Contents

Introduction

The *RHS Plant Finder* exists to put enthusiastic gardeners in touch with suppliers of plants. The book is divided into two related sections – **Plants** and **Nurseries**. **Plants** includes an A–Z Plant Directory of about 70,000 plant names, against which are listed a series of nursery codes. These codes point the reader to the full nursery details contained in the **Nurseries** section towards the back of the book.

The *RHS Plant Finder* is comprehensively updated every year.

As you will see from the entries in the **Nursery Details by Code** many nurseries do not now publish a printed catalogue but produce an online version only.

It is important to remember when ordering that many of the nurseries listed in the book are small, family-run businesses that propagate their own material. They cannot therefore guarantee to hold large stocks of the plants they list. Some will, however, propagate to order.

New in this edition

The 2014 edition of the book reflects the decisions made by the RHS Nomenclature and Taxonomy Advisory Group during 2013. The Nomenclatural Notes section (see p.24) gives a quick overview of this and other changes made during the past year.

This year's essay is a reflection by James Armitage, RHS Principal Scientist (Horticultural Taxonomy), on Taxonomic Consensus and *The Hillier Manual of Trees and Shrubs*. This important work of reference has recently been thoroughly revised by the team of RHS botanists and will be published in March 2014.

Available from the Compiler

Application for Entry

Nurseries appearing in the *RHS Plant Finder* for the first time this year are printed in bold type in the *Nursery Index by Name* starting on p.927.

If you wish your nursery to be considered for inclusion in the next edition of the *RHS Plant Finder* (2015), contact the Compiler at the address below. Entries to the book are free.

Plants Last Listed in Earlier Editions

Plants cease to be listed for a variety of reasons. For more information turn to *How to Use the Plant Directory* on p.18. A listing of more than 60,000 plants listed in earlier editions, but for which we currently have no known supplier, is available online at www.rhs.org.uk/rhsplantfinder/documents.asp.

Lists of Nurseries for Plants with more than 30 Suppliers

To prevent the book from becoming too big, we do not print the nursery codes where more than 30 nurseries offer the same plant. The plant is then listed as being "Widely available". This is detailed more fully in *How to Use the Plant Directory* on p.18.

If any readers have difficulty in finding a plant, a full list of all the nurseries held on file as current suppliers can be found at RHS Plant Finder Online by visiting the RHS website at: www.rhs.org.uk. Alternatively, we can send a printed list by post, provided enquirers include the full name of the plant (as given in the *RHS Plant Finder*) together with a SAE, and send it to:

The Compiler, *RHS Plant Finder*, RHS Garden Wisley, Woking, Surrey GU23 6QB
Email: plantfinder@rhs.org.uk
Tel: 01483 224234

The RHS Plant Finder Online

The *RHS Plant Finder* is available on the Internet. Visit the Royal Horticultural Society's website **www.rhs.org.uk** and search the *RHS Plant Finder Online*.

RHS Plant Finder 2014

Devised by Chris Philip
and Realised by Tony Lord

Editor-in-Chief
Janet Cubey

RHS Editors
James Armitage
Dawn Edwards   Neil Lancaster

Compiler
Judith Merrick

Published and compiled by
The Royal Horticultural Society
80 Vincent Square
London SW1P 2PE

Reg charity no: 222879/SC038262

First edition 1987
Twenty-eighth edition 2014

British Library Cataloguing Publication Data
A catalogue record for this book is available from the British Library

ISBN 978-1-9070-5746-5

Publisher – Rae Spencer-Jones

RHS Editor – Simon Maughan

Designer – Peter Cooling

Illustrations – Sarah Young

Maps – Alan Cooper

Printed and bound by Polestar Wheatons, Marsh Barton, Exeter, Devon EX2 8RP

The compiler and the editors of the *RHS Plant Finder* have taken every care, in the time available, to check all the information supplied to them by the nurseries concerned. Nevertheless, in a work of this kind, containing as it does hundreds of thousands of separate computer encodings, errors and omissions will inevitably occur. The RHS, the Publisher and the Editors cannot accept responsibility for any consequences that may arise from such errors.

If you find any mistakes we hope that you will let us know so that the matter can be corrected in the next edition.

Front cover photograph: *Primula* Harlow Carr hybrids (RHS/Lee Beel)
Back cover from top to bottom: *Lantana camara* (RHS/Tim Sandall)
Hamamelis × *intermedia* 'Aphrodite' (RHS/Carol Sheppard)
Euonymus europaeus 'Red Cascade' (RHS/Carol Sheppard)
Abutilon 'Orange Glow' (RHS/Carol Sheppard)
Cornus alba 'Spaethii' (RHS/Carol Sheppard)
Helenium 'Moerheim Beauty' (RHS/Carol Sheppard)

The Royal Horticultural Society is the UK's leading gardening charity dedicated to advancing horticulture and promoting good gardening. Its charitable work includes providing expert advice and information, training the next generation of gardeners, creating hands-on opportunities for children to grow plants and conducting research into plants, pests and environmental issues affecting gardeners.

For more information visit www.rhs.org.uk or call 0845 130 4646

Acknowledgements

This edition was compiled by Judith Merrick with help from Gill Skilton, June Skinner and Deborah Chubb. Richard Sanford managed the editing of plant names in the database. Rupert Wilson and Julia Barclay administered the RHS Horticultural Database, using the BG-Base™ Collection Management Software.

RHS botanists James Armitage, Dawn Edwards and Neil Lancaster undertook the task of editing the new plant names for this edition of the book.

We also acknowledge the contributions of the following colleagues: Simon Maughan, Rae Spencer Jones, Diana Levy and Louise Bowering, RHS Media; Christopher Whitehouse and Melanie Underwood, RHS Science. We are indebted to Kerry Walter of BG-BASE (UK) Ltd, Max Phillips of Strange Software Ltd and Alan Cooper, without whose professional assistance we would be unable to produce the book. Finally, we thank Peter Cooling for his skill in turning our mass of raw data into a publishable form.

Our colleagues on the RHS Nomenclature and Taxonomy Advisory Group, along with the RHS International Cultivar Registrars, have all provided valuable guidance and information. Many nurseries have supplied helpful information on plants, which has proved useful in verifying some of the more obscure names, and have suggested corrections to existing entries. Some of these remain to be checked and will be entered in the next edition, although those that contravene the Codes of Nomenclature may have to be rejected. We appreciate your patience while these checks are made. We are also grateful to all our regular correspondents and to the many readers who have made comments and suggestions.

Clematis	D. Donald, Int. Cultivar Registrar, RHS
Chrysanthemum	J. Barker (2007–08, 2013)
Conifers	S. McDonald, Int. Cultivar Registrar, RHS
Dahlia	R. Hedge (Hon. Asst. Cultivar Registrar), S. McDonald, Int. Cultivar Registrar, RHS
Dianthus	Dr A.C. Leslie, Int. Cultivar Registrar, RHS
Heathers	Dr E.C. Nelson, Int. Cultivar Registrar
Ilex	S. Andrews (2006)
Iris	J. Hewitt (2005, 2007–08)
Lilium	D. Donald, Int. Cultivar Registrar, RHS
Meconopsis	Dr E. Stevens (2003, 2005 & 2007)
Narcissus	M.R. Underwood, Int. Cultivar Registrar, RHS
Nerine	Dr J.C. David (2009)
Rhododendron	Dr A.C. Leslie, Int. Cultivar Registrar, RHS
Sorbus	Dr H. McAllister
Thymus	M. Easter (2003–11)
Viburnum	C. Sanders

Janet Cubey
RHS Editor-in-Chief
February 2014

CONSERVATION AND THE ENVIRONMENT

Invasive Plants

As the *RHS Plant Finder* demonstrates, gardens in Britain have been greatly enriched by the diversity of plants introduced to cultivation from abroad. While the vast majority of those introduced have enhanced our gardens, a few have proved to be highly invasive and to threaten native habitats. Once such plants are established it is very difficult, costly and potentially damaging to native ecosystems to eradicate or control the invasive "alien" species. Gardeners can help by choosing not to buy or distribute non-native invasive plants and by taking steps to prevent them escaping into the wild and by disposing of them in a responsible way.

Ten of the most serious invasive non-native species are no longer listed in the *RHS Plant Finder*. Any cultivars or varieties of them that are listed are believed to be less invasive than the species themselves. These 10 plants are:

**Azolla filiculoides* – fairy fern
**Crassula helmsii* – New Zealand pygmy weed
Elodea nuttalli – Nuttall's waterweed
Fallopia japonica – Japanese knotweed
Heracleum mantegazzianum – giant hogweed
**Hydrocotyle ranunculoides* – floating pennywort
Impatiens glandulifera – Himalayan balsam
Lagarosiphon major – curly waterweed
**Ludwigia grandiflora* – water primrose
**Myriophyllum aquaticum* – parrot's feather

From April 2014 the five aquatic species indicated by * above will be banned from sale. After that point anyone trading in these species will be liable to up to a £5000 fine or a six months prison sentence.

Further species are considered to present a threat to UK habitats and gardeners are encouraged to grow alternative plants. Guidance on this can be found in three booklets:

Gardening without harmful invasive plants
Landscaping without harmful invasive plants
Keeping ponds and aquaria without harmful invasive plants

These are available on the Plantlife website www.plantlife.org.uk. For further information on non-native invasive species see the GB non-native species secretariat website www.nonnativespecies.org and www.rhs.org.uk/advicesearch/Profile.aspx?pid=530.

Bringing plants back from abroad

Travelling can be a great source of inspiration for gardeners and often provides an opportunity to encounter new and interesting plants. Anyone wishing to bring plants back into Britain from overseas must realise, however, that this is a complex matter. Various regulations are in force that apply to amateur gardeners as well as to commercial nurseries. The penalties for breaking these can be serious.

Some of the most important regulatory instruments are listed below.

Plant Health regulations are in place to control the spread of pests and diseases. Plants are divided into the categories of prohibited, controlled and unrestricted, but there are also limits that vary according to the part of the world you are travelling from. For full details contact the Food and Environment Research Agency, www.fera.defra.gov.uk/plants/plant Health/imports/travellers.cfm.

The Convention on International Trade in Endangered Species (CITES) affects the transport of animal and plant material across international boundaries. Its aim is to prevent exploitative trade and thereby to prevent harm and the ultimate extinction of wild populations. A tighter regime on trade in species of wild fauna and flora exists in the EU that requires export permits for any plants listed in Appendices A, B & C and import permits for Appendices A & B. There is a further Appendix D for non-CITES listed species that the EU consider to be endangered. A broad range of plants is covered in these Appendices, including *Cactaceae* and *Orchidaceae* and, although species are mentioned in the convention title, the restrictions cover all cultivars and hybrids of listed species too, except for specific exclusions, where there are annotations in the Appendices. Details of the plants listed in the Appendices can be found on the website of the UK's CITES Management Authority, Animal Health, www.defra.gov.uk/ahvla-en/imports-exports/cites.

The Convention on Biological Diversity (CBD or the "Rio Convention") recognises the property rights of individual countries in relation to their own biodiversity. It exists to enable access to that biodiversity, but equally to ensure the sharing of any benefit derived from it. In principle it is possible to collect plant material from other countries that have asserted their rights under the CBD, by ensuring that you have obtained documentary evidence of prior informed consent on the basis of mutually agreed terms for any uses that the material will be put to in the future. In practice the legal requirements for collecting plant material varies from country to country and it is advisable to contact the National Focal Point for further information. These details and other information on the

Convention can be found on the CBD website www.cbd.int.

European Habitats Directive. The full implementation of this Directive into UK law in 2007 extended protection to all of the European Protected Species (EPS) listed in the Appendices of that Directive (these are Appendices II(b) and IV(b) for plants) whether they are native to the UK or not. This requires a licence for material of any of these species collected in the wild after 1994. These are issued by Natural England (for England), the Countryside Council for Wales (in Wales) and Scottish Natural Heritage (for Scotland), www.jncc.gov.uk/page-1374.defra.

The UK authorities issue licences for UK plants. For other EU states a collector would need to contact the relevant national authorities.

Contact addresses:

Plantlife
14 Rollestone Street
Salisbury
Wiltshire
SP1 1DX
Tel: (01722) 342730

Wildlife Licensing and Registration Service (WRLS)
Animal Health
1/17 Temple Quay House
2 The Square
Temple Quay
Bristol
BS1 6EB
Tel: 0117 372 8774

Plant Health
Room 10GA01
The Food and Environment Research Agency
Sand Hutton
York
YO41 1LZ
Tel: (01904) 465625

Joint Nature Conservation Committee
Monkstone House
City Road
Peterborough
PE1 1JY
Tel: (01733) 562626

Department for Environment, Food & Rural Affairs (Defra)
Nobel House
17 Smith Square
London
SW1P 3JR
Email for general biodiversity queries:
biodiversity@defra.gsi.gov.uk

Taxonomic Consensus and *The Hillier Manual of Trees and Shrubs*

By amalgamating a great diversity of information sources, *RHS Plant Finder* offers perhaps the best hope of establishing a list of approved names for garden plants. The move towards a general consensus is greatly strengthened this year by the publication of a revised edition of *The Hillier Manual of Trees and Shrubs.*

The Hillier Manual was first published in 1971 as an expansion of the Hillier Nurseries catalogue and, with its compendious entries and breadth of coverage, became immediately popular. It has since become a classic of horticultural literature. The original book included something over 3,000 entries; these have been added to over the years, so that this latest edition, the eighth, contains in excess of 13,000.

What makes this version different to previous editions is that, working with noted plantsmen John Hillier and Roy Lancaster, the revision of the book has been undertaken by RHS botanists. This has presented an opportunity to harmonise the nomenclature of the *Manual* and *RHS Plant Finder*, making cross-referencing the works far simpler than before and offering to gardeners a robust and durable set of names for woody plants.

The process of harmonisation was not a simple one. Since the last edition of the *Manual* was published, in 2002, much taxonomic water has passed under the bridge. DNA analysis, already well-established in the first years of this millennium, has become commonplace, bringing with it new insights into how plants are related, particularly at the familial level. The last twelve years have seen a wealth of published research, including monographs, encyclopedias, registers, papers and articles, which has added to our knowledge of garden plants and influenced our view of how they should be classified. The resources now accessible online dwarf those available at the beginning of the last decade. Other discrepancies between the texts were not the consequence of a progression in understanding but of differences in approach. What for one author is a plant worthy of recognition as a species is for another merely a subspecies or variety or not taxonomically distinct at all. Conflicts over the use of Group and infraspecific names, differences in interpretation of nomenclatural codes, issues concerning the treatment of trade designations: all had to be addressed and resolved.

The consequence of all this effort is that *The Hillier Manual* is now a more robust botanical document than ever before. The authorities for names have been exhaustively brought into line with the International Plant Names Index (a surprisingly rare thing in botanical texts), while the nomenclature adopted is supported by the huge resource of the RHS Lindley Library. The new book is the most comprehensive edition to date, containing an additional 1,500 entries which range from highly bred hybrids set to become stalwarts of car parks across the country to obscure species destined never to grace more than a handful of specialist collections.

The disharmony that previously existed between the listings of *RHS Plant Finder* and *The Hillier Manual* draws attention to the fact that, where taxonomy is concerned, there is no one-size-fits-all solution. This is perhaps not fully appreciated by many gardeners, who often believe that proposed taxonomic changes are akin to enforceable diktats. In fact, rather than any legal imperative, the basis of all biological taxonomy and nomenclature is nothing more than a common agreement to adhere to sets of rules. These universally accepted rules, in the form of nomenclatural codes, provide a framework of procedure and priority that is responsible for some unavoidable name changes. Beyond satisfying the requirements of these rules, however, there is no obligation to accept any one way of classifying living things over another. The taxonomic approach favoured by an organisation compiling a checklist of taxa present in a large geographical area, for example, may be very different to that taken by the evolutionary biologist, the wildflower enthusiast, the author of a detailed monograph or the nurseryman. In each instance the needs of the user are different; and who is to say one system is intrinsically more correct than the others.

Though there is taxonomic freedom, the taxonomy employed has nomenclatural consequences, and this can cause problems where, in the interests of effective communication and mutual understanding, a high level of nomenclatural consistency is very desirable. In horticulture, for reasons of trade, phytosanitary regulation, logistics and legislation, there is a strong need for consensus, but this is threatened by the taxonomic and nomenclatural difficulties presented by garden plants. Taxonomically, the diversity of people with an interest in horticultural plants, from tradesmen to scientists, tends not to favour wide agreement, while the complex parentage of many plants leads to frequent discrepancies in the attribution of cultivars. Nomenclaturally, the ease with which names can be established and the difficulty in tracing first publication, combined with the sheer number of names being generated, makes homonymy common and priority difficult to discern. In horticulture there is often an economic incentive to change a commercially unappealing name, and such problems are compounded by a lack of good record-keeping and a poorly indexed, highly dispersed literature. Nowadays these challenges are joined by the pitfalls of intellectual property and trademark law and the increasingly complicated name-like marketing that surrounds plant retailing, for example in Series and trade designations.

Given all these factors, it seems astonishing that horticultural nomenclature doesn't descend into complete chaos. That it hasn't says much for the value attached to it. However, there is more that can be done by people in all areas of horticulture to promote clarity. From retailers and publishers to collection holders, gardeners and botanists, everyone has a role to play.

This effort is greatly aided by access to a comprehensive, reliable list of plant names to use as a widely accepted reference point. The *RHS Plant Finder* remains the most complete and thoroughly researched guide to the current nomenclature of plants on sale in the British Isles, particularly in the nursery trade. It is a work that promotes nomenclatural stability and unity and is at the heart of the RHS's charitable purpose.

In aligning *RHS Plant Finder* and *The Hillier Manual*, two great works of horticultural taxonomy, the RHS has made a significant advance in the effort to elucidate and quantify the diversity of plants in cultivation and the taxonomic consistency attained offers the hope that still wider consensus may be achieved. This work emphasises the enormous potential and benefits of a complete catalogue of the cultivated plants of the British Isles, something that should be progressed as soon as resources allow.

James Armitage
Principal Scientist – Horticultural Taxonomy

RHS PLANT TRIALS BULLETINS

The Trials Bulletins give the results and findings of RHS Trials. Detailed descriptions and images of the plants given the Award of Garden Merit are included, as well as updates on nomenclature, cultivation details and a table comparing the different characteristics of the entries in the trial.

Begonia Rex Cultorum Group
Canna
Clematis alpina and *C. macropetala*
Dahlia
Daisies (yellow perennial)
Fuchsia, hardy
Geranium, hardy (Stage 1)
Geranium, hardy (Stage 2)
Geranium, hardy (Stage 3)
Hyacinthaceae (little blue bulbs)
Hydrangea paniculata
Iris, bearded
Lavandula, hardy
Miscanthus
Peppers, chilli
Peppers, sweet
Potatoes, salad
Potentilla, shrubby
Rhododendron yakushimanum and hybrids
Runner Beans
Saxifraga, silver
Sedum, herbaceous

If you would like a copy of any of these, please contact:
The Trials Office, RHS Garden Wisley, Woking, Surrey GU23 6QB.
Please enclose an A4 SAE and a cheque for £2.00 per copy (as a donation towards costs) made out to the Royal Horticultural Society.

In addition to the above there are four bulletins that are only available on the RHS Website: *Caryopteris, Delphinium, Perovskia, Pittosporum* and *Spiraea japonica*.
To view and download any of these RHS Plant Trials Bulletins online, please visit:
www.rhs.org.uk/trials

EXTENDED GLOSSARY

This glossary combines some of the helpful introductory sections from older editions in an alphabetical listing. A fuller, more discursive account of plant names, *Guide to Plant Names*, and a detailed guide to the typography of plant names, *Recommended Style for Printing Plant Names*, are both available as RHS Advisory Leaflets. To request a copy of either please send an A4 sae to The Compiler at the contact address given on page 4.

ADVISORY COMMITTEE ON NOMENCLATURE AND TAXONOMY

See **Nomenclature and Taxonomy Advisory Group**

AUTHORITIES

In order that plant names can be used with precision throughout the scientific world, the name of the person who coined the name of a plant species (its author, or authority) is added to the plant name. Usually this information is of little consequence to gardeners, except in cases where the same name has been given to two different plants or a name is commonly misapplied. Although only one usage is correct, both may be encountered in books, so indicating the author is the only way to be certain about which plant is being referred to. This can happen equally with cultivars. Authors' names, where it is appropriate to cite them, appear in a smaller typeface after the species or cultivar name to which they refer and are abbreviated following Brummitt and Powell's *Authors of Plant Names*.

🏆 AWARD OF GARDEN MERIT

The Award of Garden Merit (AGM) is intended as a practical guide for the gardener and is therefore awarded only after a period of assessment by the RHS Standing and Joint Committees. The AGM is awarded only to plants that are:

- excellent for ordinary use in appropriate conditions
- available
- of good constitution
- essentially stable in form and colour
- reasonably resistant to pests and diseases

The AGM symbol is cited in conjunction with the **hardiness** rating. A full list of AGM plants may be found on the RHS website at www.rhs.org.uk/agmplants.

The AGM plant list has, to date, been re-examined every 10 years. The latest review was carried out during 2012 and published in February 2013.

BOTANICAL NAMES

The aim of the botanical naming system is to provide each different plant with a single, unique, universal name. The basic unit of plant classification is the species. Species that share a number of significant characteristics are grouped together to form a genus (plural **genera**). The name of a species is made up of two elements; the name of the genus followed by the specific epithet, for example, *Narcissus romieuxii*.

Variation within a species can be recognised by division into subspecies (usually abbreviated to subsp.), varietas (or variety abbreviated to var.) and forma (or form abbreviated to f.). Whilst it is unusual for a plant to have all of these, it is possible, as in this example, *Narcissus romieuxii* subsp. *albidus* var. *zaianicus* f. *lutescens*.

The botanical elements are always given in italics, with only the genus taking an initial capital letter. The rank indications are never in italics. In instances where the rank is not known it is necessary to form an invalid construction by quoting a second epithet without a rank. This is an unsatisfactory situation, but requires considerable research to resolve.

In some genera, such as *Hosta*, we list the cultivar names alphabetically with the species or **hybrid** to which they are attributed afterwards in parentheses. For example, *Hosta* 'Reversed' (*sieboldiana*). In other situations where the aim is not to create a list alphabetically by cultivar name we would recommend styling this as *Hosta sieboldiana* 'Reversed'.

CLASSIFICATION OF GENERA

Genera that include a large number of species or with many cultivars are often subdivided into informal horticultural classifications or more formal Cultivar Groups, each based on a particular characteristic or combination of characteristics. Colour of flower or fruit and shape of flower are common examples and, with fruit, whether a cultivar is grown for culinary or dessert purposes. How such groups are named differs from genus to genus.

To help users of the *RHS Plant Finder* find the plants they want, the classifications used within cultivated genera are listed using codes and plants are marked with the appropriate code in brackets after its name in the Plant Directory. To find the explanation of each code, simply look it up under the genus concerned in the **Classification of Genera** starting on p.25. The codes relating to edible fruits are also listed here, but these apply across several genera.

COLLECTORS' REFERENCES

Abbreviations (usually with numbers) following a plant name refer to the collector(s) of the plant. These abbreviations are expanded, with a collector's name or expedition title, in the section **Collectors' References** starting on p.20.

A collector's reference may indicate a new, as yet unnamed range of variation within a species. The inclusion of collectors' references in the *RHS Plant Finder* supports the book's role in sourcing unusual plants.

The Convention on Biological Diversity calls for conservation of biodiversity, its sustainable use and the fair and equitable sharing of any derived benefits. Since its adoption in 1993, collectors are required to have prior informed consent from the country of origin for the acquisition and commercialisation of collected material.

COMMON NAMES

In a work such as this, it is necessary to refer to plants by their botanical names for the sake of universal comprehension and clarity. However, at the same time we recognise that with fruit and vegetables most people are more familiar with their common names than their botanical ones. Cross-references are therefore given from common to botanical names for fruit, vegetables and the commoner culinary herbs throughout the Plant Directory.

CULTIVAR

Literally meaning cultivated variety, cultivar names are given to denote variation within species and that generated by hybridisation, in cultivation. To make them easily distinguishable from botanical names, they are not printed in italics and are enclosed in single quotation marks. Cultivar names coined since 1959 should follow the rules of the International Code of Nomenclature for Cultivated Plants (**ICNCP**).

DESCRIPTIVE TERMS

Terms that appear after the main part of the plant name are shown in a smaller font to distinguish them. These descriptive elements give extra information about the plant and may include the **collector's reference**, **authority**, or what colour it is. For example, *Clematis henryi* B&SWJ 3402, *Penstemon* 'Sour Grapes' M.Fish, *Lobelia tupa* dark orange-flowered.

FAMILIES

Genera are grouped into larger groups of related plants called families. Most family names, with the exception of eight familiar names, end with the same group of letters, *-aceae*. While it is still acceptable to use these eight exceptions, the modern trend adopted in the *RHS Plant Finder* is to use alternative names with *–aceae* endings. The families concerned are *Compositae* (*Asteraceae*), *Cruciferae* (*Brassicaceae*), *Gramineae* (*Poaceae*), *Guttiferae* (*Clusiaceae*), *Labiatae* (*Lamiaceae*), *Leguminosae* (split here into *Caesalpiniaceae*, *Mimosaceae* and *Papilionaceae*), *Palmae* (*Arecaceae*) and *Umbelliferae* (*Apiaceae*).

Apart from these exceptions we now follow (from 2010) *Mabberley's Plant Book* (3rd edition).

GENUS (plural – GENERA)

Genera used in the *RHS Plant Finder* were originally based on Brummitt's *Vascular Plant Families and Genera* but are now based on a range of sources. For spellings and genders of generic names, Greuter's *Names in Current Use for Extant Plant Genera* has also been consulted. See **Botanical Names**.

GREX

Within orchids, hybrids of the same parentage, regardless of how alike they are, are given a grex name. Individuals can be selected, given cultivar names and propagated vegetatively. For example, *Pleione* Versailles gx 'Bucklebury', where Versailles is the grex name and 'Bucklebury' is a selected **cultivar**.

GROUP

This is a collective name for a group of cultivars within a genus with similar characteristics. The word Group is always included and, where cited with a cultivar name, it is enclosed in brackets, for example, *Actaea simplex* (Atropurpurea Group) 'Brunette', where 'Brunette' is a distinct cultivar in a group of purple-leaved cultivars.

Another example of a Group is *Rhododendron polycladum* Scintillans Group. In this case *Rhododendron scintillans* was a species that is now botanically 'sunk' within *R. polycladum*, but it is still recognised horticulturally as a Group.

Group names are also used for swarms of hybrids with the same parentage, for example, *Rhododendron* Polar Bear Group. These were formerly treated as

grex names, a term now used only for orchids. A single clone from the Group may be given the same cultivar name, for example, *Rhododendron* 'Polar Bear'.

HARDINESS

Hardiness ratings are shown for **Award of Garden Merit** plants. To assist gardeners to determine more clearly which plants are hardy in their local area, the RHS introduced a new, enhanced, hardiness rating scheme in 2013, to coincide with the publication of the new **Award of Garden Merit** plant list. The categories now used are as follows:
Temperature ranges given are intended to be absolute minimum winter temperatures (°C).
H1a = Heated greenhouse – tropical >15
H1b = Heated greenhouse – subtropical 10 to 15
H1c = Heated greenhouse – warm temperate 5 to 10
H2 = Tender – cool or frost-free greenhouse 1 to 5
H3 = Half-hardy – unheated greenhouse/mild winter 5 to 1
H4 = Hardy – average winter -10 to -5
H5 = Hardy – cold winter -15 to -10
H6 = Hardy – very cold winter -20 to -15
H7 = Very hardy <-20

Further definition of these categories can be found on the RHS website, in the Feb 2013 edition of *The Garden* and in the *RHS Plant Finder 2013* essay.

HYBRIDS

Some species, when grown together, in the wild or in cultivation, are found to interbreed and form hybrids. In some instances a hybrid name is coined, for example hybrids between *Primula hirsuta* and *P. minima* are given the name *Primula* × *forsteri*, the multiplication sign indicating hybrid origin. Hybrid formulae that quote the parentage of the hybrid are used where a unique name has not been coined, for example *Rhododendron calophytum* × *R. praevernum*. In hybrid formulae you will find parents in alphabetical order, with the male (m) and female (f) parent indicated where known. Hybrids between different genera are also possible, for example × *Mahoberberis* is the name given to hybrids between *Mahonia* and *Berberis*.

There are also a few special-case hybrids called graft hybrids, where the tissues of two plants are physically rather than genetically mixed. These are indicated by an addition rather than a multiplication sign, so *Laburnum* + *Cytisus* becomes + *Laburnocytisus*.

ICNCP

The ICNCP is the International Code of Nomenclature for Cultivated Plants. First published in 1959, the most recent (8th) edition was published in 2009.

Cultivar names that do not conform to this Code, and for which there is no valid alternative, are flagged I (for invalid). This code states that the minimum requirement is for a cultivar name to be given in conjunction with the name of the genus. However, in the *RHS Plant Finder* we choose to give as full a name as possible to give the gardener and botanist more information about the plant, following the Recommendation in the Code.

NOMENCLATURE AND TAXONOMY ADVISORY GROUP

This Group advises the RHS on individual problems of nomenclature regarding plants in cultivation and, in particular, use of names in the *RHS Horticultural Database*, reflected in the annual publication of the *RHS Plant Finder*.

The aim is always to make the plant names in the *RHS Plant Finder* as consistent, reliable and stable as possible and acceptable to gardeners and botanists alike, not only in the British Isles but around the world. Recent proposals to change or correct names are examined with the aim of creating a balance between the stability of well-known names and botanical and taxonomic correctness. In some cases the conflicting views on the names of some groups of plants will not easily be resolved. The Group's policy is then to wait and review the situation once a more obvious consensus is reached, rather than rush to rename plants only to have to change them again when opinions have shifted.

In 2014 the Group is chaired by Dr Alan Leslie (RHS) and includes: Dr Crinan Alexander, Susyn Andrews, Chris Brickell, Dr James Compton, Mike Grant, Dr John Grimshaw, Dr Stephen Jury, Dr Tony Lord, Prof David Mabberley, Dr Charles Nelson, Chris Sanders, with James Armitage, Dr Janet Cubey, Dr John David and Julian Shaw (attending RHS staff), and Dr Christopher Whitehouse (RHS) as Secretary.

NOTES ON NOMENCLATURE AND IDENTIFICATION

The **Notes on Nomenclature and Identification**, p.24, give further information for names that are complex or may be confusing. See also **Nomenclature and Taxonomy Advisory Group**.

PLANT BREEDERS' RIGHTS

Plants covered by an *active* grant of Plant Breeders' Rights (PBR) are indicated throughout the Plant Directory. Grants indicated are those awarded by both UK and EU Plant Variety Rights offices. Because grants can both come into force and lapse at any time, this book can only aim to represent the situation at one point in time, but it is hoped that this will act as a useful guide to growers and gardeners. UK and EU grants represent the published position as of the end of December 2013. We do not give any indication where PBR grants may be pending.

To obtain PBR protection, a new plant must be registered and pass tests for distinctness, uniformity and stability under an approved name. This approved name, under the rules of the **ICNCP**, established by a legal process, has to be regarded as the cultivar name. Increasingly however, these approved names are a code or "nonsense" name and are therefore often unpronounceable and meaningless, so the plants are given other names designed to attract sales when they are released. These secondary names are often referred to as selling names but are officially termed **trade designations**.

For further information on UK PBR contact:
Plant Variety Rights Office,
Food and Environment Research Agency,
Eastbrook,
Shaftesbury Road,
Cambridge CB2 8DR
Tel: (0300) 060 0740
Website: www.fera.defra.gov.uk/plants/plantVarieties/

For details of plants covered by EU Community Rights contact:
Community Plant Variety Office (CPVO),
3 Boulevard Maréchal Foch, BP 10121,
FR-49101 Angers Cedex 02, France
Tel: 00 33 (02) 41 25 64 00
Fax: 00 33 (02) 41 25 64 10
Website: www.cpvo.europa.eu

The *RHS Plant Finder* takes no responsibility for ensuring that nurseries selling plants with PBR are licensed to do so.

Reverse Synonyms

It is likely that users of this book will come across names in certain genera that they did not expect to find. This may be because species have been transferred from another genus (or **genera**). A list of **Reverse Synonyms** is available online at www.rhs.org.uk/rhs plantfinder/documents.asp. Alternatively, a copy can be requested by sending a sae (1 × 2nd class letter stamp) to The Compiler at the address given on page 4.

Selling Names

See **Trade Designations**

Series

With seed-raised plants and some popular vegetatively-propagated plants, especially bedding plants and pot plants such as *Petunia* or *Verbena*, Series have become increasingly popular. A Series contains a number of similar cultivars, but differs from a **Group** in that it is a marketing device, with cultivars added to create a range of flower colours in plants of similar habit. Individual colour elements within a Series may be represented by slightly different cultivars over the years.

The word Series is always included and, where cited with a cultivar name it is enclosed in brackets, for example *Aquilegia* 'Robin' (Songbird Series). The Series name usually follows the rest of the plant name, but sometimes in this book we list it before the cultivar name in order to group members of a Series together when they occur next to one another on the page.

Species

See under **Botanical Names**

Subspecies

See under **Botanical Names**

Synonyms

Although the ideal is for each species or cultivar to have only one name, anyone dealing with plants soon comes across a situation where one plant has received two or more names, or two plants have received the same name. In each case, only one name and application, for reasons of precision and stability, can be regarded as correct. Additional names are known as synonyms. Further information on synonyms and why plants change names is available in *Guide to Plant Names*. See the introduction to this glossary for details of how to request a copy.

See also **Reverse Synonyms**.

Trade Designations

A **trade designation** is the name used to market a plant when the cultivar name is considered unsuitable for selling purposes. It is styled in a different typeface and without single quotation marks.

In the case of **Plant Breeders' Rights** it is a legal requirement for the cultivar name to appear with the trade designation on a label at the point of sale. Most plants are sold under only one trade designation, but some, especially roses, are sold under a number of names, particularly when cultivars are introduced from other countries. Usually, the correct cultivar name is the only way to ensure that the same plant is not bought unwittingly under two or more different trade designations. The *RHS Plant Finder* follows the recommendations of the **ICNCP** when dealing with trade designations and PBR. These are always to quote the cultivar name and trade designation together and to style the trade designation in a different typeface, without single quotation marks, for example *Choisya* × *dewitteana* Goldfingers = 'Limo'PBR. Here Goldfingers is the trade designation and 'Limo' is the cultivar name that has been granted **Plant Breeders' Rights**. This may also be styled in other ways, such as *Choisya* × *dewitteana* GOLDFINGERS ('Limo')PBR.

Translations

When a cultivar name is translated from the language of first publication, the translation is regarded as a **trade designation** and styled accordingly. We endeavour to recognise the original cultivar name in every case and to give an English translation where it is in general use.

Variegated Plants

Following a suggestion from the Variegated Plant Group of the Hardy Plant Society, a (v) is cited after those plants which are "variegated". The dividing line between variegation and less distinct colour marking is necessarily arbitrary and plants with light veins, pale, silver or dark zones, or leaves flushed in paler colours, are not shown as being variegated unless there is an absolutely sharp distinction between paler and darker zones.

For further details of the Variegated Plant Group, please write to:

Brian Dockerill
19 Westfield Road
Glyncoch
Pontypridd
Mid-Glamorgan
CF37 3AG

Variety

See under **Botanical Names** and **Cultivar**

SYMBOLS AND ABBREVIATIONS

SYMBOLS APPEARING TO THE LEFT OF THE NAME

- * Name not validated. Not listed in the appropriate International Registration Authority checklist nor in works cited in the Bibliography. For fuller discussion see p.11
- I Invalid name. See *International Code of Botanical Nomenclature 2006* and *International Code of Nomenclature for Cultivated Plants 2009*. For fuller discussion see p.11
- § Plant listed elsewhere in the Plant Directory under a synonym
- × Hybrid genus
- + Graft hybrid genus

SYMBOLS APPEARING TO THE RIGHT OF THE NAME

- ✿ Plant Heritage National Plant Collection® exists for all or part of this genus. Further details can be found in the *2014 National Plant Collections® Directory* available from: www.plantheritage.com or Plant Heritage, 12 Home Farm, Loseley Park, Guildford, Surrey GU3 1HS
- ♀H4 The Royal Horticultural Society's Award of Garden Merit, see p.11
- (d) double-flowered
- (F) Fruit
- (f) female
- (m) male
- (v) variegated plant, see p.15
- PBR Plant Breeders Rights see p.13
- **new** New plant entry in this edition

For abbreviations relating to individual genera see **Classification of Genera** p.25

For **Collectors' References** see p.20

For symbols used in the **Nurseries** section see p.829

SYMBOLS AND ABBREVIATIONS USED AS PART OF THE NAME

- × hybrid species
- aff. affinis (akin to)
- agg. aggregate, a single name used to cover a group of very similar plants, regarded by some as separate species
- ambig. ambiguous, a name used by two authors for different plants and where it is unclear which is being offered
- cf. compare to
- cl. clone
- f. forma (botanical form)
- gx grex
- sensu lato in the broadest sense
- sp. species
- subsp. subspecies
- subvar. subvarietas (botanical subvariety)
- var. varietas (botanical variety)

It is not within the remit of this book to check that nurseries are applying the right names to the right plants or to ensure nurseries selling plants with Plant Breeders' Rights are licensed to do so.

Please, never use an out of date edition

PLANTS

WHATEVER PLANT YOU ARE LOOKING FOR, MAYBE AN OLD FAVOURITE OR A MORE UNUSUAL CULTIVAR, SEARCH HERE FOR A LIST OF THE SUPPLIERS THAT ARE CLOSEST TO YOU.

How to Use the Plant Directory

Nursery Codes

Look up the plant you require in the alphabetical Plant Directory. Against each plant you will find one or more four-letter codes, for example WCru, each code represents one nursery offering that plant. The first letter of each code indicates the main area of the country in which the nursery is situated. For this geographical key, refer to the **Nursery Codes and Symbols** on p.828.

Turn to the **Nursery Details by Code** starting on p.832 where, in alphabetical order of codes, you will find details of each nursery which offers the plant in question. If you wish to visit any nursery, you may find its location on one of the maps (following p.933). Please note that not all nurseries choose to be shown on the maps. For a fuller explanation of how to use the nursery listings please turn to p.829. **Always check that the nursery you select has the plant in stock before you set out.**

Plants with more than 30 Suppliers

In some cases, against the plant name you will see the term 'Widely available' instead of a nursery code. If we were to include every plant listed by all nurseries, the *RHS Plant Finder* would become unmanageably bulky. We therefore ask nurseries to restrict their entries to those plants that are not already well represented. As a result, if more than 30 nurseries offer any plant the Directory gives no nursery codes and the plant is listed instead as being 'Widely available'.

You should have little difficulty in locating these in local nurseries or garden centres. However, if you are unable to find such plants, we will be pleased to send a full list of all the nurseries that we have on file as stockists. To obtain a list, please see the Introduction on p.4 or go to www.rhs.org.uk/rhsplantfinder/.

Finding Fruit, Vegetables and Herbs

You will need to search for these by their botanical names. Common names are cross-referenced to their botanical names in the Plant Directory.

If you have Difficulty Finding your Plant

If you cannot immediately find the plant you seek, look through the various species of the genus. You may be using an incomplete name. The problem is most likely to arise in very large genera such as *Phlox* where there are a number of possible species, each with a large number of cultivars. A search through the whole genus may well bring success. Please note that, for space reasons, the following are not listed in the Plant Directory: annuals, orchids, except hardy terrestrial orchids; cacti, except hardy cacti.

Cross-references

It may be that the plant name you seek is a synonym. Our intention is to list nursery codes only against the correct botanical name. Where you find a synonym you will be cross-referred to the correct name.

Plants Last Listed in Earlier Editions

It may be that the plant you are seeking has no known suppliers and is thus not listed.

The loss of a plant name from the Directory may arise for a number of reasons – the supplier may have gone out of business, or may not have responded to our latest questionnaire and has therefore been removed from the book. Such plants may well be available but we have no knowledge of current suppliers. Alternatively, some plants may have been misnamed by nurseries in previous editions, but are now appearing under their correct name.

To obtain a listing of plants last listed in earlier editions please see the Introduction on p.4 or go to the RHS website where it is available as a pdf.

Please, never use an out of date edition

USING THE PLANT DIRECTORY

The main purpose of the Plant Directory is to help the reader correctly identify the plant they seek and find its stockist. Each nursery has a unique identification code which appears to the right of the plant name. Turn to Nursery Details by Code on p.832 for the address, opening times and other details of the nursery. The first letter of each nursery code denotes its geographical region. Turn to the map on p.933 to find your region code and then identify the nurseries in your area.

Another purpose of the Directory is to provide more information about the plant through the symbols and other information. For example, if it has an alternative names, is new to this edition or has received the RHS Award of Garden Merit.

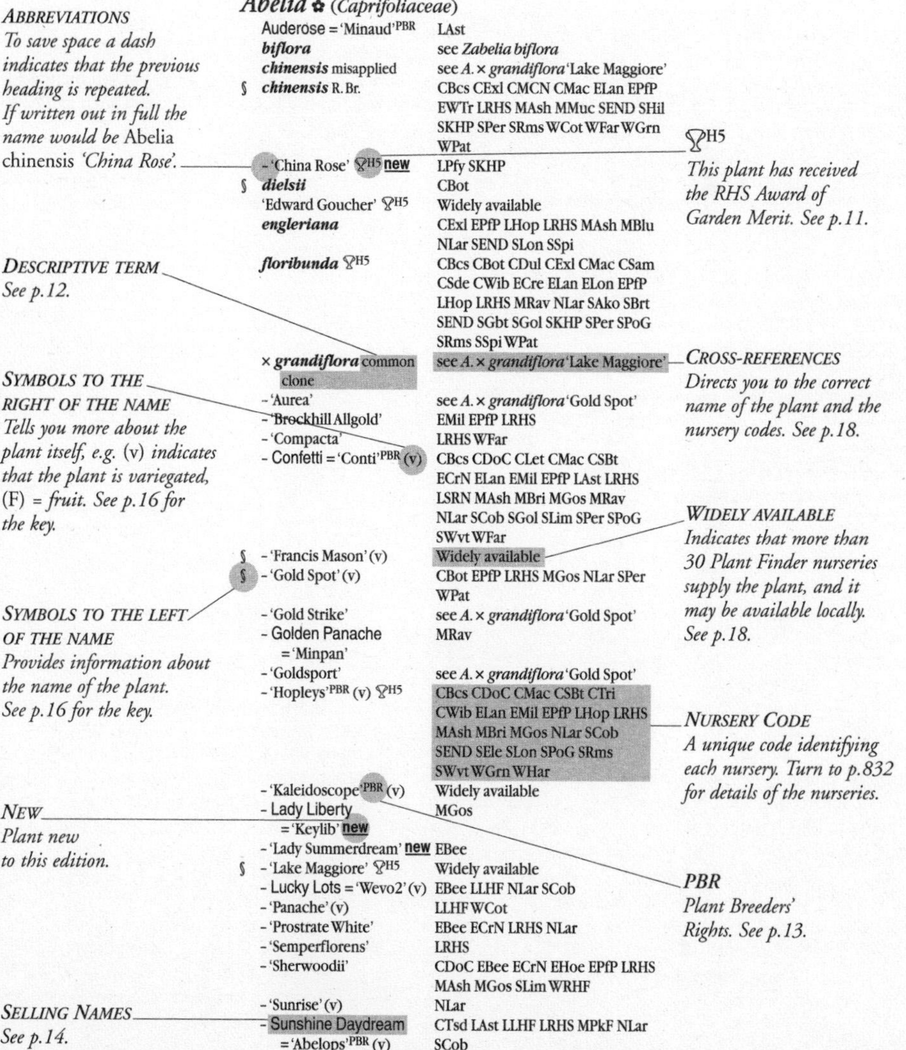

Supplementary Keys to the Directory

Collectors' References

Abbreviations following a plant name, refer to the collector(s) of the plant. These abbreviations are expanded below, with a collector's name or expedition title. For a fuller explanation, see p.12.

A&JW Watson, A. & J.
A&L Ala, A. & Lancaster, Roy
AB&S Archibald, James; Blanchard, John W. & Salmon, M.
AC Clark, Alan J.
AC&H Apold, J.; Cox, Peter & Hutchison, Peter
AC&W Albury; Cheese, M. & Watson, J.M.
ACE AGS Expedition to China (1994)
ACL Leslie, Alan C.
AER Robinson, Allan
AGS/ES AGS Expedition to Sikkim (1983)
AGSJ AGS Expedition to Japan (1988)
AH Hoog, A.
AIM Avent, Tony Mexico (1994)
Airth Airth, Murray
Akagi Akagi Botanical Garden
AL&JS Sharman, Joseph L. & Leslie, Alan C.
APA Cox, K.; Hootman, S.; Hudson, T.; et al, Expedition to Arunchal Pradesh (2005)
ARG Argent, G.C.G.
ARGS Alaska Rock Garden Society trip to China
ARJA Ruksans, J. & Siesums, A.
B Blanchard, John
B&F MA Brown, Robert & Fisher, Rif & Middle Atlas (2007)
B L. Beer, Len
B&L Brickell, Christopher D. & Leslie, Alan C.
B&M & BM Brickell, Christopher D. & Mathew, Brian
B&S Bird P. & Salmon M.
B&SWJ Wynn-Jones, Bleddyn & Susan
B&V Burras, K. & Vosa, C.G.
BB Bartholomew, B.
BBJMT Boland, Brownless, Jamieson & McNamara
BC Chudziak, W.
BC&W Beckett; Cheese, M. & Watson, J.M.
Beavis Beavis, Derek S.
Berry Berry, P.
Berry & Brako Berry, P. & Brako, Lois
BKBlount Blount, B.K.
BKN Bis, J., Kupčák, P. & Novak, H.
BL&M University of Bangor Expedition to NE Nepal
BM Mathew, Brian F.
BM&W Binns, David L.; Mason, M. & Wright, A.
BOA Boardman, P.
Breedlove Breedlove, D.
BR Rushbrooke, Ben
BS Smith, Basil
BSBE Bowles Scholarship Botanical Expedition (1963)
BSSS Crûg Expedition, Jordan (1991)
Bu Bubert, S.
Burtt Burtt, Brian L.
BWJ Wynn-Jones, Bleddyn
C Cole, Desmond T.
C&C Cox, P.A. & Cox, K.N.E.
C&Cu Cox, K.N.E. & Cubey, J.
C&H Cox, Peter & Hutchison, Peter
C&K Chamberlain & Knott
C&R Christian & Roderick
C&S Clark, Alan & Sinclair, Ian W.J.
C&V K.N.E. Cox & Vergera, S.
C&W Cheese, M. & Watson, J.M.
CC Chadwell, Christopher
CC&H Chamberlain, David F.; Cox, Peter & Hutchison, P.
CC&McK Chadwell, Christopher & McKelvie, A.
CC&MR Chadwell, Christopher & Ramsay
CCH&H Chamberlain, D.F.; Cox, P.; Hutchison, P. & Hootman, S.
CD&R Compton, J.; D'Arcy, J. & Rix, E.M.
CDB Brickell, Christopher D.
CDC Coode, Mark J.E.; Dockrill, Alexander
CDC&C Compton; D'Arcy; Christopher & Coke
CDPR Compton; D'Arcy; Pope & Rix
CE&H Christian, P.J.; Elliott & Hoog
CEE Chengdu Edinburgh Expedition China (1991)

CGG	Glendoick Gardens Expedition to Guizou (2009)
CGV	Vosa, Canio
CGW	Grey-Wilson, Christopher
CH	Christian, P. & Hoog, A.
CH&M	Cox, P.; Hutchison, P. & Maxwell-MacDonald, D.
CHP&W	Kashmir Botanical Expedition
CL	Lovell, Chris
CLD	Chungtien, Lijiang & Dali Exped. China (1990)
CM&W	Cheese M.; Mitchel J. & Watson, J.
CN&W	Clark; Neilson & Wilson
CNDS	Nelson, C. & Sayers D.
Cooper	Cooper, R.E.
Cox	Cox, Peter A.
CPC	Cobblewood Plant Collection
CPN	Compton, James
CS	Stapleton, Christopher
CSE	Cyclamen Society Expedition (1990)
CT	Teune, Carla
CWJ	Colley, Finlay; Wynn-Jones, Bleddyn, Taiwan (2007)
Dahl	Dahl, Sally
DBG	Denver Botanic Garden, Colorado
DC	Cheshire, David
DF	Fox, D.
DG	Green, D.
DHTU	Hinkley, D., Turkey (2000)
DJF	Ferguson, Dave
DJH	Hinkley, Dan
DJHC	Hinkley D., China
DJHS	Hinkley, D., Sichuan
DJHV	Hinkley, D., Vietnam
DM	Millais, David
Doleshy	Doleshy, F.L.
DS&T	Drake, Sharman J. & Thompson
DWD	Rose, D.
DZ	Zummell, D.
ECN	Nelson, E. Charles
EDHCH	Hammond, Eric D.
EGM	Millais, T.
EKB	Balls, Edward K.
EM	East Malling Research Station
EMAK	Edinburgh Makalu Expedition (1991)
EMR	Rix, E.Martyn
EN	Needham, Edward F.
ENF	Fuller, E. Nigel
ETE	Edinburgh Taiwan Expedition (1993)
ETOT	Kirkham, T.S.; Flanagan, Mark
F	Forrest, G.
F&M	Fernandez & Mendoza, Mexico
F&W	Watson, J. & Flores, A.
Farrer	Farrer, Reginald
FK	Kinmonth, Fergus W.
FMB	Bailey, F.M.
G	Gardner, Martin F.
G&K	Gardner, Martin F. & Knees, Sabina G.
G&P	Gardner, Martin F. & Page, Christopher N.
GDJ	Dumont, Gerard
GG	Gusman, G.
GS	Sherriff, George
Green	Green, D.
Guitt	Guittoneau, G.G.
Guiz	Guizhou Expedition (1985)
GWJ	Goddard, Sally; Wynne-Jones, Bleddyn & Susan
G-W&P	Grey-Wilson, Christopher & Phillips
H	Huggins, Paul
H&B	Hilliard, Olive M. & Burtt, Brian L.
H&D	Howick, C. & Darby
H&M	Howick, Charles & McNamara, William A.
H&W	Hedge, Ian C. & Wendelbo, Per W.
Harry Smith	Smith, K.A.Harry
Hartside	Hartside Nursery
HCM	Heronswood Expedition to Chile (1998)
HECC	Hutchison; Evans; Cox, P.; Cox, K.
HEHEHE	Zetterlund, H. et al, Gothenburg Botanic Gardens Expedition to northern China
Hird	Hird
HH&K	Hannay, S & S & Kingsbury, N.
HK	Kuenzler, Horst
HLMS	Springate, L.S.
HM&S	Halliwell, B.; Mason, D. & Smallcombe
HOA	Hoog, Anton
HRS	Hers, J.
Hummel	Hummel, D.
HW&E	Wendelbo, Per; Hedge, I. & Ekberg, L.
HWEL	Hirst, J.Michael; Webster, D.
HWJ	Crûg Heronswood Joint Expedition
HWJCM	Crûg Heronswood Expedition
HWJK	Crûg Heronswood Expedition, East Nepal (2002)
HZ	Zetterlund, Henrik
ICE	Instituto de Investigaciónes Ecológicas Chiloé & RBGE
IDS	International Dendrological Society
ISI	Int. Succulent Introductions
J&JA	Archibald, James & Jennifer
J. Jurasek	Jurasek, J.
JCA	Archibald, James
JE	Jack Elliott
JJ	Jackson, J.
JJ&JH	Halda, J. & Halda, J.
JJH	Halda, Joseph J.
JL	Lode, Joel
JLS	Sharman, J.L.
JM-MK	Mahr, J.; Kammerlander, M.
JMT	Mann Taylor, J.
JN	Nielson, Jens
JR	Russell, J.
JRM	Marr, John
JW	Watson, J.M.

K	Kirkpatrick, George
K&LG	Gillanders, Kenneth & Gillanders, L.
K&Mc	Kirkpatrick, George & McBeath, Ronald J.D.
K&P	Josef Kopec & Milan Prasil
K&T	Kurashige, Y. & Tsukie, S.
KC	Cox, Kenneth
KEKE	Kew/Edinburgh Kanchenjunga Expedition (1989)
KGB	Kunming/Gothenburg Botanical Expedition (1993)
KM	Marsh, K.
KMR	Kupčák, M.
KR	Rushforth, K.D.
KRW	Wooster, K.R. (distributed after his death by Kath Dryden)
KW	Kingdon-Ward, F.
KWJ	Crûg-World of Ferns Joint Expedition, Vietnam (2007)
L	Lancaster, C. Roy
L&S	Ludlow, Francis & Sherriff, George
LA	Long Ashton Research Station clonal selection scheme
LB	Bercht, L. (*Cactaceae*)
LB	Bird P.; Salmon, M.
LEG	Lesotho Edinburgh/Gothenburg Expedition (1997)
Lismore	Lismore Nursery, Breeder's Number
LM&S	Leslie, Mattern & Sharman
LP	Palmer, W.J.L.
LS&E	Ludlow, Frank; Sherriff, George & Elliott, E. E.
LS&H	Ludlow, Frank; Sherriff, George & Hicks, J. H.
LS&T	Ludlow, Frank; Sherriff, George & Taylor, George
LZ	Lutz, Eberhard
M&PS	Mike & Polly Stone
M&T	Mathew & Tomlinson
Mac&W	McPhail & Watson
McB	McBeath, R.J.D.
McLaren	McLaren, H.D.
MDM	Myers, Michael D.
MECC	Scottish Rock Garden Club, Nepal (1997)
MESE	Alpine Garden Society Expedition, Greece (1999)
MF	Foster, Maurice
MH	Heasman, Matthew T.
MK	Kammerlander, Michael
MP	Pavelka, Mojmir
MPF	Frankis, M.P.
MS	Salmon, M.
MS&CL	Salmon, M. & Lovell, C.
MSF	Fillan, M.S.
MUG	Uhlig, M.
NAPE	Hootman, S.; et al, Expedition to Naglaland and Arunachal Pradesh (2003)
NICE	North India Expedition (1997)
NJM	Macer, N.J.
NN	Nielsen & Nielsen (2009)
NNS	Ratko, Ron
NS	Turland, Nick
NVD	Expedition to Vietnam
NVFDE	Northern Vietnam First Darwin Expedition
Og	Ogisu, Mikinori
ORO	Oron, Peri
OS	Sonderhousen, O.
P. Bon	Bonavia, P.
P&C	Paterson, David S. & Clarke, Sidney
P&W	Polastri & Watson, J. M.
PAB	Barney, P.A.
PB	Bird, Peter
PC&H	Pattison, G.; Catt, P. & Hickson, M.
PD	Davis, Peter H.
PDM	Purdom, William
PF	Furse, Paul
PG	Pichler, G.
PJC	Christian, Paul J.
PJC&AH	P.J. Christian & A. Hogg
PNMK	Nicholls, P.; Kammerlander, M.
Polunin	Polunin, Oleg
Pras	Prasil, M.
PS&W	Polunin, Oleg; Sykes, William & Williams, John
PW	Wharton, Peter
R	Rock, J.F.C.
RB	Brown, R.
RBS	Brown, Ray, Sakharin Island
RCB AM	Brown, Robert, Expedition to Armenia
RCB/Arg	Brown, Robert, Argentina, (2002)
RCB E	Brown, Robert, Expedition to Spain (Andalucia)
RCB/Eq	Brown, Robert, Ecuador, (1988)
RCB RA	Brown, Robert
RCB RL	Brown, Robert, Expedition to Lebanon
RCB/TQ	Brown, Robert, Turkey (2001)
RE	Evans, Ron
RH	Hancock, R.
RKMP	Ruksans, J.; Krumins, A.; Kitts, M.; Paivel, A.
RM	Ruksans, J. & Kitts, M.
RMRP	Rocky Mountain Rare Plants, Denver, Colorado
RS	Suckow, Reinhart
RSC	Richard Somer Cocks
RV	Richard Valder
RWJ	Crûg Farm-Rickards Ferns Expedition to Taiwan (2003)
S&B	Blanchard, J.W. & Salmon, M.
S&F	Salmon, M. & Fillan, M.
S&L	Sinclair, Ian W.J. & Long, David G.
S&SH	Sheilah & Spencer Hannay
Sandham	Sandham, John
SB	Brack, Steven
SB&L	Salmon, Bird & Lovell

SBEC Sino-British Expedition to Cangshan
SBEL Sino-British Lijiang Expedition
SBQE Sino-British Expedition to Quinghai
Sch Schilling, Anthony D.
SD Sashal Dayal
SDR Rankin, Stella & David
SEH Hootman, Steve
SEP Swedish Expedition to Pakistan
SF Forde, P.
SG Salmon, M. & Guy, P.
SH Hannay, Spencer
Sich Simmons, Erskine, Howick & Mcnamara
SJ Johansson, Stellan
SLIZE Swedish-Latvian-Iranian Zagros Expedition to Iran (May 1988)
SOJA Kew/Quarryhill Expedition to Southern Japan
SS&W Stainton, J.D. Adam; Sykes, William & Williams, John
SSNY Sino-Scottish Expedition to NW Yunnan (1992)
T Taylor, Nigel P.
T&K Taylor, Nigel P. & Knees, Sabina
TCM Mitchell, Thomas Carly
TG Thomas, H-P. & Gilmer, K.
TH Hudson, T.
TJR Roberts, Tim
TS&BC Smythe, T. & Cherry, B.
TSS Spring Smyth, T.L.M.
TW Weston, Tony
USDAPI US Department of Agriculture Plant Index Number
USDAPQ US Dept. of Agriculture Plant Quarantine Number
USNA United States National Arboretum
VHH Vernon H. Heywood
VV Victor, David
W Wilson, Ernest H.
W&B Watkins, D. & Brown, R., Bulgaria (2012)
WM McLewin, William
Woods Woods, Patrick J.B.
Wr Wraight, David & Anke
WWJ Wharton, Peter; Wynn-Jones, Bleddyn & Susan
Yu Yu, Tse-tsun

NOMENCLATURAL NOTES

The following changes have been made during 2013 to the names used by the *RHS Plant Finder* based upon decisions of the Nomenclature and Taxonomy Advisory Group. If you have any comments on these changes or suggestions for other changes within the *RHS Plant Finder*, then please write, stating your reasons in full, to:

The Chairman
Nomenclature and Taxonomy Advisory Group
Royal Horticultural Society
RHS Garden Wisley
Woking
Surrey
GU23 6QB

- *Bomarea boliviensis* misapplied should be cross-referenced to *Alstroemeria isabellana.*
- *Cytisus* × *boskoopii* should be used for cultivars as listed in *Hanburyana* 7.
- *Dichroa versicolor* collections from Thailand should be placed under *Dichroa* sp.
- *Dorotheanthus bellidiformis* becomes *Cleretum bellidiforme.*
- *Euphorbia epithymoides* should be used for *E. polychroma* and all its cultivars.
- *Ficaria* is accepted as a genus distinct from *Ranunculus.*
- The remaining taxa from *Scilla* that belong to *Hyacinthoides* have now been moved.
- *Hypericum* × *hidcoteense* should be used for the cultivar 'Hidcote'.
- The genus *Menziesia* is sunk into *Rhododendron.*
- *Oldeania alpina* has been adopted for *Yushania alpina* and *Bergbambos tessellata* for *Thamnocalamus tessellatus.*
- The cultivar name 'Ken Aslet' has been adopted as a clonal name for the AGM plant of *Oxalis melanosticta.*
- *Paradisea liliastrum* misapplied should point to *P. lusitanica.*
- *Parochetus communis* will be used for plants cultivated in the UK unless stated that they specifically come from Africa.
- *Persicaria microcephala* 'Purple Fantasy' should not be attributed to a species.
- *Polyxena* is sunk into *Lachenalia.*
- Some *Prunus* names are changed to agree with Manual of Japanese Flowering Cherries.
- *Sinocalycanthus* and ×*Sinocalycalycanthus* are sunk into *Calycanthus.*
- In cultivation, pink-fruited *Sorbus hupehensis* should be referred to *S. pseudohupehensis*, while white-fruited *S.hupehensis* are *S. glabriuscula. S. hupehensis* itself is now a synonym of *S. discolor.*
- *Wisteria brachybotrys* 'Shiro-beni' is a mistake for 'Showa-beni'.
- *Zabelia* has been adopted as a split from *Abelia.* It includes the species *Z. biflora* and *Z. triflora.*
- *Zephyranthes minuta* is the correct name for *Z. grandiflora.*

This is not an exhaustive list of the changes made to the RHS Horticultural Database; many more changes are made during the year by the botanical team at the RHS. This list is to highlight the changes of the Nomenclature and Taxonomy Advisory Group.

CLASSIFICATION OF GENERA

Genera including a large number of species, or with many cultivars, are often subdivided into informal horticultural classifications, or formal cultivar groups in the case of *Clematis* and *Tulipa*. The breeding of new cultivars is sometimes limited to hybrids between closely-related species, thus for *Saxifraga* and *Primula*, the cultivars are allocated to the sections given in the infrageneric treatments cited. Please turn to p.11 for a fuller explanation.

ACTINIDIA

(s-p) Self-pollinating

BEGONIA

(C) Cane-like
(R) Rex Cultorum
(S) Semperflorens Cultorum
(T) × *tuberhybrida* (Tuberous)

CHRYSANTHEMUM

(By the National Chrysanthemum Society)
(1) Indoor Large (Exhibition)
(2) Indoor Medium (Exhibition)
(3a) Indoor Incurved: Large-flowered
(3b) Indoor Incurved: Medium-flowered
(3c) Indoor Incurved: Small-flowered
(4a) Indoor Reflexed: Large-flowered
(4b) Indoor Reflexed: Medium-flowered
(4c) Indoor Reflexed: Small-flowered
(5a) Indoor Intermediate: Large-flowered
(5b) Indoor Intermediate: Medium-flowered
(5c) Indoor Intermediate: Small-flowered
(6a) Indoor Anemone: Large-flowered
(6b) Indoor Anemone: Medium-flowered
(6c) Indoor Anemone: Small-flowered
(7a) Indoor Single: Large-flowered
(7b) Indoor Single: Medium-flowered
(7c) Indoor Single: Small-flowered
(8a) Indoor True Pompon
(8b) Indoor Semi-pompon
(9a) Indoor Spray: Anemone
(9b) Indoor Spray: Pompon
(9c) Indoor Spray: Reflexed
(9d) Indoor Spray: Single
(9e) Indoor Spray: Intermediate
(9f) Indoor Spray: Spider, Quill, Spoon or Any Other Type
(10a) Indoor, Spider
(10b) Indoor, Quill
(10c) Indoor, Spoon
(11) Any Other Indoor Type
(12a) Indoor, Charm
(12b) Indoor, Cascade
(13a) October-flowering Incurved: Large-flowered
(13b) October-flowering Incurved: Medium-flowered
(13c) October-flowering Incurved: Small-flowered
(14a) October-flowering Reflexed: Large-flowered
(14b) October-flowering Reflexed: Medium-flowered
(14c) October-flowering Reflexed: Small-flowered
(15a) October-flowering Intermediate: Large-flowered
(15b) October-flowering Intermediate: Medium-flowered
(15c) October-flowered Intermediate: Small-flowered
(16) October-flowering Large
(17a) October-flowering Single: Large-flowered
(17b) October-flowering Single: Medium-flowered
(17c) October-flowering Single: Small-flowered
(18a) October-flowering Pompon: True Pompon
(18b) October-flowering Pompon: Semi-pompon
(19a) October-flowering Spray: Anemone
(19b) October-flowering Spray: Pompon
(19c) October-flowering Spray: Reflexed
(19d) October-flowering Spray: Single
(19e) October-flowering Spray: Intermediate
(19f) October-flowering Spray: Spider, Quill, Spoon or Any Other Type
(20) Any Other October-flowering Type
(21a) Korean: Anemone
(21b) Korean: Pompon
(21c) Korean: Reflexed
(21d) Korean: Single
(21e) Korean: Intermediate
(21f) Korean: Spider, Quill, Spoon, or any other type
(22a) Charm: Anemone
(22b) Charm: Pompon
(22c) Charm: Reflexed
(22d) Charm: Single
(22e) Charm: Intermediate
(22f) Charm: Spider, Quill, Spoon or Any Other Type
(23a) Early-flowering Outdoor Incurved: Large-flowered

(23b) Early-flowering Outdoor Incurved: Medium-flowered
(23c) Early-flowering Outdoor Incurved: Small-flowered
(24a) Early-flowering Outdoor Reflexed: Large-flowered
(24b) Early-flowering Outdoor Reflexed: Medium-flowered
(24c) Early-flowering Outdoor Reflexed: Small-flowered
(25a) Early-flowering Outdoor Intermediate: Large-flowered
(25b) Early-flowering Outdoor Intermediate: Medium-flowered
(25c) Early-flowering Outdoor Intermediate: Small-flowered
(26a) Early-flowering Outdoor Anemone: Large-flowered
(26b) Early-flowering Outdoor Anemone: Medium-flowered
(27a) Early-flowering Outdoor Single: Large-flowered
(27b) Early-flowering Outdoor Single:Medium-flowered
(28a) Early-flowering Outdoor Pompon: True Pompon
(28b) Early-flowering Outdoor Pompon: Semi-pompon
(29a) Early-flowering Outdoor Spray: Anemone
(29b) Early-flowering Outdoor Spray: Pompon
(29c) Early-flowering Outdoor Spray: Reflexed
(29d) Early-flowering Outdoor Spray: Single
(29e) Early-flowering Outdoor Spray: Intermediate
(29f) Early-flowering Outdoor Spray: Spider, Quill, Spoon or Any Other Type
(29Rub) Early-flowering Outdoor Spray: Rubellum
(30) Any Other Early-flowering Outdoor Type

CLEMATIS

(Cultivar Groups as per Matthews, V. (2002) *The International Clematis Register & Checklist 2002*, RHS, London.)

(A) Atragene Group
(Ar) Armandii Group
(C) Cirrhosa Group
(EL) Early Large-flowered Group
(F) Flammula Group
(Fo) Forsteri Group
(H) Heracleifolia Group
(I) Integrifolia Group
(LL) Late Large-flowered Group
(M) Montana Group
(T) Texensis Group
(Ta) Tangutica Group
(V) Viorna Group
(Vb) Vitalba Group
(Vt) Viticella Group

DAHLIA

(Classification according to The International Dahlia Register (1969), 22nd Supp. (2012) formed through consultation with national dahlia societies.)

(Sin) 1 Single
(Anem) 2 Anemone-flowered
(Col) 3 Collerette
(WL) 4 Waterlily
(D) 5 Decorative
(Ba) 6 Ball
(Pom) 7 Pompon
(C) 8 Cactus
(S-c) 9 Semi-cactus
(Misc) 10 Miscellaneous
(Fim) 11 Fimbriated
(SinO) 12 Single Orchid (Star)
(DblO) 13 Double Orchid
(P) 14 Peony-flowered
(B) Botanical
(DwB) Dwarf Bedding
(Lil) Lilliput

DIANTHUS

(By the RHS)

(b) Carnation, border
(M) Carnation, Malmaison
(p) Pink
(p,a) Pink, annual
(pf) Carnation, perpetual-flowering
(pt) Carnation, pot

FRUIT

(B) Black (*Vitis*), Blackberry (*Rubus*), Blackcurrant (*Ribes*)
(Ball) Ballerina (*Malus*)
(C) Culinary (*Malus, Prunus, Pyrus, Ribes*)
(Cider) Cider (*Malus*)
(D) Dessert (*Malus, Prunus, Pyrus, Ribes*)
(F) Fruit
(G) Glasshouse (*Vitis*)
(O) Outdoor (*Vitis*)
(P) Pinkcurrant (*Ribes*)
(Perry) Perry (*Pyrus*)
(R) Red (*Vitis*), Redcurrant (*Ribes*)
(S) Seedless (*Citrus, Vitis*)
(W) White (*Vitis*), Whitecurrant (*Ribes*)

FUCHSIA

(E) Encliandra
(T) Variants and hybrids of *F. triphylla*

GLADIOLUS

(B) Butterfly
(E) Exotic
(G) Giant

(L) Large
(M) Medium
(Min) Miniature
(N) Nanus
(P) Primulinus
(S) Small
(Tub) Tubergenii

Hepatica nobilis

(Adapted from the International Hepatica Society classification for *Hepatica nobilis*)
(1) Hyoujun (normal)
(2) (degenerated anther)
(3) Otome (degenerated stamen)
(4) Henka (petal deformity)
(5/d) Herashibe (semi-double, primitive)
(5A/d) Choji (semi-double, primitive)
(6/d) Nidan (semi-double, advanced)
(7/d) Sandan (double, primitive)
(8/d) Karako (double, advanced)
(9/d) Sene-e (double, completed)

Hydrangea macrophylla

(H) Hortensia
(L) Lacecap

Iris

(Adapted from the American Iris Society Classification)
(AB) Arilbred
(BB) Border Bearded
(Cal-Sib) Series *Californicae* × Series *Sibiricae*
(CH) Californian Hybrid
(DB) Dwarf Bearded (not assigned)
(Dut) Dutch
(IB) Intermediate Bearded
(J) Juno (subgenus *Scorpiris*)
(La) Louisiana Hybrid
(MDB) Miniature Dwarf Bearded
(MTB) Miniature Tall Bearded
(Rc) Regeliocyclus (Section *Regelia* × Section *Oncocyclus*)
(SDB) Standard Dwarf Bearded
(Sib) Siberian
(Sino-Sib) Series *Sibiricae*, chromosome number 2n=40
(SpH) Species Hybrid
(Spuria) Spuria
(TB) Tall Bearded

Lilium

(Classification according to *The International Lily Register* (ed. 4, 2007))
(I) Asiatic hybrids derived from *L. amabile, L. bulbiferum, L. callosum, L. cernuum, L. concolor, L. dauricum, L. davidii, L.* × *hollandicum, L. lancifolium, L. lankongense, L. leichtlinii, L.* × *maculatum* and *L. pumilum, L.* × *scottiae, L. wardii* and *L. wilsonii.*
(II) Martagon hybrids derived from *L. dalhansonii, L. hansonii, L. martagon, L. medeoloides and L. tsingtauense*
(III) Euro-Caucasian hybrids derived from *L. candidum, L. chalcedonicum, L. kesselringianum, L. monadelphum, L. pomponium, L. pyrenaicum* and *L.* × *testaceum.*
(IV) American hybrids derived from *L. bolanderi, L.* × *burbankii, L. canadense, L. columbianum, L. grayi, L. humboldtii, L. kelleyanum, L. kelloggii, L. maritimum, L. michauxii, L. michiganense, L. occidentale, L.* × *pardaboldtii, L. pardalinum, L. parryi, L. parvum, L. philadelphicum, L. pitkinense, L. superbum, L. vollmeri, L. washingtonianum* and *L. wigginsii.*
(V) Longiflorum lilies derived from *L. formosanum, L. longiflorum, L. philippinense and L. wallichianum.*
(VI) Trumpet and Aurelian hybrids derived from *L.* × *aurelianense, L. brownii, L.* × *centigale, L. henryi, L.* × *imperiale, L.* × *kewense, L. leucantheum, L. regale, L. rosthornii, L. sargentiae, L. sulphureum* and *L. sulphurgale* (but excluding hybrids of *L. henryi* with all species listed in Division VII).
(VII) Oriental hybrids derived from *L. auratum, L. japonicum, L. nobilissimum, L.* × *parkmanii, L rubellum* and *L. speciosum* (but excl. all hybrids of these with *L. henryi*).
(VIII) Other hybrids not covered by any of the previous divisions (I-VII)
(IX) Species and cultivars of species
a/ upward-facing flowers
b/ outward-facing flowers
c/ downward-facing flowers
/a trumpet-shaped flowers
/b bowl-shaped flowers
/c flat flowers (or with only tepal tips recurved)
/d recurved flowers

Malus *see* Fruit

Narcissus

(By the RHS, revised 1998)
(1) Trumpet
(2) Large-cupped
(3) Small-cupped
(4) Double
(5) Triandrus
(6) Cyclamineus

(7)	Jonquilla and Apodanthus
(8)	Tazetta
(9)	Poeticus
(10)	Bulbocodium
(11a)	Split-corona: Collar
(11b)	Split-corona: Papillon
(12)	Miscellaneous
(13)	Species

Nymphaea

(H)	Hardy
(D)	Day-blooming
(N)	Night-blooming
(T)	Tropical

Papaver

(Not a horticultural classification, used to save space in this publication)

(SPS)	Super Poppy Series

Paeonia

(S)	Shrubby

Pelargonium

(A)	Angel
(C)	Coloured Foliage (in combination)
(Ca)	Cactus (in combination)
(d)	Double (in combination)
(Dec)	Decorative
(Dw)	Dwarf
(DwI)	Dwarf Ivy-leaved
(Fr)	Frutetorum
(I)	Ivy-leaved
(Min)	Miniature
(MinI)	Miniature Ivy-leaved
(R)	Regal
(Sc)	Scented-leaved
(St)	Stellar (in combination)
(T)	Tulip (in combination)
(U)	Unique
(Z)	Zonal

Primula

(Classification by Section as per Richards. J. (2002) *Primula* (2nd edition). Batsford, London)

(Ag)	*Auganthus*
(Al)	*Aleuritia*
(Am)	*Amethystinae*
(Ar)	*Armerina*
(Au)	*Auricula*
(A)	Alpine Auricula
(B)	Border Auricula
(S)	Show Auricula
(St)	Striped Auricula
(Bu)	*Bullatae*
(Ca)	*Capitatae*
(Cf)	*Cordifoliae*
(Ch)	*Chartaceae*
(Co)	*Cortusoides*
(Cr)	*Carolinella*
(Cu)	*Cuneifoliae*
(Cy)	*Crystallophlomis*
(Da)	*Davidii*
(De)	*Denticulatae*
(Dr)	*Dryadifoliae*
(F)	*Fedtschenkoanae*
(G)	*Glabrae*
(Ma)	*Malvaceae*
(Mi)	*Minutissimae*
(Mo)	*Monocarpicae*
(Mu)	*Muscarioides*
(Ob)	*Obconicolisteri*
(Or)	*Oreophlomis*
(Pa)	*Parryi*
(Pe)	*Petiolares*
(Pf)	*Proliferae*
(Pi)	*Pinnatae*
(Pr)	*Primula*
(Poly)	Polyanthus
(Prim)	Primrose
(Pu)	*Pulchellae*
(Py)	*Pycnoloba*
(R)	*Reinii*
(Si)	*Sikkimenses*
(So)	*Soldanelloides*
(Sp)	*Sphondylia*
(Sr)	*Sredinskya*
(Su)	*Suffrutescentes*
(Y)	*Yunnannenses*

Prunus *see* Fruit

Pyrus *see* Fruit

Rhododendron

(A)	Azalea (deciduous, species or unclassified hybrid)
(Ad)	Azaleodendron
(EA)	Evergreen azalea
(G)	Ghent azalea (deciduous)
(K)	Knap Hill or Exbury azalea (deciduous)
(M)	Mollis azalea (deciduous)
(O)	Occidentalis azalea (deciduous)
(R)	Rustica azalea (deciduous)
(V)	Vireya rhododendron
(Vs)	Viscosa azalea (deciduous)

Ribes *see* Fruit

Rosa

(A)	Alba
(Bb)	Bourbon
(Bs)	Boursault
(Ce)	Centifolia
(Ch)	China
(Cl)	Climbing (in combination)

(D)	Damask
(DPo)	Damask Portland
(F)	Floribunda or Cluster-flowered
(G)	Gallica
(Ga)	Garnette
(GC)	Ground Cover
(HM)	Hybrid Musk
(HP)	Hybrid Perpetual
(HT)	Hybrid Tea or Large-flowered
(Min)	Miniature
(Mo)	Moss (in combination)
(N)	Noisette
(Patio)	Patio, Miniature Floribunda or Dwarf Cluster-flowered
(Poly)	Polyantha
(Ra)	Rambler
(RH)	Rubiginosa hybrid (Hybrid Sweet Briar)
(Ru)	Rugosa
(S)	Shrub
(SpH)	Spinosissima Hybrid
(T)	Tea

Rubus *see* Fruit

Saxifraga

(Classification by Section from Gornall, R.J. (1987). *Botanical Journal of the Linnean Society,* 95(4): 273-292)

(1)	*Ciliatae*
(2)	*Cymbalaria*
(3)	*Merkianae*
(4)	*Micranthes*
(5)	*Irregulares*
(6)	*Heterisia*
(7)	*Porphyrion*
(8)	*Ligulatae*
(9)	*Xanthizoon*
(10)	*Trachyphyllum*
(11)	*Gymnopera*
(12)	*Cotylea*
(13)	*Odontophyllae*
(14)	*Mesogyne*
(15)	*Saxifraga*

Tulipa

(Classification by Cultivar Group from *Classified List and International Register of Tulip Names* by Koninklijke Algemeene Vereniging voor Bloembollencultuur 1996)

(1)	Single Early Group
(2)	Double Early Group
(3)	Triumph Group
(4)	Darwin Hybrid Group
(5)	Single Late Group (including Darwin Group and Cottage Group)
(6)	Lily-flowered Group
(7)	Fringed Group
(8)	Viridiflora Group
(9)	Rembrandt Group
(10)	Parrot Group
(11)	Double Late Group
(12)	Kaufmanniana Group
(13)	Fosteriana Group
(14)	Greigii Group
(15)	Miscellaneous

Verbena

(G)	Species and hybrids considered by some botanists to belong to the separate genus *Glandularia.*

Viola

(C)	Cornuta Hybrid
(dVt)	Double Violet
(ExVa)	Exhibition Viola
(FP)	Fancy Pansy
(PVt)	Parma Violet
(SP)	Show Pansy
(T)	Tricolor
(Va)	Viola
(Vt)	Violet
(Vtta)	Violetta

Vitis *see* Fruit

THE PLANT DIRECTORY

A

Abelia ✿ (*Caprifoliaceae*)

	Auderose = 'Minaud'PBR	LAst
	biflora	see *Zabelia biflora*
	chinensis misapplied	see *A.* × *grandiflora* 'Lake Maggiore'
§	***chinensis*** R. Br.	CBcs CExl CMCN CMac ELan EPfP EWTr LRHS MAsh MMuc SEND SHil SKHP SPer SRms WCot WFar WGrn WPat
	- 'China Rose' 🏆H5 **new**	LPfy SKHP
§	***dielsii***	CBot
	'Edward Goucher' 🏆H5	Widely available
	engleriana	CExl EPfP LHop LRHS MAsh MBlu NLar SEND SLon SSpi
	floribunda 🏆H5	CBcs CBot CDul CExl CMac CSam CSde CWib ECre ELan ELon EPfP LHop LRHS MRav NLar SAko SBrt SEND SGbt SGol SKHP SPer SPoG SRms SSpi WPat
	× ***grandiflora*** common clone	see *A.* × *grandiflora* 'Lake Maggiore'
	- 'Aurea'	see *A.* × *grandiflora* 'Gold Spot'
	- 'Brockhill Allgold'	EMil EPfP LRHS
	- 'Compacta'	LRHS WFar
	- Confetti = 'Conti'PBR (v)	CBcs CDoC CLet CMac CSBt ECrN ELan EMil EPfP LAst LRHS LSRN MAsh MBri MGos MRav NLar SCob SGol SLim SPer SPoG SWvt WFar
§	- 'Francis Mason' (v)	Widely available
§	- 'Gold Spot' (v)	CBot EPfP LRHS MGos NLar SPer WPat
	- 'Gold Strike'	see *A.* × *grandiflora* 'Gold Spot'
	- Golden Panache = 'Minpan'	MRav
	- 'Goldsport'	see *A.* × *grandiflora* 'Gold Spot'
	- 'Hopleys'PBR (v) 🏆H5	CBcs CDoC CMac CSBt CTri CWib ELan EMil EPfP LHop LRHS MAsh MBri MGos NLar SCob SEND SEle SLon SPoG SRms SWvt WGrn WHar
	- 'Kaleidoscope'PBR (v)	Widely available
	- Lady Liberty = 'Keylib' **new**	MGos
	- 'Lady Summerdream' **new**	EBee
§	- 'Lake Maggiore' 🏆H5	Widely available
	- Lucky Lots = 'Wevo2' (v)	EBee LLHF NLar SCob
	- 'Panache' (v)	LLHF WCot
	- 'Prostrate White'	EBee ECrN LRHS NLar
	- 'Semperflorens'	LRHS
	- 'Sherwoodii'	CDoC EBee ECrN EHoe EPfP LRHS MAsh MGos SLim WRHF
	- 'Sunrise' (v)	NLar
	- Sunshine Daydream = 'Abelops'PBR (v)	CTsd LAst LLHF LRHS MPkF NLar SCob
	- 'Variegata'	see *A.* × *grandiflora* 'Francis Mason'
§	'Lynn'	EBee MPkF SCob
	mosanensis	CAbP CBot CMCN ELan EPfP LLHF LRHS MBlu MGil NLar SLon SPoG SSpi WSHC
	parvifolia	Widely available
	Petite Garden = 'Minedward'PBR	CDoC EMil LLHF LRHS
	Pinky Bells	see *A.* 'Lynn'
	rupestris misapplied	see *A.* × *grandiflora* 'Lake Maggiore'
	rupestris Lindl.	see *A. chinensis* R. Br.
	triflora	see *Zabelia triflora*
	zanderi	see *A. dielsii*

Abeliophyllum (*Oleaceae*)

	distichum	CBcs CDoC CWib ECrN ELan ELon EPfP IDee LBMP LRHS MAsh MBlu SGol SSpi SWvt WBod WCFE WSHC
	- Roseum Group	CBcs CExl ELan ELon EPfP EWTr LCro LHop LRHS MAsh MMuc MRav SKHP SLon SPer SPoG

Abelmoschus (*Malvaceae*)

	esculentus	SVic

Abies (*Pinaceae*)

	alba	CDul NWea
	- 'Bystricka'	MAsh NLar
	- 'Compacta'	CKen
	- 'Green Spiral'	NLar
	- 'King's Dwarf'	CKen
	- 'Microphylla'	CKen
	- 'Münsterland'	CKen NLar
	- 'Nana' misapplied	see *Picea glauca* 'Nana'
	- 'Nana' ambig.	CKen
	- 'Pendula'	CKen
	- 'Pyramidalis'	NLar
	amabilis 'Spreading Star'	SLim
	balsamea	GKin
	- 'Cook's Blue'	CKen
	- Hudsonia Group	CDoC CKen CMac EFry LRHS NWad SLim WIce
	- - 'Nana'	CKen EFry LRHS MJak NWad WGor
	- 'Jamie'	CKen NLar
	- 'Le Feber'	CKen
	- var. ***phanerolepis*** 'Bear Swamp'	CKen NHol
	- 'Piccolo'	CKen NLar SBod WGor
	- 'Renswoude'	CKen
	- 'Tyler Blue'	CKen NLar
	- 'Verkade's Prostrate'	CKen
*	***borisii-regis*** 'Pendula'	CKen
	- 'Spring Delight' **new**	LRHS
	brachyphylla dwarf	see *A. homolepis* 'Prostrata'
	cephalonica	CDul CKen NWea
	- 'Greg's Broom'	CKen
§	- 'Meyer's Dwarf'	CMac NEgg NLar SBod SLim

	Name	Suppliers
	- 'Nana'	see *A. cephalonica* 'Meyer's Dwarf'
	cephalonica	MHtn
	× ***nordmanniana*** **new**	
	chensiensis	CDul
	cilicica 'Spring Grove'	CKen
	colimensis NJM 09.074	WPGP
	concolor	CBcs CDul CTho LRHS MMuc NWea SEND WMou
	- 'Archer's Dwarf'	CKen NEgg NLar SLim
	- 'Aurea'	NEgg NLar
	- 'Birthday Broom'	CKen
	- 'Blue Sapphire'	CKen
§	- 'Compacta' ♀H7	CDoC CKen LRHS MBri MGos NEgg NHol NLar NWea SLim
	- 'Fagerhult'	CKen
	- 'Gable's Weeping'	CKen
	- 'Glauca'	see *A. concolor* (Violacea Group) 'Violacea'
	- 'Glauca Compacta'	see *A. concolor* 'Compacta'
	- 'Hillier Broom'	see *A. concolor* 'Hillier's Dwarf'
§	- 'Hillier's Dwarf'	CKen
	- 'Husky Pup'	CKen
	- (Lowiana Group) 'Creamy'	CKen NEgg NLar
	- 'Masonic Broom'	CKen
	- 'Mike Stearn'	CKen
	- 'Mora'	CKen
	- 'Ostrov nad Ohri'	CKen
	- 'Piggelmee'	CKen MAsh
	- 'Pygmy'	CKen
	- 'Scooter'	CKen NLar
	- 'Sherwood's Blue'	NEgg
	- Violacea Group	CKen MGos SLim
	- - 'Violacea' ♀H7 **new**	WMat
	- - 'Violacea Prostrate' ♀H7	EUJe NHol NLar
	- 'Wattezii'	CKen
	- 'Wintergold'	CKen LRHS MBlu MGos NEgg NHol NLar SLim
	delavayi	CDul EPfP NWea
	- var. ***delavayi***	CExl
	- - Fabri Group	see *A. fabri*
	- 'Major Neishe'	CKen
§	***fabri***	CDul CKen
	fargesii	CKen
	forrestii	CKen
	- var. ***georgei***	NWea
	fraseri	CDul CTho NWea WMou
	- 'Blue Bonnet'	CKen NLar
	- 'Kline's Nest'	SLim
	- 'Raul's Dwarf'	CKen
	grandis	CBcs CDul CJun ELan EPfP MMuc NWea
	- 'Compacta'	CKen
	- 'Van Dedem's Dwarf'	CKen NLar SLim
	holophylla	NWea
	homolepis	CDul CKen NWea
§	- 'Prostrata'	CKen
	koreana ♀H7	CBcs CCVT CDoC CDul CJun CKen CMac CTho EFry ELan EPfP GKin LAst LRHS MAsh MBlu MGos MJak MMuc NHol NPol NWea SBod SGol SLim SPoG SWvt WHar WMat WMou
	- 'Alpin Star'	CKen MAsh NEgg NLar
	- 'Blaue Zwo'	CKen LRHS
	- 'Blauer Eskimo' ♀H7	CKen MAsh SLim
	- 'Blauer Pfiff'	CKen
	- 'Blinsham Gold'	CKen
	- 'Blue Emperor'	MBlu
	- 'Blue Magic'	CKen NLar
	- 'Blue 'n' Silver'	NLar
	- 'Bonsai Blue'	IVic
I	- 'Brevifolia'	NLar
	- 'Brilliant'	CKen NLar
	- 'Cis' ♀H7	CDoC CKen NHol NLar NWad SLim WGor
	- 'Crystal Globe'	see *A. koreana* 'Kristallkugel'
	- 'Dark Hill'	NLar
	- 'Doni-tajuso'	CKen NLar
	- 'Eisregen'	CKen
	- 'Festival'	NEgg NHol NLar
	- 'Fliegender Untertasse'	IVic
	- 'Frosty'	SLim
	- 'Gait'	CKen NLar
	- 'Golden Glow'	NLar SLim
	- 'Goldener Traum'	CKen NLar
	- 'Green Carpet'	CKen
	- 'Horstmann'	CKen
	- 'Ice Breaker' ♀H7	MAsh SLim
	- 'Inverleith'	CKen
	- 'Kleiner Prinz'	NLar
	- 'Kohout'	CKen
	- 'Kohout's Ice Breaker'PBR	CKen
§	- 'Kristallkugel'	CKen MAsh NEgg NLar
	- 'Lippetal'	CKen
	- 'Luminetta'	CKen NHol
	- 'Nadelkissen'	CKen NHol
	- 'Nisbet'	NEgg NHol NLar SCoo
	- 'Oberon'	CDoC CKen MAsh MBri NHol NLar NWad SAko
	- 'Piccolo'	CKen
	- 'Pinocchio'	CDoC CKen NHol NWad
	- 'Ry'	NLar
	- 'Schneestern'	NLar
	- 'Sherwood Compact'	CKen
	- 'Shorty'	CKen NLar
	- 'Silberkugel'	CKen CMen MAsh NLar NWad SLim
	- 'Silberlocke' ♀H7	CDoC CDul CKen LRHS MAsh MBlu MBri MGos NLar SCoo SLim WMat
	- 'Silbermavers'	CKen
	- 'Silberperl'	CKen CMen NLar SAko SLim
	- 'Silberschmelze'	NLar
	- 'Silberzwerg'	NLar
	- 'Silver Show'	CDoC CDul LRHS NHol NLar SLim
	- 'Threave'	CKen NHol NLar
	- 'Tundra'	NEgg NLar
	- 'Verdener Dom'	NLar
	- 'Wellenseind'	CKen
	lasiocarpa 'Alpine Beauty'	CKen NLar
	- var. ***arizonica*** 'Compacta' Hornibr. ♀H7	CDoC CKen CMac LRHS MAsh MBri MGos NEgg NHol NLar SBod SLim SPoG WMat
	- - 'Kenwith Blue'	CKen NEgg SLim
	- 'Beano Broom' **new**	CKen
	- 'Chikov'	CKen
	- 'Day Creek'	CKen NLar
	- 'Duflon'	CKen MAsh
	- 'Elaine'	CKen
	- 'Green Globe'	CKen NLar SLim
	- 'Joe's Alpine'	CKen
	- 'Kyle's Alpine'	CKen
	- 'Logan Pass'	CKen
	- 'Lopalpun'	CKen
	- 'Mulligan's Dwarf'	CKen
	- 'Prickly Pete'	CKen NLar
I	- 'Prostrata'	CMac
	- 'Stevens Blue'	CKen MAsh NLar
	- 'Toenisvorst'	CKen

	- 'Utah'	CKen
I	***magnifica*** 'Nana'	CKen
	- witches' broom	CKen
	nebrodensis	CKen
	- 'Sicilian Gold'	NLar
	nobilis	see *A. procera*
	nordmanniana	CCVT CDul CJun CMac CTho EFry ELan EPfP EWTr LBuc MJak MMuc NWea SEND SLim SPoG WHar WMou
	- 'Arne's Dwarf'	CKen
	- 'Barabits' Compact'	NLar
	- 'Barabits' Spreader'	CKen
	- 'Dahlheim'	MAsh
	- 'Dobřichovice' **new**	NLar
	- subsp. ***equi-trojani***	CDul NWea
	- - 'Archer'	CKen
	- - 'Franke'	NLar
	- 'Golden Spreader' 🏆H7	CDoC CKen CMac LRHS MAsh MBlu MBri MGos NEgg NLar SCoo SLim WThu
	- 'Hasselt'	CKen
	- 'Jakobsen'	CKen
	- 'Midwinter Gold' **new**	NLar
	- 'Pendula'	MBlu SMad
	- 'Silberspitze'	CKen
	numidica	CKen
	- 'Glauca'	CKen
	- 'Lawrenceville'	NEgg
	pindrow	CDul NWea
	pinsapo	CDul
	- 'Atlas'	MAsh
	- 'Aurea' 🏆H5	CKen MPkF NHol SLim
I	- 'Aurea Nana'	CKen
	- 'Fastigiata'	MPkF NLar SGol
	- 'Glauca' 🏆H5	CDoC CDul CKen CTho ELan MBlu NLar SLim
	- 'Hamondii'	CKen
I	- 'Horstmann'	CKen NEgg NHol SLim
	- 'Kelleriis'	EUJe
	- 'Marokko'	NLar
	- 'Pendula'	CKen LRHS
	- 'Quicksilver'	CKen
	- 'San Pedro'	CKen
§	***procera***	CBcs CDul EPfP EWTr NWea
	- 'Bizarro'	NEgg
	- 'Blaue Hexe'	CKen IVic MAsh NEgg SLim
	- 'Delbar Cascade'	CKen
	- Glauca Group	CDoC CTho ECrN EPfP GKin MAsh MBlu MBri NHol NLar SLim
	- - 'Glauca Prostrata' 🏆H6	EUJe SLim
	- 'La Graciosa'	NLar
	- 'Noble's Dwarf'	SLim
	- 'Prostrata'	MAsh
	- 'Rat Tail'	NLar
	- 'Sherwoodii'	CKen SLim
	Rosemoor hybrid	CKen
	sachalinensis	CKen
	sibirica	EPfP NWea
	spectabilis	EPfP
	veitchii	CTho NEgg NWea
	- 'Heddergott'	CKen NEgg NHol SLim
	- 'Heine'	CKen
	- 'Kramer'	CKen
	- 'Otovenack' **new**	NLar
I	- 'Pendula'	CKen IVic
	- 'Rumburk'	CKen SLim
	- var. ***sikokiana***	NLar
	- 'Syców'	CKen
	vejarii	SLim

Abromeitiella see *Deuterocohnia*

Abutilon ✿ (*Malvaceae*)

	'Amiti'	GFai WTcb
	'Apricot Belle'	GFai WTcb
	'Ashford Red'	CBcs ELan LRHS SKHP WKif WTcb
	'Bartley Schwarz' **new**	WTcb
	'Bella Red' (Bella Series) **new**	WTcb
	'Boule de Neige'	CBot GFai WTcb
	'Canary Bird' misapplied	see *A.* 'Golden Fleece'
	'Canary Bird' 🏆H1b	CBcs CHll CSde WKif WTcb
	'Cannington Carol' (v) 🏆H1b	CHll CLet ELan LLHF LSRN SEND SLim WTcb
	'Cannington Peter' (v) 🏆H1b	GFai LSRN WTcb
	'Cannington Sally' (v)	GFai WTcb
	'Cloth of Gold'	CMac GFai WTcb
	'Cynthia Pike' (v)	LRHS WTcb
	'Eric Lilac'	WTcb
	'Eric's Wotsit' **new**	WTcb
§	'Feuerglocke'	GFai
	Firebell	see *A.* 'Feuerglocke'
	'Flamenco'	CWGN WTcb
	'Fool's Gold' **new**	WTcb
	'Frances Elizabeth'	WTcb
	'Gloucestershire Belle' **new**	WTcb
§	'Golden Fleece'	GFai
	'Heather Bennington'	GFai WTcb
	'Henry Makepeace'	GFai WTcb
	'Herefordshire Belle' **new**	WTcb
	'Hinton Seedling'	CRHN GFai WTcb
	× ***hybridum*** apricot-flowered	WTcb
	- red-flowered	WTcb
	indicum	WCot WTcb
	'Ines'	EBee GFai SAko SChF WPGP WTcb
	'Jacqueline Morris'	LRHS
	'John Thompson'	CWGN LSRN WCot WTcb
	'Johore' **new**	WTcb
	'Julia' **new**	GFai WTcb
	'Juliet' **new**	WTcb
	'Kentish Belle' 🏆H3	Widely available
	'Kreutzberger'	WTcb
	'Lemon Queen'	WTcb
	'Linda Vista Peach' 🏆H1b	GFai WTcb
	'Louis Marignac'	GFai WTcb
	Lucky Lantern Tangerine = 'Nuabtang' **new**	SPad
	'Marion' 🏆H1b	CRHN LRHS LSRN SPlb WTcb
	'Master Michael'	CMac GFai SEND WTcb
	megapotamicum 🏆H3	Widely available
	- 'Compactum'	WTcb
	- 'Joy Bells' **new**	GFai
	- 'Pink Charm' **new**	WTcb
	- 'Variegatum' (v) 🏆H3	CBcs CBot CMac ELan ELon EPfP EUJe IDee LRHS SEle SKHP SLim SLon SPer SPoG SWvt WCot WGrn WTcb XLum
	- 'Wisley Red'	CBcs CRHN CTsd LRHS SAko SKHP
	× ***milleri*** hort. 🏆H3	CMac CRHN WCot WTcb
	- 'Variegatum' (v)	CMac LRHS WCot WTcb
	'Millie Houghton'	WTcb
	'Moonchimes'	WTcb
	'Nabob' 🏆H1b	CBcs CBot CDoC CExl CRHN CSde EUJe LSou MOWG SAko SPoG WTcb
	'Old Rose Belle'	GFai WTcb
	'Orange Glow' (v) 🏆H1b	GFai
	'Orange Hot Lava'	CExl EBee GFai SAko SMad WPGP WTcb

'Orange Vein'	GFai WTcb
'Paddy's Nephew' **new**	WTcb
'Patrick Synge'	CHGN CHll CMHG MOWG SAko SPhx WPGP WTcb
pictum	WTcb
- 'Thompsonii' (v) ♀H1b	GFai WTcb
'Pink Lady'	WTcb
'Pink Lipstick' **new**	WTcb
'Red Bells'	GFai WTcb
'Red Goblin'	GFai WTcb
'Red Hot Lava'	SChF
'Red Queen'	WTcb
'Red Tiger' **new**	WTcb
Red Trumpet = 'Oostredtrump'PBR **new**	GFai WTcb
'Redisch' **new**	GFai WTcb
'Rose Glow' **new**	WTcb
roseum **new**	WTcb
'Rotterdam'	WTcb
'Russels Dwarf'	WTcb
'Satin Pink Belle'	GFai WTcb
'Savitzii' (v) ♀H1b	GFai MSCN WTcb
'Simcox White'	WTcb
'Snowfall'	GFai WTcb
'Sophia Jackson'	WTcb
'Souvenir de Bonn' (v) ♀H1b	CBcs CHll WTcb
'Sunflower Cream' **new**	WTcb
× ***suntense***	CBcs CMHG CSBt CWld EBee ELan EPfP EUJe EWld GGal LRHS MSCN NPer SChF SPer WTcb
- 'Jermyns' ♀H4	CAbP CExl ELan EPfP LSRN MBri MGos SAko SCoo SKHP SPoG SWvt
- 'Violetta'	CBot WSHC
'Tango'	CBot CKel CWGN EUJe SEND WTcb
'Teri Turner' **new**	WTcb
variegated, salmon-flowered (v)	GFai LAst WTcb
'Victorian Lady' **new**	WTcb
'Victory'	CWGN SKHP WTcb
vitifolium	CBcs CBot CDTJ CWib EPfP NEgg SEND SPad SPtp WKif WTcb
- 'Album'	CBcs CExl CHll ELan SPer WTcb
- 'Ice Blue'	CBot
- 'Tennant's White' ♀H4	CAbP CBot CExl EPfP GGal LRHS MBri SAko SKHP
- 'Veronica Tennant' ♀H4	CExl EBee EPfP LRHS SChF WTcb
'Voodoo' **new**	WTcb
'Wakehurst'	GFai
'Waltz'	CWGN EUJe LLHF SEND WCot WTcb
'Westfield Bronze' (v)	CRHN WTcb
'White King'	WTcb
White Trumpet = 'Oostwhitru'PBR **new**	GFai WTcb
'Worcestershire Belle' **new**	WTcb
Yellow Trumpet = 'Oosttrump'PBR **new**	CBot GFai WTcb

Acacia (*Mimosaceae*)

sp.	LSRN
acinacea	IDee SPlb
adunca	SPlb
alata **new**	WBod
angustissima	SPlb
armata	see *A. paradoxa*
axillaris	SPlb
baileyana ♀H2	CBcs CLet CMac COtt CSBt EHoe ELan EPfP EUJe IDee LPfy LRHS LSRN MAsh MGos SBig SCoo SEND SPer SPlb SWvt WBod WFar WPat
- var. ***aurea***	SPlb
- 'Purpurea' ♀H3	Widely available
- 'Songlines'	LRHS MBri MGos SHil
boormanii	SAko SPlb WPGP
caven NJM 08.0021	WPGP
covenyi	WPGP
cultriformis	CTsd ESwi SEND
dealbata ♀H2	Widely available
- 'Argentea'	MGos
- 'Gaulois Astier'	CSBt LPfy LRHS LSRN MBri MGos SHil SWvt
- subsp. ***subalpina***	WPGP
drummondii	COtt
'Exeter Hybrid'	CSBt
fimbriata	CRHN
glaucoptera	SPlb
gregorii	SPlb
jibberdingensis **new**	SPlb
julibrissin	see *Albizia julibrissin*
karroo	CDTJ SPlb
longifolia	CBcs CDTJ IDee LRHS
macradenia	SPlb
mearnsii	EBee
melanoxylon	CBcs CDTJ ESwi MTPN SEND SPlb
nanodealbata	SPad
§ ***paradoxa***	IDee
pataczekii	CSBt EPfP WPGP
pendula	SPlb
podalyriifolia	SPlb
pravissima ♀H3	Widely available
- 'Bushwalk Baby'	MOWG
retinodes	CBcs CDTJ CTsd EPfP LRHS MTPN SEND SPad SWvt
- 'Lisette'	LRHS MGos SHil
riceana	CTsd SVen
rubida	CTsd IDee SPlb
sentis	see *A. victoriae*
spectabilis	SPlb
suaveolens	SPlb
truncata **new**	SPlb
verticillata	CBcs CDTJ CDoC CHGN CHll CSde EBee EPfP MOWG MTPN
- riverine form	CExl EPfP LRHS SAko SEND
§ ***victoriae***	SPlb

Acaena (*Rosaceae*)

adscendens misapplied	see *A. affinis*, *A. saccaticupula* 'Blue Haze'
adscendens ambig. 'Glauca'	EHoe NBir
§ ***affinis***	ECou MCot
anserinifolia misapplied	see *A. novae-zelandiae*
buchananii	CTri EBee ECho ECou EHoe EPPr GAbr GBin GEdr MBrN MMuc NLar SCob SRms
caerulea hort.	see *A. caesiiglauca*
§ ***caesiiglauca***	CTri GAbr GMaP GQue MLHP
inermis	SPlb
- 'Purpurea'	CSam EBee ECha ECou ECtt EHoe EWes GAbr GBin GEdr GKev GQue MAvo NDov NHol NLar NWad SPlb WMoo XLum
magellanica	GCal GKev
microphylla ♀H5	CSam CTri ECou GBin MBel MBrN NLar SPlb SRms WMoo
- Copper Carpet	see *A. microphylla* 'Kupferteppich'
- 'Glauca'	see *A. caesiiglauca*
§ - 'Kupferteppich'	CSam ECho ECtt EHoe ELan EPPr GAbr GBin GCal GCrg GKev GMaP

	GQue LHop MBri MHol MRav NBir NBro NChi NLar NPri SCob SRms WMoo XLum
minor var. ***antarctica***	GBin
§ ***novae-zelandiae***	CTri EBee ECou SDix WMoo XLum
'Pewter'	see *A. saccaticupula* 'Blue Haze'
'Purple Carpet'	see *A. microphylla* 'Kupferteppich'
'Purple Haze'	CSpe SCob
saccaticupula	GKev
§ - 'Blue Haze'	EBee ECha ECho ECou EDAr LHop LRHS MBrN MRav SPlb SRms WMoo
tesca	GBin

Acalypha (*Euphorbiaceae*)

'Mini Red'	LAst
pendula	see *A. reptans*
§ ***reptans***	EShb

Acanthocalyx see *Morina*

Acantholimon (*Plumbaginaceae*)

acerosum	XSen
androsaceum	see *A. ulicinum*
armenum	XSen
- var. ***balansae***	LLHF
glumaceum	LLHF
§ ***ulicinum***	XEll XSen

Acanthopanax see *Eleutherococcus*

ricinifolius	see *Kalopanax septemlobus*

Acanthus ✿ (*Acanthaceae*)

arboreus	XLum
balcanicus misapplied	see *A. hungaricus*
'Candelabra'	MAvo WWEG
caroli-alexandri	see *A. spinosus* L.
dioscoridis	GCal SMHy WHil
- var. ***perringii***	CCon CDes EBee ECha GBin MNrw NLar WCot WFar XLum
eminens	CDes WCot
hirsutus	CFis EPri IFoB WCot
- subsp. ***syriacus***	CCon EHrv EWTr GCal
'Hollande du Nort'	GBin XLum
§ ***hungaricus***	CCon CHid CMHG CMac EAEE EBee ELan GBin ILea LCro LOPS LRHS MBel MMuc MRav NLar SCob SDix SPer SWat WCot WFar WHil WMnd XLum
- AL&JS 90097YU	WHil
- MESE 561	EPPr
- 'White Lips' **new**	EBee
longifolius Host	see *A. hungaricus*
mollis	Widely available
- 'Fielding Gold'	see *A. mollis* 'Hollard's Gold'
- free-flowering	ESwi GCal MAvo XLum
§ - 'Hollard's Gold'	Widely available
- 'Jefalba'	see *A. mollis* (Latifolius Group) 'Rue Ledan'
- Latifolius Group	MRav SRms WHil WHoo
§ - - 'Rue Ledan'	EBee ECtt EPPr GBin LHop LRHS MAvo NGdn NLar SCob SMHy SPhx WCot WWEG XLum
- 'Long Spike'	GCal
- 'Tasmanian Angel' (v)	CBct CSpe CWGN EBee ECtt ESwi IBoy LBMP LHop MAsh MHol SCob SMad SPoG WCot XLum
'Morning's Candle'	CBct EBee ECtt NGdn NLar SGol WFar WHil XLum
sennii	CAby CCse CDes CEvo IMou LTro SMad SPhx WHil WSHC XLum
spinosus misapplied	see *A. spinosus* Spinosissimus Group
§ ***spinosus*** L.	Widely available
- Ferguson's form	WCot XLum
- 'Lady Moore' (v)	NLar XLum
- 'Royal Haughty'	MAvo WFar XLum
§ - Spinosissimus Group	CBct CCon CMHG CTsd ECha ELan GBin GCal GCra IBoy LEdu MAvo MGos MRav SMad SWat WCot WFar WHar WMnd
'Summer Beauty'	ECtt EWes GBin LHop MAvo MRav WCot WFar WHil WHoo WWEG XLum
'Whitewater' (v)	CWGN EBee ECtt GEdr LHop LRHS MAsh MAvo MHol NLar NSti NWad SBig SCob SMad SPoG SRms WCot WHil

Acca (*Myrtaceae*)

sp.	LPar
sellowiana (F)	Widely available
- 'Apollo' (F)	LRHS
- 'Mammoth' (F)	CBcs
- 'Triumph' (F)	CBcs
- 'Unique' (F)	ERea EUJe

Acer ✿ (*Sapindaceae*)

sp.	ETod
acuminatum	CEvo
amoenum B&SWJ 10916	WCru
- B&SWJ 10977	WCru
- 'Firecracker'	see *A. palmatum* (Dissectum Group) 'Firecracker'
'Ample Surprise' **new**	MBlu
buergerianum	CDul CJun CLnd CMCN CMen MMuc MPkF NLar SGol WMou
- B&SWJ 12676 from South Korea	WCru
- var. ***formosanum*** CWJ 12477	WCru
- 'Mino-yatsubusa'	MPkF
- 'Miyasama-yatsubusa'	MPkF
- 'Naruto'	CMCN MPkF
campbellii	MBlu
- subsp. ***campbellii*** GWJ 9360	WCru
- - NJM 12.069 **new**	WPGP
- 'Exuberance'	CJun
campestre ♀H6	Widely available
- 'Carnival' (v) ♀H6	CCVT EBee ECrN ELon MAsh MBlu NLar NOrn SCob SGol SPer SWvt WHar WPat
- 'Eco Sentry'PBR	EBee
- 'Elsrijk'	CCVT CLnd SCoo SGol
- 'Evelyn'	see *A. campestre* 'Queen Elizabeth'
- 'Evenley Red'	EBee MBlu WPGP
- 'Postelense'	EBee MBlu
- 'Pulverulentum' (v)	NEgg
§ - 'Queen Elizabeth'	CDul MGos SGol
- 'Red Shine'	SGol
- 'Royal Ruby'	MGos
I - 'Silver Celebration' (v)	CJun
- 'William Caldwell'	CTho EBee MBlu MBri
capillipes	CBcs CDul CMCN CTho CWib ELan EWTr MGos MJak MMuc NOrn NWea SCob SPer SPlb WHCr WHar WMat WPGP
- 'Antoine'	LRHS MBlu MBri
- 'Candy Stripe'	see *A.* × *conspicuum* 'Candy Stripe'
- 'Honey Dew'	CJun SSta

Name	Suppliers
aff. ***capillipes***	LAst
cappadocicum	CCVT CDul CMCN ECrN MMuc MSnd NWea WMou
- 'Aureum' ♀H6	CBcs CDoC CDul CLnd CMCN CNWT CTho EBee ECrN ELan EPfP GBin GKin IArd MAsh MBlu MBri MGos MRav NLar NOrn SCob SGol SMad SPer SWvt WFar WHar WHor WMat
- var. ***mono***	see *A. pictum*
- 'Rubrum' ♀H6	CArg CBcs CDul CLnd CMCN EBee ECrN EPfP GBin GKin IDee LRHS MBlu MGos MMuc MRav NOrn SCob SEND SGol SPer WFar WHar WHer WHor WMat
- var. ***tricaudatum***	CExl
carpinifolium	CDul EBee EBtc EPfP IArd MBlu MPkF NLar WPGP
- B&SWJ 10955	WCru
- B&SWJ 11124	WCru
§ ***caudatifolium***	WPat
- CWJ 12403	WCru
- RWJ 9843	WCru
§ ***caudatum*** GWJ 9279	WCru
- GWJ 9317	WCru
- HWJK 2240	WCru
- HWJK 2338	WCru
- subsp. ***ukurunduense***	MPkF
- - B&SWJ 8658	WCru
circinatum	CBcs CCVT CDul CEvo CJun CMCN ECrN IVic MBlu MMuc MSnd NEgg NLar SEND SPlb
- B&SWJ 9565	WCru
- 'Burgundy Jewel'	CJun
- 'Little Gem'	CJun
- 'Monroe'	CJun SGol
- 'Pacific Fire'	CJun
- 'Sunglow'	CJun
- 'Sunny Sister' **new**	LRHS
circinatum* × *palmatum	SBig
cissifolium	CMCN EPfP NLar
- B&SWJ 10801	WCru
§ × ***conspicuum*** 'Candy Stripe'	CJun NLar WPGP
- 'Elephant's Ear'	CJun MBlu NLar
- 'Phoenix'	CJun CMCN CRos CTho EPfP GKin IVic LRHS MBlu NLar SAko SSta WCot WHar WPGP WPat
- 'Silver Ghost'	SWvt
§ - 'Silver Vein'	CDoC CJun CMCN EPfP NLar SSta SWvt WPGP
crataegifolium	SSta
- B&SWJ 11036	WCru
- B&SWJ 11355	WCru
- 'Ittai-san-nishiki'	SSta
- 'Meuri-keade-no-fuiri' (v)	MPkF
- 'Meuri-no-ōfu' (v)	MPkF SSta
- 'Veitchii' (v)	CJun EBee EPfP MBlu MPkF NLar SBig SSpi SSta
creticum misapplied	see *A. sempervirens*
dasycarpum	see *A. saccharinum*
davidii	CBcs CDoC CDul CExl CLnd CMCN CTsd ECrN LCro MBlu MGos MMuc MRav NOrn SCob SGol SSta WPat
- AC 1471	MSnd
§ - 'Canton'	CJun SSta
- 'Cantonspark'	see *A. davidii* 'Canton'
- 'Cascade'	CJun LRHS MBlu SSta WHor
- 'Ernest Wilson'	NLar SSta
- 'George Forrest' ♀H5	CBcs CDul CExl CJun CMCN CMac CTho EBee ELan EPfP GBin LAst MMuc NLar NOrn NWea SCob SEND SPer SPoG SSta SWvt WHar WMat WMou
- 'Hagelunie'	SBir SSta
- 'Hansu-suru' (v)	SSta
- 'Karmen'	CBcs CDul CJun EPfP SSta WPGP
- 'Madeline Spitta'	MBri
- 'Purple Bark'	CExl CJun SBir SSta
- 'Rosalie'	CBcs CJun EPfP LRHS MBlu MBri NLar SBir SSta WHor
- 'Sekka'	SSta
- 'Serpentine'	CBcs CDoC CJun CMCN CNWT ELan EPfP GBin IDee MBlu MBri NEgg NLar SSta WHor
- 'Silver Vein'	see *A.* × *conspicuum* 'Silver Vein'
- Viper = 'Mindavi'	CDoC CDul EBee EPfP GQue LRHS MBri NWea SPer SPoG WMat
elegantulum	CExl CJun GBin WPGP
erythranthum B&SWJ 11733	WCru
- DJHV 06147	WCru
- FMWJ 13157 **new**	CEvo
fabri	CDul CExl
- WWJ 11614	WCru
flabellatum	CJun CMCN WPat
- NJM 11.017 **new**	WPGP
- PAB 9865 **new**	LEdu
- var. ***yunnanense***	MMuc MSnd
forrestii	CExl NEgg
- BWJ 7515	WCru
- 'Alice'	CJun SSta
- 'Inoense'	SSta
- 'Sirene'	CJun SSta
- 'Sparkling'	CJun NLar
× ***freemanii***	CMCN
- 'Armstrong'	CCVT SGol
- Autumn Blaze = 'Jeffersred' ♀H6	CBcs CCVT CDoC CDul CMCN COtt EPfP IArd MBlu MGos MMuc NLar NOrn SBir SCoo SEND SGol SPer SPoG WHar WMat
- Celebration = 'Celzam'	CArg CCVT CDul EBee MGos
- 'Indian Summer'	see *A.* × *freemanii* 'Morgan'
§ - 'Morgan'	CJun NLar
fulvescens	see *A. longipes*
ginnala	see *A. tataricum* subsp. *ginnala*
- 'Compactum' **new**	LRHS
glabrum subsp. ***douglasii***	CEvo
globosum	see *A. platanoides* 'Globosum'
grandidentatum	see *A. saccharum* subsp. *grandidentatum*
griseum ♀H5	Widely available
- 'Golden Lucky' **new**	NLar
grosseri	CDul CMCN CTri SGol
- var. ***hersii***	CBcs CDoC CDul CMac CWib EBee ECrN ELan EPfP GBin MBri MMuc MRav NLar NOrn NWea SCob SPer SPoG SSta SWvt WHar WMat
- 'Leiden'	EPfP
heldreichii	CMCN IArd
henryi	CBcs CDul EPfP NEgg NLar
heptaphlebium B&SWJ 11695	WCru
- B&SWJ 11713	WCru
- DJHV 06063	WCru
- FMWJ 13369	CEvo WCru
japonicum	CMCN MMuc SEWo

- B&SWJ 8417	WCru
- B&SWJ 12847 **new**	WCru
§ - 'Aconitifolium' ♀H6	Widely available
- 'Aki-hi'	NLar
- 'Ao-jutan'	CJun
- 'Attaryi'	CMen MPkF NEgg NLar WPat
- 'Aureum'	see *A. shirasawanum* 'Aureum'
- 'Emmit's Pumpkins'	CJun
- 'Ezo-no-momiji'	see *A. shirasawanum* 'Ezo-no-momiji'
- 'Fairy Lights'	NLar
- 'Filicifolium'	see *A. japonicum* 'Aconitifolium'
- 'Green Cascade' ♀H6	CJun CMCN CMac CMen IVic LRHS MGos MPkF NEgg NLar SBig SGol WPat
- 'Indian Summer' **new**	SAko
- 'King's Copse'	CJun LRHS
- 'Laciniatum'	see *A. japonicum* 'Aconitifolium'
- f. ***microphyllum***	see *A. shirasawanum* 'Microphyllum'
- 'Ogurayama'	see *A. shirasawanum* 'Ogurayama'
- 'Ō-isami'	MPkF SBig
- 'Ō-taki'	CJun
- 'Vitifolium' ♀H6	CDoC CJun CMCN CMac ELan EPfP GBin LPar LRHS MBlu MBri MGos MPkF NEgg NLar SBig SGol SPer SSta WCFE WPGP
kawakamii	see *A. caudatifolium*
laevigatum B&SWJ 11684	WCru
- FMWJ 13378	WCru
- NJM 10.049	WPGP
§ - var. ***reticulatum*** B&SWJ 11698	WCru
laurinum NJM 10.048	WPGP
- NJM 10.087	WPGP
- NJM 10.111	WPGP
- NJM 10.112	WPGP
laxiflorum	SSta
§ ***longipes***	CMCN
macrophyllum	CDul CMCN EPfP MBlu
mandshuricum	CDul MBlu
- B&SWJ 12592 **new**	WCru
§ ***maximowiczianum***	CBcs CMCN CTho MMuc MPkF SGol SSta
maximowiczii	MPkF WHCr
metcalfii	CFil
micranthum ♀H6	CDul CMCN EBee EPfP MBlu NLar SSpi WHar WPGP WPat
miyabei	MPkF
mono	see *A. pictum*
monspessulanum	CDul MMuc SEND
- subsp. ***oksalianum*** **new**	WMat
morifolium B&SWJ 11473	WCru
morrisonense Hayata	see *A. caudatifolium*
negundo	CDul CMCN CTho CWib ECrN NWea SCob SWvt
- 'Auratum'	CMCN SGol
- 'Aureomarginatum' (v)	CCVT ECrN SGol
- 'Aureovariegatum' (v)	CBcs
§ - 'Elegans' (v)	CDul CMCN SCoo WHar
- 'Elegantissimum'	see *A. negundo* 'Elegans'
- 'Flamingo' (v)	CBcs CCVT CDoC CDul CMac CWib ECrN ELan ELon EPfP LHop LRHS MAsh NLar NWea SCob SGol SHil SPer SPoG SWvt WFar WHar WMat
- 'Kelly's Gold'	CBcs CCVT CTho NLar NOrn NWea SCob SGol WHar WMat
- subsp. ***mexicanum***	CFil

- 'Sensation'	NLar
- 'Variegatum' (v)	CBcs ECrN SGol
- var. ***violaceum*** ♀H6	SVen
- 'Winter Lightning' ♀H6	CTho NLar
nikoense misapplied	see *A. maximowiczianum*
nipponicum	CDul
'Norwegian Sunset'	CCVT
oblongum	CMCN
- FMWJ 13449 **new**	CEvo
- KWJ 12232	WCru
- WWJ 11851	WCru
oliverianum	CDul CExl MBlu
- subsp. ***formosanum*** CWJ 12437	WCru
opalus	CMCN SEND
orientale misapplied	see *A. sempervirens*
orizabense	EBee
Pacific Sunset = 'Warrenred'	NLar
palmatum	CBar CBcs CCVT CDul CMCN CMHG CMen CSBt CTri CWib EPfP ETod GKin LCro LPar MBlu MGos NEgg NWea SCob SEWo SGol SPlb SWvt WFar WHar WPat
- (Amoenum Group) 'Ariake-nomura'	CMen MPkF
- - 'Atropurpureum'	Widely available
- - 'Bloodgood' ♀H6	Widely available
- - 'Boskoop Glory'	GKin
- - 'Chikuma-no'	CMen MPkF NLar
§ - - 'Fireglow'	CBcs CDoC CJun CMCN CMen CWib ESMi GBin LMil LPal LPar LRHS MBri MGos MJak MPkF NEgg NLar SAko SBod SCob SCoo SGol SPer WCFE WPat
- - 'Golden Pond'	CJun
- - 'Green Star'	WPat
- - 'Hōgyoku'	CJun CMCN CMen MPkF
- - 'Hondoshi'	NLar
- - 'Ichigyōji'	CJun CMen IVic MAsh NEgg NLar SBig WPGP WPat
- - 'Kagero' (v)	MPkF
- - 'Kogane-sakae'	CJun MPkF
- - 'Lutescens'	CMen MPkF NEgg
- - 'Margaret Bee'	CJun NLar
- - 'Matsuyoi'	CJun MPkF NLar
- - 'Mizu-kuguri'	MPkF NLar
- - 'Monzukushi'	CJun MPkF
- - 'Murogawa'	CJun CMen
- - 'Nanase-gawa'	MPkF
- - 'Nigrum'	CMCN CTri WPat
- - 'Ōgon-sarasa'	CJun MPkF
- - 'Omato'	CJun MAsh MPkF SBig
- - 'Ōsakazuki' ♀H6	Widely available
- - 'Ōshio-beni'	CJun CMen NEgg
- - 'Red Baron'	CJun IBoy WPat
- - Red Emperor = 'Emperor 1'	CBcs ELan EUJe IBoy LMil LRHS MBri MPkF NLar SBod SCob SPer WMat WPat
- - 'Red Flash'	CJun CMen MPkF
- - 'Rubrum'	CMen
- - 'Samidare'	CJun MPkF NLar
- - 'Saoshika'	CJun CMen MPkF NLar
§ - - 'Shigi-tatsu-sawa' (v)	CJun CMCN CMac CMen LRHS MGos MPkF NEgg NLar SBig
- - 'Shōjō'	CJun CMCN NLar
- - 'Shōjō-nomura'	CMen MPkF NLar WPat
- - 'Tana'	CJun CMCN CMen EPfP MPkF NLar WPat
- - 'Tsukushigata'	MPkF SGol WPat

	- - 'Tsuma-gaki'	CDoC CJun CMCN CMen EPfP ESMi LPar LRHS MBri MGos MPkF NEgg NLar WPat
	- - 'Umegae'	CJun
	- - 'Utsu-semi'	CJun MPkF
	- - 'Westonbirt Orange'	MBri
	- - 'Whitney Red'	CMen
	- - 'Yezo-nishiki' (v)	CMen MBlu MPkF NLar
	- 'Ao-seigen'	CJun
	- 'Aoshime-no-uchi'	see *A. palmatum* 'Shinobuga-oka'
	- 'Aoyagi-gawa'	CJun
	- 'Arakawa-ukon'	CJun NLar
	- 'Ashurst Wood'	SBig
	- 'Atropurpureum Novum'	MPkF NLar SGol
*	- 'Autumn Showers'	CJun
	- 'Beni-musume'	MPkF
	- 'Beni-otome'	MPkF
	- 'Beni-shigitatsu-sawa'	see *A. palmatum* 'Aka-shigitatsu-sawa'
	- 'Beni-tsuru'	MPkF
	- 'Berry Broom'	MPkF NLar
	- 'Bonfire' misapplied	see *A. palmatum* 'Seigai'
	- 'Bonfire' ambig.	CJun
	- 'Bonnie Bergman'	CJun
I	- 'Carlis Corner Broom'	SAko
	- 'Carminium'	see *A. palmatum* 'Corallinum'
§	- 'Chiyo-hime'	CRos ELan EPfP LOPS NEgg NLar NPri
	- 'Collingwood Ingram'	SGol
	- var. ***coreanum*** B&SWJ 8606	WCru
	- 'Crimson Prince'	CJun MPkF SCoo
	- 'Diane Verkade'	MPkF
	- var. ***dissectum***	see *A. palmatum* (Dissectum Group)
	- Dissectum Group	Widely available
	- - 'Ao-shidare'	CJun
	- - 'Autumn Fire'	CJun
	- - 'Balcombe Green'	SBig
	- - 'Baldsmith'	CJun EUJe LRHS MGos MPkF SBod WPat
	- - 'Barrie Bergman'	CJun WPat
	- - 'Beni-shidare'	NLar SCob
	- - 'Beni-shidare Tricolor'	see *A. palmatum* (Dissectum Group) 'Toyama-nishiki'
	- - 'Beni-shidare Variegated'	see *A. palmatum* (Dissectum Group) 'Toyama-nishiki'
	- - 'Berrima Bridge'	CJun
	- - 'Bewley's Red'	CJun
	- - 'Brocade'	CJun IVic MPkF WPat
	- - 'Bronzewing'	CJun
	- - 'Chantilly Lace'	CJun IBoy MPkF
	- - 'Crimson Princess'	CBcs EPfP LMil LRHS MBri MJak MPkF WMat
	- - 'Crimson Queen' ♀H6	Widely available
	- - 'Crippsii'	CBcs CMac CMen ESMi GBin LRHS MGos MPkF SCoo SGol
	- - 'Dissectum Flavescens'	CJun CMac CMen MBlu MGos MPkF NEgg SBod WMat
§	- - 'Dissectum Nigrum'	CJun CMac CMen LRHS MPkF NEgg NLar WPat
	- - 'Dissectum Palmatifidum'	CDoC CMen EUJe LRHS MPkF NEgg SBod SCoo SGol SPer
	- - 'Dissectum Rubrifolium'	MPkF
§	- - 'Dissectum Variegatum' (v)	CJun LRHS MPkF
	- - 'Ellen'	CJun MPkF NLar WPat
	- - 'Emerald Lace' ♀H6	CJun CRos EBee GKin LBuc LCro LMil LOPS LPfy LRHS MBri MGos MPkF NEgg NLar SHil SPoG SSta WCFE WPat
	- - 'Emma'	NLar
	- - 'Felice'	CJun MPkF WPat
	- - 'Filigree' (v)	CJun CMCN CMen EPfP LRHS MAsh MGos MPkF NLar SBig SBod SSta WCFE WPat
§	- - 'Firecracker' PBR	MPkF NEgg NLar
	- - 'Garnet' ♀H6	Widely available
	- - 'Germaine's Gyration'	CJun
	- - 'Goshiki-shidare'	see *A. palmatum* (Dissectum Group) 'Toyama-nishiki'
	- - 'Green Globe'	CJun LRHS
	- - 'Green Hornet'	CJun
	- - 'Green Lace'	CMen MPkF
	- - 'Green Mist'	CJun LRHS WPat
	- - 'Hanzel'	WPat
	- - 'Heartbeat'	CJun LRHS MPkF SBod WPat
	- - 'Inaba-shidare' ♀H6	Widely available
I	- - 'Kawaii'	CJun
	- - 'Kiri-nishiki'	CJun CMen LRHS MPkF NLar
*	- - 'Lionheart'	CJun CMen CWGN ESMi LRHS MGos MPkF NLar SBod SCoo
	- - 'Marlo' PBR	LCro LOPS LPfy LRHS MAsh MGos NLar SHil
	- - 'Nomura-nishiki' (v)	CMen
	- - 'Octopus'	CJun NLar
	- - 'Orangeola' ♀H6	CJun CMen COtt CSBt CTri ESMi EUJe IBoy IVic LRHS MAsh MGos MJak MPkF NEgg NHol NLar NOrn SBig SBod SCob SCoo SGol SPer SPoG SSta WMat WPat
	- - 'Ornatum' ♀H6	CMCN CMen CWib EPfP ESMi GBin LPar LRHS LSRN MGos MPkF MRav NEgg NLar NPri SBod SCob SCoo WCFE
	- - 'Otto's Dissectum'	CJun
	- - 'Pendulum Julian'	CMCN LRHS MPkF
	- - 'Pink Ballerina' (v)	CJun NLar
	- - 'Pink Filigree'	CJun CMen EPfP MPkF NLar
	- - 'Raraflora'	CJun
	- - 'Red Autumn Lace'	CJun WPat
	- - 'Red Dragon'	CDoC CJun CMen CWGN ESMi EUJe LMil LRHS MAsh MPkF NLar SAko SBig
	- - 'Red Feather'	CJun
	- - 'Red Filigree Lace'	CJun CMCN CMen CWGN LRHS MGos MPkF SBig WPat
	- - 'Red Select'	MPkF
	- - 'Seiryū' ♀H6	Widely available
	- - 'Sekimori'	CJun NLar SBig
§	- - 'Shōjō-shidare'	CJun CMen LRHS MPkF NLar WMat
	- - 'Shu-shidare'	CJun
	- - 'Spring Delight'	CJun MPkF
	- - 'Stella Rossa'	CJun MPkF NLar NPri
	- - 'Suisei' (v)	MPkF
	- - 'Sunset'	CJun MPkF
	- - 'Sunshine'	MPkF SBod
	- - 'Tamukeyama'	CJun CMCN CMen ELan ELon ESMi EUJe LMil LRHS MBri MGos MJak MPkF NEgg NLar SAko SBod SCob SCoo SGol SLau WHor WMat WPat
§	- - 'Toyama-nishiki' (v)	CJun CMCN CMen CWGN ESMi LRHS MPkF NLar SBod
	- - 'Vic Pink'	CJun
	- - 'Waterfall'	CJun CMCN
	- - 'Watnong'	CJun EUJe LRHS MPkF SBod WPat
	- - 'Zaaling'	CMen CTho NEgg
	- Dissectum Viride Group	CBcs CJun CMCN CMac CMen CSBt ELan EPfP ESMi LAst LMil LPfy

		LRHS MAsh MBlu MGos MSwo NEgg SBod SLim SPer SSta SWvt WCFE WMat
	- 'Donzuru-bo'	CJun
	- 'Dormansland'	SBig
	- 'Dragon's Fire'	CJun
	- (Dwarf Group) 'Akita-yatsubusa'	MPkF
	- - 'Aoba-jo'	CJun CMen MPkF NEgg
	- - 'Aratama'	CJun CMen ESMi MJak MPkF SAko
	- - 'Baby Lace'	CWGN IVic SAko
	- - 'Beni-hime'	MBri MPkF SAko WPat
	- - 'Beni-hoshi'	MPkF
	- - 'Berry Dwarf'	CJun MPkF
	- - 'Brandt's Dwarf'	CDoC NLar WPat
	- - 'Caperci Dwarf'	MPkF
	- - 'Carlis Corner'	CJun MPkF
	- - 'Coonara Pygmy'	CJun CMCN CMac CMen ESMi GKin MGos MPkF SBod SCoo
	- - 'Coral Pink'	CJun CMen MPkF SGol SSta
	- - 'Diana'	CJun CMen MPkF NLar SGol
	- - 'Eimini'	MPkF
	- - 'Elizabeth'	CJun
	- - 'Englishtown'	NLar SAko WPat
	- - 'Garyū'	MPkF
	- - 'Geisha'	MPkF
I	- - 'Globosum'	IBoy MPkF
	- - 'Goshiki-kotohime' (v)	CJun CMCN NLar
	- - 'Groundcover'	MPkF
	- - 'Hanami-nishiki'	CMen MPkF WPat
	- - 'Hoshi-kuzu'	MPkF
	- - 'Hupp's Dwarf'	CJun MPkF
	- - 'Iso-chidori'	MPkF
	- - 'Jerre Schwartz'	CRos EPfP LCro LPfy LRHS MGos MPkF NLar SHil WPat
	- - 'Kaba'	CMen IVic MPkF SPoG
	- - 'Kamagata'	CBcs CJun CMCN CMen ESMi IVic LRHS MAsh MGos MPkF NLar SBod SCoo WPat
	- - 'Kandy Kitchen'	CJun CMen MGos
	- - 'Kashima'	CJun CMCN CMen LRHS MPkF NEgg NLar SBod WPat
	- - 'Kiyohime' ♀H6	CDoC CMCN CMen MPkF NEgg WPat
	- - 'Komachi-hime'	CJun CMen MPkF WPat
	- - 'Kotohime'	CJun CMCN CMen CRos IVic LPfy MGos MPkF NLar SBig SCoo SHil SPoG
	- - 'Koto-ito-komachi'	CJun CMen ESMi LRHS MPkF NEgg SBod
	- - 'Koto-maru'	MPkF NLar SBod SGol
	- - 'Koya-san'	CMen MPkF NLar
	- - 'Kuro-hime'	WPat
	- - 'Kurui-jishi'	MPkF
	- - 'Mapi-no-machi-hime'	CJun CMCN CMen ELan LRHS MAsh MGos MPkF NHol WPat
	- - 'Midori-no-teiboku'	CJun MPkF
	- - 'Mikawa-yatsubusa'	CMCN CMac CMen IVic LRHS MGos MPkF NEgg NLar SAko SBod SGol WPat
	- - 'Momoiro-koya-san'	CJun MPkF NLar SBod SGol WPat
	- - 'Murasaki-hime'	MPkF
	- - 'Murasaki-kiyohime'	CJun CMCN CMen LRHS MPkF SBod WPat
	- - 'Ojishi'	CMen MPkF SAko
	- - 'Oto-hime'	CJun CMen LRHS MPkF SBod
	- - 'Pixie'	CJun CMen IVic LRHS MGos MPkF NLar SAko SBod SCob SPoG WMat WPat
	- - 'Red Elf'	MPkF
	- - 'Ryuzu'	CJun MPkF
	- - 'Sandra'	CMen MPkF
	- - 'Seigen'	CJun CMCN CMen LRHS MBlu MPkF
	- - 'Shidava Gold'	CJun MPkF WPat
	- - 'Shishio-hime'	MPkF
	- - 'Skeeter's Broom'	CBcs CJun CMen ELan EPfP ESMi GBin IArd IBoy LBuc LMil LPfy LRHS MBri MGos MPkF NEgg NLar SBig SBod SCoo SPoG WPat
	- - 'Tama-hime'	CJun CMen ESMi LRHS MPkF NEgg
	- - 'Tarō-yama'	CJun MPkF WPat
	- - 'Wilson's Pink Dwarf'	CJun CMen COtt CWib EBee IVic LPfy LRHS MBri MGos MPkF NLar SAko SCoo SPoG SSpi WPat
	- - 'Yatsubusa'	MPkF
	- - 'Yuri-hime'	MPkF
	- 'Earthfire'	MJak MPkF WPat
I	- 'Ebbingei'	CMac
	- 'Effegi'	see *A. palmatum* 'Fireglow'
	- 'Eono-momiji'	CMen
	- 'Ever Red'	see *A. palmatum* (Dissectum Group) 'Dissectum Nigrum'
	- 'Fireball'	CJun
	- 'Fransman' **new**	NLar
	- 'Frederici Guglielmi'	see *A. palmatum* (Dissectum Group) 'Dissectum Variegatum'
	- 'Fujian Red'	LRHS
	- 'Gentaku'	CJun
	- 'Gibbsii'	CMen
	- 'Goten-nomura'	NLar
	- 'Grace'	CJun
	- 'Green Flag'	CJun
§	- 'Hagoromo'	CMac CMen ESMi MPkF NEgg SCoo
	- 'Hana-matoi' PBR (v)	CMCN SAko
	- 'Haru-iro'	CJun
	- 'Hazeroino' (v)	CMen MPkF
	- 'Heffner's Red'	CJun MPkF
	- 'Helena'	see *A. shirasawanum* 'Helena'
	- var. ***heptalobum***	CMCN
	- 'Heptalobum Elegans Purpureum'	see *A. palmatum* 'Hessei'
	- 'Hino-tori-nishiki'	CMen NLar SGol
	- 'Hōno-o'	MPkF SAko
	- 'Hupp's Red Willow'	NLar WMat
	- 'Ightham Gold'	SSta
	- 'Irish Lace'	CJun
	- 'Isobel'	SBod
	- 'Issai-nishiki'	CMen MPkF
*	- 'Issai-nishiki-kawazu'	MPkF
	- 'Jane'	CJun MPkF
	- 'JJ'	CJun
	- 'Julia D.'	CJun
	- 'Kashima-yatsubusa'	MPkF
	- 'Katja'	CJun CMen MPkF
	- 'Katsura-nishiki'	MPkF
	- 'Kawahara Rose'	MPkF
	- 'Kokobunji-nishiki' (v)	MPkF
§	- 'Koshimino'	CJun
	- 'Kyōryū'	MPkF
	- 'Kyra'	CMen MPkF
	- 'Leather Leaf'	MPkF
	- (Linearilobum Group) 'Atrolineare'	CMen MPkF NEgg NLar SPoG
	- - 'Beni-otake'	CBcs CJun CMen ELan EPfP ESMi EUJe IVic MBri MGos MPkF NEgg NLar SAko SBig SCob
	- - 'Enkan'	CJun CMen COtt CWGN EBee ESMi LRHS MBri MGos MPkF NLar NPri SBod SGol SPoG WMat WPat

	Name	Suppliers
	- - 'Fairy Hair'	CJun
	- - 'Kinshii' 🏆H6	CJun CMCN CMen EPfP GBin IVic LRHS MPkF NEgg NLar SAko WMat WPat
	- - 'Koto-no-ito'	CMCN LRHS MBlu MGos MPkF NLar SAko SBod SGol SPoG WPat
§	- - 'Linearilobum'	CBcs CDoC CMen EPfP GBin IVic LMil LRHS MGos MPkF NEgg NLar SCoo SLau WMat
	- - 'Red Cloud'	CJun MPkF
	- - 'Red Pygmy' 🏆H6	Widely available
	- - 'Red Spider'	CJun
	- - 'Shime-no-uchi'	CJun MPkF SBig
§	- - 'Shinobuga-oka'	CBcs CJun CMCN CMen MPkF SGol SLau
	- - 'Villa Taranto' 🏆H6	CDoC CJun CMCN CMen EPfP ESMi EUJe IVic LMil LRHS MBlu MBri MGos MPkF NEgg NLar SCoo SGol WMat WPGP WPat
	- 'Little Princess'	see *A. palmatum* 'Chiyo-hime'
	- 'Lydia'	MPkF
	- 'Marasaki-yama'	MPkF
	- 'Mardi Gras'	CJun
	- 'Margaret'	MPkF WPat
	- 'Masamurasaki'	CMen MPkF
	- 'Matsukaze'	CJun CMCN CMen
	- var. ***matsumurae*** B&SWJ 11100	WCru
	- - B&SWJ 11195	WCru
§	- (Matsumurae Group) 'Aka-shigitatsu-sawa'	CBcs CJun CMCN CMen ESMi LRHS MGos MJak MPkF NLar SAko SGol
	- - 'Akegarasu'	CMen NLar
	- - 'Amagi-shigure'	CJun MPkF
	- - 'Amber Ghost'	CJun
	- - 'Ariadne' (v) 🏆H6	CJun CWib LRHS MBri MGos MPkF NLar SBig SCoo SPoG WMou WPat
	- - 'Autumn Glory'	CJun CMac CMen WPat
	- - 'Autumn Red'	CMen ESMi NEgg
	- - 'Azuma-murasaki'	CJun CMen MPkF NEgg NLar
	- - 'Beni-gasa'	CJun MPkF WPat
	- - 'Beni-kagami'	CJun CMCN LRHS MPkF NLar SGol
	- - 'Black Lace' **new**	MPkF NLar
	- - 'Burgundy Lace' 🏆H6	CBcs CDoC CJun CMCN CMen CWib ELan EPfP ESMi EUJe GKin LMil LRHS LSRN MAsh MBri MGos MJak MPkF NEgg SBig SCoo SGol SPer SPoG SSta WPat
	- - 'Chitose-yama' 🏆H6	CDul CJun CMCN CMen EPfP GBin GKin LPar LRHS MAsh MBri MGos MPkF NEgg NLar SBod SGol SLim SSta WPat
	- - 'Edna Bergman'	CJun
§	- - 'Elegans' 🏆H6	CMen EPfP LRHS MPkF NEgg NLar
	- - 'Fascination'	CJun
	- - 'Fior d'Arancio'	CJun IVic MPkF NLar WPat
	- - 'First Ghost' (v)	CJun
	- - 'Grandma Ghost'	CJun
	- - 'Green Trompenburg'	CJun CMen GBin MPkF NEgg NLar
§	- - 'Hessei'	CMen MPkF NLar
	- - 'Iijima-sunago'	CMen MPkF
	- - 'Inazuma'	CBcs CDoC CJun CMCN CMen MGos MPkF NLar SBod SCoo SGol SLau WPat
	- - 'Kasagiyama'	CJun CMen LRHS MPkF NLar SAko
	- - 'Ki-hachijō'	CJun CMCN CMen MPkF NLar WPat
	- - 'Killarney'	CJun
	- - 'Kinran'	CMen LRHS MPkF NEgg
	- - 'Ki-shuzan' **new**	CJun
	- - 'Koba-shōjō'	MPkF
	- - 'Korean Gem'	CJun CMen MPkF NEgg
	- - 'Kurabu-yama'	CMen MPkF
	- - 'Marjan'	CJun MPkF
	- - 'Mikazuki' (v)	CJun
	- - 'Mirte'	CDoC CJun CMen MPkF NLar SBig SGol
	- - 'Mon Papa'	CJun CMen NLar
	- - 'Moonfire'	CBcs CJun CMCN ELan EPfP MAsh MGos MPkF SGol WPat
	- - 'Mure-hibari'	CJun CMen MPkF
	- - 'Musashino'	CJun SGol
	- - 'Nicholsonii'	CMen IVic MPkF NEgg NLar WPat
	- - 'Nuresagi'	CJun MPkF WPat
	- - 'Omure-yama'	CBcs CDoC CJun CMCN CMen EPfP ESMi LRHS MGos MPkF NEgg NLar SCob SCoo SGol SPer SSta
	- - 'Oregon Sunset'	CJun LRHS MGos MPkF NLar WMat WPat
	- - 'Ōshū-shidare'	CJun CMen IBoy MPkF
	- - 'Peaches and Cream' (v)	CBcs CJun CMen ELon MGos MPkF NLar SGol SPer
	- - 'Purple Ghost'	CJun NLar
	- - 'Red Falcon' **new**	LRHS
	- - 'Ruby Ridge'	CJun
	- - 'Satsuki-beni'	CJun CMen ELon ESMi MPkF NEgg SBod
	- - 'Sazanami'	CJun CMen MPkF NEgg NLar WPat
§	- - 'Seigai'	CJun MPkF
	- - 'Semi-no-hane'	CJun NLar
	- - 'Sherwood Flame'	CDoC CJun CMen CWib LRHS MAsh MBlu MGos MPkF NEgg NLar SCoo SGol
	- - 'Shigure-bato'	CJun MPkF
	- - 'Shigurezome'	MPkF NLar
	- - 'Shinonome'	CJun CMen MPkF NLar
	- - 'Sister Ghost'	CJun
	- - 'Sumi-nagashi'	CBcs CCVT CDoC CMen ESMi GBin LRHS MGos MJak MPkF NEgg NLar SBod SCoo SGol SLau WMat WPat
	- - 'Tiger Rose'	CJun
	- - 'Trompenburg' 🏆H6	Widely available
	- - 'Tsuri-nishiki'	CJun CMen MPkF
	- - 'Uncle Ghost'	CJun
	- - 'Wakehurst Pink' (v)	CMCN MPkF NOrn WPat
	- - 'Westonbirt Red'	MBri
	- - 'Yasemin'	CJun CMen CWGN IVic LRHS MPkF NEgg NLar SAko SBig
	- - 'Yūba-e'	MPkF WPat
	- - 'Yūgure'	IVic MPkF
	- 'Meihō-nishiki'	CJun
	- 'Melanie'	CJun SBig
	- 'Meoto'	CJun
	- 'Mimaye'	CJun
	- 'Mini Mondo'	MPkF
*	- 'Muncaster'	SBig
	- 'Nakata'	NLar
	- 'Nishiki-yamato'	NLar
	- 'Nomura'	CJun CMen
	- 'Nomurishidare' misapplied	see *A. palmatum* (Dissectum Group) 'Shōjō-shidare'
	- 'Nomurishidare' Wada	SSpi
	- 'Ōgi-no-sen'	MPkF
	- 'Okina'	NLar
	- 'Oranges and Lemons'	CJun SGol
	- 'Oriental Mystery'	CJun
	- (Palmatum Group) 'Akane'	CMen
	- - 'Alpenweiss'	CJun
	- - 'Anne-Irene' **new**	MPkF

	Cultivar	Suppliers
	- - 'Ao-kanzashi' (v)	MPkF NLar
	- - 'Aoyagi'	CJun CMCN CMen ELon LRHS MGos MPkF NEgg NLar SBod WPat
§	- - 'Arakawa'	CMCN CMac CMen MPkF NEgg SBod
	- - 'Asahi-zuru' (v)	CBcs CJun CMCN CMen LPfy LRHS MBri MGos MPkF NLar SBod SHil SPer WMat
	- - 'Attraction'	CMCN CMen NEgg
	- - 'Aureum'	CMCN CMen CTri CWib ELan EPfP IBoy LMil LPar LRHS MAsh MBlu MGos MPkF NEgg NLar SPoG SSpi WCFE
	- - 'Beni-chidori'	CMen
	- - 'Beni-fushigi'	MPkF
	- - 'Beni-kawa'	CJun CMen MPkF SBig SGol WPat
	- - 'Beni-komachi'	CBcs CJun CMCN CMen EPfP ESMi LRHS MBri MGos MPkF NLar SCob SHil SSta
	- - 'Beni-maiko' ♀H6	CJun CMCN CMen CRos CWib EPfP ESMi LPfy LRHS MBri MGos MJak MPkF NBes NLar NOrn SBig SBod SCob SCoo SHil SWvt WPat
	- - 'Beni-schichi-henge' (v)	CBcs CDoC CJun CMCN CMen CRos CWGN ELon ESMi GKin LPfy LRHS MAsh MBri MGos MJak MPkF NEgg NHol NLar SAko SBig SBod SCob SCoo SGol SHil SSta WMat WPat
	- - 'Beni-shi-en'	CJun MPkF NLar WPat
	- - 'Beni-tsukasa' (v) ♀H6	CJun CMen EPfP ESMi LRHS MAsh MPkF NLar SSpi SSta
	- - 'Beni-yubi-gohon'	CBcs CJun MJak MPkF NLar
	- - 'Beni-zuru'	WPat
	- - 'Bi Hō'	CJun IVic LRHS NLar SAko SGol WPat
	- - 'Butterfly' (v)	Widely available
	- - 'Calico'	CJun
	- - 'Chirimen-nishiki' (v)	MPkF
	- - 'Chishio'	CBcs CMCN CMen LMil LRHS MPkF SBig SBod SSpi WPat
	- - 'Chishio Improved'	CJun CMCN CMac CMen CTho EPfP LRHS MAsh MGos MPkF NHol NLar NOrn SBig SWvt
§	- - 'Corallinum' ♀H6	CJun CMCN CMen LRHS MPkF NLar SAko WCFE WPat
	- - 'Deshōjō'	CMCN CMen COtt CWSG CWib ESMi LPar MBlu MGos MPkF NLar SAko SCoo SGol WMat
	- - 'Eddisbury' ♀H6	CJun CMen CSBt EPfP GBin MBlu MPkF NLar SSta WPGP WPat
	- - 'Fall's Fire'	CJun NLar
	- - 'Geisha Gone Wild' (v)	CJun
	- - 'Glowing Embers'	CJun MPkF WPat
	- - 'Harusame' (v)	MPkF NLar WPat
	- - 'Herbstfeuer'	CDoC CJun MPkF
	- - 'Higasa-yama' (v)	CBcs CJun CMCN CMen CWGN ESMi IVic MGos MPkF NLar SBod SGol WPat
	- - 'Hiryu'	WPat
	- - 'Ibo-nishiki'	CMen ESMi MPkF NEgg
	- - 'Japanese Sunrise'	CJun WMat
	- - 'Jirō-shidare'	CJun EPfP LRHS MPkF NLar SBig
§	- - 'Kagiri-nishiki' (v)	CBcs CJun CMCN CMac CMen CWGN IVic MPkF NEgg NLar SPoG
	- - 'Karaori-nishiki' (v)	CMen MPkF NLar SPer
	- - 'Karasu-gawa' (v)	CJun CMen CWGN MPkF
	- - 'Kasen-nishiki'	CMen MPkF
	- - 'Katsura' ♀H6	Widely available
	- - 'Kingsville Variegated' (v)	MPkF
	- - 'Kinky Krinkle'	CJun SAko
	- - 'Kogane-nishiki'	CMen NLar SGol
	- - 'Komon-nishiki' (v)	CJun CMen MPkF NEgg
	- - 'Koriba'	CJun MPkF NLar
	- - 'Koshibori-nishiki'	MPkF
	- - 'Limelight' **new**	SBod
	- - 'Lozita'	NLar WPat
	- - 'Maiko'	CMen MPkF
	- - 'Mama'	CMen
	- - 'Marakumo'	MPkF
	- - 'Masukagami' (v)	CJun MPkF NLar
	- - 'Matsu-ga-e' (v)	CMen MPkF
	- - 'Mizuho-beni'	CJun CMen NLar
	- - 'Nishiki-gasane' (v)	CMen MPkF
§	- - 'Nishiki-gawa'	CJun CMen LRHS MPkF NEgg SBod
	- - 'Nishiki-momiji'	CMen
	- - 'Ōgi-nagashi' (v)	MPkF NLar
	- - 'Ō-kagami'	CBcs CDoC CJun CMac CMen CSBt ELon EPfP ESMi LRHS MAsh MGos MPkF NLar SBod SCoo WCFE WPat
	- - 'Okukuji-nishiki'	CJun
	- - 'Okushimo'	CJun CMCN CMen ETod IVic LRHS MPkF NEgg NLar SSta WPat
	- - 'Orange Dream' ♀H6	Widely available
	- - 'Oridono-nishiki' (v)	CDoC CJun CMCN CMac CMen CWGN ELan ELon EPfP ESMi LRHS MAsh MBlu MGos MPkF NEgg NLar SBod SLim SPoG SSta
	- - 'Otome-zakura'	CJun CMen LRHS MPkF
	- - 'Phoenix'	CJun CRos EBee LPfy LRHS MAsh MBri MGos MPkF NLar SAko SBod SHil
	- - 'Purpureum'	LPar
	- - 'Red Wood'	CJun SGol SLau
	- - 'Redwine'PBR	CRos EBee EPfP GBin LRHS MPkF NLar SHil
	- - 'Rokugatsu-en-nishiki'	WPat
	- - 'Rufescens'	MPkF WPat
	- - 'Ryokū-ryū'	CMen MPkF
	- - 'Sango-kaku' ♀H6	Widely available
	- - 'Sa-otome'	CMen MPkF
	- - 'Seiun-kaku'	CJun CMen MPkF NLar WPat
	- - 'Sekka-yatsubusa'	CMCN CMen MPkF NLar
	- - 'Shaina'	CBcs CDoC CJun CMen COtt CRos CSBt CWGN CWib EPfP ESMi IVic LPfy LRHS MBlu MBri MGos MPkF NLar SAko SCob SCoo SGol SHil SLim SPoG
	- - 'Sharp's Pygmy'	CJun CMen MPkF SBod SGol WPat
	- - 'Shichihenge'	NLar
	- - 'Shigarami'	CJun CMen MPkF
	- - 'Shikageori-nishiki'	CJun CMen MPkF
	- - 'Shin-chishio'	CJun
	- - 'Shindeshōjō' ♀H6	Widely available
	- - 'Shirazz' (v)	CDoC CWGN ESMi IBoy LMil LPfy LRHS LSRN MBri MGos MPkF NLar SBod SCob SPer SPoG SWvt WMat
§	- - 'Shishi-gashira' ♀H6	CDoC CJun CMCN CMac CMen EBee ESMi IVic LPar LRHS MBlu MBri MGos MPkF NEgg NLar SBod SCoo SGol SPoG WPat
	- - 'Shōjō-no-mai'	CJun
*	- - 'Sode-nishiki'	CJun MPkF NLar
I	- - 'Summer Gold'	CJun COtt MPkF NLar SAko SWvt
	- - 'Taiyō-nishiki'	CJun MPkF
	- - 'Takao'	CMen
	- - 'Taylor'PBR (v)	COtt CRos CWGN EPfP IVic LPfy LRHS MAsh MGos MPkF NEgg NLar NPri SCoo SHil SPoG
	- - 'Tennyo-no-hoshi'	CMen MPkF NLar
	- - 'Tobiosho'	CJun

- - 'Tsuchigumo'	CJun CMen MPkF NLar
- - 'Ueno-homare'	CMen LRHS MPkF
- - 'Uki-gumo' (v)	CBcs CJun CMCN CMac CMen CWib ELan ESMi LRHS MGos NHol NLar SBig SCoo SPer SPoG SSta
- - 'Versicolor' (v)	CJun CMCN MPkF
- - 'Volubile'	CMCN CMen MPkF NEgg WPat
- - 'Wabito'	CJun CMen MPkF
- - 'Waka-momiji' (v)	CJun
- - 'Wendy'	CJun CMen IVic MPkF NLar SGol
- - 'Wild Goose'	MPkF
- - 'Winter Flame'	CJun GBin LMil LRHS MPkF NHol NOrn WPat
- 'Peve Chameleon'	MPkF
- 'Peve Dave'	MPkF NLar WPat
- 'Peve Multicolor'	CJun MPkF NLar
- 'Peve Ollie'[PBR]	MPkF NLar
- 'Peve Stanley'	MPkF NLar
- 'Pine Bark Maple'	see *A. palmatum* 'Nishiki-gawa'
- 'Pink Passion' (v)	NLar
- 'Princetown Gold'	EUJe NLar
- 'Pung-kil'	IVic MPkF SAko
- 'Red Blush'	CJun
- 'Red Flame'	NLar
- 'Red Jonas'	MPkF
- 'Renjaku-maru'	MPkF
- 'Reticulatum'	see *A. palmatum* 'Shigi-tatsu-sawa'
- 'Ribesifolium'	see *A. palmatum* 'Shishi-gashira'
- 'Rising Sun'	CJun NLar
- 'Roseomarginatum'	see *A. palmatum* 'Kagiri-nishiki'
- 'Rough Bark Maple'	see *A. palmatum* 'Arakawa'
I - 'Rubrum Kaiser'	CJun
- 'Ruby Star'	CJun MPkF
- 'Ryusen'	CJun NLar
- 'Sagara-nishiki' (v)	CJun CMen LRHS MPkF NEgg
- 'Sai-ho'	MPkF
- 'Saint Jean'	MPkF
- 'Scolopendriifolium'	see *A. palmatum* 'Linearilobum'
- 'Senkaki'	see *A. palmatum* 'Sango-kaku'
- 'Septemlobum Elegans'	see *A. palmatum* 'Elegans'
- 'Septemlobum Purpureum'	see *A. palmatum* 'Hessei'
- 'Sessilifolium' dwarf	see *A. palmatum* 'Hagoromo'
- 'Sessilifolium' tall	see *A. palmatum* 'Koshimino'
- 'Sharon'	WPat
- 'Shichigosan'	CMen
- 'Shimofuri-nishiki'	MPkF
- 'Shin-nyo'	MBlu
- 'Shishi-yatsubusa'	CJun MPkF
- 'Starfish'[PBR]	MPkF
- 'Susan'	MPkF
- 'Tatsuta'	CMen MPkF
- 'Tiny Tim'	CJun MPkF
- 'Tsukasa Silhouette'	CJun MPkF WPat
- 'Tsukuma-no'	MPkF
- 'Twombly's Red Sentinel'	CJun MBlu MPkF
- 'Ueno-yama'	CBcs CJun EUJe MPkF NEgg NLar SGol SPer WPat
- 'Ukon'	CJun CMen ESMi LMil LRHS MJak MPkF NEgg SCoo
- 'Usu-midori'	CJun
- 'Van der Akker'	CJun
- 'Victoria'	SGol
- 'Waka-midori'	CMen
- 'Wetumpka Red'	CJun
- 'Will's Devine'	CJun
- 'Wolff's Broom'	WPat
- 'Wou-nishiki'	CMCN CMen MPkF
- 'Yana-gawa'	CMen
papilio	see *A. caudatum*
pauciflorum 'Blaze Away'	CJun LRHS
pectinatum	GKev
- GWJ 9354	WCru
- 'Mozart'	CJun MBlu MBri MPkF NLar SMad SSta
- subsp. ***pectinatum*** B&SWJ 8270	WCru
- - HWJ 569	WCru
- - HWJ 944	WCru
pensylvanicum	CBcs CDul CMCN CTho ELan EPfP LRHS MGos MMuc MRav NEgg NWea SCob SEND SPer SSpi SSta WHor WPat
- 'Erythrocladum'	CBcs CJun CMCN EPfP IArd MAsh MGos NHol NLar NOrn SLim WPGP
pentaphyllum	SBig
§ ***pictum***	CMCN
- subsp. ***okamotoanum***	CMCN
- - B&SWJ 12623	WCru
- subsp. ***pictum*** f. ***ambiguum*** B&SWJ 8806	WCru
- 'Shufu-nishiki'	CMCN
- 'Usugomo'	WPat
aff. ***pictum*** MCN0931	CMCN
- MCN0951	CMCN
platanoides	CBcs CCVT CDoC CDul CLnd CMCN CSBt CTri CWib ECrN ELan EPfP MGos MMuc MSwo NOrn NWea SEND SEWo SGol SPer WHar WMat WMou
- 'Cleveland'	CBcs
- 'Columnare'	CLnd CMCN CWib SCoo
- 'Crimson King' 🏆H6	Widely available
- 'Crimson Sentry'	CArg CCVT CDoC CDul CLet CLnd CTri EBee ECrN ELan EPfP EUJe IVic LAst LCro LSRN MAsh MGos MRav NOrn SBmr SGol SPoG SWvt WHar
- 'Deborah'	CBcs CDul CLnd CTho EWTr SGol SPer
- 'Dissectum'	WPat
- 'Drummondii' (v)	Widely available
- 'Emerald Queen'	CDul ECrN
- 'Faassen's Black'	CDul
§ - 'Globosum'	CDul CLnd CMCN ECrN NLar SWvt
- 'Goldsworth Purple'	CLnd
- 'Laciniatum'	CMCN EBtc GBin WPat
- 'Marit'	WPat
- 'Nowush' **new**	SAko
- Princeton Gold = 'Prigo'[PBR] 🏆H6	CBcs CDoC CDul EBee ECrN ELan EMil GQue LBuc LRHS MAsh MBri MGos NEgg NOrn NWea SBmr SCoo SEWo SGol SLim SPoG SWvt WHar WMat
- 'Reitenbachii'	CDul
- 'Royal Red'	CDul CWib ECrN MRav NLar SCoo SEWo
- 'Schwedleri' 🏆H6	CMCN SGol
- 'Stollii'	WPat
- subsp. ***turkestanicum***	CMCN SSta
- 'Ulmers Select' **new**	WMat
pseudoplatanus	CBcs CCVT CDul CLnd CMCN CSBt CTri ECrN ELan LBuc MGos NWea SGol SPer WHar WMou
§ - 'Atropurpureum'	CDul ECrN NWea SEWo WHar
- 'Brilliantissimum' 🏆H6	Widely available
- 'Corstorphinense'	CDul
- f. ***erythrocarpum*** 'Erythrocarpum'	CMac
- 'Gadsby'	CDul

	Name	Suppliers
	- 'Negenia'	CDul
	- 'Prinz Handjéry'	CBcs CDul CMCN CTri CWib MGos NHol NLar NOrn NWea SGol SPer WHar WMat
	- 'Spaethii' misapplied	see *A. pseudoplatanus* 'Atropurpureum'
	- f. ***variegatum*** 'Esk Sunset' (v)	EBee ELan LSRN MGos MPkF NLar SPoG WHar
	- - 'Leopoldii' ambig. (v)	CBcs CCVT CDul CMCN ECrN ELan SWvt
	- - 'Simon-Louis Frères' (v)	CBcs CCVT CDul CLnd CMCN CWib ECrN LAst MAsh MGos NLar NOrn SGol SPer SWvt WHar WMat
	- 'Worley'	CBcs CDul CLnd CMCN CMac ECrN MRav NWea SGol SLim SPer
	pseudosieboldianum	CMCN MBlu MPkF
	- B&SWJ 8468	WCru
	- B&SWJ 8746	WCru
	- B&SWJ 8769	WCru
	- var. ***microsieboldianum*** B&SWJ 8766	WCru
	- subsp. ***takesimense*** B&SWJ 8500	WCru
	- - B&SWJ 8540	WCru
	pubipalmatum	LRHS
	pycnanthum	EPfP
	'Red Flamingo' (v)	CJun CWSG EPfP LPfy LRHS MBlu MBri MGos NLar SGol SMad SPoG WMat
	reticulatum	see *A. laevigatum* var. *reticulatum*
	rubescens CWJ 12438	WCru
	rubrum	CAgr CBcs CDul CLnd CMCN CSBt CTho CTri EBee ECrN ELan EPfP EWTr LCro LEdu LOPS MGos MMuc NEgg NWea SCoo SEWo SGol WCFE WHar WMat WMoo
	- Autumn Flame	see *A. rubrum* 'Pete's Red'
	- 'Autumn Spire'	CJun
	- 'Brandywine'	CDul CJun COtt CTho EBee EPfP LCro LOPS LRHS LSRN MAsh MBlu MBri NLar NWea SBir SCoo WHar WMat
	- 'Candy Ice' (v)	CJun
	- var. ***drummondii*** new	SBmr
	- 'Embers'	CJun
	- Fairview Flame	see *A. rubrum* 'Pete's Fairview'
	- Fireball = 'Firzam'	CJun
	- 'Firedance'	CJun
	- 'Joseph'	NLar
	- 'New World'	SCoo
	- 'Northwind'	CJun
	- 'Northwood'	CJun
	- 'October Glory' 🏆H6	Widely available
§	- 'Pete's Fairview'	CJun CLnd MMuc SEND SPer
§	- 'Pete's Red'	MPkF
	- 'Red King'	CJun
	- Red Sunset = 'Franksred' 🏆H6	CDul CJun CMCN CTho EBee ELan EPfP LHop NLar SBir SCoo SGol SLim SPer SPoG
	- 'Scanlon'	CBcs CDul CJun CMCN CTho ELan EPfP LAst SLim SPer
	- 'Schlesingeri'	CJun CLnd CMac EPfP
I	- 'Sekka'	MBlu
	- 'Somerset'	CDul CJun CTho CTri EBee LRHS SCoo WHar WMat
	- Summer Red = 'Hosr'	EPfP LRHS SCoo WMat
	- 'Sun Valley'	CJun EBee NOrn NWea WHar WMat
	- 'Tilford'	CJun SSta
§	***rufinerve***	CBcs CDoC CDul CLnd CMCN CTho CTri EBee ELan EPfP LCro MBri MMuc NEgg NLar NWea SCoo SGol SPer SSta SWvt WHar WMat
	- B&SWJ 10845	GKin WCru
	- B&SWJ 10924	WCru
	- B&SWJ 10959	WCru
	- B&SWJ 11571	WCru
	- 'Albolimbatum' (v)	CJun CMCN EBee MBri SBig SSta
	- 'Erythrocladum'	CJun MBlu SKHP
	- 'Ko-fuji-nishiki'	SSta
I	- 'Sunshine'	SSta
	- 'Winter Gold'	CJun EPfP NLar SSta
	- 'Yellow Ribbon'	WHor
§	***saccharinum***	CBcs CCVT CDul CLnd CMCN CTri CWib ELan EPfP LRHS MGos MMuc MSnd NLar NWea SCoo SGol SPer WHar WMat
	- 'Born's Gracious'	CJun
	- 'Fastigiatum'	see *A. saccharinum* 'Pyramidale'
	- f. ***laciniatum***	MBlu MMuc SGol SPer
	- - 'Laciniatum Wieri'	CDul CMCN NLar SGol
	- 'Lutescens'	CDul
§	- 'Pyramidale'	CLnd ECrN NWea SPer
	saccharum	CAgr CBcs CDul CMCN CTho ECrN EPfP MBlu NEgg
	- 'Brocade'	CJun
	- 'Fiddlers Creek'	CJun
§	- subsp. ***grandidentatum***	EPfP
§	***sempervirens***	EBee EPfP LEdu MPkF SChF
	'Sensu'	CJun
	'Serendipity'	SSta
	serrulatum CWJ 12437	WCru
	shirasawanum	CMCN
§	- 'Aureum' 🏆H6	Widely available
	- 'Autumn Moon'	CBcs CJun CMCN CMen CWGN EPfP LPar LRHS MBri MPkF NEgg NLar SBod SCob SCoo SGol SPer SPoG WMat WPat
§	- 'Ezo-no-momiji'	CJun CMen MPkF NEgg
	- 'Gloria'	MPkF SGol
§	- 'Helena'	MPkF WPat
	- 'Jordan' PBR	CDul CLet COtt CRos CWGN LCro LPfy LRHS LSRN MBri MGos MPkF SHil SPoG SWvt WPat
	- 'Lovett'	CJun
§	- 'Microphyllum'	MPkF NEgg
	- 'Mr Sun'	CJun
§	- 'Ogurayama'	CJun CMen
	- 'Palmatifolium'	CJun LRHS SBod
	- 'Red Dawn'	CJun
	- 'Susanne'	CJun CMen MPkF SGol
	- var. ***tenuifolium*** B&SWJ 11073	WCru
	sieboldianum 🏆H6	CDul CMen CTho CTri ECrN LRHS MAsh MBlu MMuc SGol WHCr WHar WMou WPGP WPat
	- B&SWJ 10849	WCru
	- B&SWJ 11049	WCru
	- B&SWJ 11090	WCru
	- 'Sode-no-uchi'	CJun CMen MPkF
	- var. ***tsushimense*** B&SWJ 10962	WCru
	sikkimense B&SWJ 11689	WCru
	- B&SWJ 11703	WCru
	- FMWJ 13166 new	CEvo WCru
	- WWJ 11601	WCru
	- WWJ 11613	WCru
	- WWJ 11853	WCru
	'Silver Cardinal' (v)	CBcs CJun CMCN EPfP LRHS MBlu MGos MPkF NLar SSta WHar
	'Silver Vein'	see *A.* × *conspicuum* 'Silver Vein'

	Name	Suppliers
	sinense	CMCN
	spicatum	NLar
§	***stachyophyllum***	GQui
	- BWJ 8101	WCru
	sterculiaceum subsp. ***franchetii***	NLar
	tataricum	CMCN
§	- subsp. ***ginnala***	CArg CBcs CDul CLnd CMCN CNWT CTri ECrN LRHS MBlu MGos NLar NWea SGol SPer
	- - 'Flame'	CDul CJun EBee ECrN EPfP MGos MMuc MSnd NLar
	- - 'Red Wing'	CJun
	tegmentosum ♀H5	CJun CMCN EPfP IArd MBlu NLar SSta WHor
	- subsp. ***glaucorufinerve***	see *A. rufinerve*
	- 'Joe Witt'	NLar
	tetramerum	see *A. stachyophyllum*
	tonkinense subsp. ***liquidambarifolium*** DJHV 06173	WCru
	trautvetteri	CMCN
	triflorum ♀H6	CBcs CCVT CDul CJun CMCN EBee EPfP LRHS MBlu MBri NLar SSpi WMat
	truncatum	CDul MPkF
	- B&SWJ 8914	WCru
	- 'Akikaze-nishiki' (v)	CJun MPkF
	tschonoskii subsp. ***koreanum***	MPkF
	- - B&SWJ 12596 **new**	WCru
	'Valley Phantom'	SSta
	velutinum	CMCN
	'White Tigress' ♀H6	CBcs CDoC CJun CTho EPfP GQue LRHS MBri NWea SPoG SSta WHar WMat WPGP WPat
	× ***zoeschense***	CMCN MPkF
	- 'Annae'	SEND SGol

Aceriphyllum see *Mukdenia*

Achillea (Asteraceae)

	Name	Suppliers
	ageratifolia ♀H5	CMea ECha ECho ECtt EDAr GJos NGdn SRms XLum XSen
§	***ageratum***	CArn CBod CLau CPrp ECho ENfk GPoy LEdu MHer MNHC SIde SRms WFar WGwG WHer WJek XLum
	'Alabaster'	LRHS SPhx
	Anthea = 'Anblo'PBR	CKno CPrp CWCL EAJP EBee ECtt GBBs IBoy LRHS LSRN MCot MRav MSpe NLar SHar SRms SWvt WCAu
§	'Apfelblüte' (Galaxy Series)	CAby CCon EBee ECha ECtt ELan EWTr GKin LPfy LRHS LSRN MBel MMuc MRav NGdn NHol NQui NSti SBod SCob SEND SPer SRms WMnd WWEG
	Appleblossom	see *A.* 'Apfelblüte'
	'Apricot Beauty'	ECtt ELan EWTr GQue
	'Apricot Delight' (Tutti Frutti Series)	MNrw
	argentea misapplied	see *A. clavennae, A. umbellata*
	argentea Lamarck	see *Tanacetum argenteum*
I	***argentifolia*** hort.	WKif
	aurea	see *A. chrysocoma*
	'Bahama'	GBin GQue
	'Belle Epoque'	WWEG
	biebersteinii	XLum
	brachyphylla	EPot
	'Breckland Bouquet'	EWes
	'Breckland Cream'	EBee
	'Breckland Ruby'	EWes
	'Carmina Burana'	CMea
	cartilaginea	see *A. salicifolia*
	'Christine's Pink'	MSpe
§	***chrysocoma***	ECho MWat WMoo
	- 'Grandiflora'	ECha LPla MMuc NGdn WBrk WWEG
§	***clavennae***	GKev MWat SRms WIce XSen
	clypeolata Sibth. & Sm.	CCon EBee EPPr LRHS NLar SPlb SRms XLum
	coarctata	NBir XSen
	Colorado Group	CBod CNec LPfy LRHS WHar
	'Coronation Gold' ♀H7	CWCL EBee ECtt ELan EPfP GBuc IBoy LAst LRHS MAsh MRav MWat NChi NDov SCob SPer SWvt WBod WCAu WCot WWEG XLum XSen
	'Credo' ♀H7	CAby CWld EAJP ECha ECtt EPPr EPfP EWTr EWoo GBin IBoy LCro LOPS LPla LRHS MBel MRav MSpe NGdn NHol NLar NSti SBea SMad SPer SWat WBrk WCAu WMnd WWEG
	crithmifolia	XLum
	decolorans	see *A. ageratum*
	(Desert Eve Series) Desert Eve Cream = 'Deseve' **new**	EBee LRHS
	- Desert Eve Deep Rose = 'Desderos'	EBee LRHS MAsh WTor
	- 'Desert Eve Light Yellow'	LRHS
	- Desert Eve Red = 'Desred'PBR	EBee LRHS MAsh
	- Desert Eve Yellow = 'Desyel'PBR	EBee
	erba-rotta subsp. ***moschata***	NBro
§	'Fanal'	CAby CLet CPrp CWCL EBee ECha ECtt ELan EPfP GBuc GKin IBoy LRHS MCot MRav MSpe MTis NBir NDov NEgg NHol NLar SPer SWvt WBrk WCAu WCot WMnd WWEG
	'Faust'	ELon
	'Federsee'	MArl
	'Feuerland'	CBod CMac CSam EBee ECha ECtt ELon EPPr EPfP GBin GKin GQue LRHS MRav MSpe NBir NDov NGdn SMad SPer SPoG WFar WWEG
	filipendulina 'Cloth of Gold' ♀H7	Widely available
	- 'Gold Plate' ♀H7	Widely available
	- 'Parker's Variety' ♀H7	EBee GQue NBre WFar WMoo XLum XSen
	'Fleur van Zonneveld'	MSpe NDov
	Flowers of Sulphur	see *A.* 'Schwefelblüte'
	(Forncett Series) 'Forncett Beauty'	LHop SWvt
	- 'Forncett Candy'	WWEG
	- 'Forncett Citrus'	EPPr MAvo
	- 'Forncett Fletton'	CWCL ECtt EHrv ELon EPPr EPfP GBin GKin LHop MAsh MBel MNrw MRav MSpe NGdn NHol WCAu WWEG
	- 'Forncett Ivory'	EBee EPPr
	fraasii	XSen
	'Gloria Jean'	SHar
	'Gold and Grey'	WWEG
	grandifolia misapplied	see *Tanacetum macrophyllum* (Waldst. & Kit.) Sch.Bip.

§	***grandifolia*** Friv.	CSam LPla MHin NBro WBor WFar WMnd WMoo WOld WOut
	'Great Expectations'	see *A.* 'Hoffnung'
	'Heidi' $\mathbb{Y}^{H7}$	MRav WWEG
	'Heinrich Vogeler'	EBee
	'Hella Glashoff' $\mathbb{Y}^{H7}$	CWCL EBee ELon GBin LRHS NDov
§	'Hoffnung'	CWCL MSpe WBod WWEG
	× ***huteri***	ECho ECtt EDAr GCrg MMuc MRav NGdn SEND SIgm SRms SWvt
	'Inca Gold'	CSam CWCL ECGP ECha ECtt EHoe EHrv EPPr EShb GBuc GQue LRHS MCot MRav MSpe NCGa NHol NSti SRms SWvt WFar WGwG WHoo WWEG WWtn
	'Jacqueline'	MTis
	× ***kellereri***	XSen
	'King Alfred'	CMea
	× ***kolbiana***	MWat SRms
§	'Lachsschönheit' (Galaxy Series) $\mathbb{Y}^{H7}$	CAby CKno CWCL EBee ECha ECtt ELan EPfP EWTr GMaP IBoy LAst LBMP LHop LRHS MBNS MCot MRav NBir NDov NHol NLar NSti SCob SPer SRms WBrk WHoo WMnd WWEG
	× ***lewisii*** 'King Edward' $\mathbb{Y}^{H5}$	ECho EDAr GMaP NBir SRms WAbe WFar WIce
	ligustica	WCot
	'Lucky Break' $\mathbb{Y}^{H7}$	ECtt LEdu MHol MTis SDix WBrk WCot
	macrophylla	MBNS
	'Marie Ann'	CWCL GQue LSRN NLar
	'Marmalade'	MRav NDov WWEG
	'Martina' $\mathbb{Y}^{H7}$	CAby CPrp CSam ECtt EPPr EWoo GBin GBuc GKin GQue LAst LHop LRHS MAsh MBNS MBel MCot MRav NDov NGdn NHol SRGP WCAu WCot WHea WHoo WWEG
	'McVities'	CWCL ECtt EPPr MSpe MTis WMnd WWEG
	millefolium	CArn CHab CLau ENfk GPoy MNHC NMir SRms WHer WJek WOut WSFF XLum
	- 'Bloodstone'	ECtt EWes MRav
	- 'Carla Hussey'	WFar
	- 'Cassis'	CSpe GQue LRHS MCot NGBl NLar SPtp WBor WBrk WMoo WOut
§	- 'Cerise Queen'	Widely available
	- 'Chamois'	MNrw
	- 'Cherry King'	NBir
	- 'Christel'	EWes GBin
	- 'Circus'	XLum
	- 'Dark Lilac Beauty'	CWCL
	- Kirschkönigin	see *A. millefolium* 'Cerise Queen'
	- 'Lansdorferglut' $\mathbb{Y}^{H7}$	EBee EPPr LRHS MTis NDov SPhx WWEG
	- 'Laura'	CSam CWGN EBee LSou MBel MNrw
	- 'Lavender Beauty'	see *A. millefolium* 'Lilac Beauty'
§	- 'Lilac Beauty'	Widely available
*	- 'Lilac Queen'	MArl
	- 'Little Suzie'	CWGN
	- 'Old Brocade'	EShb NDov WWEG
	- Pastel Shades	IFoB IFro WFar
	- 'Peggy Sue'	CBod CWGN EBee ECtt WFar
	- 'Pomegranate' (Tutti Frutti Series)	CMos CWCL CWGN IPot MNrw NLar SCob SHar XLum
	- 'Pretty Woman'	CSam CWGN EBee
	- 'Raspberry Ripple'	GBin
	- 'Red Beauty'	CWCL ELan EPfP EWTr GBin MBNS MSpe SRms WWEG XLum XSen
	- 'Red Salmon'	EWes
	- 'Red Velvet'	Widely available
	- 'Rose Madder'	Widely available
	- 'Salmon Pink'	IBoy
	- 'Salmon Queen'	NHol WFar
	- 'Sammetriese'	ELon MNrw SMad SPhx WWEG
	- 'Schneetaler'	GBin
	- 'Serenade'	ECtt MSpe
	- 'Sue's Pink'	CSam
	- (Summer Fruits Series) 'Summer Fruits Carmine'	EBee LRHS WHar
	- - 'Summer Fruits Lemon'	EBee LRHS SBea WHar
	- - 'Summer Fruits Salmon'	EBee LRHS WHar
	- 'Summertime'	WFar
	- 'White Queen'	EBee
	- 'Wonderful Wampee'	EBee LRHS MBri MNrw NLar SCob WCot
	'Mondpagode' $\mathbb{Y}^{H7}$	CAby CPrp ECGP EPPr EWTr LRHS MBNS MCot MRav NCGa NGdn NHol SMHy SPhx SWvt WGwG WHoo WWEG
*	'Moonbeam'	GKin SEND
	'Moonshine' $\mathbb{Y}^{H7}$	Widely available
	'Moonwalker'	CAbP EPfP SPav WCot XLum
	nana	WFar
	nobilis subsp. ***neilreichii***	ECGP EHoe EHrv EWTr GQue IBoy IKil LAst MMuc MNrw NDov NSti SEND SPer SWvt WWEG
*	***odilis***	EWTr
	'Paprika' (Galaxy Series)	Widely available
	'Petra'	ILea MNrw XLum
	pindicola subsp. ***integrifolia***	EWes
	'Pineapple Mango'[PBR] **new**	MTis SCob
	pink-flowered from Santa Cruz Island	CWCL
	'Pink Grapefruit' (Tutti Frutti Series)	LRHS MAsh MNrw MTis NLar SCob WCAu
	'Pretty Belinda'	EBee ECtt EPfP ILea IPot LAst LRHS LSRN LSou MAsh MAvo MBel MCot MSpe NDov NLar NSti SKHP SPoG SRms WCAu WFar
	'Prospero'	WBrk WCot WWEG
	ptarmica	CArn CBod CBre CLau MHer NMir SCob SRms WWtn XLum
*	- 'Ballerina'	MBNS MWhi NBre NDov NLar
	- 'Major'	WCot
	- 'Nana Compacta'	CSpe EPPr GBin IBoy LRHS NBir SPlb WCFE WFar WWEG
	- 'Noblessa'	MHol
	- 'Perry's White' (d)	CBcs CBre ECha MNrw SRGP WCot
	- 'Stephanie Cohen'	see *A. sibirica* 'Stephanie Cohen'
	- The Pearl Group seed-raised (d)	CTri CWld ELan MMuc SGbt SPlb SWat WBod WFar WMoo
	- - 'Boule de Neige' (clonal) (d)	GKin IBoy MRav MSpe NPer NSti SPer XLum
	- - 'The Pearl' (clonal) (d)	Widely available
	pyrenaica	XLum
	'Ruby Wine'	WFar
	'Safran'	EBee LRHS XLum
§	***salicifolia***	WFar
	- 'Silver Spray'	GQue IPot NLar SPav WOut
	'Sally'	EPPr
	Salmon Beauty	see *A.* 'Lachsschönheit'
	'Sandra Wagg'	ECtt
	'Sandstone'	see *A.* 'Wesersandstein'

§ 'Schwefelblüte' MRav NBir
'Schwellenburg' NBre WCot
sibirica CHid EBee IPot LHop MHol MMuc
subsp. ***camschatica*** MNrw NLar SGbt SPer SPtp WWEG
'Love Parade' XLum
§ - 'Stephanie Cohen' CPrp GBee GBin LHop WFar WWEG
sipikorensis **new** SIgm
'Stephanie' ECtt EPPr EWes LSRN
Summer Berries Group LRHS NFav
Summer Pastels Group EPfP IBoy LRHS MGos NLar SRms WFar WWtn XLum
- (Seduction Series) 'Peachy Seduction'PBR MBri
- - 'Saucy Seduction' CWCL ELon MBri MHol NLar
- - 'Sunny Seduction' ECtt ELon MBri
- - 'Strawberry Seduction' ECtt MBri
'Summerwine' ♀H7 Widely available
'Sunbeam' SHar
I 'Taygetea' ELan EPPr EPfP EWTr LCro LOPS LPal MBNS SCob SPer SRkn WCAu WCot XLum
'Terracotta' Widely available
'The Beacon' see *A.* 'Fanal'
'Tissington Flame' MAvo
'Tissington Old Rose' MAvo MNrw
tomentosa ♀H5 CTri ECha ECho ECtt XSen
§ - 'Aurea' ECho NBro
- 'Goldie' EDAr LRHS SWvt
- 'Maynard's Gold' see *A. tomentosa* 'Aurea'
'Tri-colour' NGdn
§ ***umbellata*** EPot NSla SIgm WAbe XSen
'W.B. Childs' ELan MNrw MRav NDov SHar
'Walther Funcke' Widely available
§ 'Wesersandstein' CWCL ECtt EPPr GBin GMaP LCro LOPS MNrw NBir SCob SGbt WWEG
'Wilczekii' SRms
'Yellowstone' EWes

× *Achimenantha* (*Gesneriaceae*)

'Aries' EABi WDib
'Cool Inferno' WDib
'Golden Jubilee' **new** WDib
'Himalayan Sunrise' LAma WDib
'Inferno' ♀H1c EABi WDib
'Pisces' WDib
'Texas Blue Bayou' WDib
'Tyche' EABi

Achimenes (*Gesneriaceae*)

'Addano' WDib
admirabilis **new** WDib
'Ambroise Verschaffelt' ♀H1c EABi LAma WDib
'Ami Salib' **new** EABi
'Ami Van Houtte' WDib
'Apricot Glow' EABi WDib
'Aquamarine' WDib
'Aurora Charm' **new** WDib
'Ballerina' WDib
'Beautiful Fire' **new** WDib
'Big Weiss' **new** WDib
'Blue David' EABi
'Blue Sparkles' EABi SDeJ
'Boy David' EABi
'Caligula' EABi WDib
'Cameo Rose' WDib
'Camille Brozzoni' EABi
'Candy Shop' **new** WDib
'Cascade Fairy Pink' WDib
'Cascade Fashionable Pink' WDib
'Cascade Rose Red' WDib
'Cascade Violet Night' WDib
'Cattleya' LAma
cettoana WDib
'Charity' WDib
'Charm' LAma SDeJ WDib
'Cherry Blossom' EABi
'Claret' EABi WDib
'Clouded Yellow' EABi
'Coral Cameo Mix' EABi
'Côte d'Ivoire' EABi
'Crackerjack' WDib
'Crummock Water' WDib
'Dale Martens' **new** EABi
'Donna' EABi
'Dot' EABi
'Double Picotee Rose' (d) WDib
'Double Pink Rose' (d) WDib
erecta EABi WDib
'Erlkönig' WDib
'Escheriana' LAma
'Extravaganza' WDib
'Firefly' **new** WDib
'Flamenco' WDib
'Flaming Embers' EABi
'Fluffy Wambler' **new** EABi
'Glory' EABi WDib
'Golden Butterfly' **new** WDib
'Good Mood' **new** EABi
grandiflora 'Robert Dressler' EABi
'Grape Wine' EABi
'Harry Williams' LAma WDib
'Hilda Michelssen' ♀H1c EABi WDib
'Himalayan Angel' EABi LAma
'Himalayan Double' LAma
'Himalayan Mandarin' EABi LAma
'Himalayan Sunset' EABi
'Hugues Aufray' **new** WDib
'Ice Tea' **new** WDib
'Improved Dale Martens' **new** EABi
'Improved Peach Cascade' **new** EABi
'India' EShb
'Jay Dee Coral' WDib
'Jay Dee Large White' WDib
'Jay Dee Pink' WDib
'Jay Dee Purple' WDib
'Jennifer Goode' EABi WDib
'Johanna Michelssen' WDib
'Jubilee Gem' EABi
'Just Divine' EABi WDib
'Kim Blue' WDib
'Lady in Black' WDib
'Light Lilac' WDib
'Little Beauty' WDib
longiflora 'Major' WDib
'Maxima' LAma
'Melon Ice Cream' **new** WDib
'Menuett' WDib
mexicana LAma SDeJ
misera WDib
'Nocturne' **new** EABi
'Opal' WDib
'Orange Delight' EABi WDib
'Orange Orchard' **new** EABi
'Palette Salmon' (Palette Series) EABi

'Pally'	WDib
'Patens Major'	EABi WDib
'Peach Blossom'	LAma SDeJ WDib
'Peach Cascade' **new**	EABi
'Peach Glow'	EABi WDib
'Peach Orchard' **new**	EABi
'Pearly Queen'	EABi
pedunculata	WDib
'Petite Fadette'	EABi WDib
'Petite Marquise' **new**	EABi
'Pink Beauty'	EABi
'Pink Rose' (d)	EABi
'Platinum'	EABi
'Primadonna'	SDeJ WDib
'Pulcherrima'	SDeJ
'Purple King'	WDib
'Purple Queen'	WDib
'Purple Triumph'	WDib
'Queen of Queens'	WDib
'Rai' **new**	WDib
'Rainbow'	EABi WDib
'Rainbow Warrior'	WDib
'Red Elfe'	EABi
'Red Hilda Michelssen'	WDib
'Rhino'	EABi
'Rosa Charm'	EABi
'Rose Dream'	EABi
'Rozi Roza' **new**	WDib
'Santa Claus'	WDib
'Schneewittchen'	WDib
'Serge Saliba'	EABi WDib
'Serge's Fantasy' **new**	WDib
'Show-off'	WDib
'Shy Sun' **new**	EABi WDib
skinneri	WDib
'Snow Princess'	SDeJ
'Stan's Delight' (d) ♀H1c	EABi WDib
'Sterntaler'	WDib
'Sugarland' **new**	WDib
'Summer Sunset'	EABi
'Sun Dance' **new**	EABi
'Sun Wind' **new**	WDib
'Sweet & Sour'	EABi WDib
'Tango'	WDib
'Tarantella'	EABi WDib
'Teresa'	EABi
(Tetra Series) 'Tetra Himalayan Purple'	LAma WDib
- 'Tetra Verschaffelt'	EABi
- 'Tetra Wine Red Charm'	EABi
'Tiger Eye'	WDib
'Valse Bleu'	WDib
'Vie-en-Rose'	EABi
'Violacea Semiplena' (d)	WDib
'Vivid'	EABi LAma WDib
'Weinrot Elfe'	WDib
'Wetterlow's Triumph'	EABi WDib
'Yellow Beauty'	WDib

Achlys (*Berberidaceae*)

japonica	WCru
triphylla	IMou WCru

Achnatherum see *Stipa*

Achyranthes (*Amaranthaceae*)

bidentata var. ***longifolia*** PAB 8037	LEdu

Acidanthera see *Gladiolus*

Acinos (*Lamiaceae*)

§ ***alpinus***	EBee EDAr GJos LLHF SBch SRms WJek XLum
§ ***corsicus***	WHoo WKif

Aciphylla (*Apiaceae*)

aurea	GBin GCal GKev SPlb
congesta	CMen
crosby-smithii	EPot
dieffenbachii	EUJe
glaucescens	EUJe GCal GKev SPlb
hectorii	CMen
'Lomond'	EBee
montana	CMen
pinnatifida	CMen
simplex	CMen
spedenii	CMen
subflabellata	GKev

Acis (*Amaryllidaceae*)

§ ***autumnalis*** ♀H5	CAby CAvo CBro CDes CElw CTal CTca CTri ECha ECho EPot EWes GKev LRHS NBir SBch SRms SRot WAbe WHea WHil WHoo WOld WPGP WSHC
- var. ***oporantha***	CWCL EPri LAma
- var. ***pulchella***	ECho GKev NRog
- 'September Snow'	ELan GKev LAma NRog
nicaeensis	CDes CTal ECho EPot GCal GKev LLHF LRHS NWad WAbe WCot WThu
§ ***rosea***	CTal ECho NRog WAbe
§ ***tingitana***	CBro
§ ***trichophylla***	EPot GKev
- f. ***purpurascens***	CDes WCot
§ ***valentina***	NRog SRot WCot

Acmena (*Myrtaceae*)

smithii	ECou

Acnistus (*Solanaceae*)

australis	see *Iochroma australe*

Aconitum (*Ranunculaceae*)

CNDS 036 from Burma	WCru
alboviolaceum	WCot
- var. ***alboviolaceum*** f. ***albiflorum*** B&SWJ 4105	WCru
- - - B&SWJ 8444	WCru
- var. ***purpurascens*** B&SWJ 8477	WCru
altissimum	see *A. lycoctonum* subsp. *vulparia*
anglicum	see *A. napellus* subsp. *napellus* Anglicum Group
* ***angulosum***	EWld
§ ***anthora***	CArn EPfP IKil MHol NLar
arcuatum	see *A. fischeri* var. *arcuatum*
austroyunnanense	CMea WHal WSHC
- BWJ 7902	WCru
autumnale misapplied	see *A. carmichaelii* Wilsonii Group
autumnale Rchb.	see *A. fischeri* Rchb.
× ***bicolor***	see *A.* × *cammarum* 'Bicolor'
'Blue Lagoon' PBR	CMos CWGN EBee
'Blue Opal'	CDes EBee ECtt EWes MAvo
'Blue Sceptre'	GBin NLar
'Bressingham Spire' ♀H7	Widely available
bulbilliferum HWJK 2120	WCru WSHC

	Name	Suppliers
§	× ***cammarum*** 'Bicolor' ♀H7	Widely available
	- 'Eleanora'	CCon ECtt EPPr EPfP EWTr EWes GBuc GCra GMaP LHop LSou NLar SRms WCAu
	- 'Grandiflorum Album'	CAby LPla MNrw NDov
	- 'Pink Sensation' PBR	CAby GQue LLHF NDov NLar
§	***carmichaelii***	CMea CSam ELan EPfP GBin GBuc GCra GKin IFoB IFro LAst LRHS LSou MMuc MNrw NBro NEgg NGdn SEND SGol SRms WBod WCot WFar WHil WHoo WWtn
	- Arendsii Group	ECtt GKev LAst LEdu SRot WCAu
	- - 'Arendsii' ♀H7	Widely available
	- - 'Cloudy' PBR	LHop MAvo NLar
	- 'Moody Blues'	EBee
	- 'Redleaf'	see *A. carmichaelii* 'Royal Flush'
	- 'River Devon'	WCot
	- 'River Finn'	WCot
	- 'River Lugg'	WCot
	- 'River Medway'	WCot
	- 'River Nene'	WCot
	- 'River Ouse'	ECtt WCot
	- 'River Spey'	WCot
	- 'River Tees'	WCot
	- 'River Teifi'	WCot
	- 'River Trent'	WCot
	- 'River Welland'	WCot
§	- 'Royal Flush' PBR	CAby CHVG CWGN EBee ECtt EPfP GBin IBoy MBNS MHol MNrw NEgg NLar SPad SPer WCot
	- var. ***truppelianum***	WCot
	- - HWJ 732	EBee WCot
§	- Wilsonii Group	EBee ECGP EWoo GMaP LPla LRHS MCot MRav MWat MWhi NCGa NDov NEgg WHoo XLum
	- - 'Barker's Variety'	CKno ELon GBuc GCal GQue LHop LRHS NGdn NLar NSti SRms WCot
	- - 'Kelmscott' ♀H7	ECtt EWes MCot MRav SDix SMHy WFar WRHF
	- - 'Spätlese'	CSam CWGN EBee ECtt ELon GCal LEdu LRHS LSou LSun MCot MHol NBir NGdn NLar SGbt SMHy WCot
§	***chasmanthum***	LRHS
	- GWJ 9393	WCru
	chiisanense B&SWJ 4446	WCru
	cilicicum	see *Eranthis hyemalis* Cilicica Group
	'Cloudy'	EBee ECtt LEdu NGdn SPer WCot
	compactum	see *A. napellus* subsp. *vulgare*
	confertiflorum	see *A. anthora*
	delphiniifolium	CExl
	elliotii	EBee
	elwesii	EBee
	episcopale	CTal WCot WCru
	aff. ***episcopale*** CLD 1426	GBuc WFar
	excelsum	see *A. lycoctonum* subsp. *lycoctonum*
	ferox	EBee EWes LLHF
	- GWJ 9333 from Sikkim	WCru
	- HWJK 2217	WCru
	fischeri misapplied	see *A. carmichaelii*
§	***fischeri*** Rchb.	CBod CWib EBee LRHS NBid NCGa NLar WCot
	- B&SWJ 8809	WCru
§	- var. ***arcuatum*** B&SWJ 774	WCru
	formosanum B&SWJ 3057	WCru
	fukutomei B&SWJ 337	MRav WCru
	gammiei GWJ 9418	WCru

	Name	Suppliers
	gmelinii	see *A. lycoctonum* subsp. *lycoctonum*
	grossedentatum	LPla NLar
§	***hemsleyanum***	CAby CExl CMea CRHN CTal CWGN ECtt EWTr EWld GCra GKev NBid SGSe WCot WCru WHea WOld
	- dark blue-flowered	MLHP
	- 'Red Wine'	WCot
	hyemale	see *Eranthis hyemalis*
	'Ivorine'	Widely available
	jaluense B&SWJ 8741	WCru
	japonicum	EBee GCal NLar WCot
	- var. ***hakonense***	CExl
	- var. ***montanum*** B&SWJ 5507	WCru
§	- subsp. ***napiforme***	EWes WCot
	- - B&SWJ 943	EBee ELon WCru
§	- subsp. ***subcuneatum*** B&SWJ 6228	WCru
	kitadakense B&SWJ 11173 **new**	WCru
	krylovii	WCot
	kusnezoffii	WCot
	laciniatum GWJ 9254	WCru
	- GWJ 9324	WCru
	lamarckii	see *A. lycoctonum* subsp. *neapolitanum*
	lasianthum	see *A. lycoctonum* subsp. *vulparia*
	leucostomum	EBee GCal
	loczyanum B&SWJ 11529	WCru WSHC
	longecassidatum B&SWJ 4277	WCru
	- B&SWJ 8486	WCru
	lycoctonum	CTal NLar
	- 'Darkeyes'	CAbP WCot WFar
§	- subsp. ***lycoctonum***	SRms WCot
§	- subsp. ***moldavicum***	WCot
§	- subsp. ***neapolitanum***	EBee GCal GMaP IMou MMuc NLar
	- 'Russian Yellow'	EWld GCal
§	- subsp. ***vulparia***	CArn CCon CMac EBee GPoy MLHP MNrw MRav MSCN NEgg NGdn SRms WCot
	mairei	see *A. vilmorinianum*
	moldavicum	see *A. lycoctonum* subsp. *moldavicum*
	nagarum	WCot
	- KR 7589	CDes WPGP
	napellus	CAby CArn CBod CMHG ECtt EPfP GAbr GKev GPoy LAst LCro LEdu LOPS LRHS MBel MCot MMuc MNHC MWat SEND SRms SWat WBor WFar WHar WHoo WPnP WShi XLum
	- 'Bergfürst'	CAby CMea EBee LPla NDov
	- 'Blue Valley'	COtt EBee ELan EPfP EWes
	- 'Gletschereis'	EBee LRHS
	- subsp. ***napellus***	SRms
§	- - Anglicum Group	MCot MHol MMuc WCot
	- 'Rubellum'	ELan EWTr GQue IBoy IMou LRHS NBir NBro NLar NPri SPoG WMnd
	- 'Schneewittchen'	CSpe EBee EWes GQue SAko
§	- subsp. ***vulgare***	CTal
	- - 'Albidum'	CAby CBod CCon CMea EHrv ELan ELon EPfP EWTr EWoo GAbr GMaP LAst LEdu LRHS MBel NBid NHol NLar NPri SBea SGol SPer SPoG WBor WWtn
	- - 'Carneum'	GCra WHer WKif

napiforme	see *A. japonicum* subsp. *napiforme*
nasutum	WCot
neapolitanum	see *A. lycoctonum* subsp. *neapolitanum*
'Newry Blue'	CKno EBee ECtt GBuc IMou LRHS MRav NBir NLar NWad SBod SRms
orientale misapplied	see *A. lycoctonum* subsp. *vulparia*
paniculatum misapplied	see *A. variegatum* subsp. *paniculatum*
piepunense	EBee GKev
proliferum	WCot
- B&SWJ 4107	WCru
pseudohuiliense	CExl
pseudolaeve B&SWJ 8663	WCru
- var. ***erectum*** B&SWJ 8466	WCru
pubiceps white-flowered	GCal
pyramidale	see *A. napellus* subsp. *vulgare*
pyrenaicum misapplied	see *A. lycoctonum* subsp. *neapolitanum*
ranunculifolius	see *A. lycoctonum* subsp. *neapolitanum*
sachalinense	WCot
- subsp. ***yezoense***	NLar WCot
senanense var. ***incisum*** B&SWJ 11032	WCru
- subsp. ***paludicola*** B&SWJ 10866	WCru
seoulense B&SWJ 694	WCru
- B&SWJ 864	WCru
- BWJ 4107	IMou
septentrionale	see *A. lycoctonum* subsp. *lycoctonum*
'Shirui Blue'	LEdu
'Spark's Variety' ♀H7	Widely available
spicatum GWJ 9394	WCru
'Stainless Steel' ♀H7	Widely available
subcuneatum	see *A. japonicum* subsp. *subcuneatum*
× ***tubergenii***	see *Eranthis hyemalis* Tubergenii Group
uchiyamae	CEvo
- B&SWJ 1005	WCru
- B&SWJ 1216	ELon EPPr WCru
- B&SWJ 4446	NLar
variegatum	EBee GCal
§ - subsp. ***paniculatum***	MLHP WCot
§ ***vilmorinianum*** BWJ 8055	WCru
violaceum var. ***robustum***	see *A. chasmanthum*
volubile misapplied	see *A. hemsleyanum*
volubile Pall.	CCon EBee
vulparia	see *A. lycoctonum* subsp. *vulparia*
yamazakii	EBee WCru
zigzag var. ***ryohakuense*** B&SWJ 8906	WCru

Aconogonon see *Persicaria*

Acorus ✿ (*Acoraceae*)

calamus	CArn CBen CKno CLau CWat EHon GPoy MNHC MSKA MWts NPer SWat WHer WMAq
- subsp. ***angustatus***	GPoy
- 'Argenteostriatus' (v)	CBen CWat ECha EHon MCot MMuc SCob SGSe SRms SWat WMAq WWEG
* ***christophii***	ELon EPPr EWes
gramineus	CLau GPoy MSKA NPer SWat WBod WHer
- 'Golden Delight'	SCob SGSe
- 'Golden Edge' (v)	ELon EWes MBri
- 'Hakuro-nishiki' (v)	EHoe GBin LRHS NBid NWad SCob SGSe SRms SWvt WMoo XLum
- 'Kinchinjunga' (v)	IFro
- 'Licorice'	GBin GCal WGrn
- 'Masamune' (v)	EWes GBin GCal
- 'Minimus Aureus'	CBre GCal
- 'Oborozuki' misapplied	see *A. gramineus* 'Ōgon'
- 'Oborozuki' (v)	EHoe
§ - 'Ōgon' (v)	Widely available
- var. ***pusillus***	NBro WWEG
- 'Variegatus' (v)	Widely available
'Intermedius'	NPer

Acradenia (*Rutaceae*)

frankliniae	CBcs CMHG CMac EBee EPfP IDee LRHS MBlu SAko SEND SKHP SPlb WHor WPGP

Actaea (*Ranunculaceae*)

alba misapplied	see *A. pachypoda*, *A. rubra* f. *neglecta*
arizonica	CTal EBee LPla LRHS NLar SPhx WCru
asiatica	CDes CEvo
- B&SWJ 616	WCru
- B&SWJ 6351 from Japan	WCru
- B&SWJ 8694 from Korea	WCru
- BWJ 8174 from China	WCru
biternata B&SWJ 8917	NLar WCru
- B&SWJ 11190	WCru
'Chocoholic'	CLAP CMos EBee ECtt ELan GBBs GBin IKil IPot LRHS MAvo MCot
§ ***cimicifuga***	CLAP ECha GCal GPoy
§ ***cordifolia***	EBee GBin GMaP LHop LRHS NGdn NLar SHar SWvt
- variegated (v)	EBee
dahurica	GBin GQue SWat
- B&SWJ 8426	WCru
- B&SWJ 8573	WCru
- tall	GBin NBid
elata	IMou
erythrocarpa	see *A. rubra*
frigida B&SWJ 2966	WCru
heracleifolia B&SWJ 8843	WCot WCru
§ ***japonica***	GCal NLar SHar
- B&SWJ 5828	WCru
- B&SWJ 11136	WCru
- B&SWJ 11526	WCru
- from Cheju Do	EBee IMou LEdu NDov WPGP
- var. ***acutiloba*** B&SWJ 6257	WCru
- compact	GBin
- - B&SWJ 8758A	WCot WCru
mairei	IMou LRHS
- BWJ 7635	WCru
- BWJ 7939	WCru
§ ***matsumurae***	CExl
- B&SWJ 11187	WCru
- B&SWJ 11528	WCru
- 'Elstead Variety' ♀H7	CExl GCal MRav
- 'White Pearl'	Widely available
§ ***pachypoda***	CBro CExl CTal EBee EPfP EWTr GBin GCal GLog GPoy MBel NBid NLar SMad WCru
- 'Misty Blue'	CAby CBct CBod CBro CLAP CWGN EBee ECtt ESwi GEdr IPot LBMP LPla MAvo MBel MHol NLar NMyG SCob SMad SPoG WCot
- f. ***rubrocarpa***	GCal

§	***podocarpa***	EBee SPlb SRms WCru
	'Queen of Sheba' **new**	EBee
	racemosa ♀H7	CArn CBod CMac EBee ELan EPfP GBin GCal GPoy NBid NGdn NLar NSti SPer SWvt WFar
§	***rubra***	CBod CBro CEvo CLAP CTal EBee ECha ELan GCal MMHG MNrw NBid NLar SMad WCru
	- B&SWJ 9555	WCru
	- ***alba***	see *A. pachypoda*, *A. rubra* f. *neglecta*
§	- f. ***neglecta***	GQue SKHP WCot WCru
	simplex	EBee GCra NEgg SWat WCot
	- B&SWJ 8653	WCru
	- B&SWJ 8664	WCru
	- B&SWJ 10957	WCru
	- B&SWJ 11133	WCru
§	- Atropurpurea Group	Widely available
	- - 'Black Negligee'	Widely available
	- - 'Brunette' ♀H7	Widely available
	- - 'Carbonella'	EBee ECtt GBin MAsh MBri SMDP SPoG
	- - 'Hillside Black Beauty'	CLAP ECtt GBin GEdr GKin GMaP LRHS MBri MNrw NBir SCob WCot
	- - 'James Compton' ♀H7	Widely available
	- - 'Mountain Wave'	ECtt WCot WPGP
	- 'Pink Spike'	Widely available
§	- 'Prichard's Giant'	CLAP EBee GBin GCal MRav NLar WFar
	- ***ramosa***	see *A. simplex* 'Prichard's Giant'
	- 'Silver Axe'	GCal NGdn
	- variegated (v)	CDes WCot
	spicata	EPPr GBin GCra GPoy LEdu NLar WCru WPGP
	- PAB 8131 **new**	LEdu
	- from England	WCru
	taiwanensis B&SWJ 3413	WCru
	- RWJ 9996	WCru
	yesoensis B&SWJ 6355	WCru
	- B&SWJ 10860	WCru
	yunnanensis	GCal

Actinella see *Tetraneuris*

Actinidia (*Actinidiaceae*)

	BWJ 8161 from China	WCru
	arguta	CPne CRHN
	- (f/F)	CAgr NLar
	- B&SWJ 4823 from Japan	WCru
	- B&SWJ 4455 from Jejudo, South Korea	WCru
	- B&SWJ 8529 from Ulleungdo, South Korea	WCru
	- 'Ambrosia' (f/F)	LRHS WMat
	- 'Ambrosia Grande'	NLar
	- 'Ananasnaya' (f/F)	CAgr
	- 'Bayern' (F)	CAgr
	- 'Geneva 2' (f/F)	CAgr
	- 'Honigbeere'	NLar
	- 'Issai' (s-p/F)	CAgr CBcs EPfP LBuc LCro LRHS MGos NLar SVic WCot
	- 'Jumbo' (f/F)	CAgr SVic
	- 'Ken's Red' (F)	CAgr SVic
	- 'Meader' (m)	CAgr
	- 'MSU' (F)	CAgr
	- 'Purpurna Sadowa' (f/F)	NLar
	- 'Shoko' (f)	WCru
	- 'Unchae' (m)	WCru
	- 'Weiki' (m)	CAgr LRHS SVic
	chinensis misapplied	see *A. deliciosa*
	chinensis Planch. var. ***setosa*** B&SWJ 3563	WCru
§	***deliciosa***	MRav WSHC
	- 'Atlas' (m)	CAgr NLar SDea
	- 'Hayward' (f/F)	CAgr CBcs CMac EPfP LSRN NLar SCob SDea SWvt WFar
	- 'Jenny' (s-p/F)	CAgr CMac CSut CTri ELan EPfP EPom LAst LBuc LCro LRHS MBri MGos MJak SBmr SCob SDea SPoG SPre SVic WFar
	- Solissimo = 'Renact'	CDoC LRHS MBri MCoo SEND WMat
	- 'Solo' (s-p/F)	CBcs CMac CSBt ECrN EPfP LRHS LSRN NLar NPri SLim SPer SWvt WPGP
	- 'Tomuri' (m)	CBcs CMac COtt EBee EPfP LSRN NLar SWvt
	hypoleuca B&SWJ 5942	WCru
	kolomikta ♀H5	Widely available
	- (m)	MBlu NPla SDix
	- B&SWJ 4243	LSRN WCru
	- 'Doctor Szymanowski'	WPGP
	- 'Sentyabraskaya' (f/F) **new**	NLar
	- 'Tomoko' (f/F)	NLar WCru
	- 'Yazuaki' (m)	WCru
	melanandra	SPlb WPGP
	petelotii FMWJ 13137	WCru
	- HWJ 628	WCru
	pilosula misapplied	see *A. tetramera* var. *maloides*
	pilosula (Finet & Gagnep.) Stapf ex Hand.-Mazz.	CKel ELan GGal IArd LRHS SHil SPoG SRms WKif
	polygama	GCal
	- B&SWJ 5444	WCru
	- B&SWJ 8525 from Korea	WCru
	- B&SWJ 8923 from Japan	WCru
	- B&SWJ 12564 from Korea	WCru
	rufa B&SWJ 3525	WCru
	aff. ***strigosa*** HWJK 2367	WCru
	tetramera B&SWJ 3564	WCru
§	- var. ***maloides*** ♀H5	CBcs CBot CDoC CExl CWGN EBee EUJe GCal GGal LHop MGil MGos NLar SBrt SCoo SDix SKHP WBor WCru WPGP WSHC

Adansonia (*Malvaceae*)

grandidieri	SPlb
madagascariensis	SPlb
rubrostipa	SPlb
za	SPlb

Adelocaryum see *Lindelofia*

Adenanthos (*Proteaceae*)

sericeus	SPlb SVen

Adenium (*Apocynaceae*)

obesum ♀H1a	LToo
- subsp. ***boehmianum***	LToo
- subsp. ***socotranum*** **new**	LToo
- subsp. ***swazicum***	LToo

Adenocarpus (*Papilionaceae*)

decorticans	SPlb SVen

Adenophora (*Campanulaceae*)

sp.	MHol
'Afterglow'	see *Campanula rapunculoides* 'Afterglow'
asiatica	see *Hanabusaya asiatica*
aurita	WCot

bulleyana	CCon CHVG ELan GCra GJos LRHS MNHC NBid NGdn NLar SGSe SPav SPlb WCot
capillaris subsp. ***leptosepala***	WCot
- - BWJ 7986	WCru
coelestis	CExl EBee NBid
- B&SWJ 7998	WCru
confusa	WHer WSHC
* ***cymerae***	WTcb
divaricata B&SWJ 11018 **new**	WCru
'Gaudi Violet' **new**	SPad
grandiflora B&SWJ 8555	WCru
jasionifolia	LLHF
khasiana	CExl LLHF NLar XLum
lamarkii B&SWJ 8738	WCru
latifolia misapplied	see *A. pereskiifolia*
latifolia ambig. white-flowered	MMuc
liliifolia	ELan EPfP GCal LHop MMuc NLar NPer WFar XLum
maximowicziana B&SWJ 11008	WCru
morrisonensis RWJ 10008	WCru
§ ***nikoensis***	GEdr NBid
§ ***pereskiifolia***	EWes SGSe SHar SPlb WCot
polyantha	EWTr NLar SRms
polymorpha	see *A. nikoensis*
potaninii	EBee ELan MMuc SEND WHal
- lilac-flowered	WFar
- pale-flowered	MAvo WHal
remotiflora B&SWJ 8714	WCru
- B&SWJ 11016	WCru
takedae	EBee SBrt
- B&SWJ 11424	WCru
- var. ***howozana***	MLHP
taquetii	CPBP GEdr
tashiroi	XLum
triphylla	GKev SGSe
- B&SWJ 8608	WCru
- B&SWJ 10916	WCru
- var. ***hakusanensis***	LLHF
- var. ***japonica*** B&SWJ 10933	WCru
uehatae	GEdr
- B&SWJ 126	SKHP WCru

Adesmia (*Papilionaceae*)

longipes	SPlb

Adiantum (*Pteridaceae*)

sp.	CMac
aethiopicum	NLos XBlo
§ ***aleuticum*** ♀H6	CLAP LPal NBro NLar SPlb WFib WPGP
- 'Imbricatum'	CElw CLAP EBee ECha ELon EShb GEdr GKev IKil ISha IVic LPal LRHS MAvo MGos NBid NLar NMyG SDix SRms WCot WFib XLum
§ - 'Japonicum'	WPGP
- 'Miss Sharples'	CBod CDTJ CLAP ECha ELon GEdr LRHS MGos NBid NLar NMyG SPoG SRms WPGP WRHF
§ - 'Subpumilum' ♀H5	CLAP GKev NBid WFib
andicola B&SWJ 10448	WCru
bonatianum	CExl
capillus-veneris	EBee ISha SGSe WFib
- 'Mairisii'	see *A.* × *mairisii*
hispidulum	EBee ISha LRHS NLos
- 'Bronze Venus'	ISha LRHS SRms
§ × ***mairisii*** ♀H5	ISha LRHS NLos
pedatum misapplied	see *A. aleuticum*
pedatum ambig.	CCon ISha NLos SPer
pedatum L.	CBcs CLAP ECha EFer ELan ELon EPfP EShb GMaP LAst LPot LRHS MBri SWat WPGP
- Asiatic form	see *A. aleuticum* 'Japonicum'
- 'Japonicum'	see *A. aleuticum* 'Japonicum'
- 'Roseum'	see *A. aleuticum* 'Japonicum'
- var. ***subpumilum***	see *A. aleuticum* 'Subpumilum'
poiretii	WCot
pubescens	ISha
raddianum 'Fragrans'	see *A. raddianum* 'Fragrantissimum'
§ - 'Fragrantissimum'	EShb ISha
- 'Lady Geneva'	WCot
- 'Legrand Morgan'	NLos
- 'Monocolor'	ISha
reniforme	NLos
tenerum 'Bicolor' **new**	ISha
venustum ♀H7	CExl CFil CHVG CLAP CTsd EBee EFer EPot ISha IVic LRHS MCot MLHP MWat NCGa SBrt SChr SKHP SPlb SRms SWat WCot WFib WHal WPGP

Adina (*Rubiaceae*)

rubella	NLar

Adlumia (*Papaveraceae*)

fungosa	CSpe LRHS

Adonis (*Ranunculaceae*)

amurensis misapplied	see *A.* 'Fukujukai', *A. multiflora*
amurensis ambig.	CMea EBee ECGP EPot GEdr LEdu LLHF LRHS WCot
- 'Pleniflora'	see *A. multiflora* 'Sandanzaki'
- 'Sakhalin' **new**	EBee
brevistyla	GBuc GEdr WAbe
'Chichibu-beni'	GEdr
§ 'Fukujukai'	ECha GKev XEll
§ ***multiflora***	ECho EHrv SRot
- 'Beni-nadeshiko'	GEdr
- 'Hakuju'	GEdr
- 'Hanazono' (d)	GEdr
§ - 'Sandanzaki' (d)	EBee EPot GEdr NLar
ramosa	GEdr
vernalis	EBee GPoy NLar WCot

Adoxa (*Adoxaceae*)

moschatellina	CBre EBee ECho EWld LEdu MNrw NMir NRya WHer WSFF WShi

Adromischus (*Crassulaceae*)

maculatus ♀H2 **new**	LToo

Aechmea (*Bromeliaceae*)

sp.	XBlo
abbreviata **new**	NEve
aquilega **new**	NEve
'Blue Rain' PBR	LAir NEve
'Blue Tango' **new**	LAir
blumenavii	LAir NEve
bracteata	LAir NEve
calyculata	LAir NEve
caudata	LAir NEve NLos
- short	LAir
- var. ***variegata***	NLos
chlorophylla	LAir

coelestis new NEve
- var. ***albomarginata*** new NEve
- dwarf new NEve
cylindrata 'Bicolor' LAir
- 'Blue Cone' new WCot
dichlamydea new NEve
distichantha NEve
'Echidna' LAir SPlb
fasciata ♀H1a LAir NEve XBlo
- 'Primera'PBR LAir NEve
filicaulis new NEve
'Flamingo' LAir
'Foster's Favorite' new NEve
fulgens NEve
var. ***discolor*** ♀H1a new
gamosepala NEve NLos
- var. ***nivea*** LAir
kertesziae NEve
lamarchei new NEve
lindenii 'Makoyana' new NEve
lueddemanniana new NEve
mariae-reginae new NEve
mexicana new NEve
miniata var. ***discolor*** new NEve
nudicaulis ♀H1a NEve NLos
- var. ***capitata*** NLos
I - - f. ***albomarginata*** NLos
- 'La Tigra' LAir
- 'Parati' LAir
- var. ***plurifolia*** LAir
orlandiana ♀H1a new NEve
racinae ♀H1a new NEve
ramosa NEve XBlo
recurvata LAir NEve NLos
- 'Artichoke' LAir
- var. ***benrathii*** LAir NEve
- 'Paraguay' NEve NLos
- var. ***recurvata*** LAir NLos
servitensis new NEve
'Suenos' LAir
victoriana NEve XBlo
- var. ***discolor*** NLos
wittmackiana 'Warren Loose' LAir

Aegle (*Rutaceae*)

sepiaria see *Citrus trifoliata*

Aegopodium (*Apiaceae*)

podagraria 'Dangerous' (v) CHid
- gold-margined (v) EPPr WWEG
- 'Variegatum' (v) CBod CLet EBee ECha EHoe EHrv EPPr EShb GKev GMaP LHop LRHS LSou MBel MRav MWhi NBid NEgg NSti SEND SPer SPoG WCFE WCot WMoo WSHC WWEG XLum

Aeonium (*Crassulaceae*)

sp. CArn
arboreum CDTJ CTre ELan EShb GCal SEND WCot
- 'Atropurpureum' CAbb CDTJ CRos CSde CSuc ELan EShb NPer SEND SPer
- var. ***holochrysum*** CSuc
I - 'Magnificum' EShb ESwi ETod GBin
- 'Variegatum' (v) CSuc NPer
balsamiferum CDTJ CSuc CTre SChr
'Black Magic' CSuc
'Blushing Beauty' ♀H1c CSuc
'Bronze Medal' CSuc
canariense CDTJ CSuc SVen
- var. ***palmense*** SVen
castello-paivae SChr
ciliatum CSuc SPlb
'Copper Kettle' CSuc
'Cornish Tribute' CTre
'Cristata Sunburst' CDTJ WCot
cuneatum CSde
'Cyclops' CSuc
davidbramwellii CSuc
* ***decorum*** 'Variegatum' (v) WCot
'Dinner Plate' CDTJ MHin
× ***domesticum*** see *Aichryson* × *aizoides* var. *domesticum*
'Emerald Flame' new CSuc
* ***escobarii*** CSuc SPlb
'Garnet' CSuc
glandulosum CSuc SVen
glutinosum CSuc
goochiae CSuc SBch
gorgonium CSuc
haworthii ♀H1c CDTJ LAll SEND SVen
- 'Variegatum' (v) ♀H1c CDTJ CSuc CTre EShb LAll SVen
hierrense CSuc CTre SPlb WCot
holochrysum Webb & Berth. CAbb
'Lemon-Lime' (v) CSuc WCot
leucoblepharum CSuc
lindleyi CSuc SChr
'Logan Rock' CTre
× ***mascaense*** CSuc
* ***multiflorum*** 'Variegatum' (v) CDTJ
nobile CBrP CSuc
'Phoenix Flame' new CSuc
'Plum Purdy' CSuc
'Poldark' new CTre
I 'Pygmaeum' CSuc
sedifolium CSuc CTre LAll
simsii CSuc
simsii × 'Zwartkop' CSuc CTre ELan ETod MHer SChr
spathulatum CSuc
'Sunburst' (v) ♀H1c CSuc CTre WCot
'Suncup' CSuc
tabuliforme ♀H1c CDTJ CSpe CSuc CTre SMad SPlb WCot
- 'Cristatum' WCot
undulatum SPlb
urbicum EShb
valverdense CSuc
'Velour' CSuc
'Voodoo' CSuc ESwi ETod EUJe WCot
'Zwartkin' CSuc
'Zwartkop' ♀H1c CAbb CBcs CHVG CHll CSpe CTre ECtt EShb EUJe GBin LSou MCot MSCN NLos NPer NPla SChr SDix SEND SEle SMad SPlb SRot SWvt WCot WWFP

Aeschynanthus ✿ (*Gesneriaceae*)

'Big Apple' WDib
Black Pagoda Group WDib
buxifolius KR 7798 WAbe WCot
'Fire Wheel' WDib
hildebrandii WDib
'Hot Flash' WDib
'Little Tiger' WDib
longicalyx WDib
§ ***longicaulis*** ♀H1c WDib
marmoratus see *A. longicaulis*

	radicans 🏆H1c	WDib
	'Scooby Doo'	WDib
	speciosus 🏆H1c	WDib

Aesculus ✿ (*Sapindaceae*)

	arguta	see *A. glabra* var. *arguta*
	× ***arnoldiana***	CDul CMCN NLar
	assamica NJM 10.030	WPGP
	- WWJ 11886	WCru
	'Autumn Splendor'	EPfP
§	× ***bushii***	CDul CMCN NLar
	californica	CBcs CDul CMCN CMac EPfP ERod SKHP WPGP
	- 'Blue Haze'	WMat
	- 'Canyon Pink' **new**	CMCN
	× ***carnea***	CDul SGol WHar
	- 'Aureomarginata' (v)	ERod LLHF WHar
	- 'Briotii'	CBcs CCVT CDul CLnd CMac CSBt CTho CWib EBee ECrN ELan EPfP LRHS MGos MMuc NLar NOrn NWea SCob SEND SEWo SPer WFar WHar WMat
	- 'Plantierensis'	CDul ECrN
*	- 'Variegata' (v)	CDul CMCN
	chinensis	CBcs CMCN
	flava 🏆H5	CDul CLnd CMCN CTho ELan EPfP EWTr MBri MMuc SEND
	- f. ***vestita***	CDul MBlu MBri NLar
	georgiana	see *A. sylvatica*
	glabra	CDul CMCN CTho
§	- var. ***arguta***	CMCN NLar WPat
	- 'Autumn Blaze'	EPfP
	- 'October Red'	EPfP LRHS MBri
	glaucescens	see *A.* × *neglecta*
	hippocastanum	CBcs CCVT CDul CMac CSBt CTho CTri CWib EBee ECrN ELan MGos MMuc MSwo NLar NWea SCob SEND SEWo SGol SPer WFar WHar WMat
	- 'Aureomarginata' (v)	CMac
§	- 'Baumannii' (d)	CDul CLnd CMCN ECrN ELan ERod MGos MSwo NWea SCob SPer
	- 'Digitata'	CDul CMCN WPat
	- 'Flore Pleno'	see *A. hippocastanum* 'Baumannii'
	- 'Gimborn's Pride'	NLar
	- 'Hampton Court Gold'	CDul CMCN CMac
	- f. ***laciniata***	CDul CMCN ERod NLar SMad WPat
	- 'Monstrosa'	WPat
	- 'Wisselink'	CDul CMCN ECrN WCot WPat
	indica	CDul CLnd CMCN ECrN ELan EPfP EWTr LEdu SEND SGol
	- 'Sydney Pearce' 🏆H5	CBcs CDul CJun CMCN EPfP ERod MBlu MBri MGos NLar SLim WMat WPat
	× ***marylandica***	CDul WPat
	× ***mississippiensis***	see *A.* × *bushii*
	× ***mutabilis*** 'Harbisonii'	WPat
	- 'Induta'	CDul CLnd CMCN EPfP GBin MBri SKHP WMat
§	- 'Penduliflora'	CDul
§	× ***neglecta***	CMCN NLar
	- 'Autumn Fire'	EBee EPfP GBin NOrn SLim SPoG WMat WPat
	- 'Erythroblastos' 🏆H5	CBcs CDul CJun CMCN EPfP ERod EUJe MBlu MBri SCoo SMad SPer SPoG WCot WMat WPat
	parviflora 🏆H5	CBcs CDul CMCN CMac CTri EBee ELan EPfP EWTr GKin IDee MBlu MGos MMuc MPkF MRav NLar SEND SGol SMad SPer SWvt WHar WMat
§	***pavia***	CBcs CDul CMCN EPfP
	- 'Atrosanguinea' 🏆H5	CMCN EPfP ERod MBri SKHP
I	- 'Biltmore Buckeye'	MPkF
	- var. ***discolor*** 'Koehnei'	CMCN EPfP MBri NLar WMat
	- 'Penduliflora'	see *A.* × *mutabilis* 'Penduliflora'
	- 'Purple Spring'	WPat
	- 'Rosea Nana'	CMCN WPat
	- Splendens Group **new**	CMCN
	splendens	see *A. pavia* Splendens Group
§	***sylvatica***	CMCN
	turbinata	CBcs CDul
	wilsonii	CBcs CDul CExl

Aethionema (*Brassicaceae*)

	armenum	GKev
	capitatum	CPBP ECho SIgm
	coridifolium	GJos
	glaucinum	ECho
§	***grandiflorum*** 🏆H5	ECho ELan GJos NBro SRms XLum XSen
	- Pulchellum Group 🏆H5	GJos
	iberideum	SRms
*	***kotschyi***	EDAr GJos WAbe
	membranaceum	GJos
	oppositifolium	LLHF
	pulchellum	see *A. grandiflorum*
	saxatile	GKev
	schistosum	CPBP GJos LLHF
	subulatum **new**	GEdr LLHF
	'Warley Rose' 🏆H5	ECho ELan EPot GCrg GKev LHop LRHS MAsh NBir NSla SBch SRms WIce WThu XSen
	'Warley Ruber'	CMea ECho WAbe

Afrocarpus (*Podocarpaceae*)

	falcatus	ECou

Agapanthus ✿ (*Agapanthaceae*)

	sp.	ETod LPar WBod
	'Aberdeen'	IBal
	'Adagio' **new**	WCot
	'Adonis'	IBlr
	'African Moon'	CPen CPne CPrp IBal
	'African Skies'	CPne CPrp IBal LRHS NHoy SFai
	africanus misapplied	Widely available
	- 'Albus' misapplied	Widely available
	'Aimee'	CBro IBal
	'Alan Street'	IBal
	'Albus' ambig.	GKev GMaP MHer MWat
I	'Albus Nanus'	IBal
I	'Albus Roseus'	IBal
	'Alice Gloucester'	CPrp
	'Amsterdam'	CPen EBee IBal IMou NHoy
	'Angela'	CPen CPrp IBal MAvo NHoy
	'Aphrodite'	IBlr
	'Aquamarine'	CAvo EPri IBal LLWG LPla NHoy
	'Arctic Star'	CAvo CExl CKno CMac CPen CPne CPou CPrp CTca CWCL EBee ELon EWoo IBal LLWG LRHS LSRN LSou NHoy NLar SDys SFai SPoG WHil
	'Ardernei' **new**	CEvo
	'Ardernei Hybrid'	CAvo CExl ECha ECtt EWes GAbr GCal IBal IBlr LSou WCot WGwG WPGP
§	'Argenteus Vittatus' (v) 🏆H2	CPen NHoy
	'Arosa'	IMou
	'Atlas'	IBlr
	'Aureovittatus' (v)	IBal NHoy

	Name	Suppliers
	'Autumn Mist' **new**	IBal
	'Azure Blue' **new**	WCot
	'Baby Blue'	see *A.* 'Blue Baby'
	'Baby Pete'^{PBR}	CPen EBee NHoy
	Back in Black = 'B in B'^{PBR}	CBro CExl COtt CWCL ELan EPfP EWes IBal MBNS MRav NBid NHoy SCob SHyH SMad SPer WCot WFar
	'Ballerina'	CPne IBal
	'Ballyrogan'	IBal IBlr
	'Bangor Blue'	IBlr
	'Barley Blue' **new**	IBal
	'Barnfield Blue'	CPne CPrp EBee IBal NHoy SFai
	'Barnsley'	NHoy
	'Basutoland'	LRHS
	'Becky'	CPne IBal
	'Beeches Dwarf'	IBal NHoy
	'Beloved'	NHoy
	'Ben Hope'	CBro IBlr NHoy WCot
	'Best Barn Blue' **new**	SMHy
	'Beth Chatto'	see *A. campanulatus* 'Albovittatus'
	'Bethlehem Star'	CPne EPri
	'Bicton Bell'	CEvo IBlr
	'Bicton Bride'	CPne
	'Big Ben' **new**	IBal
	'Big Blue'	CMac CPrp CWCL EBee LSou SEND SLdr SRkn
	'Black Beauty'	IBal LRHS
	'Black Buddhist'	CBod COtt CPen CWCL EBee ECtt EPfP EPri GBuc IBal LRHS MWat NGdn NHoy SAko SFai SGol SPer XSen
	'Black Magic'	CAbb CEvo CPne CPrp CSpe EBee IBal LCro LOPS LSou NHoy NSti SFai SPoG WCot
	'Black Pantha'^{PBR}	Widely available
§	'Blauwe Valk'	EPfP LPfy
§	'Blue Baby'	CChe CPen ELan ELon LRHS MJak NHoy SGSe XTur
	'Blue Bayou' **new**	IBal
	'Blue Beauty' **new**	LRHS
	Blue Bird	see *A.* 'Blauwe Valk'
	'Blue Bird'	CRos LRHS SHil
	'Blue Brush'	EPfP IBal LRHS NHoy SCoo WCot
	'Blue Cascade'	IBlr
	'Blue Companion'	CPrp IBlr NHoy WMnd
	'Blue Diamond' ambig.	CMac NHoy
	'Blue Dot'	CPrp ECtt EPfP LLHF LRHS LSou SDys SGSe
	'Blue Dragon'	NHoy
	'Blue Flare' **new**	IBal
	'Blue Flash' **new**	IBal
	'Blue Formality'	IBal IBlr
	'Blue Giant'	CBro CChe CKno CPrp EBee LRHS MGos NHoy SCob SWat WPGP WWEG
	'Blue Globe'	CBod CHid EBee EPri GMaP LRHS
	'Blue Gown'	CSam
	'Blue Heaven'^{PBR}	CPne CWGN EWoo IBal LHop LSun NHoy SCob
	'Blue Horizons' (v)	IBal NHoy
	'Blue Ice'	CAbb CPen CPne CPou CPrp EBee IBal LRHS NHoy SAko
	'Blue Imp'	CBro IBlr
	'Blue Jay'	CPen
	'Blue Magic'	EBee IBal NHoy
	'Blue Moon'	CAbP CAvo CBro CPen CPrp EBee ECha ECtt EPri EWoo IBal IBlr ILea LLWG LPla LRHS LSun MCot MHol NHoy NLar SEND SHyH SLdr WCot
	'Blue Nile'	IBal

	Name	Suppliers
	'Blue Pixie' **new**	IBal
	'Blue Prince'	CPen EBee NHoy
	'Blue Ribbon'	CPne
	'Blue Rinse'	CAvo IBal
	'Blue Skies' ambig.	NCGa NHoy
I	'Blue Skies' Dunlop	IBlr
	'Blue Spear'	CPen
	'Blue Triumphator'	CBod CTca EPfP EWTr GBin GKev GMaP LRHS MHer NHoy SCob
	'Blue Umbrella'	COtt NHoy SRkn
	'Blue Velvet'	LSun
	'Blue Yonder'	EBee NHoy
	blue-flowered	WCFE
	Bluestorm = 'Atiblu'^{PBR}	CPrp EPfP IBal LBuc LRHS MBri NHoy SCob SEND
	'Bluety'^{PBR}	CPen IBal NHoy
	'Bray Valley'	CPne
	'Bressingham Blue'	CAbb CBro CPrp CSam CTri EAEE EWes GCal IBal IBlr LRHS MRav NHoy SFai SWat
	'Bressingham Bounty'	EAEE IBal LRHS
	'Bressingham White'	LRHS MRav NHoy SWat
	'Bridal Bouquet'	EBee GBin IBal LCro LOPS LSRN NHoy SFai
	'Brilliant Blue'	IBal NHoy SFai
	'Bristol'	IBal
	'Buckingham Palace'	CBro CDes CPne EBee EWes GAbr IBal IBlr NChi NHoy WCot WPGP
	'Cally Blue'	GAbr GCal IBal NHoy
	'Cally Longstem'	EBee EPri GCal
	'Cally Pale Blue'	IBal
	campanulatus	CBlu CMac CPrp CTre ELan EPfP GKin IBal IBlr LRHS MRav NEgg NHoy SWat WFar WPGP
	- var. ***albidus***	CPrp ECha ELan EPfP GKin IBlr LHop LRHS MMuc NBid NGdn NHoy SEND SPer WGwG WHoo WPGP
§	- 'Albovittatus' (v)	ECho IBal LSou NHoy
	- bright blue-flowered	GCal IBal
	- 'Cobalt Blue'	CPrp EPri GBin GKin IBal LPal LRHS LSou MAvo MNrw NEgg NGdn NHoy
	- 'Oxford Blue'	IBal IBlr NHoy
	- subsp. ***patens*** ♀^{H4}	CLet EAEE EPfP IBal LRHS MRav SWat WPGP
	- - deep blue-flowered	CCon IBlr LRHS NHoy
	- - 'Rosie Palmer' **new**	CDes
	- 'Profusion'	CBro CPne CPrp ECha EPri IBal IBlr LRHS NHoy
	- 'Ultramarine' **new**	IBal
	- variegated (v)	EBee ECha NPer
	- 'Wedgwood Blue'	EBee IBal IBlr LRHS NHoy
	- 'Wendy'	CPne EBee IBal IBlr LRHS NHoy
	- 'White Hope'	IBal IBlr
	'Carefree'	IBal
	'Carnival Heaven' **new**	NHoy
	'Castle of Mey'	CAvo CBro CExl CFil CPrp EBee GAbr IBal IBlr LCro LOPS LPla LRHS LSou NHoy SFai WPGP
§	***caulescens*** ♀^{H2}	CPrp IBal IBlr LRHS SMHy WPGP
	- subsp. ***angustifolius***	CCon CHid ELon IBal IBlr LPla MHol SEND SMad SPer WCot WPGP
	- subsp. ***caulescens***	IBlr SWat
	'Cedric Morris'	CPen EPri IBal IBlr NHoy
	'Celebration'	CPne IBal
	'Chandra'	IBlr
	'Charlotte'^{PBR}	CMac CPen EBee EPfP IBal LRHS NHoy SPoG
	'Cherry Holley'	ELon

	Name	Suppliers
	'Chika's Blue'	MAvo
	'Clarence House'	CBro CPen CPrp
	coddii	CExl EPri EWes IBlr MHer WCot
	'Colin Edward'	NHoy
	'Columba'	CPen CPrp EBee ELon IBal LAma NBid NHoy XSen
	comptonii	see *A. praecox* subsp. *minimus*
	'Congratulations'	NHoy
	'Corina'	EBee
	'Crystal Drop'	CExl CPen CPne CPou CPrp EBee EPri IBal LRHS NHoy SFai SWat WPGP
	'Dainty Lady'	NHoy
	Danube	see *A.* 'Donau'
	'Dart Valley'	CPne CPrp
	'Dartmoor'	CPne
	'Dayspring'	SGSe
	'Delft'	CPrp EBee IBal IBlr SAko
	'Delft Blue'	IBal LRHS LSun
	'Density'	IBlr
	'Devon Dawn'	IMou
	'Dnjepr'	CBro EBee
	'Dokter Brouwer'	CKno EWTr GKev IBoy IKil ILea LRHS LSRN MCot NHoy SHyH
§	'Donau'	CBro CPen EBee EPri EWoo IBal NBir NHoy SGol SWat WCot
	Double Diamond = 'Rfdd'	CPen CPne CWCL EBee EPfP EPri EWes IBal LRHS LSRN LSou NHoy SAko SCob SFai SPoG
	'Dream'	NHoy
	'Dublin'	IBal
	dyeri	see *A. inapertus* subsp. *intermedius*
	'Early Blue'	EBee EWTr EWoo NHoy
	'Ed Carman' (v)	LSou
	'Eggesford Sky'	CPne CPrp EBee IBal NHoy SFai
	'Elaine' **new**	IBal
	'Elaine Anne'	NHoy
	'Elisabeth'	NHoy
	'Elizabeth Salisbury'	CPne IBal
	'Ellamae' **new**	IBal
	'Enigma'	Widely available
	'Enigma Variations'	EBee
	'Essence of Summer'	WCot
	'Ethel's Joy'	CPen EPri
	'Eve'	IBlr
	'Evening Eclipse'	IBal
	'Evening Star'	CPne EPri
	'Exmoor'	CPne IBal
	'Findlay's Blue'	LRHS MAvo SMHy
	'Finnline' (v)	CPen CPne SRms
	'Flore Pleno' (d)	CAby CBcs CBod CDes CExl CMac COtt CPen CPrp EBee ECha ECtt EHrv ELan GKin IBal IBlr LRHS LSou MHer MHol NEgg NGdn NHoy SFai WCot WFar WPGP WSHC WWEG
	'Forget-me-not'	NHoy
	'Gayle's Lilac'	CBcs CElw CExl COtt CPen CPrp ECtt ELan ELon EPfP EWTr GKin LHop LRHS MRav NGdn NHoy WGwG XTur
	'Gem'	CPne ELon MAvo
	'Getty White'	EWTr LRHS
	'Glacier'	NHoy
	'Glacier Stream'	CBro CPen EPri EWTr GBuc IKil NHoy XSen XTur
	'Glen Avon'	CAbb CCon CExl COtt CPen CPrp CRos EBee EPfP GBin IBal LRHS MWat NHoy NLar SCoo SFai SLon
	'Gold Strike'[PBR] (v)	LRHS NHoy SFai
	'Golden Drops' (v)	MGos NHoy
	'Golden Rule' (v)	EHoe GBuc IBlr
	'Goliath'	CPne
	'Grey Ruler'	MAvo
	'Hanneke'	CPen CPne IBal
	'Happy Birthday'	NHoy
	'Harvest Blue'	IBal
§	Headbourne hybrids	Widely available
	Headbourne hybrids dark blue-flowered	GBuc LRHS
	Headbourne hybrids dwarf	GBuc MNHC
	'Headbourne White'	CAvo EPri
	'Heather Gail'	NHoy
	'Heavenly Blue'	CPne
	'Helen'	IBlr
	'Holbeach'	CPen
	'Holbrook'	CSam
	'Holly Ann'	NHoy
	'Hoyland'	NHoy
	'Hoyland Blue'	NHoy
	'Hoyland Brilliant White'	NHoy
	'Hoyland Chelsea Blue'	NHoy
	'Hoyland Little Prince' **new**	NHoy
	'Hyacinth'	NHoy
	'Ice Blue Star'	CBro
	'Ice Lolly'	CBro CPen IKil
	inapertus	CAvo CBro CFil CPrp CTre EWes GGal LPla SMHy SWat WPGP
	- dwarf	IBlr
	- subsp. ***hollandii***	EBee IBal IBlr NHoy SWat
	- - 'Zealot'	IBlr
	- 'Ice Cascade'	CPen EBee IBal LRHS NHoy SWat
	- 'Icicle'	GCal
	- subsp. ***inapertus***	IBlr SWat
I	- - 'Albus'	CDes IBlr SMHy
	- - 'Cyan'	IBlr
	- - 'White'	CPrp IBal
§	- subsp. ***intermedius***	CPrp EPfP GKev IBlr NHoy SWat
	- - 'Long Tom'	CExl CPne CPrp CSpe EPri IBal LRHS WPGP
	- - white-flowered	CPen CPou
	- large	IBal
	- 'Little Black Number'	CPen
	- 'Midnight Cascade'	CExl CPar CPen EBee ECtt ELan IBal IPot LRHS NBid NHoy SBod SCob SFai SRms SWat
I	- 'Nigrescens'	CCon CPen
	- subsp. ***parviflorus***	IBlr
	- subsp. ***pendulus***	CCon IBal IBlr LRHS WPGP
	- - 'Black Magic'	NHoy
	- - 'Graskop'	Widely available
	- - 'Violet Dusk'	IBlr
	- 'Sapphire Cascade'	CPen IBal NHoy SWat
	'Indigo Dreams'	CAbb CPne CPrp NHoy SFai
	'Inkspots'	CMac CPen CRos CSpe CWCL EPfP GBin IBal LOPS LRHS LSou NHoy SFai SPoG
	'Intermedius' Leichtlin	CWCL
I	'Intermedius' van Tubergen	EBee NBid
	'Isis'	CAvo CBro CCon CPrp CSam CSde CTri EAEE ECha EPri GBuc IBlr LRHS MAvo NHoy
	'Jacaranda'	CMac EBee IBal LRHS NHoy SFai
	'Jack Elliott'	MAvo
	'Jack's Blue'	CBod CBro CElw CPen CPne CPrp CSam EBee ECtt ELan ELon EPri EWoo GMaP IBal LRHS LSRN MAvo MBri MHol MNrw NGdn NLar SBod SEND SLdr SPer WCot WPGP
	'Jersey Giant'	NHoy

'Jodie'	CPne ELon SGSe
'Johanna'	CPen
Johannesberg hybrids	ECha EPfP
'Jolanda'	CPrp ELon IBal LAma
'Jonie' **new**	IBal
'Kalmthout Blue'	IBal
'Kilmurry Blue' **new**	IBal IKil
'Kilmurry White' **new**	IBal IKil
'Kingston Blue'	IBal IBlr LRHS NBid NHoy SBea
'Kobold'	CBro NHoy WFar
'Lady Edith'	IBlr
§ 'Lady Grey'	IBlr
'Lady Moore'	IBlr SMHy
'Lapis'	CHid CMac CPne CPrp EBee EPri IBal NHoy SFai SHyH SLdr
'Latent Blue'	IBlr
'Lavender Haze'	CMac CPen EPfP IBal LRHS MBri MWat NHoy SFai
'Leanne' **new**	IBal
'Leicester'	CPen IBal
'Liam's Lilac'	CAvo CExl CKno CPar CPen CPne CPou CPrp ELon EWoo IBal LCro LOPS LRHS MAvo MWat NHoy NLar SFai
'Lilac Flash'	CPen IBal
'Lilac Time'	CExl CPne CPrp IBlr WCot
'Lilliput'	CBcs CBro CMac CMea CPrp CSpe ECha ECtt ELan EPfP EShb EWTr GBuc GKev GMaP IBal LHop LLWG LRHS MRav NGdn SPer SRms WFar WMnd XEll XSen
'Little Beauty'	NHoy
'Little Blue Heaven' **new**	NHoy
'Little Snow Heaven' **new**	NHoy
'Little White'	CPen
'Littlecourt'	CBro
'Loch Hope' ♀H6	CAvo CBro CPrp CSam ECtt ELon EPfP EWoo GCal IBal LCro LRHS MAvo MHol MRav NHoy SLdr SPer WCot WHoo
'Loch Inch'	EBee
'Luly'	CPen CPne CPrp CRos EPfP IBal LPfy LRHS MAvo MGos NHoy SHil SWat
'Luna'	EBee IBal NHoy
'Lydenburg'	CPen CPne EBee EPri IBal IBlr NHoy
'Lyn Valley'	CPrp EBee IBal NHoy SFai
'Mabel Grey'	see *A.* 'Lady Grey'
'Magnifico'	IBlr
'Marchants Cobalt Cracker'	SMHy
'Marchant's Midnight Blue' **new**	SMHy
'Marcus'	IBal
'Margaret'	IBal LRHS LSRN NHoy SBod
'Mariètte'	CPen EBee
'Marijke' **new**	IBal
'Marnie'	CPne
'Martine'	CPen EBee
'Maureen'	CPne CPrp NHoy SFai
'Maurice' **new**	IBal
'May Snow' (v)	WCot
'Medusa' **new**	IBal
'Megan's Mauve'	CAvo CKno CPne CPou CPrp EBee ELon EPri IBal LCro LOPS LRHS LSou NSti SFai SHyH
'Meibont' (v)	IBal WCot
'Mercury'	IBlr
'Metalica'	NHoy
'Michelle' **new**	IBal
Midknight Blue = 'Monmid'	NHoy WSHC XTur
'Midnight'	CPen EWes MAvo
'Midnight Blue' ambig.	CAby CPen ELan IBal MGos
'Midnight Blue' P.Wood	GCal IBlr LRHS
'Midnight Dream'	CPen EBee ECtt IBal NHoy STPC
§ 'Midnight Star'	Widely available
'Miniature Blue'	SWat
'Misty Dawn' (v)	EBee ECtt IBal MHol NHoy SFai SHyH SLdr WCot
mixed seedlings	IBal NHoy
mixed white-flowered	WCFE
'Mole Valley'	CPne IBal
'Molly Howick'	EBee LRHS NHoy
'Mood Indigo'	CAbb CPne EBee IBal NHoy SFai
'Moonlight Star'	EBee NHoy
'Moonshine'	CPen
I 'Mooreanus' misapplied	EBee EPfP IBal NBid
'Mooreanus' H.R.Wehrh.	GCal
'Morning Star'	IBal
'Mount Stewart'	IBal IBlr
'My Love'	NHoy
'Nana Blue'	SHyH
'Navy Blue'	see *A.* 'Midnight Star'
'Newa'	EBee
'Night Sky'	LRHS
'Nikki'	CMea CPne
'Norman Hadden'	IBlr
'Northern Light'	CPen LLHF
'Northern Star'[PBR]	CAbb CCon CDoC CExl CHVG CKno COtt CPen CPne CPrp EAEE EBee ELon EPri EWes EWoo IBal LOPS LRHS LSRN LSou MWat NHoy NSti SCob SFai SLon SPoG WPGP
nutans	see *A. caulescens*
'Nyx'	IBlr
'Oslo'	NHoy
'Oxbridge'	CEvo IBlr
'Pacific Blue'	CWCL EBee IBal NHoy SHyH SLdr
Palmer's hybrids	see *A.* Headbourne hybrids
'Paris'	CPen
'Patent Blue'	CPrp IBal IBlr
'Patriot'	EPfP LRHS
'Pauline'	NHoy
'Penelope Palmer'	CEvo CPrp IBlr
'Peter Franklin'	CPne CPrp EBee IBal NHoy SFai
'Peter Pan' ambig.	Widely available
'Peter Pan' Giridlion	LLWG
'Phantom'	CAbb CDes CPne CPrp EBee IBal IBlr IMou LCro LOPS LRHS NHoy SAko SFai SPer WPGP
Pine Cottage hybrids	CPne
'Pinocchio'	CPen CWib IMou NHoy SDeJ
'Plas Merdyn Blue'	IBlr
'Plas Merdyn White'	IBal IBlr NHoy
'Podge Mill'	IBlr
'Polar Ice'	CCon CPen EBee ELon EPri EWoo GKev IBal IBlr IBoy IPot LAma LRHS LSRN NHoy WCAu XTur
'Polar White'	NHoy
'Porcelain'	IBal IBlr
praecox ♀H2	CPrp IBal IBlr NHoy
- 'Albiflorus' ♀H2	CBro CPou CPrp CTri EPri IBal LRHS NEgg NHoy SEND
- 'Floribundus'	SWat
- 'Maximus Albus'	CPne CPou IBal IBlr
§ - subsp. ***minimus***	CElw CPou IBal IBlr NHoy SEND SWat
- - 'Adelaide'	CPrp IBal
- - blue-flowered	SWat
- - white-flowered	SWat

- 'Neptune'	IBlr
§ - subsp. ***orientalis***	CBro IBlr SWat
- - 'Cape Blue'	CPrp
- - 'Mount Thomas'	CPrp
- - 'Silver Star' (v)	CPen NHoy
- subsp. ***praecox***	IBlr
- - azure-flowered	CPrp SWat
- - 'Variegatus'	see *A.* 'Argenteus Vittatus'
- 'Saturn'	IBlr
- Slieve Donard form	IBlr
- 'Storms River'	IBal
- 'Uranus'	IBlr
- 'Venus'	IBlr
- 'Vittatus' (v)	NHoy
'Premier'	CPrp IBlr LRHS NHoy
'Princess Margaret'	IBal
§ 'Purple Cloud'	Widely available
'Purple Delight'	CPne CPrp IBal
'Purple Emperor'	CPne NHoy SFai
'Purple Fountain'	CPne CPrp NHoy SFai WCot
'Purple Haze'	CPen IBal
'Purple Ripple'	CPne IBal
'Purple Star'	CKno
'Queen Anne'	IBal LPfy NHoy
'Queen Mother'	CHid IBal LRHS
Queen Mum = 'Pmn06'PBR	Widely available
'Queen of the Ocean' **new**	IBal
'Quink Drops'	SMHy
'Radiant Star'	IBal LRHS NHoy
'Regal Beauty'	CBro CPen CPne CPrp CSBt EBee EWoo IBal LRHS LSRN NBid NHoy NLar SFai
'Remembrance'	NHoy
'Rhapsody in Blue'	CPne
'Rhone'	CBro IBlr
'Rosewarne'	CBcs CBod CExl CPrp GBin IBal IBlr NHoy NLar
'Rotterdam'	CPen NHoy XSen
'Royal Blue'	CBro GMaP IBal LPla NHoy
'Royal Knight' **new**	IBal
'Ruan Vean'	CPrp
'Sally Anne'	CPne
'San Gabriel' (v)	CPne
'Sandringham'	CDes CPen CPne CPrp EBee EPfP EWes IBal LSou NHoy SEND SFai WPGP
'Sapphire'	CPrp IBlr
'Sarah'PBR	CPen CPne IBal LSRN NHoy SEND SFai SHyH SLdr WCot WHil
'Sea Coral'	CCon CMac CPrp EBee EPri LRHS MAvo NHoy NSti
'Sea Foam'	CMac CPen CPne NLar
'Sea Mist'	CPne EBee
'Sea Spray'	EBee EPri IBal NHoy
'Selma Bock'	CPen CPne IBal
'Senna'PBR	CExl EBee IBal LSou NHoy WCot
'Septemberhemel'	CPen IBal
'Silver Anniversary'	NHoy
'Silver Baby'	CAbb CKno COtt CPen CPne CPrp ELon EPfP EPri ETod IBal LEdu LRHS LSou NHoy SFai SRms
'Silver Jubilee'	IBal
'Silver Lining'	ECtt IBal LRHS NHoy
'Silver Mist'	CPen CPne IBlr LRHS SWat
Silver Moon = 'Notfred'PBR (v)	CAbb CPen EBee ELan EPfP EWes EWoo GKev IBal LBMP LRHS LSou MBri MGos MJak NHoy NSti SCob SFai SPoG WCot XTur
'Silver Sceptre'	IBlr
'Silver Stream'	NHoy
'Silver Suzy' **new**	IBal
'Sky'	CAbb CCon CEvo CPne CSBt EPfP EPri EWTr EWoo IBal IBlr LCro LOPS LRHS LSRN MWat NBid SFai SKHP SRkn SRms SWat
'Sky Pendulous'	CBcs
'Sky Rocket'	CPne IBal IBlr
'Sky Star'	IBal
'Slieve Donard'	IBlr
'Snow Cloud'	CAbb CBro CExl CPen CRos CSBt EBee EPfP IBal LCro LOPS LRHS MWat NHoy NLar SEND SFai SLdr SLon
'Snow Pixie'	CBro CSpe EBee IBal LSRN LSou NHoy SFai SHyH SLdr
'Snow Princess'	CPen ELon EPfP IBal
'Snow Shadows'	CBro
'Snowball'	CBcs CChe CExl CPen LSou NHoy NLos SGSe WWEG
'Snowdrops'	EBee ELan LHop SGSe SKHP
'Snowstorm'PBR	EBee EPfP IBal LBuc LRHS MBri
'Sofie'PBR	CPen EBee MBri NHoy SCob SFai STPC XTur
'Southern Cross'	EBee IBal LRHS SFai
'Southern Star'	IBal
'Spokes'	IBlr
'Star Quality'	IBal LBuc LRHS SFai
'Starburst'	IBlr
'Stardust'	CRos IBal LBuc LPfy LRHS
'Stargazer'	EBee LBuc LRHS
'Stars and Stripes'	IBal LRHS
'Stéphanie Charm'	CPen
'Storm Cloud' Reads	see *A.* 'Purple Cloud'
'Storm Cloud' (d)	CBro CCon
'Strawberry Ice' **new**	IBal SFai WHlf
'Streamline'	CBcs CBro CElw CKno CMea COtt CTca EBee ECtt ELon EPfP EShb ETod GAbr GKin GMaP IBal LAst LRHS LSou MRav NHoy SDys SEND SFai
'Summer Blue' **new**	IBal
'Summer Clouds'	ELan NHoy
'Summer Days'	CPne CPrp EBee IBal NHoy SFai
'Summer Skies'	CPne IBal NHoy
'Sunfield'	CKno CPrp EPfP IBal ILea IPot LAma LRHS NHoy NLar NPer
'Super Star'	CBro
'Sweet Surprise' **new**	IBal SFai
'Sylvia'PBR	IBal NHoy
'Sylvine'	CPen CPne IBal
'Tall Boy'	IBal IBlr
'Tarka'	CExl CPen CPne CPrp CRos CWCL ELon EPfP EPri EWoo IBal LPfy LRHS LSou MBri NHoy NLar SDys SFai SHil
'Taw Valley'	CAbb CAvo CHVG CKno COtt CPen CPne CPrp EBee ELon EWoo IBal LCro LPfy LRHS MBri MGos NHoy SFai SHil SHyH SLon SPoG WHil WPGP
'Thorn'	IBal
'Thumbelina'	CBro CKno CMac CWCL EBee IBal LRHS LSou NHoy NLar SFai XLum
'Thunder Storm' (v) **new**	NHoy
'Timaru'	CBod CBro CCon CElw CPen EBee ECtt ELan ELon EPfP EWoo GAbr GMaP IBal LAst LPla MBri MHol NGdn NHoy NLar SFai SHyH SLdr WCot WWEG

'Tinkerbell' (v)	CBcs CBro CLet COtt CPne CPrp EBee EHoe ELan EPfP EPri EShb IBal LEdu LHop LRHS LSou MBri MGos MRav NPer SGSe SPoG SRms SWvt
'Tiny Tim'	SGSe
'Tiny White' **new**	EPri
'Titan'	IBlr
'Titch'	CPne IBal
'Tom Thumb'	CAvo CExl CPrp ECtt EPfP GBin IBal LAst LRHS LSou NHoy SFai SRkn SRot
'Torbay'	CElw CPrp EAEE ECtt ELon EPfP EShb GAbr GCal GKin IBal LLWG LRHS MAvo MNrw NCGa NEgg NHol SEND WHoo WWEG
'Tornado'	CBod CPen EBee ECtt ELon IBal ILea LPla LRHS MNrw NHoy SEND SFai STPC WCot
'Tranquil'	NHoy
'Tresco Select'	NHoy
'Triangle'	CPen
'Tsolo'	CPne IBal
'Twilight'	IBlr
'Twilight Zone'	IBal
'Twister' **new**	SFai
umbellatus L'Hérit.	see *A. africanus*
umbellatus Redouté	see *A. praecox* subsp. *orientalis*
'Underway'	EWes GCal GKev IBal IBlr LPla
'Vallée Blanche'	XTur
'Vallée Bleue'	XTur
'Vallée de la Belle'	XTur
'Vallée de la Loire'	MNHC XTur
'Vallée de la Sarthe'	XTur
'Vallée de l'Authion'	XTur
'Vallée du Cap'	XTur
'Vallée du Lathan'	XTur
'Velvet Night'	CPen
'Volendam' **new**	IBal
'Wavy Navy'	CPen IBal
'Wedding Day'	IBal NHoy SFai
'Wembworthy'	CPne CPrp EBee IBal NHoy SFai
'White Avon'	CPen CPne
'White Baby'	XTur
'White Cloud' **new**	IBal
'White Dragon'	NHoy
'White Dwarf'	see *A.* white-flowered, dwarf
'White Flash' **new**	IBal
'White Heaven' PBR	Widely available
'White Ice'	CBcs CPen LRHS
'White Orb'	NHoy
'White Pixie' **new**	IBal
'White Smile'	EPri
'White Starlet'	NHoy
'White Superior'	CPen EBee EPfP GMaP LAst
'White Swan'	SCob
'White Umbrella'	LRHS NHoy
'White Wings' **new**	IBal
§ white-flowered, dwarf	CBro CKno CPen EBee ECha ECtt EPfP EShb GBuc IBal LRHS MWat NBir NGdn NHol
'Whitestorm'	NHoy SCob
'Whitney' PBR	CPen IBal IBlr
'Windlebrooke'	EAJP EPri LPla
'Windsor Castle'	CPen CPrp IBal IBlr
'Windsor Grey'	Widely available
'Winsome'	IBlr
'Winter Sky'	IBal
'Wolga'	CBro EBee
'Wolkberg' Kirstenbosch	IBal IBlr
'Yves Klein'	CEvo IBlr
'Zachary'	CPen CPne CPou CPrp EBee ELon LRHS
'Zeal Thomas' **new**	IBal
'Zebra'	NHoy

Agapetes (*Ericaceae*)

'Ludgvan Cross' ♀H2	CTsd EShb SEle SPad
serpens ♀H2	CHll CWib EBee SLon
- 'Scarlet Elf'	CTsd LRHS
smithiana var. ***major***	GGGa

Agastache (*Lamiaceae*)

sp.	NBFr
'After Eight'	EBee ECtt IBoy ILea LCro LRHS MAvo NCGa NDov
anethiodora	see *A. foeniculum* (Pursh) Kuntze
anisata	see *A. foeniculum* (Pursh) Kuntze
aurantiaca	SPhx
- 'Apricot Sprite'	CWld EPfP LRHS MHer MSCN NGdn SRkn WHar
- 'Navajo Sunset'	EBee
- 'Raspberry Daiquiri' (Cocktail Series)	MAvo
- 'Sunset Yellow' **new**	CWld
'Blackadder'	Widely available
'Blaue Sangria' **new**	MAvo NDov
'Blue Boa'	CWGN ECtt LRHS MHol NCGa NLar
'Blue Delight'	SBch
'Blue Fortune' ♀H6	CBcs ECha LCro LHop LOPS LPfy LPla LRHS MAvo MBri MCot MRav NDov NLar SCob SMad SPhx SRms SWvt WCAu WWEG
'Bolero'	CSpe EBee LRHS MHol MSpe SPhx WCot WHoo
breviflora	EBee
§ ***cana***	SPhx
- 'Heatwave' PBR	LRHS NDov
- 'Purple Pygmy'	EPfP LHop SRot
'Cotton Candy' PBR	IBoy WHlf
cusickii	EBee SPhx
'Firebird'	EAEE EBee ECtt ELan GKin LHop LSou SPer SRms SWat SWvt
foeniculum misapplied	see *A. rugosa*
§ ***foeniculum*** (Pursh) Kuntze	CArn CMea EBee ELan ENfk GMaP GPoy MCot MHer MNHC SPav SPhx SRms WJek WWEG XLum
- 'Alabaster'	CBcs EBee NLar
- 'Alba'	NBre SHDw SPav
'Globetrotter'	ELan LPla SPhx
'Grapefruit Nectar' (Nectar Series) **new**	SCob
'Kolibri'	ECtt LHop LRHS NDov
'Linda'	NDov WCot
§ ***mexicana***	SPav
- 'Champagne'	NWad
- 'Red Fortune' PBR	CAbP CWGN CWld EAEE ECtt ILea LHop LRHS MCot MHol MHtn MPie MSCN NEgg NLar NSti SCob SMad SPad WCot WRHF
- 'Rosea'	see *A. cana*
- 'Sangria'	LHop LRHS NGdn SPad SPhx SRms
micrantha **new**	SPhx
nepetoides	EPPr NDov SPav
occidentalis	EBee SPhx
Orange Nectar (Nectar Series) **new**	MHol WCot
'Painted Lady'	CSpe ECtt WHea WTcb
pallidiflora var. ***neomexicana***	SPhx

- - 'Rose Mint' new	EBee
'Pink Beauty'	GBBs NLar
'Pink Panther'	WSHC
'Pink Pop'	EPfP SPad
'Purple Flame'	EAEE
'Purple Haze'	LRHS MTis NDov WWEG
'Raspberry Summer'PBR	CBod CWGN ECtt EPfP LHop LRHS LSou MNHC NCGa NLar SCob SPad WAul WHil
'Rose Mint'	CSpe
§ ***rugosa***	CAby CArn CBod CLau ECha GPoy LEdu LHop MNHC SPav SPhx SPlb SRms SWat WJek WMoo
- B&SWJ 4187 from Korea	WCru
- f. ***albiflora***	NBre WCAu
- - 'Alabaster'	MAvo NDov
- - 'Liquorice White'	CBod EBee ELan EPfP MBel NGBl NLar SPer SPlb SRms
- 'Golden Jubilee'	CAby CBct CBod CSpe EAEE EBee ECha ECtt ELan IBoy LRHS MAvo MHer MHtn MNHC MSpe NBFr NLar NSti SCob SPoG SRms SWvt WJek WMoo XLum
- 'Heronswood Mist' new	EBee
- 'Korean Zest'	WCru
- 'Liquorice Blue'	CKno CTsd ELan EPfP LPot LRHS MBel MSpe NEgg NGBl NGdn SPoG SRms SWvt WHea WMoo WWEG
rupestris	CSpe CWld SPhx XLum XSen
- 'Apache Sunset'	SPlb
'Serpentine'	ECtt MAvo NDov SPhx WWEG
'Spicy'	NDov
'Summer Fiesta'PBR	ECtt IBoy LSou MBri MNrw NCGa NDov
'Summer Glow'PBR	CKno CMos CWGN EBee ECtt GBin LHop LLHF LSou MBel MNrw NCGa NDov SCob SDys SPoG WBod WHil WHlf
'Summer Love'PBR	ECtt LSou MNrw NCGa NDov NLar
'Summer Sky'PBR	EBee ECtt LRHS NCGa NDov
'Summer Sunset'	CMea CWGN EAEE EBee ELan LBMP LHop LRHS LSou MHol MPie NCGa NDov SCob SPoG WCot WHil
'Tangerine Dreams'	ECtt EPfP LHop MAvo NCGa NEgg SCoo WHil
'Tango'	EBee LRHS NBFr SGbt
'Tutti-frutti'	ECtt LRHS

Agathaea see *Felicia*

Agathis (*Araucariaceae*)

australis	CBrP

Agave ✿ (*Asparagaceae*)

sp.	WCot
albomarginata	CDTJ EAla
americana ♀H2	CAbb CBcs CBen CBot CDoC EAla ELan EPfP EShb EUJe IDee LPal LRHS LSun LTro NLos SChr SCob SEND SMad SPlb SPre SVen SWvt WCot
§ - subsp. ***americana*** JL 2007-01 new	CCac
- 'Marginata' (v) ♀H2	CBot CBrP CDTJ CFil CHll NQui SEND SVen WCot WSFF
- 'Mediopicta' misapplied	see *A. americana* 'Mediopicta Alba'
- 'Mediopicta' (v) ♀H2	CDTJ CFil LEdu SBig
§ - 'Mediopicta Alba' (v) ♀H2	CBrP CDTJ CFil CJun CTre ESwi WCot
- 'Mediopicta Aurea' (v)	CFil WCot
- var. ***oaxacensis***	WPGP
- subsp. ***protamericana***	CDTJ EAla
- subsp. ***protamericana*** × ***scabra*** F&M 310	WPGP
- 'Striata' (v)	EShb WCot
- 'Variegata' (v) ♀H2	CAbb CBcs CBen CDoC CFil CLet CSde CTre EAla ELan EPfP EShb EUJe LPal LRHS LSun MGos NPer NPla SChr SCob SGSe SPlb SWvt WCot
angustifolia	see *A. vivipara* var. *vivipara*
- var. ***marginata*** hort.	SBig WCot
applanata	CFil CJun EAla WPGP
× ***arizonica***	EAla
asperrima	CDTJ EAla
§ - subsp. ***maderensis***	SPlb
asperrima × ***lechuguilla*** new	CCac
atrovirens	WCot
- from Carneros, Coah, Mexico new	CCac
- from Concepción del Oro, Mexico new	CCac
- var. ***mirabilis***	CDTJ CFil EAla
- - F&M 245	WPGP
attenuata	CAbb CBrP CDTJ SBig SPlb WCot WPGP
avellanidens	EAla
beauleriana	EAla
'Bloodspot'	WCot
boldinghiana	WCot
bovicornuta	WCot
bracteosa	CDTJ EAla WCot
celsii	see *A. mitis* var. *mitis*
cerulata subsp. ***nelsonii***	CDTJ
chiapensis	EAla
chrysantha	CDTJ CTre EAla EBee WCot WGrn
- 'Black Canyon'	WCot
colimana	see *A. ortgiesiana*
colorata	CDTJ CJun WCot
cordillerensis	see *A. americana* subsp. *americana*
'Cornelius'	WCot
cupreata	CDTJ EAla LTro
datylio	EAla
de-meesteriana	MHin
deserti	CDTJ CJun CTre LRHS WCot
- var. ***deserti*** new	LTro
- var. ***simplex***	LTro WCot
difformis	CDTJ EAla
- NJM 05.034	WPGP
durangensis	SPlb
elongata	see *A. vivipara* var. *vivipara*
ensifera	CJun
felgeri	CDTJ
ferdinandi-regis	see *A. victoriae-reginae*
ferox	see *A. salmiana* var. *ferox*
filifera ♀H2	CDTJ CJun CTre LTro SChr SMad SPlb WCot
flexispina	EAla SPlb
- from Parral, Chihuahua, Mexico new	CCac
garciae-mendozae	CDTJ
geminiflora	CDTJ CFil CJun CTre EShb
gentryi	CDTJ CEvo CFil EAla LPal LTro SPlb WCot
- F&M 213A	WPGP
ghiesbreghtii	CTre EAla
gigantea	see *Furcraea foetida*

	goldmaniana	see *A. shawii* subsp. *goldmaniana*
	× ***gracilipes***	WPGP
§	***gracillima*** new	CDes
	guadalajarana	CDTJ CTre EAla
	guttata	WCot
	havardiana	CEvo CFil CTre EAla LTro WCot XSen
	- DJF 1326 from Davis Mountains, Texas	CCac WCot
	horrida	CDTJ CFil CJun EAla SBig
	- subsp. ***horrida***	LTro SPlb
	- 'Perotensis'	EAla EShb
	hurteri	CDTJ EAla
	impressa	WCot
	kerchovei	WCot
	lechuguilla	CDTJ EAla LTro SChr WCot XSen
	lophantha	see *A. univittata*
	- var. ***caerulescens***	see *A. univittata*
§	'Macha Mocha'	WCot
	macroacantha ♀H1c	CDTJ
§	***maculosa***	WCot
	marmorata	CJun WCot
	maximilliana	SPlb
	mckelveyana	CEvo WCot
	- DJF 1575 from Bagdad, Arizona new	CCac WCot
	- from Hillside, Arizona new	CCac
	mitis var. ***albidior***	EAla
§	- var. ***mitis***	CDTJ EAla SPlb
	- var. ***mitis*** × ***variegata***	WCot
	mitriformis	EAla
	montana	CBlu CCac CDTJ CFil EAla ETod EUJe LPal LTro NLos SChr SPlb
	- F&M 221	WPGP
	- F&M 289	WPGP
	neomexicana	see *A. parryi* subsp. *neomexicana*
	× ***nigra***	EAla
§	***obscura***	CDTJ EAla WCot
	ocahui	EAla
	oroensis	WCot
	- from Estanción Margarita, Zacatecas, Mexico new	CCac
§	***ortgiesiana***	WCot
	ovatifolia	CBlu CDTJ CFil CJun EAla SKHP SPlb WCot
	- NJM 09.002	WPGP
	palmeri	CCac CFil EBee LTro WCot
	panamana	see *A. vivipara* var. *vivipara*
	parrasana ♀H2	CDTJ EAla WCot WPGP
	- from Sierra Parras, Mexico new	CCac
	parryi ♀H2	CDTJ CDoC CEvo CTre EAla ETod LPal SPlb WCot WPGP XSen
	- DJF 138 new	CCac
	- HK 1684 new	CCac
	- var. ***couesii***	CCac LTro SKHP XSen
	- 'Cream Spike' (v)	CBcs CFil ESwi WCot WGrn
	- var. ***huachucensis***	CCac CDTJ LTro WCot
§	- subsp. ***neomexicana***	CDTJ CFil EAla EBee LTro SPlb XSen
	- - SB 948 from W of Artesia, New Mexico	CCac WCot
	- 'Ohi-kissho-ten-nishiki' (v)	WCot
	- subsp. ***parryi***	CDTJ LTro WCot WPGP
	- small	EAla ETod
	- small, variegated (v)	EAla
	- var. ***truncata***	CBlu CCac EAla ETod
	- - variegated (v)	WCot
	parviflora ♀H2	EAla WCot
	pendula	EAla
	polyacantha var. ***xalapensis***	see *A. obscura*
	potatorum ♀H2	EAla
	- 'Gary Fisher'	WCot
	salmiana	CCac CDTJ CFil EAla SBig SPlb
	- F&M 290	WPGP
	- subsp. ***crassispina***	SPlb
§	- var. ***ferox***	CCac CDTJ CDoC CTre EAla SBig SPlb
	- - from Tlacotepec, Pue, Mexico new	CCac
	scabra	CTre EAla WCot
	- subsp. ***maderensis***	see *A. asperrima* subsp. *maderensis*
	schidigera	EAla LPal
	- 'Shira-ito-no-ohi' (v)	WCot
	schottii	CDTJ EAla WCot
	'Sharkskin Shoes'	WCot
§	***shawii*** subsp. ***goldmaniana***	EAla
	shrevei subsp. ***magna***	EAla SPlb
§	***sileri***	WCot
	stictata	WCot
	striata	EAla
	- subsp. ***falcata***	WCot
*	- 'Rubra'	CDTJ LTro SPlb WCot
	- subsp. ***striata*** new	LTro
	stricta ♀H2	CDTJ EAla LTro WCot
	- 'Nana'	CDTJ
	aff. ***stricta***	WCot
	toumeyana ♀H2	CAbb CTre EAla WCot
	- from Globe, Arizona new	CCac
	- var. ***bella***	CDTJ CEvo XSen
	triangularis	CDTJ EAla
§	***undulata***	CDes WCot
	- 'Chocolate Chips'	CDes WCot
§	***univittata***	CDTJ CJun EAla LPal WCot
	- 'Quadricolor' (v)	CDTJ NLos SMad SPlb WCot
	utahensis ♀H3	CCac EAla SEND SPlb WCot XSen
	- DJF 1521 from Peach Springs, Arizona new	CCac WCot
	- LZ 2042 from Beaver Dam Mountains, Utah new	CCac
	- from Kingman, Arizona new	CCac
	- var. ***eborispina***	CCac EAla WCot XSen
	- subsp. ***kaibabensis***	CCac WCot XSen
	- var. ***nevadensis***	EAla
	- subsp. ***utahensis*** new	LTro
§	***variegata***	WCot
	- B&SWJ 10234	WCru
§	***victoriae-reginae*** ♀H2	CDTJ CJun CTre EAla IDee LPal SChr WCot
	- dwarf	WCot
	- variegated (v)	EAla
§	***virginica***	CEvo GKev WCot
§	***vivipara*** var. ***vivipara***	EAla EBee WCot
	vizcainoensis	EAla
	wocomahi	EAla WCot
	xylonacantha	EAla SChr SPlb WCot
	- blue-leaved	EAla
	zebra	EAla

Ageratina (*Asteraceae*)

§	***altissima***	CHid CMac EBee
	- 'Braunlaub'	CBod MMuc NBir NLar SAko SEND SHar SWat WMnd WPtf WWtn
	- 'Chocolate'	Widely available
§	***aromatica***	MRav NBro SHar SWat
§	***ligustrina***	CExl CLet CMHG CRHN CSde CTri CWib EBee ECha EHoe ELan EWTr EWoo LHop LRHS MBlu SBrt SDix

	SEND SPer SPoG SRkn SRms WPGP WPat WSFF WSHC

Ageratum (*Asteraceae*)

'Blue Champion'	LAst NPri
corymbosum	CHll CSpe
houstonianum 'Blue Danube'	CWCL
- 'High Tide Blue'	NPri
petiolatum **new**	LRHS

Agrimonia (*Rosaceae*)

eupatoria	CArn CBod CHab CWld ENfk GPoy MHer MNHC NMir SRms SWat WHer WHfH
* - var. ***alba***	NLar
grandiflora	EBee
odorata misapplied	see *A. procera*
odorata (L.) Mill.	see *A. repens*
pilosa	CArn EBee
§ ***procera***	EBee
§ ***repens***	WMoo

Agropyron (*Poaceae*)

glaucum	see *Elymus hispidus*
magellanicum	see *Elymus magellanicus*
pubiflorum	see *Elymus magellanicus*

Agrostemma (*Caryophyllaceae*)

coronaria	see *Lychnis coronaria*
githago	CHab CWld MNHC SRms
- 'Ocean Pearl'	CSpe MCot SPhx

Agrostis (*Poaceae*)

calamagrostis	see *Stipa calamagrostis*
§ ***canina*** 'Silver Needles' (v)	NBir WWEG
capillaris	CHab
§ ***montevidensis***	NWsh SMad
nebulosa	SPhx
- 'Fibre Optics'	see *Panicum* 'Fibre Optics'
stolonifera 'Julia Ann' (v)	WCot

Aichryson (*Crassulaceae*)

§ × ***aizoides*** var. ***domesticum***	CSuc LAll
- - 'Variegatum' (v) ♀H1c	CTre EBak WCot

Ailanthus (*Simaroubaceae*)

§ ***altissima***	CBcs CCVT CDul CExl CMac EBee EPfP EUJe IDee LEdu NWea SPer SPlb SWvt
- var. ***tanakae*** CWJ 12452	WCru
- - RWJ 9906	WCru
glandulosa	see *A. altissima*

Ainsliaea (*Asteraceae*)

acerifolia B&SWJ 4795	WCru
- var. ***subapoda*** B&SWJ 11537	WCru
apiculata B&SWJ 11397	WCru
- var. ***acerifolia*** B&SWJ 6059	WCru
chapaensis B&SWJ 11720	WCru
- B&SWJ 11732	WCru
latifolia FMWJ 13426	WCru
nervosa B&SWJ 11344	WCru
petelotii FMWJ 13427	WCru
tonkinensis B&SWJ 11819	WCru
uniflora	GEdr
- B&SWJ 11336	WCru

Ajania (*Asteraceae*)

§ ***pacifica***	ELan
- 'Silver Edge'	XLum

Ajuga (*Lamiaceae*)

ciliata var. ***villosior***	CCon
genevensis	SIgm SPhx
incisa	EBee EWld GBin GCal
- 'Bikun' (v)	CDes EBee SRGP WCot WSHC
- 'Blue Enigma'	CExl CLAP EWes IMou NLar
'Little Court Pink'	see *A. reptans* 'Purple Torch'
metallica	see *A. pyramidalis*
'Pink Lightning' (v)	ECtt LSou WHil
'Pink Spires'	WFar
§ ***pyramidalis***	CArn
- 'Metallica Crispa'	CBct CBre EBee ECho ELan EPri EWes GKin NBir NEoE NHol NLar SRms SWvt WFar
reptans	CArn CHab CTri ECtt ENfk GKev GPoy LRHS MBel MHer MNHC NMir SRms WJek WOut XLum
- f. ***albiflora***	CBar WHfH
- - 'Alba'	CArn CBre ELon MRav NBro SRms WMoo
- 'Arctic Fox' (v)	LSou MRav MSCN SWvt
- 'Argentea'	see *A. reptans* 'Variegata'
§ - 'Atropurpurea'	CBar ECha ECho ELan EPfP GAbr LCro LRHS MGos MLHP MMuc MSpe NWad SEND SGol SPer SPlb SRms SWvt WBrk WJek WTcb XLum
- Black Scallop = 'Binblasca'PBR	Widely available
- 'Blueberry Muffin' **new**	NPri
- 'Braunherz'	CBct CTri ECho ECtt EHoe ELan EPfP GMaP LHop LRHS MAsh MBri MHer MWat NBir NLar NPri SCob SGol SPer SRms SWvt WFar WHar WHil WMoo
- 'Burgundy Glow' (v)	Widely available
§ - 'Catlin's Giant' ♀H7	Widely available
- 'Choc Ice'	EPPr
- 'Chocolate Chip'	see *A. reptans* 'Valfredda'
- 'Delight' (v)	ECho
- 'Ebony'	LSRN
- 'Evening Glow'	NPri WMoo
- 'Flisteridge'	CNat
- 'Golden Beauty'	SRms WOut
- 'Grey Lady'	GBuc
- 'Harlequin' (v)	SWvt
- 'John Pierpoint'	SHar
- 'Jumbo'	see *A. reptans* 'Jungle Beauty'
§ - 'Jungle Beauty'	EPfP MRav XLum
- 'Macrophylla'	see *A. reptans* 'Catlin's Giant'
- 'Mahogany'	CBod NPri SRms
§ - 'Multicolor' (v)	CBcs CBct ECho ELan LRHS MRav NPri SPer SPlb SPoG SRms SWvt WMoo
- Party Colors = 'Binparcol'PBR	CLAP SCob
- 'Pink Elf'	CMHG ECho GCra MRav NBro SWat WFar
- 'Pink Surprise'	EHoe EPri MHer MLHP NRya
- 'Purple Brocade'	EHoe
§ - 'Purple Torch'	NLar SRms WCAu
- 'Purpurea'	see *A. reptans* 'Atropurpurea'
- 'Rainbow'	see *A. reptans* 'Multicolor'
- 'Rosea'	EAEE ELon WMoo XLum
- 'Rowden Amethyst'	MHCG WHil

- 'Rowden Royal Purple' EBee
- 'Toffee Chip'PBR (v) LSou SGol
- 'Tricolor' see *A. reptans* 'Multicolor'
§ - 'Valfredda' CBod ECrN ECtt EPfP GAbr GKev LBMP LRHS MHCG NLar NPri SRms SWvt WBrk WCot WMoo
§ - 'Variegata' (v) CBct ECho ECtt EPfP LBMP MMuc SEND SPer SPoG SRms SWat WFar WTor
Sugar Plum = 'Binsugplu'PBR ELon

Akebia ✿ (*Lardizabalaceae*)

sp. GGal
longeracemosa CRHN SBrt SChF
- B&SWJ 3606 CExl LEdu WCot WCru WPGP
× ***pentaphylla*** CWld EBee ELan EPfP EWTr LRHS MAsh MRav NLar SPer
- B&SWJ 2829 WCru
quinata Widely available
- B&SWJ 4425 WCru
- 'Amethyst Glow' EBee EMil EPfP LHop LRHS NLar SKHP SPer SPoG
- cream-flowered CBot CKel CRHN CWld EBee EMil EPfP EWld LCro LOPS LRHS LSRN MGos MRav NLar SKHP SPer SPoG SRms SSta SWvt WBor WCru WPGP
- 'Shirobana' CBcs CHll CMen CWGN MBlu NLar SMDP WPat
- variegated (v) CBcs LLHF SMad WPat
- 'White Chocolate' ♀H5 ESwi NLar WCru WSHC
trifoliata CBcs CRHN ELan EPfP EWld LRHS MGos SEND SLim SLon WOld
- B&SWJ 2829 WCru
- B&SWJ 5063 WCru
- 'Amethyst' CBot

Alangium (*Cornaceae*)

platanifolium CAbP CBcs CBot CExl EBee ESwi SBrt WPGP WPat
- var. ***macrophyllum*** EBee EPfP MMHG MMuc WBor

Albizia (*Mimosaceae*)

chinensis EPfP LRHS
distachya see *Paraserianthes lophantha*
§ ***julibrissin*** CArn CDTJ CWib EBee EPfP IDee NEgg NLos
- 'Ernest Wilson' MTPN WGrn
- 'Evy's Purple' SGol
- Ombrella = 'Boubri'PBR CBcs ELan EPfP MBri WHar WMat WPGP
- f. ***rosea*** ♀H2 CArn CBcs CDul CExl CLet CLnd CMCN CWGN EBee ELan ELon EPfP EUJe LEdu LHop LRHS SEND SHil SLim SPad SPlb SPoG SPtp SSpi WPGP WSHC
I - 'Rouge Selection' EPfP LRHS SPoG
- 'Shidare' LRHS WMat
- 'Summer Chocolate'PBR ♀H2 CBcs CDul CWGN EBee ELan EPfP IDee LPfy LRHS MPkF NPri SCoo SHil SPer SPoG WHar WMat WPGP
kalkora SPlb
lophantha see *Paraserianthes lophantha*

Albuca ✿ (*Asparagaceae*)

JCA 15856 CTca WAbe
§ ***abyssinica*** EBee GKev
acuminata CDes
angolensis CPou
aurea CTca
bainesii see *A. abyssinica*
* ***batliana*** ECho
batteniana ECho
canadensis (L.) F.M. Leight. CPou WHil
cooperi ECho
'Dirk Wallace' CExl
fragrans EBee
glauca EBee
humilis CExl ECho LLHF WAbe WHil
namaquensis WHil
nelsonii CAvo CDes CPne CPrp CTca EBee ECho GKev LAma WCot WHil
setosa CDes CTca EBee
shawii CAvo CBod CCon CDes CMos CPne CPou CTca EAJP EBee ECho EHoe EHrv EPot EPri ERCP EWld GKev GKin LAst MHer MMuc NCGa SPoG WAbe WGwG WHil
trichophylla WHil
wakefieldii WHil

× *Alcalthaea* (*Malvaceae*)

suffrutescens 'Parkallee' (d) CAbP CDes EBee ECha ECtt ELon GMaP LHop LPla LRHS LSun MAvo MHol MNrw NGdn NLar SEND SPad SPhx WBrk WCot XLum
- 'Parkfrieden' (d) CDes CSpe ECtt ELon LRHS MAvo MNrw SPhx WCot XLum
- 'Parkrondell' (d) CBod CDes ECha ECtt ELon LHop LPla LRHS MAvo MNrw SHar SPad SPhx WCot XLum
- 'Poetry' EBee ECtt LRHS
- white-flowered IFro

Alcea (*Malvaceae*)

'Apple Blossom' (d) EPfP
'Arabian Nights' SPav
'Blackcurrant Whirl' SPav
'Burgundy Towers' **new** WCAu
ficifolia NChi SPav WMoo
'Happy Lights' ELon
'Las Vegas' ECtt LSun NCGa
pallida XSen
'Peaches 'n' Dreams' EPfP LHop NGBl
§ ***rosea*** SVic
- 'Blacknight' (Spotlight Series) EPfP MHer
- Chater's Double Group (d) EPfP IBoy MBri SPoG SRms WBor WHar
- - chamois (d) EPfP
- - chestnut-brown-flowered (d) EPfP
- - maroon-flowered (d) EPfP LAst LCro SPoG
- - pink-flowered (d) CBod ELan EPfP
- - red-flowered (d) CBod ELan EPfP SPoG
- - salmon-pink-flowered (d) CBod EPfP
- - scarlet-flowered (d) EPfP SPoG
- - violet-flowered (d) CBod EPfP
- - white-flowered (d) CBod ELan EPfP LCro SPoG
- - yellow-flowered (d) CBod EPfP LCro SPoG SRms
- 'Crème de Cassis' ELan EPfP LRHS NGBl SPav
- double apricot-flowered (d) EBee
- - yellow-flowered (d) EBee
- 'Fiesta Time' (d) **new** EBee
- (Halo Series) 'Halo Apricot' LRHS SPoG
- - 'Halo Blush' LRHS SPoG
- - 'Halo Cerise' LRHS SPoG
- - 'Halo Cream' LRHS SPoG
- - 'Halo Red' EBee LRHS SPoG
- - 'Halo White' **new** LRHS SPoG

	- 'Mars Magic' (Spotlight Series)	EPfP MHer MNHC
	- 'Nigra'	CBod CSpe ECtt ELan EPfP IBoy LAst LCro LHop LOPS LPal LRHS LSRN MNHC NGBl NGdn SBod SPer SPhx SRms WCAu WHar XEll
	- 'Polarstar' (Spotlight Series)	MNHC
	- single pink-flowered	EWoo
	- single-flowered	MMuc SRms
	- Summer Carnival Group	CWib SRms
	- 'Sunshine' (Spotlight Series)	EPfP
§	***rugosa***	MSpe SHar SPav XSen

Alcea × *Althaea* see × *Alcathaea*

Alchemilla ✿ (*Rosaceae*)

	abyssinica	EBee
	alpina misapplied	see *A. conjuncta*, *A. plicatula*
	alpina ambig.	MCot SCob
	alpina L.	CMea EBee ECho EHoe ELan EPfP EWTr GKev GPoy LEdu LHop LRHS MMuc MRav NChi SBch SEND SRms SWat WMoo WPGP WSHC
§	***conjuncta***	CArn CMac CSam EBee ECha EHrv ELan EPfP EShb GAbr GMaP LHop MHer MLHP MRav NBid NChi NRya NSti SPer SPlb SRms WHoo WJek WKif
	ellenbeckii	ECho GAbr IMou WPGP WWFP
	epipsila	EBee ELan EPfP EShb GCal LRHS LSun NLar SPhx
	erythropoda 🏆H5	Widely available
	- (Cepa Group) 'Alma' new	NPri
	- Turkish form	ECha
	faeroensis	WMoo WPtf XLum
	- var. ***pumila***	EBee GEdr
	fissa new	EPPr
	glaucescens	CNat
	hoppeana misapplied	see *A. plicatula*
	hoppeana (Reichenb.) Dalla Torre	EBee
	iniquiformis	EBee WPGP
	lapeyrousei	EBee NChi
	mollis 🏆H7	Widely available
I	- 'Auslese'	SWvt
	- 'Robustica'	MMuc SEND SPlb SWat WFar WMoo WPnP
	- 'Thriller'	CBod EPfP LRHS WFar
	'Mr Poland's Variety'	see *A. venosa*
	pedata	CHid NChi
	peristerica	EBee
§	***plicatula***	NLar
	saxatilis	EBee MWhi NLar
	sericata 'Gold Strike'	ECtt ELan EPfP IMou LBMP MWhi SHar SWvt WHil
	straminea	MRav
	valdehirsuta	EBee
§	***venosa***	EBee SMHy
	vetteri	EBee LRHS
	vulgaris misapplied	see *A. xanthochlora*
§	***xanthochlora***	CArn GPoy NLar SRms WFar WHer

Aldrovanda (*Droseraceae*)

vesiculosa	EFEx

alecost see *Tanacetum balsamita*

Alectorurus (*Liliaceae*)

yedoensis var. ***platypetalus***	EBee GEdr

Alectryon (*Sapindaceae*)

excelsus	CBcs ECou

Alisma (*Alismataceae*)

lanceolatum	MSKA
plantago-aquatica	CBen CHab EHon MSKA MWLS MWts NPer SWat WMAq WWtn XBlo
- var. ***parviflorum***	MSKA SPlb SWat

Alliaria (*Brassicaceae*)

petiolata	GPoy WHer WOut WSFF

Allium (*Alliaceae*)

	sp.	GEdr
	RCB AM 21 new	WCot
	RCB UA 5	WCot
	SSSE 250	GEdr
	aciphyllum	WCot
§	***acuminatum***	ECho GBin NBir NRog
I	- 'Album'	ECho LRHS
	acutiflorum	LAma NRog
	aflatunense misapplied	see *A. hollandicum*
	aflatunense ambig.	LCro LRHS LSRN SCob SDeJ SEND WCot
	akaka	NRog
	'Akbulak'	EBee LAma
	albopilosum	see *A. cristophii*
	alexeianum	NRog
	altissimum	LAma NRog
	- 'Goliath'	CTca GKev NRog WCot
	amabile	see *A. mairei* var. *amabile*
	'Ambassador'	CBro CMea CTca CWCL ERCP ILea LAma LRHS NRog SPhx WCot
	amethystinum 'Red Mohican'	EBee ERCP LAma LOPS WCot
	ampeloprasum	EBee ECha ECho LAma NRog SPlb WHer WShi
	- var. ***babingtonii***	CAgr CArn CTca GPoy LEdu NRog SRms WHer WPGP WShi
§	- 'Elephant'	LCro LEdu LOPS
	amphibolum	EBee ECho LAma NRog
	amplectens	LAma LLHF NRog
	- 'Graceful Beauty'	EPot ERCP LAma LCro LOPS NRog SCob SDeJ WCot XEll
	anceps	NRog
§	***angulosum***	CAvo CTca ECho GKev LAma LEdu LPla NRog SEND WCot
	aschersonianum	EBee ERCP SDeJ WCot
	atropurpureum	EBee ECha EHrv ELan EPfP ERCP LAma LCro LOPS LRHS MCot NRog SDeJ SPer SPhx
	atropurpureum × ***schubertii***	LSRN
	auctum new	EBee
	azureum	see *A. caeruleum*
	backhousianum	LAma NRog
	barszczewskii	NRog
	'Beau Regard' 🏆H7	CTca CWCL EBee ELan ERCP ILea LAma LRHS NLar NRog
	beesianum misapplied	see *A. cyaneum*
	beesianum W.W. Sm. 🏆H5	CDes EBee LLHF NBir NRya
	bisceptrum	NRog
	'Bizar' new	LAma LEdu
	blandum	see *A. carolinianum*
	bodeanum	see *A. cristophii*
	'Bolero'	EBee LAma LRHS NRog
	bulgaricum	see *Nectaroscordum siculum* subsp. *bulgaricum*

§	***caeruleum*** 🏆H5	CAvo CBro CSpe CTca CTri CWld EAJP EBee ECho EPfP EPot ERCP LAma LCro LHop LPot LRHS MBri MGos MNrw NBir NLar NPer NRog NRya SCob SDeJ SPer SPhx WBor
	- ***azureum***	see *A. caeruleum*
	caesium 🏆H5	ECho ERCP NRog
	caespitosum	ECho
	callimischon subsp. ***callimischon***	ECho EPot NRog
	- subsp. ***haemostictum***	CDes ECho NRog WAbe WCot
	'Cameleon'	EBee ECho ERCP LAma LCro LOPS LRHS NRog SCob
	campanulatum	NRog
	canadense	CArn
§	***carinatum***	ECho GKev MBel
§	- subsp. ***pulchellum*** 🏆H5	CBro CMea EBee ECha ECho EPot GKev LAma LHop LLWP LRHS MHer MMuc MNrw MWat NRog SPhx WThu
	- - f. ***album*** 🏆H5	CBro EBee ECha ECho GKev LEdu LLWP MNrw MWat NRog SPhx WHlf WPtf
	- - 'Bill Baker' **new**	LEdu
§	***carolinianum***	LAma NRog
	cepa	CBod SVic
	- Aggregatum Group	CLau GPoy SRms
	- - 'Golden Gourmet' 🏆H3	LCro LOPS SVic
	- - 'Longor' PBR 🏆H3 **new**	LCro LOPS
	- - 'Matador' 🏆H3	SVic
	- - 'Pikant'	SVic
	- - 'Red Sun' PBR **new**	LCro
	- 'Electric' PBR **new**	LCro
	- 'Kew White'	WCot
	- 'Perutile'	CArn CHby GPoy LEdu MHer SHDw
	- Proliferum Group	CAgr CArn CPrp GPoy LEdu MHer MNHC SIde SRms WGwG WHer WJek XLum
	- 'Red Brunswick'	SVic
	- var. ***viviparum***	ECho LAma NRog
	- 'White Lisbon' 🏆H4	LCro SVic
	cernuum	Widely available
§	- 'Hidcote' 🏆H5	CSam EBee WKif
	- 'Major'	see *A. cernuum* 'Hidcote'
	- pink-flowered	NBir
	- 'White Dwarf'	EBee ECho LAma NRog
	chinense	GPoy LEdu
	cirrhosum	see *A. carinatum* subsp. *pulchellum*
	cneorum **new**	LAma
	colchicifolium	NRog
	convallariodes **new**	LAma
	cowanii	see *A. neapolitanum* Cowanii Group
	crenulatum	LAma NRog
	crispum	NRog
§	***cristophii*** 🏆H7	Widely available
	cupanii	ECho
	cupuliferum	NRog
	curtum RCB RL 13	WCot
§	***cyaneum*** 🏆H5	CPBP ECho GEdr LAma LBee LRHS MHer NRog NRya WCot
	cyathophorum	ECho
§	- var. ***farreri***	CArn CAvo CBro CElw ECho EPot GKev LAma LEdu LLWP LRHS MHer MLHP MNrw MRav NChi NRya WCot WPtf WThu
	darwasicum RM 8274	WCot
	decipiens	LAma NRog
	diabaloense	NRog
	dichlamydeum	NRog
	douglasii	NRog
§	***drummondii***	EBee LRHS
	'Early Emperor'	CWCL EBee EPfP ERCP LAma LRHS NRog SCob
	elatum	see *A. macleanii*
	elburzense	NRog
	'Emir'	NRog
	ericetorum	NRog WCot
	- PAB 1009 **new**	LEdu
	'Eros' **new**	EBee LAma LCro LOPS
	falcifolium	CTal ECho GKev LAma LLHF NRog WCot
	farreri	see *A. cyathophorum* var. *farreri*
	fasciculatum	LAma
	fimbriatum	ECho NRog
	- var. ***purdyi***	NRog
	'Firmament'	CAvo CBro CWCL ECha ERCP LAma LRHS NRog SDeJ SPhx WCot XEll
	fistulosum	CAgr CArn CHby CLau ECho ENfk GBin GKev GPoy LAma LEdu MHer MMuc MNHC NPri SEND SIde SRms SVic WCot WGwG WJek XLum
	- 'Red Welsh'	SRms WJek
	flavum 🏆H4	CArn CBro CMea CTca ECGP ECha ECho EPot ERCP GKev LAma LRHS NSla SDeJ WGwG WThu WWEG
§	- 'Blue Leaf'	ECho NBir
	- subsp. ***flavum***	EBee ECho NRog
	- - var. ***minus***	ECho MMuc NRog SEND
	- 'Glaucum'	see *A. flavum* 'Blue Leaf'
	- var. ***nanum***	ECho EPot NRog
	- subsp. ***tauricum***	CSpe ECho NRog SPhx WCot
	'Forelock'	CAvo CTca EBee EPfP ERCP LAma MNrw NRog SCob WCot XEll
	forrestii	WCot
	geyeri	EBee ECho GBin WCot
	giganteum	Widely available
	- 'Twinkling Stars' **new**	LAma
	'Gladiator' 🏆H7	CAvo CTca CWCL EBee EPfP ERCP GMaP LAma LCro LOPS LPfy LRHS LSRN NRog SCob SDeJ
	glaucum	see *A. senescens* subsp. *glaucum*
	'Globemaster' 🏆H7	CAby CAvo CBro CMea CTca CWCL EBee EHrv ELan EPfP EPot ERCP ILea LAma LCro LEdu LOPS LRHS LSRN LSun MBri MMHG NLar SCob SDeJ SPer SPhx WCot
	'Globus'	CTca EBee LAma NRog
	guttatum subsp. ***dalmaticum***	NRog
	- subsp. ***sardoum***	NRog
	gypsaceum	NRog
	'Haarlem Superglobe' **new**	CPne
	haemanthoides	WCot
	haematochiton	ECho NRog
	'Hair'	see *A. vineale* 'Hair'
	heldreichii	EBee ECho NRog
*	***hirtifolium*** var. ***album***	EBee LAma NRog
	'His Excellency'	CCon CWCL EBee ERCP ILea LAma LRHS NRog SCob
§	***hollandicum*** 🏆H7	CAvo CBro CTca ECGP ECha EPfP GKev LAma LCro LOPS NRog SPer SPlb WFar
	- 'Purple Sensation' 🏆H7	Widely available
	- 'Purple Surprise' 🏆H7	NBir WCot

hookeri LEdu
- ACE 2430 EPot LEdu WCot
- var. ***muliense*** GEdr LEdu
- 'Zorami' LEdu WPGP

howellii var. ***clokeyi*** NRog
humile GEdr
hyalinum NRog
- pink-flowered EBee

I ***incensiodorum*** **new** CEvo
inconspicuum LAma NRog
§ ***insubricum*** ♀^{H5} CDes EPot GEdr MNrw NBir NRog NRya SChF WAbe WPtf
'Jackpot' CWCL EBee ERCP ILea LAma NRog
jajlae see *A. rotundum* subsp. *jajlae*
jesdianum 'Michael Hoog' see *A. rosenorum* 'Michael H. Hoog'
- 'Purple King' LAma LRHS NRog
- 'White Empress'^{PBR} CAvo CWCL EBee NRog SPhx

kansuense see *A. sikkimense*
karataviense ♀^{H5} CAby CAvo CTca EBee ECha ELan EPot GAbr GKev LAma LCro LHop LOPS LRHS MBri MCot NBir NLar NRog SCob SDeJ SWvt
- subsp. ***henrikii*** LAma NRog
- 'Ivory Queen' CAby CAvo CBro CTca EBee ECha EPfP ERCP GKev LAma LCro LOPS LRHS LSRN NLar NRog SCob SDeJ SPlb WWFP

kharputense NRog
komarovianum see *A. thunbergii*
komarovii LAma NRog
lacunosum NRog
- var. ***lacunosum*** NRog

ledebourianum GKev LAma NRog
lemmonii NRog
lenkoranicum ECho GKev LAma NRog WCot
libani XLum
litvinovii LAma NRog
loratum EBee LAma NRog
'Lucy Ball' EPfP ERCP ILea LAma LRHS NBir NLar NRog SDeJ
§ ***lusitanicum*** CBro CTca ECha ECho ERCP GKev LEdu NBre NRog SRms WCot
§ ***macleanii*** EBee ECho EPfP LAma LRHS NRog
macranthum CSpe EBee ECho GBin GEdr GKev LAma NRog
mairei ECho LAma LHop LRHS MMuc NRya
§ - var. ***amabile*** ECho GEdr NRya NSla WThu
- - pink-flowered ECho
- - red-flowered ECho

maximowiczii ECho
- white-flowered ECho LAma

'Mercurius'^{PBR} EBee LAma MNrw NRog SPhx WCot
meteoricum CDes NRog WCot
'Miami' EBee ERCP LAma NRog
'Millennium' WCot
moly CArn CWCL EBee ECho GKev LAma LCro MBri MRav MWat NRog NRya SCob SDeJ SRms WCot XLum
- 'Jeannine' ♀^{H5} CBro CTca EBee ECho EPot GBin LAma LRHS NRog WShi

'Mont Blanc' EBee ELan ERCP GBin GKev GQue ILea LAma LRHS NLar NRog SCob
multibulbosum see *A. nigrum*
murrayanum misapplied see *A. unifolium*
murrayanum Regel see *A. acuminatum*
myrianthum NRog
- KMT-19-04 EBee

narcissiflorum misapplied see *A. insubricum*
§ ***narcissiflorum*** Vill. CSpe EBee ECho GCal LEdu MNrw NWad
neapolitanum CAgr ECGP ECho EPot LAma LRHS MBri MCot NRog SEND SPer SRms WGwG
§ - Cowanii Group ECGP ECho LCro LOPS LRHS NRog SDeJ WCot
- 'Grandiflorum' ECho GKev

§ ***neriniflorum*** CDes WAbe
nevii NRog
nevskianum LAma NRog SKHP
§ ***nigrum*** CAvo CBro ECha EHrv EPfP EPot ERCP LAma LCro LOPS LRHS MCot NBir NPer NRog SCob SDeJ SPhx WCot WRHF
nutans CPrp LAma LEdu MHer NRog SHDw SRms WHal WHil WJek
nuttallii see *A. drummondii*
§ ***obliquum*** CAvo CBro CSpe ECha ERCP GEdr LRHS NRog SPhx WCot
ochotense WCot
odorum L. see *A. ramosum* L.
oleraceum WHer
olympicum CDes NRog
§ ***oreophilum*** CSam ECha ECho LAma LCro LOPS LRHS NRog SPer SRms WCot
- 'Agalik Giant' NRog
- 'Samur' WCot
- 'Zwanenburg' ♀^{H5} ECho EPot

orientale NRog
oschaninii LAma NRog
ostrowskianum see *A. oreophilum*
ovalifolium var. ***leuconeurum*** GEdr WCot
pallasii NRog
pallens CBre NBir
§ ***paniculatum*** LAma NRog
* - var. ***minor*** LAma NRog
paradoxum ECho LEdu NBir
- var. ***normale*** CBro CDes ECho EPot EWld NBir NRog WCot

parciflorum NRog
parvum NRog
pedemontanum see *A. narcissiflorum* Vill.
pendulinum NRog
'Pinball Wizard' CBro CTca CWCL ERCP LAma LRHS NRog
'Pink Jewel' EBee ERCP LAma NRog WCot
platycaule LAma NRog SKHP WCot
plummerae EBee GKev NRog SKHP
plurifoliatum ECho LAma
polyphyllum see *A. carolinianum*
porrum 'Musselburgh' NPri SVic
'Powder Puff' **new** LAma
prattii EBee
protensum NRog
przewalskianum LAma LEdu NRog
pskemense LAma NRog WCot
pulchellum see *A. carinatum* subsp. *pulchellum*
'Purple Rain' CBro CWCL ELan ERCP LAma NRog
'Purple Suze' **new** LAma
pyrenaicum misapplied see *A. angulosum*
ramosum Jacq. see *A. obliquum*
§ ***ramosum*** L. ECho GKev LAma LEdu NRog
'Red Eye' **new** EBee
'Rien Poortvliet' LAma
roborowskianum GKev WCot
robustum NRog

	rosenbachianum misapplied	see *A. stipitatum*
	rosenbachianum Regel	CBro LRHS
	- 'Akbulak'	LRHS
	- 'Album'	EPfP LAma NRog WCot
	- 'Michael Hoog'	see *A. rosenorum* 'Michael H. Hoog'
	- 'Shing'	IBal LAma
§	***rosenorum*** 'Michael H. Hoog'	ECho EPot LAma NRog
	roseum	EPfP EPot LAma LCro LOPS LRHS NRog SCob SDeJ
§	***rotundum*** subsp. ***jajlae***	LAma NRog WCot
	'Round and Purple'	ERCP LAma LRHS NRog
	sarawschanicum	NRog
	sativum	ENfk LBMP MHer NPri SIde SPoG SRms
	- 'Albanian Late'	LEdu
	- 'Elephant'	see *A. ampeloprasum* 'Elephant'
	- var. ***ophioscorodon***	GPoy LAma SPlb
	- - 'Purple Wight'	LOPS
	saxatile	GKev NRog
	aff. ***saxatile*** from Russia **new**	WCot
	schoenoprasum	Widely available
	- f. ***albiflorum***	CPbn CPrp ECha ECho GKev LEdu MHer NBir NCGa SIde WHer
	- 'Black Isle Blush'	CDes CPbn CTca EBee GPoy LEdu LPla MHer SMHy WPGP
	- 'Colesbourne Giant' **new**	CDes
	- 'Corsican White'	LEdu
	- fine-leaved	CLau NDov
	- 'Forescate'	CPrp CTca ECha GKev LAma LEdu LHop LRHS MRav NBir SIde SRms WAul XLum
	- medium-leaved	CLau NPri
	- 'Pink Perfection'	GPoy LEdu LPla MHer NDov SMHy
	- 'Polyphant'	CBre
	- 'Shining Silver'	LEdu
	- var. ***sibiricum***	SDix WShi
	- 'Silver Chimes'	CDes EBee MRav
	- thick-leaved	CLau
	- 'Wallington White'	LEdu
	- 'Wilau'	CLau
	schubertii 🏆^{H4}	CAvo CBod CBro CSpe CTca CWCL ELan EPfP EPot ERCP GKev LAma LCro LOPS LRHS MBri NDov NFav NRog SCob SDeJ SPer SPhx WCot WWFP
	scorodoprasum	ECho LAma SIde
	- 'Art'	ERCP LAma NRog
	- subsp. ***jajlae***	see *A. rotundum* subsp. *jajlae*
	- 'Passion'	ERCP LAma NRog
	- subsp. ***scorodoprasum***	ECho NRog
	senescens	CArn CBro CTca CTri ECGP EDAr EPot GJos IMou LAma LEdu LRHS MBel MRav SBch SRms XLum XSen
§	- subsp. ***glaucum***	CArn CAvo CMea CPBP CPrp CSpe CTal EAEE EBee ECha ECho EWTr LAst LEdu LRHS NDov NGdn NLar NRog NRya SBod SEND SWat WBor WBrk WCot WHoo XSen
	- subsp. ***senescens***	ECho GKev LEdu NRog WPGP
	sewerzowii	NRog
	shelkovnikovii	CTal WCot
	sibthorpianum	see *A. paniculatum*
	siculum	see *Nectaroscordum siculum*
§	***sikkimense***	CCon CSpe EBee ECho EWTr GBin GEdr LRHS MHer MMuc NSla SEND WCot
	'Silver Spring'	EPot ERCP LCro MNrw NRog SDeJ
	sphaerocephalon	Widely available
	- subsp. ***arvense***	NRog
	'Spider'	CWCL EBee ERCP ESwi LAma NRog SPhx WCot
I	***splendens*** var. ***kurilense***	GEdr
	stamineum W&B BGF-2 **new**	WCot
	stellatum	LRHS NRog WGwG
	stellerianum var. ***kurilense***	WAbe WThu
§	***stipitatum***	ERCP LAma NRog SPhx WCot
	- 'Album'	NRog
	- 'Mars'	EBee EPfP ERCP LAma LRHS NRog
	- 'Mount Everest'	CAvo CBro CCon CHid CTca CWCL EPfP EPot ERCP GBin GKev GMaP ILea LAma LCro LOPS LRHS LSRN MHtn MWat NRog SDeJ SPer SPhx WCot
	- 'Violet Beauty'	CCse CWCL GKev LAma LCro LOPS LRHS WCot
	- 'White Giant'	CTca CWCL EBee ERCP ILea LAma LRHS NRog
	stracheyi	WCot
	'Stratos'	EBee ERCP LAma WCot
	suaveolens	SEND
	subhirsutum	NRog XLum
	subvillosum	NRog
	'Summer Beauty'	see *A. lusitanicum*
	'Summer Drummer'	CTca EBee EPfP ERCP LEdu LRHS NRog SDeJ SPhx
	suworowii	NRog
	'Sweet Discovery'	LAma NRog
	taquetii	see *A. thunbergii*
	tauricola	NRog
	texanum	LAma NRog
§	***thunbergii*** 🏆^{H5}	EBee ECho EPot LAma LHop MHer NBir NRog NRya SPhx WAbe WWEG
	- PAB 3821	LEdu
	- 'Album'	ECho WAbe
	- 'Ozawa'	CDes EBee ECho GEdr SRms WAbe WCot WOld
	tibeticum	see *A. sikkimense*
	tolmiei var. ***platyphyllum***	NRog
	- var. ***tolmiei***	NRog
*	***tournefortii***	ECho
	triquetrum	CLau EDAr ELan EPot LAma LEdu NBir SEND WCot WHer WMoo WPnP XLum
	tschimganicum	EBee LAma NRog SKHP
	tuberosum	Widely available
	- B&SWJ 8881	WCru
	- purple/mauve-flowered	CHby CLau
	tuncelianum	LEdu
	umbilicatum	NRog
§	***unifolium*** 🏆^{H4}	CAvo CMea EBee ECho EPfP EPot ERCP GBin GKev LAma LCro LOPS MRav NBir NPer NQui NRog SDeJ SEND SRms WCot
	ursinum	CArn CHab CHby CWld ECho ENfk GKev GPoy LAma LEdu MHer MMuc NRog SRms WJek WSFF WShi
	validum NNS 06-41	WCot
	victorialis	ECho
	- 'Cantabria'	EBee GKev NRog WCot
	vineale	CArn NMir WHer
	- PAB 2763	LEdu
	- 'Dready'	ECho ERCP GKev LAma NRog
§	- 'Hair'	CAby CTca EPfP ERCP GKev LAma MCot NBir NPer NRog SCob WTor

violaceum	see *A. carinatum*
virgunculae	CDes CMea
wallichii	EBee EWes GQue LEdu LLHF MBNS NBir NChi SKHP WCot XLum
- CC 2643 **new**	WCot
- CLD 1500	CDes
- PAB 2976	LEdu WPGP
- dark-flowered	WCot
'White Cloud' **new**	XEll
'World Cup'	LAma
woronowii	NRog
zaprjagajevii	WCot
zebdanense	EBee ECho LAma NRog

almond see *Prunus dulcis*

Alniphyllum (*Styracaceae*)

eberhardtii FMWJ 13121 **new**	WCru

Alnus ✿ (*Betulaceae*)

cordata ♀H5	CBcs CCVT CDoC CDul CLnd CMCN CMac CSBt CSto CTho CTri EBee ECrN ELan EPfP EWTr LBuc MGos NEgg NLar NWea SCob SEND SEWo SGol SPer SPlb WMat WMou WOut
cremastogyne	EBtc
fauriei **new**	GKev
- from Niigata, Japan	CSto
firma	CSto
formosana	IArd
glutinosa	CArg CBcs CCVT CDoC CDul CHab CLnd CMac CSBt CTho CTri EBee ECrN EPfP LBuc MGos MJak NBes NWea SCob SEWo SGol SPer WHar WMat WMou WSFF
- 'Aurea'	CDul CTho CWib MBlu MGos
- var. ***barbata***	CSto
- 'Imperialis' ♀H6	CCVT CDoC CDul CLnd CTho EBee ECrN ELan EPfP EWTr GBin IDee LHop MBlu MBri MMuc MPkF NBro NLar NOrn NWea SCob SEND SGol SKHP SPer WHar WMat
- 'Laciniata'	CCVT CDoC CDul CLnd CMac CTho ECrN MGos NLar NWea WMou
- 'Pyramidalis'	CDul
hirsuta	CSto GKev
incana	CBcs CCVT CDoC CDul CLnd CMCN CTho CWib ECrN LBuc MGos NLar NWea SCob SGol SPer WHar WMat WMou
- 'Aurea' ♀H6	CBcs CCVT CDul CMac CTho EBee ECrN ELan EPfP IArd MBlu MGos MRav NBro NEgg NLar NOrn NWea SEWo SGol SPer SPoG WFar WHar WMat
- 'Laciniata'	CTho ELan MGos NLar SCoo WFar WMou
- 'Pendula'	CTho
japonica	MBlu
maximowiczii	CSto
- from Ulleungdo	WCru
oregana	see *A. rubra*
pendula B&SWJ 10895	WCru
rhombifolia	EBtc
§ ***rubra***	CDul CMCN CTho ELan MCoo NWea WMat
- f. ***pinnatisecta***	CDul CMCN CTho MBlu
sieboldiana	GKev WCru
× ***spaethii***	MBlu MMuc
subcordata	CSto
viridis	CAgr CSto EBtc MCoo NWea
- subsp. ***sinuata***	CAgr CSto NWea

Alocasia (*Araceae*)

× ***amazonica*** ♀H1a	XBlo
'Calidora'	CDTJ IDee MHin SPlb
cucullata	XBlo
gageana	CDTJ
macrorrhiza	CCon CDTJ NLos SBig SPlb
- 'Variegata' (v) ♀H1a	EUJe
'Mayan Mask'	EUJe
odora	CAbb CDTJ SPlb XBlo
plumbea	XBlo

Aloe ✿ (*Asphodelaceae*)

africana	CAbb
antandroi **new**	LToo
arborescens	CDTJ CDoC CTre EShb EUJe SEND
aristata ♀H3	CCac EAla EUJe LTro SChr SEND SPlb WPGP XLum
- 'Cathedral Peak' **new**	SChr
- 'Green Pearl' PBR	SMad
aristata × ***striatula*** **new**	CCac
barbadensis	see *A. vera*
barberae	CTre
betsileensis	LToo
boylei	CTre
brevifolia ♀H2	CAbb CTre EShb
broomii	CAbb CTre LToo SPlb
camperi 'Maculata'	SEND
ciliaris	CCac CHII EShb SChr
comptonii	CAbb
cooperi	CDTJ
descoingsii ♀H1b	LToo
descoingsii × ***haworthioides***	CSuc
dichotoma	CAbb CSuc CTre SPlb
dinteri	CSuc
distans	MHin
'Doran Black'	LToo
ecklonis	CBlu CSuc SPlb
elegans	LToo
excelsa	CSuc
ferox	CAbb CBod CDTJ CDoC CSuc CTre SBig
fosteri	CDTJ CSuc
gerstneri	CSuc
greatheadii	CSuc
- var. ***davyana***	SChr
humilis	CSuc SChr SEND
juvenna	SRms
kedongensis	SEND
krapohliana	CAbb
'Lime Fizz' **new**	LToo
lineata	CAbb
littoralis	CAbb
lutescens	CAbb
maculata	CDTJ CDoC CSuc
marlothii	CAbb CSuc SPlb
melanacantha	CAbb
microstigma	CDoC CTre
millotii	LToo
mitriformis	NGBl SEND
mutabilis	SChr SEND
peglerae	SRms
petricola	CAbb
plicatilis ♀H2	CBlu CDTJ CSuc EShb

pluridens	CAbb
polyphylla ♀H3	CAbb CBlu CCac CSuc CTre SChr WCot WPGP
pratensis	CDTJ
rauhii ♀H1b	CTre LToo
reitzii	CAbb CBlu CTre SPlb
rivae	CSuc
rugosifolia	CSuc
sheilae	CSuc
sinkatana	CSuc
'Snowflake'	CSuc
somaliensis ♀H1b	LToo
speciosa	CAbb
spectabilis	CSuc
spicata	CAbb
× ***spinosissima***	SChr SMad
striata	CAbb CSuc CTre EShb LToo SPlb
striatula ♀H3	CAbb CBrP CCac CDTJ CDoC CSam CSde CSuc CTca CTre EAla ETod EUJe IBlr LEdu LTro SBig SChr SEND SKHP SMad SPlb SVen WCot WPGP
succotrina	CAbb
suprafoliata	CAbb CBlu
thraskii	CAbb
tomentosa	LToo
vanbalenii	CSuc
variegata (v) ♀H1b	EShb LSun MHin
§ ***vera*** ♀H1b	CArn CDoC CSpe ELan EOHP GPoy MHer MNHC NPer NPla NPri SBch SChr SEND SIde SMad SPlb SPre SRms SVic WJek
wickensii	LToo
yavellana	SPlb

Aloe × *Haworthia* see × *Alworthia*

Alonsoa (*Scrophulariaceae*)

'Bright Spark'	CSpe
incisifolia	CSpe
meridionalis	CDes
- 'Rebel'	CBod ECtt SRkn WBor
- 'Salmon Beauty'	LRHS
'Pink Beauty'	CSpe ELan
'Scarlet Lucky Lips' (v)	LSou
warscewiczii	ELan MSCN
- 'Peachy-keen'	CSpe

Alopecurus (*Poaceae*)

borealis subsp. ***glaucus***	ELan EPPr LPot
pratensis	CHab
- 'Aureovariegatus' (v)	EHoe EPPr EShb GMaP NBid SPer SRms XLum
- 'Aureus'	NBro SPlb
- 'No Overtaking' (v)	EPPr

Alophia (*Iridaceae*)

lahue	see *Herbertia lahue*

Aloysia (*Verbenaceae*)

chamaedryfolia	EPfP LRHS
citriodora	see *A. citrodora*
§ ***citrodora*** ♀H3	Widely available
gratissima	WJek
triphylla	see *A. citrodora*

Alpinia (*Zingiberaceae*)

formosana	LEdu
galanga	CArn
japonica	CExl LEdu
- B&SWJ 8889	WCru
- PAB 6441	LEdu
zerumbet 'Variegata' (v)	EUJe MPkF NLos XBlo

Alsobia see *Episcia*

Alstroemeria ✿ (*Alstroemeriaceae*)

'Adonis'PBR	EWoo LRHS SPer WViv
'Aimi'	CCon ELan MNrw SPer SWvt WViv
'Alexis'PBR	WViv
'Aliénor' (Midi Series)	XTur
'Amarillo' **new**	WViv
'Andez Red' **new**	EWTr
'Andigné' (Garden Series)	XTur
'Angelina'	SWvt
'Anne' (Midi Series)	XTur
'Antoine' (Maxi Series)	LSou XTur
'Apollo' ♀H4	CBcs CTsd ELan EWoo LRHS MBNS MNrw NBre SWvt WViv
'Arthur' (Maxi Series)	XTur
'Athena'	WViv
'Aubance' (Garden Series)	XTur
aurantiaca	see *A. aurea*
§ ***aurea***	MRav SRms XLum
- 'Apricot'	GCal
- 'Lutea'	GKev NLar SDeJ SPlb
- 'Orange King'	CTsd ELan EPfP EWTr GKev NLar SDeJ
'Authion' (Garden Series)	XTur
'Avanti'	ELan LRHS WViv
'Avrillé' (Garden Series)	XTur
'Baracé' (Garden Series)	XTur
'Baugé' (Garden Series)	XTur
'Béatrice' (Midi Series)	XTur
'Blanche' (Midi Series)	XTur
'Blushing Bride'	CCon MBNS SWvt WViv
'Bodega'PBR **new**	WViv
'Bolero'	WViv
'Bonanza'	SLon SPer WViv
brasiliensis	CCon CTsd GCal GKev SBrt WCot WSHC WViv XLum
- 'Cally Star' (v)	GCal NLar
'Brezé' (Garden Series)	XTur
'Briançon' (Garden Series)	XTur
'Cahors' (Planet Series) ♀H4	LCro LOPS
'Camille' (Mini Series)	XTur
'Candé' (Garden Series)	XTur
'Candy' **new**	WViv
'Candy Floss'	ELan EPfP
'Caroline' (Midi Series)	XTur
'Charles' (Maxi Series)	LSou XTur
'Charm'	CTsd WViv
'Chartrené' (Garden Series)	XTur
'Chi Chi'	WCot
'Chinon' (Garden Series)	XTur
'Chloé' (Mini Series) **new**	XTur
§ 'Christina'PBR	MBNS SLon SWvt WViv
'Christine Marsh' **new**	WViv
'Christine' (Midi Series)	XTur
'Cindy' **new**	WViv
'Coronet' ♀H4	MBNS
'Dandy Candy'	CDoC EBee ECGP GKev LRHS MCot MHol NGdn NLar WBrk WCot
'Davina'PBR	NLar
'Dayspring Delight' (v)	GCal MNrw
§ Diana, Princess of Wales = 'Stablaco'	LRHS
'Diane' (Midi Series)	XTur
diluta subsp. ***chrysantha*** F&W 8700	WCot
'Distré' (Garden Series)	XTur

Name	Suppliers
Doctor Salter's hybrids	SRms
'Dorothée' (Midi Series)	XTur
'Elvira'	ELan MNrw SPer WViv
'Etna' PBR **new**	WViv
'Evening Song'	LRHS MBNS MNrw SLon SPer SWvt
exserens	WCot
'Flaming Star'	WViv
'Fougeré' (Garden Series)	XTur
'Frances' (v)	CAvo CBro
'François' (Maxi Series)	XTur
'Freedom'	CBod CWGN ECtt ELon EWoo LSou MBNS MHol NEgg NLar NSti SCob SMad SPoG WCot WOut
'Friendship' ♀H5	CBcs CTsd ELan EWoo LRHS NBre SWvt WViv
'Gaspard' (Mini Series)	XTur
'Georges' (Maxi Series) **new**	XTur
'Gloria'	CCon MBNS SWvt WViv
'Glory of the Andes' (v)	CWGN NLar
'Golden Delight'	ELan LRHS MNrw WViv
haemantha	GKev
I 'Hatch Hybrid'	GCal
'Hawera'	GCal
'Héloïse' (Mini Series)	XTur
'Henri' (Maxi Series)	XTur
hookeri	WCot
subsp. ***cummingiana***	
Inca Adore = 'Koadore'	CExl SLon SPoG
Inca Avanti = 'Koncavanti' PBR	LBuc SCob WViv
Inca Azure = 'Konazur' PBR	WViv
Inca Classic	WViv
Inca Coral = 'Konocoral'	IBoy WViv
Inca Devotion = 'Konevotio' PBR	EBee LHop NLar
Inca Dream = 'Kodream'	WViv
Inca Exotica = 'Koexotica'	EBee SLon SPoG WViv
Inca Glow = 'Koglow'	CBod CDoC CExl CWGN EBee ELon GKev LAst LRHS LSou MHol NLar SDeJ SLon SPoG SRms WViv
Inca Goal = 'Koncagoal' **new**	WViv
Inca Husky = 'Konhusky'	CBcs CWGN MHol SCob SPoG WViv
Inca Ice = 'Koice' (Inca Series)	CWGN NLar SPoG WViv
Inca Joli = 'Koncajoli' PBR	LBuc WViv
Inca Lake = 'Koncalake'	CWGN EBee LBuc SCob WViv
Inca Lolly = 'Koncalolly' **new**	WViv
Inca Mambo = 'Koncamambo' PBR	WViv
Inca Milk = 'Koncamilk'	WViv
Inca Noble = 'Koncanoble' **new**	WViv
Inca Obsession = 'Koobsion'	WViv
Inca Pulse = 'Konpulse' PBR	CDoC CWGN EBee ELon GBin GKev LSou NLar SDeJ SLon SPoG WViv
Inca Serin = 'Koserin' PBR	LHop WViv
Inca Smile = 'Koncasmile'	SCob WViv
Inca Sweety = 'Koncasweet' **new**	WViv
Inca Toto = 'Koncatoto' **new**	WViv
Inca Tropic = 'Kotrop'	CExl EBee WViv
Inca Tulsa = 'Kontulsa' **new**	WViv
Inca Vito = 'Koncavito'	CBcs CWGN LAst LSou MHol NLar SCob SPoG WViv
Inca Yuko = 'Koncayuko' PBR	CBcs CBod CDoC CWGN EBee LAst LBuc LRHS LSou MHol SLon SPoG WViv
Indian Summer = 'Tesronto' PBR	CWGN EPfP LRHS SPoG WHlf WViv
Inticancha Bryce = 'Tesbryce' **new**	EBee WViv
Inticancha Creamy Dark Pink = 'Tescreda'	SDeJ WViv
Inticancha Dark Purple = 'Tesdarklin' PBR	EBee IBoy LSou SPoG WFar WViv
Inticancha Machu = 'Tesmach' PBR	WFar WViv
Inticancha Maya = 'Tesmaya' PBR	CWGN LSou WFar WViv
Inticancha Navayo = 'Tesnava' PBR	EBee SPoG WFar
Inticancha Passion = 'Tespassion' **new**	LSou
Inticancha Purple = 'Tespurplin' PBR	CWGN WFar WViv
Inticancha Red = 'Tesrobin' PBR	CWGN EBee SPoG WFar WViv
Inticancha Sunday = 'Tessunday' PBR	WViv
Inticancha Sunlight = 'Tessunlight' PBR	LSou WViv
Inticancha White Pink Blush = 'Tesblushin' PBR	WFar
Inticancha White = 'Teswhitin' PBR	WViv
Isabella = 'Stalis'	LSRN
§ ***isabellana***	WCot WCru
'Isabelle' (Midi Series)	MGos XTur
'Jacques' (Maxi Series)	XTur
'Jalesne' (Garden Series)	XTur
'Joséphine' (Midi Series) **new**	XTur
'Junon' (Planet Series) **new**	LCro
'Laguna'	WViv
Laura = 'Stalauli' PBR **new**	SCob
'Layon' (Garden Series)	XTur
'Léo' (Mini Series) **new**	XTur
ligtu hybrids	CAvo CBcs CCon ECha EPfP LCro LOPS MNrw NLar NPer SDeJ SRms SWvt WBrk WHoo XLum
- var. ***ligtu***	SMHy
'Liré' (Garden Series)	XTur
'Little Eleanor'	CCon LRHS WViv
'Little Miss Catherine' **new**	WViv
'Little Miss Christina'	see *A.* 'Christina'
'Little Miss Davina'	LRHS MBri WViv
'Little Miss Emily' **new**	WViv
'Little Miss Gina'	LRHS WViv
'Little Miss Isabel'	WViv
'Little Miss Jessica' **new**	WViv
'Little Miss Lucy'	CBod LRHS WViv
'Little Miss Matilda'	WViv
'Little Miss Miranda' **new**	WViv
'Little Miss Natalie'	see *A.* 'Natalie'
'Little Miss Rosanna'	WViv
'Little Miss Roselind'	see *A.* 'Roselind'
'Little Miss Sophie'	see *A.* 'Sophie'
'Little Miss Tara'	see *A.* 'Tara'
'Little Miss Veronica'	MBNS WViv
'Longué' (Garden Series) **new**	XTur
'Louis' (Maxi Series)	XTur
'Louise' (Midi Series)	LSRN XTur

'Lucca' **new**	WViv
'Lucinda'	CBcs CCon SWvt WViv
'Maestro'PBR	WViv
magnifica subsp. ***magnifica***	WCot
- subsp. ***maxima***	WCot
'Marcé' (Garden Series)	XTur
'Margot' (Mini Series)	XTur
'Marguerite' (Midi Series)	XTur
'Marie' (Midi Series)	XTur
'Marina'	MBNS
'Marissa'	GMaP
'Mars' (Planet Series)	LRHS
'Mathilde' (Midi Series)	NLar XTur
'Mauve Majesty'	ELon IBoy ILea LRHS MHol NLar SPoG WBrk WCot
'Mazé' (Garden Series)	LSou XTur
'Montsoreau' (Garden Series)	XTur
'Moulin Rouge'	ELan MBNS SLon WViv
§ 'Natalie'PBR	LRHS MBri WViv
'Neptune'	LOPS
'Nicolas' (Maxi Series)	XTur
'Nina' **new**	WViv
'Océane' (Mini Series)	XTur
'Orange Gem' ♀H4	MBNS
'Orange Glory' ♀H4	ELon EWoo GMaP IBoy LRHS MBNS SWvt WViv
'Orange Supreme'	CBcs LRHS WViv
'Oriana' ♀H4	EWoo SWvt WViv
'Pandora'PBR **new**	WViv
patagonica	ECho WAbe
'Pauline' (Mini Series)	XTur
pelegrina	ECho
'Perfect Blue' ♀H4	WViv
'Perfect Orange' **new**	WViv
'Philippe' (Maxi Series)	XTur
philippii	WCot
'Phoenix' (v) ♀H4	SLon SWvt WViv
'Pink Lady'	WViv
'Pink Perfection'	NLar
'Pink Sensation'	LRHS WViv
'Polka'	EWoo MBNS WViv
presliana RB 94103	WCot
Princess Amina = 'Zapriamin'PBR	EPfP LRHS WViv
Princess Angela = 'Staprilan'	ELan MBNS NLar
Princess Anouska = 'Zaprinous'PBR	ELan NLar SLon SPer WViv
Princess Ariane = 'Zapriari'PBR	WViv
Princess Camilla = 'Stapricamil'PBR	CBcs COtt EPfP LRHS SLon SPer SPoG
Princess Daniela = 'Stapridani'	SCoo SPoG
Princess Diana	see *A.* Diana, Princess of Wales = 'Stablaco', *A.* Princess Diana = 'Zapridapal'
§ Princess Diana = 'Zapridapal'PBR	EPfP WViv
Princess Eliane = 'Zaprielia'PBR	LRHS WViv
Princess Fabiana = 'Zaprifabi'PBR	COtt ELan EPfP LRHS NLar SPoG WViv
Princess Felicia = 'Zapricia'PBR	CBcs COtt ELan SPer
Princess Frederika = 'Stabronza'	ECha
Princess Isabella = 'Zapribel'PBR	COtt LRHS LSRN WViv
Princess Ivana = 'Staprivane'PBR	ELan NLar SPoG
Princess Juliana = 'Staterpa'	SPoG
Princess Julieta = 'Zaprijul'PBR	IBoy NLar SPoG WViv
Princess Kate = 'Zaprikate' **new**	EBee
Princess Letizia = 'Zaprilet'PBR	EPfP LRHS
Princess Leyla = 'Stapriley'PBR	CBcs COtt MBNS SLon SPer SPoG
Princess Lilian = 'Zaprilian'PBR	EBee LRHS WViv
Princess Louise = 'Zaprilou'PBR	EBee LRHS LSRN WViv
Princess Margaret = 'Staprimar'	NLar
Princess Marilene = 'Staprilene'PBR	COtt MBNS WViv
Princess Mary = 'Zaprimary'PBR	NLar
Princess Mathilde = 'Zaprimat'PBR	LRHS WViv
Princess Monica = 'Staprimon'PBR	MBNS SPoG
Princess Oxana = 'Staprioxa'PBR	EBee NLar
Princess Paola = 'Stapripal'PBR	LRHS MBNS SCoo WViv
Princess Sara = 'Staprisara'PBR	COtt EPfP LRHS SPoG WViv
Princess Sarah = 'Stalicamp'	MBNS
Princess Sissi = 'Staprisis'	SPoG
§ Princess Sophia = 'Stajello'	SPoG
Princess Susana = 'Staprisusa'	NLar SCoo SPoG
Princess Theresa = 'Zapriteres'PBR	COtt EPfP NLar
Princess Zavina = 'Staprivina'PBR	CBcs ELan MBNS NLar SPer
§ ***psittacina***	CAvo CBro CHll CMea CSam CTsd ECha EHrv ELan EPfP GBin GBuc GCal GCra LHop MCot MHer SGSe SHar SRms WSHC WViv XLum
- 'Mona Lisa'	CBod GBuc LSou XLum
- 'Royal Star' (v)	CAby CBod CBro CExl CWCL EAEE ELan ELon EPfP EPri GBuc LHop LRHS MAsh MAvo SGSe SHar SPoG SRms WCot WHoo WSHC WWEG XLum
pulchella Sims	see *A. psittacina*
'Purple Rain'	ELan MNrw SLon SPer SWvt WViv
'Querré' (Garden Series)	XTur
'Red Beauty' (v)	see *A.* 'Spitfire'
'Red Beauty'	CCon ELan GMaP LRHS MBNS SPer SWvt WViv
'Red Elf' ♀H4	IBoy MBNS SWvt WViv
'René' (Maxi Series)	XTur
'Rhubarb and Custard'	ELan EPfP
'Rivale' **new**	LCro
§ 'Roselind'	CCon ELan LRHS MBNS MBri SWvt WViv
'Rosie' (Mini Series)	MGos XTur
'Saturne' (Planet Series)	EPfP LCro
'Segré' (Garden Series)	XTur

'Selina' EWoo LRHS MBNS MNrw NBre WViv
'Serenade' CBcs ELan WViv
'Serrant' (Garden Series) XTur
'Sirius' (Planet Series) ♀H4 LCro LOPS
'Sonata' ♀H4 WViv
§ 'Sophie'PBR ELan LRHS MBNS SLon SWvt WViv
§ 'Spitfire' (v) ♀H4 EPfP IBoy LCro LOPS LRHS SLon SWvt WCot WViv
'Spring Delight' (v) WCot
'Strawberry Lace' EBee ELan EPfP
'Summer Breeze' new LSou NPri
'Sunstar' GMaP
'Sweet Laura'PBR CBod ECtt ELon EWoo ILea LEdu LLHF LRHS LSRN MBri MHol MPie NEgg NGdn NLar NSti SHar SMad SPoG WCot WViv
'Tangerine Tango' new WViv
'Tanya' EWoo LRHS MNrw WViv
§ 'Tara'PBR MBNS MBri NLar SWvt WViv
'Tessa' ♀H4 LRHS MBNS NBre SLon SPer WViv
'Thorigné' (Garden Series) XTur
'Tiercé' (Garden Series) XTur
'Turkish Delight' EPfP
'Ventura' LRHS WViv
'Venus' (Planet Series) LCro
'William' (Maxi Series) XTur
'Yellow Friendship' ♀H4 MBNS MNrw NLar SWvt WViv
Yellow King see *A.* Princess Sophia
'Yellow Queen' IBoy WBod
'Zoé' (Mini Series) XTur

Alternanthera (*Amaranthaceae*)

reineckii new XBlo

Althaea (*Malvaceae*)

armeniaca EBee GCal NLar WCot WOut
cannabina CAby CArn CFis CSpe ELan EPPr GCal IPot LHop LPla MHer MNrw NGBl SGSe SHar SPhx WBor WCot WHal WHil WOld WSHC
officinalis CArn CBod CHab ELan ENfk EPPr GPoy MHer MNHC NLar SIde SRms WHer WHfH WJek WOut XLum
- ***alba*** LSou NLar
§ - 'Romney Marsh' GCal MRav WKif
rosea see *Alcea rosea*
rugosostellulata see *Alcea rugosa*

Altingia (*Hamamelidaceae*)

poilanei B&SWJ 11756 WCru

× *Alworthia* (*Asphodelaceae*)

'Black Gem' EBee EPfP EShb MHer

Alyogyne (*Malvaceae*)

'Attraction' ECou
hakeifolia ECou
- 'Elle Maree' ECou
- 'Melissa Anne' ECou
§ ***huegelii*** CBod ECou EShb EUJe IDee SEle SPlb SRkn SRms WBod
- 'Lavender Lass' ECou
- 'Santa Cruz' CHll CSpe LHop MOWG WPGP
- 'White Delight' ECou
'Joy' ECou
Magic Moments = 'Hutwow'PBR CSpe CWGN LAst LCro
'Shepherds Delight' ECou

Alyssoides (*Brassicaceae*)

utriculata GEdr WHil

Alyssum (*Brassicaceae*)

argenteum ECho
bornmuelleri LLHF
caespitosum WAbe
montanum ECha ECho SPlb SRms
§ - 'Berggold' EPfP GAbr MMuc XLum
- 'Luna' WHil
- Mountain Gold see *A. montanum* 'Berggold'
oxycarpum EPot WAbe
saxatile see *Aurinia saxatilis*
- 'Summit' NPri
spinosum GKev
- 'Roseum' ♀H5 CMea CSpe CTri ECha ELan EPot GCrg MLHP NSla WAbe
tortuosum WAbe
wulfenianum EDAr GAbr IFoB WIce XLum

Amaranthus (*Amaranthaceae*)

'Autumn Palette' CSpe
caudatus 'Viridis' SPhx
hypochondriacus 'Pygmy Torch' CSpe
'Red Army' new LCro
tricolor SRms

× *Amarcrinum* (*Amaryllidaceae*)

'Dorothy Hannibal' WCot
memoria-corsii CPrp
- 'Howardii' CCon CDes EShb LEdu NRog SDeJ WCot

× *Amarine* (*Amaryllidaceae*)

'Fletcheri' WCot
tubergenii CAvo
- 'Zwanenburg' CDoC LAma WCot

× *Amarygia* (*Amaryllidaceae*)

§ ***bidwillii*** 'Alba' CAvo CBro CPrp NRog WCot
- 'Rosea' NRog

Amaryllis (*Amaryllidaceae*)

§ ***belladonna*** ♀H3 CAby CBcs CBro CPne CPrp CTal CTca CTsd EBee ECho EPfP ERCP EShb LAma NRog SDeJ SEND SPer WCot
- 'Johannesburg' WCot
- 'Kimberley' CPne
- 'Parkeri Alba' see × *Amarygia bidwillii* 'Alba'
- 'Purpurea' WCot
- white-flowered CDes SDeJ

Ambrosina (*Araceae*)

bassii WCot

Amelanchier (*Rosaceae*)

alnifolia CTho EBtc ERea
- 'Forestburg' MBlu NLar
- 'Obelisk'PBR CDoC CDul ELan EPfP GKin GQue LAst LBuc LHop LLHF LRHS LSRN MAsh MBri MCoo MGos MJak NLar NPri SCoo SPer SPoG WCot WHar WMat WPat
- pink-fruited NLar
§ - var. ***pumila*** LHop MMHG WCot
- 'Regent' (F) NLar
- var. ***semi-integrifolia*** NLar

- 'Smokey' CDul MBlu NLar
§ ***arborea*** CTho
- Tradition = 'Trazam' NLar
'Autumn Glory' EPfP NLar
bartramiana CTho SSta
- 'Eskimo' NLar
canadensis K. Koch see *A. lamarckii*
canadensis Sieb. & Zucc. see *A. arborea*
canadensis ambig. CDul CTsd IBoy NEgg NPri SCob SEND SEWo SPoG WFar WHar WMou
canadensis (L.) Medik. CAgr CDoC CJun CLnd CMac CSBt CSam CTho CTri CWSG CWib EBee ECrN ELan EPfP LEdu LRHS MGos MRav MSwo NWea SPer WMat WMoo WPat
§ - 'Glenn Form' EBee LRHS MGos SGol SLim SPoG WHar WMat
- 'Prince William' CAgr MCoo
- Rainbow Pillar see *A. canadensis* 'Glenn Form'
× ***grandiflora*** SCob
- 'Autumn Brilliance' CJun EPfP MBlu NHol NLar SGol
- 'Ballerina' Widely available
- 'Cole's Select' EMil LRHS SAko SKHP SWvt
- 'Forest Prince' NLar
- 'Princess Diana' 🏆H6 NLar SCoo
- 'Robin Hill' 🏆H6 Widely available
- 'Rubescens' CJun EBee NLar SLon SWvt WPat
'La Paloma' 🏆H6 EPfP LRHS LSRN MBri MGos NOrn SCoo SLim SPoG WHar WMat
laevis CBcs CDul CTri EPfP NLar
- 'Cumulus' NLar
- 'Prince Charles' NLar
- 'R.J. Hilton' 🏆H6 EPfP LRHS MBri NLar SCoo WHar WMat
- 'Snow Cloud' CDoC EPfP
- 'Snowflakes' CJun EWTr LRHS LSRN MAsh NLar NOrn SEWo SLim SPer SPoG SWvt WHar WMat WMou
§ ***lamarckii*** 🏆H6 Widely available
- 'Snowberry' **new** SBmr
nantucketensis SSta
ovalis misapplied see *A. spicata* (Lam.) K. Koch
ovalis Medik. SPlb
- 'Edelweiss' CJun IArd MRav NEgg NLar SCoo WPat
pumila see *A. alnifolia* var. *pumila*
rotundifolia ambig. CAgr CNWT MCoo NEgg
sanguinea 'Chimney Rock' NLar
sinica NLar
§ ***spicata*** (Lam.) K. Koch CAgr MCoo
stolonifera CTri

× *Amelasorbus* (*Rosaceae*)

raciborskiana MBlu

Amicia (*Papilionaceae*)

zygomeris CAbb CBcs CCse CHGN CHll CSpe EUJe EWes GCal LHop MCot SDix SEle WCot WPGP WPtf
- 'John's Big Splash' (v) WCot

Ammi (*Apiaceae*)

majus CArn CBod CSpe LCro LEdu LRHS MNHC SDix SPhx WCot WHfH WJek
visnaga CBre CHby CLau CSpe MNHC SPhx SRms WHal

Ammobium (*Asteraceae*)

calyceroides ECou

Ammocharis (*Amaryllidaceae*)

coranica CEvo WCot
longifolia **new** WCot

Ammophila (*Poaceae*)

arenaria CKno IMou SMea XLum
breviligulata IMou XLum

Amomyrtus (*Myrtaceae*)

§ ***luma*** CBcs CDoC CDul CTri CTsd EBee ELan GGal IDee WJek

Amorpha (*Papilionaceae*)

canescens EBee EWTr LRHS MNrw SPhx SPlb
fruticosa CBcs EBtc MBlu SEND SPlb
herbacea NLar
nana XLum
paniculata NLar

Amorphophallus ✿ (*Araceae*)

albus CDTJ LEdu SPlb WCot
bulbifer CDTJ ESwi LAma LRHS LTro SBig SDeJ SPlb XLum
dunnii CDTJ LEdu
henryi WCot
kerrii CExl WCot
kiusianus B&SWJ 4845 WCru
konjac CDTJ CDes CExl CFil CSpe CTal EUJe LEdu SChF SPlb WPGP XLum
nepalensis WCot
ongsakulii WCot
rivieri GCal LEdu LRHS SDeJ WCot
stipitatus LEdu WCot
yuloensis WCot

Ampelocalamus (*Poaceae*)

§ ***mocrophyllum*** ERod WJun
scandens WPGP

Ampelocissus (*Vitaceae*)

sikkimensis HWJK 2066 WCru

Ampelodesmos (*Poaceae*)

mauritanicus CHid CKno CSam EBee ECha EHoe EShb EWes IDee LPla MAvo SEND SMad SPlb WCot XLum XSen

Ampelopsis (*Vitaceae*)

aconitifolia NLar WCru
- 'Chinese Lace' EBee EShb EUJe EWTr LRHS MRav NLar
arborea WCru
brevipedunculata ELan MMHG SCoo SKHP SLim SPer WHar
- 'Citrulloides' WCru
- 'Elegans' (v) CBcs CMac CWib EBee ELan EPfP EShb LAst LHop LRHS MGos MMuc MRav NBro SPer SPoG SWvt WCot WPat WSHC
delavayana EShb MMuc
glandulosa var. ***hancei*** B&SWJ 1793 **new** WCru
henryana see *Parthenocissus henryana*
megalophylla CBot ELan EShb GCal NLar SKHP
sempervirens see *Cissus striata*

tricuspidata 'Veitchii' — see *Parthenocissus tricuspidata* 'Veitchii'

Amphicome see *Incarvillea*

Amsonia (*Apocynaceae*)

'Blue Ice' — CAby EBee IPot LSun MHol MNrw NDov SPad SPoG WCot WRHF
ciliata — ELan GKev IKil LEdu NLar SHar SKHP XLum
- 'Spring Sky' — EBee
§ ***elliptica*** — EBee SPhx
'Ernst Pagels' — LHop MAvo SMHy
fugatei new — EBee
hubrichtii — CAby CCon CCse CHid CLet CSpe EBee ECha EPPr IPot LEdu LHop LPla LRHS LSun MNHC NDov SMad SPhx SWvt WPGP WPtf WSHC WWEG
illustris — CAbP EPPr GCal LEdu LPla LRHS NLar SHar SMHy SPhx WHil WHoo WWEG
jonesii — EBee SBrt SMHy SPhx
§ ***orientalis*** — CHll CMea CSpe CTri ECha EHrv IPot LEdu LHop LRHS MCot MLHP MRav NCGa NDov NLar SPhx SVen SWvt WBor WCot WFar XEll
- 'Cally Dark Stem' — GCal
peeblesii — EBee SPhx
rigida new — GEdr
sinensis — see *A. elliptica*
tabernaemontana — Widely available
- 'Montana' — SPer SWvt
- var. ***salicifolia*** — CAby EBee IMou IPot LCro LEdu LRHS WCAu
- 'Stella Azul' — IPot
tharpii new — EBee SPhx
tomentosa var. ***stenophylla*** — EBee SPhx

Amygdalus see *Prunus*

Amyris (*Rutaceae*)

madrensis — CFil

Anacampseros (*Portulacaceae*)

namaquensis new — LToo

Anacamptis (*Orchidaceae*)

§ ***laxiflora*** — NLAp
§ ***morio*** — NLAp
papilionacea — NLAp
pyramidalis — EFEx NLAp WHer

Anacyclus (*Asteraceae*)

pyrethrum — GPoy
- var. ***depressus*** 🏆^{H4} — CTri ECho ELan EPfP GMaP MAsh MHol MMuc NEgg SEND SPlb SRot WCFE XLum
- - 'Garden Gnome' — CTri ECho SRms
- - 'Silberkissen' — CMea EDAr NSla

Anagallis (*Primulaceae*)

monellii Blue Compact ='Wesanacomp' — LSou
- subsp. ***linifolia*** 'Blue Light' — CSpe
- 'Skylover' — LAst
tenella — LLWG MWts
- 'Studland' — MHer WAbe

Ananas (*Bromeliaceae*)

comosus (F) — SPre
- 'Champaca' (F) — SPre

Anaphalioides (*Asteraceae*)

§ ***bellidioides*** — CTri SBrt

Anaphalis (*Asteraceae*)

alpicola — EBee EPot
margaritacea — CBcs ECha ECtt GMaP NBid NLar SRms WBod WFar WHar WMoo
§ - 'Neuschnee' — CTri GJos ILea NBre NLar WWEG XLum
- New Snow — see *A. margaritacea* 'Neuschnee'
- var. ***yedoensis*** — CTri MLHP NBre SDix SPer
§ ***nepalensis*** var. ***monocephala*** — EBee NBre NSti SRms
nubigena — see *A. nepalensis* var. *monocephala*
transnokoensis — EBee EWes
§ ***trinervis*** — CExl GCra LSun XLum
triplinervis 🏆^{H7} — EHoe ELan ELon EPfP EWTr EWld EWoo GAbr GMaP IBoy IFoB ILea LPal LRHS MLHP MMuc MRav NBid NLar NPri NSti SPer WBod WCAu WFar WHoo WMoo WWEG
- CC 1620 — EPPr NBir
§ - 'Sommerschnee' 🏆^{H7} — CMac EAJP ECha ECtt EHoe EPfP IBoy LPot LRHS MCot MHol MRav NEgg NLar NWad SEND SPer WMnd WPtf WWtn
- Summer Snow — see *A. triplinervis* 'Sommerschnee'

Anchusa (*Boraginaceae*)

sp. — CHab
§ ***azurea*** — NLar
- 'Dropmore' — CTri EBee EPfP EWTr LRHS MRav NBFr NEgg NLar SCob SPoG SRms WHar
- 'Feltham Pride' — EBee ELan EPfP SRms SWvt WHoo
- 'Little John' — SRms
- 'Loddon Royalist' — Widely available
- 'Opal' — CWCL ECtt LRHS MAsh MBel WTor
capensis 'Blue Angel' — CWCL MNHC SWvt
cespitosa Lam. — ECho ELan EWes LLHF WAbe
italica — see *A. azurea*
laxiflora — see *Borago pygmaea*
myosotidiflora — see *Brunnera macrophylla*
officinalis — MNHC SRms
sempervirens — see *Pentaglottis sempervirens*

Ancylostemon (*Gesneriaceae*)

convexus B&SWJ 6624 — WCot WCru
- B&SWJ 7182 — WCru

Andrachne (*Phyllanthaceae*)

colchica — EWTr WCot

Andromeda (*Ericaceae*)

glaucophylla f. ***latifolia*** — IVic
polifolia — ECho LPar WFar
- 'Alba' — ECho ELan LRHS MAsh SPer SPlb SWvt WFar
- 'Blue Ice' — ELan IDee LRHS LSRN MAsh NHar NLar SPer SPoG SSpi WFar
- 'Blue Lagoon' — LRHS NLar SRms
- 'Compacta' 🏆^{H5} — CDoC CMac ECho GEdr LSRN MAsh MGil MGos NLar NWad SRms SWvt WFar WGwG WHlf
- 'Compacta Alba' 🏆^{H5} — ECho

	- 'Grandiflora'	ECho ELan GKev
	- 'Kirigamine'	LRHS MAsh NHar
	- 'Macrophylla' ♀H5	ECho GEdr NHar WThu
	- 'Nana'	EPfP LRHS
	- 'Nikko'	CMac
	- 'Shibutsu'	NHar

Andropogon (*Poaceae*)

	gerardii	CKno EBee EHoe EPPr LRHS NWsh SGSe XLum
	scoparius	see *Schizachyrium scoparium*

Androsace (*Primulaceae*)

	adenocephala	WAbe
	alashanica	WAbe
	alpina	WAbe
*	***bayanharshanensis***	WAbe
	bisulca var. ***aurata***	CPBP EPot GKev
	brachystegia	EPot GKev
	bulleyana	WAbe
	cantabrica	EPot
	carnea	ECho GKev IFoB
	- SDR 6357	GKev
	- subsp. ***brigantiaca***	GKev NSla WAbe WHoo
	- var. ***halleri***	see *A. carnea* subsp. *rosea*
	- subsp. ***laggeri*** ♀H5	ECho GKev LLHF NSla WAbe
	- - 'Andorra'	NHar
§	- subsp. ***rosea*** ♀H5	ECho GKev IFoB ITim NHar
	carnea × ***pyrenaica***	CPBP ECho EPot GKev LLHF
	chaixii	IFoB
	chamaejasme	ECho
	- subsp. ***carinata***	LLHF
	ciliata	WAbe
	cylindrica	ECho EPot GKev ITim LRHS WAbe
	cylindrica × ***hirtella***	ECho EPot LRHS WAbe
	delavayi	WAbe
	- ACE 1786	WAbe
	elatior	WAbe
	flavescens	CPBP WAbe
	geraniifolia	ECha SRms WAbe
	globifera	WAbe
	halleri	see *A. carnea* subsp. *rosea*
	hausmannii × ***hirtella*** new	LLHF
	hedraeantha	EPot WAbe
	himalaica	CPBP EPot GEdr GKev WAbe
	hirtella	IFoB ITim LLHF WAbe
	idahoensis	WAbe
	idahoensis × ***laevigata***	WAbe
	jacquemontii	see *A. villosa* var. *jacquemontii*
	kosopoljanskii	CPBP GKev
	lactea	GKev WAbe
	laevigata	ITim WAbe
	- 'Gothenburg'	WAbe
	- 'Saddle Mount'	WAbe
	lanuginosa ♀H5	CBod CMea CSpe CTal ECho ECtt EDAr EHoe EPot GBin GEdr MMuc MWat NHol SBch SRms SRot WAbe WIce WOld
	- 'Wisley Variety'	SIgm
	lehmanniana	GKev WAbe
	- 'Gotëborg Yellow'	WAbe
	limprichtii	see *A. sarmentosa* var. *watkinsii*
	mariae	GKev WAbe
	- white-flowered new	GKev
	× ***marpensis***	EPot WAbe WHal
	mathildae	GKev
	microphylla	see *A. mucronifolia* G.Watt
	'Millstream'	IFoB
	minor	WAbe
§	***mollis***	CPBP
	montana	WAbe
	mucronifolia misapplied	see *A. sempervivoides*
§	***mucronifolia*** G.Watt	EPot GKev
	mucronifolia G.Watt × ***sempervivoides***	CTal SIgm WAbe
	muscoidea	WAbe
	- SEP 132	CPBP
	- 'Breviscapa'	EPot
	- 'Dolpo Lilac'	WAbe
	- Schacht's form	EPot WAbe
	nivalis Chumstick form	GKev LLHF
	obtusifolia new	GKev
	ochotensis	WAbe
	× ***pedemontana***	GKev LLHF
	primuloides	see *A. studiosorum*
	pubescens	ECho EPot ITim LLHF LRHS
	pyrenaica	ECho EPot GKev ITim LLHF LRHS WAbe
	rigida	EPot LLHF WAbe
	- SDR 7865 new	GKev
	- SDR 7898 new	GKev
	robusta	EPot
	- subsp. ***purpurea***	WAbe
	- - 'Dolpo Dwarf'	WAbe
	rotundifolia	GEdr
	sarmentosa misapplied	see *A. studiosorum*
	sarmentosa ambig.	XLum
	sarmentosa Wall.	GKev SRms WHoo
	- CC 5557	GKev
	- from Namche, Nepal	WAbe
	- Galmont's form	see *A. studiosorum* 'Salmon's Variety'
	- 'Sherriffii'	ECho EPot SIgm SRms WIce
§	- var. ***watkinsii***	CTal EPot GKev
	- var. ***yunnanensis*** misapplied	see *A. studiosorum*
	- var. ***yunnanensis*** Knuth	see *A. mollis*
	selago	GKev WAbe
	- 'Red Eye'	WAbe
§	***sempervivoides*** ♀H5	ECho EDAr EPot GBin GCrg GJos GKev GMaP LHop LRHS NHar NHol NSla SBch SIgm SPlb SRms WIce WOld
	- 'Susan Joan'	EPot GEdr GKev WAbe WOld
	septentrionalis 'Stardust'	MHol
	spinulifera	GKev LLHF
	stenophylla	GKev MAsh
	strigillosa	GKev WAbe
§	***studiosorum*** ♀H5	CPBP EPot GAbr GCrg GEdr GKev IFoB WAbe
	- 'Chumbyi'	EPot GEdr LLHF SHar SIgm SRms WIce WThu
	- 'Doksa'	CPBP CTal EPot GEdr IFoB SHar WAbe WIce
§	- 'Salmon's Variety'	CMea CTri SBch SIgm WAbe
	tangulashanensis	LLHF WAbe
	tapete	WAbe
	- ACE 1725	WAbe
	vandellii	WAbe
	villosa	EPot IFoB NSla WAbe
§	- var. ***jacquemontii***	CPBP CTal NHar
	- - lilac-flowered	EPot WAbe
	- - pink-flowered	EPot WAbe
	- subsp. ***taurica***	WAbe
	vitaliana	see *Vitaliana primuliflora*
	wardii	WAbe
	watkinsii	see *A. sarmentosa* var. *watkinsii*
	yargongensis	LLHF WAbe
	zambalensis	WAbe

Andryala (Asteraceae)

agardhii	GKev
lanata	see *Hieracium lanatum*

Anemanthele (Poaceae)

§ **lessoniana** ♀H4	Widely available
- 'Autumn Tints'	EHoe
- 'Gold Hue'	EHoe
- 'Sirocco'	CBod WCot

Anemarrhena (Asparagaceae)

asphodeloides	CArn WCot

Anemia (Schizaeaceae)

mexicana new	ISha
tomentosa	ISha LRHS

Anemone ✿ (Ranunculaceae)

Chen Yi T49	WCot
aconitifolia Michx.	see *A. narcissiflora*
altaica	NLar SRms
amurensis	CExl
apennina ♀H4	CAvo ECGP ECho GEdr WShi
- var. **albiflora**	ECho EPPr EPot MAvo
- double-flowered (d)	ECho EPPr MAvo WCru
- 'Petrovac'	ECho EPot LEdu LLHF WCot
baicalensis	WOut
baldensis	ECho GBuc GEdr GKev ITim SRms
barbulata	CExl EAJP EBee EWes GBuc GEdr GKev NLar
biflora	ECho
- var. **petiolulosa**	GKev
blanda ♀H4	ECho LAma LPfy LRHS MAsh MBri MLHP MNHC MWat NChi NLar SCob SEND WBor WFar WHar WOut WShi
I - 'Alba'	LRHS NChi WBod
- blue-flowered	CAvo CBro CHVG CMea CSam CTri ECho ELan EPfP EPot ERCP GAbr GKev GMaP LCro LEdu LOPS LRHS MBri SCob SDeJ SPer SPhx SPoG SRms WCot WHoo
- 'Charmer'	CGrW EPot GKev SDeJ
- 'Ingramii'	EPot WCot
- var. **rosea**	ECho ELan GKev LAma LRHS SDeJ SPer SPoG
- - 'Pink Star'	CAvo ERCP GKev LAma NBir WRHF
- - 'Radar' ♀H4	CAvo ECho EPot ERCP LAma MNrw NBir SDeJ
- 'Violet Star'	GKev SDeJ
- 'White Splendour' ♀H4	CAvo CBro CHVG CMea CSam CTri ECho ELan EPfP EPot ERCP GAbr GKev IFro LAma LCro LOPS LRHS NBir SDeJ SPer SPhx SPoG SRms WCot WWFP
- white-flowered	LRHS
'Bowles's Mauve'	GEdr
caerulea	LEdu
canadensis	CSpe ECGP ELon EPPr GBuc GEdr LEdu NLar NWad WCot
caroliniana	ECho GKev
chapaensis HWJ 631	WCru
'Cinderella' (Fantasy Series) new	LRHS
coronaria	SCob SVic
- De Caen Group	CHid EPfP GKev LAma LOPS LPfy LRHS SCob SPoG WBod WBor
- - 'Bicolor'	CHid GKev LAma SDeJ
- - blue-flowered	LRHS
- - 'Bordeaux' new	EPfP LCro LOPS SCob
§ - - 'Die Braut'	ERCP GKev LAma LCro NBir SDeJ
- - 'His Excellency'	see *A. coronaria* (De Caen Group) 'Hollandia'
§ - - 'Hollandia'	GKev LAma LPot SDeJ
- - 'Mister Fokker'	CTca ERCP GKev LAma LCro LPot SBod SDeJ WRHF
- - pink-flowered	LRHS
- - red-flowered	LRHS
- - The Bride	see *A. coronaria* (De Caen Group) 'Die Braut'
- - 'The Governor'	CMea CTca GKev SDeJ
- (Harmony Series) 'Harmony Orchid'	LRHS
- - 'Harmony Pearl'	LRHS
- - 'Harmony Scarlet'	LRHS
- Saint Bridgid Group (d)	EPfP GKev LAma LRHS
- - 'Lord Lieutenant' (d)	CMea EPfP ERCP GKev NBir SBod SDeJ
- - 'Mount Everest' (d)	ERCP GKev NBir SBod SDeJ
- - 'Saint Bridgid' (d)	CHid
- - 'The Admiral' (d)	EPfP GKev NBir SDeJ
- 'Sylphide' (Mona Lisa Series)	ERCP GKev LAma LPot NBir SDeJ
crinita	NLar
cylindrica	MHer NLar XEll
'Danish White'	MNrw
decapetala	GBuc LLHF MHer
deltoidea	GBuc
demissa	GKev LLHF WCot
- SDR 4306	GKev
- SDR 7842 new	GKev
- var. **major**	EBee
'Dreaming Swan' new	SHar
drummondii	GBuc GKev
eranthioides	EBee
'Fantasy' new	GBin
fasciculata	see *A. narcissiflora*
flaccida	CAby CBro CLAP ECho EPPr GBin GEdr LEdu LRHS MAvo MMHG MNrw WCru WHal WSHC
globosa	see *A. multifida* Poir.
'Guernica'	ECho EWes
'Hatakeyama Double' (d)	GCal WSHC
'Hatakeyama Single'	CDes
hepatica L.	see *Hepatica nobilis*
§ **hortensis**	EBee
§ **hupehensis**	CExl EBee GMaP LSun
- BWJ 8190	WCru
- NJM 11.068 new	WPGP
- f. **alba**	CExl CLAP CSpe IFro WPGP
§ - 'Bowles's Pink' ♀H7	CElw CExl WPGP
- 'Crispa'	see *A.* × *hybrida* 'Lady Gilmour' Wolley-Dod
- 'Eugenie'	ECtt EPfP GBuc LRHS NBir
- 'Hadspen Abundance' ♀H7	Widely available
- var. **hupehensis**	WFar
§ - var. **japonica**	CPou SRms XLum
- - B&SWJ 4886	WCru
- - PAB 8884	LEdu
- - 'Bodnant Burgundy'	CDes LRHS SWvt WBod WBrk WPGP
§ - - 'Bressingham Glow'	CExl CMHG CMac ECtt ELan EPfP EPot EShb GKin ILea LRHS LSou NBir NEgg SPer WBrk WCAu WFar
§ - - 'Pamina' ♀H7	Widely available
- - 'Pink Saucer'	EBee

	Name	Suppliers
	- - Prince Henry	see *A. hupehensis* var. *japonica* 'Prinz Heinrich'
§	- - 'Prinz Heinrich'	Widely available
§	- - 'Rotkäppchen'	CBct CHVG ECtt GBin GKin GQue IVic LRHS LSou MCot MHol MSCN NGdn NHol NLar NSti SPad SWvt WCot WSHC
	- - 'Splendens'	CMHG EPfP LHop LRHS MBri MCot NGdn NLar SCob SHil SPer SPoG SRms SWvt WHal XLum
	- 'Little Princess'PBR	ECtt MNrw
	- 'Ouvertüre'	ECtt GBuc GQue WPGP
	- 'Praecox'	CMea CNec EPfP LPfy LRHS LSou MBNS NBir NSti SHil SWvt WCAu WHil WMnd
	- 'September Charm'	see *A.* × *hybrida* 'September Charm'
	- 'Superba'	GBin
§	× ***hybrida***	ECho NChi NEgg WHar WMoo
	- 'Alba' misapplied (UK)	see *A.* × *hybrida* 'Honorine Jobert'
	- 'Alba Dura'	see *A. tomentosa* 'Albadura'
	- 'Albert Schweitzer'	see *A.* × *hybrida* 'Elegans'
	- 'Andrea Atkinson'	Widely available
	- 'Bowles's Pink'	see *A. hupehensis* 'Bowles's Pink'
	- 'Bressingham Glow'	see *A. hupehensis* var. *japonica* 'Bressingham Glow'
	- 'Coupe d'Argent'	EBee EWTr IKil
§	- 'Elegans' 🏆H7	ECtt GMaP LHop LOPS LRHS MMuc NBir SEND SWat SWvt WFar
§	- 'Honorine Jobert' 🏆H7	Widely available
	- 'Josephine'	WFar
§	- 'Königin Charlotte' 🏆H7	Widely available
	- 'Lady Gilmour' misapplied	see *A.* × *hybrida* 'Montrose'
	- 'Lady Gilmour' ambig.	GMaP MBel WBod WHoo XLum
§	- 'Lady Gilmour' Wolley-Dod	CSam CSpe ECtt EPfP GCra LEdu LRHS MRav NBir NChi WCot WCru WPGP XLum
	- 'Loreley'	EPfP NLar SCob SWvt WWEG
	- 'Luise Uhink'	CPou
	- 'Märchenfee'	EBee MNrw
	- 'Margarete' Kayser & Seibert	CExl CPar ECtt ELan EPfP LRHS MBri NGdn WCot WCru
	- 'Max Vogel'	see *A.* × *hybrida* 'Elegans'
	- 'Monterosa'	see *A.* × *hybrida* 'Montrose'
§	- 'Montrose'	CPou EBee ECha EHrv EWes GCal GMaP LOPS LRHS LSou MBri NBir NLar SRms SWat
	- 'Nightingale' (Fantasy Series) **new**	EBee
	- 'Pamina'	see *A. hupehensis* var. *japonica* 'Pamina'
	- (Pretty Lady Series) 'Pretty Lady Diana'PBR	LBuc LRHS MBri NPri SCob SLon SWvt
	- - 'Pretty Lady Emily'PBR	LBuc LRHS MBri NPri SCob SLon SWvt
	- - 'Pretty Lady Julia'PBR	LBuc LRHS NPri SCob SHar SLon
	- - 'Pretty Lady Maria' **new**	EBee LRHS
	- - 'Pretty Lady Susan'	CWGN EBee LBuc LRHS MBri NPri SCob SHar SLon SWvt
	- Prince Henry	see *A. hupehensis* var. *japonica* 'Prinz Heinrich'
	- 'Profusion'	CTri EBee LBuc LRHS WHal
	- Queen Charlotte	see *A.* × *hybrida* 'Königin Charlotte'
	- 'Richard Ahrens'	CBod ECtt EPfP EShb EWoo GBuc GCal GMaP LAst LHop LRHS LSRN MGos MLHP MSCN NEgg NGdn NLar SWat SWvt WCru WMnd WWEG
§	- 'Robustissima'	CBod COtt EBee EPfP GMaP ILea LLWP LRHS LSRN MCot MNrw NBir NEgg NGdn NLar NSti SEND SPer SWat SWvt WMnd WMoo WWEG
	- 'Rosenschale'	LRHS MNrw WCru
	- 'Rotkäppchen'	see *A. hupehensis* var. *japonica* 'Rotkäppchen'
§	- 'September Charm' 🏆H7	Widely available
	- 'Serenade'	CSam ECtt EPfP GBBs LHop LPfy LRHS LSRN MBri MRav MTis NBir NLar SPoG SRkn WCAu WMoo XLum
	- Tourbillon	see *A.* × *hybrida* 'Whirlwind'
§	- 'Whirlwind'	Widely available
	- Wirbelwind	see *A.* × *hybrida* 'Whirlwind'
	japonica	see *A.* × *hybrida*, *A. hupehensis*, *A. hupehensis* var. *japonica*
	- 'Crustata'	CMac
	keiskeana	GEdr WCru
§	× ***lesseri***	CBro CSpe ECha ECho ELan GKev LHop SPhx SRms
	leveillei	CAby CElw CLAP CSpe CWCL EHrv EPPr EWTr GBuc GEdr GKev IPot LCro LOPS LPla LRHS LSou MSCN NBir NGdn NLar NQui NSti SPhx SWvt WAbe WCru WKif
	- BWJ 7919	WCru
§	× ***lipsiensis***	CAvo CBro CDes EBee ECho EPPr EPfP EPot GAbr GBBs GBin GMaP IFro LEdu MAvo MNrw NLar SBch WCru WFar WHal WPGP WSHC
	- 'Pallida' 🏆H5	CSam CSpe ECho ELon GBuc GEdr GKev LEdu LLWP MAvo NHar NLar SKHP WCot WShi XEll
	- 'Schwefelfeuer'	LEdu MAvo
	- 'Vindobonensis'	GEdr MAvo WCot
	magellanica hort. ex Wehrh.	see *A. multifida* Poir.
	matsudae B&SWJ 1452	WCru
	multifida misapplied, red-flowered	see *A.* × *lesseri*
§	***multifida*** Poir.	CEvo ECha ECho EPfP GJos ILea LHop LRHS NBir NSti SRms WFar WHoo
	- Annabella Series	GKev
	- - 'Annabella Deep Rose'	GAbr
	- - 'Annabella White'	GJos
	- var. ***globosa***	GKev
	- 'Major'	CMea CSpe EPfP SPhx WIce
	- 'Rubra'	EPfP GBin GEdr GKev LPot LRHS LSou MPie NBir NEgg NLar WBor WHar WHoo
	- yellow-flowered	CBro GEdr NSum
§	***narcissiflora***	CSpe GKev NBir NChi WPtf
	nemorosa 🏆H5	Widely available
	- 'Alba'	WFar
	- 'Alba Plena' (d)	CSam EAJP ECha ECho EPPr EPfP GBuc MAvo NGdn NLar WFar WSHC
	- 'Allenii' 🏆H5	CBro CElw ECho ELon EPPr EPot GBin GBuc GMaP ITim LRHS MAvo MRav NRya WShi
	- 'Amy Doncaster'	ECho
	- 'Apuseni' **new**	LEdu
	- 'Atley'	EBee GEdr MAvo
	- 'Atrocaerulea'	GBuc IBlr NLar
	- 'Ballyrogan Blue'	MAvo MNrw
	- 'Behemoth Blue'	MAvo
	- 'Bill Baker's Pink'	CDes CLAP LEdu WPGP
	- 'Blue Beauty'	CLAP EBee ELon GBuc GMaP IBlr MAvo NSla SBch

- 'Blue Bonnet'	ECho GBuc ITim LEdu MAvo
- 'Blue Eyes' (d)	CElw CLAP EBee GAbr GBuc GEdr GKev GMaP IBlr ITim LEdu MAvo NBir NSla WCot WHlf WSHC
- 'Blush'	LEdu
- 'Bohemia' **new**	MAvo
- 'Bowles's Purple'	CSam EBee ECho ELon EPot GBBs GBuc GEdr GMaP IBlr LRHS MAvo MHol MNrw NBid NHar NRya SBch SKHP WBor WCot WFar
- 'Bracteata'	CBro ECho EWld GBuc GEdr MMHG
- 'Bracteata Pleniflora' (d)	CCon CLAP ECho ELon EPot GBuc GKev GMaP IBlr LHop MAvo MNrw NBir SBch WCot WHal WShi XEll
- 'Buckland'	CLAP EBee EPfP EPot IBlr MAvo SKHP
- 'Caerulea'	EPot ITim
- 'Cedric's Pink'	CLAP EPPr IBlr LLHF MAvo MNrw WFar
- 'Celestial'	EBee ECho ELan EPPr GBuc MAvo
- 'Dee Day'	CLAP EBee GBuc LEdu MAvo NHar
- 'Dell Garden'	EPPr
- 'Evelyn Meadows' ♀H5	CLAP
- 'Flore Pleno' (d)	CDes ECho GAbr IFro MAvo NBir WBor WFar
- 'Flushing' **new**	EBee
- 'Frühlingsfee'	GKev MAvo
- 'Frühlingsfest' **new**	EBee
- 'Gerda Ramusen'	CDes CLAP ECho ELan ELon EWes GBuc LEdu LLHF
I - 'Gigantea Rubra'	WCot
- 'Good Blue'	MAvo
- 'Green Dream'	MAvo WSHC
- 'Green Fingers'	ECho EPPr GBuc GKev GMaP ITim MMHG WCot WSHC
- 'Hakumane Senjuizaki'	MAvo WCot
- 'Hannah Gubbay'	CLAP IBlr MAvo
- 'Hilda'	CBct EBee ECho GBuc GEdr LEdu MAvo MNrw NBir NHar NRya
- 'Ice and Fire'	LEdu
- 'Jack Brownless'	LEdu
- 'Kentish Pink'	GBBs GBin GMaP
- 'Knightshayes Vestal' (d)	CExl CLAP MRav
- 'Kyffhäuser Rote'	WCot
- 'Lady Doneraile'	CLAP EPot GBuc NBir WFar
- 'Latvian Pink'	ECho EPot GEdr LEdu MAvo
- 'Leeds' Variety'	CLAP EPot GBin GBuc GMaP ITim LEdu MAvo MNrw NSla
- 'Lionel Bacon'	LEdu MAvo
- 'Lismore Blue'	ECho EPPr EPot
- 'Lismore Pink'	LEdu
- 'Lucia'	EPot GEdr LEdu MAvo
- 'Lychette'	ECho EPPr GAbr GBuc GEdr GKev IBlr ITim MAvo MNrw
- 'March Blue'	EPfP
- 'Marie Rose'	EPot
- 'Mart's Blue'	EBee EPfP GBuc MAvo WCot
- 'Miss Eunice'	CLAP
- 'Monstrosa'	ECho EPot GBuc MAvo WHlf
- 'New Pink'	IBlr MAvo
- 'Noémie'	XEll
- 'Parlez Vous'	CExl ECho EPPr GEdr LEdu MAvo MNrw WPnP XEll
- 'Pat's Pink'	WShi
- 'Pentre Pink'	EPot IBlr MAvo
- 'Picos Pink'	GBuc
- 'Pink Carpet'	GEdr LEdu
- pink-flowered	ECho MMuc
- 'Ploeger's Plena' (d)	EBee MAvo
- 'Robinsoniana' ♀H6	Widely available
- 'Rosea'	CLAP ECho LEdu NLar
- 'Royal Blue'	CBct CBro CLAP EBee ECho ELon EPPr EPot ERCP GAbr GBin GEdr GKev GMaP LAma LEdu MAvo NDov NLar WCot WPnP
- 'Salt and Pepper'	LEdu MAvo
- 'Slack Top Pink'	MAvo
- 'Stammheim' (d)	CLAP EPPr MAvo
- 'Super Allenii'	GBuc
- 'Tilo'	MAvo
- 'Tinney's Blush'	CLAP
- 'Tomas'	CLAP EBee ECho ELon EPot GBuc GEdr LEdu MAvo NHar NRya
- 'Vestal' (d) ♀H5	Widely available
- 'Virescens' ♀H5	CBct CLAP CWCL ECho ELon EPPr EPot GBuc GEdr GKev GMaP LEdu MAvo NBir NHar WPtf WShi
- 'Viridiflora'	CExl CLAP ECho EPfP GBuc LHop MNrw NBir NSti WSHC
- 'Westwell Pink'	CLAP ECho EPPr LLHF MAvo MNrw WBor WCot WShi
- white-flowered	LRHS
- 'Wilks' Giant'	MAvo
- 'Wilks' White'	ELon EPPr GEdr
- 'Wisley Pink'	LEdu MAvo
I - 'Wisley White' **new**	MAvo
- 'Wyatt's Pink'	CLAP ELon EPot LEdu MAvo
- 'Yerda Ramusem'	ECho EPPr GBuc LEdu MAvo WSHC
nemorosa* × *ranunculoides	see *A.* × *lipsiensis*
obtusiloba	GBuc GEdr LLHF NSla SRms WAbe
- CLD 1549	GEdr
- 'Alba'	GEdr WAbe
- blue-flowered	WAbe
- 'Large Blue'	GEdr WAbe
- 'Pradesh'	GEdr
I - 'Sulphurea'	GEdr WAbe
- yellow-flowered	WAbe
palmata	EWes GEdr LEdu SBea SGSe SMad WCot WTor
parviflora	GKev XEll
patens	see *Pulsatilla patens*
pavonina	CAby CMea CSpe ECha EUJe IBoy LRHS MHol NBir SLon SPoG WCot
- lilac-flowered	NBir
- pink-flowered	NBir
'Pocohontas' (Fantasy Series) **new**	ECtt LRHS MNrw
polyanthes	EBee GEdr LRHS
prattii	CExl CLAP EPPr GEdr LEdu
pseudoaltaica	GEdr LEdu WCru
- blue-flowered	GEdr
- 'Yuki-no-sei' (d)	GEdr
pulsatilla	see *Pulsatilla vulgaris*
quinquefolia	WCot
raddeana	ECho
* - f. ***rosea***	GEdr
ranunculoides ♀H5	Widely available
- 'Bill Baker'	LEdu
- 'Frank Waley'	WCot
- 'Fuchsis Traum'	WCot
* - ***laciniata***	CLAP GBuc MAvo WCot
- 'Pleniflora' (d) ♀H5	CLAP ECha ECho EPPr GBBs GBuc GKev LRHS MAvo NLar WFar
- subsp. ***ranunculoides***	ECho GKev
- 'Semi-Plena'	ECho GEdr LEdu
- subsp. ***wockeana***	CDes CSam EBee ECho GBuc LEdu MAvo
reflexa	EBee GKev LLHF

riparia	see *A. virginiana* var. *alba*
rivularis	Widely available
- BWJ 7611	WCru
- CC 4588	CExl
- PAB 2477	LEdu
- SDR 4229	GKev
- SDR 7806 **new**	GKev
- 'Glacier'	EBee MAsh MAvo NLar NSti
'Ruffled Swan' **new**	SHar
rupicola	NBir
× ***seemannii***	see *A.* × *lipsiensis*
stellata Lam.	see *A. hortensis*
stolonifera double-flowered (d)	GEdr LPla WCot WSHC
sulphurea misapplied	see *Pulsatilla alpina* subsp. *apiifolia*
sumatrana B&SWJ 11265	WCru
sylvestris	Widely available
- 'Elise Fellmann' (d)	CSpe EBee GBin GBuc WHal WHil
- 'Macrantha'	EPfP WCot
tetrasepala	WCot
§ ***tomentosa***	LRHS SDix SRms SWat
§ - 'Albadura'	EBee
- 'Robustissima'	see *A.* × *hybrida* 'Robustissima'
trifolia L.	EBee EPPr GBuc LEdu NBid NLar SRms WCot WFar
- pink-flowered	WFar
trullifolia	EBee GBee GBin GBuc GCal GCra LLHF WAbe
- 'Alba'	WSHC
- var. ***coelestina***	WAbe
- var. ***linearis***	WAbe
udensis	GEdr
vernalis	see *Pulsatilla vernalis*
virginiana	EBee GCal LEdu LPla MNrw NBid NWad WHrl WWEG
§ - var. ***alba***	NLar
vitifolia misapplied	see *A. tomentosa*
Wild Swan = 'Macane001'^PBR	Widely available

Anemonella (*Ranunculaceae*)

thalictroides	CCon CElw CEvo CLAP ECho EFEx ELon EPot GAbr GBuc GEdr GKev ITim LAma MAvo NHar NLar NRya WAbe WFar WSHC XLum
- 'Alba Plena' (d)	ECho GBuc
- 'Amelia'	CLAP EPPr GBuc GEdr
- 'Babe'	WCot
- 'Betty Blake' (d)	ECho EPot GEdr GKev MMHG NRya WCot
- 'Cameo'	ECho EFEx EPPr EPot GEdr GKev MAvo NHar NRya WCot
- 'Charlotte'	GEdr
- 'Dark Pink'	CWCL EBee
- 'Diamante'	CElw WCot
- 'Double Green' (d)	EFEx
- 'Flore Pleno' (d)	GBuc
- 'Full Double White' (d)	ECho EFEx GKev
- 'Green Hurricane' (d)	ECho EFEx GEdr GKev WCot
- 'Jade Feather'	EPot
- large white-flowered	CDes
- f. ***rosea***	CAby CElw ECho ELan GBuc GKev LLHF NLar WAbe
- - 'Oscar Schoaf' (d)	ECho GBuc GEdr GKev WAbe WCot
- - semi-double pink-flowered (d)	CElw MAvo
- semi-double white-flowered (d)	CElw EPPr WAbe
- 'Spring Nymph' **new**	SMHy
- 'Tairin'	GEdr
- white-flowered	GKev

Anemonopsis (*Ranunculaceae*)

macrophylla	CCon CExl CPBP CSpe CTal EBee ECho EPfP EWes GCal GEdr GKev LEdu MNrw MRav NLar SBch SBea SMad SPhx WCru WFar WOld WPGP WSHC
- 'Alba' **new**	GKev
- double-flowered **new**	GKev
- 'White Swan'	CTal GBin GEdr WCru WSHC

Anemopsis (*Saururaceae*)

sp.	CArn
californica	EBee EWay GBin GEdr IFoB LLWG MSKA MWts NLar SBrt WCot WPGP

Anethum (*Apiaceae*)

graveolens	ENfk GPoy MHer MNHC NPri SIde SRms SVic
- 'Dukat'	CLau

angelica see *Angelica archangelica*

Angelica (*Apiaceae*)

sp.	CHab
acutiloba	WFar
- var. ***iwatensis*** B&SWJ 11197	WCru
anomala B&SWJ 10886	WCru
archangelica	Widely available
atropurpurea	CBod ECtt EPfP GQue LRHS MHer MNrw MRav SWat SWvt WFar
cartilaginomarginata B&SWJ 12663	WCru
dahurica	CBot EWTr NDov WOut
- B&SWJ 8603	WCru
decursiva	CArn
- B&SWJ 5746	WCru
edulis	SPhx WPGP
- B&SWJ 10968	LEdu WCru
gigas	Widely available
- B&SWJ 4170	WCru
hendersonii **new**	LEdu
hispanica	see *A. pachycarpa*
japonica B&SWJ 11480	WCru
keiskei **new**	LEdu
montana	see *A. sylvestris*
morii RWJ 9802	WCru
§ ***pachycarpa***	CBod EBee ELan EPri GBin GMaP LHop LRHS MAvo MHer MRav MSpe NBir NLar WJek WWEG
pubescens	NDov
- B&SWJ 5593	WCru
- B&SWJ 11129	WCru
- var. ***matsumurae*** B&SWJ 6387	WCru
sachalinensis	EBee
sinensis	GPoy LEdu
'Summer Delight'	see *Ligusticum scoticum*
§ ***sylvestris***	CArn CHab LLWG WOut
- PAB 8136 **new**	LEdu
- 'Ebony'	CAby CBod CBre CSpe CWld EBee ECtt GAbr GBin LEdu LHop LLWG LRHS MAvo MBel MHer MHol MTis NCGa NDov SCob SHil SMDP SMad SPad SPoG WCot WPGP

- 'Purple Giant' **new** EBee
* - 'Purpurea' EWes GQue NGBl WPGP
- 'Vicar's Mead' CBot CDes EBee LEdu LPla LRHS MSpe NBir NChi NDov NLar NSti SHar SPer SPhx SWvt WBor
taiwaniana CArn CBre CDTJ CSam EBee ELan ESwi IMou LRHS MSpe NLar
ursina IMou WCru

Angelonia (*Plantaginaceae*)

angustifolia Angelface Blue Improved = 'Anbluim'PBR (Angelface Series) NPri
- 'Zebra' NPri
Archangel Deep Rose **new** LRHS
Carita Cascade Deep Purple = 'Cartbas Depur' **new** LAst
SunDancer Pink = 'NuAn607' **new** LAst

Anigozanthos (*Haemodoraceae*)

flavidus SPlb
- red-flowered SPlb
manglesii ♀H1c SPlb SVen

Anisacanthus (*Acanthaceae*)

quadrifidus var. **wrightii** WCot

anise see *Pimpinella anisum*

Anisodontea (*Malvaceae*)

bryoniifolia SVen
§ **capensis** CHGN CHll CTre ELan EPri GBee LAst LPmr MCot SChF SLim SPlb SRkn SRms SVen SWvt
'Crystal Rose' LRHS MGos SHil XLum
'Donatella' SLim
'El Rayo' CSpe CWGN ECtt LHop LSou MAvo MHol MPie SDys SPad WCot XLum
'Elegant Lady' GFai
huegelii see *Alyogyne huegelii*
× **hypomadara** misapplied see *A. capensis*
julii SPlb SVen
'Large Magenta' CPne LSou SWvt
malvastroides LHop
scabrosa CChe
- 'Miss Pinky'PBR LRHS MGos

Anisodus (*Solanaceae*)

carnioliciodes BWJ 7501 WCru
§ **luridus** EWld GCal

Anisotome (*Apiaceae*)

imbricata var. **imbricata** WAbe

Annona (*Annonaceae*)

cherimola (F) XBlo

Anoiganthus see *Cyrtanthus*

Anomalesia see *Gladiolus*

Anomatheca (*Iridaceae*)

cruenta see *Freesia laxa*

Anopterus (*Escalloniaceae*)

glandulosus CFil WSHC

Anredera (*Basellaceae*)

§ **cordifolia** CRHN ECho EShb GKev LEdu

Antennaria (*Asteraceae*)

aprica see *A. parvifolia*
dioica CTri ECtt EDAr GAbr GBin GJos GPoy NSla SPlb SRms XLum
- 'Alba' EHoe
- 'Alex Duguid' EPot GEdr NWad SBrt
- 'Aprica' see *A. parvifolia*
- 'Minima' ECho EPot GCrg ITim NBro NHar NSla WAbe
- 'Nyewoods Variety' NPri
- red-flowered ECho
- var. **rosea** see *A. rosea*
- 'Rotes Wunder' CMea ECha EPot GCrg SBch WAbe
* - 'Rubra' ECha ECho ECtt EDAr ITim MHer MMuc NPri WIce XLum
'Joy' EPot NWad WHal
macrophylla see *A. microphylla*
§ **microphylla** SRms
§ **parvifolia** CTri ECho SRms SRot
- var. **rosea** see *A. microphylla*
plantaginifolia EBee
§ **rosea** ♀H5 ECho GMaP LRHS MAsh NSla SPlb SRms WHal WHoo WIce

Antenoron see *Persicaria*

Anthemis ✿ (*Asteraceae*)

from Turkey ECtt EWes LLWP
arvensis CHab
§ 'Beauty of Grallagh' GBuc
'Cally Cream' GCal NCGa SMHy SPhx
'Cally White' GBin GCal LPla WBrk WHil
carpatica NBro
- 'Karpatenschnee' LRHS NPri SAko SRms
cretica EWes
subsp. **tenuiloba** **new**
frutescens Voss see *Argyranthemum frutescens*
'Grallagh Gold' misapplied, orange-yellow see *A.* 'Beauty of Grallagh'
'Grallagh Gold' ECtt EWes NPer SPhx
§ **marschalliana** CFis CMea ECha ECho ECtt EDAr LRHS SPlb WCot
- subsp. **pectinata** GCrg
nobilis see *Chamaemelum nobile*
punctata subsp. **cupaniana** ♀H4 Widely available
- - 'Nana' NPer SHar
rudolphiana see *A. marschalliana*
sancti-johannis CBod CMHG CWib EAEE EPfP LRHS NPer NWad SAko SRms WMoo
Susanna Mitchell = 'Blomit' EBee ECtt ELon GMaP LRHS LSRN MAvo MBel MHol MNrw NBir NDov NLar NWad SWvt WMnd WSHC WWEG XLum
'Tetworth' CPrp ECha ELan EPfP LCro LOPS LRHS SAko SMad WCot WWEG
tinctoria CArn CBod CHby CMac EBee ENfk GPoy MHer NPer SRms SWvt WHfH WJek WSFF XLum
- 'Alba' EBee LRHS NWad WFar WWEG XLum
- 'Charme'PBR EBee EPfP LAst LRHS NLar SAko SRms SWvt WMnd
- 'Compacta' EWes GCal MNrw WBrk XLum
- dwarf SAko

	- 'E.C. Buxton'	Widely available
	- 'Eva'	NDov WWEG
I	- 'Golden Rays'	SDix WWEG
	- 'Hall Farm Frilly'	ECtt ELon
	- 'Kelwayi'	CSBt CTri EPfP LRHS NBro NLar NPer SPer SRms SWat WMoo WWEG XLum
	- 'Lemon Ice'	EBee
	- 'Lemon Maid'	ECtt ELon GBin LRHS
	- 'Sauce Hollandaise'	Widely available
	- 'Waddow Gold'	NWad
	- 'Wargrave Variety'	CElw CMac CPrp CSam CWCL ECha ECtt ELan EPfP LRHS MAvo NBir NBro NChi NGdn NWad SDix SPhx SWvt WCAu WFar WMnd
	'Tinpenny Sparkle'	CAbP CBod CSam EBee ECtt GAbr GMaP MHol MPie NLar NSti WAul WCot WFar WHoo WMnd WRHF WWEG
	triumfettii	NDov NPer WCot
	tuberculata	NChi SBch
	zyghia	EBee

Anthericum (*Asparagaceae*)

	algeriense	see *A. liliago*
*	***bovei***	CBro
§	***liliago***	CSpe ECho ELan EWld GCal GKev GMaP IFoB LHop LRHS LSun MCot MRav NLar SPer WAul WPtf WWEG XEll
	- 'Major' ♀H5	CAvo CBro CDes EBee ECGP ECha ECho MLHP SPhx WPGP
	plumosum	see *Trichopetalum plumosum*
	ramosum	CDes CFis CSpe ECha ECho EPot EPri EWes GCal GKev LPla LRHS MBrN NBid NBir NLar SPhx WCot WPGP

Antholyza (*Iridaceae*)

coccinea	see *Crocosmia paniculata*
× ***crocosmioides***	see *Crocosmia* × *crocosmioides*
paniculata	see *Crocosmia paniculata*

Anthoxanthum (*Poaceae*)

odoratum	CHab CLau GPoy XLum

Anthriscus (*Apiaceae*)

cerefolium	CHby CLau ENfk GPoy MHer MNHC SRms WJek WSFF
sylvestris	CBre CHab NMir SPhx WFar WOut WSFF
- 'Going for Gold'	CNat
- 'Kabir'	LEdu
- 'Ravenswing'	Widely available

Anthurium (*Araceae*)

andraeanum 'Glowing Pink'	XBlo
- 'Red Heart'	XBlo
- 'Tivolo'	XBlo
'Aztec'	XBlo
Baleno = 'Anthauf4'PBR	XBlo
'Caribo'	XBlo
crenatum	XBlo
'Crimson'	XBlo
'Jungle Bush'	LPal
'Magenta'	XBlo
'Mikra'	XBlo
'Octavia'	XBlo
Pico Bello = 'Anthcupcup'PBR	XBlo
Pink Champion = 'Antinkeles'PBR	XBlo
'Porcelaine White'	XBlo
Red Champion = 'Anthbnena'PBR	XBlo
'Vitara'	XBlo
White Champion = 'Anthefaqyr'PBR	XBlo

Anthyllis (*Papilionaceae*)

	hermanniae 'Compacta'	see *A. hermanniae* 'Minor'
§	- 'Minor'	WAbe
	montana	XSen
	- subsp. ***atropurpurea***	ECho LRHS
	- 'Rubra' ♀H5	ECho EDAr EPot LHop LLHF NSla
	- 'Rubra Compacta'	WAbe
	vulneraria	CHab NMir NRya SPhx WSFF
	- var. ***coccinea***	ELan GAbr GBin MBel NSla SGSe SPhx WCFE WHal WIce
	- dark red-flowered	CSpe

Antirrhinum (*Plantaginaceae*)

	asarina	see *Asarina procumbens*
	barrelieri	SEND
	braun-blanquetii	GCra GLog SEND SPhx WCot WHil
	'Eternal'	LRHS
	glutinosum	see *A. hispanicum* subsp. *hispanicum*
	hispanicum 'Avalanche'	ECtt
§	- subsp. ***hispanicum***	CSpe
	- - 'Roseum'	CMea LPot
	majus Appeal Bicolour Mix **new**	NPri
	- 'Black Prince'	CSpe ECtt LHop SPhx
	- 'Cheerio' (mixed)	CWCL
	- 'June Blake' (v)	WCot
	- Liberty Classic Series	NPri
	- - 'Liberty Classic Yellow'	NPri
	- 'Night and Day'	CSpe WMoo
	molle	CSpe GKev MCot NPer SChF WAbe
	- pink-flowered	MCot WAbe
	- white-flowered	GKev WAbe
	sempervirens	MHer WAbe XLum
	siculum	WHil

añu see *Tropaeolum tuberosum*

Aphelandra (*Acanthaceae*)

squarrosa 'Citrina'	XBlo

Aphyllanthes (*Asparagaceae*)

monspeliensis	SBrt XLum

Apios (*Papilionaceae*)

§	***americana***	CAgr CCon ECho EWes GBin LEdu NBir WCot WCru WSHC
	- 'Nutty' **new**	CAgr
	tuberosa	see *A. americana*

Apium (*Apiaceae*)

graveolens	CArn CHab CLau ENfk GPoy MHer MNHC SIde SRms SVic WJek
- var. ***rapaceum*** 'Prinz' ♀H4	SVic
- (Secalinum Group) 'Par-cel'	MHer SRms

Apium × Petroselinum (*Apiaceae*)

hybrid, misapplied	see *A. graveolens* Secalinum Group

Apocynum (*Apocynaceae*)

cannabinum	CArn GPoy

Aponogeton (*Aponogetonaceae*)

desertorum	EWay LLWG
distachyos	CBen CBod CWat EHon EWay LCro MSKA MWts NPer SVic SWat WMAq WPnP XLum

apple see *Malus domestica*

apricot see *Prunus armeniaca*

Aptenia (*Aizoaceae*)

cordifolia	NPer SChr SPlb SVen WHil

Aquilegia ✿ (*Ranunculaceae*)

sp.	SVic
from China **new**	CEvo
akitensis misapplied	see *A. flabellata* var. *pumila*
'Alaska' (State Series) ♀H5	LPfy LRHS MBri NPri SHil
alpina	CBod CBot CMea EBee ECho EPfP GJos LCro LPal MAsh MNHC NGdn SCob SPer SRms WMoo XLum
amaliae	see *A. ottonis* subsp. *amaliae*
'Apple Blossom'	NBir
aragonensis	see *A. pyrenaica*
§ ***atrata***	CBot CCon CLAP CPou ECho
atrovinosa	GKev
aurea misapplied	see *A. vulgaris* golden-leaved
aurea Janka	LLHF
barnebyi	CWCL
bertolonii ♀H5	CMea ECho GKev LHop LRHS SRms WHoo
- 'Blue Berry'	WThu
Biedermeier Group	EAJP ECho EPfP LRHS NGdn NNor SRot WFar WTou
'Blackcurrant'	CWCL
'Blue Star' (Star Series)	CWCL ELan EPfP GBin GMaP LRHS NEgg SPer SPtp WTou
'Bluebird' (Songbird Series) ♀H4	LBuc LRHS NBir NPer WFar
brevistyla	NNor
'Fruit and Nut Chocolate'	CAby CDes EBee EUJe IKil MBNS MHol MPie WCot WFar
buergeriana	SPhx
- 'Calimero'	CFis CTsd LHop MBNS NLar SPtp
- var. ***oxysepala***	see *A. oxysepala*
aff. ***buergeriana*** **new**	CCon
'Bunting' (Songbird Series) ♀H4	MHer SGbt
canadensis ♀H3	CBot CLAP CSpe ECho ELan GCrg LCro NBir NBro SPad SPhx SRms WFar XEll XLum
- 'Corbett'	NLar WAbe
- 'Little Lanterns'	EAJP ECho LHop NLar SGSe WIce
- 'Nana'	WThu
- 'Pink Lanterns'	LBMP
'Cardinal' (Songbird Series)	LBuc LRHS
chaplinei	GBin GKev NBir SBch
chrysantha	CBot ECho EWld GBin GJos SGSe SIgm SRms SWvt WBod WKif WTou
- 'Denver Gold'	CHVG CSam EShb MWhi
I - 'Flore Pleno' (d)	CBot
- 'Yellow Queen'	CCon CExl CWCL EPfP EShb EWoo GBin GMaP LBMP LHop LPal LRHS MWat NCGa NGdn NPri SBea SCob SDix SGbt SMHy SPad SWvt WCFE WHil WTor XLum
clematiflora	see *A. vulgaris* var. *stellata*
Clementine Series	EPfP NPri
coerulea ♀H5	GJos GKev NNor SRms
- var. ***ochroleuca***	CWCL
'Colorado' (State Series)	LPfy LRHS SHil
'Crimson Star'	CWCL ELan EPfP LRHS SPoG WMoo WTou
'Danish Dwarf' **new**	LBMP
desertorum	SIgm
dichroa	WPGP
discolor	LLHF WThu XEll
double black-flowered (d) **new**	WHil
'Double Rubies' (d)	ELan LSRN WMoo WTou
'Dove' (Songbird Series) ♀H5	LBuc LRHS MHer SGbt SHar SPer
I 'Dragonfly'	CBcs CWib EAJP ELan EPfP LRHS MBel MJak NEgg NGdn SPer SPoG WTou
'Dragon's Breath' (mixed)	WTou
ecalcarata	see *Semiaquilegia ecalcarata*
einseleana	ECho LLHF
'Elegance'	WTou
'Elegant Gold Leaf' **new**	WHil
'Elegant Moonstone'	WTou
'Elegant Opal'	WTou
'Elegant Ruby'	WTou
elegantula	CCon
'Firecracker'	GJos
flabellata ♀H5	GCra
- f. ***alba***	CTri ECho ELan
- - 'White Jewel' (Jewel Series)	GKev
- 'Blackcurrant Ice'	CWCL EPfP LRHS
- Cameo Series	GJos GMaP WFar
- - 'Cameo Blue and White'	CWib NCGa SRms SRot WFar
- - 'Cameo Pink and White'	MHer NCGa
- - 'Cameo Rose'	WFar
- - 'Cameo Rose and White'	SRms
- - 'Cameo White'	SRot WFar
- 'Georgia' (State Series) ♀H5	LPfy LRHS MBri
- Jewel Series	ECho
- 'Ministar'	ECho EDAr GCrg MHol WFar WHil XLum
- 'Nana Alba'	see *A. flabellata* var. *pumila* f. *alba*
§ - var. ***pumila*** ♀H5	CCon CWCL ECha ECho EDAr EWTr GEdr LHop LRHS LSun NGdn
§ - - f. ***alba*** ♀H5	EAJP ECha ECho EDAr GKev LHop LRHS LSun SRms
- - 'Atlantis'	EPPr LBMP LRHS NPri
I - - f. ***kurilensis*** 'Rosea'	CCon EDAr GKev WAbe
'Flamboyant'	WTou
'Florida' (State Series) ♀H5	EBee LPfy LRHS MBri NPri SHil
formosa	CBot ECho EPPr NChi WHil WKif WTou
- var. ***truncata***	SIgm
§ ***fragrans***	CCon CLAP GEdr GJos GKev SGbt WTou
- CC 7371 **new**	GKev
glandulosa	LLHF
glauca	see *A. fragrans*
'Goldfinch' (Songbird Series)	LBuc LRHS MHer NBir SGbt SPer WFar
grahamii	WAbe
'Heavenly Blue'	CBod EBee EShb LRHS WTou
'Hensol Harebell'	EBee SRms

japonica	see *A. flabellata* var. *pumila*
jonesii	GKev SPlb
jonesii × ***saximontana***	GKev
'Kansas' (State Series)	MBri SDix
'Koralle'	CBod WTou
'Kristall'	EShb LCro SGbt XLum
laramiensis	CPBP
'Leprechaun Gold' (v)	EPfP MHol NGdn SDix
'Lime Sorbet'	LRHS SRms
longissima	CWld GKev MHer SGSe SHar WFar WHoo
long-spurred hybrids	WTou
long-spurred hybrids, white	WTou
'Louisiana' (State Series) ♀^{H5}	EBee LPfy LRHS MBri NPri SCob SHil
'Magpie'	see *A. vulgaris* 'William Guiness'
'Maxi'	CBod
McKana Group	CTri EAEE ELan ELon EPfP GAbr GJos GMaP LAst LBMP LHop LRHS MGos NEgg NGdn NHol SBea SCob SPer SPlb SPoG SRms SWvt WFar WHar WMnd WMoo WTou XLum
'Montana' (State Series)	MBri
Mrs Scott-Elliot hybrids	CSBt ECtt EPfP LAst MHol
Music Series	SRms
'Nightingale' (Songbird Series)	SGbt
nigricans	see *A. atrata*
nivalis	LLHF
olympica	WTou
'Oranges and Lemons'	SGSe WFar
'Oregon' (State Series)	MBri
§ ***ottonis*** subsp. ***amaliae***	CPBP EWTr LLHF SIgm WAbe
§ ***oxysepala***	CExl GCal WFar
- B&SWJ 4775	WCru
Perfumed Garden Group	CPla CWld WFar
pleated burgundy-flowered	CBot
'Purple Emperor'^{PBR}	EPfP
§ ***pyrenaica***	GKev
- dwarf	WAbe
'Red Hobbit'	CBct CSpe EAEE EBee ELan EPfP IBoy LHop LPfy LRHS MBel MHol NEgg NGdn NLar SBea SHil SPtp WBor WFar WHoo
'Red Star' (Star Series)	CWCL EAEE EAJP EPfP NEgg SPer WHil WTou
'Rhubarb and Custard'	LRHS
'Robin' (Songbird Series)	MHer SGbt SPer
rockii	CLAP GKev
- B&SWJ 7965	WCru
'Roman Bronze'	see *Aquilegia* × *Semiaquilegia* 'Roman Bronze'
'Rose Queen'	CWCL EPfP NNor SPtp WFar WHoo WTou
'Roundway Chocolate'	CBot
saximontana	EPot GEdr GKev NSla
§ 'Schneekönigin'	CWCL LRHS WCFE
scopulorum	GKev LLHF SIgm WAbe
Shooting Stars (mixed)	WTou
sibirica	CCon GKev LLHF
'Silver Queen'	EBee ELan EWoo LHop
'Simone's White'	EBee
skinneri	CBot CExl CSpe ELan GEdr GLog WMnd
- 'Tequila Sunrise'	CSpe CWCL CWib ELan GBin MHer NNor SPad SPtp
Snow Queen	see *A.* 'Schneekönigin'
'Spitfire'	LRHS NCGa
(Spring Magic Series) Spring Magic Blue and White	LRHS SCob WTou
- Spring Magic Pink and White	WTou
- Spring Magic Rose and Ivory	WTou
- Spring Magic White	SCob WTou
- Spring Magic Yellow	WTou
stellata	see *A. vulgaris* var. *stellata*
'Sunburst Ruby'	CPla WMoo
(Swan Series) 'Swan Lavender' **new**	NPri
- 'Swan Pink and Yellow' **new**	NPri
- 'Swan Red and White' **new**	NPri
'Sweet Rainbows' (d)	CPla
'Touchwood Black & Bruises' mixed doubles (d)	WTou
'Touchwood Crinoline Ladies' mixed doubles (d)	WTou
'Touchwood Glimmers' mixed **new**	WHil
'Touchwood Gold' golden-leaved, mixed **new**	WHil
'Touchwood Harmony' mixed	WTou
'Touchwood Night Lights' mixed doubles (d)	WTou
'Touchwood Sunrise Surprises' mixed doubles (d)	WTou
triternata	NNor
'Virginia' (State Series)	LPfy LRHS MBri NPri SHil
viridiflora	CBot CLAP EBee ELan EPfP GCal WAbe WCot WHil WKif WMnd
- 'Chocolate Soldier'	CSpe CWCL
'Volcano!' (mixed)	WTou
vulgaris	CArn CHab CMHG CWCL CWld EPfP EWoo GKev GPoy LLWP LRHS MHer MNHC NBro NGdn NMir SPlb WCAu WMoo WShi
- 'Adelaide Addison'	EBee ECha WHoo
- var. ***alba***	CMea CWCL EPfP EWoo LRHS MMuc SCob WTou
- 'Aureovariegata'	see *A. vulgaris* Vervaeneana Group
- 'Blackbird' (Songbird Series) (d)	CWCL
- 'Burnished Rose'	CPla
- ***clematiflora***	see *A. vulgaris* var. *stellata*
- (Clementine Series) 'Clementine Blue' (d)	CCVN EPfP LRHS SPoG WCot
- - 'Clementine Dark Purple' (d)	CWCL EPfP LRHS SPoG WHil
- - 'Clementine Purple' (d) **new**	CCVN
- - 'Clementine Red' (d)	EPfP
- - 'Clementine Rose' (d)	CCVN LRHS SPoG
- - 'Clementine Salmon Rose' (d)	CCVN CWCL EPfP LRHS SPoG
- - 'Clementine White' (d)	CCVN EPfP LRHS SPoG
- 'Crystal Star'	LRHS
- var. ***flore-pleno*** (d)	LLWP WFar WTou
- - bicoloured (d)	WTou
- - black-flowered (d)	MMuc SEND WCot WTou
- - blue-flowered (d)	WTou
- - 'Dorothy Rose' (Dorothy Series) (d)	EWTr LHop SPad SPtp
- - 'Double Pleat' (d)	EPfP
- - 'Double Pleat' blue/white-flowered (d)	CBot

- - 'Double Pleat' pink/ white-flowered (d) CWCL
- - 'Jane Hollow' (d) CPou
- - pale blue-flowered (d) WCot WTou
- - pink-flowered (d) WTou
- - purple-flowered (d) WTou
- - red-flowered (d) WTou
- - 'Strawberry Ice Cream' (d) NBro NNor WTou
* - - 'White Bonnet' (d) CWCL
- - white-flowered (d) WTou
§ - golden-leaved ECho WTou
- Grandmother's Garden Group CBod
- 'Heidi' MMuc SEND
- 'Mellow Yellow' CPla CTsd EHoe ELon LRHS SDix SGSe WMoo
- 'Miss M. J. Huish' LPla
- Munstead White see *A. vulgaris* 'Nivea'
§ - 'Nivea' ♀H7 CBot CPou CSpe EBee ECha ELan EPfP EWoo LOPS NChi SEND WCot WTor
- 'Pink Spurless' see *A. vulgaris* var. *stellata* pink-flowered
- 'Pom Pom Crimson' (Pom Pom Series) NBro WCot
- scented WTou
§ - var. ***stellata*** CTsd ELan GAbr GKev MWhi NBir NBro NNor SPad WFar WHea WMoo WTou
- - Barlow Series (d) MJak WFar WTou
- - - 'Black Barlow' (d) Widely available
- - - 'Blue Barlow' (d) CBot CSpe EBee ECtt EPfP GMaP GQue ILea LCro LPfy LRHS LSRN MJak SCob SHil SPer SWvt WBor WCot WMnd WTou XLum
- - black-flowered WTou
- - 'Blue Fountain' WTou
- - blue-flowered MMuc NBir SEND WTou
- - 'Bordeaux Barlow' (Barlow Series) (d) LRHS WTou
- - 'Christa Barlow' (Barlow Series) (d) EBee EPfP LRHS MBel NLar WTou
- - double-flowered (d) WTou
- - 'Firewheel' WMoo
- - 'Greenapples' (d) CBre CCVN CNor CWCL EBee ELan EPfP EWoo GBin GKev GQue LPla LRHS MCot SCob WCot WHoo
- - 'Nora Barlow' (Barlow Series) (d) Widely available
§ - - pink-flowered WTou
- - red-flowered WTou
- - 'Rose Barlow' (Barlow Series) (d) EPfP GBin LRHS LSRN WMnd WTou
- - 'Royal Purple' (d) NBro NNor WMoo
- - 'Ruby Port' (d) Widely available
- - 'Ruby Port' crimped (d) WPnP
- - 'Touchwood Dreamtime' WTou
- - 'White Barlow' (Barlow Series) (d) CAby EPfP GMaP IBoy LCro LOPS LPfy LRHS SHil SPer SWvt WTou
- - white-flowered CSpe GCra NBir NBro WTou
- variegated foliage see *A. vulgaris* Vervaeneana Group
§ - Vervaeneana Group (v) CMHG CWCL ELan EPfP LRHS NBir NPer SGSe SPlb SRms SWat WBor WFar WHoo WMoo WTou
- - 'Woodside Blue' (v) NWad WTou
- - 'Woodside White' (v) NBir WBrk WTou
§ - 'William Guiness' Widely available
- 'William Guiness Doubles' (d) WMoo WTou

'White Star' (Star Series) CWCL EBee ELan EPfP GMaP LAst LRHS WTou
white-flowered WTou
Winky Series ELan GJos NCGa NNor SWvt WFar WTou
- 'Winky Blue-White' GBin LRHS NLar NPri WCFE WTou
- 'Winky Double Red-White' (d) LRHS
- 'Winky Double White-White' (d) NPri
- 'Winky Purple-White' LRHS NPri
- 'Winky Red-White' LRHS NPri SWvt WTou
- 'Winky Rose-Rose' LRHS NPri
- 'Winky Wooh' (Winky Series) CWld GBin NEgg WBor
yabeana GKev WMoo
'Yellow Star' (Star Series) ♀H4 CWCL ECtt EPfP

Aquilegia × *Semiaquilegia* (*Ranunculaceae*)

hybrid, blue-flowered NGdn
§ 'Roman Bronze' CBod CPla WMoo

Arabis (*Brassicaceae*)

albida see *A. alpina* subsp. *caucasica*
alpina MAsh SPlb
§ - subsp. ***caucasica*** ECho
- - 'Corfe Castle' ECtt
- - 'Douler Angevine' (v) CBod ECtt LBMP LHop MAvo NPri SPoG SRms WIce
- - 'Flore Pleno' (d) ♀H5 CElw CFis CHid CSpe CTri CWCL ECho ECtt ELan EWld GAbr GJos GMaP MHer SBch SIgm SRms WHoo WWFP
- - 'Hedi' **new** MJak
- - 'Pinkie' ECho LPal
- - 'Pixie Cream' ECtt EDAr MHol MMuc NGdn NPri
- - 'Rosea' GJos LRHS NBir NPri SRms
§ - - 'Schneehaube' ♀H6 CTri CWib EAJP ECho ECtt EPfP GMaP LRHS MJak NBir NGdn NPri SPoG SRms WBor
- - Snowcap see *A. alpina* subsp. *caucasica* 'Schneehaube'
- - 'Variegata' (v) ECho ELan GMaP LAst NPri SPoG SRms
androsacea SRms
× ***arendsii*** 'Compinkie' GJos SPlb SRms
- 'Rosabella' (v) NPri
blepharophylla EPfP MHol NPri WSHC
§ - 'Frühlingszauber' ♀H5 CTri EAJP ELan EPfP GJos MMuc NBir NGdn NPri SPoG SRms WRHF
- 'Rose Delight' LRHS
- 'Rote Sensation' ELan NGdn
- Spring Charm see *A. blepharophylla* 'Frühlingszauber'
bryoides LLHF
carduchorum XLum
caucasica see *A. alpina* subsp. *caucasica*
ferdinandi-coburgi ECho NHol
- 'Aureovariegata' (v) CMea CTri ECho ECtt ELan SWvt
- 'Old Gold' CTal ECho EHoe EPfP LPot MAsh MHer NHol NPri NRya SPoG SRms SRot SWvt WCFE
- 'Variegata' see *A. procurrens* 'Variegata'
procurrens WCot XSen
- 'Glacier' GJos NPri
§ - 'Variegata' (v) ♀H5 CTal CTri ECho ECtt EHoe ELan EPfP EWes GKev MBrN MHer MJak NPri SPlb SRms SRot

pumila GKev
purpurea WMoo
Snow Cap see *A. alpina* subsp. *caucasica* 'Schneehaube'
× ***wilczekii*** EPot

Arachniodes (*Dryopteridaceae*)

aristata NLos
davalliaeformis EBee ISha LRHS NLos
miqueliana ISha NLos
simplicior EBee ISha NLos SCob WCot
standishii EBee EShb ISha LEdu LRHS NLos WCot

Araiostegia (*Davalliaceae*)

faberiana CExl
hymenophylloides SKHP
parvipinnata see *A. perdurans*
§ ***perdurans*** CFil EBee NLos WPGP
- B&SWJ 1608 WCru
pulchra HWJ 1007 WCru

Aralia ✿ (*Araliaceae*)

apioides IMou
- EDHCH 9720 WCru
armata B&SWJ 6916 WCru
- RWJ 10060 WCru
bipinnata Blanco WPGP
- CWJ 12407 **new** WCru
- RWJ 10101 WCru
cachemirica CDTJ CLAP GCal MBrN NBid NLar SDix SMad SPlb WCru WHal WMoo
californica EBee GCal GPoy LEdu NLar SDix SKHP WCru
castanopsidicola CWJ 12411 WCru
chapaensis B&SWJ 11812 WCru
- HWJ 1013 WCru
chinensis misapplied see *A. elata*
chinensis L. BWJ 8102 WCru
continentalis CLAP LEdu NLar WHoo
- B&SWJ 8437 WCru
- B&SWJ 8524 WCru
cordata Thunb. GCal LEdu WFar
- B&SWJ 5511 CDes
- B&SWJ 5596 WCru
- var. ***sachalinensis*** NLar
- - B&SWJ 4773 WCru
- 'Sun King' CAby CBct CBod EBee ECtt EPfP ESwi EUJe IBoy LHop LLWG LRHS LSun MHol MNrw MPie MSCN NLar NSti SCob SPoG SWvt WCot WFar WHil
decaisneana B&SWJ 6794 WCru
- RWJ 9910 WCru
echinocaulis SBrt
- PAB 9052 LEdu
§ ***elata*** CBcs CDoC CDul CExl CHll CMac CTsd EBee ELan EPfP IDee LPal LRHS LSRN MBlu MGos MHtn MMuc SCob SGol SPer SPoG SWvt WFar
- B&SWJ 5480 WCru
- 'Albomarginata' see *A. elata* 'Variegata'
- 'Aureo-marginata' (v) CMac
- 'Aureovariegata' (v) ♀H5 CBcs ELan EWes NLar SCob
- 'Golden Umbrella' (v) EUJe LSRN NLar
- 'Silver Umbrella' (v) EUJe NLar
§ - 'Variegata' (v) ♀H5 CBcs CDul ELan MGos NLar SCob SWvt
foliolosa B&SWJ 8360 WCru
kansuensis BWJ 7650 WCru
- CD&R 2289 WCru
leschenaultii B&SWJ 9515 WCru
- B&SWJ 11789 WCru
papyrifera see *Tetrapanax papyrifer*
racemosa CArn EUJe GPoy GQue LEdu NLar SRms WJek WMoo
- B&SWJ 9570 WCru
searelliana B&SWJ 11736 WCru
sieboldii de Vriese see *Fatsia japonica*
spinosa L. CArn EBtc GQue LEdu MBlu NChi SPlb
subcordata HWJK 2385 WCru
verticillata B&SWJ 11797 WCru
vietnamensis B&SWJ 12349E WCru

Araucaria (*Araucariaceae*)

sp. LPar
angustifolia WPGP
angustifolia × ***araucana*** CFil SMad
§ ***araucana*** Widely available
cunninghamii ECou
excelsa misapplied see *A. heterophylla*
§ ***heterophylla*** ♀H2 CBcs CDoC LPal SEND
imbricata see *A. araucana*

Araujia (*Apocynaceae*)

sericifera CHll CMac CRHN ECre IDee LRHS SVen WCot WSHC

Arbutus ✿ (*Ericaceae*)

andrachne NJM 12.018 **new** WPGP
× ***andrachnoides*** ♀H4 CAbP CDul CHGN CJun CTho ELan EPfP GGal LEdu LRHS LSRN MAsh MRav SPer SPoG WPGP WPat
menziesii CBcs CMCN EPfP MBlu MMuc WFar
× ***reyorum*** 'Marina' CAbP CJun EBee ELan EPfP IVic LEdu LHop LRHS MAsh MBlu NOrn SAko SEND SMad SPer SPoG SSpi WPGP WPat
unedo Widely available
- 'Atlantic' ♀H5 CDoC CJun EPfP LPfy LRHS LSRN MAsh MBri MGos SBig SGbt SGol SHil SWvt WPGP WPat
- 'Compacta' CBcs CDoC EUJe LRHS MAsh NLar SLon SPoG SWvt
- 'Elfin King' EPfP LRHS MAsh NLar SLon SWvt
- 'Quercifolia' CHll CJun EBee ELan LEdu LLHF MAsh NLar WHor WPat
- Roselily = 'Minlily'PBR SBig
- f. ***rubra*** ♀H5 Widely available
xalapensis CFil SPlb

Archidendron (*Mimosaceae*)

glandulosum **new** EBee

Archontophoenix (*Arecaceae*)

alexandrae LPal
cunninghamiana CBrP XBlo

Arctanthemum (*Asteraceae*)

§ ***arcticum*** ECha MMuc NLar XLum
- 'Roseum' EBee

Arcterica see *Pieris*

Arctium (*Asteraceae*)

lappa	CArn GPoy SIde SRms SVic WHer WSFF
minus	NMir

Arctostaphylos (*Ericaceae*)

uva-ursi	GBin GPoy NLar SPlb
- 'Massachusetts'	NLar
- 'Snowcap'	MAsh
- 'Vancouver Jade'	ELan GKin LRHS LSRN MAsh SCoo SLon SPer SPoG SRms SWvt

Arctotheca (*Asteraceae*)

calendula	CDes EBee WPGP

Arctotis (*Asteraceae*)

Hannah = 'Archnah'PBR	CAby ECtt MBNS
Hayley = 'Archley'PBR	ECtt MBNS
'Heidi'	LAst MBNS
'Holly'	LAst MBNS
'Hope'	MBNS
× ***hybrida*** hort. 'Apricot'	ECtt LAst SVen
- 'Flame' 🏆H2	CAby ECtt LAst MBNS SCoo SRms SVen
- 'Red Devil'	EWoo LAst LSou MBNS SCoo SVen WBod
- 'Wine'	LAst LSou MBNS SCoo SRkn

Ardisia (*Primulaceae*)

PAB 7988 from Mizoram, India **new**	LEdu
japonica	WCot
- B&SWJ 1032	SMad WCru
- var. ***angusta***	WCot
- 'Houkan' (v)	EBee WPGP
- var. ***minor*** B&SWJ 1841	WCru
- - B&SWJ 3809	WCru

Areca (*Arecaceae*)

triandra	XBlo

Arecastrum see *Syagrus*

Arenaria (*Caryophyllaceae*)

§ ***alfacariensis***	EPot NLar WAbe WOld
balearica	CWCL ECho EDAr EWes GCrg LLWG MAsh NRya NSla SPlb SRms
capillaris	CTri
grandiflora	XLum
kansuensis	GKev NLar
ledebouriana	EDAr NLar
montana 🏆H5	CAby CMea CTal ECha ECho ECtt EDAr EPfP EWoo GMaP LHop LRHS MGos NPri SDix SPhx SPlb SRms SRot WAbe WIce WWFP
- 'Avalanche'	ECtt LSun MHol
- 'Blizzard'	EPfP NPri
norvegica	ITim
pseudacantholimon	LLHF
pulvinata	see *A. alfacariensis*
purpurascens	ECho EPot EWes GCrg LLHF NLar SRms SRot WAbe
tetraquetra	SIgm
- subsp. ***amabilis***	EPot
'The Pearl' **new**	CBod
verna	see *Minuartia verna*

Arenga (*Arecaceae*)

engleri	LPal
micrantha	WCot

Argania (*Sapotaceae*)

spinosa	CFil WPGP

Argemone (*Papaveraceae*)

grandiflora	CSpe SBch
hispida **new**	EBee
mexicana	ELan IMou

Argyranthemum ✿ (*Asteraceae*)

'Beth'	GBee
'Bridesmaid'	MHom
broussonetii	MHom
Butterfly = 'Ulyssis' 🏆H2	LAst
canariense hort.	see *A. frutescens* subsp. *canariae*
Cherry Harmony = 'Supa532' (Daisy Crazy Series) (d)	MCot
'Citronelle'	MCot
'Cornish Gold' 🏆H2	CBcs ECtt EShb
'Dana'	LAst
'Donington Hero' 🏆H2	MHom
double pink-flowered (d)	SVen
'Everest' **new**	LRHS
'Flamingo'	see *Rhodanthemum gayanum*
§ ***foeniculaceum*** misapplied	CTri ELan
§ ***foeniculaceum*** (Willd.) Webb & Sch.Bip.	MCot
- 'Royal Haze' 🏆H2	CHll NPer
§ ***frutescens***	SEND WKif
§ - subsp. ***canariae*** 🏆H2	MHom
'Gill's Pink'	MHom WPnn
gracile	CHll
- 'Chelsea Girl' 🏆H2	MCot MHom WKif
'Guernsey Pink'	MHom
'Jamaica Primrose' 🏆H2	CSpe CTri ECtt SDix
'Jamaica Snowstorm'	see *A.* 'Snow Storm'
(LaRita Series) LaRita Banana Split = 'Kleaf10067' 🏆H2	LAst LRHS
- LaRita Red	LAst
'Levada Cream' 🏆H2	MHom WCot
Madeira Crested Merlot = 'Bonmadmerlo'PBR (Madeira Series) (d)	SVen
§ ***maderense*** 🏆H2	CHll MHom
'Mary Wootton' (d)	ECtt MHom
mawii	see *Rhodanthemum gayanum*
Meteor Red = 'Supa742' (Daisy Crazy Series)	CBcs CWGN MBNS MCot
§ 'Mrs F. Sander' (d)	MHom
ochroleucum	see *A. maderense*
Pacific Gold = 'Pacargone'PBR (d)	CBcs CWGN
'Pink Australian' (d)	MHom
Pomponette Pink = 'Supa392'PBR (d)	CBcs
'Powder Puff' (d)	ECtt
Sassy Red = 'Chqz0001' **new**	LAst
Sassy Rose Single **new**	LAst
Sassy Watermelon **new**	LAst
'Shirley's Yellow'	MHom
'Silver Queen'	see *A. foeniculaceum* misapplied
§ 'Snow Storm' 🏆H2	MHom
'Snowflake' misapplied	see *A.* 'Mrs F. Sander'
Sole Mio = 'Supa3047' (d)	CWCL
'Starlight' 🏆H2	MCot MHom
'Summer Cloud'	MCot

'Summer Melody' (d)	CBcs
'Summer Stars' (Daisy Crazy Series) (d) ♀H2	MHom
'Vancouver' (d) ♀H2	CWCL ECtt EShb WBod
'Weymouth Pink'	MHom
'White Spider'	ELan

Argyrocytisus (*Papilionaceae*)

battandieri	Widely available
- 'Yellow Tail' ♀H4	CBot ELan EMil EPfP EUJe LPfy LRHS MBri MGos NLar NOrn SHil SKHP SSta WHar WMat

Arisaema ✿ (*Araceae*)

CC 4904	CExl
CC 5511	CExl
album	XLum
amurense	CElw CFil CLAP EBee ECho GBuc GKev LAma LLHF SGSe
§ - subsp. ***robustum***	GKev WBor
asperatum	LAma
auriculatum	GKev LAma
- var. ***hungyaense*** new	LRHS
brachyspathum	see *A. heterophyllum*
brevipes	CExl
candidissimum ♀H4	CBro CCon CElw CFil CLAP CPne CWCL ECha ELon EPfP EPot GBuc GCra GEdr GKev LAma LPla MRav NHar NLar NSla SDeJ SKHP WBor WCot WHal WPGP
- red-flowered	LAma
- white-flowered	CFil GEdr GKev LAma
- yellow-flowered	LAma
ciliatum	GBuc GEdr GKev LAma NLar SRot
- var. ***liubaense***	CAby CFwr CWCL EPfP EPot GBuc GKev WCot
- - CT 369	CDes CExl CLAP EPfP SDys SKHP WPGP WSHC
- - GG 97091	WCot
concinnum	CCon EWld GBin GEdr GKev LAma LPal WPnP XLum
consanguineum	CAby CBcs CBro CExl CFwr CLAP EBee EPfP GBin GCal GEdr GKev LAma NLar WCot WPGP WPnP XLum
- B&SWJ 071	WCru
- CLD 1519	ECho GBuc
- subsp. ***kelung-insulare*** B&SWJ 256	WCru
- 'The Perfect Wave' new	WCot
- variegated (v)	WCot
cf. ***consanguineum***	WBod
costatum	CFil EBee ECho EPfP EPot GBin GKev LAma LPal SChF WCot WPGP XLum
dilatatum	GKev
dracontium	EPot XLum
ehimense	LAma
elephas	LAma
engleri	GKev LAma LRHS
erubescens	GBin
exappendiculatum	CAby CExl CFil EBee EPfP GKev LAma LRHS
fargesii	CExl CFil EPot GKev LAma SChF SKHP XLum
flavum	CDes CFil CWCL ECho EPfP EPot EWld GBuc GCal GKev LAma NHar SGSe SPlb
- CC 6303	EBee ITim
- subsp. ***abbreviatum***	GBin GBuc
- - CC 6300	ITim
formosanum B&SWJ 280	WCru
§ ***franchetianum***	CExl EBee GKev LAma
galeatum	EPot GBin GKev LAma LRHS WCot XLum
grapsospadix B&SWJ 7000	WCru
§ ***griffithii***	ECho GBin GBuc GEdr GKev LAma NBid NLar SDeJ XLum
- 'Numbuq'	GCra
- var. ***pradhanii***	GBin GEdr GKev LAma XLum
handelii	LAma
helleborifolium	see *A. tortuosum*
§ ***heterophyllum***	GKev LAma
inkiangense	LAma
intermedium	GBin GKev LAma MNrw XLum
iyoanum subsp. ***nakaianum***	LAma
jacquemontii	CAby CFil EBee ECho EWld GCra GEdr GKev GLog LAma NLar XLum
- CC 5184	ITim
japonicum Blume	see *A. serratum* var. *mayebarae*
japonicum Komarov	see *A. serratum*
jinshajiangense	CExl LAma
kishidae	GEdr GKev LAma
kiushianum	EFEx GKev LAma LRHS
lichiangense	EBee GKev LAma LRHS
lingyunense	LAma
§ ***lobatum***	CExl LAma
maximowiczii	GEdr GKev LAma
meleagris	LAma
§ ***nepenthoides***	CFil ECho EPot GBin GEdr GKev LAma WPnP XLum
ochraceum	see *A. nepenthoides*
onoticum	see *A. lobatum*
petelotii B&SWJ 9706	WCru
polyphyllum B&SWJ 3904	WCru
propinquum	EBee ECho GBin GKev LAma NLar XLum
purpureogaleatum	see *A. franchetianum*
rhizomatum	LAma
rhombiforme	LAma
ringens misapplied	see *A. amurense* subsp. *robustum*
ringens ambig.	GEdr GKev LRHS SKHP
ringens (Thunberg) Schott	CDes EFEx LAma LEdu
- f. ***praecox*** B&SWJ 1515	WCru
- f. ***sieboldii*** B&SWJ 551	WCru
robustum	see *A. amurense* subsp. *robustum*
saxatile	GKev LAma
sazensoo	GEdr GKev LAma
§ ***serratum***	GKev LAma MNrw
§ - var. ***mayebarae***	GEdr GKev LAma
- var. ***serratum***	LAma
sikokianum	CBro EBee ECho EFEx EPot GEdr GKev LAma LLHF NLar SKHP WPnP
- variegated (v)	GEdr
speciosum	CExl CFil EBee ECho EWld GBin GEdr GKev LAma LPal SDeJ SPlb WCot WPnP XLum
* - var. ***magnificum***	CBcs GBin GEdr GKev LAma NLar XLum
- var. ***mirabile***	EBee GKev LAma LRHS XLum
taiwanense	CAby GEdr SKHP WCot
- B&SWJ 269	WCru
- var. ***brevipedunculatum*** B&SWJ 1859	WCru
- f. ***cinereum*** B&SWJ 3602	CDes
- - B&SWJ 19121	WCru
tashiroi	GKev LAma
ternatipartitum	GKev LAma LRHS
thunbergii	EFEx GEdr LAma WBor

- subsp. ***autumnale*** B&SWJ 1425	WCru
- subsp. ***urashima***	EBee EFEx GKev LAma
§ ***tortuosum***	CDes CExl CFil CPne ECha ECho EPfP EWld GBin GBuc GKev LAma LEdu LTro NLar SChF WPGP WPnP XLum
- 'Black Rod'	CFil
- var. ***helleborifolium***	NBid XLum
tosaense	GKev LAma LRHS
triphyllum	CElw CExl CLAP EBee EPot GKev GPoy LAma NLar SPlb WPnP
- subsp. ***triphyllum*** var. ***atrorubens***	CLAP
§ ***utile***	EBee ECho EPot GBin GEdr GKev LAma XLum
verrucosum	see *A. griffithii*
- var. ***utile***	see *A. utile*
yamatense	GKev
- subsp. ***sugimotoi***	LAma
yunnanense	LAma

Arisarum (*Araceae*)

proboscideum	Widely available
vulgare	ECho
- subsp. ***simorrhinum***	ECho
- - from Spain	ECho

Aristea (*Iridaceae*)

sp.	GGal
§ ***capitata***	CHll IDee WHil
- pink-flowered	CPrp CTre
ecklonii	CBcs CCon CExl CPou CPrp CTca CTsd EBee EPri EShb MHer MSCN
- GWJ 9469	WCru
ensifolia	ELan
thyrsiflora	see *A. capitata*

Aristolochia (*Aristolochiaceae*)

baetica	CExl
californica	LEdu SKHP WPGP
chilensis	SPlb
clematitis	CArn ECho GPoy LEdu
contorta	WCru
- B&SWJ 12613 new	WCru
cucurbitifolia B&SWJ 7043	WCru
delavayi	SVen
durior	see *A. macrophylla*
gigantea ♀H1b	CHll
griffithii B&SWJ 2118	WCru
heterophylla	see *A. kaempferi* f. *heterophylla*
kaempferi B&SWJ 293	WCru
§ - f. ***heterophylla*** B&SWJ 3109	WCru
liukiuensis B&SWJ 4960	WCru
§ ***macrophylla***	CArn CBcs CMac EPfP MRav SLim
manshuriensis	EBee
- B&SWJ 12557	WCru
moupinensis BWJ 8181	WCru
onoei B&SWJ 4960	WCru
paucinervis	SBrt
rotunda	CArn SKHP
sempervirens	CMac LEdu SBrt SGSe SKHP WCru WSHC
sipho	see *A. macrophylla*
tomentosa	SKHP

Aristotelia (*Elaeocarpaceae*)

§ ***chilensis***	IVic LEdu
- 'Variegata' (v)	CMCN CMac CWib EBee GQui SPlb
fruticosa (m)	ECou
- (f)	ECou
- black-fruited (f)	ECou
- white-fruited (f)	ECou
macqui	see *A. chilensis*
peduncularis	CExl
serrata	ECou SVen
- (f)	ECou
- (m)	ECou

Armeria (*Plumbaginaceae*)

§ ***alliacea*** (Cav.) Hoffmanns. & Link	ECha XSen
- f. ***leucantha***	SRms WMoo
'Bloodgood'	ECho
'Brutus'	CDes MAvo MHCG
caespitosa	see *A. juniperifolia*
- 'Bevan's Variety'	see *A. juniperifolia* 'Bevan's Variety'
gaditana new	XSen
Joystick Series	MMuc SEND
- 'Joystick Lilac Shades'	EBee ELan EPfP LBMP LRHS
- 'Joystick Red'	ELan EPfP EShb LRHS WHil WWFP
- 'Joystick White'	ELan EPfP LRHS WHil
§ ***juniperifolia*** ♀H5	CMea ECho ELan EPfP GCrg GMaP LRHS MHer NPri NSla SPlb SPoG SRms WIce XLum
- 'Alba'	CBod CMea ECho ELan EPfP EPot GCrg GMaP MHer MMuc NPri SPoG SRms SRot WAbe WHoo WThu
- 'Beechwood'	GCrg
§ - 'Bevan's Variety' ♀H5	ECha ECho ECtt ELan EPfP EPot GEdr GMaP MHer MMuc NLar NPri NRya SPoG SRms SRot WAbe WHoo
- dark-flowered	WAbe
- rose-flowered	ITim
juniperifolia × ***maritima***	ECho
§ ***maritima***	CArn CHab CNec CWld ECho ECtt ELan EPfP GJos LAst LPot LRHS MBel MSCN NEgg SWvt WCFE WHfH WMoo WRHF
- 'A Little in the Red'	EPot GCrg WAbe
- 'Alba'	CBcs CNec CTri ECha ECho ELan EPfP GJos GMaP LEdu LPfy LSun MBel MCot MHol MMuc NPri NRya SEND SPlb SPoG SRms WCFE WMoo XSen
- 'Armada Rose'	LRHS
- 'Bloodstone'	CTri ECho ELan MWat
- 'Corsica'	CTri ECha MMuc NBir
- Düsseldorf Pride	see *A. maritima* 'Düsseldorfer Stolz'
§ - 'Düsseldorfer Stolz'	CElw CNec CWld ECha ECho ECtt EDAr ELan EPfP EPot GCrg GMaP LHop LRHS MCot MLHP NPri SPoG SWvt WHlf WIce XLum
- 'Glory of Holland'	EPot
- 'In the Red'	CAby CBod CMea ECha ECtt EHoe EPPr EShb GCal GCrg GMaP LAst MAvo MHer MMuc NHol NPri NRya SEND SPoG SRms SRot SWvt WAbe WHoo WIce
- 'Laucheana'	WHoo WMoo
- 'Ministicks Rose'	LRHS
- 'Ministicks White'	LRHS
- 'Nifty Thrifty' (v)	CBod CTri ECho ECtt EHoe EWes MHer NPri SPoG SRms
- 'Pink Lusitanica'	NLar
- 'Ruby Glow'	CTri
- 'Schöne von Fellbach'	XLum

- 'Splendens'	CBcs CTri ECho EDAr EPfP GMaP LAst LRHS MBel MCot MGos MHer MHol MJak MMuc NMir NPri NRya SEND SPhx SPoG WMoo XLum XSen
- 'Splendens Alba'	XLum
- 'Vindictive' ♀^{H5}	CMea CTri EPfP
- white foliage **new**	LRHS
plantaginea misapplied	see *A. alliacea* (Cav.) Hoffmanns. & Link
pseudarmeria	ELan EPfP LPot XLum
- (Ballerina Series) 'Ballerina'	LEdu
- - 'Ballerina Red'	CWld GEdr LPfy LRHS NPri SHil SRms WTor
- - 'Ballerina White'	LPfy LRHS SHil
- hybrids	CTri ELan
pungens	GKev XSen
'Rosi' **new**	NPri
splendens 'Perfecta'	LRHS
'Vesuvius'	NPri XLum
vulgaris	see *A. maritima*
welwitschii	IFoB SRms

Armoracia (*Brassicaceae*)

§ ***rusticana***	CArn CBod CHby CLau CTri ENfk GAbr GPoy LCro LOPS MHer MMuc MNHC NPer NPri SIde SPoG SRms SVic WHer WJek
- 'Variegata' (v)	EBee ELan GCal IFoB LEdu LHop NSti SMad SRms WHer WJek WMoo

Arnebia (*Boraginaceae*)

densiflora	LLHF
echioides	see *A. pulchra*
longiflora	see *A. pulchra*
§ ***pulchra***	LLHF

Arnica (*Asteraceae*)

angustifolia subsp. ***alpina***	SRms
- subsp. ***iljinii***	NBir
chamissonis Schmidt	see *A. sachalinensis*
chamissonis Less.	CBod CHby EBee ENfk MNHC NLar SRms WJek XLum
montana	CArn EBee GPoy MHer MNHC SRms SWat WHfH
§ ***sachalinensis*** RBS 0206	EPPr

Arnoglossum (*Asteraceae*)

§ ***plantagineum***	SBrt SPhx

Aronia ✿ (*Rosaceae*)

arbutifolia	CBcs CDul CTri EPfP LSRN MBlu SGol SLon SPlb
- 'Erecta'	CDul CTho EBee ELan EWTr GBin LHop LRHS MBlu MMuc NLar SPoG SRms SWvt WCFE
melanocarpa	CCVT CDul CMCN CSpe CTsd CWib ELan EPfP EWTr GKin LEdu LRHS MAsh WGrn
- var. ***grandifolia***	CJun
- 'Hugin'	CAgr CJun LEdu MCoo NLar
× ***prunifolia***	CDoC GAbr LEdu WGrn
- 'Aron' (F)	CAgr CJun
- 'Autumn Magic'	CBcs CDoC CJun CTho EBee ELan EPfP GBin LAst LHop LRHS LSou MAsh MMuc NEgg NLar
- 'Brilliant'	CBcs CDoC CDul CTri EPfP GBin LRHS MBri NEgg NLar SGol SPer WHar WMat
- 'Karhumäki' (F)	NLar
- 'Nero' (F)	CAgr CBcs GBin GGGa LEdu LRHS MCoo NLar WMat
- 'Serina' (F)	CJun NLar
- 'Viking' (F)	CAgr CDul CJun CTho ECrN EPfP EPom EWTr GBin GGGa LBuc LCro LEdu LOPS LRHS MBlu NLar SGol

Arrhenatherum (*Poaceae*)

elatius	CHab
- var. ***bulbosum*** 'Variegatum' (v)	EBee EHoe ELan EPPr GBin GKev GMaP MMuc MWhi NBid NOak NWad SEND WMoo

Artemisia ✿ (*Asteraceae*)

RBS 0207	CExl
from Taiwan	WHer
§ ***abrotanum***	Widely available
* - 'Variegata' (v)	ELan
absinthium	CArn CBod CEls CHab ELan ENfk GPoy MHer MNHC NLar NSti SIde SRms SVic WHer WJek XLum XSen
- 'Lambrook Giant'	CEls
- 'Lambrook Mist'	CEls CFis CMac CPrp ECtt ELan EPfP EWoo GCal GQue LRHS MRav SWat WMnd WWEG XLum
- 'Lambrook Silver'	CEls CExl CSam EBee ECha ELan EPfP EWoo GCal GMaP LHop LPot LRHS LSRN MHer MMuc MRav NBro SCob SEND SLim SPer SRms SWat SWvt WMnd WWEG
- 'Silver Ghost'	CEls
afra	CEls XSen
§ ***alba***	CBod CEls GPoy MHer SRms WJek XSen
§ - 'Canescens' ♀^{H4}	CBot CEls CSam CTri EBee ECha ELan EPfP GMaP LAst LRHS MAsh MHer MRav SBrt SEND WCFE WMnd WWEG XSen
annua	CEls
anomala	CArn CEls
arborescens ♀^{H3}	CArn CBot CEls GAbr SPer
- 'Brass Band'	see *A.* 'Powis Castle'
- 'Faith Raven' ♀^{H3}	CEls GBin MBNS NLar
- 'Porquerolles'	CEls
arctica var. ***saxatilis***	EBee
argentea L'Hér.	CEls
argyi	CEls
§ ***armeniaca***	CEls ECho WHer XSen
assoana	see *A. caucasica*
atrata	CEls
barrelieri	CEls
caerulescens	WCot
subsp. ***cretacea*** **new**	
- subsp. ***gallica***	CEls
californica	CEls
- 'Canyon Gray'	CEls
campestris	XLum XSen
- subsp. ***borealis***	CEls
- subsp. ***campestris***	CEls
- subsp. ***maritima***	CEls
- - from Wales	CEls
camphorata	see *A. alba*
cana	CEls
canariensis	see *A. thuscula*
canescens misapplied	see *A. alba* 'Canescens'
canescens Willd.	see *A. armeniaca*
capillaris	CEls XLum
§ ***caucasica*** ♀^{H4}	CEls ECho EWes MHer SChF SPhx SRms SRot

	Plant	Suppliers
	chamaemelifolia	CBod CEls MHer SRms WJek XSen
	cretacea	see *A. nutans*
	discolor Dougl. ex Besser	see *A. michauxiana*
	douglasiana	CEls
	- 'Valerie Finnis'	see *A. ludoviciana* 'Valerie Finnis'
	dracunculus	ECha EWTr MJak MNHC MRav SPlb SRms WBrk WHfH
	- French	CArn CBod CEls CHby CLau CTsd ENfk GPoy LEdu MHer NPri SEND SIde WGwG WJek XLum
	- Russian	CEls ENfk SVic
	- 'Thüringen'	IMou
	ferganensis	CEls
	filifolia	CEls
	fragrans Willd.	CEls
	frigida ♀H5	CEls
	genipi	CEls
	glacialis	CEls
	gmelinii	CEls
	gnaphalodes	see *A. ludoviciana*
	gorgonum	CEls SEND
	'Hausserman'	XLum
	herba-alba	CEls XSen
	indica var. ***momiyamae***	CEls MAvo
	japonica	CEls
	kawakamii B&SWJ 088	WCru
	kitadakensis	CEls
	- 'Guizhou'	see *A. lactiflora* Guizhou Group
	laciniata	CEls
	lactiflora ♀H7	CEls CPrp EBee ECha ELan GBee GMaP MRav NGdn SDix SPer SRms WHfH WMoo XLum
	- NJM 11.010	WPGP
	- 'Elfenbein'	EBee EPPr GCal IMou LHop LPla MRav SMHy
§	- Guizhou Group	Widely available
	- - 'Dark Delight'	CEls CMos EBee ECtt EWes
	- 'Jim Russell'	CDes CEls CElw EBee ECtt EWes MAvo SPhx WWFP
	- 'Laigong'	LEdu
	- ***purpurea***	see *A. lactiflora* Guizhou Group
	- 'Weisses Wunder'	EBee
	lanata Willd.	see *A. caucasica*
	lanata Lam.	XSen
	laxa	see *A. umbelliformis*
	'Little Mice'	CEls WWEG
§	***ludoviciana***	CEls ELan GBee IFoB NLar NPer SRms WCFE WFar XLum
	- var. ***latifolia***	see *A. ludoviciana* subsp. *ludoviciana* var. *latiloba*
	- subsp. ***ludoviciana*** var. ***incompta***	CEls
	- - var. ***latiloba***	CEls EHoe LHop NBro SWvt WCot
	- subsp. ***mexicana*** var. ***albula***	CEls
	- 'Silver Queen'	Widely available
	- 'Valerie Finnis' ♀H7	Widely available
	maritima	CArn
	- 'Coca-Cola'	EBee
	- var. ***maritima***	CEls
	mauiensis	CEls
§	***michauxiana***	CEls EBee
	molinieri	CEls XSen
	mutellina	see *A. umbelliformis*
	niitakayamensis	CEls
	nitida	CEls
§	***nutans***	CEls MRav
	palmeri hort.	see *A. ludoviciana*
	aff. ***parviflora*** CLD 1531	CEls
	pedemontana	see *A. caucasica*
	pontica	CArn CBod CEls EBee ECha EHoe ELan GMaP GPoy LEdu MAvo MBNS MHer MNHC MRav NBro NLar NSti SPhx SRms WFar WHfH WHoo WPGP WWEG XSen
§	'Powis Castle' ♀H3	Widely available
	princeps	CArn CEls GPoy LEdu SIde
	procera Willd.	see *A. abrotanum*
	purshiana	see *A. ludoviciana*
	pycnocephala	CEls
	- 'David's Choice'	CEls
	ramosa	CEls
	'Rosenschleier'	CEls EWes GCal LPla MAvo SHar WPGP WWEG WWtn
	schmidtiana ♀H5	CEls CFis ECha MWat SDix WKif
	- 'Nana' ♀H5	Widely available
	- 'Nana Attraction'	EUJe LBMP LRHS NLar SRot
	selengensis	CEls
	spinescens	EBee
	splendens misapplied	see *A. alba* 'Canescens'
	splendens Willd.	SPhx
	- var. ***brachyphylla***	MAsh
	stelleriana	CEls CTri ECha EDAr GBee GKev IFoB LHop MAvo MHer NBro NLar SPer SRms
	- RBS 0207	CEls
	- 'Boughton Silver'	CBod CEls CWCL EBee ECtt EHoe ELan EPfP GMaP IKil LCro LRHS LSun MAsh MRav NEgg NLar NSti SPer SRms SWvt WWEG
	- 'Mori'	see *A. stelleriana* 'Boughton Silver'
	- 'Nana'	CEls SWvt
	- 'Prostrata'	see *A. stelleriana* 'Boughton Silver'
	- 'Silver Brocade'	see *A. stelleriana* 'Boughton Silver'
	taurica	CEls
§	***thuscula***	CEls
	tridentata	WHer
§	***umbelliformis***	CEls
	vallesiaca	CEls
	verlotiorum	CEls
	vulgaris	CArn CBod CEls CLau GPoy MHer MNHC WHer
	- 'Cragg-Barber Eye' (v)	EBee
	- Oriental Limelight = 'Janlim' (v)	CEls CLet CWld EBee ECtt EHoe EPPr EPfP GAbr MNHC NBir NEgg NLar SWvt WBod
	- 'Variegata' (v)	CEls EBee EPfP NBir SEND SRms WMoo XLum
	× ***wurzellii***	CEls

Arthropodium (*Asparagaceae*)

Plant	Suppliers
candidum	ECho ECou MPie
- 'Capri'	LPot
- 'Maculatum'	ECho LEdu SBrt SGSe SPlb
- ***purpureum***	ECho IKil
cirratum	CSpe CTre CTsd ECho IDee IKil MHer MPie
- 'Matapouri Bay'	CBcs ECre
milleflorum	SBrt
minus	CExl ECou

artichoke, globe see *Cynara cardunculus* Scolymus Group

artichoke, Jerusalem see *Helianthus tuberosus*

Arum (*Araceae*)

Plant	Suppliers
alpinum	see *A. cylindraceum*
'Chameleon'	CDes EPri LRHS NBir SEND SKHP SMad SPer WCot WRHF WWEG

§ ***concinnatum***	CEvo CTal ECho SChr SKHP
- 'Mount Ida'	ECho SKHP
cornutum	see *Sauromatum venosum*
creticum	CBro CCon CEvo CFil CPne EBee ECho GCal MNrw SKHP WBor
- 'Karpathos'	CExl CTal EPot GKev SKHP WCot
- 'Marmaris White'	CDes
- white-spotted	EWes
creticum* × *italicum	EBee
§ ***cylindraceum***	GKev
cyrenaicum	CFil ECho
dioscoridis	ECho EPot GKev
- JCA 195.197	WCot
- var. ***cyprium***	EBee
§ - var. ***dioscoridis***	GKev
- var. ***liepoldtii***	see *A. dioscoridis* var. *dioscoridis*
- var. ***smithii***	see *A. dioscoridis* var. *dioscoridis*
dracunculus	see *Dracunculus vulgaris*
hygrophilum	CEvo WCot
italicum	CLAP CTri ECho IBoy LAma LCro LOPS LPal MAvo MHol SDeJ SWat WCot WShi
- 'Angelique' **new**	CDes
- 'Edward Dougal'	MAvo WCot
- 'Green Marble'	SEND WFar WWEG
- subsp. ***italicum***	GKev WBrk
- - 'Cyclops'	WWEG
§ - - 'Marmoratum' ♀H6	Widely available
- - 'Sparkler'	WCot
- - 'Spotted Jack'	MAvo WCot WWEG
- - 'Tiny'	CDes CExl GCal SMHy SWvt WHil WRHF WWEG
§ - - 'White Winter'	CDes MAvo WBrk WCot WWEG
- 'Nancy Lindsay'	CEvo
- subsp. ***neglectum***	SChr
- - 'Miss Janay Hall' (v)	EHoe WCot
- 'Pictum'	see *A. italicum* subsp. *italicum* 'Marmoratum'
- 'Tresahor Beauty'	MAvo WWEG
italicum* × *lucanum	CEvo
italicum* × *maculatum	WHer
korolkowii	WCot
maculatum	EPot GKev GPoy LAma MHer MRav NLar WHer WShi
- 'Pleddel'	MRav WWEG
- Tar Spot Group	SEND
nickelii	see *A. concinnatum*
§ ***nigrum***	EWes GKev LLHF SBrt
orientale	EPot
palaestinum	CEvo
petteri misapplied	see *A. nigrum*
pictum	CExl CLAP CMac CTal ECho EWes LEdu
- 'Primrose Warburg'	CDes
- 'Taff's Form'	see *A. italicum* subsp. *italicum* 'White Winter'
purpureospathum	CFil EBee ECho WCot WPGP
'Streaked Spectre'	WWEG

Aruncus ✿ (*Rosaceae*)

aethusifolius ♀H7	Widely available
- 'Little Gem'	ECho WCru
asiaticus B&SWJ 8624	WCru
'Bastei'	IMou
dioicus	Widely available
§ - (m) ♀H7	CBen CMac EHoe ELan IBoy MBNS MRav MWts NBro NSti SMad SPer SRms SWat WMoo
- var. ***acuminatus***	EBee
- Child of Two Worlds	see *A. dioicus* 'Zweiweltenkind'
- 'Glasnevin'	ECtt GBee MRav NHol WFar
- var. ***kamtschaticus***	EWes NLar NWad WHrl
- - RBS 0208	NGdn
- 'Kneiffii'	Widely available
- 'Whirlwind' **new**	LPla
§ - 'Zweiweltenkind'	GCal LPla LRHS NLar SMad WCot XLum
'Guinea Fowl'	ECtt ELon GQue LEdu LPla MHol NGdn NLar NSti SCob
'Horatio'	CBod CSam EBee ECtt ELan GBin IMou IPot LEdu LHop LPla LRHS MAvo MBel MHol MMuc MPie NLar SCob SMHy SMad SPhx WCot WWtn
'Johannifest'	CDes EBee ECtt IMou IPot MAvo WCot
'Misty Lace'	ECtt GBin NGdn NLar SAko
'Netzwerk'	IMou
'Noble Spirit'	MBel NGdn NLar SGSe SWat
'Perlehuhn'	CDes EBee IMou
plumosus	see *A. dioicus*
sinensis	GAbr NBre
sylvestris	see *A. dioicus*
- 'Sommeranfang'	IMou
'Woldemar Meier'	EBee GBin IMou SAko WCot

Arundinaria (*Poaceae*)

anceps	see *Yushania anceps*
auricoma	see *Pleioblastus viridistriatus*
disticha	see *Pleioblastus pygmaeus* 'Distichus'
falconeri	see *Himalayacalamus falconeri*
fargesii	see *Bashania fargesii*
fastuosa	see *Semiarundinaria fastuosa*
fortunei	see *Pleioblastus variegatus*
§ ***gigantea***	CDTJ MWht
- subsp. ***tecta***	CBcs
hindsii	see *Pleioblastus hindsii*
hookeriana misapplied	see *Himalayacalamus falconeri* 'Damarapa'
hookeriana Munro	see *Himalayacalamus hookerianus*
humilis	see *Pleioblastus humilis*
japonica	see *Pseudosasa japonica*
jaunsarensis	see *Yushania anceps*
maling	see *Yushania maling*
marmorea	see *Chimonobambusa marmorea*
murielae	see *Fargesia murielae*
nitida	see *Fargesia nitida*
oedogonata	see *Clavinodum oedogonatum*
palmata	see *Sasa palmata*
pumila	see *Pleioblastus argenteostriatus* f. *pumilus*
pygmaea	see *Pleioblastus pygmaeus*
quadrangularis	see *Chimonobambusa quadrangularis*
simonii	see *Pleioblastus simonii*
spathiflora	see *Thamnocalamus spathiflorus*
tessellata	see *Bergbambos tessellata*
vagans	see *Sasaella ramosa*
variegata	see *Pleioblastus variegatus*
veitchii	see *Sasa veitchii*
viridistriata	see *Pleioblastus viridistriatus*
'Wang Tsai'	see *Bambusa multiplex* 'Floribunda'

Arundo (*Poaceae*)

donax	CAbb CKno CLet CPla EAla ELan EPPr ETod EUJe EWes GCra GGal GMaP IDee LRHS MAvo MBlu

		MBrN MNrw MRav SDix SEND SMad SPlb SPoG WHal WWEG
	- 'Golden Chain' (v)	CKno EPPr EWes LRHS SEND SMad
	- 'Macrophylla'	CExl CFil CHGN CKno ETod LEdu WPGP
	- 'Variegata'	see *A. donax* var. *versicolor*
§	- var. ***versicolor*** (v)	CAbb CBcs CBod CKno EAla ELan ELon EPPr ETod EUJe EWes LEdu LHop LLWG LRHS MBel MRav NLos SDix SEND SMad SPlb SPoG WWEG XLum XSen
I	- - 'Aureovariegata' (v)	CDTJ
	formosana	CKno EPPr
	- 'Golden Showers'	ESwi EUJe NLos

Asarina (*Plantaginaceae*)

	barclayana	see *Maurandya barclayana*
	erubescens	see *Lophospermum erubescens*
§	***procumbens***	CTri CWld EBee ECho IBoy NBir NRya SPhx SRms WAbe WBrk WKif

Asarum (*Aristolochiaceae*)

albomaculatum B&SWJ 1726	WCru
arifolium	EBee EPPr
- 'The Giant' new	EBee
campaniflorum	ECho WCru
canadense	CArn EBee ECho EWld GEdr GKev GPoy LEdu NLar WCru WWEG
cardiophyllum B&SWJ 11742	WCru
caudatum	CLAP EBee ECha ECho EPfP GEdr LEdu NBro NLar SRms WCot WCru
- deciduous	WCru
- white-flowered	SKHP WCru
caudigerum B&SWJ 1517	WCru
- HWJ 641 from Vietnam	WCru
caulescens	ECho EPPr LAma WCru
- B&SWJ 5886	WCru
delavayi	ECho GKev LAma LEdu NLar WCot WCru
- giant new	XEll
epigynum 'Silver Web'	WCru
europaeum ♀H6	Widely available
- PAB 4377	LEdu WPGP
fauriei	WCru
forbesii	ECho
hartwegii	CEvo CLAP IMou WThu
himalaicum GWJ 9341	WCru
hypogynum B&SWJ 3628	WCru
infrapurpureum B&SWJ 1994	LEdu WCru
- 'Taroko Web'	WCru
lemmonii	LEdu
leptophyllum B&SWJ 1983	WCru
longirhizomatosum	GEdr WCru
macranthum B&SWJ 1691	WCru
maculatum B&SWJ 1114	WCru
magnificum	LAma WCru
maximum	CCon ECho GKev LAma WCru
- 'Green Panda'	NLos
- 'Silver Panda'	CBct CDes CExl ESwi EUJe GEdr MPie SKHP WCot
megacalyx	CEvo
nipponicum B&SWJ 2839	WCru
petelotii HWJ 1043	WCru
pulchellum	WCot WCru
sieboldii	GPoy WCru
splendens	CBct CBro CHid ECho ELan EPfP EPot EUJe GBin GKev LAma LEdu LPal MHol MPie MRav MSCN NLar NLos NSti SGSe SKHP SMad SPlb WCot WCru WFar XLum
taipingshanianum B&SWJ 1688	WCru
- 'Elfin Yellow'	WCru
* takasago-saishin	GEdr NLar
wulingense	CExl CTal WCru

Asclepias ✿ (*Apocynaceae*)

	'Cinderella'	GKev SGol
	curassavica	EShb LLWG LTro SRkn XLum
	- 'Red Butterfly'	SLon
	exaltata	SBrt
§	***fascicularis***	SBrt
	fasciculata	see *A. fascicularis*
	fruticosa	see *Gomphocarpus fruticosus*
	hallii	EBee SIgm
	incarnata	ELan IFoB LRHS MRav MWhi SBea SBrt SPhx SPlb WOld XLum
	- 'Ice Ballet'	CAbP CBod ELan GKev IFoB LHop LLWG NLar SGSe SPer SPoG
*	- 'Iceberg'	SGol
	- 'Soulmate'	CBod EBee ELan EPfP GKev LPot SGSe SPer WHil
	latifolia	EBee
	physocarpa	see *Gomphocarpus physocarpus*
	purpurascens	CArn EBee
	rubra	SBrt
	speciosa	EBee MMuc NBre SBea SBrt WHil WPGP
	sullivantii	SBrt
	syriaca	EBee EWTr LPla MBel MMuc SGSe XLum
	tuberosa	CArn CBcs CBod CWib EBee ECtt GKev GPoy LAst LRHS MHer MNHC MPie SBea SCob SGSe SMad SPer SPoG WGwG XLum XSen
	- 'Hello Yellow'	SGSe
	verticillata	SBrt
	viridis	SBrt

Asimina (*Annonaceae*)

triloba (F)	CBcs EBee IBal MBlu NLar SGol SPlb

Asparagus (*Asparagaceae*)

hardy, from Malawi	SKHP
acutifolius new	XSen
asparagoides ♀H1c	EShb
densiflorus 'Mazeppa'	EShb
- 'Myersii' ♀H1c	EShb SEND
- Sprengeri Group ♀H1c	NGBl SEND
falcatus	SEND
filicinus	XBlo
- var. ***giraldii***	WCot
aff. ***meioclados*** B&SWJ 8309	WCot WCru
officinalis 'Ariane'	LCro LOPS WHar
- 'Backlim' ♀H4	ECrN EMil EPom SBmr
- 'Connover's Colossal' ♀H4	CHid CSBt ELan LCro LHop LOPS LSRN MMuc MNHC SBmr SEND SVic WHar
- 'Crimson Pacific'	SVic
- 'Dariana' ♀H4	SDea
- 'Gijnlim' ♀H4	ECrN EMil EPom LCro LOPS MMuc SBmr SDea
- 'Guelph Millennium' ♀H5	EPom LCro LEdu LOPS SBmr
- 'Jersey Knight'	SVic
- 'Mondeo'	EPom LCro LOPS

- 'Pacific 2000'	EPfP EPom LCro LOPS LSRN WMat
- 'Pacific Purple'	EPfP EPom LCro LEdu LOPS SBmr
- 'Stewart's Purple'	EPom WHar
pseudoscaber 'Spitzenschleier'	EBee EShb SDix WCot
retrofractus	WCot
scandens	EShb WCot
schoberioides	LEdu
- B&SWJ 8814	WCru
verticillatus	SGSe
virgatus	CTre EShb SPlb WPGP

Asperula (*Rubiaceae*)

§ ***arcadiensis*** ♀H3	ECho EPot WAbe
aristata subsp. ***scabra***	CSpe ECha LPla WCot
- subsp. ***thessala***	see *A. sintenisii*
boissieri	ECho EPot WAbe WThu
cynanchica	MMuc
daphneola	ECho EWes WAbe
gussonei	ECho SIgm WAbe WOld
lilaciflora	ECho
- var. ***caespitosa***	see *A. lilaciflora* subsp. *lilaciflora*
§ - subsp. ***lilaciflora***	ECho
nitida	ECho
- subsp. ***puberula***	see *A. sintenisii*
odorata	see *Galium odoratum*
§ ***sintenisii***	CMea ECho EPot WAbe WHoo WThu
suberosa misapplied	see *A. arcadiensis*
taurina	WPtf
- subsp. ***caucasica***	NLar WBor
tinctoria	CArn GPoy MHer SRms

Asphodeline (*Asphodelaceae*)

§ ***brevicaulis***	XSen
liburnica	CBro CSam ECha ELan EPri IMou SEND SPhx WCot XSen
§ ***lutea***	Widely available
§ - 'Gelbkerze'	CEvo EBee EPfP LRHS
- Yellow Candle	see *A. lutea* 'Gelbkerze'
taurica	CEvo MBNS SMHy WCot

Asphodelus (*Asphodelaceae*)

acaulis	CTal ECho LLHF WCot WWFP XLum
§ ***aestivus***	EBee EWes GCal MBel WCot XSen
albus	CArn CAvo CBro CSam CSpe ECha EPPr GJos IFoB MLHP NBid SPlb SRms XLum XSen
brevicaulis	see *Asphodeline brevicaulis*
cerasiferus	see *A. ramosus*
fistulosus	GJos LEdu XSen
lusitanicus	see *A. ramosus*
luteus	see *Asphodeline lutea*
microcarpus	see *A. aestivus*
§ ***ramosus***	CPar CTal ECho GCal LPla MCot WCot XSen

Aspidistra (*Asparagaceae*)

B&SWJ 6645 from Thailand	WCru
Chen Yi 135	WCot
attenuata	IBlr IMou
- B&SWJ 377	WCru
aff. ***attenuata*** B&SWJ 2001	WCru
caespitosa 'Jade Ribbons'	see *A. hainanensis* 'Jade Ribbons'
'China Star'	ESwi WCot
daibuensis	IBlr
- B&SWJ 312b	ESwi WCru
- B&SWJ 6863 new	WCru
- 'Totally Dotty' (v)	WCru
aff. ***daibuensis*** 'Tidy Trim'	ESwi WCru
elatior ♀H2	CBct CTsd EBak EBee EShb ESwi IBlr LEdu MMuc MRav NPla SAko SEND SMad WCot
- 'Akebono' (v)	WCot
- 'Asahi' (v)	IBlr WCot
- 'Hoshi-zora' (v)	IBlr WCot
- 'Lennon's Song' (v)	WCot
- 'Milky Way' misapplied	see *A. sichuanensis* 'Ginga'
- 'Milky Way' (v)	EBee EShb ESwi IBlr SAko SEND
- 'Okame' (v)	WCot
- 'Variegata' (v) ♀H2	IBlr IFoB NBir SEND
- 'Variegata Exotica' (v)	XBlo
§ ***hainanensis*** 'Jade Ribbons'	IBlr WCot
leshanensis (v)	IBlr
linearifolia 'Leopard'	ESwi IBlr WCot
lurida	EShb
- 'Ginga Giant' (v)	WCot
- 'Irish Mist' (v)	IBlr
minutiflora	WCot
mushaensis B&SWJ 1953	WCru
- B&SWJ 3727 new	WCru
aff. ***mushaensis*** 'Spotty Dotty' (v)	ESwi WCru
omeiensis	WCot
saxicola 'Uan Fat Lady'	see *A. zongbayi* 'Uan Fat Lady'
§ ***sichuanensis*** 'Ginga' (v)	WCot
sutepensis B&SWJ 5216	WCru
tonkinensis	WCru
typica 'China Sun'	WCot
zongbayi	WCot
§ - 'Uan Fat Lady'	ESwi WCot WCru

Asplenium ✿ (*Aspleniaceae*)

antiquum 'Osaka'	LRHS
bulbiferum misapplied	see *A.* × *lucrosum*
bulbiferum ambig. × ***oblongifolium***	GBin
bulbiferum Forst.f.	ESwi GBin
§ ***ceterach***	EBee WHer XLum
daucifolium	NWad
§ × ***lucrosum*** ♀H1c	CKel ESwi LPal
'Maori Princess'	EBee GBin WFib
nidus ♀H1b	XBlo
oblongifolium	GBin
§ ***scolopendrium*** ♀H6	Widely available
- 'Angustatum' ♀H6	Widely available
- Crispum Group ♀H6	CLAP EFer ELan NBid SRms SRot WFar WFib WPGP
- - 'Crispum Bolton's Nobile'	WFib
- - 'Golden Queen'	CLAP
- Crispum Cristatum Group	CBod CLAP CTal LCro MBri MMuc SCob
- - 'Crispum Cristatum Bolton'	WCot
- Crispum Fimbriatum Group	CLAP
- Cristatum Group	CLAP CWCL EBee ECtt ELan ELon EPfP LAst LRHS MGos MRav NBro NLar SPad SPer SPoG SRms SRot SWat WBor WFib WMoo
- Fimbriatum Group	CLAP LRHS
- 'Furcatum'	CDTJ CLAP EBee ELan MMuc NLar SEND
- 'Kaye's Lacerated' ♀H5	CLAP EFer WFib
- Laceratum Group	CLAP
- Marginatum Group	EFer GKev SRms
- 'Muricatum'	CLAP ELan GBin MRav NBid WFib

- 'Ramocristatum'	CLAP
- Ramomarginatum Group	CLAP
- 'Sagittato-crispum' **new**	SRms
- 'Sagittatoprojectum Sclater'	WFib
- Undulatum Group	CDTJ CLAP EAEE EBee ECha EPfP EUJe GEdr LPal LRHS MMuc NBir NEgg NLar SEND SRms WCot WPnP XLum
- Undulatum Cristatum Group	CLAP
trichomanes ♀[H6]	Widely available
- Cristatum Group	SRms
- Incisum Group ♀[H6]	EBee EFer SRms WAbe
- 'Ramocristatum'	WAbe

Astartea (*Myrtaceae*)

fascicularis	ECou

Astelia (*Asteliaceae*)

alpina	IBlr
banksii	CBcs CSpe EBee IBal LPfy LRHS LSRN MBri MGos SCoo SHil SLim SPoG WCot
§ ***chathamica*** ♀[H3]	Widely available
- 'Silver Spear'	see *A. chathamica*
chathamica* × *fragrans	ECou
cunninghamii	see *A. solandri*
fragrans	CCon ECou IBlr LEdu
graminea	GCal
grandis	CBcs IBlr LEdu WPGP
nervosa	ECou IBlr LSRN
- 'Alpine Ruby'	IBlr
- 'Bronze Giant'	IBlr
- 'Silver Sabre'	IBlr
- 'Westland'	CBcs CDoC COtt CPne CSpe CTsd GCal IBlr ILea LEdu LHop LPfy LRHS LSRN MBri MGos NLos SCob SEND SHil SLim SPoG SWvt WCot
nivicola 'Golden Gem'	IBlr
- 'Red Gem'	LEdu
petriei	IBlr
'Red Devil'	CBcs CDoC CSpe ECou EPfP GBin IBoy LPfy LRHS MGos MHol SHil WHer
'Silver Mound'	EPfP SCob
'Silver Shadow'[PBR]	CBod CDoC EBee EPfP LCro LPfy LRHS MBri NLos SHil SPad SWvt WCot
§ ***solandri***	ECou IBlr

Aster ✿ (*Asteraceae*)

acris	see *A. sedifolius*
ageratoides	CPou WOld
- 'Ashvi'	ECtt MAvo MHol MTis SPoG WCot WOld
- 'Asran'	CHVG EBee ECtt EHoe EPPr EWes EWld GCal LSou MMuc MPie SEND WBrk WCot WOld WTor WWEG XLum
- 'Ezo Murasaki'	NDov WCot
- var. ***firmus*** **new**	WPGP
- - PAB 9347 **new**	LEdu
- 'Harry Smith'	NDov WCot WWEG
- 'Little Theo'	EBee
- 'Stardust'	WOld
- 'Starshine'[PBR]	ECtt EPPr IBoy LRHS SHil WCot
alpigenus	WHil
- var. ***alpigenus***	LLHF
- var. ***haydenii***	LLHF
alpinus ♀[H5]	EBee ECho EPfP GJos LPot MAsh MHol NRya SRms XSen
- var. ***albus***	EDAr EPfP NLar NPri WCot
- 'Antje'	MNrw
- blue-flowered **new**	NPri
- Dark Beauty	see *A. alpinus* 'Dunkle Schöne'
- var. ***dolomiticus***	NSla
§ - 'Dunkle Schöne'	EAJP EDAr SRms
- 'Goliath'	EPfP NLar SPlb
- 'Happy End'	CNec CRos LRHS MGos NLar SRms XLum
- 'Pinkie'	EAJP EBee EDAr EPfP NLar NPri
- 'Trimix'	ECho NBir SRms
- 'White Beauty'	SRms
amelloides	see *Felicia amelloides*
amellus 'Blue King'	ECtt GBuc NWsh SWvt
- 'Breslau'	EBee
- 'Brilliant'	CBod CPrp ECha ECtt EPPr GBuc LAst LRHS LSou MAvo MBNS MMuc MRav MWat NEgg SAko SEND SPer WGwG WHoo WOld
- 'Butzemann'	WCot
- 'Doktor Otto Petschek'	ELon WCot
- Empress	see *A. amellus* 'Glücksfund'
- 'Forncett Flourish'	ECtt MHCG WCot WOld
- 'Framfieldii' ♀[H7]	ECtt NDov SMHy WCot WOld WWEG
§ - 'Glücksfund'	SAko
- 'Gründer'	IMou MAvo MHCG WOld
- 'Jacqueline Genebrier' ♀[H7]	ELon GBuc MHCG NDov WOld
- 'King George' ♀[H7]	Widely available
- 'Kobold'	WOld
- 'Lac de Genève'	WCot
- 'Lady Hindlip'	CSam ECtt IMou WCot
- 'Louise'	MBrN MHCG SBch
- 'Mira'	MNrw SAko
- 'Moerheim Gem'	IMou WOld
- 'Mrs Ralph Woods'	WOld
- 'Nocturne'	IKil WCot WOld
- 'Peach Blossom'	WOld
- Pink Zenith	see *A. amellus* 'Rosa Erfüllung'
§ - 'Rosa Erfüllung'	CBod CMac EAJP EBee ECtt ELan ELon EPPr EPfP GBin GBuc GMaP IVic LAst LHop LRHS LSou MNrw MRav NWsh SBod SCob SPhx SRGP SWvt WCAu WMnd WOld
- 'Rotfeuer'	ELon GQue SAko
- 'Rudolph Goethe'	CNec EBee ECtt ELan EMil EPPr EPfP GBee IKil LAst LPot LRHS NLar WOld
- 'Silbersee'	CSam IMou SAko
- 'Sonia'	EBee ECtt GBuc LRHS SWvt WOld
- 'Sonora'	LHop LPla MNrw SPhx WKif WOld WWEG
- 'Sternkugel'	WOld
- 'Ultramarine'	WOld
- 'Vanity'	WOld
§ - 'Veilchenkönigin' ♀[H7]	Widely available
- Violet Queen	see *A. amellus* 'Veilchenkönigin'
- 'Weltfriede'	ECtt WOld
× ***amethystinus***	MNrw WCot
- 'Freiburg'	MNrw
'Anita Pfeiffer'	LRHS
'Anja's Choice'	EBee LHop WOld
'Ann Leys' **new**	SCob
'Aqua Compact' (Autumn Jewels Series) **new**	LSou
asperulus misapplied	see *A. peduncularis*
'Beauté du Nord' **new**	WCot

	'Betel Nut' **new**	SDix
	'Blue Butterfly'	SPhx
	'Blütenregen'	WCot
	capensis 'Variegatus'	see *Felicia amelloides* variegated
	'Carmen'	WCAu
§	***carolinianus***	XEll
	'Cassandra'	NCGa
	'Cheavers'	LRHS
	'Chilly Fingers'	MAvo MTis
	ciliolatus	EBee
	'Climax' misapplied	see *A. laevis* 'Arcturus', *A. laevis* 'Calliope'
	'Climax' ambig.	CElw EBee ELan GCal GQue MMuc MRav NBid SDix SEND WBrk XLum
	'Climax' Vicary Gibbs	MNrw WOld
	coelestis	see *Felicia amelloides*
	coloradoensis	LLHF NSla
	'Connecticut Snow Flurry'	see *A. ericoides* f. *prostratus* 'Snow Flurry'
	conspicuus	MAvo
	'Coombe Fishacre' ♀H7	CBot CPrp EBee ECtt ELan ELon GBuc GCal LEdu LPla LRHS MNrw NDov NLar SPhx SRGP SWvt WCAu WCot WHoo WOld
	cordifolius	EWoo SPhx
	- from Piney Fork	EPPr
	- 'Aldebaran'	NDov WOld
	- 'Blue Heaven' **new**	SAko
	- 'Chieftain' ♀H7	MHCG MNrw SMHy SPhx WOld
	- 'Elegans'	CSam EBee SDix WMnd WOld
	- 'Ideal'	NLar XLum
	- 'Silver Queen'	WHil
	- 'Silver Spray'	CKno ECtt ELon GMaP GQue MHom MWat SRGP WOld XLum
	- 'Sweet Lavender' ♀H7	EBee LRHS WOld WWEG
	- 'White Chief'	WOld
	corymbosus	see *A. divaricatus*
	'Cotswold Gem'	ECtt WCot WOld
	diffusus	see *A. lateriflorus*
	diplostephioides	EPPr EPfP GBin GBuc GKev IKil MBNS MMHG NLar SGSe SPlb WOld WPtf
§	***divaricatus***	Widely available
§	- 'Eastern Star'	NCGa WCot WOld
	- Raiche form	see *A. divaricatus* 'Eastern Star'
	- 'Tradescant'	IMou MNrw
	'Duchess' (mixed)	CWCL
	dumosus	CExl
	- 'Biteliness'	NLar WOld
	- Sapphire = 'Kiesapphire'PBR (Autumn Jewels Series)	CPrp ELon EWoo LBMP LHop LRHS LSRN MBri MHol NEgg SRGP SRkn SWvt WBod
	'Dwarf Barbados'	EPfP LRHS
	'Early Blue'	IBoy ILea
	ericoides	CKno NBre WOld WWEG
	- 'Blue Star' ♀H6	CPrp LRHS NLar WMnd WOld WWEG
	- 'Blue Wonder'	XLum
	- 'Brimstone' ♀H6	MRav WOld
	- 'Cinderella'	CPrp EBee LRHS NSti WOld WWEG
	- 'Constance'	WOld
	- 'Deep Danziger'	SPhx
	- 'Erlkönig'	CBod EBee EPri EShb GCal GQue LAst NGdn NLar SDix SPer SWat SWvt WCot WMnd WOld XLum
	- 'Esther'	CPrp ECha ELan WOld
	- 'First Snow'	WCot
	- 'Golden Spray' ♀H6	EBee ELon EPfP EWes GMaP GQue NLar WMnd WOld
	- 'Herbstmyrte'	LRHS
	- 'Hon. Edith Gibbs'	WOld
	- 'Monte Cassino'	see *A. pilosus* var. *pringlei* 'Monte Cassino'
	- 'Pink Cloud' ♀H6	CBod CBot CHVG CPrp ECtt EPfP EPri EShb GBuc GCal LAst LEdu LRHS MSpe NCGa NWad SAko SDix SPhx SWat WBrk WCot WMnd WOld WWEG
	- f. ***prostratus***	EPot GBuc GQue MRav SAko XEll XSen
§	- - 'Snow Flurry' ♀H6	CMea ECha ECtt ELon GBuc IMou LEdu LPla MAvo MHol MNrw MWat NLar SBch SWvt WCot WHoo WMnd WOld WOut XLum
	- 'Rosy Veil'	MHom NBir NGdn WOld
	- 'Schneegitter'	LRHS SPhx WCot XSen
	- 'Schneetanne'	SAko
	- 'Sulphurea'	MWat
	- 'Vimmer's Delight'	WCot
	- 'White Heather'	ECtt NLar WMnd WOld
	- 'Yvette Richardson'	CSam SMHy WOld
	falcatus	WCot
	- var. ***commutatus***	WCot WOld
	'Fanny's Fall'	see *A. oblongifolius* 'Fanny's'
	foliaceus from Montana	EPPr
	- var. ***parryi***	EBee
	× ***frikartii***	CMac ELan EPfP MRav SWvt WSHC
	- 'Eiger'	WOld
	- 'Flora's Delight'	EBee ECtt GCal LRHS MNrw MRav NLar SPoG SRms WCAu WHoo WOld WWEG
	- 'Jungfrau'	CWGN EBee EPPr GBuc GMaP GQue IKil LRHS MRav NLar SPhx WOld WWEG
	- 'Mönch' ♀H7	Widely available
	- Wonder of Stafa	see *A.* × *frikartii* 'Wunder von Stäfa'
§	- 'Wunder von Stäfa' ♀H7	CDes CExl CKno EAEE EBee ECtt ELan ELon EPfP GBuc GMaP LHop LRHS LSRN LSou MBNS MCot MHol MWat MWhi NBir NLar SRGP SWvt WCot WMnd WOld XLum
	furcatus	XLum
	glehnii	SDix
	- 'Aglenii'	IMou NDov SMad
	'Glow in the Dark'	CDes EBee MAvo MSpe NLar WBrk WCot WHoo WOld
	greatae	EBee
	'Herfstweelde'	CPrp EBee SMad SPhx WOld
§	× ***herveyi***	CBod CCon CPrp CSam ECha ECtt EPPr GLog GQue IKil IMou LCro LEdu LOPS LRHS MMuc MSpe MTis NDov NLar NSti SDix SPer SPhx WCAu WCot WMnd WOld WPtf WSHC
	himalaicus	NSla
	'Hon. Vicary Gibbs' (*ericoides* hybrid)	WOld WOut
	hybridus luteus	see *Solidago* × *luteus*
	'Ivy House'	ECtt
*	***kotarimus***	XLum
	'Kylie'	CBot CHVG CPrp ECtt LEdu LSRN MHom MNrw MTis SPhx SRGP WBor WBrk WHil WOld
	laevis	LEdu NLar SPhx
§	- 'Arcturus'	CCon CElw MAvo MBel MHom MNrw MTis NBir NCGa SDix WCot WMnd WOld WWEG XLum
	- 'Blauhügel'	LPla NDov
	- 'Blue Bird'	WOld
§	- 'Calliope'	Widely available

	Name	Suppliers
	- 'Cally Compact'	GQue NLar WOld
	- var. ***geyeri***	MNrw WOut
	- 'Nightshade'	MAvo MNrw MTis WBrk WOld
	- 'Vesta'	MTis WOld
	- white-flowered	WBrk WOld
	lanceolatus Willd.	EPPr NCGa
	- 'Edwin Beckett'	CBre MHom MNrw SWvt WOld
§	***lateriflorus***	SWvt WOld
	- 'Bleke Bet'	WCot WOld
	- 'Buck's Fizz'	ELan NDov WOld WWEG
	- 'Chloe'	CSam NCGa SPhx WCot
	- 'Datschi'	XLum
	- var. ***horizontalis*** ♀H7	Widely available
	- 'Jan'	WOld
	- 'Lady in Black'	Widely available
	- 'Lovely'	CSam SRGP WCot
	- 'Prince'	Widely available
	laterifolius 'Snow Flurry'	see *A. ericoides* f. *prostratus* 'Snow Flurry'
	'Les Moutiers'	MAvo MHom MNrw SDix WBrk WOld
§	***linosyris***	EWes GBin MAvo NLar SPer SPhx WHer WOld XLum
	- 'Gold Dust'	GBin
	- 'Goldilocks'	see *A. linosyris*
	'Little Carlow' (*cordifolius* hybrid) ♀H7	Widely available
	'Little Dorrit' (*cordifolius* hybrid)	ECtt NWsh
	maackii	WCot
	macrophyllus	CFis ELan LRHS MSpe NLar SPhx WFar WOld WWtn
	- 'Albus'	EPPr WFar WOld
	- 'Twilight'	see *A.* × *herveyi*
	mongolicus	see *Kalimeris mongolica*
	'Mrs Dean'	ECtt
	natalensis	see *Felicia rosulata*
	'Natasha'	LSRN
	(Newstars Series) 'Newstars Fantasy'	CBot WCot WOld
	- 'Newstars Glory'	CBot ECtt WCot
	'Nicholas'	ECtt WCot WOld
	'Noreen'	MAvo MHCG WOld
	novae-angliae	GKev WOld
	- 'Abendsonne' **new**	SAko
	- 'Alex Deamon'	ELon MAvo WBrk WOld
	- 'Anabelle de Chazal'	ECtt ELon MAvo WBrk WOld
	- 'Andenken an Alma Pötschke'	Widely available
	- 'Andenken an Paul Gerber'	ECtt ELon LHop MAvo MHom MNrw NLar SRGP WOld
	- 'Augusta'	ELon MAvo NLar SPhx WBrk WOld
	- Autumn Snow	see *A. novae-angliae* 'Herbstschnee'
	- 'Badsey Pink' **new**	WCot
	- 'Barr's Blue'	CMac EBee ECtt ELan ELon EPfP GCra MAvo MHom MMuc MTis MWat NLar NWsh SEND SPer SRms WBrk WCAu WFar WMoo WOld
	- 'Barr's Pink'	CBot CBre CMac EBee ECtt ELan ELon EPfP MAvo MCot MHom MLHP MMuc MPie MTis MWat NLar SEND SRGP WBrk WFar WOld WSFF
*	- 'Barr's Purple'	ECtt WBrk WCFE WFar WOld
	- 'Barr's Violet'	CHVG CPrp ECtt MAvo MHom NSti SRms WCot WFar WHal WHoo WHrl WMoo WOld
	- 'Bishop Colenso'	EPPr
	- 'Brockamin'	MAvo MNrw WBrk
	- 'Brockamin Margaret'	WOld
	- 'Brunswick'	WOld

	Name	Suppliers
	- 'Christopher Harbutt'	LEdu SRGP WBrk
	- 'Colwall Century'	MAvo WBrk WOld
	- 'Colwall Constellation'	MAvo WBrk WOld
	- 'Colwall Galaxy'	MAvo WBrk WHrl WOld
	- 'Colwall Orbit'	ECtt ELon MAvo WOld
	- 'Connie'	MNrw MSpe
	- 'Constanze' **new**	EBee MTis
	- 'Crimson Beauty'	ECtt ELon MAvo MHCG MHer MHom MNrw MWat SAko WBrk WOld WWEG
	- 'Dapper Tapper'	ECtt MAvo WCot WOld
	- 'Evensong'	ECtt LEdu MAvo MNrw WBrk WOld
	- 'Festival'	WBrk
	- 'Foxy Emily'	ECtt MHCG WBrk WOld
	- 'Harrington's Pink' ♀H7	Widely available
	- 'Helen Picton'	CSam ECtt ELon EWld LEdu MAvo MBrN MHer MHom MPie MWat NLar NWsh SAko WBrk WHoo WOld
§	- 'Herbstschnee'	Widely available
	- 'James'	MAvo
	- 'James Ritchie'	CSam ELon LLHF MAvo WHoo WOld
	- 'John Davies'	MAvo MNrw SBch WHil WOld
	- 'Jon Baker'	CBot MAvo WBrk
	- 'Kate Deamon'	ECtt WOld
	- 'Lachsglut'	ELon MAvo NLar SAko WBrk WCot WOld
	- 'Ladies Day'	WOld
	- 'Little Bella'	ECtt WOld
	- 'Lou Williams'	ECtt ELon LPla MAvo MNrw MWat NLar WBrk WHil WOld
I	- 'Lucida'	MAvo SPhx WHal WOld WWEG
	- 'Lucinda'	ECtt
	- 'Lye End Beauty'	CKno ECtt ELon LLWP MAvo MHer MHom MNrw MWat SBch SRGP WBod WBrk WCot WHoo WMoo WOld
	- 'Mabelle'	NDov
	- 'Marina Wolkonsky'	CAby ECGP ECtt ELon EWes LEdu LHop MAvo MNrw MTis MWat NLar SAko SPhx WBrk WCot WKif WOld WWEG
	- 'Millennium Star'	ECtt ELon WOld
	- 'Miss K.E. Mash'	CPrp ECtt MHom NLar SRGP WBrk WOld WWEG
	- 'Mrs S.T. Wright'	CPrp CTri ECtt EWes LEdu MAvo MBrN MNrw SRGP WFar WOld
	- 'Mrs S.W. Stern'	WBrk WOld
	- 'Nachtauge' **new**	SAko
	- 'Naomi'	WBrk WOld
	- 'Pink Parfait'	CSam ECtt IKil MAvo NGdn SRms WBrk WCot WOld
	- 'Pink Victor'	CTri MAvo SRms WMoo
	- 'Pride of Rougham'	EWes LLWP MAvo
	- 'Primrose Upward'	MAvo MNrw NDov NWsh SPhx WCot WOld
	- 'Purple Cloud'	CSam ELon LHop MAvo MHer MHom MWat NGdn WBrk WHal WOld
I	- 'Purple Dome'	Widely available
	- 'Quinton Menzies'	ELon MAvo WOld WWEG
	- 'Red Cloud'	ECtt ELon LEdu MAvo MHer WBrk WOld
	- 'Rosa Sieger' ♀H7	CAby CBre CPrp CSam ECtt ELon GMaP GQue LEdu MAvo MHom MNrw MTis NGdn NLar SPhx SRGP WBor WBrk WHil WHoo WOld WWEG XLum
	- 'Rose Williams'	LEdu MAvo SBch WOld

- 'Röter Stern'	ECtt MPie WBrk WOld
- 'Roter Turm' **new**	SAko
- 'Rougham Pink'	MAvo WBrk
- 'Rougham Purple'	EWes
- 'Rougham Violet'	EPPr WBrk
- 'Rubinschatz'	EBee ELon MAvo MHom MTis MWat NWsh SRms WOld XLum
- 'Rudelsburg'	EBee ECtt MAvo WBrk
- 'Rudolph' **new**	EWes
- 'Saint Michael's'	MAvo WBrk WOld
- 'Sayer's Croft'	ECtt ELon MAvo MHom MWat WCot WHil WHoo WOld WOut
- September Ruby	see *A. novae-angliae* 'Septemberrubin'
§ - 'Septemberrubin'	CAby CMea EBee ECtt ELan ELon EPfP IFoB LEdu LHop LSou MAvo MBel MMuc MRav MTis NSti NWsh SAko SEND SPhx SRGP SRms WOld XLum
- 'Treasure'	CBre ECtt ELon EWes LRHS MAvo NBre SPhx SRGP WBrk WMoo WOld
- 'Vibrant Dome'PBR	LRHS MTis NLar
- 'Violet Dusk'	WBrk
- 'Violet Haze'	CMea ELon WBrk
- 'Violetta'	CBot ECtt ELon GMaP LCro LRHS LSou MAvo MHom MNrw MTis SCob SPhx WHil WHoo WKif WOld
- 'W. Bowman'	ECtt MNrw WBrk WOld
- 'Wow'	ELon WHil
'Novemberlaan'	MSpe
novi-belgii	WHer WMoo
- 'Ada Ballard'	CBod CFis CMac EBee LHop LRHS LSRN NEgg SPer SRGP WMoo WOld WWEG
- 'Albanian'	WOld
- 'Alderman Vokes'	WOld
- 'Algar's Pride'	ECtt WHlf WOld WWEG
- 'Alice Haslam'	CMac EBee ECtt ELan LRHS MHol MJak NLar SRGP SRms WOld WWEG
- 'Angela Peel'	LRHS
- 'Anita Ballard'	WOld
- 'Anita Webb'	NBir WOld
- 'Anneke'	NLar SRGP WOld
- 'Apollo'	LRHS MWat NLar WOld
- 'Apple Blossom'	WOld
- 'Aramis Rose' **new**	EBee
- 'Audrey'	CMac GMaP LPot LRHS LSRN MBNS NGdn SBea SRGP SRms WOld
- 'Autumn Beauty'	WOld
- 'Autumn Days'	WOld
- 'Autumn Glory'	WOld
- 'Autumn Rose'	WOld
- 'Baby Climax'	WOld
- 'Bahamas' (Island Series)	CBod CNec EPfP LBMP LRHS NEgg NLar NWsh SPoG SRms SWvt WCot WHil
- 'Barbados' (Island Series)	CBod EPfP LOPS NLar SPoG SWvt WCot
- 'Beauty of Colwall'	WOld
- 'Beechwood Challenger'	MHCG MPie WBrk WOld
- 'Beechwood Charm'	SDix WOld
- 'Beechwood Rival'	CTri WOld XEll
- 'Blandie'	CTri SRGP WOld
- 'Blauglut'	SAko WHlf WOld
- 'Blue Baby'	CMac
- 'Blue Bouquet'	CTri SRms WOld
- 'Blue Boy'	WOld WWEG
- 'Blue Danube'	WOld
- 'Blue Eyes'	MAvo WOld
- 'Blue Gown'	CCse GCal GQue WOld WOut
- 'Blue Lagoon'	CBot CFis CMea ELan LSRN MMuc SRGP WBrk WOld
- 'Blue Lapis' **new**	EBee LRHS
I - 'Blue Moon' Old Court Nurseries	WOld
- 'Blue Patrol'	WOld
- 'Blue Radiance'	WOld
- 'Blue Spire'	WOld
- 'Blue Whirl'	WOld
- 'Boningale Blue'	WOld
- 'Boningale White'	MHCG NDov WHil WOld
- 'Bridesmaid'	WOld
- 'Bridgette'	WOld
- 'Bright Eyes'	SRGP WOld
- 'Brightest and Best'	WOld
- 'Brigitte'	CBod NLar
- 'Cameo'	WOld
- 'Cantab'	WOld
- 'Carlingcott'	WOld
- 'Carnival'	CMac EBee ECtt IVic LRHS SRGP WOld
- 'Cecily'	WOld WWEG
- 'Charles Wilson'	CFis WOld
- 'Chatterbox'	EBee ELan EPfP LPot LRHS MRav MWat NEgg NLar SRGP SRms WHar WOld
- 'Chelwood'	WOld
- 'Chequers'	CElw EBee MBNS MHer NEgg SRGP WOld
- 'Christina'	see *A. novi-belgii* 'Kristina'
- 'Christine Soanes'	WOld
- 'Cliff Lewis'	WOld
- 'Climax Albus'	see *A.* 'White Climax'
- 'Cloudy Blue'	WOld
- 'Colonel F.R. Durham'	WOld
- 'Coombe Gladys'	WOld
- 'Coombe Margaret'	WBrk WOld
- 'Coombe Radiance'	WOld
- 'Coombe Ronald'	WOld
- 'Coombe Rosemary'	ECtt NLar WBor WOld
- 'Coombe Velvet' **new**	WHlf
- 'Coombe Violet'	MWat WOld
- 'Countess of Dudley'	CFis WOld
- 'Court Herald'	WOld
- 'Crimson Brocade'	ECtt ELan EPfP LPfy LRHS NLar SAko SHil SPoG SRGP SRms SWvt
- 'Dandy'	CMac ELan EPfP LRHS NBir NGdn SRGP WOld
- 'Daniela'	SRms WBrk WOld WWEG
- 'Daphne Anne'	WOld
- 'Dauerblau'	EBee WOld
- 'Davey's True Blue'	CTri WOld XLum
- 'David Murray'	WOld
- 'Dazzler'	ECtt WOld WWEG
- 'Destiny'	WOld
- 'Diana'	ECtt NWsh
- 'Diana Watts'	WOld
- 'Dietgard'	ELon MWat WOld WWEG
- 'Dolly'	CElw NBir SRms WOld WWEG
- 'Dora Chiswell'	WOld
- 'Dusky Maid'	ELon WOld
- 'Elizabeth Hutton'	SRGP WOld
- 'Elsie Dale'	WOld
- 'Elta'	WOld
- 'Erica'	CElw MWat WOld
- 'Ernest Ballard'	WOld
- 'Eva'	ELon SRms WOld

- 'Eventide'	CTri LSRN WOld
- 'Fair Lady'	MWat WOld
- 'Faith'	WOld
- 'Fellowship' ♀H6	CBod CBot CDes CHVG EAJP EBee ECtt ELon IKil LEdu LRHS MAvo MMuc MNrw NLar SAko SHar SRGP SRms SWvt WBrk WCot WOld WWEG
- 'Flamingo'	EBee LRHS WOld
- 'Freda Ballard'	CFis ECtt GMaP LRHS MWat SRGP WOld WWEG
- 'Freya'	CElw LSRN WOld WSHC
- 'Fuldatal'	WOld
- 'Gayborder Blue'	WOld
- 'Gayborder Royal'	CCon WOld
- 'Goliath'	WOld
- 'Grey Lady'	WOld WWEG
- 'Guardsman'	WOld
- 'Gulliver'	WBrk WOld WWEG
- 'Gurney Slade'	WOld
- 'Guy Ballard'	WOld
- 'Harrison's Blue'	MWat WOld
- 'Heinz Richard'	CFis ECha MHer MMuc NBir NGdn SRGP SRms WOld WWEG
- 'Helen'	ELon WOld
- 'Helen Ballard'	NBid SRms WOld
- 'Herbstgruss vom Bresserhof'	LRHS NBre NLar SAko WOld
- 'Hilda Ballard'	WOld
- 'Ibiza'	WCot
- 'Ilse Brensell'	WOld WWEG
- 'Irene'	WOld
- 'Janet Watts'	WOld
- 'Jean'	ELon SRms WOld
- 'Jean Gyte'	WOld
- 'Jeanette'	SRms WOld
- 'Jenny'	Widely available
- 'Jollity'	WOld
- 'Jugendstil'	XLum
- 'Julia'	WOld
- 'Kassel'	SRms WOld
- 'King of the Belgians'	WOld
§ - 'Kristina'	EBee ECha EPPr ITim LRHS MMuc MNrw MRav NBir WOld WWEG
- 'Lady Frances'	EBee SRms WOld
- 'Lady in Blue'	CSBt ECtt ELan EPPr EPfP LAst LEdu LHop LPfy LRHS MBNS MGos MWat NEgg NGdn NWad SBod SGbt SHil SPer SPoG SRGP SRms SWat SWvt WCAu WHar WOld WWEG
- 'Lassie'	MWat WHlf WOld
- 'Lavender Dream'	WOld
- 'Lawrence Chiswell'	WOld
- 'Lederstrumpf'	NDov
- 'Lisa Dawn'	WOld
- 'Little Boy Blue'	CBod SRms WOld XLum
- 'Little Man in Blue'	WOld WWEG
- 'Little Pink Beauty'	CNec ECtt ELan EPfP IBoy ITim LAst LHop LRHS MBNS NGdn NHol NWad SBea SPer SRGP SRms WBod WCAu WHar WOld WWEG
- 'Little Pink Lady'	MHCG SRms WOld
- 'Little Pink Pyramid'	SRms WOld WWEG
- 'Little Red Boy'	WOld
- 'Little Treasure'	WOld
- 'Madge Cato'	SRms WOld
- 'Mammoth'	WOld
- 'Margery Bennett'	WOld
- 'Marie Ann Neil'	SRms WOld
- 'Marie Ballard'	CMac CSBt GMaP LEdu LRHS MHer MRav MWat MWhi NGdn NHol NLar NPer SGol SPer SRGP SRms SWat SWvt WCAu WOld WWEG XLum
- 'Marie-Theres' **new**	SAko
- 'Marie's Pretty Please'	WOld
- 'Marjorie'	LSRN SRGP WOld XLum
- 'Mary Deane'	WOld
- 'Mauve Magic'	MWat SRms WOld WWEG
- 'Melbourne Belle'	WOld
- 'Melbourne Magnet'	WOld
- 'Midget'	WOld
- 'Mistress Quickly'	ECtt WOld
- 'Mittelmeer'	LRHS WOld XLum
- 'Mount Everest'	WOld WWEG
- 'Mrs Leo Hunter'	WOld
- 'Nachtlicht' **new**	SAko
- 'Neron'	IMou MNrw MPie
- 'Nesthäkchen'	WOld
- 'Newton's Pink'	WOld
- 'Niobe'	SAko WOld
- 'Norman's Jubilee'	EBee EPfP LRHS MHer NBir SRGP WOld WWEG
- 'Nursteed Charm'	WOld
- 'Oktoberschneekuppel'	WOld
- 'Pamela'	WOld
- 'Patricia Ballard'	CBcs CBod CBot CCon CMac CSBt EBee ELan GCra GMaP LRHS MHer MWat MWhi NBir NLar NPer NWad SGol SPer SRGP WOld WWEG
- 'Peace'	WOld
- 'Percy Thrower'	WOld
- 'Peter Chiswell'	SRms WOld
- 'Peter Harrison'	EBee GMaP LRHS MHol NBir WMnd WOld XLum
- 'Peter Pan'	NLar
- 'Petunia'	CBod
- 'Pink Lace'	MBNS WOld
- 'Pink Topas' **new**	LRHS
- 'Plenty'	WOld
- 'Porzellan'	CElw CFis EBee ECtt MAvo MBNS MNrw NGdn NLar SRGP WCot WHal WOld
- 'Pride of Colwall'	SRms WBrk WOld
- 'Priory Blush'	CElw WOld
- 'Professor Anton Kippenberg'	CFis ELan EPfP EWTr GMaP LRHS MNrw MRav NDov NLar SAko SPer SRGP SRms SWvt WMnd WOld WWEG XLum
- 'Prosperity'	WOld
- 'Purple Dome'	CFis CNec ECha ELan LEdu LOPS LSRN MHer MWat SCob SHar SRkn WOld WOut
- 'Ralph Picton'	WOld
- 'Rector'	see *A. novi-belgii* 'The Rector'
- 'Red Robin'	MWat WHlf
- 'Red Sunset'	SRms WOld
- 'Rembrandt'	ECtt NGdn SRGP
- 'Remembrance'	MWat SRms WOld
- 'Reverend Vincent Dale'	WOld
- 'Richness'	WOld
- 'Rose Bonnet'	CSBt LRHS SPlb WOld
- 'Roseanne'	WOld
- 'Rosebud' Ballard	WOld
- 'Rosenquartz'	NLar
- 'Rosenwichtel'	ILea NLar WHil WOld WWEG
- 'Royal Ruby'	CFis EBee ECtt LRHS NLar WOld WWEG
- 'Royal Velvet'	WOld

Name	Suppliers
- 'Rozika'	MNrw WOld
- 'Rufus'	WOld
- 'Saint Egwyn'	WOld
- 'Sam Banham'	MNrw WOld
- 'Samoa' (Island Series)	CBod CNec EPfP EUJe LRHS LSou NEgg NLar SPoG SRms WCot
- 'Sandford White Swan'	GBuc MHom WOld WWEG
- 'Sarah Ballard'	LRHS NLar SHil SRGP WBrk WOld
§ - 'Schneekissen'	CBod ECtt ELan EPfP GMaP LRHS MBNS MHer MJak SPer SRGP SRms SWvt WCAu WHar WOld XLum
- 'Schneezicklein'	GBin
- 'Schöne von Dietlikon'	CKno MWat WOld XLum
- 'Schoolgirl'	WOld
- 'Sheena'	WOld
- 'Silberblaukissen'	WOld
§ - 'Silberteppich'	EBee
- Silver Carpet	see *A. novi-belgii* 'Silberteppich'
- Snow Cushion	see *A. novi-belgii* 'Schneekissen'
- 'Snowsprite'	CSBt ELan LRHS MWat NLar SGbt SGol SRGP SRms SWat WOld
- 'Sonata'	GMaP WOld
- 'Sophia'	MWat WOld
- 'Starlight'	CBod ECtt IBoy ILea NLar WRHF
- 'Steinebrück'	WOld
- 'Sterling Silver'	WOld
- 'Sun Queen'	WOld
- 'Sunset'	WOld
- 'Susan'	SRGP WOld
- 'Sweet Briar'	CElw WOld
- 'Tapestry'	WOld
- 'Terry's Pride'	SRGP WOld WWEG
- 'The Archbishop'	ECtt WOld XEll
- 'The Bishop'	WOld
- 'The Cardinal'	WOld
- 'The Dean'	WOld
§ - 'The Rector'	WOld
- 'The Sexton'	WOld
- 'Thundercloud'	MWat WOld
- 'Timsbury'	CElw SRms WOld
- 'Tovarich'	WOld
- 'Trudi Ann'	NBir WOld
- 'Twinkle'	WOld
- 'Victor'	WOld
- 'Vignem'	NSti
- 'Violet Lady'	WOld
- 'Violetta'	LRHS
- 'Waterperry'	MWat WBrk WOld
- 'White Ladies'	CBcs ECtt GCra GMaP LRHS MMuc MNrw MWat NLar SHil SPer SRGP WHlf XLum
- 'White Swan'	ECtt
- 'White Wings'	MWat WOld
- 'Winston S. Churchill'	CBod CTri EAJP ELan EPfP GMaP IKil LEdu LPfy LRHS MHer MWat NEgg SPer SPlb SPoG SRGP WOld
- 'Zwergenhimmel' **new**	SAko
oblongifolius	NWsh WOld XSen
§ - 'Fanny's'	CBod CPrp ECtt GCal GQue NGdn NWad SRGP WCAu WOld
- 'October Skies'	CSpe EBee EWes MNrw
'Ochtendgloren' (*pringlei* hybrid) 🏆H4	CDes CPrp CSam EBee ECtt EPPr EWes GBuc MHom MNrw NCGa NLar WCAu WHal WHoo WOld WWEG
Octoberlight	see *A.* 'Oktoberlicht'
§ 'Oktoberlicht'	EBee LRHS MNrw NCGa WOld
oolentangiensis	NLar WOld
'Orchidee'	EBee EPri EWTr EWes MAvo
'Orpheus'	ECGP MAvo MNrw WBrk

Name	Suppliers
pappei	see *Felicia amoena*
patens **new**	CEvo
'Pearl Star'	WOld
§ ***peduncularis***	CAby EBee EPPr IMou LPla LRHS MAvo MHol MTis SGSe WCot WOld
petiolatus	see *Felicia petiolata*
'Photograph' 🏆H7	CHVG CSam EBee ECtt ELon EWes LEdu LRHS MAvo WOld WPGP
pilosus **new**	WCot
§ - var. ***demotus*** 🏆H7	ECha EWes MRav NWad WOld
§ - var. ***pringlei*** 'Monte Cassino'	CBot CSBt EAEE EPfP GQue LHop LPot LRHS MBNS MRav MWat SPer SPhx SRGP SRms WOld WWEG XLum
- - 'October Glory'	CCse
- - 'Phoebe'	WOld
'Pink Star'	CBot EBee ECtt ELon GMaP LEdu LRHS MRav MWat NDov NSti SBch SPhx WOld XLum
'Pinwheel'	WCot
'Pixie Dark Eye' (*ericoides* hybrid)	CDes EBee ECtt SDix SMHy WCot
'Pixie Red Eye' (*ericoides* hybrid)	EBee WCot
'Prairie Lavender'	WOld
'Prairie Pink'	SMHy WOld
'Prairie Purple'	ECtt MTis SMHy WCot WOld
'Prairie Violet'	WOld
'Primrose Path'	LEdu MNrw NCGa SPhx WBrk WCot WOld
ptarmicoides	see *Solidago ptarmicoides*
puniceus	CAby NLar XLum
'Purple Diamond' (Autumn Jewels Series) **new**	LBMP
pyrenaeus 'Lutetia'	CKno CPrp CSam ECha GBuc GCal GMaP LRHS MAvo MHom MNrw MPie MWat NLar SPoG SPtp SRGP WCAu WKif WOld XLum
radula	CSam EBee EPPr EWes IMou LPla MAvo MNrw NLar WOld WSHC
- 'August Sky'	EPPr MTis NDov WCot WHoo WRHF
'Ringdove' (*ericoides* hybrid) 🏆H6	CPrp MAvo MHom NCGa NSti SRGP SWvt WCot WOld
'Rosa Star'	WOld
'Rose Queen'	MNrw NWsh
rotundifolius 'Variegatus'	see *Felicia amelloides* variegated
rugulosus 'Asrugo'	CKno
sagittifolius Wed.	XLum
× ***salignus***	WOld
- Scottish form	WOld
§ ***scaber***	WCot
scandens	see *A. carolinianus*
schreberi	CCon EPPr EWes LEdu LPla MAvo MSpe NCGa NWsh WBor WCot WOld WPGP WWtn
'Sea Spray'	WCot
§ ***sedifolius***	ECtt ELan ELon GAbr GQue LEdu LRHS MAvo MWat NBid NEgg NSti SDix SEND SPoG WCot WMnd WOld
- RCB AM 5	WCot
- 'Nanus'	CExl EBee ELan GCal MHom MRav NBir NLar NWsh SPer WCot WHil WMnd WOld WTor XLum
- 'Roseus'	IMou
sericeus	SPhx
§ ***sibiricus***	NLar WOld
'Small-Ness' **new**	NWad

'Snow Flurry'	see *A. ericoides* f. *prostratus* 'Snow Flurry'
'Soft Lass'	WCot
souliei	GKev NSla
spathulifolius	WCot XLum
spectabilis	EBee IMou LRHS SPhx WOld
- 'JS Macho Blue' **new**	MNrw
'Star of Chesters'	MAvo WOld
stracheyi	ITim
subcaeruleus	see *A. tongolensis*
'Sunhelene'	CDes EBee ECtt WCot
Sunplum = 'Danasplum'^PBR	LEdu SRGP
'Sunspring'	SRGP
tataricus	LPla
- 'Jindai'	EBee MAvo
thomsonii	WCot WOld
- 'Nanus'	CAby EBee GBee GMaP ILea LRHS MCot MRav SPer SPhx SPoG WCot WOld WSHC
Tonga = 'Dasfour'	EPfP EWTr LRHS MHol NBir NLar NPri NWsh SPoG SRms SWvt WBod WCot WHil
§ ***tongolensis***	GKev
- 'Berggarten'	CWCL LRHS MHol MNrw MPie
- 'Dunkleviolette'	SRms
- 'Napsbury'	LRHS WOld
- 'Wartburgstern'	CCon EPfP LRHS MMuc SEND SGbt WWEG XLum
tradescantii misapplied	see *A. pilosus* var. *demotus*
tradescantii L.	ELan MBNS MRav NSti SMad WBrk WCot WOld
'Treffpunkt'	IMou SAko
trinervius var. ***harae***	WOld
tripolium	WHer
'Triumph'	WCot
turbinellus ambig.	MHom
turbinellus misapplied ♀H6	CKno EPfP EWes GGal IKil LPla LRHS MMuc NGdn NWsh SDix SMHy SPhx SRkn SWvt WWEG
turbinellus Lindl.	CSam EBee EPfP EWTr GBee MWat NCGa NLar NQui WCot WOld
- 'El Fin'	EWld MNrw
- hybrid	WOld
umbellatus	CBre CKno ECha EPPr GQue MMuc NBir NDov NLar WCot WOld
'Vasterival'	IMou LEdu MPie MSpe MTis NCGa NDov SMHy WOut WWEG XLum
vimineus Lam.	see *A. lateriflorus*
- 'Ptarmicoides'	see *Solidago ptarmicoides*
§ 'White Climax'	CSam MHom MNrw WCot
'Wood's Blue'	LRHS
'Wood's Pink'	LRHS WHil
'Wood's Purple'	EBee LRHS WHil
'Yvonne'	CBre

Asteranthera (*Gesneriaceae*)

ovata	CExl CFil EPfP GGGa LRHS LSou SLon SPoG WAbe WPGP WSHC

Asteromoea (*Asteraceae*)

mongolica	see *Kalimeris mongolica*
pinnatifida	see *Kalimeris pinnatifida*

Asteropyrum (*Ranunculaceae*)

cavaleriei	GEdr
peltatum **new**	GEdr

Asterotrichion (*Malvaceae*)

discolor	ECou SPlb SVen

Astilbe ✿ (*Saxifragaceae*)

CC 5201	CExl
'Alive and Kicking'	SCob
'Amerika' (× *arendsii*)	CMHG CSBt SRms
'Amethyst' (× *arendsii*)	CMHG CMac ELon EPfP LRHS MRav NBir NHol SPer WFar WMoo
'Angel Wings' (× *arendsii*)	NEoE
'Anita Pfeifer' (× *arendsii*)	CMHG ELon GBin IBoy NLar XLum
'Aphrodite' (*simplicifolia* hybrid)	CBcs GCal LLWG MLHP
× ***arendsii***	EPfP IFoB NBre WHar WMoo XLum
(Astary Series) 'Astary Pink' (× *arendsii*)	LRHS
- 'Astary Red' (× *arendsii*)	LRHS
- 'Astary White' (× *arendsii*)	LRHS
astilboides	CMHG SWvt
'Atrorosea' (*simplicifolia* hybrid)	SRms
'Avalanche'	CAby CTsd GBin NHol SPad WMnd
§ 'Beauty of Ernst' (× *arendsii*)	CBod EBee ELon EPfP LRHS LSou MAsh MSCN SLon SRms WMoo
§ 'Beauty of Lisse' (× *arendsii*)	ELon LSou MSCN WHil WOut
Bella Group (× *arendsii*)	WMnd
'Bergkristall' (× *arendsii*)	CMHG
'Betsy Cuperus' (*thunbergii* hybrid)	CMHG EBee GBin NBre WCAu
'Bonn' (*japonica* hybrid)	CWCL CWat MMuc NLar NQui SCob SCoo SRms
'Boogie Woogie'^PBR (× *arendsii*)	MAsh
§ 'Brautschleier' (× *arendsii*) ♀H7	CExl CMHG CMac CPrp CTri ECtt EPfP GBin GCra GKev LRHS LSRN MHol NEgg NGdn NLar NQui WPnP XLum
'Bremen' (*japonica* hybrid)	CMHG GBin
'Bressingham Beauty' (× *arendsii*)	Widely available
Bridal Veil (× *arendsii*)	see *A.* 'Brautschleier'
§ 'Bronce Elegans' (*simplicifolia* hybrid) ♀H7	CCon CMHG ECha ELon EPfP GBin GBuc GMaP NEoE NHol NLar SCob SPer WMoo WOut
'Bronze Sprite' (*simplicifolia* hybrid)	WFar
'Bronzelaub' (× *arendsii*)	CMHG
* ***bumalda*** 'Bronze Pygmy'	NHol
'Bumalda' (× *arendsii*)	CCon CSBt CWCL ELon GBin GMaP IBoy LRHS MAsh MBri NChi NEoE NGdn SPlb WMoo WWtn
'Burgunderrot' (× *arendsii*)	EBee MNrw NLar
* 'Carmine King'	MMuc
'Carminea'	CMHG
'Carnea' (*simplicifolia* hybrid)	CMHG
'Catherine Deneuve'	see *A.* 'Federsee'
'Cattleya Dunkel' (× *arendsii*)	CMHG
'Cattleya' (× *arendsii*)	CMHG CSam GBin GBuc LRHS NLar SAko WMoo
'Ceres' (× *arendsii*)	CMHG
'Cherry Ripe'	see *A.* 'Feuer'
chinensis	CMHG ECho LRHS WSHC
- B&SWJ 8178	WCru
- from Russia	GCal
- 'Brokat'	GBin
- 'Christian'	GBin
- var. ***davidii***	CMHG
- - B&SWJ 8583	WCru
- - B&SWJ 8645	WCru

	Name	Suppliers
	- 'Diamonds and Pearls'[PBR]	CWGN ECtt LLWG LSou SCob WFar WHil
	- 'Finale'	ELon NEoE NHol SPer WFar WOut
	- 'Frankentroll'	CMHG
	- 'Intermezzo'	GBin GCal GMaP NEoE NLar
	- 'Little Vision in Pink'[PBR]	MSCN WFar WHil
	- 'Love and Pride'	LSou MBri
	- 'Milk and Honey'[PBR]	CWGN ECtt ELon EWTr LSou MBNS SGol WFar
§	- var. ***pumila*** 🏆[H5]	Widely available
	- - 'Serenade'	CMac LRHS NGdn
	- 'Purple Glory'	CMHG IKil
	- 'Spätsommer'	CMHG
	- var. ***taquetii***	CMac ELan EPfP LRHS NSti SRms
	- - Purple Lance	see *A. chinensis* var. *taquetii* 'Purpurlanze'
§	- - 'Purpurlanze'	Widely available
§	- - 'Superba' 🏆[H7]	CMHG CMac CTri ECha GBin IBoy LRHS MLHP NBro NWad SDix SMad SPer SRms WMoo
	- 'Troll'	GBin
	- 'Veronika Klose'	CMHG GBin NEoE NLar
	- 'Vision in Pink'[PBR]	CWCL ELan EPfP LSou LSun MBNS MHol MNrw WFar WHil
	- 'Vision in Red'[PBR]	CWCL CWat ECtt ELan EPfP IBoy LSou MBNS MHol MNrw NEgg NLar NPri SAko SGbt SPoG WCAu WFar WMoo
	- 'Vision in White'	NEoE SAko SPoG WFar WHil
	- 'Visions'	CMHG CMac CWCL EPfP IBoy LRHS LSou MBNS MBri NBro NEoE NGdn WMoo
	'Chocolate Shogun' **new**	CMos WCot
	Cologne	see *A.* 'Köln'
	Color Flash	see *A.* 'Beauty of Ernst'
	Color Flash Lime	see *A.* 'Beauty of Lisse'
	'Country and Western'[PBR] (× *arendsii*)	LSou SCob
	'Crimson Feather'	see *A.* 'Gloria Purpurea'
	× ***crispa*** 'Lilliput'	ECtt GBee NBir NEoE NHar NLar NRya NWad SCob
§	- 'Perkeo' 🏆[H5]	CBcs CCon EBee ECho ECtt ELan EPfP GMaP LRHS NBir NEoE NHar NLar NMyG SRms WCot WMoo
	- 'Peter Pan'	see *A.* × *crispa* 'Perkeo'
	- 'Red Rog'	NEoE
	- 'Snow Queen'	NBir NEoE
	'Darwin's Dream'	IBoy MNrw NEoE NLar
	'Darwin's Favourite' (× *arendsii*)	CWCL
	'Delft Lace'	EBee LBuc LRHS MAsh WMoo
	'Deutschland' (*japonica* hybrid)	Widely available
§	'Diamant' (× *arendsii*)	CMHG LSRN MMuc MNrw NBir NGdn NHol SEND WFar
	Diamond	see *A.* 'Diamant'
	'Drayton Glory' (× *arendsii*)	see *A.* × *rosea* 'Peach Blossom'
	'Drum and Bass'[PBR]	IBoy LSou NLar
	'Dunkelachs' (*simplicifolia* hybrid)	EBee
	'Dusseldorf' (*japonica* hybrid)	CMHG CSam CWCL
	'Eden's Odysseus'	GBin IBoy NHol
	'Eden's Twinkle'	EBee
	'Elegans' (*simplicifolia* hybrid)	CMHG CMac
	'Elisabeth' (× *arendsii*)	NBir
	Elizabeth Bloom = 'Eliblo'[PBR] (× *arendsii*)	CAby CHVG ELon GAbr LLWG LRHS MHol MRav NDov NEgg NGdn NHol SGol
	'Elizabeth' (*japonica* hybrid)	CMHG
	'Ellie' (× *arendsii*)	CMHG CMac GBin GQue LSRN LSou MAsh MBNS MSCN NGdn NHol NLar WFar
	'Else Schluck' (× *arendsii*)	ECha
	'Erica' (× *arendsii*)	CAby CExl CMHG CTri CTsd LRHS NEoE NLar SPad WMoo
	'Etna' (*japonica* hybrid)	CBcs CMHG CSam ECtt IBoy NEgg NGdn NLar SGSe SRms WFar WHar
	'Europa' (*japonica* hybrid)	CMHG CMac ECtt GBin LRHS MGos NEgg NGdn NLar SPoG WHar WMoo
	'Fanal' (× *arendsii*) 🏆[H7]	Widely available
	'Fata Morgana' (× *arendsii* hybrid)	CMHG
§	'Federsee' (× *arendsii*)	CBcs CHVG CMHG CWCL EBee ECha ECtt ELan LRHS MBNS NBro NEoE NGdn WFar WWtn XLum
§	'Feuer' (× *arendsii*)	CMHG CMac ECtt ELan GBin GBuc LBMP NEgg NEoE NGdn NHol NLar WBor WGwG WMoo
	Fire	see *A.* 'Feuer'
	'Fireberry'[PBR] (Short 'n' Sweet Series)	EBee LSou NLar
	'Flamingo'[PBR] (× *arendsii*)	ECtt GBin MBNS MBel
§	***formosa*** B&SWJ 10946	WCru
	'Gertrud Brix' (× *arendsii*)	CBcs CWat MMuc NBir NGdn XLum
§	***glaberrima***	NBid
§	- var. ***saxatilis*** 🏆[H5]	EPfP GBin GEdr IFro NHar WAbe WHal WThu
	- - 'Candy Floss' **new**	NEoE
	- ***saxosa***	see *A. glaberrima* var. *saxatilis*
§	'Gloria Purpurea' (× *arendsii*)	CMHG ELon NQui WMoo
	'Gloria' (× *arendsii*)	CMHG CMac CTri ECtt LRHS MRav
	Glow	see *A.* 'Glut'
§	'Glut' (× *arendsii*)	CCon CMHG CWCL EBee ECtt LRHS MMuc NGdn NHol SAko SEND SRms WFar
	'Granat' (× *arendsii*)	CAby CMHG CMac EAEE GBuc NBir NDov NEgg NGdn NHol NLar WMoo
*	Grande Group (× *arendsii*)	NBre
	grandis	CMHG GBee WHer
	- BWJ 8076A	NLar
	'Grete Püngel' (× *arendsii*)	ECha GBin
	'Harmony' (× *arendsii*)	CMHG
	'Heart and Soul'[PBR]	CWGN EPfP LSou SAko
	'Hennie Graafland' (*simplicifolia* hybrid)	CBcs CMHG COtt CWCL GBin LSou NLar SHar WFar
	'Henry Noblett'	GBin
	'Holden Clough' (*japonica* hybrid)	NHol
	Hyacinth	see *A.* 'Hyazinth'
§	'Hyazinth' (× *arendsii*)	CExl CMHG CPrp EBee GMaP LBMP LLWG LRHS LSou NBir NHol WFar
	'Icecream' (× *arendsii*)	CBod MAsh
	'Inshriach Pink' (*simplicifolia* hybrid)	CBcs CMHG ECtt EHoe ELan LRHS MBri NBir NHar NHol NLar SBch WHal WOut
	'Irrlicht' (× *arendsii*)	CMHG CMac EBee ELan EPfP EShb EWTr GBin GBuc IBoy LHop LRHS NWad SGSe SPer SRms SWat WPnP
	'Isa Hall'	CMHG NEoE
	japonica	CExl GKev
*	- 'Pumila'	NBir NGdn
	- var. ***terrestris***	see *A. glaberrima*

	Name	Suppliers
	'Jo Ophorst' (*davidii* hybrid)	CMHG EBee ECtt GBuc LRHS NGdn NLar
	'Jump and Jive'[PBR]	LSou WFar
	'Juno'	XLum
	'Koblenz' (*japonica* hybrid)	CMHG CWCL
§	'Köln' (*japonica* hybrid)	CMHG CWat ELon GBin LRHS
	koreana	WCot
	- B&SWJ 8611	WCru
	- B&SWJ 8680	WCru
	'Kriemhilde'	CMHG MSCN
	'Kvële' (× *arendsii*)	CMHG LRHS WMoo
§	'Lachskönigin' (× *arendsii*)	CMHG
	'Lilli Goos' (× *arendsii*)	CMHG GBin GCal
	'Lollipop'	ECtt MBNS NEoE SRms
	longicarpa B&SWJ 6711	WCru
	'Look at Me' (× *arendsii*) new	LLWG MBel MHol
	macroflora	GCal
	'Magenta'	CMHG
	'Maggie Daley'	IBoy NBro NEoE WMoo
	'Mainz' (*japonica* hybrid)	CHVG CMHG ECtt
	'Mars' (× *arendsii*)	CMHG
	microphylla	CMHG
	- B&SWJ 11085	WCru
	- pink-flowered	CMHG
	'Midnight Arrow' (*davidii* hybrid)	CMHG
	'Moerheim Glory' (× *arendsii*)	GBin IBoy NBre NGdn NLar
	'Moerheimii' (*thunbergii* hybrid)	CMHG
	'Mont Blanc' (× *arendsii*)	CMHG
	'Montgomery' (*japonica* hybrid)	CMHG EBee ELon EShb GAbr GBin IKil ILea LBMP LRHS LSRN MBNS MNrw NBro NEgg NGdn NHol NLar
	'Nemo'	MAsh
	'New Wave'	MAsh
	'Nikki'	NEoE NLar
§	***okuyamae*** B&SWJ 10975	WCru
	'Opal'	CMHG
	Ostrich Plume	see *A.* 'Straussenfeder'
	'Paul Gaärder' (× *arendsii*)	CMHG
	'Peaches and Cream'	NBro NLar
	'Peter Barrow' (*glaberrima* hybrid)	GBin SRms
	'Pink Lightning'[PBR] (*simplicifolia* hybrid)	CWCL ECtt GAbr MBNS NLar WFar
	Pink Pearl (× *arendsii*)	see *A.* 'Rosa Perle'
	'Poschka'	CCon NEoE
	'Professor van der Wielen' (*thunbergii* hybrid)	CCon CMHG EBee ECha GQue LRHS NHol NLar SAko SPer SRms
	pumila	see *A. chinensis* var. *pumila*
	'Purple Rain'[PBR] (× *arendsii*)	CBod
	'Radius'	COtt ELon NGdn NLar WPnP
	'Red Baron'	CAby CTsd SPad
	Red Light	see *A.* 'Rotlicht'
	'Red Sentinel' (*japonica* hybrid)	CBcs CCon COtt CWat EBee ELon EPfP EWoo GBin GMaP IBoy LRHS LSou LSun MAsh MHol NBro NCGa NEgg NEoE NGdn NHol NLar SGSe WHil WOut WWtn
	'Red Thunder'	EBee
	'Rheinland' (*japonica* hybrid) 𝕐H7	CBcs CLet CMHG CWCL ELon GBin LPfy LRHS MBel MMuc NGdn NLar SCob SEND SHil SRot WHoo WMnd WPnP
	'Rhythm and Blues'[PBR]	ECtt NEgg NLar
	rivularis	CMHG EBee SDix WCot
	- CC 5201	GKev
	- CC 6857	GKev
	- GWJ 9366	WCru
	- PAB 7353 new	LEdu
	- PAB 9763 new	LEdu
I	- 'Grandiflora'	GBin
§	- var. ***myriantha***	NBre WMoo WPGP
	- - BWJ 8076a	WCru
	- - SICH 757	CExl
	'Robinson's Pink'	NGdn
	'Rock and Roll'[PBR]	CBod LSRN MSCN
§	'Rosa Perle' (× *arendsii*)	CHVG CMHG CSam NHol
§	× ***rosea*** 'Peach Blossom'	CBcs CMHG CPrp ELon GCra IBoy ILea LRHS MBri NBir NEoE NGdn SGbt SPoG SWvt WHoo WMnd WMoo WOut
	'Rosea' (*simplicifolia* hybrid)	NHol
	'Rot Straussenfeder' (× *arendsii*)	GBin
§	'Rotlicht' (× *arendsii*)	CMHG CMac GBin LRHS NEgg NEoE NGdn NHol NLar
	'Salland'	EBee LRHS
	Salmon Queen	see *A.* 'Lachskönigin'
	'Salmonea' (*simplicifolia* hybrid)	CMHG
	'Saxosa'	see *A. glaberrima* var. *saxatilis*
	'Sheila Haxton' (*chinensis*)	LRHS
	Showstar Group (× *arendsii*)	SRms WHil WRHF WWtn
	simplicifolia 𝕐H5	CAby SKHP WFar
	- 'Alba'	CMHG
I	- 'Angustifolia' new	LLWG
	- Bronze Elegance	see *A.* 'Bronce Elegans'
	- 'Darwin's Snow Sprite'	CMac GBin MBri MWts NHol NLar WFar
	- 'Jacqueline'	LSou MAsh NHol
*	- 'Nana Alba'	NEoE
	- 'Praecox Alba'	GBin
	- 'Rose of Cimarron'	NEoE
	- 'White Sensation'[PBR]	EBee GQue LRHS NLar SAko
	'Snowdrift' (× *arendsii*)	CHid CMHG CWat GMaP IKil LBMP LLWG LRHS MBNS MBel MMuc NBir NEgg NEoE SPer SWat
	'Solferino' (× *arendsii*)	CMHG
	'Spartan' (× *arendsii*)	see *A.* 'Rotlicht'
	'Spinell' (× *arendsii*)	CWCL GBuc NBre WMoo WPnP
	'Sprite' (*simplicifolia* hybrid) 𝕐H7	Widely available
	'Stand and Deliver'[PBR]	ECtt
§	'Straussenfeder' (*thunbergii* hybrid) 𝕐H7	CBod CMHG CMac CMos CTri EBee ECtt EPfP GBin GMaP LBMP LHop LRHS NBid NBir NBro NEgg NGdn NHol NLar SPer WCAu WMoo
	'Sugar Plum' (*simplicifolia* hybrid)	NGdn
	'Sugarberry'[PBR] (Short 'n' Sweet Series)	NLar
	'Superba'	see *A. chinensis* var. *taquetii* 'Superba'
	thunbergii	CExl
	- var. ***congesta*** B&SWJ 10961	WCru
	- var. ***formosa***	see *A. formosa*
	- var. ***hachijoensis***	EBee
	- - B&SWJ 5622	WCru
	- var. ***okuyamae***	see *A. okuyamae*
	- var. ***sikokumontanum*** B&SWJ 11164	WCru
	- var. ***terrestris*** B&SWJ 6125	WCru

	'To Have and To Hold'	LSou MNrw
	'Venus' (× *arendsii*)	ECtt GMaP LRHS MBNS MCot MMuc NGdn NHol SEND SPer SWat WFar WMoo
	'Vesuvius' (*japonica* hybrid)	CBcs NBro NLar
	virescens	see *A. rivularis* var. *myriantha*
	'Walküre' (× *arendsii*)	CMHG
	'Walter Bitner'	GBin LLWG LRHS MBNS NBre NHol
	'Washington' (*japonica* hybrid)	EWTr LAst LRHS NBre NGdn WPnP
§	'Weisse Gloria' (× *arendsii*)	CAby CHVG CMHG CMac CPrp ECha GBin GBuc LLWG LPfy LRHS NBro NDov NEgg NEoE NHol SCoo SHil WBor WCAu WMoo WWtn
	'White Diamond' (× *arendsii*)	WFar
	White Gloria	see *A.* 'Weisse Gloria'
	'White Wings'PBR (*simplicifolia* hybrid)	NLar
	'William Reeves' (× *arendsii*)	CMHG NHol
	'Willie Buchanan' (*simplicifolia* hybrid)	CAby CBcs CBod CHid CMHG CPrp EHoe GAbr GBin GCrg GMaP NCGa NEgg NGdn NHar NHol SRms WAbe WCFE WFar WMoo
	Younique Carmine = 'Verscarmine'PBR	LSou MBri
	Younique Pink = 'Verspink'PBR	MAsh
	Younique Silvery Pink = 'Versilverypink'PBR	LAst MBri WFar WHil
	Younique White = 'Verswhite'PBR	MBri
	'Zuster Theresa' (× *arendsii*)	CMHG CMos EBee ELon IBoy LRHS MBNS MNrw NBro

Astilboides (*Saxifragaceae*)

§	***tabularis***	Widely available

Astragalus (*Papilionaceae*)

	angustifolius	XSen
	canadensis	GJos LRHS
	centralpinus	GJos
	glycyphyllos	CArn CWld GJos GKev SPhx
	looseri	WCot
	membranaceus	CArn
	neglectus	EBee
	odoratus	EBee

Astrantia ✿ (*Apiaceae*)

	'Atomic Sunburst'	GQue
	bavarica	GCal GKev MFie
	'Berendien Stam'	ECGP GLet MAvo MFie NLar
	'Bloody Mary'	CWCL EBee ELan GBuc GLet MAvo MFie NGdn NLar
	'Buckland'	Widely available
	'Bury Court'	MAvo NDov
	carniolica	NEgg
	- ***major***	see *A. major*
	- 'Rubra'	CBcs EWoo GMaP MFie
	- 'Variegata'	see *A. major* 'Sunningdale Variegated'
	'Clear Pink'	NDov
	'Dark Shiny Eyes'	CExl CWCL ECtt GBin GLet IBoy ILea LHop LLHF LPal MAvo NGdn NLar NSti SPoG SWvt
	'Good Pink'	GLet LRHS
	'Hadspen Blood'	Widely available
	'Helen'	NLar
	helleborifolia	see *A. maxima*
	'Larch Cottage Clear Pink'	NLar
	'Larch Cottage Magic'	MAvo
	'Madeleine'	see *A. major* 'Madeleine van Bennekom'
§	***major***	Widely available
	- 'Abbey Road'PBR	CExl CKno CLAP CWCL ECtt EWoo GBin GLet IBoy IKil LBMP LHop LRHS LSou MFie NLar SCob SPoG SRkn SRms
I	- 'Alba'	CBcs CMHG CWCL EBee EWTr GLet IKil LPal LRHS MCot MFie MRav NBir NGdn NPer SPer WMnd WMoo
	- 'Berdien'	EBee
	- 'Best Pink'	MAvo
	- subsp. ***biebersteinii***	EBee LRHS MFie NBir
	- 'Bo-Ann'	CWCL GLet IBoy MFie NLar WFar
	- 'Can Candy'	MAvo
	- 'Celtic Star'	CSpe MFie SWvt
	- 'Claret'	Widely available
	- Cliff's form	MFie
	- 'Cottage Herbery'	MAvo
	- 'Dark Desire'	GLet NDov
	- 'Elaine's Pink'	WHoo
	- 'Elmblut'	IMou MAvo MFie
	- 'Florence'PBR	CBct CBod CNor CWCL CWGN ECtt EPfP GBin GLet LRHS MBri MTis NCGa NDov NLar SPoG SWvt
	- Gill Richardson Group	Widely available
	- 'Gracilis'	EBee
	- 'Greenfingers'	EWes
	- 'Gwaun Valley'	WFar
	- subsp. ***involucrata***	LRHS MFie SWat
	- - 'Avondale'	MAvo
	- - 'Barrister'	CSam GBuc GLet MAvo MFie NLar
	- - 'Canneman'	EBee EWes LPla MFie NLar WCot
	- - 'Huntsman'	MAvo
	- - 'Jumble Hole'	MAvo NDov
	- - 'Margery Fish'	see *A. major* subsp. *involucrata* 'Shaggy'
	- - 'Moira Reid'	CExl CLAP CSam CWCL ECtt ELan GCal GLet GMaP LSRN MFie MRav
	- - 'Orlando'	CLAP MFie
§	- - 'Shaggy' 🏆H7	Widely available
	- - 'Snape Cottage'	CDes EBee
	- 'Jade Lady'	WFar
	- 'Jitse'	MAvo
	- 'Large White' **new**	LCro
	- 'Lars'	CExl CWCL CWib ECtt ELan ELon EWoo GBin GCra GLet IFoB LRHS LSRN MBri MFie MHol MNrw MWhi NBid NGdn NLar SPer SPoG SRms SRot SWvt WCAu
	- 'Lola'	CBcs EBee EWTr GBuc GLet IBoy MTis NLar
§	- 'Madeleine van Bennekom'	CLAP CNor EBee ECha GBin GLet
	- 'Midnight Owl' **new**	EBee MHol MTis
	- 'Penny's Pink'	CWCL EBee ELan EWoo GLet LCro MAvo MFie NCGa SHar
	- 'Pink Crush'	EBee LRHS
	- 'Pink Pride'	CWCL GLet LSou MHol MNrw MTis WCAu
	- 'Pink Sensation'	EBee GLet
	- 'Pink Surprise'	GLet MAvo MBri
	- 'Primadonna'	EPri GLet GMaP LBMP LRHS MFie MHol NLar SPlb WMnd
	- 'Princesse Sturdza'	CWCL EBee LSou
	- 'Reverse Sunningdale Variegated' (v)	LSou MAvo MFie

- 'Rosa Lee'	CWCL MFie
- var. ***rosea***	CBod CWCL EPfP GLet LHop LRHS LSRN MFie MLHP MRav MSpe MWhi NGdn SPer WFar WMoo
- - George's form	CBct CLAP CWCL ECtt LSRN MFie NCGa
- 'Rosensinfonie'	CWCL EBee GLet GMaP MFie NBro
§ - 'Rubra'	CNec CSBt CSpe CWCL ELan EPfP GKin IBoy LAst LCro LOPS LPfy LRHS MFie MGos MHol NBir NChi NPer SCob SPad SRms SWat WBod WBor WCAu WCru WHal WHar
- 'Ruby Cloud'	CBod CHid CWCL ECtt ELon EPri EWTr GBuc GLet LBMP MFie NBro NGdn NSti SGSe SRot WMnd
- 'Ruby Giant'	GKin
- 'Ruby Glow'	MFie
- 'Ruby Wedding'	Widely available
- 'Silver Glow'	EBee ECtt
- 'Star of Beauty'PBR	CLAP CWCL ECtt ELan GBin GLet IBoy LLWG LPfy LRHS LSou MBri MCot MFie NCGa NGdn NLar NSti SCob SPoG SRms SRot SWvt WHlf
- 'Star of Billion'PBR	CBod CLAP EBee ECtt ELan EWTr GBin GLet IBoy IKil LHop LLWG LRHS LSun MAvo MBri MHol NDov SCob SGol SPoG SWvt WCot WHlf WPtf WRHF
- 'Star of Fire'PBR	EBee GLet LLWG LSou MBel SCob SRot WFar
- 'Star of Royals'PBR	CLAP ECtt GBin GLet IPot LSou MBri WFar
- 'Star of Summer'	CBod EBee LSou
- 'Starburst'	EBee MFie
- 'Stardust'	EBee
- 'Sue Barnes' (v)	GCal MFie
§ - 'Sunningdale Variegated' (v) ♀H7	Widely available
- 'Titoki Point'	MFie WCot
- 'Venice'PBR	CBct CLAP CMos CWCL CWGN ECtt GBuc IBoy IPot LLWG LRHS LSou MAvo MHol MNrw NEgg NLar NSti SPoG SRms STPC SWvt WCAu
§ ***maxima*** ♀H6	Widely available
- 'Mark Fenwick'	MFie NBir
* - ***rosea***	ECtt GQue MNrw MWhi NBir NGdn
minor	EBee LRHS WCru
'Moulin Rouge'PBR	Widely available
'Old Warwickshire Pink'	MAvo
'Queen's Children'	GBuc GLet SGol
'Rainbow'	MFie NLar
'Roma'PBR ♀H7	Widely available
rubra	see *A. major* 'Rubra'
'Ruby Bere' **new**	LEdu
'Ruby Star'PBR	CLAP CMil EBee ECtt ELon GAbr GMaP IBoy IPot LRHS LSun MFie MHol MSCN NDov NEgg NLar NSti SPer SWvt WCot WHoo WMnd WPnP
'Sheila's Red'	EAEE GLet LRHS LSRN MBNS NDov
'Snow Star'PBR	CWCL CWib EBee EPfP EWoo GBin GLet IKil LPfy LRHS MBNS MBri MFie NLar SHil SPoG
'Star of Heaven'	NLar
'Star of Passion'	GLet LPfy LRHS NLar SCob
'Star of Treasure'	GLet NLar WHlf
'Stonehouse Perpetual'	CElw
'Superstar'PBR	Widely available
'Warren Hills'	CLAP EBee GMaP MFie NLar
'Washfield'	CWCL GLet NDov

Astrodaucus (*Apiaceae*)

orientalis	LEdu

Astrolepis (*Adiantaceae*)

sinuata	ISha WCot

Astrophytum (*Cactaceae*)

myriostigma ♀H2	SRms

Asyneuma (*Campanulaceae*)

campanuloides **new**	SIgm
canescens	ELan LRHS LSou
limonifolium	WAbe
- var. ***alpinum***	LLHF
pulvinatum	CPBP EPot WAbe

Asystasia (*Acanthaceae*)

bella	see *Mackaya bella*

Athamanta (*Apiaceae*)

cretensis	CArn
turbith	CSpe LEdu MNrw SBrt SIgm WPtf
vestina	SBrt SPhx

Athanasia (*Asteraceae*)

§ ***parviflora***	SPlb SVen
pinnata	SVen

Atherosperma (*Atherospermataceae*)

moschatum	CBcs CDoC CFil CHll SKHP

Athrotaxis (*Cupressaceae*)

cupressoides	CBcs CDoC CDul CKen WThu
laxifolia	CDoC CKen WThu
selaginoides	CDoC

Athyrium ✿ (*Woodsiaceae*)

'Branford Beauty'	CLAP ISha LPal NLar WPGP
'Branford Rambler'	CLAP ISha
filix-femina ♀H7	Widely available
§ - subsp. ***angustum*** ♀H7	CLAP ELan GBin LRHS MRav NGdn WMoo
- - f. ***rubellum*** 'Lady in Red' ♀H7	CBod CDoC CKel CLAP CWCL EBee ESwi ISha LEdu LLWG LPal LPfy LRHS LSRN MGos MSCN NEgg NLar SCob SPoG WMoo
- 'Corymbiferum'	SRms
- 'Crispum Grandiceps Kaye'	NGdn SRms
- Cristatum Group	CLAP EFer ELan LSRN NGdn SWat WFib
- 'Dre's Dagger'	EBee SCob SPoG WFar
- 'Fieldii'	CLAP SRms
- 'Frizelliae' ♀H7	Widely available
- 'Frizelliae Capitatum'	CLAP WFib WPGP
- 'Frizelliae Cristatum'	SRms
- 'Grandiceps'	CLAP SRms
- 'Lady Victoria'	CLAP
- 'Lady-in-Lace' ♀H7	CLAP ITim LLHF LLWG SMDP SMad WCot
- 'Minutissimum'	CDes CLAP ELan ISha LRHS WCot
* - 'Nudicaule'	SRms
- Plumosum Group	CLAP EShb MRav WFib XLum
- 'Plumosum Axminster'	CLAP EFer NLar WFar
- 'Plumosum Divaricatum'	SRms
- 'Plumosum Druery'	CLAP EFer
- Red Stem	see *A. filix-femina* 'Rotstiel'

	Plant	Suppliers
§	- 'Rotstiel'	CDTJ CLAP EBee LPal MBri NBro NLos WMoo WPnP
	- 'Setigerum Cristatum'	WFar
	- 'Vernoniae' ♀H7	CLAP ELan GAbr MRav NLar SGSe
	- 'Vernoniae Cristatum'	CLAP WFib
	- 'Victoriae'	CDTJ CDes CWCL EBee EFer ELan GMaP ISha LLWG LRHS NBid NGdn NLar SBod SGSe WMoo XLum
	- 'Victoriae' seedling	MBri
	- aff. 'Victoriae'	CKel CTal
	- Victoriae Group	see *A. filix-femina* subsp. *angustum*
	'Ghost' ♀H6	CDes CLAP EBee ESwi ISha LRHS MAvo MGos MPie NLar NSti SPoG WCot WFar
	goeringianum 'Pictum'	see *A. niponicum* var. *pictum*
	niponicum	NMyG WHal
	- f. ***metallicum***	see *A. niponicum* var. *pictum*
§	- var. ***pictum*** ♀H5	Widely available
	- - 'Apple Court'	EBee ESwi ISha LRHS NLar SPoG
	- - 'Burgundy Lace'	CLAP EBee ECtt ESwi LPal MAvo MPnt NLar SMDP SPoG WCot WPat
*	- - 'Cristatoflabellatum'	CDes CLAP EBee LRHS
	- - 'Pewter Lace'	EBee ECtt NLar SMDP
	- - 'Red Beauty'	CBcs CDTJ CLAP ECha ECtt ELan EPfP EWld GBin LPfy LRHS LSRN MBri MMuc NLar NPri SBod SEND SGol SHil SPoG SRkn WCot WMoo WPat WPnP
	- - 'Regal Red'	EBee ISha LRHS NLos
	- - 'Silver Falls' ♀H5	CLAP EShb ESwi GEdr LRHS NMyG SMDP SMad SPoG WCot WPGP
	- - 'Ursula's Red'	CLAP EBee EShb LBMP LHop LOPS LPal LRHS LSRN MNrw MSCN NBid NBir NLar SPoG WCot WFar WPGP
	- - 'Wildwood Twist'	CLAP NMyG WCot
	'Ocean's Fury'	CAby CCon CLAP EBee ECtt ESwi GBin SPoG
	otophorum ♀H4	ISha MRav NBid NLos SRms WPGP
	- var. ***okanum*** ♀H5	Widely available
	vidalii	CLAP EBee ISha LLWG LRHS LSou NLar NMyG WCot WFib XLum

Atractylodes (*Asteraceae*)

Plant	Suppliers
japonica	EFEx GEdr LEdu
macrocephala	CArn EFEx

Atragene see *Clematis*

Atriplex (*Amaranthaceae*)

Plant	Suppliers
canescens	CAgr NLar
cinerea	ECou
halimus	CAgr CArn CBcs CLau CSde ECha EHoe EPPr MRav NLar SDix SLon SPer SPlb WCot
hortensis	ENfk
- var. ***rubra***	CSpe ELan LSou MHer MNHC SHDw SIde SRms WJek

Atropa (*Solanaceae*)

Plant	Suppliers
bella-donna	CArn GPoy MMuc SEND
mandragora	see *Mandragora officinarum*

Aubrieta (*Brassicaceae*)

	Plant	Suppliers
	sp.	MLHP MMuc SEND
	'Alba'	see *A.* 'Fiona'
	albomarginata	see *A.* 'Argenteovariegata'
	'Alix Brett'	CMea ECtt
	'Ann Kendall'	ECtt
§	'Argenteovariegata' (v) ♀H5	ECho ELan LRHS MJak
	(Audrey Series) 'Audrey Blue'	NPri
	- 'Audrey Light Blue' **new**	NPri
	- 'Audrey Red and Purple' **new**	NPri
§	'Aureovariegata' (v) ♀H5	CMea ECho ELan NPer XLum
	(Axcent Series) Axcent Antique Rose = 'Audelanro'[PBR]	LRHS NPri
	- Axcent Blue with Eye = 'Audelbley'[PBR]	LBuc LRHS NPri
	- Axcent Burgundy **new**	LRHS
	- Axcent Deep Purple = 'Audelpur'[PBR]	LBuc LRHS
	- Axcent Light Blue **new**	LRHS
	- Axcent Magenta = 'Audelmag'[PBR]	LRHS
	- Axcent Violet with Eye = 'Audelvioe'[PBR]	NPri
	bicoloured	CMea
	Blaue Schönheit	see *A.* 'Blue Beauty'
	'Blaumeise'	LRHS
§	'Blue Beauty'	CBod CMea ECtt EPfP GBin GMaP NLar WHoo
	'Blue Emperor'	ECtt
	'Blue Whale'	CBod ECtt ELon GAbr NLar SRms SRot SWvt
§	'Bob Saunders' (d)	CMea ECtt
	'Bressingham Pink' (d) ♀H5	ECtt ELan EPfP SRms
	'Bressingham Red'	ECtt ELan EPfP GCrg GMaP LHop NPri SRms
	'Bubble Purple'	EPfP
	canescens	CPBP GKev XSen
	- subsp. ***cilicica***	EPot
	Cascade Series	CWCL GJos SPoG
	- 'Blue Cascade'	GMaP MBNS NPri SPlb SPoG SRms
	- 'Lilac Cascade'	SPoG
	- 'Purple Cascade'	CTri CWib LBMP LCro LSRN MAsh MBNS MJak NPri SPlb SPoG SRms WRHF
	- 'Red Cascade' ♀H5	CTri CWib ECtt LBMP LSRN MBNS MJak NPri SPlb SPoG
	deltoidea	SVic XSen
	- 'Tauricola Variegata' (v)	ECtt
	- Variegata Group (v)	ECtt NPri
	- - 'Nana Variegata' (v)	CMea EPot
	'Doctor Mules' ♀H5	ECtt SRms
	'Doctor Mules Variegata' (v)	ECho ECtt EHoe ELan ELon EPfP GMaP LAst MAsh MHer NLar NPri NWad SPoG SWvt WHoo
	double pink-flowered (d)	CBod EPfP GMaP MHol WRHF
	'Downers Variegata' (v)	ECtt EPot NWad
	'Elsa Lancaster'	NSla
§	'Fiona'	ECtt EWoo MMuc
	glabrescens	CMea CPBP WAbe WTor
	'Gloria'	CBod CMea ECtt EPot GAbr NLar NSla SBod SRot WHoo WIce
	'Golden Emperor'	MHer
	'Golden King'	see *A.* 'Aureovariegata'
	gracilis	CTal NSla
	- 'Kitte Rose'	ECtt LBuc LRHS MHol NPri
	'Greencourt Purple' ♀H5	ECho ECtt ELan MHer
	'Hamburger Stadtpark'	CWCL ECtt ELan EPfP EWoo GCrg LHop NPri SRot
	'Ida' **new**	CSma
	'Ida Meadhome' **new**	NPri
	'Kitte'	CSma ECtt ELan EPfP GBin GCrg LRHS MHer NLar SPoG SRms
	'Kitte Blue'	EPfP LBuc LRHS MHol NPri SPoG WIce
	'Kitte Purple'	CSma ELan EPfP NPri SPoG
	'Leichtlinii'	XLum

'Lime Variegated' (v)	NPri WIce
macedonica	EPot
pinardii	EPot XSen
'Pink Beauty'	ECtt WIce
'Purple Charm'	SRms
'Red Carpet'	ECtt ELan EPot MAsh MHer SRms
'Rose Queen'	CMea ECtt
(Royal Series) 'Royal Blue'	EPfP MJak NEgg NLar SRms SRot WMoo XLum
- 'Royal Red'	EPfP SRms WMoo
- 'Royal Violet'	EPfP WMoo XLum
'Schofield's Double'	see *A.* 'Bob Saunders'
'Shobden' (v)	WIce
'Silberrand' (v)	ECha NSla
'Somerfield Silver'	ELan EPfP
'Somerford Lime' (v)	ECtt ELan EPfP LSou SRms
'Swan Red' (v)	CBod ECtt EHoe ELon EPot LAst LBMP MHer NEgg NLar NSla SRot WIce
thessala	CMea CTal
'Triumphante'	ECtt
'Valerie' (v)	ECtt EPot
'Westacre Gold' (v)	ECtt MHol
'Whitewell Gem'	NPri WMoo XLum
'Winterberg' **new**	ECtt

Aucuba ✿ (*Garryaceae*)

sp.	LPar
chlorascens B&SWJ 11815	WCru
himalaica	CFil
var. ***dolichophylla***	
- - Og 95038	WCru
japonica	CCVT CDul CLet LPar SCob SEWo WCru WFar
- 'Angelon'	LRHS
- var. ***borealis*** (f) CWJ 12898	WCru
- 'Crassifolia' (m)	EBtc ELon GBin
- 'Crotonifolia' (f/v) 🏆^{H5}	Widely available
- 'Crotonifolia' (m/v)	CMac MAsh SGol SRms
- 'Dentata'	WCru
- 'February Star' (f/v)	SDix
- 'Gold Splash' (v)	WFar
- 'Golden King' (m/v) 🏆^{H5}	CDoC CLet CMac CWib ELan ELon EPfP LRHS MAsh MBri MGos NLar SCob SGol SLim SPoG WFar
- 'Golden Spangles' (f/v)	CBcs CDoC EBee IVic LRHS NLar SWvt
- 'Goldstrike' (v)	LRHS MAsh SMad
- 'Hillieri' (f)	EBtc
- f. ***longifolia***	CBot CMac EPfP NLar SDix WCru
- - 'Longifolia' (f)	MGos
- - 'Salicifolia' (f) 🏆^{H5}	ESwi MRav NLar SCob WCru
- 'Maculata' misapplied	see *A. japonica* 'Variegata'
- 'Marmorata'	CRos LPfy LRHS MBri MGos SHil
- 'Mr Goldstrike' (m/v)	EPfP LPmr LRHS
- Pepper Pot = 'Shilpot' (m/v) 🏆^{H5} WFar	EPfP LRHS MAsh MJak SLon SPoG
- 'Pepperspot'^{PBR} (m/v)	CDoC MJak WMoo
- 'Picturata' (m/v)	CDul CLet CMac CSBt ELan ELon LRHS MAsh MJak MMuc NLar SEND SHil WFar
- 'Rozannie' (f/m) 🏆^{H5}	Widely available
- 'Sulphurea Marginata' (f/v)	CBcs CMac COtt CTri EBee EShb ESwi LRHS NLar WFar
§ - 'Variegata' (f/v)	Widely available
- 'Variegata' white-flowered, male (m/v)	SGbt
omeiensis	CExl CFil
- B&SWJ 2864	WCru
- BWJ 8048	WCru
- L 614	CFil WPGP

Aulax (*Proteaceae*)

cancellata	SPlb

Aurinia (*Brassicaceae*)

§ ***saxatilis*** 🏆^{H5}	ECho EPfP MMuc SEND SPlb XSen
- 'Argentea'	ECho
- 'Citrina' 🏆^{H5}	ECha ECtt SRms
- 'Compacta'	CTri ECtt GJos WIce
- 'Dudley Nevill Variegated' (v)	ECha ECho ECtt EWes GCrg MHer
- Gold Ball	see *A. saxatili* 'Goldkugel'
- 'Gold Dust'	ECho NRya SRms
- 'Golden Queen'	CNor MHer
§ - 'Goldkugel'	ECho EPfP NPri SPoG
- 'Variegata' (v)	NPri SPoG SRms
sinuata 'Pebbles'	GJos

Austrocedrus (*Cupressaceae*)

§ ***chilensis***	CKen SBig SLim

Avena (*Poaceae*)

candida	see *Helictotrichon sempervirens*

Avenula see *Helictotrichon*

avocado see *Persea americana*

Azalea see *Rhododendron*

Azara ✿ (*Salicaceae*)

sp.	NEgg
alpina	MGil
dentata	CBcs CHll CMac GGal WFar
- 'Variegata'	see *A. integrifolia* 'Variegata'
integrifolia	MGil
§ - 'Variegata' (v)	CWib LRHS
lanceolata	CBcs CDul CExl CTri CTsd GBin GGal IDee LEdu
microphylla 🏆^{H4}	CBcs CDul CExl CLet CMac CTri EBee ELan ELon EPfP EUJe GGal IVic LRHS LSRN MAsh MGil MGos MMuc SEND SLim SPer SPlb SSpi WBod WFar WPGP WSHC
* - 'Albovariegata' (v)	CTri
- 'Gold Edge' (v)	CBcs EPfP LRHS WFar
- 'Variegata' (v)	CBcs CBct CDoC CExl CMac CWib EBee EHoe ELan EPfP GQui LBMP LRHS MAsh MGil MMuc NLar SEND SLon SSpi WFar WPat
* ***patagonica***	MBlu
petiolaris	CTri EBee LEdu MGil
serrata 🏆^{H4}	CBcs CBot CDul CTsd CWib EPfP EShb EUJe GBin LHop LRHS MGil NCGa NLar SDix SEND SGol SPer SRms SVen WBor WFar WHar WKif WSHC
uruguayensis	CExl CTsd EBee EBtc GBin

Azorella (*Apiaceae*)

filamentosa	WAbe
glebaria misapplied	see *A. trifurcata*
glebaria A. Gray	see *Bolax gummifer*
gummifer	see *Bolax gummifer*
lycopodioides	EPot WAbe
patagonica	EPot SPlb WAbe
§ ***trifurcata***	CPar CSpe CTri ECho GAbr GCrg MMuc NBir SPlb WAbe

- 'Nana' ECho GEdr WThu XLum

Azorina (*Campanulaceae*)

§ ***vidalii*** SPlb

B

Babiana (*Iridaceae*)

angustifolia ECho
'Blue Gem' ECho
patersoniae SPlb
pygmaea WCot
sambucina NRog
stricta ♀H2 ECho GKev SDeJ WHil
- Kew hybrids GKev
- 'Purple Star' CExl ECho GKev NRog
- 'Tubergen's Blue' ECho
thunbergii CTre
tubulosa NRog
villosa ECho WCot
* ***volubile*** NRog
'Zwanenburg's Glory' CPrp ECho WHil

Baccharis (*Asteraceae*)

halimifolia CBcs SEND
- 'Baccador'PBR EBee LRHS SPoG
patagonica LRHS MMuc SEND SPhx SVen

Backhousia (*Myrtaceae*)

citriodora CArn MHer

Bacopa (*Plantaginaceae*)

sp. SEND SWvt
'Snowflake' see *Sutera cordata* 'Snowflake'

Baeckea (*Myrtaceae*)

gunniana CExl
linifolia SPlb
virgata ECou SPlb

Baimashania (*Brassicaceae*)

pulvinata WAbe

Baldellia (*Alismataceae*)

ranunculoides WMAq
- f. ***repens*** LLWG

Ballota (*Lamiaceae*)

acetabulosa CMHG ECha EWes WCot XSen
'All Hallow's Green' see *Marrubium bourgaei* var. *bourgaei* 'All Hallows Green'
hirsuta XSen
nigra CArn GPoy MHer NMir SRms WHfH
§ - 'Archer's Variegated' (v) MAvo
- 'Variegata' see *B. nigra* 'Archer's Variegated'
pseudodictamnus ♀H4 CBcs CBod CMac EBee ECha EHoe ELan EPfP EWoo GMaP LEdu LHop LRHS LSRN MBel MRav NPer NSti SCob SDix SEND SGSe SLon SPer WSHC XLum XSen
- B&M 8119 WCot
- from Crete ECha
rupestris 'Frogswell Carolyn' (v) IFro XSen

Balsamita see *Tanacetum*

Bambusa (*Poaceae*)

glaucescens see *B. multiplex*
§ ***multiplex*** XBlo
- 'Alphonso-Karrii' ERod SBig
- 'Elegans' see *B. multiplex* 'Floribunda'
- 'Fernleaf' see *B. multiplex* 'Floribunda'
§ - 'Floribunda' EShb XBlo
- 'Golden Goddess' XBlo
- 'Silverstripe' see *B. multiplex* 'Variegata'
§ - 'Variegata' (v) XBlo
- 'Wang Tsai' see *B. multiplex* 'Floribunda'
pubescens see *Dendrocalamus strictus*
ventricosa SBig XBlo
vulgaris XBlo
- 'Vittata' ERod XBlo

banana see *Ensete*, *Musa*

Banksia (*Proteaceae*)

canei SPlb
ericifolia CDTJ CTre
- var. ***macrantha*** SPlb
grandis CTre
integrifolia CDTJ CTre SPlb
marginata SPlb
media SPlb
oblongifolia SPlb
paludosa SPlb
robur SPlb
serrata SPlb
speciosa SPlb
spinulosa CTre
- var. ***collina*** SPlb
- var. ***spinulosa*** CBcs
violacea SPlb

Baptisia (*Papilionaceae*)

§ ***alba*** EBee GBBs GBin MNrw SBea WCAu
- var. ***alba*** 'Wayne's World' EBee
§ - var. ***macrophylla*** EWes LRHS SDix SPhx WCot
australis ♀H7 Widely available
- 'Caspian Blue' CExl LEdu LHop WHil WSHC
- 'Exaltata' ♀H7 LHop MHol WCot
- var. ***minor*** MMHG SPhx WSHC
- 'Nelson's Navy' SMHy
× ***bicolor*** 'Starlite' (Prairieblues Series) IPot MNrw SKHP SPoG
bracteata SIgm
- var. ***leucophaea*** LEdu LRHS LSou SPhx
'Carolina Moonlight' EBee EWes IPot LHop MAvo MNrw SKHP SPoG
'Chocolate Chip' LHop
lactea see *B. alba* var. *macrophylla*
leucantha see *B. alba* var. *macrophylla*
megacarpa SKHP
pendula see *B. alba*
'Purple Smoke' CAbP CAby CDes CExl CSpe EBee ECtt EPPr GBuc ILea LEdu LHop LRHS MAvo MHol MNrw NSti SMHy SPad SPhx WAul WCAu WCot WPtf WRHF
sphaerocarpa EBee SPhx SPlb WCot
tinctoria CArn SPhx
× ***variicolor*** 'Twilite' (Prairieblues Series) EBee EPfP EWes MNrw SKHP SPoG WNPC

Barbarea (*Brassicaceae*)

praecox see *B. verna*
rupicola 'Sunnyola' MMuc

§ ***verna*** GPoy MHer SRms SVic
vulgaris 'Variegata' (v) NBro WHer WMoo

Barleria (*Acanthaceae*)

suberecta see *Dicliptera sericea*

Bartlettina (*Asteraceae*)

§ ***sordida*** EUJe

Basella (*Basellaceae*)

rubra SHDw SPre SVic

Bashania (*Poaceae*)

§ ***fargesii*** ENBC ERod MMuc MRav MWht SEND WJun
I ***qingchengshanensis*** ERod MWht WJun

basil see *Ocimum basilicum*

Bauhinia (*Caesalpiniaceae*)

bowkeri **new** SPlb
galpinii MOWG
natalensis SPlb
purpurea L. SPlb
scandens MOWG
yunnanensis SBrt

Baumea see *Machaerina*

bay see *Laurus nobilis*

Beaucarnea (*Dracaenaceae*)

recurvata ♀H1c EAla LPal SPlb

Beaufortia (*Myrtaceae*)

elegans SVen
schaueri SVen
sparsa CTsd MOWG SVen
squarrosa SPlb

Beauverdia see *Leucocoryne*

Beckmannia (*Poaceae*)

eruciformis XLum

Bedfordia (*Asteraceae*)

linearis SPlb SVen

Beesia (*Ranunculaceae*)

calthifolia CBct CCon CDTJ CHid CMHG CSpe CTal EBee EPfP GBBs GEdr IMou LEdu LHop LLHF SMad WCru WPGP WSHC
- DJHC 98447 CDes CExl
deltophylla EWld WCot

Begonia ✿ (*Begoniaceae*)

'Abel Carrière' (R) WDib
aconitifolia (C) EShb
albopicta (C) EBak
- 'Rosea' (C) MOWG WDib
'Albuquerque Midnight Sky' (R) SBrm
'Amazon Delta' (R) SBrm
'Angela Jane' (T) **new** WFib
§ ***annulata*** ♀H1b HWJK 2424 ESwi WCru
'Apricot Delight' (T) WFib
'Arctic Breeze' PBR (R) SBrm
'Argentea' (R) EBak
'Argenteo-guttata' EShb
'Axel Lange' (R) SBrm
'Aya' (C) WDib
'Baronessa' SBrm
'Beatrice Haddrell' WDib
Belleconia Soft Orange = 'Imbellpea' (Belleconia Series) LAst
'Benitochiba' (R) ♀H1b CDes CDoC CExl CHll CSpe EBee ECtt ESwi EUJe LRHS LSou MAvo MHol NLar SGSe WCot WDib WGrn
'Beryl Rhodes' (T) **new** WFib
'Bethlehem Star' WDib
§ 'Bettina Rothschild' (R) SBrm WDib
'Billy Langdon' (T) **new** WFib
'Black Fang' **new** WDib
'Blackberry Swirl' (R) WDib
'Blazing Star' (T) **new** LOPS
Blissful (Million Kisses Series) **new** LSou
'Blushing Star' (T) **new** LOPS
'Bokit' WDib
'Bokit' × ***imperialis*** WDib
boliviensis (T) CDoC ESwi GCal SEND
- 'Firecracker' WDib
Bonfire = 'Nzcone' PBR ♀H1b EPfP SPoG
'Bouton de Rose' (T) SDeJ
'Brown Twist' WDib
'Burgundy Velvet' WDib
'Burle Marx' ♀H1b WDib
'Buttermilk' (T) WFib
'Can-can' (T) WFib
'Candy Floss' CDes WCru
'Captain Nemo' (R) SBrm
carolineifolia ♀H1b WDib
'Casey Corwin' (R) SBrm WDib
cathayana EBee GCal
'Cathedral' WDib
'Champagne' LCro LOPS
I ***chapaensis*** HWJ 642 WCru
Cherry Bon Bon LBuc
'China Curl' (R) ♀H1b WDib
chitoensis B&SWJ 1954 GCal WCru
chloroneura WDib
'Cleopatra' ♀H1b WDib
coccinea (C) WDib
'Comte de Lesseps' (C) WDib
'Connee Boswell' ♀H1b CHll WDib
§ ***corallina*** (C) EBak
cucullata (S) SKHP
- var. ***arenosicola*** (S) CDoC CFil ECtt ESwi SEND SKHP WCot
'Curly Fireflush' (R) ♀H1b SBrm WDib
'David Blais' (R) ♀H1b WDib
'Dawnal Meyer' (C) WDib
I 'De Elegans' WDib
Devil Series (S) NPri
- 'Devil Red' (S) LAst
- 'Devil Rose' (S) LAst
- 'Devil White' (S) LAst
Devotion = 'Yadev' PBR (Million Kisses Series) ♀H1b WGor
'Dewdrop' (R) ♀H1b WDib
'Dibleys Pink Showers' PBR ♀H1b WDib
discolor see *B. grandis* subsp. *evansiana*
'Don Miller' (C) WDib
Dragon Wing Red = 'Bepared' PBR EShb

	'Elda Haring' (R)	SBrm
	Elegance = 'Yagance'[PBR] (Million Kisses Series) ♀H1b	LAst LSou WGor
	emeiensis	CFil CSpe EBee SGSe SKHP
	'Emerald Beauty' (R) ♀H1b	SBrm
	'Emerald Giant' (R)	WDib
	'Escargot' (R) ♀H1b	WDib
	'Etna' (R)	SBrm
	'Fairy Lights' (T) **new**	WFib
	Fimbriata Group (T)	SDeJ
	'Fire Flush'	see *B.* 'Bettina Rothschild'
	'Fireworks' (R) ♀H1b	WDib
	'Flo'Belle Moseley' (C)	WDib
§	***foliosa*** var. ***miniata*** ♀H1b	CDoC CHll CTsd EBak MArl SDix WCot WDib
	- - pink-flowered	MOWG
	- - 'Rosea'	CDoC
	fuchsioides	see *B. foliosa* var. *miniata*
	'Gay Gordon' (T) **new**	WFib
	'Glowing Embers'	LBuc NWad
	gracilis (T) F&M 266	CFil
	- F&M 337	CFil
	grandis (T)	IDee WBod XLum
§	- subsp. ***evansiana*** ♀H3	CAby CBot CCon CHll CPne CTal CTsd ELon EShb EUJe GCal LEdu LPla SBch SDix SEND SGSe SKHP SPlb WCot WCru WMoo
	- - B&SWJ 11188	WCru
	- - var. ***alba*** hort. ♀H5	CAby CCon CDoC CFil CTal EBee EPPr EShb ESwi EWld GCal LEdu LPla LRHS NLos SBch SDix SGSe SKHP SPoG SSpi WCot WMoo WPGP XLum
	- - 'Claret Jug'	CDoC CExl CFil EBee ECtt ESwi WCot WGrn WPGP WWEG
	- - 'Pink Parasol'	ESwi SMad WCru
	- - pink-flowered	NLos
	- - 'Sublime'	LEdu WPGP
	- 'Sapporo'	CFil EBee EPPr ESwi GCal SChr WCru
§	- subsp. ***sinensis*** (T)	EBee SGSe
I	- - 'Red Undies'	ESwi WCru
	- aff. subsp. ***sinensis*** (T)	SKHP
	- - BWJ 8133	WCru
	'Green Gold' (R) ♀H1b	SBrm WDib
	griffithii	see *B. annulata*
	'Gryphon'	EShb
	haageana hort. ex W.Watson	see *B. scharffii*
	hatacoa silver-leaved	EShb WDib
	Heaven Series (S)	LAst NPri
	'Helen Teupel' (R)	WDib
	'Helena Hall' (T) **new**	WFib
	'Hilo Holiday' (R) ♀H1b	WDib
	Honeymoon = 'Yamoon' (Million Kisses Series)	NPri
	'Houston Fiesta' (R)	SBrm
	(Illumination Series) 'Illumination Apricot' (T/d)	SCoo
	- 'Illumination Rose' (T/d)	SCoo
	- 'Illumination Salmon Pink' (T/d)	SCoo
	- 'Illumination White' (T/d)	SCoo
	'Inca Fire'[PBR] (R)	SBrm
	incarnata 'Metallica'	see *B. metallica*
	'Indian Summer'[PBR] (R)	SBrm
	× ***intermedia*** 'Bertinii' (T)	LOPS SDeJ
	'Ironstone' (R) ♀H1b	SBrm
	'Jennifer Wilson' (T) **new**	WFib
	'Jessie Cruickshank' (T) **new**	WFib
	'La Paloma' (C)	WDib
	Large-flowered Double Group (T/d)	SDeJ
	'Lianne' (T) **new**	WFib
	'Lime Swirl'	WDib
	'Limeade' ♀H1b	WDib
	'Linda Jackson' (T) **new**	WFib
	listada ♀H1b	CDoC WDib
	'Little Brother Montgomery' ♀H1b	EShb SDix WDib
	'Little Girl' **new**	LOPS
	'Lois Burks' (C)	WDib
	'Looking Glass' (C)	WDib
	'Lucerna' (C)	EBak EShb NLos WDib
	'Lucky Colours' (R)	SBrm
	luxurians ♀H1b	CBot CDoC CHll CSpe EBee ECtt ESwi EUJe MNrw MPie SEND SMad SPad SPlb WCot WGrn WPGP
	macduffieana	see *B. corallina*
	maculata 'Wightii' (C)	CDoC CSpe WDib
	'Magma' (R)	SBrm
	'Majesty' (T)	WFib
	'Maori Haze'[PBR] (R)	SBrm
	Marginata Group (T)	SDeJ
	'Marmaduke' ♀H1b	WDib
	'Marmorata' (T)	SDeJ
	'Martin Johnson' (R) ♀H1b	WDib
	masoniana ♀H1b	GCal WDib WSFF
I	'Matador' (T)	WFib
	'Melissa' (T)	WFib
	'Merry Christmas' (R)	WDib
	'Metallic Mist'[PBR]	CSpe ESwi LSou WGrn
§	***metallica*** ♀H1b	CDoC
	'Midnight Magic' (R) ♀H1b	WDib
	'Mikado' (R) ♀H1b	SBrm
	Million Kisses Series	LBuc NPri
	'Mishmi Silver'	GCal WPGP
	'Mother's Day' (T) **new**	LCro LOPS
	'Mr Kartuz' (R)	SBrm
	'Mrs E. McLaughlan' (T) **new**	WFib
	'Mrs Peters' (T) **new**	WFib
	'Munchkin' ♀H1b	WDib
	'My Best Friend'	WDib
	'Namur' (R) ♀H1b	WDib
	Nonstop Series (T/d)	LAst SDeJ
	(Nonstop Mocca Series) 'Nonstop Mocca Orange' (T/d) **new**	LAst
	- 'Nonstop Mocca Scarlet' (T/d) **new**	LAst
	- 'Nonstop Mocca Yellow' (T/d) **new**	LAst
	'Ollykey' (T) **new**	WFib
	'Orange Rubra' (C) ♀H1b	WDib
	'Organdy' (mixed)	LAst
	'Pachea' (R)	SBrm
	palmata	CDTJ CExl GCal SKHP
	panchtharensis	CFil
	- B&SWJ 2692	WCru
	Passion = 'Yabos' (Million Kisses Series)	LSou
	pedatifida	SKHP
	- DJHC 98473	EWld WCru
	Pendula Group (T)	SDeJ
	- 'Pink Giant' (T) **new**	LCro LOPS
	- 'Red Giant' (T) **new**	LCro LOPS
	- 'White Giant' (T) **new**	LCro LOPS
	'Picotee' (T)	CSut SDeJ

	'Pink Champagne' (R) ♀H1b	WDib
	'Pink Flamingo' (T) **new**	LCro LOPS
	'Pink Pop' (R)	SBrm
	'Pollux' ♀H1b	WDib
	'Powder Puff' (T) **new**	WFib
	'Princess Alice' (T) **new**	WFib
	'Princess of Hanover' (R) ♀H1b	WDib
	putii B&SWJ 7245	WCru
	'Queen Olympus'	WDib
	'Raspberry Swirl' (R)	WDib
	ravenii (T)	EBee SKHP
	'Razzmatazz' (R)	WDib
	'Red Dragon' (R)	WDib
	'Red Glory' (T) **new**	LCro LOPS
	'Red Kiss' (R)	SBrm
	'Red Robin' (R) ♀H1b	SBrm WDib
	'Red Undies' (*grandis*)	see *B. grandis* subsp. *sinensis* 'Red Undies'
	'Regal Minuet' (R) ♀H1b	SBrm WDib
	rex (R)	SBrm
	'Richard Galle'	LAst
	'Rocheart' (R) ♀H1b	SBrm WDib
	'Roy Hartley' (T/d)	WFib
	'Sal's Comet' (R) ♀H1b	WDib
	'Sal's Moondust'	WDib
	'Sandra Haynes' (T) **new**	WFib
	'Savannah Pink Parfait' (R)	SBrm
	'Sceptre' (T)	WFib
	'Sceptre Cross' (T) **new**	WFib
§	***scharffii***	EBak EUJe SDix
	'Scherzo'	WDib
	'Sea Urchin' **new**	WDib
	serratipetala ♀H1b	CDoC EBak WDib
	'Shamus'	WDib
*	***shepherdii***	WDib
	sikkimensis	GCal
	silletensis **new**	WCot
	- subsp. ***mengyangensis***	GCal
	'Silver Cloud' (R) ♀H1b	WDib
	'Silver Jewell' ♀H1b	WDib
	'Silver Lace'	WDib
	'Silver Splendor'	CSpe EBee ECtt ESwi IBoy WCot WPGP XEll
	'Silver Spray' (R)	SBrm
	sinensis	see *B. grandis* subsp. *sinensis*
	sizemoreae	GCal WDib
	'Snow Storm'	WDib
*	'Snowcap' (C) ♀H1b	CDoC WDib
	solananthera A. DC. ♀H1b	WDib
	'Solid Silver' (R)	WDib
	soli-mutata	WDib
	sonderiana (T)	GCal
	'Stained Glass'	WDib
	'Sugar Candy' (T/d)	WFib
	'Sugar Plum'	MAsh
	(Summerwings Series) Summerwings Orange = 'Innbolora'PBR	ESwi
	- Summerwings White = 'Innbolwhi'PBR	ESwi
	'Sun Set'	LAst
	Supercascade Series **new**	LAst
	- 'Supercascade Apricot Shades' **new**	LAst
	- 'Supercascade Pink Bi-colour' **new**	LAst
	- 'Supercascade Salmon' **new**	LAst
	- 'Supercascade Yellow' **new**	LAst
	sutherlandii (T) ♀H2	CDoC CExl CFil EABi EBak EBee EShb ESwi EWld LRHS NPer SAdn SBch SDix WCot WDib WPGP
	- 'Papaya' (T)	CSpe
	'Sweet Dreams' (T/d)	WFib
	'Switzerland' (T)	SDeJ
	taliensis	SKHP
	- EDHCH 042	WCot WCru
	- 'White-boned Demon'	SKHP
	'Tessa Robinson' (T) **new**	WFib
	'Texastar'	WDib
	'Thrush' (R)	SBrm
	'Thurstonii' ♀H1b	EShb
	'Tim Anderson' (R)	SBrm
*	***tripartita*** (T)	WDib
	'Tuscan Bonfire' (R)	SBrm
	'Two Face'	WDib
	'Tye Dye'	GCal WPGP
	venosa	EShb
	'Vera Coates' (T) **new**	WFib
	'Vesuvius' (R)	WDib
	'Vibrant Star' (T) **new**	LOPS
	'Vista' (R)	SBrm
	'Wavy Green'	GCal WPGP
	'Whispers' (T) **new**	WFib
	Whopper Series **new**	LBMP
	'Wild Swan'	WCru
*	***wynn-jonesiae*** 'Pink Lady' **new**	WCru
	'Ziggy' (T) **new**	WFib

Belamcanda see *Iris*

	chinensis	see *Iris domestica*

Bellevalia (*Asparagaceae*)

	'Cream Pearl'	ECho WCot
	desertorum JCA 0.227.690	WCot
	dubia	CDes EBee ECho WCot
	forniculata	WCot
	hyacinthoides	ECho WCot
	mauretanica	ECho
§	***paradoxa***	CAby CHid CMea EBee ECho EHrv ERCP MNrw SDeJ WCot
	- white-flowered	ECho
	pycnantha misapplied	see *B. paradoxa*
	pycnantha ambig.	EPfP
	- 'Green Pearl'	ECho SDeJ
	romana	EBee ECho ERCP GKev SDeJ WCot
	tabriziana	CDes WCot

Bellis (*Asteraceae*)

§	***caerulescens***	GAbr
	perennis 'Alice'	GAbr WCot
	- 'Big Bob' (d)	WCot
	- f. ***discoidea*** **new**	NPri
	- 'Dresden China'	EWes
	- 'Galaxy White' (Galaxy Series)	EPfP
	- Hen and Chickens	see *B. perennis* 'Prolifera' single-flowered
	- 'Low and Behold'	CNat
	- old strain	WCot
§	- 'Prolifera' single-flowered	CFis ECtt WCot
	- 'Rusher Rose'	EPfP
	- 'Single Blue'	see *B. caerulescens*
	- 'The Pearl'	WCot
	- 'Upper Seagry'	CNat
	rotundifolia 'Caerulescens'	see *B. caerulescens*
	sylvestris	CArn WCot

Belloa (*Asteraceae*)

chilensis	SPlb

Beloperone see *Justicia*

guttata	see *Justicia brandegeeana*

Bensoniella (*Saxifragaceae*)

oregona	CExl

Benthamiella (*Solanaceae*)

nordenskjoldii	WAbe
patagonica	CPBP EPot WAbe
- F&W 9345	ITim WAbe
- white-flowered	WAbe
- yellow-flowered	WAbe

Berberidopsis (*Berberidopsidaceae*)

corallina	CBcs CDoC CKel CMac CTri CWSG ELan EPfP GGal IArd IDee IVic LBMP LHop LRHS MGos MOWG MRav NLar SAko SLim SPer SPoG SWvt WBod WHar WSHC

Berberis ✿ (*Berberidaceae*)

sp.	SCob
CC 4730	CExl
aggregata	NBir SPer SRms
amurensis	WPat
- var. ***latifolia*** B&SWJ 8539	WCru
aquifolium	see *Mahonia aquifolium*
- 'Fascicularis'	see *Mahonia* × *wagneri* 'Pinnacle'
aristata ambig.	CArn
asiatica	CExl GPoy WPGP
- PAB 5438 **new**	LEdu
'Baby Bear'	CJun
bealei	see *Mahonia bealei*
'Boughton Red'	WHor
× ***bristolensis***	SRms
buxifolia 'Nana' misapplied	see *B. microphylla* 'Pygmaea'
calliantha	WFar
candidula C.K. Schneid.	CDul EBee EPfP LRHS MMuc MSwo NLar SCob SPer
- 'Jytte'	see *B.* 'Jytte'
× ***carminea*** 'Pirate King'	CSBt EBee EPfP LHop LRHS MAsh SPer SPoG SWvt
darwinii Υ^{H5}	Widely available
I - 'Compacta'	CChe CDoC CMac CRos ELan EPfP LAst LBuc LHop LPfy LRHS MAsh MGos NEgg NLar SBod SCob SHil SLim SPoG SWvt WCot
deinacantha AC 1010	MSnd
dictyophylla	CBot CDul EBee ELan EPfP LHop LRHS MGos MMuc NLar SCob SKHP SLon SPer SPoG SSpi WSHC
dulcis 'Nana'	see *B. microphylla* 'Pygmaea'
dumicola	MSnd
empetrifolia	LEdu
× ***frikartii*** 'Amstelveen' Υ^{H5}	CCVT CDoC CLet ECrN ELan EPfP LAst LRHS MBNS MMuc MRav NLar SCob SEND WMoo
- 'Telstar'	EBtc EWTr NEoE NLar SCob WMoo
gagnepainii misapplied	see *B. gagnepainii* var. *lanceifolia*
gagnepainii C.K. Schneid.	CDul CMac SCob
§ - var. ***lanceifolia***	CBcs CTri EBee MGos MMuc NWea SEND SGol WHar
- - 'Fernspray'	EBee EPfP MRav SRms
- 'Purpurea'	see *B.* × *interposita* 'Wallich's Purple'
'Georgei' Υ^{H5}	CWib EPfP GQui LRHS WPat
'Goldilocks'	CDul CJun EBee EPfP LSRN MBlu SCob SMad
goudotii B&SWJ 10769	WCru
haematocarpa	SIgm
heterophylla	GKev
× ***hybridogagnepainii*** 'Chenault'	ELan
- 'Robin Hood'	NEgg
hypokerina	CMac
insignis	GCal IDee
- subsp. ***insignis*** var. ***insignis***	ELon LLHF WPat
- - B&SWJ 2432	WCru
§ × ***interposita*** 'Wallich's Purple'	WMoo CCVT EPfP MRav MSwo SPer
jamesiana	LLHF MSnd WCFE WPat
julianae	CArg CBcs CDul CMac ELan EPfP MGos MJak MMuc MSwo NBes NEgg NWea SCob SEND SGol SPer SRms SWvt WFar WHar WSHC
§ 'Jytte'	EBee
koreana	CDul EPfP NLar
'Little Favourite'	see *B. thunbergii* f. *atropurpurea* 'Atropurpurea Nana'
× ***lologensis*** 'Apricot Queen' Υ^{H5}	CBcs CLet CMac CRos EBee EPfP GBin LRHS MAsh MGos NLar SCob SPer SPoG SWvt WPat
- 'Mystery Fire'	COtt IArd MAsh MBri MGos MJak NEgg NLar SGol SWvt WHar WMoo
- 'Stapehill'	CMac ELan EPfP LRHS MAsh
lycium	CEvo
× ***media*** 'Dual Jewel'^{PBR}	NLar
- Park Jewel	see *B.* × *media* 'Parkjuweel'
§ - 'Parkjuweel'	CBcs CMac IArd MRav SCob SRms WFar WMoo
- 'Red Jewel' Υ^{H5}	CDoC CMac ECrN EMil EPfP LRHS MAsh MBri MGos MMuc MRav NEgg SCob SEND SPer SPoG WCFE WFar WMoo
× ***mentorensis***	WCFE
microphylla	EPfP GKev WCFE WFar
§ - 'Pygmaea'	CBcs CSBt EBee ELan EMil EPfP LRHS MAsh MGos MMuc MRav SCob SLim SPer
mitifolia	NLar
montana	WPGP WPat
morrisonensis	GBin
× ***ottawensis*** 'Auricoma'	NBes SGol SWvt
- f. ***purpurea***	CCVT CMac CWib LRHS WHar
§ - - 'Silver Miles' (v)	EHoe MRav NLar WFar WHar WPat
§ - - 'Superba'	Widely available
panlanensis 'Cally Rose'	GCal
poiretii	CExl
polyantha var. ***polyantha***	CTri
pruinosa	GKev
'Red Tears'	MMHG MRav NLar SPer WFar WMoo WPat
× ***rubrostilla*** 'Cherry Ripe'	CMac
- 'Wisley'	LRHS
sieboldii	ELon LLHF MAsh MRav WCFE WPat
§ ***soulieana***	EPfP NWea
stenophylla Hance	see *B. soulieana*
× ***stenophylla*** Lindl. Υ^{H5}	CCVT CDoC CDul CMac CSBt CTri EBee EPfP LBMP LBuc MBri MMuc MRav NBes NWea SEND SGol SPer WFar WHar WMoo
- 'Autumnalis'	NEgg
- 'Claret Cascade'	EMil MRav NLar

- 'Compacta'	NEgg WFar
- 'Corallina Compacta' ♀H5	CMac CMea CRos ECho ELan EPfP EPot LHop LRHS MAsh MHer SCob SIgm SPoG SRms WPat
- 'Crawley Gem'	GBin NLar
- 'Etna'	ELan LRHS MAsh SCoo SPoG
- 'Irwinii'	CMac LRHS
- 'Nana'	LRHS SRms
- 'Pink Pearl' (v)	CMHG
subacuminata FMWJ 13290	WCru
- NJM 09.165	WPGP
sublevis PAB 8943 new	LEdu
taliensis	CExl
temolaica ♀H5	CJun EBtc EHoe EPfP EWes MAsh MGos MSnd NLar NWea SCob WCFE WPGP WPat
thunbergii	CArg CBcs CDoC CDul CMac CNec EPfP LBuc NBes NLar NWea SCob SPer SWvt WFar WMou
- f. ***atropurpurea***	CBar CBcs CCVT CMac CSBt CTri EAEE EBee ELan EPfP LBuc MGos MRav MSwo NBes NEgg NLar NWea SCob SGol SPer SPlb SRms WHar WMoo WMou
- - 'Admiration'PBR ♀H7	Widely available
§ - - 'Atropurpurea Nana' ♀H7	Widely available
- - 'Bagatelle'	CDoC CLet CRos ELan EPfP EPot IArd IVic LAst LBMP LHop LRHS LSRN MAsh MBri MGos MRav NLar SCob SLim SPer SPoG SWvt WCFE WHar WMoo WPat
- - 'Concorde' ♀H7	ELan EPfP LRHS MAsh SCob
- - 'Dart's Red Lady' ♀H7	CExl CRos CSBt CWib EHoe ELan EPfP LRHS MAsh NLar SCob SPer SWvt WFar
- - 'Golden Ring' (v) ♀H7	CBcs CChe CDoC CDul CLet CMac EHoe ELan EPfP LBMP LHop LRHS MAsh MGos MRav NEgg SCob SGbt SPer SPoG SWvt WFar WMoo WPat
- - 'Harlequin' (v) ♀H7	CBcs CChe CDoC COtt CRos ELan EPfP LBMP LCro LOPS LPfy LRHS LSRN MAsh MBri MGos NEgg NLar SCob SEle SGol SHil SPer SPoG SRms SWvt WFar WHar WPat
- - 'Helmond Pillar'	Widely available
- - 'Pink Queen' (v)	CDul COtt EAEE ELan EPfP EWTr LHop LRHS MAsh NLar SCob WFar WPat
- - 'Red Chief'	CBcs CMac COtt CRos EHoe ELan EPfP LPfy LRHS MAsh MGos MJak MSwo NEgg SCob SGol SHil SLim SLon SPer SPoG SRms SWvt WFar WHar WMoo WPat
- - 'Red Pillar'	CChe CDoC CMac CRos EHoe ELan IVic LAst LPfy LRHS MAsh MBri MGos NEgg SHil SWvt WPat WRHF
- - 'Red Rocket'	EBee ELan EPfP EUJe LRHS MPkF NEgg NLar SCob SCoo SPer WMoo
- - 'Rose Glow' (v) ♀H7	Widely available
- - 'Rosy Rocket'PBR (v)	CWGN EBee ELan EPfP LRHS MAsh MRav NHol SPer SPoG
- 'Atropurpurea Superba'	see *B.* × *ottawensis* f. *purpurea* 'Superba'
- 'Aurea'	CBcs CDoC CDul CMac EHoe ELan EPfP EPot LPmr LRHS LSRN MBlu MGos MRav NLar SBod SCob SLim SPlb SRms SSpi SWvt WMoo
- Bonanza Gold = 'Bogozam'PBR	CBcs CDoC CMac CRos EBee ELan EPfP LRHS MAsh MRav NLar SCob SLim SPer WPat
- 'Carpetbagger'	WHar
- 'Crimson Pygmy'	see *B. thunbergii* f. *atropurpurea* 'Atropurpurea Nana'
- 'Diabolic'	LBuc LPfy LRHS MAsh MGos NHol SPer SPoG WGrn
- 'Erecta'	CMac EPfP MRav SPer WCFE
- 'Fireball'PBR ♀H7	EPfP LRHS
- 'Golden Rocket'PBR	CRos ELan EPfP LHop LLHF LRHS MAsh MGos MJak MPkF MRav NEgg SCoo SPer SPoG WFar
- 'Golden Torch'	CDoC CNec CRos CSBt EBee ELan EPfP LPfy LRHS MAsh MBri MRav NEgg NHol SHil SLim SWvt WPat
- 'Green Carpet'	CMac LHop LRHS MBlu NLar SGol SPoG SWvt WFar
- 'Green Mantle'	see *B. thunbergii* 'Kelleriis'
- 'Green Marble'	see *B. thunbergii* 'Kelleriis'
- 'Green Ornament'	NHol
§ - 'Kelleriis' (v)	LHop LRHS MRav
- 'Kobold'	CMac EPfP LHop LRHS MAsh MGos NEgg SCob SPer SPoG WMoo
- 'Maria'PBR ♀H7	CRos CWGN EBee EHoe ELon GBin LBMP LLHF LPfy LRHS LSou MBri MGos MJak MMuc MPkF NBes NLar NPri SCob SHil SPoG WGrn WHar WMoo
- 'Minor'	SRms
- 'Orange Rocket'PBR	CBod CRos ELan EMil EPfP LPfy LRHS MAsh MBri MGos MPkF MRav NEgg NHol SCoo SEle SHil SPer SPoG WFar WPat
- 'Pink Attraction' (v)	NLar
- 'Pow-wow'	COtt EBee ELan LRHS MAsh MGos NLar SCob SCoo SLim SPoG SWvt WPat
- 'Silver Mile'	see *B.* × *ottawensis* f. *purpurea* 'Silver Miles'
- 'Somerset'	CMac
- 'Starburst'PBR (v)	CBcs CDoC CDul COtt CRos CSBt EBee EPfP LPfy LRHS LSRN MAsh MBri MGos MJak MPkF NEgg NHol SCoo SHil SLim SLon SPoG SRms SWvt
- 'Tiny Gold'PBR	CRos ELan GBin LAst LCro LRHS LSou MAsh MGos NEgg NLar SCob SLim SLon SWvt WFar
* - 'Tricolor' (v)	CMac MRav WFar WPat
trigona 'Orange King'	CBcs CMac COtt CRos CTri ELan EPfP LRHS MAsh MGos NEgg NLar SCob SPer SPoG WHar WPat
valdiviana ♀H4	CBcs CExl CJun CMHG EBee EPfP IArd IDee SChF SKHP SMad SSpi WPGP WPat
verruculosa ♀H5	CBcs CDul EPfP EWTr LHop LRHS MBlu MGos NLar NWea SCob SPer SRms SWvt WFar
- 'Hard's Rob'	NLar
aff. ***verticillata*** B&SWJ 10672	WCru
virescens B&SWJ 2646D	WCru
vulgaris	CAgr CArn CNat GPoy MCoo NWea
- 'Wiltshire Wonder' (v)	CNat
wilsoniae	CBcs CDul CFil CMac CTri ECre ELan EPfP GLog LHop MMuc NWea SCob SEND SPer SRms WFar
- blue-leaved	MAsh WFar
- var. ***guhtzunica***	EWes

	xanthoclada NJM 11.007	WPGP

Berchemia (*Rhamnaceae*)

	racemosa	NLar WSHC

bergamot see *Citrus* × *limon* Bergamot Group

Bergbambos (*Poaceae*)

§	***tessellata***	ERod MMuc MWht SEND WJun

Bergenia ✿ (*Saxifragaceae*)

	'Abendglocken'	CMac ECGP ECha ECtt EPfP GQue NSti WCot
§	'Abendglut'	Widely available
	'Admiral'	CBct CMac ECha MLHP WCot
	afghanica	XLum
*	***agavifolia***	CBct XLum
	'Andrea'	WCot
	'Angel Kiss' (Dragonfly Series)	EBee ECtt LBrs WCot
	'Apple Blossom'	EPfP LRHS
	'Apple Court White'	CBct
	'Autumn Magic'	CBct CBod ELon EPfP GQue LAst LHop LRHS LSou MGos NPri
	'Baby Doll'	Widely available
	'Bach'	CBct EBee ECtt EPfP GEdr GQue LPfy LRHS LSou LSun MBel MCot MMuc NLar NSti NWad SCob SWvt WCot
§	'Ballawley' clonal	ECha GCal IMou LRHS MLHP MRav NEgg WCot WMnd WWEG XLum
	'Ballawley Guardsman'	CBct
§	Ballawley hybrids	CMac SDix
	'Ballawley' seed-raised	see *B.* Ballawley hybrids
	'Bartók'	CBct CBot CLAP CMil EBee ECtt ESwi GQue IKil LPla LRHS WCAu WCot WRHF
	beesiana	see *B. purpurascens*
	'Beethoven'	CBct ECha GCra MRav NBir WCot WPGP
	Bell Tower	see *B.* 'Glockenturm'
	'Biedermeier' ♀H7	ECha
	'Bizet'	CBct XLum
	'Borodin'	CBct
	'Brahms'	CBct WCot
	'Bressingham Bountiful'	CBct
	'Bressingham Ruby'PBR	CBct CBod CLAP EBee ECha ECtt ELon LPal LRHS LSRN MBel MGos MHol MRav NBir NEgg SCob SGol SPer SWvt WCot WHil WPGP
	'Bressingham Salmon'	CBct EBee ECha ECtt ELan ELon GMaP LSRN MRav NLar SRms WCot WMnd
	'Bressingham White' ♀H6	Widely available
	'Britten' ♀H7	CBct CMac IMou WCot
	ciliata	CBct CLAP CMac CTal CTca ECha EPri EShb EUJe GCra GEdr LEdu LPfy LRHS MLHP MRav NHol NLar SDix SGSe SPer WKif WPGP WSHC XLum
	- 'Dumbo'	CBct GBin LLHF
	- f. ***ligulata***	see *B. pacumbis*
	- 'Patricia Furness'	CLAP
	- 'Wilton'	CBct CDes CLAP CTal MAvo WCot WSHC WWEG
	ciliata* × *crassifolia	see *B.* × *schmidtii*
	'Claire Maxine' ♀H7	CBct CLAP EBee ECtt GBin GCal LPla MPie NFav NLar NWad WCAu WCot
	cordifolia	Widely available
	- 'Flore Pleno'	CBct
	- 'Jelle'	CBct EBee WCAu
	- 'Lunar Glow'	CBct EBee ECha ECtt ELan ELon EPfP ESwi EUJe LHop LSou MBri NEgg NLar SPoG SRms WHil
	- 'Purpurea'	CBcs CLet CMac CNec CWCL EBee ECha ELan EPfP LBuc LCro LOPS LRHS MLHP MRav NBir SCob SPer SRms SWvt WCAu XLum
	- 'Rosa Schwester'	CBct ECha
	- 'Rosa Zeiten' ♀H7	CBct GBin IMou
	- 'Rose'	LRHS
	- 'Tubby Andrews' (v)	CBct CMac EBee EShb LEdu LRHS MAvo MBel MBrN NEgg NEoE NLar SRms WHil WHrl WWEG
	- 'Vinterglöd'	CBod CBot EAEE EBee ELan ELon EPfP GMaP GQue IFoB LAst LRHS LSun MGos MWat NGdn NLar SPad SWvt WPnP XLum
	crassifolia	GKev SRms WWEG XLum
	- DF 90028	CBct GBin
	- 'Autumn Red'	CBct ECha WWEG
	- 'Orbicularis'	see *B.* × *schmidtii*
I	- var. ***pacifica***	XLum
	- - 'Cally Gem'	EBee GCal
*	***cyanea***	CLAP WCot
	'David'	CBct ECha EWes WWEG
	'Delbees'	see *B.* 'Ballawley' clonal
	'Doppelgänger'	EBee
	'Dragonfly Angel Kiss'	GBin LRHS MNrw
	'Dragonfly Sakura'	GBin LRHS MNrw
	'Eden's Dark Margin'	CBct CBod ECtt ELan ELon GBin GEdr GQue IKil LRHS LSou MBri MHol MNrw NEoE NLar NMyG SPoG WCot WHil WHoo
	'Eden's Magic Giant' ♀H7	CAbP CBct CCon ECGP ECtt ELon GBin IKil LPla LRHS MPie NEgg NLar SDix SPoG SRms WCot
	emeiensis	CBct CDes CEvo CLAP CTal GCal IMou LEdu SDix WCot WPGP
	- hybrid	MWat
	'Eric Smith' ♀H7	CBct ECha GCal GCra MBri SWvt WCAu WMnd
	'Eroica' ♀H7	Widely available
	'Evening Glow'	see *B.* 'Abendglut'
	'Frau Holle' ♀H7	MBri
§	'Glockenturm'	CBct NEgg
	'Godfrey Owen' **new**	CDes
	'Goldfisch'	GBin
	'Harzkristall'	CBct CMac CMea EPfP GBin LAst LHop LRHS SPoG STPC SWvt
	'Hellen Dillon'	see *B. purpurascens* 'Irish Crimson'
	'Herbstblute'	WCAu
	'Ice Queen'	CBct CMil EBee GBin LLHF MBel SWvt WCAu WCot
	'Jo Watanabe'	CBct MRav
	'Kashmir'	XLum
	'Lambrook'	see *B.* 'Margery Fish'
	'Little Pine' **new**	WCot
§	'Margery Fish'	CBct CFis ECha SPer
	milesii	see *B. stracheyi*
§	'Morgenröte' ♀H6	CBcs CBct CBod CMac ECha ELon EPfP GMaP LHop LRHS LSRN MMuc MRav NHol NLar NSti SAko SCob SPer SRms SWvt WCFE WCot WWEG
	'Morning Light'	ECtt ELon NEoE
	Morning Red	see *B.* 'Morgenröte'
	'Mrs Crawford'	ECha
	'Oeschberg'	CBct GBin GCal

'Opal'	CBct EBee GBin
'Overture'	Widely available
§ ***pacumbis***	CLAP EBee GBin GCal NBid NSti
- B&SWJ 2693	WCru
- CC 1793	SBch WCot
- CC 3616	CBct CDes WCot WPGP
'Perfect'	WMnd
'Pink Dragonfly'	CMac ECtt ELon EPfP GBin LPfy LPla LRHS NLar SPoG SWvt WCAu WCot
'Pink Frostwork'	ECtt WCot
'Pink Ice'	CBct CDes
'Pinneberg'	CBct GBin
'Pugsley's Pink' ♀H7	CBct
§ ***purpurascens*** ♀H5	CMac EBee EPfP GMaP LBMP SDix SPer WWEG
- SDR 4548	GKev
- var. ***delavayi*** ♀H5	CWCL EBee LRHS MBri NLar SRms
§ - 'Irish Crimson' ♀H7	CBct CDes ECha WCot
aff. ***purpurascens***	NGdn
- ACE 2175	WCot
'Purpurglocken'	EBee ECtt GCal WCAu
'Red Beauty'	EHoe EPfP IBoy LRHS MSnd
'Red Rush'	EBee
'Rietheim'	CBct EBee GBin
'Rosi Klose'	CBct CLAP EBee ECha ECtt EHoe ELon EWes GBin GCra LHop LRHS MBri MHol MRav NGdn WCot WWEG
'Rosi Ruffles'	EBee
'Rotblum'	CBct CNec ECtt EHoe ELon EPfP GMaP LEdu NBir NGdn SCob SHar WCAu WHar WWEG
§ × ***schmidtii***	CBct CMac GBin MRav NBir NLar WWEG
'Schneekissen'	CBct CMac ECGP ECtt EPri LBMP LRHS MCot WCAu
§ 'Schneekoenigin'	CBct ECha GBin GCal SWvt WCot
§ 'Silberlicht' ♀H6	Widely available
Silverlight	see *B.* 'Silberlicht'
'Simply Sweet'	WCot
Snow Queen	see *B.* 'Schneekoenigin'
§ ***stracheyi***	CBct CExl ECha GBin GCal MLHP NBid NLar SDix WCot WFar WWEG
- CC 4609	EBee
- CC 7166 **new**	EWld
- Alba Group	ECha GCal SMHy WPGP WWEG
'Sunningdale' ♀H7	CBcs CBct CBod CMac ECha ELan EPfP GCra GMaP LHop LRHS MRav NBir NGdn SPer SWvt WCAu WMnd WWEG
tianquanensis	EBee
'Tim'	EBee
'Walter Kienli'	EBee GBin
Winter Fairy Tales	see *B.* 'Wintermärchen'
§ 'Wintermärchen' ♀H7	CBct CBod CBot CChe ECha ECtt ELan ELon EPfP EShb GBin GCra LAst LRHS MLHP MMuc MRav NEoE NHol SCob SEND SWvt WCot WWEG
'XXL' **new**	WCot

Bergeranthus (*Aizoaceae*)

multiceps	SChr

Berkheya (*Asteraceae*)

cirsiifolia **new**	EBee
macrocephala	SPlb
multijuga	LRHS
- 'Golden Spike'	CBod
purpurea	CAby CBcs CBod CSpe EAJP ELon EPfP EUJe IBoy LRHS MHol MMuc MNrw SBea SPlb WCot WHer WKif WMnd WSHC
- 'Silver Spike'	EPfP GBin LSRN NGdn
- 'Zulu Warrior'	CMac NGBl SRkn

Berlandiera (*Asteraceae*)

lyrata	CArn MSCN

Berula (*Apiaceae*)

erecta	NPer

Berzelia (*Bruniaceae*)

galpinii	SPlb

Beschorneria (*Asparagaceae*)

albiflora	CEvo CFil EBee WCot
calcicola	WCot
'Red Bells'	WCot
rigida	WCot
septentrionalis	CAbP CAby CCon CDTJ CDoC CFil CSpe EAla ESwi EUJe IBoy IKil LRHS LSou LSun MBNS MSCN NLos SEND SPad WCot WGrn
- variegated	WCot
septentrionalis × ***yuccoides***	CFil CHll EBee WPGP
tubiflora	CDTJ CFil
wrightii	CFil WCot
yuccoides ♀H3	CAbb CBcs CExl CFil CPne EAla ESwi LEdu SEND SPlb
- subsp. ***dekosteriana***	CFil
- 'Quicksilver'	CBcs CDoC CExl CKno CSBt ELan EPfP EUJe IVic LRHS MBri MHtn NLos SDix SLim SSpi WGrn WPGP

Bessera (*Asparagaceae*)

elegans	CAby CAvo CCon CGrW EBee ECho EPot GKev LAma MHer SDeJ WCot

Beta (*Amaranthaceae*)

vulgaris	SHDw SRms SVic WHer
- subsp. ***cicla*** var. ***flavescens***	SRms
- subsp. ***maritima***	CAgr

Betonica see *Stachys*

Betula ✿ (*Betulaceae*)

alba	see *B. pendula*, *B. pubescens*
albosinensis misapplied	see *B. utilis*
albosinensis Burkill	CLnd CMCN EBee EPfP MMuc SEND
- W 4106	CSto
- from Gansu, China	CSto
- 'Bowling Green'	CExl CJun EBee MBlu WPGP
§ - 'China Rose' ♀H6	CJun CSto WMat WPGP
- 'China Ruby' K.Ashburner	see *B. albosinensis* 'China Rose'
- 'China Ruby' ambig.	CJun EBee EPfP LRHS SSpi
- 'China Ruby' B. Humphrey ♀H6	CBcs CDul
- 'Chinese Garden'	CJun EBee WPGP
- clone F	see *B. albosinensis* 'Ness'
- hybrid	CDul
- 'K.Ashburner'	CJun CTho
§ - 'Ness'	CJun CTho

Name	Suppliers
- 'Pink Champagne'	CJun CSto EPfP MBlu WPGP
- 'Red Panda' ♀H6	CJun EBee GQue LRHS MBri NLar WHCr WMat WPGP
- 'Rhinegold'	MBlu
- 'Sable'	SLim
- var. ***septentrionalis***	CBcs CCVT CDoC CDul CMac CTho CWib EBee ECrN ELan ELon EPfP EWTr GBin LAst MBlu MGos MMuc MRav MSwo NOrn NWea SCob SGol SLim SPer WMou WPGP
- - PDM 752	WPGP
- - 'Kansu'	CJun CLnd CTsd EBee LRHS MBri NLar NWea SBig WHCr WHar WMat
- - 'Purdom'	CJun CLnd SBig
§ ***alleghaniensis***	CCVT CDul CMCN CSto EPfP GBin MMuc NLar NWea SEND SGol WCru
apoiensis 'Mount Apoi'	CJun CLnd SBig
ashburneri new	GKev
chichibuensis	CJun MMHG MSnd WHer
chinensis	CMCN
'Conyngham'	CJun CTho MBlu SLau
cordifolia	see *B. papyrifera* var. *cordifolia*
costata misapplied	see *B. ermanii* 'Grayswood Hill'
costata ambig.	CMCN SGol
costata Trautv.	CTho EBee MSwo
- 'Daleside' new	EBee WMat
* - 'Fincham Cream'	CJun SBig
'Crimson Frost'	EBee
dahurica Pall.	CSto
- 'Maurice Foster'	CDoC CJun CSto CTho WPGP
- 'Stone Farm'	CJun
delavayi	EBee
ermanii	CBcs CCVT CDoC CDul CLnd CMCN CMac CSBt CTri ECrN ELan GBin LAst MBlu MGos MMuc MRav NLar NOrn NWea SCob SEND SGol WMou
- from Hokkaido, Japan	CSto
- B&SWJ 8801 from South Korea	WCru WPat
- B&SWJ 10852 from Aomori, Japan	WCru
- B&SWJ 12600 from South Korea	WCru
- 'Blush'	CJun MBlu SBig SCoo
- var. ***ermanii***	LSRN
- - MSF 825	EBee
- - MSF 865	WPGP
§ - 'Grayswood Hill' ♀H6	CDul CJun CLnd CMCN CMHG CSBt CTho CTri EBee EPfP LCro LOPS MBlu SAko SCoo SMad SWvt WPGP
- 'Hakkoda Orange'	CJun CTho SAko SCoo WHar WPGP
- 'Holland'	IArd NLar
- 'Kwanak Weeping'	CJun EBee GBin LLHF MBlu NWea SBig SBir SCoo
- 'Mount Zao'	CJun CSto IVic WPGP
- 'Polar Bear'	CJun CLnd EBee EPfP GBin MAsh MBlu MBri NLar NOrn SAko SCoo SMad SSta WHCr WMat WPGP
- 'Zao Purple'	CDul
'Fascination' ♀H6	CCVT CDul CJun CLnd CMCN EBee IArd IDee MBlu MBri MGos NLar NOrn NWea SCob SCoo SKHP SLim SSpi SSta WHCr WHar WMat WMou
'Fetisowii'	CDul CJun EBtc MBlu NLar SBig WHar WMat
fruticosa	see *B. humilis*
globispica	CJun GKev
gmelinii	see *B. ovalifolia*
'Haywood'	WMat
'Hergest' ♀H6	CDoC CJun EBee ECrN EPfP MAsh MBri MGos SCoo SLau WHCr WHar WMat WPat
§ ***humilis***	EBee
insignis	CSto WPGP
- subsp. ***fansipanensis*** B&SWJ 11751	WCru
'Inverleith'	see *B. utilis* var. *jacquemontii* 'Inverleith'
jacquemontii	see *B. utilis* var. *jacquemontii*
kamtschatica H. Buek	see *B. humilis*
lenta	CDul CMCN CSto EPfP IArd MBlu MMuc
luminifera	CJun EBee EBtc NLar
lutea	see *B. alleghaniensis*
maximowicziana	CMCN CSto CWib MBlu NLar SGol
medwediewii	CDul CJun CMCN CSto EBee EPfP GKev NLar NWea WPGP
- 'Gold Bark' ♀H7	CJun CMCN EPfP MBlu
megrelica new	GKev
michauxii	GKev NLar WCru
nana	CDul GQue MGos MRav NWea
- 'Glengarry'	EPot GBin GCrg GEdr NLar
nigra	CBcs CCVT CDoC CDul CLnd CMCN CNWT CTho CTri EBee EWTr MAsh NLar SCob SEWo SGol WMou
- 'Black Star'	EBee WMat
§ - 'Cully'	CCVT CDoC CDul CLnd CTho ECrN MRav NOrn NWea SBig SGol WHCr WMat
- Dura-Heat = 'Bnmtf'	MGos NLar
- Heritage	see *B. nigra* 'Cully'
- 'Little King'	CJun
- 'Peter Collinson'	CJun
- 'Shiloh Splash'	SReu SSta
- 'Summer Cascade' PBR	CDoC EBee LSRN MAsh NOrn SLon WHCr WMat
- Tecumseh Compact = 'Studetec'	MPkF SGol
- Wakehurst form	EPfP SPer SPoG WPGP
§ ***ovalifolia***	GKev
papyrifera	CCVT CDul CLnd CMCN CMac CSBt CSto CTri ECrN ELan EPfP LBuc LRHS LSRN MBlu MGos MMuc MSwo NWea SCob SEND SGol SPer WHar WMat
- 'Belle Vue'	CSto EBee
§ - var. ***cordifolia***	CSto
- - 'Clarenville'	CJun CSto EBee
- var. ***papyrifera***	CSto
- 'Saint George'	CJun CSto CTho EBee LRHS WHCr WMat
- 'Vancouver'	CJun CTho MBlu
§ ***pendula***	Widely available
- 'Bangor'	CJun SSta
- 'Black Prince'	WHCr
- f. ***crispa***	see *B. pendula* 'Laciniata'
- 'Dalecarlica' misapplied	see *B. pendula* 'Laciniata'
- 'Dalecarlica' ambig.	CBcs CSBt ECrN LRHS MRav SWvt WHCr WMat
- 'Dark Prince'	CJun NOrn
- 'Fastigiata'	CCVT CDul CJun CLnd CSBt CTho EBee ECrN ELan MGos NWea SCoo SGol SPer SPoG
- 'Golden Beauty'	CDoC CDul CJun CMac EBee EMil LAst MAsh MGos MJak NLar NOrn

	NWea SGol SLim SPer SSpi WHar WMat
- 'Golden Cloud'	MJak
- hybrid	COtt
§ - 'Laciniata' ♀^{H7}	CDul CMCN CMac CTho CWib EBee ELan EPfP MAsh MBlu MGos MSwo NWea SCob SCoo SGol SPer WCFE WHar WMou
- 'Long Trunk'	CDul EBee LAst LLHF MBlu NOrn SGol SLim WHar
- 'Purpurea'	CCVT CDul CMCN CMac CSBt CWib EBee ECrN ELan ELon EWTr GKin LAst LSRN MGos MSwo NLar NOrn NWea SCoo SGol SPer WFar
- 'Silver Grace'	CJun ECrN LSRN SKHP
- 'Tristis' ♀^{H7}	Widely available
- 'Youngii'	Widely available
- 'Zwitsers Glorie'	CDul CJun NLar SKHP
§ ***pendulata*** 'Spider Alley'[PBR]	EBee EUJe GBin NEgg NLar WMat
platyphylla misapplied	see *B. platyphylla* subsp. *mandshurica*
platyphylla Sukaczev Dakota Pinnacle = 'Fargo'	CDul EBee NLar SCoo WHar WMat
§ - subsp. ***mandshurica***	CSto MMuc MSnd
- subsp. ***platyphylla***	MSnd
populifolia	CSto
- 'Whitespire'	CDul
potaninii	GKev MSnd
§ ***pubescens***	CCVT CDul CHab CSto CTri EBee GQue MMuc NWea SCob SEND WMou
- var. ***pubescens***	CSto
raddeana	EBtc GKev
'Royal Frost'	CBcs CDul CJun EBee EUJe GQue IArd LSRN MAsh MBlu NEgg NLar NWea SPoG WHar WMat
'Silver Trestles'	see *B. pendulata* 'Spider Alley'
szechuanica 'Liuba White'	CJun CTho
- 'Moonlight'	SLau
§ ***utilis***	CDul CMCN CSBt CSto ECrN MMuc SEND SSta
- BL&M 100 from central Nepal	CSto
- GWJ 9259	WCru
- H&M 1480 from Sichuan, China	CSto
- HWJK 2250	WCru
- HWJK 2345	WCru
- S&L from Nepal	CDul
- SCH 2168	EBee
- SICH 667 from Sichuan, China	CSto
- Yu 10163 from Yunnan, China	CSto
- from eastern Nepal	CSto
- 'Bhutan Sienna'	CJun CSto
- 'Buckland'	EBee
- 'Buddha'	CJun SAko WPGP
- 'China Bronze'	EBee WPGP
- 'Cobhay Amber' **new**	CJun
- 'Cobhay Sentinel' **new**	CJun
- 'Darkness'	EBee LRHS SLon WHCr WMat WPGP
* - 'Fastigiata'	CJun SBig SSta
- 'Forest Blush' ♀^{H6}	CDul CJun CSto EBee LSRN MBri SBig WHar WPGP
§ - var. ***jacquemontii***	Widely available
- - Polunin	WPGP
- - 'Doorenbos' ♀^{H6}	Widely available
- - 'Grayswood Ghost' ♀^{H6}	Widely available
§ - - 'Inverleith'	CDul CJun EBee GBin GQue SBig SCoo WPGP
- - 'Jermyns' ♀^{H6}	CBcs CDul CJun CLnd CMHG CTri EBee EPfP IVic LSRN MBlu MBri SAko SCoo SLau SLim SSta SWvt WHCr WHar WMat WPGP
- - 'McBeath'	SLau
- - 'Moonbeam'	CDul CJun CSBt EBee GQue LRHS MAsh MBri NWea SBig SCoo SPoG WHCr WHar WMat
- - 'Silver Shadow' ♀^{H6}	CDul CJun CLnd CTho EBee EPfP LRHS LSRN MAsh MBlu NLar NOrn NWea SBig SCoo SKHP SLau SLim SPer SPoG SSta WHCr WMat
- - 'Trinity College'	CDul CJun CTri EBee MBri SBig SSpi WHCr WHar WMat WPGP
- 'Knightshayes'	CTho EBee WPGP
- 'Mount Luoji'	CJun CSto EBee WPGP
- 'Nepalese Orange'	CJun CSto EBee WPGP
- var. ***occidentalis*** 'Kyelang'	CJun CTho IVic
- 'Park Wood' ♀^{H6}	CJun CSto WPGP WPat
- var. ***prattii***	CJun CTho MBlu
- 'Ramdana River'	CDoC CJun CMHG WPGP
- 'Schilling'	CJun
- 'Sichuan Red'	CSto
- subsp. ***utilis*** 'Edinburgh' **new**	CLnd WMat
- 'Wakehurst Place Chocolate' ♀^{H6}	CJun CSBt CTho EBee GBin MBlu MBri NWea SBig SCoo SLim SSta WHCr WHar
* - var. ***yunnanensis***	EBee
cf. ***utilis***	CTri SGol
verrucosa	see *B. pendula*

Biarum (*Araceae*)

SB&L 597	WCot
S&L 604	WCot
bovei	ECho
carratracense from Spain	WCot
davisii	ECho EPot LAma WCot
dispar SB&L 294	WCot
- SB&L 564	WCot
ditschianum from Turkey	WCot
marmarisense	ECho NRog WCot
tenuifolium	ECho WCot
- LB 295	WCot
- PB 357	WCot
- S&L 174	WCot
- subsp. ***abbreviatum*** MS 974	WCot
- - from Greece	ECho
- subsp. ***arundanum***	WCot
- subsp. ***galianii*** PB 435	WCot
- subsp. ***idomenaeum*** MS 738	WCot
- subsp. ***zelebori***	ECho WCot
- - CRL 502	WCot
- - LB 300	WCot
- - PB 224	WCot
- - PB 334	WCot

Bidens (*Asteraceae*)

atrosanguinea	see *Cosmos atrosanguineus*
§ ***aurea***	EAJP ECtt EPPr EWes LAst LEdu MSpe NPer WBor XLum
- 'Cream Streaked Yellow'	GQue

- cream-flowered	MNrw
- 'Golden Drop'	LSou
- 'Hannay's Lemon Drop'	CAby CDes CKno EAJP EBee ECtt ELon EPPr EPfP ILea LHop LPla LPot MNrw MSpe SDix SGbt SPoG SRms WBor WPGP
* - 'Lemon Queen'	LEdu SMad
- 'Mellow Yellow' new	WCot
- 'Rising Sun'	EWes
- 'Super Nova'	EPPr
- white-flowered	EBee EPPr GCal NSti
ferulifolia	NPer
- 'Golden Eye' new	LSou
- 'Golden Glory' new	LAst
- Peter's Gold Rush = 'Topteppich'	LSou
- Yellow Charm = 'Danyel9'	LSou
heterophylla Ortega	see *B. aurea*
heterophylla misapplied	CAby ECtt MCot MMuc MRav MWat WFar WHal WMoo XLum
- CD&R 1515	LPla
humilis	see *B. triplinervia* var. *macrantha*
integrifolia	SMad
'Pirate's Treasure'	ECtt
'Rockstar' new	LSou NPri
§ ***triplinervia*** var. ***macrantha***	ELon LHop

Bignonia (*Bignoniaceae*)

capreolata	CRHN EBee ECre EWld WCot WSHC
- 'Dragon Lady'	SKHP
lindleyana	see *Clytostoma calystegioides*
tweedieana	see *Macfadyena unguis-cati*
unguis-cati	see *Macfadyena unguis-cati*

Bilderdykia see *Fallopia*

Billardiera (*Pittosporaceae*)

cymosa	CTsd MOWG
longiflora ♀H3	Widely available
- 'Cherry Berry'	CBcs CFlo CMac EBee ELan EPfP EUJe LRHS LSRN MMuc NLar SLim SPer SPoG SRms SWvt WHlf
- 'Fructu-albo'	CBcs CFlo EBee ELan EPfP EWes LRHS NLar SLon SPer SWvt

Billbergia (*Bromeliaceae*)

'Borracho'	LAir NLos
buchholtzii new	NEve
'Carnaval'	LAir
'Casa Blanca'	LAir
chlorosticta Saunders new	NEve
'Déjà Vu'	LAir
distachya	NEve
- var. ***maculata***	NLos
elegans	LAir
euphemiae new	NEve
- var. ***purpurea*** new	NEve
- var. ***purpurea*** × ***gireaudiana*** new	NEve
'Flamenco'	LAir
'Fosters Striate'	NLos
'Gerda'	LAir
'Hallelujah'	LAir NEve
horrida new	NEve
- var. ***tigrina*** hort. ex Baker new	NEve
'Las Manchas'	LAir
magnifica new	NEve
manarae	LAir
nutans	CHll EBak ECou ESwi EUJe IMou LAir LEdu LTro NEve NLos SChr SEND SPlb WSFF
- var. ***schimperiana***	EShb
* - 'Variegata' (v)	CCon CHll EShb EUJe NLos SChr WCot
'Pink Patches'	LAir
pyramidalis ♀H1a	NEve NLos XBlo
rosea hort. ex Beer new	NEve
'Santa Barbara' (v)	NEve SChr
vittata ♀H1a new	NEve
× ***windii*** ♀H1a	EBak NEve NLos
zebrina	NEve

Bismarckia (*Arecaceae*)

nobilis	LPal

Bistorta see *Persicaria*

Bituminaria (*Papilionaceae*)

bituminosa	WCot

blackberry see *Rubus fruticosus*

blackcurrant see *Ribes nigrum*

Blechnum (*Blechnaceae*)

alpinum	see *B. penna-marina* subsp. *alpinum*
attenuatum new	NLos
australe	NLos
brasiliense ♀H1a	EBee EShb ESwi ISha NLos
§ ***chilense*** ♀H4	CBcs CCon CDTJ CDes CLAP EBee EPfP EWes GBin GCal GCra IBlr LEdu LPal LPar LRHS NLos SBig SGSe SKHP SPlb SRms WCru WMoo WPat
cycadifolium new	NLos
discolor	NLos
divergens new	NLos
fluviatile	CDTJ CLAP NLos SGSe
gibbum	ISha LPal NLos
- 'Silver Lady'	ISha NLos
gracile new	NLos
magellanicum misapplied	see *B. chilense*
magellanicum (Desv.) Mett.	SBig SKHP
novae-zelandiae	NLos
nudum	CDTJ EBee ESwi ITim LPal NLos SGSe
penna-marina ♀H4	CDoC CExl CKel CLAP CTal CWCL ECou EFer ELon GAbr GBin GCal GMaP LEdu LHop LPal LRHS MMuc MRav NBir NLos SCob WFib WMoo XLum
§ - subsp. ***alpinum***	CLAP ECha EPfP GEdr GKev NWad SGSe WMoo
- - BR 68	GEdr
- 'Cristatum'	CLAP GAbr GEdr NWad SGSe
procerum	NLos
punctulatum	ISha
spicant ♀H6	Widely available
tabulare misapplied	see *B. chilense*
tabulare (Thunb.) Kuhn	CBcs CDTJ CKel EPfP GGal NLos
wattsii	CDes NLos

Blepharocalyx (*Myrtaceae*)

§ ***cruckshanksii***	CBod CExl CSde CTsd EBee ELon LRHS NLar SEle SVen WPGP WPat
- 'Heaven Scent'	see *B. cruckshanksii*

Blephilia (*Lamiaceae*)

ciliata	SPhx

Bletilla (*Orchidaceae*)

sp.	NDav
Brigantes gx	CDes
Coritani gx	NLAp
formosana	NLAp
hyacinthina	see *B. striata*
ochracea	CExl LAma NLAp
Penway Paris gx	CTal
sinensis	CExl
§ ***striata*** 🏆H4	CAby CBct CCon CDes CEvo CExl CTri ECho EPot GKev LAma LCro LEdu LOPS LRHS MNrw NLAp SDeJ WCot WPGP XLum
- ***alba***	see *B. striata* f. *gebina*
- 'Albostriata'	CBct CCon CExl ECho ELan LAma NLAp WCot XLum
§ - f. ***gebina***	CCon CDes CEvo CExl CTal CTri ECho GKev LCro LEdu LOPS LRHS NLAp SDeJ WPGP
- - variegated (v)	GKev LEdu
- 'Kuchi-beni'	LAma NLAp
- 'Soryu'	ECho LAma NLAp
- variegated (v)	GKev
Yokohama gx	CTal

Bloomeria (*Asparagaceae*)

crocea	ECho
- var. ***aurea***	ECho
- var. ***montana***	ECho

blueberry see *Vaccinium corymbosum*

Blumea (*Asteraceae*)

balsamifera	CHab

Bocconia (*Papaveraceae*)

cordata	see *Macleaya cordata* (Willd.) R. Br.
frutescens B&SWJ 10654 **new**	WCru
microcarpa	see *Macleaya microcarpa*

Boehmeria (*Urticaceae*)

nivea	WCot
platanifolia	IMou
sieboldiana **new**	EBee
tricuspis	IMou SBrt

Boenninghausenia (*Rutaceae*)

albiflora	CPne
- B&SWJ 1479	WCru
- B&SWJ 3112 pink-flowered	WCru
- BWJ 8141 from China	WCru
japonica B&SWJ 11186	WCru

Bolax (*Apiaceae*)

glebaria	see *B. gummifer*
§ ***gummifer***	ECho EPot GEdr WAbe

Bolboschoenus (*Cyperaceae*)

§ ***maritimus***	SMea WDra

Boltonia (*Asteraceae*)

asteroides	GCra MMuc SEND SPer SWat WRHF XLum
- var. ***latisquama***	GMaP GQue LSou MAvo MRav MWat NCGa NLar SHar SMad WBor WHal WHil
- - 'Nana'	SGSe
- - 'Snowbank'	ELan LHop NDov
decurrens	CBod EBee IMou LPla WBor
- 'Warrior's Blush'	MNrw
incisa	see *Kalimeris incisa*

Bolusanthus (*Papilionaceae*)

speciosus	SPlb

Bomarea (*Alstroemeriaceae*)

from Veracruz, Mexico **new**	WCot
acutifolia	CFil WCot
- B&SWJ 10388	WCru
- B&SWJ 9094	WCru
- B&SWJ 9130	WCru
aff. ***andreana*** B&SWJ 10617	WCru
boliviensis misapplied	see *Alstroemeria isabellana*
boliviensis Baker **new**	EWld WCot
caldasii	see *B. multiflora*
costaricensis	GCal
- B&SWJ 10467	WCru
distichifolia	CExl WCot WCru
§ ***edulis*** 🏆H1c	CDes CPne CRHN EWld GKev SBrt WBod WCot WHil
- B&SWJ 9017	WCru
- F&M 104	CExl
'Fiesta' **new**	WCot
'Flare' **new**	WCot
frondea	see *B. multiflora*
aff. ***frondea*** B&SWJ 10681	WCru
hirsuta B&SWJ 10774	WCru
hirtella	see *B. edulis*
§ ***multiflora*** 🏆H2	CBcs CCon CExl CTre EBee GCal MOWG NLos SKHP WCot WCru WSHC
'Orange Sunset' **new**	WCot
patacocensis JCA 13987	WCot
salsilla 🏆H1c	CAvo CFil EBee GKev NLos SBrt SKHP WSHC
'Tangerine' **new**	WCot
yellow-fruited **new**	WCot

Bombax (*Malvaceae*)

ceiba	SPlb

Bongardia (*Berberidaceae*)

chrysogonum	CAvo ECho EPot GKev LLHF LRHS

Bonia (*Poaceae*)

§ ***solida***	ERod MMuc MWht SEND WJun

Boophone (*Amaryllidaceae*)

disticha	CEvo
haemanthoides **new**	CEvo

borage see *Borago officinalis*

Borago (*Boraginaceae*)

laxiflora	see *B. pygmaea*
officinalis	CHby CLau CWld ENfk EPfP GPoy LCro MHer MNHC NBir NPri SBch SRms SVic WJek
- 'Alba'	CBre CLau ENfk MNHC SIde SRms WJek
- 'Bill Archer' (v)	CNat

§	***pygmaea***	CArn CExl CHid CSpe ELan GCal LEdu MHer MNrw NBir NSti SRms WJek WMoo

Borinda (*Poaceae*)

	KR 4558	ERod
	KR 5287	MWht
	KR 5600	MWht
	KR 5950	ERod
	KR 6438	MWht
	KR 6439	MWht
	KR 7346	MWht
	KR 7613 new	MWht
	KR 7662	MWht
	from Muli County, Sichuan	WJun
	albocerea ♀H4	EPfP ERod MAvo MWht WJun
	- Yunnan 1	ERod WJun
	- Yunnan 2	CDTJ CEnt ERod WJun
	- Yunnan 3a	CDTJ CEnt ERod WJun
	- Yunnan 3b	ERod WJun
	- Yunnan 4	see *B. lushuiensis* Yunnan 4
	angustissima	CDTJ CEnt CExl CFil EPfP ERod MMuc MWht SBig SEND WJun
	boliana	SBig WJun
	edulis	WJun
	frigida	CDTJ CEnt WJun
	- KR 4059	ERod MWht
	fungosa	ESwi IBoy LTro WJun
	grossa	WJun
	- KR 5931	MWht
	lushuiensis	WJun
§	- Yunnan 4	CDTJ CEnt MWht
	macclureana KR 5050	WJun
	- KR 5051	MWht
	- KR 5177 from Gyala, Nepal	ERod ESwi MWht WJun
	- KR 5602	ERod
	- KR 5950	ERod
	- KR 6236	ESwi
	- KR 6243	ERod WJun
	- KR 6400 from Show La	ESwi
	- KR 6438 from Pasm Tso	ESwi
	aff. ***macclureana*** KR 6900	MWht
	nujiangensis new	WJun
	papyrifera	CEnt ERod WJun WPGP
	- CS 1046	MWht WJun
	- KR 3968	WJun
	- KR 7613	WJun
	perlonga	WJun
	scabrida ♀H4	CDTJ CEnt ENBC ERod MWht WJun WPGP
	- 'Asian Wonder'	CBod LRHS MBlu NLar SPoG
	Yunnan 4	see *B. lushuiensis* Yunnan 4

Boronia (*Rutaceae*)

	heterophylla	CBcs CSde CTsd EPfP IDee IVic LRHS MOWG MPkF SEle SPoG
	- 'Ice Charlotte'	CBcs

Bossiaea (*Papilionaceae*)

	riparia	SPlb
	scolopendria new	SPlb

Bothriochloa (*Poaceae*)

§	***bladhii***	CKno EPPr
	caucasica	see *B. bladhii*

Bougainvillea (*Nyctaginaceae*)

	'African Sunset'	SPlb
	'Alexandra'	SPre
	'Brilliant' misapplied	see *B.* × *buttiana* 'Raspberry Ice'
§	× ***buttiana*** 'Raspberry Ice' (v)	EShb
	glabra ♀H1c	EShb IDee SPre
	'Tropical Rainbow'	see *B.* × *buttiana* 'Raspberry Ice'

Boussingaultia (*Basellaceae*)

	baselloides Hook.	see *Anredera cordifolia*

Bouteloua (*Poaceae*)

	curtipendula	CBod SGSe
§	***gracilis***	CAby EAJP EBee EHoe LEdu LRHS MSCN NWsh SGSe SMad SMea WWEG XLum

Bouvardia (*Rubiaceae*)

	ternifolia	CSpe CWGN EBee ESwi EWld LSou MNrw MPie SPoG WCot

Bowiea (*Asparagaceae*)

	volubilis	EBee

Bowkeria (*Stilbaceae*)

	cymosa	SPlb SVen
	verticillata	CHll

Boykinia (*Saxifragaceae*)

	aconitifolia	CMac GLog IMou MRav NRya SMad WCru WMoo WSHC
	elata	see *B. occidentalis*
	heucheriformis	see *B. jamesii*
§	***jamesii***	GKev WAbe
	lycoctonifolia	LEdu NLar
	major	EBee
§	***occidentalis***	WCru WMoo WPtf XLum
	rotundifolia	GJos NBir WCru WMoo
	tellimoides	see *Peltoboykinia tellimoides*

boysenberry see *Rubus* 'Boysenberry'

Brachychilum see *Hedychium*

Brachychiton (*Malvaceae*)

	acerifolius	SPlb
	populneus	SPlb
§	***rupestris***	EShb

Brachyelytrum (*Poaceae*)

	japonicum	EPPr NLar

Brachyglottis (*Asteraceae*)

§	***bidwillii***	CBcs IVic
	- 'Basil Fox'	WAbe
§	***compacta***	ECou ELan EPfP LRHS SLon SPer
	compacta × ***monroi***	ECou
	'County Park'	ECou
	Dunedin Group	WHar
	- 'Drysdale'	EBee ELan EPfP LPfy LRHS SBod SHil SKHP SLon SRGP SWvt
§	- 'Moira Reid' (v)	CExl CTsd
§	- 'Sunshine' ♀H4	Widely available
	'Frosty'	CBod EAEE ECou ECrN
	greyi misapplied	see *B.* (Dunedin Group) 'Sunshine'
§	***greyi*** (Hook. f.) B. Nord.	CMac COtt EPfP EWTr MGos SGol
	greyi × ***repanda***	CDoC
	huntii	SVen
	huntii × ***stewartii***	SEND
	laxifolia misapplied	see *B.* (Dunedin Group) 'Sunshine'
§	***monroi***	CBcs CMac CSBt CTsd CWib ECou EHoe ELan EPfP IVic LRHS MRav SGol SKHP SLon SVen

- 'Clarence'	ECou
repanda	CBcs EWld
- 'Purpurea'	CBcs
- var. ***rangiora***	CTsd
'Silver Waves'	ECou LRHS
I 'Sunshine Improved'	CBcs EHoe
'Sunshine Variegated'	see *B.* (Dunedin Group) 'Moira Reid'
Walberton's Silver Dormouse = 'Walbrach'PBR ♀H4	CBct CBot EAEE EBee EPfP LBMP LPfy LRHS MBri MGos MJak MRav SPoG SRkn STPC SWvt WHil

Brachyotum (*Melastomataceae*)

ledifolium	CPne

Brachypodium (*Poaceae*)

phoenicoides	XSen
pinnatum	EPPr
sylvaticum	CHab MMuc SEND

Brachyscome (*Asteraceae*)

'Metallic Blue'	NPri
rigidula	CPBP
Surdaisy Strawberry Pink = 'Bonbrapi'PBR	LAst

Brachystachyum (*Poaceae*)

densiflorum	ERod

Bracteantha see *Xerochrysum*

Brahea (*Arecaceae*)

sp.	ETod
armata	CBrP CDTJ CPHo EPfP EShb ETod LPal SPlb WCot
dulcis	NLos
edulis	CPHo EAla ETod LPal NLos
'Super Silver'	EAla NLos WCot

Brassaia see *Schefflera*

Brassica (*Brassicaceae*)

juncea	SVic
oleracea	CAgr SVic WHer
* ***rapa*** var. ***japonica***	MNHC SHDw

Bravoa (*Agavaceae*)

geminiflora	see *Polianthes geminiflora*

Brimeura (*Asparagaceae*)

§ ***amethystina*** ♀H5	CExl ECho GBin GKev LEdu SDeJ SPhx WCot WPGP WThu
- 'Alba'	ECho GKev SDeJ SPhx

Briza (*Poaceae*)

maxima	CTri EHoe LEdu LHop NGdn NSti NWad SPhx WHer WTou
media	Widely available
- 'Golden Bee'	CKno CWCL EHoe ELon EPPr EPfP LEdu LRHS MMHG NDov NLar SMad SPhx WPGP
- 'Limouzi'	CCon CElw CKno CWCL EBee EHoe EHrv ELon EPPr GCal LEdu LRHS MAvo NSti NWsh SMad SMea SPoG WPGP XLum
- 'Russells'PBR	CBod CHid CKno EBee EHoe ELan EPPr EPfP LHop LPot LRHS MAvo MGos NWad NWsh SCob SHil SMea SPer SPoG SRms SWvt WGrn
subaristata	EPPr LPal
triloba	LRHS MMHG NWsh SMea

Brocchinia (*Bromeliaceae*)

hechtioides	NLos

Brodiaea (*Asparagaceae*)

§ ***californica***	CEvo EBee ECho ERCP GKev WCot
- NNS 00-109	WCot
- NNS 06-102	WCot
- 'Babylon'	CAvo ERCP GKev
'Corrina'	see *Triteleia* 'Corrina'
elegans	CEvo ECho
ida-maia	see *Dichelostemma ida-maia*
laxa	see *Triteleia laxa*
peduncularis	see *Triteleia peduncularis*

Bromus (*Poaceae*)

erectus	CHab
inermis 'Skinner's Gold' (v)	EBee EHoe EPPr NLar SMea WCot WWEG

Broussonetia (*Moraceae*)

kazinoki	LHop
papyrifera	CAbP CBcs CDul CMCN CTsd EBtc EGFP ELan ESwi GBin IVic SPer WBor
- 'Billardii'	NLar
- 'Laciniata'	EBee EPfP IDee SChF SMad WCot

Browallia (*Solanaceae*)

from Sikkim	CSpe
americana new	SPhx

Bruckenthalia see *Erica*

Brugmansia ✿ (*Solanaceae*)

'Angel' (d)	MNai
'Angels Applause' (d)	MNai
'Angel's Baby' (d) new	WOth
'Angels Cloud' (d)	MNai
'Angels Daydream' (d)	MNai
'Angels Endless Summer' (d)	MNai
'Angels Exotic' (d)	MNai
'Angels Fantasy' (d)	MNai
'Angels Glamour' (d)	MNai
'Angels Honeymoon' (d)	MNai
'Angels Innovation' (d)	MNai
'Angels Inspiration' (d)	MNai
'Angels Love' (d)	MNai
'Angels Moonlight' (d)	MNai
'Angels Paradise' (d)	MNai
'Angels Phenomenal' (d)	MNai
'Angels Prima Donna' (d)	MNai
'Angels Proud' (d)	MNai
'Angels Sensation' (d)	MNai
'Angels Shredded Dress' (d)	MNai
'Angels Surprise' (d)	MNai
'Angels Swingtime' (d)	MNai
'Anja' (d)	MNai
'Apricot Queen'	MNai
'Apricot Queen Variegated' (v)	MNai
§ ***arborea***	CBcs CDTJ
§ - 'Knightii' (d) ♀H1c	CDTJ MNai
- 'Rosea' variegated (v)	ELan
- variegated (v)	ELan
aurea	EUJe SAdn
- 'Citronella'	MNai
'Bergfee' (d)	MNai
'Bergische Symphonie' (d)	MNai WOth

	'Birgit' (d)	MNai
	'Bolero' (d)	MNai
	'Borner Gold'	MNai
	'Bridesmaid' (d)	MNai
	'Canarybird'	MNai
	× ***candida***	MNai SAdn
	- 'Angels Summertime' (d)	MNai
	- 'Angels Sunsilk' (d)	MNai
	- 'Blush'	EUJe
	- 'Double White' (d)	MNai
§	- 'Grand Marnier' ♀H1c	CDTJ CHll WOth
	- 'Maya'	MNai
	- 'Pink Perfektion' (d)	MNai
	- 'Plena'	see *B. arborea* 'Knightii'
	- f. ***plena*** 'Angels Flight' (d)	MNai
	- - 'Angels Flight Variegated' (v/d)	MNai
	- - 'Salmon Perfektion' (d)	MNai
	- 'Rosalla'	MNai WOth
§	- 'Variegata' (v)	CDTJ CHll
	'Caribbean Night'	MNai
	'Carousel' (d)	MNai
	'Cerise Baby'	MNai
	'Cerise Wonder'	MNai
	'Creamsickle' (d)	MNai
	'Dalen's Pink Amour' (d)	MNai WOth
	'Dalen's Princess' (d)	MNai
	'Dark Rossetta'	MNai
	'Day Dreams' (d)	MNai
	'Dottie'	MNai
	'Double Dark Rossetta' (d)	MNai
	'Dream Angel' (d)	MNai
	'Elfi' (d)	MNai
	'Exotic Variegated Pink' (v)	MNai
	'Fandango' (d)	MNai
	'Fascination' (d)	MNai
	'Fleming Island Spider' (d) **new**	WOth
	'Flieder'	MNai
	'Flowerdream' (d)	EUJe
	'Frosty Pink'	MNai
	'Gelber Riese'	MNai
	'Golden Princess'	MNai
	'Goldtraum'	MNai
	'Grand Marnier'	MNai
	'Grazie'	MNai
	'Herzenbrücke'	MNai
§	× ***insignis***	CHll
	- 'Pink Delight'	MNai
§	- pink-flowered	SEND
	'Kani Spirit'	MNai
	'Kleine Aap'	MNai
	'Kongmansia'	MNai
	'L'Amour'	WOth
	'Lemon Giant'	MNai
	'Lilac 1'	MNai
	'Lilac Touch'	MNai
	'Lime Wonder'	MNai
	'Logee's Species' (d)	MNai
	'Louise'	MNai
	'Lovely Lady' (d)	MNai
	'Madame Bovary' **new**	WOth
	'Marie Stöppler' (d)	MNai
	'Midnight Passion'	MNai
	'Midsummer Magic' (d)	MNai
	'Miss Emily Mackenzie'	WOth
	'Morgensonne'	WOth
	'Mystic Fire'	MNai
	'Nicoline' **new**	WOth
	'Painted Lady'	WOth
	'Pink Flamingo'	MNai
	'Pink Honour'	MNai
	'Pink Lady'	MNai
	'Pink Smitty' (d)	MNai
	'Prince of Colombia'	MNai
	'Red Devil'	MNai
§	***sanguinea***	SEND SPlb WOth
	- 'Rosea'	see *B.* × *insignis* pink-flowered
	'Schloss Burg'	MNai
	'Shredded Fantasy' (d)	MNai
	'Snowbank' (v)	MNai
	'Sonja' (d)	MNai
	'Splashes'	MNai
§	***suaveolens*** ♀H1c	CBcs CHll EUJe MNai
	- pink-flowered	EShb
	- ***rosea***	see *B.* × *insignis* pink-flowered
	- 'Variegata' (v)	EShb
	- yellow-flowered	EShb
	suaveolens × ***versicolor***	see *B.* × *insignis*
	'Super Pink'	MNai
	'Tangie Tigress'	MNai
	'Tante Erna' (d)	MNai
	'Thea's Liebling' (d)	MNai
	'Tropicana' (d)	MNai
	'Variegata Sunset'	see *B.* × *candida* 'Variegata'
	versicolor misapplied	see *B. arborea*
	'Violet Crush'	MNai
	'Wildfire' (d)	MNai
	'Wuppergold' (d)	MNai
	'Wupperstolz' (d)	MNai
*	'Yellow Trumpet'	ELan

Brunfelsia (*Solanaceae*)

	americana	MOWG
	calycina	see *B. pauciflora*
	eximia	see *B. pauciflora* 'Eximia'
	jamaicensis	MOWG
§	***pauciflora*** ♀H1c	ELan EShb IDee
§	- 'Eximia'	SPer
	- 'Floribunda'	MOWG

Brunia (*Bruniaceae*)

	albiflora	SPlb

Brunnera ✿ (*Boraginaceae*)

§	***macrophylla***	Widely available
	- 'Agnes Amez'	IMou
	- 'Aimee Angus'	EPPr
	- 'Alba'	see *B. macrophylla* 'Betty Bowring'
	- 'Alexander's Great' **new**	SCob
§	- 'Betty Bowring'	Widely available
	- 'Blanc d'Adoué' **new**	CBot
	- 'Blaukuppel'	CLAP CTal EWes GBin GCal LRHS NBir SBod WCAu WPtf
	- 'Dawson's White' (v)	CBcs CBod CLAP CWCL ECha ECtt ELan ELon EPfP EPri GBuc GEdr GJos GMaP IKil LAst LBMP LHop LRHS LSRN MLHP NBid NBir NLar SCob SPer SRGP SRms SWvt WFar
	- 'Diane's Gold' PBR	CTal EBee ECtt GEdr LRHS MBri MHol MPnt NLar SCob SMDP
	- 'Emerald Mist' PBR (v)	EBee ECtt EPfP GBin MGos NLar NSti SPad SPoG SWvt
	- 'Gordano Gold' (v)	EHoe NBir WCot
	- 'Green Gold' (v)	EBee MBri NLar SPoG
	- 'Hadspen Cream' (v) ♀H6	Widely available
	- 'Henry's Eyes' **new**	EBee MAsh
	- 'Hopley's Gold'	LHop
	- 'Jack Frost' PBR ♀H6	Widely available
	- 'Jennifer'	WCAu

- 'King's Ransom'PBR (v)	CBct CNor CWGN ECtt NLar NSti SPoG
- 'Langford Hewitt' (v)	MNrw
- 'Langtrees'	CBct CMac EBee ECha EHoe GAbr GBin GBuc GCal GCra LHop LRHS MCot MHol MMuc NBir NGdn SEND SWat WCFE WHea WWEG
- 'Looking Glass'PBR ♀H6	Widely available
- 'Marley's White'	CLAP ELan LLHF MBri NLar SCob SGbt WPnP
§ - 'Mister Morse'PBR (v)	Widely available
- 'Sea Heart'	ECtt GBin NLar SCob
- 'Silver Heart'	ECtt MAsh SCob SMad SPad
- 'Silver Lace'	IFro
- 'Silver Wings'	CBod CElw CWCL EAEE EBee ECtt EPfP GEdr GKev LRHS LSou MBel MGos NBir NGdn NLar NSti NWad SGol SPoG SWat WCAu WFar
- 'Spring Yellow'	ECtt NLar
- 'Starry Eyes' **new**	SCob
'Mrs Morse'	see *B. macrophylla* 'Mister Morse'
sibirica	CLAP EBee EPPr EWes NBid WWEG

Brunsvigia (*Amaryllidaceae*)

bosmaniae	WCot
elandsmontana **new**	WCot
gregaria	WCot
josephinae	WCot
- LAV 30394	WCot
litoralis **new**	WCot
marginata	WCot
multiflora	see *B. orientalis*
§ ***orientalis***	WCot
pulchra	WCot
radulosa	WCot
rosea 'Minor'	see *Amaryllis belladonna*
striata	WCot

Bryonia (*Cucurbitaceae*)

dioica	CArn GPoy NMir

Bryophyllum see *Kalanchoe*

Buddleja ✿ (*Scrophulariaceae*)

HCM 98.017 from Chile	WPGP
agathosma	CBot CExl CFil MOWG SLon WKif WLav WSHC
albiflora	SLon WLav
alternifolia ♀H5	Widely available
- 'Argentea'	CBcs CBot CDoC CNec EBee ELan EMil EPfP EWTr LRHS MBNS MRav NLar SKHP SPer SWvt WCot WLav WSHC XSen
asiatica ♀H2	CHid CSde IDee MOWG SLon WLav
- B&SWJ 11278	WCru
auriculata	CBcs CBot CExl CHll CMCN CNec CSde CWib EBee ELan EPfP LRHS MOWG SDix SKHP SLon SPlb SVen WLav
'Bel Argent' **new**	WPGP
'Blue Chip'PBR (Lo and Behold Series)	CBot CDoC EMil EPfP GBin LBuc LRHS MAsh MBri MGos MJak MPkF NLar SCob SKHP SLim SLon SRms SWvt WCot WLav
* 'Blue Trerice'	CExl
caryopteridifolia	EBtc GQui SEND SLon WCot
colvilei	CBcs CDul CWCL CWld ELan EPfP GCal GGal GKin IArd IDee LAst SBrt SLon SWvt WBor
- B&SWJ 2121	WCru
- GWJ 9399	WCru
- 'Kewensis'	CBot CExl CHGN CHid CNec CRHN CWCL CWld EWTr EWes GCal GGal NLar SBrt SLon SVen WCFE WCru WLav WPat WSHC
cordata	CFil SLon
- B&SWJ 10433	WCru
coriacea	SLon
§ ***crispa***	CBcs CBct CBot CExl CHid CSpe EBee ECha ELan EPfP GCal LRHS MOWG SEND SLon SPer SRkn SVen SWvt WFar WKif WPGP WSHC XSen
- var. ***farreri***	CBot CHGN CHid EUJe SLon
crotonoides subsp. ***amplexicaulis***	SLon
curviflora f. ***venenifera***	SLon
- - B&SWJ 6036	WCru
'David Griffin'	LRHS
davidii	CCVT NPol NWea SCob
- B&SWJ 8083	WCru
- Adonis Blue = 'Adokeep'PBR	CBcs CNec CSBt CWCL LBuc LRHS MBri SLon STPC WLav
- 'African Queen'	LRHS SLim SLon SRGP WLav
- var. ***alba***	CWib
§ - 'Autumn Beauty'	CAni CNec SLon WLav
- 'Autumn Delight'	SLon
- 'Bath Beauty'	CAni
- 'Beijing'	see *B. davidii* 'Autumn Beauty'
- 'Bishop's Velvet'	CAni
- 'Black Knight' ♀H5	Widely available
- 'Blue Eyes'	WLav
- 'Blue Horizon' ♀H5	CAni LRHS NLar SLon SRGP WCot WLav WMoo
- 'Border Beauty'	CAni CNec LRHS SCob SLon WLav
- 'Brown's Beauty'	CAni
- 'Butterfly Heaven'PBR	WLav
- Buzz Series	LBuc NHol SLon
- - Buzz Ivory = 'Tobuivo'	CMac CNec CRos ELan ELon ESwi LCro LOPS LPfy LRHS LSRN LSou MBri MGos NHol NLar SHil SLim SLon SMDP SPer SPoG WHil WLav
- - Buzz Lilac	ELan MGos NHol SCob SLon
- - Buzz Magenta = 'Tobudpipur'PBR	CBod CMac CMea CNec CNor CRos ELan ELon LAst LBMP LCro LHop LPfy LRHS LSou MBri MGos NEgg NHol NLar NPri SCob SHil SLim SLon SPad SPoG SWvt WHil WLav
- - Buzz Sky Blue = 'Tobuskyblu'	CMac CRos LAst LBMP LHop LPfy LRHS LSou MBri MGos NEgg NHol NLar NPri SHil SLim SMDP SPad SPoG WLav
- - Buzz Velvet = 'Tobudvelve' **new**	CRos LRHS SPer
- - Buzz Violet = 'Tobudviole'	CHid CMac CMea CRos CWld ELan ELon GBin LCro LRHS LSou MBri MGos NHol NLar NPri SBod SLim SLon SPer SWvt WLav
- Camberwell Beauty = 'Camkeep' (English Butterfly Series) ♀H5	CDoC CHll CNec LRHS MBri SLon WLav
- 'Car Wash'	CAni
- 'Castle Blue'	LRHS SLon
- 'Castle School'	CAni CSam WLav
§ - 'Charming'	CDul WMoo WSHC
- 'Clive Farrell'	see *B. davidii* 'Autumn Beauty'
- 'Corinne Tremaine'	WHer
- 'Cotswold Blue'	WLav
- 'Darent Valley' ♀H5	SLon

- 'Dartmoor' ♀H5 Widely available
- 'Dart's Ornamental White' CNec MRav SLon WLav
- 'Dart's Papillon Blue' CAni SLon WLav
- 'Dart's Purple Rain' CAni CNec LRHS SLon WLav
- 'Dubonnet' CAni SLon WLav
- 'Dudley's Compact Lavender' CAni
- 'Ecolonia' CAni SLon WLav
- 'Empire Blue' CAni CBar CBcs CDoC CDul CNec CSBt ECtt EPfP GKin LRHS LSRN MGos NBir NPer NWea SCob SEND SPer SPlb SPoG SRGP SRms SWat SWvt XSen
- 'Fair Lady' WLav
- 'Fascinating' CAni CNec GCal MRav NBir SLon WLav
- 'Flaming Violet' CAni SLon WLav
- 'Florence' CNec LLHF LSRN MBri NEgg NLar SLon WMoo
- 'Fortune' CAni
- 'Foxtail' WLav
- 'Glasnevin Hybrid' CAni CNec LRHS NLar SDix SLon WLav
- 'Gonglepod' CAni CNec LRHS SLon WLav
- 'Greenway's River Dart' CAni SLon
- 'Grey Dawn' WLav
- 'Griffin Blue' MAsh WLav
- 'Gulliver'PBR LRHS NLar SGol SLon WFar WLav
- 'Harlequin' (v) Widely available
- 'Île de France' CAni CBcs CNec CWib NLar NWea SLon SRms WLav
- 'Leela Kapila' SLon
- 'Les Kneale' CAni CNec SLon WLav
- 'Lilac Moon' WLav
- 'Lyme Bay' CAni
- Marbled White = 'Markeep'PBR (English Butterfly Series) CNec EBee LRHS MBri SLon STPC WLav WMoo
- Masquerade = 'Notbud' (v) CLet MRav SLon
- Moonshine = 'Buddma'PBR LSou

§ - Nanho Blue = 'Mongo' CAni CMHG CMac CNec COtt CRos CSBt EBee ECrN ECtt ELan EPfP GKev GKin LAst LRHS MAsh MGos MJak MLHP MRav MSwo NBir NLar SCob SGol SLim WHar WMoo XSen
- 'Nanho Petite Indigo' see *B. davidii* Nanho Blue
- 'Nanho Petite Plum' see *B. davidii* Nanho Purple
- 'Nanho Petite Purple' see *B. davidii* Nanho Purple

§ - Nanho Purple = 'Monum' ♀H5 CDoC CMHG CMac CNec COtt CRos CTri CWib EBee ELan EPfP LAst LRHS LSRN MBri MGos MRav NLar SCob SGol SLim SLon SPer SPlb SPoG SRms XSen
- Nanho White = 'Monite' ♀H5 CRos ELan EPfP LRHS SCob SGol SLon SPer SRms
- var. ***nanhoensis*** CAni CDul SEND SGol WFar WLav
- - blue-flowered EPfP NWad SLon SPer
- 'Orchid Beauty' CAni SLon WLav
- 'Orpheus' CAni CNec SLon WLav
- 'Panache' CNec EPfP LRHS MAsh SLon WLav
- 'Peace' CMac CTri CWCL LSRN MRav NLar SLon SPoG WLav
- Peacock = 'Peakeep'PBR (English Butterfly Series) CBcs CNec CSBt MAsh MBri NEgg SPoG STPC WLav
- 'Persephone' SLon WLav
- 'Petite Indigo' see *B. davidii* Nanho Blue
- 'Pink Beauty' LAst LSRN MBlu SRGP WFar
- 'Pink Charming' see *B. davidii* 'Charming'
- 'Pink Pearl' CAni LRHS SEND SLon WLav
- 'Pink Spreader' CAni LRHS SLon WLav
- 'Pixie Blue' CAni LBMP LRHS MAsh NLar SLon WLav
- 'Pixie Red' CAni LBMP LBuc LRHS MAsh MHer NLar SEND WLav
- 'Pixie White' LBuc LRHS MAsh NLar SEND SGol WLav
- Purple Emperor = 'Pyrkeep' (English Butterfly Series) CNec MBri NBir NEgg SLon SPoG STPC WLav
- 'Purple Friend' CAni SLon WLav
- 'Purple Prince' CAni
- 'Red Admiral' CAni LLHF LRHS MAsh SLon SRGP
- Rêve de Papillon Blue = 'Minpap3' WLav
- Rêve de Papillon = 'Minpap' CNec CRos LRHS MAsh WLav
- 'Royal Purple' CAni SLim SWvt
- 'Royal Red' ♀H5 Widely available
- 'Saith Ffynnon Early' WSFF
- 'Santana' (v) CAni CBcs CBod CDul CMac CNec EBee EHoe ELon EMil EPfP EWes LAst LRHS LSou MRav NEgg NHol NLar SGol SPoG SRms SWvt WCFE WCot WMoo WPat XSen
- 'Shapcott Blue' CAni
- 'Shire Blue' WLav
- 'Southcombe Splendour' CAni LRHS
- 'Summer Beauty' CAni CDul CWib MBlu SLon WLav XSen
- 'Summer House Blue' LRHS SLon WLav
- 'Twotones' WLav
- 'Variegata' (v) CAni MAsh SLon SWvt WLav
- 'White Ball' ELan NLar SLon WLav
- 'White Bouquet' CAni CCVT CSBt EAEE EPfP GKin LAst LRHS MHer MSwo NLar NWea SCob SEND SPer SRGP SWvt WLav XSen
- 'White Cloud' CAni ECrN GQui LRHS SRms WGwG
- 'White Harlequin' (v) SLon WCFE
- 'White Profusion' ♀H5 Widely available
- 'White Wings' CNec LRHS SLon WLav
- 'Widecombe' CAni
- 'Windtor' CNec LRHS

§ ***delavayi*** CBot CExl ECre SEND WCru
'Ellen's Blue' CExl CFil CNec LRHS NLar WLav
fallowiana misapplied see *B.* 'West Hill'
fallowiana Balf.f. & W.W.Sm. CRos ELan GQui LRHS WLav
- ACE 2481 LRHS
- BWJ 7803 WCru
- var. ***alba*** ♀H5 CBot CDoC CHGN CMac CRos ECrN ELan EPfP LRHS MAsh MRav NLar SDix SLon SPer WPGP WSHC
- 'Bishop's Violet' CTsd
'Flower Power' see *B.* × *weyeriana* 'Bicolor'
Flutterby Petite Blue Heaven = 'Podaras No 8' **new** NLar
Flutterby Petite Dark Pink = 'Podaras No 10' **new** NLar
forrestii WCru
globosa ♀H5 Widely available
- RCB/Arg C-11 WCot
- 'Cally Orange' GCal WGwG
- 'Lemon Ball' CNec MBlu NPer SLon WLav
glomerata CBod CNec CWCL EShb SLon
- 'Silver Service' CBod CBot EBee ELan LRHS SKHP

heliophila	see *B. delavayi*
'Ice Chip' (Lo and Behold Series) new	EPfP
indica	SLon WLav
InSpired Pink	see *B.* × *weyeriana* 'Pink Pagoda'
japonica	SLon
- B&SWJ 8912	WCru
* ***knappii***	CBot
× ***lewisiana*** 'Margaret Pike'	SLon
'Lilac Chip' (Lo and Behold Series)	LRHS MBri MPkF NLar
limitanea	SLon
lindleyana	Widely available
aff. ***lindleyana***	CBot EWTr
- B&SWJ 11478	WCru
'Lochinch' ♀H5	Widely available
longifolia	SLon XSen
'Longstock Gem' new	LRHS SLon
'Longstock Silver'	SLon
loricata	CBot CDoC CExl CHGN CNec CTsd CWib EBee EPfP GBin GQui IDee LRHS MOWG SEND SKHP SLon SPlb WCot WLav WPat
macrostachya HWJ 602	WCru
- PAB 4198	LEdu WPGP
- WWJ 12016	WCru
§ ***madagascariensis*** ♀H2	CRHN MOWG NLar SLon SPlb SVen
'Malvern Blue'	CAni
megalocephala B&SWJ 9106	WCru WPGP
'Miss Ruby' PBR ♀H5	CDoC EBee EPfP LBuc LPfy LRHS MAsh MBri MPkF SGol SHil WCot WLav
§ 'Morning Mist' PBR	Widely available
myriantha	CExl SLon WPGP XSen
nappii	CBot SLon
nicodemia	see *B. madagascariensis*
nivea	CBot CExl CHid CMHG CWCL MOWG SLon WLav XSen
- B&SWJ 2679	WCru
- pink-flowered	SLon
aff. ***nivea***	CBot
officinalis ♀H2	CBot CExl CSde MOWG SLon WLav
paniculata	SLon
- GWJ 9286 from Sikkim	WCru
parvifolia	SLon
- MPF 148	WLav
× ***pikei*** 'Hever'	SRms XSen
'Pink Delight' ♀H5	Widely available
'Pink Perfection'	CAni WFar
'Pride of Hever'	MOWG SDys
'Pride of Longstock'	LRHS SLon SPoG
'Purple Chip' (Lo and Behold Series)	LRHS
saligna	SLon
'Salmon Spheres'	SLon WLav
salviifolia	CBcs CBot CExl CHid CMac CSde CTsd CWCL EBee ELan GGal LRHS MBlu NLar SEND SPlb SVen WGwG WHer WLav WPGP
- white-flowered	EBee SLon WPGP
Silver Anniversary	see *B.* 'Morning Mist'
stachyoides	WLav
stenostachya	CExl SLon
sterniana	see *B. crispa*
'Sugar Plum'	CNec CSBt EPfP LRHS SLon
tibetica	see *B. crispa*
tubiflora	MOWG SLon WLav
utahensis new	SIgm
venenifera B&SWJ 895	WCru
wardii KR 4881 new	WPGP
§ 'West Hill' ♀H5	SLon WLav
× ***weyeriana***	CBot CDul ECtt GGal GQui MGil MMuc MNrw MSwo NBir SBod SPad SPlb SWvt WOut
§ - 'Bicolor'	CNec EPPr EPfP EWTr IDee LCro LLHF LOPS MNrw NLar SCob SLon SRms WLav
- 'Boy Blue'	SLon WLav
- 'Golden Glow'	CNec CTri ECrN GBin LSRN NLar SLon SWvt WLav WSFF
- 'Honeycomb'	CBod EPfP GBin MGos NLar
- 'Lady de Ramsey'	SEND
- 'Moonlight'	CBcs CExl CNec ELan GBin LRHS SLon SPer WCot WLav
§ - 'Pink Pagoda' PBR	CNec EPfP LRHS SLon SPoG
- 'Sungold' ♀H4	Widely available
'White Chip' (Lo and Behold Series) new	LRHS
'Winter Sun'	SLon
yunnanensis	CBcs GCal NLar SLon
- B&SWJ 8146	WCru

Buglossoides (*Boraginaceae*)

§ ***purpurocaerulea***	CHll CSpe ECha ELan EPfP EWld MLHP MNrw MWhi NBid NChi WCot WHea WSHC XLum

Bukiniczia (*Plumbaginaceae*)

cabulica	GKev WAbe

Bulbine (*Asphodelaceae*)

SH 74	CCse
alooides	ECho WCot
caulescens	see *B. frutescens*
§ ***frutescens***	CBod CDoC CHll IDee MHer MMuc SMad SVen WJek
- 'Hallmark'	EAJP

Bulbinella (*Asphodelaceae*)

angustifolia	MHer
cauda-felis	WCot
elata	WCot
hookeri	CExl EBee ECho EWld GBee GBin GEdr GKev ITim LRHS MHer NChi SRms WHal WThu
latifolia subsp. ***latifolia***	IBlr
nutans	CDes EBee ECho WPGP
- white-flowered new	CPne

Bulbinopsis see *Bulbine*

Bulbocodium (*Colchicaceae*)

vernum	ECho EPot GKev LAma LLHF SDeJ

bullace see *Prunus insititia*

Bunias (*Brassicaceae*)

orientalis	CAgr LEdu

Bunium (*Apiaceae*)

bulbocastanum	CAgr CSpe EBee IMou LEdu SDix SHDw WPGP XLum

Buphthalmum (*Asteraceae*)

salicifolium	EBee ELan EPfP MMuc NBro NGdn SEND SPer SRms SWat WCot WWtn XLum
- 'Alpengold'	CSam ECha GMaP NBre NLar

	- 'Dora'	ECtt WCot
	- 'Sunwheel'	LRHS MHol SRms
	speciosum	see *Telekia speciosa*

Bupleurum (*Apiaceae*)

	angulosum	NBir WTcb
	- copper-leaved	see *B. longifolium*
	dianthifolium new	CSpe
	falcatum	ECGP ECha LRHS NDov WCot
	fruticosum	CBcs CFil CSpe EAJP EBee ELan EPfP EUJe GBin LRHS MAsh SCob SDix SEND SKHP SLon SMad SPer SPoG SSpi WCot WPGP WPat XSen
§	***longifolium***	CElw CMea CSpe EBee EWes LEdu LRHS MNrw NBir NCGa NChi NSti SKHP SMad WPGP WSHC
	- subsp. ***aureum***	SPhx
	- 'Bronze Beauty'	GEdr
	- bronze-leaved	LPla
	ranunculoides	SPhx XLum
	rotundifolium	CSpe IMou LEdu SBod SPhx WCot
	spinosum	CSpe SMad

Burchellia (*Rubiaceae*)

	capensis	SPlb

Bursaria (*Pittosporaceae*)

	spinosa	CHII

Butia (*Arecaceae*)

	sp.	ETod
	capitata	CAbb CBcs CDTJ CPHo EAla ETod LPal
§	- var. ***odorata***	SPlb
	odorata	see *B. capitata* var. *odorata*
	yatay	LPal NLos SBig

Butomus (*Butomaceae*)

	umbellatus	CBen CWat ECha EHon EPfP EWay GQue MNrw MRav MSKA MWLS MWts NBir NPer SRms SWat WMAq WWtn XLum
	- f. ***albiflorus***	MSKA
	- 'Rosenrot'	EWay LLWG
	- 'Schneeweisschen'	EWay GQue LLWG MNrw MWts

butternut see *Juglans cinerea*

Buxus ✿ (*Buxaceae*)

	sp.	ETod LPar MJak
	aurea 'Marginata'	see *B. sempervirens* 'Marginata'
	'Green Mound'	LBMP
	harlandii misapplied	CMen SRiv
	japonica 'Nana'	see *B. microphylla*
§	***microphylla***	MHer NWad NWea SGol
	- 'Asiatic Winter'	see *B. microphylla* var. *japonica* 'Winter Gem'
§	- 'Compacta'	CMen LLHF MHer NWad SRiv WCot WPat WThu
	- 'Curly Locks'	NWad
	- 'Faulkner' Υ^{H5}	CCVT ELan EPfP LHop LSRN LTop MAsh MGos NPri SCob SGol SPer SRiv SRms WMoo
	- Golden Dream = 'Peergold'[PBR]	NLar SRms
	- 'Golden Triumph'[PBR]	EBee LBMP SRms
	- 'Green Pillow'	MHer SRiv
	- var. ***japonica*** 'Morris Midget'	NWad
	- - 'National'	NLar
§	- - 'Winter Gem'	MHer MRav NLar
	- 'John Baldwin'	SRiv
	- var. ***sinica***	LTop
	'Newport Blue'	see *B. sempervirens* 'Newport Blue'
	sempervirens	Widely available
§	- 'Angustifolia'	MHer MRav NWad SMad
	- 'Arborescens'	CNWT
	- 'Argenteo-variegata' (v)	IFoB MJak SGol
	- 'Aurea'	see *B. sempervirens* 'Aureovariegata'
	- 'Aurea Maculata'	see *B. sempervirens* 'Aureovariegata'
	- 'Aurea Marginata'	see *B. sempervirens* 'Marginata'
	- 'Aurea Pendula' (v)	CJun
§	- 'Aureovariegata' (v)	EBee EPfP EShb LRHS LTop MGos MHer MRav NLar SBod SRiv SRms WMoo
	- 'Bentley Blue'	LTop NWea
	- 'Blauer Heinz'	ELan EWTr IVic MHer MRav SRiv WMoo
	- 'Bowles's Blue'	EWes
I	- 'Brilliantissima'	WMoo
	- clipped ball	CLet CWib EPfP LSRN MGos NLar SGol SLim SRiv SRms
	- clipped bird	SRiv
	- clipped cone	CLet LSRN SGol SRiv SRms
	- clipped pyramid	CWib EPfP LSRN MGos NLar SGol SLim SRiv SRms
	- clipped spiral	LSRN SGol SRiv SRms
	- 'Elegans'	IFoB LRHS
§	- 'Elegantissima' (v) Υ^{H5}	Widely available
	- 'Fiesta'	SRms
	- 'Gold Tip'	see *B. sempervirens* 'Notata'
	- 'Golden Frimley' (v)	LHop
§	- 'Graham Blandy' Υ^{H5}	IVic MHer SAko SGol SRiv
	- 'Green Balloon'	EPfP
	- 'Greenpeace'	see *B. sempervirens* 'Graham Blandy'
	- 'Handsworthensis'	CLnd CTri NWea SEND SRms WMoo
	- 'Japonica Aurea'	see *B. sempervirens* 'Latifolia Maculata'
	- 'King Midas'	IVic SAko
	- 'Kingsville'	see *B. microphylla* 'Compacta'
	- 'Kingsville Dwarf'	see *B. microphylla* 'Compacta'
	- 'Latifolia Macrophylla'	SLon
§	- 'Latifolia Maculata' (v) Υ^{H5}	CAbP CWib EPfP LRHS MHer MMuc NPer SEND SPoG SRiv WRHF
	- 'Longifolia'	see *B. sempervirens* 'Angustifolia'
§	- 'Marginata' (v)	CArn CPne IFoB LHop LRHS LTop SGol SLon WHar
	- 'Memorial'	LTop MHer NWad SMHy SRiv
	- 'Myosotidifolia'	NEoE SRiv WCot
	- 'Myrtifolia'	MHer
§	- 'Newport Blue'	NLar
§	- 'Notata' (v)	IFoB MAsh WHar WMoo
	- 'Parasol'	MHer
	- 'Prostrata'	NWad
	- 'Rosmarinifolia'	MHer MRav
	- 'Rotundifolia'	ELan MMuc SEND WMoo
	- 'Silver Variegated'	see *B. sempervirens* 'Elegantissima'
	- 'Suffruticosa'	Widely available
	- 'Suffruticosa Variegata' (v)	SRms SWvt
	- 'Twisty'	WFar
	- 'Vardar Valley'	NEoE SRiv
*	- 'Variegata' (v)	MSwo
	- 'Waterfall'	MHer
	sinica var. ***insularis*** 'Justin Brouwers'	MHer SRiv
	- var. ***insularis*** 'Tide Hill'	LTop MHer SRiv

C

Cacalia (*Asteraceae*)
plantaginea see *Arnoglossum plantagineum*

Cachrys (*Apiaceae*)
alpina SPhx

Caesalpinia (*Caesalpiniaceae*)
gilliesii ♀H1c CBcs CSpe EAla LRHS LSRN MOWG NLos SBrt SPlb WCot WSHC
spinosa SPlb

Caiophora (*Loasaceae*)
coronata SPlb

Caladium (*Araceae*)
'Candidum' (v) SDeJ
'Carolyn Whorton' SDeJ
'Florida Cardinal' (v) SDeJ
'Freida Hemple' SDeJ
'White Christmas' (v) SDeJ

Calamagrostis (*Poaceae*)
× **acutiflora** XLum
- 'Avalanche' CKno ECha EHoe EPPr EShb EWes LHop LRHS MAvo MWhi NWsh WWEG
- 'Eldorado' (v) SMHy WCot
- 'Karl Foerster' Widely available
- 'Overdam' (v) Widely available
- 'Stricta' EBee EPPr NWsh WWEG
- 'Waldenbuch' CKno
argentea see *Stipa calamagrostis*
arundinacea CElw CExl CMac CSpe SPlb WMoo WPGP XLum XSen
'Avalanche' CKno GBin GCal GQue MAsh NOak WPtf
§ **brachytricha** ♀H7 Widely available
- 'Mona' NDov
canadensis EPPr
emodensis CAby CMea CSam EBee ECha EHoe EPPr GCal MAvo MMuc MWhi NBid NOak NWsh SEND SMad WGrn WHea WMoo WPGP WWEG
epigejos CKno LEdu WHrl WPGP
foliosa EPPr
splendens misapplied see *Stipa calamagrostis*
splendens Trin. LPla NDov
varia CKno EBee EHoe GBin WHrl

Calamintha (*Lamiaceae*)
alpina see *Acinos alpinus*
§ **ascendens** EBee ECGP WMoo
clinopodium see *Clinopodium vulgare*
* 'Fritz Kuhn' WWEG
§ **grandiflora** CArn CBod CMea ECha ELan GJos GPoy ITim LEdu MHer MMuc MNHC MNrw MRav NBir NPer SPer SPlb SRms WBod WCAu WHea WJek WMoo XSen
- 'Elfin Purple' EBee EPfP
- 'Variegata' (v) ECtt ELan ENfk EPfP LSou MPie SPoG SRms
'Harrogate' NDov
§ **menthifolia** NBre NLar SRms WJek
§ **nepeta** CArn CHab CMea ECha ENfk GMaP LAst LRHS MHer MNHC NBFr NBro SCob SEND SPhx SPlb SPoG SRms SWat WCAu WJek WMoo WOut WPtf XSen
- subsp. **glandulosa** ECGP WMoo
- - ACL 1050/90 EBee WHoo
- - 'White Cloud' EBee ECGP ECtt ELan GQue LLWP MMuc MRav NBir SPoG SRms WCAu WHea WMoo
- 'Gottfried Kuehn' LPla MRav
§ - subsp. **nepeta** ELan ELon EPfP IMou MCot MHer MLHP MMuc MRav NDov NSti SPer WFar WHal WWEG XLum
- - 'Blue Cloud' CFis CSam CSpe EBee ECha EPfP EPri MRav MSpe NBir NDov SPhx SPtp SRms WCAu WFar WMoo WTor WWEG
- 'Weisse Riese' CMea EBee SPhx
nepetoides see *C. nepeta* subsp. *nepeta*
officinalis misapplied see *C. ascendens*
sylvatica see *C. menthifolia*
I - 'Menthe' LPla
- subsp. **sylvatica** **new** WJek
vulgaris see *Clinopodium vulgare*

calamondin see *Citrus* × *microcarpa*

Calandrinia (*Portulacaceae*)
* **ranunculina** CPBP
sibirica see *Claytonia sibirica*
umbellata EDAr LBMP MAsh WIce
- 'Ruby Tuesday' XLum

Calanthe (*Orchidaceae*)
alismifolia EFEx LAma
arcuata EFEx
arisanenesis EFEx
aristulifera EFEx GKev LAma LRHS
bicolor see *C. striata*
brevicornu NLAp
discolor CDes CEvo EBee EFEx GKev LAma LRHS NLAp
- subsp. **amamiana** EFEx
- var. **flava** see *C. striata*
- subsp. **tokunoshimensis** EFEx
graciliflora EFEx
Kozu gx LEdu NLAp WPGP
- 'Brown' **new** NLAp
- 'Orange' **new** NLAp
- 'Purple' **new** NLAp
mannii EFEx
nipponica CBct EBee EFEx GKev LAma LRHS
reflexa EFEx GKev LAma LRHS
sieboldii see *C. striata*
§ **striata** CBct CEvo EFEx GKev LAma LRHS WCot
sylvatica EBee GKev LAma
Takane gx GKev
tricarinata CBct EBee EFEx GKev LAma NLAp
triplicata GKev LAma

Calathea (*Marantaceae*)
argyrophylla 'Exotica' XBlo
louisae 'Maui Queen' XBlo
majestica ♀H1b XBlo
makoyana ♀H1b XBlo
picturata 'Argentea' ♀H1b XBlo
roseopicta ♀H1b XBlo
- 'Rosastar' XBlo

rufibarba ♀H1b	NGBl XBlo
* ***stromata***	XBlo
veitchiana 'Medaillon'	XBlo
zebrina ♀H1b	XBlo
'Zoizia'	XBlo

Calceolaria (*Calceolariaceae*)

sp.	WBod
acutifolia	see *C. polyrhiza* Cav.
andina	GKev
arachnoidea	CDes EBee GEdr SKHP SPlb
§ ***biflora***	ECho GKev
- 'Goldcap'	ECho
- 'Goldcrest Amber'	SPlb
corymbosa	GKev GLog
falklandica	ECho GBin NSla SRms
filicaulis	CDes GKev
fothergillii	GAbr GKev GLog WAbe
'Goldcrest'	ECho LRHS NPri SRms
integrifolia ♀H1c	CAbb CBcs CDTJ CExl CFis CTri ECtt ELan EShb MGil MSCN SAdn SDix SEND SPer SRms WAbe WBor
- bronze	MSCN SPer
- 'Gaines' Yellow'	EBee GCal
'John Innes'	ECho
'Kentish Hero'	CDes CSpe EBee GBin GCal SDys WAbe
pavonii	MGil
aff. ***pavonii***	CRHN
perfoliata B&SWJ 10638	WCru
plantaginea	see *C. biflora*
§ ***polyrhiza*** Cav.	ECho
rugosa	see *C. integrifolia*
tenella	ECho WAbe
uniflora var. ***darwinii***	ECho GKev WAbe
'Walter Shrimpton'	ECho WAbe

Calendula (*Asteraceae*)

'Bronze Beauty'	CSpe
officinalis	CLau ENfk GPoy LCro MHer MNHC SIde SPav SRms SVic SWvt WJek WSFF
- 'Art Shades'	CWCL
- 'Calypso Orange' (Calypso Series)	CWCL
- Fiesta Gitana Group	WJek
- 'Indian Prince' (Prince Series) **new**	LCro SPhx
- 'Touch of Red Buff' (Touch of Red Series)	CSpe
'Tarifa'	SEND

Calibanus (*Asparagaceae*)

hookeri	EShb

Calibrachoa (*Solanaceae*)

Aloha Midnight Purple = 'Duealmidpu'PBR (Aloha Series) **new**	LBMP
(Cabaret Series) Cabaret Bright Red = 'Balcabrite'	LBMP NPri
- Cabaret Deep Blue = 'Balcabdebu'PBR	LBMP NPri
- Cabaret Deep Yellow = 'Balcabdepy'	NPri
- Cabaret Hot Pink = 'Balcabhopi'PBR	LBMP NPri
- Cabaret White = 'Balcabwit'	LBMP NPri
Callie Sunrise = 'Cal Sunre'PBR (Callie Series)	LSou
(Can-can Series) Can-can Black Cherry	LAst LBMP LSou NPri
- Can-can Double Blue **new**	NPri
- Can-can Double Dark Yellow **new**	NPri
- Can-can Double Magenta **new**	NPri
- Can-can Hot Pink Star = 'Balcanosar' **new**	LBMP
- Can-can Primrose **new**	LBMP
- Can-can Terracotta = 'Balcantera' **new**	LBMP NPri
Celebration Lemon Ice = 'Wescalei' **new**	LAst
Dream Kisses Orange Sunset = 'Wescaosu'PBR (Dream Kisses Series)	LAst
(Million Bells Series) Million Bells Crackling Fire = 'Sunbelfire'	LAst
- Million Bells Trailing Blue = 'Sunbelkubu'PBR	LAst
- Million Bells Trailing Fuchsia = 'Sunbelrkup'	LAst
- Million Bells Trailing Ice = 'Sunbelkuriho'PBR	LAst
- Million Bells Trailing Lavender Vein = 'Sunbelbura'PBR	LSou
- Million Bells Trailing Lemon	LSou
Noa Tangerine = 'Danoa52' **new**	LSou
(Superbells Series) Superbells Cherry Star	NPri
- Superbells Imperial Purple = 'Uscali100'PBR	LSou
- Superbells Lemon Slice = 'Uscal5302m'	NPri
- Superbells Orange = 'Uscali41109'	LSou NPri
- Superbells Pink = 'Uscali11'PBR	LSou
Trailing Million Bells Red (Million Bells Series) **new**	LAst

Calla (*Araceae*)

aethiopica	see *Zantedeschia aethiopica*
palustris	CBod CWat EBee EHon EWay MSKA MWts NPer SRms SWat WMAq

Calliandra (*Mimosaceae*)

eriophylla	SPlb
tweediei ♀H1c	MOWG

Callianthemum (*Ranunculaceae*)

anemonoides	GEdr LLHF WAbe WCot
coriandrifolium	GEdr
kernerianum	GEdr WAbe

Callicarpa (*Lamiaceae*)

acuminata	CFil
americana	CExl NLar
- var. ***lactea***	CMCN
bodinieri	CHII WBod WHar
- var. ***giraldii***	GBin MRav NLar SGol

- - 'Profusion' ♀[H5]	Widely available
'Cardinal'	CJun
cathayana	NLar
dichotoma	CBcs CExl NLar
- f. ***albifructa***	NLar
- 'Issai'	EBee EPfP ESwi LRHS MBlu NLar
- 'Variegata' (v)	CJun
japonica	CExl CMen NLar
- B&SWJ 12621	WCru
- f. ***albibacca***	ESwi
- 'Heavy Berry'	NLar
- 'Koshima-no-homate'	NLar
- 'Leucocarpa'	CBcs CExl CMac EBee ELan EPfP ESwi EWTr MRav NLar SPer SPoG
- var. ***luxurians*** B&SWJ 8521	WCru
kwangtungensis	CBcs EPfP ESwi MMHG MMuc NLar
mollis	CBcs CExl
shikokiana	NLar
× ***shirasawana***	NLar
aff. ***tikusikensis*** B&SWJ 7127	WCru
Van den Broek selection	NLar
yunnanensis	NLar

Callirhoe (*Malvaceae*)

bushii	EBee
involucrata	LPla SBrt WHrl WSHC XLum
- var. ***tenuissima***	GCal SMad

Callisia (*Commelinaceae*)

fragrans	EOHP EShb

Callistemon (*Myrtaceae*)

'Awanga Dam'	ECou
brachyandrus	SVen
'Burgundy'	MOWG
'Candy Pink'	MOWG
citrinus	CBcs CHll CTri CWSG ECou EPfP EPri LPfy MMuc SEND SPlb SRms WGrn WHar
- 'Albus'	see *C. citrinus* 'White Anzac'
- 'Angela'	MOWG
- 'Firebrand'	LRHS MAsh
- 'Splendens' ♀[H3]	Widely available
§ - 'White Anzac'	CDoC CMac CSde ELan EMil EPfP LRHS MOWG SAko SPoG
glaucus	see *C. speciosus*
'Hannah's Child'	MOWG
'Happy Valley'	ECou MOWG
'Inferno'	LRHS NEgg
'Injune'	MOWG
'Kings Park Special'	MOWG
laevis hort.	see *C. rugulosus*
linearifolius	LSRN
linearis ♀[H2]	CBcs CMac CSde CTri ECou ECrN ELan EPfP IDee LRHS LSRN MAsh MHer MHin MOWG SEND SLim SLon SPlb SRms SWvt WSHC
macropunctatus	SPlb SVen
'Masotti'[PBR]	LPfy LRHS MPkF SPoG
'Mauve Mist'	CDoC CHll ELan EMil EPfP GBin LRHS MOWG SAko SPoG SVen WGrn
'Millie Marsden'	MOWG
pachyphyllus	MOWG
- var. ***viridis***	MOWG
pallidus	CBcs CMCN CMac CTsd CWib ECou ELan EPfP IDee LRHS MAsh MMuc MOWG MRav SAko SEND SPer SPlb SPoG SVen WBod
- 'Candle Glow'	MOWG
- 'Father Christmas'	MOWG
paludosus	see *C. sieberi* DC.
pearsonii 'Rocky Rambler'	MOWG
'Perth Pink'	CBcs CDoC CSde ELan EPfP LHop LRHS MOWG SLim SPad SVen
phoeniceus	MOWG
- 'Pink Ice'	MOWG
pinifolius	EAla SPlb SVen
- 'Sockeye'	MOWG
'Pink Champagne'	MOWG
§ ***pityoides***	CExl CTsd EAla ECou MOWG NLar SVen
- from Brown's Swamp, Australia	ECou
recurvus	MOWG
'Red Clusters'	CMac ELan EMil EPfP IArd LRHS MAsh MJak MOWG NPri SAko SWvt
'Reeve's Pink'	MOWG
rigidus	CBcs CChe CDoC CHll CMHG CTri CTsd CWib ELan EPfP EPri GAbr IArd LRHS LSRN MGos MHtn MMuc MRav NLar SEle SPer SVen SWvt WBod
§ ***rugulosus***	MOWG SVen SWvt
salignus ♀[H2]	CBcs CDoC CDul CLet CMac CTri CTsd EPfP IDee LPal LRHS MHer MOWG MRav NEgg NLar SEle SLim SPer SVen
sieberi misapplied	see *C. pityoides*
§ ***sieberi*** DC.	CBcs CDoC CMCN ELan EPfP LRHS MMuc MOWG NBir NLar SEND SLim SPlb
- purple-flowered	MOWG
§ ***speciosus***	CDul MOWG NLar SPlb
subulatus	ECou GGal MOWG SPlb
- 'Crimson Tail'	ECrN MMuc NLar SEND SPtp
I - 'Packer's Selection'	ECou MOWG
'Taree Pink'	MOWG
viminalis	CBcs LPal MOWG SPlb
- 'Captain Cook'	CMac ECou IDee LRHS LSRN MOWG NEgg SRms SVen SWvt WGrn
- 'Endeavor'	SLim
- 'Hannah Ray'	EUJe IDee MOWG
- Hot Pink = 'Kkho1'[PBR]	LPfy LRHS MPkF SHil SLim
- 'Little John'	CSde LRHS LSRN MAsh MOWG SPad SWvt
- 'Malawi Giant'	MOWG
'Violaceus'	NLar SPlb SVen
viridiflorus	CMCN ECou GGal MMuc SEND SPlb WGwG
- 'County Park Dwarf'	ECou
'White Anzac'	see *C. citrinus* 'White Anzac'

Callistephus (*Asteraceae*)

chinensis	SVic

Callitriche (*Plantaginaceae*)

sp.	WSFF
brutia subsp. ***hamulata***	LLWG
§ ***palustris***	CBen MSKA MWts
stagnalis	WMAq
verna	see *C. palustris*

Callitropsis see *Chamaecyparis*

× ***leylandii***	see × *Cuprocyparis leylandii*

Calluna ✿ (*Ericaceae*)

vulgaris	SWhi WOut
- 'Adrie'	SWhi
- 'Alba Elongata'	see *C. vulgaris* 'Mair's Variety'
§ - 'Alba Rigida'	CFst
- 'Alexandra'PBR (Garden Girls Series)	IVic SCoo SPoG
- 'Alicia'PBR (Garden Girls Series) ♀H7	SCoo SPoG SWhi
- 'Allegro'	EPfP MMuc SCoo
- 'Amethyst'PBR (Garden Girls Series)	MJak MMuc SPoG SWhi
- 'Amilto'	CFst SPer
- 'Anette'PBR (Garden Girls Series)	MJak SCoo SWhi
- 'Annabel' (d)	SWhi
- 'Annemarie' (d) ♀H7	CBcs CFst CSBt EPfP SCoo SPlb SWhi
- 'Anne's Goldzwerg'	CFst
- 'Anne's Zwerg'	CFst
- 'Aphrodite'PBR (Garden Girls Series)	CFst SWhi
- 'Arabella'PBR	SWhi
- 'Arina'	MAsh SCoo
- 'Athene'PBR (Garden Girls Series)	CFst SWhi
- 'Aurea'	MJak
- 'Beoley Crimson'	SCoo
- 'Beoley Gold' ♀H7	CSBt CTri EPfP MAsh NHol SCoo
- 'Beoley Silver'	SCoo SWhi
- 'Blazeaway'	CTri EPfP MAsh MJak SCoo
- 'Bonfire Brilliance'	CSBt NHol
- 'Bonita'PBR (Garden Girls Series)	CFst
- 'Boskoop'	IVic MAsh NHol SWhi
- 'C.W. Nix'	CSBt
- 'Con Brio'	CFst CSBt SCoo SWhi
- 'Cottswood Gold'	SCoo
- 'County Wicklow' (d) ♀H7	CTri EPfP MMuc NHol SCoo SWhi
- 'Cuprea'	EPfP MJak SCoo SWhi
- 'Dark Beauty'PBR (d) ♀H7	CBcs CFst CSBt EPfP IVic MAsh NHol SCoo SPer SWhi
- 'Dark Star' (d) ♀H7	CFst CSBt EPfP LCro MAsh NHol SCoo SWhi
- 'Darkness' ♀H7	CBcs CFst CTri EPfP MAsh MJak SCoo SWhi
- 'David Hagenaars'	SWhi
- 'Disco Queen'	SWhi
- 'Dunnet Lime'	SPlb
- 'Easter-bonfire'	SCoo
- 'Elsie Purnell' (d) ♀H7	CFst EPfP MAsh NHol SCoo SPlb
- 'Feuerwerk'	SCoo
- 'Firefly' ♀H7	CFst CSBt EPfP MJak MMuc NHol NWea SCoo SPer SWhi
- 'Flamingo'	MMuc SCoo
- 'Forest Fire'	CFst
- 'Foxii Nana'	CFst NHol SWhi
- 'Fred J. Chapple'	MJak SWhi
- 'Galaxy'PBR	CFst
- Garden Girls Series	MMuc
- 'Glenfiddich'	CSBt MAsh
- 'Gold Haze'	CTri MAsh NHol SCoo
- 'Gold Knight'	EPfP MAsh SCoo
- 'Gold Spronk'	SWhi
- 'Golden Carpet'	CFst MAsh NHol
- 'Golden Fleece'	CFst
- 'Golden Turret'	MAsh
- 'Grey Carpet'	CFst
- 'Guinea Gold'	MAsh SWhi
§ - 'H.E. Beale' (d)	CTri EPfP MJak NHol SCoo
- 'Hammondii Aureifolia'	SPlb
- 'Hammondii Rubrifolia'	SWhi
- 'Highland Rose'	SPlb
- 'J.H. Hamilton' (d)	CTri MAsh NHol SCoo SWhi
- 'Jan Dekker'	MAsh SPer
- 'Jana' (d) **new**	CFst
- 'Joan Sparkes' (d)	SPer
- 'Johnson's Variety'	SCoo
- 'Josefine'	SWhi
- 'Joy Vanstone'	EPfP
- 'Julia'	SWhi
- 'Kerstin' ♀H7	CFst NHol SCoo SPer SPlb SWhi
- 'Kinlochruel' (d) ♀H7	CBcs CFst CSBt CTri EPfP MAsh NHol SPlb SWhi
- 'Kirby White'	MAsh SPlb SWhi
- 'Klaudine'PBR (Garden Girls Series)	CFst IVic
- 'Lemon Queen'	CFst
- 'Leslie Slinger'	SCoo
- 'Little John'	LSRN
- 'Loch Turret'	SPer
- 'Long White'	CFst SWhi
§ - 'Mair's Variety'	SCoo SWhi
- 'Marleen'	MJak
- 'Melanie' (Garden Girls Series)	NHol SCoo SWhi
- 'Mrs Pat'	MAsh
- 'Multicolor'	MAsh NHol
§ - 'My Dream' (d)	CSBt EPfP SCoo
- 'Nana Compacta'	CFst
- 'October White'	CFst
- 'Orange Queen'	CSBt
- 'Peter Sparkes' (d) ♀H7	CBcs CSBt EPfP MAsh MMuc NHol SCoo
- 'Pink Beale'	see *C. vulgaris* 'H.E. Beale'
- 'Purple Passion'	EPfP SCoo
- 'Radnor' (d)	CSBt
- 'Ralph Purnell'	SCoo
- 'Red Beauty'	CBcs CFst SPer SWhi
- 'Red Favorit' (d)	CFst SWhi
- 'Red Fred'	SCoo
- 'Red Haze'	EPfP NHol SCoo
- 'Red Pimpernel'	EPfP SCoo SWhi
- 'Red Star' (d)	NHol
- 'Rigida Prostrata'	see *C. vulgaris* 'Alba Rigida'
- 'Robert Chapman' ♀H7	CFst CSBt CTri MAsh NHol SWhi
- 'Rosalind' ambig.	EPfP
- 'Rosalind, Underwood's'	EPfP NHol
- 'Rosita'PBR	CFst
- 'Roswitha'	CFst
- 'Ruby Slinger'	NHol
- 'Ruth Sparkes' (d)	NHol
- 'Safari'	CFst
- 'Sandy'PBR (Garden Girls Series)	SPoG SWhi
- 'Schurig's Sensation' (d)	IVic
- 'Serlei Aurea'	CSBt EPfP MAsh
- 'Silvana'PBR	CFst
- 'Silver Fox'	CFst
- 'Silver Knight'	CSBt EPfP MAsh MJak NHol SCoo SPlb SWhi
- 'Silver Queen' ♀H7	CFst MAsh MJak NHol SWhi
- 'Sir John Charrington'	CFst CSBt EPfP MAsh NHol SWhi
- 'Sister Anne' ♀H7	CFst CSBt EPfP MJak MMuc SCoo
- 'Snow White' **new**	SWhi
- 'Snowball'	see *C. vulgaris* 'My Dream'
- 'Sonja' (d)	IVic
- 'Spitfire'	MAsh

- 'Spring Cream' ♀H7 CBcs CFst MAsh MMuc NHol SCoo SPer SPoG SWhi
- 'Spring Torch' CBcs CFst CSBt MAsh MJak NHol SCoo SPer SPoG SWhi
- 'Stefanie' SWhi
- 'Strawberry Delight' (d) EPfP SCoo
- 'Sun Sprinkles' CFst
- 'Sunrise' EPfP
- 'Sunset' CFst
- 'Theresa' (Garden Girls Series) CFst
- 'Tib' (d) ♀H7 CSBt MAsh SWhi
- 'Tricolorifolia' EPfP MAsh SCoo
- 'Velvet Fascination' ♀H7 EPfP SCoo SWhi
- 'White Coral' (d) ♀H7 EPfP IVic SCoo
- 'White Lawn' CFst MMuc NHol
- 'Wickwar Flame' ♀H7 CBcs CFst CSBt EPfP LCro MAsh MJak NHol SCoo SPlb SWhi
- 'Winter Chocolate' CSBt EPfP MAsh NHol SCoo
- 'Yellow Beauty'PBR CFst
- 'Yvette's Gold' CFst
- 'Yvette's Silver' CFst

Calocedrus (*Cupressaceae*)

§ ***decurrens*** ♀H6 CBcs CDoC CDul CLnd CMac CMen CTho EFry EPfP EUJe MBlu NWea SLim SPoG
- 'Aureovariegata' (v) ♀H6 CBcs CWib EFry SCoo
- 'Berrima Gold' ♀H6 CDoC NLar SLim
§ - 'Depressa' CKen
- 'Intricata' SLim
- 'Maupin Glow' (v) NLar SLim
- 'Nana' see *C. decurrens* 'Depressa'
- 'Pillar' CKen NLar

Calochortus (*Liliaceae*)

'Cupido'PBR CExl GKev LAma
luteus Douglas ex Lindl. EPot
- 'Golden Orb'PBR CExl ECho GKev LAma SDeJ
splendens 'Violet Queen' ECho GKev LAma
superbus ECho EPot GKev SDeJ
'Symphony'PBR CExl ECho EPot GKev LAma SDeJ
venustus ECho EPot GKev LAma SDeJ
- 'Burgundy' ECho EPot GKev SDeJ

Calomeria (*Asteraceae*)

§ ***amaranthoides*** WJek

Calonyction see *Ipomoea*

Caloscordum see *Allium*

neriniflorum see *Allium neriniflorum*

Calothamnus (*Myrtaceae*)

quadrifidus ECou
- yellow-flowered MOWG
validus SPlb
villosus new SPlb

Calpurnia (*Papilionaceae*)

aurea SPlb

Caltha (*Ranunculaceae*)

howellii see *C. leptosepala* subsp. *howellii*
introloba SWat
laeta see *C. palustris* var. *palustris*
leptosepala EBee EWay GEdr GKev LLHF LLWG NLar
§ - subsp. ***howellii*** EBee
- - NNS 07-87 GKev
natans LLWG
palustris Widely available
- var. ***alba*** Widely available
- 'Auengold' EBee LLWG
- 'Auenwald' LLWG
- var. ***barthei*** GEdr
- 'Flore Pleno' (d) ♀H7 Widely available
- 'Himalayan Snow' new LLWG
- 'Honeydew' CAby CDes EWay LLWG WCot WSHC
§ - var. ***major*** new CAby
- 'Marilyn' LLWG
- 'Multiplex' (d) ECtt GBin GBuc SRot
- Newlake hybrid LLWG
- 'Pallida Plena' (d) SCob
§ - var. ***palustris*** CBen CBre ECha EHon ELan EUJe EWay GCal SWat WWtn
- - 'Plena' (d) CWat EWay LRHS MCot MSKA SGol SPoG
- var. ***radicans*** EWay GEdr
- - 'Flore Pleno' (d) WWtn
- 'Stagnalis' MSKA MWts
- 'Yellow Giant' MSKA
polypetala misapplied see *C. palustris* var. *major*
polypetala Hochst. ex Lorent CCon CWat GCal GJos MSCN MSKA NPer SMad SWat WMAq
- from Turkey SGSe
sagittata WSHC
scaposa GKev

Calycanthus (*Calycanthaceae*)

§ ***chinensis*** CBcs CHll CJun CMCN EBee ELan EPfP EUJe GKin IDee LRHS MBlu MMHG MPkF NLar SMad SSpi
fertilis see *C. floridus* var. *glaucus*
floridus Widely available
- 'Athens' CBcs CJun NLar
§ - var. ***glaucus*** EPfP LPfy LRHS MAsh MGil SHil
- - 'Purpureus' CBcs CJun MBlu NLar
- var. ***laevigatus*** see *C. floridus* var. *glaucus*
- 'Michael Lindsay' CJun NLar
mohrii NLar
occidentalis CArn CBcs CDul CMCN CWib EPPr MBlu SBrt WCFE
§ × ***raulstonii*** CAbP
- 'Hartlage Wine' ♀H5 CBcs CJun EBee EPfP EUJe GBin GKev GKin IArd IDee LCro LLHF LRHS MAsh MBlu NLar SAko SHil SPoG SSpi
§ 'Venus' CBcs CMCN EPfP LLHF LRHS MBlu NLar SPoG SSpi

Calylophus (*Onagraceae*)

fendleri new EBee

Calystegia (*Convolvulaceae*)

'Angel's Trumpets' SKHP
§ ***hederacea*** 'Flore Pleno' (d) SMad
japonica 'Flore Pleno' see *C. hederacea* 'Flore Pleno'
soldanella NNS 99-85 WCot

Calytrix (*Myrtaceae*)

tetragona SPlb

Camassia ✿ (*Asparagaceae*)

'Blue Candle' EBee LAma SPhx
'Blue Heaven' CMea EBee ECGP ERCP LAma SDeJ SPhx

	cusickii	CBod CBro CExl CTca CTri CWCL EBee ECho ECtt ELan EPfP EPot ERCP GKev IFro LAma LPot LRHS MBel MBri MCot MNrw NBir NLar SDeJ SDix WCot
	- white-flowered	IFoB NChi
	- 'Zwanenburg'	CTca EBee ERCP GKev IPot WCot
	esculenta Lindl.	see *C. quamash*
	'John Treasure' (d)	CDes
	leichtlinii misapplied	see *C. leichtlinii* subsp. *suksdorfii*
	leichtlinii (Baker) S.Watson	see *C. leichtlinii* subsp. *leichtlinii*
	'Alba' misapplied	
*	- 'Alba Plena'	MNrw NBir
I	- 'Atrocaerulea'	GMaP
	- Blue Danube	see *C. leichtlinii* subsp. *suksdorfii* 'Blauwe Donau'
	- 'Blue Wave'	NWad SBch
§	- subsp. ***leichtlinii***	Widely available
	- 'Plena' (d)	ECha
	- 'Sacajawea'	CAvo CMea CTca EBee ERCP LAma LRHS SBch SDeJ WTor
	- 'Semiplena' (d)	CAvo CBro CMea CTca EBee ECtt EPfP ERCP LAma LHop LRHS MBel MCot MNrw NSti SDix SPhx WBor WCot WHoo WShi
§	- subsp. ***suksdorfii***	GCra LCro WCot
	- - 'Alba'	CBod LOPS LRHS SCob
§	- - 'Blauwe Donau'	ILea SMHy
	- - Caerulea Group	Widely available
	- - 'Electra'	CAvo ECha
§	***quamash***	CArn CAvo CBro CTca CWCL EBee ECha ELan EPfP EPot ERCP GKev LAma LEdu LLWG LRHS MBel MBri MCot NBir SCob SDeJ SDix SRms WFar WShi XLum
	- 'Blue Melody' (v)	CAvo CBro CSam CTca EBee EPot GKev GMaP LEdu SDeJ WRHF
	- 'Orion'	CBro EBee LRHS WCot

Camellia ✿ (*Theaceae*)

	'Adorable' (*pitardii* hybrid)	CDoC LRHS LSRN
	'Alpen Glo'	LRHS MPkF
	'Annette Carol'	CDoC
	'April Blush'	SCog
	'Ariel's Song'	CDoC
	'Auburn White'	see *C. japonica* 'Mrs Bertha A. Harms'
	azalea **new**	LPar
	'Baby Bear'	LRHS MPkF
	'Barbara Clark' (*reticulata* × *saluenensis*)	CDoC LRHS LSRN MAsh SCog SCoo
	'Bertha Harms Blush'	see *C. japonica* 'Mrs Bertha A. Harms'
	'Bett's Supreme'	CDoC
	'Black Lace' 𝕐^{H5}	CDoC CTrh CTri EPfP LPfy LRHS LSRN MAsh MMuc NPri SCog SCoo SEND SHil
	'Blissful Dawn'	CDoC CTrh
	'Bonnie Marie'	CDoC SCam SCog
	'Califonia Sunset' **new**	LRHS
	'Canterbury'	LRHS MPkF
	'Champêtres Spring Awakening'	MPkF
*	'Chatsworth Belle'	CDoC
	chekiangoleosa	CPne
	'China Lady' (*granthamiana* × *reticulata*)	SCam
	'Christmas Daffodil' (*japonica* hybrid)	CBcs MPkF
	'Cinnamon Cindy'	CDoC LRHS MPkF
	'Cinnamon Sensation'	LRHS MPkF SCog
	'Congratulations'	COtt CSBt LSRN
	'Contessa Lavinia Maggi'	see *C. japonica* 'Lavinia Maggi'
	'Cornish Snow' (*cuspidata* × *saluenensis*) 𝕐^{H4}	CBcs CDoC CSBt CTri ELan GGal SCam SCog SSpi
	'Cornish Spring' (*cuspidata* × *japonica*) 𝕐^{H4}	CDoC CSBt CTrh CTsd LRHS SCam SCog SPer
	'Crimson Candles' 𝕐^{H5}	LRHS MPkF SCam
	Cupido	see *C. rosthorniana* 'Elina'
	cuspidata	SCam SCog
	'Czar'	see *C. japonica* 'The Czar'
	'Dainty Dale'	CDoC SCam
	'Delia Williams'	see *C.* × *williamsii* 'Citation'
	'Diamond Head' (*japonica* × *reticulata*)	LSRN
	'Diana's Charm'	CDoC
	'Doctor Clifford Parks' (*japonica* × *reticulata*) 𝕐^{H4}	CDoC CTrh
	'Donckelaeri'	see *C. japonica* 'Masayoshi'
	edithae	LRHS
	'El Dorado' (*japonica* × *pitardii*)	CDoC
	'Extravaganza' (*japonica* hybrid) 𝕐^{H5}	CTrh IArd
	'Fairy Blush'	LRHS MPkF
	'Fairy Wand'	CDoC LRHS MPkF
	'Fascination'	SWvt
	'Felice Harris' (*reticulata* × *sasanqua*)	CDoC SCog
	'Festival of Lights'	MPkF
	'Fiesta Grande'	MPkF
	'Fire 'n' Ice'	CDoC
	'Forty-niner' (*japonica* × *reticulata*)	CBcs LRHS
	'Fox's Fancy'	CDoC
	'Fragrant Pink'	CDoC CTrh
	'Francie L' 𝕐^{H4}	CDoC CMac EPfP SCam
	'Free Spirit'	CTrh
	'Freedom Bell' 𝕐^{H5}	CDoC CMHG CTrh EPfP GGal GKin LRHS MAsh MBri MPkF SCam SCog SCoo
	'Frosted Star' **new**	LRHS
	'Gay Baby'	CDoC MPkF
	'Golden Anniversary'	see *C. japonica* 'Dahlohnega'
	grijsii	CExl CTrh LRHS
	handelii	CExl
	'Happy Anniversary'	COtt CSBt LSRN SWvt
§	***hiemalis*** 'Bonanza'	CTrh LRHS MPkF
	- 'Chansonette'	CDoC ELon SCog
§	- 'Dazzler'	CDoC LRHS MGos SCam SCog
	- 'Elfin Rose' **new**	LRHS
	- 'Interlude'	MPkF
	- 'Kanjirō'	CDoC SCam
	- 'Shishigashira'	CTrh
	- 'Shōwa-no-sakae'	CDoC LRHS MPkF SCog
	'High Fragrance'	LRHS MPkF
	'Hooker'	CDoC LRHS MAsh SCoo
	'Imbricata Rubra'	see *C. japonica* 'Imbricata'
	'Inspiration' (*reticulata* × *saluenensis*) 𝕐^{H4}	CDoC CMac COtt CTrh EPfP LSRN MGos NLar SCam SCog SPer
	japonica	SEWo SPre
	- 'Aaron's Ruby'	CDoC COtt ELon LRHS SCam SCog
	- 'Ace of Hearts'	LPfy
	- 'Ada Pieper'	CTrh
	- 'Adelina Patti' 𝕐^{H5}	CBcs CDoC CMHG CTrh ELan ELon
	- 'Adeyaka' **new**	LRHS
	- 'Adolphe Audusson' 𝕐^{H5}	Widely available
§	- 'Akashigata' 𝕐^{H5}	CBcs ELon EPfP LRHS LSRN SCam SCog SLim SSta WHar

- 'Alba Plena' 🏆H5 CTrh ELan LRHS SCog SWvt
- 'Alba Simplex' CDoC CMac CTrh ELan EPfP IVic NPri SCam SCob SCog SSta
- 'Alexander Hunter' 🏆H5 CDoC LRHS SCog
- 'Alison Leigh Woodroof' CDoC
§ - 'Althaeiflora' CBcs CDoC ELon LRHS SCog
- 'Amazing Graces' CDoC
- 'Anemoniflora' CBcs CDoC CTsd EPfP LRHS SCog
- 'Angel' CBcs LSRN SCam WBor
- 'Angello' LRHS
- 'Ann Sothern' CBcs
- 'Annette Gehry' CBcs
- 'Annie Wylam' 🏆H5 CTrh ELan
- 'Apollo 14' COtt
- 'Apollo' ambig. CBcs CDoC LRHS MBri MGos MMuc SPer
- 'Apollo' Paul, 1911 MSwo SCam SCog
§ - 'Apple Blossom' CTrh CTsd LRHS
- 'Arajishi' misapplied see *C. japonica* subsp. *rusticana* 'Beni-arajishi'
* - 'Augustine Supreme' CMac
- 'Ave Maria' 🏆H5 CDoC CTrh LRHS
- 'Baby Pearl' LSRN
- 'Baby Sis' CDoC LRHS
- 'Ballet Dancer' 🏆H5 CDoC ELon LSRN SCam SCog
- 'Bambino' CDoC
- 'Barbara Woodroof' CBcs
- 'Baron Gomer' see *C. japonica* 'Comte de Gomer'
- 'Baronne Leguay' SCam
- 'Beau Harp' LRHS SCam
- 'Bella Lambertii' SCog
- 'Bella Romana' SCam
- 'Berenice Boddy' 🏆H5 CBcs ELan LRHS
- 'Berenice Perfection' SCog
- 'Betty Foy Sanders' CDoC CTrh
- 'Betty Robinson' CDoC LRHS
- 'Betty Sheffield' COtt LRHS MAsh SCog
- 'Betty Sheffield Pink' LRHS SCam
- 'Betty Sheffield Supreme' CBcs
- 'Betty's Beauty' LRHS
- 'Black Magic' CTrh LRHS
- 'Black Tie' CDoC CTrh CWSG ELan ELon LRHS MBri MGos NEgg SCam SCog
- 'Blackburnia' see *C. japonica* 'Althaeiflora'
- 'Blaze of Glory' SCog
§ - 'Blood of China' CBcs CDoC CSBt ELan LPfy LRHS LSRN MGos MMuc SCam SCog SCoo SHil
- 'Blush Tinsie' **new** LRHS
- 'Bob Hope' 🏆H5 CBcs CDoC CTrh CTri LRHS
- 'Bob's Tinsie' 🏆H5 CBcs CDoC CMHG CSBt CTsd ECre LRHS LSRN MGos MPkF
§ - 'Bokuhan' 🏆H5 CDoC MPkF
- 'Bonomiana' NLar
- 'Bright Buoy' LRHS
- 'Brushfield's Yellow' CBcs CDoC CMHG COtt CSBt CTrh CTsd EBee ELan ELon EPfP IArd LBrs LMil LRHS LSRN MAsh MBri MGos NLar SCam SCog SCoo SPer SSta
- 'Bush Hill Beauty' see *C. japonica* 'Lady de Saumarez'
§ - 'C.M. Hovey' 🏆H5 CMHG CMac LRHS
- 'C.M. Wilson' CMac SCog
- 'Campsii Alba' CTsd
- 'Can Can' CDoC ELon SCam SCog
- 'Candy Apple' CDoC CTrh
- 'Candy Stripe' CDoC
- 'Captain Blood' CDoC
- 'Cara Mia' CBcs CDoC CTsd LRHS SCam
- 'Carolyn Tuttle' LRHS
- 'Carter's Sunburst' 🏆H5 CBcs CDoC ELan EPfP SCog
- 'Cassandra' EPfP LPfy MGos SHil
- 'Chandleri Elegans' see *C. japonica* 'Elegans'
- 'Charlotte de Rothschild' CTrh CTri
- 'Cheryll Lynn' CDoC
- 'Cinderella' CDoC LRHS SCam SCog
- 'Clarke Hubbs' CDoC
- Classique = 'Kerguelen'[PBR] CDoC LBrs LRHS MPkF SCog
- 'Colonel Firey' see *C. japonica* 'C.M. Hovey'
- 'Commander Mulroy' 🏆H5 CDoC CTrh SCam
§ - 'Comte de Gomer' CDoC ELan ELon EPfP LRHS MGos NPri SCam SCog
- 'Conspicua' CBcs
- 'Contessa Samailoff' CDoC
§ - 'Coquettii' 🏆H5 LRHS
- 'Coral Pink Lotus' CDoC
- 'Coral Queen' CDoC
- 'Cornish Excellence' CDoC
- 'Curly Lady'[PBR] CDoC MJak MMuc NPri WMoo
§ - 'Dahlohnega' CDoC COtt CSBt CTrh ELon LRHS LSRN MGos MHtn MPkF SCam
- 'Daikagura' CBcs CDoC
- 'Dainty' CBcs
- 'Daitairin' see *C. japonica* 'Dewatairin'
- 'Daphne du Maurier' LRHS
- 'Dark of the Moon' CDoC LRHS MAsh
- 'Dear Jenny' CBcs
- 'Debutante' CBcs CDoC CMac COtt ELon MGos MMuc SCam SCog
- 'Deep Secret' 🏆H5 CDoC
- 'Desire' 🏆H5 CBcs CDoC CMHG CSBt CTrh CTsd CWSG ELan EPfP LBrs LCro LMil LRHS LSRN MAsh MBri MGos MPkF NEgg SCam SCog SCoo SPoG
- 'Devonia' CBcs SCog
§ - 'Dewatairin' (Higo) CBcs CDoC MGos SCam SCog
- 'Diddy's Pink Organdie' CDoC LRHS
- 'Dixie Knight' CDoC LRHS MGos SCam SCog
- 'Dobreei' CMac
- 'Doctor Burnside' CBcs CDoC CTrh LPar LRHS SCam SCog
- 'Doctor King' EPfP LRHS MBri MGos NPri SPoG
- 'Doctor Tinsley' 🏆H5 EPfP LRHS MAsh NPri SCoo
- 'Dona Herzilia de Freitas Magalhães' CBcs CDoC ELon MGos SCam SCog
- 'Dona Jane Andresson' SCam
- 'Donckelaeri' see *C. japonica* 'Masayoshi'
- 'Donnan's Dream' CTrh
- 'Drama Girl' 🏆H5 CBcs CDoC CTsd ELan LRHS SCam SCog
- 'Duc de Bretagne' SCog
- 'Duchesse Decazes' CBcs
- 'Edelweiss' CDoC ELon SCam SCog
- 'Effendee' see *C. sasanqua* 'Rosea Plena'
§ - 'Elegans' CBcs CDoC ELon EPfP LCro LMil LPar LRHS MBri MGos MMuc SCam SCog SCoo SLim SPoG SWvt
- 'Elegans Champagne' EPfP
- 'Elegans Splendor' CDoC
- 'Elisabeth' CDoC LRHS
- 'Elizabeth Arden' CTsd
- 'Elizabeth Cooper' CTrh LSRN
- 'Elizabeth Dowd' SCog
- 'Elizabeth Hawkins' CTrh LRHS MAsh NCGa
- 'Emily Wilson' CDoC
- 'Emmett Pfingstl' SCam
- 'Emperor of Russia' CBcs LRHS WBod
- 'Eric Baker' SCam

– 'Erin Farmer'	CBcs
– 'Eugène Lizé'	SCam
– 'Eximia'	CDoC EPfP LRHS
– 'Faith'	CBcs
– 'Fanny'	SCog
– 'Faustina' **new**	LRHS
– 'Feast Perfection'	CDoC
– 'Finlandia Variegated'	CDoC ELon MMuc SCam SCog
– 'Fire Dance'	CDoC
– 'Fire Falls' ♀H5	CMHG
– 'Firebird'	CBcs CTsd
– 'Flamingo'	CDoC
– 'Flashlight'	ELan EPfP LRHS
§ – 'Fleur Dipater'	CBcs LRHS SCam
– 'Flowerwood'	SCog
– 'Frans van Damme'	CBcs
– 'Fred Sander'	CBcs CDoC ELan ELon LRHS MGos SCam SCog
– 'Frosty Morn'	CDoC ELan
– 'Gertrude Preston' **new**	CDoC
§ – 'Gigantea'	ELan LRHS SCam
– 'Giuditta Rosani'	LRHS
– 'Gladys Wannamaker'	SCog
– 'Glen 40'	see *C. japonica* 'Coquettii'
– 'Gloire de Nantes' ♀H5	CTrh SCam SCog
– 'Gold Tone'	CDoC ELon MGos SCam
* – 'Golden Wedding' (v)	SCog
– 'Goshozakura'	CDoC
– 'Grace Albritton' (d)	LRHS MPkF
– 'Grace Bunton'	CBcs CDoC ELon MGos SCog
– 'Granada'	SCog
– 'Grand Prix' ♀H5	CDoC ELan ELon LSRN MGos NLar SCam SCog SPer
– 'Grand Slam' ♀H5	CDoC SCam
– 'Guest of Honor'	CDoC COtt LRHS
– 'Guilio Nuccio' ♀H5	CBcs CDoC COtt CTri ELan ELon EPfP IArd LRHS LSRN MBri NEgg NPri SCam SCog SCoo SLim SPer
– 'Gus Menard'	SCam
– 'Gwenneth Morey'	CBcs CDoC ELan
– 'H.A. Downing'	CDoC SCam
§ – 'Hagoromo' ♀H5	CBcs CDoC CSBt CTrh CTsd ELan LRHS SCam
– 'Hakugan'	EPfP
§ – 'Hakurakuten' ♀H5	CTrh CTri SCog
– 'Hanafūki'	CDoC LRHS SCam SCog
– 'Happy Birthday'	LSRN
– 'Haru-no-utena'	CTrh MPkF
– 'Hatsuzakura'	see *C. japonica* 'Dewatairin'
– 'Hawaii'	CBcs CMac CTrh ELon LRHS SCam
– 'Her Majesty Queen Elizabeth II'	CDoC
– Herme	see *C. japonica* 'Hikarugenji'
– 'High Hat'	CBcs SCog
– 'High, Wide 'n' Handsome'	CDoC
§ – 'Hikarugenji'	CDoC LRHS SCog
– 'Hinomaru'	CMac
– 'Holly Bright'	CDoC CTrh MPkF
– 'Honeyglow'	CDoC
– 'Ichisetsu'	SCog
§ – 'Imbricata'	CTrh LRHS MAsh MMuc SCog
– 'Italiana Vera'	LRHS MAsh
– 'J.J. Whitfield'	CMac
– 'Jack Jones Scented'	CMHG
– 'Janet Waterhouse'	CBcs
§ – 'Japonica Variegata' (v)	LRHS
– 'Jean Clere'	CDoC SCog
– 'Jennifer Turnbull'	CDoC
– 'Jingle Bells'	CBcs
– 'Jitsugetsusei'	CDoC
– 'Joseph Pfingstl' ♀H5	CTri EPfP LRHS MMuc NLar SCam SCog
– 'Jovey Carlyon'	CBcs LRHS
– 'Joy Sander'	see *C. japonica* 'Apple Blossom'
– 'Juan XXIII'	MGos SHil
– 'Jubilee Gem' **new**	CTsd
– 'Jules Verne' **new**	CDoC
– 'Julia France'	SCog
– 'Juno'	CBcs LRHS SCoo
– L. 'Jupiter' Paul, 1904 ♀H5	CBcs CDoC CMac COtt CTri EPfP LSRN SCam SCog WHar
– 'Kellingtoniana'	see *C. japonica* 'Gigantea'
– 'Kenny'	CBcs
– 'Kentucky'	LRHS SCam
– 'Kick-off'	CTrh MMuc SCam SCog
– 'Kimberley'	CDoC LSRN MPkF SCog
– 'King Size'	CDoC MGos
– 'King's Ransom'	CDoC CMac LRHS
– 'Kingyoba-shiro-wabisuke'	CDoC
– 'Kingyo-tsubaki'	SCam SSta
– 'Kitty Berry'	CDoC CTrh
– 'Kokinran'	CDoC SCam
§ – 'Konronkoku' ♀H5	CDoC LRHS
– 'Kouron-jura'	see *C. japonica* 'Konronkoku'
– 'Kramer's Beauty'	COtt
– 'Kramer's Supreme' ♀H5	CBcs ELon LPar LPfy LRHS LSRN MGos SCam SCog SCoo SGol SHil
§ – 'Kumasaka'	CTri LRHS
– 'Lady Campbell'	CTri EPfP LPfy LRHS MBri MGos NPri SCam
– 'Lady Clare'	see *C. japonica* 'Akashigata'
§ – 'Lady de Saumarez'	CBcs CDoC CMac COtt CTsd
– 'Lady Erma'	CBcs
– 'Lady Loch'	CTrh SCam
– 'Lady Marion'	see *C. japonica* 'Kumasaka'
– 'Lady McCulloch'	LRHS
– 'Lady Saint Clair'	CDoC
– 'Lady Vansittart'	CDoC CTrh ELan EPfP GGal LBrs LMil LRHS LSRN MAsh MBri MGos MPkF NEgg SCam SCog SCoo SLim SPer SPoG SSta
§ – 'Lady Vansittart Pink'	CMac
– 'Lady Vansittart Red'	see *C. japonica* 'Lady Vansittart Pink'
– 'Lady Vansittart Shell'	see *C. japonica* 'Yours Truly'
– 'Lady Vere de Vere' (d)	CDoC
– 'Latifolia'	SCam
– 'Laura's Red'	CTsd
– 'Laurie Bray'	SCog
§ – 'Lavinia Maggi' ♀H5	CBcs CDoC CTri ELan ELon EPfP LMil LPfy LRHS LSRN MAsh MBri MGos MMuc NPri SCam SCog SCoo SHil SPoG SReu SRms SSta
– 'L'Avvenire'	SCog
– 'Lemon Drop'	CBcs COtt CTrh
– 'Leonora Novick'	CDoC SCog
– 'Lily Pons'	CTrh
– 'Little Bit'	CBcs CDoC CMHG ELon MGos SCam SSta
– 'Little Man'	COtt LRHS
– 'Look-away'	LRHS
– 'Lovelight' ♀H5	CTrh LRHS
– 'Lucy Hester'	CDoC
– 'Ludgvan Red'	LRHS
– 'Lulu Belle'	SCog
– 'Mabel Blackwell'	ELon SCam
– 'Madame de Strekaloff'	CMac CSBt SCam
– 'Madame Hahn'	CDoC
– 'Madame Lebois'	CBcs CDoC SCam
– 'Madge Miller'	LRHS

- 'Magnoliiflora'	see *C. japonica* 'Hagoromo'
- 'Maiden's Blush'	CMac COtt
- 'Man Size'	CDoC
- 'Manuroa Road'	LRHS
- 'Margaret Davis' 𝕐H5	CDoC COtt CSBt CWSG EBee ELan ELon EPfP LBrs LCro LOPS LPfy LRHS LSRN MAsh MBri MGos MPkF NEgg NPri SCam SCoo SHil SLim WFar
- 'Margaret Davis Picotee'	CBcs CMHG CTrh SCog SPer
- 'Margaret Rose'	SCam
- 'Margaret Short'	CTsd
- 'Margherita Coleoni'	CBcs
- 'Marguérite Gouillon' Drouard-Gouillon	CBcs SSta
- 'Marian Mitchell'	SCam
- 'Mariana'	CDoC ELon SCog
- 'Marie Bracey'	CBcs
- 'Mariottii Rubra'	CMac
- 'Marjorie Magnificent'	LRHS MAsh SCoo
- 'Mark Alan'	CDoC LRHS LSRN
- 'Maroon and Gold'	CDoC LRHS LSRN SCog
- 'Mars' 𝕐H5	CBcs SCam SCog SPer
- 'Marshmallow' **new**	LRHS
- 'Mary Alice Cox'	CDoC
- 'Mary Costa'	CBcs CDoC CTrh
- 'Mary J. Wheeler'	LSRN
§ - 'Masayoshi' 𝕐H5	CBcs CSBt LRHS MAsh SCam SCog
- 'Mathotiana Alba'	CDoC CMac CTri CTsd ELan EPfP LSRN MGos MMuc SCam SCog SEND SPer
§ - 'Mathotiana Rosea'	CMac NLar SCam
- 'Mathotiana Supreme'	CDoC SCam SCog
- 'Matilija Poppy'	CTrh
- 'Matterhorn'	CDoC CTrh LCro
- 'Mattie Cole'	CDoC SCam
- 'Mercury' 𝕐H5	CBcs CMac EPfP GGGa NEgg SCog
- 'Mercury Variegated' (v)	CMHG
- 'Mermaid'	CDoC LRHS
- 'Midnight'	CBcs CMHG CTsd LRHS MAsh SCoo
- 'Midnight Magic'	CTrh CTri LRHS MAsh
- 'Midnight Serenade'	CDoC LRHS
- 'Midnight Variegated'	LRHS MPkF
§ - 'Mikenjaku'	CBcs CDoC EBee LBrs LPfy LRHS SCog
- 'Miriam Stevenson'	SCam
- 'Miss Charleston'	CBcs SCog
- 'Miss Lyla'	MMuc
- 'Modern Art'	MPkF
- 'Momiji-gari'	CDoC
- 'Monsieur Faucillon'	CBcs
- 'Monstruosa Rubra'	see *C. japonica* 'Gigantea'
- 'Monte Carlo'	CDoC SCam SCog
- 'Moshe Dayan'	CDoC EBee LRHS MAsh SCam SCog SCoo
- 'Moshio'	CDoC
§ - 'Mrs Bertha A. Harms'	CDoC LRHS MGos SCam SCog
- 'Mrs Charles Cobb'	LRHS
- 'Mrs D.W. Davis'	CDoC EPfP
- 'Mrs William Thompson'	LRHS SCam
- 'Nagasaki'	see *C. japonica* 'Mikenjaku'
- 'Nigra'	see *C. japonica* 'Konronkoku'
- 'Nobilissima' 𝕐H5	CBcs CDoC CMac CTrh CTri CWSG EPfP LBrs LCro LMil MBlu MBri MJak MMuc NEgg NLar SCam SCog SCoo SPer SPoG WFar WHar
- 'Nokogiriba-tsubaki'	MPkF
- 'Nuccio's Cameo' 𝕐H5	CDoC CTrh LRHS MAsh NPri SCoo
- 'Nuccio's Gem' 𝕐H5	CDoC CMHG EPfP LRHS MAsh MMuc SCoo SGol
- 'Nuccio's Jewel' 𝕐H5	CDoC CSBt CTrh ELan ELon EPfP LRHS LSRN MAsh SCog WMoo
- 'Nuccio's Pearl' 𝕐H5	CDoC EPfP LRHS LSRN MAsh SCog SCoo
- 'Nuccio's Pink Lace'	CTri LRHS
- 'Okan' (Higo) **new**	CDoC
- 'Onetia Holland'	CBcs CDoC EPfP LSRN MGos SCam SCog SLim
- 'Oo-La-La'	CTrh LRHS MPkF
- 'Optima'	CBcs CDoC ELon LRHS MMuc SCam SCog SCoo
- 'Orandakō'	LPfy SCob SHil
- 'Patricia Ann'	LSRN
- 'Paulette Goddard'	SCam
- 'Paul's Apollo'	see *C. japonica* 'Apollo' Paul, 1911
- 'Peachblossom'	see *C. japonica* 'Fleur Dipater'
- 'Pearl Harbor'	SCam
- 'Pensacola Red'	CDoC
- 'Pink Chiffon' **new**	LRHS
- 'Pink Clouds'	CBcs
- 'Primavera'	CTrh SCog
- 'Prince Murat'	CDoC LRHS
- 'Princess Baciocchi'	SCam
- 'Princess du Mahe'	CMac
- 'R.L. Wheeler' 𝕐H5	CBcs CSBt CTri EPfP LRHS LSRN MBri NPri SCog SCoo SPoG
- 'Raspberry Ripple'	MPkF
- 'Red Dandy'	CDoC SCam SCog
- 'Red Red Rose'	CDoC LRHS
- 'Reg Ragland'	CDoC MGos SCog
- 'Robert Lasson' **new**	LRHS
- 'Roger Hall'	CBcs CDoC CTrh LRHS LSRN SCoo SPoG
- 'Rosa Baroveira Nella'	NLar
- 'Rosularis'	ELon SCog
- 'Royal Velvet'	CTrh
- 'Rubescens Major'	CBcs
- 'Ruddigore'	CTrh
§ - subsp. ***rusticana***	CBcs SCog
- - 'Arajishi' misapplied	see *C. japonica* subsp. ***rusticana*** 'Beni-arajishi'
- - 'Arajishi' Ko'emon	SCam
§ - - 'Beni-arajishi'	CDoC LRHS
- - 'Reigyoku' (v)	CBcs CDoC
- 'Sabiniana'	LRHS
- 'Saint André'	CMac LRHS MAsh SCoo
- 'San Dimas' 𝕐H5	CDoC CTrh LRHS MGos MPkF SCam SCog
- 'Sanpei-tsubaki' **new**	LRHS
- 'Saturnia'	CDoC ELon LRHS WBor
- 'Sawada's Dream'	CDoC MMuc SCog
- 'Scentsation' 𝕐H5	CDoC CMHG CTri LPfy LRHS MBri SCog SHil
- 'Sea Foam'	LRHS
- 'Sea Gull'	CTrh
- 'Senator Duncan U. Fletcher'	CDoC
- 'Shikibu'	CTrh
- 'Shiragiku'	CBcs CDoC EPfP SCog
- 'Shiro Chan'	CDoC ELon MGos SCam
- 'Shirobotan'	CDoC ELon LRHS MAsh SCam SCog SCoo
- 'Shūgetsu' **new**	LRHS
- 'Silver Anniversary' 𝕐H5	Widely available
- 'Silver Chalice'	MAsh
- 'Silver Ruffles'	CDoC CTrh ELon LRHS SCam

	– 'Silver Waves'	MPkF
	– 'Souvenir de Bahuaud-Litou' ♀H5	CBcs CDoC SCam SCog
	– 'Splendens Carlyon'	LRHS SCoo
	– 'Spring Fling'	CTrh
	– 'Spring Formal'	CTrh
	– 'Spring Frill'	CWSG SCam
	– 'Stacy Susan'	MPkF
	– 'Strawberry Blonde'	MMuc SCog WFar
	– 'Strawberry Parfait'	CDoC COtt
	– 'Strawberry Swirl'	CBcs SCog
	– 'Sugar Babe'	CDoC CTrh LRHS SCoo WHar
	– 'Suibijin'	SSpi
	– 'Sunset Glory'	SCam
	– 'Sweetheart'	SCog
	– 'Sylva' ♀H5	EUJe GGGa GGal
	– 'Sylvia'	CMac
	– 'Takanini'	CBcs CDoC CTrh MPkF
	– 'Tama Electra'	MPkF
	– 'Tammia'	CDoC COtt LRHS
	– 'Tarō'an'	GGal
	– 'Teresa Ragland'	CDoC SCam
§	– 'The Czar'	CBcs
	– 'The Mikado'	LRHS SCog
	– 'Tickled Pink'	CDoC
	– 'Tiffany'	CBcs ELon LRHS SCam SCog SCoo
	– 'Tinker Bell'	CDoC ELon MGos SCam SCog
	– 'Tinker Toy'	CTrh
	– 'Tom Pouce'	LRHS MPkF
	– 'Tom Thumb' ♀H5	CDoC CTrh LRHS SRms
	– 'Tomorrow'	CBcs CDoC NEgg SCam SCog
	– 'Tomorrow Park Hill'	CBcs SCog
§	– 'Tomorrow Variegated' (v)	SCam
	– 'Tomorrow's Dawn'	CDoC
	– 'Touchdown'	SCam
	– 'Trewithen White'	CDoC LRHS
§	– 'Tricolor' ♀H5	CDoC CMHG CMac COtt CSBt CTrh ELon LRHS MAsh MGos MMuc SCam SCog SCoo
	– 'Tricolor Red'	see *C. japonica* 'Lady de Saumarez'
	– 'Trinkett'	CDoC
	– variegated (v)	SCog
	– 'Victor Emmanuel'	see *C. japonica* 'Blood of China'
	– 'Ville de Nantes'	LRHS
	– 'Virginia Carlyon'	CBcs
	– 'Visconti Nova'	LRHS
	– 'Vittorio Emanuele II'	CDoC CTrh LRHS SCoo
	– 'Volcano'	CDoC MPkF
	– 'Volunteer'	EPfP LRHS MBri SPoG
	– 'Vosper's Rose'	CDoC
	– 'Warrior'	CDoC SCog
	– 'Wheel of Fortune'	LRHS MAsh
	– 'White Nun'	CBcs SCog
	– 'White Swan'	CMac COtt CSBt LRHS MAsh SCoo
	– 'Wilamina' ♀H5	CDoC CMHG
	– 'Wildfire'	CDoC LRHS
	– 'William Bartlett'	CDoC CTrh MBri MMuc
	– 'William Honey'	CTrh
	– 'Wisley White'	see *C. japonica* 'Hakurakuten'
	– 'Witman Yellow'	CTrh
§	– 'Yours Truly'	CDoC CMac COtt CTrh CTsd LRHS LSRN MAsh SCog
	– 'Yukimi-guruma'	CDoC
	'John Tooby'	CDoC COtt
	'Jury's Yellow'	see *C.* × *williamsii* 'Jury's Yellow'
	'Kichō'	MPkF
	'Lasca Beauty' (*japonica* × *reticulata*)	CTrh
	'Leonard Messel' (*reticulata* × (× *williamsii*)) ♀H5	CBcs CDoC CMHG CMac CTrh CTri CTsd EPfP GGal LRHS MAsh MBri MGos MPkF NLar SCam SCog SCoo SPer SReu WHor
	'Liz Henslowe'	CTsd
	lutchuensis	LRHS
	'Magic Mum'	LSRN
	'Mandalay Queen' (*reticulata* hybrid)	SCam
	'Maud Messel' (*reticulata* × (× *williamsii*))	SCam
	'Milo Rowell'	CDoC
	'Mimosa Jury'	CDoC LRHS
	'Nicky Crisp' (*japonica* × *pitardii*)	CDoC CTrh LRHS MPkF
	oleifera	CExl CTrh
	'Phyl Doak' (*reticulata* × *saluenensis*)	CDoC
	'Pink Goddess'	LRHS MPkF
	'Pink Icicle' (*oleifera* hybrid)	CWSG ELon SCam
	'Pink Spangles'	see *C. japonica* 'Mathotiana Rosea'
	pitardii	CDoC
	– 'Snippet'	CDoC
	'Polar Ice'	CDoC SCog
	'Polyanna'	CDoC SCog
	'Portuense'	see *C. japonica* 'Japonica Variegata'
	'Quintessence' (*japonica* × *lutchuensis*)	CDoC CTrh SCog
	'Red Crystal'	CTrh
	reticulata Lindl.	CPne
	– 'Arch of Triumph'	LRHS
	– 'Captain Rawes'	LRHS
	– 'Jean Morel'	LRHS
	– 'Mary Williams'	MMuc SCoo
	– 'Miss Tulare'	CDoC
	– 'Mouchang'	CBcs
	– 'Satsuma-kurenai'	LRHS
	– 'Simpatica'	LRHS
	'Rose du Steir' (*reticulata* hybrid)	MPkF
§	***rosthorniana*** 'Elina' **new**	CWSG ELan EPfP LCro WCot
	rusticana	see *C. japonica* subsp. *rusticana*
	saluenensis	WBod
I	***sasanqua*** 'Alba'	CMac CTri
	– 'Baronesa de Soutelinho'	ELan ELon SCam SCog
	– 'Bettie Patricia'	SCog
	– 'Bonanza'	see *C. hiemalis* 'Bonanza'
	– 'Brocéliande'	MPkF
	– 'Cleopatra'	EPfP LPar SCob
	– 'Cotton Candy'	CDoC
	– 'Crimson King' ♀H4	CDoC CTrh LRHS
	– 'Dazzler'	see *C. hiemalis* 'Dazzler'
	– 'Dwarf Shishi'	CTrh
	– 'Early Pearly'	CDoC LRHS
	– 'Flamingo'	see *C. sasanqua* 'Fukuzutsumi'
	– 'Fragrans'	ELon MGos SCam SCog
	– 'Fuji-no-mine'	ELon SCam SCog
§	– 'Fukuzutsumi'	CSBt
	– 'Gay Border'	LRHS
	– 'Gay Sue'	CTrh SCam
	– 'Hinode-gumo' **new**	SEWo
	– 'Hiryū'	LRHS MBri SCam SPoG
	– 'Hugh Evans' ♀H4	CBcs CDoC COtt CTrh ELan ELon EPfP LRHS SCam SCog SCoo SSta
	– 'Jean May' ♀H4	CBcs ELan ELon EPfP LRHS MBri SCam SCog SCoo SPer WCot
	– 'Kenkyō'	ELon SCam SCog SPer SSta
	– 'Maiden's Blush'	LRHS MBri SCog WCot
	– 'Mignonne'	CTrh
	– 'Narumigata' ♀H4	CAbP CBcs CDoC CDul CMac CTrh CTsd ELon EPfP LCro LRHS MBlu MBri MGos SCam SCog SSta WSHC

- 'New Dawn'	SCam SCog
- 'Nyewoods'	CMac
- 'Papaver'	SCam SCog WBod
- 'Paradise Audrey'	LMil LRHS
- 'Paradise Belinda'^{PBR}	CAbP EPfP LMil LRHS
- 'Paradise Blush'	CBcs LRHS SCog
- 'Paradise Glow'	CBcs LMil LRHS SCam
- 'Paradise Helen'	LRHS SCam SPoG
- 'Paradise Hilda'	CAbP CDoC LRHS
- 'Paradise Little Liane'^{PBR}	CBcs
- 'Paradise Pearl'	EPfP LMil LRHS SSpi
- 'Paradise Venessa'^{PBR}	CBcs CTsd EPfP LRHS SCam SPoG
- 'Peach Blossom'	CBcs
- 'Plantation Pink'	CTrh ELan EPfP LCro LOPS LRHS MBri SCam SCog SRkn WCot
- 'Rainbow'	CAbP CDoC CTrh ECre ELan ELon EPfP GGal LRHS MAsh MBri MPkF SCam SCoo SSta
- 'Rosea'	CMac ELon LRHS SCam SCog
§ - 'Rosea Plena'	CBcs SCam
- 'Sasanqua Rubra'	CMac SCam SCog
- 'Sasanqua Variegata' (v)	CTrh ELon MPkF SCam SCog
- 'Sekiyō' **new**	LRHS
- 'Setsugekka'	LRHS SCog
- 'Shishigashira' Nihon Engei Kai Zasshi, 1894	SCog
- 'Snowflake'	SCam SSta
- 'Sparkling Burgundy'	see *C.* 'Sparkling Burgundy'
- 'Tanya'	CDoC CTrh
- 'Versicolor'	EPfP LRHS MBri MPkF
- 'Winter's Joy'	CBcs
- 'Winter's Snowman'	CBcs CDoC LCro LOPS LRHS SCam SCog
'Satan's Robe' (*reticulata* hybrid)	CDoC MGos SCog
'Scented Gem'	LRHS
'Scented Sun'	CDoC CTrh
'Show Girl' (*reticulata* × *sasanqua*) ♀H4	CDoC LRHS SCam SCog
§ ***sinensis***	CBcs CTrh CTsd ELon GPoy LRHS NLar SCam SPlb SPre
- var. ***assamica***	SPre
- 'Benibana-cha' **new**	CDoC
- 'Tea Breeze' **new**	WCot
'Sir Victor Davis'	CDoC
'Snow Flurry'	CBcs CTrh CWSG LRHS NEgg SCog
§ 'Sparkling Burgundy' ♀H5	CBcs CDoC ELon EPfP LCro LRHS MBri MGos SCam SCog SPoG
'Spring Festival' (*cuspidata* hybrid) ♀H4	CDoC CMHG CSBt CTrh LCro LPfy LRHS MMuc MPkF NPri SCam SCog
'Spring Mist' (*japonica* × *lutchuensis*)	CDoC CMHG CTrh
'Sugar Dream'	CTrh LRHS
'Superscent'	CTrh
'Survivor'	LRHS MPkF
'Swan Lake'	COtt LRHS MAsh NPri SCog
'Sweet Emily Kate' (*japonica* × *lutchuensis*)	LRHS MPkF
'Sweet Jane'	LRHS MPkF SCam
'Sweet Olive' (d)	LRHS MPkF
'Tamzin Coull' (d)	CDoC MPkF
'Tarōkaja' (wabisuke)	SCam
thea	see *C. sinensis*
'Tinsie'	see *C. japonica* 'Bokuhan'
'Tiny Princess' (*fraterna* × *japonica*)	CMac
'Tom Knudsen' (*japonica* × *reticulata*) ♀H4	CTrh LRHS
'Tomorrow Supreme'	see *C. japonica* 'Tomorrow Variegated'
transnokoensis ♀H4	CExl CMac CTrh LRHS MPkF
'Tricolor Sieboldii'	see *C. japonica* 'Tricolor'
'Tristrem Carlyon' (*reticulata* hybrid)	CTri EPfP LRHS
'Valley Knudsen' (*reticulata* × *saluenensis*)	SCog
× ***vernalis*** 'Star Above Star'	CMHG
- 'Yuletide'	CDoC CTrh LCro LOPS LRHS LSRN MAsh MPkF SCob SCog
'Volcano'	CDoC
'White Retic' (*japonica* × *reticulata*)	LRHS
× ***williamsii*** 'Angel Wings'	LRHS
- 'Anticipation' ♀H5	Widely available
- 'Anticipation Variegated'	LRHS
- 'Ballet Queen'	CBcs CDoC CSBt SCam
- 'Ballet Queen Variegated'	CDoC ELon SCog
- 'Bartley Number Five'	CMac
- 'Beatrice Michael'	CBcs CMac
- 'Bow Bells'	CDoC CDul CTri ELan SCam
- 'Bowen Bryant' ♀H5	CTrh GGGa GGal LRHS NPri SCog
- 'Brigadoon' ♀H5	CBcs COtt CTri EPfP GGGa GGal LRHS MBri SCog
- 'Burncoose'	CBcs
- 'Buttons 'n' Bows'	CDoC LRHS MPkF SCog
- 'C.F. Coates'	CDoC MGos SCam SCog
- 'Caerhays'	CBcs
- 'Celebration'	CBcs COtt CSBt LSRN
- 'Charles Colbert'	CDoC LRHS
- 'China Clay' ♀H5	CDoC EPfP LRHS
§ - 'Citation'	CBcs CMac SCog
- 'Clarrie Fawcett' ♀H5	CDoC
- 'Contribution'	CDoC CTrh
- 'Coral Delight'	LRHS MPkF
- 'Crinkles'	CDoC SCam
- 'Daintiness' ♀H5	CDoC SCog
- 'Dark Nite'	CMHG
- 'Debbie' ♀H5	Widely available
- 'Debbie's Carnation'	CDoC LRHS
- 'Deloraine' **new**	CTsd
- 'Donation' ♀H5	Widely available
- 'Dream Boat'	CDoC LRHS MPkF
- 'E.G. Waterhouse'	CBcs CDoC CSBt CTrh CTri ELan ELon EPfP GKin LRHS MAsh MGos MJak NEgg SCam SCog SPoG SSta
- 'E.T.R. Carlyon' ♀H5	CDoC CTrh CTri ELan EPfP LMil LRHS MAsh MBri MGos NLar SCog SCoo SLim SPoG
- 'Elegant Beauty' ♀H5	CDoC COtt CTrh ELon LRHS NLar SCam SCog SPer
- 'Elizabeth Anderson'	CDoC CTrh CTsd
- 'Elizabeth de Rothschild'	GGGa
- 'Ellamine'	CBcs
- 'Elsie Jury' ♀H5	CDoC CMac COtt CTri ELan GKin LRHS MGos NLar SCam SCog SGol SPer
- 'Exaltation'	CDoC SCog
- 'Fiona Colville'	CDoC
- 'Francis Hanger'	CBcs CDoC CTrh LRHS SCam SCog SPer
- 'Galaxie'	CBcs CDoC SCog
- 'Gay Time'	CBcs LRHS SCog
- 'George Blandford' ♀H5	CBcs CMac GGal
- 'Glenn's Orbit' ♀H5	CDoC NLar SCam SCog
- 'Golden Spangles' (v)	CBcs CMac ELan EPfP GKin LBrs LRHS MGos MMuc NEgg SCam SCog SEND SLim SPer WHor
- 'Grand Jury'	CDoC LRHS
- 'Gwavas'	CBcs CDoC CTrh LRHS MAsh SCog SCoo

	- 'Hilo'	SCam
	- 'Hiraethlyn'	CBcs WBod
	- 'J.C. Williams' ♀H5	CBcs CMac CTri LRHS MMuc SCog SEND WBod
	- 'Jean Claris'	CDoC
	- 'Jenefer Carlyon'	CBcs
	- 'Jill Totty'	CDoC CTrh
	- 'Joan Trehane' ♀H5	CDoC
	- 'John Pickthorn'	CBcs
	- 'Julia Hamiter' ♀H5	LRHS
§	- 'Jury's Yellow' ♀H5	Widely available
	- 'Lady's Maid'	CBcs
	- 'Laura Boscawen'	CDoC CTrh
	- 'Les Jury' ♀H5	CDoC CMHG COtt CSBt CTrh LBrs LMil LRHS LSRN MGos NLar SCog SLim
	- 'Lucky Star' (d)	MPkF
	- 'Margaret Waterhouse'	CBcs SCam SCog
	- 'Marjorie Waldegrave'	LRHS MAsh
	- 'Mary Christian'	GGal
	- 'Mary Larcom'	CBcs
	- 'Mary Phoebe Taylor' ♀H5	CBcs CDoC GGal NLar SCog SCoo SLim
	- 'Mirage'	CDoC CTrh SCam
	- 'Monica Dance'	CBcs CDoC
	- 'Muskoka' ♀H5	CBcs
	- 'Night Rider'	CDoC MPkF
	- 'Phillippa Forward'	CBcs CMac
	- 'Pink Wave'	LRHS
	- 'Plymouth Beauty' **new**	CDoC
	- 'Red Dahlia'	CBcs
	- 'Rendezvous'	CDoC CTrh SCam SCog
	- 'Rose Bouquet'	CDoC
	- 'Rosemary Williams'	CBcs CMac
	- 'Ruby Bells'	CMHG
	- 'Ruby Wedding' (d) ♀H5	CBcs CDoC COtt CSBt CTrh CTsd EPfP LBrs LMil LRHS LSRN MAsh MBri MGos MHtn NEgg NPri SCog SCoo SLim SPer SPoG SWvt
	- 'Saint Ewe' ♀H5	CBcs CDoC CSBt CTrh CTri ELan EPfP GGal LRHS MAsh MBri MGos SCam SCog SCoo SPer WBod
	- 'Saint Michael'	CDoC
	- 'Sayonara'	CBcs CDoC SCog
	- 'Senorita' ♀H5	CDoC CTrh ELan ELon MBri NLar SCam SCog
	- 'Shocking Pink'	LRHS MAsh
	- 'Sun Song'	SCog
	- 'The Duchess of Cornwall'	CDoC LRHS SCam
	- 'Tiptoe'	CDoC CTrh
	- 'Toni Finlay's Fragrant'	CTrh
	- 'Tulip Time'	LRHS MPkF
	- 'Twinkle Star'	LRHS
	- 'Waltz Time'	CDoC SCam
	- 'Water Lily' ♀H5	CBcs CDoC CTri ELan ELon EPfP LRHS MAsh NLar SCam
	- 'Wilber Foss'	CBcs CDoC ELon LRHS MGos MMuc SCam SCog
	- 'William Carlyon'	LRHS
	- 'Winter Gem'	MPkF
	- 'Wynne Rayner'	CDoC
	- 'Yesterday'	COtt MBri
	'Winter's Charm'	LRHS
	'Winter's Dream'	SCog
	'Winter's Interlude'	CDoC LRHS
	'Winter's Joy'	SCog
	'Winter's Toughie'	LRHS SCog
	'Winter's Waterlily'	COtt
	'Winton' (*cuspidata* × *saluenensis*)	CBcs CDoC
	'Yoimachi' (*fraterna* × *sasanqua*)	CTrh LRHS
	'Yume' **new**	LRHS

Camissonia (*Onagraceae*)

	bistorta 'Sunflakes'	CSpe

Campanula ✿ (*Campanulaceae*)

	sp.	WCot
	RCB AM 13	WCot
	from Sicily	WCot
	from Zigana Pass, Turkey	CPBP
	abietina	see *C. patula* subsp. *abietina*
	alata	EACa EWTr NBir SRms SWat WMoo WOut XLum
	'Albert Kirkham' **new**	CDes
§	***alliariifolia***	Widely available
	- DHTU 0126	WCru
	- 'Ivory Bells'	see *C. alliariifolia*
	allionii	see *C. alpestris*
§	***alpestris***	NSla
I	- 'Silver Bells'	MSCN
	alsinoides	GEdr
	americana	XLum
	arvatica	EACa ECho EPot GMaP LRHS NHar NSla
	aucheri	see *C. bellidifolia* subsp. *aucheri*
	'Audrey Widdison' **new**	ECtt LRHS WCot
	'Barbara Valentine'	SCob
	barbata	EACa EBee ECho EPfP GKev SIgm WAbe WMoo
	'Belinda'	CPBP EPot SIgm
	bellidifolia	LLHF NSla
§	- subsp. ***aucheri***	EPot EWTr GEdr
	- subsp. ***saxifraga***	GEdr
§	***betulifolia*** ♀H5	EACa GEdr NSla
	biebersteiniana	LLHF NSla
	'Birch Hybrid'	EACa ECho ECtt ELan GCrg LRHS MMuc NPri SAko SEND SRms WBod XLum
	'Blithe Spirit'	WAbe
	'Blue Octopus'	IBoy LRHS SCob WHlf WNPC
	bononiensis	LLHF NWad SRms XLum
	bornmuelleri	CPBP
	'Bumblebee'	WAbe
	'Burghaltii'	CAby EACa ELan GBee GCal NLar SHar WOut WWEG
	'Cantata'	CPBP EPot WAbe
§	***carnica***	ECho XLum
	carpatha white-flowered	WHar
	carpatica ♀H5	ECho EPfP NBro NGdn NPri SPlb SRms SWat WFar WHar XLum
	- f. ***alba***	ECho LRHS NGdn NPri SPlb SWat XLum
	- - 'Bressingham White'	EACa
§	- - 'Weisse Clips'	CBar EAEE ECho ECtt ELan EPfP GBin GKin GMaP LAst LCro LHop LRHS MAsh NEgg NGdn NHol SCob SPer SPoG SRms SWvt WFar
	- 'Albescens'	EWoo
§	- 'Blaue Clips'	CBar CBcs ECho ECtt ELan EPfP GKin GMaP IFoB LAst LCro LHop LRHS MAsh MGos NEgg NGdn SCob SPer SPoG SRms SWvt WFar
	- Blue Clips	see *C. carpatica* 'Blaue Clips'
	- 'Blue Moonlight'	EACa ECho LHop LRHS
	- 'Caerulea'	COtt
	- 'Chewton Joy'	CTri EACa ECho LLHF LRHS
	- dwarf	EACa
	- 'Karpatenkrone'	GBin

	Name	Suppliers
	- 'Kathy'	EPot GBuc GCrg
	- 'Pearl White' **new**	MHol
*	- var. ***pelviformis***	SMHy
	- var. ***turbinata***	ECho NSla SRms
	- - 'Foerster'	EACa ECho GCrg LHop LRHS XLum
	- - 'Isabel'	EACa ECho LLHF LRHS XLum
	- - 'Jewel'	EACa ECho EPot LHop LRHS
	- White Clips	see *C. carpatica* f. *alba* 'Weisse Clips'
	cashmeriana 'Blue Cloud'	CWib
	cenisia	WAbe
	cephallenica	see *C. garganica* subsp. *cephallenica*
§	***chamissonis***	ECho EPot GEdr LLHF NWad
	- 'Major'	EWes
	- 'Oyobeni'	EACa NHar
§	- 'Superba' ♀H5	EACa ECho NRya SIgm WAbe
	choruhensis	LLHF SPlb
§	***cochlearifolia*** ♀H5	CSpe CTri EBee ECho EDAr EPfP GAbr GJos GMaP LRHS MAsh MLHP MMuc NFav SBch SEND SPoG WHoo XLum
	- var. ***alba***	CSpe CTri EDAr ITim MHer MMuc NRya SBch SEND SIgm SRms WHoo XLum
	- - 'White Baby' (Baby Series)	EACa ECho ECtt EPfP EPot ITim LRHS NPri NWad SPoG XLum
	- 'Bavaria Blue'	ECho ELon GJos IPot NHol NWad XLum
	- 'Blue Baby' (Baby Series)	ECho ECtt EPfP GJos LRHS MHer NPri SPoG SRms SRot
	- 'Bells Blue' **new**	NPri
	- 'Blue Wonder'	ECtt GBin GCrg ITim
	- 'Elizabeth Oliver' (d) ♀H5	CTri CWld EACa ECho ECtt EDAr EPau EPot GCal GCrg GEdr GMaP LHop LRHS MHer MHol NBir NPri SPlb SRms WFar WHoo WIce WRHF
	- 'Flore Pleno' (d)	WFar
	- var. ***pallida*** 'Silver Chimes'	ITim
	- 'R.B. Loder' (d)	LRHS MHer WAbe
	- 'Tubby'	EACa ECho EPot ITim LLHF LRHS MHer SRms
	- 'Warleyensis'	see *C. × haylodgensis* W. Brockbank 'Warley White'
	collina	CTri EACa LLHF WCFE XLum
	'Constellation'	EACa
	'Covadonga'	CMea CPBP EACa ECho EPot LHop LLHF LRHS SBch WAbe WThu
	cretica	MHol WRHF
	'Crystal'	CDes CFis ECtt MAvo MNrw WCot
	dasyantha	see *C. chamissonis*
	dolomitica	EACa EBee GKev LLHF
	'E.K. Toogood'	CCon CElw CPBP EACa ECho ECtt MWat SRms XLum
	'Faichem Lilac'	LLHF
	fenestrellata	EACa SRms XLum
	- subsp. ***fenestrellata***	EPot
	finitima	see *C. betulifolia*
	foliosa	EACa
	fragilis	ECho IFoB WAbe
	- 'Hirsuta'	ECho
	garganica ♀H5	EACa ECho EPfP EWoo GKev GMaP LAst LRHS MAsh MMuc MRav NFav SEND SRms SVic SWvt WFar WMoo XLum
	- 'Aurea'	see *C. garganica* 'Dickson's Gold'
	- 'Blue Diamond'	EACa ECho IVic LHop NLar
§	- subsp. ***cephallenica***	EACa NBro
§	- 'Dickson's Gold'	Widely available
	- 'Erinus Major'	EACa IVic XLum
	- 'Major'	LAst SPoG
	- 'Mrs Resholt'	ECtt ESwi EWoo LAst LRHS NLar SWvt
	- 'W.H. Paine' ♀H5	EACa ECho ECtt IFoB NLar NSla WAbe WHoo
	'Glandore'	EACa SAko XLum
	glomerata	CExl CWld GAbr GJos LSRN MHer NBir NBro NEgg NGBl NMir WBrk WFar WOut XSen
	- var. ***acaulis*** hort.	EACa EAJP EPfP GKev LEdu NEgg NLar WFar XLum
	- var. ***alba***	CBcs CCon CSpe EACa EAEE ECtt ELan EPfP GJos GMaP LRHS MBel NEgg SCob SPer SPlb SPoG SWat WCAu WGwG WMnd WWEG XLum
§	- - 'Schneekrone'	ECha LCro LOPS WFar
	- Bellefleur Blue (Bellefleur Series)	EACa
	- 'Caroline' ♀H7	Widely available
	- Crown of Snow	see *C. glomerata* var. *alba* 'Schneekrone'
	- var. ***dahurica***	CCon EAJP ELon ILea LRHS NEgg NLar XLum
	- 'Emerald'	EACa EBee ECtt LRHS MBri MHer NLar SRms WFar
	- 'Freya' PBR ♀H7	CBod EACa EBee MHol SCob WCot WFar WHil
	- 'Genti Twisterbell' **new**	WHlf
	- 'Genti White' **new**	NLar
	- 'Joan Elliott'	EACa EBee ECha ECtt EShb GBuc LEdu LSRN MWat
	- 'Purple Pixie'	LRHS MBri SRms
	- 'Superba' ♀H7	Widely available
	grossekii	CCon EBee LLHF LRHS
	hakkiarica	EBee WCot
	'Hannah'	EACa ECho EPot LHop LRHS
	× ***haylodgensis*** misapplied	see *C. × haylodgensis* 'Plena'
§	× ***haylodgensis*** W. Brockbank 'Marion Fisher' (d)	CPBP ECtt EPot WAbe WHoo
§	- 'Plena' (d)	EACa ECho ECtt ELan EPot LHop LRHS SRms WAbe WCot WKif
§	- 'Warley White' (d)	ECho EPot XLum
	- 'Yvonne'	CBod ECtt EPot GCrg LHop NPri WHil
	hercegovina	SIgm
	- 'Nana'	CPBP WAbe
	hierapetrae	WAbe
	'Hilltop Snow'	NHar
	hofmannii	CTsd GJos GKev NWad WCot
	hypopolia	CPBP WAbe
§	***incurva***	EACa ELan EWld GJos GKev LHop WMoo
	× ***innesii***	see *C.* 'John Innes'
	isophylla ♀H2	ECho EPot
	- 'Alba' ♀H2	ECho
	- 'Pamela' **new**	EPot
	Jenny = 'Harjen' PBR	CWGN EBee SHar
	'Joe Elliott'	CPBP NSla WAbe
§	'John Innes'	CPBP
	kemulariae	EDAr LLHF WCot XLum
	- 'Alba'	ITim
	'Kent Belle' ♀H7	Widely available
	khasiana	EBee GKev
	komarovii	WCot
	lactiflora	CAby CElw CMac EACa EBee ECha GAbr GCra IFoB ITim LCro LRHS

	MCot MLHP MNrw NEgg SDix SPer WBod WCAu WFar WMoo WWEG XLum
- ***alba***	see *C. lactiflora* white-flowered
- 'Alba' 🏆H7	CAby COtt EACa EBee ECha EPfP GBin GMaP IBoy IVic MAvo MBel MHol MTis SCob WBod WBrk WCot WMnd WRHF
- 'Avalanche'	EACa ECtt MBNS MTis NLar
- 'Blue Cross'	EBee
- 'Border Blues'	EACa EBee ECtt ELon EPfP MHol WFar
- dwarf pink-flowered	EACa EBee EPfP
- 'Favourite' 🏆H7	CSpe ECtt EWoo MNrw NGdn
- hybrids	CBod GJos
- 'Lidie's Choice'	CSam
- 'Loddon Anna' 🏆H7	Widely available
- 'Macrantha'	WRHF
- 'Moorland Rose'	WMoo
- 'Pouffe'	CHid COtt EACa EAEE EAJP EBee ECtt ELan EPfP GMaP IVic LRHS MHol MNrw MRav NBro NGdn NLar SBod SGbt SPer SPoG SWat SWvt
- 'Prichard's Variety' 🏆H7	Widely available
- 'Superba' 🏆H7	ECtt IVic
- 'Violet'	SWat
- 'White Pouffe'	EACa ECtt ELan EPfP EWTr GBin GMaP IVic LRHS LSRN MBri MLHP NChi NLar SGbt SPer SPoG SWat WCAu WFar
§ - white-flowered	ECha GBin NBir NEgg SPer SWat
latifolia	EACa GJos LPot MCot NBid NMir SPer SRms WMoo WShi
- var. ***alba***	EBee ELan EPfP GCra GJos LRHS MMuc MSCN NGdn SEND SPav SPer SRms WHal WWEG
* - 'Amethyst'	LSun
- blue-flowered	NChi
- 'Brantwood'	CFis CSpe EBee EPfP GAbr LRHS MRav NLar SPad SRms SWat WCAu WMnd
- 'Buckland'	CDes
- 'Gloaming'	ECtt GBBs LRHS
- var. ***macrantha***	EBee ELan ELon EPfP GMaP LHop LRHS NEgg NSti SWat SWvt WMoo WWEG
- - 'Alba'	ECtt GLog GMaP LHop MAvo MHol MRav NLar WMoo WRHF WWEG
latiloba	CMHG MLHP WCot WKif
§ - 'Alba' 🏆H7	EBee ELan GCal GCra MCot NEgg NLar NWad WBrk
- 'Hidcote Amethyst'	CAby CWGN ECtt ELan ELon GBuc GCal IKil LRHS LSun MCot MHol MRav MSpe NBid NBir NChi NGdn NLar WBod WCot WMnd
- 'Highcliffe Variety' 🏆H7	EACa ECtt ELan EPfP GBuc GCra LRHS MRav NLar SGSe WCot WMnd
* - 'Highdown'	GBuc
- 'Percy Piper' 🏆H7	EACa EBee ECtt ELan GBuc LRHS MRav NBro NLar
'Linda'	LSRN
linifolia Scop.	see *C. carnica*
longestyla 'Isabella Blue'	LRHS
'Lynchmere'	CMea EPot WAbe
makaschvilii	CHid CPla CSpe EACa EBee GEdr GKev ILea ITim LHop MHer SGSe SRkn WCot WSHC WTcb
- pink-flowered **new**	GKev
makaschvilii* × *trachelium	WCot
'Margaret Brine' **new**	CPBP WAbe
'Marion Fisher'	see *C.* × *haylodgensis* W. Brockbank 'Marion Fisher'
medium	EPfP LAst
'Mevr. V. Vollenhove'	EBee MAvo MHol NSti WCot
'Misty Dawn'	MAvo WCot
moesiaca	GKev
'Monic'	EPfP
muralis	see *C. portenschlagiana*
myrtifolia	WAbe
nitida	see *C. persicifolia* var. *planiflora*
'Norman Grove'	EPot
ochroleuca	CMea EBee GBin GEdr IMou LHop SGSe SWat WCFE WCot WNPC
- 'White Beauty'	CWib
odontosepala from Iran	EPPr NLar
'Oliver's Choice'	WHrl
olympica misapplied	see *C. rotundifolia* 'Olympica'
oreadum	EPot
orphanidea	IMou
ossetica	EBee ECtt MLHP WBor
patula	EACa NLar WCot WKif XLum
§ - subsp. ***abietina***	NLar
'Paul Furse'	ECtt MSpe NCGa NSti WCot
pelia **new**	GEdr
pendula	EBee EWes GJos MBNS SRot XLum
persicifolia	Widely available
- var. ***alba***	Widely available
§ - 'Alba Coronata' (d)	CBod EWoo GAbr SRms WHar
- 'Alba Plena'	see *C. persicifolia* 'Alba Coronata'
- 'Azure Beauty'	CSpe EBee ECtt ELan NCGa NLar WCot
- 'Beau Belle'	LSou NLar
§ - 'Bennett's Blue' (d)	EPfP MRav SRms SWat
- 'Blue Bell'	COtt
- 'Blue Bloomers' (d)	CLAP ECtt EPri EWes GBin IKil LRHS MBel MBri MRav MSCN NQui NWad SRms WBrk WCAu WCFE WCot WHal WRHF XLum
- blue cup-in-cup (d)	WPtf
- 'Blue-eyed Blonde'[PBR] (v)	LSou NLar
- blue-flowered	IFoB SGSe SPlb
- 'Boule de Neige' (d)	WWEG
- 'Caerulea Coronata'	see *C. persicifolia* 'Coronata'
* - 'Caerulea Plena' (d)	EWoo
§ - 'Chettle Charm'[PBR]	CBod CMos CTri CWCL ECtt ELan EPfP EShb GAbr LAst LRHS LSou MBel MCot MRav NBir NChi NLar SCob SPer SRms SWat SWvt WCot WFar WMnd WWEG
- 'Cornish Mist'	CBod CCon CExl EACa EBee ECtt ELan EPfP GBin LPla MBel MHol MPie NLar WCAu WCot
§ - 'Coronata' (d)	GCra NLar
- cup and saucer blue (d)	GCra
- double white-flowered (d)	ELan
- 'Fleur de Neige' (d)	MRav WWEG
- 'Frances' (d)	WCot
- 'Gawen'	CAby CMac EACa EBee ECtt GMaP LRHS MTis NBre SGbt SPtp WCot
- 'George Chiswell'	see *C. persicifolia* 'Chettle Charm'
- 'Grandiflora'	EAJP
- 'Grandiflora Alba'	EAJP NLar NWad XLum
§ - 'Hampstead White' (d)	GCal NLar WHil WWEG
- 'Hetty'	see *C. persicifolia* 'Hampstead White'
- 'Kelly's Gold'	LRHS MHol NBir NLar SRms
- 'La Belle' (d)	COtt EBee MNrw NLar WBor WCot

- 'La Bello'PBR EBee MNrw
- 'La Bonne Amie' (d) EBee GBin IBoy IKil NLar SPoG XEll
- 'Moerheimii' (d) EPfP
- 'Perry's Boy Blue' NPer
§ - var. ***planiflora*** CPBP WCot
- - f. ***alba*** WAbe
- - 'Coerulea' WAbe
- 'Powder Puff' (d) ECtt EPfP GBin LRHS MHol MSCN NEgg WCot XEll
- 'Pride of Exmouth' (d) ♀H7 ELan IBoy LPot MHer MRav WMnd
- subsp. ***sessiliflora*** 'Alba' see *C. latiloba* 'Alba'
- 'Snowdrift' SRms
- (Takion Series) 'Takion Blue' EBee ELan GBin LRHS SPoG
- - 'Takion White' ELan EPfP SPoG
- 'Telham Beauty' ambig. CBod CLet COtt CWCL MCot NEgg NGBl SCob SPad SRkn SWvt WWEG XLum
- 'Telham Beauty' misapplied CSBt EBee ELan EPfP LRHS MRav SPer SRms SWvt WMnd
- 'Telham Beauty' D.Thurston CAby NLar
- 'Tinpenny Blue' WCot
- 'Wortham Belle' misapplied see *C. persicifolia* 'Bennett's Blue'
- 'Wortham Belle' ambig. MRav
- 'Wortham Belle' Blooms ECtt LRHS MBNS NEgg WGwG
'Peter Nix' new EACa
petrophila WAbe
pilosa see *C. chamissonis*
- 'Superba' see *C. chamissonis* 'Superba'
'Pink Octopus'PBR Widely available
planiflora see *C. persicifolia* var. *planiflora*
× ***portenscharskyana*** new WBor
§ ***portenschlagiana*** ♀H5 Widely available
- 'Biokovo' XLum
- 'Blue Ocean' GBin
- 'Catharina' EACa ECtt EPPr LRHS MHol NPri SHil SPoG
- 'Lieselotte' CElw ECtt EPot LLHF SAko
- 'Major' CBod EACa LAst LBMP WGwG WMoo
- 'Resholdt's Variety' CBar CMea CSam EACa ECho ECtt EDAr ELan EPfP GMaP LHop LRHS MCot MHol MMuc MRav NPri SAko SRms WMoo XLum
poscharskyana Widely available
- 'Blauranke' EACa EWes SAko XLum
- 'Blue Gown' EACa ECtt GCrg SAko XLum
- 'Blue Rivulet'PBR ECtt
- 'Blue Waterfall' CWGN EACa ECtt LRHS LSun MBNS NCGa NDov WCot XLum
- 'E.H. Frost' CElw EACa ECho ECtt EDAr ELan EPPr EPfP GKev GMaP IBoy LHop MCot MMuc NRya SAko SEND SPer SRGP SRms SWvt WAbe WBrk WMnd WMoo XLum
- 'Erich G.Arends' new SAko
I - 'Freya' EACa SAko XLum
- 'Frühlingszauber' new WCot
- 'Hirsch Blue' new EPfP LAst
- 'Lilacina' EACa EPPr
- 'Lisduggan Variety' CElw EACa EBee ECtt EDAr EPPr EWes GMaP IBoy LHop MAvo MHer NBro NLar SAko SRms WBrk WCot WIce WMoo XLum
- 'Nana Alba' EACa EPPr SAko WBrk
- 'Pinkins'PBR EACa
- 'Silberregen' new SAko
- 'Stella' ♀H5 EACa ECha ECho ECtt ELan EPPr EPfP EWoo IBoy IPot LRHS LSRN MAvo MRav NBro NDov SAko SPer SWvt WHoo WMoo XLum
- 'Trollkind' EACa EPPr SAko XLum
- variegated (v) EHoe EPPr
- white-flowered CTri ECho ELan
× ***pseudoraineri*** hort. EACa ECho EWes LRHS
pulla CAby CPBP CWld EACa ECho EDAr ELan ELon EPot GCrg GEdr LRHS NPri NSla SCob SPoG SRms SRot WAbe WIce
- 'Alba' EACa ECho EPot LRHS NSla WAbe
× ***pulloides*** hort. 'G.F. Wilson' ♀H5 EACa ECho ECtt EPot GMaP NLar SRkn
- 'Jelly Bells'PBR ECtt IPot NLar
punctata CMHG LEdu MCot NBro NSti SWat WCAu WFar WGwG WMoo WTcb
- f. ***albiflora*** WFar WMnd
- - 'Nana Alba' GEdr
- 'Alina's Double' (d) MSCN MSpe NLar WWEG
- 'Cherry Pie' EPfP
- dwarf CPBP
- 'Einhorn JP' IVic
- 'Golddrache JP' IVic
- 'Hexe JP' IVic
- var. ***hondoensis*** EBee GKev
- hose-in-hose (d) MMHG WGwG
- 'Hot Lips' CMac EPfP MHol
* - var. ***howozana*** EBee GKev
- 'Kurokawa' new SBrt
- var. ***microdonta*** B&SWJ 5553 WCru
- 'Milly' IVic
- 'Moorgeist JP' IVic
* - 'Nana' GEdr
- 'Nasachtal' IVic
- 'Pantaloons' (d) CMac CWGN EWTr NLar SRms WCot
- 'Pink Chimes' IVic LSou MBNS MHol NLar
- 'Plum Wine' MSpe NWad
- 'Pumpernickel JP' IVic
- 'Reifrock' IVic
- 'Rosea' SRms
- f. ***rubriflora*** CBod CSpe ECtt ELan EPfP GCra LHop LRHS MCot MHol MNrw NEgg SCob SPer SRms WBor WCAu WMnd WTcb WWEG XLum
- - 'Beetroot' IKil IVic MHer MTis NLar WHrl
- - 'Bowl of Cherries' ECtt ELan EPfP IVic LRHS MMHG NLar SRkn SRms SRot
- - 'Cherry Bells' EACa ECtt IVic LSRN
- - 'Vienna Festival' CSBt NLar
- - 'Wine 'n' Rubies' EACa EBee ECtt GBee LSRN MAvo MHol WCot
- 'Seejungfrau JP' IVic
I - 'Silver Bells' EACa EBee ECtt EPfP IPot NSti SRms WFar WHil
- 'Troll JP' IVic
- 'Wedding Bells' EACa EAJP EBee ELan EPri LAst LRHS LSRN MHer MHol MSpe MTis NEgg NLar NSti SCob SRkn SRms WHil WWEG
- 'Weisser Schwan JP' IVic
- 'Weisser Turm JP' IVic
I - 'White Bells' MJak
- white hose-in-hose (d) MNrw WBrk XLum
'Purple Sensation'PBR CAbP CSpe EBee EPfP LSou MAvo MBel MBri MHol MNrw NCGa NLar NSti WCot

	Name	Suppliers
	pusilla	see *C. cochlearifolia*
	pyramidalis	CSpe EACa EBee ELan EPfP GJos NGBl SPav SPlb SRms XLum
	- 'Alba'	CSpe CWib EACa ELan EPfP GJos NGBl SPav SPlb XLum
	- lavender blue-flowered	CWib
	raddeana	EACa EBee SBrt WBrk
	raineri ♀H5	ECho EPot WAbe
*	- 'Alba'	ECho EPot WAbe
	- 'Nettleton Gold'	ECho LRHS
§	***rapunculoides***	GJos GKev LHop SWat WCFE XLum
§	- 'Afterglow'	MAvo
	- 'Alba'	EACa MAvo XLum
	rapunculus	MNHC WCot XLum
	recurva	see *C. incurva*
	rhomboidalis Gorter	see *C. rapunculoides*
	rhomboidalis L.	WCot XLum
	rigidipila	WHer
	rotundifolia	CArn CMac CWld EACa ECho ELan EPfP GEdr GJos GLog MCot MHer MMuc MNHC NGBl SGSe SIde SPhx SPlb SRms SWat WBrk XLum
	- var. ***albiflora***	CElw EWes WAbe
	- 'Jotunheimen'	EACa WAbe
§	- 'Olympica'	EACa ECtt EWoo MMuc WHoo
	- 'Superba'	ECho
	- 'Thumbell Blue'	EACa NPri WHar
	- 'White Gem'	CMea EACa EBee EPfP GJos LRHS NBre WHoo
	'Royal Wave'	CAbP EBee ECtt GEdr IPot MBel MHol MSCN NCGa NLar SCob WCot WHoo
	rupestris	LLHF
	rupicola	EPot WAbe
	'Samantha'	EACa ECtt ELon GBin IBoy LHop LRHS LSRN SHar WTor XEll
	'Sarastro'	Widely available
	sarmatica	EACa EBee EPfP NBid SBch SRms
	- 'Hemelstraling'	MAvo NLar
	sartorii	SIgm
	scheuchzeri	WTcb
	'Senior'	ECtt EPPr EWoo IVic LPla MHol SAko SHar WBrk WCot
	'Serafinental'	IVic
	sibirica 'Royal Wedding'	IPot
	speciosa	EBee
	'Stansfieldii'	EACa ECho EPot LLHF LRHS
§	***stevenii*** subsp. ***turczaninovii*** new	EPot
	suanetica	GMaP
	subramulosa	see *C. cochlearifolia*
	'Summer Pearl'	CBod CPBP ECtt
	'Summertime Blues' PBR	ECtt IBoy LSou NCGa NLar
§	'Swannables'	CPou EACa LRHS MAvo MRav NCGa NChi WOut
	takesimana	CBod CBro CSpe ECtt ELan EPfP GKev GKin LEdu LHop LRHS MLHP MMuc NEgg NSti SPad SPer SRms SWvt WMnd WMoo WTcb WWEG XLum
	- B&SWJ 8499	WCru
I	- 'Alba'	GBBs ILea WFar WHea WMoo
	- 'Beautiful Trust'	CLAP EBee SGSe WCot
	- 'Elizabeth'	Widely available
	- 'Elizabeth II' (d)	EPPr WCot WPtf
	- 'Feenrock JP'	XLum
	- purple-flowered	WWtn
	thyrsoides	CSpe EACa EBee GKev SPav XLum
	'Timsbury Perfection'	EPot NHar WAbe
	tommasiniana ♀H5	WAbe
	trachelium	CMHG EACa EBee ELon GJos GKev LRHS MHer MNHC MRav NMir SWat WCot WFar WHer WMoo WOut XLum
	- f. ***alba***	CLAP EBee IFro IMou LRHS NLar SGbt SWat WCot WMoo
	- - 'Alba Flore Pleno' (d)	CLAP LEdu SMHy
	- 'Bernice' (d)	Widely available
	- lilac-blue-flowered	SWat
	- 'Purple Break'	EBee LPla MHol WCot
	- 'Snowball'	CMac LSRN
	tridentata	GEdr
	troegerae	EACa EPot
	turczaninovii	see *C. stevenii* subsp. *turczaninovii*
	'Tymonsii'	ECho LLHF
	'Van-Houttei'	CDes EBee EWes NLar WCot
	versicolor	SRms
	vidalii	see *Azorina vidalii*
	waldsteiniana	CPBP WAbe
	wanneri	EAJP GJos
	'Warley White'	see *C.* × *haylodgensis* W. Brockbank 'Warley White'
	'Warleyensis'	see *C.* × *haylodgensis* W. Brockbank 'Warley White'
	'White Octopus'	IBoy SCob WHlf WNPC
	× ***wockei*** 'Puck'	CHid EACa ECho ECtt EPot GCrg LHop LLHF LRHS SIgm WAbe WOld
	zangezura	EACa EDAr GJos GKev IKil SGbt XLum
	zoysii	EPot WAbe

Campanula × *Symphyandra* see *Campanula*

Campanumoea see *Codonopsis*

Campsis (*Bignoniaceae*)

	Name	Suppliers
	grandiflora	CArn CBcs CFlo CKel CSBt CWGN ELan EPfP LRHS LSRN SPer SRms SWvt WCFE
	radicans	CArn CBcs CMac CRHN CWib ECrN ELan EPfP LRHS LSRN MJak MSwo NEgg SLon SPer SPlb WHlf
	- 'Atrosanguinea'	SVen
	- 'Flamenco'	CBcs CDoC CMac CWCL EBee ELan EUJe LRHS LSRN SAdn SCoo SLim SVen SWvt
§	- f. ***flava*** ♀H4	CBcs CDoC CFlo CLet CMac COtt CTri CWCL EBee ELan EPfP LHop LRHS MBlu MGos MJak NPla SLim SPer SPoG SVen SWvt WSHC
	- 'Stromboli'	EPfP
	- 'Yellow Trumpet'	see *C. radicans* f. *flava*
	× ***tagliabuana*** Dancing Flame = 'Huidan' PBR	CWCL CWGN EBee LRHS
	- Indian Summer = 'Kudian' PBR	CBcs CFlo CKel COtt CSBt CWCL CWGN ELon EPfP LRHS LSRN LSou MBri MGos SCoo
	- 'Madame Galen' ♀H4	Widely available

Camptosema (*Papilionaceae*)

Name	Suppliers
praeandinum	WPGP

Camptosorus see *Asplenium*

Camptotheca (*Nyssaceae*)

Name	Suppliers
acuminata	WPGP
- NJM 11.049	WPGP

Campylandra see *Tupistra*

Campylotropis (*Papilionaceae*)

	macrocarpa	SBrt WSHC

Canarina (*Campanulaceae*)

	canariensis ♀H2	CFil CPne CTsd ECho MOWG SVen
	- from Anaga Mountains, Tenerife	CLak WCot
	- from Los Silos, Tenerife	CLak WCot

Candollea see *Hibbertia*

Canna ✿ (*Cannaceae*)

	'Adam's Orange'	CDTJ XBlo
	'Alaska' ♀H3	SAdu
	'Alberich'	SHaC
	altensteinii	CDTJ SAdu SHaC SPlb XBlo
	'Ambassador'	LAma SAdu SDeJ
	'Ambassadour'	SAdu SHaC
	'Angel Pink'	SAdu
	'Annaeei' ♀H3	SAdu
	'Annei-Rubra'	SAdu
	'Anthony and Cleopatra' (v)	WCot
	'Argentina'	SAdu SHaC
	'Assaut'	SAdu SHaC
	'Atlantis'	XBlo
	'Australia'	CDTJ EUJe SAdu SHaC XBlo
	'Austria'	SAdu
	'Baron Seguier'	XLum
	'Bethany' ♀H3	SAdu
	'Black Knight'	CCon ECGP LAma LPal LSRN MSCN SAdu SDeJ SHaC XBlo XTur
	'Bonfire'	CDTJ
	'Bonnezeaux'	XTur
	brasiliensis	CCon CHll SAdu SHaC XBlo
	'Brillant'	LAma SAdu SDeJ SHaC XTur
	'Britannia'	SAdu
	'Caballero'	SHaC XLum
	'Caliméro'	SHaC
	'Canary'	XBlo
	'Carnaval'	SHaC XTur
	'Centenaire de Rozain-Boucharlat'	SAdu SDeJ SHaC XLum XTur
	'Champion'	SAdu XTur
	'Chocolate Sunrise'	LCro LOPS SAdu
	'Chouchou'	SHaC
I	'Citrina'	XBlo
§	'City of Portland'	LAma XTur
§	'Cleopatra'	EBee LAma SAdu SHaC XBlo
*	'Cléopâtre'	SAdu
	compacta	SHaC
	'Corail'	XTur
	'Corrida'	XLum
	'Corsica' (Island Series)	SAdu
	'Creamy White'	SHaC XBlo
	'Député Hénon'	SAdu
	'Di Bartolo'	XBlo
	'Durban' Hiley, orange-flowered	see *C.* 'Phasion'
	'Durban' ambig.	CWGN EPfP LAma LPal XTur
	'E. Neubert'	SAdu SHaC
	edulis	CDTJ SAdu
	- purple-leaved	SAdu
§	× ***ehemanii*** ♀H3	CDTJ SAdu SDix SHaC
	'En Avant'	SHaC SPlb XTur
	'Endeavour'	EUJe MSKA SAdu SHaC
	'Erebus' ♀H3	EUJe MSKA SAdu SDix SHaC
	'Ermine'	EUJe
	'Étoile du Feu'	XBlo
	'Fatamorgana'	SHaC
	'Feuerzauber'	SHaC XTur
	'Fiesta'	SHaC
	Firebird	see *C.* 'Oiseau de Feu'
	flaccida	SAdu SHaC
	'Flame'	XBlo
§	'Florence Vaughan'	SAdu
	'Foulquier'	XLum
	'General Eisenhower' ♀H3	SAdu SHaC
	generalis × ***indica***	SHaC
	glauca	SAdu SDix SHaC
	'Gnom'	SAdu SDeJ SHaC
	'Golden Girl'	SAdu
	'Golden Lucifer'	EBee LAma
	'Golden Orb'	SHaC
	'Gran Canaria'	SAdu
	'Grande'	CCon SAdu SHaC SPlb XLum
	'Grandiose'	SHaC
	'Heinrich Seidel'	CHll SAdu
	Henlade hybrids	CDTJ
	'Henlade Pink'	SAdu
	'Henlade Red'	SAdu
	'Hercule'	SAdu
	'Horn'	XTur
	'Hossegor'	XLum
	'Hungaria'	SAdu
	hybrids	SHaC
	'Ibis'	XTur
	'Ibiza' (Island Series)	SAdu
	'Indiana'	SHaC
	indica	CAbb CDTJ SAdu SBrt SHaC SPlb
	- 'Kreta' (Island Series)	SAdu
	- 'Purpurea'	CDTJ EUJe SAdu SDix SHaC SPlb
	- 'Russian Red' ♀H3	SAdu SHaC
	- Tropicanna Gold = 'Mactro'PBR	EPfP LCro LOPS SAdu
	'Ingeborg'	XTur
	'Intrigue'	EUJe SAdu
	iridiflora misapplied	see *C.* × *ehemanii*
	iridiflora Ruiz & Pav.	CCon CDTJ CSpe
	'Italia'	SAdu
	jacobiniflora	SAdu SHaC
	jaegeriana new	SHaC
	'Jivago'	SHaC
	'Kalimpong'	CDTJ
I	'King Humbert' (blood-red)	CBcs CBod CDTJ EPfP XBlo
	King Humbert (orange-red)	see *C.* 'Roi Humbert'
	'King Midas'	see *C.* 'Richard Wallace'
	'Königin Charlotte'	SAdu SDeJ SHaC
	'La France'	SAdu
	'La Gloire'	XTur
	latifolia	SHaC
	'Lesotho Lil'	CHll SAdu SHaC
	'Libération'	XLum
	'Liberté'	see *C.* 'Wyoming'
	'Lion Rouge'	XLum
	'Lippo's Kiwi'	SAdu
	'Llanthony'	SAdu
	'Lolita'	SHaC
	'Louis Cayeux' ♀H3	LAma SHaC XTur
	'Louis Cottin'	CBcs CDTJ EPfP LAma SAdu XTur
	'Love Child'	SAdu
	'Lucifer'	LAma NPer XLum
	lutea	SHaC XBlo
	'Madame Angèle Martin'	XBlo XTur
	'Madame Crozy' new	SAdu
	'Madeira' (Island Series)	EUJe SAdu
	'Malawiensis Variegata'	see *C.* 'Striata'
	'Marabout'	SAdu XTur

'Montaigne'	SHaC XLum
'Moonshine'	LCro LOPS
'Mrs Kate Gray'	SAdu
'Musifolia' ♀H3	CDTJ EUJe EWes SAdu SDix SHaC XBlo
I 'Musifolia Rubra'	SAdu
'Mystique' ♀H3	EWes SAdu SDix SHaC
'Ointment Pink'	XBlo
§ 'Oiseau de Feu'	SAdu XLum
'Oiseau d'Or'	XLum XTur
'Orange Beauty'	SAdu
'Orange Chocolate' **new**	SHaC
'Orange Perfection'	CCon
'Orange Punch'	SAdu XTur
'Orchid'	see *C.* 'City of Portland'
'Panache'	CDTJ EUJe SAdu SHaC WCot
'Panama'	SHaC
paniculata	SHaC
'Peach Pink'	XBlo
'Pearlescent Pink'	XBlo
'Perkeo'	SAdu SHaC
§ 'Phasion' (v) ♀H3	CHll CSpe ELan EPfP EUJe EWes LAma LCro LOPS LPal MSCN NPer NPla SAdu SDix SHaC WCot XBlo
'Picadore'	XTur
'Picasso' ♀H3	CBcs CDTJ CExl LAma SAdu XBlo
'Pink Champagne'	XBlo
'Pink Perfection'	SHaC
'Pink Sunburst' (v)	SAdu
'Plantagenet'	XTur
'Plaster Pink'	XBlo
'Pony'	XTur
'President'	LAma SAdu SHaC XBlo XLum
'Pretoria'	see *C.* 'Striata'
'Pretoria Variegata'	see *C.* 'Striata'
'Prince Charmant'	SHaC XTur
'Pringle Bay' (v)	SAdu
'Professor Lorentz'	see *C.* 'Wyoming'
'Puck'	SHaC
'Ra' ♀H3	MSKA SHaC
'Red Cherry'	XTur
'Red Stripe'	SAdu
§ 'Richard Wallace'	CExl SAdu SHaC SPlb XBlo
'Robert Kemp'	SHaC
§ 'Roi Humbert'	SAdu SHaC
'Roi Soleil'	SHaC XLum XTur
'Roma'	SAdu SHaC
'Rosemond Coles'	SAdu SHaC XBlo
'Saladin'	SHaC XLum
'Saumur'	SHaC
Savennières = 'Turcasav'	XTur
'Sémaphore'	EUJe SAdu WCot XBlo
'Shenandoah' ♀H3	SAdu SHaC
'Singapore Girl'	SAdu SHaC
'Snow-white'	XBlo
'Society Belle' **new**	SHaC
'Soudan'	CDTJ SAdu
speciosa	CDTJ SPlb XBlo
'Statue of Liberty'	SAdu
'Strasbourg'	NPer SAdu XLum
'Strawberry Pink'	XBlo
'Striata' misapplied	see *C.* 'Stuttgart'
§ 'Striata' (v) ♀H3	CDTJ CSpe CWGN EPfP EUJe LPal SAdu SEND SHaC SMad WCot XBlo XTur
'Striped Beauty' (v)	CDTJ EUJe LAma SAdu
§ 'Stuttgart' (v)	CDTJ CSpe ESwi EWes SAdu SHaC XTur
'Südfunk'	SAdu
'Summer Gold'	XBlo
'Sunset'	WCot
'Tafraout'	XTur
'Tali'	SAdu SHaC
'Talisman'	XBlo
'Taney'	EUJe MSKA SHaC
'Taroudant'	SHaC XLum
'Tenerife' (Island Series)	SAdu
'Triomphe'	SHaC
(Tropical Series) 'Tropical Bronze Scarlet'	SAdu SHaC
- 'Tropical Orange'	XTur
- 'Tropical Red'	SAdu SHaC XTur
- 'Tropical Rose'	SAdu SHaC XTur
- 'Tropical Salmon'	SAdu SHaC
- 'Tropical White'	SAdu SHaC XTur
- 'Tropical Yellow'	SAdu SHaC XTur
Tropicanna	see *C.* 'Phasion'
Tropicanna Black = 'Lon01'PBR	EPfP LCro LOPS SAdu
tuerckheimii	SAdu SHaC
'Valentine'	ECGP WCot
'Vanilla Pink'	XBlo
'Verdi' ♀H3	LAma SAdu SHaC
warscewiczii	CDTJ CExl SAdu SHaC
'Weymouth'	CDTJ SAdu
'Whithelm Pride' ♀H3	SAdu SDeJ SHaC
'Wintzer's Colossal'	SAdu
'Woodbridge Pink'	XBlo
§ 'Wyoming' ♀H3	CBcs CDTJ ECGP EUJe LAma LCro LOPS LPal SAdu SDeJ SEND SHaC XBlo XTur
'Yara'	SAdu SDeJ SHaC
'Yellow Humbert' misapplied	see *C.* 'Richard Wallace', *C.* 'Cleopatra', *C.* 'Florence Vaughan'
'Yellow Humbert'	SAdu
'Zoodikers!'	SAdu

Cannomois (*Restionaceae*)

grandis **new**	CTre

Cantua (*Polemoniaceae*)

buxifolia ♀H2	CAbb CBcs CDes CExl CHid CHll CPne ECre LRHS MOWG
- 'Alba'	CBcs CHid ESwi
- 'Dancing Oaks'	WCot
pyrifolia **new**	WCot

Cape gooseberry see *Physalis peruviana*

Capnoides see *Corydalis*

Capparis (*Capparaceae*)

spinosa CC 7159 **new**	GKev
- subsp. ***rupestris***	SPlb WJek

Capsicum (*Solanaceae*)

annuum	SVic
- 'Ancho'	SVic
- var. ***annuum*** (Grossum Group) 'Bell Boy' **new**	LCro NPri
- - - 'Cecilia' **new**	NPri
- - - 'Gusto' **new**	NPri
- - (Longum Group) jalapeno	SVic
- - - 'Joe's Long Cayenne'	SVic
- - - 'Ring of Fire'	SVic
- - - 'Serrano'	SVic
- - 'Marconi Rosso'	SVic
- 'Apache' ♀H1c	NPri SPre
- 'Basket of Fire' ♀H1c **new**	SVic

- 'Bulgarian Carrot' new SVic
- 'Cayenne Red' NPri SVic
- 'Demon Red' ♀H1c new SVic
- var. ***glabriusculum*** SVic
- 'Hungarian Hot Wax' ♀H1c SVic
- 'Krakatoa' ♀H1c new SVic
- 'Las Cruces Cayenne' SVic
- 'Numex Big Jim' SVic
- 'Numex Garnet' SVic
- 'Numex Piñata' SVic
- 'Numex Primavera' SVic
- 'Numex Twilight' SVic
- 'Peter Pepper' SVic
- 'Pinocchio's Nose' SVic
- 'Purple Gusto' new NPri

baccatum 'Aji Limon' SVic
- 'Aji Omnicolor' SVic
- 'Christmas Bell' SVic

chinense (Habanero Group) 'Habanero Caribbean Red' SVic
- - 'Naga Morrich' SVic
- 'Numex Suave Orange' SVic
- 'Numex Suave Red' SVic

frutescens Tabasco Group SVic
'Rodeo' SVic

Caragana (*Papilionaceae*)

CC 3945 CExl
arborescens CAgr CDul CMCN EBee ELan EPfP NLar NWea SCob SPer SPlb
- 'Lorbergii' GBin MBlu NLar SPer
- 'Pendula' CMac CWib ELan GBin LAst LHop MAsh NEgg NLar NOrn SCoo SPer
- 'Walker' CMac CWib ELan GBin MAsh MBlu MGos NHol NLar NWea SCoo SPer

aurantiaca NLar
pygmaea NLar

Caralluma (*Asclepiadaceae*)

hesperidum LToo

carambola see *Averrhoa carambola*

caraway see *Carum carvi*

Cardamine ✿ (*Brassicaceae*)

asarifolia misapplied see *Pachyphragma macrophyllum*
bulbifera CLAP EBee ELon EPPr GBin GEdr LEdu MAvo NRya WCot WCru
bulbosa GBuc
californica EPPr LEdu MAvo NRya WCru WMoo
concatenata WCru
digitata CWCL EBee NCGa
diphylla CDes CLAP EBee LEdu SKHP WCru
- 'American Sweetheart' CExl WCot
- 'Eco Cut Leaf' CAby CDes CExl EBee MAvo WCot WCru
- 'Eco Moonlight' WCru

aff. ***diphylla*** CTal WCot
enneaphylla CLAP EWld GKev NBid
glanduligera CElw EBee ECha ELon EPPr EPri GBuc GEdr LEdu MAvo MNrw WCot WCru
§ ***heptaphylla*** CAby CLAP ECha ECho ELon GBin GKev ILea WSHC
- from the Pyrenees GCal NLar
- 'Big White' EBee GBuc GCal MAvo NCGa WPnP
- Guincho form CLAP EPPr WCot
- white-flowered CLAP

§ ***kitaibelii*** CAby CLAP CTal GBin GCal LEdu NLar WCot WCru
latifolia Vahl see *C. raphanifolia*
macrophylla CLAP EBee GBin GKev LEdu SWat WCot WSHC
- CD&R 561 NCGa
- 'Bright and Bronzy' CExl GBin IMou WCru

maxima LEdu WCru
pachystigma GBuc
pentaphylla ♀H5 CBro CSpe ECho ELan ELon EPPr EPot EWTr GAbr GBin GBuc GKev GMaP IFro LEdu MCot NBir NHar SPhx WCot
- bright pink-flowered CLAP WCot

pratensis CArn CWat CWld EHon GJos LCro MCot MHer MNHC MSKA NMir SPhx SWat WHer WMoo WSFF WShi
- 'Diane's Petticoat' MAvo MHer MNrw WHoo
- 'Edith' (d) CLAP EBee MNrw
- 'Flore Pleno' (d) CBre ECha EPfP GAbr GBuc GCal GMaP IFro LEdu MAvo MHer MNrw NBid NBir NBro NCGa NLar NSla SWat WBor WPGP WSFF
- 'Flore Pleno' white-flowered (d) LEdu
- white-flowered GAbr
- 'William' (d) LEdu MAvo MNrw

quinquefolia CDes CElw CLAP CMea ECha ELon GBuc ILea LEdu LRHS MAvo MBel MCot MNrw NCGa NLar SDys WBrk WCot WCru WOut
§ ***raphanifolia*** CBre CDes CExl EBee GBin GCal IFro IMou LLWG MAvo NBid NBro NRya NSti SKHP SWat WBor WMoo WOut WPGP
- PAB 204 LEdu

trifolia CAby CElw CMac CTal EBee ECha EPPr GBin GCal GEdr GMaP IFro IMou LEdu MRav NBir NBro NRya SWat WCot WCru WMoo
waldsteinii CDes CElw CExl CLAP CTal EBee ECho EPPr GBuc GEdr LEdu MAvo NCGa WCru WPGP WSHC
yezoensis B&SWJ 4659 EBee WCru

cardamon see *Elettaria cardamomum*

Cardiandra (*Hydrangeaceae*)

alternifolia B&SWJ 5719 WCru
- B&SWJ 5845 WCru
- B&SWJ 6177 WCru
- B&SWJ 6354 WCru
- subsp. ***moellendorffii*** CExl CFil WPGP
- 'Pink Geisha' WCru

amamiohshimensis WCru
formosana CExl CFil WPGP
- B&SWJ 2005 WCru
- 'Crûg's Abundant' WCru
- 'Hsitou' WCru
- 'Hsitou Splendour' WCru

Cardiocrinum ✿ (*Liliaceae*)

cathayanum GEdr GKev
cordatum GKev
- B&SWJ 2812 WCru
- B&SWJ 4841 WCru
- B&SWJ 5427 WCru

- B&SWJ 6336	WCru
- var. ***glehnii***	GBuc LRHS
- - B&SWJ 4722	WCru
- - B&SWJ 4758	WCru
- - B&SWJ 10827	WCru
- red-veined	MNrw
giganteum	CBcs CBct CBro CHid CTca EBee ECho GAbr GBin GBuc GCra GEdr GKev LAma LOPS LRHS MNrw NBid NLar WAbe WBod WCru WPnP XLum
- B&SWJ 2419	WCru
- GWJ 9219 from Sikkim	WCru
- HWJK 2158 from Nepal	WCru
- var. ***yunnanense***	EPfP GAbr GBuc GEdr ITim NBid WCru WPGP

cardoon see *Cynara cardunculus*

Carex (*Cyperaceae*)

sp.	LPar
acuta	CHab MSKA
- 'Variegata' (v)	CBen CMac CWat EHoe EShb GMaP IFro LLWG MWts NBro NOak WMoo WWtn
acutiformis	NMir WDra
alba	CKno EPPr WCot
'Amazon Mist'	COtt MBri NWsh WFar
appalachica	EPPr
arenaria	CKno GBin
atrata	EHoe WHrl
§ - subsp. ***pullata***	GCal
- - KEKE 494	EBee
aurea	EPPr IFoB WDra
baccans	CAby CExl ECou GCal SBrt SGSe
berggrenii	CSde ECou EHoe ELan EPPr GBin LPot SPlb
brizoides	IMou
brunnea	CMac SHDw
- 'Jenneke' (v)	LRHS SGSe SHDw SLim SWvt
- 'Variegata' (v)	EHoe SHDw
buchananii	Widely available
- 'Firefox'	CLet MWhi
- 'Green Twist'	EShb LPla NWsh
- 'Red Rooster'	COtt EWoo NWsh WHar WRHF
- 'Viridis'	ELan GBin XLum
chathamica	LRHS SVen
'China Blue'	SGSe
colchica	XLum
comans	EPPr EPfP NBro
- 'Bronze Perfection'	SMea XLum
- bronze-leaved	Widely available
- 'Copper Green'	SMea
- 'Dancing Flame'	CWCL ELon
- 'Frosted Curls'	Widely available
- red-leaved	CBcs EUJe NLar SRms
- 'Small Red'	see *C. comans* 'Taranaki'
§ - 'Taranaki'	ELan MBNS SCoo
conica	MWat
- 'Hime-kan-suge'	see *C. conica* 'Snowline'
- 'Kiku-sakura' (v)	EPPr
§ - 'Snowline' (v)	CMac CMea EHoe ELan EShb GKev GMaP LEdu LLWP NBro NLar NWsh SGSe SGol SWvt XLum
crinita	EPPr
cristatella	EPPr
dallii	SGSe WHrl
davalliana	EBee
davisii	EPPr
depauperata	EHoe
dioica	LLWG WDra
dipsacea	CKno CMac CWCL EHoe EPPr EShb GMaP LRHS NLar NWad NWsh SBea WHal
- 'Dark Horse'	EHoe MMuc SEND SMea WPtf
dissita	GAbr
divulsa	CKno NDov
- subsp. ***leersii***	EPPr
§ ***dolichostachya*** 'Kaga-nishiki' (v)	CSBt EPPr GKev LEdu LHop LRHS SLim
duthiei	see *C. atrata* subsp. *pullata*
eburnea new	CEvo
§ ***elata*** 'Aurea' ♀H6	Widely available
- 'Bowles's Golden'	see *C. elata* 'Aurea'
- 'Knightshayes'	CKno MWhi SGSe WCot
elongata new	CHab
'Evergold'	see *C. oshimensis* 'Evergold'
firma 'Variegata' (v)	GEdr WThu
flacca	CHab CKno EHoe EPPr GBin WBor XLum XSen
- 'Blue Zinger'	CKno WWEG
§ - subsp. ***flacca***	EBee NSti SMea
flagellifera	CBcs CBod CEvo CMac COtt CSde CSpe CTri CWCL EBee EHoe ELan ELon EPPr EPfP EShb GCal GMaP LRHS MLHP MMuc MWhi NBir NPri NWsh SCob SEND SPlb WWEG WWtn
- 'Auburn Cascade'	CBod ELan LHop NWad SPtp WPtf
- 'Coca-Cola'	NOak SGSe WRHF
- 'Kiwi'	EAEE EShb LPla NWsh
flava	CKno EHoe EPPr WDra
fortunei	see *C. morrowii* Boott
fraseri	see *Cymophyllus fraserianus*
fraserianus	see *Cymophyllus fraserianus*
glauca Bosc. ex Boott	see *C. glaucescens*
glauca Scop.	see *C. flacca* subsp. *flacca*
§ ***glaucescens***	EPPr
'Gold Fountains'	see *C. dolichostachya* 'Kaga-nishiki'
granularis	EPPr
grayi	CDes CWCL EAJP EHoe LEdu LLWG LRHS MBlu MSKA NLar NOak SGSe SPlb SPtp WBor WPGP XLum
- 'Saladin' new	EBee
'Ice Dance' (v)	Widely available
kaloides	EHoe EPPr XLum
'Kan-suge'	see *C. morrowii* Boott
laxiculmis Bunny Blue	see *C. laxiculmis* 'Hobb'
§ - 'Hobb' new	LRHS NLar
* ***leformeri***	XLum
limosa	LLWG
lupulina	GBin
lurida	EPfP MBNS XLum
- 'Silver'	EPPr
melanocephala new	EBee
mertensii NNS 07-98	EPPr
Milk Chocolate = 'Milchoc' PBR (v)	EPfP MBri MGos NOak SCob
morrowii misapplied	see *C. oshimensis*
§ ***morrowii*** Boott	CWCL EPPr
I - 'Fisher's Form' (v)	CKno CTri ELan EPPr LHop MRav NLar NWsh SCob SGSe SWvt WGrn WWEG
- 'Gilt' (v)	EHoe EPPr MBNS NWad
- 'Gold Band'	CBod
- 'Nana Variegata' (v)	CTri
- 'Pinkie'	ECou WPtf
- var. ***temnolepis***	IMou
- - 'Silk Tassel' (v)	EPPr SGSe WWEG

- 'Variegata' (v)	CBod EHoe ELan EPPr EWoo GCal GMaP LAst MJak MMuc NBir NSti SRms XLum
muehlenbergii	EPPr
muricata	EPPr XSen
muskingumensis	CExl CKno CWCL CWib EHoe ELan EPPr EPfP EShb GBin GCal LCro LEdu NBro NLar NOak SDix SLim SMad WMoo WPnP WWEG
- 'Ice Fountains' (v)	EPPr WWEG
- 'Little Midge'	CKno CMac EPPr EShb GBin GCal LEdu NLar NOak WWEG
- 'Little Titch'	SMHy
- 'Oehme' (v)	CBod CKno CWCL EBee EPPr EShb GBin LEdu LLWG LRHS NBid NHol NWad SGSe WPtf WWEG
- 'Silberstreif' (v)	CKno EBee EPPr EShb GBin LEdu MMuc XLum
nigra (L.) Reichard	EHon EPPr XLum
§ - 'On-line' (v)	CKno EHrv EPPr
- 'Variegata'	see *C. nigra* 'On-line'
No 4, Nanking (Greg's thin leaf)	EPPr
normalis	EPPr
obnupta	CKno EPPr
ornithopoda 'Aurea'	see *C. ornithopoda* 'Variegata'
§ - 'Variegata' (v)	EBee GBin NHol NWsh WMoo WWEG
§ ***oshimensis***	EPPr WCot
- 'Everdi' **new**	LRHS
- Everest = 'Fiwhite'[PBR] (v)	CBod CKno COtt EBee EShb GBin LHop LRHS MAvo NWad SCob SMad SPoG WCot WRHF WSHC
§ - 'Evergold' (v) Y[H7]	Widely available
- 'Evergreen' **new**	LRHS
- 'Everillo'[PBR]	CKno EBee ESwi LRHS MAsh NLar NWad SMad SPoG WCot WRHF
- 'Everoro' (v)	LRHS WCot
- 'Variegata' (v)	NBir
otrubae	CHab WDra XLum
panicea	CKno CWCL EBee EHoe EPPr EShb LLWG MSKA SGSe WMoo
paniculata	WDra XLum
parviflora	SMea
pendula	Widely available
- 'Cool Jazz' (v)	EPPr MSKA
- 'Moonraker' (v)	EHoe EPPr ESwi MSKA NOak NWad WCot WWEG
petriei	CWCL EBee ECha ELon LLWP XLum
phyllocephala	EShb
- 'Sparkler' (v)	EHoe EPfP EUJe LRHS SGSe SPad SWvt XLum
plantaginea	EBee EHoe EPPr EShb GBin LEdu WMoo WPGP WWEG
praegracilis	CKno EPPr
Pritchard's selection (v)	IFro
projecta	EPPr
pseudocyperus	CBen EHoe EHon GBin MSKA MWts NPer NWsh SWat WMoo WPnP
punctata	XLum
remota	CKno EHoe EPPr EShb LPla SMea WDra
riparia	CHab MMuc MSKA NPer SMea SWat WShi
- 'Bowles's Golden'	see *C. elata* 'Aurea'
rostrata	MMuc
sabynensis	see *C. umbrosa* subsp. *sabynensis*
* ***saxatilis*** 'Variegata' (v)	EWoo
scaposa KWJ 12304	WCru
secta	CKno ECou EPPr EPfP GBin GMaP IMou LPla LRHS MNrw SGSe SHDw WMoo
- from Dunedin, New Zealand	EPPr
siderosticha	WSHC
- 'Banana Boat'	see *C. siderosticha* 'Golden Falls'
§ - 'Golden Falls' (v)	EShb LEdu LRHS NOak SGSe SMad SPtp
- 'Golden Fountains'	WCot
- 'Kisokaido' (v)	EShb
- 'Old Barn'	EBee
- 'Shima-nishiki' (v)	EBee EPfP LRHS NOak
- 'Variegata' (v)	CTsd EBee EHoe ELan ELon EPPr EShb GCal GKev LEdu NBir NLar NOak NSti NWsh SGSe SLim WBor WWEG WWtn
'Silver Sceptre' (v)	CChe EAEE EPPr EShb GMaP LPar LRHS MBNS MBri MGos NSti NWad NWsh SLim SPlb SWvt WBrk WHar WMoo
'Silver Streams'	WWEG
solandri	CKno LEdu NWsh SGSe SHDw WPtf XLum
spicata	CHab
spissa	MNrw
stricta Gooden. 'Bowles's Golden'	see *C. elata* 'Aurea'
stricta Lam.	MMuc
sylvatica	CHab EHoe WDra
tenuiculmis	CBod CWCL EAJP EBee EPPr LHop LRHS LSRN NOak NSti NWad SGSe SPtp WCot WWEG XLum
testacea	Widely available
- dark-leaved	EPfP
- 'Limeshine'	EWes
- 'Old Gold'	ELan EWes NOak SMad SPlb WMoo
- 'Prairie Fire'	CSpe LHop LRHS NLar WGrn
texensis	EPPr
'The Beatles'	EHoe EPPr EShb EWoo NBir
'Triffid'	WPtf
trifida	CKno ECou EHoe
- 'Chatham Blue'	CBod GBin MMuc SEND
* - 'Glauca'	CWCL
- 'Rekohu Sunrise'[PBR] (v)	CBct CKno EBee ELon EPfP ESwi LHop LRHS SEND SGSe SLon SPoG WCot
umbrosa subsp. ***sabynensis*** 'Thinny Thin' (v)	EBee EPPr EShb
vesicaria	WDra
vulpina	EPPr

Carica (*Caricaceae*)

papaya (F)	XBlo
pubescens	SPlb

Carlina (*Asteraceae*)

acanthifolia	SPhx
acaulis	ECho ELan SPlb
- subsp. ***acaulis***	GPoy
- 'Bronze Form'	EBee
- bronze-leaved	ELan
- var. ***caulescens***	see *C. acaulis* subsp. *simplex*
§ - subsp. ***simplex***	ECha NPri
- - bronze-leaved	SPhx
vulgaris 'Silver Star'	SPhx

Carmichaelia (*Papilionaceae*)

'Abundance'	ECou

'Angie'	ECou
angustata 'Buller'	ECou
appressa	ECou
- 'Ellesmere'	ECou
astonii	ECou
- 'Ben More'	ECou
- 'Chalk Ridge'	ECou
australis	WSHC
- Aligera Group	EAla
'Clifford Bay'	ECou
fieldii 'Westhaven'	ECou
flagelliformis 'Roro'	ECou
kirkii	ECou
monroi	ECou
- 'Rangitata'	ECou
- 'Tekapo'	ECou
odorata	CExl ECou
- 'Lakeside'	ECou
- 'Riverside'	ECou
petriei	ECou SMad
- 'Aviemore'	ECou
- 'Lindis'	ECou
- 'Pukaki'	ECou
'Spangle'	ECou
stevensonii	MBlu WPGP
'Tangle'	ECou
uniflora	ECou
williamsii	ECou

× *Carmispartium* see *Carmichaelia*

Carpenteria (*Hydrangeaceae*)

californica	CJun CSBt CTri EBee ELan EPfP ESwi EWTr LAst LCro LOPS LRHS MBri MGos SCob SPer SSpi SWvt WBod WFar WSHC
- 'Bodnant' ♀H4	CBcs CBot CDul ELan LPfy LRHS LSRN MAsh MBri MGos SEle SHil SPoG SWvt WFar WPGP
- 'Elizabeth' ♀H4	CAbP CJun CSBt CWGN ELan EPfP LRHS LSRN MAsh NLar SPer SSpi SSta WPGP WPat
- 'Eskimo'	LRHS SWvt
- 'Ladhams' Variety'	CBcs CDul CJun CMac EPfP LRHS MRav NPri SEle SRkn SWvt

Carpinus ✿ (*Betulaceae*)

sp.	CMen LSRN SWvt
betulus ♀H6	Widely available
* - 'A. Beeckman'	SGol
- 'Columnaris'	CDul CLnd CTho
* - 'Columnaris Nana'	LLHF MPkF WCot WPat
§ - 'Fastigiata' ♀H6	CBcs CCVT CDoC CDul CLnd CMCN CMac CNWT CSBt CTho CWib ECrN ELan EPfP LAst LBuc LHop MGos NEgg NPri NWea SCob SCoo SEWo SGol SSta SWvt WHar WMat WMou
- 'Frans Fontaine'	CCVT CDoC CDul CLnd CMCN CTho EBee EPfP EWTr IArd LHop MBlu MBri MGos NLar NWea SCoo SEWo SGol SLim SPer SPoG WHar WMat
- 'Globus'	MBlu
- 'Incisa'	WMou
- 'Lucas'	EBee LRHS MBlu SBir SGol WMat
- 'Monument'	MPkF
- 'Pendula'	CDul CTho EBee IArd IDee MBlu SWvt WPat
- 'Purpurea'	CDul CLnd MBlu MGos WPat
- 'Pyramidalis'	see *C. betulus* 'Fastigiata'
- 'Quercifolia'	CDul EBee
- 'Stegemanns Primus'PBR **new**	EBee WMat
caroliniana	CDul CLnd CMCN EPfP SBir
- 'Red Fall' **new**	MBlu
- 'Sentinel Dries'	LRHS MBlu MBri
cordata	CDul MBlu SSta
coreana	CMCN SBir
fangiana	CExl CTho EBee EPfP IVic MBlu SKHP WPGP WPat
fargesii	see *C. viminea*
henryana	CExl CMen EBtc SBir
- var. ***simplicidentata*** **new**	MBlu
japonica ♀H6	CDul CLnd CMCN CMen EBee EPfP MBlu MBri NLar SAko SBir SCoo SEWo SMad SSta WMat
- B&SWJ 10803	WCru
- B&SWJ 11072	WCru
- 'Chinese Lantern' **new**	SGol
kawakamii	CMCN
- CWJ 12412	WCru
- CWJ 12449	WCru
laxiflora	CExl CMen
- B&SWJ 10809	WCru
- B&SWJ 11035	WCru
- var. ***longispica*** B&SWJ 8772	WCru
- var. ***macrostachya***	see *C. viminea*
omeiensis KR 280	WPGP
orientalis	CMCN SBir
polyneura	SBir SSta WPGP
pubescens	EBee WPGP
- 'Abbotsbury'	SSta
rankanensis	SSta
- RWJ 9839	WCru
× ***schuschaensis***	EBtc LRHS WPat
shensiensis	CDul EBee WPGP
tschonoskii B&SWJ 10800	WCru
- BBJMT 297 **new**	WPGP
turczaninowii	CMCN CMen MBlu NLar SBir SSta
§ ***viminea***	CExl CMCN SSta WPat

Carpobrotus (*Aizoaceae*)

acinaciformis	SVen
§ ***edulis***	CCac CDTJ SEND SVen WHer XLum
- 'Gugh Dawn' (v) **new**	CCac SVen
- var. ***rubescens***	CCac
muirii	SVen

Carpodetus (*Rousseaceae*)

serratus	CBcs IVic WPGP

Carrierea (*Salicaceae*)

calycina	IArd IDee IVic SAko WPGP

carrot see *Daucus carota*

Carthamus (*Asteraceae*)

mitissimus	GEdr
tinctorius	MNHC SPav SRms SVen

Carum (*Apiaceae*)

carvi	CArn CBod CLau ENfk GPoy MHer MJak MNHC SIde SRms SVic WJek
petroselinum	see *Petroselinum crispum*

Carya ✿ (*Juglandaceae*)

cordiformis	CTho MBlu

illinoinensis (F)	CAgr CBcs CDul CMCN EGFP WPGP
- 'Carlson No 3' seedling (F)	CAgr
- 'Colby' seedling (F)	CAgr
- 'Cornfield' (F)	CAgr
- 'Lucas' (F)	CAgr
laciniosa (F)	CTho EPfP WPGP
- 'Henry' (F)	CAgr
- 'Keystone' seedling (F)	CAgr
ovata (F)	CAgr CBcs CDul CLnd CTho EPfP MBlu SSpi WPGP
- 'Grainger' seedling (F)	CAgr
- 'Neilson' seedling (F)	CAgr
- 'Weschcke' seedling (F)	CAgr
- 'Yoder No 1' seedling (F)	CAgr
tomentosa	EPfP NLar WPGP

Caryophyllus see *Syzygium*

Caryopteris (*Lamiaceae*)

× ***clandonensis***	CMac ECtt MGil NBir
- 'Arthur Simmonds' ♀H4	CTri ECha ELan LHop SCob SPer
- 'Dark Knight'	CBot CMea COtt CSpe CTsd EBee ECtt ELan EPfP LAst LBuc LCro LPfy LRHS LSun MAsh MBri MCot SBod SCob SEle SHil SMDP SPoG SWvt WFar WHil WHoo WTor
- 'Ferndown'	COtt CWib ELon NLar SEND SPoG SRms
- 'First Choice' ♀H5	CLet CMac ECrN ECtt ELan EPfP LAst LHop LRHS LSRN MAsh MGos SLim SPer SPoG SRkn SWvt WSHC
- 'Gold Giant'	LRHS MAsh
- Grand Bleu = 'Inoveris'[PBR]	CDoC CDul CMac CSBt ELan EPfP LRHS LSRN MBri MGos NLar SCob SGbt SGol SWvt WPat
- 'Heavenly Baby' ♀H4	EPfP LRHS MAsh SKHP SLon
- 'Heavenly Blue'	Widely available
- Hint of Gold = 'Lisaura'[PBR] ♀H4	CDoC CSBt ELan EPfP LRHS MAsh MBri SPoG STPC
- 'Kew Blue'	CBcs CDul CMac COtt CSBt EHoe ELan EPfP EShb IVic LRHS LSRN MAsh MGos MHer MNHC MSwo NLar SCob SCoo SGol SLim SLon SPer SRms SSta SWvt WSHC XSen
- 'Longwood Blue'	EPfP LRHS SRms
- 'Pershore'	WAvo
- Petit Bleu = 'Minbleu'[PBR]	EBee LRHS MPkF
- Sterling Silver = 'Lissilv'[PBR] ♀H4	CDoC CMac EBee EHoe EPfP LRHS LSRN MAsh SCob SPer SPoG SRms
- 'Summer Gold'	CMac MAsh
- 'Summer Sorbet'[PBR] (v) ♀H4	CBot CDoC CLet CMac COtt CWGN CWld EBee ECrN EHoe ELan EPfP EWes LRHS MAsh MGos MJak MTPN NLar SCob SCoo SEND SGol SLim SPer SPoG SRms SWvt WHar WHil
- 'White Surprise'[PBR]	CBcs CMac CWGN ELan EMil EPfP LAst LRHS MBri MGos NEgg NLar SCob SGol SPer SPoG WCot WHil
- 'Worcester Gold' ♀H4	Widely available
divaricata	CMCN SBrt WHil
- 'Electrum'	CDes EBee LSou WCot
- 'Jade Shades'	EBee LSou
- pink-flowered **new**	SBrt
§ ***incana***	SPer
- 'Autumn Pink'[PBR]	ELan EPfP
- 'Blue Cascade'	EBtc ELan LRHS MRav NLar SRms WGrn WPat
- 'Delft Blue'	CChe LRHS
§ - 'Jason'[PBR]	CBcs ECrN ELon MBri NEgg NLar SCob SPoG SWvt WHil WRHF
- Sunshine Blue	see *C. incana* 'Jason'
mastacanthus	see *C. incana*

Caryota (*Arecaceae*)

mitis	SPlb
- 'Himalaya'	LPal NLos

Cassandra see *Chamaedaphne*

Cassia (*Caesalpiniaceae*)

corymbosa Lam.	see *Senna corymbosa*
marilandica	see *Senna marilandica*
nemophila	SPlb

Cassinia (*Asteraceae*)

fulvida	CBcs SVen
leptophylla	CBcs
- 'Avalanche Creek'	ECou
vauvilliersii	EBee ELan SEle SVen
'Ward Silver'	ECou EHoe EWes

Cassinia × *Helichrysum* (*Asteraceae*)

hybrid	WKif

Cassiope ✿ (*Ericaceae*)

'Askival Snowbird'	ITim
'Askival Snow-wreath'	see *C.* Snow-wreath Group
'Askival Stormbird'	ITim
'Badenoch'	ECho GBin
'Edinburgh' ♀H5	ECho GBin NHar NWad WThu
lycopodioides 'Beatrice Lilley'	GBin GKev NHar NLar WThu
- 'Jim Lever'	NHar WAbe
- 'Rokujō'	ITim
mertensiana	ECho
- 'California Pink'	GKev NWad
- var. ***californica***	ITim NLar NWad WThu
- var. ***gracilis***	NHar NLar NWad WThu
'Muirhead' ♀H5	ECho NHar NLar WThu
'Randle Cooke' ♀H5	ECho NHar WIce WThu
selaginoides	GBin
- LS&E 13284	WAbe WThu
§ Snow-wreath Group	ITim
tetragona	ITim

Castanea ✿ (*Fagaceae*)

'Bouche de Bétizac' (F)	CAgr
crenata	CAgr CDul
dentata	CBcs
'Maraval' (F)	CAgr CTho ERea MBlu MBri MCoo SGol WHar WMat
'Maridonne' (F)	CAgr
'Marigoule' (F)	CAgr EPom ERea MCoo NWea SPer WHar WMat
'Marsol' (F)	CAgr ECrN MCoo SGol WMat
mollissima	CBcs
'Précoce Migoule' (F)	CAgr
sativa	Widely available
§ - 'Albomarginata' (v) ♀H6	EBee EPfP LHop MBlu MBri WMat
- 'Anny's Red'	MBlu SPer
- 'Anny's Summer Red'	CDul EUJe
- 'Argenteovariegata'	see *C. sativa* 'Albomarginata'
- 'Aspleniifolia'	CDul
- 'Aureomarginata'	see *C. sativa* 'Variegata'
- 'Belle Epine' (F)	CAgr
- 'Bournette' (F)	CAgr
* - 'Doré de Lyon'	CAgr
- 'Marlhac' (F)	CAgr NOra WMat

- 'Marron Comballe' (F)	CAgr
- 'Marron de Goujounac' (F)	CAgr
- 'Marron de Lyon' (F)	CAgr CDul CHab CTho EPfP EPom IVic MBri NWea SVic
- 'Regal' (F)	EPom
§ - 'Variegata' (v)	CMCN ELan SPer

Castanopsis (*Fagaceae*)

sclerophylla	CBcs
sieboldii	CBcs

Castilleja (*Orobanchaceae*)

angustifolia new	GKev
haydenii new	GKev
integra	SPlb
miniata	CDes SPlb WAbe
sulphurea	CDes

Casuarina (*Casuarinaceae*)

cunninghamiana	SPlb

Catalpa ✿ (*Bignoniaceae*)

bignonioides 🏆^{H6}	Widely available
- 'Aurea' 🏆^{H6}	Widely available
- 'Nana'	EBee LPal WHar WPat
- 'Purpurea'	see *C.* × *erubescens* 'Purpurea'
- 'Variegata' (v)	ELon EPfP LHop LRHS MAsh WPat
bungei	CCVT CMCN CTho MBlu SGol
§ × ***erubescens*** 'Purpurea' 🏆^{H6}	CBcs CBot CDul CLnd CMCN CMac CTho EBee ELan ELon EPfP EUJe IDee LAst MAsh MBlu MGos MRav NLar NOrn SCob SWvt WHar WMat WPGP WPat
fargesii f. ***duclouxii*** 🏆^{H5}	CBcs CDul EBee EPfP IVic MBlu SAko SChF WHor WPGP
ovata	CMCN CTho
- 'Slender Silhouette'	NLar
speciosa 🏆^{H6}	CDul CMCN CTho SVen
- 'Frederik'	NLar
- 'Pulverulenta' (v)	CDul EBee LLHF MBlu SBig SMad WCot WPat

Catananche (*Asteraceae*)

caerulea	CMea CSBt CTri EAJP ECha ELan EPfP EShb LPot LRHS MBel MBri MHer MNHC MSCN MSpe NEgg NPri SBea SCob SPad SPer SPoG SWvt WCAu WHar WHoo WMoo WSHC XLum
- 'Alba'	CMea EAJP ECha ELan EPfP IFoB LPot LRHS MBel MNrw NBir SCob SPad SPer SPoG SWvt WHar WMoo
- 'Amor Blue'	EPfP LRHS
- 'Bicolor'	MHer MSpe WMoo
- 'Major' 🏆^{H5}	LRHS SHil SRms
caespitosa	SIgm

Catha (*Celastraceae*)

edulis	CArn GPoy WHfH WJek

Catopsis (*Bromeliaceae*)

morreniana	LAir NEve

Caulokaempferia (*Zingiberaceae*)

petelotii B&SWJ 11818	LEdu WCru

Caulophyllum (*Berberidaceae*)

thalictroides	CEvo EPPr GKev IMou LEdu SRot WCru WMoo WPGP WPnP WSHC
- subsp. ***robustum***	WCru

Cautleya ✿ (*Zingiberaceae*)

cathcartii	CExl LEdu
- 'Tenzing's Gold'	CDes EBee WCru WSHC
§ ***gracilis***	CDTJ CExl EBee EPfP EUJe GCal IBlr SBig
- BWJ 7843	WCru
- NJM 09.105	WPGP
- 'Crûg Gold'	LEdu WCru WPGP
- var. ***gracilis***	NLos
- var. ***robusta***	NLos
* ***humilis*** new	GKev
lutea	see *C. gracilis*
spicata	CAby CBct CDTJ CSpe CTsd ECho EUJe GKev IBlr LTro NLos SBig
- CC 3676	CExl
- 'Arun Flame'	GCal LEdu WCru WPGP
- 'Bleddyn's Beacon' new	WCru
- 'Crûg Canary'	LEdu WCru
* - var. ***lutea***	CBct LEdu WBor WPGP
- 'Robusta'	CAvo CExl EBee GCal GCra IBlr LEdu MNrw SGSe SMad WBor WCru WPGP

Cayratia (*Vitaceae*)

japonica B&SWJ 6636	WCru
§ ***thomsonii*** BWJ 8123	WCru

Ceanothus ✿ (*Rhamnaceae*)

sp.	LPar
'A.T. Johnson'	SGol SRms
americanus	CArn
arboreus 'Trewithen Blue' 🏆^{H4}	Widely available
'Autumnal Blue' 🏆^{H4}	Widely available
'Blue Cushion'	CBcs CDoC CLet COtt CTri CWSG LRHS MAsh MGos MJak SLon SWvt
'Blue Diamond'^{PBR}	LSRN
'Blue Jeans'	LRHS MMuc NLar
'Blue Mound' 🏆^{H4}	Widely available
'Blue Sapphire'^{PBR}	CBcs CDoC CWGN EAEE ELan ELon EPfP LRHS LSRN MAsh MGos NEgg NLar NPri SPer SWvt
'Burkwoodii' 🏆^{H4}	CBcs CDoC CDul CSBt EPfP LAst LCro LRHS MAsh MGos MRav NEgg SCob SLim SPer SPoG SWvt
'Cascade' 🏆^{H4}	CBcs COtt LSRN SLim SLon SPer SPlb WHar
'Concha' 🏆^{H4}	Widely available
§ ***cuneatus*** var. ***rigidus***	WSHC
'Cynthia Postan'	EPfP LRHS LSou MHer NEgg NLar SCob
'Dark Star' 🏆^{H4}	CBcs CDoC CSBt CTri CWGN CWSG ELan ELon EPfP EUJe LBMP LRHS LSRN MAsh MGos MOWG NHol SBod SCob SLim SPoG SSta SWvt
'Delight'	CBcs EPfP SPer
× ***delileanus*** 'Gloire de Versailles' 🏆^{H4}	CBcs CDoC CDul CTri CWib EAEE ELan EPfP EWTr LBMP LHop LPfy LRHS MGos MRav MSwo NLar SCob SCoo SGol SPer SWvt WSHC
- 'Henri Desfossé'	ELan EPfP LRHS LSRN MRav MSwo NLar SCob SPer SPoG WKif
- 'Topaze' 🏆^{H4}	ELan EPfP LRHS MOWG MRav NLar SGol SLon SPoG WHar WKif
dentatus misapplied	see *C.* × *lobbianus*
dentatus Torr. & A. Gray	SPer SPlb
'Diamond Heights'	see *C. griseus* var. *horizontalis* 'Diamond Heights'

'Edinburgh'	COtt NEgg
El Dorado = 'Perado' (v)	ELan
gloriosus 'Anchor Bay'	EPfP LRHS
- 'Emily Brown'	CBcs CDoC ELan MRav NLar
§ ***griseus*** var. ***horizontalis*** 'Diamond Heights' (v)	CBcs CMac EPfP LSRN MGos SPer
- - 'Silver Surprise'[PBR] (v)	ELan EPfP LBuc LSRN MGos NEgg NLar SRms
- - 'Yankee Point'	CBcs CDoC CMac CSBt CWib ECrN EPfP LPar LRHS LSRN MBri MGos MRav MSwo NLar SCoo SEND SLim SPlb SPoG SVen SWvt
- 'Kurt Zadnik'	LRHS
impressus	CTri EPfP LPfy MAsh SHil SVen SWvt
'Italian Skies'	CBcs CDoC COtt CRos CSBt CWib ELan EPfP LAst LBMP LHop LPar LRHS LSRN MAsh MGos MSwo NEgg NLar SCob SCoo SGol SLim SLon SPer SPlb SPoG SWvt WBod
'Joan Mirov'	EBee NLar
'Lemon and Lime'[PBR]	LBuc LRHS
§ × ***lobbianus***	CTri
'Madagascar'	SCoo SPoG WFar
microphyllus	COtt
× ***pallidus***	WHar
- 'Marie Simon'	CBcs CWib ELan EPfP EWTr LRHS LSRN MAsh MGos SCob SGol SPer SPoG SRms SWvt WCFE WHar WKif
- 'Perle Rose' ♀H4	CBcs EAEE EPfP LLHF LRHS MGos MOWG NLar SPer WKif WSHC
papillosus	IArd SBrt
§ 'Pershore Zanzibar'[PBR] (v)	CBcs CBod CChe CDoC CLet CMac COtt CSBt CTri EHoe ELan EPfP EShb LAst LBuc LRHS LSRN MGos MHtn MRav MSwo NEgg NLar NPri SGol SLim SPer SPoG SRms SWvt
'Pin Cushion'	CWib EPfP LRHS MAsh
'Point Millerton'	see *C. thyrsiflorus* 'Millerton Point'
'Popcorn'	CDoC
prostratus	SMad
'Puget Blue' ♀H4	Widely available
'Ray Hartman'	NLar
repens	see *C. thyrsiflorus* var. *repens*
rigidus	see *C. cuneatus* var. *rigidus*
'Skylark' ♀H4	Widely available
'Snow Flurries'	see *C. thyrsiflorus* 'Snow Flurry'
'Southmead' ♀H4	CDoC CTri ECrN ELan EPfP LBMP LPfy LRHS MGos MSwo NEgg SHil SLim SPer WHar
thyrsiflorus	CTri CWib SRms SWvt WHar
§ - 'Millerton Point'	EPfP LRHS NLar SCoo SLim WHar
- 'Mystery Blue' ♀H4	EPfP LPfy LRHS SHil SWvt
§ - var. ***repens*** ♀H4	Widely available
§ - 'Snow Flurry'	CWib ELan MSwo NEgg
'Tilden Park'	LRHS
'Tuxedo'[PBR]	MAsh MRav NLar
× ***veitchianus***	CSBt EPfP LRHS SEND
'Victoria'	CBod CDoC EAEE EBee LPfy LRHS LSRN NLar SHil SRGP SRms WHar
'Zanzibar'	see *C.* 'Pershore Zanzibar'

Cedrela (*Meliaceae*)

sinensis	see *Toona sinensis*

Cedronella (*Lamiaceae*)

§ ***canariensis***	CArn CBod EBee ENfk GPoy MHer MNHC SRms SWat WJek
mexicana	see *Agastache mexicana*
triphylla	see *C. canariensis*

Cedrus (*Pinaceae*)

sp.	LPar
atlantica	CDul CMac CMen EFry NWea SEND SGol WMat WMou
- 'Aurea' ♀H6	ESwi MBri MGos MJak NLar NWea SLim SSta WHar
- 'Fastigiata'	CDul EFry MGos NEgg NLar SLim
- Glauca Group	Widely available
- - 'Glauca Pendula' ♀H6	CCVT CDoC CDul EBee EFry LRHS MBlu MGos NEgg NLar NWea SGol SLim SSta WHar WMat
- - 'Silberspitz'	CKen NLar
- 'Pendula'	MAsh SMad
- 'Sahara Frost'	NLar
- 'Sapphire Nymph'	CKen MAsh NLar SLim
brevifolia	LRHS NLar
- 'Epstein'	NLar
- 'Hillier Compact'	CKen NLar
- 'Jade Medusa' **new**	LRHS
- 'Kenwith'	CKen NLar
deodara ♀H6	Widely available
- 'Albospica' (v)	SWvt
- 'Aurea' ♀H6	CDoC CKen CTho EFry EPfP MAsh MBri MGos NEgg NHol NLar NOrn NWea SGol WFar WHar WMat
- 'Blue Dwarf'	CKen
* - 'Blue Mountain Broom'	CKen
- 'Blue Snake'	CKen IVic
- 'Blue Surprise'	SLim
- 'Bush's Electra'	MBlu NLar
- 'Devinely Blue'	CKen
- 'Eisregen' **new**	LRHS
- 'Feelin' Blue' ♀H6	CDoC CKen LRHS MAsh MBri MJak NEgg NLar SBod SLim SMad SWvt WFar
- 'Gold Cascade'	SLim
- 'Golden Horizon'	CDoC CKen CMen EFry MAsh MBri NEgg SLim WFar
- 'Golden Jubilee'	SGol
- 'Karl Fuchs'	LRHS NLar
- 'Klondyke'	MAsh
- 'Lime Glow'	NEgg SLim
- 'Nana'	CKen
- 'Pendula' ♀H6	CKen EFry NWea SLim
- 'Pygmy'	CKen
- 'Roman Candle'	NEgg WFar
- 'Silver Mist'	CKen
- 'Silver Spring'	NLar WFar
libani ♀H6	CCVT CDoC CDul CLnd CMCN CTho ECrN EFry ELan EPfP EUJe EWTr LPar LRHS MAsh MBlu MMuc NLar NWea SEND SGol SLim SPlb SWvt WFar WHar WMou
- 'Blue Angel'	NLar SLim
- 'Comte de Dijon'	LRHS NLar
- 'Fontaine'	NLar
- 'Glauca'	EWTr
- 'Home Park'	CKen
- 'May'	LRHS NLar
- Nana Group	CKen ELan NEgg
- 'Pendula'	WFar
- 'Sargentii'	EFry LRHS MBlu NEgg NLar
- 'Taurus'	NLar

Ceiba (*Malvaceae*)

pentandra	SPlb

Celastrus (*Celastraceae*)

FMWJ 13173 **new**	CEvo

FMWJ 13442 **new**	CEvo
dependens CWJ 12478	WCru
flagellaris B&SWJ 8572	WCru
hookeri B&SWJ 11667	WCru
kusanoi CWJ 12445	WCru
orbiculatus	CBcs CDoC ELan LHop LRHS MRav SLon SPer WBod WHar WHer
- 'Diana' (f)	CMac
- 'Hercules' (m)	CMac
- Hermaphrodite Group ♀H6	EWTr MMuc SDix SEND SKHP WSHC
- var. ***papillosus*** B&SWJ 591	WCru
- var. ***punctatus*** CWJ 12439	WCru
scandens	CMac SPhx SPlb
stephanotiifolius B&SWJ 4727	WCru

Celmisia (*Asteraceae*)

allanii	GKev WAbe
argentea	WAbe
bellidioides	EPot NSla WAbe
coriacea misapplied	see *C. semicordata*
coriacea (G. Forst.) Hook. f.	GBin
discolor	WAbe
'Eggleston Silver'	NBir
glandulosa	GCra
gracilenta	GKev NSla WAbe
graminifolia	GKev
haastii* × *viscosa **new**	NSla
hectorii	WAbe
hectorii* × *ramulosa	WAbe
holosericea	GKev
hookeri	GBin ITim
longifolia	IBlr
monroi	IBlr
prorepens	EPot
ramulosa	EPot ITim WAbe
- var. ***tuberculata***	NSla
§ ***semicordata***	GCra IBlr
- subsp. ***semicordata***	GKev
- subsp. ***stricta***	IBlr
sessiliflora	WAbe
verbascifolia	GKev
§ ***walkeri***	GKev
webbiana	see *C. walkeri*

Celosia (*Amaranthaceae*)

argentea var. ***cristata*** (Plumosa Group) (Fresh Look Series) 'Fresh Look Orange' **new**	NPri
- - - - 'Fresh Look Red' **new**	NPri
- - - - 'Fresh Look Yellow' **new**	NPri
- - - Kimono Series	LAst

Celsia see *Verbascum*

× *Celsioverbascum* see *Verbascum*

Celtica see *Stipa*

Celtis (*Cannabaceae*)

australis	CBcs CDul CLnd EBee EBtc LEdu LPar MBlu MGos
biondii	NLar
bungeana	NLar
caucasica	CFil
choseniana B&SWJ 12774	WCru
occidentalis	CDul ELan EWTr
sinensis	CMen

Cenolophium (*Apiaceae*)

denudatum	CDes CSam CSpe EPPr EWes GBin LCro LEdu LHop LPfy LRHS MMuc MPie MSpe NChi NDov SPtp WCot WHil WPGP

Centaurea ✿ (*Asteraceae*)

HH&K 271	NBid
RCB AM 6	WCot
W&B BGB-1	WCot
alpestris	GJos NLar SPhx WPGP
'Amethyst' **new**	LRHS
'Amethyst on Ice'	LBuc LRHS
§ ***atropurpurea***	CAby CDes CFis CSpe EAJP EBee ELon EPfP EWes GQue LPot LRHS MMuc MSpe NBid NLar NSti SEND SHar SPhx SPlb WHea WPGP
bella	CDes EAEE EBee ECtt ELon GCal LPla LRHS LSou MBel MLHP MMuc MRav MSpe NBro NSti SBod SEND SGSe SMHy SPhx SWat WKif WMnd XLum XSen
- 'Katherine' (v)	MSpe
benoistii misapplied	see *C. atropurpurea*
benoistii ambig.	CSpe MRav
benoistii* × *orientalis ambig.	SPhx
'Blewit'	CAby CDes CElw EBee ECtt ELon MAvo MSpe NLar WOut WPGP
cana	see *C. triumfettii* subsp. *cana*
candidissima misapplied	see *C. cineraria*
'Caramia'	CDes EBee ECtt LBMP MAvo MBri MSpe NBid SPad SPoG WHil
carniolica SDR 5443	EBee GKev
cheiranthifolia	CDes EPPr MAvo MNrw MSpe NBid NBir NLar SHar WBrk WPGP
§ ***cineraria***	ECre XSen
- subsp. ***cineraria*** ♀H3	SEND WCot
cyanus	CHab CSpe MHer MNHC SVic WJek
- 'Black Ball'	CSpe MNHC SPhx
- 'Blue Ball'	CSpe
- 'Pinkie' (d)	MNHC
- 'Snowman' **new**	SPhx
cynaroides	see *Stemmacantha centaureoides*
dealbata	CMac COtt CWib EAJP EBee ELon EPfP GJos IFoB LRHS MBel MHol MLHP MMuc MSpe NBro NLar NMir NPri SCob SEND SPhx WHar WMoo XLum
- 'Steenbergii'	CMac ELan GCal LLWP MSpe NBid NBir NEgg NGdn NPer NSti SGSe SPer SPoG WCot WMnd
declinata RCB UA 18	WCot
deflexa	GKev
drabifolia subsp. ***cappadocica***	SIgm
fischeri Willd.	WPGP
gigantea **new**	GKev
glastifolia	CDes EBee GCal LEdu MSpe WPGP
gymnocarpa	see *C. cineraria*
hypoleuca	NBid
jacea	GQue LEdu MMuc MSpe NBid NDov NLar SEND SPhx WCot WOut WPGP

- var. ***nemoralis***	NLar
'John Coutts'	Widely available
'Jordy'	Widely available
karabaghensis	EBee GCal GKev MAvo MSpe WPGP
kotschyana	EBee LPla WPGP
kotschyi	GKev
var. ***decumbens*** new	
macrocephala	Widely available
microptilon	EBee LEdu
mollis	NBid
montana	Widely available
- 'Alba'	Widely available
- 'Amethyst Dream'PBR	CBod EBee LRHS NLar SPoG
- 'Amethyst in Snow'	EBee ECtt GBin LRHS LSun MAvo MBri MHol MMHG MSpe NHol NLar NWad SCob SPoG WBor
- 'Black Sprite'	CNor CPar CSpe CWGN EBee ECtt EPfP LRHS MBri MNrw NLar NSti SBea SPoG STPC WBrk WFar WNPC WOut
§ - 'Carnea'	CElw GCra GMaP LCro LOPS MSpe NBir NChi NLar NQui SPhx WBrk WCAu WFar WMoo WOut
- 'Elworthy Glacier'	CElw
- 'Gold Bullion'	CSpe EBee ECtt ELan ELon EPfP EWes GMaP LRHS MAvo MHer MHol MRav NBid NLar SMad SPoG WSHC
- 'Grandiflora'	EBee ELon MJak MPie MSpe
- 'Joyce'	CElw MAvo MSpe MTis NBid NLar WCAu WOut WSHC
- 'Lady Flora Hastings'	CBre CCse CElw CSpe EBee ELon LRHS MSpe NBid WBrk WPGP
- lilac-flowered	NBid
- 'Ochroleuca'	CDes CElw MSpe NBid WPGP
- 'Parham'	CBod ECtt ELan ELon GCal LBMP LLWP LRHS LSou MBel MMuc MNrw MRav MSpe NDov NEgg NLar NSti SPer SPlb SPoG WMnd WMoo WSHC WTor
- 'Purple Heart'	CAby CDes EBee ECtt ELon EWTr LHop MBNS MBel MBri MHer MNrw MSpe NLar NPri SPer SRot WCAu WCot
- 'Purple Prose'	MAvo
- 'Purpurea'	CDes CElw MSpe NBFr WOut
- 'Rosea'	see *C. montana* 'Carnea'
* - ***violacea***	NBid
- 'Violetta'	MAvo MSpe NBid NBir WBrk WMoo
montana × ***triumfettii***	SHar
nervosa	ELon NBid NBro NLar XLum
nigra	CArn CHab CWld EPfP GJos MSpe NLar NMir SPhx SRms WMoo WOut WSFF
- var. ***alba***	CBre NBid
- 'Elstead'	MSpe
- 'Mardi Gras' (v) new	ECtt
- subsp. ***rivularis***	MMuc NBid XLum
nogmovii	MAvo MSpe
orientalis	CSpe ELon EWes GCal IBoy LRHS LSou MPie MSpe NLar SPhx WBor WHoo
pannonica subsp. ***pannonica*** HH&K 259	NBid WSHC
parilica	GKev
'Phoenix Bronze' new	LEdu
phrygia	MBel MMuc MSpe NFav NLar
pterocaula RCB/TQ 18	WCot
pulcherrima	MMuc MNrw NDov SCob XSen
'Pulchra Major'	see *Stemmacantha centaureoides*
rhapontica	see *Stemmacantha rhapontica*
rupestris	EBee EPfP SPhx
ruthenica	CFis MMuc NDov NSti SCob SEND SKHP SPhx SPlb
salicifolia	NBir
salonitana RCB AM 1	WCot
scabiosa	CArn CHab CWib CWld IBoy MHer MNHC MSpe NBid NBir NLar NMir SPhx SRms
'Silver Feather'	CAby LAst LRHS MBri
simplicicaulis	CSam MAsh MSpe SBch SHar SRms WHoo WSHC XSen
thracica	CSpe EBee WCot
triumfettii	CPBP NDov
- 'Blue Dreams'	CDes
I - subsp. ***cana*** 'Rosea'	MSpe WBrk
- 'Hoar Frost'	CDes EBee ELon MAvo NDov WPGP
- subsp. ***stricta***	MSpe
uniflora	EBee
vallesiaca	WOut
woronowii	MAvo MSpe

Centaurium (*Gentianaceae*)

erythraea	GPoy MMuc
scilloides	CPBP GCrg NSla WAbe

Centella (*Apiaceae*)

§ ***asiatica***	CArn GPoy LEdu WJek

Centradenia (*Melastomataceae*)

sp.	LAst

Centranthus (*Caprifoliaceae*)

§ ***lecoqii***	ECha ECtt EPPr EWes LPla SPhx WCot
§ ***ruber***	Widely available
§ - 'Albus'	Widely available
- 'Atrococcineus'	ECha MMuc SPer
- var. ***coccineus***	CBcs CBod CWld EBee ELan EPfP GAbr GBin GKin GMaP LBMP LRHS LSun MJak MRav MWat NPri SCob SEND SHil SPhx SRot SWat WCot WGwG XSen
- mauve-flowered misapplied	see *C. lecoqii*
- mauve-flowered	NBir
- 'Roseus'	EBee EPfP LRHS WMoo
- 'Snowcloud'	EBee ECtt ENfk EPfP MNHC SRms WHil
'White Cloud'	SPad

Centropogon (*Campanulaceae*)

§ ***ayavacensis*** subsp. ***ayavacensis*** B&SWJ 10663	WCru
costaricae B&SWJ 10455	WCru
ferrugineus B&SWJ 10665	WCru
hirsutus B&SWJ 10657	WCru
willdenowianus	see *C. ayavacensis* subsp. *ayavacensis*

Cephalanthera (*Orchidaceae*)

falcata	EFEx
longibracteata	EFEx

Cephalanthus (*Rubiaceae*)

occidentalis	CDul CLet CWib EBee GBin IVic LLWG LRHS LSou MAsh MBNS

MBlu NLar NQui SLim SMad SPer SPoG WBor WCFE

Cephalaria (*Caprifoliaceae*)

§ ***alpina*** EPPr EPfP LRHS MAsh MHer MNrw SDix SGSe SHar SPhx SRms SWat WBrk WCot XLum
caucasica see *C. gigantea*
dipsacoides LPla MSpe SKHP SPhx SRms WMoo WTcb
§ ***flava*** EBee LRHS
galpiniana SPlb
§ ***gigantea*** Widely available
graeca see *C. flava*
leucantha CFis EBee GBin MMuc NLar SEND SPhx WMoo
litvinovii SPhx
natalensis LEdu
radiata NDov
tatarica hort. see *C. gigantea*
tchihatchewii ILea NLar WCot
transsylvanica CSpe
- W&B BGJ-1 WCot

Cephalotaxus (*Taxaceae*)

fortunei CDul
harringtonia CMCN
- 'Fastigiata' CDoC CDul EFry IArd IDee LRHS MAsh MBri MGos NLar NWea SLim SPoG
- 'Gimborn's Pillow' MAsh NLar
- 'Korean Gold' SLim

Cerastium (*Caryophyllaceae*)

alpinum ECho IFoB SRms
- var. ***lanatum*** ECho EWes XLum
arvense 'Compactum' XLum
biebersteinii XLum
candidissimum EWes
fontanum CHab
tomentosum CBar CNec ECho ELan EPfP EWTr GAbr GBin LPot MMuc NPri SEND SPer SPlb SPoG
- var. ***columnae*** ECha ECho EHoe EWes XLum XSen

Ceratonia (*Caesalpiniaceae*)

siliqua CBcs SEND SPlb

Ceratophyllum (*Ceratophyllaceae*)

demersum CBen CWat EHon EWay MSKA MWts SWat WMAq WSFF XBlo
submersum LLWG

Ceratostigma (*Plumbaginaceae*)

abyssinicum ELan ESwi LEdu LHop MGil
asperrimum B&SWJ 7260 WCru
'Autumn Blue' EPfP LRHS
capensis CMac
griffithii CBcs CDoC CDul CMac COtt EAEE EBee EHoe ELan EPfP LBMP LRHS MAsh MRav MSwo NLar SCoo SEND SGol SLim SPer SPoG SRms SVen SWvt WGwG WKif WSHC XLum XSen
§ ***plumbaginoides*** ♀H4 Widely available
willmottianum ♀H4 Widely available
- BWJ 8140 WCru
- Desert Skies = 'Palmgold'PBR CBcs CMac ELan EPfP NLar SCob SGol SLim SPer SWvt
- Forest Blue = 'Lice'PBR ♀H4 Widely available
- Sapphire Ring = 'Lissbrill' **new** ELan LRHS SCoo SPoG

Cercidiphyllum ✿ (*Cercidiphyllaceae*)

japonicum ♀H5 Widely available
- 'Boyd's Dwarf' CJun CRos ELan EPfP LLHF LRHS MAsh MBlu NLar SPoG SSta
- 'Chameleon' (v) NLar
- 'Herkenrode Dwarf' MBlu NLar
- 'Heronswood Globe' ♀H5 CJun EPfP MBlu NLar SSta
- 'Kreukenberg Dwarf' CJun NLar SSta
- f. ***miquelianum*** NLar
- 'Morioka Weeping' CDoC CJun CTho MPkF NLar SChF SMad SSta WPGP
- 'Peach' CJun NLar
§ - f. ***pendulum*** ♀H5 Widely available
- - 'Amazing Grace' CTho MBlu NLar SSta
- 'Raspberry' CJun MBlu NLar
- Red Fox see *C. japonicum* 'Rotfuchs'
§ - 'Rotfuchs' CBcs CJun CLet CMCN CMac CRos EBee ELan EPfP EWTr GBin IVic LRHS MAsh MBlu MBri MGos MPkF NLar SCob SHil SPoG SSpi SSta WFar WHar WMat WPat
- 'Ruby' CJun MBlu NLar SChF WPGP
- 'Strawberry' CBcs CJun MBlu NLar SSta
- 'Tidal Wave' CJun MBlu NLar SSta
- 'Titania' NLar SSta
magnificum CBcs CDoC CDul CExl CMCN IMou MBlu NLar WPGP
- f. ***pendulum*** see *C. japonicum* f. *pendulum*

Cercis ✿ (*Caesalpiniaceae*)

canadensis CBcs CDul CMCN CWGN MGos MMuc NEgg NLar NWea SCob SPer WPat
- 'Ace of Hearts'PBR MPkF NLar
- f. ***alba*** CBcs ESwi LSRN
- - 'Royal White' CDul CJun EPfP IArd LRHS MBlu
- 'Appalachian Red' CJun CTho ESwi LSRN MBlu MGos NTre SKHP WCot
- 'Cascading Hearts' CBcs ESwi LRHS NLar NTre
- 'Flame' CJun NLar SKHP SSta WPat
- 'Forest Pansy' ♀H5 Widely available
- 'Hearts of Gold'PBR CTho CWGN EBee EBtc EPfP EWTr LCro LRHS MAsh MGos MPkF MRav NLar NOrn NTre SHil SKHP SLon SPoG WHar WMat
- Lavender Twist = 'Covey' CBcs EBee ELan EPfP ESwi LRHS LSRN MBlu MBri MGos NLar NOrn NTre SCob SGol SKHP SLon SPoG WHar WMat WPat
- Little Woody = 'Litwo'PBR MGos MPkF NLar SGol
- 'Melon Beauty' NLar SKHP WPat
- 'Merlot' EBee ESwi LRHS NTre NWea WMat
- 'Pauline Lily' EBee ESwi NLar
- 'Pink Heartbreaker' SGol
- Red Force = 'Minrouge3'PBR **new** CDoC
- 'Ruby Falls'PBR ♀H5 CBcs EBee LRHS MBri MGos NLar NTre NWea SCob SPoG WMat
- 'Rubye Atkinson' CJun NLar SSpi
- 'Silver Lining' (v) EBee NTre
- 'Tennessee Pink' CJun NLar SCob
- var. ***texensis*** 'Oklahoma' CJun ESwi LSRN MGos MPkF NLar NTre SKHP WHar WMat WPGP WPat

- - 'Texas White'	CBcs CJun EPfP MPkF NLar SCob SGol SKHP SPoG WHar WMat WPat
- - 'Traveller'	EBee ESwi SGol
- 'The Rising Sun'	NTre
- 'Whitewater' (v)	NTre
chinensis	NLar SPer WMou
- B&SWJ 12665	WCru
- NJM 11.047	WPGP
- f. ***alba***	CTho MGos
- 'Avondale' ♀H5	Widely available
- 'Don Egolf' ♀H5	CJun EUJe LSRN MBlu MGos MPkF NLar SGol SKHP
- 'Shirobana'	EBee NTre WMat
chingii	CExl WPGP
gigantea	NLar WPGP WPat
griffithii	NLar SSta
occidentalis	LEdu SSta
racemosa	CExl WPGP
siliquastrum	Widely available
- f. ***albida***	CTho ECrN ELan EPfP EWes LRHS SKHP
- 'Bodnant' ♀H4	CDul CTho EPfP EWes IArd IDee LLHF LPfy LRHS LSRN MBlu MBri MGos NLar NTre SCob SHil SSta WHar WMat WPGP WPat
- 'White Swan'	CJun CTho EWes NTre
yunnanensis	NLar

Cerinthe (*Boraginaceae*)

glabra	SPlb
major	SWvt WBod
- 'Kiwi Blue'	CHll
- 'Purpurascens'	CSpe CWCL ELan EPfP LBMP LCro LOPS MNHC NWad SPer SPhx SPoG WKif

Ceropegia (*Apocynaceae*)

§ ***linearis*** subsp. ***woodii*** ♀H1c	EShb LToo
woodii	see *C. linearis* subsp. *woodii*

Cestrum (*Solanaceae*)

aurantiacum	EShb SEND
auriculatum	MOWG
× ***cultum***	CHll
- 'Cretan Pink'	MOWG
- 'Cretan Purple'	CBcs CHGN CHll ELan ELon EPfP EShb IDee LHop LRHS MOWG SEND SPoG SWvt WBod WKif WSHC
diurnum* × *nocturnum	EShb
§ ***elegans***	CExl CHll CLet CTsd EBee ELon EPfP IDee LHop LRHS MOWG NQui SEND SLon SWvt WCFE
fasciculatum	EShb MOWG SDix
'Newellii' ♀H1c	CBcs CDoC CExl CMHG CRHN CWib EBak EBee ELan ELon EPfP EShb EUJe LRHS MOWG SEND SPlb SVen SWvt WKif WSHC
nocturnum	CHll CPne EBak EShb MOWG
parqui ♀H3	CAbb CBcs CHll CTsd CWib ELan EPfP EUJe LHop LRHS MGil MOWG SDix SEND SLon SMad SWvt WJek WKif WSHC
psittacinum	CExl
purpureum (Lindl.) Standl.	see *C. elegans*
roseum	CExl WBod
- B&SWJ 10255 from Oaxaca State, Mexico	WCru
* ***splendens***	MOWG

Ceterach see *Asplenium*

officinarum	see *Asplenium ceterach*

Chaenomeles (*Rosaceae*)

sp.	CWSG
cathayensis	CAgr CDul CTho EBee GKev LEdu NLar WCru WHer WPGP
§ ***japonica***	MMuc SEND
- 'Chojubai'	CMen
- 'Cido'	CAgr LEdu MCoo
- 'Orange Beauty'	LRHS NHol SPer
- 'Rising Sun' **new**	NLar
- 'Sargentii'	CMac ELan MBlu NLar SGol
lagenaria	see *C. speciosa*
Madame Butterfly = 'Whitice'	CLet EBee EPfP LRHS LSRN MAsh MBri MMuc MRav SCob SEND SGol SLim SPer SPoG SRms
maulei	see *C. japonica*
sinensis	see *Pseudocydonia sinensis*
§ ***speciosa***	NWea
- 'Apple Blossom'	see *C. speciosa* 'Moerloosei'
- 'Brilliant'	EPfP
- 'Cardinalis'	CMac
- 'Contorta'	LRHS MAsh WFar
I - 'Contorta Rosea' **new**	LBMP
- 'Eximia'	LRHS
- 'Falconnet Charlet' (d)	EWTr LRHS MBri MRav SRms
- 'Flocon Rose'	EPfP LRHS
- 'Friesdorfer'	LRHS
- 'Geisha Girl' (d) ♀H6	CBcs CDoC CMac COtt CSBt EBee EPfP EWTr LAst LCro LHop LRHS LSRN MAsh MBri MGos MRav MSwo NPri SCob SGbt SGol SHil SLim SPer SPoG SRms SWvt WFar WPat
- Hot Fire = 'Minvesu'	CDoC EBee EPfP LRHS MBri
- 'Kinshiden'	CLet EBee EPfP LRHS NLar
- 'Knap Hill Radiance'	SLim
§ - 'Moerloosei' ♀H6	Widely available
- 'Nivalis'	Widely available
- 'Rosea Plena' (d)	ELan LCro
- 'Rubra Grandiflora'	LRHS
- 'Simonii' (d)	CBcs MRav NWea
- 'Snow'	MAsh MSwo SRms
- 'Umbilicata'	MBlu SPer SRms
- 'Winter Snow' (d)	SPer
- 'Yukigotan' (d)	CDoC LCro LLHF LRHS MBri NLar SCob SGol SHil SWvt WPat
× ***superba***	IBoy
- 'Boule de Feu'	CTri CWib MCoo
- 'Cameo' (d)	CChe CLet ELon EPfP LHop LRHS MAsh MBNS MRav NLar SGol SRms WBor WFar
- 'Clementine'	CWib NLar
- 'Coquelicot'	NLar
- 'Crimson and Gold' ♀H6	Widely available
- 'Elly Mossel'	CMac CWib NLar WFar
- 'Ernst Finken'	NLar
- 'Etna'	WFar
- 'Fascination'	NLar
- 'Fire Dance'	CDul CHll CWib MSwo NLar SGol SPer WRHF
- 'Fusion'	CAgr
- 'Hollandia'	SRms
- 'Issai White'	MRav NLar
- 'Jet Trail'	CBcs CMac CSBt ECrN ELan EPfP LHop LRHS LSRN MAsh MBri MGos MJak MRav MSwo NLar SCob SGol SHil SLim SRms SWvt WFar

	- 'Knap Hill Scarlet'	CDoC CDul EBee ELan EPfP GGal LRHS MAsh MBri MGos SCob SEND SLim SPer SPoG SRms SWvt
	- 'Lemon and Lime'	ELan EWTr LRHS MAsh MGos MRav NLar SLon SPer SRms
	- 'Nicoline' ♀H6	CBcs CDoC CDul EAEE EPfP IBoy LRHS MGos NEgg SCob SLim WMoo
	- 'Orange Trail'	MBri
	- 'Pink Lady' ♀H6	Widely available
	- 'Pink Trail'	MBri NLar SRms
	- 'Red Joy'	EBee EPfP LHop LRHS MBri MRav NLar WGrn
	- 'Red Trail'	MRav
	- 'Rowallane' ♀H6	CHll ELan EPfP MRav
	- 'Salmon Horizon'	EWTr IArd NLar
	- 'Texas Scarlet'	ELan
	- 'Tortuosa'	EBee LHop LRHS NLar WGrn
	'Toyo-nishiki'	LCro MBlu

Chaenorhinum (*Plantaginaceae*)

§	***origanifolium***	ECho SPlb WHea
	- 'Blue Dream'	CSpe ECho EPfP GKev IPot LRHS MAsh NPri SCob SPoG SWvt WIce WMoo
	- 'Dreamcatcher'	EPfP

Chaerophyllum (*Apiaceae*)

	azoricum	SIgm
	hirsutum	IMou
	- 'Roseum'	Widely available

Chamaebatiaria (*Rosaceae*)

	millefolium	SBrt

Chamaecyparis ✿ (*Cupressaceae*)

	sp.	LPar
	formosensis	CKen
	funebris	see *Cupressus funebris*
	lawsoniana	CDul EFry NWea SLim WMou
	- 'Allumii Aurea'	see *C. lawsoniana* 'Alumigold'
	- 'Allumii Magnificent'	CDul
§	- 'Alumigold'	MAsh MGos MJak NOrn
	- 'Alumii'	CMac MAsh MGos MJak NOrn NWea
	- 'Aurea'	CDul
	- 'Aurea Densa' ♀H6	CKen CSBt CTri EFry EPfP MAsh MGos
	- 'Bleu Nantais' ♀H6	CKen EFry LBee LRHS MAsh MGos SCoo SLim SPoG WCFE WGor
	- 'Blom'	CKen
§	- 'Blue Gown'	EFry LBee
	- 'Blue Surprise'	CKen EFry
	- 'Brégéon'	CKen NLar
	- 'Broomhill Gold' ♀H6	CSBt EFry LBee MAsh MGos NOrn SCoo SLim SPoG WGor
	- 'Caudata'	CKen NLar
	- 'Chantry Gold'	EFry
§	- 'Chilworth Silver' ♀H6	CSBt EFry LBee LRHS MAsh SRms
	- 'Columnaris'	CBcs CDoC EPfP LAst LBee MBri MJak NEgg NWea SCoo SPoG
	- 'Columnaris Aurea'	see *C. lawsoniana* 'Golden Spire'
	- 'Columnaris Glauca'	CLet CMac CWib EFry MAsh MGos NEgg NLar NPri NWea SCoo SPer
	- 'Cream Crackers'	EFry
	- 'Cream Glow'	CKen CSBt MAsh MGos
	- 'Croftway'	EFry
	- 'Dik's Weeping' ♀H6	CDoC NLar NWea SLim
	- 'Duncanii'	EFry
	- 'Dutch Gold'	EFry MAsh MGos
	- 'Eclipse'	CKen
	- 'Elegantissima' ambig.	CMac SLim
	- 'Ellwoodii' ♀H6	CDul CMac COtt CSBt CTri CWib EFry ELan EPfP LAst LRHS MGos NEgg NPri NWea SCoo SLim SPer SRms
I	- 'Ellwoodii Glauca'	SPlb
	- 'Ellwood's Empire'	EFry
	- 'Ellwood's Gold' ♀H6	CBcs CDoC CDul CLet CMac CSBt CWib EFry ELan EPfP LBMP LBee LRHS MAsh MBri MGos MJak NOrn NPri NWea SPer SPlb SPoG SRms
	- 'Ellwood's Gold Pillar' ♀H6	COtt EFry LBee MAsh MBri MGos NHol SLim WGor
§	- 'Ellwood's Nymph'	CKen MAsh
	- Ellwood's Pillar = 'Flolar' ♀H6	CDoC CMac EFry LAst LBee LRHS MBri MGos NLar SCoo SLim WCFE WGor
	- 'Ellwood's Pygmy'	CMac
	- 'Ellwood's Silver'	MAsh
	- 'Ellwood's Silver Threads'	CMac LBee
*	- 'Ellwood's Treasure'	MBri
	- 'Ellwood's Variegata'	see *C. lawsoniana* 'Ellwood's White'
§	- 'Ellwood's White' (v)	CMac CSBt EFry EPfP
	- 'Emerald Spire'	MAsh
	- 'Erecta Viridis'	CBcs MJak NEgg NWea
	- 'Ericoides'	EFry
	- 'Filiformis Compacta'	EFry
	- 'Filip's Golden Tears'	ELan MAsh SLim
	- 'Fleckellwood'	CWib EFry MAsh
	- 'Fletcheri' ♀H6	CMac EFry NWea
	- 'Fletcheri Aurea'	see *C. lawsoniana* 'Yellow Transparent'
	- 'Forsteckensis'	EFry NLar NWea
I	- 'Forsteckensis Aurea'	NLar
	- 'Fraseri'	NWea
	- 'Gimbornii' ♀H6	CDul EFry LBee
	- 'Glauca'	CDul
	- 'Globosa'	MGos
	- 'Gnome'	CDoC CKen CMac EFry LAst NHol SCoo SLim SPoG WGor WThu
§	- 'Golden Pot'	COtt CSBt CWib EFry LBee
	- 'Golden Showers'	EFry
§	- 'Golden Spire'	MGos
	- 'Golden Triumph'	EFry
	- 'Golden Wonder' ♀H6	MAsh NEgg NLar NWea SCoo
	- 'Goldfinger'	NLar
	- 'Grayswood Feather' ♀H6	CDoC EFry LBee MAsh SPlb
	- 'Grayswood Gold'	EFry
	- 'Grayswood Pillar'	EFry MGos
	- 'Green Globe' ♀H6	CDoC CKen CMen CSBt EFry LBee MAsh WGor WThu
§	- 'Green Hedger'	CSBt NWea
§	- 'Green Pillar'	CDul CWib LAst LBee NEgg SCoo
	- 'Green Spire'	see *C. lawsoniana* 'Green Pillar'
	- 'Hogger's Blue Gown'	see *C. lawsoniana* 'Blue Gown'
	- 'Imbricata Pendula' ♀H6	CDoC CKen MBlu NLar SMad
	- 'Intertexta'	SLim
	- 'Ivonne' ♀H6	CDoC CDul EFry EPfP LRHS MAsh MBri MGos NLar SCoo SLim SPoG
	- 'Jackman's Green Hedger'	see *C. lawsoniana* 'Green Hedger'
	- 'Jackman's Variety'	see *C. lawsoniana* 'Green Pillar'
	- 'Jeanette'	CKen
	- 'Killarny Salmon'	CMac
	- 'Kilmacurragh' ♀H6	CDul CMac MAsh MGos NWea WCFE
	- 'Kilworth Column'	CDoC LRHS NLar NWea
	- 'Kingswood'	CDoC
	- 'Knowefieldensis'	CMac
	- 'Lane' misapplied	see *C. lawsoniana* 'Lanei Aurea'

	Name	Suppliers
	- 'Lane' den Ouden	CWib MJak MRav NEgg
§	- 'Lanei Aurea' 🏆H6	MGos MJak NWea SPoG
	- 'Lemon Pillar'	COtt
	- 'Lemon Queen'	LBee NOrn
	- 'Little Spire' 🏆H6	CDoC EUJe LRHS MBri MGos NLar SLim
	- 'Lutea'	CMac MGos
§	- 'Lutea Nana'	CMac EFry MAsh NLar
	- 'Luteocompacta'	LBee
*	- 'MacPenny's Gold'	CMac
	- 'Minima Argentea'	see *C. lawsoniana* 'Nana Argentea'
	- 'Minima Aurea' 🏆H6	CDoC CKen CMac CSBt CWib EFry EPfP LAst LBee MAsh MBri MGos MJak NEgg NWea SLim SPoG WCFE
	- 'Minima Glauca' 🏆H6	CLet CMac EFry EPfP LAst MBri MJak NEgg NWea SCoo SLim SRms
	- 'Moonsprite' 🏆H6	CKen EFry LAst NLar SCoo SLim SPoG
	- 'Nana'	CMac
	- 'Nana Albospica' (v)	EFry LBee MBri MGos
§	- 'Nana Argentea'	CKen CMac EFry SPoG WGor
	- 'Nana Lutea'	see *C. lawsoniana* 'Lutea Nana'
	- 'Nicole'	EFry LAst MAsh MBri MGos NWea SCoo SLim WGor
	- 'Nidiformis'	EFry NWea
	- 'Nyewoods'	see *C. lawsoniana* 'Chilworth Silver'
	- 'Nymph'	see *C. lawsoniana* 'Ellwood's Nymph'
	- 'Pearly Swirls' (v)	LRHS NLar SPoG
§	- 'Pelt's Blue'	CBcs CDoC CDul CSBt MGos NLar
	- 'Pembury Blue' 🏆H6	CCVT CDoC CDul CLet CWib EFry EPfP LBee LRHS MAsh MGos MJak MRav NEgg NLar NOrn NWea SCoo SLim SPer SPoG
	- Pot of Gold	see *C. lawsoniana* 'Golden Pot'
	- 'Pottenii'	CMac EFry LBee MAsh MGos NLar NOrn NWea
	- 'Pygmaea Argentea' (v) 🏆H6	CKen CLet CMac CSBt CWib EFry ELan MAsh MBri MGos NEgg NWea SLim SPoG SRms WCFE
	- 'Pygmy'	EFry NLar NWea SLim
	- 'Rijnhof'	EFry LBee
	- 'Rimpelaar'	CDoC NWad SPoG
	- 'Silver Queen' (v)	CKen
	- 'Silver Threads' (v)	COtt EFry ELan EPfP LBee LRHS MBri MGos SPoG
	- 'Silver Tip' (v)	EFry SLim
	- 'Snow Flurry' (v)	CKen EFry
	- 'Snow White'[PBR] (v) 🏆H6	COtt EFry LBee LRHS MAsh MBri MGos NHol NOrn SCoo SLim SPoG WGor
	- 'Springtime'[PBR]	COtt CSBt EFry LBee LRHS MBri
	- 'Stardust' 🏆H6	CBcs CDoC CDul CLet CSBt CWib ELan MAsh MGos MJak MRav NEgg NOrn NPri
	- 'Stewartii'	CDul NEgg NWea
*	- 'Summer Cream'	EFry
	- 'Summer Snow' (v) 🏆H6	EFry EPfP MGos NHol SCoo
	- 'Sunkist'	SLim
	- 'Tamariscifolia'	CDoC WCFE
	- 'Tilford'	EFry
	- 'Treasure' (v)	COtt CSBt EFry MAsh MGos SLim
	- 'Van Pelt'	see *C. lawsoniana* 'Pelt's Blue'
	- 'Westermannii' (v)	CMac MGos NOrn
	- 'White Spot' (v)	EFry MGos
	- 'Winston Churchill'	MGos NOrn
	- 'Wisselii' 🏆H6	CDoC CKen CMac EFry LAst MGos NLar NWea SCoo SLim SRms WCFE
	- 'Wisselii Nana'	CKen EFry
	- 'Wissel's Saguaro' 🏆H6	CDoC CKen IVic MGos NLar SLim
	- 'Witzeliana'	CDul NLar
§	- 'Yellow Transparent'	CMac MBri
	× ***leylandii***	see × *Cuprocyparis leylandii*
	obtusa 'Albovariegata' (v)	CKen
	- 'Arneson's Compact'	CKen
	- 'Aurea'	CDoC SCoo
	- 'Aurora' 🏆H7	CKen ELan MAsh SLim SPoG WGor
	- 'Bambi'	CKen WAbe WThu
	- 'Barkenny'	CKen
	- 'Bartley'	CKen
	- 'Bassett'	CKen
	- 'Bess'	CKen
	- 'Brigitt'	CKen
	- 'Bronze Pygmy' **new**	LRHS NLar
	- 'Butterball' **new**	CKen
	- 'Caespitosa'	WAbe
	- 'Chabo-yadori'	CDoC NLar
	- 'Chilworth'	CDoC CKen NWad
	- 'Chima-anihiba'	CKen
	- 'Chirimen'	CDoC CKen NLar NWad SAko SLim
	- 'Clarke's Seedling'	CDoC CKen
	- 'Confucius'	CDoC EFry MGos
	- 'Corley Gold'	NLar
§	- 'Crippsii' 🏆H7	CBcs CDoC CMac
	- 'Crippsii Aurea'	see *C. obtusa* 'Crippsii'
	- 'Dainty Doll'	CKen NHol NLar NWad
	- 'Densa'	see *C. obtusa* 'Nana Densa'
	- 'Draht'	CDoC MGos NLar
	- 'Draht Hexe'	CKen
	- 'Elf'	CKen
	- 'Ellie B'	CKen
	- 'Ericoides'	CKen
	- 'Erika'	NLar
	- 'Fernspray Gold' 🏆H7	CCVT CDoC CDul CKen CMac CTri EFry EPfP LRHS MAsh MBri MGos NEgg NLar SCoo SLim SPer SPoG
	- 'Flabelliformis'	CKen NWad
	- 'Gitte'	SLim
	- 'Gnome'	CKen CMen
	- 'Gold Fern'	CKen
	- 'Golden Fairy'	CKen NLar
	- 'Golden Filament' (v)	CKen
	- 'Golden Nymph'	CKen
	- 'Golden Sprite'	CKen WAbe
	- 'Goldilocks'	EFry
	- 'Gracilis' **new**	NEgg
	- 'Gracilis Aurea'	CKen CMac
	- 'Green Cushion'	CKen
	- 'Green Diamond'	CKen
	- 'Hage'	CKen
	- 'Hannah'	NLar
	- 'Hypnoides Nana'	CKen
	- 'Intermedia'	CKen WAbe
	- 'Ivan's Column'	CKen
	- 'Junior'	CKen
	- 'Juniperoides'	CKen
	- 'Juniperoides Compacta'	WAbe
	- 'Kamarachiba' 🏆H7	CDoC CKen CSBt EFry LBee MAsh NEgg NLar SCoo SLim SPoG WGor
	- 'Kerdalo'	NLar
	- 'Konijn'	EFry NWea
	- 'Kosteri' 🏆H7	CDoC CKen CMac EFry ELan LBee LPot MAsh NHol SCoo SLim WGor
	- 'Kyoto Creeper'	CKen
	- 'Leprechaun'	WAbe
	- 'Limerick'	CKen
	- 'Little Markey'	CKen
	- 'Lucas'[PBR]	LRHS NLar
	- 'Marian'	CKen NLar

§	– 'Mariesii' (v)	CKen LRHS
	– 'Melody'	CKen
	– 'Meroke'	NLar
	– 'Minima'	CKen
	– 'Nana' ♀H7	CDoC CKen CMac CMen LBee NHol NWad SRms
	– 'Nana Aurea' ♀H7	CDoC CMac CSBt EFry EPfP LRHS MAsh MJak NEgg NHol WGor
§	– 'Nana Densa'	CDoC CKen CMac
	– 'Nana Gracilis' ♀H7	CDoC CDul CKen CMen CSBt EFry ELan EPfP EUJe IVic LAst LRHS MAsh MBri MGos MJak NEgg NWad NWea SBod SCoo SLim SPoG
I	– 'Nana Gracilis Aurea'	CMen EFry NEgg
I	– 'Nana Lutea' ♀H7	CDoC CKen EFry ELan EPfP LBee MAsh MGos NHol NWad SLim
	– 'Nana Rigida'	see *C. obtusa* 'Rigid Dwarf'
	– 'Nana Variegata'	see *C. obtusa* 'Mariesii'
	– 'Pygmaea'	CSBt EFry MGos NEgg SCoo SLim
§	– 'Rigid Dwarf'	CDoC CKen EFry LBee SLim
	– 'Saffron Spray'	NLar SLim
	– 'Snowflake' (v)	CKen ELan NEgg NWad
	– 'Snowkist' (v)	CKen
	– 'Sparkles' **new**	NLar
	– 'Spiralis'	CKen
	– 'Split Rock'	NLar
	– 'Stoneham'	CKen NEgg
	– 'Tempelhof'	CKen EFry MAsh NEgg NLar SCoo SLim
	– 'Tetragona Aurea'	CBcs CMac EFry NWad
	– 'Timothy'	CMac
	– 'Tonia' (v)	CKen EFry
	– 'Tsatsumi'	NLar
	– 'Tsatsumi Gold' ♀H7	CKen EFry ELan EPfP MPkF NLar SCoo SLim SPoG
	– 'Verdon'	CKen
	– 'Villa Marie' **new**	NLar
	– 'Wissel'	CKen
	– 'Wyckoff'	CKen
	– 'Yellowtip' (v)	CKen EPfP MAsh NEgg
	pisifera 'Aurea'	LPar
	– 'Aurea Nana'	see *C. pisifera* 'Strathmore'
	– 'Avenue'	EFry
	– 'Baby Blue'	EFry ELan EPfP MGos SCoo SLim SPoG WGor
	– 'Blue Globe'	CKen
	– 'Boulevard' ♀H7	CBcs CDoC CDul CJun CLet CMac CSBt CWib EFry ELan EPfP LAst LBee LRHS MAsh MGos MJak NEgg NWea SLim SPer WBor
	– 'Compacta Variegata' (v)	NEgg SRms
	– 'Curly Top' ♀H7	CSBt EFry NHol SCoo SLim WGor
	– 'Devon Cream'	NEgg
	– 'Filifera'	CMac CSBt SCoo
	– 'Filifera Aurea' ♀H7	CKen CLet CMac CWib EFry ELan EPfP LBee MGos MJak NEgg NHol NWea SCoo WCFE
	– 'Filifera Aureovariegata' (v)	EFry
	– 'Filifera Nana'	EFry ELan LRHS MGos SLim
	– 'Filifera Nana Aurea'	see *C. pisifera* 'Golden Mop'
	– 'Filifera Sungold'	see *C. pisifera* 'Sungold'
	– 'Fuiri-tsukomo'	CKen
	– 'Gold Cushion'	CKen
	– 'Gold Dust'	see *C. pisifera* 'Plumosa Aurea'
	– 'Gold Spangle'	CKen EFry
§	– 'Golden Mop'	CKen EFry NLar
	– 'Green Pincushion'	CKen CMen
	– 'Hime-himuro'	CKen
	– 'Hime-sawara'	CKen CMen
	– 'Iceberg' **new**	NLar
	– 'Lime Tart'	CKen
	– 'Nana'	CKen CMen EFry MAsh MBri NHol WGor
I	– 'Nana Albovariegata' (v)	CDoC MAsh WThu
	– 'Nana Aurea'	NWad
	– 'Nana Aureovariegata' (v)	CDoC CSBt EFry LBee MBri
I	– 'Nana Compacta'	CMac SRms
	– 'Nana Variegata' (v)	CMac LBee NWad
I	– 'Parslorii'	CKen
	– 'Pici'	CKen
§	– 'Plumosa Aurea'	CKen EFry MAsh NWea
	– 'Plumosa Aurea Compacta'	CKen
	– 'Plumosa Aurea Nana'	MAsh
I	– 'Plumosa Aurea Nana Compacta'	CMac
	– 'Plumosa Aurescens'	CDoC CMac
I	– 'Plumosa Compacta Nana'	SRms
§	– 'Plumosa Compressa' ♀H7	CDoC CKen EUJe NWad
	– 'Plumosa Densa'	see *C. pisifera* 'Plumosa Compressa'
	– 'Plumosa Flavescens'	EFry
I	– 'Plumosa Juniperoides'	CKen EFry MBri
§	– 'Plumosa Rogersii'	EFry
I	– 'Pygmaea Tsukumo'	NLar
	– 'Rogersii'	see *C. pisifera* 'Plumosa Rogersii'
	– 'Silver and Gold' (v)	EFry
	– 'Silver Lode' (v)	CKen
	– 'Snow' (v)	CKen
	– 'Snowflake'	CKen EFry
	– 'Spaan's Cannon Ball'	CKen
	– 'Squarrosa Dumosa'	CKen EFry
I	– 'Squarrosa Lombarts'	CLet CMac CSBt EFry SRms
	– 'Squarrosa Lutea'	CKen
	– 'Squarrosa Sulphurea'	CSBt EFry ELan MBri
§	– 'Strathmore'	EFry NWad
§	– 'Sungold' ♀H7	CDoC CKen CSBt EFry ELan LRHS MAsh MGos NWea SCoo SLim SPoG SRms
	– 'Tama-himuro'	CKen
	– 'Teddy Bear'	MBri NEgg NLar
	– 'True Blue'	EFry ELan NWea WGor
	thyoides 'Andelyensis'	CMac CSBt EFry MBri
	– 'Aurea'	EFry
	– 'Conica'	MAsh
	– 'Ericoides'	CKen CTri EFry LBee SPlb
	– 'Little Jamie'	CKen
	– 'Red Star'	see *C. thyoides* 'Rubicon'
§	– 'Rubicon'	CLet CMac CSBt EFry EPfP LBee LRHS MAsh MBri NEgg SLim SPoG
	– 'Top Point'	LAst LBee MAsh SCoo SPoG
	– 'Variegata' (v)	EFry

Chamaecytisus see *Cytisus*

Chamaedaphne (*Ericaceae*)

	calyculata	CBcs
	– 'Nana'	NHar

Chamaedorea (*Arecaceae*)

	elegans ♀H1a	LPal
	erumpens	see *C. seifrizii*
	metallica misapplied	see *C. microspadix*
§	***microspadix***	CPHo LPal SChr
	radicalis	CBrP CPHo NLos SChr
§	***seifrizii***	LPal

Chamaemelum (*Asteraceae*)

§	***nobile***	CArn CBod CHby CLau CPrp CTri CWld ENfk EPfP GPoy LCro MBri MHer MMuc MNHC NGdn NPri SEND SPlb SRms SVic WJek

- dwarf SMor SVic
- dwarf, double-flowered (d) LEdu
- 'Flore Pleno' (d) CBod CBre CElw CLau CMea CPrp CTri CWld ECha ENfk EPfP GPoy LAst MBri MHer MHol MMuc MNHC MRav NBro NGdn SEND SIde SPer SRms WAbe WHal WJek WWEG
- 'Treneague' CBod CBre CPrp CTri ECha ECho ELan ENfk EPfP GAbr GKin GPoy LAst MBri MCot MHer MNHC MRav NPri SIde SMor SPer SPlb SRms WAbe WHal WHer WJek

Chamaenerion (*Onagraceae*)

§ ***angustifolium*** SWat WSFF
§ - 'Album' CAby CDes CElw CMea CSpe ECha ELan EPfP LEdu LRHS MBel MMuc MNrw MRav NBid NBir NSti SEND SPad SPer SPhx SPoG SWat WCot WHal WMoo WPGP WSFF WSHC
- 'Isobel' MRav WCot
- 'Stahl Rose' CAby CElw CHid CMea EPfP EWes LEdu LPla NSti SGbt SMad SPhx SWat WCot WSHC
§ ***dodonaei*** CFis ELan EWes IMou LPla SPhx WCot
§ ***fleischeri*** MMuc SEND

Chamaepericlymenum see *Cornus*

Chamaerops (*Arecaceae*)

sp. ETod LPar
excelsa misapplied see *Trachycarpus fortunei*
excelsa Thunb. see *Rhapis excelsa*
humilis ♀H4 CAbb CBcs CBrP CTsd EAla ELan EPfP ESwi ETod EUJe LPal LPar LPfy LRHS MGos NPla SChr SEND SHil SPlb SPoG STrG WCot XSen
§ - var. ***argentea*** CBlu CBrP CDTJ CPHo ETod LPal LPar LRHS LTro MGos SChr SPlb WCot
- var. ***cerifera*** see *C. humilis* var. *argentea*
- 'Stella' new ETod
- 'Vulcano' CDTJ LPal SChr

Chamaespartium see *Genista*

Chamaesphacos (*Lamiaceae*)

ilicifolius misapplied see *Siphocranion macranthum*

Chamelaucium (*Myrtaceae*)

uncinatum MOWG

Chamerion see *Chamaenerion*

Chasmanthe (*Iridaceae*)

aethiopica CTre EBee EPri
bicolor CExl CPrp CTca EBee EPri EWld
floribunda CPrp CTca EBee EPri GKev LTro
- var. ***duckittii*** CCon CPrp ECho EPfP GKev
- - 'Golden Wave' CPrp GKev
- 'Saturnus' GKev MHer

Chasmanthium (*Poaceae*)

§ ***latifolium*** CBod CKno CLet CSde EAJP ECha EHoe ELan ELon EPPr EShb EUJe LHop LRHS MAvo MBrN MBri SCob SDix SGSe SGol SMad SPad SPoG WBor WCot WSHC WWEG XLum

- 'Golden Spangles' CKno
- 'River Mist' (v) EBee ECha ELon LRHS SCob SPoG
laxum CBod SMea

Cheilanthes (*Pteridaceae*)

argentea EBee ISha
bonariensis WCot
distans SRms
lanosa CHid CLAP EBee EFer EWes ISha LRHS NLos SGSe SPlb WCot
tomentosa CLAP EBee ISha LPal LRHS

Cheiranthus see *Erysimum*

Cheirolophus (*Asteraceae*)

benoistii misapplied see *Centaurea atropurpurea*
benoistii (Humb.) Holub CSpe EBee MRav SKHP WSHC

Chelidonium (*Papaveraceae*)

japonicum see *Hylomecon japonica*
majus CArn GEdr GPoy GQui MHer NMir WHer WSFF
- 'Flore Pleno' (d) CBre GJos NBid NBro WHer WTou
- var. ***laciniatum*** WCot

Chelone (*Plantaginaceae*)

barbata see *Penstemon barbatus*
§ ***glabra*** Widely available
lyonii EBee ELan ILea NLar SPad SPhx WMoo WShi
- 'Hot Lips' LHop WCAu WHlf
- 'Pink Temptation' EBee GEdr
obliqua Widely available
- var. ***alba*** see *C. glabra*
- 'Forncett Foremost' GQui
- 'Ieniemienie' EBee LEdu
- 'Pink Sensation' WFar
I 'Pink Turtle' EBee GBin

Chelonopsis (*Lamiaceae*)

moschata EBee GBin GEdr LEdu MHer SBrt SMad SPlb WMoo
yagiharana CAby NBid SHar WMoo WOut

Chenopodium (*Amaranthaceae*)

bonus-henricus CAgr CArn CHab CHby ENfk GPoy LPot MCoo MHer MNHC SIde SRms WHer WJek
giganteum MNHC SHDw SRms WJek

cherimoya see *Annona cherimola*

cherry, Duke see *Prunus* × *gondouinii*

cherry, sour or morello see *Prunus cerasus*

cherry, sweet see *Prunus avium*

chervil see *Anthriscus cerefolium*

chestnut, sweet see *Castanea sativa*

Chiastophyllum (*Crassulaceae*)

§ ***oppositifolium*** ♀H5 CBcs CSam CTri EBee ECha ECho EDAr ELan EPfP GAbr GJos GKev ITim LAst LRHS MLHP MMuc MRav NBid SIgm SPlb SRms WKif WMoo WSHC XLum
- 'Frosted Jade' see *C. oppositifolium* 'Jim's Pride'
- 'Jane's Reverse' (v) EBee WCot

§ - 'Jim's Pride' (v)	ECha ECho ECtt EHoe EWes GBuc GKev GMaP LPfy MHer MPie MRav NHar NPer NWad SPlb SRGP SRms SRot WIce WKif WMoo WSHC WTor
simplicifolium	see *C. oppositifolium*

Chiliotrichum (*Asteraceae*)

diffusum	CWib MMuc SEND
- 'Lanceolatum'	GAbr

Chilopsis (*Bignoniaceae*)

linearis (Cav.) Sweet	CArn

Chimonanthus ✿ (*Calycanthaceae*)

fragrans	see *C. praecox*
nitens	CBcs CMCN NLar
§ ***praecox***	Widely available
- 'Brockhill Goldleaf'	NLar
- 'Grandiflorus' 🏆H5	CJun EPfP LRHS SPoG SSta WPGP WPat
- 'Luteus' 🏆H4	CJun ELan EPfP LEdu LRHS MGos NLar SPoG SSpi WCot WPGP WPat
- 'Sunburst'	CJun
- 'Trenython' 🏆H4	CJun WPat
yunnanensis misapplied	IDee

Chimonobambusa (*Poaceae*)

KR 7592	MWht
hookeriana misapplied	see *Himalayacalamus falconeri* 'Damarapa'
§ ***marmorea***	CDTJ CEnt ERod MMuc MWht SBig
- 'Variegata' (v)	CDTJ ERod ESwi
§ ***quadrangularis***	CBcs CDTJ CDoC CEnt EPfP ERod ESwi IMou MWht SBig
- 'Nagaminei' (v)	ERod
- 'Suow' (v)	CDTJ
- 'Tatejima'	ERod
tumidissinoda	CDTJ CEnt ERod ESwi IMou MWhi MWht SBig WJun

Chinese chives see *Allium tuberosum*

Chiogenes see *Gaultheria*

Chionanthus (*Oleaceae*)

retusus	CBcs CDul CMCN EBee EPfP LRHS MPkF NLar SAko SHil SKHP SSpi
- 'Arnold's Pride'	NLar WPGP
- 'Tokyo Tower'	CJun
virginicus	CBcs CDoC CDul CJun CMCN ECrN ELan EPfP EWTr GBin IArd IDee LHop LRHS MBlu MMuc MRav NEgg NLar SAko SKHP SPer SPlb SPoG SSpi WCot

Chionochloa (*Poaceae*)

conspicua	CAby CBod EBee GAbr GBee GBin GCal MAvo MMuc NBid NBir SGSe SMea WPGP
- 'Rubra'	see *C. rubra*
flavescens	EHoe GBin MAvo MMuc WPGP
flavicans	IMou MHin SMad SMea
rigida	MAvo
§ ***rubra*** 🏆H7	CBcs CElw CKno CSpe EBee EHoe ELan EWes GBin GCal ILea IMou MAsh MRav SGSe SMad WCot WMoo WPGP
- PAB 67	LEdu
- subsp. ***cuprea***	CAby CBod GBin

Chionodoxa ✿ (*Asparagaceae*)

§ ***forbesii***	CBro ECGP ECho EPfP EPot GKev LAma LRHS NBir SCob SDeJ SPer SRms WShi
- 'Alba'	ECho
- 'Blue Giant'	ECho ELan EPot ERCP SCob
- 'Rosea'	ECho LAma
- 'Violet Beauty'	ECho GKev SDeJ
- 'Zwanenburg'	ECho
gigantea	see *C. luciliae* Gigantea Group
luciliae misapplied	see *C. forbesii*
luciliae ambig.	CAvo ECho LCro LOPS LRHS SEND
luciliae Boiss. 🏆H5	CAby CBro EPfP LAma MBri SPer
- 'Alba'	ECho LAma LRHS SDeJ SPer
§ - Gigantea Group	ECho GKev
- - 'Alba'	EPot GKev SCob
- 'Rosy Queen' **new**	LAma MPie
'Pink Giant'	CAvo CBro ECho ELan EPfP EPot ERCP GKev LAma LRHS SCob SDeJ WBor XLum
sardensis 🏆H5	CBro CPrp ECho EPot ERCP GKev LAma LRHS SDeJ SPhx WShi
'Valentine Day'	EPot

Chionographis (*Melanthiaceae*)

japonica	EFEx WCru

Chionohebe (*Plantaginaceae*)

§ ***densifolia***	EPot
pulvinaris	NSla WAbe
'Vera Cox' **new**	WAbe

Chionophila (*Scrophulariaceae*)

tweedyi **new**	EBee

× *Chionoscilla* (*Asparagaceae*)

§ ***allenii***	ECho SPhx WCot

Chiranthodendron (*Malvaceae*)

pentadactylon	SPlb

Chirita (*Gesneriaceae*)

'Aiko'	WDib
'Candy'	WDib
'Chastity'	WDib
'Diane Marie'	WDib
'Erika'	WDib
flavimaculata	WDib
heterotricha	WDib
'Keiko'	WDib
linearifolia	WDib
linearifolia* × *sinensis	WDib
linearifolia* × *sinensis 'Latifolia'	WDib
longgangensis	WDib
'New York'	WDib
sinensis 🏆H1c	WDib
- 'Hisako'	WDib
speciosa 'Crûg Cornetto'	WCot WCru
'Stardust'	WDib
'Sweet Dreams'	WDib
tamiana	WDib

Chironia (*Gentianaceae*)

baccifera	SPlb

× *Chitalpa* (*Bignoniaceae*)

tashkentensis	CBcs EPfP ESwi MTPN
- 'Morning Cloud'	MBlu

- 'Pink Dawn'	ESwi MBlu SPad
- Summer Bells = 'Minsum'	CDoC ELon LHop WCot

chives see *Allium schoenoprasum*

Chlidanthus (*Amaryllidaceae*)

fragrans	ECho GKev SDeJ SEND XLum

Chloranthus (*Chloranthaceae*)

fortunei	CDes SCob
- 'Domino'	WCot
glaber B&SWJ 11102	WCru
- var. ***flavus***	see *Sarcandra glabra* f. *flava*
henryi	WCot
japonicus	GBuc GEdr WCru
oldhamii	CTal WPGP
- B&SWJ 2019	GEdr LEdu WCru
serratus	GEdr WCru

Chloris (*Poaceae*)

distichophylla	see *Eustachys distichophylla*

Chlorogalum (*Asparagaceae*)

pomeridianum	CFil CLak

Chlorophytum (*Asparagaceae*)

comosum	EShb SEND SVic
- 'Aureomarginata' (v)	SEND
- 'Variegatum' (v) 🏆[H2]	CTsd EShb NGBl SEND SPre SRms
- 'Vittatum' (v) 🏆[H2]	EShb NGBl SRms
krookianum	CCon CDes WCot
macrophyllum	EShb
nepalense	IMou
- B&SWJ 2528	WCru
saundersiae	CExl

Choisya (*Rutaceae*)

sp.	LPar
× ***dewitteana*** 'Aztec Gold'[PBR]	CRos EPfP LCro LPfy LRHS MAsh MGos SCob SHil
- 'Aztec Pearl' 🏆[H4]	Widely available
- Golden Gift = 'Lismarty'[PBR]	LRHS SSpi
- Goldfingers = 'Limo'[PBR]	CBcs CDul CMac CRos CWGN EBee ELan EPfP EShb LAst LHop LRHS LSRN MBri MGos MJak MRav NEgg NHol NLar NPri SCob SGbt SLim SLon SPer SPoG SWvt
- Snow Flurries = 'Lisflurry'[PBR]	CRos ELan EPfP LLHF LRHS MAsh MRav SPoG
- White Dazzler = 'Londaz'[PBR] 🏆[H4]	Widely available
dumosa	LHop
'Royal Lace'	LRHS SLon
ternata 🏆[H4]	Widely available
- Moonshine = 'Walcho'[PBR]	EBee NLar
- Moonsleeper	see *C. ternata* Sundance
§ - Sundance = 'Lich'[PBR] 🏆[H4]	Widely available

Chondrosum (*Poaceae*)

gracile	see *Bouteloua gracilis*

Chordospartium see *Carmichaelia*

Chorisia (*Bombacaceae*)

speciosa	SPlb

Chorizema (*Papilionaceae*)

cordatum 🏆[H2]	ECou SVen
dicksonii	SPlb
rhombeum **new**	ECou

Chromolaena (*Asteraceae*)

arnottiana	CDes

Chronanthus see *Cytisus*

Chrysalidocarpus see *Dypsis*

Chrysanthemopsis see *Rhodanthemum*

Chrysanthemum ✿ (*Asteraceae*)

E.H. Wilson s.n.	MNrw WCot
'Action Bronze' (22)	EPfP NWsh
'Agnes Ann' (21d)	EWoo MNrw
'Alan Brown' (25a) **new**	MCms
'Alan Foxall Yellow' (3b)	MCms
'Alec Bedser' (25a)	NHal
'Alehmer Rote' (21)	MNrw WWEG
'Alex Young' (25b)	MCms
'Aline' (21)	EWoo MNrw
'Alison' (29c)	ELon EWoo MNrw
'Alison's Dad'	MNrw
'Allouise' (25b) 🏆[H3]	NHal
'Allouise Pink' (25b)	MCms
'Allyson Peace' (14a)	MCms NHal
alpinum	see *Leucanthemopsis alpina*
'Amber Gigantic' (1)	NHal
'Amber Matlock' (24b)	MCms
'American Beauty Lemon' (5b)	MCms
'American Beauty White' (5b)	MCms
'Anastasia' ambig.	SAko
'Anastasia' (21c)	CHid EBee ECtt ELon GCal LRHS MNrw MRav NSti WBor WWEG
'Anderton' (6b)	MCms
'Angela Blundell' (19b)	WCot
'Angela Cosimini' (25b)	MCms
'Angelic' (21b) 🏆[H4]	EWoo
'Anne Ratsey' (21)	CHVG CSam MNrw WBrk
'Anne, Lady Brocket' (21d)	ECtt NWsh
'Anthony Peace' (25b)	MCms NHal
'Antigua'[PBR]	MCms
'Apollo' H. Shoesmith	LLHF MNrw WCot
'Apollo' (21)	SPhx WHoo
'Apricot'	see *C.* 'Cottage Apricot'
'Apricot Chessington' (25a)	MCms NHal
'Apricot Courtier' (24a)	MCms NHal
'Apricot Enbee Wedding'	see *C.* 'Bronze Enbee Wedding'
'Apricot Mundial' (6b)	MCms
'Arctic Queen'[PBR] (23a)	MCms
'Arctic Queen Yellow' **new**	MCms
arcticum L.	see *Arctanthemum arcticum*
argenteum	see *Tanacetum argenteum*
'Astro' (25b)	MCms NHal
'Aunt Millicent' (21d) 🏆[H4]	EWoo LLHF NHal WCot
'Balcombe Perfection' (5a)	MCms NHal
balsamita	see *Tanacetum balsamita*
Barbara = 'Yobarbara' (22)	NHal
'Barca' **new**	MCms
'Beacon' (5a) 🏆[H2]	MCms NHal
'Beechcroft' (29Rub)	MNrw
'Belle' (21d)	EWoo MNrw
'Beppie Bronze' (29e)	MCms
'Beppie Purple' (29e)	MCms
'Beppie Red' (29e)	MCms
'Beppie Rose' (29e)	MCms
'Beppie Yellow' (29e)	MCms

	Name	Suppliers
	'Best Man' (29d)	MCms
	'Betty' (21)	EWoo
	'Bill Holden' (14a)	MCms NHal
	'Bill Wade' (25a)	MCms NHal
	'Billy Bell' (15a)	MCms NHal
	'Blanche Poitevene' (5b)	EMal NHal
	'Bob Green' (13b)	MCms
	'Bobby Swinburn' (13b)	MCms NHal
	'Branroyal'[PBR]	NLar
	Bravo = 'Yobra' (22c) 🏆H3	NHal
*	'Breitner's Supreme'	ECtt MHCG MNrw WWEG
	'Brennpunkt'	MNrw
	'Bretforton Road'	ECtt MNrw WCot WOld
	'Brierton Violet' (17b)	NHal
	'Brightness' (21)	EWoo MNrw
	'Bronze Cassandra' (5b) 🏆H2	MCms NHal
	'Bronze Darren Pugh' (3b)	NHal
	'Bronze Dee Gem' (29c)	MCms NHal
§	'Bronze Elegance' (21b) 🏆H4	CTri ECtt LRHS MNrw NBir NGdn NSti NWsh SRms
§	'Bronze Enbee Wedding' (29d) 🏆H3	MCms NHal
	'Bronze Gigantic' (1)	NHal
	'Bronze Matlock' (24b)	NHal
	'Bronze Max Riley' (23b) 🏆H3	MCms NHal
	'Bronze Mayford Perfection' (5a) 🏆H2	MCms
	'Bronze Mei-kyo'	see *C.* 'Bronze Elegance'
	'Bronze Talbot Parade' (29c) 🏆H3	MCms
	'Bronze William Florentine' (15a)	MCms
	'Brown Eyes' (21b) 🏆H4	EWoo
	'Bryony Wade' (13b)	MCms NHal
	'Buff William Florentine' (15a)	MCms
	'Bunty' (28)	SMad
	burnt orange-flowered	CAby CFis MNrw
	'Burntwood Belle' (3b)	MCms
	'Buxton Ruby'	EWTr EWoo
	'Candy John Wingfield' (14b)	MCms
	'Capel Manor'	EBee LLHF MHCG MNrw WCot
	'Capella' (10a)	MCms
	'Cardinal Red' **new**	LRHS
	'Carlene Welby' (25b)	MCms
	'Carmine Blush' (21d) 🏆H4	EWoo LHop MNrw WBrk WCot WWEG
	'Caroline Barclay' (14b)	MCms
	'Casablanca' (25a)	NHal
	'Cassandra' (5b) 🏆H2	MCms NHal
	'Cawthorne' (29d)	MCms
	'Charles Tandy Yellow' (15b)	MCms
	'Charlie' (24b) **new**	MCms
	'Chatsworth' (29c) **new**	NHal
	'Chelsea Physic Garden'	CAby EBee EWoo LEdu MNrw WCot WWEG
	'Chempak Rose' (14b)	MCms
	'Cherry Chessington' (25a)	MCms NHal
	'Cherry Riley's Dynasty' (14a)	MCms
	'Chesapeake Primrose' (10a)	MCms
	Chesapeake = 'Yochesapeake'[PBR] (10a)	MCms NHal
	'Chessington' (25a)	MCms
	'Chessington Oyster' (25a) **new**	MCms
	'Chesswood Beauty' (7b)	MCms
	'Chestnut Talbot Maid' (29c)	MCms
	'Chestnut Talbot Parade' (29c) 🏆H3	MCms
	'Chloe Ball' (13b)	MCms
	'Christmas'	MNrw
	'Christopher Lawson' (24b)	MCms NHal
	'Cinderella'	WMnd WWEG
	cinerariifolium	see *Tanacetum cinerariifolium*
	'Clapham Delight' (23a)	MCms NHal
	'Clara Curtis' (21d)	Widely available
	'Clare Louise' (24b)	MCms
	'Clarksdale' (15b)	MCms NHal
	coccineum	see *Tanacetum coccineum*
	'Colsterworth'	MNrw
	'Contralto' (22)	EWoo
	'Coral Reef' (10b)	MCms NHal
	'Corinna' (21d)	GBin MNrw
	'Cornetto' (25b)	MCms NHal
	corymbosum	see *Tanacetum corymbosum*
§	'Cottage Apricot' (21)	ECGP EPfP EWoo LRHS MBNS MLHP MRav SRms
	'Cottage Bronze'	MNrw
	'Cottage Lemon'	MNrw
	'Cottage Pink'	see *C.* 'Emperor of China'
	'Courtier' (24a)	NHal
	'Cousin Joan' (21d) 🏆H4	EBee EWoo LHop LLHF MNrw NCGa WCot WOld
	'Cream Dorridge Crystal' (24a) **new**	MCms
	'Cream Elegance' (9c)	NHal
	'Cream John Hughes' (3b)	MCms NHal
	'Cream Patricia Millar' (14b)	NHal
	'Cream Talbot Maid' (29c)	MCms
	'Cream Talbot Parade' (29c) 🏆H3	MCms
	'Cream West Bromwich' (14a)	MCms
	Dana = 'Yodana' (25b) 🏆H3	MCms NHal
	Dance = 'Fidance'[PBR] (9f)	MCms
	'Dance Red' (9f)	MCms
	Dance Salmon = 'Fidancesal'[PBR] (9f)	MCms
	'Dance Sunny' (9f)	MCms
	'Dance White' (9f)	MCms
	'Daniel Cooper' (21d) 🏆H4	EBee EWoo MNrw SBch
	'Danny Peace' (25b) **new**	MCms
	'Daphne' (21d)	EWoo
	'Daphne Davis' (29d)	NHal
	'Darren Pugh' (3b)	MCms NHal
	'Dawn Charlton' (14a) **new**	MCms
	'Dee Gem' (29c) 🏆H3	MCms NHal
	'Delianne'[PBR]	MCms
	'Delianne Yellow'[PBR]	MCms
	'Delistar'[PBR] (9f)	MCms
	'Delistar Bronze' (9f)	MCms
	'Delistar Cream'[PBR] (9f)	MCms
	'Delistar Lemon' (9f)	MCms
	'Delistar Lilac' (9f)	MCms
	'Delistar Mint' (9f)	MCms
	'Delistar Pink' (9f)	MCms
	'Delistar Pink Star' (9f)	MCms
	'Delistar Saffira' (9f)	MCms
	'Delistar Sunny' (9f)	MCms
	'Delta' (5b)	NHal
	'Delta Copper Bronze' (9d)	NHal
	'Delta Crimson' (29d)	NHal
	'Delta Yellow' (29)	NHal
	'Denise Oatridge' (5a)	MCms
	'Dennis Gill' (25b)	MCms
	'Dennis Turner' (25b)	MCms

	Name	Suppliers
	'Dennis Turner Primrose' (15b)	MCms
	'Dernier Soleil'	MNrw SAko XLum
	'Deva Glow' (25a)	MCms
	'Dixter Orange'	EBee GCal MHCG SDix SMad
	'Dixter Pink' **new**	SDix
§	'Doctor Tom Parr' (21c)	CExl ELan EWoo LHop MNrw
	'Domingo' (14b)	MCms
	'Don't Start' (7a)	MCms
	'Doreen Hall' (15a)	MCms NHal
	'Doreen Statham' (4b)	MCms NHal
	'Doris Ozols' (25a)	MCms NHal
	'Dorothy Stone' (25b)	MCms NHal
	'Dorridge Crystal' (24a)	MCms NHal
	'Downpour' (10a)	MCms
	'Dublin'	MCms
	'Duchess of Edinburgh' (21d)	CFis EBee ECtt ELan EPfP EWoo GBin LRHS LSun MNrw SPhx XLum
	'Dulwich Pink' (21d) ♀^{H4}	WCot WOld
	'Dutchy'^{PBR} (9d)	MCms
	'Early Yellow'	EBee ELon EWoo MNrw WCot
	'Edelweiss' (21)	CAby
	'Edmund Brown'	WCot
	'Edward Shaw' (5a)	MCms
	'Egret' (23b)	MCms NHal
	'Elegance' (9c)	NHal
	'Elizabeth Lawson' (5b)	MCms NHal
	'Elizabeth Shoesmith' (1)	NHal
§	'Emperor of China' (21)	CAby CElw ECha ECtt EWoo LSun MNrw MRav NHal SPhx SRms WBor WMnd WWEG XLum
	'Enbee Wedding' (29d) ♀^{H3}	MCms NHal
	'Energy'^{PBR} (9)	MCms
	'Esther' (21d)	ELon MNrw NCGa SMad
	'Eva Allen' (25b)	MCms
	'Fairweather' (3b)	MCms NHal
	'Fairweather Cream' (3b) **new**	MCms
	'Fairweather Peach' (3b)	MCms
	'Fanfare Cherry' **new**	LRHS
	'Fanfare Claret' **new**	LRHS
	'Fanfare Flame' **new**	LRHS
	'Fanfare Glowing Embers' **new**	LRHS
	'Fanfare Orange' **new**	LRHS
	'Fanfare Pink Blush' **new**	LRHS
	'Fanfare Pink Pastel' **new**	LRHS
	'Fanfare Rosetta' **new**	LRHS
	'Fanfare Ruby' **new**	LRHS
	'Fanfare Salmon' **new**	LRHS
	'Fanfare Sunset' **new**	LRHS
	'Feeling Green Dark'^{PBR} (9b)	MCms
	'Fleur de Lis' (10a)	MCms
	foeniculaceum misapplied	see *Argyranthemum foeniculaceum* misapplied
	foeniculaceum (Willd.) Desf.	see *Argyranthemum foeniculaceum* (Willd.) Webb & Sch.Bip.
	'Folk Song' (4b) **new**	MNrw
	'Fondant'	NHal
	'Formcast' (24a)	MCms
	'Foxtrot'^{PBR} ♀^{H3}	NLar
	'French Rose'	MNrw
	'Froggy'^{PBR} (9)	MCms
	frutescens	see *Argyranthemum frutescens*
	'Gala Burgundy'	EPfP NLar
	'Gambit' (24a)	MCms NHal
	'Geoff Aird' (15b)	MCms NHal
	'Geoff Amos' (3b)	MCms
	'Geoff Brady' (5a)	MCms NHal
	'George Griffiths' (24b) ♀^{H3}	MCms NHal
	'Gigantic' (1)	NHal
	'Gillette' (23b)	MCms
	'Ginger Nut' (25b)	MCms
	'Ginger Nut Yellow' (25b)	MCms
I	'Gladys' (12a)	NHal
	'Gladys Emerson' (3b)	MCms NHal
	'Gold Enbee Wedding' (29d) ♀^{H3}	MCms
	'Gold Mundial' (6b) ♀^{H2}	MCms
	'Golddukaten' (21) **new**	NWad
	'Golden Cassandra' (5b) ♀^{H2}	MCms NHal
	'Golden Chalice' (12a)	NHal
	'Golden Courtier' (24a)	MCms NHal
	'Golden Masons' (7b)	MCms
	'Golden Mayford Perfection' (5a) ♀^{H2}	MCms
	'Golden Plover' (22)	NHal
	'Golden Rain' (10a) ♀^{H2}	MCms NHal
	'Golden Roy Coopland' (5b) **new**	MCms
	'Golden Splendour' (10a)	MCms
	'Golden Wedding' (21)	MNrw
	'Golden William Florentine' (15a)	MCms
	'Golden Woolman's Glory' (7a)	NHal
	'Goldengreenheart' (21d) ♀^{H4}	EBee ECtt ELon EShb LLHF MHCG MNrw WBrk WHoo WWEG
	'Goldmarianne' (21)	GBin XLum
	'Goodlife Sombrero' (29a) ♀^{H3}	MCms
	'Goshu Penta' (10a)	MCms
	'Grandchild' (21c) ♀^{H4}	MNrw NHal SBch
	'Hanenburg' (25b)	MCms NHal
	haradjanii	see *Tanacetum haradjanii*
	'Harold Lawson' (5a)	MCms NHal
	'Harry Gee' (1)	NHal
	'Harry Tolley' (14b)	MCms
	'Heather James' (3b)	MCms NHal
	'Hebe' (21d)	EBee
	'Heide' (29c) ♀^{H3}	NHal
	'Helen Louise' (25b)	MCms NHal
	'Herbie McCauley' (24b)	MCms
	'Herbstbrokat'	EBee GBin XLum
	'Herbstfeuer' (21) **new**	NWad
	'Hesketh Knight' (5b) ♀^{H2}	MCms NHal
	'Hillfield Apricot' **new**	EShb
	'Hoagy' (29d)	MCms NHal
	'Holly Elizabeth' (14a)	MCms
	Holly = 'Yoholly' (22b) ♀^{H3}	NHal
	'Honey Enbee Wedding' (29d)	MCms NHal
	'Horningsea Pink' (19d)	ECGP WBor
	hosmariense	see *Rhodanthemum hosmariense*
	'Imp' (21e) ♀^{H4}	EWoo
	indicum	SVic
	'Innocence' (21d) ♀^{H4}	CFis ECtt ELan EWoo LEdu MNrw MRav NGdn SHar WBrk WHoo WWEG
	'Isabellarosa' (21d) ♀^{H4}	GBin
	'Janet South'	EWoo MNrw
	'Jante Wells' (21b) ♀^{H4}	MNrw WBor WWEG
	'Jennifer Shephard' (25b) **new**	MCms
	'Jenny Wren' (12a)	NHal
	'Jessie Cooper' misapplied	see *C.* 'Mrs Jessie Cooper' (21)

'Jimmy Simpson' (25b)	MCms NHal
'Jimmy Tranter' (14b)	NHal
'Joan Waugh' (14b)	MCms
'John Harrison' (25b)	MCms NHal
'John Hughes' (3b)	MCms NHal
'John Lowry' (24a)	MCms NHal
'John Riley' (14a)	MCms NHal
'John Wingfield' (14b)	MCms NHal
'John Wingfield Honey' (14b)	MCms
'John Wingfield Pearl' (14b)	MCms
'Jolie Rose'	WCot
'Joyce Fountain' (24a)	MCms NHal
'Joyce Frieda' (13b)	MCms NHal
'Julia' (28)	EPfP MNrw
'Julia Arnold'	WHoo
'Julia Peterson'	MHCG MHer MNrw WCot WHoo
'Julie Lagravère' (28)	EWoo LHop MNrw XLum
'Karen Taylor' (29c) 🏆H3	NHal
'Kath Stephenson' (7b)	MCms NHal
'Kath Stephenson Honey' (7b)	MCms
'Kath Stephenson Peach' (7b)	MCms
'Kath Stephenson Primrose' (7b)	MCms NHal
'Kath Stephenson Rose' (7b)	MCms NHal
'Kath Stephenson Salmon' (7b)	MCms
'Kay Woolman' (13b)	MCms NHal
'Kay Woolman Yellow' (13b)	MCms
'Killerton Tangerine'	MNrw
'Kimberley Marie' (15b)	MCms NHal
'Kiyomi-no-meisui'	MCms NHal
'Kleiner Bernstein'	MNrw
'La Damoiselle'	WCot
'Lakelanders' (3b)	MCms NHal
'Laura Jayne' (25a) **new**	MCms
'Lava' (10a)	MCms
'Leo' (21b) 🏆H4	EBee EWoo
leucanthemum	see *Leucanthemum vulgare*
'Lexy'[PBR] (9)	MCms
'Lexy Red'[PBR] (9)	MCms
'Lighthouse' **new**	NHal
'Lilac Chessington' (25a)	MCms NHal
Linda = 'Lindayo' (22c) 🏆H3	NHal
'L'Innocence' (21)	CAby
'Little Dorrit' (21f) 🏆H4	EWoo
'Liverpool Festival' (23b)	MCms
'Lollipop'[PBR] (9)	MCms
'Lorna Wood' (13b)	MCms NHal
'Louise Park' (24a)	MCms
'Luba' (9c) **new**	MCms
'Luba Bronze' (9c) **new**	MCms
'Luba Orange' (9c) **new**	MCms
'Lucy' (29a)	MCms NHal
'Lucy Simpson' (21d)	EWoo SBch
'Lundy' (2)	NHal
'Lydia Mannion' (7b)	MCms
'Lynn Johnson' (15a)	MCms
Lynn = 'Yolynn' (22c) 🏆H3	NHal
macrophyllum	see *Tanacetum macrophyllum* (Waldst. & Kit.) Sch.Bip.
'Malcolm Perkins' (25a)	MCms NHal
'Mancetta Comet' (29a)	MCms NHal
'Mancetta Symbol' (5a)	MCms
'Mandarin' (5b)	SAko
maresii	see *Rhodanthemum hosmariense*
'Margaret Dear' (25a)	MCms
'Margaret Lawson' (14b) **new**	NHal
'Margery Fish'	MNrw
'Marion' (25a)	MNrw WCot
'Martin Bell' (29d) **new**	MCms
'Mary' (21f)	NHal
'Mary Stoker' (21d)	CAby EBee ECtt ELan ELon EPfP EPri EWoo LRHS MNrw MPie MRav NCGa NHal NLar NWsh SPer WAul WCAu WMnd WWEG XLum
'Mary's Miracle' (24a)	MCms
'Mason's Bronze' (7b)	MCms
'Matlock' (24b)	NHal
'Mauve Gem' (21f) 🏆H3	MNrw NHal
'Mavis' (21) 🏆H3	MNrw
mawii	see *Rhodanthemum gayanum*
'Max Riley' (23b) 🏆H3	MCms NHal
maximum misapplied	see *Leucanthemum* × *superbum*
maximum Ramond	see *Leucanthemum maximum* (Ramond) DC.
'Maxine Charlton' (24b)	MCms NHal
'Maxine Johnson' (25b)	MCms NHal
'May Shoesmith' (5a) 🏆H2	MCms NHal
'Maybach' (9)	MCms
'Mayford Perfection' (5a) 🏆H2	MCms
'Mei-Kyō' (28b) 🏆H4	CFis CMea CTri ECtt EWoo LRHS MNrw MPie SRms WBor WBrk WCAu WHil WWEG
'Membury' (24b)	MCms NHal
'Michelle Preston' (13b)	NHal
'Millennium' (25b) 🏆H3	MCms NHal
'Millie Mathews' (14b)	MCms
'Misty Cream' (25b)	MCms
'Misty Golden' (25b)	MCms
'Misty Lemon' (25b)	MCms
'Moonlight' (29d/K)	MRav
'Morning Star' (12a)	NHal
'Mount Fuji' (10b)	MCms
§ 'Mrs Jessie Cooper' (21d) 🏆H4	CAby CHGN EBee ELon EWoo GBee GQue LHop MNrw NLar SDys SRms WCot WHil WHoo WPtf WWEG
'Mrs Jessie Cooper No 1'	NCGa NWsh SBch
'Mrs Jessie Cooper No 2'	MNrw
'Mundial' (6)	MCms
'Mundial Peach' (6b/9a)	MCms
'Mundial Rose' (6b)	MCms
'Mundial Ruby' (6b)	MCms
'Muriel Odell' (7b)	MCms
'Music' (23b)	MCms NHal
'Muxton Sable' (10a)	MCms
'Myss Carol' (29c) 🏆H3	NHal
'Myss Debbie' (29e)	NHal
'Myss Dorothy' (29c)	MCms NHal
'Myss Eliza' (29c)	MCms NHal
'Myss Goldie' (29c)	MCms
'Myss Macy' (29c) **new**	NHal
'Myss Rihanna' (29c)	MCms NHal
'Myss Saffron' (29c) 🏆H3	MCms NHal
'Nancy Perry' (21d)	CSam GBee MNrw MRav XLum
'Nantyderry Sunshine' (28b) 🏆H4	ELon LLHF LRHS MNrw MPie NWsh SPhx WCot WMnd WWEG
'Naru' (9c)	NHal
'Naru Crimson' (9c)	NHal
'Natalie Rachelle' (25b) **new**	MCms
'Natalie Sarah' (29d) 🏆H3	MCms NHal
'Nell Gwynn' (21d)	EWoo MNrw NHal
'New Stylist' (24b) **new**	MCms

Nicole = 'Yonicole' (22c) ♀H3	NHal
nipponicum	see *Nipponanthemum nipponicum*
'Nora Brook' (25b) **new**	MCms
'Olwyn' (4b)	MCms
'Olwyn Yellow' (4b) **new**	MCms
'Orange Allouise' (25b)	MCms NHal
'Orange Enbee Wedding' (29d)	NHal
pacificum	see *Ajania pacifica*
'Paloma Mist' (29d) **new**	NHal
'Paloma Redeye' (29d)	NHal
'Paloma Regent' (29d)	NHal
'Paloma Sands' (29d) **new**	NHal
parthenium	see *Tanacetum parthenium*
'Patricia Millar' (14b)	MCms NHal
'Patricia Millar Cerise' (14b)	MCms
'Patricia Millar Coral' (14b)	MCms
'Patricia Millar Orange' (14b)	MCms
'Patricia Millar Yellow' (14b)	MCms NHal
'Paul Boissier' (30Rub)	CAby CFis ECtt EWoo MNrw NLar NSti SPhx WBor WMnd WWEG
'Paul Cornelius' (24b)	MCms NHal
'Pauline White' (15a)	MCms
'Peach Courtier' (24a)	NHal
'Peach Enbee Wedding' (29d) ♀H3	MCms NHal
'Peach John Wingfield' (14b)	MCms NHal
'Peach Patricia Millar' (14b)	MCms
'Pearl Celebration' (24a)	MCms
'Pearl Enbee Wedding' (29d)	MCms
'Pennine Bullion'	NHal
'Pennine Gambol' (29a) **new**	MCms
'Pennine Jude' (29a) **new**	MCms
'Pennine Marie' (29a) ♀H3	MCms
'Pennine Oriel' (29a) ♀H3	MCms NHal
'Pennine Point' (19c)	NHal
'Pennine Polo' (29d) ♀H3	MCms NHal
'Pennine Poppet' (29a) **new**	MCms
'Pennine Ranger' (29d)	NHal
'Pennine Swan' (29c)	MCms NHal
'Pennine Sweetheart' (29c) ♀H3	MNrw
'Penny's Yellow'	LHop LLHF WBrk
'Percy Salter' (24b)	NHal
'Perry's Peach' (21d) ♀H4	EWoo LLHF MHCG MNrw NCGa NHal NPer SPhx
'Peter Jolley' (25b) **new**	MCms
'Peter Rowe' (23b)	MCms NHal
'Peterkin'	CMac EBee ECtt ELon LRHS WWEG XLum
'Picasso'	MNrw
'Ping Pong' (8a) **new**	MCms
'Pink John Wingfield' (14b)	NHal
'Pocahontas' (10a)	MCms
'Poesie'	SAko WCot
'Polar Gem' (3a)	MCms NHal
'Pomander' (25b)	MCms
'Pot Black' (14b)	MCms
'President Osaka'	MNrw
'Primrose Allouise' (24b) ♀H3	MCms NHal
'Primrose Chessington' (25a)	MCms
'Primrose Courtier'	see *C.* 'Yellow Courtier'
'Primrose Dorothy Stone' (25b)	MCms NHal
'Primrose Dorridge Crystal' (24a)	MCms
'Primrose Egret' (23b)	MCms
'Primrose Enbee Wedding' (29d) ♀H3	MCms NHal
'Primrose Fairweather' (3b)	MCms
'Primrose John Hughes' (3b)	MCms
'Primrose Mayford Perfection' (5a) ♀H2	MCms
'Primrose Olwyn' (4b) **new**	MCms
'Primrose Pauline White' (15a)	MCms
'Primrose Pennine Oriel' (29a)	MCms
'Primrose West Bromwich' (14a)	MCms
'Princess' (21d)	LLHF
'Promise' (25a)	MCms NHal
'Purleigh White' (28b)	ECtt ELon MNrw NSti WCot WWEG
'Purple Chempak Rose' (14b)	MCms NHal
'Purple Dee Gem' (29c) **new**	NHal
'Purple Doreen Hall' (15a) **new**	MCms
'Purple Glow' (5a)	MCms
'Ralph Lambert' (1)	NHal
'Raquel' (21)	MNrw
'Red Balcombe Perfection' (5a)	MCms NHal
'Red Chempak Rose' (14b)	MCms
'Red Goodlife Sombrero' (29a)	MCms
'Red Louise Park' (14a)	MCms
'Red Mayford Perfection' (5a)	MCms
'Red Pennine Gift' (29c)	NHal
'Red Regal Mist' (25b)	MCms NHal
'Red Shirley Model' (3a)	MCms NHal
'Redbreast' (12a)	NHal
'Regal Mist' (25b)	NHal
'Regal Mist Purple' (25b)	MCms
I 'Rhumba'	WCot
'Riley's Dynasty' (14a)	MCms
'Ringdove' (12a)	NHal
'Rita Fox' (25b) **new**	MCms
'Rita McMahon' (29d) ♀H3	NHal
Robin = 'Yorobi' (22c)	NHal
'Roen Sarah' (29c)	NHal
'Romantica'	MNrw
'Romany' (2)	CElw
'Rose Enbee Wedding' (29d)	MCms NHal
'Rose Madder'	EWoo LPot MNrw WCot
'Rose Mayford Perfection' (5a) ♀H2	MCms
'Rose Patricia Millar' (14b)	MCms NHal
'Rose Talbot Parade' (29c)	MCms
'Rosensilber' **new**	SAko
'Rosetta'	MNrw WCot
roseum	see *Tanacetum coccineum*
'Roter Spray' **new**	NWad
'Roy Bevan' (29d)	MCms
'Roy Coopland' (5b) ♀H2	MCms
'Royal Command' (21a)	MNrw WCot
rubellum	see *C. zawadskii*
'Ruby Enbee Wedding' (29d) ♀H3	MCms NHal

Cultivar	Suppliers
'Ruby Glow' (7b)	MCms
'Ruby Mound' (21c) ℽH3	EWoo MHCG MNrw NHal SDys SHar SPhx WCot
'Ruby Raynor' (21c) ℽH4	MNrw NHal WCot
'Rumpelstilzchen' (21d)	CFis CMea ECtt EWoo MNrw NWsh WWEG
'Salhouse Dream' (10a)	MCms NHal
'Salhouse Joy' (10a)	MCms NHal
'Salmon Allouise' (25b)	MCms NHal
'Salmon Enbee Wedding' (29d) ℽH3	NHal
'Salmon Fairweather' (3b)	MCms
'Salmon John Wingfield' (24b)	MCms
'Salmon Patricia Millar' (14b)	MCms
'Salmon Pauline White' (15a)	MCms
'Salmon Talbot Maid' (29c)	MCms
'Salmon Talbot Parade' (29c) ℽH3	MCms
'Salmon Venice' (24b)	MCms
'Sam Vinter' (5a)	MCms NHal
'Samba'	WCot
'Sarah Louise' (25b)	NHal
'Savanna Charlton' (25a)	MCms NHal
'Sea Urchin' (21f) ℽH3	MNrw NHal SDys
'Seaton's Ashleigh' (10b)	MCms
'Seaton's Galaxy' (10a)	MCms NHal
'Senkyo Karyu' (10a)	MCms
'Senkyo Kenshin' (10a)	MCms NHal
'Shamrock' (10b)	MCms
'Sheffield'	XLum
'Sheila Coles' (7b)	MCms NHal
'Sheila Harris' (3b)	MCms
'Shenley Orange'	LLHF
'Shining Light' (21f)	EWoo MNrw
'Shirley Primrose' (1)	NHal
'Sonnenschein'	LHop
'Sound' (9d)	MCms
'Southway Semtex' (29d) **new**	MCms
'Southway Sheba' (29d) ℽH3	MCms NHal
'Southway Sheba Bronze' (29d)	MCms NHal
'Southway Shimmer' (29d)	MCms NHal
'Southway Shiraz' (29d)	MCms NHal
'Southway Sloe' (29d)	MCms NHal
'Southway Spectacular' (29d)	MCms NHal
'Southway Spritzer' (29d) **new**	MCms NHal
'Southway Strontium' (29d)	MCms NHal
'Southway Sunbeam' (29d) **new**	MCms
'Spartan Canary' (21d) ℽH4	EWoo
'Spartan Display'	EWoo
'Spartan Seagull' (21d)	MNrw
'Stallion' PBR (9)	MCms
'Stallion Yellow' **new**	MCms
'Stan Addison' (5b) **new**	MCms
'Starlet' (21f) ℽH4	EWoo NHal
'Steve Packham' (23b)	MCms NHal
'Stockton' (3b) ℽH2	MCms NHal
'Suffolk Pink'	ECtt EShb EWoo MNrw
Sundoro = 'Yosun' (22d)	NHal
'Sunny John Wingfield' (14b)	MCms
Swan = 'Fiswan' PBR (9)	MCms
'Syllabub' (21f) ℽH3	ECtt MNrw
'Symphony' (10a)	MCms NHal
'Talbot Maid' (29c)	MCms
'Talbot Parade' (29c) ℽH3	MCms
'Talbot Parade Pink' (29c)	MCms
'Tapestry Rose' (21d)	CMea EWoo MNrw NCGa NWsh SPhx WBor WHoo
'Tara Olivio' (24b) **new**	MCms
'Terry Brook' (29e)	MCms NHal
'Terry Morris' (7b)	MCms
'Thoroughbred' (24a)	MCms NHal
'Tickle Pink' (29f/K)	MNrw
'Tim Sandall' (25a) **new**	MCms
'Tom Parr'	see *C.* 'Doctor Tom Parr'
'Tom Snowball' (3b)	MCms
'Topsy' (21d) ℽH4	ELon EWoo
'Tracey Waller' (24b) **new**	MCms
Triumph = 'Yotri' (22)	NHal
uliginosum	see *Leucanthemella serotina*
'Uri'	CAby CFis EBee LHop SPhx
'Vagabond Prince'	ELon EWoo LHop MHCG MNrw NCGa WBor WBrk WHoo
'Venice' (24b)	MCms NHal
'Venice Peach' (24b) **new**	MCms
'Venice Rose' (24b) **new**	MCms
'Venus' (21)	NCGa WCot
'Venus One' (7)	ECtt EWoo MNrw NHal SPhx
'Vibrant' (9c) ℽH2	NHal
'Viking' (9)	MCms
'Vision On' (24b) **new**	MCms
'Vulcano Dark' (9)	MCms
'Warm Yoigloo' PBR	SPoG
'Wedding Day' (29k)	EWoo MNrw
'Wedding Sunshine' (21)	MNrw
welwitschii	see *Glebionis segetum*
'Wembley' (24b)	MCms
'Wendy Tench' (21d)	ECtt EWoo NWsh
'West Bromwich' (14a)	MCms
weyrichii	EBee ECho GCrg IKil LEdu MMuc NLar SBch SEND SRms WWEG
'White Allouise' (25b) ℽH3	MCms NHal
'White Beppie' (29e)	MCms
'White Cassandra' (5b)	MCms NHal
'White Denise Oatridge' (5a)	MCms
'White Enbee Wedding' (29d)	MCms NHal
'White Fairweather' (3b)	MCms NHal
'White Gem' (21f)	NHal
'White Gloss' (21e)	MNrw SPhx
'White Pearl Celebration' (24a)	MCms
'White Tower' (27)	MNrw NWad
'Wilder Charms'	WHil
'William Florentine' (15a)	MCms NHal
'Win' (9c)	NHal
'Wind Dancer' (10a)	MCms
'Winning's Red' (21)	EWoo NCGa SMad WCot
'Winter Queen' (5b)	MCms
'Winter Queen Yellow' (5b) **new**	MCms
'Woolley Globe' (15b)	MCms
'Woolman's Glory' (7a)	MCms NHal
'Woolman's Glory Red' (7a)	MCms
'Woolman's Star' (3a)	MCms NHal
'Woolman's Venture' (14b)	MCms NHal
'Xiang' **new**	NWad
'Yellow Allouise' (25b)	MCms
'Yellow American Beauty' (5b) ℽH2	MCms
'Yellow Billy Bell' (15a)	NHal

'Yellow Clapham Delight' (23a) MCms NHal
§ 'Yellow Courtier' (24a) MCms NHal
'Yellow Duke of Kent' (1) NHal
'Yellow Egret' (23b) MCms
'Yellow Enbee Wedding' (29d) MCms NHal
'Yellow Fair Lady' (5a) **new** LAst
'Yellow Goodlife Sombrero' (29a) MCms
'Yellow Heide' (29c) ♀H3 NHal
'Yellow John Harrison' (25b) **new** MCms
'Yellow John Hughes' (3b) ♀H2 MCms NHal
'Yellow John Wingfield' (14b) MCms NHal
'Yellow May Shoesmith' (5a) NHal
'Yellow Mayford Perfection' (5a) ♀H2 MCms
'Yellow Pennine Oriel' (29a) ♀H3 MCms NHal
'Yellow Spider' (10a) MCms
'Yellow Starlet' (21f) ♀H4 EWoo LLHF MNrw
'Yellow Talbot Parade' (29c) MCms
'Yellow Woolman's Glory' (7a) MCms
yezoense MNrw SRms
- B&SWJ 10872 WCru
- 'Roseum' ECtt
'Yonashville' SRms
'Yvonne Gray' (25b) **new** MCms
'Yvonne's Rot-Goldene' **new** SAko
§ ***zawadskii*** CMac SRms
'Zembla'PBR **new** MCms
'Zembla Yellow'PBR **new** MCms

Chrysocephalum (*Asteraceae*)

'Desert Flame' LRHS

Chrysogonum (*Asteraceae*)

australe LRHS
virginianum CMea EWes SBch SPer WFar WWEG
- 'Golden Acres' ECtt

Chrysopogon (*Poaceae*)

gryllus EBee WPGP

Chrysopsis (*Asteraceae*)

§ ***mariana*** WOld
villosa (Pursh) Nutt. ex DC. see *Heterotheca villosa*

Chrysosplenium (*Saxifragaceae*)

alternifolium GEdr
davidianum CBre CSam EBee EPot EWld GCal GEdr GJos GKev IMou NLar NSla WBor WCru WMoo WSHC
- SBEC 233 CExl
flagelliferum B&SWJ 8902 WCru
hebetatum B&SWJ 9835 WCru
lanuginosum var. ***formosanum*** GEdr
- - B&SWJ 6979 ESwi WCru
macrophyllum CDes CDoC CExl CTal EBee EPPr EWld GCal GKev GMaP IMou LEdu MAvo MPie MTPN NLar SHar WBor WCot WCru WSHC
macrostemon var. ***shiobarense*** B&SWJ 6173 WCru
oppositifolium ECha NMir WSFF WShi

Chusquea (*Poaceae*)

breviglumis misapplied see *C. culeou* 'Tenuis'
culeou ♀H4 CAbb CBcs CDoC CEnt CHid EPfP LEdu LPal MGos MWht SBig SPlb SSta WJun
- 'Breviglumis' see *C. culeou* 'Tenuis'
- 'Purple Splendour' WJun
§ - 'Tenuis' ERod
- weeping CDTJ
delicatula from Machu Picchu, Peru CExl CFil
gigantea ♀H3 CDTJ CEnt CExl CFil CHid EPfP ERod ESwi LEdu MWht SBig WJun WPGP
mulleri F&M 104A from Mexico CExl
nigricans CFil

Cibotium (*Cibotiaceae*)

barometz NLos

Cicerbita (*Asteraceae*)

§ ***alpina*** GAbr NBid SPlb
bourgaei MMuc
macrorhiza CC 6912 EBee
plumieri EWes GAbr MMuc SBrt WCot WFar WMoo
- 'Blott' (v) WCot

Cichorium (*Asteraceae*)

intybus CArn CHby CLau CSpe CWld ELan ENfk GAbr GPoy LHop LSun MBel MCot MHer MNHC NBir NCGa NGBl NMir NPri SIde SPer SPlb SPoG SRms SVic WHrl WJek WMoo WSHC
- f. ***album*** CBod EBee ECha ECtt LHop LRHS MBel MCot SBea SPer SPoG SWat
- 'Palla Rossa' ♀H4 SRms
- 'Red Rib' **new** SRms
- 'Roseum' CBod CMos CWld ECha ECtt ELan GKin LHop LRHS MBel MPie NCGa SBea SBod SHar SPer SPoG SWat WCAu WHrl

Cicuta (*Apiaceae*)

virosa LLWG

Cimicifuga see *Actaea*

acerina see *Actaea japonica*
americana see *Actaea podocarpa*
cordifolia (DC.) Torrey & A.Gray see *Actaea cordifolia*
cordifolia Pursh see *Actaea podocarpa*
foetida see *Actaea cimicifuga*
racemosa var. ***cordifolia*** see *Actaea cordifolia*
- 'Purpurea' see *Actaea simplex* Atropurpurea Group
ramosa see *Actaea simplex* 'Prichard's Giant'
rubifolia see *Actaea cordifolia*
simplex var. ***matsumurae*** see *Actaea matsumurae*

Cineraria (*Asteraceae*)

maritima see *Senecio cineraria*

Cinnamomum (*Lauraceae*)

camphora	CBcs CExl IDee SAko SPlb WHfH

Circaea (*Onagraceae*)

alpina	EBee
lutetiana	WHer
- 'Caveat Emptor' (v)	NBid WCot

Cirsium (*Asteraceae*)

arvense	WSFF
* ***atroroseum***	SWat
canum	CSpe GQue
ciliatum	EBee
diacantha	see *Ptilostemon diacantha*
helenioides	see *C. heterophyllum*
§ ***heterophyllum***	CHid EBee EWld GQue LEdu LRHS MAvo MMuc NChi NLar SHar WCot WHil
- PAB 067	LEdu WPGP
japonicum 'Murakumo' (v)	WCot
- 'Rose Beauty'	EBee SCob WBor
'Mount Etna'	CBod CFis CMHG EBee ELan GKin GQue LHop LRHS MBNS MMuc MSpe NDov NGdn SEND SPoG WCAu
oleraceum	LEdu NBid NLar
purpuratum	MNrw WCot
rivulare 'Atropurpureum'	Widely available
- 'Trevor's Blue Wonder'	CAby CBod CSam EBee ECtt GAbr GBin IBoy MAvo MBel MCot MHol MMuc MNrw MSCN NDov NEgg NLar SCob SMad SPer WCAu WCot WPtf WTor
tuberosum	CAby LEdu LRHS SKHP SPhx
vulgare	WSFF

Cissus (*Vitaceae*)

antarctica ♀H1c	EShb SEND
pedata B&SWJ 2371	WCru
rhombifolia ♀H1c	EOHP EShb
- 'Ellen Danica' ♀H1c	EShb
§ ***striata***	CBcs CDoC CMac CWCL EBee ELon EShb IBoy LRHS MGil MRav NChi SEND SLim SWvt WSHC

Cistus ✿ (*Cistaceae*)

acutifolius misapplied	see *C. inflatus*, *C.* × *pulverulentus*
× ***aguilarii***	CBcs CSBt CTri LAst MRav SPhx WSHC XSen
- 'Maculatus' ♀H4	CBcs CDoC CDul CExl CSam ELan EPfP LRHS LSRN MMuc NLar SEle SPer SPoG SWvt WBod WKif WPGP
albidus	CArn GKev SVen XSen
algarvensis	see *Halimium ocymoides*
'Anne Palmer'	see *C.* × *fernandesiae* 'Anne Palmer'
× ***argenteus*** 'Blushing Peggy Sammons'	ELan NLar SVen SWvt XSen
- Golden Treasure = 'Nepond' (v)	SWvt
- 'Paper Moon'	EWTr LSRN NLar SVen
§ - 'Peggy Sammons'	CBot CDoC CDul COtt ECha ELan EPfP EWTr LPot LRHS LSRN MAsh MGos MOWG NLar SAko SCob SEND SLim SPer SPhx SWvt WHar WSHC XSen
- 'Silver Ghost'	EPfP LRHS SLim SVen SWvt
- 'Silver Pink' ambig.	Widely available
atriplicifolius	see *Halimium atriplicifolium*
'Blanche'	see *C. ladanifer* 'Blanche'
× ***bornetianus*** 'Jester' ♀H4	CSBt EPfP EWTr LRHS MAsh NLar SVen SWvt WBor
× ***canescens***	SVen
- f. ***albus***	CWib WKif XSen
§ ***clusii***	NLar SBod
- subsp. ***multiflorus***	XSen
× ***corbariensis***	see *C.* × *hybridus*
creticus	CBcs CDoC CExl CSam LAst LPfy LRHS MAsh MBri MGos MOWG NEgg NLar SAko SHil SLon SPoG SRms SVen SWvt WBod WKif
- subsp. ***corsicus***	XSen
§ - subsp. ***creticus***	EBee ELan EPfP MRav SCoo SPer
§ - subsp. ***incanus***	WCot
× ***crispatus***	XSen
§ - 'Warley Rose'	GMaP SIgm WKif XLum
crispus misapplied	see *C.* × *pulverulentus*, *C.* × *purpureus*
§ ***crispus*** L.	ELan SEND SGol
- 'Prostratus'	see *C. crispus* L.
- 'Sunset'	see *C.* × *pulverulentus* 'Sunset'
§ × ***cyprius*** ♀H4	CArn CDul EBee ELan EPfP GBin LRHS SDix SEND SPer SRms SWvt
§ - var. ***ellipticus*** 'Elma' ♀H4	ELan EPfP LRHS MAsh NLar SPer XSen
§ × ***dansereaui***	CBot CMac COtt CSBt CWib EAEE LRHS NLar SVen SWvt
- 'Decumbens' ♀H4	CChe CDul CLet COtt CSde CTri CTsd EBee ELan EPau EPfP LPfy LRHS MAsh MBNS MBri MJak MRav MSwo NEgg NLar SAko SCoo SGbt SHil SPer SPhx SPoG SWvt WPGP
- 'Jenkyn Place' ♀H4	CBod CDoC EBee GMaP IVic LSRN MBNS MMuc NLar SPer SPoG WKif
× ***dubius***	SVen
'Elma'	see *C.* × *cyprius* var. *ellipticus* 'Elma'
'Enigma'	CDoC
§ × ***fernandesiae*** 'Anne Palmer'	EPfP LLHF LRHS MAsh NLar
× ***florentinus*** misapplied	see × *Halimiocistus* 'Ingwersenii'
× ***florentinus*** ambig.	SVen XLum
§ × ***florentinus*** Lam.	GMaP XSen
- 'Fontfroide'	SEND SVen
* - 'Tramontane'	XSen
'Gordon Cooper' ♀H4	LSRN MMuc NLar SPoG WBor
× ***heterocalyx*** 'Chelsea Bonnet'	CBod COtt GMaP MBNS MMuc NLar SCoo SEND SLim SPoG XSen
heterophyllus	SVen
'Highlights'	EPfP LRHS MAsh
hirsutus Lam. 1786	see *C. inflatus*
- var. ***psilosepalus*** misapplied	see *C. inflatus*
§ × ***hybridus***	Widely available
- 'Gold Prize' (v)	CMHG COtt CWGN ELan NLar SWvt WGrn
- Little Miss Sunshine = 'Dunnecis'PBR (v)	LPfy LRHS MAsh MGos NHol NLar SHil SPoG SRms SWvt
- Rospico = 'Rencis'PBR (v)	LRHS NLar SIgm
incanus	see *C. creticus* subsp. *incanus*
§ ***inflatus***	XSen
ingwerseniana	see × *Halimiocistus* 'Ingwersenii'
'Jessamy Beauty'	SVen WHar WIce
'Jessamy Bride'	SVen
'Jessamy Charm'	SPhx
ladanifer misapplied	see *C.* × *cyprius*
ladanifer ambig.	CMac ECha WKif
ladanifer L.	CBcs CBot CDoC CLet COtt CSBt CSde CTri ELan EPfP GPoy LRHS MRav MSwo SPer SWvt WHar XSen

§	- 'Blanche'	CBot CDoC EPfP EWTr LLHF LSRN NLar SEND SPer SSpi SWvt WKif
§	- 'Paladin'	LRHS MNHC
	- Palhinhae Group	see *C. ladanifer* var. *sulcatus*
	- 'Pat'	COtt ELan EPfP LRHS LSRN MAsh NBir NLar SAko SPer SPoG SSpi SWvt
§	- var. ***sulcatus***	ELan LHop LRHS
	lasianthus	see *Halimium lasianthum*
	laurifolius	CLet EPfP LRHS MGos NBir NLar SCob SEND SKHP SPer SVen SWvt XLum XSen
	- subsp. ***atlanticus***	XSen
	× ***laxus*** 'Snow White' ♀H4	CDoC CWGN EBee EPfP LAst MGos NLar NPer SLim SLon
	× ***ledon***	EBee
§	× ***lenis*** 'Grayswood Pink' ♀H4	Widely available
	libanotis	COtt SVen
	- 'Major'	XSen
	× ***longifolius***	see *C.* × *nigricans*
	× ***loretii*** misapplied	see *C.* × *dansereaui*
	× ***loretii*** Rouy & Foucaud	see *C.* × *stenophyllus*
	× ***lusitanicus*** Maund	see *C.* × *dansereaui*
	'Merrist Wood Cream'	see × *Halimiocistus wintonensis* 'Merrist Wood Cream'
	monspeliensis	CAbP CMac EPfP GKev LRHS LSun MAsh MBNS SEND SLon SPer XSen
	- 'Vicar's Mead'	MBNS MMuc
	monspeliensis × ***salviifolius***	see *C.* × *florentinus* Lam.
§	× ***nigricans***	XSen
	× ***oblongifolius***	SWvt XSen
	× ***obtusifolius*** misapplied	see *C.* × *nigricans*
	× ***obtusifolius*** ambig.	ELan LRHS MRav SAko SKHP
	× ***obtusifolius*** Sweet	EPfP WPGP XSen
§	- 'Thrive' ♀H4	EPfP LCro LRHS MBri MGos SCoo SHil WBod
	ocymoides	see *Halimium ocymoides*
	'Paladin'	see *C. ladanifer* 'Paladin'
	palhinhae	see *C. ladanifer* var. *sulcatus*
	parviflorus misapplied	see *C.* × *lenis* 'Grayswood Pink'
	parviflorus Lam.	WSHC
	aff. ***parviflorus***	MOWG
*	× ***pauranthus*** 'Natacha'	XSen
	'Peggy Sammons'	see *C.* × *argenteus* 'Peggy Sammons'
	× ***platysepalus***	SPhx
	populifolius	CBot CMHG CMac ECha EPfP LLHF LRHS NLar SGol SPer SWvt
	- var. ***lasiocalyx***	see *C. populifolius* subsp. *major*
§	- subsp. ***major***	EPfP EWTr LRHS LSRN MOWG SKHP WPGP
	psilosepalus misapplied	see *C. inflatus*
§	× ***pulverulentus***	CExl CTri ECha LRHS MMHG SVen WSHC XSen
*	- Delilei Group	XSen
	- - 'Fiona'	XSen
§	- 'Sunset' ♀H4	Widely available
	- 'Warley Rose'	see *C.* × *crispatus* 'Warley Rose'
§	× ***purpureus*** ♀H4	Widely available
	- 'Alan Fradd'	Widely available
	- 'Betty Taudevin'	see *C.* × *purpureus*
	- f. ***strictus***	EPfP LRHS LSRN SVen XSen
	× ***rodiaei*** 'Jessabel'	CBot EPfP EWTr LRHS MAsh MRav NLar SPer SWvt WPGP
	- 'Jessica'	NLar
	rosmarinifolius	see *C. clusii*
	'Ruby Cluster'	LRHS LSRN MMuc NLar
	sahucii	see × *Halimiocistus sahucii*
	salviifolius	CAbP CArn MOWG SVen XSen
	- 'Avalanche'	MRav WAbe
	- 'Gold Star'	ELan NLar
	- 'May Snow'	EHoe LRHS MAsh
	- 'Prostratus'	CSde ELan EPfP LRHS SAko SWvt WPGP
	'Silver Pink' misapplied	see *C.* × *lenis* 'Grayswood Pink'
	× ***skanbergii***	CLet CMac CTri CWib ELan EPfP LHop MGos MLHP MMuc MOWG MRav NBir NLar SDix SEND SPer WCFE XLum XSen
	'Snow Fire' ♀H4	CDoC CWSG EBee ELan EPfP LRHS LSRN MAsh MGos MMuc NEgg NLar SAko SBod SCoo SEle SWvt WGrn WHar
§	× ***stenophyllus***	CWib
	'Stripey'	SVen
	× ***tephreus***	XSen
	'Thrive'	see *C.* × *obtusifolius* 'Thrive'
	× ***verguinii***	LHop XSen
	villosus	see *C. creticus* subsp. *creticus*
	wintonensis	see × *Halimiocistus wintonensis*

Citharexylum (Verbenaceae)

	quadrangulare Jacq.	see *C. spinosum*
	spicatum	CExl CFil WBor
§	***spinosum***	CHII

citrandarin see *Citrus reticulata* × *C. trifoliata*

citrange see *Citrus* × *insitorum*

citrangequat see *Citrus* × *georgiana*

citremon see *Citrus* × *limon* × *C. trifoliata*

× *Citrofortunella* (Rutaceae)

	mitis	see *Citrus* × *microcarpa*

citron see *Citrus medica*

Citronella (Icacinaceae)

§	***gongonha***	SVen
	mucronata	see *C. gongonha*

Citrullus (Cucurbitaceae)

	lanatus 'Charleston Gray'	SVic

Citrus (Rutaceae)

	sp.	ETod
§	× ***aurantiifolia*** (F)	EPfP ETod SCit SPre SVic
	- key lime	see *C.* × *aurantiifolia*
	× ***aurantium*** 'Aber's Narrowleaf' (F)	SCit
	- subsp. ***bergamia***	see *C.* × *limon*
	- 'Bouquet de Fleurs'	see *C.* × *aurantium* - 'Bouquet'
	- 'Gou-tou Cheng' (F)	SCit
§	- Grapefruit Group (F)	SPre SVic
	- - 'Foster' (F)	SCit
	- - 'Golden Special' (F)	SCit SVic
	- - 'Marsh' (F)	SCit
	- - 'Oroblanco' (F)	SCit
	- - 'Red Blush' (F/S)	SCit
	- - 'Star Ruby' (F/S)	SCit
	- - 'Wheeny'	see *C. maxima* 'Wheeny'
	- 'Robinson' (F)	SCit
§	- (Sour Orange Group) 'Bouquet' (F)	SCit
	- - 'Bouquetier de Nice' (F)	SCit
	- - 'Chinotto' (F)	SCit SPre
	- - 'Seville' (F)	LSRN SCit

	Plant	Suppliers / cross-reference
	- - 'Smooth Flat Seville' (F)	SCit
§	- Sweet Orange Group (F)	ETod SCit SHil SPre SVic
§	- - 'Baia' (F/S)	SCit
	- - 'Embiguo' (F)	SCit
	- - 'Jaffa'	see *C.* × *aurantium* (Sweet Orange Group) 'Shamouti'
	- - 'Lane Late' (F)	NLar SCit
§	- - 'Malta Blood' (F)	SCit
	- - 'Maltaise Sanguine'	see *C.* × *aurantium* (Sweet Orange Group) 'Malta Blood'
	- - 'Navelate' (F)	SCit
	- - 'Navelina' (F/S)	CDoC SCit SPre
	- - 'Newhall' (F/S)	NLar SCit
	- - 'Ruby' (F)	ELan
	- - 'Salustiana' (F/S)	SCit
§	- - 'Sanguinelli' (F)	SCit
§	- - 'Shamouti' (F)	SCit
	- - 'Spanish Sanguinelli'	see *C.* × *aurantium* (Sweet Orange Group) 'Sanguinelli'
	- - 'Succari' (F)	SCit
	- - 'Tarocco' (F)	SCit
	- - 'Valencia' (F)	SCit SVic
	- - 'Washington'	see *C.* × *aurantium* (Sweet Orange Group) 'Baia'
	- - 'Washington Navel'	see *C.* × *aurantium* (Sweet Orange Group) 'Baia'
§	- (Tangelo Group) 'Minneola' (F)	SCit
§	- - 'Nova' (F/S)	SCit
	- - 'Orlando' (F)	SCit
	- - 'Ugli' misapplied	see *C.* × *aurantium* 'Minneola'
	- - 'Ugli' (F)	SCit
	- (Tangor Group) 'Ellendale' (F)	SCit
	- - 'Murcott' (F)	SCit
	bergamia	see *C.* × *limon*
	- bergamot	see *C.* × *limon* Bergamot Group
	'Buddha's Hand'	see *C. medica* 'Fingered'
	calamondin	see *C.* × *microcarpa*
	deliciosa	see *C. reticulata* 'Willowleaf'
	× ***floridana*** 'Eustis' (F)	SCit SPre
§	***hystrix***	CDoC ELan IDee LSRN NLar NPla SCit SPre
	× ***insitorum*** 'C-35' (F)	SCit
	- 'Carrizo' (F)	SCit
	- 'Swingle' (F)	SCit
§	***japonica*** (F) ♀H1c	CDoC ELan EPfP SCit SHil SPre
	- Hong Kong kumquat (F)	SCit
	- 'Nagami' (F)	SPre
	kinokuni	see *C. japonica*
	'Kucle' (F)	SCit
	kumquat	see *C. japonica*
	'La Valette' (F)	LSRN SPre
	× ***latifolia*** (F/S)	CDoC EPfP NLar SCit SPre
	- 'Bearss' (F)	SCit
	- variegated (v)	SPre
	latipes Hook. f. & Thomson ex Hook. f.	see *C. hystrix*
	limetta (F)	SVic
	limettioides (F)	SCit SPre
§	× ***limon*** (F)	ETod LSRN SCit SHil SVic
§	- Bergamot Group (F)	SPre
	- 'Eureka'	see *C.* × *limon* 'Garey's Eureka'
	- 'Eureka Variegated' (F/v)	SCit
	- 'Fino' (F)	SCit
	- 'Four Seasons'	see *C.* × *limon* 'Garey's Eureka'
§	- 'Garey's Eureka' (F)	ELan EPfP LSRN NLar SCit SPre
	- 'Imperial' (F)	SCit
	- 'Improved Meyer'	see *C.* × *limon* 'Meyer'
	- 'Lemonade' (F)	SCit
	- 'Lisbon' (F)	SCit
	- 'Lunario' (F)	SCit
§	- 'Meyer' (F) ♀H2	CBcs CHll CTri ELan EPfP LSRN NLar SCit SPre
	- 'Ponderosa' (F)	SCit
	- 'Quatre Saisons'	see *C.* × *limon* 'Garey's Eureka'
	- 'Rangpur' (F)	SCit
	- 'Sfusato d'Amalfi' (F)	SCit
	- 'Siracusano' (F)	SCit
	- 'Variegata' (F/v) ♀H2	SCit SPre
	- 'Verna' (F)	SCit
	- 'Villa Franca' (F)	SCit
	- 'Yen Ben' (F)	SCit
	- 'Zagara Bianco' (F)	SCit
	× ***limonia***	see *C.* × *limon*
	'Lipo' (F)	NLar SPre
	macrophylla (F)	SCit
	madurensis	see *C. japonica*
§	***maxima*** 'Wheeny' (F)	SCit
	medica 'Cidro Digitado'	see *C. medica* 'Fingered'
	- var. ***digitata***	see *C. medica* 'Fingered'
	- 'Ethrog' (F)	SCit SPre
§	- 'Fingered' (F)	SCit SPre
	- var. ***sarcodactylis***	see *C. medica* 'Fingered'
	× ***meyeri***	see *C.* × *limon*
§	× ***microcarpa*** (F) ♀H1c	CDoC NLar SCit SHil SPre
	- Philippine lime	see *C.* × *microcarpa*
§	- 'Tiger' (F/v)	SCit
	- 'Variegata'	see *C.* × *microcarpa* 'Tiger'
	× ***mitis***	see *C.* × *microcarpa*
	× ***nobilis*** Lour.	see *C. reticulata* 'Willowleaf'
	- var. ***inermis***	see *C. japonica*
	- Ortanique Group	see *C.* × *aurantium* Sweet Orange Group
	× ***obovata*** (F)	SPre
§	- 'Fukushu' (F)	SCit
	× ***paradisi***	see *C.* × *aurantium* Grapefruit Group
	- 'Wheeny'	see *C. maxima* 'Wheeny'
§	***reticulata*** (F)	SPre
	- 'Clausellina' (F/S)	SCit
	- 'Clemenlate'PBR (F) **new**	ELan
	- var. ***deliciosa***	see *C. reticulata* 'Willowleaf'
	- 'Fina' (F/S)	SCit
	- 'Hashimoto' (F/S)	SCit
	- Mandarin Group (F)	CDoC EPfP
	- - 'Clemenpons'PBR (F) **new**	ELan
	- - 'Clementine' (F)	CDoC EPfP SPre
	- - 'Encore' (F)	SCit
	- - 'Fortune' (F)	SCit
	- - 'Fremont' (F)	SCit
	- - 'Nules' (F/S)	SCit
	- 'Marisol' (F/S)	SCit
	- 'Miyagawa' (F)	SCit
	- 'Nour' (F)	SCit
	- 'Nova'	see *C.* × *aurantium* (Tangelo Group) 'Nova'
	- 'Okitsu' (F/S)	SCit
	- 'Owari' (F/S)	SCit
	- Satsuma Group	see *C. reticulata*
§	- 'Willowleaf' (F)	SCit
	sinensis	see *C.* × *aurantium* Sweet Orange Group
	- 'Jaffa'	see *C.* × *aurantium* (Sweet Orange Group) 'Shamouti'
	- 'Washington'	see *C.* × *aurantium* (Sweet Orange Group) 'Baia'
§	× ***taitensis*** rough lemon (F)	SCit
	- Schaub rough lemon	see *C.* × *taitensis* rough lemon

§ ***trifoliata*** CAgr CArn CBcs CDoC CDul EBee ELan EPfP IDee LRHS MBlu MGil MRav SCit SMad SPlb SVic
- 'Flying Dragon' IVic LEdu SCit SMad
unshiu see *C. reticulata*
volkameriana see *C. × limon*

Cladium (*Cyperaceae*)

mariscus XLum

Cladrastis (*Papilionaceae*)

§ ***kentukea*** CBcs CDul CLnd CMCN CTho EBee ELan EPfP EUJe EWTr LRHS MBlu MRav NLar WHar WMat
§ - 'Perkins Pink' MBlu
- 'Rosea' see *C. kentukea* 'Perkins Pink'
lutea see *C. kentukea*
sinensis CBcs CExl CFil EPfP IArd MBlu SKHP WPGP

Clavinodum (*Poaceae*)

§ ***oedogonatum*** MWht

Claytonia (*Portulacaceae*)

alsinoides see *C. sibirica*
caroliniana EBee
§ ***perfoliata*** GPoy MNHC WHer
§ ***sibirica*** CAgr IMou LPot LSou MSCN XLum
- f. ***albiflora*** LPla MPie WCot WMoo
virginica EBee ECho LAma MPie WFar WMoo WPnP

Clematis ✿ (*Ranunculaceae*)

BWJ 7630 from China WCru
CC 711 CExl
CC 4710 CExl
CC 5904 GKev
'Abigail' (Vt) NHaw
Abilene = 'Evipo027' (EL) CFlo CKel CRos ELan EPfP ETho LBuc LRHS NTay SPoG SWCr
'Abundance' (Vt) ♀H6 CDoC CFlo CKel CRHN CWCL ETho LCro LRHS LSRN MAsh MBri NHol NTay SDix SPer WBod WFar
acuminata var. ***sikkimensis*** B&SWJ 7202 WCru
addisonii NHaw WSHC
afoliata WThu
'Ai-Nor' (EL) ETho
'Akaishi' (EL) ETho
akebioides NHaw
aff. ***akebioides*** **new** CEvo
Alabast = 'Poulala'PBR (EL) ♀H6 LRHS MBri SCoo
Alaina = 'Evipo056' (EL) CRos ELan LRHS NTay SLon SPoG SWCr
'Alba Luxurians' (Vt) CBcs CCon CDoC CFlo CKel CRHN CSam CTri CWCL ELan ELon EPfP ETho LCro LRHS LSRN MAsh MBri MGos MLHP NHol NTay SCob SDix SLim SPer SPoG SWCr
'Albatross' (EL) LSRN
albicoma LLHF
'Albiflora' (A) NTay
'Albina Plena' (A/d) ETho LRHS SLon
'Aleksandrit' (EL) NHaw
'Alice Fisk' (EL) CKel ETho LRHS LSRN MBri MSwo NHaw SLim
'Aliide' (LL) NHaw
'Alionushka' (I) ♀H6 CKel CRHN CWCL ELan EPfP ETho LRHS LSRN MBri NLar SDix SLim SPoG SWCr
Alita = 'Evipo070' (Vt) LCro NTay
'Allanah' (LL) ELon ETho LRHS LSRN NHaw SCoo SLim SPoG WHar
alpina GKin IBoy LCro LRHS LSRN MAsh MRav NHaw NPer SCob SEWo SPlb SPre SWvt
- 'Albiflora' see *C. sibirica*
- 'Columbine White' see *C.* 'White Columbine'
I - 'Odorata' (A) NHaw
§ - 'Pamela Jackman' (A) ♀H6 CDoC CKel CMac CWCL ELan LRHS LSRN MAsh MBri MMuc NEgg NTay SCoo SDix SLim SPer SPoG SRkn SWCr SWvt WFar
- pink-flowered GKev
- 'Stolwijk Gold' (A) CWGN ETho MBlu NHaw NTay SRms
alternata CWGN EBee ETho
'Amelia' (I) SMDP
'Ameshisuto' (EL) ETho
'Amethyst Beauty' (A) EPfP LBuc LRHS
Amethyst Beauty = 'Evipo043' (LL) CRos ETho NTay SLon SWCr
'Andante' (I) CWGN
'Andromeda' (EL) CLng ETho LRHS MBri NHaw NTay SDix SWCr
Aneta = 'Evipo055'PBR CFlo CWGN EBee LCro LRHS NTay
Angela = 'Zoang'PBR (EL) ELan NTay
Angelique = 'Evipo017' (EL) CFlo CKel CLng COtt CRos CWGN ELan EPfP ETho LRHS NPri NTay SCoo SLon SPer SWCr
§ ***angustifolia*** EBee
'Anita' (Ta) CFlo EBee EPfP ETho IPot LSRN NHaw SLim SMDP
Anna Louise = 'Evithree'PBR (EL) ♀H6 CLng COtt CRos EPfP ETho LRHS LSRN MBri NTay SCoo SLim SLon SWCr
'Annabel' (EL) LSRN MAsh
Anniversary = 'Pynot' (EL) LSRN SCoo
'Aotearoa' (LL) ♀H6 IPot MBri NHaw
'Aphrodite' (I) CCon CRos
'Aphrodite Elegafumina' (I) CCon CRHN CWGN LRHS NHaw SWCr
apiifolia TCM 12-956 **new** CEvo
'Apollonia' CWGN IPot
'Apple Blossom' (Ar) ♀H4 Widely available
'Arabella' (I) ♀H6 CFlo CKel COtt CRHN CRos CWCL CWGN ELan ELon EPfP EShb ETho LCro LRHS LSRN MAsh MBri NEgg NLar NTay SDix SLim SPer SPoG SRkn SWCr SWvt WHar WSHC
§ Arctic Queen = 'Evitwo'PBR (EL) ♀H6 CFlo CKel CRos EPfP ETho LBuc LCro LRHS LSRN MAsh MBri NPri NTay SCoo SLon SPoG SWCr WHar
armandii Widely available
- 'Enham Star' LPfy LRHS MBri MGos
§ - 'Little White Charm' EBee ELan LRHS MBri SKHP SWCr
- 'Meyeniana' see *C. armandii* 'Little White Charm'
§ - 'Snowdrift' CBcs CFlo CKel CLet CSBt CWSG ELan EPfP ETho LCro LRHS LSRN MAsh MGos MSwo NLar NTay SCob SKHP SPer SPoG SRms SWCr
× ***aromatica*** CFlo CKel CWGN EAEE ELan EPfP ETho LRHS NTay SCoo WHlf
§ 'Asagasumi' (EL) ETho
'Asao' (EL) CLng CRos ELan EPfP ETho IBoy LRHS MBri NTay SCoo SPoG SWCr

'Ascotiensis' (LL) CLng CRHN EPfP ETho LRHS MBri NHaw NTay SCoo SLim SLon SPoG SWCr
'Ashva' (LL) CWGN
Avant-garde = 'Evipo033'PBR (Vt) CFlo CKel CLng COtt CRos CWCL CWGN ELan EPfP ETho EUJe LRHS NTay SLon
§ Aztek = 'Daihelios' (Ta) CDoC CKel LRHS SCoo
Baby Doll = 'Zobadol' (EL) CWGN ETho NTay
Baby Star = 'Zobast' (EL) CWGN ETho NTay
§ 'Bagatelle' (LL) CLng LRHS MBri MGos NHaw
'Bal Maiden' (Vt) CRHN NHaw
'Barbara' (LL) LSRN NTay SDix
'Barbara Dibley' (EL) CFlo CKel CTri CWCL LRHS MAsh NHaw SCoo SLim
'Barbara Harrington'PBR (LL) CLng COtt LRHS LSRN SLon SWCr
'Barbara Jackman' (EL) CKel CLng CWCL ETho LRHS LSRN MAsh MSwo NEgg NTay SCoo SLon SPer SWCr
'Beata' (LL) CWCL MGos NHaw
'Beautiful Bride'PBR (EL) **new** LCro NTay
'Beauty of Worcester' (EL) CCon CKel CWCL CWSG ELan ELon EPfP ETho LRHS LSRN MAsh MSwo NEgg NHaw NTay SCoo SDix SLim SPer
'Bees' Jubilee' (EL) CBcs CKel CMac CRos CWCL CWSG ELan ELon ETho LCro LRHS LSRN MAsh MSwo NBir NEgg NLar NTay SLim SPer SPoG SWvt
'Bella' (EL) LSRN
'Belle Nantaise' (EL) LRHS NTay SCoo SRms
'Belle of Woking' (EL) CLng ELan ELon LRHS LSRN MAsh NEgg NTay SCoo SLim SWCr SWvt
'Ben's Beauty' (A) CDoC CFlo
Bernadine = 'Evipo 061' **new** LRHS
'Berry Red' (A) CWGN
'Best Wishes'PBR CKel LRHS NTay SLon SPoG SWCr
§ 'Beth Currie' (EL) CLng EPfP LRHS SWCr
'Betty Corning' (Vt) CFlo CKel CLng CRHN CWGN EBee ELan EPfP ETho IPot LRHS LSRN MBri MGos NTay SCoo SLon SPoG SRms SWCr SWvt
'Betty Risdon' (EL) ETho
Bijou see *C.* Thumbelina
'Bill MacKenzie' (Ta) ♀H6 CFlo CMHG CMac CSam CSpe CTri CWib ELan EPfP ETho LHop LPfy LRHS LSRN MAsh MBri MGos MRav NHol NPri NTay SCob SDix SLim SPer SPoG SRms SWCr SWvt WSHC
'Black Prince' (Vt) CFlo CKel CRHN CWGN ELan EPfP ETho IPot LCro LRHS LSRN MBri NHaw NLar NTay SLim SLon SMDP SPer SRms
'Black Tea' (LL) CKel EPfP IPot LRHS LSRN NEgg NHaw NTay SLim SLon SWCr
§ 'Błękitny Anioł' (LL) ♀H6 CFlo CKel CLng CMac CRHN CRos CWCL CWGN EBee ELon ETho LRHS MAsh MBri MLHP NLar NTay SCob SCoo SPer SWCr
Blue Angel see *C.* 'Błękitny Anioł'
'Blue Belle' (Vt) CRHN ELan LRHS NEgg SLon WFar
'Blue Bird' (A/d) CBcs CWCL ELan LRHS MAsh NTay SRms
Blue Blood see *C.* 'Königskind'
'Blue Boy' (EL) see *C.* 'Elsa Späth'
'Blue Boy' (I) see *C.* × *diversifolia* 'Blue Boy'
'Blue Dancer' (A) CBcs CKel CLng COtt EPfP ETho LRHS MBri MGos NLar NTay
'Blue Eclipse' (A) CFlo CKel CWGN MBri NHaw NHol NTay
'Blue Eyes' (EL) ELon ETho LSRN MBri NHaw NTay
§ 'Blue Light'PBR (EL/d) CFlo CWGN ELan LRHS NLar NTay
Blue Moon = 'Evirin'PBR (EL) CLng CRos ETho LRHS LSRN MBri NLar NTay SCoo SLon SWCr
Blue Pirouette = 'Zobluepi'PBR (I) CWCL IPot LRHS MBri MJak NEgg
Blue Rain see *C.* 'Sinii Dozhd'
'Blue Ravine' (EL) EPfP LRHS MBri NLar NTay SCoo
Blue River = 'Zoblueriver'PBR CWCL CWGN ELan
§ 'Blushing Ballerina' (A/d) MBri
'Bolam Belle' (Vt) NHaw
Bonanza = 'Evipo031'PBR (Vt) CLng CRos EPfP LRHS MBri NLar NTay SCoo SLon SPoG
× ***bonstedtii*** 'Crépuscule' (H) ECtt SMDP
Bourbon = 'Evipo018'PBR (EL) CLng CRos ELan EPfP ETho LRHS NTay SCoo SLon SWCr
brachyura B&SWJ 8854 WCru
'Brocade' (Vt) CRHN NHaw
'Broughton Bride' (A) CBot CFlo CKel CLng CWGN ETho LCro LRHS MBri NHol NTay SMDP WHar
'Broughton Star' (M/d) ♀H4 Widely available
'Brunette' (A) CFlo CKel EBee ELan EPfP ETho LCro LOPS LRHS MAsh MBri NHaw NLar NTay SLon SWCr
buchananiana Finet & Gagnep. see *C. rehderiana*
buchananiana DC. B&SWJ 8333a WCru
'Buckland Beauty' (V) CFlo CLng CWGN ETho LRHS MJak NHaw SMDP
'Buckland Cascade' ETho SMDP
'Buckland Pixie' (Vt) NHaw
'Burford Bell' (V) NHaw
'Burford Princess' (Vt) CRHN NHaw
'Burford White' (A) MBri NLar
'Burma Star' (EL) CFlo CKel CWCL CWGN EPfP ETho LRHS MBri NTay SDix
'By the Way' (M) SMDP
Caddick's Cascade see *C.* 'Semu'
calycina see *C. cirrhosa* var. *balearica*
§ ***campaniflora*** EShb ETho GCal NHaw
'Candida' (EL) MBri
'Candleglow' (A) MBri NHaw
'Candy Stripe' CLng CRos LRHS NTay SCoo SPoG
'Capitaine Thuilleaux' see *C.* 'Souvenir du Capitaine Thuilleaux'
'Cardinal Wyszynski' see *C.* 'Kardynał Wyszyński'
'Carmencita' (Vt) CRHN EBee LRHS LSRN NHaw SCoo SLon
'Carnaby' (EL) CBcs CKel COtt CWCL ELan ELon EPfP ETho LRHS LSRN MAsh MBri NEgg NTay SCoo SLim SPoG SWCr SWvt WHar
'Carol Klein' (I) NHaw
'Carol Leeds' (Vt) NHaw
'Caroline' (LL) CWGN ETho LSRN NTay SDix
× ***cartmanii*** hort. 'Avalanche'PBR (Fo/m) CFlo CKel CRos ELan EPfP ETho GBin LRHS MBri MGos NLar NPri NTay SCoo SLim SLon SPoG SWCr SWvt
- 'Joe' (Fo/m) ♀H4 CBcs CFlo CKel ELan EPfP ETho EWes ITim LCro LOPS LRHS LSRN NTay SCob SCoo SPoG SWCr SWvt WIce
- 'Joe' × ***marmoraria*** (Fo) ECho MAsh SWCr

- 'Joe' × 'Sharon' LSRN
- Michiko = 'Evipo044' PBR (Fo) LRHS NTay
- 'White Abundance' PBR (Fo/f) LRHS NLar SPoG

× ***cartmanii*** hort. × ***petriei*** (Fo) ECho
Cassis = 'Evipo020' PBR CKel CLng COtt ELan ETho LRHS LSRN MBri NTay SCoo SLon SPer
'Catherine Clanwilliam' (T) CWGN SMDP
'Celebration' Caddick see *C.* 'Pink Celebration'
'Celebration' PBR Godfrey (EL) CFlo NTay SLim
Cezanne = 'Evipo023' PBR (EL) CFlo CKel CLng COtt CRos ELan EPfP ETho LRHS MGos NTay SCoo SLon SWCr
'Chacewater' (Vt) CRHN
'Chalcedony' (EL) CWCL CWGN ETho
Chantilly = 'Evipo021' PBR (EL) CFlo CKel CLng COtt CRos ELan EPfP ETho LBuc LRHS LSRN NTay SCoo SLon SWCr
'Charissima' (EL) CWGN LRHS NLar SCoo SWCr
'Charlie Brown' (LL) CRHN NHaw
'Chatsworth' (Vt) CRHN CWGN LRHS NHaw SLon SWCr
Chelsea = 'Evipo100' LRHS NTay SLon SWCr
Cherokee see *C.* Ooh La La
Chevalier = 'Evipo040' PBR (EL) CRos ELan EPfP LRHS NTay SLon SPoG SWCr
chiisanensis WSHC
- B&SWJ 4560 WCru
- B&SWJ 8800 WCru
- B&SWJ 12725 WCru
- 'Korean Beauty' (A) CRos
- 'Lemon Bells' (A) CRos ELan EPfP LRHS MAsh SCoo SLon SPoG SWCr
- 'Love Child' (A) ELan IPot NTay
chinensis misapplied see *C. terniflora*
chinensis Osbeck PAB 3751 LEdu
- RWJ 10042 WCru
Chinook = 'Evipo013' PBR CLng LRHS SLim
'Chris' (H) **new** SMDP
chrysantha see *C. tangutica*
chrysocoma misapplied see *C. spooneri*
chrysocoma Franch. SMDP
'Cicciolina' (Vt) CRHN ETho NHaw
cirrhosa CTri LRHS MAsh SCob
§ - var. ***balearica*** CBcs CDoC CFlo CKel CMac CTri CWCL ELan EPfP ETho LCro LHop LRHS LSRN MAsh MBri MGos MRav MSwo NTay SCob SDix SEND SLim SPer SPoG SWCr SWvt
- 'Jingle Bells' (C) CFlo CKel CLng CMac COtt CWCL EPfP ETho LCro LOPS LRHS LSRN MAsh MBri MGos NLar NTay SCob SCoo SLim SLon SPoG SWCr
- 'Ourika Valley' (C) CWGN ELon ETho LOPS LRHS MAsh MBri NLar NTay
- var. ***purpurascens*** 'Freckles' (C) 🏆H4 Widely available
- - 'Lansdowne Gem' (C) CFlo CKel CMac CWCL CWGN CWib LCro LRHS NLar NTay SKHP SMDP SPoG SWCr SWvt
- 'Wisley Cream' (C) 🏆H4 CBcs CFlo CKel CMac COtt CWCL CWib ELan EPfP ETho LCro LRHS LSRN MAsh MBri MJak MSwo NLar NTay SCob SCoo SEND SKHP SLim SPer SPoG SRms SWCr SWvt
clarkeana misapplied see *C. urophylla* 'Winter Beauty'

§ ***columbiana*** var. ***tenuiloba*** GKev LLHF
- - 'Ylva' (A) WAbe
'Columbine' (A) CDul EBee LRHS MBri MSwo NTay SDix SPer
'Columella' (A) EBee ETho MGos NLar
'Comtesse de Bouchaud' (LL) 🏆H6 CDoC CFlo CKel CMac COtt CTri CWCL EBee ELan ELon EPfP EShb ETho LRHS LSRN MAsh MBri MGos MRav NPri NTay SDix SLim SPer SPoG SWCr WBor
Confetti = 'Evipo036' PBR (Vt) CFlo CLng EBee EPfP ETho LRHS LSRN MBri NTay SLim SLon
'Congratulations' (EL) ELon LRHS LSRN
connata GQui
- B&SWJ 2956 WCru
- CC 7137 **new** CEvo
aff. ***connata*** GWJ 9431 from West Bengal WCru
- HWJK 2176 from Nepal WCru
'Constance' (A) 🏆H6 CFlo CKel CLng CMac CWCL EBee EPfP ETho LRHS LSRN MBri NEgg NLar NTay SCoo SPer SPre SRms SWCr WFar
'Continuity' (M) CWGN
'Cora' (I) CWGN
'Cornish Spirit' (Vt) CRHN
'Corona' (EL) CLng ELon EPfP LRHS MBri SCoo
'Côte d'Azur' (H) CBcs CCse CExl GCal LRHS
'Countess of Lovelace' (EL) CBcs ELan EPfP ETho LRHS LSRN MBri NTay SCoo
Country Rose = 'Zocoro' (A) **new** EPfP
§ 'Crimson King' (LL) MBri NHaw NLar
'Crinkle' PBR (M) SPoG
§ ***crispa*** NHaw
§ Crystal Fountain = 'Evipo038' PBR (EL) CFlo CKel CLng COtt CRos CWCL CWGN ELan EPfP ETho LBuc LCro LRHS LSRN MBri NTay SCoo SLim SLon SPoG SWCr
'Danae' (Vt) NHaw
Dancing Dorien = 'Zodado' PBR (EL) IPot
Dancing Queen = 'Zodaque' PBR (EL) ETho MBri NTay
Dancing Smile = 'Zodasmi' PBR (EL) NTay
Dancing Teruko see *C.* 'Teruko'
'Daniel Deronda' (EL) 🏆H6 CDoC CFlo CKel CWCL CWGN CWSG ELan ETho IBoy IPot LRHS LSRN MAsh MBri NBir NTay SCoo SDix SLim SPoG SWCr
'Dark Eyes' (Vt) CKel CWGN ETho IPot
'Dark Secret' (A) MBri NHaw NHol NTay
dasyandra NJM 11.075 **new** WPGP
'Dawn' (EL) CFlo ETho LRHS LSRN MBri NTay SCoo SWCr
'De Vijfhoeven' (Vt) NHaw
'Débutante' (EL) NHaw
'Denny's Double' (EL/d) CWGN ETho LRHS NTay
'Destiny' (EL) CWGN
Diamantina = 'Evipo039' PBR (EL) CFlo CKel CRos EPfP ETho LBuc LRHS NTay SLon SPoG SWCr
'Diamond Anniversary' (A) **new** CWCL NTay
'Diana' (LL) EBee ETho LSRN NHaw
Diana's Delight = 'Evipo026' CKel CRos EPfP ETho LRHS LSRN NTay SLon SPoG SWCr
dioscoreifolia see *C. terniflora*

§ × ***diversifolia*** CRHN LRHS NHaw SDix SWvt WCot
§ - 'Blue Boy' (I) CRHN NHaw SLon
- 'Heather Herschell' (I) CFlo CRHN CTsd NHaw SMDP
§ - 'Hendersonii' (I) CFlo CWCL EAEE ELan ETho GBuc LHop LRHS LSRN MBri MCot MRav MSwo NBir SPer SWat SWvt WCot
§ - 'Olgae' (I) CExl NHaw
'Doctor Mary' (V) NHaw
'Doctor Penelope' (M) WNPC
'Doctor Ruppel' (EL) CFlo CKel CMac COtt CWCL EBee ELon ETho IBoy LRHS LSRN MAsh MBri MSwo NBir NTay SCob SDix SLim SPer SWCr
'Dominika' (LL) NHaw
'Dorath' CKel CWGN LRHS NHaw NTay SWCr
'Dorothy Barbara' (M) SMDP
'Dorothy Tolver' (EL) ETho
'Dorothy Walton' see *C.* 'Bagatelle'
'Double Delight' (M) CFlo CWGN WNPC
'Duchess of Albany' (1897) (T) CFlo CKel CLng CTri CWCL CWib ELan EPfP ETho LCro LRHS LSRN MAsh MBri MGos NEgg NHol SDix SPer SWCr
'Duchess of Edinburgh' (EL) CBcs CKel CMac CWCL EBee ELan ELon EPfP IBoy LRHS LSRN MAsh MBri MGos MSwo NEgg NHol NTay SDix SLim SPoG SWCr SWvt WHar
'Duchess of Sutherland' (EL) NHaw
× ***durandii*** ♀H6 CBcs CFlo CKel COtt CRHN CSpe CWCL EBee ELan EPfP ETho LRHS LSRN MAsh MBri MGos MRav NTay SCoo SPer SPoG SWCr SWvt WCot
'Dutch Sky' (LL) CWGN ETho MBri
'Early Sensation' (Fo/f) CBcs CFlo CKel CTri CWib ELan ELon EPfP ETho EUJe LCro LRHS LSRN MAsh MBri NEgg NTay SCob SCoo SDix SLim SPer SPoG SPre SWCr SWvt
East River = 'Zoeastri' PBR (I) ELan IPot
'Eclipse' (H) EBee
Edda = 'Evipo074' (Boulevard Series) **new** LRHS
'Edith' (EL) ♀H6 CWCL ETho LSRN MBri NHaw NLar NTay
'Edomurasaki' (EL) MBri
'Édouard Desfossé' (EL) LRHS MBri
'Edward Prichard' CFlo CKel EPfP MAsh NTay SDix SMDP
'Eetika' (LL) CRHN ETho NHaw
'Ekstra' (LL) NHaw
'Eleanor' (Fo/f) GEdr
'Elf' (Vt) CWGN
'Elizabeth' (M) ♀H4 Widely available
§ 'Elsa Späth' (EL) CExl CKel CLng CMac COtt CTri ELan EPfP ETho LRHS LSRN MAsh MBri NEgg NTay SLim SPer SPoG SWCr SWvt
'Elten' (M) CKel
'Elvan' (Vt) CRHN NHaw NLar
'Ember' (I) CWGN
'Emerald Dream' **new** EBee
'Emilia Plater' (Vt) CRHN ETho LRHS MBri NHaw NTay SLon
Empress = 'Evipo011' PBR (EL) CFlo CLng CRos EBee ELan EPfP LRHS NTay SLon SWCr
Endellion = 'Evipo076' **new** LRHS
'Entel' (Vt) CRHN NHaw
× ***eriostemon*** see *C.* × *diversifolia*
'Ernest Markham' (LL) ♀H6 CBcs CDoC CKel CMac COtt CWCL ELan EPfP ETho IBoy LRHS LSRN MAsh MBri MGos MJak MSwo NEgg NPri NTay SDix SLim SPer SPoG SWCr SWvt
Esme = 'Evipo048' NTay
'Esperanto' (LL) NHaw
'Étoile de Malicorne' (EL) MBri
'Étoile de Paris' (EL) MBri
'Étoile Rose' (Vt) CCon CMac CRHN CTri CWCL EBee ELan EPfP ETho IPot LRHS LSRN MAsh NEgg NHaw NHol NTay SCoo SDix SLim SLon SPer SWCr WBod
'Étoile Violette' (Vt) ♀H6 Widely available
Evening Star = 'Evista' (EL) EPfP MBri
'Everett' (V) **new** SMDP
Exciting = '20exci' (EL) NTay
'Fair Rosamond' (EL) MBri NHaw NLar NTay
'Fairy' (Fo/f) ECou
Fairy Blue see *C.* Crystal Fountain
'Fairydust' (Vt) NHaw
× ***fargesioides*** see *C.* 'Paul Farges'
fasciculiflora CMHG
- KWJ 12160 WCru
- L 657 CBot EPfP WCru WPGP
'Fascination' PBR (I) CFlo CWGN EBee MBri NTay
fauriei WSHC
Filigree = 'Evipo029' PBR CFlo CLng COtt CRos LBuc LRHS MGos NTay SPoG SWCr
'Firefly' (EL) EBee
'Fireworks' (EL) CFlo CKel CWCL CWGN ELon EPfP ETho IBoy LRHS LSRN MAsh MBri MRav NEgg NLar NTay SLim SPer SPoG SWCr
flabellata B&SWJ 8431 **new** WCru
flammula CCon CFlo CKel CWib ELan EPfP LCro LRHS LSRN MAsh MBlu MBri MRav NTay SDix SPer SPoG SRms SWCr SWvt WSHC XSen
- 'Rubra Marginata' see *C.* × *triternata* 'Rubromarginata'
Fleuri = 'Evipo042' PBR (Boulevard Series) (EL) CFlo CKel CLng CRos CWCL EPfP ETho LBuc LRHS LSRN LSou NTay SCoo SLon SPoG SWCr
florida CWGN SWvt
- 'Bicolor' see *C. florida* var. *florida* 'Sieboldiana'
- var. ***flore-pleno*** 'Plena' (d) CFlo CLng CWCL ELan EPfP ETho LCro LRHS LSRN MAsh NEgg NTay SPoG SWCr
§ - var. ***florida*** 'Sieboldiana' (d) CBcs CFlo CKel CWCL CWGN CWSG ELan ELon EPfP ETho LCro LOPS LRHS LSRN MAsh MBri NEgg NTay SLim SPoG SRkn SWCr SWvt WFar
- var. ***normalis*** Pistachio = 'Evirida' PBR (LL) CFlo CKel CLng CRos CWGN ELan EPfP ETho LRHS LSRN MAsh MGos NLar NTay SLim SLon SPoG SWCr
- - 'Thorncroft' (LL) ETho
'Floris V' (I) MCot NHaw NLar
'Fluffy Duck' (Vt/d) NHaw
foetida × 'Lunar Lass' (Fo) ECho
foetida × ***petriei*** ECho
'Fond Memories' (EL) CFlo CKel CWCL CWGN EPfP ETho IPot LCro LOPS LRHS LSRN MBri NLar NTay SLon SWCr
Forever Friends = 'Zofofri' PBR (LL) CWGN ETho IPot LRHS NTay SLon SWCr
'Forget-me-not NLP1' LSRN MBri NLar WHar

	Name	Suppliers
	forrestii	see *C. napaulensis*
§	***forsteri***	WSHC
	'Foxtrot' (Vt)	CRHN
	'Foxy' (A) ♀H6	CFlo CLng LRHS MBri NLar NTay SLon
	Fragrant Oberon = 'Hutbron'PBR (Fo)	CFlo ECou LCro LOPS NTay SMDP SWvt
	'Fragrant Spring' (M)	CKel CSBt CWGN ELon ETho IBoy LCro LOPS LRHS MMuc NLar NTay SLim SMDP SPoG SWCr
	'Frances Rivis' (A) ♀H6	CBot CFlo CKel CMac CWCL ELan EPfP ETho LCro LOPS LRHS LSRN MAsh MBlu MBri MRav MSwo NFav NLar NTay NWea SDix SPer SPoG SRms SWCr
	'Francesca' (A)	LSRN
	'Frankie' (A) ♀H6	CFlo CKel CLng COtt EBee ELan EPfP ETho LRHS LSRN MAsh MBri MGos MHer NTay SCoo SWCr
	Franziska Maria = 'Evipo008' (EL)	CFlo CLng EPfP LCro LRHS MAsh MBri MGos NTay SCoo SLon SWCr
	'Frau Mikiko' (EL)	MGos
	'Frau Susanne' (EL)	ETho
	'Freda' (M) ♀H6	CKel CRHN CTri CWGN ELan EPfP ETho LCro LRHS LSRN MAsh MBlu MBri MRav NEgg NHol NTay SDix SLim SPer SPoG SWCr WFar
	fremontii	NHaw SBrt
	'Fryderyk Chopin' (EL)	EBee NHaw NLar
	'Fudō' (V) **new**	NHaw
	'Fujimusume' (EL) ♀H6	CFlo CKel CLng CWGN ETho IPot LRHS MAsh NHaw NTay SPoG SWCr
	fujisanensis B&SWJ 11370	WCru
	'Fukuzono'	ETho LRHS LSRN NHaw NTay SDix SWCr
	fusca misapplied	see *C. japonica*
	fusca Turcz.	GBin
	- dwarf	CWGN
§	- var. ***fusca***	ETho WSHC
	- var. ***kamtschatica***	see *C. fusca* Turcz. var. *fusca*
	'Fusca Peveril' (V) **new**	NHaw
	'Fuyu-no-tabi' (EL)	ETho
	'Gabrielle'	LSRN MBri
	Galore	see *C.* Vesuvius
	'Garnet' (V)	NHaw
	Gazelle = 'Evipo014'PBR	CLng LRHS SKHP
	'Generał Sikorski' (EL)	CBcs CFlo CKel CMac CWCL ELan EPfP ETho LRHS LSRN MAsh MBri MGos NTay SCoo SLim SPer SWCr SWvt
	gentianoides	WAbe
	'Geoffrey Tolver' (LL)	ETho NHaw
	'Georg' (A/d)	EBee
	'Georg Ots' (LL)	NHaw
	Giant Star = 'Gistar'PBR (M)	CKel CLng EBee ELon IBoy LRHS NEgg NLar NPer SLim SRkn WNPC
	'Gillian Blades' (EL) ♀H6	CFlo CKel CLng COtt ELan EPfP ETho LBuc LRHS LSRN MAsh MBri MGos NHaw NTay SCoo SWCr SWvt
§	'Gipsy Queen' (LL) ♀H6	CBcs CMac CWCL ELan ELon EPfP ETho IBoy LRHS LSRN MAsh MBri MGos NEgg NTay SDix SLim SPer SPoG SWCr SWvt
	Giselle = 'Evipo051'	EPfP LRHS NTay SLon SPoG
	'Gladys Picard' (EL)	MBri NHaw
	glauca Turcz.	see *C. intricata*
	glaucophylla	WCru WSHC
	'Golden Harvest' (Ta)	NLar
	Golden Tiara = 'Kugotia'PBR (Ta) ♀H6	CKel CWGN ETho GBin LSRN MBri NLar NTay SRms WCot
	'Gothenburg' (M)	MBri
	'Grace' (Ta)	EPfP NHaw NLar
	gracilifolia BWJ 8002	WCru
I	'Grandiflora' (F)	COtt WFar
	grandiflora	LBuc SLim SRms
	'Grandiflora Sanguinea' (Vt)	NTay
	grata misapplied	see *C.* × *jouiniana*
	'Gravetye Beauty' (T)	CFlo CKel CMac COtt CRHN CWCL ELan EPfP ETho LRHS LSRN MAsh MBri MGos MJak NHol NTay SDix SLon SPoG SRms SWCr SWvt
	grewiiflora B&SWJ 2956	WCru
	'Guernsey Cream' (EL)	CCon CFlo CWCL EPfP ETho LCro LOPS LRHS LSRN MAsh MBri NLar NTay SCoo SDix SLim SRkn SWCr
	Guiding Promise = 'Evipo053'	CLng LRHS NTay SLon
	'Gunta' (LL)	NHaw
	'H.F. Young' (EL)	CFlo CKel ELan EPfP ETho LRHS LSRN MAsh MBri MGos NLar NTay SCoo SDix SPer SWvt
	'Hågelby Pink' (Vt) ♀H6	CRHN CWGN NHaw
	'Hagley Hybrid' (LL)	CDoC CMac COtt CWCL EBee ELan EPfP ETho LRHS LSRN MAsh MBri MGos MJak MRav NEgg NLar NTay SCob SDix SLim SPer SPoG SRms SWCr SWvt
	'Hakuōkan' (EL)	EPfP ETho LRHS LSRN MBri NLar SCoo
	'Hakuree' ambig.	CKel
	'Hakuree' K. Ozawa (I)	EBee ETho LRHS MLHP SMDP
	'Hanaguruma' (EL)	CKel ETho LSRN MBri
	'Hanajima' (I)	SChF SMDP
	'Hania' (EL)	EBee ETho
	'Happy Anniversary' (EL)	LBuc LSRN MBri NLar NTay
§	Happy Birthday = 'Zohapbi'PBR (LL)	LCro LSRN NTay
	Harlow Carr = 'Evipo004'PBR	CLng CMac EPfP LRHS MBri NTay SCoo SLim SRms SWCr
	'Haru Ichiban' (EL)	ETho
	'Hayate'	CWGN EBee
	'Helen Cropper' (EL)	ETho
	'Helios'	see *C.* Aztek
	'Helsingborg' (A) ♀H6	CFlo CKel CLng COtt EBee ELan EPfP ETho LRHS MAsh MBri NPri NTay SCoo SPoG SRms SWCr
I	'Hendersonii' (I)	CFlo CKel GBuc LSRN
	hendersonii Koch	see *C.* × *diversifolia* 'Hendersonii'
	hendersonii Stand.	see *C.* × *diversifolia*
I	'Hendersonii Rubra' (Ar)	LRHS
	'Hendryetta'PBR (I)	LRHS MBri NEgg SWvt
	henryi	CRos EShb LSRN MAsh MBri NTay
	- B&SWJ 3402	WCru
	- var. ***morii*** B&SWJ 1668	WCru
	'Henryi' (EL)	CFlo CKel CMac CTri CWCL EBee ELan EPfP ETho LCro LRHS LSRN MBri MRav MSwo NEgg SDix SPer SPoG SWCr
	heracleifolia	CCon CFis CMac CPou ECtt GLog LRHS MWhi NLar SGSe WBor WOld XLum
	- Alan Bloom	see *C. tubulosa* Alan Bloom
	- 'Blue Dwarf' (H)	ETho MGos SMDP WAbe
	- 'Cassandra' (H)	CFlo CSpe CWGN CWld EAEE ECtt ELon EPfP EShb ETho EWld GLog LCro LRHS LSRN MAvo MCot MWhi NCGa SChF SMDP SPoG WGwG

	Name	Suppliers
	- 'China Purple' (H)	CExl CPou GBin LRHS MCot MHol MWhi NLar
	- var. ***davidiana***	see *C. tubulosa*
	- 'Pink Dwarf' (H)	CWGN ETho NLar NTay SMDP WAbe
	- 'Roundway Blue Bird' (H)	CBot LHop NHaw SMDP
	'Herbert Johnson' (EL)	NHaw
	hexapetala	see *C. angustifolia*
	hexapetala Forster	see *C. forsteri*
	hexasepala	see *C. forsteri*
	hirsutissima	SBrt
	'Honora' (LL)	CFlo CWGN LRHS MAsh MBri NTay SCoo
	'Horn of Plenty' (EL)	LRHS MBri NHaw
	'Huldine' (LL) ♀H6	CBcs CKel CLng CRHN CWCL ELan EPfP ETho LRHS LSRN MAsh MBri MRav NTay SDix SLon SPer SWCr SWvt
	'Huvi' (LL)	CWGN ETho MGos NHaw
	'Hybrida Sieboldii' (EL)	EUJe SCoo
	Hyde Hall = 'Evipo009'PBR (EL)	CFlo CKel CLng CMac CWGN ELan EPfP LRHS MAsh MBri MGos NTay SCoo SLim SLon SPer SRms SWCr
	'Hythe Egret' (Fo)	ECho LLHF
	I Am a Little Beauty = 'Zolibe' (Vt)	CRHN NHaw NTay
	I am Happy = 'Zoiamha' (Vt) **new**	SCob
	I am Lady J = 'Zoiamlj' (Vt)	IPot NHaw SCob
	I Am Lady Q = 'Zoiamladyq'PBR (Vt)	CWGN LRHS NHaw NTay SCob
	I Am Red Robin = 'Zorero'PBR (A)	MBri
	ianthina 'Josie's Midnight Blue' (V) **new**	NHaw
	- var. ***kuripoensis***	NHaw WSHC
	- - B&SWJ 700	WCru
	'Ibi' (EL)	CWGN
	Ice Blue = 'Evipo003'PBR (Prairie Series) (EL)	CLng CRos ELan EPfP ETho LRHS MBri NTay SCoo SLim SLon SWCr
	'Ice Queen' (EL)	MAsh
	'Ingrid Biedenkopf' (Vt)	NHaw
	Inspiration = 'Zoin'PBR (I)	ELan MBri NLar SCoo
	integrifolia	CExl CFis CPou ELan EPfP GKev IFoB LHop LRHS MBel MBri MHer NLar NPer NTay SRms WHil WHoo
	- RCB UA 10	WCot
I	- 'Alba' (I)	CCon CFlo ECtt LRHS LSRN MBri NBir NHaw NTay SCoo SRms
	- 'Blue Ribbons' (I)	CSpe SPhx WSHC
	- 'Hendersonii' Koch	see *C. × diversifolia* 'Hendersonii'
	- mid-blue-flowered	MGos
	- 'Olgae'	see *C. × diversifolia* 'Olgae'
	- 'Ozawa's Blue' (I)	CWGN ETho MBNS MLHP
	- violet-flowered **new**	GKev
	- white-flowered	see *C. integrifolia* 'Alba'
	'Intermedia Rosea' (I)	NChi
§	***intricata***	CExl
	'Iola Fair' (EL)	EBee
	ispahanica	NHaw
	'Iubileinyi-70' (LL)	NHaw
	'Ivan Olsson' (EL)	CWCL ETho IPot
	'Izumi' M.Takeuchi (LL)	ETho
	'Jackmanii' (LL) ♀H6	CBcs CKel CMac COtt CTri EBee EPfP ETho IBoy LCro LRHS LSRN MAsh MBri MGos MJak NWea SCoo SEND SLim SPoG SWCr SWvt WHar
	'Jackmanii Alba' (EL)	CWCL ELan ELon EPfP ETho LRHS LSRN MAsh MBri SCoo SLim SPoG
	Jackmanii Purpurea = 'Zojapur'PBR (LL)	ETho LRHS NTay
	'Jackmanii Rubra' (EL)	ETho
	'Jackmanii Superba' misapplied	see *C.* 'Gipsy Queen'
	'Jackmanii Superba' ambig. (LL)	CDul CFlo CKel CMac CWCL CWSG ELan EPfP ETho LRHS MAsh MBri MGos MMuc MRav MSwo NEgg NPer NPri NTay SCob SDix SLim SPer SPoG SWCr
	'Jacqueline du Pré' (A) ♀H6	CBcs CFlo CKel CMac EBee ELan EPfP ETho LRHS MBri NTay SMDP
	'Jacqui' (M/d)	CKel CWCL
	'James Mason' (EL)	ETho LSRN MBri
	'Jan Fopma'PBR (I)	CWGN LRHS NTay
	'Jan Lindmark' (A/d)	CLng ETho LRHS MAsh MBri NLar NTay SCoo SPre
§	'Jan Paweł II' (EL)	ELan ETho LRHS MBri SCoo SPer
§	***japonica***	NHaw WSHC
	- B&SWJ 11204	WCru
	'Jasper' (V)	EBee IPot
	'Jean Caldwell' (Vt)	NHaw
	'Jeanne's Pink' **new**	CWCL LCro
	'Jenny' (M/d)	CFlo CKel CWCL ETho LRHS LSRN SPoG
	'Jenny Caddick' (Vt)	ETho MGos NHaw
	'Jerzy Popiełuszko' (EL)	ETho
	Jessica = 'Evipo012'PBR	CLng LRHS
	Jewel of Merk	see *C.* Happy Birthday
	John Howells = 'Zojohnhowells'PBR (Vt)	CFlo CWCL ETho LSRN MBri NTay SLon
	'John Huxtable' (LL) ♀H6	CFlo CKel CLng ETho LRHS MBri NHaw NTay
	John Paul II	see *C.* 'Jan Paweł II'
	'John Treasure' (Vt)	CRHN LRHS NHaw NLar NTay
	'John Warren' (EL)	LRHS MAsh MBri NHaw NTay SCoo SWCr
	'Jolly Jake' (Vt)	CFlo
	Josephine = 'Evijohill'PBR (EL)	CFlo CKel CLng COtt CRos CWCL CWGN EPfP ETho EUJe LCro LRHS LSRN MAsh MBri MGos NLar NTay SCoo SLim SPer SPoG SRkn SWCr SWvt WHar
§	× ***jouiniana***	MRav SEND SWvt WSHC
	- 'Chance' (H)	NHaw
	'Julka' (EL)	CFlo CWCL ETho NHaw NTay
	'June Pyne' (EL)	MBri
	'Justa' (Vt)	NHaw
	'Juuli' (I)	LRHS LSRN MBri
	'Kaaru' (LL)	CRHN
	'Kacper' (EL)	ETho NHaw
	'Kaen' (EL)	EBee ETho NTay
	'Kaiu' (V)	CFlo CKel CWCL CWGN LRHS NHaw NTay SLim SMDP SWCr
§	'Kakio' (EL)	CLng CWCL ETho LRHS LSRN MAsh MBri NEgg NTay SDix SLim SPer SPoG SWCr
I	'Kamilla' (EL)	CWGN
§	'Kardynał Wyszyński' (EL)	ETho MBri
§	'Kasmu' (Vt)	NHaw
	'Kathleen Dunford' (EL)	LSRN MBri NHaw NTay SCoo
	'Kathryn Chapman' (Vt)	CRHN NHaw
	'Kaunitar' (LL)	NHaw
	'Ken Donson' (EL) ♀H6	LRHS MBri SCoo
	'Ken Pyne' (LL)	CFlo
	'Kermesina' (Vt) ♀H6	CCon CKel CRHN EBee ELan EPfP ETho IBoy LCro LRHS MAsh MBri MJak SCoo SDix SLim SPer SPoG SRms SWCr
	'Ketu Õde' (LL)	NHaw

	Name	Suppliers
	'Kiev' (Vt)	NHaw
	'Killifreth' (Vt)	CRHN NHaw
	'King Edward VII' (EL)	LRHS MBri
	Kingfisher = 'Evipo037'PBR (EL)	CFlo CKel CRos ELan EPfP LBuc LRHS NTay SCoo SLon SWCr
	'Kinju Atarashi' (LL)	ETho NTay
	'Kiri Te Kanawa' (EL)	CKel CWCL ELon ETho LRHS LSRN MBri NLar NTay
	'Kommerei' (LL)	ETho NHaw
§	'Königskind' (EL)	ETho NLar
	koreana	MAsh WCru
	'Krakowiak'PBR (Vt) **new**	NHaw
	'Külli' (LL)	NHaw
	ladakhiana	GQui NHaw
	- CC 7134	ITim
	- CC 7135	EWld
	'Lady Betty Balfour' (LL)	CMac ETho LRHS MBri NTay SCoo SWvt
	'Lady Bird Johnson' (T)	CFlo CWCL LRHS LSRN NTay SCoo
	'Lady Caroline Nevill' (EL)	LRHS MBri
	'Lady Londesborough' (EL)	MBri NHaw NTay SCoo SDix
	'Lady Northcliffe' (EL)	CKel CLng CTri CWCL EPfP ETho LRHS MAsh MBri NTay SDix
	'Lambton Park' (Ta) ♀H6	CCon CDoC CKel CRHN CWCL ETho LRHS LSRN NHaw NLar NTay SMDP
	lasiandra	NHaw
	'Last Dance' (Ta)	CRHN
	'Lasurstern' (EL) ♀H6	CBcs CExl CFlo CKel CMac CTri ELan EPfP ETho LCro LRHS LSRN MAsh MBri NEgg NTay SDix SPer SPoG SWCr SWvt WFar
	'Laura Denny' (EL)	ETho
	'Lavender Twirl'	CRHN
	'Lawsoniana' (EL)	CMac LRHS MBri
	'Lech Wałęsa' (EL)	ETho
	'Lemon Chiffon' (EL)	CLng LRHS NTay
	Liberation = 'Evifive'PBR (EL)	CLng LRHS MBri NLar NTay SCoo SLim SLon SPoG SWCr
§	***ligusticifolia***	NHaw
	'Lily the Pink' (V/Vt) **new**	NHaw
	'Lincoln Star' (EL)	CLng CMac ELon LRHS MAsh MBri NEgg SDix SLim SPer SWvt
	'Lisboa' (Vt)	NHaw
	'Little Bas' (Vt)	CRHN IPot MBri NHaw NLar NTay SLon
	'Little Butterfly' (Vt)	CRHN NHaw
	'Little Mermaid' (EL)	CFlo CWCL EBee ETho
	'Little Nell' (Vt)	CRHN ELan EPfP ETho LRHS LSRN MAsh NTay SCoo SDix SLon
I	'Longiflora'	CFlo
	'Lord Herschell'	CFlo CKel CWCL CWGN ETho LRHS MBri SMDP
	'Lord Nevill' (EL)	EPfP LRHS MBri
	'Louise Pummell' (Fo)	ECou
	'Louise Rowe' (EL)	CFlo CLng CWCL ELan ETho LRHS LSRN MBri NHaw NTay SWCr
	loureiroana HWJ 663	WCru
	'Love Jewelry' (EL)	ETho
	'Lunar Lass' (Fo/f)	CFlo EBee ECho ETho LRHS NTay WAbe
	'Lunar Lass Variegata' (Fo/v)	ECho LLHF
	'Luxuriant Blue' (Vt)	CRHN NHaw
	'M. Koster' (Vt)	CDoC CRHN ETho LRHS NHaw SLon SRms
	macropetala (d)	CBcs CLng CSBt ELan EPfP ETho GKev LAst LRHS MAsh MGos MMuc MRav MWhi NTay SDix SPer
	- 'Alborosea'	see *C.* 'Blushing Ballerina'
	- 'Blue Lagoon'	see *C. macropetala* 'Lagoon' Jackman 1959
	- 'Lagoon' Jackman 1956	see *C. macropetala* 'Maidwell Hall' Jackman
	- 'Lagoon' ambig.	LSRN SWCr
§	- 'Lagoon' Jackman 1959 (A/d) ♀H6	ETho LCro LRHS LSRN MAsh MBri MSwo NHol NTay SCoo SPoG
	- 'Maidwell Hall' ambig. (A)	SCob
§	- 'Maidwell Hall' Jackman (A/d)	CTri EPfP ETho LSRN MAsh MGos NTay
	- 'Wesselton' (A/d) ♀H6	CFlo CKel CTri CWCL EBee EPfP ETho LCro LRHS MAsh MBri NHaw NTay SPre SRms SWCr
	- 'White Moth'	see *C.* 'White Moth'
	'Madame Baron-Veillard' (LL)	CLng LRHS MBri SCoo
	'Madame Edouard André' (LL)	CLng CWCL EPfP LRHS MAsh MBri NTay SCoo SWCr
	'Madame Grangé' (LL) ♀H6	LRHS MBri NHaw SCoo
	'Madame Julia Correvon' (Vt) ♀H6	Widely available
	'Madame le Coultre'	see *C.* 'Mevrouw Le Coultre'
	'Majojo' (Fo)	GEdr LLHF
	mandschurica	ETho GCal NHaw NLar XEll XLum
	'Margaret Hunt' (LL)	ELan ETho IBoy LSRN MBri NHaw NTay
	'Mari' (LL)	NHaw
	'Maria' Kivistik (LL)	NHaw
	'Maria Băsescu'	NTay
	'Maria Cornelia'PBR (Vt)	CWGN EBee ETho LCro LOPS NTay
	'Marie Boisselot' (EL) ♀H6	CBcs CFlo CKel CMac CTri CWCL ELan EPfP ETho IBoy LRHS LSRN MAsh MBri MRav MSwo NPri NTay SDix SPer SPoG SWCr SWvt
	'Marie-Louise' (EL) **new**	EBee
	'Marinka'	EBee
	'Marjorie' (M/d)	CBcs CDoC CKel COtt CTri CWCL CWSG ELan EPfP GKin IBoy LRHS LSRN MAsh MBri MGos MRav NEgg NTay SLim SPer SPoG SRms SWCr WFar
	'Markham's Pink' (A/d) ♀H6	Widely available
	marmoraria	EAEE ECho EPot LHop LRHS SPlb SRms WAbe
	- 'Timpany Treasure'	ITim
	marmoraria × petriei	ECho
	'Marmori' (LL)	CWGN ETho NHaw
	'Mary Habberley' (Vt)	NHaw
	'Mary Rose'	see *C. viticella* 'Flore Pleno'
§	'Maskarad' (Vt)	MBri
	Masquerade (Vt)	see *C.* 'Maskarad'
I	'Masquerade' (EL)	MBri
	maximowicziana	see *C. terniflora*
	'Mayleen' (M) ♀H4	CPou CSBt CSam CTri EPfP ETho IBoy LRHS MAsh MBri MRav NEgg NTay SCoo SLim SPer SPoG SRms SWCr SWvt
	'Mazury' (LL)	ETho
I	'Melodie' (Vt)	NHaw
§	'Mevrouw Le Coultre' (EL)	MJak
	meyeniana var. ***insularis*** B&SWJ 6700	WCru
	Mienie Belle = 'Zomibel'PBR (T)	CWGN ETho IPot NHaw
	'Mikelite' (Vt)	MGos NHaw
	'Miniseelik' (LL)	NHaw NTay
	'Minister' (EL)	MBri
	'Minuet' (Vt) ♀H6	CRHN ELon EPfP ETho LCro LOPS LRHS MAsh MGos NTay SCob SCoo SDix SLon SPer SWvt

	Miranda = 'Floclemi'PBR (I)	CWGN SMDP
	'Miriam Markham' (EL)	MBri
	'Miss Bateman' (EL)	CDoC CFlo CKel CMac COtt CTri CWCL CWSG ELan EPfP ETho LCro LRHS LSRN MAsh MBri MGos NEgg NTay SDix SLim SPer SPoG SWCr WBor
	'Miss Christine' (M)	CFlo CSam ELan LCro LSRN NTay SMDP
	Mississippi River = 'Zomisri' (I) new	IPot
	'Mister Hans Horn' (Vt)	NHaw
	Mon Amour = 'Zomoa' (EL)	CWGN EBee NTay
	'Moniuszko' (EL)	CWGN
	montana	CExl CSBt GGal MAsh SCob SDix SEWo
	- B&SWJ 6724 from Taiwan	WCru
	- B&SWJ 6930	WCru
	- var. ***alba***	see *C. montana* var. *montana*
	- 'Alexander' (M)	CPou CRHN EPfP LRHS SWCr
	- 'Da Yun' (M) new	IPot
	- var. ***grandiflora*** (M) 🏆H4	CDul CKel CMac CSam CWSG EBee ELan EPfP ETho GKin LBuc LCro LHop LPot LRHS MBri MJak MMuc NBir NPri NTay SCob SEND SLim SPer SPoG SRms SWCr SWvt
§	- var. ***montana***	CBar LRHS MAsh MGos MJak SCob SPer SPoG
	- var. ***rubens*** misapplied	see *C. montana* var. *montana*
	- var. ***rubens*** E.H.Wilson	CDoC CSBt CTri ELan EPfP ETho GGal LRHS MBri NHol NWea SDix SPlb
I	- - 'Odorata' (M)	EPfP ETho GKin LRHS MRav NTay SCoo SLim WHar
	- - 'Pink Perfection' (M)	CDoC CKel CMac CRHN CWSG EBee ELan EPfP GKin LCro LRHS LSRN MAsh MBri NTay SCob SCoo SLim SPer SPoG SWCr SWvt WFar WHar
	- - 'Tetrarose' (M) 🏆H4	Widely available
I	- 'Rubens Superba' (M)	COtt CTri GKin NEgg NTay SRms SWCr WFar
	- var. ***sericea***	see *C. spooneri*
	- 'Superba' (M)	MBri
	- var. ***wilsonii***	CFlo CKel CSam ELan EPfP ETho GKin LRHS LSRN MBri MRav MSwo NTay SDix SMDP SPer SPoG SRms SWCr SWvt
	'Monte Cassino' (EL)	CWGN EBee NTay
	'Moonbeam' (Fo)	ECou EPot GEdr ITim MRav
	Moonfleet = 'Evipo046' (LL)	CLng LRHS MGos NTay SWCr
§	'Moonlight' (EL)	LRHS MAsh
	'Moonman' (Fo)	ECou LLHF
	Morning Cloud	see *C.* 'Yukikomachi'
	'Morning Heaven' (Vt)	NHaw
	Morning Star = 'Zoklako'PBR (EL)	CWGN ETho IPot LRHS
	Morning Yellow = 'Cadmy'PBR (M)	IBoy LRHS
	'Mrs Cholmondeley' (EL) 🏆H6	CKel CWCL ELan EPfP ETho LRHS LSRN MAsh MBri MGos MSwo NPri NTay SCob SLim SPer SPoG SWCr
	'Mrs George Jackman' (EL) 🏆H6	CFlo CLng CWCL ETho LRHS NLar NTay SCoo
	'Mrs James Mason' (EL)	EBee
	'Mrs N.Thompson' (EL)	CKel CMac COtt CTri CWCL ELan ELon ETho IBoy LRHS LSRN MAsh MBri NBir NEgg NHol NPer NTay SDix SLim SPer SPoG SWCr
	'Mrs P.B.Truax' (EL)	LRHS NTay
	'Mrs Robert Brydon' (H)	ECtt LSRN MSCN NLar NTay SRms
	'Mrs T. Lundell' (Vt)	CRHN MGos NHaw
	'Multi Blue' (EL)	CBcs CFlo CKel COtt CWCL CWSG ELan ELon EPfP EUJe IBoy LRHS LSRN MAsh MBri MGos MMuc NTay SLim SPer SPoG SRkn SRms SWCr WHar
	'My Angel'PBR (Ta)	ELan IPot NHaw NLar NTay SCob
	'Myojō' (EL)	LRHS
§	***napaulensis***	CFlo CTri CWCL EPfP ETho LCro NHaw SMDP WCru WSHC
I	'Natacha' (EL)	CRos NHaw NTay SCoo
	'Natascha' (EL)	CLng CWCL LRHS LSRN MBri SWvt
	'Negritianka' (LL)	LRHS LSRN MBri NHaw
	'Negus' (LL)	NHaw
	'Nelly Moser' (EL) 🏆H6	Widely available
	'Nelly Moser Neu' (EL)	NTay
	Neva = 'Evipo050' (Boulevard Series) new	LRHS
	'New Dawn' (M)	NHaw
	'New Love'PBR (H)	ETho LSRN NHaw NLar NTay
	'Night Veil' (Vt)	NHaw
	'Niobe' (EL) 🏆H6	CBcs CKel CMac COtt CRos CWCL ELan EPfP EShb ETho EUJe IBoy LCro LRHS LSRN MAsh MBri MGos MSwo NEgg NHol NTay SCob SDix SLim SPer SPoG SRms SWCr WFar
	'North Star' (EL)	CKel EPfP NTay
	North Star (LL)	see *C.* 'Põhjanael'
	'Nunn's Gift' (Fo)	ETho NTay
	nutans var. ***thyrsoidea***	see *C. rehderiana*, *C. veitchiana*
	'Oberek' (Vt) new	NHaw
	'Ocean Pearl' (A)	CFlo ETho LSRN MBri NLar NTay
	ochotensis	LLHF
	Octopus = 'Zooct'PBR (A)	CFlo NTay
	'Odoriba' (V)	CRHN CWGN ETho LRHS NHaw SMDP
	'Olimpiada-80' (EL)	NHaw
	'Omoshiro' (EL)	CWGN ETho IPot LRHS NHaw NTay
§	Ooh La La = 'Evipo041'PBR (Boulevard Series) (EL)	CFlo CKel CLng COtt CRos CWCL ELon EPfP ETho LBuc LRHS LSou NTay SCoo SPer SPoG SWCr
	Opaline	see *C.* 'Asagasumi'
	orientalis L.	EBee GCra SCoo SWvt
	- 'Orange Peel'	see *C. tibetana* subsp. *vernayi* var. *vernayi* 'Orange Peel'
*	- 'Rubromarginata' (Ta)	MBri
	- 'Sherriffii'	see *C.* 'Sherriffii'
	- var. ***tenuiloba***	see *C. columbiana* var. *tenuiloba*
	orientalis × tangutica	SWvt
	otophora	NHaw
	'Ovation'PBR (Fo) new	EBee
	'Paala' (EL)	NHaw
	'Pagoda' (Vt)	CDoC CRHN EBee EPfP IPot LRHS MBri SCoo SLon SRms
	Palette = 'Evipo034'PBR (Vt)	CLng LRHS MBri SLon
	'Pamela' (F)	ETho NHaw NTay
	'Pamela Jackman' (Vt)	MBri NEgg
	'Pamela Jackman' (A)	see *C. alpina* 'Pamela Jackman'
	'Pamiat Serdtsa' (I)	ELon ETho NHaw
	'Pamina' (EL)	ETho
	'Pangbourne Pink' (I) 🏆H6	CFlo CKel CWCL EPfP ETho LRHS MBri NHaw NTay SCoo SWCr
	paniculata Thunb.	see *C. terniflora*
	paniculata J.G.Gmel. (f)	ETho
	'Paola' (EL/d)	EBee
	'Paradise Queen' (EL)	LBuc MBri NLar NTay

'Parasol' (EL) EBee MBri
Parisienne = 'Evipo019'PBR (Boulevard Series) (EL) CFlo CLng COtt CRos EPfP ETho LRHS LSou NTay SCoo SLon SPoG SWCr
parviflora DC. see *C. campaniflora*
parviloba var. ***bartlettii*** B&SWJ 6788 WCru
'Pastel Blue' (I) ETho
'Pastel Princess' (EL) NHaw
'Pat Coleman' (EL) CWCL ETho
patens CCse
- 'Korean Moon' (EL) WCru
§ - 'Manshuu Ki' (EL) CFlo CWCL ELon ETho LRHS NEgg SPer SRms
- 'Yukiokoshi' (EL) ETho IPot
§ 'Paul Farges' (Vb) 🏆H6 CKel CWGN EShb ETho GLog MBri MNrw NEgg NHaw NTay SMDP
'Pauline' (A/d) 🏆H6 CBcs LRHS LSRN MBri NTay SCoo SLim SWCr
'Pendragon' (Vt) CRHN NHaw
'Pennell's Purity' (LL) CFlo NTay
Peppermint = 'Evipo005'PBR (d) CFlo CLng CRos ELan EPfP LRHS NTay SCoo SLon
'Perida' (LL) CWGN EBee
'Perle d'Azur' (LL) CBcs CKel CMac CRHN CTri CWCL ELan ELon EPfP ETho LAst LCro LOPS LRHS LSRN MAsh MBri MSwo NEgg NTay SCob SDix SLim SPer SPoG SRms SWCr WFar
'Perrin's Pride' (Vt) CLng LRHS MBri MGos NHaw NLar NTay SCoo SWCr
Petit Faucon = 'Evisix'PBR (I) 🏆H6 CFlo CLng COtt EPfP ETho LRHS LSRN MBri MGos NLar NTay SCob SCoo SLim SPer SWCr SWvt
petriei WThu
'Peveril Pearl' (EL) NTay
'Peveril Pristine' (Vt) CWGN
'Peveril Profusion' (T) SMDP
Picardy = 'Evipo024'PBR (EL) CFlo CLng COtt CRos EPfP ETho LRHS NTay SCoo SLim SPoG SWCr
I 'Picton's Variety' (M) CTri MBri
'Piilu' (EL) CKel COtt CRos CWCL CWGN ELan ETho LRHS LSRN LSou MAsh MBNS MBri NHaw NLar NTay SCob SCoo SLim SPoG SRkn SWCr
'Pille' (LL) NHaw
§ 'Pink Celebration' (EL) ETho
Pink Champagne see *C.* 'Kakio'
'Pink Fantasy' (LL) CFlo CRHN CTri ETho LRHS MAsh MBri NLar NTay SCob SCoo SLim SRkn SWCr
'Pink Flamingo' (A) 🏆H6 CLng CWCL ELan EPfP LRHS MBri NTay SCoo SLim SPoG SRkn SWCr WBor
'Pink Ice' (I) CKel CWCL LRHS NHaw NTay
'Pirko' (Vt) NHaw
§ ***pitcheri*** NHaw
'Pixie' (Fo/m) CFlo CKel CLng EBee ECou ELan ELon EPfP ETho LRHS MGos NLar NTay SCoo SLim SPoG
pogonandra NHaw
§ 'Põhjanael' (LL) MBri NLar
Polar Bear see *C.* Arctic Queen
'Poldice' (Vt) 🏆H6 CRHN
'Polish Spirit' (LL) 🏆H6 Widely available
'Polonez' (Vt) NHaw
potaninii CCon GCra NSti
- 'Summer Snow' see *C.* 'Paul Farges'
'Praecox' (H) 🏆H6 CRHN CWCL CWld EAEE EBee ELan EPfP ETho LHop LRHS MBri MCot NBir NSti NTay SDix SPer WAul WCot
Pretty in Blue = 'Zopre'PBR (F) MBri SCob SWvt
'Primrose Star' see *C.* 'Star'
'Prince Charles' (LL) 🏆H6 CFlo CKel CPou CRHN CTri CWCL ELan EPfP ETho LRHS LSRN MAsh MBri MJak NHaw NLar NTay SCoo SDix SLim SPer SPoG SWCr SWvt WBod
'Prince George' new CWCL LCro LOPS LSRN NPri WHlf
§ 'Princess Diana' (T) 🏆H5 CFlo CKel COtt CRHN CTri CWGN EBee ELan ETho IPot LAst LBuc LCro LRHS LSRN MAsh MBlu MSwo NHol NTay SCob SCoo SLim SPer SPoG SRms SWCr SWvt
Princess Kate = 'Zoprika' (T) CWGN EBee EPfP ETho IPot LCro LOPS LRHS MBlu NTay SPoG
§ 'Princess of Wales' (1875) (EL) CWCL LSRN NLar SLon SWvt
'Prinsesse Alexandra'PBR (EL) ETho NTay
'Propertius' (A) CFlo CKel CWCL CWGN EBee ETho GEdr LRHS MGos NHaw NTay SMDP
'Prosperity' (M) CRHN ETho
'Proteus' (EL) CLng EBee ELan ELon EPfP LRHS MAsh MBri MGos NTay SCoo SLim SWCr WHar
psilandra CWJ 12377 WCru
'Purple Haze' (Vt) CRHN NHaw
'Purple Princess' (H) NTay
'Purple Spider' (A/d) CFlo CMac EPfP ETho LRHS MAsh MBlu MBri MLHP NHaw NLar NTay SCoo
'Purpurea Plena Elegans' (Vt/d) 🏆H6 Widely available
quadribracteolata NHaw
'Queen Alexandra' (EL) EBee
Queen Mother = 'Zoqum' (Vt) CWGN EPfP ETho LRHS
'Radiance' CWGN
'Ragamuffin' (EL/d) MGos
'Rahvarinne' (LL) ETho
'Ramona' (LL) CLng LRHS LSRN NHaw
ranunculoides NHaw
'Rapture' (T) MBri
'Rasputin' (LL) CWCL ETho
Rebecca = 'Evipo016'PBR (EL) CFlo CKel CLng COtt CRos CWCL CWGN ELan EPfP EUJe LBuc LCro LOPS LRHS LSRN MBri NTay SCob SCoo SLon SPer SPoG SWCr
recta CWCL ECtt MNrw NLar
- 'Lime Close' seedlings CAby CDes
- 'Purpurea' (F) CFlo CMea CWld EHoe ELan EPfP GKev IPot LHop LRHS MNrw NBir NChi NSti NTay SChF SDix SEND SPer SWCr XLum
- 'Velvet Night' (F) CSpe ECtt ETho GBuc LRHS MAvo MBel NEgg NLar SMDP WCot
'Red Ballon' (Ta) IPot
'Red Cooler' see *C.* 'Crimson King'
'Red Pearl' (EL) CFlo LRHS LSRN MBri NTay SWCr
I 'Red Star' (d) NTay
Reflections = 'Evipo035' (LL) CRos EPfP LRHS NTay SLon SWCr
§ ***rehderiana*** 🏆H5 CCon CDul CKel CRHN CSam EBee ELan EPfP ETho IDee LRHS MBlu MBri NBir NSti NTay SChF SDix

		SPer SWvt WCot WHea WPGP WSHC
	'Reiman' (LL)	NHaw
	'Remembrance' (LL)	CFlo EPfP ETho LSRN MBri
	repens 'Bells of Emei Shan'	ETho NTay
	'Rhapsody' ambig.	CLng EPfP ETho MAsh MBri MGos NTay SCoo SWCr
	'Rhapsody' B. Fretwell (EL)	LRHS LSRN NHaw
	'Ribble Red' (V)	NHaw
	'Richard Pennell' (EL) ♀H6	LRHS MAsh SWCr
	'Richard's Picotee' (Vt)	NHaw
	'Rising Star'	NHaw
	'Ristimägi' (LL)	NHaw
	'Robud'^{PBR} (M/d)	NPer
	'Roelie' (Vt)	NHaw
	'Roko-Kolla' (LL)	ETho NHaw
	'Romance' (Vt)	MBri
	'Romantika' (LL)	CFlo ELan ELon ETho IBoy IPot LCro LRHS LSRN MAsh MBri NHaw NTay SCoo XEll
	'Rooguchi' (I)	CFlo CWCL CWGN EBee ETho IPot LRHS MBri NHaw SDix
	'Rooran' (EL)	CWCL EBee ETho
	'Rosa Königskind' (EL)	ETho
	'Rosamunde' (LL)	ETho
	'Rose Supreme' (EL)	ETho
I	'Rosea' Westphal. (Vt)	NHaw
I	'Rosea' (I)	EPfP ETho LHop LRHS LSRN NTay
	Rosemoor = 'Evipo002'^{PBR} (EL)	CFlo CKel CLng COtt CRos CWCL CWGN EPfP ETho LRHS MAsh MBri NTay SCoo SLim SLon SWCr SWvt
	'Rosy O'Grady' (A) ♀H6	MAsh MBri NLar NTay SRms
	'Rosy Pagoda' (A)	ELan LRHS MBri NHaw NLar NTay SLim WBod
	'Rouge Cardinal' (LL)	CFlo CMac CWSG ELan ELon EPfP ETho IBoy LRHS LSRN MAsh MBri MGos MJak NEgg NTay SCob SDix SLim SPer SPoG SRms SWCr
	'Royal Velours' (Vt)	CDoC CFlo CKel CRHN CTri CWCL ELan EPfP ETho LCro LRHS LSRN MAsh MBri MGos NHol NTay SCob SCoo SDix SLim SPer SPoG SWCr
	Royal Velvet = 'Evifour'^{PBR} (EL)	LRHS LSRN MBri NTay SCoo
	'Royalty' (EL)	CWCL EBee ELan EPfP LRHS LSRN MAsh MBri MJak NBir NTay SCoo SWCr
	'Rubens Superba'	see *C. montana* 'Rubens Superba'
	'Ruby' (A)	CLng CWCL ELan EPfP ETho LRHS LSRN MAsh NEgg NTay SCoo SPer SRms
	'Ruby Glow' (EL)	CLng EBee EPfP LRHS LSRN NTay SCoo SWCr
	'Ruby Wedding' Fretwell (T)	CDoC CFlo CWCL CWGN EPfP LBuc LSRN MBri NTay SWvt
	'Rüütel' (EL)	CFlo CKel ELon ETho LRHS MAsh MBri NHaw NTay SCoo SMDP
	'Saalomon' (LL)	NHaw
	'Sally Cadge' (EL)	NHaw
	Sally = 'Evipo077' **new**	LRHS
	Samaritan Jo = 'Evipo075'	LRHS NTay SPoG SWCr
	'Sander' (H)	SMDP
	'Saturn' (EL)	MGos
	Savannah = 'Evipo015'^{PBR} (Vt)	CLng LRHS SLim
	'Scartho Gem' (EL)	CLng COtt LRHS MBri SCoo
	'Sealand Gem' (EL)	MBri NHaw
§	'Semu' (LL)	CWGN ETho NHaw
	'Serenata' (EL)	MBri
	serratifolia	CRHN ECtt ETho GAbr GEdr GLog MWhi SDix SPlb
	- B&SWJ 8458 from Korea	WCru
	'Sheila Thacker' (EL)	ETho
I	'Sherriffii' (Ta)	SWvt
	'Shikoo' (EL)	CWCL ETho LSRN NTay
	Shimmer = 'Evipo028' (LL)	CKel EPfP LRHS NTay SLon SWCr
	'Shirayukihime' (EL)	NLar
§	'Shiva' (A)	MBri
	'Shooun' (EL)	MBri
	'Sialia' (A/d)	CFlo CKel
§	***sibirica***	EPfP LRHS MBri
	'Signe' (Vt)	see *C.* 'Kasmu'
	'Siirus' (EL)	NHaw
	'Silver Moon' (EL)	CFlo CLng CWCL EPfP ETho LRHS MAsh MBri NLar NTay SCoo
	simensis	LEdu
	'Simplicity' (A)	MBri
	simsii Small	see *C. pitcheri*
	simsii Sweet	see *C. crispa*
	'Sinee Plamia' (LL)	NHaw
§	'Sinii Dozhd' (I)	CWCL NHaw
	'Sir Eric Savill' (M)	EBee ETho
	'Sir Garnet Wolseley' (EL)	MBri SDix
	'Sir Trevor Lawrence' (T)	LRHS NHaw
	'Sireen' (LL)	NHaw
	smilacifolia NJM 10.094	WPGP
	aff. ***smilacifolia*** HWJ 1049	WCru
	'Snow Queen' (EL)	CCon CFlo CKel ELon EPfP ETho LRHS MBri NTay SLim SPoG SRms WBod
	'Snowbird' (A/d)	CFlo CKel LRHS NHaw NTay SPer SPoG
	'Snowdrift'	see *C. armandii* 'Snowdrift'
	'Södertälje' (Vt)	CRHN EPfP ETho MBri SCoo
	'Solidarność' (EL)	ETho
	'Solina' (Vt) **new**	NHaw
	'Sonnette' (V)	CFlo CWGN NHaw
§	'Souvenir du Capitaine Thuilleaux' (EL)	CKel ELon LRHS MBri NTay
	'Special Occasion' (EL)	CLng COtt CWGN LRHS LSRN MBri NHaw NLar NTay SCoo SPoG SWCr
	Spiky = 'Zospi'^{PBR} (A/d)	CFlo
§	***spooneri***	CTri LRHS NTay SCoo SLim SWvt
	'Sputnik' (I)	CWGN NHaw
	stans	CEvo CExl CPou EBee IFro LLHF LRHS NLar SWCr
	- B&SWJ 5073	WCru
	- B&SWJ 6345	WCru
§	'Star'^{PBR} (M/d)	CDoC ELan EPfP LRHS MBri MSwo NLar SPer
	'Star of India' (LL)	CKel CLng COtt CWCL EPfP ETho LRHS MBri MGos NTay SCoo SLim SPer
	Star River = 'Zostarri'^{PBR} (I)	ELan IPot
I	'Starfish' (EL)	NHaw
	'Starlight' (M)	CKel CWCL ELon LRHS NTay SLim
	'Stasik' (LL)	NHaw
	'Stephanie' (A)	CFlo CKel
	Still Waters = 'Zostiwa'^{PBR} (EL)	CWGN ETho LRHS NTay
	'Strawberry Kiss' (V) **new**	NHaw
	Sugar Candy = 'Evione'^{PBR} (EL)	CLng LRHS MAsh MBri NTay SCoo SLim SWCr
	Summer Snow	see *C.* 'Paul Farges'
	Summerdream = 'Zosumdre' (EL)	ETho IPot NTay
	'Sundance' (Ta)	SMDP
	Sunny Sky = 'Zosusk'^{PBR} (Vt)	CFlo CKel NHaw NTay

	Name	Suppliers
	'Sunrise' (M/d)	IPot LRHS MBri MSwo NHaw NLar NTay
	'Sunset' (EL) Y^{H6}	CLng CWCL ELon LRHS LSRN MBri MGos NEgg NLar NTay SCoo SLim SWCr
	'Swedish Bells' (I)	CWGN
	'Sweet Scentsation' (F)	CFlo EPfP LCro LOPS MBri NHaw NLar NTay
	'Sweet Summer Love'PBR (F)	CWGN NHaw
	Sweetheart = 'Witswe'PBR (I)	ELan EPfP NTay
	'Sylvia Denny' (EL)	ELan EPfP ETho MAsh MBri
	'Syrena' (LL)	NHaw
	szuyuanensis B&SWJ 6791	WCru
	- CWJ 12455	WCru
	'Tae' (EL)	ETho
	'Tage Lundell' (A)	CFlo EBee EPfP LRHS MBri NLar
	'Tango' (Vt)	CRHN NHaw
§	***tangutica***	Widely available
	'Tapestry' (I)	NHaw
	'Tartu' (EL)	NHaw
	tashiroi purple-flowered B&SWJ 7005	WCru
	- 'Yellow Peril'	WCru
	Tekla = 'Evipo069'	NTay
	'Teksa' (LL)	NHaw
	Temptation = 'Zotemp'PBR (EL)	MJak NTay
	tenuiloba	see *C. columbiana* var. *tenuiloba*
§	***terniflora***	EPfP ETho NHaw SKHP WHar
	- B&SWJ 5751	WCru
§	'Teruko' (EL)	IPot
	'Teshio' (EL)	IPot
	texensis	NHaw WSHC
	- 'The Princess of Wales'	see *C.* 'Princess Diana'
	'The Bride' (EL)	CWCL CWGN EBee ETho LRHS LSRN
	The Countess of Wessex = 'Evipo073' (EL)	EPfP ETho LRHS NTay SPoG SWCr
	'The First Lady' (EL)	CWCL ETho MBri
	'The President' (EL) Y^{H6}	CDul CKel CMac COtt CTri CWCL CWSG ELan EPfP ETho IBoy LCro LRHS LSRN MBri MGos MSwo NEgg NPri NTay SCob SDix SLim SPer SPoG SRms SWCr WFar
	'The Princess of Wales' (EL)	see *C.* 'Princess of Wales' (1875)
	'The Princess of Wales' (T)	see *C.* 'Princess Diana'
	'The Vagabond' (EL)	CWCL ELan EPfP ETho LRHS LSRN MAsh MBri NHaw NLar NTay SCoo SLim SPoG SWCr
§	Thumbelina = 'Evipo030'PBR (EL)	CKel CLng COtt CRos CWCL LRHS MGos NTay SPoG SWCr
	thunbergii misapplied	see *C. terniflora*
	'Thyrislund' (EL)	CKel
	tibetana	NHaw
	- 'Black Tibet' (Ta)	CWGN
	- subsp. ***vernayi*** 'Glasnevin Dusk' (Ta)	SMDP WSHC
§	- - var. ***vernayi*** 'Orange Peel' LS&E 13342 (Ta)	CBcs CDoC ETho LRHS SEND
	'Tie Dye' (LL)	CWGN ELan EPfP ETho NHaw NTay
	'Tiiu' (LL)	NHaw
	'Tinkerbell'	see *C.* 'Shiva'
	'Titipu' (V) **new**	NHaw
	'Toki' (EL)	CWGN
	tongluensis GWJ 9358	WCru
	- HWJK 2368	WCru
	'Tranquility'	CWGN
	'Treasure Trove' (Ta)	SMDP
	'Triinu' (Vt)	NHaw
	'Trikatrei' (LL)	EBee
	× ***triternata***	LSRN
§	- 'Rubromarginata'	Widely available
	'Tsunami Child' (M)	IMou
§	***tubulosa***	SMDP
§	- Alan Bloom = 'Alblo'PBR (H)	LRHS
	- 'Wyevale' (H)	CFlo CMac CWld EAEE ELan ELon EPfP LHop LRHS MCot MRav NCGa NSti NTay SCoo SDix SMDP SPer SPoG WAul WCAu WCot
	'Twilight' (EL)	CFlo CKel CLng EPfP LRHS MAsh MBri NTay SWCr
	Twinkle = 'Zotwi' (I)	CWGN IPot
	uncinata B&SWJ 11368	WCru
	- CWJ 12373	WCru
	'Uno Kivistik'PBR (LL)	NHaw
§	***urophylla*** 'Winter Beauty'	CDoC CFlo CWCL EBee ELan ETho LCro LOPS LSRN MBri NTay SBrt SMDP SPoG WPGP
	urticifolia B&SWJ 8651	WCru
	- B&SWJ 8852	WCru
	'Utopia' (EL)	CWGN
	'Valge Daam' (LL)	CWGN ETho NHaw
	'Valle' (LL)	NHaw
	'Van Gogh' (M)	SMDP
	'Vanessa' (LL)	CRHN
	'Vanso'	see *C.* 'Blue Light'
§	***veitchiana***	NHaw
	'Venosa Violacea' (Vt) Y^{H6}	CCon CFlo CKel CRHN ELan EPfP ETho LRHS LSRN MAsh NHaw NHol NTay SCoo SDix SPer SPoG SRms SWCr
	'Vera' (M)	LRHS LSRN NTay SCoo SLim
	'Veronica's Choice' (EL)	CFlo CWCL ELan LRHS MBri MGos NHaw NTay
	Versailles = 'Evipo025'PBR (EL)	CLng EPfP LRHS NTay SLim SWCr
	versicolor	WSHC
§	Vesuvius = 'Evipo032'PBR (Vt)	CLng LRHS MBri SCoo SLim SLon SWCr
	'Vetka'PBR (LL)	NHaw
	Victor Hugo = 'Evipo007'PBR (LL)	CFlo CLng EBee LRHS NLar NTay SCoo
	'Victoria' (LL) Y^{H6}	CRHN ETho LRHS LSRN MBri NHaw NTay SCoo SWCr
	Viennetta = 'Evipo006'PBR (d)	CFlo CKel CLng CWCL CWGN EPfP ETho LRHS MGos MHtn NTay SCoo SLon SRms SWCr
	'Vihma' (LL)	NHaw
	'Ville de Lyon' (LL)	CBcs CFlo CKel COtt CRHN CWCL CWSG ELan EPfP GGal IBoy LRHS LSRN MAsh MBri MGos NEgg NTay SDix SLim SPer SPoG SWCr WBod WHar
	'Vince Denny' (Ta)	EBee MBri NHaw SMDP
	Vino = 'Poulvo'PBR (EL)	CLng LRHS MBri NHaw NTay SCoo SLim
	'Viola' (LL)	CFlo CWGN ELon ETho LRHS LSRN MBri NHaw NTay SDix SMDP
	'Violet Charm' (EL)	MBri NEgg
	'Violet Elizabeth' (EL)	EBee
	viorna	NHaw WCru
	virginiana misapplied	see *C. vitalba*
	virginiana Hook.	see *C. ligusticifolia*
§	***vitalba***	CArn CWld ECrN ETho NHaw NTay NWea WHer WSFF

viticella	CDul CRHN CWib ETho GKev MBri NHaw WSHC
- subsp. ***campaniflora***	see *C. campaniflora*
§ - 'Flore Pleno' (Vt/d)	CFlo CKel CRHN EBee ELan ELon EPfP ETho IPot LRHS LSRN NHaw NTay SLon SWCr
- 'Hågelby Blue' (Vt)	NHaw
- 'Hågelby White' (Vt)	CRHN CWGN NHaw
- 'Hanna' (Vt)	CRHN LSRN NHaw
- 'Mary Rose'	see *C. viticella* 'Flore Pleno'
'Vivienne'	see *C.* 'Beth Currie'
'Voluceau' (Vt)	CLng CPou CRHN CWCL ELan LRHS LSRN SRms SWCr
'Vostok' (LL)	MGos NHaw NTay
'Vyvyan Pennell' (EL)	CBcs CFlo CKel CMac COtt CTri CWCL CWSG ELan EPfP ETho EUJe IBoy LRHS LSRN MAsh MBri MSwo NEgg NLar NTay SLim SPer SPoG SWCr SWvt WFar
'W.E. Gladstone' (EL)	ETho LRHS
Wada's Primrose	see *C. patens* 'Manshuu Ki'
'Walenburg' (Vt) ♀H6	CKel CRHN CWGN ETho NHaw SLon
'Walter Pennell' (EL)	CBcs LRHS SCoo
'Warsaw' (Ta)	COtt NLar SWCr
'Warszawska Nike' (EL) ♀H6	CLng CMac CRHN CWCL ELan EPfP ETho LCro LRHS MAsh MBri MGos NTay SCob SCoo SLim SPer SPoG
'Warszawska Olga' (EL)	ETho
'Warwickshire Rose' (M)	CFlo CKel CLng CMac CRHN CTri CWGN ELan ETho LRHS LSRN MAsh NEgg NHaw NTay SLim SPoG SWCr WHar
'Wedding Day' (EL)	CFlo ETho LCro LSRN NLar NTay
'Wee Willie Winkie' (M)	SCoo
'Westerplatte' (EL)	CFlo CKel CLng CRHN CWCL CWGN EPfP ETho MBri MGos NHaw NTay SLim SPoG SWCr WHar
§ 'White Columbine' (A) ♀H6	CWCL ELan ETho LRHS MBri NTay SDix SLim SPer
'White Lady' (A/d)	NHaw
'White Magic' PBR (Vt)	ETho
§ 'White Moth' (A/d)	ELan ETho LSRN MAsh NHaw NHol SLim
'White Prince Charles' (LL) **new**	NHaw
'White Satin' (A)	EPfP LRHS SRms SWCr
'White Swan' (A/d)	MAsh MBri NHol NLar SCoo
'White Wings' (A/d)	CFlo LSRN
'Will Goodwin' (EL) ♀H6	CBcs CLng COtt CWCL ELan EPfP LRHS MBri SLim SRms
'William Kennett' (EL)	CWCL ELan ETho IBoy LRHS MBri MJak
williamsii	SMDP
'Willy' (A)	CBcs CLng COtt CWCL EBee ELan EPfP ETho LRHS MAsh MBri MGos MSwo NLar NTay SDix SLim SPer SRms WBod
Wisley = 'Evipo001' PBR (Vt) ♀H6	CBcs CKel CLng EPfP LRHS MBri MGos NLar NTay SLim SLon SWCr
'Xerxes' misapplied	see *C.* 'Elsa Späth'
'Yatsuhashi' ambig.	CCon LRHS
'Yellow Queen' Holland	see *C. patens* 'Manshuu Ki'
'Yellow Queen' Lundell/ Treasures	see *C.* 'Moonlight'
§ 'Yukikomachi' (EL)	ETho NHaw NTay
yunnanensis	WPGP
'Yvonne Hay' (I)	SMDP
Zara = 'Evipo062' (EL)	CRos ELan ETho LRHS NTay SLon SPoG SWCr
'Zephyr' (Vt)	NHaw

Clematopsis see *Clematis*

Clementsia see *Rhodiola*

Cleome (*Cleomaceae*)

hassleriana 'Helen Campbell' ♀H2	CSpe
Senorita Rosalita = 'Inncleosr' PBR	CSpe NPri

Clerodendrum (*Lamiaceae*)

bungei	CAbb CBcs CDul CExl CHll CMac CWib EBee ELan EPfP EUJe IDee LAst LRHS MAsh MBlu MGos NLar NSti SDix SEND SKHP SLim SMad SPer SPoG SSpi SWvt WBor WHor
- PAB 8953	LEdu
- 'Pink Diamond' (v)	CDoC CWGN ELan EUJe EWes LRHS LSRN LSou MGos NLar SKHP SLim SMDP SPer SPoG SWvt
§ ***chinense*** var. ***chinense*** (d) ♀H1b	CHll
- 'Pleniflorum'	see *C. chinense* var. *chinense*
colebrookianum B&SWJ 6651	WCru
- PAB 7794 **new**	LEdu
fragrans var. ***pleniflorum***	see *C. chinense* var. *chinense*
myricoides 'Ugandense' ♀H1b	CHll CRHN EShb MOWG WSFF
philippinum	see *C. chinense* var. *chinense*
speciosissimum	MOWG
aff. ***subscaposum*** WWJ 11735	WCru
thomsoniae ♀H1b	EShb MOWG WSFF
trichotomum	CBcs CDul CExl CMCN CSam CSpe CTho CTri CWib EPfP EUJe IArd LCro LOPS LRHS NLar SLim SLon SPer WBor WHor WMat
- var. ***fargesii*** ♀H4	Widely available
- - 'Carnival' (v) ♀H4	CAbP CBcs CExl CMac EBee ELan EPfP EWes LRHS MAsh MBri NLar SEND SKHP SLim SMDP SPer SPoG SWvt WCot WPat
- 'Purple Blaze'	EBee
- 'Purple Haze'	CJun MMHG NLar
- 'Shiro'	WCru
wallichii	CSpe EShb

Clethra ✿ (*Clethraceae*)

acuminata	NLar
alnifolia	CBcs CDul CExl CMHG CTsd MPkF SRms WCFE WCot WFar
- 'Anne Bidwell'	MBlu NLar
- 'Creel's Calico' (v)	NLar
- 'Fern Valley Pink'	CMac EBee ELon LLHF LRHS NLar SRms WFar
- 'Hokie Pink'	NLar
- 'Hummingbird' ♀H5	CDoC CExl CMac CWib ELan EPfP LRHS MAsh MBlu NEgg NLar SChF SPad SPoG SSpi SWvt WFar WSHC
- 'Paniculata'	CDoC ELon EPfP LRHS MMuc WBor
- 'Pink Spires'	CDoC CExl CWld ECrN EWTr GKin LSou MMHG MMuc MRav NEgg NLar SCob SCoo SEle SMad
- 'Rosea'	CTri GKin GQui MMHG MPkF SPer

– 'Ruby Spice' ♀H5	CBcs CExl CJun CLet CMac CWib EBee ELan ELon GBin GGGa GKin IDee LAst LRHS LSRN MAsh MBlu NLar SEle SPad SPer SPoG SWvt
– 'September Beauty'	CJun NLar
– 'Sixteen Candles'	GGGa GKin MPkF NLar
– Vanilla Spice = 'Caleb'	NLar
arborea	CBcs EBee NLar
barbinervis ♀H5	CBcs CDoC CExl CTho EPfP GGGa IDee IVic LRHS MBlu MGil NLar WPGP WSHC
– B&SWJ 11562	WCru
– Great Star = 'Minbarb' **new**	CDoC EPfP
– 'White Star' **new**	LRHS SPer
delavayi Franch.	CBcs CFil CPne EBee EPfP GGGa GQui IDee NLar SKHP SSpi
– SBEC 1513	CExl
– Stone's hardy strain	SKHP
fabri B&SWJ 11702 **new**	WCru
fargesii	CExl CFil EPfP NLar
kaipoensis	WPGP
NJM 11.020 **new**	
– NJM 11.058 **new**	WPGP
luzmariae	CFil
mexicana	CFil
monostachya	CExl GGGa NLar
pringlei	CFil NLar WPGP WSHC
tomentosa 'Cottondale'	CJun NLar

Cleyera (*Pentaphylacaceae*)

fortunei	see *C. japonica* 'Fortunei'
– 'Variegata'	see *C. japonica* 'Fortunei'
§ ***japonica*** 'Fortunei' (v)	CMHG CMac CWib LRHS MGos SHil
– var. ***japonica***	WPGP
– 'Tricolor' (v)	CBcs IDee MPkF SAko

Clianthus ✿ (*Papilionaceae*)

maximus	GDun
§ ***puniceus*** ♀H3	CAbb CExl CHll CKel CSpe CTsd CWib EAla EBee EPfP GDun IBoy LHop LRHS MGil MOWG SEle SGbt SIgm SPer SPlb SPoG SWvt WBor WCot WKif WSHC
§ – 'Albus' ♀H3	CBcs CExl CHGN CHll CKel CSpe CWib EBee EPfP GDun IBoy IDee LRHS MGil MOWG SPer SPoG SWvt WCot
– 'Flamingo'	see *C. puniceus* 'Roseus'
– 'Kaka King'	CBcs EWes LRHS MGil SPoG
– 'Red Admiral'	see *C. puniceus*
– 'Red Cardinal'	see *C. puniceus*
§ – 'Roseus' ♀H3	CBcs CExl CKel EPfP EUJe GDun IVic LRHS SPer SPoG WCot
– 'White Heron'	see *C. puniceus* 'Albus'

Clinopodium (*Lamiaceae*)

ascendens	see *Calamintha ascendens*
calamintha	see *Calamintha nepeta*
grandiflorum	see *Calamintha grandiflora*
§ ***vulgare***	CHab CSpe EBee MHer MNHC NMir SRms WJek WMoo WOut
– PAB 7562 **new**	LEdu

Clintonia (*Liliaceae*)

andrewsiana	ECho EWes WCru
udensis	WCru
– HWJK 2339 from Nepal	WCru
umbellulata	GCal WCru
uniflora	ECho EWes

Clivia ✿ (*Amaryllidaceae*)

caulescens	WCot
– pink-flowered **new**	WCot
gardenii	WCot
gardenii × ***miniata***	WCot
miniata ♀H1c	CAbb CBcs CEvo CTca CTsd ECho EWoo SAdn SEND SPlb SRms WCot
– 'Anshan Variegated' (v) **new**	WCot
– 'Arturo's Yellow'	WCot
– 'Ato-Shan'	WCot
– 'Aurea'	CSpe EWoo
– Belgian hybrids	WCot
– 'Beverley's Delight'	WCot
– broad-leaf, variegated (v)	WCot
– broad-leaved	EWoo
– broad-leaved, dark orange-flowered	EWoo
– var. ***citrina*** ♀H1c	CTca ECho LAma WCot
– – variegated (v) **new**	WCot
– Daruma Group	WCot
– green-centred	EWoo WCot
– 'Light of Buddha' (v)	WCot
– 'Mitsuhashi Multipetal' **new**	WCot
– 'Orange Spider'	CFwr
– pastel shades	CFwr EWoo WCot
– 'Pink Perfection' **new**	WCot
– 'Red Dawn' **new**	WCot
– 'Striata' (v)	CBlu WCot
– 'Terracotta Treasure' (v) **new**	WCot
– 'Vico Shima' **new**	WCot
– 'Vico Yellow'	EWoo
– 'Wide Leaf Monk'	WCot
nobilis ♀H1c	SPlb WCot
'Pale Quail' **new**	WCot
robusta	WCot
'San Marcus Yellow' × 'Solomone Yellow'	WCot
'Sweet Undress' **new**	WCot

Clytostoma (*Bignoniaceae*)

§ ***calystegioides***	CBcs CHll CRHN

Cneorum (*Rutaceae*)

tricoccon	SKHP

Cnidium (*Apiaceae*)

officinale	GPoy LEdu

Cobaea (*Polemoniaceae*)

pringlei	CRHN WPGP WSHC
– CD&R 1323	WCot
scandens ♀H2	CDTJ CSpe ELan EShb SPer
– f. ***alba***	CSpe EShb LCro SPer

cobnut see *Corylus avellana*

Cocculus (*Menispermaceae*)

laurifolius	EBee EUJe
§ ***orbiculatus***	CExl
– B&SWJ 535	WCru
trilobus	see *C. orbiculatus*

Cochlearia (*Brassicaceae*)

armoracia	see *Armoracia rusticana*
officinalis	CLau MHer WHer

Cocos (*Arecaceae*)

plumosa	see *Syagrus romanzoffiana*
weddelliana	see *Lytocaryum weddellianum*

Codonanthe (*Gesneriaceae*)

gracilis	WDib
'Paula'	WDib

× *Codonatanthus* (*Gesneriaceae*)

'Golden Tambourine'	WDib
'Sunset'	WDib
'Tambourine'	WDib

Codonopsis (*Campanulaceae*)

HWJK 2105 from Nepal	WCru
affinis	EBee
- HWJCM 70	WCru
- HWJK 2151	WCru
benthamii GWJ 9352	WCru
cardiophylla	EBee EWld GCal
clematidea	CCon CSpe EBee ECha ECho EPfP EWld GCal GKev MNHC MNrw NEgg NLar NSum SGSe SPhx SPlb SWvt WSHC
- 'Lilac Eyes'	NEgg SGSe
convolvulacea misapplied	see *C. grey-wilsonii*
- 'Alba'	see *C. grey-wilsonii* 'Himal Snow'
- Forrest's form	see *C. forrestii* Diels
convolvulacea ambig.	GKev
- var. **hirsuta** B&SWJ 7812	WCru
'Dangshen'	see *C. pilosula*
aff. **deltoidea** SSSE 86 new	EWld
dicentrifolia	NLar
- HWJCM 267	WCru
forrestii misapplied	see *C. grey-wilsonii*
§ **forrestii** Diels	CPne EBee ECho EPot EWld NHar WCot WTcb
- BWJ 7776	WCru
- BWJ 7847	WCru
§ **grey-wilsonii** ♀H5	CAby CBro CPne EWld GEdr MNrw NSum
- B&SWJ 7532	WCru
§ - 'Himal Snow'	CAby CPne EPot EWld GEdr GKev WCru
inflata GWJ 9442	WCru
javanica FMWJ 13329	WCru
kawakamii	EBee
- B&SWJ 1592	WCru
- RWJ 10007	WCru
§ **lanceolata**	CAby EWld GCal SBrt SGSe
- B&SWJ 562	EBee WCru
mollis	ECho NSum
nepalensis Grey-Wilson	see *C. grey-wilsonii*
obtusa	EBee EWld
ovata	CPne EBee EWld NBro NLar
§ **pilosula**	EBee EWld GPoy SBrt SGSe WSHC WTcb
- BWJ 7910	WCru
- var. **modesta** new	EBee
§ **rotundifolia** var. **angustifolia**	EBee EWld WCru
- var. **grandiflora**	EBee EWld GKev
silvestris	see *C. pilosula*
subsimplex BWJ 7502	WCru
tangshen misapplied	see *C. rotundifolia* var. *angustifolia*
tangshen Oliv.	CArn GKev WSHC
ussuriensis	see *C. lanceolata*
vinciflora	CPne ECho EWld GEdr GKev WAbe
viridiflora	WCru
viridis HWJK 2435	WCru

Coffea (*Rubiaceae*)

arabica	SPlb SPre

coffee see *Coffea*

Coincya (*Brassicaceae*)

wrightii PJL 20098	CHid

Colchicum (*Colchicaceae*)

byzantinum ambig.	NRog
agrippinum ♀H4	CAvo CBro CTal CTca ECha ECho EPot GBin GKev MRav NBir NRog NRya WAbe WHoo WThu
'Antares'	ECha NRog
atropurpureum	LAma
'Autumn Herald'	ELan GKev LAma NRog
'Autumn Queen' ♀H5	CTca GKev NRog
§ **autumnale**	CArn CAvo CBro CHab EPot GKev GPoy IFro LAma NRog NRya SDeJ WShi
- 'Alboplenum'	CTca ERCP GKev LAma NBir NRog
- 'Album'	CAvo CBro CTca EPot ERCP GKev LAma LCro LOPS NBir WShi
- 'Atropurpureum'	NRog
- var. **major** hort.	see *C. byzantinum* Ker Gawl.
- var. **minor** hort.	see *C. autumnale*
§ - 'Nancy Lindsay' ♀H5	CBro CTal EPot NRog WCot WShi XEll
- 'Pannonicum'	see *C. autumnale* 'Nancy Lindsay'
§ - 'Pleniflorum' (d)	GKev LAma NRog
- 'Roseum Plenum'	see *C. autumnale* 'Pleniflorum'
baytopiorum	GKev NRog
'Beaconsfield'	NRog
§ **bivonae**	EPot
- 'Apollo'	GKev NRog
- 'Mount Giona'	GKev
bornmuelleri misapplied	see *C. speciosum* var. *bornmuelleri* hort.
bornmuelleri Freyn	CBro EPot GKev LAma NRog
bowlesianum	see *C. bivonae*
§ **byzantinum** Ker Gawl. ♀H5	CBro GKev LAma SDeJ
- **album**	see *C. byzantinum* 'Innocence'
§ - 'Innocence'	NRog WCot
cilicicum	LAma NRog
- 'Purpureum'	CTca EPot GKev LAma NRog
'Conquest'	see *C.* 'Glory of Heemstede'
corsicum	ECho GKev WThu
cupanii var. **pulverulentum**	NRog
davisii	CTal NRog
'Dick Trotter'	EPot GKev NRog SDeJ WOld
'Disraeli'	EPot NRog
falcifolium	NRog
§ **giganteum**	LAma NRog
§ 'Glory of Heemstede'	GKev NRog WCot
'Gracia'	NRog
'Harlekijn'	EPot ERCP NRog
hungaricum	ECho EPot NRog
- f. **albiflorum**	EPot GKev NRog
- 'Velebit Star'	GKev NRog
illyricum	see *C. giganteum*
'Jaroslavna'	NRog
'Jochem Hof'	NRog
kesselringii	GKev NRog
laetum misapplied	see *C. parnassicum*
laetum Stev.	EPot NRog
'Lilac Bedder'	NRog

	'Lilac Wonder'	ELan EPfP GKev LAma MRav NRog SDeJ SEND WCot
	longifolium	see *C. neapolitanum*
	lusitanum	LAma
	luteum	NRog
	macrophyllum	LAma NRog
	minutum	NRog
	munzurense	NRog
§	***neapolitanum***	NRog
	'Neptun'	NRog
	'Oktoberfest'	EPot
	parlatoris	NRog
§	***parnassicum***	ECha NRog WThu
	'Pink Goblet' ♀H5	CBro LAma
	'Poseidon'	NRog
	pusillum	NRog
	'Rosy Dawn' ♀H5	CBro CTca ECha GKev NRog WOld
	'Rosy Wonder' **new**	GKev
	sibthorpii	see *C. bivonae*
	speciosum ♀H5	CAvo CBro ELan EPot GKev LAma NBir NRog WCot
	- 'Album' ♀H5	CAvo CBro ECha EPfP EPot ERCP GAbr GKev LAma NBir NRog SDeJ
	- 'Atrorubens' ♀H5	ECha EPot
I	- var. ***bornmuelleri*** hort.	WOld
	- 'Dombai'	NRog
	- var. ***illyricum*** hort.	see *C. giganteum*
	szovitsii 'Tivi'	ECho NRog
	- white-flowered	ECho
	tenorei ♀H4	CTal EPot GKev LAma NBir NRog
	'The Giant'	CAvo CBro EPfP EPot GKev LAma NRog SCob SDeJ
	triphyllum	NRog
	'Violet Queen'	EPot GAbr GKev LAma NRog
	'Waterlily' (d) ♀H5	CAvo CBro CTca ECho ELan EPfP EPot ERCP GBin GKev LAma LCro LOPS NBir NRog SCob SDeJ WCot WHoo
	'William Dykes'	NRog
	'Zephyr'	LAma

Coleonema (*Rutaceae*)

	album	EBee
§	***pulchellum***	CSpe SVen SWvt
	- 'Pink Fountain'	CAbb EPfP LRHS MPkF SEND SEle SPoG
	- 'Sunset Gold'	CAbb CBod CSpe CWGN EPfP LBuc LRHS MPkF SAko SCoo SEle SPoG
	pulchrum misapplied	see *C. pulchellum*
	'Sunset Gold'	COtt CSpe SPlb

Coleus see *Solenostemon*, *Plectranthus*

Colignonia (*Nyctaginaceae*)

	ovalifolia B&SWJ 10644	WCru

Colletia (*Rhamnaceae*)

	armata	see *C. hystrix*
	cruciata	see *C. paradoxa*
§	***hystrix***	CBcs CMac CTri CTsd EAla ELon IVic NLar SMad
	- 'Rosea'	CMac GCal MBlu SKHP
§	***paradoxa***	CBcs CDoC CWib EAla ELan EPfP LAst SKHP SMad
	paradoxa × ***spinosissima***	SMad
	ulicina	SVen

Collinsonia (*Lamiaceae*)

	canadensis	CArn LEdu

Collomia (*Polemoniaceae*)

	grandiflora	WCot

Colocasia (*Araceae*)

	affinis var. ***jeningsii***	CDTJ
	antiquorum	see *C. esculenta*
§	***esculenta*** ♀H1a	CDTJ EUJe LCro LLWG LOPS MSKA NLos SPlb XBlo
	- 'Black Coral'	CAbb LRHS SPad
	- 'Black Magic'	CBct CDTJ CHll ECtt EUJe IKil LAma LRHS MPie NLos SBig SDix WCot XBlo
	- 'Blue Hawaii'	LRHS
	- burgundy-stemmed	CDTJ LAma SBig
	- 'Diamond Head'	CWGN EUJe LRHS SPad
	- 'Fontanesii'	CDTJ EUJe MPkF SDix
	- 'Hawaiian Eye'	LRHS
	- 'Hilo Bay'	ESwi LRHS MPie WCot
	- 'Hilo Beauty'	XBlo
	- 'Illustris'	CDTJ LLWG
	- 'Mammoth'	EUJe
	- 'Pineapple Princess' (v)	ECtt LRHS WCot
	- 'Ruffles'	EUJe
	- 'Sangria'	EUJe
	fallax	CCon
	formosana B&SWJ 6909	WCru
	gaoligongensis	CCon
	gigantea	CDTJ
	- 'Thailand Giant'	EUJe
	'Himalayan Dragon'	SKHP
	'Kachhu' **new**	LAma

Colquhounia (*Lamiaceae*)

	coccinea	CHll CMHG CSde ESwi EUJe GGal MBlu MGil MRav NLar SBrt SChF SLon WBod WSHC
	- Sch 2458	WPGP
§	- var. ***mollis*** B&SWJ 7222	WCru
	- var. ***vestita*** misapplied	see *C. coccinea* var. *mollis*
	- var. ***vestita*** (Wall.) Prain	CBcs CTsd EBee EPfP LRHS SEND

Columnea (*Gesneriaceae*)

	'Aladdin's Lamp'	WDib
	× ***banksii*** ♀H1c	WDib
§	'Broget Stavanger' (v) ♀H1c	WDib
	'Chanticleer' ♀H1c	WDib
I	'Firedragon'	WDib
	'Gavin Brown'	WDib
	gloriosa	EBak
	'Inferno'	WDib
	'Katsura'	WDib
	'Merkur'	WDib
I	'Midnight Lantern'	WDib
	'Rising Sun'	WDib
	schiedeana	WDib
	'Sherbert'	WDib
	'Stavanger' ♀H1c	WDib
	'Stavanger Variegated'	see *C.* 'Broget Stavanger'

Coluria (*Rosaceae*)

	geoides **new**	WCot

Colutea (*Papilionaceae*)

	arborescens	CBcs CExl CWib ELan EWTr LRHS MBlu MGil MGos NWea SCob SEND SPer SPlb XSen

cilicica EGFP
× ***media*** CTsd ECre
- 'Copper Beauty' CBcs ELan LRHS NLar SCob SPer
orientalis CSde EBee

Colvillea (*Caesalpiniaceae*)

racemosa SPlb

Comarum see *Potentilla*

Commelina (*Commelinaceae*)

coelestis see *C. tuberosa* Coelestis Group
dianthifolia GEdr LEdu SMad SRms WPtf
- 'Electric Blue' ELan LRHS SVic WCot
robusta CSpe SBrt WCot
tuberosa NWad
- B&SWJ 10353 WCru
- blue-flowered SDeJ
§ - Coelestis Group CAby CSpe ECha LHop SDys SRms WKif WSHC
- - 'Sleeping Beauty' MSpe WHea

Comptonia (*Myricaceae*)

peregrina WPGP

Conandron (*Gesneriaceae*)

ramondoides B&SWJ 8929 WCru

Conanthera (*Tecophilaeaceae*)

campanulata EBee

Conicosia (*Aizoaceae*)

pugioniformis SVen

Coniogramme (*Pteridaceae*)

japonica WFib
- 'Flavomaculata' ♀H4 **new** WCot

Conium (*Apiaceae*)

maculatum CArn
- 'Golden Nemesis' (v) EBee WCot

Conoclinium (*Asteraceae*)

§ ***coelestinum*** CBod EBee LHop SBrt XLum

Conopodium (*Apiaceae*)

majus SRms WOut WShi

Consolida (*Ranunculaceae*)

ajacis Giant Imperial Series SVic

Convallaria ✿ (*Asparagaceae*)

japonica see *Ophiopogon jaburan*
keiskei EPPr MAvo WHil WWEG
I - 'Marginata' (v) WCot
majalis ♀H7 Widely available
- 'Albostriata' (v) CBct CBot CFwr CLAP CTal CWCL ECho EHoe ELan EPPr EUJe GKev GMaP LEdu LPal LRHS MAvo MHol MMuc MNrw MRav NBir NEgg NSti SGSe WCot WHer WHoo WPnP
- 'Berlin Giant' NRya SDeJ
- 'Bordeaux' CBro CExl CWld EBee EPPr MHer NEgg NLar WCot
- 'Bridal Choice' EBee ELan GBin GKev NLar
- 'Dorien' CBct CBre EPPr IMou MAvo
- 'Fernwood's Golden Slippers' CAvo LLHF
- 'Flore Pleno' (d) GEdr SGSe WWEG
- 'Géant de Fortin' CAvo CBct CBro CCon CExl CLAP CLet ECho EPot GCal GEdr MRav NBir NLar NMyG SBch WCot WWEG
- 'Gerard Debureaux' see *C. majalis* 'Green Tapestry'
- 'Golden Jubilee' **new** CBct
§ - 'Green Tapestry' (v) CBct MAvo
- 'Haldon Grange' (v) CDes CLAP EPPr
- 'Hardwick Hall' (v) CBct CCse CExl CLAP CTal EBee ECho EHoe GEdr GKev MAvo NMyG WAul WCot WHil WWEG XEll
- 'Hitschberger Riesenperle' XLum
- 'Hofheim' (v) CLAP LEdu MAvo WCot WHal WWEG
- 'Prolificans' CBct CCon CCse CLAP CTal EBee ECho ECtt EPPr EPfP GKev LAma LCro LOPS LSou MAvo MRav NBir NLar NSti WCot WPnP
- var. ***rosea*** Widely available
- 'Rosea Plena' (d) EWoo
- 'Silbercconfolis' (v) WCot
- 'Variegata' (v) CAvo EAJP EPot LHop MLHP NMyG SBch SMad WHil WThu WWEG
- 'Vic Pawlowski's Gold' (v) CAby CBct CDes CExl CLAP CMac ELon EPPr GEdr LEdu MAvo NSla WPGP WSHC
transcaucasica EBee GKev

Convolvulus (*Convolvulaceae*)

althaeoides CFis CMea ECho ELan EPri SEND WSHC
§ - subsp. ***tenuissimus*** EWes
§ ***boissieri*** WAbe XEll
cantabrica LRHS SGSe SPhx XLum XSen
cneorum ♀H4 Widely available
- 'Snow Angel' LRHS LSou SWvt
compactus LLHF
elegantissimus see *C. althaeoides* subsp. *tenuissimus*
humilis ECho
lineatus ECho EWes
mauritanicus see *C. sabatius*
nitidus see *C. boissieri*
§ ***sabatius*** ♀H3 CSam CSde CTri ECho ECtt ELan EPfP EPot EShb EWoo LAst LHop MCot SEND SLim SPer SPlb SPoG SVen SWvt WCFE WSHC XLum XSen
- dark-flowered CSpe ECho
- 'Moroccan Beauty'PBR CSpe ECtt

× *Cooperanthes* see *Zephyranthes*

Cooperia see *Zephyranthes*

Coprosma (*Rubiaceae*)

acerosa 'Hawera' CBcs
- 'Live Wire' (f) ECou
atropurpurea (f) ECou
- (m) ECou
'Autumn Orange' (f) ECou
'Autumn Prince' (m) ECou
baueri misapplied see *C. repens*
'Beatson's Gold' (f/v) CBcs CDTJ CExl CHGN CHll ELan EShb IVic LRHS SEND SLim SWvt WGrn WSHC
'Black Cloud' CBcs ELon LRHS SEND
'Blue Pearls' (f) ECou
'Blue Skies' NHar WThu

brunnea ECou
- (f) WThu
- (m) WThu
- 'Blue Beauty' (f) ECou
- 'Violet Fleck' (f) ECou
'Bruno' (m) ECou
'Cappuccino' CBcs EShb
cheesemanii (f) ECou
'Coppershine' CExl
× ***cunninghamii*** (f) ECou
× ***cunninghamii*** × ***macrocarpa*** (m) ECou
depressa ECou WThu
- 'Orange Spread' (f) ECou
'Evening Glow'PBR (f/v) CDTJ CDoC CSBt CWSG ELan EShb EUJe IVic LPfy LRHS MBri MGos SEle SHil SLim SRms WHar
'Fire Burst'PBR (f/v) CBcs EBee ELan EShb EUJe LBuc LHop LPfy LRHS MBri MGos SHil SLim SLon SRms WHar
grandifolia ECou
'Green Globe' CHll
'Hinerua' (f) ECou
'Inferno' LPfy LRHS MGos SEle SHil
'Karo Red'PBR (v) CBcs SLim SRms
I × ***kirkii*** 'Kirkii' (f) CHll
- 'Variegata' (f/v) CBcs CSde CTsd EBee ECou ELan EPfP EShb LRHS SLim
'Lemon and Lime'PBR (v) CDoC CWSG EBee ELan EUJe LBuc LHop LPfy LRHS MGos SEle SHil SPoG SRms WHar
'Lemon Drops' (f) ECou
lucida IDee
macrocarpa (f) ECou
- (m) ECou
parviflora red-fruited (f) ECou
'Pearly Queen' (f) ECou
petriei ECou WThu
- 'White Pearls' WThu
propinqua (f) ECou
- (m) ECou
- 'Autumn Haze'PBR **new** LRHS
- var. ***latiuscula*** (m) ECou
- - (f) ECou
quadrifida ECou
'Rainbow Surprise'PBR (v) CExl CSBt ELan LPfy LRHS MBri MGos SHil SLim SRms WHar
§ ***repens*** CBcs CExl EShb SPlb SVen
- (f) ECou
- (m) ECou
- 'County Park Plum' (v) CBcs ECou
- 'County Park Red' ECou
- 'Exotica' (f/v) ECou
- 'Marble King' (m/v) ECou
- 'Marble Queen' (m/v) ♀H2 CBcs ECou EShb
- 'Midnight Martini' (v) LPfy LRHS SHil SPoG
- 'Orangeade' (f) ECou
- 'Pacific Lady' ECou
- Pacific Night = 'Hutpac'PBR (m) CDoC CSBt ECou ELan EUJe IVic LBuc LHop LPfy LRHS MBri MGos SHil SLon
- Pacific Sunset = 'Jwncopps' (v) LCro SEle SLon
- 'Painter's Palette' (m) ECou SVen
- 'Picturata' (m/v) ♀H2 ECou EShb
- 'Pina Colada'PBR (v) CSBt LBuc LPfy LRHS SEle SHil SPoG
- 'Pink Splendour' (m/v) CBcs ECou
- 'Rangatiri' (f) ECou
- 'Tequila Sunrise' LBuc LPfy LRHS SEle SHil
- 'Variegata' (m/v) ECou
rigida ECou
- 'Ann' (f) ECou
- 'Tan' (m) ECou
robusta ECou
- 'Tim Blunt' (m) ECou
- 'Variegata' (m/v) ECou
'Roy's Red' (m) EShb LRHS LSRN
rugosa (f) CExl ECou
'Scarlet O'Hara' SEle
'Snowberry' (f) ECou
'Translucent Gold' (f) ECou
'Violet Drops' (f) ECou
virescens (f) ECou
'Walter Brockie' CHGN CHll CSde EShb

Coptis (*Ranunculaceae*)

japonica GPoy WCru
- var. ***dissecta*** WCru
- var. ***major*** CDes EBee WCru WSHC
omeiensis WCru
quinquefolia CTal
- B&SWJ 1677 WCru
ramosa B&SWJ 6000 WCru
- B&SWJ 6030 WCru
trifolia WCru

Corallospartium see *Carmichaelia*

Cordyline ✿ (*Asparagaceae*)

sp. LPar
australis ♀H3 Widely available
- 'Albertii' (v) ♀H3 MBri
- 'Atlantic Green' LPfy LRHS MGos SHil
- Burgundy Spire = 'Jel01'PBR EPfP LRHS
- Charlie Boy = 'Ric01'PBR (v) **new** EBee SPad
- 'Claret' CBcs COtt
- multi-stemmed **new** CLet
- 'Purple Heart' MSwo
- Purpurea Group CBcs CDTJ ELan LPar MGos MMuc SEND SPer SPlb WFar
- 'Red Sensation' LRHS SWvt
- 'Sparkler' LRHS MBri MGos SCob
- 'Torbay Dazzler' (v) ♀H3 CAbb CBcs CBod CDoC CLet COtt CSBt ELan EPfP IVic LPal LPar LPfy LRHS LSRN MAsh MBri MGos MJak NEgg NPla NPri SCob SEND SHil SLim SPer SPoG SWvt WFar
- 'Torbay Sunset' LPfy LRHS SCob
- 'Variegata' (v) LPar
banksii CTsd IDee
'Cardinal'PBR CBcs
'Cherry Sensation' (v) CBod LBuc LRHS SHil
'Dark Star' CDTJ SLim
Electric Pink = 'Sprilecpink' EBee
'Eurostripe'PBR LRHS MBri
Festival Grass = 'Jurred' LRHS
'Firecracker' LRHS MBri SHil
fruticosa 'Kiwi' LRHS
- 'Red Edge' ♀H1b XBlo
§ ***indivisa*** CBcs CBrP CDTJ CTsd EUJe IDee NLos SPlb WPGP
kaspar CTsd
mauritiana **new** WCot
'Pink Champagne' ELan LRHS MGos MSwo SCob
Pink Passion = 'Seipin'PBR EPfP LBuc LPfy LRHS MBri

'Pink Stripe' (v)	CDoC ELan EPfP LSRN MBri SLim SWvt
pumilio	LRHS
'Purple Sensation'	LRHS
'Red Bush'	XBlo
'Red Heart'	LRHS MJak
'Red Star'	CAbb CBcs CChe CLet COtt CSBt CWGN CWSG CWib EPfP LCro LPal LPar LPfy LRHS MBri MSwo NPer SCob SHil SPoG SWvt WFar
'Southern Splendour'	ELan LPfy LRHS MBri MGos NPri SHil SPoG
'Sundance' 🏆H3	CBcs CBod CDoC COtt CWib EPfP LRHS MAsh MBri MGos MMuc MSwo NPer SCob SEND SLim SPoG SRms SWvt
'Sunrise' (v)	CWGN EUJe LPfy LRHS MBri SHil
terminalis	see *C. fruticosa*
'Torbay Red' 🏆H3	CDoC CLet CMac CTsd EPfP LRHS LSRN MAsh MBri NPri SWvt

Coreopsis (*Asteraceae*)

'Astolat'	CBod LSou MRav NEgg SPer
auriculata Cutting Gold	see *C.* 'Schnittgold'
- 'Elfin Gold'	EDAr
- 'Nana'	CCon ELon MNrw NBre
- 'Superba'	MRav
- 'Zamphir'	EBee EPfP MNrw WCot
'Baby Gold'	see *C. lanceolata* 'Sonnenkind' (unblotched)
Baby Sun	see *C.* 'Sonnenkind' (red-blotched)
'Calypso' (v)	EWes SMad
'Cherry Pie' PBR (Pie Series)	SCob
'Citrine' (Hardy Jewel Series)	CWGN WHlf
'Cosmic Eye' (Big Bang Series)	MSCN
'Cranberry Ice'	CWGN NLar
'Desert Coral' (Hardy Jewel Series)	CWGN LBMP LSou WHlf
'Dream'	SRkn
'Fool's Gold'	EBee
'Fruit Punch' (Punch Series)	LRHS
'Full Moon' PBR (Big Bang Series)	CBod EBee MAvo NLar STPC WFar XLum
'Garnet' PBR (Hardy Jewel Series)	MAvo WHlf
gigantea	SPlb
'Golden Pompom' (d)	EBee
grandiflora	NEgg
- 'Bernwode' (v)	CMac EBee LSou SWvt
- 'Domino'	EAJP EBee LSun
- 'Early Sunrise' 🏆H5	COtt CSBt EAJP EBee ECtt EPfP EShb IBoy LPot LRHS MAsh MBri MNHC NBir NGBl NPer SCob SGbt SPoG SWvt WHar WWEG XLum
- Flying Saucers = 'Walcoreop' PBR	EPfP LRHS SCoo SPoG
- 'Heliot'	MBri
- 'Illico'	EBee MBri
- 'Mayfield Giant'	CCon CSBt EBee ELan EPfP LHop MNrw NPri SPer SRms SWvt
- 'Presto' (d)	CNor SPad
- 'Rising Sun'	ELan MAvo MBri
- 'Sunburst'	EPfP NBre XLum
- 'Sunfire'	LPfy LRHS MBri MHer SHil
- 'Sunray'	CBcs CSBt CWib EAJP ECtt ELon EPfP LRHS MAvo MBri NGdn NPri SHil SPlb SPoG SRms SWvt WCAu WMoo XLum
- 'Tetra Riesen'	NBre
'Jethro Tull' PBR	EBee LSou SPoG
'Jive' PBR (Coloropsis Series)	CWGN SCob
lanceolata	LPal NBre
- 'Goldfink'	MRav SRms
- 'Goldteppich'	EBee EPfP LRHS
- 'Little Sundial'	LSou MBri
§ - 'Sonnenkind' (unblotched)	GMaP XLum
- 'Walter'	LSou MAsh MNrw MPie NDov NEgg SPoG WCot WWEG XLum
'Limbo' (Coloropsis Series)	SCob
'Limerock Passion' PBR	EPfP ILea LRHS MBNS SRkn
'Limerock Ruby' PBR	ECtt GMaP ILea LRHS LSou SCob SPer SRkn SWvt WHar XLum
major	EBee
'Mango Punch' (Punch Series)	EBee
maximiliani	see *Helianthus maximiliani*
'Pineapple Pie' PBR (Pie Series)	SCob
'Pink Lady' PBR	WBod
'Pink Sapphire'	WHlf
'Pinwheel'	WHlf
pubescens	LSou
- 'Sunshine Superman'	EBee ELan
'Pumpkin Pie' PBR (Pie Series)	SCob
rosea	NGBl
- 'American Dream'	CBod CSBt ELan EPfP GMaP LAst LRHS NBir NEgg NGdn SGSe SPer SPlb SRms SWvt WMnd XLum
- 'Heaven's Gate' PBR	LAst NGBl SCob
- 'Nana'	XLum
- 'Sweet Dreams' PBR	SRkn
'Route 66' PBR	WFar
'Rum Punch' PBR (Punch Series)	LHop
§ 'Schnittgold'	NBre SHar
Solanna Golden Sphere	MBri
I 'Sonnenkind' (red-blotched)	EBee LRHS NBre
'Star Cluster' (Big Bang Series)	CWGN EBee MBri MSCN
'Sterntaler'	CCon EBee ECtt ELon EPfP LHop LRHS LSun MBri SPad SWvt WWEG XLum
Sun Child	see *C.* 'Sonnenkind' (red-blotched)
'Tequila Sunrise' (v)	MNrw
tinctoria	MNHC SRms
tripteris	CAby CCon ELan ELon EPfP LPla MMuc SEND SGSe SMad WMoo XLum
- 'Mostenveld'	EBee
- 'Pierre Bennerup'	SAko
verticillata	CMac EBee ECha GCal MBel MBrN MHer MWat NLar NPer SRms WCAu WHal WOld
- Crème Brûlée = 'Crembru' PBR	ECtt EPau EWes LRHS MJak SCoo SRkn
I - 'Golden Gain'	ECtt GBuc LHop MArl NGdn WFar WMnd WWEG
- 'Golden Shower'	see *C. verticillata* 'Grandiflora'
§ - 'Grandiflora' 🏆H5	CBcs CBod CPrp EAEE ELan EPfP GMaP LRHS MRav NGdn NHol NWad SHar SPer WFar WMnd XLum
- 'Limerock Dream' PBR	ILea MBNS SCob
- 'Moonbeam'	Widely available
- 'Old Timer' 🏆H5	SDix
- 'Ruby Red'	CAbP LRHS MBri
- 'Sunbeam'	ELon SCob
- 'Tweety'	WFar
- 'Zagreb' 🏆H6	Widely available

coriander see *Coriandrum sativum*

Coriandrum (*Apiaceae*)

* ***citratus***	CLau
sativum	ENfk GPoy MHer MNHC NPri SIde SPoG SRms
- 'Leisure'	SVic
- 'Santo'	CLau
- 'Slobolt'	CLau

Coriaria ✿ (*Coriariaceae*)

arborea	WCru
intermedia B&SWJ 019	WCru
japonica	CDes NLar SVen WCru
- B&SWJ 2833	WCru
- subsp. ***intermedia*** B&SWJ 3877	WCru
kingiana	WCru
§ ***microphylla***	WCru
- B&SWJ 8999	WCru
myrtifolia	NLar WCru
nepalensis	NLar WCru
- BWJ 7755	WCru
pteridoides	WCru
ruscifolia	WCru
- HCM 98178	WCru
sarmentosa	WCru
terminalis	GCal WCru
var. ***xanthocarpa***	
- - GWJ 9204	WCru
- - HWJK 2112c	WCru
thymifolia	see *C. microphylla*

Cornus ✿ (*Cornaceae*)

alba L.	CArg CBar CCVT CDoC CDul CLnd ECrN MHer MRav NWea SCob SEWo SRms WMou
- 'Argenteovariegata'	see *C. alba* 'Variegata'
- 'Atrosanguinea'	WWtn
- 'Aurea' 🏆H7	Widely available
- Baton Rouge = 'Minbat' PBR	CDoC CRos ELon EPfP LHop LPfy LRHS MAsh SPoG SWvt
- 'Cream Cracker' PBR (v)	EBee MRav
- 'Elegantissima' (v) 🏆H7	Widely available
- 'Gouchaultii' (v)	CBcs CMac CRos EPfP GKin LPfy LRHS MGos MRav NEgg NLar SGol SHil SPer SRms WFar WMoo
- 'Hessei' misapplied	see *C. sanguinea* 'Compressa'
- 'Hessei' Hesse	WPat
- Ivory Halo = 'Bailhalo' PBR	EAEE EBee EMil EPfP LRHS LSRN MAsh MBri MRav NWea SLim SPer SPoG
- 'Kesselringii'	Widely available
- Red Gnome = 'Regnzam'	ELon LLHF MAsh
- 'Siberian Pearls'	ELan GKin MBlu NLar
§ - 'Sibirica' 🏆H7	Widely available
- 'Sibirica Variegata' (v) 🏆H7	CDoC CMac CRos CWSG EBee ELon EPfP GCra GKin LPfy LRHS LSRN MAsh MBlu MGos NEgg SCob SHil SLim SPer SPoG SSpi SWvt WCFE WHar WMoo
- 'Spaethii' (v) 🏆H7	Widely available
§ - 'Variegata' (v)	LAst WFar
- 'Westonbirt'	see *C. alba* 'Sibirica'
- 'Wintersun'	NLar
alternifolia	CBcs CCVT CMCN CTho EAEE ELan EWTr IDee WMou
§ - 'Argentea' (v) 🏆H6	Widely available
- 'Brunette'	CJun MBlu NLar
- Golden Shadows = 'Wstackman' PBR (v)	EBee IArd LRHS NLar SAko SPoG WHor
- 'Golden Surprise'	CJun
- 'Goldfinch' (v)	CJun MBlu
- 'Moonlight' (v)	CJun
- Pinky Spot = 'Minpinky'	LSRN NLar
- 'Silver Giant' (v)	CJun GBin IArd NEgg NLar SAko
- 'Variegata'	see *C. alternifolia* 'Argentea'
- 'Yellow Spring'	CJun NLar
amomum	CAbP EBtc NLar
- 'Lady Jane'	NLar
'Ascona'	CBcs CJun EWTr NLar SPer SSta
Aurora = 'Rutban' (Stellar Series)	CJun MBlu NLar SGol
canadensis	Widely available
capitata	CAby CBcs CDoC CDul CHid CJun CMac CPne CTsd EBee EPfP ESwi EWTr GKev IArd IDee IMou LRHS MGos SAko SEND SKHP WCru WFar WPGP
- subsp. ***emeiensis***	CJun
- 'Foreness Fog' (v)	SEND
§ Celestial = 'Rutdan' (Stellar Series)	CBcs CDul CJun LRHS NEgg NLar SGol SKHP
'Celestial Shadow'	MGos MPkF SGol
'Centennial'	LRHS
chinensis	SSta SWvt
Constellation = 'Rutcan' (Stellar Series)	CJun MAsh SGol
controversa	CBcs CCVT CDul CLnd CMCN COtt CTri ECrN ELan EPfP EWTr GBin LCro LOPS LPar MBlu MBri MJak NLar NWea SEND SEWo SGol SSpi SSta SWvt WHar
I - 'Aurea'	LRHS
- 'Candlelight'	MBlu NLar
§ - 'Frans Type' (v)	CJun LSRN
- 'Green Carpet'	NLar
- 'Laska'	CJun NLar WPGP
- 'Lucia'	CJun NLar
I - 'Marginata Nord'	NLar
- 'Pagoda'	CJun MBlu NLar
- 'Troya Dwarf'	CJun NLar
- 'Variegata' (v) 🏆H5	Widely available
- 'Variegata' Frans type	see *C. controversa* 'Frans Type'
'Dorothy'	CJun NLar
'Eddie's White Wonder' 🏆H5	Widely available
elliptica	EBee IDee SAko SKHP
- 'Full Moon'	CJun
florida	CDul CLnd CMCN CTho ESwi EWTr LCro MMHG MMuc NOrn NWea SPer WHar WMat
- 'Alba Plena' (d)	CJun
- 'Appalachian Spring'	CTho
- 'Apple Blossom'	CJun CMac CMen
- 'Aurea' × ***kousa***	MPkF
- 'Autumn Gold'	SSta
- Cherokee Brave = 'Comco No 1'	CBcs CJun CMen CTho ESwi EWTr LMil LRHS MAsh MGos NEgg SGol SPoG SSta
- 'Cherokee Chief'	CBcs CDul CJun CLet CMac CMen COtt CTho CTri IVic LSRN MGos MPkF NEgg SAko WHar
- 'Cherokee Daybreak'	see *C. florida* 'Daybreak'
- 'Cherokee Princess'	CJun EWTr LRHS MAsh SGol SPoG SSta WMat
- 'Cherokee Sunset'	see *C. florida* 'Sunset'
- 'Cloud Nine'	CBcs CDoC CJun CLet CMen CTho EWTr GKin MGos MPkF NEgg SAko SSpi WHar

	Plant	Suppliers
§	- 'Daybreak' (v) 🏆^{H5}	CBcs CJun CLet ESwi LPfy LRHS LSRN MAsh MGos MPkF NOrn SHil SPer WHar WMat
	- 'Eternal Dogwood' (d)	ESwi LSRN SGol
	- 'First Lady' (v)	CJun CMac CMen NEgg SSpi
	- 'Fragrant Cloud'	SWvt
	- 'Golden Nugget' (v)	CJun
	- 'Granary Gold'	SSta
	- 'Moonglow'	CJun
	- 'Pendula'	CJun
	- 'Pink Flame' (v)	CJun SSta
	- f. ***pluribracteata*** (d)	NLar
	- var. ***pringlei***	CJun
	- 'Purple Glory'	CBcs CJun NLar SPer
	- 'Pygmaea'	NLar
	- 'Rainbow' (v) 🏆^{H5}	CAbP CBcs CJun CLet CWib GKin LRHS MAsh MGos MPkF SHil SPoG WHar WMat
	- f. ***rubra***	CLnd CTri CWib ELan ESwi GKin LRHS MGos MRav NEgg SPer WMat
	- - 'Red Giant'	CAbP CBcs CJun EWTr
	- - 'Spring Song'	CJun CMac CMen NEgg
	- 'Spring Day'	CMac CMen NEgg
	- 'Springtime'	CJun
	- 'Stoke's Pink'	CJun CMac CMen NEgg
§	- 'Sunset' (v)	CBcs CJun CLet CMen CWib ELan LRHS MAsh MGos NEgg NLar NOrn SSta SWvt WHar WMat
	- 'Sweetwater'	CJun
	- subsp. ***urbiniana***	WPGP
	- 'Variegata'	GKin
	- 'White Cloud'	CJun WMat
	'Gloria Birkett'	CAbP CJun ELan EPfP LMil LRHS MAsh NEgg SSpi
	'Gold Splash' (v)	NEgg
	hessei misapplied	see *C. sanguinea* 'Compressa'
	hongkongensis	LRHS MAsh NLar WPGP
	- B&SWJ 11700	WCru
	- HWJ 1033	EBee EPfP WPGP
	- PAB 8237 **new**	LEdu
	- aff. subsp. ***gigantea*** KWJ 12225	WCru
	- aff. subsp. ***tonkinensis*** B&SWJ 11791	WCru
	'Jerry Mundy'	CMac IVic NEgg
	'Kelsey Dwarf'	see *C. sericea* 'Kelseyi'
	'Kenwyn Clapp'	CJun
	kousa	CCVT CDoC CMCN CMHG CMac CTho ELan EPfP GKin LCro MJak NEgg NLar SCob SPer SPlb WFar WHar WMou
	- B&SWJ 12610 from Korea	WCru
	- 'Akabana'	CJun
	- 'Akatsuki' (v)	CJun MPkF SSta
	- 'All Summer'	CJun
	- 'Angyo Issai'	NLar
	- 'Autumn Rose'	CJun EPfP IArd NLar SAko
	- 'Beni-fuji'	CJun EBee EWTr LRHS NLar
	- 'Big Apple'	CJun CRos LLHF LMil LRHS NLar SBir
	- 'Blue Shadow'	CJun LRHS MBlu NLar SSta
	- 'Bonfire' (v)	CJun
	- 'Bultinck's Beauty'	LRHS NLar
	- 'Bultinck's Giant'	LRHS NLar
	- 'Bush's Pink'	CJun
	- 'Cherokee'	CJun NLar
	- 'China Dawn' (v)	CJun SSta
	- var. ***chinensis***	Widely available
	- - 'Bodnant Form'	CAby CJun CMac CTho EPfP ESwi NEgg NLar SSta WBor
	- - 'China Girl' 🏆^{H5}	Widely available
	- - 'Claudia'	CDoC EPfP IVic LRHS NLar SAko SSta
	- - 'Great Star'	LRHS MAsh
	- - 'Greta's Gold' (v)	CJun SSta
	- - 'Ikone'	IVic
	- - 'PVG'	CJun
	- - 'Snowflake'	CJun
	- - 'Spinners'	CJun NEgg
	- - 'Summer Stars'	CJun
	- - 'Tri-Splendor'	NLar
	- - 'White Dusted' (v)	CJun EPfP MBlu NLar
	- - 'White Fountain'	EPfP LSRN MPkF MPnt NLar NOrn SLim WHar WMat
	- - 'Wieting's Select'	CJun IArd IVic MBlu MPkF NEgg NLar SAko
	- - 'Wisley Queen' 🏆^{H5}	CAbP CJun CMHG EPfP LMil LRHS MAsh SSta WPGP
	- 'Claudine'	CJun SAko
	- 'Copacabana'	MBlu
	- 'Daybreak' **new**	SGol
	- 'Doctor Bump'	CJun
	- 'Doubloon'	CJun WPat
	- 'Dwarf Pink'	CJun LRHS
	- 'Ed Mezitt'	CJun NLar
	- 'Eline'^{PBR}	MPkF
	- 'Elizabeth Lustgarten'	CJun MBlu MPkF SSta
	- 'Eurostar'	ELan IArd IVic LRHS MBlu SAko
	- 'Eva'^{PBR}	MPkF
	- 'Fanfare'	CJun
	- 'Fernie's Favourite'	CJun
	- Galilean = 'Galzam'	CJun MPkF SAko
	- 'Gay Head'	CJun
I	- 'Girard's Nana'	CJun
	- 'Gold Cup' (v)	CJun MPkF SSta
	- 'Gold Star' (v)	CBcs CJun CMac ELan LMil LRHS MBlu MGos MPkF NEgg NLar SPoG SSta
	- 'Greensleeves'	CJun EPfP LLHF LMil LRHS SSta
	- 'Heart Throb'	CJun MBri MGos NLar SGol
	- 'Highland'	CJun
	- 'John Slocock' 🏆^{H5}	CJun NLar
	- 'Kim'	NEgg
	- 'Koree' **new**	NLar
	- 'Kreutzdame'	CJun LRHS MBlu
	- 'Laura'	IArd MBlu SAko SSta
	- 'Little Beauty'	CJun
	- 'Lizzie P'	NLar
	- 'Lustgarten Weeping'	CJun
	- 'Madame Butterfly'	CJun IDee LRHS MBlu MBri NEgg NLar
	- 'Marwood Dawn'	CMHG SSta
	- 'Marwood Twilight'	CMHG
	- 'Melanie'^{PBR}	GQue MBlu MPkF WMat
	- 'Milky Way'	CBod CDoC CJun CMCN CTho EPfP ESwi EWTr GBin LRHS LSRN MAsh MBlu MGos MPkF MRav NEgg NLar SGol SSpi WPat
	- 'Milky Way Select'	CBcs CJun LRHS MGos
	- 'Miss Petty'	CJun MBri MPkF NLar
	- 'Miss Satomi' 🏆^{H5}	Widely available
	- 'Moonbeam'	CJun NLar WPat
	- 'Mount Fuji'	CJun MBlu NLar SSta
	- 'National'	CJun LMil MAsh MGos MPkF NLar SSta WPat
	- 'Nicole'	CDoC LRHS NLar WPat
	- 'Ohkan'	CJun
	- 'Pevé Foggy'	LRHS NLar
	- 'Pevé Limbo' (v)	CJun NLar
	- 'Pevé Satomi Compact'	CJun NLar

- 'Piff Frocky' **new**	EBee
- 'Polywood'	CJun NLar
- 'Radiant Rose'	CJun MPkF NLar SBir SSpi SSta
- 'Rasen'	CJun NLar
- 'Rel Whirlwind'	CJun NLar
* - 'Robert'	NLar
- 'Rosea'	CJun
- Samaratin = 'Samzam' (v)	CBcs CJun LRHS LSRN MGos MPkF SGol SKHP SSta
- 'Satomi Akatuki' (v)	CJun NLar
- 'Schmetterling'	CJun EWTr MBlu NLar SAko WPat
- 'Snowbird'	CJun
- 'Snowboy' (v)	CBcs CDul CJun CMac MBlu SMad
- 'Snowflurries'	CJun
- 'Southern Cross'	CJun GBin
- 'Square Dance'	CJun
- 'Steeple'	CJun MBri NEgg
- 'Summer Fun' 🏆H5	CJun LRHS SPoG SSta
- 'Summer Gold' (v)	MPkF
- 'Summer Majesty'	CJun
- 'Sunsplash' (v)	CJun LRHS SSta
- 'Temple Jewel' (v)	CJun
- 'Teresa'	LRHS
- 'Teutonia' 🏆H5	CJun IArd IVic LPfy MGos NLar SAko SHil SSta
- 'Trinity Star'	CJun
- 'Triple Crown'	CJun WPat
- 'Tsukubanomine'	CJun CLnd NLar
- 'Vale Milky Way' (v)	NLar
- 'Weaver's Weeping'	CJun MPkF NLar
- 'Weisse Fontäne'	CJun NLar
- 'White Dream'	CJun LRHS NLar
- 'White Giant'	CJun SLim SPer SPoG
- 'Willy Boy'	WHor
- 'Wolf Eyes' (v) 🏆H5	CBcs CJun LMil MAsh MBlu MPkF NLar SGol SPoG SSta
macrophylla Wall.	LRHS WCru
mas	Widely available
- 'Aurea' (v) 🏆H6	CAbP CBcs CJun ELan EPfP LRHS MAsh MBlu MGos MRav NEgg NLar SGol SSpi SSta WPat
§ - 'Aureoelegantissima' (v)	CJun CMac LRHS MAsh NLar SPer SSpi WCot WPat
- 'Devin' (F)	NLar
- 'Elegant' (F)	CAgr
- 'Elegantissima'	see *C. mas* 'Aureoelegantissima'
- 'Golden Glory' 🏆H6	CJun CLnd EPfP NLar SKHP WHor
- 'Gourmet' (F)	CAgr
- 'Happy Face'	NLar
- 'Hillier's Upright'	CJun
- 'Jolico' (F) 🏆H6	CAgr CJun LEdu MBlu NLar SKHP WMat
- 'Kasanlaker' (F)	CAgr NLar
- 'Pancharevo' (F)	CAgr
- 'Pioneer' (F)	CJun NLar
- 'Redstone' (F)	CJun
- 'Schönbrunner Gourmet Dirndl' (F)	MCoo
- 'Shan' (F)	CAgr
- 'Shumen' (F)	CAgr
- 'Spring Glow'	CJun NLar
- 'Titus' (F)	NLar
- 'Variegata' (v) 🏆H6	CAbP CBcs CDul CJun CMCN CMac EBee EPfP LRHS MAsh MBlu MGos NLar SKHP SPer SSpi WPat
- 'Xanthocarpa'	CJun NLar
- 'Yellow'	CAgr
'Norman Hadden' 🏆H5	Widely available
nuttallii	CDul CTho CTri CWib ELan EPfP ESwi MMuc SPer SWvt
- 'Colrigo Giant'	CJun
- 'Gold Spot' (v)	CJun CMac NWea
- 'Monarch'	CJun CTho NEgg SKHP WPat
- 'North Star'	CDul CJun NLar
- 'Portlemouth'	CJun LRHS NLar
- 'Zurico'	CJun MPkF
oblonga	CExl LEdu WPGP
officinalis	CAgr CBcs CDul CMCN EMil EPfP IMou LCro LRHS NLar SKHP SWvt
- 'Kintoki' 🏆H6	ESwi NLar SKHP
'Ormonde' 🏆H5	CJun EPfP NEgg NLar SSpi SSta WPGP
'Pink Blush'	CJun
'Porlock' 🏆H5	CDul CJun CMCN CRos EPfP IArd ITim LPfy LRHS MAsh MBri NLar SHil SWvt WHor WPat
pumila	NLar
racemosa	EBtc NLar
rugosa	EBtc NLar
I × ***rutgersiensis***	LRHS
- Galaxy	see *C.* Celestial
Ruth Ellen = 'Rutlan' (Stellar Series)	CJun NLar
sanguinea	CBcs CCVT CDul CHab CLnd CMac CTri ECrN EPfP LBuc MJak MMuc MRav MSwo NBes NWea SCob SEWo SGol SPer SVic WHar WMat WMou
§ - 'Anny'	CJun MBlu MRav WCot WPat
- 'Anny's Winter Orange' 🏆H6	CJun MAsh
§ - 'Compressa'	MBlu MGil MRav NLar
- 'Magic Flame' 🏆H6	CJun ELon EMil EPfP LRHS MAsh NLar SWvt WPat
- 'Midwinter Fire'	Widely available
- 'Winter Beauty'	CJun CSBt CWib EPfP EUJe LBMP MAsh MBlu NEgg NLar NWea SLon SWvt WCFE WHar WPat WWtn
- 'Winter Flame'	see *C. sanguinea* 'Anny'
§ ***sericea***	SRms
- 'Bud's Yellow'	CRos ELon EPfP LRHS MBlu MBri NLar SHil
- 'Cardinal'	CHGN CRos EBee ELon EPfP ESwi LPfy LRHS MAsh MBri MGos NLar SHil
- 'Flaviramea' 🏆H7	Widely available
- 'Hedgerows Gold' (v) 🏆H7	CRos EBee ELan ELon EMil EPfP LHop LPfy LRHS MAsh MBri MGos SHil SPoG WCot WPat
§ - 'Kelseyi'	CMac EBee ELan EPfP MRav NLar SCob WMoo
- Kelsey's Gold = 'Rosco'	MAsh SPoG WPat
- subsp. ***occidentalis*** 'Sunshine'	NEoE NLar
§ - 'White Gold' (v)	CDoC EAEE EHoe ELon EPfP EWTr MBri MRav NEoE NLar SAko SMad SPer SPoG WMoo
- 'White Spot'	see *C. sericea* 'White Gold'
Stardust = 'Rutfan' (Stellar Series)	CJun
Stellar Pink = 'Rutgan' (Stellar Series)	CBcs CJun CTho LRHS MAsh MGos MPkF NLar SGol SKHP WPGP
stolonifera	see *C. sericea*
suecica	CTal NHar
× ***unalaschkensis***	LLHF
- NNS 08-101	EBee GKev
Venus = 'Kn30 8'PBR 🏆H5	CBcs CJun CWGN ELan EPfP LBuc LCro LRHS MBlu MBri MPkF SLon SSta WPGP
walteri	CBcs EBtc

	- B&SWJ 8776	WCru
	'Winter Orange'	CJun NLar SAko WHor

Corokia (*Argyrophyllaceae*)

	buddlejoides	CBcs CHGN CMHG CSde CTsd ECou NLar SEND WFar
	'Coppershine'	CMHG
	cotoneaster	CAbP CBcs CChe CDul CMac CSde CTri ECou ECre ELan EPfP EUJe IDee LRHS MAsh MGil MGos NLar SBod SCob SDix SEle SIgm SPer SPoG SWvt WCot WFar WGrn WPat
	- 'Boundary Hill'	ECou
	- 'Brown's Stream'	ECou
	- 'Swale Stream'	ECou
	- 'Wanaka'	ECou
	macrocarpa	ECou
	× ***virgata***	CAbP CChe CTri CTsd ECou ELan EPfP GBin GGal LRHS NLar SWvt WKif WSHC
	- 'Bronze King'	LPal LRHS MOWG SPer SVen
	- 'Bronze Lady'	ECou
	- 'Cheesemanii'	ECou
	- 'County Park Orange'	ECou
	- 'County Park Red'	ECou
	- 'Frosted Chocolate'	CMHG CSde CTsd EBee ECou ELan EPfP IVic LHop LLHF LRHS MOWG SEND SKHP SLim SPoG SVen SWvt WGrn
	- 'Geenty's Green'	ECou LRHS WGrn
	- 'Havering'	ECou
	- 'Pink Delight'	ECou EPfP ESwi LBMP MAsh MRav
	- 'Red Wonder'	CMHG CMac EBee ELan EPfP IVic LRHS SAko SEND SLim SPoG SVen WGrn
	- 'Silver Ghost'	ECou
	- 'Sunsplash' (v)	CBcs CDoC CMac CTsd EBee ECou EPfP ESwi LBMP LHop LLHF LRHS MAsh MPkF NLar SAko SEND SEle SPoG SWvt WGrn
I	- 'Virgata'	ECou
	- 'Yellow Wonder'	CBcs CMHG EBee ESwi LRHS NLar SEND SLim SWvt

Coronilla (*Papilionaceae*)

	comosa	see *Hippocrepis comosa*
	coronata	LRHS
	emerus	see *Hippocrepis emerus*
	glauca	see *C. valentina* subsp. *glauca*
	juncea **new**	XSen
	minima	WAbe XSen
	'Nan Hicks'	EWld
	valentina	CDoC CRHN LHop MGil SDix WSHC
	- 'Clotted Cream'	CHid
§	- subsp. ***glauca*** ♀H4	CDul CMac CSBt CSde CTri CWib EBee ELan EPfP LPfy LRHS LSRN MGil MMuc SEND SLim SPer SRms SVen SWvt WAbe WBod WOut WPat XLum XSen
	- - 'Brockhill Blue'	EBee IVic LRHS SAko WCot
	- - 'Citrina' ♀H4	Widely available
*	- - 'Pygmaea'	MCot SEle SRms WCot
	- - 'Variegata' (v)	CBcs CDoC CKel CMac COtt CTri CWib CWld EBee EHoe ELan EPfP LBMP LRHS MCot MGil MRav NQui SEle SLim SLon SPer SPoG SRms SVen WCot
	- 'Variegata' **new**	SEle
	varia	see *Securigera varia*

Correa (*Rutaceae*)

	aemula	MOWG
	alba	CExl EPfP
	- 'Pinkie' ♀H2	CExl CSde CTsd ECou MOWG WAbe
	alba × ***backhouseana***	MOWG
	backhouseana ♀H2	CAbb CBcs CDoC CExl CHll CMac CSde CTri CTsd ECou ELan EPfP EWld GCal IDee IVic LHop LPot LRHS MOWG NLar SEle SVen WSHC
	- 'Mount Congreve'	MOWG
	- 'Peaches and Cream'	IVic SEle SRkn
	decumbens	MOWG
	'Dusky Bells' ♀H2	CAbb CBcs CHll CSde CTri CTsd ECou EPfP IVic LBMP LHop LRHS MAsh MHtn MOWG SEND SEle SLim SPlb SPoG SRkn SVen
	'Dusky Maid'	CExl
	'Federation Belle'	ECou MOWG SPlb SVen
	glabra	MOWG SEle
	'Harrisii'	see *C.* 'Mannii'
	'Ivory Bells'	ECou
	lawrenceana	CExl CFil CTsd SEND SVen WPGP
	- from Mount Wellington, Tasmania **new**	SBrt
	- var. ***grampiana***	SVen
§	'Mannii' ♀H2	CBcs CDoC CExl CTsd ECre ELan ELon EPfP IVic LRHS MOWG SEle SPoG WSHC
	'Marian's Marvel' ♀H2	CDoC CExl CSde ECou ECre EPfP LBMP MAsh MOWG SEND SEle SPoG SRkn SVen WAbe
	'Peachy Cream'	CAbb CDoC LRHS
	'Poorinda Mary'	ECou MOWG
	pulchella ♀H2	CExl CTri SEle
	- orange-flowered	MOWG
	- 'Pink Mist'	ECou MOWG WAbe
	reflexa ♀H2	CDoC CExl
	- from Hobart, Tasmania **new**	SBrt
	- var. ***nummulariifolia***	ECou MAsh MGil MOWG SBrt WAbe WCot
	- var. ***reflexa***	CExl
*	- ***virens***	CExl
	schlechtendalii	ECou LHop LRHS SEle

Cortaderia ✿ (*Poaceae*)

	argentea	see *C. selloana*
	fulvida misapplied	see *C. richardii* (Endl.) Zotov
§	***fulvida*** (Buchanan) Zotov ♀H6	EWes IArd IDee SMad SWvt WCot
	richardii misapplied	see *C. fulvida* (Buchanan) Zotov
	richardii ambig.	CBod CCon CExl EHoe GBin IMou MMuc NBir SDix SMad SWvt WHrl
§	***richardii*** (Endl.) Zotov ♀H5	CAby CBcs CBot CKno EBee ECha ESwi EWes IDee IMou LRHS MAvo MHin MWhi WMnd WPGP
	- Brown's strain	LSun WCot
§	***selloana***	CBcs CBod CLet CTri CWib IBoy MGos MHtn MJak NBir SCob SGol SPlb
§	- 'Albolineata' (v)	CBcs CBot ELon EWes MWht SEND SLim SPoG SWvt
§	- 'Aureolineata' (v) ♀H5	CBcs CBot CLet CMac CSde ELan EPfP GMaP IVic LRHS MHin NBid SCob SEND SLim SPer SPoG SWvt
	- 'Evita'PBR ♀H5	CKno ECtt NLar SMad SPer SWvt
	- 'Gold Band'	see *C. selloana* 'Aureolineata'
	- 'Golden Goblin'PBR	EHoe NLar NPri SCob

	- 'Icalma'	CSde EPPr
	- 'Monstrosa' 🏆H5	SEND SMad
	- 'Patagonia' 🏆H5	EHoe EPPr
	- 'Pink Feather'	EPfP SEND SPer
	- 'Pointe du Raz'	CBot SWvt
	- 'Pumila' 🏆H5	Widely available
	- 'Rendatleri'	CBcs CDoC ELan LSRN SCoo SLim SPoG SWvt
	- 'Rosea'	CBod CLet EPfP MJak NGdn NLar SCob SGol
	- 'Senior'	NLar
	- Silver Feather = 'Notcort' (v) 🏆H5	SCob
	- 'Silver Fountain' (v)	ELan EPfP LRHS MAsh
	- 'Silver Star'PBR (v) **new**	EBee
	- 'Silver Stripe'	see *C. selloana* 'Albolineata'
	- 'Splendid Star'PBR (v)	CBcs CDoC EHoe LHop LRHS MAsh MGos MJak NLar SLim SPoG SWvt
	- 'Sunningdale Silver' 🏆H5	CBcs CDoC CDul CMac ECha ECtt ELan ELon EPfP LRHS LSRN MGos SCob SEND SLim SMad SPer SPoG SWvt
*	- 'White Feather'	CBod NGdn SCob SPer WHar
	Toe Toe	see *C. richardii* (Endl.) Zotov

Cortia (*Apiaceae*)

	depressa CC 7379 **new**	EWld

Cortusa (*Primulaceae*)

	altaica	CPne
	- 'Amelia Chekiangolios' **new**	CPne
	brotheri	EBee ECho
*	***caucasica***	EBee EWld GKev
*	- 'Alba'	EBee GKev
	matthioli	ECho GBin GEdr GKev SRms WFar
	- 'Alba'	CCon ECho GBuc GKev NLar NWad SRms
	- var. ***congesta***	GEdr GKev
	- subsp. ***pekinensis***	CCon ECho EDAr MLHP MPnt NBid NLar SGSe SRms
	- - var. ***sachalinensis***	EBee GKev
	turkestanica	ECho GEdr LLHF

Corydalis ✿ (*Papaveraceae*)

	anthriscifolia	CLAP EWes LPla MMHG
	'Blackberry Wine'	CExl CWCL EBee ECtt EPfP LRHS MPnt SPad WOut
	Blue Line = 'Couriblue' **new**	CSpe LSou SPoG
	'Blue Panda'	see *C. flexuosa* 'Blue Panda'
	'Bronze Beauty'	WFar WMoo
	brunneovaginata **new**	WCot
	bulbosa misapplied	see *C. cava*
	bulbosa (L.) DC.	see *C. solida*
	buschii	CAby EBee ECho ELon GBin GBuc GEdr NHar NMyG WCot
	'Canary Feathers'PBR	ECtt GEdr LRHS MBNS NPri
	cashmeriana	GKev LRHS NBid WAbe WHal
	- 'Kailash'	EBee LRHS
	cashmeriana × ***flexuosa***	CBro CLAP ECho GKev LHop WAbe
	caucasica	ECho GBuc
	- var. ***alba*** misapplied	see *C. malkensis*
§	***cava***	CLAP EBee ECho LAma WShi
	- 'Albiflora'	CLAP ECho EPot
	cheilanthifolia	CExl EPfP EWld IMou LEdu LPla SRms WHea XLum
	- 'Manchu'	NPri
	'Craigton Blue'	CLAP EBee EPPr GBuc GEdr GKev IMou IPot MNrw NHar WAbe
	curviflora subsp. ***rosthornii***	CExl EWes
	- - 'Blue Heron'	CWGN ECtt GEdr LBMP LRHS MPnt WSHC
	davidii	CExl
	decipiens Schott, Nyman & Kotschy	see *C. solida* subsp. *incisa*
I	***decipiens*** misapplied	ECho EPot
	densiflora	GKev
	'Early Bird'	ECtt
	elata	CLAP CSpe EWes GAbr GBin GBuc GEdr IFro LHop LRHS MArl MBel MCot MMuc MNrw NBid NBir NChi NSla SPhx SPoG WCot WCru WHal WHoo WOut WSHC
	- 'Blue Summit'	CLAP ECtt EPPr IMou LRHS
	elata × ***flexuosa***	IMou
	elata × ***flexuosa*** clone 1	CCse CExl CLAP GEdr
	flexuosa 🏆H5	CSpe EPfP GBin MArl MNrw WAbe WBor WSHC XLum
	- CD&R 528	CBot IFro NRya
	- 'Balang Mist'	CExl CLAP
	- 'Blue Dragon'	see *C. flexuosa* 'Purple Leaf'
§	- 'Blue Panda'	CExl EPPr EWes GBuc GKev GMaP MNrw MPnt NLar WCru
	- 'Blue Skies'	MHol
	- 'China Blue'	Widely available
	- 'Golden Panda' (v)	NLar
	- 'Hale Cat'	ECtt EPPr
	- 'Hidden Purple'	CHid
	- 'Nightshade'	CExl EWld LLHF NBid WCot WHoo
I	- 'Norman's Seedling'	EBee EPPr IVic WPGP
	- 'Père David'	CLet CMac COtt CSBt CSpe CWCL EBee ECha ECho ELan EPPr EPfP GBin LRHS MHer NBir NCGa NEgg NMyG SPlb SPoG SWvt WCru WPnP WSHC WWEG XLum
§	- 'Purple Leaf'	Widely available
	'Golden Spinners'	IVic
	'Heavenly Blue'	GKev
	heterocarpa	IMou
	incisa	ECho LAma
	- B&SWJ 4417	WCru
	'Kingfisher'	CBot CLAP CSma GBuc LEdu NHar NLar NSla WAbe
	leucanthema DJHC 752	CDes CExl CLAP
	- 'Silver Spectre' (v)	CExl WMoo
	linstowiana CD&R 605	CExl CLAP
§	***lutea***	CBcs EBee EPfP IFoB IFro MMuc NBir NPer NPri NWad SEND SRms WCot WMoo
§	***malkensis*** 🏆H5	CWCL EBee ECho EPot GBin GBuc GKev LLHF NBir NRya WCot WThu XLum
	'Maya' (v)	XLum
	moorcroftiana	CExl
	nobilis	EBee ECho IFoB LLHF SPhx
	ochotensis	IMou LRHS
§	***ochroleuca***	CElw CSpe EPot GCal LPla NLar WMoo
	omeiana **new**	WCot
	ophiocarpa	EHoe ELan GCal WMoo
	pachycentra	CExl WAbe
	paczoskii	ECho GBuc LRHS MNrw
	pseudofumaria alba	see *C. ochroleuca*
	'Rainier Blue'	IVic
	rosea 'American Dream'	CSam
	'Rukšāns Red'	CWCL
	'Sapphire'	CBro
	scandens	see *Dactylicapnos scandens*
	scouleri	IMou NBir

shimienensis 'Berry Exciting'[PBR]	CAby CBct CWGN EBee ECtt ELon EPfP LBMP LHop LRHS LSou MBNS MHol MPnt NPer SPoG
siamensis	IFoB IMou
- B&SWJ 7200	WCru
§ ***solida***	CAvo CBro CElw EBee ECho ECtt ELan EPfP EPot ITim LAma LEdu LHop LRHS MPie MRav NLar NPri NRya SDeJ SPhx WCot WShi
- 'Advocet'	GEdr
- 'Endres Traum' **new**	EBee
- 'Evening Shade'	GEdr
- 'Fire Bird'	ECho GEdr GKev
- 'Firecracker'	CBro ECho LHop LLHF LRHS SPhx
- 'Frodo'	ECho LAma
- 'Gandalf'	NHar
- 'Gaviota'	GEdr
§ - subsp. ***incisa*** ♀H5	ECho EPot GKev SDeJ SPhx
- lilac-flowered	IFoB
- pink and red shades	GBuc
- 'Purple Beauty'	GEdr GKev MNrw SPhx
- 'Purple Bird'	CAvo GKev
§ - subsp. ***solida***	CLAP EPot GBin GKev NBir NRya SPhx WCot
- - from Penza, Russia	GBuc GKev LLHF
- - 'Beth Evans'	Widely available
- - 'Blushing Girl'	ECho GEdr LAma
- - 'Dieter Schacht' ♀H5	EPPr EPot GKev ITim LAma NLar WAbe
- - 'Evening Shade'	ECho GEdr LAma
- - 'George Baker' ♀H5	Widely available
- - 'Lahovice'	WAbe
- - Prasil Group	EPot GEdr GKev SPhx WBor
- - 'White Knight'	ECho LAma WCot
- f. ***transsylvanica***	see *C. solida* subsp. *solida*
- 'White King'	WCot
- 'White Swallow'	ECho EPot GEdr GKev
'Spinners'	CElw CFis CLAP EBee ECha ECtt ELon EPPr GKev GLog IMou IVic NEgg NMyG NQui WPnP WSHC WWEG XLum
stipulata B&SWJ 2951	WCru
taliensis	CExl GLog
tauricola	GEdr
temulifolia 'Chocolate Stars'	CBod CSpe CWGN EBee ECtt EWld LEdu LHop LLHF MBNS MHol MPie NCGa SCob WCot WSHC
tomentella	NSla
'Tory MP'	CBct CExl CHid CLAP CSam CSpe EBee EPPr GEdr IFro LRHS MNrw MPie NBid NCGa NChi NHar NMyG WHoo WPGP
transsylvanica hort.	see *C. solida* subsp. *solida*
turtschaninovii	SKHP
vittae	IFoB
wendelboi	IFoB
'Wildside Blue'	CLAP EWld
wilsonii	CExl IFoB

Corylopsis ✿ (*Hamamelidaceae*)

SDR 7921 **new**	GKev
glabrescens	CHGN CJun LRHS
- var. ***gotoana***	CJun EPfP LRHS MAsh NLar SSpi WPat
- - 'Chollipo'	CAbP LRHS NLar SSta
- 'Lemon Drop'	CJun NLar
glandulifera	CJun
multiflora	SSpi
pauciflora ♀H5	CBcs CDoC CDul CJun CMHG CTho CTri CWib ELan EPfP IDee IVic LCro LRHS LSRN MAsh MRav NEgg NLar NPri SChF SCob SGol SKHP SLim SPer SPoG SSpi WPGP WPat
platypetala	see *C. sinensis* var. *calvescens*
- var. ***laevis***	see *C. sinensis* var. *calvescens*
sinensis	CBcs EPfP
§ - var. ***calvescens***	CBcs CJun CTho EPfP WPat
§ - - f. ***veitchiana*** ♀H5	CJun EPfP IArd IDee IMou LRHS MAsh NLar
§ - var. ***sinensis*** ♀H5	CDoC CDul CJun CTho ELon EPfP IVic LAst LRHS MAsh NLar SLon
- - 'Spring Purple'	CAbP CBcs CDoC CJun CMac EPfP IDee IVic LRHS MGos NLar SChF SHil SKHP SPoG SSpi WCot WPGP WPat
- 'Veitch's Purple'	CJun NLar
spicata	CBcs CDul CJun IArd IDee LRHS MBlu MRav NEgg NLar SCob SGol SLim WHor WPat
- 'Golden Spring'	CBcs NLar
- 'Red Eye'	CJun IVic NLar
veitchiana	see *C. sinensis* var. *calvescens* f. *veitchiana*
willmottiae	see *C. sinensis* var. *sinensis*

Corylus ✿ (*Betulaceae*)

sp.	MAsh
avellana (F)	Widely available
- 'Anny's Purple Dream'[PBR]	MBlu NLar
- 'Anny's Red Dwarf'	IArd NLar
- 'Aurea'	CBcs CDoC CDul CLet CSBt CTho CTri EBee ELan EPfP EUJe GBin LRHS MAsh MBlu MBri MGos MRav NLar NWea SCob SLim SPer SSta SWvt
- 'Bollwylle'	see *C. maxima* 'Halle'sche Riesennuss'
§ - 'Butler' (F)	CAgr CDul CMac CTho CTri ERea IArd MBri MJak SDea SKee WHar
- 'Casina' (F)	CAgr CTho
- 'Contorta' ♀H6	Widely available
- 'Corabel' (F)	CAgr MBri NOra WMat
- 'Cosford' (F)	CAgr CCVT CDul CMac CSBt CTho CTri ECrN EPom ERea GTwe IArd LBuc LEdu MBlu MBri MGos NLar NOra SDea SEWo SGol SKee SPer SWvt WHar WMat
- Emoa Series	WMat
§ - 'Ennis' (F)	CAgr MBri NOra SDea SKee WHar
§ - 'Fuscorubra' (F)	CJun EPom EShb MRav NLar SWvt
- 'Gustav's Zeller' (F)	NOra WMat
§ - 'Heterophylla'	CDul EBee EPfP MBri NLar SSta WHar WPat
- 'Laciniata'	see *C. avellana* 'Heterophylla'
§ - 'Lang Tidlig Zeller' (F)	CAgr ERea MBri NOra NWea WMat
- 'Louis Berger' (F)	MCoo
- 'Merveille de Bollwyller'	see *C. maxima* 'Halle'sche Riesennuss'
- 'Nottingham Prolific'	see *C. avellana* 'Pearson's Prolific'
- 'Pauetet' (F)	CAgr
§ - 'Pearson's Prolific' (F)	CAgr CSBt GTwe LBuc SDea SGol SKee
- 'Pendula'	EBee MAsh MBlu SCoo WCot WHar WPat
- 'Princess' (F)	SVic
- 'Purpurea'	see *C. avellana* 'Fuscorubra'
- 'Red Majestic'[PBR] ♀H6	Widely available
- 'Tonda di Giffoni' (F)	MCoo NOra WMat

- 'Webb's Prize Cob' (F) CAgr CDul ERea GBin GTwe IArd LEdu MBlu MJak MMuc NLar SBmr SDea SEND SGol SKee SVic
colurna ♀H5 CAgr CCVT CDul CMCN CMac EBee ECrN EPfP IArd LEdu MBlu MGos NLar NOrn NWea SCoo SGol SPer WHar WMat WMou
× **colurnoides** 'Chinoka' (F) CAgr MCoo WHar WMat
- 'Freeoka' (F) CAgr MCoo WHar WMat
Early Long Zeller see *C. avellana* 'Lang Tidlig Zeller'
fargesii WPGP
ferox CJun
maxima (F) CDul CLnd CMac CTri EPom GTwe MSwo NWea SDea
- 'Butler' see *C. avellana* 'Butler'
- 'Ennis' see *C. avellana* 'Ennis'
- 'Fertile de Coutard' see *C. maxima* 'White Filbert'
- 'Frühe van Frauendorf' see *C. maxima* 'Red Filbert'
- 'Grote Lambertsnoot' see *C. maxima* 'Kentish Cob'
- 'Gunslebert' (F) CCVT CDul CMac CTho CTri ECrN ERea GTwe LCro MBri NOra SDea SKee SPoG WHar WMat
- Halle Giant see *C. maxima* 'Halle'sche Riesennuss'
§ - 'Halle'sche Riesennuss' (F) CAgr ECrN ERea GTwe MBri MMuc NLar NOra SEND SKee WHar WMat
§ - 'Kentish Cob' (F) CAgr CBcs CDul CMac CSBt CTho ECrN ELan EPfP EPom ERea GTwe IArd LBuc LRHS MBri MGos NLar SDea SEWo SKee SLim SPer SPoG SRms SVic SWvt WHar WMat WMou
- 'Lambert's Filbert' see *C. maxima* 'Kentish Cob'
- 'Longue d'Espagne' see *C. maxima* 'Kentish Cob'
- 'Monsieur de Bouweller' see *C. maxima* 'Halle'sche Riesennuss'
- 'Nottingham Cobnut' (F) ERea SBmr SVic
- 'Purple Filbert' see *C. maxima* 'Purpurea'
§ - 'Purpurea' (F) Widely available
§ - 'Red Filbert' (F) ♀H6 CDul CHab CTho EPom ERea GTwe IArd LEdu MAsh MBlu MBri NLar NOra SBmr SCoo SGol SKee SLim SSta WHar WPat
- 'Red Zellernut' see *C. maxima* 'Red Filbert'
- 'Spanish White' see *C. maxima* 'White Filbert'
§ - 'White Filbert' (F) CHab ERea GTwe SKee WHar
- 'White Spanish Filbert' see *C. maxima* 'White Filbert'
- 'Witpit Lambertsnoot' see *C. maxima* 'White Filbert'
'Nottingham Early' (F) NLar
sieboldiana B&SWJ 11056 WCru
'Te Terra Red' CDul CJun CMCN EBee MAsh MBlu MBri NOrn SLon WHar WMat
tibetica LEdu

Corymbia see *Eucalyptus*

Corynabutilon see *Abutilon*

Corynephorus (*Poaceae*)

canescens NBir

Corynocarpus (*Corynocarpaceae*)

laevigatus CBcs ECou

Corynopuntia (*Cactaceae*)

grahamii SB 1885 from Candelaria, Texas **new** CCac

Cosmos (*Asteraceae*)

§ **atrosanguineus** CBcs CMea COtt CSBt CSpe CWGN CWib ECho ECtt ELan EPfP EWTr IVic LAst LCro LHop LOPS LPal LSRN MBri MRav NLar SCob SDeJ SPer SPoG SWvt WHoo
- Chocamocha = 'Thomocha'PBR CAvo CBcs CBod CChe CHid CWCL CWGN ECtt EPfP EUJe GMaP IBoy LAst LBMP LCro LHop LOPS LPfy LRHS MGos NCGa NLar NPri SCob SHil SPer SPoG SRot WBor
- Dark Secret = '3013/01' **new** CSpe
- 'New Choco'PBR LSou
- 'Spellbound' **new** ECtt
bipinnatus 'Antiquity' NPri SPhx
- 'Dazzler' **new** LCro SPhx
- 'Purity' CSpe LCro SPhx
- 'Rubenza' **new** LCro SPhx
- 'Sea Shells' (mixed) CWCL
- (Sonata Series) 'Sonata Carmine' LSou NPri SPoG
- - 'Sonata Pink' LSou NPri SPoG
- - 'Sonata White' CSpe LAst LSou NPri SPoG
- 'Sweet Sixteen' **new** SPhx
caudatus WJek
peucedanifolius CSpe NGBl WSHC
- 'Flamingo' CGrW EBee EPfP ERCP SDeJ
'Razzmatazz Pink' NPri
sulphureus 'Bunte Lichter' CSpe

Cosmos × *Dahlia* (*Asteraceae*)

'Mexican Black' ECtt ERCP NJRG WCot WPGP

costmary see *Tanacetum balsamita*

Cotinus ✿ (*Anacardiaceae*)

americanus see *C. obovatus*
§ **coggygria** CArn CBcs CDoC CDul CMCN CMac CWSG EBee ECrN ELan EPfP LHop LPal MBri MRav MSwo NLar NWea SCob SEND SGol SPer SWvt WFar WHar XSen
- Golden Spirit = 'Ancot'PBR ♀H5 Widely available
- Green Fountain = 'Kolcot'PBR EBee EMil LHop LRHS
- 'Kanari' NLar WPat
- 'Nordine' WPat
- 'Notcutt's Variety' MRav
- 'Old Fashioned'PBR MGos MPkF
- 'Pink Champagne' CBcs EPfP MAsh NLar SSta WPat
- Purpureus Group SGol
- 'Red Beauty' NLar
- 'Royal Purple' ♀H5 Widely available
- Rubrifolius Group CBcs EPfP SEND SGol SPer SWvt
- Selection EPfP
- Smokey Joe = 'Lisjo'PBR CBcs EPfP LRHS MAsh SLon SPoG SSta SWvt WHar
- 'Smokey Joe Purple' LSou
- 'Velvet Cloak' CAbP EBee ELan EPfP LRHS MGos MPkF NLar SLon SPer SWvt
- 'Young Lady'PBR ♀H5 Widely available
Dusky Maiden = 'Londus'PBR CSBt ELon EPfP GBin LLHF LRHS MAsh MBri MGos NLar SCob SLon WPat
'Flame' ♀H5 CBcs CDul ECrN ELan ELon EPfP EUJe LRHS MAsh MBri MGos MRav NLar SCob SGbt SHil SKHP SLim SPer SPoG SWvt WFar WPat

	'Grace'	Widely available
§	***obovatus***	CMCN EBtc ELon EPfP IArd LLHF LRHS MBlu MPkF MRav NLar SSta WPGP WPat
	'Ruby Glow' **new**	LRHS

Cotoneaster ✿ (*Rosaceae*)

	SDR 5804	GKev
	acuminatus	SRms
	acutifolius var. ***laetevirens***	see *C. laetevirens*
	adpressus	SCob
§	- 'Little Gem'	ECho NHar NLar
	- var. ***praecox***	see *C. nanshan*
	- 'Tangstedt'	SGol
	- 'Tom Thumb'	see *C. adpressus* 'Little Gem'
	affinis	SRms
	albokermesinus	SRms
	ambiguus Rehder & E.H.Wilson	NLar
	amoenus	NLar SRms
	- AC 829	MSnd
§	***apiculatus***	NLar SRms
§	***ascendens***	SRms
	assamensis	SRms
§	***astrophoros***	CMac MBlu NHar NLar
	atropurpureus	NLar SRms
§	- 'Variegatus' (v) ♀H6	Widely available
	aurantiacus	NLar
	boisianus	NLar SRms
	bradyi	SRms
	brickellii	NLar
§	***bullatus***	CDul CTri EPfP MMuc NLar SPer SRms WHil
	- 'Firebird'	see *C. ignescens*
	- f. ***floribundus***	see *C. bullatus*
	- var. ***macrophyllus***	see *C. rehderi*
	bumthangensis	NLar SRms
	buxifolius blue-leaved	see *C. lidjiangensis*
	- 'Brno'	see *C. marginatus* 'Brno'
	- f. ***vellaeus***	see *C. astrophoros*
	camilli-schneideri	NLar SRms
	canescens	NLar SRms
	chadwelli	NLar
	chuanus **new**	NLar
	chungtiensis	NLar
	cinnabarinus	SRms
§	***cochleatus***	LAst SRms
§	***congestus***	CDul CSBt CWib MSwo NLar SPlb SRms WHar XLum
	- 'Nanus'	CMea ELan GCrg GEdr
	conspicuus	CBcs SPer SRms
	- AC 3176	MSnd
	- 'Decorus' ♀H6	CDoC CDul CLet CSBt EAEE EPfP LAst LHop LPfy LRHS MBri MGos MJak MMuc MSwo NEgg NLar NWea SCob SEND SGol SHil SLim SPer SPlb SPoG SWvt WHar WMoo
	- 'Leicester Gem'	SRms
	- 'Red Glory'	CMac
	cooperi	SRms
	cordifolius	MBlu NLar SRms
	cornifolius	SRms
§	'Cornubia' ♀H6	Widely available
	crispii	NLar
	cuspidatus	MBlu NLar
	dammeri	Widely available
§	- 'Major'	CBar CDul LBuc NLar SPoG WFar
§	- 'Mooncreeper'	CWSG MMuc SCob WHar
	- 'Oakwood'	see *C. radicans*
	- var. ***radicans*** misapplied	see *C. dammeri* 'Major'
	- var. ***radicans*** (Dammer ex C.K.Schneid.) C.K.Schneid.	see *C. radicans*
	dammeri × ***microphyllus*** **new**	MJak SBod
	dielsianus	NLar NWea SRms
	divaricatus	EPfP NLar NWea SPer SRms
	duthieanus	NLar
	- 'Boer'	see *C. apiculatus*
	elatus	SRms
	elegans	SRms
	emeiensis	NLar SRms
	encavei	NLar
	'Erlinda'	see *C.* × *suecicus* 'Erlinda'
	'Exburiensis'	CBcs CBod CCVT CDoC CDul ECrN EPfP LAst MAsh MBri MGos MMuc MRav NLar SCob SEND SGol SPer WFar WHar WMat
	falconeri	SRms
	fastigiatus	SRms
	flinckii	NLar SRms
	floccosus	IArd NWea SEND
	floridus	SRms
	forrestii	NLar SRms
	franchetii	Widely available
	cf. ***franchetii***	COtt
	frigidus	NOrn SRms
§	- 'Pershore Coral'	WAvo
	fulvidus **new**	NLar
	gamblei	SRms
	ganghobaensis	SRms
	- B&L 12234	WCru
	glabratus	SRms
	glacialis	SRms
	glaucophyllus	IArd NLar SAko SRms
§	***glomerulatus***	NLar SRms
	gracilis	SRms
	granatensis	NLar SRms
	harrovianus	NLar SRms
	harrysmithii	NLar
	hebephyllus	NLar
I	***hedegaardii*** 'Fructu Luteo'	SRms
	henryanus	SRms
	- 'Corina'	SRms
	'Herbstfeuer'	see *C. salicifolius* 'Herbstfeuer'
	'Highlight'	see *C. pluriflorus*
	hillieri	NLar
§	***hjelmqvistii***	LBuc NLar SRms
	- 'Robustus'	see *C. hjelmqvistii*
	- 'Rotundifolius'	see *C. hjelmqvistii*
	hodjingensis	SRms
	horizontalis	Widely available
	- 'Variegatus'	see *C. atropurpureus* 'Variegatus'
	- var. ***wilsonii***	see *C. ascendens*
	hualiensis	NLar SRms
	- B&SWJ 3143	WCru
	humifusus	see *C. dammeri*
	hummelii	SRms
§	'Hybridus Pendulus'	Widely available
§	***hylmoei***	NLar SRms
	hypocarpus	SRms
	ignavus	SRms
§	***ignescens***	NLar NWea SRms
	ignotus	SRms
	incanus	NLar
	induratus	SRms
	insculptus	SRms

	insolitus	NLar
	integerrimus	SRms
§	***integrifolius***	MMuc NLar SRms WMoo
	kangdingensis	SRms
	kingdonii	NLar
	kitaibelii	NLar
	konishii	NLar
	kweitschoviensis	NLar
	lacteus ♀H6	Widely available
	- 'Milkmaid' (v) new	NLar
§	***laetevirens***	NLar
	lancasteri	NLar SRms
	langei	SRms
	laxiflorus	SRms
§	***lidjiangensis***	SRms
§	***linearifolius***	GCra
	lucidus	NLar SRms
	ludlowii	SRms
	magnificus	SRms
§	***mairei***	NLar NWea SRms
	marginatus Lindl. ex Loudon	SRms
§	- 'Blazovice'	NLar SRms
§	- 'Brno'	SRms
	marquandii	NLar SRms
§	***meiophyllus***	MBlu NLar
	melanocarpus	NLar
	meuselii	NLar SRms
	meyeri	GKev NLar
	microphyllus misapplied	see *C. purpurascens*
	microphyllus ambig.	CBcs EAEE SCob
	microphyllus Wall. ex Lindl.	CDul CTri LRHS MGos NWea SDix SPer SPoG WMoo
	- NICE 004	WCFE
	- var. ***cochleatus*** (Franch.) Rehder & E.H.Wilson	see *C. cochleatus*
	- var. ***cochleatus*** ambig.	EPot NSla
	- 'Donard Gem'	see *C. astrophoros*
	- 'Teulon Porter'	see *C. astrophoros*
	- var. ***thymifolius*** misapplied	see *C. linearifolius*
	- var. ***thymifolius*** (Lindl.) Koehne	see *C. integrifolius*
	- var. ***thymifolius*** ambig.	LRHS
	milkedandaensis	SRms
	miniatus	SRms
	mirabilis	NLar SRms
	monopyrenus	SRms
	- F 11422 new	GKev
	'Mooncreeper'	see *C. dammeri* 'Mooncreeper'
	morrisonensis	SRms
	moupinensis	GLog SRms
	- BWJ 8167	WCru
	mucronatus	NLar SRms
§	***nanshan***	CAbP NLar NWea SRms WHar
	- 'Boer'	see *C. apiculatus*
	naoujanensis	EPfP NLar
	- 'Berried Treasure'	EPfP LRHS SHil
	nepalensis	NLar
	newryensis	SRms
	nitens	NLar SRms
	nitidifolius	see *C. glomerulatus*
	nohelii	NLar SRms
	notabilis	SRms
	nummularioides	SRms
	nummularius Fisch. & C.A.Mey.	SRms
	obscurus	SRms
	obtusus Wall. ex Lindl.	NLar SRms
	ogisui	NLar

	omissus	NLar
	pangiensis	SRms
	pannosus	SRms
	paradoxus	SRms
	parkeri	NLar SRms
	pekinensis	SRms
	permutatus	see *C. pluriflorus*
	perpusillus	SRms
	'Pershore Coral'	see *C. frigidus* 'Pershore Coral'
§	***pluriflorus***	NLar SRms
	poluninii	NLar SRms
	polycarpus	SRms
	praecox 'Boer'	see *C. apiculatus*
	procumbens	SRms
	- 'Queen of Carpets' ♀H6	CBod CDoC CLet ELan EPfP IBoy LHop LPfy LPmr LRHS LSRN MAsh MBri MGos MRav NEgg NLar SBod SCoo SHil SLim SPoG SRms SWvt WMoo
	- 'Streib's Findling'	see *C.* 'Streib's Findling'
	prostratus	SRms
	przewalskii	SRms
	pseudo-obscurus	SRms
§	***purpurascens***	CSBt LRHS
	pyrenaicus misapplied	see *C. congestus*
	qungbixiensis	NLar SRms
	raboutensis	NLar
	racemiflorus	SRms
§	***radicans***	MGos NWad
§	***rehderi***	CMHG NLar SRms
	reticulatus new	NLar
	rokujodaisanensis	NLar
	roseus	NLar SRms
	'Rothschildianus' ♀H6	Widely available
	rubens W.W.Sm.	NLar
	rugosus E. Pritz. ex Diels	NLar SRms
	'Saint Monica'	MBlu
	salicifolius	CTri MSwo NLar NWea SRms WFar
	- Autumn Fire	see *C. salicifolius* 'Herbstfeuer'
§	- 'Avonbank'	CDoC NLar WAvo WHar
	- 'Brno Orangeade'	SRms
	- 'Emerald Carpet' new	SEND
	- 'Gnom' ♀H6	CDul CMac ELan EPfP LRHS MAsh MGos MMuc MRav NBir NEgg SCob SEND SLim SPer SPoG SRms WHar WMoo
§	- 'Herbstfeuer'	MRav MSwo SRms WMoo
	- Park Carpet	see *C. salicifolius* 'Parkteppich'
§	- 'Parkteppich'	NWea
	- 'Pendulus'	see *C.* 'Hybridus Pendulus'
	- 'Pink Champagne' ♀H6	CMac MRav
	- 'Repens'	CDoC CWib EPfP NPla NWad NWea SCob SGol SLim SPer SPoG SRms WHar WMat
	- var. ***rugosus***	see *C. hylmoei*
	salwinensis	SRms
	sandakphuensis	SRms
	Saphyr Green = 'Belka'[PBR]	EAEE
	scandinavicus	SRms
	schantungensis	NLar SRms
	schlechtendalii 'Blazovice'	see *C. marginatus* 'Blazovice'
	- 'Brno'	see *C. marginatus* 'Brno'
	schubertii	SRms
	serotinus misapplied	see *C. meiophyllus*
	serotinus Hutch.	SRms
	shannanensis	SRms
	shansiensis	NLar SRms
	sherriffii	NLar SRms

sikangensis SRms
simonsii CBcs CCVT CDoC CDul CLnd CMac EBee ECrN ELan EPfP LBuc LRHS MGos NBes NHol NLar NWad NWea SCob SGol SPer SPoG SRms WHar
soczavianus NLar
§ ***splendens*** SRms
- 'Sabrina' see *C. splendens*
spongbergii SRms
staintonii SRms
sternianus ♀H6 EPfP NLar SRms
- ACE 2200 EPot
§ 'Streib's Findling' IBoy MAsh SCob SGol
suavis SRms
subacutus SRms
subadpressus SRms
submultiflorus **new** NLar
× ***suecicus*** 'Coral Beauty' ♀H6 Widely available
§ - 'Erlinda' (v) SRms
- 'Ifor' SRms
- 'Juliette' (v) ♀H6 EHoe LRHS LSRN MAsh MMuc MRav NLar NOrn SCob SCoo SLim SPer WMat
- 'Skogholm' CBcs CWib ELan EPfP LRHS MAsh MGos MMuc NWea SCob SPer SRms WHar
svenhedinii NLar
taoensis SRms
tardiflorus NLar SRms
tauricus SRms
teijiashanensis NLar SRms
tengyuehensis SRms
thimphuensis NLar SRms
tomentellus WCFE
tomentosus SRms
transcaucasicus **new** NLar
turbinatus NLar SRms
'Valkenburg' SRms
vandelaarii NLar SRms
veitchii NLar SRms
verruculosus SRms
vestitus NLar
villosulus SRms
vilmorinianus SRms
wardii misapplied see *C. mairei*
wardii W.W. Sm. GGal SRms
washanensis NLar
× ***watereri*** CBod CCVT COtt CWib EAEE ECrN ELon LPfy MJak MMuc MSwo NWea SHil WJas
- 'Avonbank' see *C. salicifolius* 'Avonbank'
- 'Cornubia' see *C.* 'Cornubia'
- 'John Waterer' EPfP SPer SPoG
- 'Pendulus' see *C.* 'Hybridus Pendulus'
wilsonii NLar SRms
yalungensis SRms
yinchangensis SRms
zabelii SRms

Cotula (*Asteraceae*)

coronopifolia CBen CWat EHon NPer SWat
hispida ambig. ECtt NPri SIgm SPtp
§ ***hispida*** (DC.) Harv. CTri CWCL ECho EDAr EHoe EPot GMaP MAsh MHer NPer NRya SPoG SRms WIce WJek XLum
lineariloba (DC.) Hilliard ECha ECho EWes
minor see *Leptinella minor*
pectinata see *Leptinella pectinata*
'Platt's Black' see *Leptinella squalida* 'Platt's Black'
potentilloides see *Leptinella potentillina*
pyrethrifolia see *Leptinella pyrethrifolia*
squalida see *Leptinella squalida*

Cotyledon (*Crassulaceae*)

chrysantha see *Rosularia chrysantha*
gibbiflora var. ***metallica*** see *Echeveria gibbiflora* var. *metallica*
oppositifolia see *Chiastophyllum oppositifolium*
orbiculata CTal CTre ETod SPlb
- var. ***oblonga*** EShb IDee
- 'Silver Waves' MCot
simplicifolia see *Chiastophyllum oppositifolium*
tomentosa subsp. ***ladismithensis*** ♀H1c LAll

Cousinia (*Asteraceae*)

thomsonii CC 7328 **new** GKev

Crambe (*Brassicaceae*)

cordifolia ♀H5 Widely available
maritima CArn CBod CEls CSpe ECha EMil EPfP GJos GMaP GPoy IPot LOPS LRHS MCoo MHol MRav MSCN NLar NPri NSti SEND SMad SPer SWat WCot WFar WJek WMnd WPGP XLum
- 'Lilywhite' CAgr LEdu SVic
tatarica GJos

cranberry see *Vaccinium macrocarpon*, *V. oxycoccos*

Crassula ✿ (*Crassulaceae*)

anomala see *C. atropurpurea* var. *anomala*
arborescens EShb EUJe SChr
argentea see *C. ovata*
§ ***atropurpurea*** var. ***anomala*** SChr
- subsp. ***arborescens*** 'Blue Mist' LAll SEND
coccinea CTre EShb SPlb
columella CSuc
elegans subsp. ***elegans*** CSuc
muscosa CSuc SChr SPlb SRot
obtusa SRot
orbicularis WCot
§ ***ovata*** ♀H2 CDoC EBak LAll NPer NPla SChr SEND SPlb SPre SVen WThu
- 'Blue Bird' LToo
- 'Gollum' ♀H2 LAll
- 'Horn Tree' CSuc
- 'Hummel's Sunset' (v) ♀H2 EShb LAll
- 'Minima' LAll
- 'Undulata' **new** WCot
§ - 'Variegata' (v) EBak EShb LAll WCot
pellucida subsp. ***marginalis*** f. ***rubra*** EShb
perfoliata var. ***falcata*** ♀H2 EOHP SRot WCot
perforata 'Variegata' (v) NWad SRot
portulacea see *C. ovata*
§ ***sarcocaulis*** ♀H3 CBcs CTri EAla ECho ELon GCrg GMaP MAsh SIgm SPlb SPoG SRms SRot SVen WAbe WHoo WIce WSHC XSen
sedifolia see *C. setulosa* 'Milfordiae'

sediformis see *C. setulosa* 'Milfordiae'
setulosa SPlb
§ - 'Milfordiae' CTri ECho EPot NBir NPri NRya
socialis LLHF WAbe
tetragona LAll SEND
* ***tomentosa*** 'Variegata' (v) EShb

+ *Crataegomespilus* (*Rosaceae*)

'Jules d'Asnières' IArd NLar

× *Crataegosorbus* (*Rosaceae*)

miczurinii 'Ivan's Belle' CAgr

Crataegus (*Rosaceae*)

sp. SWvt
F&M 196 WPGP
arnoldiana CAgr CDul CLnd CTri EBee ECrN EPfP MAsh MCoo MMuc NLar NWea SEND WMat
'Autumn Glory' CLnd EBee ECrN
azarolus var. ***aronia*** WCot
chrysocarpa EPfP
coccinea misapplied see *C. intricata*
coccinea ambig. NWea
§ ***coccinea*** L. CAgr CLnd CNWT CTho EBee WMat
coccinioides EPfP
cordata see *C. phaenopyrum*
crus-galli misapplied see *C. persimilis* 'Prunifolia'
crus-galli L. CCVT CDul CLnd ECrN EPfP LAst LCro LOPS MAsh NLar NWea SPer WJas
dahurica EPfP
dsungarica EPfP
× ***durobrivensis*** CAgr CDul CLnd EPfP LRHS
ellwangeriana CAgr ECrN EPfP SDix
- 'Fire Ball' MBlu
gemmosa CAgr MAsh NWea
greggiana CEvo EPfP
× ***grignonensis*** 🏆H6 CDul CLnd CTho ECrN MAsh SPer WJas
§ **intricata** NWea
jonesiae EPfP
laciniata misapplied see *C. orientalis*
§ **laevigata** CCVT NWea SCob
- 'Coccinea Plena' see *C. laevigata* 'Paul's Scarlet'
- 'Gireoudii' CBod CDul CWib LAst MGos NSti WJas
- 'Mutabilis' CTri EWTr SGol
§ - 'Paul's Scarlet' (d) 🏆H6 Widely available
- 'Pink Corkscrew' EPfP LLHF MAsh MBlu MGos WCot WPat
- 'Plena' (d) CBcs CDoC CDul CLnd CMac CSBt CTri CWib EBee ECrN ELan EPfP LAst MGos MRav MSwo NOrn NWea SEWo SGol SLim SPer SWvt WHar WMat
- 'Punicea' 🏆H6 Widely available
- 'Rosea' GKin
- 'Rosea Flore Pleno' (d) 🏆H6 Widely available
× ***lavalleei*** CCVT CDul CLnd CMCN CTri ECrN ELan LAst MMuc MRav MSwo NOrn NWea SCoo SEND SLon SPer
- 'Aurora' NLar
- 'Carrierei' 🏆H6 CDul CMac CTho EPfP EWTr IVic LHop LSRN MBri NWea SCoo SEWo SPoG WCot WMat WMou
mexicana see *C. pubescens* f. *stipulacea*
mollis CAgr CTho ECrN EPfP IArd
monogyna Widely available
§ - 'Biflora' CDul CLnd CTho CTri EBee MAsh MCoo MGos NLar NWea SLim WMat
- 'Compacta' LLHF MAsh MBlu WCot WPat
- 'Flexuosa' WCot
- 'Praecox' see *C. monogyna* 'Biflora'
- 'Stricta' CCVT CDul CLnd CSBt ECrN EPfP IDee MMuc SGol SPer
- 'Variegata' (v) ECrN
× ***mordenensis*** 'Toba' (d) CDul CLnd SGol
nigra CDul
§ ***orientalis*** 🏆H6 CCVT CDul CLnd CMCN CTho CTri ECrN EPfP IArd MAsh MBri MCoo MGos NLar NOrn NWea SCoo SLim WHar WJas WMat WMou
oxyacantha misapplied see *C. laevigata*
pedicellata see *C. coccinea* L.
persimilis <u>new</u> NOrn
§ - 'Prunifolia' 🏆H6 Widely available
- 'Prunifolia Splendens' CAgr CCVT EBee EWTr GBin LBuc MBri NOrn WMat WPat
§ **phaenopyrum** CDul CLnd CTho EBee EPfP
pinnatifida EPfP
- var. ***major*** CDul EPfP LEdu MCoo NOrn
- - 'Big Golden Star' CAgr CDoC CTho ECrN EPfP MBlu MCoo WMat
'Praecox' see *C. monogyna* 'Biflora'
prunifolia see *C. persimilis* 'Prunifolia'
§ ***pubescens*** f. ***stipulacea*** CDul CTho ECrN EPfP
punctata CTho EPfP
- f. ***aurea*** EPfP MBlu
sanguinea EPfP
schraderiana CAgr CDoC CDul CLnd CTho EBtc EPfP IVic MBri NLar NWea WHar WMat
submollis CLnd
succulenta 'Jubilee'PBR EBee MCoo WMat
- var. ***macracantha*** CMCN
tanacetifolia CAgr CDul CTho EPfP MBlu MBri WPGP
viridis 'Winter King' CAgr EPfP SLim
wattiana CDul CLnd EBee ELan EPfP

× *Crataemespilus* (*Rosaceae*)

grandiflora CDul CLnd

Craterocapsa (*Campanulaceae*)

congesta CPBP

Cremanthodium (*Asteraceae*)

arnicoides EBee GKev
ellisii CC 7220 GKev

Crenularia see *Aethionema*

Crepis (*Asteraceae*)

aurea ECho
incana 🏆H4 CMea CPla ECho ECtt GCrg NChi NSla NWad SRms WAbe
- 'Pink Mist' GBin NLar
rubra CSpe

Crinitaria see *Aster*

Crinodendron (*Elaeocarpaceae*)

hookerianum 🏆H4 Widely available
- 'Ada Hoffmann' CBcs CBot CDoC CExl CMac CTsd CWSG EBee ELan ELon EPfP GCal GKin IVic LPmr LRHS LSRN MBlu

		MGos MPkF NLar SAko SEle SKHP SLim SWvt WBor WSHC
	patagua	CBcs CBot CDul CExl CHid CMac CTsd CWib EBee ELon EPfP EPri ESwi GBin IDee LRHS MMuc NLar SAko SBrt SEND SPlb SPoG SVen WSHC

Crinum (*Amaryllidaceae*)

	sp.	CMac
§	***album*** **new**	SGSe
	amoenum	EBee GBin
	asiaticum	WCot
§	***bulbispermum***	CPrp
	campanulatum	CDes EBee
	capense	see *C. bulbispermum*
	'Carolina Beauty'	CDes WCot
	'Cintho Alpha'	CBod EPfP MNrw SDeJ SPer
	'Elizabeth Traub'	WCot
	'Ellen Bosanquet'	CCon CDoC CTca EBee ELan GBin LRHS WCot
	'Emma Jones'	WCot
	'Hanibal's Dwarf'	CFil WCot WPGP
	moorei	CBro CCon CEvo CTca IVic LEdu SChr WPGP
	- f. ***album***	CFil CTca EBee
	'Ollene'	WCot
§	× ***powellii***	CBcs CBod CBro CDoC CExl CPrp CTca EBak ECha ECho ELan ELon EPfP GCal LAma LEdu LRHS MNrw MRav MWat NWad SDeJ SDix SEND SMad SPer SRms WCot WWFP
	- 'Album'	CBod CBro CDes CDoC CPrp CTca CTri EBee ECha ECho ELan ELon EPfP EWTr EWes GCra LAma LEdu LRHS MRav SDeJ SEND SMad SPer SRms SSpi WCot WPGP WSHC
	- 'Harlemense'	CDes EBee
	- 'Krelagei'	CDes
	- 'Longifolium'	see *C. bulbispermum*
	- 'Roseum'	see *C.* × *powellii*
	'Sangria'	WCot
	'Summer Nocturne'	WCot
	'White Queen'	WCot
	yemense Deflers	see *C. album*
	yemense misapplied	IMou

Criogenes see *Cypripedium*

Crithmum (*Apiaceae*)

maritimum	CArn CEls GPoy MNHC SPlb SRms WHer WJek

Crocosmia (*Iridaceae*)

	'African Beauty' **new**	ECtt IBal
	'Anna Marie'	EBee ECtt GKev
	'Anniversary'	IBlr
	'Apricot'	CTca ECrc IBal
	'Apricot Surprise'	ECtt IBal
	aurea misapplied	see *C.* × *crocosmiiflora* 'George Davison' Davison
	aurea ambig.	EShb GCal LRHS
	aurea (Pappe ex Hook.f.) Planch.	CPou IBal IBlr LEdu
	- from Swaziland	GCal IBal
	- subsp. ***aurea***	CTca GKev IBlr
	- - 'Maculata'	IBlr
	- subsp. ***pauciflora***	IBlr
	'Auricorn'	CEvo CTca IBal IBlr LEdu
	'Auriol'	IBlr NCot
	'Aurora'	NGdn
	'Ballyrogan Sundown' **new**	IBlr
	'Beth Chatto'	CTca ECrc IBal
	'Blaze' **new**	IBal
	'Bowland Blaze'	MAvo
	Bressingham Beacon = 'Blos'	IBlr LRHS MSpe
	'Bressingham Blaze'	CBre CMHG CTca ECrc IBal IBlr LRHS NGdn NHol WHil
	Bridgemere hybrid	ECrc
	Bright Eyes = 'Walbreyes'^{PBR}	EPfP LRHS
	'Buttercups'	EWoo MTis
	'Cadenza'	IBal IBlr
	'Caistor Sunset' **new**	IBal
	'Carnival'	IBlr
	'Cascade'	IBal IBlr
	'Chinatown'	CEvo IBal IBlr
	'Chrome'	CSam
	'Chrome Spray'	IBlr
	'Citronella' misapplied	see *C.* × *crocosmiiflora* 'Honey Angels'
	'Comet' Knutty	CTca ECrc GCal IBal IBlr LRHS MAvo SDix WMoo
	'Cornish Copper'	CTca SMad
	× ***crocosmiiflora***	CTca CTri IBlr SPlb SRms WBrk WMoo WShi
	- 'A.E. Amos'	ECrc
	- 'A.J. Hogan'	CDes CPrp CTca IBal IBlr NHol
	- 'African Glow'	CTca EBee ECrc IBal LEdu
	- 'Amberglow'	CElw CExl IBal IBlr MAvo NHol NPer
	- 'Apricot Queen'	CTca IBlr NHol
	- 'Autumn Gold'	ECrc IBlr
	- 'B.A. Walker'	ECrc
	- 'Baby Barnaby'	CBre CDes EBee
	- 'Babylon'	Widely available
	- 'Best of British'	ECtt
	- 'Bicolor'	CElw CTca IBal IBlr
	- 'Burford Bronze'	CEvo CTca IBal IBlr NHol
	- 'Burnt Umber'	IBal
	- 'Butterball'	LRHS SHil
	- 'Buttercup'	CSam CTca ECrc ECtt EPfP GKev IBal IBlr IKil LRHS MAvo MCot NHol SHar SMad SRkn WMoo WOut
	- 'Canary Bird'	CBro CSam ECtt IBal NGdn NHol WBrk
	- 'Cardinale'	IBlr
§	- 'Carmin Brillant' 🏆^{H4}	CBod CSam CTca CWCL EAEE EBee ECha ECtt ELon ERCP GKev IBlr LAma LEdu LRHS MBri MGos MHol MWhi NHol SCob SGSe SHil SMad SPoG SRms WMoo WSHC
	- 'Challa'	CTca ECtt IBal
	- 'Citrina'	CTca MNrw
	- 'Citronella' J.E. Fitt	CBro CExl CSam CTri ECrc EPfP GMaP GQue LRHS MBel MWhi NGdn NHol
§	- 'Coleton Fishacre'	Widely available
§	- 'Columbus'	CAvo CMos CSam CTca ECrc ELon EPfP EPri GKev IBal IBlr ILea LHop LRHS LSou MAvo NHol SGSe SMad SPer SRms WHil WMoo
	- 'Colwall'	CEvo IBal IBlr
	- 'Comet'	CEvo EBee IBal
	- 'Constance'	CBro CSam CTca ECrc ECtt GKev IBal IBlr LRHS MAvo NBid NGdn NHol WBrk WHil
	- 'Corona'	CPrp CTca IBal IBlr MAvo NHol
	- 'Corten'	IBlr

§ - 'Croesus' CTca IBal IBlr
- 'Custard Cream' CPrp CTca ECrc IBlr LRHS NHol
- 'D.H. Houghton' IBlr
- 'Daisy Hill' IBlr
- 'David Fitt' CDes MAvo
- 'Debutante' CDes CEvo CHVG CPrp CTca EBee ECrc EPri IBal IBlr NHol WSHC
§ - 'Diadème' CSam CTca CWCL IBal
- 'Dusky Maiden' CMac CTca ECrc ECtt EHoe EPri GCal GKin GMaP IBal IBlr LAst LSou MSwo NHol SRms SWvt
- 'Dwarf Gold' IBal
§ - 'E.A. Bowles' CPou CTca ECrc
- 'Eastern Promise' CBre CEvo CTca IBal IBlr MAvo
- 'Elegans' CHVG ECrc ECtt IBal
§ - 'Emily McKenzie' Widely available
- 'Fantasie' ECrc IBal
- 'Festival Orange' ECrc
- 'Fire Jumper' CDes CEvo CTca EBee IBal MAvo
- 'Fireglow'PBR CTca ECtt IBal
- 'George Davison' misapplied see *C.* × *crocosmiiflora* 'Golden Glory' ambig., *C.* 'Sulphurea'
§ - 'George Davison' Davison Widely available
- 'Gillian' ECrc IBal
- 'Gloria' CTca ECrc IBal MAvo SGSe
- 'Golden Glory' misapplied see *C.* × *crocosmiiflora* 'Diadème'
§ - 'Golden Glory' ambig. CBod CExl COtt CTca CWCL ELan EWoo GBuc GKev IBal LCro LPfy MSwo MWat NBir SCob SEND SGSe SRms WHar
- 'Goldfinch' EBee ECrc WHil WWEG
- 'Goldie' CTca ECrc MAvo
- 'Hades' IBal IBlr
- 'Harvest Sun' IBlr
- 'His Majesty' CBro CSam CTca ECrc IBal IBlr NHol WHil
- 'Hoey Joey' ECrc
§ - 'Honey Angels' Widely available
- 'Honey Bells' ECrc WBrk WOld
- 'Irish Dawn' ECrc IBal IBlr NHol NWad
§ - 'Jackanapes' CDes CTca ECtt ELan GCal IBal IBlr LRHS MLHP STPC
- 'Jackanapes VI' IBal
- 'James Coey' misapplied see *C.* × *crocosmiiflora* 'Carmin Brillant'
- 'James Coey' J.E. Fitt EAEE ECha EHoe EPfP GKin IBal IFoB MLHP NGdn NLar WMoo
§ - 'Jessie' CTca
- 'Judith' CTca IBlr
- 'Kapoor' IBlr
- 'Kiautschou' CTca CWCL IBal IBlr NGdn NHol
- 'Lady Hamilton' CCon CElw CExl CSam CTca ECtt GCal GCra IBal IBlr LRHS MAvo NCGa NHol WMoo WOut WWEG
- 'Lady McKenzie' see *C.* × *crocosmiiflora* 'Emily McKenzie'
- 'Lady Oxford' CTca ECrc IBal IBlr NHol
- 'Lambrook Gold' CAvo ECrc IBal IBlr
- 'Lord Nelson' CExl CTca IBal NHol
- 'Loweswater' ECrc IBal MAvo
- 'Lutea' ECtt IBal
- 'Marjorie' ECrc IBal
- 'Mars' CElw ECrc EWes IBal IFoB MAvo NGdn SRkn
- 'Mephistopheles' CPrp CTca IBlr MAvo NHol
- 'Merryman' CTca ECrc IBal MAvo
- 'Météore' ECtt EPfP GKev GQue LRHS MBNS NEgg WWEG
- 'Morgenlicht' CTca MAvo NHol
- 'Moses' CTca
- 'Mount Usher' CCon CCse CTca EBee ECrc ECtt GCal IBal MNrw NHol
§ - 'Mrs Geoffrey Howard' CSam CTca IBal IBlr LRHS NCGa NHol SRms WCru
- 'Mrs Morrison' see *C.* × *crocosmiiflora* 'Mrs Geoffrey Howard'
- 'Newry Seedling' see *C.* × *crocosmiiflora* 'Prometheus'
- 'Nimbus' CHVG CTca IBal IBlr
§ - 'Norwich Canary' CMHG CTca ECha ECtt EPfP EPri GBuc GCra GKev IBal IBlr LCro LEdu LRHS MRav NBir NGdn NHol WMoo WOut WWEG
- 'Olympic Fire' ECrc IBlr NHol
- 'Olympic Sunrise' CTca
- 'Pepper' IBlr
- 'Ping Pong' CTca
- 'Plaisir' CTca IBal IBlr NBid NHol
- 'Polo' CSam CTca CWCL ECtt IBal LRHS
- 'Princess' see *C. pottsii* 'Princess'
§ - 'Princess Alexandra' IBlr
- 'Prolificans' ECrc IBal
§ - 'Prometheus' CTca IBal IBlr LRHS NHol
- 'Queen Alexandra' misapplied see *C.* × *crocosmiiflora* 'Princess Alexandra'
§ - 'Queen Alexandra' J.E. Fitt CTca ECha IBlr WHal WMoo
- 'Queen Charlotte' CTca ECrc IBal IBlr
- 'Queen Mary II' see *C.* × *crocosmiiflora* 'Columbus'
- 'Queen of Spain' CTca IBal WHil WWEG
- 'Rayon d'Or' ECrc IBal
- 'Red King' CBro EBee EPfP GKev IBal LHop LRHS NLar WBrk WMoo WRHF
- 'Red Knight' IBal
- 'Rheingold' misapplied see *C.* × *crocosmiiflora* 'Diadème'
- 'Saint Clements' CEvo CTca IBal IBlr NHol
- 'Saracen' CBcs CBod CMac CMea CTca CWCL EAEE EBee ECtt GBuc GCal GKin IBal IBoy LEdu LRHS LSou MAvo MBNS MHer MHol MNrw SKHP SPoG WAul WCot WMoo
- 'Severn Seas' ECrc ECtt
- 'Sir Mathew Wilson' IBal
- 'Solfatare' ♀H4 Widely available
- 'Solfatare Coleton Fishacre' see *C.* × *crocosmiiflora* 'Coleton Fishacre'
- 'Star of the East' ♀H4 Widely available
- 'Starfire' ECrc
- 'Sultan' CExl WMoo
- 'Tiger's Eye' CTca
- 'Twilight Fairy Gold' CPou EBee ECtt GBin IBal LLWG LSou MHol SMad SPer WCot WRHF
- 'Venus' CBre CTca ECtt ELon IBal MAvo MHer NHol WMoo WOut
- 'Vesuvius' ECrc GCal WSHC
- 'Vic's Yellow' ECrc IBal
- 'Voyager' ECtt ELon ERCP GKev IBal LRHS NHol NLar SDeJ WOut
- Wasdale strain ECrc IBal
- 'Zeal Tan' CElw CExl CMHG CSam CTca EBee ECtt ELan ELon EPri GBin GCal IBal LEdu LRHS MBNS NEgg NLar NSti SDix WCot WHoo WMoo

§ × ***crocosmioides*** CTca IBlr
- 'Castle Ward Late' CHVG CPrp CTca EAEE ECrc ECtt EPfP GBin GCal GCra GQue IBal IBlr LRHS MAvo MWhi NEgg NHol NLar SRms WCAu WCot WMoo
- 'Mount Stewart Late' IBlr
§ - 'Vulcan' Leichtlin CTca IBlr

'Darkleaf Apricot'	see *C.* × *crocosmiiflora* 'Coleton Fishacre'
'Devil's Advocate'	CTca
'Doctor Marion Wood'	IBal
'Eggs and Bacon'	ECrc
'Eldorado'	see *C.* × *crocosmiiflora* 'E.A. Bowles'
'Elegance'	IBlr
'Ellenbank Canary'	CEvo CTca MAvo
'Ellenbank Firecrest'	CDes CTca EBee MAvo NCGa
'Ellenbank Goldcrest'	NLar
'Ellenbank Skylark'	CEvo MAvo
'Emberglow'	Widely available
'Fandango'	IBal IBlr NHol
'Fernhill'	ECrc IBal IBlr
'Fire King' misapplied	see *C.* × *crocosmiiflora* 'Jackanapes'
'Fire King' ambig.	ECrc EPot ERCP GKev IBal LRHS NLar NSti SWvt WHil
'Fire Sprite'	IBlr
'Firebird'	CAby CTca ECtt GCra IBal IBlr LRHS MHol NHol SRms WCot
'Firecracker'	IBlr
'Firefly'	IBlr
'Flaire'	IBlr
'Fleuve Jaune'	CTca ECrc IBal
'Forest Fire'	IBal LLHF LSou
fucata	IBlr
- 'Jupiter'	see *C.* 'Jupiter'
fucata* × *paniculata	CTca IBal
'Fugue'	CEvo CTca IBlr
'Fusilade'	IBlr
'Gold Sprite'	IBlr
'Golden Ballerina' PBR	CAbb EBee ECtt EWes GBin IBal LBMP LSou MWat NCGa SCob SGSe SHar SPoG SRkn
'Golden Dew'	CTca ECrc ECtt GQue IBal MBNS SKHP WCot WMoo
Golden Fleece *sensu* Lemoine	see *C.* × *crocosmiiflora* 'Coleton Fishacre'
'Harlequin'	CElw CPrp CTca IBal MAvo MHer
'Harmonia'	CDes CTca EBee
'Hellfire'	Widely available
'Highlight'	ECrc IBal IBlr MAvo NHol
'Jennine'	IBal
'Jenny'	MAvo
Jenny Bloom = 'Blacro' PBR	EBee IBal LRHS NChi
'John Boots'	ECtt ELon GBuc GKev IBal LRHS MCot NBid NLar SRms
§ 'Jupiter'	CBre CSam CTca CWCL EBee GCal IBal MAvo MMuc MNrw NCGa NChi NHol NLar WHil
'Kathleen'	ECrc WBod
'Krakatoa'	CAbb CHll CPrp CTca ECrc GBin IBal LBMP LLHF MAvo MBel MHer SGSe SKHP SPoG SWvt WCot WMoo
'Lady Wilson' misapplied	see *C.* × *crocosmiiflora* 'Norwich Canary'
'Lana de Savary'	CEvo CPrp CTca EBee ECtt EWes GCal IBal IBlr MNrw NBid NHol NWad WCot
'Late Cornish'	see *C.* × *crocosmiiflora* 'Queen Alexandra' J.E. Fitt
'Late Lucifer'	CTca CTri GCal IBal IBlr SDix SMHy
'Late Yellow' **new**	IBal
× ***latifolia***	see *C.* × *crocosmioides*
'Lemon Spray'	CTca IBlr
'Limpopo'	Widely available
'Lowen Daa'	CTca
'Lucifer' ♀H5	Widely available
Lucifer's Children	EPfP NPri
'Malahide Castle Red'	SMad WMoo
'Mandarin'	ECrc IBlr
'Marcotijn'	CTca IBal
masoniorum ♀H4	Widely available
- from Satan's Nek, South Africa	CTca IBal
- 'African Dawn'	CTca ECrc ECtt
- 'Amber'	IBlr
- 'Dixter Flame'	IBlr IFoB SDix WOut
- 'Flamenco'	IBlr
- 'Golden Swan'	SRms
- Holehird strain	ECrc ECtt
- 'Kiaora'	IBlr
- 'Moira Reid'	ECtt IBal IBlr
- red-flowered	IBlr
- 'Rowallane Apricot'	IBlr
- 'Rowallane Orange'	CHVG CPrp CTca IBal IBlr
- 'Rowallane Yellow' ♀H4	CEvo CPrp CTca EBee GCal IBal IBlr IMou LRHS NCGa NHol SMHy WSHC
- 'Sherbert Orange'	MAvo
- Slieve Donard selection	CTca ECrc IBal
- 'Sunflare'	IBlr
- 'Tropicana'	IBlr
mathewsiana	IBlr
mathewsiana* × *paniculata	CEvo CTca
'Mex'	MAvo
'Minotaur'	CEvo IBlr
'Miss Scarlet'	EPfP LRHS SAko
'Mistral'	CCon COtt CTca ECtt EPot GAbr GBuc GKev IBal IBlr LAst LRHS NHol NLar SCob SPer WMoo
'Moorland Blaze'	WMoo
'Moorland Sunset' **new**	IBal
'Mount Stewart'	see *C.* × *crocosmiiflora* 'Jessie'
'Mr Bedford'	see *C.* × *crocosmiiflora* 'Croesus'
'Mullard Pink'	CTca ECrc
'Okavango' PBR	CBre CBro CMac CPrp CTca ECtt ELon EPri GAbr GQue IBal LSun MAvo MBNS MHol MNrw NEgg NLar NSti SDix SGSe SKHP WCot WFar
Old Hat	see *C.* 'Walberton Red'
'Orange Devil'	CBre CEvo ECtt GKin IBal IBlr LLHF LRHS MBNS NCGa
'Orange River'	MAvo WCot
'Orangeade'	CTca ECtt IBal IBlr NHol SRms
'Pageant'	ECrc IBal
§ ***paniculata***	CMac CPou CTca ECtt GAbr GBin NBid SCob WBrk WMoo WOut WShi
- from Howick	CTca
- from Kologha	CTca
- brown/orange-flowered	IBlr
- 'Cally Greyleaf'	GCal IBal MAvo WCot
- 'Cally Sword'	GCal IBal MAvo
- 'Major'	CTri IBlr
- 'Natal'	CPrp CTca ECtt IBal NHol
- red-flowered	CTca IBlr SWvt
- triploid	IBlr
aff. ***paniculata***	IBlr
'Paul's Best Yellow'	Widely available
pearsei	CTca IBlr
'Phillipa Browne'	CSde CTca ECtt IBal SCob SGSe WCot WMoo

	pottsii	CTca EBee IBal IBlr LEdu WHil WPtf WWEG
	- CD&R 109	CPou
	- 'Culzean Pink'	CElw CExl CPrp CTca EBee GBin GCal IBal IBlr LPla MLHP MNrw NBid NBir NCot NHol NLar WOut
	- deep pink-flowered	IBlr WMoo
	- 'Grandiflora'	CEvo IBlr
§	- 'Princess'	ECrc ECtt GKev IBal
	- tall	CTca IBal MSpe
	'Prince of Orange' **new**	ERCP
	'Quantreau'	IBlr
	'Queen Alexandria'	LRHS
	'R.W. Wallace'	CTca IBal
	'Raspberry Spray' **new**	IBlr
	'Red Star'	IBal
	rosea	see *Tritonia disticha* subsp. *rubrolucens*
	'Rowden Bronze'	see *C.* × *crocosmiiflora* 'Coleton Fishacre'
	'Rowden Chrome'	see *C.* × *crocosmiiflora* 'George Davison' Davison
	'Ruby Velvet'	IBlr
	'Rubygold'	CPrp IBlr
	'Saffron Queen'	IBlr
	'Salsa'	CDes
	'Sampford Yellow' **new**	IBal
	'Saturn'	see *C.* 'Jupiter'
	'Scarlatti'	CTca IBal IBlr NHol
	'Scarlet Wonder'	CTca
	'Severn Sunrise' 🏆H5	Widely available
	'Shocking'	IBlr MAvo
	'Sonate'	CTca
	'Sorento'	IBlr
	'Spitfire'	CExl CSam CTca ECha ECtt ELan GAbr GQue IBal IBlr LHop MArl MAvo MRav NHol SGSe SWvt
§	'Sulphurea'	CExl CPou CSam ECtt EPfP IBal IBlr LRHS MSpe NHol
	'Sunglow' **new**	EBee ERCP GKev MNrw WHil
	'Sunzest'	CTca ECrc ECtt MAvo
	'Suzanna'	EBee ECtt GKev
	'Tamar Double Red'	CTca SMad
	'Tamar Glow'	CTca WOld
	'Tamar New Dawn'	CTca
	'Tamar Peace'	CTca
	'Tangerine'	ECrc
	'Tangerine Dream'	IBlr
	'Tangerine Queen'	CTca ECrc IBal IBlr NHol WHil WMoo
	'Tangerine Spray' **new**	IBlr
	'Tiger'	CElw CTca ECrc MAvo
	'Toccata'	IBlr
	'Twilight Fairy Crimson'	CAbb CWGN EBee ECrc ECtt GBin LEdu LSou
I	'Vulcan' A. Bloom	CTca IBal IBlr MAvo
	'Vulcan' Leichtlin	see *C.* × *crocosmioides* 'Vulcan' Leichtlin
§	'Walberton Red'	CDes CTca EBee ECrc EWes IBal MAvo NCGa NWad SKHP SMad
	Walberton Yellow = 'Walcroy'[PBR]	CHVG EPfP LRHS SMHy SMad
	'Zambesi'[PBR]	CDes CMac CPrp CTca ECtt ELon GQue IBal LHop MAvo MBNS MCot MNrw NCGa NEgg SKHP SPer WCot WHil
	'Zeal Giant'	CTca ECrc ECtt IBal IBlr MAvo NHol
	'Zeal Remembrance'	CTca
	'Zeal Unnamed'	CCon CPrp CTca ECrc ECtt GBee IBal IBlr NHol

Crocus ✿ (*Iridaceae*)

	'Advance'	CAvo ECho EPot ERCP LAma MBri SDeJ
§	***albiflorus***	EPot
	ancyrensis	EPot GKev SDeJ
	- 'Golden Bunch'	ECho SDeJ WShi
§	***angustifolius*** 🏆H5	ECho EPot SDeJ
	- 'Minor'	EPot
	'Ard Schenk'	ECho GKev LAma LRHS
	asturicus	see *C. serotinus* subsp. *salzmannii*
	asumaniae	EPot NRog
	- white-flowered	NRog
	'Aubade'	EPot GKev LAma
	aureus	see *C. flavus* subsp. *flavus*
	banaticus 🏆H5	ECho EPot GKev LLHF NHar NRog
	- 'Early Bird'	NRog
	- 'Snowdrift'	EPot NHar
	baytopiorum	ECho
	biflorus 'Blue Pearl' 🏆H5	CAvo CBro ECho EPfP EPot ERCP GKev LCro MBri NBir SCob SDeJ SPer SPhx WCot WShi
	- subsp. ***melantherus***	NRog
	- 'Miss Vain'	ECho EPot ERCP GKev LAma MBri MGib
	- 'Serevan'	EPot
	- subsp. ***tauri***	EPot
	- subsp. ***weldenii*** 'Albus'	ECho EPot LAma
	- - 'Fairy'	ECho LAma
	'Blue Bird'	ECho EPot LAma
	blue-flowered **new**	LRHS
	boryi	ECho LRHS NRog
	cambessedesii	NRog
	cancellatus	SDeJ
§	- subsp. ***cancellatus***	EPot GKev LAma NRog
	- var. ***cilicicus***	see *C. cancellatus* subsp. *cancellatus*
	- subsp. ***damascenus***	NRog
	- subsp. ***lycius***	ECho EPot NRog
	- subsp. ***mazziaricus***	EPot NRog
	- subsp. ***pamphylicus***	NRog
	cartwrightianus 🏆H4	GKev LRHS NRog WShi
	- 'Albus' misapplied	see *C. hadriaticus*
	- 'Albus' Tubergen 🏆H4	EPot GKev NRog SDeJ
	- 'Marcel'	NRog
	- 'Michel'	NRog
	chrysanthus 🏆H5	CHab
	- 'Blue Peter'	EPot
	- 'Constellation' **new**	EPot
	- 'Cream Beauty' 🏆H5	CAvo CBro ECho EPfP EPot GKev LAma LCro LOPS LRHS MBri NBir SCob SDeJ WShi
	- 'E.A. Bowles' misapplied	see *C. chrysanthus* 'E.P. Bowles'
§	- 'E.P. Bowles'	ECho LAma MBri
	- var. ***fuscotinctus***	ECho EPfP EPot LAma LCro LOPS MBri SDeJ
	- 'Goldene Sonne' **new**	EPot
	- 'Uschak Orange'	ECho
	- 'Warley'	ECho
	- 'Zwanenburg Bronze' 🏆H5	ECho EPfP GKev LCro LOPS SDeJ WShi
	'Cloth of Gold'	see *C. angustifolius*
	clusii	see *C. serotinus* subsp. *clusii*
	corsicus 🏆H4	ECho EPot
	dalmaticus	EPot
	danfordiae	ECho
	'Dorothy'	EPot GKev
	'Dutch Yellow'	see *C.* × *luteus* 'Golden Yellow'

	Name	Suppliers
	etruscus ♀H5	GKev
	- 'Rosalind'	ECho GKev LAma
	- 'Zwanenburg' ♀H5	ECho EPot GKev LAma SDeJ
	'Fantasy'	ECho WShi
§	***flavus*** subsp. ***flavus*** ♀H5	ECho EPot GKev LAma WShi
	fleischeri	ECho EPot LAma
	'Flower Record'	GKev LAma NBir SDeJ
	gargaricus	GKev
	'Gipsy Girl'	CAvo EPfP EPot ERCP LAma LCro LOPS MBri SCob SPer
	'Golden Mammoth'	see *C.* × *luteus* 'Golden Yellow'
	'Goldilocks' ♀H5	GKev LAma SDeJ
	goulimyi ♀H4	CAvo CBro CTal ECho EPot GKev LAma LRHS NRog SDeJ
	- 'Albus'	see *C. goulimyi* subsp. *goulimyi* 'Mani White'
§	- subsp. ***goulimyi*** 'Mani White' ♀H4	CTal ECho EPot
	- subsp. ***leucanthus***	NRog
	'Grand Maître'	CAvo LAma MBri MGib SDeJ
§	***hadriaticus*** ♀H4	ECho GKev LAma LRHS NRog
	- var. ***chrysobelonicus***	see *C. hadriaticus*
	- 'Jumbo'	NRog
	'Herald'	LAma SPhx
	heuffelianus subsp. ***heuffelianus***	GKev WShi
§	- subsp. ***scepusiensis*** new	WShi
	imperati subsp. ***imperati*** var. ***albus***	WAbe
	- subsp. ***suaveolens***	EPot
	- - 'De Jager'	ERCP LAma
	'Jānis Rukšāns'	CAvo CDes
	'Jeanne d'Arc'	CAvo CBro ECho EPfP EPot GKev LAma LCro LOPS MBri NBir SDeJ WShi
	'Jeannine'	SDeJ
	karduchorum	EPot LAma NRog
	'Karin' new	EPot
	'King of the Striped'	ECho LAma SDeJ SPer
	korolkowii	ECho GKev LAma MGib
	- 'Golden Nugget'	EPot
	- 'Kiss of Spring'	ECho EPot
	kosaninii	GKev
	- 'April View'	EPot
	kotschyanus 'Albus'	NRog SDeJ
	- subsp. ***cappadocicus***	NRog
§	- subsp. ***kotschyanus***	EPot NRog SDeJ
	- 'Reliance'	NRog
	'Ladykiller' ♀H5	CAvo CBro ECho EPot ERCP GKev LAma LCro LOPS MBri SPhx WShi
	laevigatus ♀H3	NRog
	- CE&H 612	EPot
	- 'Fontenayi'	EPot ERCP GKev NRog
	'Large Yellow'	see *C.* × *luteus* 'Golden Yellow'
§	***ligusticus*** ♀H5	CBro EPot LAma
	- 'Millesimo'	NRog
	longiflorus ♀H4	EPot LRHS NRog
§	× ***luteus*** 'Golden Yellow' ♀H5	CAvo EPot GKev LAma LCro WShi
§	- 'Stellaris' ♀H5	EPot
	malyi ♀H4	ECho GKev
	- 'Sveti Roc'	EPot
	mathewii	ECho EPot
	- 'Dream Dancer'	EPot
	medius	see *C. ligusticus*
	minimus	ECho EPot ERCP GKev LAma LLHF
	'Negro Boy'	ECho EPot LAma
	niveus	CBro ECho EPot GKev LAma LLHF LRHS NRog WAbe
	nudiflorus	ECho EPot GKev LAma LLHF NRog
	ochroleucus	ECho EPot GKev NRog SDeJ
	olivieri subsp. ***balansae*** 'Zwanenburg'	EPot
	'Orange Monarch' new	EPfP SCob
	oreocreticus	NRog
	pallasii subsp. ***dispathaceus***	NRog
	pestalozzae	EPot
	'Peter Pan'	CAby
	'Pickwick'	CAby CAvo EPfP EPot LAma LCro MBri NBir SDeJ WShi
	'Prins Claus'	ECho EPfP EPot ERCP LAma MBri SDeJ SPer
	pulchellus ♀H4	CAvo EPot ERCP GKev LAma NRog SDeJ
	- 'Albus'	ECho EPot NRog
	- 'Inspiration'	NRog
	- 'Michael Hoog'	ECho NRog
	'Purple Heart'	NRog
	'Purpureus'	see *C.* 'Purpureus Grandiflorus'
§	'Purpureus Grandiflorus'	CBro EPot SDeJ
	'Queen of the Blues'	CBro EPot SDeJ
	'Remembrance'	CAby CAvo CBro ECho EPfP EPot GKev LAma LCro NBir SDeJ WShi
	reticulatus	EPot
	robertianus	NRog
	'Romance'	CAvo CBro EPot GKev LAma MBri SDeJ
	'Ruby Giant'	CAvo CBro ECho EPfP EPot ERCP GKev LAma LCro LOPS MBri NBir SCob SDeJ SPer SPhx WShi
	rujanensis	EPot
	salzmannii	see *C. serotinus* subsp. *salzmannii*
	sativus	CAvo CBod CBro CPrp CTca CTsd ECho ELan EPot ERCP GKev GPoy LAma LCro LOPS NBir NCGa NRog SCob SDeJ SVic
	'Saturnus'	EPot LAma
	scepusiensis	see *C. heuffelianus* subsp. *scepusiensis*
§	***serotinus*** subsp. ***clusii***	LAma NRog
§	- subsp. ***salzmannii***	LAma NRog
	- - f. ***albus***	NRog
	- - - 'El Torcal' new	WAbe
	- - 'Erectophyllus'	NRog
	sibiricus	see *C. sieberi*
§	***sieberi*** ♀H5	EPot
	- 'Albus'	see *C. sieberi* 'Bowles's White'
	- subsp. ***atticus***	ECho
	- - 'Firefly'	ECho EPfP EPot GKev LAma SDeJ
§	- 'Bowles's White' ♀H5	CBro ECho EPot GKev SDeJ
	- 'Hubert Edelsten' ♀H5	ECho EPot LAma
	- 'Ronald Ginns'	EPot
	- subsp. ***sublimis*** 'Tricolor' ♀H4	CAvo CBro CTca ECho EPfP EPot GKev LAma LCro MBri NBir NWad SDeJ SPer WOld
	- 'Violet Queen'	LAma
	'Snow Bunting' ♀H5	CAvo CBro CTca ECho EPfP EPot GKev LAma LCro LOPS NBir SCob SDeJ SPer WShi
	speciosus ♀H4	CAvo CBro CDes CTca EPfP LAma LCro LOPS MLHP NBir SDeJ WShi
	- 'Aino'	ECho NRog
	- 'Aitchisonii'	ECho GKev LAma LRHS NRog
	- 'Albus' ♀H4	CAvo CBro ECho EPot ERCP GKev LCro LOPS NRog SDeJ WShi
	- 'Artabir'	ECho GKev LRHS NRog SDeJ
	- 'Cassiope'	ECho GKev LAma LRHS NRog SDeJ
	- 'Conqueror'	ECho EPfP ERCP GKev LAma LCro LOPS LRHS NRog SDeJ

- 'Oxonian' CBro ECho EPot GKev LAma NRog WOld
- subsp. ***speciosus*** ECho EPot NBir NRog SDeJ
- subsp. ***xantholaimos*** NRog
'Spring Beauty' EPfP ERCP SDeJ
× ***stellaris*** see *C.* × *luteus* 'Stellaris'
susianus see *C. angustifolius*
thomasii NRog
tommasinianus ♀H5 CAvo CBro CGrW CHab CTca ECho EPot LAma LCro LLWP MBri MRav NBir SDeJ SPhx SRms WShi
- 'Albus' ECho EPot GKev LAma WShi
- 'Barr's Purple' ECho EPot GKev LAma LCro SDeJ
- 'Claret' ECho
- 'Eric Smith' EPot
- 'Lilac Beauty' ECho EPfP EPot LAma
- 'Pictus' ECho EPot LAma LLHF WShi
- 'Roseus' CAvo CDes ECho EPot ERCP GKev LAma SBch SDeJ SPhx WCot WShi
- 'Whitewell Purple' CAvo CBro ECho EPot ERCP GKev LAma LCro LOPS MBri NBir SDeJ WShi
tournefortii ♀H3 ECho EPot LRHS NRog
'Twinborn' EPot
'Vanguard' ♀H5 CAvo EPfP EPot GKev LAma LCro LOPS SDeJ WCot
veluchensis LLHF
veneris NRog
vernus subsp. ***albiflorus*** see *C. albiflorus*
- 'Graecus' EPot
- Uklin strain ECho
- subsp. ***vernus*** 'Grandiflorus' see *C.* 'Purpureus Grandiflorus'
versicolor 'Picturatus' EPot ERCP LAma LLHF SDeJ
'White Triumphator' LAma
'Yalta' CAvo ECho ERCP GKev MGib SPhx
'Yellow Giant' SDeJ
'Yellow Mammoth' see *C.* × *luteus* 'Golden Yellow'
'Zenith' EPot
'Zephyr' ♀H4 CBro NRog SDeJ WOld
zonatus see *C. kotschyanus* subsp. *kotschyanus*

Croomia (*Stemonaceae*)

heterosepala WCru

Crossandra (*Acanthaceae*)

infundibuliformis ♀H1a EShb

Crossyne (*Amaryllidaceae*)

flava NRog WCot
guttata new WCot

Crowea (*Rutaceae*)

exalata × ***saligna*** CExl

Crucianella (*Rubiaceae*)

stylosa see *Phuopsis stylosa*

Cruciata (*Rubiaceae*)

§ ***laevipes*** NMir

Crusea (*Rubiaceae*)

coccinea CSpe WCot
- 'Crûg Crimson' WCot WCru

Cryptanthus (*Bromeliaceae*)

alagoanus LAir
bivittatus LAir NEve
- 'Pink Starlight' (v) ♀H1a LAir
Black Mystic Group LAir
bromelioides LAir
marginatus LAir
'Red Star' LAir

Cryptocarya (*Lauraceae*)

alba GBin IDee SVen

Cryptocoryne (*Araceae*)

× ***willisii*** new XBlo

Cryptogramma (*Pteridaceae*)

crispa WHer

Cryptomeria ✿ (*Cupressaceae*)

fortunei see *C. japonica*
§ ***japonica*** CDul CLau CLet CMen CTho EPfP LPar MBlu MMuc NWea SEND SWvt WMou
- 'Antique Gold' new LRHS
- Araucarioides Group NEgg SLim
- 'Atawai' NLar
- 'Aurea' EUJe
- 'Bandai-sugi' ♀H6 CKen CMac CMen EPfP EUJe MGos NHol NLar SRms WGor
- 'Barabits Gold' LRHS MGos
- 'Birodo' CKen
- 'Black Dragon' SLim
- 'Compressa' CDoC CKen EPfP LBee MAsh MGos NWad SRms WGor
§ - 'Cristata' CBcs CDoC CMac ELan ESwi LRHS MGos MPkF NEgg NOrn SLim SRms
- 'Dacrydioides' CDoC NLar SLim
- 'Dinger' CKen NLar
- Elegans Group CBcs CDul CLet CMac CSBt EFry ELan EPfP EUJe LRHS MBri MGos NEgg NLar NOrn NWea SCoo SEND SLim SPer SPoG SRms WMat
- 'Elegans Aurea' CCVT CLet EFry ELan MAsh MBri NEgg SPoG SWvt
- 'Elegans Compacta' ♀H6 CDoC CLet CMac CSBt CWib EFry ELan GBin LBee LRHS MBri MMuc NLar NWea SLim SRms SWvt
- 'Elegans Nana' LBee SRms
- 'Elegans Viridis' ♀H6 SLim WHar WMat
I - 'Elegantissima' CCVT
- 'Globosa Nana' ♀H6 CDul EPfP LAst LBee LPal MGos NEgg NHol NPri SCoo SPoG
- 'Golden Promise' ♀H6 CBcs NHol NWad SLim SPer SWvt
- 'Jindai-sugi' NLar
- 'Kamasan' NLar
- 'Karl Fuchs' SLim
- 'Kilmacurragh' CKen NWea
- 'Kohui-yatsubusa' CKen
- 'Koshiji-yatsubusa' NLar
- 'Koshyi' CKen
- 'Little Champion' CDoC CKen LRHS SLim
- 'Little Diamond' CKen NEgg SBod
- 'Little Sonja' CKen SLim
- 'Little Yoko' CKen NLar
- 'Littleworth Dwarf' see *C. japonica* 'Littleworth Gnom'
§ - 'Littleworth Gnom' LRHS NLar
- 'Lobbii Nana' hort. see *C. japonica* 'Nana'
- 'Monstrosa' NLar
§ - 'Nana' CDoC CMac
- 'Osaka-tama' CKen
- 'Pipo' CKen
- 'Pygmaea' NHol NLar NWad SRms

	- 'Rasen-sugi'	IDee IVic MGos NLar SMad
	- 'Rein's Dense Jade'	SLim
	- 'Sekkan-sugi' ♀H6	CBcs CCVT CDoC CDul CLet CMac EFry EPfP ESwi GBin GKin IArd LAst LBee LRHS MGos NEgg NLar SCoo SLim SPoG SWvt WBor
	- 'Sekka-sugi'	see *C. japonica* 'Cristata'
§	- 'Spiralis' ♀H6	CDoC CKen CMac EFry ELan EPfP EUJe LAst LBee LRHS MAsh MGos NEgg NHol NLar NWad NWea SCoo SLim SPoG SRms SWvt
§	- 'Spiraliter Falcata'	NLar
§	- 'Tansu'	CDoC CKen SPoG WGor
	- 'Tenzan-sugi' ♀H6	CDoC CKen MGos NHol NWad WThu
	- 'Tilford Gold'	EFry MGos NHol WGor
	- 'Toda'	CKen
	- 'Vilmorin Gold'	ELan MGos NHol
	- 'Vilmoriniana' ♀H6	CDoC CKen CLet CMen CTri ELan EPfP GKin LRHS MBri MGos MMuc NEgg NHol NLar SCoo SEND SLim SPer SPoG SWvt WMoo
	- 'Winter Bronze'	CKen
	- 'Yatsubusa'	see *C. japonica* 'Tansu'
	- 'Yore-sugi'	see *C. japonica* 'Spiralis', 'Spiraliter Falcata'
	- 'Yoshino'	CKen NEgg SLim
	sinensis	see *C. japonica*

Cryptotaenia (*Apiaceae*)

	japonica	CAgr CHby CPou GPoy LEdu MHer MNHC SRms WHer WJek
	- f. ***atropurpurea***	CSpe EBee EHoe LEdu MNrw SDix SGSe WBor WPGP

Ctenanthe (*Marantaceae*)

	lubbersiana ♀H1b	XBlo
	oppenheimiana	XBlo

Cucubalus (*Caryophyllaceae*)

	baccifer	CArn EWld NLar

Cudrania see *Maclura*

cumin see *Cuminum cyminum*

Cuminum (*Apiaceae*)

	cyminum	CLau SRms SVic

Cumulopuntia (*Cactaceae*)

§	***boliviana***	CCac
	subsp. ***dactylifera*** **new**	

Cunninghamia (*Cupressaceae*)

	konishii	CExl
§	***lanceolata***	CBcs CDTJ CDoC CDul CKen CMCN CMac CTho EPfP SSpi SSta WBor WPGP
	- 'Glauca'	CExl CJun CTho GKev IVic
	sinensis	see *C. lanceolata*
	unicaniculata	see *C. lanceolata*

Cunonia (*Cunoniaceae*)

	capensis	CExl

Cuphea (*Lythraceae*)

	caeciliae	CSam
	cyanea	CMHG SDix
	'Firecracker'	LAst
	hyssopifolia ♀H1c	CTsd EShb SWvt
	- 'Alba'	CTre EShb SWvt
	- pink-flowered	CTre
	- 'Rosea'	SWvt
§	***ignea*** ♀H1c	CTsd
	'Lilac Belle' **new**	CSpe
I	***macrophylla*** hort.	CHll
	platycentra	see *C. ignea*
	'Regal Purple'	CPla
	'Torpedo'	LAst NPri
	viscosissima	CSpe MCot

× *Cupressocyparis* see × *Cuprocyparis*

Cupressus (*Cupressaceae*)

	arizonica	LPal
	- var. ***arizonica*** 'Arctic'	CDoC
§	- var. ***glabra***	CPne
	- - 'Angaston'	SLim
	- - 'Aurea'	CLet CMac EFry MAsh SGol SLim
	- - 'Blue Ice'	CBcs CDoC CDul CMac CTho EFry MAsh MGos NEgg SLim SWvt WHar
	- - 'Compacta'	CKen
I	- - 'Fastigiata'	CCVT CDoC ECrN EFry EPfP ETod NPri
*	- - 'Lutea'	NEgg
	- 'Pyramidalis' ♀H5	SEND SGol
	cashmeriana ♀H3	CBcs CDTJ CDoC CTho ELan IVic SLim SMad
§	***funebris***	CDul
	glabra	see *C. arizonica* var. *glabra*
	× ***leylandii***	see × *Cuprocyparis leylandii*
	lusitanica 'Brice's Weeping'	CKen NEgg SLim
	- 'Glauca Pendula'	CDoC
	- 'Pygmy'	CKen
	macrocarpa	CBcs CCVT CDoC CDul CTho EFry SEND
	- 'Compacta'	CKen
	- 'Gold Spread'	EFry SLim
	- 'Goldcrest' ♀H4	CBcs CCVT CDoC CDul CLet CMac ECrN EFry ELan LBMP LBee LPar LRHS MBri MGos NBir NPri SEWo SGol SLim SWvt
	- 'Golden Pillar'	CDoC EFry SWvt
	- 'Greenstead Magnificent'	SLim
	- 'Horizontalis Aurea' R.E. Harrison	EFry
	- 'Lohbrunner'	CKen
	- 'Lutea'	CDoC
	- 'Pygmaea'	CKen
	- 'Sulphur Cushion'	CKen
	- 'Wilma' ♀H4	CSBt EFry ELan LAst LBee LRHS MAsh MBri MGos SCoo SGol SLim SPer SPoG SWvt
	- 'Woking'	CKen
	sempervirens	CDul CLet EFry ELan EUJe LPal LPar SPlb
	- 'Bolgheri'	SBig
	- 'Green Pencil'	CKen
	- 'Pyramidalis'	see *C. sempervirens* Stricta Group
	- var. ***sempervirens***	see *C. sempervirens* Stricta Group
§	- Stricta Group	CBcs CCVT CDul CTho EFry EPfP EWTr LPal NLar SEND SEWo SGol WCFE
	- 'Swane's Gold'	CBcs CDoC CKen EFry MAsh NEgg WCFE
	- 'Totem Pole'	CCVT CDoC CKen CSBt CTho CTri EFry ELan EPfP EUJe LBee LPal LRHS MAsh MGos SCoo SEND SPoG SWvt

× *Cuprocyparis* (*Cupressaceae*)

§ ***leylandii*** — Widely available
I - '2001' — CCVT CDoC SGol SLim
- 'Blue Jeans'PBR — SEND
§ - 'Castlewellan' — CBcs CCVT CDoC CDul CMac COtt CSBt CTri EFry EPfP LBuc LSRN MAsh MBri MGos MJak MMuc NBes NPri NWea SCob SEND SGol SLim SPer SPoG SWvt WFar WHar
- Excalibur Gold = 'Drabb'PBR — CDoC NWea
- 'Ferngold' — MAsh
- 'Galway Gold' — see × *C. leylandii* 'Castlewellan'
- 'Gold Rider' ♀H6 — CDoC CLet CMac EFry ELan LPar MAsh MGos MMuc NEgg NWea SCob SCoo SEND SGol SMad SPer SPoG SWvt WHar
§ - 'Harlequin' (v) — CMac SEND SWvt
- 'Herculea' — CDoC
- 'Naylor's Blue' — CMac
- 'Olive's Green' — SWvt
- 'Robinson's Gold' — CLet CMac GQui NWea SGol SLim WHar
- 'Variegata' — see × *C. leylandii* 'Harlequin'
- 'Winter Sun' — WCFE

Curculigo (*Hypoxidaceae*)

capitulata — XBlo
crassifolia B&SWJ 2318 — WCru
- HWJ 683 from Vietnam — WCru

Curcuma ✿ (*Zingiberaceae*)

alismatifolia — SDeJ
longa — CArn SPre
roscoeana — LAma SDeJ
zedoaria 'White Wonder' — SDeJ

Curtonus see *Crocosmia*

Cussonia (*Araliaceae*)

paniculata — CDTJ CWGN
spicata — CDTJ SPlb

custard apple see *Annona cherimola*, *A. reticulata*

Cyananthus (*Campanulaceae*)

incanus — GEdr
integer misapplied — see *C. microphyllus*
lobatus ♀H5 — GKev LLHF
- SDR 7476 new — GKev
- 'Albus' — EPot WAbe
- giant — CTal EPot GEdr NHar WAbe
lobatus* × *microphyllus — CTal GCrg GEdr WAbe
macrocalyx — EPot
§ ***microphyllus*** ♀H5 — EPot GCrg GEdr NHar NSla WAbe
microphyllus × 'Sherriff's Variety' — NHar
sherriffii — EPot GJos IFoB WAbe
spathulifolius — WAbe

Cyanella (*Tecophilaeaceae*)

orchidiformis — NRog

Cyanotis (*Commelinaceae*)

somaliensis ♀H1c — EShb

Cyathea (*Cyatheaceae*)

australis — CDTJ CKel ESwi IDee NLos SPlb
baileyana new — NLos
brownii — NLos
cooperi — CDTJ CKel EBee ESwi NLos WFib
* - 'Brentwood' — EBee ESwi ISha NLos
- 'Cinnamon' new — NLos
- single-crested new — NLos
dealbata — CDTJ CKel GBin
dregei — SPlb
exilis new — NLos
glauca new — NLos
leichardtiana new — NLos
medullaris — CKel NLos
rebeccae — NLos
smithii — CDTJ CKel
tomentosissima — CDTJ CKel
woollsiana — NLos

Cyathodes (*Ericaceae*)

colensoi — see *Leucopogon colensoi*
fraseri — see *Leucopogon fraseri*

Cycas (*Cycadaceae*)

media — LPal
panzhihuaensis — CBrP LPal SPlb
revoluta ♀H2 — CAbb CBrP CDoC EAla EPfP ETod EUJe LPal NLos SChr SEND SMad SPlb STrG XBlo
revoluta* × *taitungensis — CBrP
§ ***rumphii*** — CBrP LPal
taitungensis — CBrP
thouarsii — see *C. rumphii*

Cyclamen ✿ (*Primulaceae*)

abchasicum — see *C. coum* subsp. *caucasicum*
africanum — CBro ECho EPot GKev LRHS MAsh
§ ***alpinum*** — CBro ECho EPot GKev LAma LRHS MAsh SDeJ XEll
- 'Nettleton White' — MAsh
balearicum — CBro CEvo ECho EPot GKev LAma LRHS MAsh
cilicium ♀H3 — CBro CEvo ECho EPfP EPot ERCP GBuc GKev LAma LCro LOPS LRHS MAsh NSla WCot WHoo WShi XEll
- f. ***album*** — CBro ECho EPot GBuc GKev LAma LLHF LRHS MAsh XEll
colchicum — CEvo MAsh
§ ***coum*** ♀H5 — Widely available
- var. ***abchasicum*** — see *C. coum* subsp. *caucasicum*
§ - subsp. ***caucasicum*** — CEvo GKev WCra
- subsp. ***coum*** — CBro ECho
- - f. ***albissimum*** — GBuc
- - - 'George Bisson' — MAsh
- - - 'Golan Heights' — MAsh
- - f. ***coum*** Pewter Group ♀H5 — ECho GBuc GKev WCot
- - - - 'Blush' — GBuc
- - - - 'Maurice Dryden' ♀H5 — CBro CLAP ECho EPot GKev LAma LHop LRHS MAsh WHoo
- - - - red-flowered — WPat
- - - - 'Tilebarn Elizabeth' — MAsh NBir WHoo
- - - 'Roseum' — CAvo GBuc
- - - Silver Group — CAvo CBro ECho EWoo LHop LRHS NRya WHoo
- - - - red-flowered — WHoo
- - magenta-flowered — WHoo
- - f. ***pallidum*** 'Album' — CAvo ECho EPot EWoo GKev GMaP LAma LPal SDeJ SPer WHoo WPat WPnP WShi
- dark pink-flowered — CAvo CLAP ECho WHoo

- hybrid	ERCP
- marble-leaved	ECho LHop WHoo
- plain-leaved	CLAP
- red-flowered	CLAP ECho
I - 'Rubrum'	GKev
creticum	ECho MAsh
cyprium	CBro CEvo ECho GKev LRHS MAsh XEll
- 'E.S.'	ECho
× ***drydeniae***	MAsh
europaeum	see *C. purpurascens*
graecum	CBro CEvo CPne CTal ECho EPot GKev LLHF LRHS MAsh WCot WHil WThu XEll
- subsp. ***candicum***	MAsh
- subsp. ***graecum*** f. ***album***	CBro ECho LRHS MAsh
- - f. ***graecum*** 'Glyfada'	EPot GKev MAsh XEll
§ ***hederifolium*** ♀H5	Widely available
- S&L 175/1	WCot XLum
- 'Amaze Me'	ECtt LEdu MHol MPie WCot
- arrow-head	CLAP ECho SBea
- var. ***hederifolium*** f. ***albiflorum*** ♀H5	CAvo CBro CTri ECho EWoo GKev LCro LEdu LOPS NWad SBea SCob SDeJ WHil WHoo WPat WPnP XLum
- - - 'Album'	CWCL WShi
- - - Bowles's Apollo Group	GBuc
- - - 'Nettleton Silver'	see *C. hederifolium* var. *hederifolium* f. *albiflorum* 'White Cloud'
- - - 'Perlenteppich'	GMaP
- - - silver-leaved	SDys
§ - - - 'White Cloud' ♀H5	CLAP ECho MAsh WHoo
- - f. ***hederifolium*** Bowles's Apollo Group	CHid CLAP GBuc
- - - 'Fairy Rings'	MAsh
- - - 'Rosenteppich'	WBor
- - - 'Ruby Glow'	CWCL GBuc LRHS MAsh NBir WPat WThu
- - - Silver Cloud Group ♀H5	CBro CHid CLAP GBuc MAsh NBir WHoo WPat
- 'Lysander'	ECho EPot GKev MAsh
- 'Pewter Mist'	LAma
- 'Red Sky'	LAma NWad
- 'Rose Pearls'	SRot
- Silver-leaved Group	ECho EPot GKev LHop LRHS SBea SRot
- - 'Silver Leaf Pink'	GMaP NWad
- - 'Silver Leaf Red' **new**	NWad
- - 'Silver Leaf White'	GMaP NWad
× ***hildebrandii***	LLHF
ibericum	see *C. coum* subsp. *caucasicum*
intaminatum	CBro CEvo ECho EPot GKev LAma LLHF LRHS MAsh XEll
- plain-leaved	WThu
latifolium	see *C. persicum*
libanoticum	CBro ECho EPot GKev LAma LRHS MAsh XEll
mirabile ♀H4	CBro CEvo CPne ECho EPot GBuc GKev LAma LLHF LRHS MAsh SDeJ WThu
- 'Alba' **new**	XEll
- f. ***mirabile*** 'Tilebarn Nicholas'	ECho MAsh WCot
neapolitanum	see *C. hederifolium*
orbiculatum	see *C. coum*
parviflorum	MAsh
§ ***persicum***	CBro CEvo CWCL ECho GBuc LRHS MAsh
- Metis Series **new**	LPfy
- white-flowered	MAsh
pseudibericum ♀H4	CBro CPne ECho EPot GKev LAma LHop LLHF LRHS MAsh SDeJ WCot WThu
- AC&W 664	NWad
- f. ***roseum***	MAsh
§ ***purpurascens***	CBro CEvo ECho GBuc GKev LLHF MAsh NSla WHoo WPat WThu
repandum	CAvo CBro ECho EPot GKev LAma LLHF LRHS WHer
- 'Pelops' misapplied	see *C. rhodium* subsp. *peloponnesiacum*
§ ***rhodium*** subsp. ***peloponnesiacum***	ECGP
rohlfsianum	CBro CEvo ECho GKev LRHS MAsh XEll
× ***schwarzii***	MAsh
'Trena'	SDeJ
trochopteranthum	see *C. alpinum*

Cyclea (*Menispermaceae*)

polypetala KWJ 12157	WCru

Cydonia ✿ (*Rosaceae*)

japonica	see *Chaenomeles japonica*
oblonga (F)	CBcs ECrN
- 'Agvambari' (F)	SKee
- 'Aromatnaya' (F)	ERea MCoo NOra WHar WMat
- 'Champion' (F)	CAgr CHab ECrN ERea GTwe LBuc MCoo NEgg NOra SBdl SKee SVic WHar WMat
- 'Early Prolific' (F)	SEND
- 'Ekmek' (F)	SKee
- 'Iranian' (F) **new**	CAgr
- 'Isfahan' (F)	ERea SKee WMat
- 'Krymsk' (F)	CAgr WWct
- 'Leskovac' (F)	CAgr EPom ERea NLar NOra WWct
§ - 'Lusitanica' (F)	CAgr CHab CLnd ELan ERea GTwe NLar NOra SBdl SKee WHar WMat
- 'Meech's Prolific' (F)	CAgr CDul CHab CLnd CTho CTri ECrN EMil EPom ERea GTwe LAst LRHS MAsh MBri MGos MRav NLar NOra NWea SBmr SDea SKee SLim SPer WHar WMat WWct
- pear-shaped (F)	CHab ECrN NEgg SPer
- Portugal	see *C. oblonga* 'Lusitanica'
- 'Rea's Mammoth' (F)	CHab ERea NLar
- 'Serbian Gold' (F)	CDoC CDul CMac CTho ECrN EPom ERea GQue GTwe LAst LRHS MAsh MBri NLar NOra SBdl WHar WMat
- 'Shams' (F)	SKee
- 'Smyrna' (F)	NLar NOra WHar WMat
- 'Sobu' (F)	SKee
- 'Vranja' ambig. (F)	CBcs MAsh NBes NWea SBdl SBmr SPoG
- 'Vranja' Nenadovic (F) ♀H5	Widely available

Cylindropuntia (*Cactaceae*)

acanthocarpa from Meadview, Arizona **new**	CCac
§ ***echinocarpa*** MUG 167 **new**	CCac
imbricata	CCac SPlb XLum XSen
- DJF 928.19 from Union County, New Mexico **new**	CCac
- DJF 1575 from Delhi, Colorado **new**	CCac
- KMR 429	CCac

	- SB 99 from Manzano Mountains, New Mexico **new**	CCac
	- from Caon City, Colorado **new**	CCac
	- from Fremont County, Colorado **new**	CCac
	- 'Pinky' **new**	CCac
	kleiniae **new**	CCac
	leptocaulis	XSen
	- from Valencia County, New Mexico **new**	CCac
	rosea PG **new**	CCac
§	***spinosior***	XLum
	versicolor	CCac XSen
	× ***viridiflora***	CCac XSen
	- SB 957 from Santa Fe, New Mexico **new**	CCac
	whipplei DJF 131.24 from Show Low, Arizona **new**	CCac
	- DJF 167 from Snowflake, Arizona **new**	CCac
	- MUG 125 from San Juan, New Mexico **new**	CCac
	- from Coconino County, Arizona **new**	CCac
	- 'Monstrosus' **new**	CCac
*	- var. ***multidigitata*** from Meadview, Arizona **new**	CCac
	- 'Waiblingen' **new**	CCac
	- 'Würzburg' **new**	CCac

Cymbalaria (*Plantaginaceae*)

	aequitriloba 'Alba'	GAbr GEdr
§	***hepaticifolia***	CSma SBrt SPlb
§	***muralis***	ECho ECtt GAbr GJos MHer MSCN NPri WBor WHer WIce XLum
	- 'Albiflora'	see *C. muralis* 'Pallidior'
	- 'Kenilworth White'	GJos WCot WMoo
	- 'Nana Alba'	MSCN
§	- 'Pallidior'	ECho
§	***pallida***	CPBP CSma MAsh MMuc SBch SEND SPlb WMoo
	- 'Alba'	EWTr NPri WMoo
§	***pilosa***	ECtt NLar
	'Snow Wave'	ECtt LSou

Cymbopogon (*Poaceae*)

citratus	CArn CBod CTsd ENfk ERea GPoy MNHC SHDw SIde SRms SVic WJek
flexuosus	CLau MHer SRms WJek
martini	GPoy
nardus	CArn GPoy

Cymophyllus (*Cyperaceae*)

§	***fraserianus***	CDes CFil EBee GBin

Cynanchum (*Apocynaceae*)

ascyrifolium	EBee GEdr IPot

Cynara (*Asteraceae*)

§	***baetica*** subsp. ***maroccana***	WHil
	cardunculus 🏆^{H6}	Widely available
	- ACL 380/78	SWat
	- 'Bianco Avorio'	SVic
I	- 'Cardy'	LCro NCGa
	- dwarf	SDix SMHy
I	- 'Florist Cardy'	NLar
	- 'Gobbo di Nizza'	LEdu SRms WHer
	- 'Porto Spineless'	CAgr WFar
§	- Scolymus Group	CBcs EHoe EPfP EWes GPoy IBoy LRHS LSRN MBri MNHC MRav MWat NPri SEND SPav SPhx SPoG SVic WHer WWEG
	- - 'Bere' **new**	LEdu
	- - 'Carciofo Violetto Precoce'	WHer
	- - 'Gigante di Romagna'	WHer
	- - 'Gros Camus de Bretagne'	MAvo WCot XLum
	- - 'Gros Vert de Lâon' 🏆^{H5}	CBcs ELan LRHS WCot
	- - 'Monica Lynden-Bell'	WCot
	- - 'Purple Globe'	LEdu SRms
	- - 'Romanesco'	SRms SVic
	- - 'Rouge d'Alger'	CAgr LEdu WCot
	- - 'Tavor'	LRHS SVic WCot
	- - 'Vert Globe'	CSBt ENfk LEdu MWat NLar NPer SPad SRms SVic SWvt WHil
	- - 'Violet de Provence'	CSBt LEdu MHer SRms
	- - 'Violetto di Chioggia' 🏆^{H4}	WHer
*	***gomerensis***	WCot
	humilis **new**	SBrt
	- white-flowered **new**	SBrt
	hystrix misapplied	see *C. baetica* subsp. *maroccana*
	scolymus	see *C. cardunculus* Scolymus Group

Cynodon (*Poaceae*)

aethiopicus	CDes EBee EHoe SEND

Cynoglossum (*Boraginaceae*)

amabile 🏆^{H3}	SPhx
- f. ***roseum*** 'Mystery Rose'	LLWG
grande	EBee SBrt
nervosum	EBee ELan EPPr LAst MLHP MMuc MRav SEND SPer SPoG WCAu WCot WGwG WWEG
officinale	CArn MHer WSFF

Cynosurus (*Poaceae*)

cristatus	CHab NMir

Cypella (*Iridaceae*)

	aquatilis	EWay LLWG
§	***coelestis***	CDes
	herbertii	CDes
	peruviana	WHil
	plumbea	see *C. coelestis*

Cyperus (*Cyperaceae*)

§	***albostriatus***	EShb
	- 'Nanus'	SGSe
	alternifolius misapplied	see *C. involucratus*
	alternifolius L.	CBen EHon EPfP EUJe LPal MHin MHtn MSKA WMAq WMoo
	- 'Compactus'	see *C. involucratus* 'Nanus'
	'Chira'	NWsh
§	***cyperoides***	EBee
	diffusus misapplied	see *C. albostriatus*
§	***eragrostis***	EHoe GCal LPot MWts NSti SDix SPlb SWat WGrn WMAq WMoo
	esculentus	CAgr CArn LEdu
	fuscus	WMoo
	glaber	IBoy
	haspan misapplied	see *C. papyrus* 'Nanus'
	haspan L.	MSKA
§	***involucratus*** 🏆^{H1c}	EShb EWay MSKA MWts SEND SGSe SMad SWat WMoo

§ - 'Nanus'	EShb
longus	CBen CWat EHoe EHon EPPr MMuc MWts NPer SEND SWat WMAq WWtn XLum
papyrus 𝕐H1a	CDTJ LPal LRHS MHer MHin MSKA SBig SPlb XBlo
§ - 'Nanus' 𝕐H1a	SKHP XBlo
- 'Perkamentus'PBR	LLWG
prolifer	LLWG
sumula	see *C. cyperoides*
vegetus	see *C. eragrostis*
'Zumila'	EShb

Cyphomandra see *Solanum*

Cypripedium (*Orchidaceae*)

sp.	LRHS
acaule	GEdr
Achim gx	GEdr XFro
Aki gx	GEdr LAma NLAp XFro
- 'Pastel'	GEdr XFro
× ***andrewsii***	GEdr
- ***ventricosum***	NLAp
Anna gx	GEdr XFro
Annegret gx	NLAp
Annette gx	GEdr NLAp
Bärbel Schmidt gx	GEdr
× ***barbeyi***	see *C.* × *ventricosum*
Barry Phillips gx	GEdr NLAp
Bernd gx	GEdr
Bill gx	GEdr
Birgit gx pastel-flowered	GEdr XFro
Boots gx	GEdr LAma NLAp
calceolus	CCon LAma NLAp
calceolus × ***henryii*** new	LAma
calceolus × ***segawae***	NLAp
californicum	LAma NLAp
Carol Ilene gx	GEdr
Carolin gx new	NLAp
Chauncey gx	GEdr NLAp XFro
Cleo Pinkepank gx	GEdr
× ***columbianum***	GEdr NLAp
cordigerum	NLAp
corrugatum	see *C. tibeticum*
corrugatum × ***fasciolatum*** new	NLAp
Dawn Edwards gx	GEdr
debile	LAma NLAp
Dietrich gx 𝕐H5	GEdr XFro
Emil gx	GEdr XFro
fasciolatum	GEdr LAma LRHS NLAp
fasciolatum × ***montanum***	NLAp
flavum	GBin GEdr LAma NLAp
- white-flowered × ***reginae***	LAma
formosanum 𝕐H3	GEdr LAma NLAp SKHP
franchetii	NLAp
froschii × ***kentuckiense*** new	NLAp
Gabriela gx	NLAp
- 'Kentucky Maxi' new	LAma LRHS
Gisela gx	GEdr LAma NLAp XFro
- 'Pastel'	GEdr
guttatum	NLAp
Hank Small gx 𝕐H5	GEdr NLAp XFro
Hans Erni gx	GEdr NLAp XFro
henryi	GKev LAma NLAp
henryi × ***segawai*** new	NLAp
Ilse gx new	NLAp
Inge gx	GEdr XFro
Ingrid gx	GEdr XFro
Irene gx	GEdr XEll
Ivory gx	GEdr LAma
James Armitage gx	GEdr NLAp
japonicum	GKev
Jens gx	GEdr
Judith Merrick gx	GEdr
Julia Barclay gx	GEdr
Kathleen Anne Green gx	GEdr NLAp
kentuckiense 𝕐H5	CCon GEdr GKev LAma LRHS NLAp
- **Lady Dorine gx**	LAma NLAp
kentuckiense × ***montanum***	NLAp
Kristi Lyn gx	GEdr NLAp XFro
lichiangense	NLAp
Lothar Pinkepank gx	GEdr LAma NLAp
Lucy Pinkepank gx	GEdr
- 'Kentucky Pink Blush' new	LAma LRHS
macranthos	GEdr NLAp
- 'Hotei'	GEdr NLAp
- var. ***hotei-atsumorianum*** Sadovsky	GEdr
- John Hagger Group	XFro
- var. ***speciosum***	GEdr
Maria gx	GEdr XFro
Memoria Gerd Kohls gx	GEdr NLAp
Memoriam Shawna Austin gx	GEdr LAma NLAp
Michael gx 𝕐H5	GEdr NLAp XFro
- 'Pastel'	GEdr
montanum × ***reginae***	NLAp
Neil Lancaster gx	GEdr
Otto gx	GEdr
parviflorum	GEdr GKev NLAp
- var. ***makasin***	NLAp
- var. ***parviflorum***	LAma
§ - var. ***pubescens***	GEdr GKev LAma NLAp
'Parville'	LRHS NLAp
Paul gx	GEdr XFro
Peter gx	GEdr XFro
Philipp gx 𝕐H5	GEdr LAma NLAp XFro
- 'Kentucky Pink' new	LAma
Pixi gx	GEdr NLAp
Pluto gx	GEdr XFro
pubescens	see *C. parviflorum* var. *pubescens*
pubescens × ***shanxiense*** new	NLAp
'Pueblo'	LRHS NLAp
Rascal gx	GEdr
reginae 𝕐H5	CCon CEvo GEdr LAma LOPS LRHS NLAp SKHP XEll
- f. ***album***	GEdr LAma LRHS NLAp
Renate gx	GEdr
Renate gx pastel-flowered	XFro
Rhodopoxis gx	GEdr
Sabine gx 𝕐H5	GEdr NLAp XFro
- pastel-flowered	GEdr XFro
Schoko gx	NLAp
Sebastian gx	GEdr XFro
- 'Frosch's Mountain King' new	XFro
- 'Multiflower White' new	LAma
segawae	LAma
Selston High School gx	GEdr NLAp
Siggi gx	GEdr
Sunny gx	GEdr NLAp XFro
§ ***tibeticum***	GEdr LAma NLAp

Tilman gx	GEdr LAma NLAp XFro
Tower Hill gx	GEdr
Ulla Silkens gx ♀H5	GEdr LAma NLAp XEll XFro
Ursel gx	GEdr NLAp XFro
§ × ***ventricosum***	GEdr LAma NLAp XFro
- 'Pastel'	XFro
Vicky's Delight gx new	NLAp
Victoria gx	GEdr NLAp XFro
Werner Frosch gx	GEdr

Cyrilla (*Cyrillaceae*)

racemiflora	CMac

Cyrtanthus (*Amaryllidaceae*)

§ ***brachyscyphus***	ECho EShb
breviflorus	CTre ECho WPGP
'Edwina'	ECho
§ ***elatus*** ♀H1c	CPne CSpe ECho LEdu NSti
- 'Pink Diamond'	ECho
'Elizabeth'	ECho
eucallus	WCot
mackenii	ECho EShb WPGP
- var. ***cooperi***	CAby CPne
- cream-white-flowered	ECho
- 'Himalayan Pink'	ECho
- orange-flowered	ECho
- red-flowered	ECho
- white-flowered	ECho
- yellow-flowered	ECho
montanus	ECho WCot
parviflorus	see *C. brachyscyphus*
purpureus	see *C. elatus*
sanguineus	ECho WCot
speciosus	see *C. elatus*

Cyrtomium (*Dryopteridaceae*)

§ ***caryotideum***	CLAP ISha
§ ***falcatum*** ♀H2	Widely available
- 'Rochfordianum'	GBin ISha LRHS MRav WFib
§ ***fortunei*** ♀H3	Widely available
- var. ***clivicola***	CKel EBee EPfP EShb ISha LPal LPot LRHS MGos MRav NLar SPad SPtp WCot XLum
macrophyllum	CLAP LPal LRHS
tukusicola	NLos

Cystopteris ✿ (*Woodsiaceae*)

bulbifera	CLAP SGSe WCot
dickieana	CLAP GBin WFib
fragilis	EFer GKev WFib
moupinensis B&SWJ 6767	WCru

Cytisus (*Papilionaceae*)

'Andreanus'	see *C. scoparius* f. *andreanus*
× ***beanii*** ♀H5	CLet EBee ELan EPfP LRHS NLar SLon
'Boskoop Glory'	NLar
× ***boskoopii*** 'Apricot Gem'	LRHS MBri NLar
- 'Boskoop Ruby' ♀H5	CDoC CLet CMac CSBt EBee EPfP EUJe GKin LBMP LRHS LSRN MAsh MBri MJak NEgg NHol NPri SCob SHil SPer SWvt WBor WHar
- 'Dukaat'	MMHG NLar
- 'Hollandia' ♀H5	CBcs CSBt EPfP GKin LBMP MMuc MRav SGol
- 'La Coquette'	EPfP LRHS MBri MMuc NEgg SPlb
- 'Windlesham Ruby'	CExl EBee ELan EPfP LRHS LSRN MMuc NEgg NLar SLim SPer WFar
- 'Zeelandia' ♀H5	CMac EPfP LCro LRHS MBri NHol SCob SPer WFar
'Burkwoodii' ♀H5	CBcs CDoC CDul ELan EPfP LRHS LSRN MMuc MSwo NEgg SPoG WFar
canariensis	see *Genista canariensis*
'Cottage'	EPot WAbe
§ ***decumbens***	MAsh
§ ***demissus*** ♀H4	WAbe
'Dorothy Walpole'	EBee WFar
'Eastern Queen'	EBee
filipes	GKin
'Garden Magic'	EBee
'Golden Cascade'	CBcs ELan LBMP LRHS MAsh NEgg SLim
'Goldfinch'	CDoC CSBt ECrN ELan LRHS MJak MSwo NEgg NHol NLar SCob WFar
§ ***hirsutus***	CExl SRms
× ***kewensis*** ♀H5	CLet ELan EPfP LRHS MAsh MGos MRav NLar NWea SPer SRms
- 'Niki'	EPfP LRHS MAsh MMuc NLar SPer WRHF
'Killiney Red'	ELan
'Killiney Salmon'	GKin LSRN MRav
'Lena' ♀H5	CDoC CLet CMac CSBt EPfP GKin LRHS LSRN MBri MGos NBir NEgg NHol NLar NPri SCob SGol SHil SLim SPoG WFar WHar
'Luna'	EPfP NEgg SHil
maderensis	see *Genista maderensis*
'Maria Burkwood'	MMuc NLar
'Minstead'	ELan SPer
'Mrs Norman Henry'	NLar
'Newry Seedling'	CMac
nigricans 'Cyni' ♀H5	ELan ESwi IArd LAst LRHS MAsh MMuc SPer SPoG
oromediterraneus	EBee
'Palette'	MMuc
'Porlock'	see *Genista* 'Porlock'
× ***praecox***	CMac ELon LAst LRHS MAsh NEgg SGol SPlb SPoG WFar WHar
- 'Albus'	CBcs CDoC CDul CMac ELan EPfP LAst LRHS LSRN MAsh MBri MGos MJak MRav NHol SCob SHil SPer WFar WHar
- 'Allgold' ♀H5	CBcs CDoC CDul CLet CMac CSBt CTri ELon EPfP LRHS LSRN MAsh MBri MGil MMuc MRav NEgg NHol NPri NWea SCob SEND SGol SHil SLon SPer SPoG SRms SWvt WFar
- 'Frisia'	WFar
- 'Lilac Lady'	LRHS
- 'Warminster' ♀H5	EPfP GKin MBri MMuc MRav NWea SEND SPer SRms
§ ***proliferus***	CExl
§ ***purpureus***	ELan EPfP LHop LRHS MRav SPer WCot WPat WSHC
§ - 'Atropurpureus'	EPfP NWea SPer
racemosus	see *Genista* × *spachiana*
'Red Wings'	MMuc SPer
scoparius	CArn CDul NWea
§ - f. ***andreanus***	CDoC CTri EPfP
- - 'Splendens'	EPfP SPer
- 'Cornish Cream'	CDul CSBt ELan EPfP NEgg SPer
- 'Firefly'	CBcs CMac
- 'Fulgens'	EPfP
- 'Golden Sunlight'	CSBt MSwo
§ - subsp. ***maritimus***	CMac
- Monarch strain	GJos
- var. ***prostratus***	see *C. scoparius* subsp. *maritimus*
× ***spachianus***	see *Genista* × *spachiana*

	supinus	see *C. hirsutus*
	supranubius **new**	SBrt
	'White Lion'	CMac

D

Daboecia ✿ (*Ericaceae*)

	cantabrica	MMuc
§	- f. ***alba***	CSBt NWad SWhi
	- - 'Bellita'	SAko
	- - 'Creeping White'	CFst
	- - 'David Moss'	MMuc
I	- - 'Early Bride'	CFst
	- 'Alberta White'	CFst IVic SWhi
	- 'Amelie'[PBR]	CFst IVic LCro SAko SWhi
	- 'Andrea' **new**	CFst SWhi
	- 'Arielle'	CFst SWhi
	- 'Atropurpurea'	CFst CSBt NWad SPer SWhi
	- 'Bicolor'	CFst
	- f. ***blumii*** 'Pink Blum'	CFst
	- - 'Purple Blum'	CFst
	- - 'White Blum'	CFst SPer SWhi
	- 'Bubbles'	CFst
	- 'Celtic Star'	CFst
	- 'Chaldon'	CFst
	- 'Cinderella'	IVic
	- 'Covadonga'	CFst
	- 'Cupido'	CTsd IVic
	- 'Glamour'	CFst SPer
I	- 'Globosa Pink'	NWad SWhi
	- 'Heather Yates'	CFst
	- 'Hookstone Purple'	NWad
	- 'Praegerae'	CTri
	- 'Rainbow' (v)	CFst
	- 'Romantic Muxoll' **new**	CFst
	- subsp. ***scotica*** 'Ben'	CFst
	- - 'Cora'	CFst
	- - 'Ellen Norris'	CFst
	- - 'Golden Imp'	CFst SWhi
	- - 'Goscote'	MGos SWhi
	- - 'Jack Drake'	CFst
	- - 'Katherine's Choice'	CBcs CFst CTri
	- - 'Red Imp'	CFst
	- - 'Robin'	CFst
	- - 'Silverwells' ♀H5	CBcs MAsh SWhi
	- - 'William Buchanan' ♀H5	CFst GAbr GJos MAsh NWad SCoo SWhi
	- 'Stardust Muxoll'	CFst
	- 'Tinkerbell'	CFst GJos SWhi
	- 'Vanessa'[PBR]	CFst IVic SAko SWhi
	- 'Waley's Red' ♀H5	NWad SWhi

Dacrycarpus (*Podocarpaceae*)

§	***dacrydioides***	CBcs CBrP ECou LEdu
	- 'Dark Delight'	ECou

Dacrydium (*Podocarpaceae*)

	bidwillii	see *Halocarpus bidwillii*
	cupressinum	CDoC SPlb WThu
	franklinii	see *Lagarostrobos franklinii*
	laxifolium	see *Lepidothamnus laxifolius*

Dactylicapnos (*Papaveraceae*)

	macrocapnos	CCon CSpe IDee IFro WBor WCru
	platycarpa	WPGP
§	***scandens***	CRHN GEdr IRos SBrt SMad
	- GWJ 9438	WCru
	- 'Shirley Clemo'	CExl
	torulosa	WTou
§	***ventii*** GWJ 9376	WCru

Dactylis (*Poaceae*)

	glomerata	CHab SVic WSFF
	- 'Variegata' (v)	MMuc NBid SEND SHDw

Dactylorhiza (*Orchidaceae*)

	sp.	NDav
	alpestris	CCon
	aristata	EFEx
	baltica **new**	LAma
	× ***braunii***	ECha
§	***elata*** ♀H5	GAbr GKev IBlr LAma WCot
§	***foliosa*** ♀H4	ECha GCra IBlr NLAp
§	***fuchsii***	CCon CMil ECho EPot GBin LEdu MNrw NLAp NRya NSla SKHP WHer WSFF
	- pink-flowered	CCon
	× ***grandis***	IBlr
	- Blackthorn hybrid	IBlr
	hybrid	LEdu
	incarnata	LAma NBid NLAp
§	***maculata***	CCon CHid EPfP LAma LRHS NLAp WBor WHer
	- subsp. ***ericetorum***	NLAp
	maderensis	see *D. foliosa*
§	***majalis***	CCon LAma LRHS MNrw NLAp WSFF XEll
	mascula	see *Orchis mascula*
	praetermissa	CCon EPot LRHS NLAp SKHP
	- subsp. ***praetermissa*** hybrid	SKHP
	purpurella	CCon GAbr GJos NLAp NRya

Dahlia ✿ (*Asteraceae*)

	'Abba' (D)	ECtt
	'Abbie' (D)	NHal
	'Abingdon Ace' (D)	SGbt
I	'Acapulco' (S-c)	ERCP
	'African Garden' (D)	CSut
	'Aitara Caress' (C)	NHal SGbt WPhe
	'Akita' (Misc)	NBri SGbt WPhe
	'Aladdin's Lamp' (WL)	NJRG
	'Alauna Clair-Obscur' (Fim)	ERCP WPhe
	'Albert Schweitzer' (S-c)	SGbt
	'Alfred Grille' (S-c)	LCro LOPS SDeJ SGbt SPer
	'Alf's Mascot' (D)	NJRG WPhe
	'Allan Snowfire' (S-c)	LAyl NHal
	'Alloway Candy' (Misc)	ERCP
	'Alloway Cottage' (D)	NHal SGbt WPhe
	'Almand's Climax' (D) ♀H3	SGbt WPhe
	'Alva's Doris' (S-c) ♀H3	LAyl
	'Alva's Supreme' (D) ♀H3	LAyl NHal WPhe
	'Amaran Relish' (D)	SGbt
I	'Amazone' (DwB)	SPoG
	'Amber Banker' (C)	SGbt WPhe
	'Amber Festival' (D)	NHal
	'Ambition' (S-c)	CAvo ERCP LCro LOPS
	'American Dawn' (D) **new**	LCro LOPS
	'American Moon' (D) **new**	LCro LOPS
	American Pie = 'Vdtg26'[PBR] (Dark Angel Series) (Sin)	LRHS SDeJ
	'Amgard Delicate' (D)	SGbt
	'Amira' (Ba)	NHal
	'Amy Cave' (Ba)	LAyl NHal
	'Andrea Clark' (D)	NHal WPhe
	'Andrea Lawson' (Ba)	NHal WPhe
	'Andrew Mitchell' (S-c)	NHal WPhe

	Cultivar	Suppliers
	'Andries' Orange' (C)	ECtt
	'Angora' (Fim)	SGbt
	'Ann Breckenfelder' (Col) Υ^{H3}	ECtt ERCP EUJe NHal NJRG SDix WPhe WWEG
	'Annika' (Sin)	LCro LOPS SDeJ
	'Anniversary Ball' (Ba)	LAyl
	'Another Pet'	see *D.* 'Mystic Enchantment'
	'Apache' (Fim)	CAby ERCP SDeJ SGbt SPer
	'Apache Blauw' (Fim)	ERCP
	'Apple Blossom' (C)	SGbt
	'Apricot Star' (Fim) **new**	NBri
	'April Heather' (Col) Υ^{H3}	NHal
	'Arabian Night' (D)	CAby CAvo CBcs CSut ECtt ELan ERCP LAyl LCro LOPS LRHS LSRN LSun MNrw NBri NHal NLar SDeJ SEND SGbt WCot WPhe WWEG
	'Arlequin' (D)	SGbt
	'Askwith Ian' (D)	NHal
	'Askwith Joan' (D)	NHal
	'Askwith Minnie' (D) **new**	NHal
I	'Atlanta' (D)	SGbt
	'Audacity' (D)	LAyl SGbt
	'Aurora's Kiss' (Ba)	ERCP NHal SGbt
	'Aurwen's Violet' (Pom)	LAyl NHal WPhe
	australis	CSpe EBee SEND
	- B&SWJ 10208	WCru
	- B&SWJ 10389	WCru
I	'Autumn Fairy' (D)	ERCP SDeJ
	'Avignon' (D)	SDeJ
	'Avoca Amanda' (D)	NHal WPhe
	'Avoca Comanche' (S-c)	NHal
	'Avoca Salmon' (D)	NHal
	'B.J. Beauty' (D)	NHal NJRG WPhe
	'Babette' (S-c)	WBor
	'Babylon' (D)	SGbt
§	'Babylon Brons' (D)	ERCP LRHS SGbt
	'Babylon Bronze'	see *D.* 'Babylon Brons'
	'Babylon Lila' (D)	SGbt
§	'Babylon Paars' (D)	LRHS SDeJ SGbt
	'Babylon Purple'	see *D.* 'Babylon Paars'
	'Babylon Rose' (D)	LRHS SGbt
	'Bacardi' (D) **new**	ERCP
	'Ballego's Glory' (D)	SGbt
	'Bantling' (Ba)	ECtt ERCP SGbt
	'Barbara's Pastelle' (S-c)	NJRG SGbt WPhe
	'Barbarry Banker' (D)	LAyl
	'Barbarry Bluebird' (D)	NHal SGbt
	'Barbarry Melody' (D)	NHal
	'Barbarry Monitor' (Ba)	SGbt
	'Barbarry Pip' (D)	NHal
	'Barbarry Sultan' (D)	NHal
	'Barbarry Sunbeam' (D)	NHal
	'Baret Joy' (S-c)	NHal
	'Bargaly Blush' (D)	NHal
	'Barry Williams' (D)	SGbt
	'Bayou'^{PBR} (Misc)	ERCP LCro LOPS NJRG SGbt SPer
	'Bednall Beauty' (Misc/DwB) Υ^{H3}	CHll CSpe CWCL ECtt ELan EUJe EWes LHop LRHS LSRN NJRG NLar WCot WHoo WPhe WWEG
	'Bell Boy' (Ba)	SGbt
	'Berliner Orange' (D)	ERCP
	'Berwick Wood' (D)	NHal SGbt
	'Beth's Chaplet' (Sin)	WCot
	'Biddenham Strawberry' (D)	SGbt
	'Bilbao'^{PBR} (Jumbo Collection) (D)	NBri
	'Bill Holmberg' (D)	SGbt
	'Bingo' (D)	SGbt
	'Bishop of Auckland'^{PBR} (Misc)	CAby CAvo CWGN ECtt EPfP EPot ERCP EWoo LCro LOPS LRHS MGos SDeJ SGbt SHil WCot WPhe
	'Bishop of Cambridge' (Sin)	WPhe
	'Bishop of Canterbury'^{PBR} (P)	ECtt EPfP LCro LOPS LRHS MGos NHal SDeJ SGbt SHil SPoG WBod WPhe
	'Bishop of Dover' (Sin)	EPfP EPot LCro LOPS LRHS NBri SDeJ SGbt WBrk WPhe
	'Bishop of Lancaster' (Misc)	LCro LOPS NLar
	'Bishop of Leicester' (Misc)	ECtt EPfP EPot LCro LOPS LRHS NBri SDeJ SGbt SHar WPhe
	'Bishop of Llandaff' (P) Υ^{H3}	Widely available
	'Bishop of Oxford' (Misc)	CAby ELan EPfP EPot ERCP LCro LOPS LRHS MGos SDeJ SGbt SHil SPoG WPhe
	'Bishop of York' (Misc)	CAby CAvo CSpe ECGP ECtt EPfP EPot LAst LCro LOPS LRHS MGos NGdn SDeJ SGbt SHil SPoG WPhe
	'Black Fire' (D)	ECtt
	'Black Jack' (D)	ERCP IPot NHal WPhe
	'Black Monarch' (D)	NHal SGbt
	'Black Narcissus' (C)	SGbt WPhe
I	'Black R Jack'	NJRG
	'Black Star' (Sin)	EPfP
	'Black Touch' (Fim)	EBee ERCP WPhe
	'Black Wizard' (S-c)	EWoo
	'Bloodstone' (D)	SGbt
	'Bloom's Kenn' (D)	SGbt
	'Blue Bell' (D)	ERCP SPer
	'Blue Boy' (D)	ERCP LCro LOPS
	'Blue Record' (S-c/DwB)	ERCP
	'Blue Wish' (WL)	LCro LOPS NJRG
	'Blyton Golden Girl' (D) **new**	NHal
	'Blyton Lady in Red' (D)	LAyl NHal NJRG WPhe
	'Blyton Romance' (D)	NHal
	'Blyton Softer Gleam' (D) Υ^{H3}	NHal NJRG SGbt WPhe
	'Bob''s Bonaventure' (D)	NHal
	'Bonesta' (D)	NBri WPhe
	'Boogie Woogie' (Anem)	SDeJ
	'Boom Boom White' (Ba)	ERCP
	'Boom Boom Yellow' (Ba) **new**	ERCP
	'Bora Bora' (S-c)	NBri
	'Border Princess' (C/DwB)	SGbt
	'Bracken Lorelei' (WL)	NHal NJRG
	'Brackenridge Ballerina' (WL)	LAyl NHal NJRG SGbt WPhe
	'Brandaris' (S-c)	SGbt
	'Brandon James' (D)	ERCP SDeJ
	'Brandysnap' (D)	SGbt
	Braveheart = 'Vdtg67'^{PBR} (Dark Angel Series) (Sin)	LCro LOPS SDeJ
	'Brian's Dream' (D)	LAyl NHal WPhe
	'Bride's Bouquet' (Col)	ERCP LRHS
	'Bridge View Aloha' (S-c) Υ^{H3}	SGbt WPhe
	'Bright Eyes' (Sin)	ERCP WPhe
	'Brigitta Alida' (S-c) **new**	EBee
	'Bryn Terfel' (D)	NHal SGbt WPhe
	'Butterball' (D/DwB)	SDeJ
	'Café au Lait' (D)	CAby EPfP ERCP IPot LCro LOPS LRHS NBri SDeJ SGbt SPer
	'Cambridge' (D)	NBri
I	'Cameo' (WL)	NHal NJRG SGbt WPhe
	'Canary Fubuki' (Fim)	ERCP SDeJ SGbt
	Candy Eyes	see *D.* 'Zone Ten'

	Name	Suppliers
	'Candy Keene' (S-c)	NHal
	'Carolina Moon' (D)	LAyl NHal SGbt
	'Carol's Spanish Dancer' (C)	NHal
	'Carstone Firebox' (Col)	LAyl NHal
	'Carstone Ruby' (D)	NHal
	'Carstone Valiant' (Ba)	NHal
	'Catherine Deneuve' (Misc)	CWGN SGbt
	'Cha Cha' (S-c)	SGbt
	'Charlie Briggs' (Ba)	NHal
	'Charlie Dimmock' (WL) ♀H3	NHal NJRG SGbt WPhe
	'Charlie Two' (D)	NHal WPhe
	'Chat Noir' (S-c) ♀H3	CAvo ERCP LCro LOPS LRHS SGbt WPhe
	'Cheerio' (S-c)	LAyl WPhe
	'Cherwell Goldcrest' (S-c)	NHal SGbt WPhe WWEG
	'Cherwell Skylark' (S-c)	NHal
	'Chic en Rouge' (Misc)	LSou
	'Chilson's Pride' (D)	SGbt
	'Chimborazo' (Col)	EUJe LAyl SDix SGbt WPhe
	'Christine' (D)	SPer WPhe
I	'Christine' (WL)	SGbt WPhe
	'Christmas Carol' (Col)	ECtt NHal NJRG
	'Christopher Nickerson' (S-c)	SGbt
	'Christopher Taylor' (WL)	NHal SGbt WPhe
	'Citizen' (S-c)	WPhe
	'City of Leiden' (S-c)	LCro LOPS
	'Clair de Lune' (Col) ♀H3	CWCL ECtt ERCP LRHS MCot NHal NJRG NLar SGbt WCot
I	'Clarion' (Sin)	CHVG
	'Classic Poème'PBR (Misc)	ERCP
	'Classic Rosamunde'PBR (Misc)	NHal NJRG
§	'Classic Swanlake'PBR (Misc)	ERCP EWoo LCro LOPS NJRG WPhe
	'Claudette' (D)	ECtt WPhe
	'Clearview Irene' (S-c)	NHal
	coccinea	CExl CFil CSpe EBee MCot SDix SGbt SMHy WPGP
	- NJM 05.072	WPGP
	- hybrids	NSti WHil
	- var. ***palmeri***	CAvo CFil EBee WPGP XEll
	'Color Spectacle' (S-c)	CSut LRHS
	'Contessa' (WL)	SDeJ WPhe
	'Coral Jupiter' (S-c)	WPhe
	'Cornel' (Ba)	ERCP LAyl NHal NJRG SGbt
	'Cornel Brons' (Ba)	ERCP
	'Cornish Ruby' (Sin)	CCon EPfP
I	'Corona' (S-c/DwB)	SDeJ
	'Coronella' (D)	SGbt
	'Coupe de Soleil' (D)	CSut
	'Craigowan' (S-c)	NHal WPhe
	'Crazy Legs' (D)	SGbt
	'Cream Moonlight' (S-c)	SGbt WPhe
	'Croydon Superior' (D)	SGbt
	'Culdrose' (D)	SGbt
	'Curiosity' (Col)	NJRG
	'Currant Cream' (Ba)	SGbt
	cuspidata	CFil EBee
	'Czardas' (C)	GCal
	Dahlietta Jenny	see *D.* 'Jenny'
	'Daleko Jupiter' (S-c)	NHal
I	'Dandy' (Col)	CWCL
	'Danjo Doc' (D)	SGbt
	'Danum Torch' (Col)	ECtt SGbt
	'Dark Desire' (Sin/DwB)	CAvo CSpe CWGN ECtt EWoo LHop WCot
	'Dark Fubuki' (Fim)	ERCP
§	'Dark Side Of The Sun'PBR (Sin)	LBMP LRHS SPoG
	'Dark Spirit' (D)	ECtt SGbt
	'David Digweed' (D)	NHal SGbt
	'David Howard' (D) ♀H3	ECtt ELan EPfP ERCP EUJe EWoo LAst LAyl LCro LHop LOPS LRHS MBri NBri NHal NJRG SBod SDix SGbt SPer SWvt WBrk WCot WFar WPhe WWEG
	'Dawn Sky' (D)	LAyl
	'Deborah's Kiwi' (C)	NHal SGbt WPhe
	'Debra Anne Craven' (S-c)	NHal
	'Decorette' (D/DwB)	SGbt
	'Deepest Yellow' (Ba)	SDeJ SGbt
	'Diamond Wedding' (D)	SGbt
	'Diamond Years' (D)	SGbt
	'Diana Gregory' (Pom)	SGbt
	'Dikara Jodie' (D)	NHal
	'Dikara Kent' (Ba) ♀H3	WWEG
	'Dikara Moon' (D)	NHal WPhe
	'Dikara Superb' (D)	NHal WPhe
	'Dilys Ayling' (Col)	NHal
I	'Disneyland' (Col)	SGbt
	dissecta	CExl CFil EBee
	- F&M 191	CDes
	'Doctor Caroline Rabbit' (D)	SGbt
	'Doctor John Grainger' (D)	LRHS
	'Don Hill' (Col) ♀H3	NJRG WPhe
	'Doris Day' (C)	NHal SGbt
	'Double Dream Fantasy' (Dreamy Series) (Misc)	EPfP LRHS
	'Downham Royal' (Ba)	ERCP LCro LOPS
	Dracula = 'Vdtg17'PBR (Dark Angel Series) (Sin)	ERCP
	Dragon Ball = 'Vdtg31'PBR (Dark Angel Series) (Sin)	LRHS SDeJ
	'Dream Fantasy' (Dream Series) (Misc)	EBee ELan LRHS
	'Dream Seeker' (Col)	MBri
	(Dreamy Series) 'Dreamy Eyes' (Misc) **new**	WHlf
	- 'Dreamy Fantasy' (Misc) **new**	WHlf
	- Dreamy Inspire (Misc)	NLar
	- 'Dreamy Nights' (Misc) **new**	WHlf
	- 'Dreamy Fusion' (Sin) **new**	LRHS
	- 'Dreamy Passion' (Sin) **new**	LRHS
	'Duddon Grace' (WL)	LAyl NHal
	'Duet' (D)	CSut ECtt NBri SGbt
	'Dusky Harmony' (WL)	SGbt
	'Dutch Explosion' (S-c)	WPhe
	'Early Harvest' (D)	SGbt
	'Eastwood Moonlight' (S-c)	NHal SGbt WPhe
I	'Edge of Joy' (D)	LCro LOPS
	'Edinburgh' (D)	ERCP NBri NHal SDeJ SGbt
	'Edith Jones' (Col)	NJRG
	'Edwin's Sunset' (WL) ♀H3	NHal WPhe
	'Elaine Huston' (S-c)	NJRG
	'Elga' (S-c)	ERCP LRHS
	'Elgico Leanne' (C)	SGbt
	'Elizabeth Snowden' (Col)	NJRG
	'Ella Britton' (D)	LRHS
	'Ellen Huston' (Misc/DwB) ♀H3	ECtt ERCP NHal SGbt WPhe
	'Elma E' (D)	ERCP LAyl NHal WPhe
I	'Embrace' (C)	NHal NJRG WPhe
	'Emory Paul' (D)	ERCP

'Engelhardt's Matador' (D) ECtt ERCP EUJe LRHS MCot NJRG SGbt WCot
'England's Glory' **new** SPer
'Etheral' (Sin) CAvo
'Eveline' (D) CAby ERCP LCro LOPS SGbt WPhe
'Evelyn Rumbold' (D) SGbt
'Evelyn Taylor' (S-c) NJRG
I 'Evita' (Anem) NJRG
excelsa (B) CHll
- B&SWJ 10238 WCru
- 'Penelope Sky' WCru
'Excentrique' (Misc) ECtt NJRG
'Exotic Dwarf' (Sin/Lil) ♀H3 ECtt NHal NJRG
'Eye Candy' (Sin) LRHS NJRG WPhe
'Fabula' (Col) LRHS
'Fairfield Frost' (Col) NHal
'Fairway Spur' (D) NHal WPhe
'Fairy Queen' (C) SGbt
§ 'Famoso' (Col) CAby CSut ERCP
'Fantastico' (Col) CSut ERCP WBor
'Fascination' (P) ♀H3 CAby CBcs ECGP ECtt ERCP LAyl LRHS MCot MSCN NJRG NLar SDeJ SGbt WHoo WWEG
'Fashion Monger' (Col) ECtt ERCP NHal NJRG SGbt
'Fata Morgana' (Anem) NJRG SGbt
'Ferncliff Illusion' (D) ERCP SGbt
'Festivo' (Col) LRHS
'Fidalgo Supreme' (D) LAyl
I 'Fiesta' (Pom) SDeJ
Figaro Series (Misc/DwB) NPri
'Figurine' (WL) ♀H3 NJRG
'Fille du Diable' (S-c) SGbt
'Finchcocks' (WL) ♀H3 LAyl
'Fire and Ice' (Misc) EBee WBor
'Fire Mountain' (D) CHVG LAyl NHal NJRG
'Firebird' (S-c) see *D.* 'Vuurvogel'
'Firebrand' ambig. (S-c) SGbt
'Firepot' (WL) ERCP MBri SGbt
'Fleur' see *D.* 'Fleurel'
§ 'Fleurel'PBR (Fim) ERCP SDeJ SPer
'Floorinoor' (Anem) ERCP NJRG SGbt WPhe
foeniculifolia **new** CFil
'Fontmell Kaz' (Col) NJRG SGbt
'Formby Art' (D) NHal
'Formby Supreme' (D) SGbt
'Fortuna' (Col/DwB) ERCP
'Frank Holmes' (Pom) NHal
'Franz Kafka' (Pom) CAvo ERCP NJRG SDeJ WPhe
'Freelancer' (C) SGbt
'Freestyle' (C) NJRG
§ 'Freya's Paso Doble' (Anem) ♀H3 LAyl NJRG SGbt
'Frigoulet' (C) ERCP SGbt
'Fringed Star' (S-c) NBri
'Furswood Park' (Pom) NJRG
'Fusion' (D) ♀H3 SGbt SHar WCot
'G.I. Joe' (D) SGbt
(Gallery Series) 'Gallery Art Deco'PBR (D) ♀H3 ERCP LRHS NHal SGbt SHil
- 'Gallery Art Fair'PBR (D) ♀H3 ERCP LRHS MBri NHal SDeJ SHil
- 'Gallery Art Nouveau'PBR (D) ♀H3 ERCP LAst LRHS NHal SHil
- 'Gallery Bellini'PBR (D) LRHS MBri SDeJ
- 'Gallery Cézanne'PBR (D) LRHS MBri SGbt
- 'Gallery Cobra'PBR (D) ERCP
- 'Gallery La Tour'PBR (D) ♀H3 SDeJ
- 'Gallery Leonardo'PBR (D) ♀H3 SDeJ
- 'Gallery Matisse'PBR (D) LRHS
- 'Gallery Pablo'PBR (D) ♀H3 LRHS SGbt SHil
- 'Gallery Pinto'PBR (D) LRHS SHil
- 'Gallery Renoir'PBR (D) ♀H3 LRHS SHil
- 'Gallery Rivera'PBR (D) SDeJ SHil
- 'Gallery Salvador'PBR (D) ERCP SGbt
- 'Gallery Serenade'PBR (D) **new** ERCP
- 'Gallery Valentin'PBR (D) LRHS
- 'Gallery Vermeer'PBR (D) SGbt
'Garden Festival' (WL) ERCP WPhe
'Garden Party' (C) ♀H3 LAyl
'Garden Princess' (C/DwB) SGbt
'Garden Wonder' (D) NBri SDeJ SPer
'Garnet Quartz' (Misc) EBee
Gateshead Festival see *D.* 'Peach Melba' (D)
'Gay Princess' (WL) LAyl
'Geerlings Babette' (Ba) ERCP
'Geerlings Cupido' (WL) NHal SGbt WPhe
'Geerlings Indian Summer' (S-c) NHal
§ 'Geerlings Sorbet' (S-c) CAby LAyl NHal SGbt WPhe
'Gelber Vulkan' (S-c) SGbt
'Genova' (Ba) CAvo EBee EPfP ERCP SGbt SPer
'Gerrie Hoek' (WL) ECtt ERCP EWoo NBri SDeJ SGbt WPhe
'Gillwood Terry G' (C) NHal WPhe
'Gina Lombaert' (S-c) SEND
'Gipsy Boy' (D) LAyl
'Gipsy Night' (Ba) ERCP SDeJ
'Giraffe' (DblO) CAby ERCP SGbt
'Glenbank Honeycomb' (Pom) WWEG
'Glorie van Heemstede' (WL) ♀H3 ERCP LAyl NHal SDeJ SEND SGbt WPhe
'Glorie van Noordwijk' (S-c) ERCP SDeJ SGbt WPhe
'Go American' (D) NHal WPhe
'Gold Crown' (S-c) SDeJ
I 'Golden Emblem' (D) ECtt NBri SDeJ
'Golden Scepter' (D) ERCP SDeJ SGbt
'Golden Torch' (D) NBri
'Goldie Gull' (Anem) NJRG
'Good Earth' (C) SDeJ
'Gracie S' (C) NJRG
'Grand Prix' (D) CSut ERCP SDeJ SGbt
'Grenadier' (D) ♀H3 ECtt ERCP EWoo LAyl LRHS NJRG NLar SDix SGbt WCot WWEG
'Grenidor Pastelle' (S-c) NHal NJRG WPhe
'Gurtla Twilight' (Pom) NHal NJRG WPhe WWEG
'Gwyneth' (WL) NJRG WPhe WWEG
'Gypsy Girl' (D) SGbt
'Hadrian's Sunlight' (Sin) **new** NHal
'Hallmark' (Pom) NJRG
'Hamari Accord' (S-c) ♀H3 LAyl
'Hamari Girl' (D) NHal SGbt
'Hamari Gold' (D) ♀H3 NHal SGbt WPhe
'Hamari Katrina' (S-c) WPhe
'Hamari Rosé' (Ba) ♀H3 NHal SGbt
'Hamari Sunshine' (D) NHal SGbt
'Hapet Charmant' (WL) NHal WPhe
'Hapet Ideal' (S-c) WPhe
'Hapet Pearl' (Ba) NHal
'Hapet Pom' (Pom) WPhe
'Hapet Vinete' (Pom) NHal

	Name	Suppliers
	Happy Days Cream = 'Hdw79'[PBR] (Sin) **new**	LAst LRHS
	(Happy Single Series) Happy Single Date = 'HS Date'[PBR] (Sin)	ERCP LRHS SDeJ WHil
	- Happy Single First Love = 'HS First Love'[PBR] (Sin)	ERCP LRHS MBri SDeJ
	- Happy Single Flame = 'HS Flame'[PBR] (Sin) 🏆[H3]	CAvo EBee ERCP LRHS MBri NPri
	- Happy Single Juliet = 'HS Juliet'[PBR] (Sin)	ERCP LRHS MBri SDeJ
	- Happy Single Kiss = 'HS Kiss'[PBR] (Sin)	CAvo LRHS
	- Happy Single Party = 'HS Party'[PBR] (Sin)	CAvo MBri NBri SDeJ
	- Happy Single Princess = 'HS Princess'[PBR] (Sin) 🏆[H3]	ERCP LRHS MBri
	- Happy Single Romeo = 'HS Romeo'[PBR] (Sin)	LRHS MBri SDeJ WHil
	- Happy Single Wink = 'HS Wink'[PBR] (Sin) 🏆[H3]	ERCP LCro LOPS LRHS LSou MBri NPri SDeJ WHil WPhe
	'Haresbrook' (Sin)	NGdn
	'Harriet G' (WL)	NHal NJRG WPhe
§	'Harvest Samantha' (Sin/Lil) 🏆[H3]	NHal
	'Hayley Jayne' (C)	ERCP NBri NJRG SGbt WPhe
	'Heather Jean' (Col)	NJRG
	'Hexton Copper' (Ba)	SGbt
	'Hillcrest Amour' (D)	SGbt
	'Hillcrest Candy' (S-c) 🏆[H3]	NHal NJRG SGbt WPhe WWEG
	'Hillcrest Cheryl' (SinO)	NHal
	'Hillcrest Delight' (D)	NHal SGbt
	'Hillcrest Desire' (C) 🏆[H3]	LAyl
	'Hillcrest Hannah' (D)	NHal
	'Hillcrest Jake' (S-c)	NHal
	'Hillcrest Kismet' (D)	LAyl NHal WPhe
	'Hillcrest Matt' (D)	NJRG
	'Hillcrest Regal' (Col) 🏆[H3]	SGbt
	'Hillcrest Royal' (C) 🏆[H3]	LAyl NHal SDix SGbt
	'Holland Festival' (D)	SGbt
	'Hollyhill Big Pink' (S-c)	SGbt
	'Honeypot' (Ba)	SGbt
	'Honka' (SinO) 🏆[H3]	ECtt ERCP LAyl LCro LOPS LRHS NHal NJRG NSti SDeJ WCot WPhe
	'Honka Fragile' (SinO)	CAby ERCP
	'Honka Orange' (SinO)	ERCP
	'Honka Pink Edge' (SinO)	NJRG
	'Honka Red' (SinO)	CAby ERCP LCro LOPS
	'Honka Rose' (SinO)	ERCP NJRG
	'Honka Surprise' (SinO)	CAby EBee ECtt ERCP EUJe NJRG SDeJ WBrk WCot
	'Honka White' (SinO)	CAby ERCP
	'Honor Francis' (Misc)	WCot WWEG
I	'Hootenanny' (Col)	NHal WPhe
	'Hot Chocolate' (D)	NJRG SGbt
	'Hugs 'n' Kisses' (D)	EPfP
	'Hy Wine Frost' (Col)	NJRG
	'Ice Crystal' (Fim) **new**	CAby ERCP
	'Ice Cube' (D)	ERCP SDeJ
	'Imagion' (D)	EPfP
	imperialis (B)	CCon CDTJ CHll EBee EWes LEdu LRHS SBig SDix SGbt
	- B&SWJ 8997	WCru
	- pink double-flowered (B)	CExl CFil
	'Impression Famosa'	see *D.* 'Famoso'
	'Inca' (Anem)	WPhe
	'Inca Dambuster' (S-c)	NHal SGbt WPhe
	'Independence' (D)	SGbt
	'Ivanetti' (Ba)	NHal SGbt WPhe
	'J.R.G.' (Misc) 🏆[H3]	NJRG
	'Jack Hood' (D)	SGbt
	'Jamaica' (WL)	SGbt
I	'Jan van Schaffelaar' (Pom)	ERCP SDeJ
	'Janal Amy' (S-c)	NHal SGbt WPhe
	'Jane Horton' (Col)	SGbt
	'Jean Fairs' (WL) 🏆[H3]	SGbt
	'Jean Marie'[PBR] (D)	ERCP
	'Jean Shaw' (D)	NHal
	'Jeanne d'Arc' (C)	EPfP
§	'Jenny' (Dahlietta Select Series) (Misc)	SGbt
	'Jescot Julie' (DblO)	CAvo ERCP LAyl LCro LOPS
	'Jescot Lingold' (D)	SGbt WPhe
	'Jessie G' (Ba)	NJRG
	'Jim Branigan' (S-c)	NHal
	'Jive' (Anem)	ERCP SDeJ
	'Joanne Taylor' (WL)	NJRG
	'Jocondo' (D)	NHal SGbt
	'Jodie Wilkinson' (L/Pom) **new**	NHal
	'Johann' (Pom)	NHal
	'John Hill' (D)	NHal
	'Jomanda' (Ba) 🏆[H3]	NHal NJRG SGbt WPhe
	'Josie Gott' (Ba) 🏆[H3]	NJRG SGbt WPhe
	'Jowey Linda' (Ba)	WPhe
	'Joyce Green' (S-c)	SGbt
	'Jules Dyson' (Misc)	SDys
	'Julie One' (DblO)	CAvo SGbt
	'Jura' (S-c)	EPfP
	'Karenglen' (D) 🏆[H3]	NHal NJRG SGbt
	'Karma Bon Bini'[PBR] (C)	CAby SGbt WPhe
	'Karma Choc'[PBR] (D) 🏆[H3]	CAby CAvo EBee EPfP ERCP EWes IPot LCro LOPS LRHS MSCN SBod SEND SGbt SPer WBor WCot WFar WHoo WPhe
	'Karma Corona'[PBR] (C)	SGbt
	'Karma Fiesta'[PBR] (D) **new**	ERCP
	'Karma Fuchsiana' (D)	ERCP LCro LOPS LRHS NPri SGbt WPhe
	'Karma Irene'[PBR] (D)	ERCP WPhe
	'Karma Lagoon'[PBR] (D)	ERCP LRHS SGbt WPhe
	'Karma Maarten Zwaan'[PBR] (WL)	ERCP WPhe
	'Karma Naomi'[PBR] (D)	ERCP SGbt WPhe
	'Karma Pink Corona'[PBR] (C)	LCro LOPS WPhe
	'Karma Prospero'[PBR] (D)	ERCP LCro LOPS WPhe
	'Karma Red Corona'[PBR] (C)	SDeJ SGbt WPhe
	'Karma Sangria'[PBR] (C)	SDeJ SGbt WPhe
	'Karma Serena'[PBR] (D)	SDeJ WPhe
	'Karma Yin Yang' (D)	SGbt WPhe
	'Kate Mountjoy' (Col)	SGbt
	'Katie Dahl' (D)	NHal
	'Kayleigh Spiller' (Col)	SGbt
	'Keith's Choice' (D)	NHal SGbt
	'Kelvin Floodlight' (D)	NBri SDeJ SGbt WPhe
	'Kennemerland' (S-c)	EPfP SDeJ SGbt
	'Kenora Challenger' (S-c)	NHal NJRG SGbt WPhe
	'Kenora Frills' (Fim)	NHal
	'Kenora Jubilee' (S-c)	SGbt WPhe
	'Kenora Macop-B' (Fim)	ERCP NHal WPhe
	'Kenora Sunset' (S-c) 🏆[H3]	LAyl NHal SGbt
	'Kenora Superb' (S-c)	SGbt WPhe
	'Kenora Valentine' (D) 🏆[H3]	LAyl NHal SGbt WPhe
	'Kenora Wow' (S-c) **new**	NHal
	'Ken's Flame' (WL)	SGbt
	'Ken's Rarity' (WL)	NJRG SGbt
	'Kidd's Climax' (D) 🏆[H3]	WPhe

	Name	Suppliers
	'Kiev' (Jumbo Collection) (D) new	NBri
	'Kikoski' (C)	SGbt
	'Kilburn Fiesta' (S-c)	NHal WPhe
	'Kilburn Glow' (WL) new	NHal
	'Kilburn Rose' (WL)	NHal WPhe
	'Kilmorie' (S-c)	NHal WPhe
	'Kingston' (D)	SGbt
	'Kiss' (D)	MBri
	'Kiss Me' (D)	EPfP
	'Kiwi Gloria' (C)	NHal NJRG WPhe
	'Klondike' (S-c)	ERCP NJRG WPhe
	'Knock Out' (S-c) new	CAby
I	'Knockout'PBR (Sin) 🏆H3	CBcs CChe EPfP ERCP LRHS LSRN LSou NBri SHar SPoG
I	'Kyoto' (WL)	SGbt
	'L.A.T.E.' (Ba)	NHal NJRG SGbt
	'La Recoleta' (D)	ERCP
	'Lady Liberty' (D) new	ERCP
	'Lady Linda' (D)	NHal SGbt
	'Lakeland Polly' (Pom)	NHal NJRG
	'Lambada' (Anem)	ERCP
	'L'Ancresse' (Ba)	LAyl NHal NJRG
	'Lauren Kitchener' (Misc)	NJRG
	'Lavender Line' (S-c)	NHal
	'Le Baron' (D)	CSut ERCP WPhe
	'Le Castel' (WL) 🏆H3	SDeJ
	'Lemon Elegans' (S-c) 🏆H3	NHal
	'Lemon Meringue' (D)	ECtt SGbt
	'Lemon Zing' (Ba)	LAyl NHal SGbt
	'Leopold Chloe' (D)	NHal
	'Leslie's Willo' (Pom)	WWEG
	'Life Force' (D)	SGbt
	'Lilac Bull' (D)	LRHS
	'Lilac Marston' (D) 🏆H3	NHal WPhe
	'Lilac Taratahi' (C) 🏆H3	CSam LAyl
I	'Lilac Time' (D)	ERCP NBri SDeJ SGbt WPhe
	'Lilianna W' (Sin)	NJRG
	'Lilliput Orange' (Sin)	NJRG
	'Linda's Baby' (Ba)	SPer
	'Lismore Carol' (Pom)	NHal WPhe
	'Lismore Moonlight' (Pom)	LAyl NHal
	'Lismore Robin' (D)	NHal
	'Lismore Sunset' (Pom)	SGbt
	'Lismore Willie' (WL) 🏆H3	NJRG WPhe
	'Little Dorrit' (Sin/Lil)	NJRG
	'Little Matthew' (Pom)	SGbt
	'Little Robert' (D)	CAvo ERCP NBri SGbt WPhe
	'Little Sally' (Pom)	SGbt
	'Little Snowdrop' (Pom)	SGbt
I	'Little William' (Ba)	SGbt WPhe
	'Lololove' (Sin) new	SPer
	'Lorona Dawn' (SinO)	ERCP LAyl NJRG
	'Louis V' (Fim)	SGbt
	'Lucky Number' (D)	ERCP
	'Ludwig Helfert' (S-c)	SEND
	'Luka Johanna' (WL) new	ERCP
	'Mabel Ann' (D)	LAyl NHal WPhe
	'Madame de Rosa' (S-c)	LAyl NHal
	'Madame Simone Stappers' (WL)	ECtt EUJe LRHS WWEG
	'Magenta Magenta' (D)	LAyl SGbt
	'Magenta Magic' (Sin/DwB)	NHal
	'Magenta Star' (Sin) 🏆H3	CAvo SGbt WPhe
	'Maldiva' (D)	ERCP
I	'Mambo' (Anem)	SDeJ
	'Manhattan Island' (D)	ERCP NBri
	'Marble Ball' (D)	ERCP SDeJ SGbt
	'Margareth Kleene' (D)	ERCP
	'Marie Schnugg' (SinO) 🏆H3	NJRG SGbt
	'Marlene Joy' (Fim)	SGbt WPhe
I	'Mars' (Col)	NJRG SGbt
	'Marston George' (Ba)	NHal
	'Martin's Yellow' (Pom)	NHal
	'Mary Eveline' (Col)	EBee ECtt NHal
I	'Mary Evelyn' (C)	ERCP LAst MSCN SGbt
	'Mary Pitt' (D)	SGbt
	'Mary's Jomanda' (Ba) 🏆H3	NHal SGbt WPhe WWEG
	'Mascot Maya' (D)	NJRG
	'Matilda Huston' (S-c)	LAyl NHal
	'Maureen Hardwick' (D)	SGbt
	'Maureen Jones' (Col)	NJRG
	'Maxime' (D)	ERCP
	'Mayan Pearl' (DblO) 🏆H3	LAyl SGbt
	'Mayan Swan' (S-c)	SGbt
	'Mediterrannee' (D)	ERCP
	'Megan Dean' (Ba)	NHal WPhe
	'Melody Dixie'PBR (D)	ERCP
	'Melody Dora'PBR (D)	MBri
	'Melody Fanfare'PBR (D) new	LCro LOPS
	'Melody Gipsy'PBR (S-c)	ERCP
	'Melody Harmony'PBR (D) 🏆H3	EPfP ERCP
	'Melody Mambo'PBR (D)	MBri
	'Melody Swing'PBR (D)	ERCP
	'Mel's Orange Marmalade' (Fim) new	LCro LOPS
	merckii	CBot CCon CExl CFil CSpe EUJe EWes EWld EWoo LRHS MCot MMHG MNrw MRav NSti SEND SHar SPtp WBod
	- 'Alba' (B)	CExl CFil CSpe
	- compact	CFil
	- dark-leaved new	WPGP
	- 'Edith Eddleman' (B)	CFil
	'Mero Star' (D) new	SPer
	'Mevrouw Clement Andries' (Fim)	ERCP
	'Mexico Mogul' (D)	SGbt
	'Mick's Peppermint' (S-c)	CAby SGbt
	'Midnight' (Pom)	SGbt
	'Midnight Star' (SinO)	NJRG
	'Mies' (Sin)	LCro LOPS
*	'Mingus Max'	ERCP
	'Mingus Randy' (S-c)	SPer
	'Mingus Toni' (D)	ERCP
	'Minley Carol' (Pom)	LAyl NHal
	'Miss Campbell' (Ba)	NJRG
	'Misterton' (D)	SGbt
	mollis	CFil
	'Mom's Special' (D)	ERCP
	'Monet Mystique' (WL)	SGbt
	'Monet Sunlight' (WL)	SGbt
	'Moonfire' (Misc/DwB) 🏆H3	CAby CWCL CWGN ECtt ELan EPfP ERCP EUJe LAyl LRHS MBri NHal NJRG SDix SGbt SPer WCot WHoo WPhe WWEG
	'Moonglow' (S-c)	ERCP LRHS
	'Moor Place' (Pom)	NHal NJRG SGbt WPhe WWEG
	moorei new	WPGP
	'Mrs Eileen' (D)	ERCP SGbt WPhe
	'Mrs H. Brown' (Col)	SGbt
	'Mrs McDonald Quill' (D)	SGbt
	'München' (D)	SDeJ SGbt
	'Murdoch' (D)	ECtt EWoo LRHS WCot
I	'Murillo'	LAyl
	'Musette' (D)	SGbt

	'My Love' (S-c)	CSut ERCP LCro LOPS NBri SEND SGbt WPhe
	'My Neddy' (D)	NJRG SGbt
	'Myama Fubuki' (Fim)	ELan ERCP
	'My-nute Blend' (Misc) **new**	WWEG
	'Myrtle's Folly' (Fim)	ERCP
	Mystic Desire	see *D.* 'Scarlet Fern'
§	'Mystic Enchantment'^{PBR} (Sin)	EBee LRHS LSou SPoG
	'Mystic Haze'	see *D.* 'Dark Side Of The Sun'
	Mystic Illusion	see *D.* 'Knockout' (Sin)
	Mystic Mars	see *D.* 'Scarlet Fern'
	'Nagano' (D)	SDeJ WPhe
	'Naples' (D)	EWoo
	'Nargold' (Fim)	LAyl
	'Narrow's Tricia' (S-c)	WPhe
	'Natal' (Ba)	CAvo EBee ECtt NBri SDeJ
	'Natalie G' (D)	EPfP NJRG
	'Nathalie's Wedding' (WL)	ERCP
	'Nepos' (WL)	NJRG SGbt WPhe
	'Nescio' (Pom)	ERCP SDeJ
I	'New Baby' (Ba)	ERCP LCro LOPS SGbt
I	'Night Queen' (Ba)	EPfP ERCP
	'Nippon' (Sin)	EBee EPfP LRHS
	'Nonette' (WL)	CWGN EBee ECtt SGbt WBrk WCot
	'Noreen' (Pom)	NHal WPhe
§	'Nuit d'Eté' (S-c)	CAby ELan ERCP EWoo LCro LRHS NBri SGbt WPhe
	'Nuland's Josephine' (Ba)	NHal NJRG
	'Oakwood Goldcrest' (S-c)	NHal WPhe
	'Offshore Dream' (D) **new**	ERCP
I	'Old Gold' (D)	SGbt
I	'Olivia' (Col)	NJRG
	'Olivia Mari' (WL)	NHal
	'Omo' (Sin/Lil) ♀H3	NJRG
	'Onesta' (D)	ERCP SDeJ WPhe
	'Opus' (D)	SGbt
	'Orange Explosion' (Misc)	SGbt
	'Orange Fubuki' (D)	ERCP
	'Orange Nugget' (Ba)	SDeJ
I	'Orange Queen' (C)	SGbt
	'Orchid Princess' (S-c)	ERCP
	'Orel' (Col)	SGbt
	'Oreti Bliss' (C)	LAyl NHal
	'Oreti Classic' (D)	NHal
	'Orfeo' (C)	ECtt ERCP MNrw SDeJ SGbt
	'Osirium' (D)	ERCP
	'Ossie Latham' (Sin)	SGbt
	'Otto's Thrill' (D)	ERCP
	'Pacific Argyle' (D)	NHal
	'Painted Girl' (D)	ERCP
	'Pale Excentrique' (Sin/DwB)	NJRG
	'Pale Roxy'	NJRG
	'Pam Howden' (WL)	NHal NJRG SGbt WPhe
	'Paradise City' (D) **new**	CAby
	'Park Princess' (C/DwB)	CSut LAyl NBri NHal SDeJ SGbt
	'Park Record' (S-c)	NBri
	'Paso Doble' misapplied	see *D.* 'Freya's Paso Doble'
	'Pat Knight' (Col)	NHal NJRG
	'Pat Mark' (S-c)	LAyl
	'Pat 'n' Perc' (Col)	NJRG SGbt
	'Patricia' (Col)	NHal
	'Peace Pact' (WL)	NJRG
	'Peach Delight' (S-c)	SGbt
§	'Peach Melba' (D)	WPhe
	'Peaches' **new**	ERCP
	'Pearl of Heemstede' (D) ♀H3	LAyl NHal WPhe
	'Pearson's Ben' (S-c)	NJRG
	'Pembroke Levenna' (Ba)	LAyl NHal
	'Penhill Autumn Shade' (S-c)	NJRG SGbt
	'Peter' (D)	ECtt SGbt
	'Petite Harvest' (Misc/DwB)	NJRG
	'Petite Sunrise' (Sin)	NJRG
	'Petite Sunset' (Misc/Lil)	NJRG
	'Petra's Wedding' (Ba) **new**	NBri
	'Pfitzer's Joker' (C)	CAby
	'Pianella' (S-c)	SGbt
	'Pinelands Princess' (Fim)	ERCP EUJe SGbt
	'Pink Carol' (Pom)	NJRG
	'Pink Giraffe' (DblO) ♀H3	CAby ERCP SGbt
	'Pink Isa'^{PBR} (D)	ERCP
	'Pink Jupiter' (S-c)	NHal SGbt
	'Pink Pastelle' (S-c) ♀H3	NHal SGbt WPhe
	'Pink Shirley Alliance' (C)	LAyl
	'Pink Skin' (D)	ECtt EWoo LRHS SDeJ
	pinnata B&SWJ 10240	WCru
	'Piperoo' (C)	SGbt
	'Piper's Pink' (S-c/DwB)	ECtt LRHS NLar SGbt
	'Playa Blanca' (C/DwB)	SGbt
I	'Polka' (Anem)	NJRG SDeJ SGbt
	'Pontiac' (C)	CAvo LAyl SGbt
	'Pooh' (Col)	see *D.* 'Pooh - Swan Island'
§	'Pooh - Swan Island' (Col) ♀H3	CHVG EBee ERCP EUJe LAyl NHal NJRG WCot WPhe
	'Pow Wow' (Anem)	EWoo
	'Preference' (C)	ERCP SDeJ SGbt
	'Preston Park' (Sin/DwB) ♀H3	LAyl NHal
	Pretty Woman = 'Vdtg43'^{PBR} (Dark Angel Series) (Sin)	ERCP LCro LOPS
	Pride of Berlin	see *D.* 'Stolz von Berlin'
	'Primrose Pastelle' (S-c)	NHal
I	'Princess' (Col)	SDeJ
	'Princesse Elisabeth' (D)	ERCP
	'Princesse Gracia' (D)	ERCP
	'Princesse Laetitia' (D)	ERCP
	'Procyon' (D)	NBri SGbt WPhe
	'Promise' (Fim)	ECtt ERCP
	aff. ***pteropoda*** F&M 312	WPGP
	Pulp Fiction = 'Vdtg61'^{PBR} (Dark Angel Series) (Sin) **new**	ERCP
	'Purple Flame'^{PBR} (D)	ERCP
	'Purple Gem' (S-c)	ERCP EUJe LAst LCro LOPS SGbt WPhe
	'Purple Haze' (Misc)	ERCP NBri NQui WPhe
	'Purple Pearl' (D)	ERCP NHal
	'Purple Petite' (Sin)	NJRG
	'Purple Puff' (Anem)	NHal NJRG
	aff. ***purpusii*** B&SWJ 10321	WCru
	'Quick Step' (Anem)	NJRG
	'Raffles' (D)	LAyl
	'Ragged Robin' (Misc)	CSpe CWGN ECtt LCro LRHS
	'Raiser's Pride' (C)	NHal WPhe
	'Raspberry Valiant' (B) **new**	NHal
*	'Raymond Guernsey'	ECtt
	'Razzle Dazzle' (D) **new**	ERCP
	'Red and White' (D)	SGbt
	'Red Diamond' (D)	NHal
	'Red Fox'^{PBR} (Ba) **new**	LCro LOPS
	'Red Fubuki' (D)	SDeJ
	'Red Majorette' (S-c)	SDeJ
	'Red Pathfinder' (Sin)	NJRG
	'Red Pygmy' (S-c)	SDeJ
	'Reginald Keene' (S-c)	NHal
	'Reputation' (C)	SGbt

	'Requiem' (D)	ECtt ERCP NJRG
	'Reverend P. Holian' (S-c)	SGbt
	'Rhanna Tammy' (D)	NHal
	'Rhonda' (Pom)	NHal WPhe WWEG
	'Richard S' (S-c)	NHal
	'Rip City' (S-c)	CAvo ERCP LCro LOPS LRHS MCot WPhe
	'Rita Shrimpton' (Misc)	NJRG
	'Rocco' (Ba)	ERCP LCro LOPS SGbt WBor WPhe
	'Rockcliffe Billy' (S-c)	NJRG
	'Rose Jupiter' (S-c)	NHal
	'Rosella' (D)	SDeJ SGbt WPhe
	'Rosemary Webb' (D)	SGbt
	'Rossendale Heide' (D) new	NHal
	'Rossendale Natasha' (Ba)	NHal SGbt
	'Rossendale Stephanie' (D)	NHal
	'Rothesay Robin' (D)	WPhe
I	'Roxy' (Sin/DwB)	CAby CBcs EBee ECtt ELan EPfP ERCP GMaP LAst LAyl LRHS LSRN MBri NHal NJRG SGbt WBrk WCot WHoo WPhe
	'Royal Mail' (D)	SGbt
	'Royal Visit' (D)	SGbt
	'Ruby Wedding' (D)	SGbt
	rudis	CExl CFil WPGP
	'Ruskin Andrea' (S-c)	LAyl NHal WPhe
	'Ruskin Avenger' (S-c)	NJRG
	'Ruskin Bride' (S-c)	NHal
	'Ruskin Buttercup' (D)	SGbt
	'Ruskin Charlotte' (S-c)	NJRG
	'Ruskin Diana' (D)	NHal WPhe
I	'Ruskin Harmony' (S-c)	NHal WPhe
	'Ruskin Limelight' (C)	NHal
	'Ruskin Marigold' (S-c)	NHal
	'Ruskin Myra' (S-c)	LAyl NHal WPhe
	'Ruskin Respectable' (S-c)	WPhe
	'Ruskin Sensation' (S-c)	NHal WPhe
	'Ruskin Tangerine' (Ba)	NHal SGbt
	'Ryecroft Brenda T' (D)	NHal NJRG WPhe
	'Ryecroft Claire' (D)	NHal
	'Ryecroft Delight' (Ba)	NHal
	'Ryecroft Ice' (D)	NHal SGbt WPhe
	'Ryecroft Jan' (Ba) ♀H3	NHal NJRG WPhe
	'Ryecroft Jim' (Anem)	NHal
	'Ryecroft Laura' (Ba)	NHal
	'Ryecroft Pixie' (C)	NHal
	'Ryecroft Rebel' (D)	NHal WPhe
	'Ryecroft Sparkler' (C)	NHal SGbt
	'Ryecroft Yellow Orb' (Ba)	NHal
	'Ryecroft Zoe' (S-c)	NHal
	'Saint-Saëns' (S-c)	ERCP SDeJ
	'Sakura Fubuki' (Fim)	ERCP
	'Salmon Wheels' (Col)	NJRG
	'Sam Hopkins' (D)	ERCP LAyl NHal WPhe
	'Sam Huston' (D)	SGbt
	'Samantha'	see *D.* 'Harvest Samantha'
	'Sandia Rose' (WL)	NHal
	'Sandia Shomei' (WL)	EWoo
	'Sandra' (D)	ERCP
	'Santa Claus' (D)	SGbt
	'Sarah' (S-c)	ECtt EUJe LRHS
	'Sascha' (WL) ♀H3	LAyl
	'Sassy' (D)	SGbt
§	'Scarlet Fern' (Sin)	LRHS LSRN WPhe
	'Scarlet O'Hara' (D)	NJRG
	'Scaur Sunrise' (D)	NJRG
	'Scaur Swinton' (D)	LAyl NHal SGbt
	'Sean C' (Col)	CHVG
	'Seattle' (D)	NBri
	'Seduction' (D)	EPfP ERCP

	'Seirō' (S-c)	SGbt
	'Shandy' (S-c)	LAyl
	'Shep's Memory' (WL) ♀H3	NJRG
	sherffii dwarf new	WPGP
	'Shirwell Greta' (D) new	NHal
	'Shooting Star' (S-c)	NBri
	'Show 'n' Tell' (Fim)	SGbt WPhe
	'Silver City' (D)	NHal SGbt WPhe
	'Sir Alf Ramsey' (D)	LAyl NHal SGbt WPhe
	'Small World' (Pom) ♀H3	LAyl NHal WWEG
	'Snow Cap' (S-c)	SDeJ
	'Snowbound' (D)	SGbt
I	'Snowflake' (WL)	ERCP SDeJ
	'Snowfox' (Anem)	NJRG
I	'Snowstorm' (D)	SGbt
	'So Dainty' (S-c) ♀H3	LAyl
	'Sophie Taylor' (SinO)	NJRG
I	'Sorbet' (D)	NHal
	'Sorbet' (S-c)	see *D.* 'Geerlings' Sorbet' (MS-c)
	'Sorrento Flush' (D)	WPhe
	'Soulman' (Anem)	CSpe EWoo NJRG SGbt
	'Souvenir d'Eté' (Pom)	SDeJ
	'Spanish Conquest' (D)	SGbt
I	'Sparkler' (S-c)	ERCP
	'Spartacus' (D)	LAyl NHal WPhe
	'Spassmacher' (S-c)	NBri
	'Spectacular' (D)	SGbt
I	'Spike' (S-c)	SGbt
	'Staleen Condesa' (S-c) ♀H3	NHal SGbt
	'Star Elite' (C)	NBri
	'Star Surprise' (C)	SDeJ
	Star Wars = 'Vdtg14'PBR (Dark Angel Series) (Sin)	ERCP LCro LOPS SDeJ WPhe
	'Star's Favourite' (C)	ERCP NBri
	'Stevie D' (D) ♀H3	SGbt
§	'Stolz von Berlin' (Ba)	ERCP SDeJ SGbt
	'Stoneleigh Cherry' (Pom)	LAyl
	'Storrs Julie' (Pom)	NJRG
	'Striped Vulcan' (S-c)	CAby
	'Suffolk Punch' (D)	LAyl
	'Sugar Diamond' (C)	ERCP
	'Summer Festival' (D)	SGbt
	'Summer Night' (S-c)	see *D.* 'Nuit d'Eté'
	'Summer Night' ambig.	ECGP LAyl NHal
	'Summer Nights' (Misc)	LOPS NJRG
	'Sunny Boy' (D)	NBri
I	'Sunshine' (Sin)	LCro LOPS LRHS
	'Sunshine Girl' (Col)	NJRG
	'Susan Carey' (S-c) ♀H3	WPhe
	'Susan Gilbert' (Col)	NHal
	'Susan Gilliott' (S-c)	NHal
I	'Suzanne' (Col)	NJRG
	'Suzette' (D/DwB)	SGbt
	'Swan Lake'	see *D.* 'Classic Swanlake'
	'Swanvale' (D)	SGbt
	'Sweet Content' (D)	SGbt
	'Sweetheart' (D)	NJRG
I	'Sylvia' (Ba)	ERCP NBri NJRG WPhe
	'Tahiti Sunrise' (S-c)	EPfP
	'Tahoma Star' (SinO)	LCro LOPS
	'Tahoma Tom Tom' (S-c)	NHal
	'Take Off' (Anem) new	WBor
	'Tally Ho' (Misc) ♀H3	ECGP ECtt EPfP LRHS NJRG SDys WCot WWEG
	'Tam Tam' (Ba)	EPfP SPer
	'Tamburo' (S-c)	EPfP ERCP SPer
I	'Tapestry' (Sin)	SGbt WPhe
	'Taratahi Ruby' (WL) ♀H3	CHVG ERCP NHal NJRG WPhe
	Taxi Driver = 'Vdtg57'PBR (Dark Angel Series) (Sin)	ERCP LRHS

Plant	Suppliers
'Teamarie Butterscotch' (Misc)	NJRG
'Teesbrooke Audrey' (Col)	CHVG ECtt LAyl NHal WPhe
'Teesbrooke Red Eye' (Col)	ERCP NHal NJRG SGbt WPhe
tenuicaulis	CDTJ CExl GGal SBig
- F&M 257	CFil
- F&M 355	CFil
'Terracotta' (DwB)	NHal
'Terrie Bandey' (Fim) **new**	NHal
'Thais' (Col)	NJRG
'The Phantom' (Anem)	ERCP NJRG WBor
'Thomas A. Edison' (D)	CAvo ERCP IPot SDeJ SGbt
'Tiger Eye' (D)	SGbt
'Timeless' (D) **new**	SPer
I 'Tiptoe' (D)	LAyl NHal
'Tisa' (Pom)	NHal
'Tohsuikyoh' (Misc)	SGbt
'Tomo' (D)	LAyl NHal
'Top Totty' (D)	NHal
'Topmix' (Sin/DwB)	SDeJ
'Topmix Mama' (Sin)	NJRG
'Topmix Pink' (Sin/DwB)	SDeJ
'Topmix Purple' (Sin)	NJRG
'Topmix Red' (Sin/DwB)	NJRG SDeJ
'Topmix Reddy' (Sin)	NJRG
I 'Topmix Rose' (Sin)	NJRG
'Topmix White' (Sin/DwB)	SDeJ
'Topmix Yellow' (Sin/DwB)	NJRG SDeJ
'Toto' (Anem)	ERCP
'Trelyn Crimson' (Col) **new**	NHal
'Trelyn Kiwi' (S-c) ♀H3	NHal NJRG SGbt WPhe
'Trelyn Rebecca' (Col)	NHal WPhe
'Trelyn Red Dragon' (SinO) **new**	NHal
'Trelyn Rhiannon' (C) ♀H3	WPhe
'Trelyn Seren' (SinO)	LAyl NHal WPhe
'Trengrove Autumn' (D)	SGbt
'Trengrove Millennium' (D)	NHal NJRG SGbt
I 'Trevor' (Col)	ECtt SGbt
'Tricolor'	MSCN
'Trooper Dan' (S-c)	NHal
'Troy Dyson' (Misc)	SDys
'Truly Scrumptious' (S-c)	SGbt
'Tsuki-yori-no-shisha' (Fim)	LCro LOPS
tubulata	CFil EBee
'Tudor 1' (Misc/DwB)	NHal
'Tui Avis' (C)	NJRG
'Tu-tu' (S-c)	SGbt
'Twiggy' (WL)	SGbt
'Twilight Time' (D)	SDeJ WPhe
* 'Twinkle Stars'	SDeJ
'Twyning's After Eight' (Sin) ♀H3	CAby CAvo CBot CExl CSpe CWGN EAJP ECtt ELan EPfP ERCP EWoo LAyl LCro LOPS LRHS LSun MBri NHal NJRG NSti SDix SDys SGbt SPer WBor WCot WHoo WPhe
'Twyning's Revel' (Sin) ♀H3	CAvo
'Twyning's Smartie' (Sin)	EBee LCro
'Tyrell' (D)	EPfP
'Uncle Hankey' (D)	ERCP
'Val's Candy' (S-c) **new**	NHal
'Vancouver' (Misc)	ERCP SDeJ
'Veritable' (S-c)	CSut NBri
'Viking' (Pom) **new**	NBri
'Vivian Russell' (WL)	NJRG
'Vulcan' (S-c)	ERCP SGbt WPhe
§ 'Vuurvogel' (S-c)	ERCP NBri SDeJ
'Waltzing Mathilda' (Misc)	ERCP LCro LOPS
'Wanda's Capella' (D)	WPhe
'War of the Roses' (D)	EWes WHer
'Westerton Folly' (Ba) ♀H3	NHal
'Westerton Lilian' (D)	NHal
'Westerton Southside' (D) **new**	NHal
'Weston Buccaneer' (C)	NHal WPhe WWEG
'Weston Corsair' (C)	NJRG WWEG
'Weston Kelpie' (C)	NJRG
'Weston Miss' (S-c)	NHal NJRG
'Weston Pirate' (C) ♀H3	LAyl NHal NJRG WPhe WWEG
'Weston Spanish Dancer' (C) ♀H3	NHal NJRG SGbt WPhe
'Weston Stardust' (C) ♀H3	NJRG WPhe
'Weston Sunup' (C)	NJRG
'Wheels' (Col)	NJRG
'White Alva's' (D) ♀H3	LAyl NHal SGbt WPhe
'White Aster' (Pom)	ERCP
'White Ballerina' (WL)	LAyl NHal SGbt WPhe
'White Ballet' (D) ♀H3	LAyl SGbt
'White Charlie Two' (D)	NHal
'White Katrina' (S-c)	WPhe
'White Knight' (D)	NHal
'White Linda' (D)	NHal
'White Moonlight' (S-c)	LAyl NHal WPhe
'White Nettie' (Ba)	SGbt
'White Onesta' (D)	SDeJ WPhe
'White Perfection' (D)	ECtt EPfP ERCP NBri SDeJ
'White Rebel' **new**	NBri
'White Star' (S-c)	ERCP LCro LOPS SDeJ
'White Swallow' (S-c)	NHal
'Who Dun It' (D)	ERCP
'Wildwood Marie' (WL)	NJRG
'Willo's Borealis' (Pom)	NHal WPhe
'Willo's Surprise' (Pom)	NHal SGbt WWEG
'Willo's Violet' (Pom)	NHal NJRG SGbt WPhe WWEG
'Wine & Roses' (WL)	SGbt
'Winholme Diane' (D)	NHal WPhe
'Winter Springs' (S-Sc)	ERCP WPhe
'Wishes n Dreams' (Sin)	NJRG
'Witteman's Best' (S-c)	ERCP MCot NBri SGbt WPhe
'Witteman's Superba' (S-c) ♀H3	NHal SDix
'Wizard of Oz' (Ba)	ERCP LCro LOPS WPhe
'Woodbridge' (Sin)	SGbt
'Woodside Finale' (D)	NHal
'Wootton Impact' (S-c) ♀H3	NHal WPhe
'Worton Blue Streak' (S-c)	ERCP SGbt
'Yellow Galator' (C)	SGbt
'Yellow Hammer' (Sin/DwB) ♀H3	LAyl NHal SGbt
'Yellow Happiness'	NBri
'Yellow Heaven' (D) **new**	NBri
'Yellow Lorona Dawn' (Col)	NJRG
'Yellow Passions' (D)	ERCP
'Yellow Star' (S-c)	ERCP EUJe SDeJ
'Yelno Enchantment' (WL)	LAyl
'York and Lancaster' (D)	EBee SGbt
* 'Zingaro' **new**	LCro
'Zingaro' (D) **new**	LOPS
§ 'Zone Ten'PBR (Sin/DwB)	CAby EPfP LRHS LSRN LSou SHar SPoG WBor
'Zorro' (D) ♀H3	ERCP NHal SGbt WPhe

Daiswa see *Paris*

Dalea (*Papilionaceae*)

Plant	Suppliers
purpurea	EBee SBrt SPhx
- 'Stephanie'	CMea LRHS

damson see *Prunus insititia*

Danae (*Asparagaceae*)

§	***racemosa*** 🏆H5	CBcs CFil CLet CMac CTri EBee EPfP MGil MGos MMuc MRav SEND SPer SRms SSpi SWvt WCot WCru WPGP

Danthonia (*Poaceae*)

§	***cincta***	WCot

Daphne ✿ (*Thymelaeaceae*)

	DJHC 98164 from China	WCru
	acutiloba	CJun GKev
	- 'Fragrant Cloud'	CExl CJun EWes SChF
	albowiana	CJun LLHF
	alpina	CJun
	altaica	CJun
	arbuscula 🏆H5	CJun EPot SIgm WAbe
	- subsp. ***arbuscula*** f. ***albiflora***	CJun
	- 'Diva'	CJun
	- 'Muran Pride'	CJun
	- f. ***radicans***	CJun
	arbuscula × ***cneorum*** var. ***verlotii***	CJun
	arbuscula × 'Leila Haines'	see *D.* × *schlyteri*
	arisanensis B&SWJ 6983	WCru
	bholua	CAbP CJun EPfP GCal GGal LRHS
I	- 'Alba'	CJun EPfP SSta WPGP
	- 'Cobhay Snow' **new**	CJun
	- 'Darjeeling'	CExl CJun EPfP GKev LRHS SKHP WPGP
	- 'Garden House Enchantress' **new**	WPGP
	- 'Garden House Ghost' **new**	WPGP
	- 'Garden House Sentinel' **new**	WPGP
	- var. ***glacialis*** 'Gurkha' 🏆H4	CExl CJun EPfP SKHP WPGP
	- 'Hazel Edwards'	LRHS
	- 'Jacqueline Postill' 🏆H4	CBcs CExl CJun CTri CWib ELon EPfP EWTr GKev IVic LCro LRHS LSRN MAsh MBlu MBri MGil MGos SCob SGbt SKHP SPoG SReu SSpi SSta SWvt WPGP WPat
	- 'Limpsfield'	CJun LRHS SSta
	- 'Penwood'	CJun
	- 'Peter Smithers'	CExl CJun EPfP LRHS LSRN SSta
	- 'Wisley Purple'	CJun
	blagayana	ECho NBir SIgm SRms
	- 'Brenda Anderson'	CJun EPot WAbe
	'Bramdean'	see *D.* × *napolitana* 'Bramdean'
	× ***burkwoodii***	EBee ECrN LSRN SCob
	- 'Albert Burkwood'	CJun
	- 'Astrid' (v)	CBcs CJun LRHS MGos NLar SCob SLon
	- 'Briggs Moonlight' (v)	NLar
§	- 'Carol Mackie' (v)	CJun LRHS
	- 'G.K.Argles' (v)	CJun MAsh
I	- 'Gold Sport'	CJun SChF
	- 'Gold Strike' (v)	CJun
	- 'Golden Treasure'	CJun MAsh SChF
	- 'Lavenirii'	CJun
	- 'Somerset' 🏆H4	CBcs CJun ELan ESwi LCro MGos MRav MSwo NLar NWea SCob
§	- 'Somerset Gold Edge' (v)	CJun
§	- 'Somerset Variegated' (v)	SChF WThu
	- 'Variegata' broad cream edge	see *D.* × *burkwoodii* 'Somerset Variegated'
	- 'Variegata' broad gold edge	see *D.* × *burkwoodii* 'Somerset Gold Edge'
	- 'Variegata' narrow gold edge	see *D.* × *burkwoodii* 'Carol Mackie'
	calcicola 'Gang-ho-ba'	CJun WThu
	caucasica	CJun
	circassica	CJun SChF
	cneorum	CBcs CJun ELan EPot EWTr GKev IVic MGos MWat
	- 'Benaco'	CJun
	- 'Blackthorn Triumph'	CJun CWib WAbe
	- 'Eximia' 🏆H5	CJun LRHS WAbe
	- 'Klaus Patzner'	CJun
	- 'Lac des Gloriettes'	CJun
	- 'Puszta'	CJun WAbe
	- var. ***pygmaea***	CJun EPot
	- - 'Alba'	CJun
	- 'Rubra'	LRHS
	- 'Ruby Glow'	CJun
	- 'Variegata' (v)	CJun EPot GEdr GKev
	- 'Velký Kosir'	CJun WAbe
	- var. ***verlotii***	EPot
	collina	see *D. sericea* Collina Group
	× ***eschmannii*** 'Jacob Eschmann'	CJun
	euboica **new**	GKev
	'Forarch'	CJun
	gemmata **new**	NLar
	genkwa	CJun SKHP WThu
	giraldii	CJun
	gnidioides	CJun
	gnidium **new**	CEvo
	- PAB 8371 **new**	LEdu
	'Guardsman'	CJun MAsh WAbe
	× ***hendersonii***	CJun
	- 'Appleblossom'	CJun WAbe
	- 'Aymon Correvon'	CJun WThu
	- 'Blackthorn Rose'	CJun WAbe
	- 'Ernst Hauser'	CJun GKev SChF WAbe WIce WThu
	- 'Fritz Kummert'	CJun WAbe WThu
	- 'Jeanette Brickell'	CJun WAbe WThu
	- 'Kath Dryden'	CJun GEdr WAbe
	- 'Marion White'	CJun WAbe
	- 'Rosebud'	CJun WThu
	- 'Solferino'	CJun
	'Hinton'	CJun
	× ***houtteana***	CJun
	× ***hybrida***	CJun
	japonica 'Striata'	see *D. odora* 'Aureomarginata'
	jasminea	CJun ECho WAbe
	jezoensis	CJun
	× ***jintyae*** 'Pink Cascade'	CJun
	juliae	CJun WAbe
	kamtschatica	CJun
	'Kilmeston Beauty'	CJun
	kosaninii	CJun
	kurdica **new**	GKev
	× ***latymeri*** 'Spring Sonnet'	CJun SChF WAbe
	laureola	CJun EPfP GKev GPoy MMHG NBid NBir NLar NPer SChr
	- 'Kingsley Green'	CJun
	- 'Margaret Mathew'	CJun EPfP EPot NLar SChF
	- subsp. ***philippi***	CBcs CJun CMac EBee ELan EPfP GKev LRHS MAsh MBlu MGil MGos NLar SKHP
	'Leila Haines'	CJun GKev NLar
	longilobata	GKev
	× ***mantensiana*** 'Audrey Vockins'	CJun
	- 'Manten'	CJun

	Name	Suppliers
	× ***mauerbachii*** 'Perfume of Spring'	CJun
	'Meon'	see *D.* × *napolitana* 'Meon'
	mezereum	CTri ECho EWld GKev GMaP GPoy IFoB LRHS MAsh MBri MGil MGos NChi NWea SChF SCob SGol SWvt WCot WHar WHil WPGP
	- PAB 7643	LEdu
	- f. ***alba***	CBcs CJun CMac ECho EWld GKev GLog MAsh MGos NChi SChF SRms SWvt WAbe
	- - 'Bowles's Variety'	CJun
	- 'Rosea'	ECho MAsh SRms
	- var. ***rubra***	CBcs CJun CMac CWSG CWib ELan GKin LRHS MGos MJak MNHC MRav MSwo SPer WAbe
	× ***napolitana*** ♀H4	CJun
§	- 'Bramdean'	CJun SChF
§	- 'Meon'	CJun GEdr MAsh WAbe WThu
	odora	CBcs CJun CWSG EPfP LCro LOPS LRHS LSRN MSwo SCob
§	- f. ***alba***	CJun CMac
	- - 'Sakiwaka'	CExl CJun SKHP WPat
§	- 'Aureomarginata' (v)	Widely available
I	- 'Aureomarginata Alba' (v)	SEle
	- 'Clotted Cream' (v)	CJun
	- 'Geisha Girl' (v)	CJun MAsh MGos
	- var. ***leucantha***	see *D. odora* f. *alba*
	- 'Limelight' (v)	CJun
	- 'Mae-jima' (v)	CAbP CExl CJun EBee ELan EPfP LRHS MAsh NLar SLon SPer SPoG
	- 'Marginata'	see *D. odora* 'Aureomarginata'
	- Marianni = 'Rogbret' (v)	CDoC CWSG EBee EUJe LCro LHop LOPS MJak NCGa NLar SGol SMad SWvt
	- Rebecca = 'Hewreb' (v) ♀H4	CBct CBod CRos CWib EPfP LBuc LRHS MAsh MBri MGos SHil SLon SPer SPoG
	- var. ***rubra***	CJun CMac GKev
	- 'Walberton' (v)	EPfP LRHS MBri
	oleoides	CJun GKev NLar
	- var. ***buxifolia***	GKev
	papyracea	CExl CFil
	petraea	CJun WAbe
	- 'Cima Tombea'	CJun
	- 'Corna Blacca'	CJun
	- 'Garnet'	CJun WAbe
	- 'Grandiflora'	CJun WAbe
	- 'Lydora'	CJun
	- 'Persebee'	CJun
	- 'Punchinello'	CJun
	- 'Tuflungo'	CJun
	'Pink Star'	CJun
	pontica	CBcs CJun CMac EBee EPfP LRHS MAsh NLar SChF SDix SKHP SSpi WPGP
	retusa	see *D. tangutica* Retusa Group
	'Richard's Choice'	CJun
	× ***rollsdorfii*** 'Arnold Cihlarz'	CJun SChF WAbe
	- 'Wilhelm Schacht' ♀H5	CAbP CJun IVic MAsh SChF WAbe WThu
	× ***rossetii*** 'Rossetii'	CJun
	'Rosy Wave'	CJun SChF
§	× ***schlyteri***	CJun
	- 'July Glow'	EPot GEdr SChF
	- 'Lovisa Maria'	CJun GEdr WAbe
	sericea	CJun
§	- Collina Group	CAbP CJun WIce
	'Spring Beauty'	CJun EPfP WPGP
	'Spring Herald'	CJun
	'Stasek' (v)	CJun
	× ***suendermannii*** 'Franz Suendermann'	WAbe WOld
	× ***susannae*** 'Anton Fahndrich'	CJun NLar SChF WThu
	- 'Cheriton' ♀H5	CJun EPot LRHS NLar SChF WAbe WThu
	- 'Tage Lundell'	CJun IVic
	- 'Tichborne'	CAbP CJun EPot SChF WThu
	tangutica ♀H5	CBcs CExl CJun CMac CSpe CTri EAla ECho ELan EPfP GKev LRHS LSRN MAsh MGil MGos NBir NHol NLar SCoo SEND SKHP SPoG SRkn SRms SSpi WAbe WBod
	- 'Golden Thread' (v)	EPfP LRHS
§	- Retusa Group ♀H5	CExl CJun ECho ELan ELon EOHP EPot GAbr GBin GEdr GKev GMaP LCro LHop LRHS MGil MHer NBir NLar SIgm SRms
	× ***transatlantica*** new	CBot
	- 'Beulah Cross' (v)	CAbP CJun LRHS MAsh SChF
	- Eternal Fragrance = 'Blafra' PBR ♀H5	CAbP CBcs CExl CWGN ELan EPfP EUJe GKev LCro LOPS LRHS LSRN MAsh MGos MJak MPkF NLar SCoo SKHP SLon SPer SPoG SSpi WPGP XEll
	- 'Jim's Pride'	SChF
§	- Pink Fragrance = 'Blapink' PBR	CDoC EBee ELan EPfP LCro LOPS MAsh SKHP SPoG XEll
	- Spring Pink Eternal Fragrance	see *D.* × *transatlantica* Pink Fragrance
	- 'Summer Ice' (v)	WAbe
	'Valerie Hillier'	CJun GKev LRHS
	velenovskyi	CJun
	× ***whiteorum*** 'Beauworth'	CJun WAbe WOld
	- 'Kilmeston'	CJun WAbe
	- 'Warnford'	CJun
	wolongensis 'Kevock Star'	CExl GKev SChF

Daphniphyllum (*Daphniphyllaceae*)

Name	Suppliers
aff. ***angustifolium*** B&SWJ 8225	WCru
- B&SWJ 11804	WCru
- WWJ 12020	WCru
chartaceum KWJ 12244 from northern Vietnam	WCru
glaucescens subsp. ***oldhamii*** var. ***kengii*** B&SWJ 6872	WCru
- - - B&SWJ 7119	WCru
- - var. ***oldhamii*** B&SWJ 7056	WCru
- - - CWJ 12351	WCru
himalaense	SMad
humile	see *D. macropodum* var. *humile*
aff. ***longeracemosum*** B&SWJ 11788	WCru
- NJM 10.147	WPGP
macropodum	CBcs CBct CFil CMCN EBee EPfP GBin LRHS NLar SDix SKHP SSpi SVen WCru WHor WPGP
- B&SWJ 581	WCru
- B&SWJ 2898	WCru
- B&SWJ 6809 from Taiwan	WCru
- B&SWJ 8507 from Ulleungdo, South Korea	WCru
- B&SWJ 8763 from Cheju-do, Korea	WCru

- B&SWJ 11489 from Yakushima, Japan — WCru
- dwarf — WCru
§ - var. ***humile*** B&SWJ 11232 — WCru
majus B&SWJ 11744 — WCru
paxianum B&SWJ 9755 — WCru
pentandrum B&SWJ 6888 — WCru
- B&SWJ 7056 — WCru
- CWJ 12393 — WCru
- RWJ 9836 — WCru
teijsmannii B&SWJ 11110 from Japan — WCru
- B&SWJ 11358 from Japan — WCru
aff. ***teijsmannii*** CWJ 12350 from Taiwan — WCru
teysmannii B&SWJ 11112 — WCru

Darlingtonia (*Sarraceniaceae*)

californica ♀H3 — EFEx WSSs

Darmera (*Saxifragaceae*)

peltata ♀H6 — Widely available
- 'Nana' — EBee ECha ELan EPfP GBuc GCal LBMP MWts NBid NHol NLar NMyG SWat WFar WMoo

Darwinia (*Myrtaceae*)

taxifolia — MOWG

Dasylirion (*Asparagaceae*)

§ ***acrotrichum*** — CDTJ CExl EAla EShb
berlandieri — CExl
cedrosanum — CDTJ CJun SPlb
durangense — EAla
glaucophyllum — CJun
gracile Planchon — see *D. acrotrichum*
longissimum — CBrP EShb ETod LPal SChr XSen
lucidum — EAla
miquihuanense — SMad
- F&M 301A — WPGP
- F&M 321 — EBee WPGP
quadrangulatum — EAla EBee LPal SPlb
serratifolium — ETod EUJe LPal
texanum — EAla LEdu
wheeleri ♀H2 — CBrP EAla LPal SIgm SPlb XSen

date see *Phoenix dactylifera*

Datisca (*Datiscaceae*)

cannabina — CArn CDTJ CSpe EBee ECha GBin GCal IMou LPla NChi SBrt SDix SMHy SMad WMoo WPGP WSHC

Datura (*Solanaceae*)

arborea — see *Brugmansia arborea*
cornigera — see *Brugmansia arborea*
rosea — see *Brugmansia* × *insignis* pink-flowered
rosei — see *Brugmansia sanguinea*
sanguinea — see *Brugmansia sanguinea*
stramonium — EBtc
suaveolens — see *Brugmansia suaveolens*
versicolor 'Grand Marnier' — see *Brugmansia* × *candida* 'Grand Marnier'

Daucus (*Apiaceae*)

carota — CHab LEdu NMir SVic WHer WHil WSFF

Davallia (*Davalliaceae*)

canariensis ♀H1c — CMen
divaricata new — NLos
mariesii ♀H2 — CCon CMen ISha NLos
- var. ***stenolepis*** — CMen
tasmanii — CMen
trichomanoides — CMen NLos
- f. ***barbata*** — CMen

Davidia (*Nyssaceae*)

involucrata ♀H5 — Widely available
- 'Crimson Spring' new — WHor
- 'Sonoma' — CLnd MBlu NLar WHor
- var. ***vilmoriniana*** ♀H5 — CBcs CWCL ELan EPfP LRHS MAsh MBlu MGos NOrn SLim SPer SPtp

Daviesia (*Papilionaceae*)

cordata — SPlb
* ***ovalifolia*** — SPlb
pectinata — SPlb

Debregeasia (*Urticaceae*)

longifolia — SVen
- WWJ 11686 — WCru

Decaisnea (*Lardizabalaceae*)

fargesii — Widely available
- B&SWJ 8070 — WCru

Decodon (*Lythraceae*)

verticillatus — LLWG

Decumaria (*Hydrangeaceae*)

barbara — CBcs CMac MMuc NLar WCru WSHC
- 'Vicki' — NBro NLar
sinensis — CBot EPfP ESwi EUJe EWTr LRHS MMuc SHil SKHP SLon SPoG SSpi WCru WSHC

Degenia (*Brassicaceae*)

velebitica — EPot GKev SIgm WOld

Deinanthe (*Hydrangeaceae*)

bifida — CDes CExl CMil EBee EPfP EWes GKev LRHS MMHG WCru WPGP
- B&SWJ 5436 — EWld WCru
- B&SWJ 5551 — WCru
- 'Pink-Kii' — WCru
- 'Pink-Shi' — EWld LEdu WCru WSHC
bifida × ***caerulea*** 'Blue Blush' — CLAP WCru / WCru
caerulea — CMil ECho GCra GKev IMou LEdu LHop MMHG NLar SKHP WCru WPGP WSHC
- 'Blue Wonder' — CExl CLAP LLHF MNrw SPoG
- white-flowered — IMou

Delonix (*Caesalpiniaceae*)

decaryi — SPlb
regia — SPlb

Delosperma (*Aizoaceae*)

from Graaf Reinet, South Africa — NSla
from Ouberg Pass, South Africa — CPBP
from Sani Pass, South Africa — CPBP ECtt EPot GCrg GEdr NSla WAbe
§ ***aberdeenense*** ♀H3 — SAko XLum
alpinum — ECho EPot EWes GEdr LRHS

	ashtonii	EWes NSla XLum
	basuticum	EWld NSla
	'Basutoland'	see *D. nubigenum*
	'Beaufort West'	EDAr EWes LRHS NSla WIce XLum
	congestum	CPBP CSma CTal ECho EDAr EPot GEdr NPri SMad WAbe WHal WIce XLum
I	- 'Album'	CSma CTal EWes GEdr WIce
	- 'Gold Nugget' ♀H3	EAEE ECho LRHS
*	- white-flowered	EDAr EPot WAbe
	cooperi	CTri EAEE ECho ECtt EDAr EPfP EPot EUJe GBin ITim LAst LRHS LSou NPri SChr SIgm SPlb SRot SVen WIce WPnn XLum
	dyeri Red Mountain = 'Psdold'	ECho EDAr GEdr LRHS SAko XLum
	ecklonis	GKev
	Fire Spinner = 'P001s'	EDAr WHlf
	floribundum Sequins = 'Balosquin'	CAbb
	- 'Starburst'	EDAr MHol
	- 'Stardust'	EWes
	jansei	NSla
	(Jewel of Desert Series) 'Jewel of Desert Garnet'PBR	CAbb ECtt LRHS SPad
	- 'Jewel of Desert Moon Stone'PBR	ECtt LRHS NPri
	- 'Jewel of Desert Peridott'PBR	CWGN ECtt LRHS SPad
	- 'Jewel of Desert Ruby'PBR **new**	CWGN LRHS
	- 'Jewel of Desert Topaz'PBR	CAbb CWGN ECtt LRHS
§	'John Proffitt'	GKev SAko SPlb XLum
	karrooicum	GEdr
	lavisiae	ELon NSla SPlb
	'Lesotho Pink'	EWes
	lineare	XLum
	Mesa Verde = 'Kelaidis'	ECtt SAko
§	***nubigenum***	CSma CTal CTri ECho ECtt EPot EUJe GAbr GCrg GKev SPlb
	'Ruby Coral'	ECho ECtt EPot LRHS NPri
	sphalmanthoides	CPBP EPot GEdr WAbe
	sutherlandii ♀H3	CSma CTal ECho EDAr EPfP GBin NPri SRot XLum
	- 'Peach Star'	EDAr GEdr NPri SBch WIce
	Table Mountain	see *D.* 'John Proffitt'

Delphinium ✿ (*Ranunculaceae*)

	sp.	MLHP SVic
	'After Midnight'	CNMi
	'Ailsa'	CNMi
	'Alice Artindale' (d)	CDes EBee EWes EWld IFoB WCot
	'Ann Woodfield'	CNMi
	'Ariel' ambig.	LRHS
	Astolat Group	CBcs CBod COtt CSBt CTri CWib ELan EPfP GJos GMaP IBoy LRHS MBri MGos MHol NHol NLar SPer SPoG SWvt WCAu WHar
	'Atholl' ♀H5	CNMi
	'Bambi'	CNMi
	Belladonna Group	CWCL ELan EPfP WHar
	- 'Atlantis'	ECha LRHS NLar
	- 'Casa Blanca'	EBee EPfP GMaP LRHS NLar
	- 'Cliveden Beauty'	CWCL EPfP GMaP LHop LRHS NLar
	- 'Gute Nacht' **new**	EBee
§	- 'Janny Arrow'	LRHS
	- 'Piccolo'	ECha MNrw NLar
	- 'Pink Sensation'	see *D.* × *ruysii* 'Pink Sensation'
	- 'Völkerfrieden'	GMaP IBoy LRHS MNrw MRav NLar
	× ***bellamosum***	EPfP GMaP LRHS MNrw
	'Berghimmel'	EBee LRHS
	'Beryl Burton'	CNMi
	Black Knight Group	Widely available
	'Black Pearl'	ECtt IKil
	'Black-eyed Angels' (New Millennium Series)	IPot LSun SCob SGbt
	'Black-eyed Beauty' **new**	MHol
	'Blauwal'	LRHS
	'Blue Arrow'	see *D.* 'Blue Max Arrow', *D.* (Belladonna Group) 'Janny Arrow', *D.* 'Kings Blue Arrow'
	Blue Bird Group	CBcs COtt CSBt CTri CWCL ELan EPfP GJos GMaP LRHS MGos MJak NMir SGbt SPer SPoG WCAu WHoo
	'Blue Butterfly'	see *D. grandiflorum* 'Blue Butterfly'
	'Blue Dawn' ♀H5	CNMi
	Blue Fountains Group	CSBt EPfP LSRN SPoG SRms
	'Blue Jay'	CBcs CTri EPfP EWoo LSRN MWat
	'Blue Lace'	IPot LCro LRHS
§	'Blue Max Arrow'	LRHS
	'Blue Mirror'	SRms
	'Blue Nile' ♀H5	CNMi LRHS
	'Blue Oasis'	CNMi
	Blue Springs Group	NGdn
	'Blue Tit'	CNMi IKil
	'Bob Geldof'	CNMi
	'Boudicca'	CNMi
	'Bruce' ♀H5	CNMi
	brunonianum	EPot
	'Butterball'	CNMi
	Cameliard Group	CBcs CBod CSBt ELan EPfP LHop LRHS NLar SPer SPoG
	'Cameliard' (Pacific Hybrid Series)	COtt
	'Can-can' ♀H5	CNMi
	carolinianum	SBrt
	cashmerianum	CPne
	(Centurion Series) 'Centurion Gentian Blue' **new**	LCro LOPS
	- 'Centurion Lavender' **new**	LCro LOPS
	- 'Centurion Sky Blue' ♀H5	LCro LOPS
	'Chelsea Star'	CNMi EBee LRHS
	'Cher'	CNMi
	'Cherry Blossom'	EPfP NLar
	'Christel'	IKil LRHS LSRN NLar
	'Claire'	CNMi
	'Conspicuous' ♀H5	CNMi
	'Coral Sunset'PBR (d)	EBee LBuc MBri MHol
	'Cranberry Delight' **new**	CNMi
	'Crown Jewel'	EBee LRHS
	'Darling Sue'	CNMi
	'Diamant'PBR	IKil LRHS
	'Dreaming Spires'	SRms
	drepanocentrum HWJK 2263	WCru
	'Dunsden Green'	CNMi
	Dusky Maidens Group	ELan IFoB LRHS LSun MHol SGbt SPoG
	dwarf, dark blue-flowered	LRHS
	elatum	GCal
	- 'Blushing Brides' (New Millennium Series)	LRHS SPoG
	- 'Dasante Blue'	NPri
	- 'Double Innocence' (New Millennium Series) (d)	LRHS MHol
	- ex GORK **new**	SMHy
	- 'Morning Lights' (New Millennium Series)	EPfP IPot LRHS MHol SPoG

	Name	Suppliers
	- 'Sweet Sensation'	CMos ECtt EPfP EWTr IBoy LCro LRHS NLar
	- 'Sweethearts' (New Millennium Series) ♀H5	IPot LCro LSun
	'Elizabeth Cook' ♀H5	CNMi
	'Elmfreude'	IBoy LRHS
	'Emily Hawkins' ♀H5	CNMi
	'Fanfare'	CNMi
	'Faust' ♀H5	CNMi IKil LRHS
	'Fenella' ♀H5	CNMi
	'Finsteraarhorn'	GBin IKil LRHS MAvo MNrw
	'Florestan'	CNMi
	'Foxhill Nina' ♀H5	CNMi
	'Franjo Sahin'	CNMi
	Galahad Group	CBcs CSBt CTri CWCL CWib ECtt ELan EPfP EWoo GMaP LRHS MBel MBri MJak MWat NGdn NHol SPer SPlb SPoG WCAu WHar WHoo
	'Galahad' (Pacific Hybrid Series)	COtt LOPS LSun MGos MHol
	'Galileo' ♀H5	CNMi
	'Gemini'	CNMi
	'Gemma'	CNMi
	'Gillian Dallas'	IKil
	glaciale HWJK 2299	WCru
	'Gossamer'	CNMi ECtt IKil
§	***grandiflorum*** 'Blauer Zwerg'	MNHC SPoG
§	- 'Blue Butterfly'	CSpe EPfP LHop SPlb SPoG WSHC
	- Blue Dwarf	see *D. grandiflorum* 'Blauer Zwerg'
	- 'Delfix'	LRHS
	- (Summer Series) 'Summer Blues'	LRHS MBri SRot
	- - 'Summer Nights'	EPfP LRHS MBri SPoG WHar
	- - 'Summer Stars'	GJos MBri
	- 'White Butterfly'	LRHS
	'Green Twist' (New Millennium Series)	LRHS SCob SPoG
	(Guardian Series) 'Guardian Blue'	EBee LCro LOPS LRHS NPri SHil SPoG
	- 'Guardian Lavender'	LCro LOPS LRHS NPri SHil SPoG
	- 'Guardian White'	LCro LOPS LRHS NPri SHil SPoG
	Guinevere Group	CBcs CSBt CWCL CWib ECtt EPfP GJos MBri SPer SPoG WCAu
	- 'Lady Guinevere'	COtt IBoy
	'Guy Langdon'	CNMi
	'Highlander Blueberry Pie'	EBee ECtt IBoy LRHS SPoG
	'Highlander Crystal Delight'	EBee ECtt LCro LRHS SPoG
	'Highlander Morning Sunrise'	SPoG
	himalayae	GKev
	'Honey Pink'	CNMi
I	'Independence'	IKil LRHS
	'Innocence'	LRHS SCob
	'Jenny Agutter'	CNMi
	'Kathleen Cooke'	CNMi
	'Kestrel' ♀H5	CNMi COtt
	King Arthur Group	CBcs CBod CSBt CWCL ELan EPfP EUJe GJos LSRN LSun MBel MGos MHol MWat SPer SPoG
§	'Kings Blue Arrow'PBR	LRHS
	'La Bohème'	CWCL
	'Lanzenträger'	LRHS
	'Leonora'	CNMi
	'Loch Leven'	CNMi
	'Lord Butler' ♀H5	CNMi EBee LRHS
	'Lucia Sahin' ♀H5	CNMi
	maackianum	IMou LLHF WCot
	Magic Fountains Series	IFoB LRHS NGBl SPlb SPoG SVic
	- 'Magic Fountains Blue/White Bee' **new**	LRHS
	- 'Magic Fountains Cherry Blossom'	EPfP SPoG
	- 'Magic Fountains Dark Blue'	EAJP EPfP GMaP LRHS LSRN NEgg NLar SPoG
	- 'Magic Fountains Deep Rose/White Bee' **new**	LRHS
	- 'Magic Fountains Lavender'	EAJP EPfP NLar
	- 'Magic Fountains Lilac Pink'	EPfP SPoG
	- 'Magic Fountains Lilac Rose'	EAJP LRHS
	- 'Magic Fountains Pure White'	EAJP EPfP LRHS NEgg
	- 'Magic Fountains Sky Blue'	EPfP SPoG
	'Margaret' ♀H5	CNMi
	'Marilyn Clarrissa'	CNMi
	'Merlin' ambig.	LRHS LSRN
	'Michael Ayres' ♀H5	CNMi
	micropetalum CNDS 031	WCru
	'Mighty Atom'	CNMi IKil
	'Min' ♀H5	CNMi
	'Misty Mauves' (New Millennium Series) (d)	LRHS
	'Molly Buchanan'	CNMi
	'Moon Light' (Highlander Series) (d)	EBee EPfP LBuc LCro LOPS LRHS MHol NLar SPad SPoG
	'Moonbeam'	LRHS
	'Moonlight Blues' (New Millennium Series)	LSun SGbt
	'Morgentau'	EBee LRHS
	'Mother Teresa'	CNMi
	'Mrs Newton Lees'	IKil LRHS NLar
	'Ned Rose'	IKil
	'Ned Wit'	IKil
	nudicaule	GKev SPlb
	- 'Laurin'	LRHS
	'Oliver' ♀H5	CNMi
	'Ouvertüre'	LRHS
	oxysepalum	LLHF
	Pacific hybrids	CWCL EPfP LSRN MHer NLar SRms SWvt WHar
	'Pagan Purples' (New Millennium Series) (d)	IFoB IPot LRHS
	'Patricia Johnson'	CNMi
	Percival Group	EPfP
	'Pericles'	CNMi
	'Pink Petticoat' (d)	CDes
	'Pink Punch' (New Millennium Series)	ELan EPfP LHop LRHS SCob
	'Pink Ruffles'	CNMi
	'Plagu Blue'PBR	MAvo NLar
	Princess Caroline = 'Odabar'PBR	CBcs
	'Purple Passion' (New Millennium Series)	ELan EPfP LCro LRHS LSun SCob SPoG
	pylzowii	EWld
	'Red Caroline'	CBcs
	requienii	CBgR CSpe MNHC NSti
	'Rona'	CNMi
	'Rose Butterfly' (d)	LRHS
	Round Table Mixture	CTri
	'Royal Aspirations' (New Millennium Series)	ELan LHop LRHS SCob SGbt SPoG
	'Ruby'	CNMi
	'Ruby Tuesday'	CNMi
	'Ruby Wedding' **new**	CNMi

Plant	Suppliers
§ × ***ruysii*** 'Pink Sensation'	CWCL EWTr NLar
'Sandpiper'	CNMi
'Schildknappe'	EBee
'Schönbuch'	LRHS
'Secret'PBR	LRHS WCot
'Shieldbearer'	LRHS
'Silver Jubilee'	CNMi
'Sky Sensation'	IBoy LRHS
'Snow Queen Arrow'	LRHS
'Sommerabend'	LRHS
'Sommerwind' **new**	EBee
'Sooty'	CNMi
'Spindrift' 🏆H5	CNMi
stapeliosmum B&SWJ 2954	WCru
staphisagria	CArn
'Starlight'PBR	LRHS
'Strawberry Fair'	IKil LRHS NLar
Summer Skies Group	CBcs CSBt CTri CWCL ELan EPfP EWTr EWoo GJos LSun MBel MBri MGos MWat SPer SPoG WCAu WHoo
'Summerfield Diana'	CNMi
'Summerfield Oberon'	WCot
'Sungleam' 🏆H5	ECtt IKil
'Sunkissed' 🏆H5	CNMi
'Sunny Skies' (New Millennium Series)	CBod ELan LRHS SPoG
'Susan Edmunds'PBR (d)	CNMi
sutchuenense BWJ 7867	WCru
'Sweetheart'	LRHS
tatsienense	IFoB SRms
'Tiger Eye'	CNMi
tricorne	CEvo EBee
'Trudy'	CNMi
'Vanessa Mae'	CNMi
'Walton Benjamin'	CNMi
'White Swan'	EPfP
Woodfield strain	WHrl
'Yvonne'	LRHS LSRN NLar
'Zauberflöte'	EBee LRHS

Dendranthema see *Chrysanthemum*

Plant	Suppliers
pacificum	see *Ajania pacifica*

Dendriopoterium see *Sanguisorba*

Dendrobenthamia see *Cornus*

Dendrocalamus (*Poaceae*)

Plant	Suppliers
asper	XBlo
calostachys	SPlb
giganteus	XBlo
§ ***strictus***	SPlb XBlo

Dendromecon (*Papaveraceae*)

Plant	Suppliers
rigida	CBcs EPfP LRHS SKHP WPGP WSHC

Dendropanax (*Araliaceae*)

Plant	Suppliers
cf. ***kwangsiensis*** FMWJ 13274 **new**	WCru
trifidus B&SWJ 11230	WCru

Dennstaedtia (*Dennstaedtiaceae*)

Plant	Suppliers
punctilobula	CLAP

Dentaria see *Cardamine*

Plant	Suppliers
pinnata	see *Cardamine heptaphylla*
polyphylla	see *Cardamine kitaibelii*

Deparia (*Woodsiaceae*)

Plant	Suppliers
conilii **new**	NLos
okuboana	ISha

Dermatobotrys (*Scrophulariaceae*)

Plant	Suppliers
saundersii	ECre

Derwentia see *Parahebe*

Deschampsia (*Poaceae*)

Plant	Suppliers
cespitosa	CBod CKno CLet CWib EPPr EPfP LCro LOPS LPot LRHS MWat SCob SPhx SPlb WCot WMoo WWEG XLum XSen
- Bronze Veil	see *D. cespitosa* 'Bronzeschleier'
§ - 'Bronzeschleier'	CBod CMea CWCL EAEE EBee EHoe ELan EPPr EPfP GMaP LRHS MAsh MAvo MBel MBrN MBri NGdn NOak NWsh SCob SPer SPhx SRms SWvt WMoo WPtf WWEG XLum
- 'Coral Cloud'	GQue
- 'Fairy's Joke'	see *D. cespitosa* var. *vivipara*
- 'Garnet Schist'	GQue LRHS SPhx
- Gold Dust	see *D. cespitosa* 'Goldstaub'
- Golden Dew	see *D. cespitosa* 'Goldtau'
- Golden Pendant	see *D. cespitosa* 'Goldgehänge'
- Golden Shower	see *D. cespitosa* 'Goldgehänge'
- Golden Veil	see *D. cespitosa* 'Goldschleier'
§ - 'Goldgehänge'	CSam EHoe NBir WWEG XLum
§ - 'Goldschleier'	CSam EBee ECha EPPr EPfP GBin GCal GMaP GQue LHop LPal LRHS NGdn NWsh SCob SPhx SWvt WMoo XLum
§ - 'Goldstaub'	EPPr
§ - 'Goldtau'	Widely available
- 'Mill End'	CKno NDov
- 'Morning Dew'	MBri WFar
- 'Northern Lights' (v)	ELan ELon EPfP LRHS MBel MBri NBro SLim SPer SPoG SRms SWvt WPtf WWEG
- 'Pixie Fountain'	EBee EPPr GQue LHop LRHS LSun MWat NOak SPhx SPtp WWEG
- 'Schottland'	CKno ELon EPPr GBin LEdu NDov WWEG
- 'Tardiflora'	CKno EPPr
- 'Tauträger'	CKno EBee ELon EPPr GQue SMHy XLum
§ - var. ***vivipara***	EHoe EPPr GBin NBro SGSe
- 'Waldschatt'	CKno EPPr
- 'Willow Green'	GCal SCoo
flexuosa	CKno EHoe LRHS NBir NWsh SPhx
- 'Tatra Gold'	CSBt CWCL ECha EHoe ELan ELon EPfP GMaP LBMP LRHS MAsh MHtn MMuc MRav NBir NBro NGdn NOak NPri NSti SCob SGSe SLim SPer SPoG SRot SWvt WWEG
holciformis 'Marin'	CKno

Desfontainia (*Loganiaceae*)

Plant	Suppliers
§ ***spinosa*** 🏆H4	CAbb CBcs CBot CDoC CDul CMHG CMac CTri CTsd CWib EBee ELan ELon EPfP GAbr GBin GGal GKin IArd LRHS MAsh MBlu MGil MMuc SLim SPer SPoG WBod WFar WPat
- 'Harold Comber'	CMac NLar WHor
- f. ***hookeri***	see *D. spinosa*

Desmanthus (*Mimosaceae*)

illinoensis	SBrt

Desmodium (*Papilionaceae*)

callianthum	CMac LRHS SBrt WSHC
canadense	EBee MNrw NLar SBrt SPhx
cuspidatum	SPhx
var. ***longifolium***	
§ ***elegans***	CBcs CExl EBee ELan EPfP LRHS NLar SBrt SChF SKHP SVen WBod WHer WPGP WSHC
praestans	see *D. yunnanense*
tiliifolium	see *D. elegans*
§ ***yunnanense***	CExl WSHC

Deuterocohnia (*Bromeliaceae*)

brevifolia ♀H2	CFil EBee WCot WPGP
lotteae	WCot

Deutzia ✿ (*Hydrangeaceae*)

CC 4548	CExl
CC 4550	CExl
bhutanensis HWJK 2180	WCru
'Bright Eyes'	WPGP
calycosa	GQui
- B&SWJ 7742	WPat
- BWJ 8007	WCru
- 'Dali'	CDoC CExl CFil NLar SDys
chunii	see *D. ningpoensis*
compacta	CMCN SLon WPGP
- GWJ 9202	WCru
- GWJ 9203	WCru
- GWJ 9339	WCru
- 'Lavender Time'	CBot CExl CMac EMil EPfP LRHS NLar SWvt
cordatula B&SWJ 3720	WCru
- B&SWJ 6917	WCru
corymbosa	MRav
crenata	CBot
- B&SWJ 8886	WCru
- B&SWJ 8896	WCru
- B&SWJ 8924	WCru
- 'Flore Pleno'	see *D. scabra* 'Plena'
- var. ***heterotricha*** B&SWJ 5805	WCru
- - B&SWJ 8879	WCru
- var. ***nakaiana***	WPat
- - B&SWJ 11184	WCru
- - 'Nikko'	see *D. gracilis* 'Nikko'
§ - 'Pride of Rochester' (d) ♀H5	CBcs CMCN CWib EAEE ECrN GKin LRHS LSou MBlu MGos MRav NLar SCob SEle SGol SLim SPoG SWvt WGrn
'Dark Eyes'	CExl CFil SAko
discolor 'Major'	CExl CFil WPGP WPat
× ***elegantissima***	SRms
- 'Fasciculata'	CBod ELan EPfP EWTr LRHS NLar SPer SWvt WBor
- 'Rosealind' ♀H5	CBar CBcs CBot CDul CExl CMac CTri EBee ELan EPfP GKin IArd LHop LRHS LSRN LSou MGil MGos MRav SEND SLim SRms SWvt WCFE WKif WPat WSHC
glabrata B&SWJ 617	GQui WCru
- B&SWJ 8427	WCru
glomeruliflora BWJ 7742	WCru
gracilis	CBod CDoC CSBt EAEE ELan EPfP GGal GKin GQui IArd LPot LRHS MAsh MGos MRav MSwo SPad SPer SPoG WFar WHar WPat
- B&SWJ 8927	WCru
- 'Aurea'	CBcs LRHS
- 'Carminea'	see *D.* × *rosea* 'Carminea'
§ - 'Nikko' ♀H4	CBcs CBot CExl CMCN CMac CMea COtt EBee ECho ELan EShb EWes GKin LHop LRHS MAsh MGos MHer MMuc MRav NLar SGol SHil SPlb SPoG SWvt WKif WSHC
- var. ***ogatae*** B&SWJ 8911	WCru
- 'Rosea'	see *D.* × *rosea*
grandiflora	NChi WPGP
'Hillieri'	CFil
hookeriana	EBee EPfP LBuc LLHF LRHS SWvt WBod
× ***hybrida*** 'Contraste' ♀H5	CMac SPer
- 'Iris Alford'	CDoC CExl EPfP LRHS MBri MGos SAko SChF SHil SLon WFar WPGP
- 'Joconde' ♀H5	CExl WFar
- 'Magicien' Lemoine	Widely available
- 'Mont Rose' ♀H5	Widely available
§ - 'Strawberry Fields' ♀H5	Widely available
× ***kalmiiflora***	CExl CJun CMac CSBt CTri GBin GKin GQui MAsh MJak MRav NLar SPer SRms WFar WPat
× ***lemoinei***	MJak
longifolia	CMCN WPGP WPat
- 'Veitchii'	CSBt GQui MGil MRav
- 'Vilmoriniae'	MRav
× ***magnifica***	CBcs CDul GQui NLar SGbt SRms
- 'Nancy'	GKin
- 'Rubra'	see *D.* × *hybrida* 'Strawberry Fields'
× ***maliflora***	CFil
maximowicziana B&SWJ 11567	WCru
monbeigii ♀H5	CBot CDoC CExl CFil EPfP LLHF LRHS MRav SWvt WKif
- BWJ 7728	CBot WCru
multiradiata	CExl CFil WPGP
§ ***ningpoensis***	CExl CFil CTsd EPfP EWTr GQui MNHC NLar SPer WBor WCFE WPGP WPat
paniculata B&SWJ 8592	WCru
parviflora var. ***barbinervis*** B&SWJ 8478	WCru
'Pink Pompon'	see *D.* 'Rosea Plena'
prunifolia B&SWJ 8588	WCru
pulchra	CAbP CBot CDoC CDul CMCN EPfP EWTr IDee LCro LRHS MRav SLon SPer SPoG SSpi WPGP WPat
- B&SWJ 1738 new	WCru
- B&SWJ 3870	WCru
- B&SWJ 6908	WCru
- pink-tinged	WPGP
purpurascens BWJ 7859	WCru
- 'Alpine Magician'	COtt
rehderiana	CFil
§ × ***rosea***	CDul CWib EPfP LAst LRHS MAsh SRms WKif
- 'Campanulata'	CExl MAsh MSwo
§ - 'Carminea'	SDix SPlb SRms WPat
§ 'Rosea Plena' (d)	CBot CDoC CExl CLet CMac CSBt CWib ECrN ELan EPfP GKin LBuc LRHS MAsh MGos NLar SEle SLim SWvt WFar WPat
rubens	LLHF WPat
scabra	CDul CTri
- B&SWJ 11127	WCru
- B&SWJ 11168	WCru

- B&SWJ 11178 WCru
§ - 'Candidissima' (d) 🏆H5 CDul CMac GQui MGil MRav SCob SPer WPat
- 'Codsall Pink' 🏆H5 CFil MRav
§ - 'Plena' (d) CExl ECrN ELan EPfP GKin NLar SPer SPoG WCFE
- 'Pride of Rochester' see *D. crenata* 'Pride of Rochester'
- 'Punctata' (v) EHoe MAsh MMuc SEND SRms
- 'Robert Fortune' SPlb
- 'Variegata' (v) CDul CMac
setchuenensis CMac GQui MRav SSpi WPat WSHC
- NJM 11.096 **new** WPGP
- PAB 7449 LEdu
- var. ***corymbiflora*** 🏆H5 CBcs CBot CDoC CDul CExl CSam CTri ECre EPfP EWTr IArd IDee LHop LRHS MSwo NLar SAko SChF SPoG SWvt WFar WKif WPGP
taiwanensis EPfP SAko SGol WPGP WPat
- B&SWJ 6858 WCru
- CWJ 12443 WCru
- CWJ 12459 WCru
* ***vidalii*** GGal
× ***wellsii*** see *D. scabra* 'Candidissima'
× ***wilsonii*** SRms

Dianella ✿ (*Hemerocallidaceae*)

brevicaulis ECou
caerulea CBcs CMac EAla EBee ECou ELan EPri IBoy IMou MOWG NBir NLar
- 'Caspar Blue' LPal
- Cassa Blue = 'Dbb03'PBR CBod CHll CLet EPfP LRHS MSpe SPad SPer
- 'Kulnura' ECou
- Little Jess = 'Dcmp01'PBR CExl EBee
- 'Variegata' see *D. tasmanica* 'Variegata'
ensifolia LEdu
nigra CBcs CExl ECou IMou LEdu LTro
- 'Margaret Pringle' (v) CBcs CExl ECou SEND
revoluta ECou
- Little Rev = 'Dr5000'PBR EAla EBee EPfP ESwi
'Silver Streak' (v) LRHS
tasmanica CAbb CBcs CCon CDoC CElw CExl CKno CMac CPne CTal CTri CTsd ECou ECre ELan EPfP EShb EUJe GBin GGal LEdu LHop LPal LTro MOWG SGSe SMad SRms WSHC
- from Logan EBee GCal
- 'Emerald Arch' ELan ESwi LEdu SPer
- 'Prosser' ECou
- 'Splice' **new** MJak
- Tasred = 'Tr20'PBR CBod CDoC CExl CTsd ELan EPfP ESwi EUJe NPla SPer
§ - 'Variegata' (v) CDTJ CExl ECou ELan LHop NLar SEND SGSe

Dianthus ✿ (*Caryophyllaceae*)

sp. SVic
AC&W 2116 ECtt
'Alan Titchmarsh' (p) CWCL CWhe ECtt EPfP LRHS LSRN MGos MTis NCGa NEgg SBod SPoG SWvt
'Albert Hill' (p) LAll
'Aldridge Yellow' (b) LAll
'Alfriston' (b) 🏆H6 LAll
'Alice' (p) LAll LSRN
'Alice Lever' (p) WAbe
§ 'Allen's Maria' (p) LAll
'Allspice' (p) CFis MRav WHoo
Allwoodii Group (p) NNor
- 'Doris' (p) CWhe SHil
Allwoodii Alpinus Group (p) NGdn SRms XLum
- 'Wink' (p) **new** NPri
'Allwood's Celebration' (p) LAll
'Allwood's Crimson' (pf) LAll
'Allwood's Delight' (p) LAll
alpinus 🏆H6 GCrg GJos ITim NSla
- 'Albus' (p) GCrg NWad SIgm
- 'Joan's Blood' (p) 🏆H6 ECho GBuc GCrg LSRN WAbe
'Alyson' (p) LAll
amurensis CBar ECho EPPr GCal LPla MLHP NNor SPhx WSHC XLum
- 'Andrey' (p) NNor
anatolicus CTri ECho EDAr LRHS MHer NGdn XLum
'Anders Cream Princess' (pf) CNMi
'Anders Fay Seagrave' (p) LAll
'Anders Irene Ann' (pf) CNMi
'Anders Kath Phillips' (pf) 🏆H2 CNMi
'Anders Melody' (p) LAll
'Anders Patricia Griffiths' (p) CNMi LAll
'Andrew Morton' (b) LAll
'Angela Carol' (pf) CNMi
'Angelo' (b) LAll
'Ann Franklin' (pf) 🏆H2 CNMi
'Annabelle' (p) LAll
'Annette' (p) CWhe EAJP ECho EDAr GCrg GEdr IPot LRHS LSRN MAsh NGdn NHol SRGP SWvt
'Annie Claybourne' (pf) CNMi
'Apricot Sue' (pf) CNMi LAll
Arctic Star see *D.* 'Devon Arctic Star'
arenarius CCon LAll LEdu NGdn SPhx SPlb XLum
- 'Little Maiden' (p) CSpe GEdr NCGa NGdn WIce WPtf
- 'Snow Flurries' ITim
'Argus' LAll
armeria CBgR CFis WHer WOut
arpadianus GKev
'Arthur Leslie' (b) LAll
§ × ***arvernensis*** (p) 🏆H6 ECha ECho EPot NPri SBch
- 'Albus' ECho
'Audrey Robinson' (pf) CNMi
'Aurora' (b) LAll
'Auvergne' see *D.* × *arvernensis*
'Averiensis' see *D.* 'Berlin Snow'
'Badenia' (p) ECha
'Bailey's Celebration' (p) CWhe MTis NCGa SRGP WMnd
'Barbara Norton' (p) ECtt
barbatus MNrw SVic
- SDR 6404 GKev
- 'Black Adder' CSpe
I - 'Darkest of All' EBee MMuc SEND
- 'Heart Attack' (p) WCot
- 'Indian Carpet' (p,a) LCro
- Midget Group (p,a) CBod
- 'Monksilver Black' (p,a) CAby CSpe ECtt MHol MPie SBod SMad WCot WRHF
- Nigrescens Group (p,a) 🏆H7 CBre CMea CSpe SPhx
I - 'Sooty' (p,a) CBod CTsd CWCL CWld EDAr MSCN
- 'Super Parfait Strawberry' (Super Parfait Series) LRHS
- 'Tuxedo Black' WMoo
'Barley Sugar' (pf) CNMi
basuticus CTre GKev
§ 'Bat's Double Red' (p) LAll
'Becky Robinson' (p) 🏆H6 CNMi LAll

	Name	Suppliers
	'Belmont Duchess' (p)	LAll
§	'Berlin Snow' (p)	CPBP ECho EPot GCrg ITim LRHS
	'Betsy' (pf)	LAll
	'Betty Miller' (b)	LAll
	'Betty Morton' (p) 🏆H6	ECtt IFoB WKif
	'Betty's Choice' (pf)	CNMi
	'Bill Smith' (pf)	CNMi
	'Blue Hills' (p)	ECho GKev
	'Blue Ice' (b)	LAll
	'Blush'	see *D.* 'Souvenir de la Malmaison'
	'Bobby' (p)	LAll
	'Bob's Highlight' (pf)	CNMi
	'Bombardier' (p)	NPri
	'Bookham Gleam' (b)	LAll
	'Bookham Grand' (b)	LAll
	'Bookham Heroine' (b)	LAll
	'Bookham Lad' (b)	LAll
	'Border Special' (b)	LAll
	'Bouquet Purple' (p)	CSpe
	'Bovey Belle' (p)	LAll
	'Bramdean' (pf)	CNMi
	brevicaulis subsp. ***brevicaulis***	LLHF
	'Brian Tumbler' (b) 🏆H6	LAll
	'Bridal Veil' (p)	LAll SBch WHer
	Bright Eyes = 'Wp07 Ame02'PBR (p) **new**	CWhe
	'Briljant'PBR **new**	CWhe
	'Brilliance' (p)	MSCN WMoo
	'Brilliant'	see *D. deltoides* 'Brilliant'
	'Brilliant Star' (p) 🏆H6	CWhe ECho ECtt LRHS MWat SEND SWvt WIce
	'Brockenhurst' (pf)	CNMi
	'Brympton Red' (p)	CFis ECha LAll
	'Bryony Lisa' (b) 🏆H6	LAll
	caesius	see *D. gratianopolitanus*
	callizonus	LLHF
	'Calypso' (pf)	CTri
	'Calypso Star' (p)	ECho ECtt SPoG
	'Camilla' (b)	CNMi
	'Can-can' (pf)	ECho ECtt MHol
	'Candy Clove' (b)	LAll
	Candy Floss	see *D.* 'Devon Flavia'
	'Candy Spice' (p)	MRav
	'Carbrooke Village' (p)	SGSe
§	'Carmine Letitia Wyatt'PBR (p) 🏆H6	CWhe ECtt LRHS NCGa SPoG
	Carmine Valda	see *D.* 'Devon Louise'
	carthusianorum	Widely available
	- W&B BGL-1 **new**	WCot
I	- 'Rupert's Pink' (p)	EBee NGdn SWvt
	caryophyllus	ENfk SVic WSFF
	Cassandra = 'Bardranasca' (pf)	LAll
	Cecil Wyatt	'Rose Devon Pearl'
	'Charles' (p)	LAll
	'Charles Edward' (p)	LAll
	'Charles Musgrave'	see *D.* 'Musgrave's Pink'
	'Chastity' (p)	LAll LLHF WHoo
	Cheddar pink	see *D. gratianopolitanus*
	'Cherly'	LSRN
	'Cherry Clove' (b)	LAll
	Cherry Sundae = 'Wp05 Enid' **new**	CWhe
	'Cheryl'	see *D.* 'Houndspool Cheryl'
	'Chesswood Dorothy Cottam' (b)	LAll
	'Chetwyn Ruth Gillies' (pf)	CNMi
	'Chianti Double' (p)	LAll
	chinensis 'Black and White' (p,a)	CSpe
I	- 'Valentine' (p,a)	LAll
	'Chris Crew' (b) 🏆H6	LAll
	'Christopher' (p)	LAll
	'Citrien'PBR (pf)	LRHS
	'Clare' (p)	LAll
	'Claret Joy' (p) 🏆H6	ECtt EPfP LAll MMuc SEND
	'Clifford Pipperoo' (pf)	LAll
	'Clunie' (b)	LAll
§	'Cockenzie Pink' (p)	LAll SBch WHer
	Coconut Sundae = 'Wp 05 Yves'PBR (Scent First Series) (p)	CWhe ECtt ELan ELon EPfP GBin LCro LOPS LRHS LSRN MCot NNor NPri SRot
	'Constance' (p)	LAll
	'Constance Finnis'	see *D.* 'Fair Folly'
	'Consul' (b)	LAll
	'Conwy Silver' (p)	WAbe
	'Conwy Star' (p)	CPBP WAbe
	'Coral Reef'PBR (Scent First Series) (p)	CWhe ECtt ELan LCro LOPS LRHS MTis NNor NPri SPoG
	'Coronation Ruby' (p) 🏆H6	LAll
	'Coste Budde' (p)	WSHC
	Cracker = 'Wp10 Sab06'PBR (Early Bird Series) (p)	CWhe GAbr NPri
	'Cranberry Crush' (pf) **new**	CNMi
	'Cranberry Ice' (p) **new**	CWhe
	'Cranmere Pool' (p) 🏆H6	CBcs CWhe ECtt ELan EPfP LAst LRHS NNor SEND SPoG SWvt WRHF WWEG
	'Cream Sue' (pf)	CNMi
	Crimson Valda	see *D.* 'Devon Kitty'
	'Crimson Warrior' (pf)	CNMi
	'Crock of Gold' (b)	LAll
	'Crompton Classic' (pf)	CNMi
	'Crompton Princess' (pf)	CNMi
	cruentus	CAby CSpe LCro LRHS MBel NDov SHar SPhx SPtp SWvt WCAu WPtf WWEG
	'D.D.R.'	see *D.* 'Berlin Snow'
	'Dad's Favourite' (p)	CFis LAll WHer
	'Dainty Dame' (p) 🏆H4	CSpe CTal CTri ECho EPfP LAll LRHS MNHC SBch WBod
§	'Dancing Queen'PBR (p)	CWhe MTis MWat NNor
	'Daphne' (p)	LAll
	'David' (p)	LAll LSRN SCob
	'David Russell' (b) 🏆H6	LAll
	'David Saunders' (b) 🏆H6	LAll
	'Dawn' (b)	LAll
*	'Dazzler'	NPri
	'Dedham Beauty'	MPie SEND WCot WWEG
	deltoides 🏆H6	CTre CWld ECha ECho ENfk EPfP LEdu MAsh MBel MMuc MNHC SPlb SRms WJek WPtf
	- 'Albus' (p)	ECha EPfP MSCN NGdn WMoo
	- 'Arctic Fire' (p)	CWib ECho EPfP GJos MBel NGdn NHol WMoo
	- 'Bright Eyes' (p)	ECho MWat
§	- 'Brilliant' (p)	CTri EAJP ECho GJos LAll LAst NGdn NHol SPhx SRms
	- 'Broughty Blaze'	GCrg
	- 'Canta Libra'	MLHP
	- 'Dark Eyes' (p)	EWes
	- 'Erectus' (p)	EPfP
	- Flashing Light	see *D. deltoides* 'Leuchtfunk'
§	- 'Leuchtfunk' (p)	ECho GJos LAst MJak NNor NPri SPoG WMoo WRHF
I	- 'Luneburg Heath Maiden Pink' (p)	NGdn SPhx
	- Microchips Group (p)	WMoo

	Name	Suppliers
	- 'Nelli' (p)	NGdn WMoo
	- red-flowered (p)	SVic
	- 'Shrimp' (p)	EAJP NGdn
	'Dennis' (p)	LAll LSRN
	'Desert Song' (b)	LAll
	'Desmond'	EPfP
§	'Devon Arctic Star' (p)	CMea CTri CWhe ECho ELan EWTr EWoo GBin GMaP LAst LHop LRHS NPri SPoG SRms SRot SWvt
	'Devon Cream'[PBR] (p)	CWhe ECtt ELan LAst LRHS MWat NEgg WMnd
	'Devon Dove'[PBR] (p) ♀[H6]	CMea CSBt CTri CWhe ECGP ECtt ELan EPfP LRHS MRav MTis MWat NCGa NEgg
	'Devon Esther'	see *D.* Pop Star
	'Devon Fatima'	see *D.* Iced Gem
§	'Devon Flavia'[PBR] (Scent First Series) (p) ♀[H6]	CWhe ELan EPfP GBin LAst LCro LOPS LRHS LSou MTis SPoG
	'Devon General'[PBR] (p)	CTri CWhe
	'Devon Glow' (p)	EPfP
§	'Devon Isolde'[PBR] (p) **new**	CWhe
§	'Devon Judith'[PBR] (p) **new**	CWhe
§	'Devon Kitty'[PBR] (p) **new**	CWhe
§	'Devon Louise'[PBR] (p) **new**	CWhe
	'Devon Magic'[PBR] (p)	CWhe ECtt ELan LRHS
	'Devon Opal'	see *D.* Lady Madonna
	'Devon Pearl'[PBR] (p)	CWhe
§	Devon Sapphire = 'Wp 05 Safire' (p) ♀[H6]	CMea CWhe ELan EWoo IPot MTis WIce
§	'Devon Siskin' (p)	CWhe
	'Devon Verity'	see *D.* 'Dancing Queen'
§	'Devon Winnie'[PBR]	CWhe MAsh MTis
	'Devon Wizard'[PBR] (p) ♀[H6]	CSBt CWhe ECtt EPfP LAst LRHS MRav MSpe MTis NCGa NDov NEgg NNor SBod SEND WCAu
§	'Devon Xera' (p) ♀[H6]	CTal CWhe MTis SRms
§	'Devon Yolande'[PBR] (Scent First Series) (p) **new**	CWhe ELon LCro LOPS
	'Devon Yvette'	CWhe
	'Devon Zane' (p) **new**	CWhe
	'Dewdrop' (p)	CMea CTri ECho LAll MAsh MHer MMuc NBir NGdn SBch SEND WHal
	'Diana'	see *D.* Dona
	'Diane' (p) ♀[H6]	CWhe ELan EPfP LAll LPal NEgg SPoG SWvt WHar WMnd
	'Dian Cape' (b)	LAll
	'Diplomat' (b)	LAll
	'Doctor James Dennison' (pf)	CNMi
§	Dona = 'Brecas' (pf)	LSRN SRGP
	'Dora' (p)	ECho LRHS
	'Doreen Hodgson' (p)	LAll
	'Doris' (p) ♀[H6]	Widely available
	'Doris Allwood' (pf)	CNMi CSBt EMal LAll
	'Doris Elite' (p)	LAll
	'Doris Galbally' (b)	LAll
	'Doris Majestic' (p)	LAll
	'Doris Ruby'	see *D.* 'Houndspool Ruby'
	'Doris Supreme' (p)	LAll
	'Dorset' (pf) **new**	CNMi
	'Double Lace'	ECtt
	Dubai = 'Bardibua' (pf)	LAll
	'Dubarry' (p)	CTri ECtt
	'Duchess of Fife' (p)	EPfP
	'Duchess of Roxburghe' (pf)	EMal LAll
	'Duchess of Westminster' (M)	EMal LAll
	'Duke of Norfolk' (pf)	EMal LAll
	'Dunkirk Spirit' (pf)	CNMi
	'Dusky Janelle' (pf)	CNMi
	'Earl Kelso' (pf)	EMal
	'Earl of Essex' (p)	LAll
	'Edenside Scarlet' (b)	LAll
	'Edenside White' (b)	LAll
	'Edna' (p)	LAll
	'Edward Allwood' (pf)	LAll
	'Edwin Cross' (b)	LAll
	'Eileen' (p)	LAll
	'Eileen Lever' (p)	CPBP IFoB MWat WAbe
	'Eileen Neal' (b) ♀[H6]	LAll
	'Eileen O'Connor' (b) ♀[H6]	LAll
	'Eira Wen' (p)	CWhe WAbe
	'Eleanor Parker' (p)	WAbe
	'Eleanor's Old Irish' (p)	ECtt ELon LRHS MBel MHol MPie NDov SEND WCot WHoo WMnd WWEG
	'Elizabethan' (p)	CFis CSpe EWTr MCot SDys
*	'Elizabethan Pink' (p)	LAll
	'Elsie Ketchen' (pf)	CNMi
	'Emile Paré' (p)	CFis
	'Emjay' (b)	LAll
	'Emmeline Pankhurst' (pf)	CNMi
	'Emperor'	see *D.* 'Bat's Double Red'
	erinaceus	ECho EPot GCrg GJos
	- var. ***alpinus***	EPot GBin ITim
	- Duguid's	WAbe WThu
	'Erycina' (b)	LAll
	'Ethel Hurford' (p)	WHoo
	'Eva Humphries' (b)	LAll
	'Evelyn Berry' (p)	CNMi
	'Evening Star' (p) ♀[H6]	CTri CWhe ECho EWoo GBin LRHS SPoG SWvt WIce
	'Eve's Holly' (pf)	CNMi
	'Exquisite' (b)	LAll
§	'Fair Folly' (p)	LAll WHer
	'Farnham Rose' (p)	LAll
	'Fenbow Nutmeg Clove' (b)	SDix
	'Fettes Mount' (p)	LPla WCot
	'Feuerhexe' (p)	ECtt GCrg
	'Fimbriatus' (p)	WHoo
	'Fiona' (p)	LAll
	Fire Star	see *D.* 'Devon Xera'
	'Firestar' (p)	CTri ELan GMaP LRHS MAsh MWat SHil SRot SWvt
	'First Lady' (b)	LAll
	Fizzy = 'Wp08 Ver03'[PBR] (Early Bird Series) (p)	CMea CTal CWhe ELan EPfP LBMP LRHS MHol NPri SHil
	'Flanders' (b) ♀[H6]	LAll
	'Flashdance' (pf)	CNMi
	'Fleur' (p)	LAll
	'Florence Franklin' (pf)	CNMi
	'Floristan Mix' (p,a)	NNor
	'Forest Princess' (b)	LAll
	'Forest Sprite' (b)	LAll
	'Forest Treasure' (b)	LAll
	'Forest Violet' (b)	LAll
	'Forge Pink'	LLHF
	'Fortuna' (p)	LAll
	'Fragrant Ann' (pf) ♀[H6]	CNMi EMal LAll
	'Fragrant Phyllis' (pf)	CNMi
	'Frances Isabel' (p)	LAll
	'Frank Bruno' (pf)	CNMi
	'Freda' (p)	LAll
	'Freda Woodliffe' (p)	ECtt GCrg SBch WAbe
	freynii	ECho EPot EWes GKev WAbe
*	- var. ***nana***	GKev
*	'Frilly'	LBMP LRHS SHil

Plant	Suppliers
Frilly = 'Wp08 Ulr03'PBR (Early Bird Series) (p)	CWhe NPri
fringed pink	see *D. superbus*
furcatus	GKev SIgm
'Fusilier' (p)	CBod CTri CWhe EAJP ECho ECtt EDAr EPfP GAbr GBuc GCrg GMaP LAll LHop LRHS MAsh NPri SEND SHar SRot SWvt WRHF
'Gail Graham' (b)	LAll
'Gail Tilsley' (b)	LAll
'Garland' (p)	CTri
'Gaydena' (b)	LAll
giganteus	WSHC
'Gingham Gown' (p)	ECtt EPot LAll NBir
* ***glacialis elegans***	GKev
'Gold Dust' (p)	ECtt EPot EWTr LAll SBch
'Gold Embrace' (pf)	CNMi
'Golden Cross' (b) ♀H6	LAll
'Grace's Scarlet Clove' (b)	LAll
'Grandma Calvert' (p)	LAll
graniticus	EPot
'Gran's Favourite' (p) ♀H6	Widely available
§ ***gratianopolitanus*** ♀H6	CArn CBod CPBP CTri CWld EDAr ENfk EPfP EPot GJos LAll LEdu MHer MNHC MRav NBid
- 'Albus'	MHer
- 'Babi Lom'	GCrg
- dwarf	SIgm WAbe
- 'Grandiflorus'	SPhx
- 'Rosenfeder' (p)	SPhx
§ - 'Tiny Rubies' (p)	CTal EDAr GCrg SDys WAbe
'Greensides' (p)	LAll
'Grey Dove' (b) ♀H6	LAll
'Gypsy Star' (p)	ECho SPoG
haematocalyx 'Alpinus'	see *D. haematocalyx* subsp. *pindicola*
§ - subsp. ***pindicola***	LLHF NSla WAbe
'Hamish Berry' (p) **new**	CNMi
'Hampshire' (pf) **new**	CNMi
'Hannah Gertsen' (p)	LAll
'Hannah Louise' (b) ♀H6	LAll
'Harkell Special' (b)	LAll
'Hayden' (pf)	CNMi
'Hayley's Choice' (b)	LAll
'Haytor Rock' (p) ♀H6	CWhe EPfP MTis NCGa NNor WGwG
Haytor	see *D.* 'Haytor White'
§ 'Haytor White' (p) ♀H6	CBcs CTri CWhe CWib EPfP LAll SCob WWEG
'Hazel Ruth' (b) ♀H6	LAll
'Heath' (p)	LAll
'Helen' (p)	ELon LAll LSRN
'Helena Hitchcock' (p)	LAll
'Herbert's Pink' (p)	SPhx
'Hercules' (pf)	CNMi
'Hereford Butter Market' (p)	EBee
'Hidcote' (p)	CTri LLHF LRHS SIgm
'Hidcote Red' (p)	ECho
'Highland Fraser' (p)	WKif
Highland Group (p)	SGbt
'Hope' (p)	LAll SBch
'Hot Spice' (p)	SPoG
§ 'Houndspool Cheryl' (p) ♀H6	CBcs CTri CWhe EPfP LAll SRGP
§ 'Houndspool Ruby' (p) ♀H6	CBcs CWhe EPfP LAll LSRN
'Ian' (p)	LAll LSRN
§ Iced Gem = 'Wp06 Fatima'PBR (Scent First Series) (p)	CWhe ELan ELon EPfP LHop LRHS LSRN LSou MTis NNor NPri SHil SPoG SRot
'Icomb' (p)	WHoo
'Inchmery' (p)	LAll LRHS WHer
'India Star'PBR (p) ♀H6	CTri CWhe EPfP LRHS MTis MWat NEgg SEND SRms SRot WIce
'Inglestone' (p)	CTri
'Inshriach Dazzler' (p) ♀H6	CPBP ECho ECtt GCrg GMaP LLHF LRHS MAsh MHer NEgg NHar NHol SRot WAbe WHal
'Irene Della-Torré' (b) ♀H6	LAll
'Janelle Welch' (pf)	CNMi
'Janet Walker' (p)	GMaP
'Jess Hewins' (pf)	CNMi LAll
'Joanne' (pf)	CNMi
'Joanne's Highlight' (pf)	CNMi
'Joy' (p) ♀H6	CWhe EPfP LAll LAst SPoG
'Julian' (p)	LAll
'Julie Ann Davis' (b)	LAll
'Julie Martin' (pf) **new**	CNMi
'Just Jodie' (pf) **new**	CNMi
'Kathleen Hitchcock' (b) ♀H6	LAll
'Kelly's Kiss' (p) **new**	CNMi
'Kent' (pf) **new**	CNMi
'Kessock Charm' (p)	MNrw
'Kesteven Chamonix' (p)	SBch
'Kesteven Kirkstead' (p) ♀H6	LAll MNrw
'Kim' (p)	NDov
'King of the Blacks' (p,a)	CWld
knappii	CFis SPhx WHer XLum
- 'Yellow Harmony' (p,a)	LAll MLHP
'La Bourboule' (p) ♀H6	CMea CTri ECho ECtt EDAr GAbr GCrg GEdr GMaP LRHS MWat NPri
'La Bourboule Alba' (p) ♀H5	CTri ECho ECtt GCrg MAsh
'Laced Joy' (p)	LAll
'Laced Monarch' (p)	CBcs CWhe ECtt ELan EPfP GCra LAll LHop LRHS MCot MMuc NCGa NEgg NNor SEND SPlb SPoG WGwG
'Laced Mrs Sinkins' (p)	CNMi LAll
'Laced Prudence'	see *D.* 'Prudence'
'Laced Romeo' (p)	LAll
'Laced Treasure' (p)	LAll
'Lady Granville' (p)	LAll MHCG SBch
Lady in Red = 'Wp04 Xanthe'PBR (p)	CSBt CWhe ECtt ELan EPfP LRHS MTis NNor
§ Lady Madonna = 'Wp04 Opal'PBR (p) ♀H6	CWhe ELan
'Lady Wharncliffe' (p)	SBch
'Lady Windermere' (M)	EMal LAll
'Lancing Monarch' (b)	LAll
'Lancing Supreme' (p)	LAll
'Langford Manor' (pf)	CNMi
'Langport Lady' (pt) **new**	CNMi
'Laura' (p)	LAll
'Layla Jane' (p)	CNMi
'Leatham Pastel' (pf)	CNMi
'Lemsii' (p) ♀H6	NGdn
'Leslie Rennison' (b)	LAll
'Letitia Wyatt' (p) ♀H6	CMea CWhe LRHS MWat SBch SPoG SRGP
'Leuchtkugel' (p)	CPBP ECho LLHF WAbe
'Lily Lesurf' (b)	LAll
Lily the Pink = 'Wp05 Idare'PBR (p) ♀H6	CWhe ELan LRHS
'Lime Crush' (pf)	CNMi
'Linfield Annie's Fancy' (pf)	CNMi
'Linfield Doreen Ashmore' (p)	LAll

'Linfield Dorothy Perry' (p) ♀H6	LAll
'Linfield Isobel Croft' (p)	LAll
'Linfield Julie' (p)	LAll
'Linfield Kathy Booker' (p) ♀H6	LAll
'Linfield Pink Margaret' (p)	CNMi LAll
'Little Ben' (p)	LAll
'Little Jock' (p)	ECho ECtt EDAr EPot GCrg GEdr LAll LRHS MAsh MHer MWat NPri SBch SPlb
'Liz Rigby' (b)	LAll
'London Brocade' (p)	LAll
'London Glow' (p)	LAll
'London Lovely' (p)	LAll
'London Poppet' (p)	LAll
'Lord Nuffield' (b)	LAll
lumnitzeri	XLum
'Lustre' (b)	LAll
'Madonna' (pf)	WHer
'Maggie' (p)	LSRN
'Maisie Neal' (b) ♀H6	LAll
'Mandy' (p)	LAll
'Manon des Sources' (pf)	CNMi
'Margaret Taylor' (p)	LAll
'Maria'	see *D.* 'Allen's Maria'
'Marielle' (pf)	LAll
'Marilyn's Highlight' (pf) **new**	CNMi
'Marjery Breeze' (p)	LAll
'Marmion' (M)	EMal LAll
'Mars' (p)	ECho
'Ma's Choice' (p)	LAll
'Matthew' (p)	WHoo
'Maudie Hinds' (b)	LAll
'Maxine' (pf)	CNMi
'Maybole' (b)	LAll
'Maybush' (pf)	CNMi
Memories = 'WP11 Gwe04' (Scent First Series) (p)	CWhe LBuc LCro LRHS MCot MTis WCot
'Mendip Hills' (b)	LAll
Mendlesham Minx = 'Russmin'PBR (p)	CTal CWhe ECho EDAr ELan EPfP LAll LAst LRHS MTis NPri SRms SWvt
Merlin	see *D.* 'Devon Siskin'
'Messines Pink' (p)	LAll
'Michael Saunders' (b) ♀H6	LAll
microlepis	ECho EDAr GKev NGdn NSla WAbe
- f. ***albus***	NSla
- ED 791562	NGdn
- var. ***musalae***	ECho LLHF
- 'Rivendell' (p)	ECho WAbe
'Mike Briggs' (b)	LAll
'Miss Farrow' (p)	LRHS SPhx
'Miss Sinkins' (p)	CTri IFoB
Mojácar = 'Barjamocar' (pf)	LAll
'Monica Wyatt' (p) ♀H6	CBcs CWhe ECtt ELan EPfP LRHS NCGa NEgg SPoG
'Montrose Pink'	see *D.* 'Cockenzie Pink'
'Monty Allwood' (p)	LAll
'Monty's Pink' (pf) **new**	EMal
'Moor Editha' (p)	CNMi
Morning Star	see *D.* 'Devon Winnie'
'Morrissey' (pf) **new**	CNMi
Mother of Pearl = 'Wp10 Ele04'PBR (Perfume Pinks Series) (p)	CWhe ELan EPfP LRHS
'Mottisfont Pink' **new**	NWad
'Moulin Rouge' (p) ♀H6	CTri CWCL CWhe ECtt ELan EPfP GAbr GCra LHop LRHS MTis NDov SPoG
'Mrs Macbride' (p)	LAll
'Mrs Roxburgh' (p)	CSam
'Mrs Sinkins' (p)	Widely available
'Musgrave's Pink' (p)	CFis ECha EWTr LAll MRav
'Musgrave's White'	see *D.* 'Musgrave's Pink'
myrtinervius	CCon ECho EDAr MHtn NGdn
'Mystic Dawn' (b)	LAll
Mystic Star	see *D.* Devon Sapphire
'Napoleon III' (p)	LAll
nardiformis	XLum
'Natalie Saunders' (b) ♀H6	LAll
'Nautilus' (b)	LAll
neglectus misapplied	see *D. pavonius*
'Neon Star'PBR (p) ♀H6	CTri CWhe ECho EDAr ELan GBuc GKev LRHS MTis MWat NPri SHil SPoG SRms SRot
'Night Star' (p) ♀H6	ECho ELan EPfP EUJe EWoo GBin GKev GMaP LHop LPot LRHS NEgg SBch SEND SRot WPtf
nivalis	GKev
noeanus	see *D. petraeus* subsp. *noeanus*
'Nomie' (pf)	CNMi
'Northland' (pf)	CNMi EMal LAll
'Nyewoods Cream' (p)	CMea CTri ECho EPot GCrg MHer NGdn NHar NPri NWad SBch
§ 'Oakington' (p)	CTri GCrg
'Oakington Rose'	see *D.* 'Oakington'
'Oakwood Erin Mitchell' (p)	CNMi
'Oakwood Sweetheart' (p)	LAll
'Odessa Red' (Odessa Series) (pt) **new**	LRHS
'Old Blush'	see *D.* 'Souvenir de la Malmaison'
'Old French Red' (pf)	EMal
'Old Red Clove' (p)	CAby ECtt GAbr LSun MBel MCot MHol MPie NDov NSti SBch WCot
§ 'Old Square Eyes' (p)	LAll MNrw SHar
'Old Velvet' (p)	GCal LAll MNrw WHoo
'Oliver' (p)	LAll
'Orange Maid' (b)	LAll
'Oscar' (b)	LRHS
'Owston Third Avenue' (p)	LAll
'Oxford Magic' (p)	LAll
'Painted Lady' (p)	LAll
'Paisley Gem' (p)	LAll
Passion = 'Wp Passion'PBR (Scent First Series) (p)	CWhe EBee ECtt ELan EPfP GBin LRHS LSou MBel MCot MHer MHol MPie MTis MWat NNor SAko SEND SHil SPoG WCot
§ ***pavonius***	EWes NGdn NSla SIgm
'Peach' (p)	SEND
'Pendle Doris Delight' (p)	LAll
'Pennine Reflections' (b)	LAll
'Peter Wood' (b) ♀H6	LAll
§ ***petraeus***	EWes NGdn WThu
§ - subsp. ***noeanus***	LHop LLHF WHal
'Petticoat Lace' (p)	LAll
'Phantom' (b)	LAll
'Pheasant's Eye' (p)	LAll WHer
* 'Picton's Propeller' (p)	GBuc GCal
Pierrot = 'Kobusa' (pf)	CNMi
'Pike's Pink' (p) ♀H6	CSpe CTal CTri ECho EDAr ELan EPfP EPot EWTr EWoo GCrg LAll LHop LRHS MAsh MHer MMuc MWat NBir NGdn NPri SEND
pindicola	see *D. haematocalyx* subsp. *pindicola*

pinifolius SBrt
'Pink Devon Pearl'[PBR] CWhe
'Pink Doris' (pf) CNMi
'Pink Fantasy' (b) LAll
Pink Fizz = 'Wp10 Xav04'[PBR] (Scent First Series)(p) CWhe LRHS
'Pink Jewel' (p) CMea CPBP ECha EDAr EPot GKev LAll LCro LOPS MAsh MNHC NPri SBch
'Pink Mrs Sinkins' (p) LAll MHer MLHP MNrw
'Pink Pearl' (b) LAll
Pink Valda see *D.* 'Devon Judith'
'Pixie' (b) EPot NPri
'Pixie Star'[PBR] (p) ♀H6 CWhe ECho EPfP NPri SPoG SRot WIce
plumarius CArn IFro LAll MLHP WHer XLum
- 'Albiflorus' XLum
- subsp. ***praecox*** **new** CPBP
pontederae NDov
§ Pop Star = 'Wp04 Esther'[PBR] (p) CTal CWhe MTis SGbt SRms
'Pretty' (p) LAll
Pretty Flamingo see *D.* 'Carmine Letitia Wyatt'
'Prince Charming' (p) ECho MAsh
'Princess of Wales' (M) EMal LAll
'Priory Pink' (p) LAll
§ 'Prudence' (p) LAll
'Pudsey Prize' (p) CPBP EPot
'Purple Frosted' (pf) EMal
'Purple Jenny' (p) LAll
'Queen of Hearts' (p) CTri ECho SEND
§ 'Queen of Henri' (p) EBee ECho LRHS
'Queen of Sheba' (p) LAll SBch WHer WHoo WKif
'Rachel' (p) LAll
'Raggio di Sole' (pf) CNMi
'Rainbow Loveliness' (p,a) LAll WOut
'Ralph Gould' (p) ECho
'Raspberry Parfait' (p,a) LRHS
'Raspberry Ripple' (p) CTal
Raspberry Sundae (p) see *D.* 'Devon Yolande'
'Raspberry Sundae' (p) ECtt ELan EPfP GBin LBMP LRHS LSRN SEND SHil SPoG WRHF
Raspberry Swirl see *D.* 'Devon Siskin'
Rebekah = 'Wp09 Mar05'[PBR] (Early Bird Series) (p) CMea CWhe LAst LRHS NPri SHil
Red Dwarf see *D.* 'Red Star'
§ 'Red Star'[PBR] (p) ♀H6 CWhe ECho ELan GJos LRHS MAsh SRot WIce
'Reine de Henri' see *D.* 'Queen of Henri'
'Richard Pollak' (b) LAll
'Ringwood Belle' (pf) CNMi
'Rizalene' (p) CNMi
'Robert Allwood' (pf) LAll
'Robin Ritchie' (p) WHoo
Romance = 'Wp09 Wen04'[PBR] (Scent First Series) (p) CWhe ELan LRHS LSou MTis SHil
'Romsey' (pf) CNMi
'Roodkapje' (p) XLum
'Rose de Mai' (p) CFis CNMi CSam LAll WHoo
§ 'Rose Devon Pearl'[PBR] CWhe
'Rose Joy' (p) ♀H6 CBcs CWhe EPfP LRHS
§ 'Rose Monica Wyatt'[PBR] (p) ♀H6 CWhe
Rosebud = 'Wp08 Ros03'[PBR] (Early Bird Series) (p) CTal CWhe LBMP LRHS NPri SHil
'Rötkappchen' (p) ELon WCot
'Royal Fragrance' (pf) **new** EMal
'Royal Salmon' (pf) **new** EMal
'Ruby' see *D.* 'Houndspool Ruby'
'Ruby Doris' see *D.* 'Houndspool Ruby'
'Ruby Wedding' (p) LSRN
rupicola WCot
'Sam Barlow' (p) LAll SBch
'Santa Claus' (b) LAll
scardicus NSla
Scarlet Beauty = 'Hilbeau' WMoo
'Seraphina' (pf) CNMi
'Seren Wen' (p) WAbe
serotinus EPot WCot XLum
Sherbet = 'Wp08 Ros03'[PBR] (Early Bird Series) (p) CWhe ELan EPfP LRHS NPri SHil
Shooting Star = 'Wp04 Flores'[PBR] (p) CWhe ELan LRHS MTis NPri SRms
'Shot Silk' (pf) LAll
'Show Aristocrat' (p) LAll
'Show Beauty' (p) LAll
Show Girl = 'Hilshow' (pt) LRHS
Showgirl = 'Wp08 Uni02'[PBR] (Scent First Series) (p) CWhe ELan LSou MTis MWat
'Show Glory' (p) LAll
'Show Harlequin' (p) LAll
'Show Satin' (p) LAll
'Shrimp' (b) CWib
Silver Star = 'Wp10 Hel01'[PBR] (p) CTal CWhe LRHS MTis SHil
'Singapore Girl' (Kiwi Series) (p) CWGN
'Siskin Clock' see *D.* 'Devon Siskin'
* 'Six Hills' NWad
Slap 'n' Tickle = 'Wp05 Pp22'[PBR] (Scent First Series) (p) CWhe EBee ECtt ELon LRHS LSRN LSou NPri SHil SPoG SRot
'Solomon' (p) CFis LAll
'Somerset' (pf) **new** CNMi
'Sops-in-wine' (p) CSam ECha ECtt LAll MSCN
§ 'Souvenir de la Malmaison' (M) EMal LAll
'Spangle' (b) LAll
'Spencer Bickham' (p) MNrw
spiculifolius CAby CFis EWTr NPri SPhx
'Spinfield Joy' (b) ♀H6 LAll
'Spring Star' (p) ECtt SRot WJek
'Square Eyes' see *D.* 'Old Square Eyes'
squarrosus CPBP ECho EPot WAbe
* - ***alpinus*** ECho
- 'Nanus' see *D.* 'Berlin Snow'
'Starburst'[PBR] (p) CTal CWhe ECho GBin LRHS MTis NPri WIce
Stardust = 'Wp07 Opr04'[PBR] (Early Bird Series) (p) CWhe LAst NPri WIce
Stargazer = 'Wp13 Gil05' (Whetman Stars Series) (p) CWhe LRHS MTis
Starlight = 'Hilstar' (pf) CMea LRHS SRms
Starlight = 'Wp 06 Parnia'[PBR] (p) CWhe
'Starry Eyes' (p) ♀H6 CBod CSam CTal CWhe EAJP ECho ELan GBin GCrg GEdr GMaP LRHS NPri SRms SRot SWvt
'Storm' (pf) CNMi EMal LAll
'Strawberries and Cream' (p) CWhe ECtt NEgg SPoG
'Strawberry Kiss' CWhe
strictus WCot
* - subsp. ***pulchellus*** GEdr

	subacaulis	EDAr IFoB NGdn NSla XLum
	- subsp. ***brachyanthus*** 'Murray Lyon'	WThu
	suendermannii	see *D. petraeus*
	Sugar Plum = 'Wp08 Ian04'PBR (Scent First Series) (p)	CWhe ECtt ELan EPfP LRHS LSou MTis
	'Summerfield Adam' (p)	LAll
	'Summerfield Amy Francesca' (p)	LAll
	'Summerfield Blaze' (p)	LAll
	'Summerfield Blush' (p)	LAll
	'Summerfield Daniel' (b)	LAll
	'Summerfield Debbie' (p)	LAll
	'Summerfield Emma Louise' (p)	LAll
	'Summerfield Jo' (p)	LAll
	'Summerfield Rebecca' (p)	LAll
	Summertime	see *D.* 'Rose Monica Wyatt'
	'Sunray' (b)	LAll
	'Sunstar' (b)	LAll
§	***superbus***	CMHG NNor SBch SHar SIgm SPhx WMoo XLum
	- 'Crimsonia' (p)	WOut
I	- 'Primadonna'	GQue
	Supernova = 'Wp11 Tyr04' (pf)	CMea CTal CWhe MTis
	'Susan' (p)	LAll
	'Susannah' (p)	LAll
*	'Susan's Seedling' (p)	LAll
	'Swanlake' (p)	LAll
	'Sway Lass' (p)	SEND
	'Sweet Cecille' (pf)	CNMi
	'Sweet Sue' (b)	LAll
	sylvestris	WOut
	'Tamsin Fifield' (b) ♀H6	LAll
	'Tatra' (pf) **new**	NQui
	'Tatra Blush' (p)	GCal
	'Tatra Fragrance' (p)	CCse GCal LAll
	'Tatra Ghost' (p)	LAll SDys
	'Tayside Red' (M)	EMal LAll
	'Terranova' (pf)	CNMi
	'Thora' (M)	EMal LAll
	'Thunderstorm' (pf) **new**	CNMi
	Tickled Pink = 'Devon Pp 11'PBR (Scent First Series) (p)	CWhe ECtt ELan ELon EPfP LBMP LCro LOPS LPla LRHS LSRN LSou MWat NPri SHil SPoG
	'Tiny Rubies'	see *D. gratianopolitanus* 'Tiny Rubies'
	'Tony's Choice' (pf)	CNMi
	'Tracy Jardine' (pf)	CNMi
	'Treasure' (p)	LAll
	'Trevor' (p)	LAll
	tristis	XLum
	'Tropic Butterfly' (p)	LPot
	'Tudor'	ELon MHCG MNrw
	turkestanicus	NNor WPtf
	Tyrolean trailing carnations	LAll
	'Uncle Teddy' (b) ♀H6	LAll
	'Unique' (p)	LAll
	'Ursula Le Grove' (p)	WHer
	'Valda Wyatt' (p) ♀H6	CBcs CWhe ELan EPfP LAll LAst MCot NCGa NEgg NNor NSti SEND SPoG SWvt WBod WGwG WMnd
	'Vic Masters'	SBch
	'Violet Clove' (b)	LAll
	'Violet Yates' (pf)	CNMi
	'W.A. Musgrave'	see *D.* 'Musgrave's Pink'
	'Waithman Beauty' (p)	CFis CTri ECtt LAll WHoo
	'Waithman's Jubilee' (p)	LAll WTor
	'Warden Hybrid' (p)	CTri CWhe ECho ECtt GCrg LAst LRHS MNHC NGdn NWad SPoG SWvt WAbe
	'Waterloo Sunset'PBR (p)	CMea CSBt CWhe MTis
	'Weetwood Double' (p)	LPot SBch
	'Welton Raspberry Ice' (p)	LAll
	'Wessex' (pf)	CNMi
	weyrichii	ECho EPot
	'Whatfield Anona' (p)	LAll
	'Whatfield Beauty' (p)	ECho ECtt
	'Whatfield Brilliant' (p)	ECho
	'Whatfield Cancan' (p) ♀H6	CBod CMea CTal CWhe ECho ECtt ELan EPot GMaP LAll LHop LRHS MNHC NEgg NGdn NHol NPri SBch SPoG SWvt WJek
	'Whatfield Cyclops' (p)	ECho LAll
	'Whatfield Dawn' (p)	ECho
	'Whatfield Dorothy Mann' (p)	ECho LAll
	'Whatfield Fuchsia Floss' (p)	LAll
	'Whatfield Gem' (p)	CFis CPBP CWhe ECho ECtt ELan ELon EPfP GCrg LAll LAst MNHC MWat NGdn SIgm SWvt WHoo
	'Whatfield Joy' (p)	ECho ECtt ELan EPfP GCrg LAll LRHS MHer NGdn
	'Whatfield Magenta' (p) ♀H6	CSam ECho ECtt ELan EPot GCrg LAll LHop LRHS MWat NPri SBch SPoG WAbe
	'Whatfield Mini' (p)	LAll SBch
	'Whatfield Miss' (p)	LAll SBch
	'Whatfield Misty Morn' (p)	ECho LAll
	'Whatfield Nine Star' (p)	ECho
	'Whatfield Peach' (p)	LAll
	'Whatfield Pretty Lady' (p)	ECho LAll
	'Whatfield Rose' (p)	ECho
	'Whatfield Ruby' (p)	ECho ECtt ELan GJos LAll
	'Whatfield Supergem' (p)	ECho
	'Whatfield White' (p)	ECho ECtt LAll
	'Whatfield White Moon' (p)	ECho
	'Whatfield Wisp' (p)	CPBP CTri ECho EPfP EPot GEdr MRav NBir
	'White and Crimson' (p)	LAll
	'White Joy'PBR (p) ♀H6	ELan MRav
	'White Ladies' (p)	LAll MRav
	White Valda	see *D.* 'Devon Isolde'
	'Whitehill' (p)	ECho
	'Whitesmith' (b) ♀H6	LAll
	'Widecombe Fair' (p) ♀H6	CTri CWhe ELan EPfP LAll LRHS MTis SPoG WTor
	'Yellow Alice' (b)	LAll
	'Zebra' (b)	LAll

Diapensia (*Diapensiaceae*)

lapponica var. ***obovata***	NHar

Diascia (*Scrophulariaceae*)

'Alice Cap'	SBch
'Andrew'	SBch
'Apricot'	see *D. barberae* 'Hopleys Apricot'
Apricot Delight = 'Codicot' (Sun Chimes Series)	EDAr
barberae 'Belmore Beauty' (v)	EWes
- 'Blackthorn Apricot' ♀H4	CBod EBee ECha ELan EPfP EWoo GBin GMaP LRHS LSRN NDov NLar NPri SPer SPlb SPoG SRms SWvt WGwG XEll
- Juliet Orange = 'Baljulor' **new**	NPri

	- Juliet Pink With Eye = 'Baljulpiney'	NPri
§	- 'Hopleys Apricot'	NLar
§	- 'Ruby Field' ♀H4	CMea EBee ECha ELan EPfP LHop LRHS LSRN SPer SRms SWvt
	Blue Bonnet = 'Hecbon'	SWvt
	'Bluebelle' (Maritana Series)	LAst MCot
	'Blush'	see *D. integerrima* 'Blush'
	(Breezee Series) Breezee Apple Blossom **new**	NLar
	- Breezee Apricot = 'Diaspritwo'PBR	LHop NLar
	- Breezee Red **new**	NLar
	- Breezee Snow = 'Inndiabzsno'PBR	LHop NLar
	Coral Belle = 'Hecbel'PBR ♀H3	ECho EWoo GBin LHop LRHS LSou
	'Denim Blue'	EDAr EPfP NLar WHea
	elegans misapplied	see *D. fetcaniensis*, *D. vigilis*
	'Emma'	NDov SMHy SWvt
	felthamii	see *D. fetcaniensis*
§	***fetcaniensis***	CMea CPne CPrp EBee EPfP GMaP LRHS MCot MHer NEgg SPer WBod WHal WHea WKif
	- 'Daydream'	LBuc MPie SBch WHrl
	flanaganii misapplied	see *D. vigilis*
	(Flying Colours Series) Flying Colours Appleblossom = 'Diastara'	EPfP
	- Flying Colours Apricot = 'Diastina'	EPfP
	- Flying Colours Red = 'Diastonia'	EPfP
	'Hector Harrison'	see *D.* 'Salmon Supreme'
	Ice Cracker = 'Hecrack'	CMea ELan LHop LRHS SRms
	Iceberg = 'Hecice'	NDov SWvt
§	***integerrima*** ♀H4	CTal ECha MCot MHer SIgm
	- 'Alba'	see *D. integerrima* 'Blush'
§	- 'Blush'	CSpe NDov
	- 'Ivory Angel'	see *D. integerrima* 'Blush'
	integrifolia	see *D. integerrima*
	'Jacqueline's Joy'	CMea NPer
	'Joyce's Choice' ♀H3	ECho LRHS SRms
	'Katherine Sharman' (v)	EWes
	'Lilac Belle' ♀H3	EDAr ELan LHop LRHS NBir NEgg SPlb SPoG SRms
	'Lilac Mist' ♀H3	NPer
	lilacina* × *rigescens	GBee
	Little Dancer = 'Pendan'PBR	ELan GBin LAst LSou NLar SLon
	'Little Dazzler'	GBin
	Little Dreamer = 'Pender'PBR	LAst NLar
	Little Drifter = 'Pendrif'PBR	LSou NLar
	Little Maiden = 'Penmaid'PBR	GBin LAst NLar
	Little Tango = 'Pentang'PBR	CBod CPrp LAst LHop LSou MCot NLar SRms WRHF
	personata	Widely available
	- 'Hopleys'	EPPr EWes LHop LRHS MAvo MSCN NCGa WHea WWEG
	'Peter'	NDov
	Pink Panther = 'Penther'	SWvt
	'Pitlochrie Pink'	GBin
	Red Ace = 'Hecrace'PBR	EPfP LAst LHop MCot NPer SWvt
	Redstart = 'Hecstart'	SWvt
	rigescens ♀H3	CBod CCon CPne CPrp CSpe CWCL ECtt ELan GBin ILea LHop MHer NLar NPer SPer SPlb SPoG SWvt WCFE WSHC
§	- 'Anne Rennie'	LRHS SWvt
	- pale-flowered	see *D. rigescens* 'Anne Rennie'
	'Ruby Field'	see *D. barberae* 'Ruby Field'
	'Rupert Lambert' ♀H3	NDov
§	'Salmon Supreme'	ELan LRHS NPer SPoG SRms
	(Sundiascia Series) Sundiascia Blush Pink **new**	LBMP LCro LOPS
	- Sundiascia Orange **new**	LSou
	- Sundiascia Rose Pink **new**	LBMP LSou
	'Twinkle' ♀H3	ECho LRHS NBir NPer SRms
*	'Twins Gully'	EWes
§	***vigilis*** ♀H3	CExl CMea EPot GBee LHop LRHS NBro NCGa SIgm SRms WHal WPnn WWEG

Dicentra ✿ (*Papaveraceae*)

	CC 4452	CExl
	'Adrian Bloom'	CExl ECtt EPfP GBuc GLet LCro MCot MWat SPer SWvt WFar WMoo
	(Amore Series) 'Amore Pink' **new**	NLar WHil WHlf
	- 'Amore Rose' **new**	NLar
	'Aurora'	CBod EBee ECtt ELon EPfP GBin GBuc LAst LCro LRHS MBel MBri MRav MTis NGdn NLar NSti SCob SPer SPoG SWvt WHil WMoo
	'Boothman's Variety'	see *D.* 'Stuart Boothman'
	'Bountiful'	CMac ECtt EPau GLet LRHS LSou MRav NGdn SWvt WGwG
	'Brownie'	GBuc
	'Burning Hearts'PBR	CMos CWCL CWGN ECtt EPot EWoo GBin GLet IKil LCro LHop LLHF LRHS LSou MPnt NSti SCob SPer WHil
	canadensis	CLAP EBee GBuc GKev LEdu MAvo NLar WAbe WCru WHal
	'Candy Hearts'PBR	EBee ECtt ELan LHop NGdn NLar SCob SGol
	cucullaria	CAby CElw CEvo CLAP CMea CPBP CTal CWCL EBee ECho ELon EPPr EPot GAbr GBuc GEdr GKev GLet ITim LRHS MNrw MRav NHar NLar WAbe WCru WFar XEll
	- 'Pink Punk'	CTal CWCL EBee LEdu LLHF MNrw NHar NLar
	- 'Pittsburg'	CAby CDes EBee EPPr GBuc MNrw
	eximia misapplied	see *D. formosa*
	eximia ambig.	MHol
	eximia (Ker Gawl.) Torr.	see *D. eximia*
	'Alba'	'Snowdrift'
§	- 'Snowdrift'	CLAP ECtt ELan EPfP LRHS MCot MTis NLar SRms WMoo
	'Fire Island'PBR	ECtt MBri
	'Firecracker'	ECtt MBri MPnt
§	***formosa***	CBcs CLet CTri ECha ELan EPfP GKev IFro LAst LRHS MLHP MWat NBro NGdn NPri SPlb SRms WMoo
	- f. ***alba***	GAbr GCra GLet GLog GMaP NBir SRms WCru WFar WKif
	- 'Bacchanal' ♀H5	Widely available
	- 'Cox's Dark Red'	CExl CLAP EWes GBuc GKev GLet LLHF SKHP
	- 'Gold Leaf'	CBod
	- 'Langtrees' ♀H5	CMac CSam ECha EPau GBuc LHop MRav NBro NLar SGSe SRms SWvt WCru WFar WHea WMoo WOut
	- 'Moorland Pearl'	WOut
	- subsp. ***oregana***	EPPr SKHP WHal

- - 'Rosea'	EPPr
- Snowflakes = 'Fusd'	EWes MRav
- 'Spring Gold'	EBee ECha ELon EPPr LRHS NLar WHil WMoo
- 'Spring Magic'	CMos EBee ECtt EPPr LRHS MRav NLar
'Ivory Hearts'PBR	CMos CWGN EBee ELan EWoo GKev GLet IKil LHop MAvo MBri MCot NLar NSti SPer
§ 'Katie'	EPPr
'Katy'	see *D.* 'Katie'
'King of Hearts'	Widely available
'Luxuriant' ♀H5	CBcs CLet COtt CSBt ECtt ELan EPfP GBuc GKev LAst LHop LRHS LSRN MCot MGos MHol MRav MTis MWhi SCob SPer SPoG SRms SRot SWvt WMoo
macrantha	see *Ichthyoselmis macrantha*
'Pearl Drops'	ELan GKev GLog GMaP LRHS MCot NBid NLar SRms WHil WMoo
peregrina	WAbe
'Red Fountain'PBR	CWCL ECtt GLet LHop NLar NSti SMad WFar WHil
scandens	see *Dactylicapnos scandens*
spectabilis	see *Lamprocapnos spectabilis*
'Spring Morning'	CElw CMHG CSam CTal EAEE ECtt EPPr EPau GLet NGdn
§ 'Stuart Boothman' ♀H5	CMac CSam CWCL ECtt ELan ELon EPfP GBuc GLet GMaP LAst LHop LRHS MCot MLHP MRav MSpe MTis NBro NCGa NGdn NLar NPri SPoG SRms SWvt WFar WKif WMoo
thalictrifolia	see *D. scandens*
ventii	see *Dactylicapnos ventii*

Dichelachne (*Poaceae*)

crinita	SMea

Dichelostemma (*Asparagaceae*)

congestum	CAvo ECho GKev LCro SDeJ
§ ***ida-maia***	CAvo CGrW CWCL EPot GKev SDeJ
- 'Pink Diamond'	EBee GKev SDeJ
volubile	ECho
- 'Pink Giant'	SDeJ

Dichocarpum (*Ranunculaceae*)

§ ***dicarpon*** B&SWJ 11555	WCru

Dichondra (*Convolvulaceae*)

argentea 'Silver Falls'	EShb LAst LBMP LSou NPri SCoo SPer SPoG
§ ***micrantha***	EShb
repens misapplied	see *D. micrantha*

Dichopogon (*Anthericaceae*)

strictus	ECou SBrt WSFF

Dichroa (*Hydrangeaceae*)

febrifuga	CAbb CBcs CBot CDoC CExl CHll CMil CWib EBee EPfP LRHS SWvt WCru WPGP
- B&SWJ 2367	WCru
- HWJK 2430	WCru
- NJM 10.042	WPGP
hirsuta B&SWJ 8207 from Vietnam	WCru
aff. ***hirsuta*** B&SWJ 8371 from Laos	WCru
aff. ***yunnanensis*** B&SWJ 9734	WCru

Dichroa × *Hydrangea* see × *Didrangea*

Dichromena see *Rhynchospora*

Dichrostachys (*Mimosaceae*)

cinerea	SPlb

Dicksonia ✿ (*Dicksoniaceae*)

antarctica ♀H3	Widely available
arborescens new	NLos
fibrosa ♀H3	CDTJ CKel
sellowiana	CDTJ CKel
squarrosa ♀H3	CDTJ CKel NLos
thyrsopteroides new	NLos

Dicliptera (*Acanthaceae*)

§ ***sericea***	CDoC CHll EShb LHop MCot MSCN SBch SRkn WHil WOut WPGP XSen
suberecta	see *D. sericea*

Dictamnus ✿ (*Rutaceae*)

albus	CArn CBcs CHll CTri CWCL EBee ECha ELan EPfP EWTr EWoo GMaP LAst LEdu LHop LRHS LSun MBel MCot MNrw MRav NPri SBrt SKHP SMHy SPer SPoG SWat SWvt WCAu
- var. ***albus*** ♀H6	IBoy LPla SWvt WAul
§ - var. ***purpureus*** ♀H6	CWCL EAEE ECha ELan EPfP GBin GMaP GPoy IBoy LAst LHop LPla LRHS LSun MBel MNrw MRav NEgg SKHP SPer SPoG SRms SWat SWvt WAul WCot WKif WWEG
* - var. ***roseus***	IMou
* - ***turkestanicus***	GCal
caucasicus	SBrt SMHy
fraxinella	see *D. albus* var. *purpureus*

× *Didrangea* (*Hydrangeaceae*)

B&SWJ 6605 from Thailand	WCru
versicolor B&SWJ 6565	WCru
ytiensis B&SWJ 11790	WCru

Didymochlaena (*Dryopteridaceae*)

lunulata	see *D. truncatula*
§ ***truncatula***	XBlo

Dierama ✿ (*Iridaceae*)

CD&R 192	CElw
adelphicum	LLHF
ambiguum	CElw EBee NLos SBea XLum
argyreum	CDoC CElw CMac CPla CTsd CWCL EBee EPri EWTr GBin GKev ITim MMuc NLar SBrt SGSe SPad SPoG SRot WHil XLum
atrum new	EBee
'Ballyrogan Red'	IBlr
Barr hybrids	CBro CWCL GAbr
'Big Pink' new	CEvo
'Black Knight'	CExl IBlr
'Blackberry Bells'	CDoC CWCL CWGN ELon GBin LAst MAvo NLar NLos WHil
Blue Belle = 'Rowblu'PBR	CWCL EBee GEdr IBal IVic LBuc LRHS NPri SPoG
'Blush'	IBlr
'Buckland White'	WPGP
'Candy Stripe'	CPla EBee IBal
'Carmine'	CWCL

'Cherry Chimes'	EPfP
'Cinnamon Fairy'	EBee EPfP IBal
cooperi	CElw CPou CTca EBee NBir WWEG
'Coral Belle'	EBee IBal LRHS
'Coral Bells'	CDes CKno GCal IBal LBuc NPri
'Cosmos'	CExl CWCL EBee EPri EUJe LRHS MHer MMuc SEND SMad WHil
'Delicacy'	IBlr
'Desire'	IBlr
dissimile	EBee
'Donard Legacy'	IBlr
§ ***dracomontanum***	Widely available
- JCA 3.141.100	WPGP
dracomontanum* × *pulcherrimum	SMad
dubium	IBlr
ensifolium	see *D. pendulum*
erectum	CBcs CBod CHid CMac CTsd CWCL EBee EPri GBin MMuc NLar NLos SGSe SRot
formosum	CCon EBee WPGP
galpinii	CPla CWCL EBee ELan EPri LHop LLHF MMuc NLos WPGP
grandiflorum	CPou IBlr
'Guinevere'	Widely available
igneum	Widely available
- CD&R 278	CExl CPou ELon GBuc
insigne	CHid CWCL EBee ESwi GBin LRHS NLos
'Iris'	IBlr
jucundum	CWCL EBee EWTr GBuc LRHS
'Juno'	CMac
'Knee-high Lavender'	WPGP
'Lancelot'	CBcs CElw CExl CKno COtt CPne EBee ECtt IBal IBlr LRHS MBri NBir NPri SWvt WFar WKif
latifolium	CHid IBlr
'Magenta' new	CEvo
'Mandarin'	IBlr
medium	ELon SWat WPGP WWEG
'Milkmaid'	CExl IBlr
'Miranda'	CKno EBee ECtt EPri IBal LRHS NLar SPhx
mossii	CBcs CCon CDoC CExl CHid CMHG CMac CPne CWCL EBee ELan EPri EWTr GBin LHop LRHS NLar NLos SBea SGSe SPhx SPlb SRot SVen WHil WPGP WWEG XLum
'Painted Lady'	CWCL EBee EPfP IBal LRHS NPri SKHP SLon
pallidum	CExl
'Pamina'	CExl CPrp IBlr
'Papagena'	IBlr
'Papageno'	IBlr
pauciflorum	CAbb CCon CExl CHid CPrp CWCL CWib EBee EPri EWTr GBin IKil LHop LRHS MNrw NBir NLar NLos SPhx SRot SWat WPGP WSHC WWEG
§ ***pendulum***	CBro ELan GBBs IBlr LRHS LSRN MRav SWvt WFar WWEG
- 'Album'	CEvo
pictum	IBlr
'Pink Rocket'	CWCL MHer NHol
Plant World hybrids	ELon SGSe
Plant World Jewels	CWCL NLos
'Pretty Flamingo'	CExl CPrp IBlr
'Puck'	CDes EBee GCal IBlr ITim MRav WPGP
pulcherrimum	Widely available
- var. ***album***	CWCL ELan IBlr MHer MNrw NDov NLos WHil WPGP
- 'Blackbird'	CBcs CCon CExl CWCL ELan EPri GAbr IBlr IBoy LAst LHop LRHS LSRN MAvo MBel MHer MMuc NHol NLar NLos SBea SGSe SKHP SPer SPoG SWvt WHil WPGP
- dark cerise seedlings	MAvo NDov
- dark pink-flowered	IBoy SGSe
- 'Falcon'	IBlr
- 'Flamingo'	IBlr
- 'Merlin'	CElw CExl CKno CPou CWCL EBee ECtt ELon EWoo GEdr GMaP IBal IBlr IBoy LRHS MBel MBri NBir NPri SCob SVen SWvt WGwG
- pale-flowered	ECha
- 'Peregrine'	IBoy
- 'Redwing'	IBlr
- Slieve Donard hybrids	CWCL GBuc LAst NLos SMad WFar WHrl WMnd
pumilum misapplied	see *D. dracomontanum*
'Queen of the Night'	IBlr
reynoldsii	CAbb CBcs CCon CExl CHid CMac CPla CTsd CWCL EBee ELan EPri IBlr IVic MBel MMuc SGSe SPhx SPlb SPoG SRkn SVen WKif
robustum	CAbb CExl CPou CWCL EWes IBlr LRHS WHoo WPGP
'Sarastro'	CExl IBlr
sertum	EBee
'Spring Dancer'	CWCL EHoe MHer NHol NLos SGSe SPlb
'Tamino'	IBlr
'Tiny Bells'	EDAr GBin GCal IBal SMHy
'Titania'	IBal IBlr
trichorhizum	CCon CElw CExl CPla CPrp CWCL ELan EPri GBin GKev IBlr LHop LPla LRHS SGSe WPGP WWEG
'Tubular Bells'	IBlr
tyrium	LLHF
'Violet Ice'	IBlr
'Westminster Chimes'	IBlr MAvo
white-flowered new	MBel
'Zulu Bells'	ELon

Diervilla ✿ (*Caprifoliaceae*)

middendorffiana	see *Weigela middendorffiana*
rivularis 'Troja Black'	EPPr NLar
§ ***sessilifolia***	CBcs CHGN CMac EBee EPPr IDee LAst LCro MRav SLon WBod WCot WFar WMoo
- 'Butterfly'	CMac EPPr LCro LSou NLar SCob WMoo
- Cool Splash = 'Lpdc Podaras'PBR (v)	CBod CMHG CMac CWGN EBee ELan EMil EPPr LBuc LCro LHop LRHS SPoG SWvt WCot
× ***splendens***	CExl CMHG CWib EHoe ELan EPPr EPfP EWTr GAbr IDee LHop LRHS MBNS MBlu MSwo NLar SEND SPer SPoG SWvt

Dietes (*Iridaceae*)

bicolor	CAbb CAby CBod CDes CExl CPrp CTca CTre EPri LEdu LRHS LSou SChr SGSe WSHC
grandiflora	CAbb CAby CArn CBod CDes CExl CHll CPne CTca CTre ECho ESwi SGSe SVen WCot WHil
§ ***iridioides***	CPrp CTca ECho ESwi LRHS WCot

Digitalis ✿ (*Plantaginaceae*)

	sp.	SVic
	'Albino'	EPfP LRHS
	ambigua	see *D. grandiflora*
	apricot hybrids	see *D. purpurea* 'Sutton's Apricot'
	canariensis	CAbb CBcs CBot CDTJ CHll CRHN CSpe CTsd EUJe LRHS MHin SEND SEle SPad SPlb SVen WCFE
	cariensis	CBot GKev
	ciliata	GKev NWad SBri
	davisiana	CExl EWld GKev GLog MNHC WMoo
	dubia	CBot EBee EPfP WAbe
	'Elsie Kelsey'	ECtt SWvt
	eriostachya	see *D. lutea*
	ferruginea ♕[H7]	Widely available
	- 'Gelber Herold'	CBod CLAP GMaP WFar
	- 'Gigantea'	CLAP ECtt ELan EPfP EWoo GBin GQue LAst LEdu MBNS MHin SCob SHar SPlb SWat WPGP WWtn
	'Foxtrot'	CRos EPfP LRHS SHil
	'Glory of Roundway'	CBod CBot CLAP CMos ECtt IBoy LBrs LEdu LSou MHol MPie NLar SPer SPoG STPC WCot
§	***grandiflora*** ♕[H5]	Widely available
	- 'Carillon'	CBod ELan EPfP GBin GJos IFoB LAst NBir SCob SGSe SRot WHoo
	- 'Cream Bell'	EPfP LRHS MHol WHar
	- 'Temple Bells'	CBot
	aff. ***grandiflora***	IBoy
	heywoodii	see *D. purpurea* subsp. *heywoodii*
	'Ice Queen' **new**	EBee
	Illumination Series	EPfP SCob
	- Illumination Apricot = 'Chelsea Gold'	CHid CRos EPfP LRHS
	- Illumination Pink = 'Tmdgfp001'	CAbb CAby CBot CHid CRos CWGN ELan ELon EPfP LAst LBMP LBuc LHop LRHS LSou MAvo MHol MNrw NLar NPri SCob SPad SPer SPoG SRkn STPC WCot
	- Illumination Raspberry	CBot EPfP LBuc LRHS LSou MAvo MHol NLar SCob
	'John Innes Tetra'	CBot MNrw SPtp WHoo
	kishinskyi	see *D. parviflora* Jacq.
	laevigata	CBot CCon GBin LEdu NBro SBri SEND SPav WMnd WMoo WPGP
	- subsp. ***laevigata***	SPtp
	- white-flowered	ESwi GBin MCot WCot
	lamarckii misapplied	see *D. lanata*
§	***lanata***	CArn CBot EBee ECtt ELan EPfP GKev LAst LRHS MBNS MNHC NGdn NWad SBea SGSe SPav SPlb SPtp SRms WMnd
	- 'Café Crème'	CAby CBot CLAP WHar
§	***lutea***	Widely available
I	- 'Aurea'	LPla
	- 'Flashing Spires' (v)	CPla
	macedonica **new**	LAst
	× ***mertonensis*** ♕[H5]	Widely available
	- 'Raspberry'	CLAP
	- 'Summer King'	CChe COtt ECtt ELan EWld GJos LAst LSRN LSun MAsh MWat NPri WFar WHil
	minor var. ***palaui*** **new**	SBrt
	obscura	CBod CBot EAJP ECho IFoB SBrt SEND SPlb SVen WCot WMnd
*	- 'Dusky Maid'	LHop
	- 'Sunset' **new**	LAst
	orientalis	see *D. grandiflora*

§	***parviflora*** Jacq.	Widely available
	- 'Milk Chocolate'	Widely available
	'Pink Chapel'	ECtt
	(Polkadot Series) 'Polkadot Pippa'	CBot LPfy LRHS SHil
	- 'Polkadot Polly' **new**	CBot
	- 'Polkadot Princess' **new**	CBot
	purpurea	CHab CWld ELan ENfk EPfP EWoo GPoy LPal LPfy MHer MLHP MMuc MNHC NMir SCob SIde SPlb SPoG WBrk WMoo WOut WSFF
	- 'Alba'	see *D. purpurea* f. *albiflora*
§	- f. ***albiflora***	Widely available
	- - 'Anne Redetzky'[PBR]	CSpe LRHS
	- 'Apricot Delight' **new**	EBee
	- Camelot Series	CNec LSqH SHar SVic
	- - 'Camelot Cream'	CBot ELan EPfP LRHS SWvt
	- - 'Camelot Lavender'	CBot COtt ELan EPfP LCro LRHS SWvt
	- - 'Camelot Rose'	CBot ELan EPfP LRHS SWvt
	- - 'Camelot White'	COtt ELan EPfP
*	- 'Campanulata Alba'	CBot
	- 'Candy Mountain'	CBot
	- CEN-type mutant **new**	CNat
	- 'Chedglow' (v)	CNat
	- (Dalmatian Series) 'Dalmatian Cream'	CBod CBot LRHS MAsh
	- - 'Dalmatian Peach'	CBod CBot EBee LCro LRHS LSou MAsh
	- - 'Dalmatian Purple'	CBod CBot LOPS LRHS LSou MAsh SHil
	- - 'Dalmatian Rose'	CBot MAsh
	- - 'Dalmatian White'	CBod EBee LAst LRHS LSou MAsh SHil
	- Excelsior Group	CBcs CBod CBot CMac CSBt CTri CWCL EAEE ECtt EPfP GJos GMaP IBoy LAst LCro LRHS MBri MJak NHol NMir SCob SPer SPoG SRms SVic SWvt WHar XLum
	- - (Suttons; Unwins) ♕[H7]	ECtt MRav
	- Foxy Group	CBot CWib EAJP EPfP LRHS MNHC SPoG WHar
	- - 'Foxy Apricot'	SPtp SWvt WCot
	- - 'Foxy Pink'	ELan GBin LHop SPtp
	- Giant Spotted Group	ECtt EPfP LRHS SPoG
	- Glittering Prizes Group	CBot SWat
	- Gloxinioides Group	CBot LCro LOPS
	- - 'The Shirley' ♕[H7]	WMoo
§	- subsp. ***heywoodii***	CBot ELan EWTr WMoo
	- - 'Silver Fox'	LSRN
	- 'Pam's Choice'	Widely available
	- 'Pam's Split'	CAby CBot EBee SCob
	- 'Primrose Carousel'	CBot LRHS MCot NEgg NLar SCob STPC
	- 'Serendipity'	CBot EPfP LPfy LRHS MBri SHil
	- 'Snow Thimble'	CAby CBod CBot CLAP COtt EAJP ELan GJos IBoy LRHS LSun MBri MHol NLar STPC
	- 'Sugar Plum' **new**	CBot
§	- 'Sutton's Apricot' ♕[H7]	Widely available
*	- 'Sutton's Giant Primrose'	CBod CBot
	- white CEN-type mutant	NChi
	'Red Skin'	GBin GJos MBel NLar NWad SGSe SPad
	'Saltwood Summer'	MBri
	sceptrum	CExl SPlb SVen WPGP
	'Spice Island'	CBod CLAP CMos EBee ECtt ELon ESwi GBin GJos IBoy LEdu LHop LPal LRHS LSou MAvo MBri MCot

	NCGa NLar NSti SCob SMad SPer SPoG STPC WCot
* ***stewartii***	ELan EWes GLog LEdu NWad WMoo
'Strawberry Fayre'	GJos
thapsi	CBod ELan EPfP GJos NChi SBri SEND WMoo XLum
- 'Spanish Peaks'	GJos
trojana	CFis EAJP ECtt GKev IFoB SCob SDix WWtn
- 'Helen of Troy'	CLAP ELan GJos LHop SKHP SPtp
viridiflora	CExl ECtt NBro SBri

Dilatris (*Haemodoraceae*)

ixioides	CLak
pillansii	CLak

dill see *Anethum graveolens*

Dimorphotheca (*Asteraceae*)

cuneata	WHil

Dionaea ✿ (*Droseraceae*)

muscipula	CHew EECP SKHP SPlb WSSs
- 'Akai Ryu' ♀H3	NLos WSSs
- 'All Green' **new**	EECP
- 'B52'	EECP WSSs
- 'Big Mouth'	EECP
- 'Bohemian Garnet' **new**	EECP
- (Dentate Traps Group) 'Dentate Traps'	WSSs
* - f. ***heterodoxa***	NLos
- large clone	NLos
- long-toothed	NLos
- 'Pink Venus'	NLos
- 'Royal Red'	CHew NLos WSSs
- 'Sawtooth'	EECP NLos WSSs
- shark-toothed	EECP NLos
- Slack's red clone	NLos
- 'South West Giant' ♀H3	NLos WSSs
- 'Spider'	EECP NLos
- 'Tiger Fangs' **new**	WSSs
- upright	NLos

Dionysia (*Primulaceae*)

'Annielle'	WAbe
aretioides ♀H5	WAbe
- 'Bevere'	EPot WAbe
- 'Phyllis Carter'	ECho
'Charlson Emma'	WAbe
'Charlson Gem'	WAbe
'Charlson Jake'	WAbe
'Charlson Petite'	WAbe
'Charlson Pip'	WAbe
'Charlson Primrose'	WAbe
'Corona'	WAbe
curviflora	WAbe
'Emmely'	WAbe
'Eric Watson'	WAbe
'Ewesley Iota'	WAbe
'Ewesley Kappa'	WAbe
'Ewesley Theta'	WAbe
'Geist'	WAbe
janthina	WAbe
'Judith Bramley'	WAbe
'Lycaena'	WAbe
'Monika'	WAbe
'Pascal'	WAbe
sarvestanica	WAbe
tapetodes	WAbe
- 'Brimstone'	WAbe
- 'Peter Edwards'	WAbe
'Tess'	WAbe
'Yellowstone'	WAbe

Dioon (*Zamiaceae*)

califanoi	CBrP
caputoi	CBrP
edule ♀H1b	CBrP LPal SPlb
- var. ***angustifolium***	CBrP
merolae	CBrP
rzedowskii	CBrP
spinulosum	CBrP SBig

Dioscorea (*Dioscoreaceae*)

araucana	LSou
batatas	CAgr CArn CRHN LEdu
deltoidea	CExl
elephantipes ♀H1c	LToo
japonica	CAgr LEdu
quinqueloba	WCru
villosa	CArn LEdu

Diosma (*Rutaceae*)

ericoides misapplied	see *Coleonema pulchellum*

Diosphaera (*Campanulaceae*)

asperuloides	see *Trachelium asperuloides*

Diospyros (*Ebenaceae*)

austroafricana	CFil SPlb
glabra	SVen
* ***hyrcanum***	NLar
kaki (F)	CBcs CMCN EPfP NLar NPla WCot WPGP
- 'Fuyu' (F)	CAgr
- 'Kostata' (F)	CAgr
- 'Mazelii' (F)	CAgr WPGP
lotus	CAgr CBcs CMCN EBee ESwi LEdu NLar SPlb WMat WPGP
- (f)	CAgr
- (m)	CAgr
lycioides	CTre SPlb
'Nikita's Gift' (F)	CAgr
'Nikita's Russian' (F) **new**	CAgr
'Nikshoo' (F) **new**	CAgr
ramulosa	SPlb
rhombifolia	CBcs NLar
'Russian Beauty' (F)	CAgr
'Russian Red' (F) **new**	CAgr
virginiana (F)	CBcs CMCN NLar SPlb SSpi
- 'Morris Burton' (F) **new**	CAgr
- 'Nc-10' (F) **new**	CAgr

Diostea (*Verbenaceae*)

juncea	MGil

Dipcadi (*Asparagaceae*)

ciliare	CLak
serotinum	ECho
- subsp. ***lividum***	WPGP
viride	CLak CTal
white-flowered	CLak

Dipelta (*Caprifoliaceae*)

floribunda ♀H5	CBcs CBot CDul CExl CFil CJun CMCN CMac EBee ELan EPfP IDee LRHS MBlu NLar SKHP SWvt WPGP WPat

ventricosa	CAbP CBcs CExl CFil CJun EBee ELan EPfP LRHS MBlu NLar SChF SKHP SSpi WPGP WPat
yunnanensis	CBcs CBot CDul CExl CJun ELan EPfP IArd IDee LRHS NLar SBrt SKHP SWvt WPGP WPat

Diphylleia (*Berberidaceae*)

cymosa	CAby CTal ECha GCal GEdr LEdu LPla MRav SPhx WCru
- red-marked	CDes
grayi	GEdr WCru
sinensis	CExl WCru

Dipidax see *Onixotis*

Diplacus see *Mimulus*

Dipladenia see *Mandevilla*

Diplarrena (*Iridaceae*)

§ ***latifolia***	CNor EBee GBBs GCal IBlr LRHS NCGa SGSe WPtf
- Helen Dillon's form	IBlr
moraea	CAbP CAby CElw CJun CMac CWCL EBee ECho GAbr GBBs GBin GCal IBlr IDee IKil LEdu MBel NCGa WPGP WSHC
- ***minor***	IBlr
- 'Slieve Donard'	IBlr
- West Coast form	see *D. latifolia*

Diplazium (*Woodsiaceae*)

maximum **new**	NLos

Diplopanax (*Cornaceae*)

stachyanthus B&SWJ 11803	WCru

Diplotaxis (*Brassicaceae*)

muralis	CLau WJek
tenuifolia	CAgr CLau ENfk MNHC SRms

Dipsacus (*Caprifoliaceae*)

asper PAB 8884 **new**	LEdu
§ ***fullonum***	CArn CBod CHab ENfk EPfP GJos LCro MBri MHer MNHC NBFr NMir NPri SDix SEND SIde SRms WHer WSFF
inermis	CSam ECha NBid NLar
japonicus	SKHP
- HWJ 695	SPhx WCru
pilosus	CBgR NDov
sativus	NLar NWad
strigosus	SPhx
sylvestris	see *D. fullonum*

Dipteracanthus see *Ruellia*

Dipteronia (*Sapindaceae*)

sinensis	CBcs CMCN WPGP

Disa (*Orchidaceae*)

aurata	NDav
Bride's Dream gx	NDav
Child Safety Transvaal gx	NDav
- 'Sonia' **new**	NDav
Constantia gx	NDav
Diores gx	NDav
- 'Inca City'	NDav
- 'Inca Gold'	NDav
- 'Inca Princess'	NDav
- 'Inca Warrior'	NDav
Diorosa gx	NDav
Foam gx	NDav
- 'Zoe' **new**	NDav
Glasgow Orchid Conference gx **new**	NDav
Ivan Watson gx	NDav
Kalahari Sands gx	NDav
Kewbett gx	NDav
Kewdior gx	NDav
Kewensis gx 'Alice'	NDav
- 'Ann'	NDav
- 'May'	NDav
- 'Milkmaid'	NDav
- 'Ruth'	NDav
Reheat gx	NDav
Riette gx	NDav
Robert Parkinson gx	NDav
Sealord gx	NDav
Tracey Parkinson gx	NDav
tripetaloides	NDav
Unidiorosa gx 'Tracey'	NDav
uniflora	NDav SPlb
- carmine-flowered	NDav
- pink-flowered	NDav
- red-flowered	NDav
Unifoam gx	NDav
- 'Firebird'	NDav
Unilangley gx	NDav
Watsonii gx 'Bramley'	NDav
- 'Candy'	NDav
- 'Don'	NDav
- 'Sandra'	NDav

Disanthus (*Hamamelidaceae*)

cercidifolius ♀H5	CAbP CBcs CJun CMCN CMac EPfP GBin GKin IArd IDee LRHS MBlu MBri MPkF NLar SPer SPoG SSpi WHor WMat WPGP
- 'Ena-nishiki' (v)	MBlu NLar WPGP

Discaria (*Rhamnaceae*)

chacaye	LEdu WPGP
toumatou	SVen

Diselma (*Cupressaceae*)

archeri	CDoC CKen SCoo SLim
- 'Read Dwarf'	CKen

Disepalum (*Annonaceae*)

petelotii B&SWJ 11690	WCru
- FMWJ 13375 **new**	WCru

Disphyma (*Aizoaceae*)

crassifolium	SChr

Disporopsis (*Asparagaceae*)

B&SWJ 229 from Taiwan	WCru
B&SWJ 1864 from Taiwan	WCru
aspersa	CAvo CSpe EBee ECho EPPr EWld GEdr GKev LEdu MAvo NBir WCru WPGP
- tall	CBct CExl WCru WWEG
fuscopicta	CAby CBct CLAP EBee EPPr LEdu MAvo MPie WCru WWEG
longifolia	CLAP
- B&SWJ 5284	WCru

- HWJ 861	CDes
luzoniensis	IMou
- B&SWJ 3891	CBct CExl ESwi GEdr LEdu WCru
'Min Shan'	CExl CTal ELon
* ***nova***	EPPr WWEG
§ ***pernyi***	Widely available
- B&SWJ 1864	CBct EPPr GEdr MAvo
- 'Bill Baker'	CBct EBee EPPr LEdu MAvo WSHC
aff. ***pernyi***	CCon
taiwanensis	IMou LEdu
- B&SWJ 3388	CBct GEdr WCru
undulata	CBct EPPr ILea IMou LEdu NBid WCru WPGP

Disporum (*Colchicaceae*)

austrosinense B&SWJ 9777	WCru
bodinieri	CExl EPfP GKev
- BWJ 8128	WCru
- DJHC 765	WCru
cantoniense	CBct CCon IMou LEdu WCru WFar
- B&L 12512	CExl CLAP
- B&SWJ 1424	WCru
- B&SWJ 9715	WCru
- DJHC 98485	LEdu SKHP WPGP
- PAB 8339 new	LEdu
I - 'Aureovariegata'	CBct EPfP LEdu WCot
- var. ***cantoniense*** f. ***brunneum*** B&SWJ 5290	WCru
- 'Leigong' new	WPGP
- var. ***multiflorum*** B&SWJ 11252	WCru
- - B&SWJ 11291	WCru
- var. ***sikkimense*** B&SWJ 2337	WCru
- - B&SWJ 2358	LEdu WCru
- - PAB 4973	LEdu
- var. ***y-tiense*** FMWJ 13348 new	CEvo
- - HWJ 1045	WCru
hookeri	see *Prosartes hookeri*
kawakamii B&SWJ 350	WCru
- RWJ 10103	CBct WCru
lanuginosum	see *Prosartes lanuginosa*
leschenaultianum B&SWJ 9484	WCru
- B&SWJ 9505	WCru
leucanthum	CTal WCru
- B&SWJ 2389	WCru
longistylum	EBee LEdu SGSe
- B&SWJ 2859	WCru
- L 1564	CBct ESwi LEdu WCru
- 'Green Giant'	CBct CDes CExl CLAP CTal EBee EPfP GEdr IDee IFoB ILea LEdu LSou MAvo MSCN NLar WFar WPtf
- 'Night Heron'	CBct CDes CExl CTal GKev IFoB IMou LEdu WCot WFar
- 'Night Heron' seedlings	WPGP
lutescens	CTal WCru
maculatum	see *Prosartes maculata*
megalanthum	CBct CExl CLAP GKev IFoB LEdu WCru
- CD&R 2412B	CExl CTal
menziesii	see *Prosartes smithii*
nantouense	CTal
- B&SWJ 359	CBct LEdu WCru
- B&SWJ 6812	WCru
oreganum	see *Prosartes hookeri* var. *oregana*
sessile	EBee ECho LEdu WCru
- AGSJ 146	GBuc
- B&SWJ 2824	WCru
I - 'Aureovariegatum' (v)	ECho WCru
- 'Awa-no-tsuki' (v)	GEdr
- 'Cricket'	GEdr
- 'Kinga' (v)	GEdr LEdu MAvo
- f. ***macrophyllum*** B&SWJ 4316	WCru
I - 'Robustum Variegatum' (v)	EBee
- 'Snow Stream' (v) new	GEdr
- 'Variegatum' (v)	CAby CExl CNor CTal EBee ECho ELan ELon EPPr EPfP IMou LEdu LRHS NLar SGSe SPhx WCru WFar WPGP
- var. ***yakushimense***	ECho LEdu
shimadae	GKev
- B&SWJ 399	WCru
smilacinum	CTal NLar SGSe WCru
- B&SWJ 713	CBct WCru
* - 'Aureovariegatum' (v)	LEdu WCru
- pink-flowered	WCot WCru
smithii	see *Prosartes smithii*
taiwanense B&SWJ 1513	WCru
- B&SWJ 2018	WCru
tonkinense B&SWJ 11672	WCru
- B&SWJ 11814	WCru
- HWJ 882	WCru
trabeculatum	CBct WCru
- 'Nakafu'	GKev IMou LEdu WCru
uniflorum	CAby CAvo CBct CLAP CTal ECho EPPr EPfP LEdu LRHS MMHG MNrw NBid SMHy WSHC
- B&SWJ 651	CBct LEdu WCru
- B&SWJ 872	WCru
- B&SWJ 4100	WCru
viridescens	CBct EBee EPPr GKev LEdu SKHP WCru WPnP
- B&SWJ 4598	WCru

Distictis (*Bignoniaceae*)

buccinatoria	CHII

Distylium (*Hamamelidaceae*)

myricoides	NLar WPat
racemosum	CBcs CMac EBee EPfP IVic MBlu NLar SSta WSHC

Dittrichia (*Asteraceae*)

viscosa	WCot

Diuranthera see *Chlorophytum*

Dizygotheca see *Schefflera*

Dobinea (*Anacardiaceae*)

vulgaris B&SWJ 2532	WCru

Dodecatheon (*Primulaceae*)

sp.	MSCN
alpinum	GKev NHar
- subsp. ***alpinum***	EBee
'Aphrodite'PBR	CBod LLWG NLar WFar
austrofrigidum	GEdr GKev NCGa NHar
clevelandii	GEdr
- subsp. ***insulare***	EBee LLHF
- subsp. ***patulum***	ECho LRHS
conjugens	GKev LLHF
cusickii	see *D. pulchellum* subsp. *cusickii*
dentatum H5	CPBP GEdr GKev LEdu NHar SBrt WAbe WFar

- subsp. ***utahense***	NHar
frigidum	GEdr WAbe
§ ***jeffreyi***	ECho EPPr GBuc GEdr GKev LEdu LRHS MBel MNrw NCGa NLar NSum WAbe WBor WFar
- subsp. ***pygmaeum***	GKev
* × ***lemoinei***	WAbe
§ ***meadia*** ♀H5	Widely available
- from Cedar County, USA	WAbe
- f. ***album*** ♀H5	CBro ECho ELan EPfP EPot LAma LEdu LHop LRHS MBel NCGa NHol NMyG NSum NWad SKHP SPer SWvt WPnP
- 'Aphrodite'	EPfP
* - 'Goliath'	GAbr GJos NSum
- membranaceous	WAbe
- 'Queen Victoria'	ECho GBuc GEdr LEdu NLar SKHP WFar
- red shades	GBuc NSum
pauciflorum misapplied	see *D. pulchellum*
pauciflorum (Dur.) E. Greene	see *D. meadia*
poeticum	SPlb
- NNS 00-259	NCGa
§ ***pulchellum*** ♀H5	CBro EBee ECho EDAr GEdr GKev IBoy LHop LLWG LRHS MNrw NRya WIce
- ***album***	ECho GKev
§ - subsp. ***cusickii***	LEdu
- subsp. ***pulchellum*** 'Red Wings'	CPne ECho ELon EPot IBoy LLHF LRHS NBir NHar NLar SKHP WHoo
- ***radicatum***	see *D. pulchellum*
- 'Sooke Variety'	WAbe
radicatum	see *D. pulchellum*
redolens	GBuc
tetrandrum	see *D. jeffreyi*

Dodonaea (*Sapindaceae*)

viscosa	CBcs SPlb
- 'Purpurea'	CBcs CExl CHGN COtt CTsd EUJe IVic LPal LRHS SPoG SVen

Doellingeria (*Asteraceae*)

scabra	see *Aster scaber*

Dolichos (*Papilionaceae*)

purpureus	see *Lablab purpureus*

Dombeya (*Malvaceae*)

× ***cayeuxii***	SVen

Dondia see *Hacquetia*

Doodia (*Blechnaceae*)

media	EBee GBin ISha LBMP LLWG LRHS NLos SPlb

Doronicum (*Asteraceae*)

austriacum	NBid
- PAB 5641	LEdu
caucasicum	see *D. orientale*
§ ***columnae***	CBcs
cordatum	see *D. columnae*
§ × ***excelsum*** 'Harpur Crewe'	EBee LEdu MRav NPer SHar
'Finesse'	COtt GCal GJos LRHS LSun SRms
'Little Leo'	CBod CMea COtt ELan ELon EPfP GJos GMaP LRHS LSRN NLar NPri SPoG SRms WHil WRHF
§ ***orientale***	ELan EPfP GJos MMuc SEND SPoG SWat
- 'Leonardo'	EBee LRHS WHar
- 'Leonardo Compact'	LPot
- 'Magnificum'	CBod CSBt EBee EPfP GMaP LRHS MBNS MBri SPoG SRms WHar
pardalianches	CArn CFis CMea GCal GJos MMuc WHal WRHF
- 'Goldstrauss'	EBee
plantagineum 'Excelsum'	see *D.* × *excelsum* 'Harpur Crewe'

Doryanthes (*Doryanthaceae*)

palmeri	CBrP

Dorycnium see *Lotus*

Doryopteris (*Pteridaceae*)

pedata var. ***palmata*** **new**	NLos

Douglasia see *Androsace*

vitaliana	see *Vitaliana primuliflora*

Dovyalis (*Salicaceae*)

caffra (F)	XBlo

Doxantha see *Macfadyena*

Draba (*Brassicaceae*)

acaulis	WAbe
aizoides	ECho EDAr GJos LRHS NPri SPlb SRms XLum
aizoon	see *D. lasiocarpa*
bertolonii Boiss.	see *D. loeseleurii*
bruniifolia	NHar
bryoides	see *D. rigida* var. *bryoides*
'Buttermilk'	WAbe
compacta	see *D. lasiocarpa* Compacta Group
cuspidata	CTal
dedeana	GJos WAbe
densifolia	IFoB
imbricata	see *D. rigida* var. *imbricata*
'John Saxton'	EPot WAbe
kotschyi	SPlb
§ ***lasiocarpa***	XLum
§ - Compacta Group	SIgm
§ ***loeseleurii***	GJos
longisiliqua ♀H4	EPot LLHF WAbe
mollissima	EPot
- 'Göteborg'	EPot
oligosperma	EDAr IFoB
paysonii var. ***treleasei***	LLHF
polytricha	EPot NSla
ramosissima **new**	GJos
§ ***rigida*** var. ***bryoides***	WThu
* - var. ***imbricata***	GCrg NSla
- - f. ***compacta***	EPot
rosularis	EDAr EPot GJos WAbe
scardica	see *D. lasiocarpa*
senilis **new**	GKev
ventosa	EPot
yunnanensis	WAbe

Dracaena ✿ (*Asparagaceae*)

cochinchinensis	SPlb
draco ♀H1c	CArn EShb MHin SPlb WCot XBlo
fragrans Deremensis Group	XBlo
indivisa	see *Cordyline indivisa*
'Lemon Lime Tips'	XBlo

marginata (v) ♀H1b	XBlo
- 'Tricolor' (v) ♀H1b	XBlo

Dracocephalum (*Lamiaceae*)

argunense	SPhx SRms WCot
- 'Blue Carpet'	LEdu NLar
- 'Fuji Blue'	CExl CSma EDAr EWes SPoG WIce XLum
- 'Fuji White'	CExl SPhx SPoG
austriacum	LRHS SBrt
botryoides	CPBP EPot MMuc SBrt SPhx
calophyllum var. ***smithianum***	IMou
forrestii	EBee GKev SBrt
grandiflorum	GEdr MMHG SBrt SPhx WCot XLum
hemsleyanum	LLHF
mairei	see *D. renatii*
peregrinum 'Blue Dragon'	IPot SPhx
prattii	see *Nepeta prattii*
§ ***renatii***	LLHF SPhx
rupestre	EBee GEdr SBrt SPhx
ruyschiana	ELan EWes GEdr MMHG SPhx XLum
sibiricum	see *Nepeta sibirica*
* ***tataricum***	LRHS
virginicum	see *Physostegia virginiana*

Dracunculus (*Araceae*)

canariensis	WCot
muscivorus	see *Helicodiceros muscivorus*
§ ***vulgaris***	CAby CHid EBee ECho EPfP EPot ESwi EUJe GKev LTro SDix SEND SMad SPlb SPoG WCot

Dregea (*Apocynaceae*)

sinensis	CBcs CBot CHll CRHN ECre ELan EPfP EShb EWes LRHS MOWG MRav SEND SKHP SPer SPoG SWvt WPGP WSHC
- 'Brockhill Silver'	CBot EPfP LRHS SKHP SWvt
- 'Variegata' (v)	EWes

Drepanostachyum (*Poaceae*)

falconeri	see *Himalayacalamus falconeri*, *Himalayacalamus falconeri* 'Damarapa'
hookerianum	see *Himalayacalamus hookerianus*
§ ***khasianum***	CExl WPGP

Drimia (*Asparagaceae*)

angustifolia ambig.	ECho
anomala	CLak
basutica	CLak
elata	CLak
§ ***indica*** new	GKev
involuta	CLak
mzimvubuensis	CLak
sphaerocephala	CLak
uniflora	CLak

Drimiopsis (*Asparagaceae*)

maculata	CEvo EShb LToo MPie WCot

Drimys (*Winteraceae*)

andina	CBct CExl EPfP MMuc
aromatica	see *Tasmannia lanceolata*
colorata	see *Pseudowintera colorata*
granadensis var. ***grandiflora*** B&SWJ 10777	WCru
* ***latifolia***	CBcs IDee
winteri ♀H4	Widely available
§ - var. ***chilensis***	CExl EPfP LRHS SSpi WCru WPGP
- Latifolia Group	see *D. winteri* var. *chilensis*
- var. ***winteri***	SRms

Drosanthemum (*Aizoaceae*)

hispidum	ECho ELan EPot LRHS MAsh SPlb SPoG WAbe
speciosum	ECho
* ***sutherlandii***	ECho

Drosera ✿ (*Droseraceae*)

admirabilis	CHew
aliciae ♀H3	CHew EECP
andersoniana	EFEx
ascendens	CHew
binata	CHew EECP
§ - subsp. ***dichotoma*** ♀H3	CHew NLos
- 'Extrema'	NLos
- 'Giant'	NLos
browniana	EFEx
bulbigena	EFEx
bulbosa subsp. ***bulbosa***	EFEx
- subsp. ***major***	EFEx
capensis	CHew SPlb
- 'Albino' ♀H3	CHew EECP
dichotoma	see *D. binata* subsp. *dichotoma*
dichrosepala	EECP
erythrorhiza	EFEx
- subsp. ***collina***	EFEx
- subsp. ***erythrorhiza***	CHew EFEx
- subsp. ***magna***	EFEx
- subsp. ***squamosa***	EFEx
filiformis	NLos
- var. ***filiformis***	CHew EECP
- var. ***tracyi***	NLos
gigantea	EFEx
graniticola	EFEx
heterophylla	EFEx
loureiroi	EFEx
macrantha	EFEx
- subsp. ***macrantha***	EFEx
macrophylla subsp. ***macrophylla***	EFEx
marchantii subsp. ***prophylla***	EFEx
menziesii subsp. ***basifolia***	EFEx
- subsp. ***menziesii***	EFEx
- subsp. ***thysanosepala***	EFEx
modesta	EFEx
nidiformis	CHew
orbiculata	EFEx
peltata	EFEx
platypoda	EFEx
ramellosa	EFEx
rosulata	EFEx
rotundifolia	WHer
salina	EFEx
scorpioides	EECP
slackii ♀H3	CHew SPlb
stolonifera subsp. ***compacta***	EFEx
- subsp. ***humilis***	EFEx
- subsp. ***porrecta***	EFEx
- subsp. ***rupicola***	EFEx

	- subsp. ***stolonifera***	EFEx
	tubaestylus	EFEx
	zonaria	EFEx

Drosophyllum (*Drosophyllaceae*)

	lusitanicum	CHew

Dryandra (*Proteaceae*)

	formosa	CTre SPlb
	quercifolia	SPlb

Dryas (*Rosaceae*)

	drummondii	EBee ECho EPot LLHF
§	***integrifolia***	CMea LLHF WAbe
	- 'Greenland Green'	WAbe
	octopetala 🏆H5	CArn CMea ECho GJos LHop LRHS NChi SPoG SRms SWvt WAbe
	- subsp. ***hookeriana***	LLHF
§	- 'Minor' 🏆H5	EPot NHar WAbe
	× ***suendermannii*** 🏆H5	CMea EBee EPot GCrg GEdr GMaP LLHF NHar NSla SBch
	tenella misapplied	see *D. octopetala* 'Minor'
	tenella Pursh	see *D. integrifolia*

Dryopteris ✿ (*Dryopteridaceae*)

	from Kunming, China **new**	NLos
	from Mount Zijin, China **new**	NLos
	from Nanjing Botanical Garden, China **new**	NLos
	aemula	EFer SRms
§	***affinis*** 🏆H5	CLAP CMac CWCL EAEE ECha EPfP ERod EWoo GMaP LBuc LPal LPfy LRHS MBri MCot MGos MWat NPri SCob SPer SPoG SRms WCot WFib WShi XLum
	- 'Angustata Crispa'	EBee
§	- subsp. ***borreri***	SRms
	- subsp. ***cambrensis***	ISha
	- - 'Crispa Barnes'	WPGP
	- - 'Insubrica'	EFer
	- 'Congesta'	CKel CLAP
	- 'Congesta Cristata'	CLAP CTal CWCL ECtt EFer GMaP LPal SRot
	- Crispa Group	CBod CLAP EHon EPfP LRHS SCob WWEG
§	- 'Crispa Gracilis' 🏆H5	CKel CLAP ELan ERod GBin ISha LPal NBir NEgg NHol NLar
*	- 'Crispa Gracilis Congesta'	GEdr MRav MWhi NGdn NWad SGSe WCot WFib WPat
§	- 'Cristata' 🏆H5	Widely available
	- 'Cristata Angustata' 🏆H5	CLAP CTal EFer ELan EPfP NBid NBro NGdn NHol SRms WFib WMoo WPGP
	- 'Cristata The King'	see *D. affinis* 'Cristata'
	- 'Grandiceps Askew'	EFer SRms WFib
	- 'Pinderi'	CLAP EBee EPfP GBin ISha LLWG LSun MPie NLar SCob SRms WCot WRHF
	- Polydactyla Group	CLAP CLet
	- - 'Polydactyla Dadds'	CLAP EBee LLHF NLar
	- - 'Polydactyla Mapplebeck' 🏆H5	CLAP CLet NBid SRms WFib
	- 'Revoluta'	SGSe
	- 'Revolvens'	CLAP EFer
	atrata misapplied	see *D. cycadina*
	atrata (Wall. ex Kunze) Ching	CDTJ CWCL LLWG LPal LRHS NEgg NLar SPoG XLum
	× ***australis***	CDes CLAP ISha NLos
	austriaca	see *D. dilatata*
	bissetiana	ISha
	blanfordii	WPGP
	- from Kashmir	ISha
	borreri	see *D. affinis* subsp. *borreri*
	buschiana	CLAP EBee LPal MRav NLar WCot
	carthusiana	CLAP EBee EFer GBin NLar XLum
	- 'Cristata'	EFer
	celsa	ISha NLos
	championii	CLAP EBee ISha LRHS
	clintoniana	CLAP EBee ECtt EFer GBin GEdr LLWG LRHS WCot WPGP
	× ***complexa***	ISha NLos
	- 'Stablerae' 🏆H7	CLAP CLet EFer GBin WFib WPGP
	- 'Stablerae' crisped 🏆H7	NMyG WFib
	coreanomontana	NLar
	crassirhizoma 🏆H6	CKel CLAP EBee ECGP ECtt GBin ISha LLWG LRHS LSun MAvo SGSe SMDP WCot WPtf WRHF
	cristata	CLAP CWCL EBee EPfP WMoo XLum
§	***cycadina*** 🏆H4	CBcs CLAP CTal EBee EFer ELan EPfP ERod EShb EUJe GBin ISha LRHS MBri MGos NBid NBir NLos SCob SPtp WFib WMoo WPnP
	cystolepidota	EFer
§	***dilatata*** 🏆H6	ECha EFer ELan EPfP ERod LPal LRHS MMuc MRav SGSe SRms WFib WHal WShi
	- 'Crispa Whiteside' 🏆H6	CDoC CLAP CLet CWCL EAEE EBee EFer ELan EPfP ERod LEdu LPfy LRHS MBri MRav NBro NEgg NLar SHil SPlb WCot WFib WMoo WPGP WPat WWEG
	- 'Grandiceps'	CLAP CMac EFer WFib
	- 'Jimmy Dyce'	CLAP ISha LRHS
	- 'Lepidota Crispa Cristata'	CLAP EBee WPat
	- 'Lepidota Cristata' 🏆H6	CLAP CWCL ELan ERod NGdn NLos NMyG SGSe SRms WFib WMoo
	- 'Lepidota Grandiceps'	CLAP
*	- 'Recurvata'	CLAP ISha LLHF NLar
	erythrosora 🏆H4	Widely available
	- 'Brilliance' 🏆H5	CDoC CLAP CSpe EBee ECtt GQue ISha LLWG LRHS LSou MPie SMDP WCot WRHF
	- var. ***koidzumiana***	EBee EShb ISha LRHS
	- var. ***prolifica***	CBod CDoC CKel CLAP EBee ELan EPfP GMaP ISha LPal LRHS MBri MGos NBir NEgg NLar NPri SBod SPoG WFib WPat
	× ***euxinensis***	CLAP
	filix-mas 🏆H7	CKel CSBt CTri CWCL ECha ELan EPfP ERod EWoo GMaP LAst LCro LEdu LOPS LPal LPfy LRHS LSun MCot MMuc MWat NHol SCob SEND SPer SRms WFib WSFF WShi XLum
	- 'Barnesii'	CBod CLAP CLet CWCL ECGP EFer ELan ERod GBin ISha LRHS MMuc NEgg NLar SEND SPlb WWEG
	- 'Crispa'	CLAP LRHS SRms WFib
	- 'Crispa Congesta'	see *D. affinis* 'Crispa Gracilis'
	- 'Crispa Cristata' 🏆H7	CLAP CWCL EBee ECtt EFer ELan EPfP ERod EUJe GMaP IKil LHop LLWG LRHS MBri NBid NBir NBro SCob SGSe SPoG SRms WFib WWEG XLum
	- 'Crispatissima'	EBee
	- 'Cristata' 🏆H7	CLAP CTal EBee ECtt EFer ELan EPfP LLWG LOPS LPot MJak MMuc SEND SRms WMoo

- Cristata Group	EFer
* - - 'Cristata Grandiceps'	EFer
- - 'Cristata Jackson'	CLAP SPlb
- - 'Cristata Martindale'	CLAP NBid SRms WFib
- - 'Fred Jackson'	CLAP WFib
- 'Depauperata'	CLAP WPGP
- 'Furcans'	CLAP EBee ECtt
- 'Grandiceps Wills' ♀H7	NBid WFib
- 'Linearis'	EFer EHon ELan EWoo ISha LAst LRHS MCot MGos MWhi SGSe SRms WFib
- 'Linearis Congesta'	WPGP
- 'Linearis Polydactyla' ♀H7	CDoC CLAP CMac CWCL EAJP EFer ELan EPPr EPfP EShb LPal LRHS MMuc MRav NEgg NGdn NHol NLar NLos NMyG SCob SEND SPoG SPtp WMoo WPnP XLum
- 'Parsley'	CLAP ISha
* - Polydactyla Group	ECha MRav NEgg SCob
I - 'Revolvens'	WFib
fragrans	SKHP
goldieana	CDTJ CLAP CLet CTal EBee ECha ECtt EFer GMaP ISha LLWG LRHS NBid NBir NEgg NLar WFar WFib WMoo WPnP XLum
hirtipes misapplied	see *D. cycadina*
intermedia	ISha
labordei	EBee EShb ISha LRHS
lacera	ISha
lepidopoda	CAby CBcs ECtt LLWG LPal LRHS LSun MAvo SGSe SMDP WCot WPtf WRHF
ludoviciana	ISha LRHS
marginalis	CDTJ CKel CLAP GBin LRHS NLar SCob WMoo
neorosthornii new	NLos
oreades	WCot
pacifica	CLAP
paleacea	CLAP
pseudofilix-mas	ISha
pseudomas	see *D. affinis*
pulcherrima new	LRHS
× ***remota***	ISha NLos
× ***separabilis***	ISha
sichotensis new	EBee
sieboldii ♀H6	Widely available
stewartii	CLAP GEdr LLHF NLar
tokyoensis ♀H6	CDTJ CLAP GBin ISha LRHS NLar WPGP
uniformis	CLAP EFer NLos
wallichiana ♀H5	Widely available
- F&M 107	WPGP
- from Yunnan, China new	GCal
yigongensis new	NLos

Duchesnea (*Rosaceae*)

chrysantha	see *D. indica*
§ ***indica***	GJos MRav SEND WHea WMoo WOut XLum
§ - 'Harlequin' (v)	CExl
* - 'Snowflake' (v)	WMoo
- 'Variegata'	see *D. indica* 'Harlequin'

Dudleya (*Crassulaceae*)

calcicola new	SPlb
cymosa	SPlb
- subsp. ***cymosa*** new	SIgm
lanceolata	SIgm

Dugaldia (*Asteraceae*)

hoopesii	see *Hymenoxys hoopesii*

Dulichium (*Cyperaceae*)

arundinaceum	LLWG
- 'Tigress'	LLWG

Dunalia (*Solanaceae*)

australis	see *Iochroma australe*
- blue-flowered	see *Iochroma australe* 'Bill Evans'
- white-flowered	see *Iochroma australe* 'Andean Snow'

Duranta (*Verbenaceae*)

§ ***erecta***	CHll EShb
- white-flowered	SVen
plumieri	see *D. erecta*
repens	see *D. erecta*

Duvernoia see *Justicia*

Dyckia (*Bromeliaceae*)

brevifolia	WCot
'Cherry Coke'	WCot
frigida	EAla WCot WGrn
goehringii	WCot
jonesiana	WCot
leptostachya	WCot WGrn
marnier-lapostollei	WCot
'Morris Hobbs'	WCot
* ***polyphylla***	WCot
remotiflora	EAla SChr
velascana	EAla WCot

Dypsis (*Arecaceae*)

§ ***decaryi***	LPal XBlo
lutescens ♀H1a	LPal XBlo

Dysosma see *Podophyllum*

E

Ecballium (*Cucurbitaceae*)

elaterium	CArn CDTJ CFil LEdu SIde WCot WPGP
- 'Lahij' new	WPGP

Eccremocarpus (*Bignoniaceae*)

scaber	CBcs CKel CWCL ELan EPfP IDee LHop LRHS MGil NPer SEND WHea
- 'Carmineus'	EPfP
- 'Coccineus'	EUJe
- cream-flowered	ESwi NLar
- orange-flowered	ESwi
- red-flowered	NLar
- 'Tangerine'	CSpe

Echeandia (*Asparagaceae*)

formosa B&SWJ 9147	WCru

Echeveria ✿ (*Crassulaceae*)

affinis	CBod CDTJ CDoC EUJe SRot
'Afterglow'	CSuc
agavoides ♀H1c	CDTJ MRav WCot
- 'Ebony' new	CSuc WCot
- 'Lipstick'	WCot

	albicans	CDoC SPlb
	alpina	see *E. secunda*
	amoena	CDoC
	'Apollo' **new**	CSuc
	ballsii	WCot
*	'Black Knight'	MAvo
*	'Black Prince'	CDTJ CDes CDoC ELan MHer NPer SPlb SRot WCot WPGP
	'Blue Prince'	CDoC
	'Blue Waves'	CSuc WCot
*	***cana***	CDTJ CDoC SRot
	cante ♀H2	SPlb
	'Chrissy 'n' Ryan'	CDoC
	coccinea	CDoC ELan
	colorata ♀H2	WCot
	- f. ***brandtii***	CDoC
	'Corymbosa'	WCot
	'Crystal Maze'	CSuc
	'Curly Locks'	WCot
	derenbergii ♀H2	MHCG
	'Derenceana'	CDoC
	× ***derosa***	CDTJ
	difractens	WCot
	'Duchess of Nuremberg'	CBod CDoC EUJe SPlb SRot
	elegans ♀H2	CBod CDTJ CDoC EPfP EUJe LSou LSun NWad SPlb
	'Frank Reinelt'	CSuc
	'Fred Wass' **new**	CDoC
	'Galaxy Mars' (Galaxy Hybrids Series)	CDoC
	'Ghost Buster'	WPGP
§	***gibbiflora*** var. ***metallica***	CDoC EBee
	× ***gilva*** ♀H2	CSuc
*	- 'Red'	CDoC LSun MHol WCot
	glauca Baker	see *E. secunda* var. *glauca*
	harmsii	CDoC CSuc
	hyalina RE 614	CDoC
	'Ileen'	CDoC
	'Imbricata'	CBod
	lilacina ♀H2	CDoC EUJe MAvo SPlb SRot WPGP
	'Mahogany'	WCot WGrn
	'Mauna Loa'	CDTJ EBee EWes LRHS WGrn
	maxonii B&SWJ 10396	WCru
	minima ♀H2	CSuc SPlb WCot
	'Miranda' **new**	CSuc
	montana B&SWJ 10277	WCru
	multicaulis	CSuc
	nodulosa	CSuc WCot
	nuda	CSuc
	peacockii	MHer MSCN SPlb
	'Perle von Nürnberg' ♀H2	CAbb SMad SPlb
	'Pollux' **new**	LToo
	prolifica	CSuc
	pulidonis ♀H1c	CDoC LToo MHer
	pulvinata ♀H1c	MHCG
	- 'Frosty'	CDoC
I	- 'Rubra'	SPlb
	purpusorum	CDoC SPlb
	'Ramillette'	CSuc
	'Ron Evans'	CDoC
	rosea ♀H1c	MHer WCot
	runyonii ♀H2 **new**	CDoC
	- 'Topsy Turvy' ♀H2	CDTJ CDoC SRot
	'Scorpio'	CSuc
§	***secunda***	CAbb CCac SPlb
§	- var. ***glauca***	CDTJ CDes CDoC ELan EShb NBir SEND WPGP
*	- - 'Gigantea'	NPer WPGP
	setosa ♀H1c	CDTJ LToo WCot
	- var. ***ciliata***	EShb
	- var. ***deminuta***	CDoC
	shaviana ♀H2	CDTJ EUJe SPlb SRot WCot
	subsessilis	WCot
	- RE 163	CDoC
	'Telstar'	CSuc
	'Violet Queen'	CDoC

Echinacea ✿ (*Asteraceae*)

§	'Adam Saul'	LRHS STPC
§	'After Midnight'PBR (Big Sky Series)	EBee ECtt IBoy
	'Aloha'	NLar
	'Amazing Dream'PBR	CWGN EBee ECtt IBoy
	angustifolia	CArn CEvo ENfk EPfP GPoy LRHS MHer MMuc NDov SPhx WJek
§	'Art's Pride'PBR	LSRN MJak SCob SPer
	'Buttercream' (d) **new**	EBee
	'Butterfly Kisses' (d) **new**	EBee
	'Caribbean Green' **new**	EBee
	'Cheyenne Spirit' mixture	LCro LOPS MAsh SPhx
	'Cleopatra' **new**	EBee
	'Coral Reef'PBR	ECtt
	'Coupe Soleil' (d) **new**	EBee
	'Cranberry Cupcake' (d)	ECtt
	Crazy Pink	see *E.* 'Adam Saul'
	Crazy White	see *E.* 'Noam Saul'
	'Daydream'PBR	CWCL CWGN ECtt LRHS LSou
	Double Scoop Bubblegum = 'Balscblum'	EBee
	Double Scoop Raspberry = 'Balsceras' (d)	EBee
	'Eccentric' (d)	CWCL CWGN EBee IBoy IPot LRHS MHol WCot WNPC WTor
	'Emily Saul'	see *E.* 'After Midnight' (Big Sky Series)
	'Evan Saul'	see *E.* 'Sundown'
	'Evening Glow'	CWGN EBee
	'Ferris Wheel' (Carnival Series)	SCob
	'Flame Thrower'PBR	CWGN ECtt LBMP LSou MHol NLar SPoG WCAu
	'Gemini Pink'	LRHS
	'Green Envy'PBR	CBcs CWGN EBee ECtt ELan EPfP EWoo GQue IBoy LOPS LRHS MBNS MBel MNrw NLar SCob SKHP SMad SPoG WCot WTor
	'Greenline'	EBee ECtt
	'Guava Ice'PBR	EBee LLHF MHol
§	'Harvest Moon'PBR (Big Sky Series)	CBcs CBod CMac CWGN CWld EBee ECtt EPfP LHop LOPS LRHS LSRN NSti SCob SKHP SPer SPoG SWvt WCot WFar
	'Heavenly Dream'PBR	CWCL ECtt ELon MHol
	'Hot Lava'PBR	CMos CWGN EBee ECtt LRHS SPoG
	'Hot Papaya'PBR (d)	CBod CWCL CWGN ECtt EWoo IBoy IPot LCro LLHF LOPS MBNS MBri MHol NPla SCob SMad SWvt WCot
	'Hot Summer'PBR	CBcs CPar CWCL CWGN EBee EWoo LCro LHop LRHS MBri NLar SCob SGbt SPoG STPC
	'Irresistible'PBR (d)	CNor CWGN EBee IPot LCro LOPS
	'Jupiter' (Big Sky Series)	ECtt SCob
	'Katie Saul'	see *E.* 'Summer Sky'
	'Leilani' **new**	WCAu
	'Mac 'n' Cheese'PBR	CWCL EBee LCro LOPS LRHS SCob
	'Mama Mia'	CPar CWGN EBee ECtt LRHS NLar SGbt SPoG
	Mango Meadowbrite = 'CBG Cone3'	EPfP LRHS

'Marmalade'PBR CBcs CWCL CWGN EBee LLHF NCGa SCob WCAu
'Matthew Saul' see *E.*'Harvest Moon'
'Maui Sunshine'PBR CAbb EBee ECtt SHar
'Maya Raya' IBoy WNPC
'Meditation'PBR EBee LRHS MHol WCot
§ 'Noam Saul' LRHS
Orange Meadowbrite see *E.*'Art's Pride'
'Orange Passion' CWGN ECtt
'Pacific Summer' **new** EBee
pallida Widely available
- 'Hula Dancer' NGdn SHar SPhx
paradoxa CArn CEvo CHid ELan EPfP EPri GPoy LHop LRHS LSRN MCot MMuc NGdn SGSe SPav SPer SPhx SPlb SPtp SWvt WTcb XLum
- var. ***paradoxa*** EAJP SPtp
- 'Yellow Mellow' ELan
paradoxa* × *purpurea IBoy
'Piccolino' CAbP CWGN ECtt LLHF LRHS MHol WCot
'Pink Mist' (Mistical Series) EBee
Pixie Meadowbrite = 'CBG Cone 2' CAbP CWGN EBee ECtt GQue IKil MNrw
§ ***purpurea*** Widely available
- 'Alaska'PBR IBoy NGdn NLar SGol
- 'Alba' CRos EPfP EWTr LBMP LPfy LRHS SHil WCot XLum
- 'Amber Mist'PBR (Mistical Series) EBee
- 'Augustkönigin' CKno EBee LRHS MNrw
- 'Avalanche'PBR EBee ELon
- 'Baby Swan Pink' EAEE LRHS SHil SPhx
- 'Baby Swan White' CBod EBee ELon GBin LRHS NLar SHil WCot WFar WWEG
- Bressingham hybrids CNec EShb EUJe LRHS MRav NDov SPer WGwG WWtn
- 'Catharina'PBR CWGN EBee ECtt
- 'Coconut Lime'PBR CWGN EPfP LOPS LSou
- dark-stemmed LPla
- Doppelganger see *E. purpurea* 'Doubledecker'
§ - 'Doubledecker' CWCL EBee ELan EPfP GBin IBoy LLHF MHol NGdn SGbt SGol SPoG SWat WCAu WFar WHar XLum
- Elton Knight = 'Elbrook'PBR ♀H7 ECtt LOPS LRHS LSRN MBri MHol STPC SWvt
- 'Fancy Frills' ECtt LSou
- 'Fatal Attraction'PBR Widely available
- 'Firebird'PBR ECtt LRHS SCob SGbt SPoG
- 'Fragrant Angel'PBR CWCL ECtt ELon EPfP LHop LRHS LSRN NLar SKHP SPoG SWat SWvt WCot WNPC
- 'Green Edge' LOPS
- 'Green Eyes' EBee ECtt NLar
- 'Green Jewel'PBR CWGN EBee ECtt EUJe EWoo GBin LRHS LSou MAsh MBel MCot NLar MNrw NSti SBod SCob SGbt SGol SPad WCAu WCot WPtf
- 'Gum Drop'PBR EBee LRHS SPoG
- 'Happy Star' EAEE LRHS LSou SHil
- 'Hope'PBR CBod CPar EBee ECtt LRHS LSou NLar WCAu
- 'Jade' CAbP EBee GQue LSRN MBNS NLar SWat
- 'JS Purple Prairie' IPot
- 'Kim's Knee High'PBR CKno CMea COtt EAEE ECtt ELan EPfP EWoo GMaP LCro LRHS LSou MCot NGdn NLar SCob SGol SPer SWat SWvt WCot
- 'Kim's Mop Head' CKno ECtt ELan EPfP EWes LRHS MCot MRav NGdn NLar WCot
§ - 'Leuchtstern' CKno ELan EPfP LRHS NBir NGdn SWat WWEG XLum
- 'Lilliput'PBR ECtt LRHS NLar
- 'Little Angel'PBR ECtt
- 'Little Giant' ELon
- 'Little Magnus'PBR CKno ECtt LRHS MAsh SPoG
- 'Lucky Star' ELan EPfP LRHS SBea SPhx WCFE
- 'Magnus' Widely available
- 'Magnus Superior' CBod EAEE ECGP LAst LRHS LSou LSun SHil SPhx SWvt WHoo
- 'Mars' SCob
- 'Maxima' CAbP ECtt LRHS
- 'Meringue'PBR IBoy SCob
- 'Merlot'PBR ECtt LRHS LSou SPoG
- 'Milkshake'PBR CWGN EBee LLHF LRHS
- 'Mistral' EBee LRHS
- 'Mozzarella' (d) **new** EBee
- 'Pica Bella' COtt CWGN ECtt EPfP LRHS
- 'Pink Double Delight'PBR LHop LRHS MRav NGdn SWat
- 'Pink Glow' NDov
- 'Pink Poodle'PBR CPar EBee EPri IBoy
- 'Pink Sorbet'PBR NLar
- 'Polar Breeze'PBR LRHS
- (PowWow Series) PowWow White = 'Pas709018' LRHS MBri SPoG WCAu
- - PowWow Wild Berry = 'Pas702917'PBR CBod IPot LRHS MBri SCob SPoG
- 'Prairie Splendor' EPfP LRHS MHol NDov SPhx
- 'Primadonna Deep Rose' CNec IFro LEdu NGBl SRot SVic
- Primadonna (mixed) ELon
- 'Primadonna White' LRHS SRot WWtn
- 'Purity'PBR ECtt LRHS SPoG WCAu
- 'Razzmatazz'PBR (d) CAbP CMac COtt EBee ECtt ELan EWes IBoy MHol MNrw MRav NGdn NSti SGol SPer SWat SWvt WCot
- 'Red Baron' EBee
- 'Red Knee High' ECtt MBri
- 'Robert Bloom' ECtt GQue LHop NBir SWvt
- 'Rubinglow' ECtt IBoy LCro LOPS NBir NDov NLar SWvt
- 'Rubinstern' Widely available
- 'Ruby Giant' ♀H7 CCon CKno ECtt ELan EWoo GBin GMaP IBoy LHop LRHS LSRN LSou MBel MHol MTis NEgg NLar SGbt SPer SPoG WCot WWEG
- 'Southern Belle'PBR CWCL EBee IPot NPla SMad
- 'Summer Salsa' CBod EUJe LCro LLHF LOPS WCot
- 'The King' LRHS NGdn NLar
- 'Tom Thumb' EBee
- 'Verbesserter Leuchtstern' NLar
- 'Vintage Wine'PBR CKno CMac CMos ECtt ELan EPfP EWoo GAbr GQue LCro LRHS LSun MBel NEgg NLar SCob SPer SPoG SWvt WCAu WCot
- 'Virgin'PBR EBee EWoo IPot LCro MAvo NDov NLar SCob WCAu
- 'White Lustre' ECha EPfP SRms
- White Natalie = 'Norwhinat'PBR EBee
- 'White Swan' Widely available
'Quills and Thrills' (Prairie Pillars Series) CWGN ECtt SCob
'Raspberry Tart' ECtt
'Raspberry Truffle'PBR EBee ECtt
(Secret Series) 'Secret Love' (d) CWGN SCob

- 'Secret Lust' (d)	ECtt
- 'Secret Passion' (d)	CWGN EBee ECtt LRHS SGbt
- 'Secret Pride' (d)	SCob
simulata	NDov
'Solar Flare' (Big Sky Series)	CPar EBee ECtt LRHS MBri
(Sombrero Series) 'Sombrero Hot Coral'	EBee LAst MAsh
- 'Sombrero Salsa Red'	CBod LRHS MAsh
- 'Sombrero Sandy Yellow'	CBod EBee MAsh
'Starlight'	see *E. purpurea* 'Leuchtstern'
'Strawberry Shortcake'	EBee
'Summer Breeze'	SCob
'Summer Cloud'	SCob
'Summer Cocktail' PBR	CMos LCro LRHS SCob SPoG
'Summer Passion'	SGol
'Summer Samba' (d) **new**	EBee
§ 'Summer Sky' PBR (Big Sky Series)	ECtt EPfP LRHS MBNS NLar
'Summer Sun' PBR	LRHS NLar
§ 'Sundown' PBR (Big Sky Series)	CMac CPar EBee ECtt EPfP GMaP IBoy LAst LOPS LRHS MBNS MWhi NLar NSti SCob SGbt SPoG SWvt WCAu
'Sunrise' PBR (Big Sky Series)	CKno CMac CMea EBee ECtt ELan EPfP EWes IPot LHop LLHF LRHS MCot NEgg NSti SCob SGbt SKHP SPer SPoG SWat SWvt WCot
'Sunset' PBR (Big Sky Series)	CAbP ECtt ELan EWes GBin GMaP LCro LLHF LRHS LSRN MBNS MBri NEgg SPoG SWat SWvt
'Supreme Elegance' (d) **new**	EBee
'Tangerine Dream'	CAbb ECtt EPfP LAst LRHS MAsh SCob SPoG WNPC
tennesseensis	CArn CEvo SPhx
- 'Rocky Top'	CBcs EPfP LRHS SKHP SPhx
'Tiki Torch' PBR	CPar ECtt EWes LCro LHop LOPS LRHS SBod SCob SPer SPoG SWvt WCot
'Tomato Soup' PBR	Widely available
'Twilight' PBR (Big Sky Series)	ECtt LRHS MBri
'White Meditation' **new**	LRHS
'White Mist' (Mistical Series)	EBee
'White Spider'	SCob
'Yellow Spider' **new**	SCob

Echinocereus (*Cactaceae*)

§ ***coccineus*** **new**	CCac
- SB 236 **new**	CCac
- from Belen, New Mexico **new**	CCac
- from Jarilla Mountains, New Mexico **new**	CCac
engelmannii var. ***variegatus*** LZ 867 **new**	CCac
reichenbachii HK 1228 **new**	CCac
- from Montemorelos, Mexico **new**	CCac
- subsp. ***baileyi*** **new**	CCac
- subsp. ***caespitosus*** **new**	CCac
- - from Mason County, Texas **new**	CCac
triglochidiatus	CCac
- SB 223 **new**	CCac
- from Sandoval Country, New Mexico **new**	CCac
- var. ***melanacanthus***	see *E. coccineus*
- var. ***mojavensis*** **new**	CCac
- - SB 686 **new**	CCac
viridiflorus DJF 713.1 from Larimer County, Colorado **new**	CCac
- SB 137/18 from Sandia Mountains, New Mexico **new**	CCac
- SB 876 from Chaffee County, Colorado **new**	CCac
* - var. ***robustior*** HK 1007 **new**	CCac

Echinops (*Asteraceae*)

albus	see *E.* 'Nivalis'
§ ***bannaticus***	CBcs CMac CSBt NBid SCob WWtn
* - 'Albus'	EBee WFar
- 'Blue Globe'	CBod CEvo CMHG EBee EHoe ELan EPfP GCal IBoy LCro LRHS LSRN LSun MBel MGos MHol NChi NGdn NHol SCob SPoG WCAu WFar WMnd XLum
- 'Star Frost'	CBod CEvo EBee ELan EPfP GQue LRHS NBFr NLar SPhx
- 'Taplow Blue'	Widely available
commutatus	see *E. exaltatus*
§ ***exaltatus***	LPla
maracandicus	GCal WCot
§ 'Nivalis'	CBre LRHS
* ***perringii***	GCal
ritro misapplied	see *E. bannaticus*
§ ***ritro*** L. ♀H7	Widely available
- 'Baby Globes' **new**	EBee
- subsp. ***ruthenicus*** ♀H7	ELan MRav WCot WWtn
- - 'Platinum Blue'	CMea ECtt ELon LRHS NDov NEgg SPhx SRms
- 'Veitch's Blue' misapplied	see *E. ritro* L.
- 'Veitch's Blue'	Widely available
sphaerocephalus	NBir NDov SPlb
- 'Arctic Glow'	CBod CEvo CMHG CMac CPou EBee ECha ECtt EHoe ELan EPfP GBin GMaP LRHS MTis MWhi NDov NGdn NLar SCob SPer SPlb SPoG SWvt WFar WMnd WWtn XLum
terscheckii	LPal
tjanschanicus	EBee LRHS MMuc NLar SEND

Echinospartum (*Papilionaceae*)

sp.	CArn

Echium (*Boraginaceae*)

amoenum	CBod IPot MNrw NBFr SPhx
bethencourtianum	SVen
'Blue Steeple'	MSCN NLos
boissieri	WOut
§ ***candicans*** ♀H1c	CAbb CBcs CBod CCon CHll CSde CSpe CTre CTsd EBee ECre ELan IBoy IDee NLos SEND SVen
decaisnei subsp. ***decaisnei***	SVen
fastuosum	see *E. candicans*
gentianoides	EBee SPlb SVen
onosmifolium	SVen
pininana ♀H2	CAbb CBcs CBod CDoC CPla CTre CTsd EAla ECre ELan EUJe IBoy IDee NLos SChr SDix SEND SIde SPav SPhx SPoG SVen
- 'Snow Tower'	CDTJ CPla ELan EUJe LRHS NLos SVen
pininana × ***wildpretii***	EUJe
'Pink Fountain'	CDTJ CPla ELan EUJe LRHS MSCN NLos

	russicum	CArn CFis CSpe EAJP EBee ELan IBoy LHop MSpe SPad SPav SPhx SPlb
	sventenii	SPlb
	tuberculatum	EWld SPhx WMoo
	virescens	SVen
	vulgare	CHab CSpe CWld ELan ENfk MHer MNHC NLar NMir SBch SIde SPhx WHer WHfH WJek WOut WSFF
	- from Armenia **new**	WCot
	- 'Blue Bedder' ♀H7	CSpe SPhx WSFF
	- Drake's form	SPhx
	webbii	MMHG SVen
	wildpretii ♀H1c	CCon CDTJ CPla CPne CTsd ECre ELan EUJe MHin NLos SIgm SPlb SVen
	- subsp. ***wildpretii***	SPav

Edgeworthia (*Thymelaeaceae*)

§	***chrysantha***	CBcs CExl CHGN CJun EBee ELan EPfP GBin LCro LOPS LPal LRHS MGos MTPN NLar SBig SHil SPer SPoG
I	- 'Grandiflora'	CJun EBee ESwi GBin LCro LOPS LRHS MGos MPkF NLar SMad WPGP
§	- 'Red Dragon'	CJun NLar
	- f. ***rubra*** hort.	see *E. chrysantha* 'Red Dragon'
	papyrifera	see *E. chrysantha*

Edraianthus (*Campanulaceae*)

	croaticus	see *E. graminifolius*
	dalmaticus	GKev
	- ***albus***	NSla
§	***graminifolius***	GKev XLum
	- ***albus***	see *E. graminifolius* subsp. *niveus*
	- subsp. ***graminifolius***	CPBP LLHF
§	- subsp. ***niveus***	CPBP EPot
	owerinianus	LLHF WAbe
	pilosulus	WAbe
§	***pumilio*** ♀H5	CPBP GEdr GKev NSla SIgm SRms WAbe
	serpyllifolius 'Major'	WAbe
	tenuifolius	WIce
	wettsteinii	GKev
	- subsp. ***lovcenicus*** **new**	GKev
	zogovicii	see *E. graminifolius*

Egeria (*Hydrocharitaceae*)

§	***densa***	CBen

Ehretia (*Boraginaceae*)

	anacua	CBcs
	dicksonii	IVic
	rigida	SPlb

Eichhornia (*Pontederiaceae*)

	crassipes	CBen MSKA
	- 'Major'	NPer

Elaeagnus (*Elaeagnaceae*)

	sp.	LPar
	angustifolia	CAgr CArg CBcs CDul EPfP MCoo MGos NLar SCob SPer SRms
	- Caspica Group	see *E.* 'Quicksilver'
	argentea Pursh	see *E. commutata*
§	***commutata***	CBcs CDul CMac ECrN EHoe EPfP LHop MBlu MWhi NLar SPer WHar
	- 'Zempin'	EPfP LRHS
§	× ***ebbingei*** ♀H5	Widely available
	- 'Coastal Gold' (v)	CBcs CDoC CDul CLet COtt CSde EBee EPfP LBMP LRHS LSRN MAsh MGos SGol SLim SRms WFar WRHF
I	- 'Compacta'	LAst LRHS LSou MGos SHil
	- 'Gilt Edge' (v) ♀H5	Widely available
	- Gold Splash = 'Lannou' (v)	CDoC CMac EPfP LRHS SGol SPoG SWvt
	- 'Limelight' (v)	Widely available
	- 'Moonlight'	EPfP LRHS MAsh
	- 'Viveleg'PBR (v)	ELan EPfP LRHS MBri MGos SCob SEWo SHil
	glabra	GGal
	macrophylla	CMac EPfP LRHS
	multiflora	CDoC SPer WPGP
	- 'Sweet Scarlet'	CAgr
	parvifolia	ELan
	pungens	CLet
	- 'Argenteovariegata'	see *E. pungens* 'Variegata'
	- 'Aureovariegata'	see *E. pungens* 'Maculata'
	- 'Dicksonii' (v)	CWib LRHS NLar SLon SPer SRms
	- 'Forest Gold' (v)	ELan EPfP LRHS MAsh
	- 'Frederici' (v)	CBcs CDoC CMac EBee EHoe ELan LAst LBMP LHop LRHS MAsh MRav NLar SCob SPer SPoG SWvt
	- 'Goldrim' (v)	CDoC
	- 'Hosoba-fukurin' (v)	EBee ELan LRHS MAsh NLar SLon
§	- 'Maculata' (v)	Widely available
§	- 'Variegata' (v)	CBcs CMac NBir SPer
§	'Quicksilver'	Widely available
	× ***submacrophylla***	see *E.* × *ebbingei*
	umbellata	CBcs CDul CExl CTho EBee EPfP LEdu MBlu NLar SPer WPat WSHC
	- 'Amber' (F)	CAgr
	- 'Big Red' (F)	CAgr
	- var. ***borealis*** 'Polar Lights'	NLar
	- 'Brilliant Rose' (F)	CAgr
	- 'Garnet' (F)	CAgr
	- 'Hidden Springs' (F)	CAgr
	- 'Jewel' (F)	CAgr
	- 'Late Scarlet' (F)	CAgr
	- 'Newgate' (F)	CAgr
	- 'Red Cascade' (F)	CAgr LEdu
	- var. ***rotundifolia*** CWJ 12835 **new**	WCru
	- 'Ruby' (F)	CAgr LEdu
	- 'Sweet 'n' Tart' (F)	CAgr

Elaeocarpus (*Elaeocarpaceae*)

	sylvestris var. ***ellipticus***	LEdu WPGP

elderberry see *Sambucus nigra*

Elegia (*Restionaceae*)

	capensis	CAbb CBod CCon CDTJ CExl CLet CTre LRHS MPkF NLos SPlb WPGP
	cuspidata	NLos
	elephantina	CTre NLos
	equisetacea	CTre NLos
	filacea	NLos
	macrocarpa	CTre NLos SPlb
	tectorum ♀H2	CAbb CSpe CTre EAEE LRHS NLos SGSe SHDw SPlb SPoG
	- dwarf	CTre
	- 'Fish Hoek' **new**	CTre

Eleocharis (*Cyperaceae*)

	acicularis	MSKA
	parvula	MSKA

Elettaria (*Zingiberaceae*)

cardamomum	CArn EOHP EShb GPoy LEdu SPre WJek

Eleutherococcus (*Araliaceae*)

sp.	CArn
from Manipur new	WPGP
divaricatus B&SWJ 5027	WCru
giraldii BWJ 8091	WCru
hypoleucus B&SWJ 5532	WCru
nakaianus B&SWJ 5027	WCru
nodiflorus PAB 8119 new	LEdu
pictus	see *Kalopanax septemlobus*
senticosus	GPoy LEdu
- B&SWJ 4568	WCru
septemlobus	see *Kalopanax septemlobus*
sessiliflorus B&SWJ 4528	WCru
- B&SWJ 8457	WCru
- B&SWJ 8618	WCru
sieboldianus	MMuc MRav SEND
- 'Variegatus' (v)	CBcs CLet EBee EHoe ELan ELon EPfP ESwi EUJe GBin LAst LRHS MRav NLar SEND SPoG WCFE WHer WSHC WWFP
trifoliatus PAB 7113	LEdu
- RWJ 10108	WCru

Elingamita (*Primulaceae*)

johnsonii	ECou

Ellisiophyllum (*Plantaginaceae*)

pinnatum	SBrt
- B&SWJ 197	CDes EBee LEdu WCru WPGP

Elmera (*Saxifragaceae*)

racemosa	EPau

Elodea (*Hydrocharitaceae*)

canadensis	MSKA NBir WMAq
densa	see *Egeria densa*

Elsholtzia (*Lamiaceae*)

stauntonii	CArn CBcs EBee ECha ELan GPoy IDee IVic LRHS MHer NLar SBch SBrt SLon SPer SRms SWvt WBor WJek XLum

Elymus (*Poaceae*)

	arenarius	see *Leymus arenarius*
	canadensis	EHoe EPPr
	- f. **glaucifolius**	CCon
	cinereus from Washington State, USA	WPGP
	glaucus misapplied	see *E. hispidus*
§	**hispidus** ♀H6	CBod EPPr MBlu MLHP NDov SPer WCFE WCot
§	**magellanicus**	Widely available
	- 'Blue Sword'	CRos ELan LRHS MBri MGos SHil SRkn SRms
	riparius	EPPr
	sibiricus	EPPr
	villosus	EPPr
	- var. **arkansanus**	EPPr
	virginicus	EPPr

Embothrium ✿ (*Proteaceae*)

coccineum	CBcs CFil CPne CTri EPfP LRHS LSou MGil MMuc SEND SPlb WBod WPGP WPat
* - var. **andina**	MGil
- Lanceolatum Group	CBcs CDoC CHll CTsd ELon EPfP EUJe IDee LRHS MBlu MPkF SLim SPer SSpi SSta SWvt WAbe WBor WPat
- - 'Inca Flame'	CJun EPfP LRHS MAsh SPoG SWvt
- - 'Ñorquinco'	GGal
- Longifolium Group	EPfP IBlr WPGP

Emmenopterys (*Rubiaceae*)

henryi	CBcs EPfP IArd MBlu NLar SAko SMad WCot WPGP

Empetrum (*Ericaceae*)

nigrum	GPoy WThu
rubrum	MGil

Empodium (*Hypoxidaceae*)

namaquensis	NRog
plicatum	NRog

Enceliopsis (*Asteraceae*)

covillei	EBee

Encephalartos ✿ (*Zamiaceae*)

altensteinii	CBrP LPal
caffer	CBrP
cycadifolius	CBrP
ferox	CBrP LPal
horridus	CBrP
lebomboensis	CBrP LPal
lehmannii	CBrP LPal
natalensis	CBrP LPal
senticosus	LPal
villosus	CBrP LPal

Endymion see *Hyacinthoides*

Enkianthus ✿ (*Ericaceae*)

	campanulatus ♀H5	Widely available
	- var. **campanulatus** f. **albiflorus**	CBcs GKin IVic NLar
I	- 'Hollandia'	GKin
I	- 'Pagoda'	CBcs IArd NLar SAko
	- var. **palibinii**	CAbP CLet EPfP GGGa GKin LRHS MAsh NLar SSpi
	- 'Red Bells'	CBcs CDul EPfP GBin GKin LRHS MAsh NLar SPer SPoG SWvt WFar
	- 'Red Velvet'	GKin NLar
	- 'Ruby Glow'	IVic SAko
	- 'Showy Lantern'	NLar
	- var. **sikokianus**	EPfP GGGa GKin NLar
	- 'Sinsetu'	NLar
	- 'Tokyo Masquerade' (v)	LRHS MAsh NLar SPoG
	- 'Venus'	CBcs GKin NLar
	- 'Victoria'	CBcs IArd IDee NLar SAko
	- 'Wallaby'	CBcs IArd LRHS NLar SAko WAbe
	cernuus f. **rubens** ♀H5	CBcs EPfP GBin GGGa GKin ITim NLar
	chinensis	CAbP CBcs EPfP GGGa LRHS MAsh
	deflexus	GGGa LRHS MAsh SSpi WPGP
	perulatus ♀H5	CBcs CDoC CDul EBee GKin LRHS MGil MGos MMuc NLar SPer SSpi WFar
	serrulatus	GGGa

Ensete (*Musaceae*)

gilletii	XBlo
- from Malawi	XBlo
- from Mozambique	XBlo

glaucum	CDTJ CDoC LPal
§ ***ventricosum*** ♀H1c	CDTJ CHll EUJe NLos SEND XBlo
§ - 'Maurelii' ♀H1c	CDTJ CDoC CHll CSpe CTsd EBee ESwi EUJe LPal NLos NPla SChr SDix SEND SPer WCot WPGP
- 'Rubrum'	see *E. ventricosum* 'Maurelii'
- 'Tandarra Red'	CAbb

Entelea (*Malvaceae*)

arborescens	ECou EShb SPlb

Eomecon (*Papaveraceae*)

chionantha	CCon CDes CExl CSam CSpe CWCL EBee GAbr GBuc GCal GCra GEdr LEdu MLHP MRav NBid SBrt WCru WHer WMoo WPGP XLum

Epacris (*Ericaceae*)

microphylla	ITim
serpyllifolia	WThu

Ephedra (*Ephedraceae*)

sp.	MPie
andina	IMou
chilensis	MGil XLum
distachya	GPoy
equisetina	CArn IFro
- RCB/TQ K-1 **new**	WCot
fedtschenkoi	XSen
gerardiana	IFro LRHS
- var. ***sikkimensis***	GEdr WOld XLum
§ ***major***	EBee XSen
minuta	MSCN
monosperma	GEdr WThu
nebrodensis	see *E. major*
nevadensis	CArn GPoy WHfH
sinica	CArn GPoy
viridis	CArn MGil XSen

Epigaea (*Ericaceae*)

gaultherioides	GGGa

Epilobium (*Onagraceae*)

angustifolium	see *Chamaenerion angustifolium*
- f. ***leucanthum***	see *Chamaenerion angustifolium* 'Album'
californicum misapplied	see *Zauschneria californica*
canum	see *Zauschneria cana*
dodonaei	see *Chamaenerion dodonaei*
fleischeri	see *Chamaenerion fleischeri*
garrettii	see *Zauschneria californica* subsp. *garrettii*
glabellum misapplied	MSCN NSla
glabellum G. Forst.	CSpe MMuc SPhx WKif
hirsutum 'Album'	EWTr GMaP MHer
microphyllum	see *Zauschneria cana*
rosmarinifolium	see *Chamaenerion dodonaei*
septentrionale	see *Zauschneria septentrionalis*
villosum	see *Zauschneria californica* subsp. *mexicana*

Epimedium ✿ (*Berberidaceae*)

from Jian Xi, China	GEdr
from Yunnan, China	CDes CLAP IFoB WPGP
acuminatum	CAby CCon CCse CElw CFil CLAP EFEx ESMi GEdr LEdu MNrw NLar SCob WMoo WPGP WSHC
- CC 031207 **new**	XPou
- L 575	CDes CElw CExl CFil XPou
- 'Galaxy'	CExl CFil CJun CLAP CMil LEdu WPGP
- 'Night Mistress'	WCot XPou
- 'Quinquin'	IMou
- yellow-flowered CC 011415	XPou
'Akakage'	CExl CLAP GBuc
'Akebono'	Widely available
Alabaster = 'Conalba'	NEgg
alpinum	CEvo CFil CFis CMac EBee EPPr EPot GKev GLog IFro LEdu LRHS SHar SKHP SPer WMoo XLum
'Amanogawa'	CAby CDes CJun CMil GEdr IFoB LEdu WPGP XPou
'Amber Queen'[PBR]	Widely available
'Anju'	GEdr
'Arctic Wings'[PBR]	CLAP CMil EBee EPfP GEdr LHop NGdn SMHy SWvt
'Asiatic Hybrid'	CJun CLAP WHal
'Autumn Raspberry'	CJun
baojingense	XPou
'Beni-goromo'	GEdr
'Beni-kujaku'	CAby CDes CJun CLAP EBee GEdr IFoB MHol
'Beni-yushima'	GEdr
'Bieke' **new**	SMHy
'Black Sea'	CElw CJun CLAP CSpe EPPr EPot ESMi EWTr GBuc IFoB IMou LHop MAvo MNrw SCob XPou
borealiguizhouense CC 020711	XPou
brachyrrhizum	CAby CExl CJun CMil LLHF NLar WPGP
- CPC 940447	XPou
- 'Elfin Magic'	IFoB
brevicornu	GEdr SKHP WPGP
- Og 82.010	CExl CFil CJun XPou
- Og 88.010	CJun XPou
'Buckland Spider'	CDes CLAP EBee ELon EPPr ESMi GEdr IFoB MNrw SMHy WCot WPGP
campanulatum	LLHF
- CC 002079 **new**	XPou
- Og 93.087	CExl CFil CJun
× ***cantabrigiense***	CBro CMac CTal ECtt ESwi GBuc GEdr GKev GMaP ILea MRav NEgg NLar SRms XLum
chlorandrum	CAby EBee IFoB LEdu WPGP
- Og 93.003	XPou
- Og 94.003	CDes EBee
creeping yellow	EBee LSou WHil
cremeum	see *E. grandiflorum* subsp. *koreanum*
davidii	CDes CFil EPPr ESMi GEdr LEdu MNrw NLar NMyG SCob SKHP WHal WPGP WSHC
- CPC 960079	CExl EBee XPou
- EMR 4125	CElw CExl CJun CLAP XPou
- dwarf	CAby CExl
dewuense	XPou
diphyllum	CExl CFil CTsd EBee GEdr IFoB IVic WHal WPGP XPou
- dwarf white	CSam
- pink-flowered **new**	XPou
dolichostemon	CElw IFoB LHop WCot WHil
- Og 81-010	CJun XPou
'Domino'	XPou
ecalcaratum	CDes CMil EBee LEdu WPGP
- Og 93.082	CExl CJun XPou
- spurred	XPou
'Egret'	CDes SMHy

elongatum	CLAP
- CC 12906	XPou
'Emperor'	see *E.* 'Phoenix'
'Enchantress'	CElw CJun CLAP CMil CTal ESMi EWTr EWld IFoB MCot MNrw NLar WHal WHil WHoo
epsteinii	CAby CDes CFil CLAP CMil CTal EBee EPPr ESMi GEdr IFoB LEdu LLHF MNrw SKHP WCot WPGP
- CPC 940347	CExl CJun IVic XPou
fangii	CExl IFoB SKHP
- CC 022008	XPou
fargesii	CAby CDes CExl CFil EBee GEdr IFoB LEdu MAvo MNrw NMyG WPGP
- Og 93.057	CTal
- 'Pink Constellation'	CDes CExl CFil CJun EBee GEdr ITim LEdu LHop SBch SMHy WPGP XPou
'Fire Dragon'[PBR]	CLAP CWCL EBee EPfP GEdr IFoB LLHF MBNS NMyG SPoG
flavum	CFil EBee SKHP WPGP
- Og 92.036	CDes CExl CJun XPou
'Flowers of Sulphur'[PBR]	CLAP EBee EPfP GEdr
franchetii	CAby CCon CElw CExl ELon GEdr IFoB SKHP WCot
- 'Brimstone Butterfly'	CAby CDes CExl CFis CJun EPPr ESMi GEdr LHop NLar SKHP WCot WPGP XPou
'Fukujuji'	GEdr
'Genpei'	GEdr
'Golden Eagle'	CExl CJun EBee EWes MNrw SMHy
§ ***grandiflorum*** ♀H5	CBcs CBod CElw CPla CTri ELan ELon EPfP GBuc GEdr GLog LPfy NBir NLar NMyG SCob SPer WPnP
- 'Akagiza Kura'	XPou
- 'Album'	CLAP
- 'Bandit'	GEdr IFoB
- 'Beni-chidori'	CJun CLAP GEdr
- 'Bicolor Giant' **new**	XPou
- 'Circe'	XPou
- 'Crimson Beauty'	CAby CJun CLAP ECha NLar WHal WHoo WSHC
- 'Elfenkönigin'	LRHS NLar
- 'Freya'	CDes CExl EBee IFoB SMHy WSHC XPou
§ - var. ***higoense***	CJun GEdr WHal WPGP XPou
- - 'Saturn'	CDes
- 'Jennie Maillard'	ELon WCot
- 'Kicho' **new**	XPou
- 'Koji'	CLAP EBee ESMi IFoB WSHC
§ - subsp. ***koreanum***	CLAP CPla ECha EFEx GEdr IFoB
- 'La Rocaille'	CAby EBee EWld XPou
- lilac-flowered	CAby CLAP WHal
- lilac-pink-flowered	SMHy
- 'Lilafee'	Widely available
- 'Mount Kitadake'	CLAP WAbe
- 'Mugawa-gen-pan'	XPou
- 'Nanum' ♀H5	CAby CJun CPBP EBee ECho EPot ESMi GBuc GKev MNrw NEgg NHar SKHP SMHy WAbe WPGP XPou
- pink-flowered	MCot
- 'Purple Pixie'[PBR]	ECtt EWTr LAst MHol NEgg WHil
- 'Purple Prince'	CDes CExl CLAP CTal EBee WPGP XPou
- 'Queen Esta'	CAby CDes CExl CJun CLAP CMil EBee IFoB LEdu MNrw MRav WPGP WSHC XPou
- 'Red Beauty'	CBod CLAP CWCL ECtt ELan ELon EPfP EWTr GBin GEdr IFoB LRHS LSou MAvo MCot MNrw WGrn WGwG WHil WPnP
- 'Red Queen'	CMac
- 'Rose Queen' ♀H5	CAby CDes CSam EBee ELan ELon EPfP ESMi EThi IFoB LEdu LPfy LRHS MBri MGos MNrw MRav NBir NEgg NMyG NSti SCob SWvt WFar WMoo WPGP
- 'Roseum'	CLAP CMac CMil ESwi GMaP IFoB SGSe SWvt
- 'Rubinkrone'	CWCL GBuc GEdr GMaP IMou LRHS MNrw
- 'Sirius'	CAby CJun CLAP MNrw
- f. ***violaceum***	CJun CLAP EBee WCFE WSHC
- 'White Beauty'	WSHC
- 'White Queen' ♀H5	CElw CJun EBee EPPr IFoB LLHF SMHy WCot WHal WHil
- 'Wildside Red'	CJun
- 'Yellow Princess'	CAby CDes CElw CJun EBee XPou
- 'Yubae'	GEdr IFoB
'Hagoromo'	GEdr
'Hakubai'	GEdr
'Harugasumi'	GEdr
'Heavenly Purple'	CJun
higoense	see *E. grandiflorum* var. *higoense*
'Hina Matsuri'	GEdr
ilicifolium	CAby CDes CFil CJun EBee LEdu WPGP
- Og 93.020	XPou
'Jean O'Neill'	CAby CDes CLAP EBee EPPr LEdu SGSe WCot WPGP WSHC
'Jenny Pym'	EBee
'Kaguyahime'	CElw CJun CMil EPPr IFoB WSHC
'Kibana Genpei' **new**	XPou
'King Prawn'	CDes LEdu SMHy WPGP
'Kodai Murasaki'	XPou
'Koki'	GEdr
koreanum 'Harold Epstein'	XPou
'Korin'	XPou
'Kotobuki'	GEdr
latisepalum	CPne CTal EBee GEdr LEdu MNrw WCot WPGP
- Og 91.002	CJun
- Og 93.009	XPou
'Lemon Meringue Pie'	CJun
leptorrhizum	CElw CExl CFil CJun CLAP EBee ELon EPPr ESMi EWld GBuc GEdr IFoB IVic LEdu MNrw NCGa NHar NLar NMyG SKHP WCot WHal
- Og Y44	CExl WSHC XPou
- 'Mariko'	CAby CDes CExl CJun CMil LEdu WPGP XPou
lishihchenii	CAby CDes CExl CFil CJun CTal GEdr WPGP
- CC 95007	XPou
- Og 93.024	XPou
'Little Shrimp'	CJun CTal CTri EBee ELon EPot GMaP LLHF LRHS MNrw NLar WSHC
macranthum	see *E. grandiflorum*
macrosepalum	GEdr XPou
'Madame Butterfly'[PBR]	MBel MTis
'Mandarin Star'	GEdr
membranaceum	CAby CCon CFil CMil EBee ESMi GEdr GKev LEdu LLHF NCGa SKHP WHal WPGP XEll XPou
- Og 93.047	CExl CJun EPPr GEdr
mikinorii	CExl GEdr

	- CC 990001	XPou
	'Milky Way'	CDes
	'Mine-no-fubuki'	GEdr
	'Myojo'	GEdr
	myrianthum	CAby CDes CJun EBee GEdr LEdu WPGP XPou
	ogisui	CAby CDes CElw CLAP CMil IFoB LEdu MRav SMHy WPGP WThu
	- Og 91.001	CExl CFil CJun EBee MNrw SKHP
§	× ***omeiense*** 'Akame'	CDes CExl CJun CMil EPPr GEdr WPGP XPou
	- 'Emei Shan'	see *E.* × *omeiense* 'Akame'
	- 'Myriad Years'	SMHy XPou
	- 'Pale Fire Sibling'	CDes CJun GEdr
	- 'Stormcloud'	CAby CDes CElw CExl CFil CJun CMil EBee EPPr EWTr MAvo WPGP XPou
	parvifolium	XPou
	pauciflorum	CFil EBee EPPr ESMi GEdr LEdu NHar NMyG WPGP XPou
	- Og 92.123	CExl CJun CLAP
	× ***perralchicum***	CAby CBro CJun CTri ECha GKev IFro MLHP NLar WSHC
	- 'Fröhnleiten'	Widely available
	- 'Lichtenberg'	CDes EBee EWes
	- 'Wisley'	CElw CJun CSam EWes
	perralderianum	CMac CSam CTal EPot GMaP MBel MCot MNrw SRms WHal WPnP XLum
	- 'Weihenstephan'	CWCL LRHS NLar WPnP
§	'Phoenix'	CAby CDes CExl EBee WCot WPGP
	'Pink Champagne'	CDes EPfP GEdr LEdu WCot WFar
	'Pink Elf' PBR	CLAP CMil CMos CWCL ECGP EPfP EWoo GEdr IFoB LBrs LLHF MNrw MPie NCGa NGdn NLar NSti SCob SRms WCAu WCot WFar WHil
	pinnatum	ECho GMaP WHal XLum
§	- subsp. ***colchicum*** ♀H7	CDoC CJun CLAP CWCL ELan EPfP EWTr GBuc GLog LEdu LRHS MCot MRav NGdn NLar SCob SDix SPer WCot WFar WHil WPnP XEll
	- - L 321	CDes GEdr WPGP
	- ***elegans***	see *E. pinnatum* subsp. *colchicum*
	platypetalum	CDes CFil CLAP CMil SBrt WCot WPGP
	- Og 93.085	CExl CJun XPou
	pubescens	CAby IFoB
	- CC 022556 from Shaanxi **new**	XPou
	- Og 91.003	CExl CFil CJun WPGP
	pubigerum	CDes CJun CSam CWCL EAEE EBee ESMi GAbr GBuc GEdr IFro ILea LEdu LRHS NEgg NLar NMyG SCob SEND SWvt WCAu WHal WHil WPGP XEll
	qingchengshanense 03124 **new**	XPou
	'Red Maximum' **new**	XPou
	reticulatum	GEdr
	rhizomatosum	CAby EPPr ESMi GEdr GMaP LLHF NMyG WPGP WSHC
	- Og 92.114	CJun WCot XPou
	× ***rubrum*** ♀H7	Widely available
	- 'Galadriel'	GBin
	- 'Sweetheart'	GEdr
	sagittatum	EFEx
	- 'Warlord'	XPou
	'Sakura-maru'	GEdr
	'Sasaki'	CLAP EPot GBin GBuc IFoB MNrw NLar XEll
	sempervirens	CAby CJun WHal
	- 'Creamsickle' (v)	GEdr
	- 'Okuda's White'	CDes EBee WPGP XPou
	- 'Violet Queen'	XPou
	- violet-flowered	CDes
	× ***setosum***	CJun ESMi WHal
	'Shiho'	EBee EWTr GBin GEdr MNrw
	shuichengense CC 030175	XPou
	'Sphinx Twinkler'	see *E.* 'Spine Tingler'
§	'Spine Tingler'	CMil CSpe ECtt ESwi EUJe GBin GEdr LEdu MBel MSCN MTis SCob SPoG WCot WPGP XPou
	'Spinners'	EBee WCot
	'Starcloud'	GBin LRHS WGrn WHil
	stellulatum	GEdr
	- long-leaved CC 970051	XPou
	- 'Wudang Star'	CDes CExl CFil CJun CLAP CMil CWCL EWes IFoB IMou IVic SCob WPGP WSHC XPou
	- 'Yukiko'	XPou
	sutchuenense CC 990394	XPou
	'Suzuka'	GEdr LEdu WPGP
	'Tama-no-genpei'	CDes CJun GEdr IFoB LEdu WPGP
	'Tanima-no-yuki'	GEdr
	'The Giant'	XPou
	'Togen'	WCot XPou
	'Tokiwa-gozen'	GEdr
	'Totnes Turbo'	CDes EBee
	truncatum	XPou
	CC 030557 **new**	
	× ***versicolor***	CExl EShb SCob
	- 'Cherry Tart'	CLAP XPou
	- 'Cupreum'	CJun CLAP CWCL EBee GBuc LPfy LRHS MGos WCAu
§	- 'Discolor'	CAby CDes CElw CFis CTal ECha EPPr EWld NBir SMHy WCot
	- 'Neosulphureum'	CAby CBro CDes CLAP EPPr WPGP WSHC WThu XPou
	- 'Sulphureum' ♀H7	Widely available
	- 'Versicolor'	see *E.* × *versicolor* 'Discolor'
	× ***warleyense***	Widely available
	- 'Orangekönigin'	Widely available
	'William Stearn'	CDes CExl CJun CLAP GEdr WCot XPou
	wushanense	CFil CLAP EPPr ESMi GEdr LEdu XPou
	- CC 014193	XPou
	- Og 93.019	CExl CJun XPou
	- 'Caramel'	CAby CDes CExl CJun CLAP CMil EBee GEdr IFoB LEdu MAvo SKHP WCot WPGP WSHC XPou
	- spiny-leaved	WCot
	- - CC 014631	XPou
	'Yachimata-hime'	GEdr
	'Yokihi'	CEvo GEdr XPou
	× ***youngianum***	IFoB NEgg
	- 'Beni-kujaku'	NEgg XPou
	- 'Merlin'	CElw CJun CLAP CMil EBee EPfP EPot ESMi GBuc GEdr IFoB MBri NSti WHal WSHC XPou
	- 'Niveum' ♀H5	Widely available
	- 'Roseum'	Widely available
	- 'Shikinomai'	CExl CJun EPPr EPot
	- 'Tamabotan'	CDes CLAP CMil EBee GEdr MNrw MRav XPou
§	- 'Typicum'	CElw GBuc WHil WSHC
	- 'Yenomoto'	CJun CLAP
	- 'Youngianum'	see *E.* × *youngianum* 'Typicum'
	zhushanense	CDes CTal GEdr LEdu WCot
	- CC 022403	XPou

Epipactis (*Orchidaceae*)

Catalina gx GEdr
gigantea CAvo CBro CCon EBee ECha ECho ELan EPot GBin GEdr GKev LRHS MHer MNrw MRav NDav NLAp WPGP
gigantea* × *veratrifolia see *E.* Lowland Legacy gx
helleborine WHer
§ **Lowland Legacy gx** GEdr
- 'Edelstein' MNrw
- 'Frankfurt' GEdr
palustris GEdr LRHS MNrw NDav NLAp WHer
Passionata gx Light Royals Group GEdr
royleana GEdr
Sabine gx CAby GEdr
- 'Frankfurt' EWld MNrw
thunbergii EFEx GEdr

Epipremnum (*Araceae*)

pinnatum 'Marble Queen' (v) XBlo

Episcia (*Gesneriaceae*)

dianthiflora WDib
'San Miguel' WDib

Equisetum ✿ (*Equisetaceae*)

arvense CArn
'Bandit' (v) CDes CNat EBee MAvo SMad WMoo
× ***bowmanii*** CNat
* ***camtschatcense*** EWay SBig SMad SPlb XLum
× ***dycei*** CNat
fluviatile CNat MSKA
giganteum LLWG
hyemale CBen CKno EHoe EWay GQue LRHS MAvo MSCN MSKA MWts NOak NPer NSti SCob SEND SPlb WMoo WWtn XLum
§ - var. ***affine*** CNat EBee ELan LEdu MSKA SCob WMAq WPGP
- var. ***robustum*** see *E. hyemale* var. *affine*
ramosissimum LEdu MMuc NLos NPla SCob SWat
var. ***japonicum*** WPGP
robustum SCob
scirpoides EBee EFer EHoe EWay MSKA MWts NPer NWad SPlb SWat WMAq WMoo XLum
telmateia LEdu SMad
variegatum EBee EFer

Eragrostis (*Poaceae*)

RCB/Arg S-7 EBee WCot
airoides misapplied see *Agrostis montevidensis*
airoides ambig. CBod WMoo
chloromelas EPPr
curvula CBod CElw CKno CMea CWCL ECha EHoe EPPr GAbr LRHS MAvo MBel MRav MWhi NBir NChi NGdn NOak NWsh SEND SGSe SPhx WMoo XLum
- S&SH 10 CElw EPPr SMHy WPGP
- 'Totnes Burgundy' CAby CDes CExl CKno CWCL EBee ECha EPPr EPfP EShb LRHS MAvo MNrw SMea SPhx SRms WMoo WPGP
elliottii CBod CKno ECha EPPr EShb LBMP LRHS MAvo NWsh SEND SHDw SMea WWEG
- 'Wind Dancer' CSde EBee WHar XSen
prolifera IMou
'Silver Needles' see *Agrostis canina* 'Silver Needles'
spectabilis CBod CCon CKno CSBt CSde CTsd EBee ELan EPfP LBMP MWhi NGdn NLar NWsh SDix SGSe SMea WMoo XLum XSen
trichodes CBod CCon CKno EBee EHoe LEdu MAvo NWsh SGSe SMea WCot

Eranthemum (*Acanthaceae*)

pulchellum 🏆H1b CTsd ECre

Eranthis (*Ranunculaceae*)

sp. MLHP
cilicica see *E. hyemalis* Cilicica Group
§ ***hyemalis*** 🏆H5 CBro CMea CTca ECho ELan ELon EPfP GBin GKev LAma LCro LOPS LRHS SCob SDeJ SPhx SWvt WBor WCot WHoo WShi
§ - Cilicica Group CBro ECho ELan EPot GEdr GKev GMaP IFro LRHS NLar SCob SDeJ SPer SPhx WBor WCot WRHF WShi
- 'Flore Pleno' (d) ECho EPot GEdr WCot
- 'Grünling' CAvo ECho WCot
- 'Orange Glow' ECho GEdr
- 'Schwefelglanz' CAvo CBro ECho EPot GEdr GKev WCot
§ - Tubergenii Group CBro ECho EPot
- - 'Guinea Gold' 🏆H5 CTca ECho
pinnatifida EFEx GEdr
× ***tubergenii*** see *E. hyemalis* Tubergenii Group

Ercilla (*Phytolaccaceae*)

volubilis CBod CExl CFil CRHN CWGN EPfP EWld GCal IDee LRHS MGil SAko SEND WCru WSHC

Eremophila (*Scrophulariaceae*)

§ ***debilis*** ECou
glabra SVen
'Kilbara Carpet' ECou
longifolia SPlb
maculata ECou IDee
- pale pink-flowered MOWG
- 'Peaches and Cream' MOWG
'Yellow Trumpet' ECou

Eremostachys (*Lamiaceae*)

laciniata XSen

Eremurus (*Asphodelaceae*)

altaicus JCA 0.443.809 WCot
'Brutus' EBee
bungei see *E. stenophyllus* subsp. *stenophyllus*
'Charleston' **new** EBee
'Disco' EBee
'Emmy Ro' EBee LAma LRHS NLar WCot
'Foxtrot' EBee
fuscus EBee SPhx
- JCA 0.444.043 WCot
'Grace' LAma NLar
'Helena' LAma LRHS
himalaicus CAvo CCon EBee ELan EPot ERCP GBin GKev GMaP ILea LAma LRHS

	MCot MHer NLar SCob SDeJ SPer SPhx
'Image'	EBee MAvo
× ***isabellinus*** 'Cleopatra'	CBod CWCL EBee EPfP EPot ERCP GKev GMaP LAma LCro LOPS LRHS MBNS MHer SCob SDeJ SPer SPhx
- 'Obelisk'	EBee LAma LRHS
- 'Pinokkio'	CWCL EBee EPot GKev LAma LCro LOPS MHer SDeJ SPad SPer
- Ruiter hybrids	ELan EPfP GKev GMaP LAma LAst LRHS MCot MGos MNrw NLar SPer
- Shelford hybrids	CBcs ELan GKev LAma SDeJ SPhx
'Jeanne-Claire'	LAma LRHS NLar
'Joanna'	LAma LRHS NLar
lactiflorus	WCot
'Line Dance'	EBee LAma
'Luca Ro'	EBee NLar
'Moneymaker'	CWCL EBee LAma
'Oase'	EBee GKev LAma LRHS SDeJ
'Paradiso'	EBee
'Pink Persuasion' **new**	EBee
'Pink Sky' **new**	EBee
'Rexona'	LAma MBNS SDeJ
robustus ♀H7	CAvo CBcs CCon CWCL ELan EPot ERCP GKev LAma LRHS MAvo MHer MNrw NLar SDeJ SPer SPhx SPlb
'Romance'	CBod EBee EPot ERCP LAma MBNS MBel MNrw NLar SCob SDeJ SPhx
'Rumba'	EBee LAma
'Samba'	LAma
stenophyllus ♀H6	CBod CTri CWib EPot ERCP GBin GKev LCro LHop LOPS LRHS MPkF NLar SDeJ SPhx SPoG
§ - subsp. ***stenophyllus***	CBcs EBee EPfP GMaP IBoy LAst MHer MNrw NPer NPri SPer
'Tap Dance'	EBee LAma
'Twist' **new**	EBee
'White Beauty Favourite'PBR	ERCP LCro LOPS
'White Plume' **new**	EBee
'White Sensation' **new**	LRHS
zenaidae JCA 0.444.409	WCot

Erepsia (*Aizoaceae*)

lacera	SPlb

Erianthus see *Saccharum*

Erica ✿ (*Ericaceae*)

aestiva	SPlb
alopecurus	SPlb
andevalensis f. ***albiflora***	CFst
arborea	CBcs SPlb XSen
- var. ***alpina*** ♀H5	CDoC CTri EPfP GAbr GGal LRHS SCob SPer SPoG SWhi
§ - - f. ***aureifolia*** 'Albert's Gold' ♀H5	CFst CSBt CTri ELan EPfP GAbr LRHS MBri MGos NHol SCob SCoo SPer SPoG SWhi
- 'Arbora Gold'	see *E. arborea* var. *alpina* f. *aureifolia* 'Albert's Gold'
- 'Arnold's Gold'	see *E. arborea* var. *alpina* f. *aureifolia* 'Albert's Gold'
- 'Estrella Gold' ♀H5	CBcs CDoC CFst CSBt CTri ELan EPfP GAbr LRHS NHol SCob SCoo SPer SPoG SWhi
- 'Golden Joy'	CFst
australis f. ***albiflora*** 'Mr Robert' ♀H2	CFst GCal
- 'Holehird'	CFst
- 'Riverslea' ♀H4	CDoC CFst CTri GCal LRHS SCob SPer SPoG SWhi
- 'Trisha'	CFst
caffra	CTre SPlb
canaliculata ♀H2	CBcs
carnea 'Adrienne Duncan' ♀H7	SCoo SRms
- f. ***alba*** 'Golden Starlet' ♀H7	CFst CSBt CTri EPfP MAsh MJak NHol NWea SCoo SPer SRms SWhi
- - 'Ice Princess' ♀H7	ELan EPfP MAsh SCoo SRms SWhi
- - 'Isabell' ♀H7	CBcs CFst CSBt EPfP IVic MAsh SCoo SRms SWhi
- - 'Rosalinde Schorn'	SRms
- - 'Schneekuppe'	SWhi
- - 'Schneesturm'	SRms
- - 'Snow Queen'	SRms
- - 'Springwood White' ♀H7	CFst CSBt CTri ELan EPfP MAsh MMuc NHol SEND SLon SRms SWhi
- - 'Whitehall'	CFst LCro SCoo SRms SWhi
- - 'Winter Snow' ♀H7	CFst CSBt ELan SCoo SPer SRms SWhi
- 'Amy Doncaster'	see *E. carnea* 'Treasure Trove'
- 'Ann Sparkes' ♀H7	CBcs CFst CSBt CTri ELan EPfP MAsh NHol SCoo SRms SWhi
- 'Atrorubra'	SWhi
- f. ***aureifolia*** 'Aurea'	SCoo SRms
- - 'Barry Sellers'	SRms
§ - - 'Bell's Extra Special'	EPfP SRms
- - 'Foxhollow' ♀H7	CBcs CFst CTri EPfP IArd MAsh MJak NHol SCoo SRms SWhi
- - 'Gelber Findling'	SRms
- - 'Hilletje'	CFst SRms
- - 'January Sun'	SRms
- - 'Westwood Yellow' ♀H7	CSBt MAsh NHol SRms
- 'Aztec Gold'	CFst
- 'Beoley Pink'	SRms
- 'C.J. Backhouse'	SRms
- 'Challenger' ♀H7	ELan EPfP MAsh SCoo SLon SRms SWhi
- 'Clare Wilkinson'	SRms
- 'Claribelle'	CFst
- 'Corinna'PBR **new**	SWhi
- 'December Red'	CFst ELan EPfP MAsh MMuc SCoo SEND SRms SWhi
- 'Diana Young'	SCoo SWhi
- 'Dømmesmoen'	CFst SRms
- 'Dorset Sunshine'	CFst
- 'Early Red'	SRms
- 'Eileen Porter'	SEND
- 'Eva' ♀H7	CBcs CFst IVic SRms SWhi
- 'Foxhollow Fairy'	SPer SRms
- 'Gracilis'	SRms
- 'Heathwood'	MAsh SRms
- 'James Backhouse'	CTri
- 'Jason Attwater'	SRms
- 'Jennifer Anne'	SRms
- 'John Kampa'	SRms
- 'John Pook'	SCoo SRms
- 'King George'	CFst CTri SRms
§ - 'Kramer's Rubin'	CFst SRms
- 'Lena'	see *E.* × *darleyensis* 'Lena'
- 'Lesley Sparkes'	CFst
- 'Lohse's Rubin'	NWea SRms
- 'Loughrigg' ♀H7	CTri MAsh MJak NHol SCoo SRms
- 'March Seedling' ♀H7	CFst EPfP MAsh NHol SCoo SLon SPer SRms SWhi
- 'Margery Frearson'	SRms
I - 'Martin'	SRms

	Name	Suppliers
	- 'Myretoun Ruby' ♀H7	CBcs CFst CSBt CTri EPfP LCro MAsh NHol SCoo SPer SRms SWhi
	- 'Nathalie' ♀H7	CFst CSBt IVic MAsh SCoo SRms
	- 'Pink Cloud'	CFst
	- 'Pink Mist'	SRms
	- 'Pink Spangles' ♀H7	CBcs CFst CSBt CTri MAsh MJak SCoo SPer SRms SWhi
	- 'Pirbright Rose'	SRms
	- 'Polden Pride'	SRms
	- 'Praecox Rubra'	NHol SCoo SRms
	- 'Queen Mary'	SRms
	- 'Queen of Spain'	MAsh SRms
	- 'R.B. Cooke'	EPfP MAsh MJak SCoo SRms
	- 'Robert Jan'	SRms
	- 'Rosalie' ♀H7	CFst EPfP IArd LCro MAsh SCoo SPer SRms SWhi
	- 'Rosantha'	CFst SRms
	- 'Rosea'	SPlb
	- 'Rosy Morn'	SRms
	- 'Rotes Juwel'	SRms
	- 'Rubinteppich'	SRms
	- 'Ruby Glow'	MJak NHol
	- 'Scatterley'	SRms
	- 'Schatzalp'	SRms
	- 'Sherwood Creeping'	SRms
	- 'Smart's Heath'	SRms
	- 'Springwood Pink'	CSBt CTri NHol SRms
	- 'Tanja'	CFst SWhi
§	- 'Treasure Trove'	CFst
	- 'Viking'	MAsh
	- 'Vivellii' ♀H7	CFst CTri MAsh MJak NHol SCoo SRms
	- 'Walter Reisert'	SRms
	- 'Wentwood Red'	SRms
	- Whisky	see *E. carnea* f. *aureifolia* 'Bell's Extra Special'
	- 'Winter Beauty'	MJak NHol
	- Winter Rubin	see *E. carnea* 'Kramer's Rubin'
	- 'Winterfreude'	SWhi
	- 'Wintersonne' ♀H7	CFst MMuc SRms SWhi
	cerinthoides	CTre
	ciliaris 'Bretagne'	SWhi
	- 'Corfe Castle'	CFst
	- 'David McClintock'	CFst SWhi
	- 'Globosa'	SWhi
	cinerea	SWhi
	- f. ***alba*** 'Alba Minor'	CFst MAsh SWhi
	- - 'Celebration'	SWhi
	- - 'Domino'	MAsh
	- 'Atropurpurea'	MAsh
	- 'Atrorubens'	CFst
	- f. ***aureifolia*** 'Apricot Charm'	CSBt
	- - 'Fiddler's Gold'	MAsh SWhi
	- - 'Golden Drop'	CFst CSBt MAsh
	- - 'Golden Hue'	MAsh
	- - 'Golden Sport'	SWhi
	- - 'Goldilocks'	CFst
	- - 'Summer Gold'	SWhi
	- 'Bucklebury Red'	CFst
	- 'C.D. Eason' ♀H7	CFst CSBt CTri IVic MAsh SCoo SWhi
	- 'Champs Hill'	CFst
	- 'Coccinea'	SWhi
	- 'Discovery'	CFst
	- 'Eden Valley'	CFst SCoo
	- 'Glasnevin Red'	IVic
	- 'Glencairn'	MMuc
	- 'Harry Fulcher'	SWhi
	- 'John Ardron'	CFst
	- 'Joseph Murphy'	CBcs CFst
	- 'Joyce Burfitt'	CFst
	- 'Katinka'	CBcs CFst IVic SWhi
	- 'Lilac Time'	CFst
	- 'Mrs E.A. Mitchell'	SPlb SWhi
	- 'My Love'	CFst SWhi
	- 'Ockham'	CFst
	- 'Pentreath'	SWhi
	- 'Pink Ice' ♀H7	CFst CTri EPfP MAsh NHol SWhi
	- 'Providence'	CFst
	- 'Purple Beauty'	SWhi
	- 'Rosita'	CFst
	- 'Roter Kobold'	SWhi
	- 'Sandford Heritage'	CFst
	- 'Sandpit Hill'	CFst SWhi
	- 'Sherry'	CFst NHol SWhi
	- 'Stephen Davis' ♀H7	NHol SCoo SWhi
	- 'Ted Oliver'	CFst
	- 'Velvet Night' ♀H7	CSBt MAsh NHol SWhi
	- 'Vivienne Patricia'	CFst
	cooperi	SPlb
	curviflora	SPlb
	× ***darleyensis***	GGal
	- 'Alba'	see *E.* × *darleyensis* f. *albiflora* 'Silberschmelze'
	- f. ***albiflora*** 'Ada S. Collings'	MAsh SRms
	- - 'Bing'	CFst SCoo
	- - 'N.R. Webster'	SRms
§	- - 'Silberschmelze'	CSBt CTri EPfP MAsh MJak MMuc SCoo SEND SRms SWhi
	- - 'White Glow'	CTri MAsh SRms
	- - 'White Perfection' ♀H6	CBcs CFst CSBt EPfP IArd IVic MAsh MJak NHol SCoo SPoG SRms SWhi
	- 'Archie Graham'	SRms
	- 'Arthur Johnson' ♀H6	CFst CSBt CTri MAsh SRms
§	- f. ***aureifolia*** 'Eva Gold'[PBR]	CFst SWhi
	- - 'Jack H. Brummage'	CSBt CTri MAsh SRms
	- - 'Mary Helen'	CSBt EPfP MAsh NHol SCoo SRms SWhi
	- - 'Moonshine'	CFst SRms SWhi
	- - 'Tweety'	CBcs CFst SRms
	- 'Aurélie Brégeon'	CFst SRms
	- 'Bert'	CFst SCoo
	- 'Cherry Stevens'	see *E.* × *darleyensis* 'Furzey'
§	- 'Darley Dale'	CFst CSBt ELan EPfP MAsh MJak MMuc SCoo SEND SLon SPer SPoG SRms SWhi
	- 'Epe'	CFst SRms
	- 'Eva'	see *E.* × *darleyensis* f. *aureifolia* 'Eva Gold'
§	- 'Furzey' ♀H6	CSBt EPfP LCro MAsh NHol NWea SCoo SRms SWhi
	- 'George Rendall'	CSBt CTri EPfP MAsh SCoo SRms
	- 'Ghost Hills' ♀H6	CSBt EPfP MAsh MJak SCoo SPoG SRms
	- 'Golden Perfect'	CFst
	- 'Irish Treasure'	CFst
	- 'J.W. Porter' ♀H6	EPfP MJak MMuc SCoo SEND SLon SRms SWhi
	- 'James Smith'	SRms
	- 'Jenny Porter' ♀H6	CSBt ELan EPfP SCoo SLon SWhi
	- 'Katia'[PBR] (Winter Belles Series)	CFst SWhi
	- 'Kramer's Rote' ♀H6	CFst CSBt CTri ELan EPfP MJak NHol SCoo SPer SPoG SRms SWhi XLum
§	- 'Lena'	CFst

- 'Lucie'PBR (Winter Belles Series)	CFst SWhi
- 'Margaret Porter'	CFst EPfP MAsh SCoo
- Molten Silver	see *E.* × *darleyensis* f. *albiflora* 'Silberschmelze'
- 'Phoebe'PBR (Winter Belles Series)	CFst SWhi
- 'Pink Perfection'	see *E.* × *darleyensis* 'Darley Dale'
- 'Rubina'PBR	CFst SWhi
- 'Snow Surprise'	SWhi
- 'Spring Surprise'PBR ♀H6	CFst EPfP SCoo
- 'W.G. Pine'	SRms
- 'White Spring Surprise'	SWhi
- 'Winter Spring Surprise' **new**	SWhi
- 'Winter Surprise'	CFst SWhi
- 'Winter Treasure'	CFst SWhi
densifolia **new**	CDes
discolor	CTre
erigena f. ***alba*** 'Brian Proudley'	CFst
- f. ***alba*** 'W.T. Rackliff' ♀H5	CBcs CSBt EPfP MAsh NHol SCoo SRms SWhi
- f. ***aureifolia*** 'Golden Lady'	CFst CSBt MAsh NHol SCoo SRms
- - 'Thing Nee'	CFst SRms SWhi
- 'Brightness'	CSBt EPfP NHol SCoo
- 'Irish Dusk' ♀H5	CBcs CSBt CTri EPfP MAsh NWea SCoo SEND SRms SWhi
- 'Rosslare'	CFst
- 'Superba'	MAsh SRms
fastigiata **new**	CDes
formosa	CTre
glandulosa **new**	CTre
glauca var. ***glauca***	SPlb
× ***griffithsii*** 'Jacqueline'	SWhi
- 'Valerie Griffiths'	NHol
× ***krameri*** 'Rudi'	IVic
lusitanica ♀H2	CFst
- f. ***aureifolia*** 'George Hunt'	CFst ELan EPfP LRHS MAsh SLon SPer SPoG
- Great Star	see *E. lusitanica* 'La Vasterival'
§ - 'La Vasterival'	CFst
- 'Sheffield Park'	CFst EPfP LRHS MAsh SPer SPoG
mackayana f. ***eburnea*** 'Doctor Ronald Gray'	CFst
- f. ***eburnea*** 'Shining Light'	CFst SWhi
- 'Errigal Dusk'	CFst
- f. ***multiplicata*** 'Ann D. Frearson' (d)	CFst
- - 'Plena' (d)	CFst WHer
mammosa ♀H2	CTre SPlb
- cream-flowered **new**	CTre
- pink-flowered **new**	CTre
- red-flowered **new**	CTre
- white-flowered **new**	CTre
mediterranea misapplied	see *E. erigena*
multiflora	XSen
× ***oldenburgensis*** 'Ammerland' ♀H6	SCoo SRms
patersonii	SPlb
perspicua	CTre SPlb
platycodon	CFst
subsp. ***maderincola*** f. ***aureifolia*** 'Levada Gold'	
scabriuscula	CTre
sessiliflora	CTre
spiculifolia 'Balkan Rose'	GCal
straussiana	CDes SPlb
× ***stuartii*** 'Irish Lemon' ♀H5	CFst CSBt NHol SWhi
- 'Irish Orange'	CSBt NHol SWhi
terminalis	WBod
tetralix	SWhi
- f. ***alba*** 'Alba Mollis' ♀H7	CFst CSBt MAsh SWhi
- f. ***aureifolia*** 'Ruth's Gold'	NHol
- 'Con Underwood'	CFst CSBt LCro SWhi
- 'Riko'	CFst
- 'Samtpfötchen'	CFst
- 'Silver Bells'	CSBt
- f. ***stellata*** 'Pink Star' ♀H7	CFst NHol SWhi
transparens	CDes
vagans f. ***alba*** 'Cornish Cream' ♀H6	EPfP NHol SWhi
- f. ***alba*** 'Diana's Gold'	SRms
- - 'Golden Triumph'	CFst
- - 'Lyonesse' ♀H6	MAsh MMuc NHol SWhi
- f. ***aureifolia*** 'Valerie Proudley' ♀H6	CSBt MAsh NHol
- - 'Yellow John'	CFst SRms
- 'Birch Glow' ♀H6	EPfP
- 'Keira'	CFst SRms
- 'Mrs D.F. Maxwell' ♀H6	CBcs CFst CSBt MAsh MMuc NHol SWhi
- 'Mrs Donaldson'	CFst
- 'Saint Keverne'	CFst CSBt IArd IVic MMuc NHol SWhi
- 'Summertime'	CFst
× ***veitchii*** 'Exeter' ♀H5	CFst CSBt ELan EPfP LRHS MAsh SPer SWhi
- 'Gold Tips' ♀H5	CFst CSBt EPfP LRHS
versicolor	CTre SPlb
verticillata	CTre
× ***watsonii*** 'Claire Elise'	CFst
- 'Mary'	SWhi
- 'Pink Pacific'	CFst SWhi
× ***williamsii*** 'Ken Wilson'	CFst
'Winter Fire' **new**	CTre
woodii	SPlb

Erigeron ✿ (*Asteraceae*)

'Adria'	EBee ECtt LLHF LRHS MMuc MSpe SEND WMnd WWEG
annuus	CSpe NCGa NDov SDix
aurantiacus	MNrw NBro WCot WHal
aureus 'Canary Bird' ♀H4	ECtt EPot GCrg NSla WAbe
- 'The Giant'	WAbe
Azure Fairy	see *E.* 'Azurfee'
§ 'Azurfee'	CSBt ELan EPfP GMaP MBNS MHol MWat NBir NLar NPri SGSe SPer SPoG SWvt WFar WMoo
Black Sea	see *E.* 'Schwarzes Meer'
'Blue Beauty'	CMac EPfP LRHS
borealis	GAbr
'Charity'	MRav WBrk
chrysopsidis	GKev MHer
- 'Grand Ridge'	ECho EPot LHop LRHS WAbe
compositus	CTri SRms
§ - var. ***discoideus***	EDAr NSla SPlb WHoo WOld
- 'Rocky'	CBod ECho MMuc NPri
coulteri **new**	EBee
Darkest of All	see *E.* 'Dunkelste Aller'
'Dignity'	ECGP ELan GBuc LHop LLHF MBrN MMuc MPie MRav NHol SEND SWvt WBrk WFar WWEG
'Dimity'	CMea ECha NBir NBre WFar WHal
'Dominator'	MNrw WCot
I 'Dunkelste Aller'	CHVG CMea CSam ELan EPfP GBin GMaP LHop LRHS LSou MBel MRav

	MTis NLar SCob SGbt SPer SPoG SRms SWvt WCAu WWEG
* ***ereganus***	NBre
flettii	ECho GKev
'Foersters Liebling' ♀H5	EBee GBin LHop MBel MNrw WWEG
formosissimus	GBin
'Four Winds'	CAbP ECho ECtt ELan EWes GKev LRHS NGdn WBrk WWEG
'Gaiety'	NBre
glaucus	CBod CSBt ECho GBee GJos LRHS MMuc MRav NGdn SEND SMad WBrk WFar
- 'Albus'	ELon LHop LRHS NLar WBor WFar
- 'Elstead Pink'	CTri ECtt ELan MBri WFar
- large-flowered	LRHS
- 'Roger Raiche'	CFis CMea MRav
- 'Rose Purple'	CFis
- 'Roseus'	CBcs SEND
- 'Sea Breeze'	CBod CNec EBee ECtt ELon GJos GMaP LHop LOPS LRHS MBel MBri MHol MLHP NDov NLar NPri SCob SGbt SHil SPoG SRms SWvt WBor WBrk WHoo
- 'Sennen'	WBrk
- 'Viewpoint Blue'	ELon LRHS
§ ***karvinskianus*** ♀H4	Widely available
- 'Kew Profusion'	LRHS MHol SHil
- 'Sea of Blossom' **new**	CBod
- 'Stallone'	LSun NLar NPri
leiomerus	LLHF
linearis	LLHF
'Mrs F.H. Beale'	LSou WCot
mucronatus	see *E. karvinskianus*
multiradiatus	GCal
'Nachthimmel'	CAby NBre NGdn
philadelphicus	CDes CElw MNrw NBir NBro WHal
'Pink Beauty'	SKHP
Pink Jewel	see *E.* 'Rosa Juwel'
'Profusion'	see *E. karvinskianus*
pygmaeus	LLHF
pyrenaicus Rouy	see *Aster pyrenaeus*
'Quakeress'	CAby CBod CPrp ECtt EPri GBin GBuc GMaP IKil LHop LRHS MBel MMuc MNrw MRav MSpe NGdn SCob SPoG SWvt WBrk WFar WGwG WWEG XLum
§ 'Rosa Juwel'	CSBt CTri ECtt ELan EPfP GBin GMaP LPfy LRHS MBNS MHol MRav NBir NPri SPad SPer SPoG SRms SWvt WCAu WFar WMnd WMoo
'Rotes Meer'	CMac EBee ELan MRav
rotundifolius 'Caerulescens'	see *Bellis caerulescens*
salsuginosus misapplied	see *Aster sibiricus*
§ 'Schneewittchen'	CSam EBee ELan EPfP LHop MBNS MBel MPie MRav NCGa NGdn SRms SWvt WWEG
§ 'Schwarzes Meer'	EBee WCot
scopulinus	ITim SBch WAbe WHal WOld
simplex	ECho LRHS
'Sincerity'	XLum
'Snow Queen'	SWvt
Snow White	see *E.* 'Schneewittchen'
'Sommerneuschnee'	GBin LPla MTis NDov SCob SPhx WMnd
'Strahlenmeer'	MSpe NBre
'Synehurst' **new**	WCot
trifidus	see *E. compositus* var. *discoideus*
tweedyi	EBee
uniflorus	LLHF SRms
'Wayne Roderick'	CBod ELan EPfP LAst LRHS WCot
'White Quakeress'	CFis CMea MHCG MRav WCot

Erinacea (*Papilionaceae*)

§ ***anthyllis*** ♀H5	SBrt WAbe WThu
pungens	see *E. anthyllis*

Erinus (*Plantaginaceae*)

alpinus ♀H4	CTri ECho ECtt EDAr GAbr GJos GKev MLHP NBir NPri NSla SBch SRms WCot XLum
- var. ***albus***	ECho NSla SRms WHoo XLum
- 'Doktor Hähnle'	ECho EDAr GJos GMaP NPri NRya SRms WHoo XLum

Eriobotrya (*Rosaceae*)

sp.	ETod LPar
'Coppertone'	see × *Rhaphiobotrya* 'Coppertone'
deflexa	CBcs EBee
japonica (F) ♀H3	CAbb CBcs CDul CLet CTho ELan EPfP ETod EUJe LPal LPar LRHS MGos MMuc NLar NLos NPla SCoo SEND SPer SPlb SPtp SSta SVic WHer WPGP
- 'Gold Nugget' (F)	XBlo
- 'Mrs Cookson' (F)	LRHS MBri WMat
- 'Oliver' (F)	LRHS MBri MGos WMat
- 'Rose-Anne' **new**	LRHS SGol

Eriocapitella see *Anemone*

Eriocephalus (*Asteraceae*)

africanus	CBod SPlb WJek

Eriogonum (*Polygonaceae*)

alatum	WCot
alleni	WCot
- 'Little Rascal'	EBee
cespitosum	LLHF WAbe
fasciculatum	EBee
grande var. ***rubescens*** **new**	EBee SBrt
umbellatum	ECho EPot GKev
- var. ***porteri***	GKev
- var. ***torreyanum***	CMea
vimineum **new**	EBee

Eriophorum (*Cyperaceae*)

angustifolium	CBen CWat EHoe EHon MSKA MWts SPlb SWat WMAq WPnP WWtn XLum
chamissonis	MWts
latifolium	LLWG MSKA MWts SGSe XLum
rousseauianum	MSKA
vaginatum	EHoe EWay LLWG MSKA SGSe XLum

Eriophyllum (*Asteraceae*)

lanatum	CFis EBee ECha EPfP NBid NGBl SHar WWEG XLum
* - 'Pointe'	WSHC

Eriostemon (*Rutaceae*)

myoporoides	see *Philotheca myoporoides*

Eritrichium (*Boraginaceae*)

aretioides	SPlb
§ ***canum***	GKev
rupestre	see *E. canum*
strictum	see *E. canum*

Erodium (*Geraniaceae*)

	absinthoides	LRHS XSen
	- var. ***amanum***	see *E. amanum*
§	***acaule***	EPPr
	'Almodovar'	WCot
§	***amanum***	CSpe ECtt EWes
	balearicum	see *E.* × *variabile* 'Album'
	'Bidderi'	XSen
	'Candy Store'	LRHS
	'Carmel'	XSen
	'Caroline'	CMea WHoo
§	***castellanum***	EBee GKev LLHF NLar
	celtibericum	EPot XSen
	- 'Javalambre'	XSen
	- 'Peñagolosa'	XSen
	'Cézembre'	WCot XSen
	chamaedryoides	see *E. reichardii*
	- 'Roseum'	see *E.* × *variabile* 'Roseum'
§	***cheilanthifolium***	XSen
	- 'David Crocker'	EPot WAbe
	chrysanthum	CElw CSam CTri EAJP ECha ECho ECtt EDAr EPfP EPot EWoo GBuc GJos GMaP ITim LHop MPnt NChi NLar SEND SRot SWvt XLum XSen
	- (f)	WFar
	- (m)	NRya
	- 'Arcadia'	CMea SPhx
	- pink-flowered	CSpe ECtt EPot LHop MMuc SEND SRot
	- ***sulphureum***	MMuc
	corsicum	ECho
	- 'Album'	ECho
	'County Park'	ECha ECou EPPr MLHP NLar SHar SRms XSen
	daucoides misapplied	see *E. castellanum*
	'Fran's Delight'	CMea ECtt EPot GJos WAbe WHoo
	'Freedom'	CSpe MHol SCob XEll
	'Fripetta'	WIce XSen
	'Géant de Saint Cyr'	ECtt
	'Gini's Choice'	WCot
	glandulosum ♀H5	ECho EPfP MAsh MMuc NLar SBch SEND SPtp SRms SRot WSHC XLum XSen
	- 'Marie Poligné'	XSen
	'Grey Blush'	SMHy
	gruinum	CHid SPhx
	guicciardii	XSen
	guttatum misapplied	see *E.* 'Katherine Joy'
	guttatum (Desf.) Willd.	EPot EWTr LHop SRms
	hymenodes L'Hér.	see *E. trifolium*
	'Julie Ritchie'	WHoo
§	'Katherine Joy'	ECtt EWes MHer NRya SBch SRot XSen
	× ***kolbianum***	SMHy WAbe WCot WHoo WPnn XSen
	- 'Natasha'	CFis CMHG ECtt EPPr EPot EWes GBuc MHer MMuc NSla SEND SPoG WAbe WIce WKif XSen
	'Las Meninas'	ECtt WCot
	× ***lindavicum***	GCrg NChi WPnn XSen
	macradenum	see *E. glandulosum*
	manescavii	Widely available
	'Marchants Mikado'	WKif
	'Maryla'	CMea WIce
	'Merstham Pink'	ELon SRms XLum XSen
	'Mesquita'	CMea
	'Pallidum'	CSam
	pelargoniiflorum	CFis CHid CSpe ELan EPfP EWTr LRHS MCot NLar SEND SRms SWvt WKif WPnn
	'Peter Vernon'	MHer XSen
	petraeum subsp. ***crispum*** misapplied	see *E. cheilanthifolium*
	- subsp. ***petraeum***	EPot
	'Pickering Pink'	EBee
	'Princesse Marion'	MLHP XSen
*	'Purple Haze'	EBee SRms SRot WFar
§	***reichardii***	CTri ECho ECtt LRHS MBrN SPoG SRms WCFE
	- 'Album'	CTal ECho GCrg LRHS MAsh MMuc MSCN NPri SPoG WHoo WPnn
	- 'Bianca'	EPfP
*	- 'Rubrum'	CElw ECho MAsh
	'Robertino'	WAbe
	rodiei	EWes
	romanum	see *E. acaule*
§	***rupestre***	ECho ECtt SRms SRot WIce
	'Sarck'	XSen
	'Shocked Pink' **new**	SMHy
	sibthorpianum	XSen
	'Souvenir d'Hélène'	XSen
	'Spanish Eyes'	CBod CWGN ECtt EWTr GCrg LRHS LSou NPri SRot SWvt WCot WKif
	'Stephanie'	CFis CMHG ECho ECtt ELan EPPr EPot EWes MHer MMuc SEND WAbe WIce XSen
	supracanum	see *E. rupestre*
	'Tiny Kyni'	XSen
	trichomanifolium misapplied	see *E. cheilanthifolium*
	trichomanifolium L'Hér.	EWes
§	***trifolium***	ECho ELan EPfP MHer SBch SPhx
	× ***variabile***	WFar
§	- 'Album'	CMea ECho EPfP EPot GMaP LAst LRHS MHer NEgg NPri NSla SRms SRot SWvt WAbe WBrk WFar
I	- 'Bishop's Form'	CMea CNec ECho ECou ECtt ELon EPfP EPot GCrg GJos GMaP LAst LRHS MAsh MHer MHol NEgg NQui NRya SPoG SRms SRot SWvt WAbe WBrk WCFE WFar WHoo WIce
	- 'Candy'	CTal ECtt MHer WBrk
	- 'Derek'	ECho SRGP
	- 'Flore Pleno' (d)	CBod ECho ELan EPfP EWes GMaP ITim LRHS MHer SPoG SRms SRot WBrk WRHF
	- 'Red Rock'	CTri
§	- 'Roseum' ♀H4	CBod ECho ECtt ELan ELon EPfP MMuc MSCN NPri NSla SEND SPlb SRms WBrk
	- 'Timpany Seedling'	ITim
	'Whitwell Superb'	XSen

Erpetion see *Viola*

Eruca (*Brassicaceae*)

	vesicaria	ENfk
	- subsp. ***sativa***	CLau CSpe GPoy MHer MNHC SIde SRms SVic

Eryngium ✿ (*Apiaceae*)

	NJM 09.072	WPGP
§	***agavifolium***	Widely available
	- giant	WPGP

alpinum	CBcs CSpe ECha ELan GKev GMaP IBoy LAst LHop MGos MHer MMuc MSCN NBir SCob SKHP SPer SRms SRot WFar
- 'Amethyst'	LRHS LSRN NBro WFar
- 'Blue Jacket'	NSti
- 'Blue Star'	CBot CExl CSpe EBee ECtt ELan ELon EWoo GBin GBuc NLar SAko SMad WBor WCFE
- 'Holden Blue'	MAvo
- 'Slieve Donard'	see *E.* × *zabelii* 'Donard Variety'
- 'Superbum'	ECtt GCal GLog LRHS MNrw SRms SWat
amethystinum	CCse ELon EPri LRHS XLum
'Blue Jackpot'	EBee EPfP EWes MBel MHol MNrw
'Blue Spikes'	EBee
'Blue Steel'	EBee LLHF
bourgatii	Widely available
- Graham Stuart Thomas's selection	CAbP CAby CElw CExl CLet CMHG CSpe ECtt ELan EPPr EWes GAbr GMaP LHop LRHS MBel MCot MHol NBir NEgg NLar SMad SPad SPer SRms WCAu WCot WHoo WHrl WPGP
- 'Oxford Blue' ♀H5	CSpe GBin MHer NLar NSla SGSe SKHP SWvt
- 'Picos Amethyst'	CBcs CBct CMac CWCL EBee ELon EPfP LCro LHop LOPS LRHS LSRN NLar NSti SCob SCoo SGSe SKHP SRms WSHC
- 'Picos Blue' PBR	Widely available
bromeliifolium misapplied	see *E. agavifolium*, *E. eburneum*
bromeliifolium ambig.	LRHS
'Cobalt Star'	MAvo MRav NLar WHoo
creticum	NBro NChi
decaisneanum misapplied	see *E. pandanifolium*
deppeanum	CFil CSpe
- F&M 54	CDes WPGP
- NJM 05.031	EBee LEdu
Dove Cottage hybrid	MAvo NDov
ebracteatum	LPla SMad SPhx
var. ***poterioides***	
§ ***eburneum***	CBod CCon EBee ECha EPfP EWes GMaP ILea LRHS NChi SIgm SKHP SMad
aff. ***eburneum***	CMac
'Electric Haze'	CSam ECtt GBuc LSou
elegans var. ***elegans***	CCon
§ ***giganteum*** ♀H7	Widely available
- 'Silver Ghost' ♀H7	CAby CBod CExl CSam CSpe ECtt EWoo GMaP LCro LHop LOPS LRHS LSun MBel NChi NDov NGdn NLar NPri NSti SKHP SMad SPhx SWat SWvt WCot
gracile B&SWJ 10351	WCru
- B&SWJ 10441	WCru
'Green Jade'	LRHS
guatemalense B&SWJ 8989	WCru
- B&SWJ 10322	WCru
- B&SWJ 10420	WCru
horridum misapplied	see *E. eburneum*
horridum ambig.	EWes MNrw NChi NLar NLos WMnd
horridum Malme	WCot
humile	CSpe
- B&SWJ 10464	WCru
'Indigo Star'	MAvo
leavenworthii	LRHS
maritimum	CArn CEls CPou EBee GPoy MNHC SPhx SPlb SRms
Miss Willmott's ghost	see *E. giganteum*
monocephalum	EBee
'Neptune's Gold' **new**	NLar SCob SHar
× ***oliverianum*** ♀H6	CBod CMea CSpe CWCL ECtt ELan EPfP GBuc GCal GKev LHop LRHS MAvo MCot MLHP MRav MTis NBir NChi NLar SDix SMad SPoG SWat SWvt WCot WHoo
palmatum	NChi
§ ***pandanifolium*** ♀H3	CBot CCon CKno ELan EUJe EWes GCal LTro SEND SGSe SMad SPlb SPoG SWvt WMnd
- 'Physic Purple'	CAby CFis CSpe EBee MAvo SDix SPhx
paniculatum	LTro
'Pen Blue'	CAby CWld MGos SAko SCob WCot
planum	Widely available
- 'Bethlehem'	NLar SWat
§ - 'Blauer Zwerg'	GMaP NLar
- 'Blaukappe'	CExl CMea EAEE EBee ELan ELon EPfP EWoo LHop LRHS LSun MMuc NLar SEND SKHP SPhx SRms WTcb
- Blue Dwarf	see *E. planum* 'Blauer Zwerg'
- 'Blue Glitter'	CBod EAJP EBee ELon LRHS LSun NLar SPhx SWvt
- 'Blue Hobbit'	Widely available
- 'Flüela'	EWes GBuc GCal LRHS LSRN NEgg SWat
- 'Jade Frost' PBR (v)	Widely available
- 'Little Blue Wonder' PBR	NHol
- 'Naughty Jackpot' (v)	EBee NLar
- 'Paradise Jackpot' PBR	SRms
- 'Seven Seas'	CCon LRHS MBNS NEgg
- 'Silver Salentino'	CBod EBee ELon WHil WOut
- 'Silver Stone'	SRms
- 'Tetra Petra'	LRHS SRms
- 'Tiny Jackpot'	CWGN GMaP IBoy NLar
- 'White Glitter'	CBod EBee ELan
proteiflorum	EPfP LPla LRHS NChi SKHP SMad SPlb
serbicum	GCal SDix WCot
serra	EWes LRHS MCot NLos
tricuspidatum	EBee ECtt LRHS
× ***tripartitum*** ♀H5	CBcs CBod CElw CTri ECha ECtt ELan EPPr EPfP GMaP LAst LHop LRHS LSRN MRav MWat NBro NEgg NLar SBod SDix SRkn SWat SWvt
* ***umbelliferum***	GCal IMou MBNS SKHP
variifolium	Widely available
- 'Miss Marbel'	CNec COtt EPfP LSun MWat SRms WSHC WWtn
venustum	CSpe EBee EUJe LRHS SMad
viviparum	WFar
yuccifolium	CBod CCon EBee EPfP EWes GCal LEdu MAvo NLar SPhx SPlb SWvt XLum XSen
× ***zabelii***	ECha NChi WBor
- 'Big Blue'	CBct CBod CSpe CWCL ELon GBin GMaP LRHS MAsh MAvo MHol MNrw MSCN MTis NEgg NLar NPri SHar SMad WCAu WCot WHil WTor
- 'Blaue Ritter'	SKHP SWat
§ - 'Donard Variety'	COtt ECtt GBBs GBuc GCal ILea LRHS MAvo NLar SWat
- 'Forncett Ultra'	GCal MNrw NChi SDix
- 'Jewel'	SWat
- 'Jos Eijking' PBR	Widely available
- 'Violetta'	MCot NLar SWat

Erysimum ✿ (*Brassicaceae*)

sp. — SVic
allionii misapplied — see *E.* × *marshallii*
alpinum misapplied — see *E. hieraciifolium*
'Andy's Oranges and Lemons' (v) — WCot
'Apricot Delight' — see *E.* 'Apricot Twist'
§ 'Apricot Twist' — CBcs CMea CSpe CWCL CWGN CWld EAJP ECtt ELan ELon EPfP GBuc GMaP LHop LRHS LSou MBri MRav NLar SCob SCoo SPer SPoG SRms SWvt WHil WHoo
arkansanum — see *E. helveticum*
asperum — GJos
'Audrey's Pink' — WHoo
'Bowles's Mauve' ♀H4 — Widely available
'Bowles's Purple' — SRms SWvt
'Bowles's Yellow' — MHCG WCot
'Bredon' — NPer
'Butterscotch' — MMHG WHoo
'Canaries Yellow' new — NBFr
capitatum var. ***purshii*** — WAbe
'Caribbean Island' new — WHlf
caricum — WAbe
cheiri MHer
- 'Baden-Powell' (d) — GCal
- 'Bloody Warrior' (d) — CElw ECtt WCot
- 'Gold Dust' new — NPri
- 'Harpur Crewe' (d) — CBot NPer SRms WHer
concinnum — see *E. suffrutescens*
'Constant Cheer' — CMea CSBt CWCL EAJP ECtt ELan ELon EPfP IFoB MCot MMuc NBFr NPer SCob SEND SPer SRGP SRkn SRms SWvt WHil WHoo WKif
'Cotswold Gem' (v) — EHoe ELan ELon LSou MHer MMuc NPer SEND SWvt
'Dawn Breaker' — ECtt MRav WCot
'Desert Island' new — ECtt
'Dorothy Elmhirst' — see *E.* 'Mrs L.K. Elmhirst'
'Emm's Variety' — ECtt
'Gogh's Gold' new — WHlf
'Gold Shot' — EAJP
'Golden Gem' — ECho EPfP
'Golden Jubilee' — ECho ECtt EPPr GBuc LRHS SRms WIce
'Hector's Gatepost' — SRGP
§ ***helveticum*** — ECho EPPr MMuc SBod SRms
§ ***hieraciifolium*** — GKev
'Jacob's Jacket' — ECha ECtt MBNS MHer NPer
'John Codrington' — GBin LHop NPer WKif
'Joseph's Coat' — MHCG
'Jubilee Gold' — WWEG
kotschyanum — ECho EPot GCrg GEdr NSla SIgm SRms WIce
'Lemon Light' — WHoo
linifolium — SRms
- 'Little Kiss Lilac' — GJos
§ - 'Variegatum' (v) — CSBt EAJP EBee ECtt ELan EPfP LPot LRHS MHol NPer NPri SCob SPer SPoG SRot WCAu XLum
- 'Variegatum' peach-flowered (v) — NQui SPad
§ × ***marshallii*** — GJos
'Moonlight' — GBuc GMaP MHer MRav NBir SRms WHoo
§ 'Mrs L.K. Elmhirst' — ELon MMHG NPer
mutabile — CTri EPfP MRav WHal
'Orange Flame' — CMea ECha ECho ELon GCrg MHer MMuc NPer SEND WHoo
'Orange King' — WIce
'Orange Zwerg' — MMuc WIce
'Paintbox' — WHlf
'Parish's' — CElw CFis CSpe CWld WHea WWFP
'Parkwood Gold' — ECho GJos
'Pastel Patchwork' — CSpe ECtt WCot
Perry's hybrid — NPer
'Perry's Peculiar' — NPer
'Perry's Surprise' — NPer
'Perry's Variegated' (v) — NPer
'Plant World Lemon' — CAby CHGN CSpe ELon MHol NLar
'Poppet' — CSpe
§ ***pulchellum*** — ECha
pumilum DC. — see *E. helveticum*
'Ray's Early Giants' (mixed) — CPla
rupestre — see *E. pulchellum*
'Ruston Royal' — ECha
Rysi Bronze = 'Innrysibro' — LRHS MHol
Rysi Gold = 'Innrysigol'[PBR] — LRHS SPoG
Rysi Moon — GBin LRHS
Rysi Star = 'Inneryrysistar' new — LRHS
scoparium — ECha ELon
'Sissinghurst Variegated' — see *E. linifolium* 'Variegatum'
'Spice Island' — ECtt EWTr
'Sprite' — CMea CTri MMuc NPer SEND
'Starbright' — CWCL
'Stars and Stripes' (v) — CBod ECtt LRHS LSou SRkn
§ ***suffrutescens*** — EBee SBrt
Sunburst = 'Listrace' — CAby CMea CWGN ECtt LRHS LSou SPoG WCot
'Sweet Sorbet' — NLar SRkn SWvt
Walberton's Fragrant Star = 'Walfrastar'[PBR] (v) — EPfP LRHS SPoG SRms
Walberton's Fragrant Sunshine = 'Walfrasun' — EPfP LRHS MBri SCoo SPoG
'Wenlock Beauty' — CFis SRms
'Winter Joy' — EPfP LLHF LRHS MBNS MHol
Winter Orchid — CSpe CWCL CWGN GBin LCro LOPS LRHS NLar
Winter Rouge — CMea CSpe CWCL LRHS
Winter Sorbet = 'Inneryws'[PBR] — ECtt ELon EPfP LRHS
witmannii — EBee
'Yellow Bird' — NPri

Erythraea see *Centaurium*

Erythrina (*Papilionaceae*)

abyssinica — SPlb
amazonica — SPlb
arborescens — SPlb
× ***bidwillii*** — WPGP
crista-galli ♀H3 — CBcs CDTJ CHll CSde CSpe EBee ELan EPfP ESwi LRHS MPie MPkF SPlb WCot WPGP
flabelliformis — SPlb
guatemalensis — SPlb
herbacea — SPlb
§ ***humeana*** — SPlb
latissima — SPlb
lysistemon — SPlb
princeps — see *E. humeana*
rubrinervia — SPlb
speciosa — SPlb
vespertilio — SPlb

Erythronium ✿ (*Liliaceae*)

albidum — ECho EPot GBuc GKev IBlr LAma

	Plant	Suppliers
	americanum	ECho EPot GKev IBlr LAma MNrw NRog SKHP WAbe
	'Apple Blossom'	ECho IBlr
	'Ballyrogan's Blaze'	IBlr
	'Beechpark'	IBlr
	'Blush'	ECho IBlr
	'Bronze Beauty'	IBlr
	'Californian Star'	IBlr
	'Californian Sunshine' **new**	IBlr
	californicum 🏆H5	CCon CLAP EBee ECho ENun GBuc IBlr LRHS MNrw NHar NRog
	- J&JA 13216	CLAP
	- 'Ballyrogan Bronze Bounty'	IBlr
	- 'Brimstone'	IBlr
	- 'Brocklamont Inheritance'	IBlr
	- 'Bronze Edge'	IBlr
	- 'Dark Delight'	IBlr
	- 'Harvington Snowgoose'	see *E.* 'Harvington Snowgoose'
	- Plas Merdyn form	IBlr
	- 'Purple Heart'	IBlr
	- 'Stellar'	IBlr
	- 'White Beauty' 🏆H5	Widely available
	californicum* × *hendersonii	IBlr NRog
	'Carol Scott'	IBlr
	caucasicum	NRog
	citrinum	GBuc LLHF NRog
	- J&JA 13462	CLAP
	- subsp. ***citrinum***	GBuc
	- var. ***roderickii***	NRog
	citrinum* × *hendersonii	IBlr NRog
	'Citronella'	CBro CCon CLAP GBuc IBlr NRog WAbe
	cliftonii hort.	see *E. multiscapideum* Cliftonii Group
	'Craigton Beauty'	IBlr
	'Craigton Cover Girl'	IBlr
	'Craigton Cream'	IBlr
	'Delicacy'	IBlr
	dens-canis 🏆H5	Widely available
	- JCA 470.001	CLAP
	- 'Charmer'	ECho GEdr MNrw NRog
	- 'Frans Hals'	CCon ECho EPot GBuc GCra GEdr GKev IPot MNrw NRog SKHP WHal
	- large-flowered	IBlr
	- 'Lilac Wonder'	EBee ECho EPot GBuc GEdr GKev GMaP IPot LAma LEdu MAvo MNrw NRog NWad SDeJ SKHP
*	- 'Moerheimii' (d)	ECho GEdr GKev IBlr NRog
	- var. ***niveum***	GEdr IBlr NRog
	- 'Old Aberdeen'	CAvo CLAP ENun IBlr LRHS MNrw NHar NRog
	- 'Pink Perfection'	EBee ECho GEdr GKev LEdu MNrw NRog SDeJ
	- 'Purple King'	EBee ECGP ECho EPot GBuc GEdr GKev GMaP IPot LAma MAvo MNrw NHol NRog NWad SDeJ
	- 'Rose Queen'	ECho EPot GBuc GEdr GKev GMaP LAma MAvo MNrw NRog NWad SDeJ WHal
*	- 'Semi-plenum' (d)	IBlr
	- 'Snowflake'	CAvo CBro CLAP ECho ENun EPot GBuc GEdr GKev LAma LEdu LRHS MAvo MNrw NBir NHol NRog NWad SDeJ SKHP WAbe
	- 'White Splendour'	ECho EPot GEdr IBlr MNrw NRog
	- white-flowered, from Serbia	ECho
	'Eirene'	IBlr
	elegans	EBee ECho GBuc NRog
	'Flaire'	IBlr
	'Flash'	IBlr
§	***grandiflorum***	CLAP ECho NRog
	- M&PS 007	CLAP
	- subsp. ***chrysandrum***	see *E. grandiflorum*
§	'Harvington Snowgoose'	CAvo CBro CLAP EBee ENun IBlr LLHF LRHS NHar SKHP SPoG
	helenae	CLAP ECho IBlr MNrw NRog WAbe
	hendersonii	CAvo CLAP EBee ECho ENun GBuc LRHS NHar NRog SKHP SPlb WAbe
	- J&JA 12945	CLAP
	'Hidcote Beauty'	ENun LLHF LRHS
	howellii	CLAP EBee ENun SKHP
	- J&JA 13441	CLAP
	'Janice'	IBlr
	japonicum	ECho EFEx EPot LAma MNrw NRog
	'Jeanette Brickell'	CLAP GBuc IBlr
	'Jeannine'	GBuc IBlr
	'Joanna'	CTal GBuc IBlr MNrw NRog
	'John Brookes'	IBlr
	'Kinfauns Pink'	CWCL EBee EPot GBuc GEdr IBlr LLHF NHar NRog
	'Kondo'	CCon CTri ECho EPfP EPot GKev GMaP IBlr LAma LRHS NBir NHol NLar NRog NWad SCob SPer WAbe WPnP
	'Lavender Eye'	IBlr
	'Margaret Mathew'	CLAP IBlr WAbe
	'Minnehaha'	GBuc IBlr
	montanum	ECho
§	***multiscapideum***	CLAP ECho GBuc LLHF MNrw WCot
	- NNS 02-166	WCot
§	- Cliftonii Group 🏆H4	CLAP GBuc SKHP WAbe WCot
	'Oregon Encore'	IBlr
	oregonum	CBro CLAP EBee ECha ECho ENun GBuc GKev IBlr LLHF LRHS MNrw NHar NRog
	- 'Ballyrogan Yellow'	IBlr
	- subsp. ***leucandrum***	GBuc
	- - 'The Giant'	IBlr
	- subsp. ***oregonum***	SKHP
	oregonum* × *revolutum	IBlr
	'Pagoda' 🏆H5	Widely available
	purdyi	see *E. multiscapideum*
	revolutum 🏆H5	CBro CLAP CWCL ECho ENun EPot GBuc GEdr GKev GMaP IBlr LAma LCro LRHS MNrw NHar NLar NRog SChF SKHP SRot WCru
	- from God's Valley, Oregon	CPne IBlr MNrw
	- 'Ballyrogan White Blusher'	IBlr
	- 'Dark Dapple'	IBlr
	- 'Guincho Splendour'	IBlr
I	- 'Inshriach Form'	IBlr
	- Johnsonii Group	EBee ECho EPot WAbe WCru
	- 'Knightshayes'	CAvo EBee GBuc IBlr LRHS NHar SKHP
	- 'Knightshayes Pink'	CLAP ENun IBlr LLHF NBir WShi
	- 'Pink Beauty'	NRog
	- Plas Merdyn form	IBlr
	- 'Rose Beauty'	ECho
	- 'Wild Salmon'	CLAP EBee ENun LLHF LRHS NHar SKHP
	'Rippling Waters'	IBlr
	'Rosalind'	IBlr NRog WAbe
	sibiricum	ECho NRog
	'Spring Fresh'	IBlr
	'Sundisc'	ECha ECho GBuc IBlr NRog WAbe
	'Sunshine'	IBlr
	'Susannah'	EBee ENun IBlr LRHS NHar

tuolumnense ♀H5	CBro CCon CLAP CTal CWCL ECho EPot GBuc GEdr GKev GMaP IBlr LAma MCot MNrw NRog NWad SDeJ WAbe WCot
- EBA clone 2	IBlr
- EBA clone 3	IBlr
- Plas Merdyn form	IBlr
- 'Spindlestone'	EBee ENun GBuc GEdr IBlr LLHF LRHS NHar SKHP
umbilicatum	EBee ECho EPot GEdr GKev IBlr
'White Star'	IBlr
'Winifred Loraine'	IBlr

Escallonia ✿ (*Escalloniaceae*)

'Alice'	SCob SPer
§ ***alpina***	MGil
'Apple Blossom' ♀H5	Widely available
§ ***bifida*** ♀H4	CBot CDul CHGN ECre ELan LRHS SDix
'C.F. Ball'	CBcs CTri ELan EPfP GKin IArd LBMP LBuc LRHS MAsh MSwo NEgg NPla NWea SEND SGol SRms WMoo
'Compacta Coccinea'	LRHS MBri
'Dart's Rosy Red'	MBri WMoo
'Donard Beauty'	SRms
'Donard Brilliance'	SGol SRms
'Donard Radiance' ♀H5	CBcs CDul CMac CSBt CWib EPfP EShb LBMP LHop LRHS LSRN MBri NLar NWad NWea SCob SGol SLim SPer SPoG SRms SWvt WMoo
'Donard Seedling'	CBcs CCVT CDul EBee ECrN ELan EPfP GKin LAst LBuc LRHS MAsh MGos MMuc MSwo NBes NEgg NPer NWea SCob SGol SLim SPer SRms SWvt WMoo
'Donard Star'	CWib EPfP NLar NWad NWea WCFE WHar
'Donard White'	CBod EPfP NLar SPoG
'Edinensis'	EAEE EPfP NLar SLim SRms WMoo
'Everest'	EPfP LRHS MMuc SLon
× ***exoniensis***	SRms
fonkii	see *E. alpina*
Golden Carpet = 'Alcaura' **new**	LRHS SCob SPoG
'Hopleys Gold'	see *E. laevis* 'Gold Brian'
illinita	CDul NLar
'Iveyi' ♀H4	Widely available
'Jamie'PBR	EAEE EShb LLHF LSRN WMoo
§ ***laevis***	LRHS
§ - 'Gold Brian'PBR	CDul CLet CMac COtt EHoe ELan EPfP LRHS LSRN MAsh MGos MJak NLar SCob SGol SPer
- 'Gold Ellen' (v)	Widely available
'Langleyensis' ♀H5	CMac CTri CWib NWea SCob SGol SRms WHar
mexicana	CBot
montevidensis	see *E. bifida*
organensis	see *E. laevis*
'Peach Blossom' ♀H5	CBar CDoC CDul COtt CWib ELan EPfP GKin LHop LRHS MAsh MLHP MMuc MSwo NEgg NHol SCob SCoo SEND SGol SLim SPer SRms
'Pink Elf'	LPfy
'Pink Elle'	LPfy LRHS MAsh MBri SCob
'Pink Pyramid'	LRHS
'Pride of Donard' ♀H5	CBod CSBt EPfP GKin MGos SCob SRms WBod
Red Carpet = 'Loncar'PBR	EAEE ELon LAst LRHS SLon WMoo WNPC
'Red Dream'	CLet CSBt CWSG EBee EPfP LBMP LPfy LRHS MAsh MBri MGos MSwo NLar NWad SCob SCoo SEWo SHil SPoG SRms SWvt
'Red Elf'	CMac EBee ELan EPfP GKin LAst LPfy LRHS MBri MGos NEgg SBod SCob SHil SPer SPlb SPoG SRms SWvt
'Red Hedger'	CBod COtt CSBt CTsd CWib EAEE ECrN ELan EShb GGal MRav SCob SRms WMoo
'Red Knight'	LRHS MAsh NEgg NHol WNPC
'Red Robin'	SPoG
resinosa	CBod CExl CTsd SPlb SRms SVen WJek
revoluta	CTri MGil
rubra 'Crimson Spire' ♀H5	Widely available
- 'Ingramii'	CWib NWea SEND
- var. ***macrantha***	Widely available
* - - ***aurea***	NPla
- 'Pygmaea'	see *E. rubra* 'Woodside'
§ - 'Woodside'	ECho LLHF NWad SGol SRms
'Silver Anniversary'	MSwo
'Slieve Donard'	CMac MRav NWad NWea SLim SRms
tucumanensis	SPlb SVen
'Ventnor'	SPlb SVen
virgata	MGil

Eschscholzia (*Papaveraceae*)

californica	MBel WBod
- 'Alba'	CSpe
- subsp. ***mexicana*** 'Sun Shades'	SPhx
- 'Red Chief'	SPhx

Escobaria (*Cactaceae*)

missouriensis **new**	CCac
vivipara SB 128 from Manzano, New Mexico **new**	CCac

Esterhuysenia (*Aizoaceae*)

alpina	CPBP

Eucalyptus ✿ (*Myrtaceae*)

sp.	LPar
aggregata	SKin WEuc
alpina	SPlb
amygdalina	SPlb
apiculata	WEuc
approximans	SKin WEuc
archeri	CDTJ CDul CTho EPfP LPfy LRHS MBri MGos MMuc NLar SHil SKin WCot WEuc
baeuerlenii	SKin
§ ***bridgesiana***	WEuc
caesia ♀H2	SPlb
- subsp. ***magna*** **new**	WEuc
camaldulensis	SPlb
camphora	CTsd ESwi MMuc SKin
cinerea	SBig SKin SPlb WEuc
citriodora	CWCL MHer SPlb WEuc
coccifera	CBcs CSBt CTsd EPfP EUJe MMuc NPer SBig SKin SPlb WEuc
cordata	EBee SKin WPGP
crenulata	SKin WEuc
crucis subsp. ***crucis***	SPlb
cypellocarpa	SPlb

dalrympleana ♀H4	CMac ELan EPfP EUJe IDee LRHS LSRN MGos NLar NPer SBig SHil SKin SLim SPer SPlb SRms WCot WEuc WHar WPGP
deanei	WEuc
debeuzevillei	see *E. pauciflora* subsp. *debeuzevillei*
deglupta new	WEuc
delegatensis	NPer SKin WEuc
divaricata	see *E. gunnii* subsp. *divaricata*
erythrocorys	SPlb
eximia	SPlb
* - 'Nana'	SPlb
ficifolia	CDTJ IDee
fraxinoides	SPlb
gamophylla	SPlb
glaucescens	CMHG ELan EPfP LPar LRHS SEWo SHil SKin SPer WEuc
globulus	CWCL SPlb
- subsp. ***bicostata***	WEuc
goniocalyx	WEuc
§ ***gregsoniana***	CDul EPfP EUJe GGal SKin SPlb WEuc
gunnii ♀H5	Widely available
- Azura = 'Cagire'PBR	COtt LCro LRHS LSRN MPkF SCob SLon WMat
§ - subsp. ***divaricata***	EPfP MBri SKin WEuc
johnstonii	CDul SKin SPer
kitsoniana	SKin WEuc
kruseana	SPlb
kybeanensis	SKin WCot WEuc
§ ***lacrimans***	WEuc
lehmannii	MSCN
leucoxylon subsp. ***megalocarpa***	SPlb WEuc
ligustrina	SKin WEuc
'Little Boy Blue'	CWib LSRN
macarthurii	SKin
macrocarpa	SPlb WEuc
mannifera subsp. ***elliptica***	SKin WEuc
mitchelliana	SKin WEuc
moorei var. ***moorei*** new	WEuc
- var. ***nana***	CDTJ
neglecta	SKin WEuc
nicholii	CBcs CDoC CSpe ECre EPfP EUJe EWes IDee LRHS MGos MMuc SCoo SKin WCot WEuc
niphophila	see *E. pauciflora* subsp. *niphophila*
nitens	CDTJ CTsd SBig SKin SPlb WEuc
§ ***nitida***	SKin WEuc
nova-anglica	SKin
obliqua	WEuc
paliformis	WEuc
parviflora	SKin
parvula	CDoC CMac EPfP MRav SCoo SEND WEuc
pauciflora	CDoC CSBt CTsd EUJe IDee MGos MMuc SPer
§ - subsp. ***debeuzevillei*** ♀H5	CBlu CDoC EPfP NOrn SBig SKin WEuc
- subsp. ***hedraia***	SKin
- var. ***nana***	see *E. gregsoniana*
§ - subsp. ***niphophila*** ♀H5	Widely available
- - 'Pendula'	see *E. lacrimans*
- subsp. ***pauciflora***	WEuc
- - from Mount Buffalo, Australia	WEuc
perriniana	CBcs CDul CLnd CMHG ECrN EPfP EUJe LRHS MBri MGos NLar NOrn SBig SCoo SHil SKin SPer SPlb SPoG SWvt WEuc WFar WMat
pulchella	WEuc
pulverulenta	CMac SKin SPlb WEuc
- 'Baby Blue'	ELan LAst LHop LRHS SHil SKin SWvt WEuc
regnans	SKin WEuc
risdonii	SKin WEuc
rodwayi	IDee SKin WEuc
rossii	SPlb
rubida	CMHG GAbr SKin WEuc
sideroxylon	SPlb
- 'Rosea'	SPlb
simmondsii	see *E. nitida*
stellulata	SKin WEuc
stricta	SKin WEuc
stuartiana	see *E. bridgesiana*
sturgissiana	WEuc
subcrenulata	CDul ELan EPfP SKin WEuc
tetraptera	SPlb
torquata	SPlb
urnigera	SKin WEuc
vernicosa	SKin WEuc
viminalis	SKin

Eucharis (*Amaryllidaceae*)

§ ***amazonica*** ♀H1b	LAma SDeJ SPav
grandiflora misapplied	see *E. amazonica*

Eucomis ✿ (*Asparagaceae*)

Aloha	see *E.* 'Leia'
autumnalis misapplied	see *E. zambesiaca*
§ ***autumnalis*** (Mill.) Chitt. ♀H3	CBlu CBro ECho EPot ERCP GKev LAma LRHS SDeJ SPav SPlb WCot
- subsp. ***autumnalis***	LTro
- - 'Peace Candles'	CTca
bicolor ♀H3	Widely available
- 'Alba'	CAvo CExl CTca ECho EPot GKev LAma
- 'Stars and Stripes'	WCru WHil
'Cabernet Candles'	CTca
§ ***comosa***	CAvo CBro CHll CPrp CSam CTal CTca EBee ERCP EShb GKev LAma LEdu LRHS SDeJ SMad SPav WWEG
- 'Cornwood'	CAvo CTca
- 'First Red'	WPGP
- green-leaved	CTca
- 'Johannesburg' new	GKev
- 'Kilimanjaro'	CTca EBee WHil
- 'Lotte'	CTca EBee GKev
- 'Oakhurst'	CAby CBct CBod CDoC CKno CMos ECtt ESwi LRHS LTro SPad SPtp WHil
- purple-leaved	CAvo EShb
- 'Sparkling Burgundy' ♀H6	Widely available
- 'Sparkling Rosy'	ECho ERCP GKev LAma SCob
- var. ***striata***	CAby CDes
'Frank Lawley'	CDes
'Freckles'	CAby CMos LSou SPad
'Glow Sticks' new	WHil
humilis	CTca XEll
- 'Twinkle Stars'	EPot ERCP GKev LAma SCob
'John Treasure'	SMHy
'Joy's Purple'	CBro CPar CTca EPri LRHS
§ 'Leia'PBR	CBro CTca ERCP GKev LAma LRHS
montana	CBlu CBro CPar CPrp CTca EBee ECho EPot GKev LAma WCot WPGP
pallidiflora ♀H3	CAvo CTal LEdu SMHy WPGP
'Pink Gin'	CAvo

	'Playa Blanca'	CTca GKev LAma
	pole-evansii	CBro CCon CExl CPar CPne CTal CTca EAEE ELan EPri EUJe GKev IVic LAma LTro MRav SDeJ WCru WPtf WWEG
	- 'Burgundy'	GBin
I	- 'Purpurea'	CExl GCal WCot
	punctata	see *E. comosa*
	regia	CTca
	- JCA 3.230.709	WCot
	'Swazi Pride'	CTca
	'Tugela Ruby'PBR	CTca
	undulata	see *E. autumnalis* (Mill.) Chitt.
	vandermerwei ♀H3	CAvo CBlu CBro CPne CTal CTca EBee ECho EPot GKev LAma LEdu SDeJ SKHP SPlb WPGP
	- 'Octopus'	CExl CKno CPrp CTca ECho ELan EPfP ESwi GBin GKev LSou LTro MHer MPie WCot WWEG
§	***zambesiaca***	CAvo CTal CTca EBee GCal LAma SMHy WWEG
	- JCA 3.230.709	WCot
	- JCA 3.231.010	WCot
	- 'White Dwarf'	ECho SPer WHil
	'Zeal Bronze'	CMHG CTal CTca EPfP GCal GCra

Eucommia (*Eucommiaceae*)

	ulmoides	CMCN EBtc EPfP IArd IDee NLar WPGP

Eucrosia (*Amaryllidaceae*)

	bicolor	CAby

Eucryphia ✿ (*Cunoniaceae*)

	cordifolia	CAbP CBcs CDoC CMac CWib IDee MBlu
§	***cordifolia* × *lucida***	CBcs GGal LAst
	glutinosa ♀H4	EPfP GGGa GKev IDee LRHS MAsh NLar SAko WBod WCru
	- 'Miniature'	CBct EPfP SChF WPGP
	× ***hillieri*** 'Winton'	CMHG GQui WPGP
	× ***intermedia***	CExl CMac GKin NLar SRms SSta
	- 'Rostrevor' ♀H4	CBcs CDoC CDul CExl CJun CMHG CMac CTho ELan EPfP GBin GGGa GGal GQui IDee LRHS LSRN MBlu MMuc NLar SAko SPoG SReu SSta WPGP
	lucida	CTho LLHF LRHS MMuc NLar
	- 'Ballerina' ♀H4	CBcs CBct CMHG CMac CTho EBee ELan ELon EPfP GKin IDee LRHS MAsh SAko SChF SCoo SPoG SSpi WPGP
I	- 'Chaplin's Variety' **new**	CBct SAko WPGP
	- 'Dumpling'	CExl WPGP
	- 'Gilt Edge' (v)	CBcs GKin LLHF LRHS
	- 'Leatherwood Cream' (v)	WHor
	- 'Pink Cloud'	CBcs CDoC CDul CExl CMac CTho ELan EPfP GKin GQui IDee IVic LHop LRHS LSRN MBlu NLar SAko SLim SWvt WPGP
	- 'Spring Glow' (v)	CExl ELan LLHF LRHS MAsh SPoG
	milliganii	CDul CFil EPfP GGGa GQui LHop LRHS MBlu MRav SAko SRms WPGP
	moorei	CBcs CExl CMac GGGa WPGP
	× ***nymansensis***	CBot CHab CWib SAko SRms SSpi
	- 'George Graham'	CMHG GGGa
	- 'Nymans Silver' (v)	CBot CJun ELan GGGa LLHF LRHS MAsh WPat
	- 'Nymansay' ♀H4	Widely available
	'Penwith' misapplied	see *E. cordifolia* × *lucida*
	'Penwith' ambig.	CTsd GKin GQui IDee SAko

Eumorphia (*Asteraceae*)

	prostrata	EBee WNPC
	sericea	CFis

Eunomia see *Aethionema*

Euodia (*Rutaceae*)

	daniellii	see *Tetradium daniellii*
	hupehensis	see *Tetradium daniellii* Hupehense Group

Euonymus ✿ (*Celastraceae*)

	B&L 12543	EWes
	CC 4522	CExl
	NJM 09.109	CRHN WPGP
	NJM 10.106	WPGP
	alatus	Widely available
	- B&SWJ 8794	WCru
	- var. ***apterus***	EBee EPfP WGrn
	- 'Blade Runner'	EPfP LRHS
	- Chicago Fire	see *E. alatus* 'Timber Creek'
	- 'Ciliodentatus'	see *E. alatus* f. *striatus*
	- 'Compactus' ♀H5	Widely available
§	- 'Fire Ball'	CJun
	- Little Moses = 'Odom'	NLar
*	- 'Macrophyllus'	CJun EPfP
	- 'Rudy Haag'	CJun
	- 'Select'	see *E. alatus* 'Fire Ball'
	- 'Silver Cloud'	EPfP NLar
§	- f. ***striatus***	CJun SBrt WPat
	- - B&SWJ 11051	WCru
§	- 'Timber Creek'	CJun EPfP LEdu LLHF MBlu NLar SAko WPat
	americanus	EPfP MBlu NLar
	- var. ***angustifolius*** B&SWJ 12905	WCru
	- 'Evergreen'	EPfP
	- narrow-leaved	EPfP
	bungeanus	EPfP
	- B&SWJ 8782 from South Korea	WCru
	- 'Dart's Pride'	CJun EPfP NLar
	- 'Fireflame'	CJun WPat
*	- var. ***mongolicus***	EPfP
	- 'Pendulus'	MBlu SCoo
	- var. ***semipersistens***	CJun WCru
§	***carnosus***	CJun
	- CWJ 12425	WCru
	- 'Red Wine'	CJun CTho EBee ELon EPfP ESwi LEdu LHop LRHS MBlu NLar SKHP WCot WPGP WPat
	chibae B&SWJ 11159	WCru
§	***clivicola***	CJun EPfP
	'Copper Wire'	EHoe
	cornutus **new**	WPGP
	- var. ***quinquecornutus*** ♀H5	CBot CJun CMCN ELan EPfP MBlu NLar WPGP WPat
	'Den Haag'	CJun EPfP NLar
	europaeus	Widely available
	- from Slovakia	WCru
	- f. ***albus***	CJun CTho EPfP LRHS NLar
	- 'Atropurpureus'	CMCN CTho EPfP NLar
	- 'Atrorubens'	CJun
	- 'Aucubifolius' (v)	CMac
*	- 'Aureus'	CNat
	- 'Brilliant'	CJun EPfP NLar
*	- f. ***bulgaricus***	EPfP

	Name	Suppliers
	- 'Chrysophyllus'	EPfP MBlu
	- 'Howard'	EPfP NLar
	- var. ***intermedius***	CJun EPfP MBlu NLar
	- 'Red Cascade' Y^{H5}	Widely available
	- 'Scarlet Wonder'	CJun EPfP
	- 'Thornhayes'	CTho EPfP NLar
	farreri	see *E. nanus*
	fimbriatus	CJun
	fortunei	LEdu
	- Blondy = 'Interbolwi'^{PBR} (v)	CDoC CDul CLet COtt CTri CWib ELan EPfP LAst LRHS MAsh MBri MGos MJak MMuc MSwo NEgg NLar NPri SCob SCoo SEND SGol SLim SPoG SRms
	- 'Canadale Gold' (v)	COtt EPfP LRHS MAsh NHol SLon SPoG
	- 'Coloratus'	CBod CMac ECrN EPfP MBlu MSwo SEND
	- 'Country Gold'	WFar
	- 'Dart's Blanket'	CDul ELan EPPr EPfP MRav SCob
	- 'Emerald Gaiety' (v) Y^{H5}	Widely available
	- 'Emerald 'n' Gold' (v) Y^{H5}	Widely available
	- 'Emerald Surprise' (v) Y^{H5}	SRGP
	- 'Gaiety Silver'	IBoy
	- 'Gold Spot'	see *E. fortunei* 'Sunspot'
	- 'Gold Tip'	see *E. fortunei* 'Golden Prince'
	- Golden Harlequin = 'Hoogi'^{PBR} (v)	CLet COtt CSBt LHop LPfy LRHS MAsh MBri MPkF NWad SPoG SWvt
§	- 'Golden Pillar' (v)	EHoe
§	- 'Golden Prince' (v)	CMac EHoe MRav MSwo SRms
	- Goldy = 'Waldbolwi'^{PBR}	LPfy LRHS NLar SGol SHil SPoG
	- 'Harlequin' (v)	CBar CBcs CMac CSBt CWGN EBee EHoe ELan ELon EShb LBuc LRHS LSRN MAsh MBlu MGos MJak MRav NBir SGol SLim SPer SPoG SRms SWvt WBod WFar
	- 'Hort's Blaze'	EBee EPPr
	- 'Kewensis' Y^{H5}	CDoC CHid CMac CWib ELan EUJe GCal GEdr LRHS MSCN SCob SPoG WCru
	- 'Kewensis Variegatus' (v) **new**	MRav
	- 'Longwood'	LRHS
	- 'Minimus'	CDul CTri EPPr MSwo SCob WBor WPGP XLum
*	- 'Minimus Variegatus' (v)	ECho EPPr EShb SPlb
§	- var. ***radicans***	EWld
	- 'Sheridan Gold'	CTri MRav
	- 'Silver Gem'	see *E. fortunei* 'Variegatus'
	- 'Silver Pillar' (v)	EHoe
	- 'Silver Queen' (v)	Widely available
	- 'Silverstone'^{PBR} (v)	EPfP LRHS SPoG
	- 'Sunshine' (v)	EBee ELan EPfP LRHS MAsh SLon SPoG
§	- 'Sunspot' (v)	CBcs CBod CMac ELan ELon MGos MJak MMuc MSwo SEND SRms WHar WRHF
	- 'Tustin'	EAEE EPPr
§	- 'Variegatus' (v)	SRms
	- 'Wolong Ghost' Y^{H5}	CBot CDoC CExl EMil EPPr GKin LRHS MBlu MGos MMuc NLar SGol SKHP SWvt WCot WPat
	frigidus	EPfP
	- var. ***elongatus*** GWJ 9378	WCru
	grandiflorus misapplied.	see *E. carnosus*
§	***grandiflorus*** Wall.	CJun EBee EPfP NLar SCoo WFar
	- f. ***salicifolius*** misapplied	see *E. grandiflorus* Wall.
	- f. ***salicifolius*** Stapf. & F. Ballard	CJun EPfP

	Name	Suppliers
	hamiltonianus	CMCN EBtc ECrN EPfP LRHS MMuc SEND SSpi
	- NJM 11.006	WPGP
	- 'Fiesta'	CJun
	- subsp. ***hians***	see *E. hamiltonianus* subsp. *sieboldianus*
	- 'Indian Summer'	CJun ELon EMil EPfP LRHS MAsh NLar SAko SCoo SKHP SPoG SSpi WMat WPGP WPat
	- 'Koi Boy'	CJun EBee MAsh WMat WPat
	- 'Miss Pinkie'	CJun EPfP IVic MAsh NLar SCoo WPat
	- 'Pink Delight'	CJun
	- 'Poort Bulten'	CJun
	- 'Popcorn'	CJun EPfP WPat
	- 'Rainbow'	CJun EPfP
	- 'Red Chief'	CJun EPfP
	- 'Red Elf'	CJun NLar
	- 'Rising Sun'	CJun EPfP NLar SMad
§	- subsp. ***sieboldianus***	CDul CExl CJun EPfP GBin MRav WPat
	- - B&SWJ 10941	WCru
	- - PAB 5337	LEdu
	- - 'Calocarpus'	CJun EPfP SCoo
	- - 'Coral Charm'	CJun EPfP NLar WPat
*	- - var. ***yedoensis*** f. ***koehneanus***	EPfP
	- 'Snow'	CJun EBee WCot WPat
	- 'Winter Glory'	CJun MMHG
	- var. ***yedoensis***	see *E. hamiltonianus* subsp. *sieboldianus*
§	***huangii***	CJun WPat
	- B&SWJ 3700	WCru
	japonicus	CBcs CBod CDoC CDul CMac CTri ECrN EPfP SBod SCob SEND SEWo SPer
	- 'Albomarginatus' (v)	CBcs CTri EHoe EPfP NPri SEND SRms
§	- 'Aureomarginatus'	LPar NPri
	- 'Aureopictus'	see *E. japonicus* 'Aureus'
	- 'Aureovariegatus'	see *E. japonicus* 'Ovatus Aureus'
§	- 'Aureus' (v)	CBcs CDoC CDul CSBt CTsd CWib EPfP LAst LPfy LRHS NPri SCoo SLon SPer WHar
	- 'Benkomasaki'	EPfP LRHS
	- 'Bravo' (v)	CDoC CDul ECrN EHoe ELon EPfP IVic LPar LPfy LRHS MAsh MBri MGos NLar NPri SCob SCoo SEWo SHil SLim SPer SPoG SWvt WCot WFar
	- 'Chollipo' (v) Y^{H5}	ELan EPfP LRHS MAsh SHil SPoG
	- 'Compactus'	SCoo
	- 'Duc d'Anjou' misapplied	see *E. japonicus* 'Viridivariegatus'
	- 'Duc d'Anjou' Carrière (v)	EBee EHoe ELan EPfP EWes MRav SPoG
	- 'Elegantissimus Aureus'	see *E. japonicus* 'Aureomarginatus'
	- Exstase = 'Goldbolwi'^{PBR} (v)	SPoG WCot
	- 'Francien' (v)	LRHS MGos NLar SHil
	- 'Gold Queen'^{PBR}	LRHS NLar
	- 'Golden Maiden' (v)	ELan EPfP LRHS MAsh SLim SLon SPoG SRms SWvt
	- 'Golden Pillar'	see *E. fortunei* 'Golden Pillar'
	- Green Millenium = 'Minmil'^{PBR}	LRHS
	- 'Green Rocket'	EBee EPfP EShb GBin LPfy LRHS MBri MGos MRav SGol SHil SLim SPoG WCot WFar WPat
	- 'Green Spider'	SPoG
	- 'Green Spire' **new**	LHop LRHS

	- 'Grey Beauty'	ELon EShb NLar
	- 'Happiness'PBR	MPkF
	- 'Hibarimisaki' (v)	EPfP
	- 'Kathy'PBR	CDoC ELan ELon EPfP LPfy LRHS MAsh NBes SCob SHil SPoG SRGP
§	- 'Latifolius Albomarginatus' (v)	CTsd ELan EPfP MRav MSwo SPer SWvt
	- 'Luna'	see *E. japonicus* 'Aureus'
	- 'Macrophyllus Albus'	see *E. japonicus* 'Latifolius Albomarginatus'
	- 'Maiden's Gold'	COtt CSBt
	- 'Marieke'	see *E. japonicus* 'Ovatus Aureus'
	- 'Microphyllus'	CDoC MRav NEgg SRms
§	- 'Microphyllus Albovariegatus' (v)	CBcs CDoC CDul CMac CSBt CTri ELan EPfP LAst LPfy LRHS MGos SCob SEND SHil SIgm SLim SRms SWvt WFar
§	- 'Microphyllus Aureovariegatus' (v)	CDoC CMac ELan ELon EPfP LRHS MAsh MMuc NLar SHil WHar
	- 'Microphyllus Aureus'	see *E. japonicus* 'Microphyllus Pulchellus'
§	- 'Microphyllus Pulchellus' (v)	CBcs CDoC CMac CSBt EBee ECrN EPfP LPfy LRHS MAsh MGos SEND SHil SWvt
	- 'Microphyllus Variegatus'	see *E. japonicus* 'Microphyllus Albovariegatus'
§	- 'Ovatus Aureus' (v) ♀H5	CBar CDoC CDul CExl CLet CMac CSBt CTri EBee ELon EPfP LAst LRHS MGos MRav NLar SCob SGol SHil SLim SPer SPlb SPoG SRms SWvt WFar
	- 'Président Gauthier' (v)	CBar CDoC EAEE EBee LRHS MBri MGos SCob SCoo SLim SPer SWvt WCFE
	- 'Pulchellus Aureovariegatus'	see *E. japonicus* 'Microphyllus Aureovariegatus'
I	- 'Pyramidatus'	EPfP
	- 'Rokujo'	GEdr
	- 'Silver King'	CMac
	- 'Silver Krista' (v)	NLar
	- 'Susan' (v) ♀H5	CDoC CMac EShb LPfy MAsh SAko SRGP
§	- 'Viridivariegatus' (v)	LRHS
	kachinensis B&SWJ 11668	WCru
	kiautschovicus 'Berry Hill'	NLar
	- 'Manhattan'	NLar
	latifolius	CJun CMCN EPfP IMou LEdu WPat
§	***laxiflorus*** GWJ 9351	WCru
	- HWJ 890	WCru
	lucidus	CBcs CExl CHll EBee SSpi
	macropterus	CJun EPfP
	mexicanus	CFil
	morrisonensis	see *E. huangii*
	myrianthus	CJun EPfP EUJe EWes MBlu MPkF NLar
§	***nanus***	CJun CWib NLar WSHC WThu
	- var. ***turkestanicus***	CFil GKin LHop LRHS SBrt SLon SRms
	obovatus	NLar
	oxyphyllus ♀H5	CDul CEvo CJun CMCN CTho EBee EPfP MBri MMuc NLar WCot WCru WPat
	- 'Waasland'	CJun EPfP
	phellomanus ♀H5	CBot CDoC CDul CTho EBee EPfP GKin IDee LHop LRHS MBlu MGil MGos MPkF MRav MSCN NLar NOrn SAko SCoo SKHP SPoG SWvt WFar WMat WPGP
	- 'Silver Surprise' (v)	CJun ELon EPfP WPat
	Pierrolino = 'Heespierrolino'PBR	LRHS MRav NLar SCoo
§	***planipes***	Widely available
	- B&SWJ 8660	WCru
	- 'Dart's August Flame'	CJun EPfP
	- 'Sancho' ♀H5	CJun EPfP MBri WPat
	porphyreus GWJ 9377	WCru
	quelpaertensis	CJun
	radicans	see *E. fortunei* var. *radicans*
	'Rokojō'	WPat
	'Rokojō Variegated' (v)	WCot
	rongchuensis 'Cliuicolus'	see *E. clivicola*
	rosmarinifolius	see *E. nanus*
	rubescens	see *E. laxiflorus*
	sachalinensis misapplied	see *E. planipes*
	sachalinensis (F. Schmidt) Maxim.	EPfP NLar WPat
	- B&SWJ 10835	WCru
	sacrosanctus	CJun MBlu
	sanguineus	CJun SSpi
	sieboldianus	WCru
	var. ***sanguineus*** B&SWJ 11140	
	- - B&SWJ 11386	WCru
	spraguei	NLar
	- CWJ 12446	WCru
	tingens	CJun
	trapococcus	EPfP
	vagans Wall.	EPfP WCot
	verrucosus	CJun NLar
	vidalii	EPfP
	wilsonii	LRHS NLar
	yedoensis	see *E. hamiltonianus* subsp. *sieboldianus*

Eupatoriadelphus see *Eupatorium*

Eupatorium ✿ (*Asteraceae*)

B&SWJ 9052 from Guatemala	WCru
FMWJ 13428 from Northern Vietnam	WCru
album misapplied	see *Ageratina altissima*
album L.	NBid SWat
altissimum	SRms
aromaticum	see *Ageratina aromatica*
atrorubens	see *Bartlettina sordida*
cannabinum	CArn CBod CHab EHon ELan EShb GLog GPoy IFoB MBNS MHer MMuc MNHC MWLS MWts NBFr NBir NMir NPer SEND SGSe SPav SWat WHfH WSFF
- f. ***cannabinum*** 'Flore Pleno' (d)	CMac CPrp ECtt ELan ELon EPfP IBoy LHop MBel MHer MRav MSpe NBir NGdn NLar SDix SWat WCot WMnd WSFF WWtn XLum
- - 'Spraypaint' (v)	WSFF
capillifolium ♀H3	CAby EBee ECtt ESwi EWes LHop MNrw MPie SDix SHar SPhx WCot WWEG
coelestinum	see *Conoclinium coelestinum*
dubium 'Baby Joe'PBR	CWGN ECtt IPot LBMP LRHS MNrw NEgg NLar WNPC
- 'Little Joe'	EBee EPPr EShb LEdu WPGP WWEG
fistulosum	CEvo EBee
- f. ***albidum***	MMuc SEND WWFP
- - 'Bartered Bride'	CKno EBee ECtt EWes GCal MAvo WCot WSFF
- - 'Ivory Towers'	EShb LRHS LSun SBea SPtp WCot WPtf WWEG

- - 'Massive White' ♀H6	CCon EBee GCal MNrw NBir NSti
- 'Berggarten'	GCal WSFF
- 'Carin'	WSFF
fortunei	CArn
- 'Fine Line' (v)	EPPr LSou WSFF WWEG
- 'Pink Elegance' (v)	CAby CBod EBee ECtt EShb LHop LLWG LRHS MPie MWts SDix SPoG SRms WMnd WWEG
- 'Pink Frost' (v)	LBMP MAsh WHil
japonicum	GPoy
ligustrinum	see *Ageratina ligustrina*
lindleyanum	CKno EBee WSFF
- var. ***trisectifolium*** B&SWJ 12742 **new**	WCru
maculatum	NBFr NGdn NLar WHrl
- Atropurpureum Group	Widely available
- - 'Ankum's August'	EBee IMou
- - 'Gateway'	CBod CKno EBee ECtt ELon GCal LHop LRHS NBid NBre NLar SWvt WHoo WMnd WMoo WSFF WWtn
- - 'Glutball'	CKno ELon GCal IMou LBMP LPla LRHS MNrw NChi SMad WWEG
- - 'Little Red'	GBin WSFF
- - 'Orchard Dene' ♀H6	SMHy
- - 'Phantom'PBR	CBod EBee ECtt ELon EWoo GQue IPot LHop LRHS MBri MHol MWts NCGa NLar SAko SMad WMoo WPtf
- - 'Purple Bush' ♀H6	CKno EBee ECtt ELon EPPr GBee GBin GCal GQue ILea LOPS LRHS MHer MTis NDov NEgg SDix SPhx SWvt WSFF WWEG
- - 'Red Dwarf'	CBod ECtt ELon GQue IKil ILea IPot LEdu LRHS MBel MHol SCob SHar SPoG SWvt WHoo WWEG
- - 'Riesenschirm' ♀H6	Widely available
makinoi	WCru
var. ***oppositifolium*** B&SWJ 8449	
micranthum	see *Ageratina ligustrina*
perfoliatum	CArn GPoy MNrw NBre NLar SPhx WSFF
purpureum	Widely available
- 'Album'	CTri MBel SWvt
rugosum	see *Ageratina altissima*
* 'Snowball'	NDov SCob
weinmannianum	see *Ageratina ligustrina*

Euphorbia ✿ (*Euphorbiaceae*)

'Abbey Dore'	SPhx WCot
aeruginosa	LToo
altissima	NWit
ambovombensis	LToo
amygdaloides	ECtt SWat SWvt WOut
- 'Craigieburn'	CBod EWes GBuc GCra LRHS MAsh MRav WPGP
- 'Frosted Flame'PBR	LRHS
§ - 'Purpurea'	Widely available
§ - var. ***robbiae***	Widely available
- - dwarf	EWes
- - 'Pom Pom'	LSou
- - 'Redbud'	EWes LSou
- 'Rubra'	see *E. amygdaloides* 'Purpurea'
aureoviridiflora	LToo
baselicis	CPla CSpe EWes
biglandulosa Desf.	see *E. rigida*
Blackbird = 'Nothowlee'PBR	Widely available
'Blue Dome'	CSpe
'Blue Haze'	CDes ECrN WCot WRHF
bupleurifolia × ***susannae*** **new**	LToo
caerulescens	LToo
capitulata	SBrt
cashmeriana CC&McK 607	EWes
ceratocarpa	CFil ECtt EWes EWoo GMaP LRHS LSou NWit SEND SIgm SMad WCot WSHC
characias	CArn CBcs CLet CMac CWCL ECtt EPfP EWoo IBoy LRHS LSun MCot MLHP MRav NPer SPer SRms SWvt WBrk WCot WMnd WWEG XLum XSen
- 'Black Pearl'	CAbb CBcs CBod CLet CRos ECtt ELan ELon EPfP LHop LPfy LRHS MAvo MBel MBri MPnt NQui SGbt SGol SHil SLim SPoG SRkn SWvt WFar
- 'Blue Wonder'	CExl ECtt ELan EPfP GAbr GBin GMaP LRHS NEgg NGdn NWit WCot
- 'BQ' **new**	WCot
- subsp. ***characias***	CBot GMaP NLar SEND
- - 'Blue Hills'	ECtt WWEG
- - 'Burrow Silver' (v)	CCon MRav NEgg SWvt
- - 'Humpty Dumpty'	CBod CExl EBee ECtt ELan ELon EPfP GMaP IBoy LRHS LSRN LSqH MBri NGdn NLar NPer NWit SCob SPer SRms SWvt
- 'Chocolate Heart' **new**	CEvo
- 'Dwarf Black Pearl'	ECtt WWEG
- 'Forescate'	EBee EPfP GBin LSRN
- 'Freckles' (v)	MAvo
- 'Glacier Blue'PBR	CAby CBct CBod CBot CMea CSpe CWGN ECha ELan EShb LAst LRHS MAsh NLar SCob SPoG WNPC WTor
- 'Goldbrook'	ECtt EHoe EPfP LRHS MRav NGdn NLar
- 'Kestrel' (v)	WCot
- 'Portuguese Velvet' ♀H7	CBod CExl ECtt ELan ELon EPfP EUJe LHop LPla LRHS MCot MRav NLar NWit SBod SKHP SLim SPhx SPtp WCAu WCot WWEG
- Silver Swan = 'Wilcott'PBR (v) ♀H2	Widely available
- 'Tasmanian Tiger'PBR (v)	CBct CWGN ECtt EWes GMaP LAst LHop LRHS LSou MAvo MBri MGos MHol SBod SCob SEle SGol SKHP SMDP SPad SPoG SRms SWvt WCot WHil WNPC
- subsp. ***wulfenii***	Widely available
- - 'Bosahan' (v)	CExl
- - 'Emmer Green' (v)	CExl ECtt ELon EWes GAbr GMaP IKil LRHS MAvo MHol NLar NSti NWit WCot WWEG
- - 'Jimmy Platt'	SRms WCot
§ - - 'John Tomlinson' ♀H4	EBee LSRN MRav
- - Kew form	see *E. characias* subsp. *wulfenii* 'John Tomlinson'
- - 'Lambrook Gold' ♀H4	CSam CWCL MRav NLar NPer SMad WCot WWEG
- - 'Lambrook Gold' seed-raised	see *E. characias* subsp. *wulfenii* Margery Fish Group
- - 'Lambrook Yellow'	WWEG
§ - - Margery Fish Group	LRHS MCot NBir SBod
- - 'Perry's Tangerine'	EWes NPer
§ - - 'Purple and Gold'	ECtt EWes MAvo NWit SWvt WWEG
- - 'Purpurea'	see *E. characias* subsp. *wulfenii* 'Purple and Gold'

- - 'Shorty'	EBee ECtt LRHS LSou
- - var. ***sibthorpii***	IBoy
- - 'Silver Shadow'	WCot
- - 'Thelma's Giant'	MAvo NWit
- - 'Westacre Giant'	EWes
clavarioides var. ***truncata***	WCot
'Copton Ash'	CSpe EBee ECtt EWes GBin IPot LRHS SKHP SPhx WCot WNPC XSen
corallioides	ECha NLar NPer NSti SPer WHer
§ ***cornigera*** 🏆H6	CElw EBee ECha EPfP GBin GBuc LRHS MAvo MMuc NBid NDov NGdn NLar NSti NWit SEND SPhx SWat WCru WFar
- 'Goldener Turm'	ECtt EPfP ESwi GBin GBuc LCro LOPS LPla LRHS LSou NWit SCob SDix SPer WCot WFar
corollata	MNrw SBrt
cyparissias	CBcs ECha ELan EWoo MLHP MRav NBir NGdn NLar SBod SPav SRms WBrk WFar XLum XSen
- 'Betten'	see *E.* × *gayeri* 'Betten'
- 'Clarice Howard'	see *E. cyparissias* 'Fens Ruby'
- clone 2	WCot
§ - 'Fens Ruby'	Widely available
- 'Orange Man'	CNec CTca ECtt EPfP EWes LRHS LSou NBro NEgg NGdn NLar SPoG SVen SWat SWvt WAul WBrk WFar WWEG
- 'Purpurea'	see *E. cyparissias* 'Fens Ruby'
- 'Red Devil'	NWit WWEG
- 'Tall Boy'	EWes
decaryi	LToo
deflexa	EBee EWes MAvo
dendroides	LRHS
'Despina'[PBR]	LRHS NPri
didiereoides	LToo
§ ***donii***	EWes MAvo NWit SDix XEll
- HWJK 2405	WCru
- 'Amjillasa'	NWit SDix SMHy WCot WWtn
dulcis	CBre IFro NBro NWit
- 'Chameleon'	Widely available
'Efanthia'[PBR]	CRos ELon EWes GBin LHop LRHS LSou NLar NPri SHil
enormis	LToo
§ ***epithymoides***	Widely available
- 'Bonfire'[PBR]	ECtt LRHS MAvo NLar SAko SPoG
§ - 'Candy'	EBee ECha EPfP LSqH MNrw WFar
- compact	NWit
- 'First Blush' (v)	EBee ECtt MAsh NLar NWit
- 'Geisha'	EWes
- 'Golden Fusion'	EPfP LRHS MAsh MBri WFar
§ - 'Lacy' (v)	EWes NBir NGdn NWit SKHP
§ - 'Major' 🏆H6	CExl EBee SDix WKif
- 'Midas'	GBin MNrw NWit SCob
- 'Senior'	GBin LRHS MAvo MNrw NLar
esula Baker's form	NWit
Excalibur = 'Froeup'[PBR]	CExl CMac CWCL ELan ELon GBin IVic LHop LSRN MBNS MMuc MNrw MRav NBir NLar NSti SEND SPer SPoG SPtp SRms SWvt
fischeriana B&SWJ 8575	WCru
flavicoma	GCal
fragifera	NWit
§ × ***gayeri*** 'Betten'	EBee EWes LPla
glauca	SKHP
globosa	LToo
'Gloria' **new**	LAst
'Golden Foam'	see *E. stricta*
'Grey Hedgehog'	CBod LSou SHar SPoG SRms WNPC
griffithii	CHll GGal IFoB NBro SWat WFar WMoo WWtn
- 'Dixter' 🏆H7	Widely available
- 'Dixter Flame'	IFoB NWit
- 'Fern Cottage'	CElw EWes WMnd
- 'Fireglow'	Widely available
- 'King's Caple'	ELon EWes GBin LRHS NLar WCru
- 'Wickstead'	CWCL EBee ESwi GBin MLHP NLar
'Helena'[PBR] (v)	CExl LSRN NLar SRms SWvt WHil
horrida 🏆H2	LToo SPlb
hyberna	SWat
hypericifolia Diamond Frost = 'Inneuphe'[PBR]	CSpe ESwi LBMP LHop LSou MCot SRkn WCot
inermis **new**	LToo
ingens	CAbb
jacquemontii	IFoB MRav NLar WCot
'Jade Dragon'	LRHS SWvt
'Jessie'	NWit
jolkinii	CExl
Kalipso = 'Innkalff'	CRos LRHS NLar SHil SRot
knobelii	LToo
'Lambrook Silver'	SRkn
lathyris	CBre MLHP NLar NPer NWit SRms SVic
longifolia misapplied	see *E. cornigera*
longifolia D. Don	see *E. donii*
longifolia Lam.	see *E. mellifera*
margalidiana	EWes MAvo NWit
× ***martini***	Widely available
- 'Aperitif'	LPal
- 'Ascot Rainbow'[PBR] (v)	Widely available
- 'Baby Charm'	CNec EAEE EBee ECtt ELon EPfP EUJe GBin GCal GKin IPot LHop LRHS LSRN MAsh MGos NLar SHil SPoG SRms WFar WNPC
- 'Cherokee'	WCot
- dwarf	CCon
- 'Helen Robinson'	WCot
- Helena's Blush = 'Inneuphhel' (v)	EPfP
- 'Kolibri'	EBee MBri SWvt
- 'Little John'	LRHS MBri
- 'Rudolph'[PBR]	CBod ECtt EPfP LRHS MAsh WTor
- Tiny Tim = 'Waleutiny'	ECtt EPfP GBin LRHS LSRN LSou MAsh SPoG SWvt
- 'Walberton's Red Flush'	EPfP LRHS
× ***martinii*** 'Colibri'	MBel MPnt
§ ***mellifera*** 🏆H2	Widely available
meloformis 🏆H2	LToo
milii 🏆H1b	EBak
* - 'Variegata' (v)	CBlu
moratii	LToo
myrsinites 🏆H4	Widely available
nereidum	EWes NWit
nicaeensis	EBee GCal LPla LRHS SEND SPer SPhx WCot XLum XSen
- subsp. ***glareosa***	NWit
- subsp. ***nicaeensis*** **new**	CBot
obesa 🏆H2	LToo
oblongata	GBin NDov NLar SEND WCot
palustris 🏆H7	Widely available
- 'Walenburg's Glorie'	CBot CWCL EBee ECha ELan EWoo GBin GQue IBoy MAvo MNrw MRav NLar NSti NWit SWat WCot WKif
- 'Woodchippings'	WCot
- 'Zauberflöte'	ELon SRms
paralias	WHer

× ***pasteurii***	CBct CBod CCon CDTJ EPfP EUJe EWes GCal LSou MNrw NBir NLos NSti NWit SMad SPhx WCot WPGP
- Brown's strain **new**	WCot WRHF
- 'Devil's Honey'	CHid
- 'John Phillips'	CBct CExl CFil EBee EPfP IVic LRHS MAvo SChF WPGP
- 'Phrampton Phatty'	LRHS WCot WPGP
pekinensis	SKHP
pentagona	SVen
pilosa 'Major'	see *E. epithymoides* 'Major'
pithyusa	ECha ELan SEND WCot WSHC XLum XSen
platyclada	LToo
polychroma	see *E. epithymoides*
- 'Purpurea'	see *E. epithymoides* 'Candy'
- 'Variegata'	see *E. epithymoides* 'Lacy'
portlandica	SVen WHer
pseudocactus 'Lyttoniana' **new**	LToo
pulcherrima	SPre
Redwing = 'Charam'PBR ♀H5	CBcs CMac ECtt EHoe ELan EPfP EWoo IKil LBuc LRHS LSou MAvo MBri MHol MRav NLar NPri NSti NWit SGol SLim SPer SPoG SWvt WCot
reflexa	see *E. seguieriana* subsp. *niciciana*
§ ***rigida*** ♀H6	CAby CBod CBro CDes CSpe EBee EHoe ELan EPfP EUJe EWes GCal GJos LPla SDix SEND SIgm SPhx WCot WPGP XSen
robbiae	see *E. amygdaloides* var. *robbiae*
'Roundway Titan'	CBot CFil EBee EMil LRHS SAko SSpi SWvt WSHC
sarawschanica	ECha GQue LPla LRHS NWit SMad SPhx
schillingii ♀H5	CBod CLet CPne CWCL EHoe ELan EPfP EWTr GCra GMaP IPot LCro LHop LRHS LSRN MRav NLar SCob SDix SMad SPer SPhx SPlb SPoG SPtp SRms SWvt WCru WWEG
schoenlandii	LToo SPlb
seguieriana	ECha EWes SPhx
§ - subsp. ***niciciana***	GBin IMou MAvo SCob WHoo
serrulata Thuill.	see *E. stricta*
sikkimensis ♀H5	CExl CMHG ECha ELan EWes GCal IMou LRHS NEgg NLar NPer SRms WBod WCru
- 'Crûg Contrast'	WCru
soongarica	NWit
spinosa	NWit SPlb XSen
stellata **new**	LToo
stellispina	LToo
§ ***stricta***	CBgR CFil LSun NWad
stygiana	CCon CExl CPne CSam CSpe ELon EUJe EWes GBin GCal IBoy LRHS SPlb WCot WCru WPGP WSHC
- subsp. ***santamariae***	CFil
- subsp. ***stygiana***	CFil WPGP
susannae	LToo
tirucalli	EShb
valdevillosocarpa	CBod NLar SPhx WFar
'Velvet Ruby'	GBin LSRN LSou SWvt WCot WNPC
viguieri	LToo
villosa Waldst. & Kit. ex Willd.	GBin LEdu NWit
§ ***virgata***	EWes NWit
× ***waldsteinii***	see *E. virgata*
wallichii misapplied	see *E. donii*
wallichii Kohli	see *E. cornigera*
wallichii ambig.	MRav
wallichii Hook. f.	CExl EPfP GCal MNrw SKHP SPhx WCot
- 'Lemon and Lime'	CWib
'Whistleberry Garnet'	CMac CWCL EAEE EBee ELan EPfP EWoo LBMP LLHF LRHS LSou NSti SCob SEND SKHP SWvt WBod WNPC
'Whistleberry Ruby'PBR **new**	EWTr

Euptelea (*Eupteleaceae*)

franchetii	see *E. pleiosperma*
§ ***pleiosperma***	NLar SSpi
polyandra	EPfP NLar SBrt

Eurya (*Pentaphylacaceae*)

japonica 'Variegata' **new**	SAko
- 'Variegata' misapplied	see *Cleyera japonica* 'Fortunei'

Euryops (*Asteraceae*)

abrotanifolius	SVen
§ ***acraeus*** ♀H4	CMea CSBt ECho EPot EWes EWld GCrg GEdr WAbe
brachypodus	SVen
§ ***chrysanthemoides***	CBcs CDoC CSde EShb SEND SVen
- 'Sonnenschein'	SPtp
evansii Schltr.	see *E. acraeus*
lateriflorus	SPlb
pectinatus ♀H3	CBcs CBod CDTJ CDoC CExl CLet CSde CTca CTri CTsd ELan EPfP EShb GGal IVic LAst LRHS MOWG MSCN SEND SPtp SVen SWvt
tenuissimus	SVen
tysonii	CTca EWes SPlb SVen
virgineus	CExl SBod SPlb SVen

Euscaphis (*Staphyleaceae*)

japonica B&SWJ 11359	WCru
- B&SWJ 12739 **new**	WCru

Eustachys (*Poaceae*)

§ ***distichophylla***	NWsh

Eustephia (*Amaryllidaceae*)

coccinea **new**	WCot

Eustrephus (*Philesiaceae*)

latifolius	ECou

Eutrochium see *Eupatorium*

Ewartia (*Asteraceae*)

planchonii	EPot WAbe

Exochorda (*Rosaceae*)

alberti	see *E. korolkowii*
giraldii var. ***wilsonii***	CDul CExl CMac EBee EPfP LHop LRHS MBlu MMuc MNHC MRav NLar SWvt
§ ***korolkowii***	LRHS MAsh NLar
× ***macrantha***	COtt LRHS
- 'Irish Pearl'	CExl
§ - 'Niagara'	CMac EPfP GBin MPkF NLar SCob SPoG
- Snow Day Surprise	see *E.* × *macrantha* 'Niagara'
- 'The Bride' ♀H6	Widely available
racemosa	EPfP MMuc NLar SPer
- 'Niagara'PBR **new**	CBcs LRHS LSRN SGol

serratifolia	CBcs EPfP LRHS MMuc SPoG SSpi
- 'Snow White'	CJun EPfP EWes GKin IArd IMou LRHS MAsh MBlu NLar NOrn SLon SPoG SWvt

F

Fabiana (*Solanaceae*)

foliosa 'Cliftonville Limelight'	WAbe
imbricata	CAbP CTre ELon EPfP LLHF LRHS MGil SLon SPer SPlb WAbe WCot
- 'Prostrata'	CBcs ELan LRHS SVen WThu
- f. ***violacea*** ♀H4	CExl CSBt CTri CTsd EBee ELan EPfP LLHF LRHS MMuc SAko SPoG SWvt WKif
- - dark-flowered	CBcs
nana	WAbe

Fagopyrum (*Polygonaceae*)

from India	GCal
cymosum	see *F. dibotrys*
§ ***dibotrys***	CSpe EBee ECha EWld LEdu

Fagus ✿ (*Fagaceae*)

§ ***crenata***	CMen MBlu
- 'Mount Fuji'	CMen LLHF NEgg SBir
engleriana	CExl SBir
grandifolia subsp. ***mexicana***	SBir
japonica	SBir
- var. ***multinervis***	SBir
longipetiolata	CExl CMCN WPGP
lucida	CExl
orientalis	CMCN SBir
- 'Iskander'	IArd MBlu NLar SGol
sieboldii	see *F. crenata*
sylvatica ♀H6	Widely available
- 'Albovariegata' (v)	CMCN
- 'Aniek'	SGol
- 'Arcuata'	SBir
- 'Asterix' new	MBlu
- Atropurpurea Group	Widely available
- - 'Purpurea Pendula'	CBcs CCVT CMCN CMac COtt CSBt CTri CWib ELan EPfP GKin IVic LAst MAsh MBri MGos MJak MSwo NEgg NWea SCoo SGol SLau SLim SPer SPoG WHar WMat
- - 'Riversii' ♀H6	CBcs CDoC CDul CLnd CMCN COtt CTho CTri CWib ECrN ELan EPfP GKin LAst MAsh MBri MGos NOrn NWea SPer WHar WMat
- 'Aurea Pendula'	CMCN MBlu SBir WPat
- 'Bicolor Sartini'	MBlu
- 'Black Swan'	CDul CLnd CMCN EBee GBin IArd LLHF LSRN MAsh MBlu MBri MGos NEgg NHol NLar NOrn SBir SLon SPoG WMat
- 'Bornyensis'	MBlu
- 'Brathay Purple'	MBlu
- 'Cochleata'	CMCN
- 'Cockleshell'	MBlu SBir
- 'Cristata'	MBlu
§ - 'Dawyck' ♀H6	CBcs CDoC CDul CLnd CMac COtt CSBt CTho ECrN ELan EPfP MBri MGos NEgg NLar NWea SBir SCob SGol SLau SPer WMou
- 'Dawyck Gold' ♀H6	CBcs CDoC CDul CMCN CMac COtt CTri EBee GKin IVic MAsh MBlu MBri MGos NEgg NOrn NWea SBir SCob SGol SLau SPer WHar WHor WMat WMou
- 'Dawyck Purple' ♀H6	Widely available
- 'Eugen'	SBir
- 'Fastigiata' misapplied	see *F. sylvatica* 'Dawyck'
- 'Felderbach'	SBir
- 'Franken' (v)	LLHF MBlu SBir
- 'Green Obelisk' new	MBlu
- 'Greenwood'	LLHF MBlu NEgg NLar
- var. ***heterophylla***	CLnd CSBt CTho NWea
- - 'Aspleniifolia' ♀H6	CBcs CDul CMCN CMac EBee ECrN ELan EPfP ESwi GKin LRHS MBlu MBri MGos NEgg SBir SCoo SGol SLau SPer SPoG WMat WMou
- - (Atropurpurea Group) 'Ansorgei'	LAst MBlu MPkF
- - 'Incisa'	MBlu
- - f. ***laciniata***	MBlu
- - 'Mercedes'	CDoC CDul CMCN LLHF MBlu NEgg WCot WPat
- 'Horizontalis'	MBlu
- 'Pendula' ♀H6	CBcs CCVT CDoC CDul CMCN CMac COtt CSBt CTho EBee ECrN ELan EPfP MGos MSwo NEgg NWea SGol SLau SPer WHar WMat WMou
- 'Prince George of Crete'	CDul CMCN
- 'Purple Fountain' ♀H6	CDoC CDul CMCN EBee ELan LAst LHop MAsh MBlu MBri MGos NLar NWea SBir SLau WMat
- Purple-leaved Group	see *F. sylvatica* Atropurpurea Group
§ - 'Purpurea Tricolor' (v)	CDul CMCN CMac MAsh MBlu MGos NEgg NWea SBir SCoo SPer WMat WMou
- 'Red Obelisk'	see *F. sylvatica* 'Rohan Obelisk'
- 'Rohan Gold'	CMCN SGol
- 'Rohan Minaret'	SGol
§ - 'Rohan Obelisk'	CDul CMCN CTho ELan EWTr IArd MBlu NEgg NLar SBir SGol SPoG
- 'Rohan Trompenburg'	CMCN MBlu
- 'Rohan Weeping'	MBlu SBir
- 'Rohanii'	CBcs CDoC CDul CMCN CTri EBee ELan EPfP GKin LAst LHop MGos NEgg SBir SLau SPer WHar
- 'Roseomarginata'	see *F. sylvatica* 'Purpurea Tricolor'
- 'Rotundifolia'	CDul MBlu NEgg SGol
- 'Spaethiana'	EWTr GKin
- 'Striata'	NEgg
- f. ***tortuosa***	MPkF NEgg
- - 'Rot Süntel'	CDul NEgg
- 'Tricolor' misapplied	see *F. sylvatica* 'Purpurea Tricolor'
- 'Tricolor' ambig.	SLau
- 'Tricolor' (v)	CBcs CLnd COtt CSBt CWib ELan LLHF NHol SGol
- 'Viridivariegata' (v)	CMCN
- 'Zlatia'	CBcs CDul CLnd CMCN CSBt CWib ELan EPfP MBlu MGos NLar NWea SBir SGol SLau

Fallopia (*Polygonaceae*)

aubertii	see *F. baldschuanica*
§ ***baldschuanica***	Widely available
§ ***japonica*** var. ***compacta***	WMoo XLum
- - 'Fuji Snow'	see *F. japonica* var. *compacta* 'Milk Boy'
§ - - 'Milk Boy' (v)	EShb

	- - 'Variegata' misapplied	see *F. japonica* var. *compacta* 'Milk Boy'
§	***multiflora***	CArn CBod LEdu
	- var. ***hypoleuca***	CSde SCoo SPoG
	- - B&SWJ 120	WCru

Farfugium (*Asteraceae*)

§	***japonicum*** B&SWJ 884	WCru
	- 'Argenteum' (v)	SMad WCot
§	- 'Aureomaculatum' (v) ♀H3	CCon CTal ECtt LEdu SGSe
	- 'Bumpy Ride'	WCot
	- 'Crispatum'	CAbP CCon CTal LAst LEdu WWEG
	- double-flowered (d)	WCru
	- 'Kaimon Dake'	WCot
	- 'Kinkan' (v)	WCot
	- 'Ryuto'	WCot
I	- 'Tsuwa-buki'	WCot
	'Last Dance' PBR	EBee ECtt NLar
	tussilagineum	see *F. japonicum*

Fargesia (*Poaceae*)

	from Jiuzhaigou, China	CDTJ CEnt EPfP ERod ETod EUJe GBin LPal MMuc MWht NLar SBig SEND WJun WPGP
	adpressa	MWht WJun
	confusa	CDTJ
	denudata	CDTJ CEnt CFil ENBC ERod NLar SBig WJun
	- L 1575	CExl MWht
	- 'Huanglong' **new**	WJun
	- Xian 1	CDTJ WJun WPGP
	dracocephala	CDoC CEnt CExl CFil ERod ESwi GBin LRHS MAvo MBrN MMuc MWht SBig SEND WJun WMoo WPGP
	- 'White Dragon'	CExl CFil SMad
§	***murielae*** ♀H4	CDoC CEnt CFil CLet ELan ENBC EPau EPfP ERod ETod LCro LOPS LPfy MGos MJak MMuc MWhi MWht NGdn NLos SCob SEND SPlb SPoG WJun WMoo
	- 'Bimbo'	CBod CEnt EPfP ERod ESwi ETod LPal LRHS MAvo MWhi MWht NLar SCob SPoG SWvt WJun WMoo
	- 'Dana Jumbo'	LRHS
	- 'Grüne Hecke'	ERod MWht SBig
	- 'Harewood'	CFil MWht SWvt
	- 'Joy'	GBin NLar WMoo
	- 'Jumbo'	CBod CEnt CSBt ELan ELon EPfP ERod ESwi ETod EUJe LPal LRHS MAvo MBri MGos MJak MWhi MWht NGdn NLar SBig SPer SPoG SRms SWvt WJun
	- 'Mae'	CDTJ MWht
	- 'Simba'	Widely available
	- 'Vampire'	EBee ERod EUJe LRHS SBig
	murieliae 'Superjumbo' PBR	ETod LPal
*	***nepalensis***	ESwi
§	***nitida***	CAbb CBcs CDoC CDul CEnt CLet CSBt ELan EPfP ERod IFro LRHS MBri MGos MJak MWht SCob SPoG SRms SWvt WHer WJun WMoo WPGP
	- 'Great Wall'	CBod ETod EUJe LPal MGos MWht NLar SCob
	- Jiuzhaigou 1	see *F.* Red Panda
	- 'Jiuzhaigou 2'	WJun
	- 'Jiuzhaigou 4'	CExl CFil WPGP
	- 'Jiuzhaigou 8'	WPGP
	- 'Jiuzhaigou Genf'	CFil NLar WPGP
	- 'Nymphenburg'	SBig
	perlonga Yunnan 6	ERod WPGP
§	Red Panda = 'Jiu' ♀H4	CExl CFil EBee LCro LOPS LPal LRHS SPoG SWvt WJun
	robusta ♀H4	CAbb CChe CDTJ CEnt ELan ENBC EPfP ERod ETod LRHS MAvo MBrN MMuc MWhi MWht NGdn NLos SBig WJun
	- 'Campbell'	LPal NLar
	- 'Ming Yunnan'	LEdu WJun WPGP
	- 'P. King'	ERod MWht
	- 'Pingwu'	CBod CDTJ CEnt ENBC ERod ETod GBin LPal MGos MWht SBig WJun
	- 'Red Sheath'	CEnt CExl CJun ERod MWht WJun WPGP
	- 'Wolong'	CDoC CExl ERod ETod MWht WJun WPGP
	rufa ♀H4	CAbb CBod CEnt CExl CFil ELan ENBC EPfP ERod ETod EUJe LCro LPal LPfy LRHS LSRN MAvo MBlu MBrN MGos MJak MMuc MWhi MWht NLar SBig SEND WJun WPGP
	spathacea misapplied	see *F. murielae*
	utilis	CEnt ERod ETod MMuc MWht SEND WJun
	yulongshanensis	ERod MWht WJun
	yunnanensis	LTro

Farsetia (*Brassicaceae*)

	clypeata	see *Fibigia clypeata*

Fascicularia (*Bromeliaceae*)

	andina	see *F. bicolor*
§	***bicolor***	Widely available
	- subsp. ***bicolor***	CFil CMac CPne EAla IBoy NLos SMad
	- subsp. ***canaliculata***	CFil IBlr LEdu MNrw SChr SKHP SPad WCot WPGP
	kirchhoffiana	see *F. bicolor*
	litoralis	see *Ochagavia litoralis*
	pitcairniifolia misapplied	see *F. bicolor*
	pitcairniifolia (Verlot) Mez	see *Ochagavia litoralis*

× *Fatshedera* (*Araliaceae*)

	lizei ♀H3	CBcs CDoC CDul CMac CSde CTri EBee ELon EPfP EUJe LRHS MAsh MRav SCob SDix SEND SPer SPlb SWvt
§	- 'Annemieke' (v) ♀H3	CBcs CBot CDoC CLet CRHN ELan ELon EPfP EUJe LHop LRHS MAsh MMuc MRav SCob SEND SEle SPer SPoG WBor
	- compact **new**	EMil
	- 'Lemon and Lime'	see × *F. lizei* 'Annemieke'
	- 'Maculata'	see × *F. lizei* 'Annemieke'
	- 'Variegata' (v) ♀H3	CMac CSde EBee EBtc ELan ELon EPfP EUJe LAst LRHS MAsh MBel MGos SCob SDix SEND SPer SWvt
	- 'Variegata' compact **new**	EMil

Fatsia (*Araliaceae*)

	sp.	SCob
§	***japonica*** ♀H5	Widely available
	- 'Annelise' (v)	SEND
	- 'Moseri'	CExl ELan ESwi LHop NGdn NLar SWvt WCot

- 'Murakumo-nishiki' (v) CBot
- 'Spider's Web' (v) CAbb CExl CHid CWGN EBee ECtt ELon ESwi ETod EUJe LBMP LHop LLWG LRHS MNrw MRav SBig SCob SDix SMad SPad SPer SPoG WCot WGrn
- 'Variegata' (v) ♀H3 CAbb CBcs CBot CLet CMac EBee ELan EPfP ESwi LLWG LRHS MAsh MBri MGos MPie MRav SCob SEND SHil SLim SLon SPer SPoG WCot WGrn

papyrifera see *Tetrapanax papyrifer*
polycarpa CBot CDTJ CExl CFil WPGP
- B&SWJ 1776 **new** WCru
- B&SWJ 3467 **new** WCru
- B&SWJ 7144 CExl WCru
- RWJ 10133 WCru
- from Tregye **new** EBee
- deeply cut leaf BWJ 12499 WCru

Feijoa see *Acca*

Felicia (*Asteraceae*)

aethiopica CTre
§ ***amelloides*** LAst SEND SPlb
- 'Blue Eyes' LAst
- 'Santa Anita' CTri SVen
§ - variegated (v) ECtt LAst MBri MSCN NPer
§ ***amoena*** CTri
- 'Variegata' (v) CTri
capensis see *F. amelloides*
coelestis see *F. amelloides*
echinata IDee
Felicitara Blue **new** LRHS
filifolia blue-flowered SVen
fruticosa CHll
natalensis see *F. rosulata*
pappei see *F. amoena*
§ ***petiolata*** CTri EWes MMuc MNrw NSti SDix
§ ***rosulata*** CSma ECho GCrg GEdr MBrN MHer MHol NBro NLar SBrt SRot WHal WIce
uliginosa EWes GCrg SBrt SPlb WIce
wrightii GEdr

Fenestraria (*Aizoaceae*)

rhopalophylla subsp. ***aurantiaca*** ♀H2 LToo

fennel see *Foeniculum vulgare*

fenugreek see *Trigonella foenum-graecum*

Ferraria (*Iridaceae*)

LP 18095 WCot
§ ***crispa*** ECho NRog WCot
- var. ***nortieri*** NRog WCot
divaricata CDes EBee NRog WCot
- subsp. ***arenosa*** NRog
schaeferi NRog WCot
undulata see *F. crispa*

Ferula (*Apiaceae*)

assa-foetida WJek
chiliantha see *F. communis* subsp. *glauca*
§ ***communis*** CArn CHVG CMea CSpe ECGP ECha ELan GBin GCra IBoy LRHS NDov SDix SPav SPhx SPlb WJek
- 'Gigantea' see *F. communis*
§ - subsp. ***glauca*** CArn EWes GKev SDix WCot WPGP
- - B&SWJ 12999 WCru
'Giant Bronze' see *Foeniculum vulgare* 'Giant Bronze'
szowitsiana NDov
tingitana 'Cedric Morris' ECha GCra SDix WCot

Ferulago (*Apiaceae*)

cassia **new** WCot
sylvatica PAB 2875 LEdu WPGP

Festuca (*Poaceae*)

actae XLum
amethystina CBod CKno CWib EHoe EShb LOPS LRHS NGdn SEND SMea SPhx SRot WMoo WWEG XLum
- 'Aprilgrün' XLum
arundinacea CHab MMuc SEND
californica CKno EPPr
coxii CHid WCot
curvula subsp. ***crassifolia*** EShb
durissima XLum
'Eisvogel' EPPr
elegans EPPr XLum
eskia EAEE EHoe EPPr XLum
filiformis CHab
gamisansii XLum
§ ***gautieri*** EBee EPPr GBin SMea XLum
- 'Hobbit' CBod
- 'Pic Carlit' GBin NLar XLum
gigantea CBod CHab SEND XLum
glacialis XLum
- 'Czakor' XLum
glauca Vill. CBar CBcs CBod CWib ELan EShb GMaP LPot MBNS MGos MRav MSCN NGdn NOak SGSe SLim SPer SPlb SRms WHea WWEG XSen
I - 'Auslese' CExl EPPr EShb LBMP NGdn
- 'Azurit' EHoe EPPr EWes LHop NLar NWad SPoG
§ - 'Blaufuchs' CLet EAEE ELan EPfP EWes GMaP LRHS MAsh MAvo MBlu MGos NLar NWad SLim SPer SPlb SWvt WFar WWEG XLum
§ - 'Blauglut' EBee EPfP LRHS MBri MRav SRms
- Blue Fox see *F. glauca* 'Blaufuchs'
- Blue Glow see *F. glauca* 'Blauglut'
- 'Elijah Blue' Widely available
- 'Euchre' LSRN
- 'Golden Toupee' CTsd ECha EHoe ELan EPfP LRHS MAsh MBlu MGos NBir NEgg NLar NSti SGSe SLim SPer SPlb SPoG SWvt WWEG XLum
- 'Harz' EHoe XLum
- 'Intense Blue' CAbP CKno CRos EPfP EWes LPfy LRHS LSRN MGos SHil SMad SPoG SRms STPC
* - ***minima*** NWsh WGrn WWEG
- 'Pallens' see *F. longifolia*
- Sea Urchin see *F. glauca* 'Seeigel'
§ - 'Seeigel' EPPr LRHS NWad
- Select see *F. glauca* 'Auslese'
- 'Seven Seas' see *F. valesiaca* 'Silbersee'
- 'Silberreiher' EPPr WWEG
- 'Solling' XLum
- 'Uchte' ELan EPPr WPtf WWEG
'Hogar' EPPr LPal
idahoensis EShb
- 'Tomales Bay' CKno
liviensis **new** XSen

§	***longifolia***	EPPr
	mairei	CKno ECha EHoe EPPr NDov SPhx XLum
	novae-zelandiae	CWCL
	ovina	CHab GBin WSFF
	- var. ***gallica***	NWsh
	- 'Söhrewald'	EPPr
*	- 'Tetra Gold'	SWvt
	paniculata	CKno EHoe EPPr XLum
	- subsp. ***spadicea***	XLum
	pratensis	CHab
	punctoria	MMuc SMea
	rubra	CHab CKno WSFF XLum
	scoparia	see *F. gautieri*
	'Siskiyou Blue'	CKno WWEG
	tatrae	MBel MMuc WCot
	tolucensis NJM 09.071	WPGP
	valesiaca	SMea XLum
	- var. ***glaucantha***	CWib EPPr NGdn WWEG XLum
§	- 'Silbersee'	EAEE EHoe EPPr GBin SRms
	- Silver Sea	see *F. valesiaca* 'Silbersee'
	violacea	EPPr
	vivipara	EHoe LEdu NBid
*	'Willow Green'	SPlb

Fibigia (*Brassicaceae*)

§	***clypeata***	XLum
I	- 'Select'	CSpe

Ficaria (*Ranunculaceae*)

	verna 'Aglow in the Dark'	CDes CHid
	- Alba Group	CHid CSam LEdu NRya WOut
	- 'Art Nouveau'	CDes
§	- Aurantiaca Group	CDes ECha ECho GCrg MHer NLar NRya SPhx SRms
	- 'Brambling'	CHid EBee ECho LEdu NLar
	- 'Brazen Child'	SHar
	- 'Brazen Daughter'	ECho
	- 'Brazen Hussy'	CBod CExl CSam CTri CTsd EBee ECha ECho EHoe EHrv ELan EPPr EPfP GBin GMaP IFro LEdu LRHS MHer NBir NLar NSti SDix SEND SPer SPoG WCot WHal WPnP XLum
	- 'Broadleas Black'	ECho
	- 'Chocolate Cream'	ECho
§	- subsp. ***chrysocephala***	CDes ECha IFro MNrw WCot
§	- 'Collarette' (d)	CHid EBee ECho GBuc LEdu MHer NBir NLar NRya WOut
	- 'Coppernob'	CHid ECho WCot WPnP
	- 'Dahlem' **new**	EPPr
	- 'Damerham' (d)	CHid
§	- 'Double Bronze' (d)	CHid ECho GBuc LEdu MHer NBir NLar NRya SHar
§	- 'Double Mud' (d)	CHid ECho EPPr EWTr GAbr GBuc IFro LEdu NLar NRya SHar WHal
	- double, green-eyed (d)	CHid LEdu
	- 'Dusky Maiden'	ECho NLar NRya
	- 'Elan' (d)	CDes
§	- Flore Pleno Group (d)	CBod CHid CMac CTri ECha ECho ELan EPPr GAbr NRya NSti SRms WCot WPnP
	- 'Fried Egg'	ECho
	- 'Granby Cream'	ECho
	- 'Green Mantle'	ECho
	- 'Green Petal'	CAby CHid EBee ECho EPPr GBuc LEdu MCot MHer NBir NRya WHal WHer
§	- 'Holly Green'	ECho
	- 'Hyde Hall'	ECho NLar WCot
	- 'Jake Perry'	MNrw
	- 'Jane's Dress'	CHid
	- 'Ken Aslet Double' (d)	CDes EPPr LEdu MHer WHal
	- 'Lambrook Variegated' (v)	CFis EPPr
	- 'Lemon Queen'	CHid
	- 'Leo'	MNrw
	- 'Mobled Jade'	CHid
	- 'Monksilver'	IFro
	- 'Montacute' **new**	CFis
	- 'Newton Abbot'	CBre
	- 'Old Master'	WCot
	- 'Orange Sorbet' (d)	LEdu MNrw NLar
§	- 'Picton's Double' (d)	MNrw
	- 'Primrose'	CHid NRya
	- 'Primrose Elf'	EBee
	- 'Ragamuffin' (d)	CDes EBee
	- 'Randall's White'	CAby EBee SHar
	- 'Richard and Val'	WCot
	- 'Rita Pirouet' **new**	WCot
	- 'Salmon's White'	CBre ECho EPPr NBir NLar NRya SHar WHal
	- 'Sheldon Silver'	CHid
	- 'Silver Collar'	LEdu
	- 'Single Cream'	MNrw
	- 'Tomas'	ECho
	- 'Tortoiseshell'	CHid EPPr
§	- subsp. ***verna***	CArn CTri ESwi MHer WHer WOut WSFF WShi
	- - 'Chedglow'	WCot
	- 'Witchampton'	CDes
	- 'Yaffle'	CHid ECho

Ficinia (*Cyperaceae*)

	truncata 'Ice Crystal' (v) **new**	LRHS

Ficus (*Moraceae*)

	sp.	LPar
	afghanistanica	ERea
	- 'Silver Lyre' **new**	WPGP
I	***binnendijkii*** 'Alii'	WCot
	carica (F)	ETod EUJe LPar MBri SEWo SLon SPad
	- 'Abicou' (F)	ERea
	- 'Adam' (F)	ERea LEdu NLar
	- 'Alma' (F)	ERea
	- 'Angélique' (F)	ERea
I	- 'Bauern Feige' (F)	NLar SRms
	- 'Black Ischia' (F)	ERea SDix
	- 'Black Jack' (F)	ERea
	- 'Bornholm' (F)	LSRN SPre
	- 'Bourjassotte Grise' (F)	CAgr ERea SDea XSen
	- 'Brown Turkey' (F) ♀H4	Widely available
	- 'Brunswick' (F)	CAgr CDoC CDul CHll CLet ELan ELon EPfP EPom ERea EShb EUJe GTwe LEdu LRHS NLar SBmr SDix SKee SLim SRms WCot WFar WMat
	- 'Califfo Blue' (F)	SRms
	- 'Castle Kennedy' (F)	ERea
	- 'Celeste' (F)	CBcs ERea SRms
	- 'Col de Dame Blanc' (F)	ERea XSen
	- 'Col de Dame Noir' (F)	ERea
	- 'Dalmatie' (F)	CAgr ELan EPfP ERea LRHS MGos NPri SRms WMat WPGP XSen
§	- 'Desert King' (F)	ERea
I	- 'Digitata' (F)	MBlu
	- 'Dorée' (F) **new**	SBmr
	- 'Drap d'Or' (F)	ERea
	- 'Excel' (F)	ERea
	- 'Figue d'Or' (F)	ERea
	- 'Goutte d'Or' (F)	CAgr EPfP ERea SDea

- 'Green Ischia' (F)	ERea
- 'Grise de Saint Jean' (F)	ERea
- 'Honey Tulip' (F) new	ERea
- 'Ice Crystal' (F) ♀H5	CDoC ECrN ELan EMil EPfP ERea EShb LRHS MBlu SPoG SRms WCot WMat WPGP
- 'Kadota' (F)	ERea IDee
- 'King'	see *F. carica* 'Desert King'
* - 'Laciniata' (F)	MBri
- 'Lisa' (F)	ERea
- 'Little Yellow Wonder' (F)	ERea
- 'Longue d'Août' (F)	XSen
- 'LSU Gold' (F) new	ERea
- 'LSU Purple' (F)	ERea
- 'Madeleine des Deux Saisons' (F)	CDoC EPom ERea SBmr
- 'Marseillaise' (F)	EPfP GTwe SDea
- 'Morena' (F)	SRms
- 'Napolitana' (F)	ERea
- 'Nero' (F)	ELon SGol
- 'Newlyn Harbour' (F)	ELon
- 'Noire de Caromb' (F)	CAgr EPfP ERea LRHS SBmr SKee SRms WMat
- 'Noire de Provence'	see *F. carica* 'Reculver'
- 'Orphan' (F) new	ERea
- 'Osborn's Prolific' (F)	EPfP SEND SGol SWvt
- 'Panachée' (F)	CSut EPom ERea SRms
- 'Pastilière' (F)	ERea
- 'Peter's Honey' (F)	ERea
- 'Petite Nigra' (F)	ERea
- 'Pingo de Mel' new	ERea
- 'Précoce de Dalmatie' (F)	CTho ERea LEdu NLar SRms
- 'Précoce Ronde de Bordeaux' (F)	ERea SEND
§ - 'Reculver' (F)	SEND
- 'Ronde de Bordeaux' (F)	XSen
- 'Rouge de Bordeaux' (F)	CDoC EPom ERea LRHS NPri SDea SPlb SRms
- 'Saint Johns' (F)	ERea SDea
- 'San Pedro Miro' (F)	ERea
- 'Sugar 12' (F)	ERea
- 'Sultane' (F)	CAgr ERea
- 'Tena' (F)	ERea
- 'Texas Everbearing' (F)	ERea
- 'Violette Dauphine' (F)	EPfP ERea LEdu NLar
- 'Violette de Bordeaux' (F)	ERea
- 'Violette de Sollies' (F)	ERea SVic
- 'Violette Normande' (F)	SEND
- 'Violette Sepor' (F)	ERea
- 'White Adriatic' (F)	CBcs ERea SRms
- 'White Genoa'	see *F. carica* 'White Marseilles'
- 'White Ischia' (F)	ERea
§ - 'White Marseilles' (F)	CAgr CMac CWib ECrN ERea LRHS MBri SDea SKee SRms WMat WPGP
microcarpa	LPal
pubigera	CExl
pumila ♀H1c	CBcs CTsd EShb
- 'Variegata' (v) ♀H1c	EShb
tikoua	CFil

fig see *Ficus carica*

filbert see *Corylus maxima*

Filipendula ✿ (*Rosaceae*)

alnifolia 'Variegata'	see *F. ulmaria* 'Variegata'
camtschatica	CCon ECha ELan IMou NBid NLar WPGP WWtn
- B&SWJ 10987	WCru
- RBS 0224	NLar
- TCM 12-668 new	CEvo
- 'Rosea'	LHop MRav
digitata 'Nana'	see *F. multijuga*
hexapetala	see *F. vulgaris*
- 'Flore Pleno'	see *F. vulgaris* 'Multiplex'
'Kahome'	CMea CPrp EAJP ELon EShb GMaP IFoB IKil LLWG LRHS MHol NBid NBir NGdn NLar SCob SPer SPhx SWat WMoo WPnP WWEG
kiraishiensis	EBee
- B&SWJ 1571	WCru
§ ***multijuga***	GCal IFoB LLWG MSCN NHol NLar NWad WBor WMoo
- B&SWJ 10950	WCru
- 'Hjördis'	CBod EBee ELon LLWG MBri WHil
- var. ***yezoensis*** B&SWJ 10828	IMou WCru
palmata	ECha IBlr LLWG MLHP NBre SWat WMoo
- 'Digitata Nana'	see *F. multijuga*
- dwarf	CDes
- 'Elegantissima'	see *F. purpurea* 'Elegans'
- 'Nana'	see *F. multijuga*
- 'Rosea'	CMac LLWG NBir
- 'Rubra'	CTri EBee GCra LRHS MRav NGdn
purpurea	CKno CSBt ECha ELon IBlr ILea MBri MMuc SBod SEND SRms WCru WMoo
- f. ***albiflora***	LLWG WMoo
§ - 'Elegans'	EBee ELon GBin ILea LLWG LRHS MLHP NBid NHol SCob SPer SRms SWat WMoo WPnP
- 'Pink Dreamland'	SPhx
* - 'Plena' (d)	NLar
'Queen of the Prairies'	see *F. rubra*
§ ***rubra***	IFro LSRN WSFF
§ - 'Venusta' ♀H5	Widely available
- 'Venusta Magnifica'	see *F. rubra* 'Venusta'
rufinervis B&SWJ 8611	WCru
§ ***ulmaria***	Widely available
- 'Aurea'	CBod CCon CMac CNor CTri CWCL EBee ECha ECtt EHoe ELan GAbr GMaP LEdu LRHS MAvo MLHP MRav NBid NLar SPer SRms WCot WFar WMoo WSHC WWEG
- 'Flore Pleno' (d)	CBre CCon CWld EBee LHop LLWG LRHS MRav NBid SPer SWat WCot WFar WHil
- 'Rosea'	LRHS MBel MHer
§ - 'Variegata' (v)	CBen CPrp EBee ECtt EHoe ELan GBuc IFoB LRHS NBid NGdn NLar SPer SRms WFar WHfH WMoo WWEG
§ ***vulgaris***	CArn CHab CWld GLog ILea MBel MLHP MMuc MNHC NBro NMir NQui SWat WHer WHfH WJek WWEG
- 'Flore Pleno'	see *F. vulgaris* 'Multiplex'
- 'Grandiflora'	CBre EBee
§ - 'Multiplex' (d)	CMac CSpe ECha ELan GMaP LLWG LRHS MHer MMuc MRav MSpe MWts NBid NBir NRya NSti SRms WFar WMoo XLum
- 'Plena'	see *F. vulgaris* 'Multiplex'
- 'Rosea'	NBre

Firmiana (*Malvaceae*)

simplex	CBcs EShb ESwi EUJe MBlu SPad WPGP

Fitzroya (*Cupressaceae*)

cupressoides	CBcs CDoC CMac CTho GBin IArd IDee SAko SLim WThu
- 'Borde Hill' (f)	WThu
- 'Westonbirt' (m)	WThu

Foeniculum (*Apiaceae*)

sp.	LBMP
vulgare	CAgr CArn CHby CLau ECha ECrN ELan ENfk EPfP EWoo GPoy LPal MGos MHer MJak MNHC NPri SCob SEND SIde SPer SPhx SPlb SPoG SRms SVic SWvt WHfH WJek
- 'Bronze'	see *F. vulgare* 'Purpureum'
- var. ***dulce***	ENfk SIde
§ - 'Giant Bronze'	EBee LCro LOPS LRHS MAvo SCob SMad SPhx WCot WGrn XSen
§ - 'Purpureum'	Widely available
- 'Smokey'	ECha MRav
- 'Sweet Florence'	SVic

Fontanesia (*Oleaceae*)

fortunei	EBtc
phillyreoides	CBcs

Forsythia (*Oleaceae*)

'Arnold Dwarf'	ECrN NBir SRms
'Beatrix Farrand' ambig.	COtt CTri NWea SEND SRms
'Beatrix Farrand' K. Sax	MMuc NLar
'Fiesta' (v)	ELon EPfP LAst LRHS MAsh MGos MRav MSwo NEgg NLar SPer SPoG WCot
giraldiana	MSwo SLon SRms
Gold Tide	see *F.* Marée d'Or
'Golden Bells'	WHar
'Golden Nugget'	CMac ELan EPfP LBuc LRHS MAsh NLar SLon SPoG WCFE WFar
'Golden Times' (v)	CMac EWes LAst LBuc LPot LSRN MAsh MGos MSwo NHol NWea SPoG SWvt
'Goldstream' (v) **new**	NWad
× ***intermedia***	EShb IBoy
- 'Arnold Giant'	MBlu
- 'Goldrausch'	ELan LPfy LRHS MAsh NLar SHil
- 'Goldzauber'	NWea
- 'Josefa' (v)	ELon
- 'Lynwood Variety' 🏆H5	Widely available
- 'Lynwood Variety' variegated (v)	CWib
- Minigold = 'Flojor'	CMac CNec CSBt EBee ELan LBMP MSwo NLar SRms
- Show Off = 'Mindor'[PBR]	LRHS
- 'Spectabilis'	CDul EPfP LBuc NWea SCob SCoo SGol SLim WFar
- 'Spectabilis Variegated' (v)	CMHG MBNS NEoE
- 'Spring Glory'	MHer
- Week End = 'Courtalyn'[PBR] 🏆H5	CBod CDoC CLet CNec EPfP LBMP LBuc LRHS MAsh MBri MJak MMuc NHol NLar SCob SEND SGol SHil SLon SPlb WFar
'Kanarek'	NLar
× ***mandshurica***	IDee IMou SAko
§ Marée d'Or = 'Courtasol'[PBR] 🏆H5	ELon EPfP IVic LRHS MAsh MGos MJak MRav NLar NWea SLon SPer SPoG
Mêlée d'Or = 'Courtaneur'	SGol
Melissa = 'Courtadic'	NWea
'Northern Gold'	MBlu
ovata 'Tetragold'	NWea
'Paulina'	GEdr NLar WAbe
suspensa	CMac CTri CWib EPfP NWea SPlb SRms
- f. ***atrocaulis***	CDul
- 'Nymans'	MBri MRav NLar NSti SEND
§ - 'Taff's Arnold' (v)	CExl
- 'Variegata'	see *F. suspensa* 'Taff's Arnold'
'Tremonia'	ECrN
viridissima	NWea
- 'Bronxensis'	CMac CTal ECho LHop LLHF MAsh NBir NLar SIgm WAbe WPat
- Citrus Swizzle = 'Mckcitrine'[PBR]	NLar
- var. ***koreana*** 'Kumsom' (v)	EBee NLar SAko SPoG
- 'Weber's Bronx'	NLar WAbe

Fortunella (*Rutaceae*)

× ***crassifolia***	see *Citrus japonica*
'Fukushu'	see *Citrus* × *obovata* 'Fukushu'
hindsii	see *Citrus japonica*
margarita	see *Citrus japonica*

Fothergilla (*Hamamelidaceae*)

gardenii	CBcs CJun ELan EPfP LRHS MBlu MRav NLar SPer SWvt
- 'Blue Mist'	CAbP CDoC CExl CJun EBee ELan ELon EPfP GQue IVic LRHS MAsh SKHP SPer SPoG WPat
- 'Brian Upchurch'	NLar
- 'Glaucophylla' **new**	NLar
- 'Suzanne'	NLar
- 'Zundert'	NLar
'Huntsman'	CDoC CTho EBee EPfP SPer
× ***intermedia*** Beaver Creek = 'Klmtwo'	NLar
- 'Blue Shadow'	CBcs CJun EPfP EUJe IDee LCro LRHS LSRN MGos MPkF MRav NLar SGol SKHP
- 'Mount Airy' 🏆H5	CDoC CDul CJun CMCN EBee EPfP LRHS MPkF NLar SKHP SSta
- 'Red Licorice'	CJun EPfP NLar
- 'Sea Spray'	CJun NLar
- 'Windy City'	CJun NLar
major 🏆H5	CBcs CDul CJun CLet CWib EBee ELan EPfP LCro LPfy LRHS LSRN MAsh MBlu MGos MJak NEgg NLar NPri SHil SPer SReu SWvt WBod WFar WHor WMat WPat
- 'Bulkyard'	CJun
- Monticola Group	CDoC CDul CJun CTho ELan EPfP LRHS MAsh MMuc SLim SPer SSpi SSta

Fouquieria (*Fouquieriaceae*)

columnaris	SPlb
splendens	SPlb

Fragaria (*Rosaceae*)

from Taiwan	WHer
alpina 'Alba'	see *F. vesca* 'Semperflorens Alba'
× ***ananassa*** 'Albion'[PBR] (F)	CSBt LCro LOPS LRHS LSRN SBdl SPer
- 'Alice'[PBR] (F) 🏆H6	CAgr CMac EPom LBuc LRHS
- 'Anablanca' (F)	CSut EMil EPom LRHS SRms
- 'Aromel' (F) 🏆H6	EPfP LBuc
- 'Bolero' (F)	MBri
- 'Buddy' (F)	EPom LCro LOPS SBmr SPer
- 'Calypso' (F)	CSBt LBuc SDea SFrt SPer

	Name	Suppliers
	- 'Cambridge Favourite' (F) ♀H6	CAgr CMac CSBt CTri EMil EPfP EPom GAbr GTwe LBuc LCro LOPS LRHS MBri MGos MJak NPri SBdl SBmr SDea SEND SFrt SPlb SRms WHar
	- 'Cambridge Vigour' (F)	LRHS
	- 'Christine' (F)	CAgr CSut EPom LRHS SDea
	- 'Cupid' (F) **new**	CArg LCro LOPS
	- 'Darselect'PBR (F)	EPom LOPS
	- 'Delia' (F) **new**	LCro LOPS LRHS
	- 'Elan'PBR (F) **new**	LRHS
	- 'Elegance'PBR (F)	EPom GTwe SFrt SRms
	- 'Elsanta' (F)	CSBt CTri EMil EPfP EPom GTwe IArd LBuc LEdu LRHS NEgg NPri SBdl SBmr SDea SPer WHar WMat
	- 'Elvira' (F)	EPfP
	- 'Eros'PBR (F)	LBuc
	- 'Everest'PBR (F)	LRHS
	- 'Fenella'PBR (F)	CMac EMil EPom GTwe LCro LOPS
	- 'Finesse' (F) **new**	GTwe LRHS
	- 'Flamenco'PBR (F)	CArg CSut EPom LEdu NWad
	- 'Florence'PBR (F)	CAgr CArg CSBt CTri EPfP EPom GTwe LBuc LEdu LRHS MBri SBmr SDea SFrt SPer
	- 'Florian' (F)	LEdu
	- (Fragoo Series) Fragoo Deep Rose = 'Tarpan'	LRHS
	- - Fragoo Pink = 'Pikan' (F)	LRHS
	- - Fragoo White = 'Belton'	LRHS
	- Fraise des Bois	see *F. vesca*
	- 'Framberry' (F) **new**	LEdu LRHS
	- 'Frau Mieze Schindler' (F)	EPom SFrt
	- 'Fruitful Summer' (F)	LRHS
	- 'Gariguette' (F)	EPom
	- 'Gasana' (F) **new**	LRHS
	- 'Hapil' (F) ♀H6	CTri EMil EPfP EPom GTwe LBuc LEdu LRHS SBdl
	- 'Honeoye' (F) ♀H6	CAgr CSBt EMil EPfP EPom GTwe LBuc LCro LEdu LOPS LRHS MBri NWad SBdl SBmr SEND SPer SRms WHar
	- 'Judibell'PBR (F)	GTwe SFrt
	- 'Korona'PBR (F)	CMac EPom
	- 'Leo Alba' (F) **new**	CArg
	- 'Loran' (F)	LRHS
	- 'Lucy'PBR (F)	LCro LOPS SFrt
	- 'Malling Opal'PBR (F)	CSut EPom
	- 'Malwina'PBR (F)	CSut EPom SVic
	- 'Manille' (F)	EPom
	- 'Merlan'PBR (F)	LRHS SRms
	- 'Pandora' (F)	LEdu
	- 'Pegasus'PBR (F) ♀H6	CAgr CSBt EPfP EPom LRHS NPri
	- pineberry (F) **new**	LEdu
	- Pink Panda = 'Frel' (F)	CBod CMac CTri EAEE EBee ELan LHop LRHS MBel MRav NEgg NGdn NLar SPer SPoG WCAu WWFP
	- pink-flowered (F)	GAbr LPot
	- 'Red Glory'PBR (F) **new**	LRHS
	- 'Red Princess'PBR (F) **new**	LRHS
	- Red Ruby	see *F.* × *ananassa* 'Samba'
	- 'Redgauntlet' (F)	EPfP GTwe LBuc LRHS
	- 'Rhapsody' (F) ♀H6	GTwe LRHS LSRN SBdl
	- 'Rosie'PBR (F)	SDea
	- 'Royal Sovereign' (F)	CMac CSut CTri EPom GTwe LEdu NBir SVic
§	- 'Samba'PBR (F)	CBod GLog LRHS MBel MNrw NDov NGdn NLar SPer SPoG WCAu
	- 'Senga Sengana' (F)	SVic
	- 'Sonata'PBR (F)	EPom LRHS NWad
	- 'Sophie'PBR (F)	LEdu NWad
	- 'Sweetheart' (F)	CSut LCro
	- 'Symphony'PBR (F) ♀H6	CAgr CSBt EPfP EPom LBuc LRHS LSRN MBri SBmr SFrt SPer
	- 'Temptation' (F)	LRHS
	- 'Toscana' (F) **new**	LRHS
§	- 'Variegata' (v)	CTri EAEE EBee MRav SPer SPoG WHea WMoo
	- 'Vibrant' (F) **new**	EMil GTwe LRHS
	- 'White Dream' (F)	LCro LOPS
	'Bowles's Double'	see *F. vesca* 'Multiplex'
	chiloensis (F)	IFro LEdu
	- 'Chaval' (F)	CHid ECha EPPr IMou MRav NChi WMoo
	- 'Variegata' misapplied	see *F.* × *ananassa* 'Variegata'
	daltoniana	GCra
	indica	see *Duchesnea indica*
	'Lipstick'	EBee LHop NFav NLar
	moschata	CAgr
	nubicola	CAgr GPoy
	'Roman'	LRHS
	'Variegata'	see *F.* × *ananassa* 'Variegata'
§	***vesca*** (F)	CAgr CArn CBcs CWld ELan EPfP GKev GPoy LCro LOPS MHer MNHC NMir NPri SFrt SIde SPlb SRms SVic WGwG WJek WOut WSFF WShi
	- 'Alexandra' (F)	CLau CPrp ENfk EPPr ERea NLar SIde WHar
	- 'Alpina Scarletta' (F)	ENfk
	- 'Alpine Yellow' (F)	EWTr
	- 'Baron Solemacher' (F)	ERea SHDw SPhx WHer
	- 'Capron Royale' (F)	CAgr
	- 'Flore Pleno'	see *F. vesca* 'Multiplex'
	- 'Fructu Albo' (F)	CAgr CArn CBre WMoo
	- 'Golden Alexandra' (F)	ECha EWes MHer NEoE WHer WOut WWFP
	- 'Golden Surprise' (F)	SHDw
	- 'Mara des Bois'PBR (F)	EPom LRHS SRms
	- 'Monophylla' (F)	SIde WHer
§	- 'Multiplex' (d)	EPPr NChi WBor WHer WOut
§	- 'Muricata'	CBre LEdu LOPS
	- 'Pineapple Crush' (F)	WHer
	- 'Plymouth Strawberry'	see *F. vesca* 'Muricata'
	- 'Reine des Vallées' (F)	ERea
	- 'Scarlet Beauty' (F)	EPom LCro LOPS
§	- 'Semperflorens Alba' (F)	CAgr WJek
	- 'Variegata' misapplied	see *F.* × *ananassa* 'Variegata'
*	- 'Variegata' ambig. (v)	EHoe LLWG
	- 'White Surprise' (F) **new**	LCro LOPS
	virginiana	CAgr
	- subsp. ***glauca***	EPPr
	viridis	CAgr

Francoa (Francoaceae)

	Name	Suppliers
	appendiculata	GAbr ILea NBir WHer WMoo
	- red-flowered	LHop
	Ballyrogan strain	IBlr
	'Confetti'	CAbP CExl IKil
*	dwarf purple	CElw
	'Purple Spike'	see *F. sonchifolia* Rogerson's form
	ramosa	CCon CTri IBlr ILea NBro SDix WKif WMoo
*	- 'Alba'	CSpe
	sonchifolia	Widely available
	- 'Alba'	WMoo
	- 'Molly Anderson'	MAvo
	- 'Petite Bouquet' **new**	EWes

- 'Pink Bouquet'	CAbb CKno CMac CMos CWGN EBee GBin SHar WOut
- 'Pink Giant'	CBod GBin GBuc GCal GKev IPot LRHS MBel NWad WHil WMoo
§ - Rogerson's form	CAby CElw CTri ELon EShb IMou IVic LHop LRHS NBir NChi SDix SGSe WMoo WWEG

Frangula (*Rhamnaceae*)

§ ***alnus***	CArg CArn CCVT CDul CHab CTri ECrN EShb LBuc MBlu MGos MMuc NWea SEWo WFar WMou WSFF
- 'Aspleniifolia'	ELan EPfP LRHS MBlu MMuc MPkF MRav NLar SMad WCFE WPat
- 'Fine Line'	ELan LRHS MBri MPkF NLar
- 'Minaret'	MBlu
- 'Ron Williams'	MBlu WMat

Frankenia (*Frankeniaceae*)

laevis	SRms
thymifolia	CTri ECho ECtt EPot MAsh MHer MMuc MSCN NPri SIgm SPlb WOld WRHF XLum

Franklinia (*Theaceae*)

alatamaha	CBcs IDee IVic MBlu SAko WPGP

Fraxinus ✿ (*Oleaceae*)

americana	CDul CMCN NWea
- 'Autumn Purple'	CDul CMCN CTho EBee EPfP MAsh NWea
angustifolia	CMCN
- 'Raywood'	CCVT CDul CMCN CMac CTho CTri CWib EBee ECrN ELan EPfP EWTr LAst LCro MAsh MGos MMuc MSwo NWea SCob SEND SGol
anomala	CDul
chiisanensis B&SWJ 12719	WCru
chinensis	CDul CMCN
excelsior	CCVT CDul CHab CMac CSBt CTho CTri CWib ECrN EPfP MAsh MBri MGos MJak MMuc NWea SCob SEND SEWo SGol
- 'Althena'	CDul
- 'Aurea Pendula'	CDul CMac CWib MGos
- 'Crispa'	NLar
- f. ***diversifolia***	CDul
- 'Jaspidea'	CCVT CDul CMCN CMac CTho CWib ECrN ELan EPfP ERod LAst MAsh MBri MGos MMuc MSwo NWea SCob SEND SGol
- 'Pendula'	CCVT CDul CMac CTsd EBee ECrN ELan NWea SGol
- 'R.E. Davey'	CDul
- variegated (v)	CMac
- 'Westhof's Glorie'	CCVT CDul
insularis var. ***henryana***	CDul CMCN
latifolia	CMCN
mariesii	see *F. sieboldiana*
ornus	CArn CCVT CDul CMCN CMac CTri ECrN ELan EPfP LAst MMuc MSwo NWea SEND
- 'Arie Peters'	CDul
- 'Obelisk'	EBee EBtc EWTr MAsh MBri
- 'Rotterdam'	EBee
pennsylvanica	CDul CMCN
- 'Variegata' (v)	EBee
quadrangulata	CDul
§ ***sieboldiana***	CDul CMCN EPfP MBri
sogdiana Potamophila Group	CEvo CFil EBee
velutina	CDul
xanthoxyloides	CDul

Freesia (*Iridaceae*)

alba Foster	see *F. lactea*
alba Watson	see *F. caryophyllacea*
§ ***caryophyllacea***	NRog
corymbosa	NRog
'Fragrant Sunburst'	SPoG
fucata	ECho
grandiflora	CExl CHll ECho WCot
grandiflora × ***laxa***	CDes
'Grumpy'	LRHS
§ ***lactea***	CDes ECho
§ ***laxa*** ♀H3	CExl CSpe CTal CTre CTri ECho EPri LRHS NLos WAbe WCot
- var. ***alba*** ♀H3	CExl CSpe CTre ECho EPri LLWP WAbe
- blue-flowered	ECho WAbe
- 'Joan Evans'	CSpe ECho LLHF
- red-spotted	CExl ECho
- ***viridiflora***	ECho
leichtlinii	NRog
refracta	CTal NRog
viridis	CDes CExl CTal EBee ECho NRog
xanthospila	NRog WCot

Fremontodendron (*Malvaceae*)

'California Glory' ♀H4	Widely available
californicum	CTri EAla EBee ELan MBri MPkF NLar SEND SLim SPlb WFar
'Dara's Gold'	LRHS
'Pacific Sunset'	CBcs EPfP LSRN MGos MRav SGol
'Tequila Sunrise' ♀H4	CBcs CJun CWGN LHop LLHF

Freylinia (*Scrophulariaceae*)

cestroides	see *F. lanceolata*
§ ***lanceolata***	CBcs CWib SPlb SVen WCot
tropica	CHll GFai WCot
visseri	SVen

Frithia (*Aizoaceae*)

pulchra ♀H2 **new**	LToo

Fritillaria ✿ (*Liliaceae*)

acmopetala ♀H4	CAvo CBro CCon CTal CWCL ECho EPot ERCP GBuc GKev ITim LAma MNrw MPie SDeJ WCot WIce
- 'Brunette'	EPot LAma
- subsp. ***wendelboi***	ECho GKev LAma
affinis	CWCL ECho EPot GBin GBuc
- NNS 00-336	WCot
§ - var. ***tristulis***	CWCL
- 'Vancouver Island'	LAma
amana	CTca CWCL ECho EPot ERCP GKev ITim LLHF WCot
- 'Cambridge' ♀H4	WCot
- 'Goksan Gold'	ECho
- yellow-flowered	EPot
arabica	see *F. persica*
armena	GKev
assyriaca	EPot GBuc MPie
aurea	LAma
- 'Golden Flag'	ECho EPot LAma LLHF
'Beethoven' (Rascal Series) **new**	GKev
biflora	ECho
- 'Martha Roderick'	ECho LAma SDeJ

§ ***bithynica***	ECho ITim LAma
bucharica	ECho EPot GKev LAma
- 'Nurek Giant'	ECho
camschatcensis	CBro CWCL ECho EFEx EPfP EPot ERCP GBin GBuc GEdr GKev GMaP LAma LRHS MAvo NBir NHar SDeJ SPhx WAbe WCot WCru
- 'Alaska'	NHar
- 'Aurea'	ECho GBuc NHar SPhx
- black-flowered	CAby ECho NHar
- double-flowered (d)	CCon ECho GBuc
- f. ***flavescens***	EFEx GBuc GEdr LAma
- green-flowered	CAby
carduchorum	see *F. minuta*
carica	ECho EPot
'Chopin' (Rascal Series) **new**	GKev
citrina	see *F. bithynica*
conica	EPot
§ ***crassifolia*** subsp. ***kurdica***	ECho EPot GKev ITim
davisii	ECho EPfP EPot GKev LAma LLHF WCot
eduardii	ECho EPot GKev WCot
elwesii	ECho EPot ERCP GKev ITim LAma LLHF SDeJ WTor
* ***glauca*** 'Golden Flag'	LLWG
- 'Goldilocks'	LAma SDeJ
graeca	ECho EPot GBuc GKev LAma SDeJ
- subsp. ***graeca***	GBuc
hispanica	see *F. lusitanica*
imperialis ♀H6	ECGP MBri
- 'April Flame'	LAma
- 'Argenteovariegata' (v)	LAma
- 'Aureomarginata' (v)	EPot LAma
- 'Aurora'	EPot ERCP GKev LAma LRHS MBri NLar NPer SDeJ SPhx WFar
- 'Garland Star'	GKev LAma NLar
- 'Grenadier'	LAma
- var. ***inodora***	GKev LAma
- 'Inodora Purpurea'	LAma
- 'Lutea'	CAvo CTca ELan ERCP GKev LAma LRHS SPoG WFar
- 'Maxima'	see *F. imperialis* 'Rubra Maxima'
- 'Maxima Lutea' ♀H6	CBro CCon ELan EPfP EPot ERCP GKev LSun MBri NLar SDeJ SPer SPhx SPoG
- 'Orange Beauty' **new**	LAma
- 'Orange Brilliant'	LAma
- 'Prolifera'	GKev LAma SDeJ
- 'Rubra'	CCon CTca EPfP ERCP GKev LAma NLar SPer WFar
§ - 'Rubra Maxima'	CBro CTca ELan EPfP EPot ERCP GKev LRHS LSun SDeJ
- 'Slagzwaard'	GKev LAma
- 'Striped Beauty'	EPot GKev LAma LSun SDeJ
- 'Sulpherino'	GKev LAma
- 'Sunset' **new**	LAma
- 'The Premier'	GKev LAma SDeJ
- 'William Rex'	CAvo EPot ERCP GKev LAma LBuc LRHS LSun SDeJ SPhx SPoG
involucrata	ECho WCot
japonica var. ***koidzumiana***	EFEx LAma
karadaghensis	see *F. crassifolia* subsp. *kurdica*
kotschyana	ECho EPot LAma
lanceolata	see *F. affinis* var. *tristulis*
latakiensis	ECho EPot GKev
§ ***lusitanica***	ITim
meleagris ♀H5	Widely available
- 'Artemis'	GBuc
- var. ***unicolor*** subvar. ***alba*** ♀H5	CAvo CBro ECho ERCP GBuc GKev LCro LLWG LOPS MBri MWat NHol SCob SDeJ SPer SPhx WShi
- - - 'Aphrodite'	EPot NBir
messanensis subsp. ***gracilis***	GKev
michailovskyi	CHid CTri CWCL ECho EPfP EPot ERCP GBuc GKev LAma LHop LRHS MNrw SDeJ SRms WFar
minima	ECho
§ ***minuta***	ECho EPot ERCP GKev LAma SDeJ
montana	ECho
nigra Mill.	see *F. pyrenaica*
olivieri	ECho
pallidiflora ♀H5	CBro CTca CWCL ECho EPot ERCP GBuc GCra GKev LAma MBri NBir SDeJ SPhx WCot
§ ***persica***	ECha ECho EPfP EPot ERCP GKev LAma LHop LRHS MBri MNrw SCob SPhx
- 'Adiyaman' ♀H4	ELan SDeJ
- 'Alba'	GKev SDeJ
- 'Chocolate'	CWCL
- 'Ivory Bells'	ECho ELan EPot ERCP LAma SDeJ SKHP SPhx
- 'Ivory Queen'	CBro
- 'Midnight Bells'	ECho GKev
pinardii	ECho LAma
- 'Ole Sonderhause'	ECho
pontica ♀H4	CAvo CBro CCon CWCL ECho EPot ERCP GBuc GKev ITim LAma LLWG MNrw SDeJ
pudica	ECho LAma WAbe
* - 'Fragrant'	ECho
- 'Giant'	ECho EPot SDeJ
purdyi	ECho
§ ***pyrenaica*** ♀H5	ECho GCra LAma LLHF
raddeana	ECho EPot ERCP GKev LAma SDeJ SPhx WCot
reuteri	ECho EPot LAma
rubra major	see *F. imperialis* 'Rubra Maxima'
ruthenica	ECho
sewerzowii	ECho EPot GKev LAma
stenanthera	ECho EPot GKev LAma
tachengensis	see *F. yuminensis*
thunbergii	CTal ECho GKev LAma LLHF WCot
uva-vulpis	CAby CCon CMea CTca ECho ECtt ELon EPfP EPot ERCP GKev LAma LHop LLWG LRHS MNrw NBir NPri SDeJ WFar
verticillata	CBro ECha LAma WCot WCru
'Vivaldi' (Rascal Series) **new**	GKev
whittallii	ECho EPot GKev LAma
§ ***yuminensis***	LAma

Fuchsia ✿ (*Onagraceae*)

'A.M. Larwick'	EBak
'A.W. Taylor'	EBak
'Aalt Hillie van de Veen'	WOth
'Abbé Farges' (d)	CLoc CWVF EBak EPts LHop SVic WOth
'Abbigayle Reine' (v)	CDoC
'Abigail' ambig.	CWVF
'Achievement' ♀H4	CLoc LCla MJac SVic
'Adalbert Bogner' (d)	CDoC
'Adinda' (T) ♀H1c	EPts LCla
'Adriaan van Bylant' (d) **new**	WOth
'Adrienne' (d)	CDoC
'Ailsa Garnett' (d)	EBak
'Aintree'	CWVF

	'Airedale'	CWVF
	'Aladna's Sander' (d)	CWVF
	'Alan Ayckbourn'	CWVF WOth
	'Alan Titchmarsh' 🏆H2	CDoC EPts LCla SLBF
	'Alaska' (d)	CLoc SVic
	'Albertina'	SVic WOth
	'Albertus Schwab'	LCla
	'Alde'	CWVF WOth
	'Alderford'	SLBF
	'Alexandra Meles' **new**	WOth
	'Alf Thornley' (d)	CWVF WOth
	'Alfonso' (d) **new**	SLBF
	'Alice Ashton' (d)	EBak
	'Alice Blue Gown' (d)	CWVF
	'Alice Doran'	CDoC LCla
	'Alice Hoffman' (d) 🏆H4	CAby CLet CLoc CMac COtt CSBt CWCL CWVF EBak EBee ELan EPfP EPts LAst LRHS MAsh MGos MJac NEgg NLar SEND SHil SLBF SLim SPer SPoG SVic WFar
	'Alice Sweetapple' (d)	CWVF
	'Alicia Sellars'	SLBF
	'Alison Ewart'	CLoc CWVF MJac SVic
	'Alison Patricia' 🏆H2	CWVF EBak LAst LCla MJac SLBF SVic WOth
	'Alison Reynolds' (d)	CWVF
	'Alison Ruth Griffin' (d)	MJac
	'Alison Ryle' (d)	EBak
	'Alison Sweetman' 🏆H2	CWVF MJac
	'Allan Taylor' **new**	WOth
	'Allen Jackson'	LCla WOth
	'Aloha'	WOth
	'Aloys Hetterscheid' **new**	WOth
	alpestris	CDoC EBak GCal LCla SVic
	'Alwin' (d)	CWVF
	'Alyce Larson' (d)	CWVF EBak MJac SVic
	'Alyssa May Garcia' (d)	CDoC EPts SLBF WOth
	'Amazing Grace' (d)	MJac
	'Amazing Maisie' (d)	SLBF WOth
	'Ambassador'	SVic
	'Amelia Rose'	SLBF
	'Amelie Aubin'	CLoc CWVF EBak SVic
	'America'	CWVF
	'Amerika' (d)	WOth
§	***ampliata***	CDoC LCla
	'Amy'	MJac
	'Amy Lye'	CLoc SVic
	'Amy Ruth'	CWVF
§	'Andenken an Heinrich Henkel' (T)	CLoc CWVF EBak SVic WOth
	'André Le Nostre' (d)	CWVF EBak SVic
	'Andreas Schwab'	LCla
	andrei	LCla
	'Andrew Carnegie' (d)	CLoc
	'Andrew Hadfield'	CWVF SVic WOth
	'Andromeda' De Groot	WOth
	'Angela King'	SLBF WOth
	'Angela Leslie' (d)	CLoc EBak SVic
	'Angela Rippon'	CWVF MJac
	'Angel's Flight' (d)	EBak
	'Angel's Kiss' (E)	CDoC LCla SLBF
	'Angie'	WOth
	'Angie Baby'	WOth
	'Anhaltiner'	WOth
	'Anita' (d)	CDoC CLoc CWVF EPts LAst MJac SLBF SVic WOth
	'Anjo' (v)	CWVF
	'Ann Allen' **new**	SLBF
	'Ann Howard Tripp'	CLoc CWVF EPts MJac SVic
	'Anna Louise'	WOth
	'Anna of Longleat' (d)	CWVF LAst MJac
	'Anna Sunshine' (T) **new**	WOth
	'Annabel' (d) 🏆H4	CDoC CLoc CTri CWVF EBak EPts LAst LCla MJac SLBF SVic
	'Anneke de Keijzer'	CDoC LCla WOth
	'Annie den Otter'	WOth
	'Annie Earle'	WOth
	'Annie Geurts'	CDoC
	'Annie Hall' (E)	WOth
	'Annie M.G. Schmidt'	EPts LCla
	'Anniek Geerlings' (T)	WOth
	'Ant and Dec' (d/v)	MJac
	'Anthea Day' (d)	CLoc
	'Antigone'	SLBF WOth
	'Apart'	WOth
	'Aphrodite' (d)	CLoc CWVF
	'Applause' (d)	CLoc CWVF EBak EPts SVic
	aprica misapplied	see *F.* × *bacillaris*
	aprica Lundell	see *F. microphylla* subsp. *aprica*
	'Apricot Ice'	CLoc SVic
	'Arabella'	CWVF
	'Arabella Improved'	CWVF SVic
	arborea	see *F. arborescens*
§	***arborescens***	CBcs CBot CDoC CHll CLoc CWCL CWVF EBak EWld IDee LCla MCot MHer SDys SVic WHil WJek
	- B&SWJ 10475	WCru
	'Arcadia Gold' (d)	CWVF WOth
	'Arcady'	CLoc CWVF
	'Arels Nina'	WOth
	'Arels Tojo' **new**	WOth
	'Ariel' (E)	CDoC LRHS SVic WOth
	'Arkie'	MJac
	'Arlendon' (d)	CWVF
	'Army Nurse' (d) 🏆H4	CDoC CLoc COtt CWCL CWVF ELan ELon EPfP EPts LRHS MBri MGos MSmi NBir NLar SEND SHil SLBF SVic WOth
	'Ashley'	CDoC LCla
	'Ashley and Isobel'	CWVF
	'Ashtede'	SLBF
	'Ashville'	SLBF WOth
	'Atahualpa' (T)	CDoC WOth
	'Atlantic Star'	CWVF MJac
	'Atlantis' (d)	CWVF
	'Atomic Glow' (d)	SVic
	'Aubergine'	see *F.* 'Gerharda's Aubergine'
	'Audrey Hepburn'	CWVF
	'Auenland'	MJac
	'Auntie Jinks' 🏆H2	CDoC CWVF EBak LAst MJac SVic WOth
	'Aurora Superba'	CLoc CWVF EBak SLBF
	'Australia Fair' (d)	CWVF
	'Autumnale' 🏆H2	CDoC CLoc CWVF EBak EPts LAst MSmi SLBF SPoG SVic WOth
	'Avalanche' ambig. (d)	CDoC CLoc EBak SLBF
	'Avalanche' Henderson (d)	WOth
	'Avocet'	CLoc
	'Avon Celebration' (d)	CLoc WOth
	'Avon Gem'	CLoc
	'Avon Glow' (d)	CLoc
	'Avon Gold'	CLoc
	'Awake Sweet Love' (T)	EPts WOth
	ayavacensis	LCla
	'Aylisa Rowan' (E)	SLBF
	'Azure Sky' (d)	MJac
	'Baby Blue Eyes' 🏆H4	CDoC CLoc CWVF ELan ELon EPfP LAst LRHS LSRN MAsh SVic WOth
	'Baby Bright'	CWVF LCla
	'Baby Brooke'	WOth

	Name	Suppliers
	'Baby Chang'	WOth
	'Baby Pink' (d)	CWVF
	'Baby Thumb' (v)	EPts
	'Babyface' Tolley (d)	SVic
§	× ***bacillaris*** (E)	CAbb CHGN EWes GCal IDee LRHS SLBF SPoG
§	– 'Cottinghamii' (E)	CDoC EWld ILea SPlb WOth WSHC
§	– 'Reflexa' (E)	CAbP LSou WOth
	'Baden Powell' (E)	SVic
	'Bagworthy Water'	CLoc
	'Baker's Tri' (T)	EBak
	'Balkonkönigin'	CLoc CWVF
	'Ballerina Dreams'	LAst
	'Ballerina Girl' (E)	SLBF
	'Ballet Girl' (d) ♀H2	CLoc CWVF EBak SLBF
	'Bambini'	CWVF EPts
	'Banks Peninsula'	GBin GQui
	'Barbara'	CLoc CWVF EBak EPts LCla MJac SVic
	'Barbara Evans'	SLBF
	'Barbara Norton'	CDoC
	'Barbara Pountain' (d)	CWVF
	'Barbara Reynolds'	WOth
	'Barbara Windsor'	CWVF MJac
	'Barry's Queen'	see *F.* 'Golden Border Queen'
	'Bartje'	SLBF
	'Bashful' (d)	CDoC EPts LCla SVic
	'Beacon'	CDoC CLoc CMac COtt CWVF EBak EPfP EPts LAst LCla LRHS MJac MLHP SLBF SPoG SVic
	'Beacon Rosa' ♀H4	CLoc CWVF ELon EPfP EPts LAst LCla LRHS MJac SLBF SPoG SVic
	'Bealings' (d)	CWVF SVic
	'Beauty of Bath' (d)	CLoc
	'Beauty of Clyffe Hall' Lye	CDoC EBak WOth
	'Beauty of Exeter' (d)	CWVF EBak WOth
	'Beauty of Meise' (d)	CDoC
	'Beauty of Prussia' (d)	CLoc CWVF
	'Beauty of Purbeck' (d)	WOth
	'Beauty of Swanley'	WOth
	'Beauty of Trowbridge'	CWVF LCla WOth
	'Beckie Lou'^{PBR} **new**	EBee
	'Beebop' **new**	MSmi
	'Belinda Jane'	WOth
	'Bella Forbes' (d) ♀H2	MSmi
	'Bella Rosella' (California Dreamers Series) (d) ♀H2	CDoC CLoc EPts LAst MJac MSmi SCoo SLBF
	'Belsay Beauty' (d)	CWVF MJac
	'Belvoir Beauty' (d)	CLoc
	'Ben de Jong'	LCla SLBF
	'Ben Jammin'	CLoc CWVF EPfP EPts LRHS SEND SVic
	'Ben-Ben'	SLBF
	'Beninkust'	WOth
	'Berba's Happiness' (d)	CWVF
	'Berba's Trio'	WOth
	'Berliner Kind' (d)	CWVF EBak
	'Bermuda' (d)	CWVF
	'Bernadette' (d)	CWVF
	'Bernie's Big-un' (d)	MJac
	'Bernisser Hardy' ♀H4	EPts LCla SLBF SLim WOth XLum
	'Beryl Clarke' (v)	EPts
	'Bessie Girl'	CDoC
	'Bessie Kimberley' (T)	LCla
	'Beth Robley' (d)	CWVF
	'Betsy Huuskes'	SLBF
	Betty = 'Shabetty'^{PBR} (Shadowdancer Series)	LAst
	'Beverley'	CWVF EBak EPts
	'Beverly Hills' (d) **new**	WOth
	'Bianca' (d)	CWVF SVic
	'Bicentennial' (d)	CLoc CWVF EBak EPts LAst MJac MSmi SVic
	'Big Slim'	WOth
	'Billy'^{PBR}	CDoC
	'Billy Green' (T) ♀H2	CDoC CLoc CWVF EBak EPts LCla MHer MJac SVic
	'Billy P'	LAst
	'Bishop's Bells' (d)	CWVF SVic
	'Bittersweet' (d)	SVic
	'Black Beauty' (d)	CWVF
	'Black Country 21'	WOth
	'Black Prince'	CDoC CWVF SVic WOth
	'Black to the Future'	WOth
	'Blackmore Vale' (d)	CWVF
	'Blacky' (d)	CDoC EBak EUJe GBin LAst MSCN SDix SDys SEND SVic
I	'Blanche Regina' (d)	CWVF MJac
	'Bland's New Striped'	CDoC EBak EPts LSou SLBF WOth
	'Blauer Engel'	WOth
	'Blaze Away' (d)	LAst MJac
	'Blood Donor' (d)	MJac
	'Blowick'	CWVF MJac WOth
	'Blue Angel' (d)	LAst MJac
	'Blue Bush'	CWVF EPts MJac SVic WOth
	'Blue Butterfly' (d)	CWVF WOth
	'Blue Eyes' (d)	CDoC
	'Blue Gown' (d)	CDoC CLoc CWVF EBak SVic
	'Blue Lace' (d)	CDoC SVic
	'Blue Lagoon' ambig. (d)	CWVF
	'Blue Lake' (d)	CWVF
	'Blue Mirage' (d)	CLoc CWVF LAst SVic
	'Blue Pearl' (d)	CWVF EBak
	'Blue Pinwheel'	CWVF EBak
	'Blue Satin' (d)	LAst WOth
	'Blue Sleighbells'	WOth
	'Blue Tit'	LCla
	'Blue Veil' (d)	CLoc CWVF MJac SCoo SVic WOth
	'Blue Waves' (d)	CLoc CSBt CWVF EBak MJac SVic
	'Blush o' Dawn' (d)	CLoc CWVF EBak SVic
	'Bob Bartrum'	EPts
	'Bob Pacey'	CWVF
	'Bobby Dazzler' (d)	CWVF
	'Bobby Shaftoe' (d)	EBak
	'Bobby Wingrove'	EBak
	'Bobby's Girl'	EPts
	'Bobolink' (d)	EBak
	'Bob's Best' (d)	CWVF EPts MJac
	boliviana Britton	see *F. sanctae-rosae*
	boliviana ambig.	CBcs MHer
§	***boliviana*** Carrière	CDoC CHll CLoc CWVF LCla WOth
§	– var. ***alba*** ♀H2	CDoC CHll CLoc EBak EPts LCla SVic WOth
	– var. ***boliviana***	CRHN SVic
	– var. ***luxurians*** 'Alba'	see *F. boliviana* Carrière var. *alba*
	– f. ***puberulenta*** Munz	see *F. boliviana* Carrière
	'Bon Accorde'	CLoc CWVF EBak EPts SLBF
	'Bon Bon' (d)	CWVF SVic
	'Bonita' (d)	CWVF SVic
	'Bonnie Lass' (d)	EBak
	'Boogie' **new**	MSmi
	'Bora Bora' (d)	CWVF SVic
	'Borde Hill' (d)	EPts
	'Border Princess'	EBak
	'Border Queen' ♀H4	CLoc CWVF EBak EPts MJac MSCN SLBF SVic WOth
	'Border Raider'	WOth
	'Border Reiver'	CWVF SVic
	'Börnemann's Beste'	see *F.* 'Georg Börnemann'

'Bouffant'	CLoc SVic
'Bountiful' Munkner (d)	CLoc CWVF
'Bow Bells'	CDoC CLoc CWVF MJac SVic WOth
'Boy Marc' (T) ♀H1c	CDoC LCla
'Brandt's 500 Club'	CLoc
'Breckland'	EBak
'Breeders' Delight'	CWVF
'Breeder's Dream' (d)	EBak
'Breevis Minimus'	SLBF
'Brenda' (d)	CWVF
'Brenda White'	CLoc CWVF EBak SVic WOth
'Brian C. Morrison' (T)	LCla
'Brian G. Soanes'	EBak
'Brian Kimberley' (T)	LCla
'Brian McFetridge' (d)	WOth
'Bridesmaid' (d)	CWVF EBak SVic
'Brighton Belle' (T)	CDoC CWVF
'Brilliant' ambig.	COtt CWVF
'Brilliant' Bull, 1865	CLoc EBak LCla
'British Jubilee' (d)	CWVF SVic WOth
'British Sterling' (d)	WOth
'Brixham Orpheus'	CWVF
'Bronze Banks Peninsula'	CDoC
'Brookwood Belle' (d) ♀H3	CWVF EPts LCla MJac SLBF
'Brookwood Joy' (d)	CWVF
'Brutus' ♀H4	CDoC CLet CLoc CWVF EBak EPfP EPts LRHS MAsh SCoo SLBF SVic WFar WOth
'Bryan Breary' (E)	LCla WOth
'Buddha' (d)	EBak
'Bugle Boy'	CDoC LCla
'Bunny' (d)	CWVF SVic
'Burgundy Velvet'	WOth
'Buster' (d)	LCla
'Buttercup'	CLoc CWVF SVic
'Butterfly Dance'	WOth
'C.J. Howlett'	EBak
'Caesar' (d)	CWVF EBak
'Caledonia'	CDoC WOth
'Callaly Pink'	CWVF
'Calverley' **new**	WOth
'Cambridge Louie'	CWVF EBak WOth
campos-portoi	CDoC CFil LCla MGil WPGP
'Candy Bells' (d)	CSBt
canescens misapplied	see *F. ampliata*
'Canny Bob'	MJac WOth
'Canopy' (d)	CWVF
'Cape Cornwall'	CDoC
'Capri' (d)	CWVF
'Cara Mia' (d)	CDoC CLoc
'Caradela' (d)	CLoc MJac
'Cardinal'	CLoc
'Cardinal Farges' (d)	CDoC CLoc CWVF SLBF SVic
'Careless Whisper'	CDoC LCla SLBF
'Carl Drude' (d)	SVic
'Carla Johnston' ♀H2	CLoc CWVF EPts MJac SVic
'Carl's Brummagem Beauty'	MJac
'Carmel Blue'	CDoC CLoc LAst LCla SVic
'Carmen' Lemoine (d)	CDoC
'Carnea'	CWib
'Carnoustie' (d)	EBak
'Carol Grace' (d)	CLoc
'Carol Nash' (d)	CLoc
'Caroline'	CLoc CWVF EBak EPts SVic WOth
'Caroline's Joy'	MJac SCoo
'Cascade'	CLoc CWVF EPts MJac SLBF
'Caspar Hauser' (d)	CWVF SLBF SVic
'Catharina' (T)	CDoC
'Catherine Bartlett'	CWVF
'Cecil Glass'	WOth
'Cecile' (d)	CWVF EPts LAst LCla MJac MSmi SLBF SVic
'Celadore' (d)	CWVF
'Celebration' (d)	CLoc CWVF
'Celia Smedley' ♀H3	CDoC CLoc CWVF EBak EPts LAst LCla LRHS MJac SLBF SVic WBod WOth
'Celtic Beauty'	CDoC
'Centerpiece' (d)	EBak
'Ceri'	CLoc
'Cerrig'	SVic
'Champagne Celebration'	CLoc WOth
'Champion'	XLum
'Chancellor' (d)	CWVF
'Chandleri'	CWVF SVic
'Chang' ♀H2	CDoC CLoc CWVF EBak LCla SLBF SVic WOth
'Chantelle Garcia' (d)	CDoC EPts SLBF
'Chantry Park' (T)	LCla
'Chapel Rossan' (E)	SLBF
'Charisma'	SVic
'Charles Edward' (d)	CDoC
'Charles Welch'	EPts
Charlie Dimmock = 'Foncha'PBR (d)	CLoc
'Charlie Gardiner'	CWVF EBak
'Charlie Girl' (d)	SVic
'Charming'	CDoC CLoc CWVF LRHS MAsh MJac SVic WOth
'Chartwell'	WOth
'Chatt's Delight'	SLBF
'Checkerboard' ♀H3	CDoC CLoc CWVF EBak EPts LAst LCla MHer MJac SLBF SVic WOth
'Cheers' (d)	CWVF
'Chelsea Louise'	EPts
'Chenois Godelieve'	CDoC
'Cherry Lee'	SLBF WOth
'Cherry Pie'	CDoC
'Chessboard'	CLoc
'Chillerton Beauty' ♀H4	CDoC CLoc CTri CWVF ELan ELon EPts LCla LRHS MJac NLar SEND SLBF SPer SVic WMnd WOth
'Chilli Red'	EPts
'China Doll' (d)	CWVF
'China Lantern'	CLoc CWVF SVic
'Chor Echo'	CDoC WOth
'Chris Bright'	MJac
'Chris Tarrant' (d)	EPts
'Christina Becker'	SVic
'Christine Bamford'	CDoC CWVF
'Christmas Ribbons' (d)	MSmi
'Churchtown'	CWVF
cinerea	LCla
'Cinnabarina' (E)	CLoc SVic WOth
'Cinque Port Liberty' (d)	SLBF
'Cinvenu'	LCla
'Cinvulca'	LCla
'Circe' (d)	CWVF
'Circus Spangles' (d)	CLoc
'Citation'	CLoc CWVF EBak SVic
'City of Adelaide' (d)	CLoc
'City of Leicester'	CWVF
'Clair de Lune'	CWVF EBak SVic
'Claire Oram'	CLoc
'Claudia' (d)	LAst LCla MJac SLBF
'Cliantha' (d)	CDoC
'Cliff's Hardy'	CDoC LCla MSmi SVic
'Cliff's Own'	SVic
'Cliff's Unique' (d)	CWVF EPts
'Clifton Beauty' (d)	CWVF MJac

'Clifton Belle' (d)	CWVF
'Clifton Charm'	EPts LCla MJac SVic
'Clipper'	CWVF WOth
'Cloth of Gold'	CLoc CWVF EBak MJac SVic
'Cloverdale Jewel' (d)	CWVF SVic WOth
'Cloverdale Pearl'	CDoC CWVF EBak SPoG SVic WOth
'Coachman' ♀H4	CLoc CWVF EBak EPts LAst LCla SLBF SVic WOth
coccinea	CDoC CTsd EWld WOth
× ***colensoi***	CDoC ECou LCla
* - var. ***purpurascens***	WOth
'Collingwood' (d)	CLoc CWVF WOth
'Come Dancing' (d)	CWVF SVic
'Comet' Banks	CWVF
I 'Comet' Tiret (d)	CLoc
'Comperen Lutea' (d)	CDoC
'Conchetta Garcia'	SLBF
'Connie' (d)	EBak SVic
'Connor's Cascade'	SLBF
'Conspicua' ♀H4	CDoC CWVF ELon SLBF SVic WOth
'Constable Country' (d)	CWVF
'Constance' (d)	CDoC CLoc CWVF LCla MJac SLBF SVic WOth
'Constance Comer'	MJac
'Constellation' ambig.	CWVF
'Constellation' Schnabel, 1957 (d)	CLoc EBak
'Coombe Park'	MJac
'Coquet Bell'	CWVF EBak
'Coquet Dale' (d)	CWVF
'Coral Baby' (E)	LCla SLBF
'Coral Rose' (d)	SVic
'Coralle' (T) ♀H1c	CDoC CLoc CWVF EBak EPts LAst LCla MHer MJac MSmi SLBF SVic WOth
'Corallina' ♀H4	CDoC CLoc MMuc SEND SVic WOth WPnn
I 'Corallina Variegata' (v)	WOth
* ***cordata*** B&SWJ 9095	WCru
- B&SWJ 10325	WCru
cordifolia misapplied	see *F. splendens*
'Core'ngrato' (d)	CLoc CWVF
'Cornelia Smith' (T)	CDoC LCla
'Cornwall Calls' (d)	EBak
'Coronation' (d) **new**	WOth
'Corsage' (d)	CWVF SVic
'Corsair' (d)	EBak SVic
corymbiflora misapplied	see *F. boliviana* Carrière
corymbiflora Ruíz & Pav.	CDoC SVic
'Costa Brava'	CLoc
'Cotta Bright Star'	CDoC CWVF LCla
'Cotta Carousel'	LCla
'Cotta Christmas Tree'	CDoC LCla SLBF
'Cotta Fairy'	CWVF
'Cotta Vino'	SVic
'Cottinghamii'	see *F.* × *bacillaris* 'Cottinghamii'
'Cotton Candy' (d)	CLoc CWVF SVic
'Countdown Carol' (d)	EPts
'Countess of Aberdeen'	CWVF EBak SLBF WOth
'Countess of Maritza' (d)	CLoc CWVF
'Court Jester' (d)	CLoc
'Cover Girl' (d)	EPts
'Coxeen'	EBak WOth
'Crackerjack'	CLoc
'Crescendo' (d)	CLoc CWVF
'Crinkley Bottom' (d)	EPts MJac SLBF
'Crosby Serendipity'	CLoc
'Crosby Soroptimist'	CWVF MJac WOth
'Cross Check'	CWVF
'Crusader' (d)	CWVF
'Crystal Blue'	EBak SVic
'Crystal Stars' (d)	SVic
'Cumbrian Lass'	WOth
'Cupid'	EBak
'Curly Q'	EBak SVic
'Curtain Call' (d)	CWVF EBak SVic
cylindracea misapplied	see *F.* × *bacillaris*
'Cymon' (d)	CWVF
'Cymru' (d)	SVic
'Dainty'	EBak
'Dainty Lady' (d)	EBak WOth
'Daisy Bell'	CLoc CWVF EBak LCla MJac SVic WOth
'Dana Samantha'	EPts
'Dancing Bloom'	EPts
'Dancing Flame' (d) ♀H3	CDoC CLoc CWVF EBak EPts LAst LCla MJac SLBF SVic
'Daniel Pfaller' (d)	MJac
'Danish Pastry'	CDoC CWVF
'Danny Boy' (d)	CLoc CWVF EBak SVic
'Dark and Delicious' (Mojo Series)	WOth
'Dark Eyes' (d) ♀H4	CLoc CWVF EBak LAst MJac SLBF SPer SVic WOth
'Dark Mystery' (d)	WOth
'Dark Secret' (d)	EBak
'Dark Treasure' (d)	CDoC
'Daryn John Woods'	CDoC LCla WOth
'David' ♀H4	CDoC CLoc CSde CWVF ELon EPfP EPts LAst LCla LSRN MJac SEND SLBF SPoG WHil WOth
'David Alston' (d)	CLoc CWVF
'David Lockyer' (d)	CLoc CWVF SVic
'David Savage' (d)	LCla
'Dawn Fantasia' (v)	CLoc EPts
'Dawn Redfern' (d)	CWVF
'Dawn Star' (d)	CLoc CWVF SVic WOth
'Dawn Thunder' (d)	SVic
'De Groot's Dream'	WOth
'De Groot's Floriant'	LCla
'De Mijnlamp' (d)	CDoC
'Debby' (d)	EBak
'Deben Petite' (E)	LCla
'Deborah Jane'	SLBF
'Deborah Street' (d)	CLoc
'DebRon's Beau Dean Richard' **new**	WOth
'DebRon's Black Cherry'	SLBF
'DebRon's Party Girls' **new**	WOth
'DebRon's Snow Fairy' **new**	WOth
'DebRon's Tonii Nicole' (d) **new**	WOth
'DebRon's White Linen' (d) **new**	WOth
'Dee Copley' (d)	EBak
'Deep Purple' (d)	CLoc LAst MJac SCoo SLBF
'Delia Smith' (d)	EPts
'Delicate Purple'	EPts
'Delilah' (d)	CWVF
'Delphobe'	EPts WOth
'Delta's Bride'	SLBF
'Delta's Dream'	CWVF WOth
'Delta's Drop'	SVic
'Delta's Fellow'	WOth
'Delta's Groom'	LCla SLBF
'Delta's Ko' (d)	SVic
'Delta's Parade' (d)	CDoC WOth

Name	Suppliers
'Delta's Sara'	CDoC COtt EPfP IDee LAst LBuc LCro LRHS MBri MJac SHil SLim SLon SPoG WFar WHar
'Delta's Symphonie' (d)	CWVF
'Delta's Wonder'	SVic
§ ***denticulata*** ♀H2	CBot CDoC CLoc CWVF EBak EPts LCla LRHS MHer SLBF SVic WBod WOth
'Derby Imp'	CWVF
'Desperate Daniel'	EPts
'Deutsche Perle'	WOth
'Devonshire Dumpling' (d) ♀H2	CDoC CLoc CWVF EBak EPts LAst MJac MSmi SLBF SVic
'Dharlah' (T)	WOth
'Diablo' (d)	EBak
'Diamond Celebration' (d)	WOth
'Diamond Wedding'	SVic WOth
'Diana Wills' (d)	CWVF
'Diana Wright'	CDoC
Diana, Princess of Wales = 'Fucdpw'PBR	LAst
'Diane Brown'	CWVF
'Diane Stephens'	SLBF
'Didi' (d)	WOth
§ 'Die Schöne Wilhelmine'	CDoC SVic
'Dilly-Dilly' (d)	CWVF
'Dipton Dainty' (d)	CLoc EBak SVic
'Display' ♀H4	CLoc COtt CWVF EBak EPfP EPts LAst LCla LRHS MAsh MBri MGos MJac NPer SHil SLBF SPoG SVic WHar
'Diva' **new**	WCot
'Doc'	CDoC EPts SVic
'Docteur Topinard'	CLoc
'Doctor'	see *F.* 'The Doctor'
'Doctor Foster' ♀H4	CDoC CLoc CTri EBak SPoG SVic
'Doctor Mason'	CWVF
'Doctor Olson' (d)	CLoc
'Doctor Robert'	CWVF EPts MJac
'Dodo'	LCla SLBF
'Doffie'	WOth
§ 'Dollar Prinzessin' (d) ♀H4	CDoC CLoc CMac COtt CWVF EBak EPfP EPts EShb LAst LCla LPfy LRHS MAsh MBri MGos MJac MLHP NPer SHil SLBF SLim SPlb SVic WFar
'Dominyana'	CDoC EBak LCla
'Dopy' (d)	EPts SVic
'Doray'	CDoC EPts WOth
'Doreen Redfern'	CLoc CWVF MJac SVic
'Doreen Stroud' (d)	CWVF
'Doris Joan'	SLBF
'Dorothea Flower'	CLoc CWVF EBak WOth
'Dorothy'	EPts LCla SLBF
'Dorothy Ann'	LCla SLBF
'Dorothy Cheal'	CWVF
'Dorothy Day' (d)	CLoc
'Dorothy Hanley' (d)	CDoC CLoc EPts LAst LRHS LSou MAsh MJac SLBF SVic WOth
'Dorothy Oosting' (d)	CDoC
'Dorothy Shields' (d)	CWVF MJac WOth
'Dorrian Brogdale' (T)	LCla
'Dorset Abigail'	CWVF
'Dorset Delight' (d)	CWVF
'Drake 400' (d)	CLoc
'Drama Girl' (d)	CWVF
'Drame' (d)	CDoC CWVF EBak SVic WHea
'Duchess of Albany'	CLoc WOth
'Duchess of Cornwall' (d)	EPts
'Duet' (d)	SVic
'Duke of Wellington' Haag, 1956 (d)	CLoc
'Dulcie Elizabeth' (d)	CWVF EBak MJac
'Dusky Beauty'	CWVF SVic
'Dusky Rose' (d)	CLoc CWVF EBak MJac SVic
'Dutch Kingsize'	WOth
'Dutch Mill'	CLoc CWVF EBak
'Duyfken'	CWVF
'Dying Embers'	CDoC CLoc MHer MSCN SVen WOth
'Dymph Werker van Groenland' (E)	LCla
'Earre Barré'	WOth
'East Anglian'	CLoc WOth
'Easter Belle'	LRHS
'Easter Bonnet' (d)	CLoc CWVF
'Ebb 'n' Flow'	EBak
'Ebbtide' (d)	CLoc
'Echo'	CWVF WOth
'Ed Largarde' (d)	EBak
'Eden Lady'	CLoc
'Eden Princess'	CWVF MJac
'Eden Rock' (d)	CLoc WOth
'Edith' ambig.	EPts
'Edith' Brown (d)	LCla SLBF
'Edna May'	CWVF
'Edna W. Smith'	CWVF
'El Camino' (d)	CWVF
'El Cid'	CLoc EBak SVic
'Elaine Ann'	EPts MJac
'Elaine Taylor' (d)	MJac
'Eleanor Clark'	WOth
'Eleanor Grace'	WOth
'Eleanor Leytham'	CWVF EBak SVic WOth
Electric Lights = 'Nufu1'PBR **new**	EPts
'Elfin Glade'	CLoc CWVF EBak SVic
'Elfrida' (d)	CDoC
'Elfriede Ott' (T) ♀H1c	CLoc EBak LCla
'Elizabeth' ambig.	WOth
'Elizabeth Honnorine'	SVic
'Ellebel'PBR **new**	LAst
'Ellen Morgan' (d)	CWVF
'Elma'	LCla MJac
'Elsa' (d)	CWVF SVic
'Elsie Mitchell' (d)	CWVF
§ 'Emile de Wildeman' (d)	CWVF
'Emily'	WOth
'Emily Austen'	CWVF
'Emma Alice' (d)	CWVF
'Emma Louise' (d)	WOth
'Empress of Prussia' ♀H4	CDoC CLoc CWVF EBak EPts MSmi SLBF SVic WOth
'Enchanted' (d)	CWVF
encliandra subsp. ***encliandra*** (E)	CDoC
§ 'Enfant Prodigue' (d)	CLoc SDix SLBF SVic
'English Rose' (d)	CWVF
'Enstone'	see *F. magellanica* var. *molinae* 'Enstone'
'Eric's Hardy' (d)	CDoC
'Eric's Majestic' (d)	MJac
'Erik'	WOth
'Erika Köth' (T)	WOth
'Erna van Wiele'	CDoC
'Ernest Rankin'	SVic
'Ernie'PBR	CDoC EPts LAst SLBF WOth
'Ernie Bromley'	CWVF WOth
'Ernie Wise' (d)	MJac SCoo
'Eroica'	SVic

'Eruption'	CDoC CLoc LAst MCot
'Estelle Marie'	CLoc CWVF EBak SVic
'Eternal Flame' (d)	CWVF EBak EPts SVic
'Ethel May' (d)	MJac
'Eusebia' (d)	SVic
'Eva Boerg' ♀H4	CLoc CTri CWVF EBak LAst SVic WKif
'Evelyn Stanley' (d)	CWVF
'Evensong'	CLoc CWVF EBak SVic
excorticata	CBcs CDoC CExl CTsd ECre GBin IDee LRHS MCot SPlb
'Fabian Franck' (T)	LCla
'Fairy Lavender'	LAst
'Falklands' (d)	EPts SLBF
'Falling Stars'	CLoc CWVF SVic
'Falmouth'	CDoC
'Fancy Pants' (d)	CLoc CWVF SVic
'Fanfare'	CDoC LCla SVic
'Fascination'	see *F.* 'Emile de Wildeman'
'Felicity Kendal' (d)	SCoo
'Feltham's Pride'	CWVF
'Fenman'	CWVF SVic
'Festival Lights' (E)	SLBF
'Fey' (d)	CWVF
'Ffion'	CDoC EPts WOth
'Fiery Spider'	EBak SVic
'Finn'	CDoC CWVF EPts
'Fiona'	CLoc CWVF EBak SVic WOth
'Fiona Pitt' (E)	WOth
'Fiorelli Flowers' (d)	CDoC
'Fire Mountain' (d)	CLoc SVic
'Firecracker'	see *F.* 'John Ridding'
'Firefly'	SVic
'Firelite' (d)	EBak
'Firenza' (d)	CWVF
'First Kiss' (d)	CWVF
'First Lady' (d)	CWVF
'First Lord'	CWVF
'First Success' (E)	CDoC CWVF LCla SVic WOth
'Flair' (d)	CLoc CWVF WOth
'Flamenco Dancer' (California Dreamers Series) (d)	CLoc LAst
'Flamingo' (d)	SVic
'Flamingo Wings' (d) **new**	EPts
'Flash' ♀H4	CLoc CTri CWVF ELan EPts LCla MJac MRav SLBF SPoG SVic WOth
'Flashlight'	CDoC CWVF EWld LAst LCla MHtn MJac SCoo WOth
'Flat Jack o' Lancashire' (d)	CDoC SLBF
'Fleur de Picardie'	SLBF
'Flirtation Waltz' (d)	CLoc CWVF EBak MJac SVic
'Flogman'	LCla
'Floral City' (d)	CLoc
'Florence Taylor' (d)	CWVF
'Florence Turner'	EBak WOth
'Florentina' (d)	CLoc CWVF EBak SVic
'Florrie's Gem' (d)	SLBF
'Flowerdream' (d)	CWVF
'Fly-by-night' (d)	CWVF
'Flying Cloud' (d)	CDoC CLoc CWVF EBak LAst SVic WOth
'Flying Scotsman' (d)	CLoc CWVF EBak EPts SCoo SVic
'Fokkos Katrientje'	WOth
'Folk' **new**	MSmi
'Foolke'	EBak
'Forget-me-not'	CLoc CWVF SVic WOth
'Fort Bragg' (d)	CWVF EBak
'Fountains Abbey' (d)	CWVF
'Four Farthings' (d)	EPts
'Foxgrove Wood' ♀H4	CWCL CWVF EBak ELon EPts SLBF WOth
'Foxtrot' (d)	CWVF
'Foxy Lady' (d)	CWVF MTis
'Frances Haskins'	WOth
'Frank Saunders'	CWVF LCla SLBF
'Frank Unsworth' (d)	CWVF EPts MJac
'Frankfurt 2006'	MJac
'Frankie's Magnificent Seven' (d)	EPts
'Franz von Zon'	LCla SLBF
'Frau Hilde Rademacher' (d)	CWVF EBak EPts SLBF SVic
'Frauke'	SVic
'Fred Hansford'	CDoC CWVF WOth
'Fred Swales' (T)	WOth
'Fred's First' (d)	SVic
'Friendly Fire' (d)	CLoc
'Frosted Flame'	CLoc CWVF LAst LCla MJac SLBF
'Frozen Tears'	EPts WOth
'Frühling' (d)	EBak
'Fuchsiade '88'	CLoc CWVF SLBF
'Fuchsiarama '91' (T) ♀H2	CDoC CWVF
'Fuji-san'	ELon EPts
'Fuksie Foetsie' (E)	CDoC WOth
fulgens (T) ♀H2	CDoC GCal LCla
* - 'Variegata' (T/v)	CDoC CLoc EPts LCla WOth
'Fulpila'	CDoC LCla SLBF
'Funk' **new**	MSmi
'Gala' (d)	EBak
'Galadriel'	CDoC WOth
'Garden News' (d) ♀H4	CDoC CLoc COtt CWCL CWVF EPfP EPts LAst LCla LRHS MAsh MBri MJac MLHP MSmi NGBl NPer SHil SLBF SPer SVic WFar WHar
'Garden Week' (d)	CDoC CWVF SVic
'Gartenmeister Bonstedt' (T) ♀H1c	CLoc CWVF EWld LCla SVic
'Gary Rhodes' (d)	EBak SCoo
'Gay Anne' (d)	WOth
'Gay Fandango' (d)	CLoc CWVF
'Gay Future'	WOth
'Gay Parasol' (d)	LAst MJac
'Gay Señorita'	EBak
'Gay Spinner' (d)	CLoc
'Gemma Fisher' (d)	EPts
Gene = 'Goetzgene' PBR (Shadowdancer Series)	LAst SCoo
'Général Monk' (d)	CDoC CWVF EBak EPts LAst SVic WOth
'General Wavell' (d)	SVic
'Genii' ♀H4	Widely available
'Geoff Amos' (d)	MSmi
'Geoff Oke'	CDoC SLBF WOth
'Geoffrey Smith' (d)	EPts
§ 'Georg Börnemann' (T) ♀H2	CLoc EBak MJac WOth
'George Allen White' (d)	CWVF
'George Barr'	CDoC LRHS
'George Johnson'	CDoC
'Georges Remy'	WOth
§ 'Gerharda's Aubergine'	CLoc CWVF
'Gerharda's Katja'	CDoC
'Gesneriana'	CLoc EBak
'Ghislaine' (d)	CDoC
'Giant Pink Enchanted' (d)	CLoc
'Gilda' (d)	CWVF MJac SVic
'Gillian Althea' (d)	CWVF
'Gilt Edge' (v)	CLoc
I 'Gina'	WOth
'Gina Bowman' (E)	EPts LCla SLBF

	Name	Suppliers
	Ginger = 'Goetzginger'^{PBR} (Shadowdancer Series)	LAst LSou SCoo
	'Gipsy Princess' (d)	CLoc
	'Girls' Brigade'	CWVF
	'Gladiator' (d)	CMac EBak SVic WOth
	'Gladys Lorimer'	CDoC CWVF EPts LRHS WOth
	'Gladys Miller'	CLoc
	glazioviana ♀^{H2}	CDoC CSde CWVF EPts GCal LCla LHop MHer SLBF SVen WOth
	'Glenby' (d)	CWVF
	'Glendale'	CWVF WOth
	'Glitters'	CWVF EBak
§	'Globosa'	CAgr
	'Glow'	WOth
	'Glowing Embers'	EBak
	'Glowing Lilac' (d)	EPts
	'Gold Brocade'	ELan
	'Gold Leaf'	CWVF
	'Golden Anniversary' (d)	CLoc CWVF EBak MJac MSmi SVic
	'Golden Arrow' (T)	LCla SVic
§	'Golden Border Queen'	CLoc EBak
	'Golden Dawn'	CLoc CWVF SVic
	'Golden Girl'	SLBF
	'Golden Herald'	SLBF
	'Golden la Campanella' (d/v)	CDoC CLoc
	'Golden Lena' (d/v)	CWVF
	'Golden Marinka' (v) ♀^{H2}	CLoc EBak SVic
	'Golden Swingtime' (d)	MJac SVic
	'Golden Treasure' (v)	CLoc CWVF
	'Golden Vergeer' (v)	SLBF
	'Golondrina'	CWVF
	'Good Girl'	WOth
	'Goody Goody'	SVic
	'Gordon's China Rose'	LCla
	'Göttingen' (T)	WOth
	'Governor Pat Brown' (d)	EBak
	'Grace Bell'	CDoC
	'Grace Darling'	CDoC CWVF EBak
	gracilis	see *F. magellanica* var. *gracilis*
	'Graf Witte'	CWVF SVic
	'Granada' (d)	WOth
	'Grand Duke' (T/d)	CWVF
	'Grand Prix' (d)	SVic
	'Grandad Fred' (d)	SLBF
	'Grandad Hobbs' (d)	LCla SLBF
	'Grandma Sinton' (d)	CLoc CWVF
	'Grandpa Jack' (d)	SLBF
	'Granny Charlton'	WCFE
	'Grasmere'	WOth
	'Grayrigg'	CDoC ELon EPts LCla LSRN SLBF WOth
	'Great Ouse' (d)	EPts
	'Great Scott' (d)	CLoc
	'Green 'n' Gold'	EBak
	'Greenpeace'	SLBF SVic
	'Greta' (T)	CDoC
	'Grey Lady' (d)	SVic
	'Gris'	WOth
	'Groene Kan's Glorie'	SVic
	'Grumpy'	CWVF EPts SVic WOth
	'Gruss aus dem Bodethal'	CLoc CWVF EBak EPts SLBF
	'Guinevere'	CWVF
	'Gunar Reich' (d)	WOth
	'Gustave Doré' (d)	EBak
	'Guy-Ann Mannens'	CDoC
	'Gwen Dodge'	SVic
	'Gypsy Girl' (d)	CWVF
	'H.G. Brown'	EBak
	'Hampshire Blue'	CDoC CWVF WOth
	'Hanna' (d)	LRHS
	'Hannah Amelia' **new**	MJac
	'Hannah Louise' (d)	EPts
	'Hans Callaars'	CDoC LCla
	'Happiness' (d)	SVic
	'Happy'	CDoC CWVF EPts LCla MSCN SVic
	'Happy Anniversary'	CLoc SVic WOth
	'Happy Fellow'	CDoC CLoc EBak WOth
	'Happy Wedding Day' (d)	CDoC CLoc CWVF EPts EShb LAst MJac MSmi SCoo SVic
	'Hapsburgh'	EBak
	'Harbour Lites'	SLBF
	'Harlow Car'	CDoC CWVF EPts WOth
	'Harlow Perfection'	CDoC
	'Harmony' Niederholzer, 1946	EBak
I	'Harmony' Tabraham	WOth
	'Harry Gray' (d) ♀^{H2}	CDoC CLoc CWVF EBak EPts LAst MJac SVic
	'Harry Lye'	WOth
	'Harry Taylor' (d)	EPts
	'Harry's Sunshine'	SLBF
	'Harti's Olivia'	CDoC
	hartwegii	CDoC LCla MHer
	'Harvey's Reward'	SLBF WOth
	'Hastings'	CDoC
	'Hathersage' (d)	EBak
	hatschbachii ♀^{H2}	CDoC CSde EWes GCal LCla MCot MHer SBrt SDix SLon SPlb SPoG SVen WHil WOth WPGP WPnn
	'Haute Cuisine' (d)	CLoc SVic
	'Hawaiian Sunset' (d)	CLoc CWVF EPts SLBF
	'Hawkshead' ♀^{H4}	Widely available
	'Hayley Jay' (d)	CDoC SLBF
	'Hazel' (d)	CWVF SVic WOth
	'Heidi Ann' (d) ♀^{H4}	CDoC CLoc CWVF EBak EPts LAst LRHS MAsh MRav SLBF SVic
	'Heidi Blue' (d)	SLBF
§	'Heidi Weiss' (d)	CLoc CWVF
	'Heinrich Henkel'	see *F.* 'Andenken an Heinrich Henkel'
	'Helen Clare' (d)	CLoc CWVF
	'Helen Gair' (d)	CWVF
	'Helen Storer'	MJac
	'Hellen Devine'	CWVF
	'Helston Flora' (d)	CDoC
	'Hemsleyana'	see *F. microphylla* subsp. *hemsleyana*
	'Hendrikje Stoffels' (d)	WOth
	'Henkelly's Chloris'	WOth
	'Henkelly's Gitano'	WOth
	'Henkelly's Hermine'	WOth
	'Henkelly's Trubia'	WOth
	'Henkelly's Vitalia' **new**	WOth
	'Henning Becker' ♀^{H3}	CDoC CWVF ELan ELon
	'Henri Poincaré'	EBak
	'Henrieke Dimi' (d)	CDoC
	'Henriette Ernst'	WOth
	'Herald' ♀^{H4}	CDoC CWCL CWVF EPfP LPfy LRHS LSou MBri MGos SHil SLBF SVic WOth
	'Herbé de Jacques'	see *F.* 'Mr West'
	'HeRi Asagi' **new**	WOth
	'HeRi Trevally'	WOth
	'Heritage' (d)	CLoc EBak
	'Herman de Graaff' (d)	SLBF
	'Hermiena'	CDoC CLoc CWVF EPts SLBF SVic WOth
	'Herps Bazuin'	WOth
	'Herps Buggy' **new**	WOth

'Herps Contrabas' **new**	WOth
'Herps Kipkar'	WOth
'Herps Martina'	WOth
'Herps Mignon' (d) **new**	WOth
'Herps Piccolo' **new**	WOth
'Herps Pierement'	SLBF
'Herps Schalmei'	WOth
'Herps Steekkar' **new**	WOth
'Herps Tamboerijn' **new**	WOth
'Herps Vierspan'	CDoC
'Hessett Festival' (d)	CWVF EBak
'Heston Blue' (d)	CWVF
'Hettenheuvel'	WOth
'Heydon'	CWVF
hidalgensis	see *F. microphylla* subsp. *hidalgensis*
'Hidcote Beauty' ♀H2	CLoc CWVF LCla SLBF SVic WOth
'Highland Pipes'	LCla SVic
'Hilary'	LAst
'Hilda May Salmon'	CWVF
'Hindu Belle'	EBak
'Hinnerike' (E)	CWVF LCla SVic
'Hiroshige' (T)	LCla
'Hobson's Choice' (d)	CWVF SLBF
'Holly's Beauty' (d)	CLoc EPts LAst
'Horsforth Beauty'	WOth
'Horsforth Dream'	WOth
'Horsforth in Bloom'	WOth
'Hot Coals'	CWVF EPts MJac SVic
'Howlett's Hardy' ♀H4	CDoC CLoc CWVF EBak SVic WMnd WOth
'Huet's Baraketh'	WOth
'Huet's Kwarts'	CDoC
'Huet's Turkoois'	CDoC
'Hula Girl' (d)	CWVF EBak MJac
'I Love You'	WOth
'Ian Storey'	CDoC LRHS
'Ice Cool' (d)	MSmi
'Iceberg'	CWVF EBak SVic
'Icecap'	CWVF SVic
'Iced Champagne'	CLoc CWVF EBak MJac
'Ichiban' (d)	CLoc
'Ida' (d)	EBak
'Igloo Maid' (d)	CLoc CWVF EBak SVic
'Imogen Faye' (d)	SLBF
'Impala' (d)	CWVF
'Imperial Fantasy' (d)	CWVF
'Impudence'	CLoc CWVF EBak
'Impulse' (d)	CLoc
'Independence' (d)	SVic
'Indian Maid' (d)	CWVF EBak
'Insetta' (d) **new**	WOth
'Insulinde' (T)	CWVF EPts LAst LCla MHer MJac SLBF
'Iolanthe' (T)	CWVF
'Irene L. Peartree' (d)	CWVF LCla
'Irene Sinton' (d)	CDoC MJac
'Iris Amer' (d)	CLoc CWVF
'Isis' Lemoine	WOth
'Island Sunset' (v)	SLBF
'Isle of Purbeck'	SVic
'Italiano' (d)	CWVF MJac SVic
'Ixion'	WOth
'Izabela Cieszyńska' (d) **new**	WOth
'Jack Acland'	CWVF
'Jack Shahan' ♀H2	CLoc CWVF EBak LAst LCla MJac SLBF WOth
'Jack Siverns'	WOth
'Jack Stanway' (v)	CDoC CWVF WOth
'Jackie Bull' (d)	CWVF
'Jackpot' (d)	EBak
'Jackqueline' (T)	CWVF
'Jadi Messingtetra'	CDoC WOth
'Jadi Netbotia'	CDoC
'James Bamber'	WOth
'James Lye' (d)	CWVF EBak WOth
'James Travis' Travis (E)	CDoC LCla
'James Travis' Thorne (d) **new**	WOth
'Jan Bremer'	SVic
'Jan van Erp'	WOth
'Jan Weijeb'	CDoC
'Jandel'	CWVF
'Jane Humber' (d)	CWVF
'Janice Perry's Gold' (v)	CLoc CNor MJac
'Janie' (d)	CDoC EPfP LBuc LRHS MAsh SVic
'Jap Vantveer' (T)	LCla
'Jasper Marnix'	WOth
'Jasper's Zuurstok'	WOth
'Jaunty Jack'	SLBF WOth
'Javelin'	WOth
'Jean Baker'	CDoC
'Jean Frisby'	CLoc WOth
'Jean Smith' (d)	MSmi
'Jean Taylor'	EPts
'Jean Webb' (v)	WCot
'Jeeves' (d)	WOth
'Jennifer'	MJac
'Jennifer Ann'	LAst SLBF WOth
'Jenny May'	CLoc EPts LCla WOth
'Jenny Sorensen' ♀H2	CWVF
'Jess'	LCla SLBF WOth
'Jessie Pearson'	CWVF
'Jessimae'	CWVF
'Jester' Holmes (d)	CLoc WOth
'Jet' **new**	MJac
'Jezebel' (d)	SVic
'Jiddles' (E)	LCla
'Jill Holloway' (T)	CDoC SLBF
'Jill Whitworth'	CDoC WPnn
'Jim Coleman'	CWVF SVic
'Jim Dodge' (d)	EPts
'Jim Muncaster'	CWVF
'Jim Watts'	CDoC WOth
jimenezii	CDoC
'Jimmy Cricket' (E)	SLBF WOth
'Joan Barnes' (d)	CWVF
'Joan Cooper'	CLoc CWVF SLBF SVic WOth
'Joan Goy'	CWVF MJac SVic
'Joan Knight'	CLoc
'Joan Margaret' (d)	MJac
'Joan Morris'	SLBF
'Joan Pacey'	CWVF
'Joan Waters' (d)	CWVF
'Joanna Lumley' (d)	EPts
'Joanne'	WOth
'Jo-Anne Fisher' (d)	EPts
'Joanne Jackson' **new**	MJac
'Joan's Delight'	SVic WOth
'Joe Kusber' (d)	CWVF EBak
'Joel'	WOth
'John Bartlett'	CLoc
'John Green'	CDoC
'John Grooms' (d)	CLoc SVic
'John Lockyer'	CLoc CWVF
'John Maynard Scales' (T) ♀H2	CWVF LCla MJac WOth
'John Nicholass'	SLBF WOth
§ 'John Ridding'PBR (T/v) ♀H1c	CLoc EPts LAst SPoG

	Name	Suppliers
	'John Wright'	CDoC LCla
	'Jomam'	CWVF
	'Jon Oram'	CLoc CWVF
	'Jonny Wilkinson'	MJac
	'Jorma van Eijk' (d)	CDoC
	'Jose's Joan' (d)	CWVF SVic
	'Jotu'	WOth
	'Joy Patmore'	CLoc CWVF SLBF
	'Joyce Adey' (d)	CWVF
	'Joyce Sinton'	CLoc CWVF
	'Judith Coupland'	CWVF
	'Judith Louise'	WOth
	'Jülchen'	CWVF
	'Jules Daloges' (d)	EBak
	'Julie Marie' (d)	CWVF MJac WOth
	'June Gardner'	CWVF
	'June Marie Shaw' **new**	MJac
	'Jungle'	CDoC LCla SLBF WOth
	'Jungle Baby'	WOth
	juntasensis	CDoC WOth
	'Just Pilk'	SLBF
	'Just Pink' (E)	CDoC WOth
	'Justin's Pride'	CDoC
	'Kames Bay'	WOth
	'Karen Isles' (E)	CDoC LCla SLBF
	'Karen Louise' (d)	CLoc
	'Kate Taylor' (d)	SLBF
	'Kath van Hanegem'	CLoc SLBF WOth
	'Kath Wilson'	LAst
	'Kathryn Maidment'	SVic
	'Katie'	WOth
	'Katie Rogers'	EPts
	'Katinka' (E)	CDoC CWVF LCla WOth
	'Katjan'	LCla SLBF WOth
	'Katrina' (d)	CDoC CLoc
	'Katrina Thompsen'	CLoc CWVF EPts SLBF WOth
	'Katy Flynn'	CWVF WOth
	'Kegworth Carnival' (d)	CWVF
	'Ken Goldsmith' (T)	CWVF
	'Ken Jennings'	CWVF
	'Ken Tudor'	MJac
	'Kenny Holmes'	CWVF
	'Kenny Walkling'	SLBF
	'Ken's Pixie'	MJac
	'Kernan Robson' (d)	CWVF EBak
	'Keystone'	EBak
	'Kilili'	WOth
	'King's Ransom' (d)	CLoc CWVF EBak SVic
	'Kirsten de Keijzer' (E) **new**	WOth
	'Kiss 'n' Tell'	CWVF
	'Kit Oxtoby' (d)	CDoC CWVF MJac SLBF WOth
	'Kiwi' (d)	EBak
	'Knockout' (d)	CWVF SVic
	'Kobold'	SLBF WOth
	'Kocarde' **new**	WOth
	'Kolding Perle'	CWVF SLBF
	'Komeet'	CDoC
	'Krommenie'	WOth
	'Kuniko Atarashi' (d)	EPts
	'Kwintet'	CWVF EBak MJac
	'La Bianca'	EBak
	'La Campanella' (d) ♀H2	CDoC CLoc CWVF EBak EPts LAst MJac SVic
	'La France' (d)	EBak
	'La Neige' ambig.	CWVF
	'La Porte' (d)	CLoc CWVF
	'La Rosita' (d)	EBak
I	'La Traviata' Blackwell (d)	EBak
	'Lace Petticoats' (d)	EBak SVic
	'Lady Beth' (d)	SVic
	'Lady Boothby' ♀H4	Widely available
	'Lady Framlingham' (d)	EPts
	'Lady Heytesbury'	WOth
	'Lady in Black'	LRHS MHer SPoG
	'Lady in Grey' (d)	MJac SVic
	'Lady Isobel Barnett'	CLoc CWVF EBak MJac SLBF SVic WOth
	'Lady Kathleen Spence'	CWVF SVic WOth
	'Lady Patricia Mountbatten'	CWVF SVic WOth
	'Lady Ramsey'	EBak
	'Lady Rebecca' (d)	CLoc
	'Lady Thumb' (d) ♀H3	Widely available
	'Laepines'	WOth
	'Laing's Hybrid'	CWVF EBak
	'Lakeland Princess'	EBak
	'Lambada'	CLoc LAst SLBF
	'Lancashire Lad' (d)	MJac
	'Lancashire Lass'	CWVF WOth
	'Lancelot'	EBak
	'Land van Beveren'	SLBF WOth
	'Landgoed Hulshorst'	WOth
	'Lapshead White'	CExl
	'Lark' (T)	CWVF
	'Lassie' (d)	CLoc CWVF EBak
	'Last Chance' (E)	SLBF
	'Laura' ambig.	CWVF SVic WOth
I	'Laura' (Dutch)	CLoc EPts LCla SLBF
	'Laura Cross' (E)	CDoC SLBF WOth
	'Lauren'	CDoC
	'Lavender Kate' (d)	CWVF EBak
	'Lazy Lady' (d)	CWVF
	'Lechlade Apache'	LCla
	'Lechlade Bullet'	LCla
	'Lechlade Chinaman'	SVic
	'Lechlade Debutante'	LCla WOth
	'Lechlade Gorgon'	CDoC CWVF LCla SLBF
	'Lechlade Magician'	CDoC EPts LCla SLBF
	'Lechlade Maiden'	CWVF WOth
	'Lechlade Martianess'	CDoC LCla SVic WOth
	'Lechlade Potentate'	LCla
	'Lechlade Tinkerbell' (E)	CDoC LCla
	'Lechlade Violet' (T)	LCla SVic
	lehmanii	LCla
	'Len Bielby' (T)	CWVF LCla
	'Lena' (d) ♀H2	CDoC CLoc CMac CTri CWVF EBak EPts MJac SLBF SPer SPlb SVic
	'Lena Dalton' (d)	CLoc CWVF EBak SVic
	'Leonhart von Fuchs'	WOth
	'Leonora'	CDoC CLoc CWVF SLBF SVic
	'Lesley' (T)	CWVF LCla
	'Lesley's Wonder'	MJac
	'Leslie Bowman'	LCla SLBF
	'Lett's Delight' (d)	CWVF EPts
	'Letty Lye'	EBak WOth
	'Leverhulme'	see *F.* 'Leverkusen'
§	'Leverkusen' (T)	CDoC CLoc EBak LCla MJac WOth
	'Lidie Bartelink' **new**	WOth
	'Liebriez' (d) ♀H4	EBak SVic
	'Liemers Lantaern'	CWVF
	'Likalin'	CWVF
	'Lilac Lustre' (d)	CLoc CWVF SVic
	'Lilac Mist'	SLBF
	'Lilac Queen' (d)	EBak
	'Lilian'	WOth
	'Lillian Annetts' (d) ♀H2	CWVF LAst MJac SLBF WOth
	'Lillibet' (d)	CLoc CWVF
	'Lime Lite' (d)	MJac
	'Linda Goulding'	CWVF EBak SVic
	'Linda Grace'	MJac
	'Linda Hinchliffe'	MJac

	Name	Suppliers
	'Linda Rosling' (d)	CDoC
	'Lindisfarne' (d)	CLoc CWVF EBak MJac WOth
	'Lindsey Victoria' (d)	SVic
	'Lionel'	WOth
	'Lipstick'	SLBF
	'Lisa' (d)	EPts
	'Lisi'	WOth
	'Little Beauty'	CWVF SVic WOth
	'Little Boy Blue'	EPts
	'Little Brook Gem'	SLBF
	'Little Catbells' (E)	SLBF
	'Little Fellow' **new**	WOth
	'Little Gene'	EBak
	'Little Nan'	SLBF
	'Little Ouse' (d)	CWVF
	'Little Scamp'	SLBF
	'Little Tony'	SLBF
	'Little Witch'	WOth
	'Liza Todman' (d)	LAst
	'Lochinver' (d)	CWVF
	'Loeky'	CDoC CLoc CWVF SVic WOth
	'Logan Garden'	see *F. magellanica* 'Logan Woods'
	'Lolita' (d)	CWVF EBak
	'London 2000'	EPts LCla MJac SLBF WOth
	'London Eye'	WOth
	'London in Bloom'	LCla SLBF
	'Lonely Ballerina' (d)	CLoc CWVF
	'Long Distance' (T)	CDoC LCla
	'Long Wings'	LCla SVic
I	'Longfellow' Lockerbie **new**	WOth
	'Lord Byron'	CLoc
	'Lord Jim'	LCla
	'Lord Lonsdale'	CWVF EPts LCla SVic
	'Lord Roberts'	CLoc CWVF SLBF
	'Lorna Swinbank'	CWVF SVic
	'Lorraine's Delight' (d)	SVic
	'Lottie Hobby' (E) 🏆H3	CLoc CMac CWVF EPfP EPts EShb LCla MLHP MSmi SVic WCot WOth
	'Louise Emershaw' (d)	CWVF EBak MJac SVic
	'Louise Nicholls'	MJac
	'Loulabel'	SVic
	'Loveliness'	CLoc CWVF SVic
	'Lovely Linda'	SLBF
	'Love's Reward' 🏆H2	CLoc CWVF MJac SLBF SVic
I	'Loxensis'	CDoC CWVF SVic
	loxensis misapplied	see *F.* 'Speciosa', *F.* 'Loxensis'
	loxensis Kunth	WOth
	'Loxhore Lullaby' (E)	LCla
	'Loxhore Minuet' (T)	LCla
	'Loxhore Posthorn' (T)	CDoC LCla
	'Lucinda'	CWVF
	'Lucy Locket'	MJac
	'Lunter's Klokje'	WOth
	'Lustre'	CWVF SVic WOth
I	'Lycioides'	LCla
	lycioides misapplied	see *F.* 'Lycioides'
§	***lycioides*** Andrews	WOth
	'Lydia'	WOth
	'Lye's Elegance'	WOth
	'Lye's Own'	SLBF
	'Lye's Unique' 🏆H3	CDoC CLoc CWVF EBak EPts LCla MJac SLBF SVic WOth
	'Lynette' (d)	CLoc
	'Lynn Cunningham'	CDoC
	'Lynne Marshall'	WOth
	'Lynne Patricia' (d)	EPts SLBF WOth
	'Mabel Greaves' (d)	CWVF
	'Machu Picchu'	CLoc CWVF EPts LCla SVic WOth
	macrophylla	WMoo
	'Madame Butterfly' (d)	CLoc
	'Madame Cornélissen' (d) 🏆H4	CLet CLoc CMac CSBt CTri CWVF EBak EBee ELan EPfP EPts LRHS MAsh MBri MRav NLar SCob SCoo SHil SLBF SLim SPer SPoG SVic WFar XLum
	'Madeleine Sweeney' (d)	MJac
	magellanica 🏆H4	CBcs CDoC CTsd CWib MGil MLHP MMuc NPer NWea SPer SVic WMoo WPnn
	- 'Alba'	see *F. magellanica* var. *molinae* 'Alba'
	- 'Alba Variegata' (v)	CLet WFar
	- 'Americana Elegans'	CDoC
	- 'Angel's Teardrop'	CDoC
	- 'Duchy of Cornwall'	CDoC
	- 'Fire Gold'	CDoC
	- 'Folius Aureus'	WFar
§	- var. ***gracilis*** 🏆H4	CAgr CDoC CLoc CSde CTri CWVF EPfP LRHS NBro SVic WMoo WOth WPnn
	- - 'Aurea' 🏆H4	CBcs CMac CSde CTsd CWVF ELan ELon EPfP LCla LRHS MHer MRav SCoo SDix SLBF SPer SRms SVic WMoo WOth
	- - 'Purple Mountain'	EPfP LRHS SPoG
	- - 'Variegata' (v) 🏆H4	CDoC CTsd EBak EPfP LCla LRHS MGos MRav SDix SVic WPnn
§	- - 'Versicolor' (v) 🏆H4	Widely available
	- 'Lady Bacon'	CBot CDoC ELon EPri EPts EWes GCal IDee LHop LRHS MCot MMuc SBod SDys SEND SLBF SMHy WBod WPGP WSHC
§	- 'Logan Woods'	CAby CDoC ELon GKin SLBF WPGP
	- 'Longipedunculata'	CDoC
	- var. ***magellanica***	SCob
	- var. ***molinae***	CDul CLoc CTri CWVF CWib EBak ECrN ELan EPfP EPts EShb EWoo GKin LCla LCro LRHS MBlu MNrw MSwo NBid NChi NPer SCob SPer SPlb WBod WFar WMnd WMoo WPnn
§	- - 'Alba' 🏆H4 **new**	CBar CDoC EUJe NLar
I	- - 'Alba Aureovariegata' (v)	CMac EPfP SPer SVic WFar XLum
§	- - 'Enstone' (v)	CDoC ELon
	- - 'Golden Sharpitor' (v)	LAst WFar
	- - 'Mr Knight's Blush'	CDul
§	- - 'Sharpitor' (v) 🏆H2	CBcs CDoC CLet CSde CTsd EBak ELan ELon EPfP LRHS MAsh NPer SVic WFar WKif WMoo WOth WSHC
	- 'Mountain Gold'	CDoC LAst
	- var. ***myrtifolia***	CDoC CTsd
	- 'Pumila'	CDoC EWes GCal MHer MLHP SMHy SRot SVic WAbe WHal WPGP WThu WTor
	- ***purpurea***	LRHS
	- 'Red Mountain'	EWes
	- 'Sea King'	CDoC
	- 'Sea Spray'	CDoC
	- 'Seahorse'	CDoC
§	- 'Thompsonii' 🏆H4	CDoC ECGP SMHy
	- 'Threave'	CDoC
	'Magenta Flush'	CWVF
	'Magic Flute'	CLoc CWVF MJac SVic
	'Maik Luijten' (d)	CDoC
	'Major Heaphy'	CDoC CWVF EBak MHer MSmi WOth
	'Malibu Mist' (d)	CWVF
	'Mama Bleuss' (d)	EBak

	Name	Suppliers
	'Mancunian' (d)	CWVF
	'Mandarin Cream' **new**	LAst WOth
	'Mandi Oxtoby' (T)	LCla
	'Mantilla' (T)	CLoc CWVF LCla MJac MSmi SVic
	'Marbled Sky'	SVic
	'Marcel Michiels' (d)	CDoC
	'Marcia'^{PBR} (Shadowdancer Series)	CLoc LAst
	'Marcus Graham' (d)	CLoc CWVF EBak SCoo SVic
	'Marcus Hanton' (d)	CWVF
	'Margaret' (d) $\mathbb{Y}^{H4}$	CDoC CDul CLoc CTri CWVF EBak EPts SEND SLBF SVic WFar
	'Margaret Bird'	LCla
	'Margaret Brown' $\mathbb{Y}^{H4}$	CDoC CLoc CTri CWVF LCla LRHS SLBF SVic WOth
	'Margaret Pilkington'	CWVF SVic WOth
	'Margaret Roe'	CDoC CWVF EBak MJac
	'Margaret Susan'	EBak
	'Margaret Viscountess Thurso'	SLBF
	'Margarite Dawson' (d)	SVic
	'Maria Landy'	CWVF MJac SLBF WOth
	'Maria Mathilde' (d)	SLBF
	'Maria Shaw'	EPts
	'Marilyn Olsen'	CWVF
	'Marin Glow' $\mathbb{Y}^{H3}$	CLoc CWVF EBak SVic
	'Marinka' $\mathbb{Y}^{H2}$	CLoc CWVF EBak EPts LAst LCla MJac SLBF SVic WOth
	'Mark Kirby' (d)	CWVF
	'Marlies de Keijzer' (E)	CDoC EPts LCla SLBF SVen
	Martha = 'Goetzmart'^{PBR} (Shadowdancer Series)	LAst LHop
	'Martina'	SLBF
	'Martin's Double Delicate' (d)	WOth
	'Martin's Inspiration'	CDoC LCla
	'Martin's Sylvia'	CDoC
	'Martin's Trompet'	CDoC
	'Martin's Yellow Surprise' (T)	LCla SLBF SVic
	'Marty' (d)	EBak
	'Martyn Smedley' **new**	WOth
	'Mary' (T) $\mathbb{Y}^{H1c}$	CDoC CLoc CWVF EPts LCla MSmi SLBF SVic WOth
	'Mary Lockyer' (d)	CLoc EBak
	'Mary Poppins'	CWVF SVic
	'Mary Reynolds' (d)	CWVF
	'Mary Thorne'	EBak
	'Mary's Beauty' (d)	MSmi
	'Mary's Millennium'	CWVF
	'Mauve Beauty' (d)	CWVF SLBF WOth
	'Mauve Wisp' (d)	SVic
	'Mavis Enderby'	MJac SLBF
	'Max Jaffa'	CWVF
I	'Maxima'	EPts LAst LCla SLBF
	'Maxine's Smile'	SLBF
	'Mayblossom' (d)	CWVF
	'Mayfield'	CWVF
	'Mazda'	CWVF WOth
	'McGee's Chocolate Mint'	SLBF
	'Meadowlark' (d)	CWVF
	'Meditation' (d)	CLoc
	'Melanie'	SVic WOth
	'Melissa Heavens'	CWVF
	'Melody'	SVic
	'Melody Ann' (d)	EBak
	'Melting Moments' (d)	SCoo
	'Mendocino Rose'	SVic
	'Menna'	CDoC
	'Mephisto' $\mathbb{Y}^{H2}$	CWVF WOth
	'Mercurius' $\mathbb{Y}^{H4}$	WOth
	'Merlin'	CDoC LCla
	'Merry Mary' (d)	CWVF EBak
	'Mersty' (d)	SLBF WOth
I	'Mexicali Rose' Machado	CLoc
	'Michael' (d)	CWVF EPts
	'Michael Wallis' (T)	CDoC LCla SLBF
	'Michelle Wallace'	SVic
	michoacanensis misapplied	see *F. microphylla* subsp. *aprica*
	michoacanensis Sessé & Moç. (E) B&SWJ 9027	WCru
	- B&SWJ 9148	WCru
	'Micky Goult' $\mathbb{Y}^{H2}$	CLoc CWVF EPts MJac SLBF SVic WOth
	'Microchip' (E)	LCla
	microphylla (E)	CAby CBcs CDoC CElw CExl CLoc CTsd CWVF EBak EBee ELon GCal IDee MGil SDix SIgm SVic
	- B&SWJ 10331	WCru
§	- subsp. ***aprica*** (E)	LCla
	- - B&SWJ 9101	WCru
	- - 'Dolly's Dress' (E)	WCru
	- 'Cornish Pixie' (E)	CDoC
§	- subsp. ***hemsleyana*** (E)	CDoC CExl CLet SVic
	- - B&SWJ 10478	WCru
	- - 'Silver Lining' (E)	GCal SCob WCot WCru
§	- subsp. ***hidalgensis*** (E)	CDoC LCla
§	- subsp. ***minimiflora*** (E)	SVic
	- 'Variegata' (E/v)	EWes
	'Midas'	CWVF
	'Midwinter'	CWVF SVic WOth
	'Mieke Meursing' $\mathbb{Y}^{H2}$	CLoc CWVF EBak MJac
	'Mieke Sarton'	CDoC
	'Miep Aalhuizen'	CDoC LCla WOth
	'Mike Oxtoby' (T)	CWVF
	'Millennium'	CLoc EBak EPts MJac SCoo SVic
	'Millie Butler'	CWVF
	'Ming'	CLoc
	'Mini'	WOth
	'Miniature Jewels' (E)	SLBF
	minimiflora misapplied	see *F.* × *bacillaris*
	minimiflora Hemsl.	see *F. microphylla* subsp. *minimiflora*
	'Minirose'	CWVF EPts SLBF WOth
	'Minnesota' (d)	EBak WOth
	'Miramere'	EPts
	'Mischief'	SVic
	'Miss California' (d)	CLoc CWVF EBak
	'Miss Great Britain'	CWVF
	'Miss Muffett' (d)	EPts
	'Miss Vallejo' (d)	EBak
	'Mission Bells'	CDoC CLoc CWVF EBak EPts SVic
	'Mistoque'	WOth
	'Misty Blue' (d)	SVic
	'Misty Haze' (d)	CWVF SVic
	Mojo Series	CDoC
	'Molesworth' (d)	CWVF MJac
	'Money Spinner'	CLoc
	'Monica Dare' (T) $\mathbb{Y}^{H1c}$	CDoC
	'Monsieur Thibaut' $\mathbb{Y}^{H4}$	SPer
	'Monte Rosa' (d)	CWVF
	'Montevideo' (d)	CWVF
	'Mood Indigo' (d)	CDoC CWVF MJac SLBF SVic WOth
	'Moonbeam' (d)	CLoc
	'Moonglow'	MJac WOth
	'Moonlight Sonata'	CLoc CWVF
	'Moonraker' (d)	CWVF SVic
	'Moorland Beauty' (d)	WOth
	'More Applause' (d)	CLoc

'Morning Light' (d)	CLoc SVic
'Morrells' (d)	EBak
'Moth Blue' (d)	CWVF EBak
'Mountain Mist' (d)	CWVF SVic
'Moyra' (d)	CWVF
'Mr A. Huggett'	CLoc CWVF EPts SLBF WOth
'Mr W. Rundle'	EBak SVic
§ 'Mr West' (v)	LRHS LSou MCot WMoo
'Mrs Churchill'	CLoc
'Mrs Lee Belton' (E)	CDoC LCla SLBF WOth
'Mrs Lovell Swisher' ♀H4	CWVF EBak LCla SVic WOth
'Mrs Marshall'	CWVF SLBF WOth
'Mrs Popple' ♀H4	Widely available
'Mrs W. Castle'	SVic
'Mrs W.P. Wood' ♀H4	CLoc CWVF ELon LRHS MSCN SVic WOth
'Mrs W. Rundle'	CLoc CWVF SLBF WOth
'Mrs Wilks' new	SLBF
'Muriel' (d)	CLoc CWVF WOth
'Murru's Pierre Marie' (d)	SLBF
'My Delight'	CWVF
'My Fair Lady' (d)	CLoc CWVF EBak
'My Honey'	WOth
'My Little Cracker'	CDoC MJac
'My Mum'	LCla SLBF
'My Pat'	SLBF
'My Reward' (d)	CWVF
'Naaldwijk 800'	WOth
'Nancy Lou' (d)	CLoc CWVF MJac SLBF SVic
'Nanny Ed' (d)	CWVF
'Napoléon' new	WOth
'Natasha Lynn' (d)	WOth
'Natasha Sinton' (d)	CDoC CWVF LAst MJac
'Nathan Rhys'	EPts SLBF WOth
'Native Dancer' (d)	CWVF
'Neapolitan' (d)	CDoC SLBF
'Neck'	LCla
'Nell Gwyn'	CLoc CWVF SVic
'Nellie Nuttall' ♀H2	CLoc CWVF EBak EPts SVic
'Neopolitan' (E)	CLoc EPts LCla SVic WOth
'Nephele'	EPts
'Nettala'	CDoC SVic WOth
'Neue Welt'	CDoC CWVF
'New Millennium' (d)	CDoC EShb LHop
'Nice 'n' Easy' (d)	LRHS MJac
'Nicki Fenwick-Raven' (E)	LCla
'Nicki's Findling'	CWVF EPts LCla MJac
'Nicola'	EBak
'Nicola Jane' (d)	CLet CWVF EBak EPts LCla MJac SHar SLBF SVic
'Nicola Storey'	CDoC
'Nicolette'	CWVF MJac
'Nightingale' (d)	CLoc
§ ***nigricans*** B&SWJ 10664	WCru
'Niula'	CDoC LCla
'Noblesse'	CDoC WOth
'Nonchalance' (T)	CDoC LCla
'Nordseebrandung' new	WOth
'Norman Welton'	MJac SLBF
'Normandy Bell'	EBak SVic
'Northern Jewel'	SLBF
'Northern Pride' (d)	WOth
'Northilda'	SVic
'Northumbrian Pipes'	CDoC LCla WOth
'Northway'	CLoc CWVF MJac SVic
'Norvell Gillespie' (d)	EBak
'Novella' (d)	CWVF
'Nuance'	CDoC LCla
'Nunthorpe Gem' (d)	CDoC
'O Sole Mio'	SVic
obconica (E)	CDoC
'Obcylin' (E)	CDoC EPts LCla WOth
'Ocean Beach'	CDoC EPts WOth
'Oddfellow' (d)	WOth
'Oetnang' (d)	CTri SCoo
'Oh Carol' (E)	LCla SLBF WOth
'Old Somerset' (v)	SVic WOth
'Olga Storey'	CDoC LRHS
'Olive Moon' (d)	WOth
'Olive Smith'	CWVF EPts LCla MJac
'Olympia'	WOth
'Olympic Lass' (d)	WOth
'Olympic Sunset'	SVic WOth
'Oosje' (E)	LCla SVic
'Oostveens Thymen'	WOth
'Opalescent' (d)	CLoc CWVF SVic
'Orange Crush'	CLoc CWVF EBak MJac WOth
'Orange Crystal'	CWVF MJac SLBF SVic
'Orange Drops'	CLoc CWVF EBak EPts SVic WOth
'Orange Flare'	CLoc CWVF EBak SLBF SVic
'Orange Heart'	LCla
'Orange King' (d)	CLoc CWVF LAst
'Orange Mirage'	CLoc CWVF SLBF SVic
'Orange Star' (E)	CDoC LCla WOth
'Orangeblossom'	SLBF WOth
'Oranje van Os'	CWVF
'Orient Express' (T) ♀H1c	CDoC CLoc CWVF MJac SVic WOth
'Oriental Sunrise'	CWVF
'Ornamental Pearl' (v)	CLoc CWVF WOth
'Orwell' (d)	CWVF
'Oso Sweet'	CWVF
'Other Fellow'	CDoC CWVF EBak EPts LCla MJac SLBF SVic WOth
'Oulton Empress' (E)	LCla SLBF
'Oulton Fairy' (E)	SLBF
'Oulton Hoya' (E)	WOth
'Oulton Red Imp' (E)	LCla SLBF
'Oulton Travellers Rest' (E)	SLBF
'Oulton Tu-Fu' (E)	WOth
'Our Carol'	SLBF
'Our Darling'	CWVF
'Our Hilary'	SLBF WOth
'Our Kid'	SLBF
'Our Nan' (d)	MJac
'Our Pamela'	MJac
'Our Spencer'	SLBF
'Our Ted' (T)	EBak EPts
'Our William'	SLBF
'Overbecks'	see *F. magellanica* var. *molinae* 'Sharpitor'
'P.E. King' (d)	SLBF
'Pabbe's Belle'	WOth
'Pabbe's Kirrevaalk'	WOth
'Pabbe's Klompnoagel'	WOth
'Pabbe's Siddeltop' (d) new	WOth
'Pacific Queen' (d)	EBak
'Pacquesa' (d)	CWVF EBak SVic
'Padre Pio' (d)	CWVF EBak MJac
'Pam Plack'	CDoC LCla SLBF WOth
'Pamela Knights' (d)	EBak
'Pamela Wallace'	WOth
'Pam's People'	LCla
'Pan' (T)	WOth
'Panache' (d)	LCla
'Pangea' (T)	CDoC
paniculata (T) ♀H2	CBot CDoC CRHN CWVF EBak EPts IDee LCla MCot MHer SLBF WCot WCru
'Panique'	CDoC LCla
'Pantomine Dame' (d)	CWVF

'Panylla Prince'	LCla SLBF
'Papa Bleuss' (d)	CWVF EBak
'Papoose' (d)	CDoC EBak LCla SLBF SVic
'Parkstone Centenary' (d)	CWVF
'Party Frock'	CDoC CLoc CWVF EBak WOth
parviflora misapplied	see *F.* × *bacillaris*
parviflora Lindl.	see *F. lycioides* Andrews
'Pat Meara'	CLoc EBak
'Pathétique' (d)	CLoc
'Patience' (d)	CDoC CWVF EBak SLBF
'Patio Princess' (d)	CLoc CWVF EPts LAst
'Patricia Ann' (d)	CDoC
'Patricia Hodge'	WOth
'Patty Evans' (d)	CWVF
'Paul Cambon' (d)	EBak
'Paul Roe' (d)	MJac
'Paul und Carole' (d) new	WOth
'Paula Jane' (d) ♀H2	CWVF LAst MJac SLBF SVic
'Pauline Rawlins' (d)	CLoc
'Peachy' (California Dreamers Series) (d)	CDoC CLoc LAst SCoo
'Peachy Keen' (d)	EBak
'Peacock' (d)	CLoc
'Pearly King' (d)	WOth
'Pearly Queen' (d)	WOth
'Peasholm'	WOth
'Pee Wee Rose'	EBak SVic
'Peggy Burford' (T)	LCla
Peggy = 'Goetzpeg' PBR (Shadowdancer Series)	LAst LSou SCoo
'Peggy King'	CDoC EBak
'Peloria' (d)	CLoc EBak
'Pennine'	WOth
'People's Princess'	MJac
'Peper Harow'	EBak
'Pepi' (d)	CWVF EBak
'Peppermint Candy' (d)	CWVF MJac
'Peppermint Stick' (d)	CLoc CWVF EBak MSmi SVic
'Percival's'	CDoC
'Perky Pink' (d)	EBak EPts
'Perry Park'	CWVF MJac SVic
'Perry's Jumbo'	NPer
perscandens	CBcs CDoC CExl LCla
'Peter Bielby' (d)	CWVF
'Peter Crookes' (T)	CWVF
'Peter Meredith'	MJac WOth
'Peter Pan'	CWVF
petiolaris	LCla
- B&SWJ 10675	WCru
'Petit Four'	CWVF WOth
'Phaidra' (T)	CDoC LCla WOth
'Pharaoh'	CLoc
'Phénoménal' (d)	CWVF EBak MLHP MSmi
'Phryne' (d)	SVic WOth
'Phyllis' (d) ♀H4	CDoC CLoc CWVF EBak EPts LCla LRHS MJac SEND SLBF SVic
'Piet van der Sande'	CDoC LCla
'Piggelmee'	CDoC WOth
'Pinch Me' (d)	CWVF EBak SVic
'Pink Aurora'	CLoc
'Pink Ballet Girl' (d)	CLoc SVic
'Pink Bon Accord'	CLoc CWVF SVic
'Pink Cloud'	CLoc EBak
'Pink Cornet'	LCla
'Pink Darling'	CLoc EBak
'Pink Dessert'	EBak
'Pink Fandango' (d)	CLoc
'Pink Fantasia' ♀H2	CLoc CWVF EBak EPts LAst LCla MJac SLBF SVic WOth
'Pink Galore' (d) ♀H2	CLoc CWVF LAst MJac SLBF
'Pink Goon' (d)	MSmi SLBF SVic
'Pink Haze'	SVic
'Pink Jade'	CWVF
'Pink la Campanella'	CDoC CWVF EBak LAst
'Pink Marshmallow' (d) ♀H4	CDoC CLoc CWVF EBak MJac SLBF SVic
'Pink Panther' (d)	CDoC
'Pink Profusion'	EBak
'Pink Quartet' (d)	CLoc CWVF EBak WCot
'Pink Rain'	CWVF MJac WOth
'Pink Slippers'	CLoc
'Pink Spangles'	CWVF SVic
'Pink Sprite'	WOth
'Pink Temptation'	CLoc CWVF SVic
'Pinto de Blue' (d)	MSmi
'Pinwheel' (d)	CLoc EBak
'Piper' (d)	CWVF
'Piper's Vale' (T)	CDoC LAst MJac SLBF WOth
'Pirbright'	CWVF WOth
'Pixie'	CDoC CLoc CWVF EBak MJac SLBF SVic
'Playboy' (d)	SVic
'Playford'	CWVF EBak
'Pledle' (T) new	WOth
'Plenty'	EBak SVic
'Plumb Bob' (d)	CWVF
'Polskie Fuksji'	CDoC
'Pop Whitlock' (v)	CWVF SVic
'Poppet'	CWVF WOth
'Popsie Girl'	SLBF WOth
'Port Arthur' (d)	EBak
'Postiljon'	CWVF EBak
'Powder Puff' ambig.	CWVF
'Powder Puff' Hodges (d)	CLoc SVic
'Prelude' Blackwell	CLoc
'President'	CDoC EBak LRHS
'President Barrie Nash'	CLoc
'President Carol Gubler' (d)	SLBF
'President George Bartlett' (d) ♀H2	CDoC CLoc EPts MJac SLBF WOth
'President Jim Muil'	SLBF
'President Joan Morris' (d)	SLBF
'President John Porter'	MJac SLBF
'President Leo Boullemier'	CWVF MJac SVic WOth
'President Margaret Slater'	CLoc CWVF SVic WOth
'President Moir' (d)	SLBF WOth
'President Norman Hobbs'	CWVF WOth
'President Roosevelt' (d)	CDoC
'President Stanley Wilson' (d)	EBak EPts
'President Wilf Sharp' (d)	SVic
'Preston'	CMac
'Preston Field' (v)	WOth
'Preston Guild' ♀H3	CLoc CWVF EBak NPer SDys SVic WOth
'Prince of Orange'	CLoc SVic WOth
'Princess Dollar'	see *F.* 'Dollar Prinzessin'
'Princessita'	CWVF EBak WOth
procumbens	CBcs CDoC CExl CLoc CWVF EBak ECou EPfP EPts EUJe GCal IDee LCla MCot MHer SBrt SLBF WHea WOth
- 'Argentea'	see *F. procumbens* 'Wirral'
- 'Variegata'	see *F. procumbens* 'Wirral'
§ - 'Wirral' (v)	CLoc CTsd EShb EWld ITim WOth
'Prodigy'	see *F.* 'Enfant Prodigue'
'Profusion' ambig.	SVic
'Prosperity' (d) ♀H3	CDoC CLoc CWVF EBak EPts LCla LRHS MJac SLBF SVic WOth

'Pumila'	CExl CMac CWib EBee ELan EPfP EPts LRHS SDix SVic WPat
'Purbeck Mist' (d)	CWVF
'Purperklokje'	CWVF EBak SVic
'Purple Emperor' (d)	CLoc
'Purple Heart' (d)	CLoc EBak
'Purple Lace'	SVic
'Purple Rain'	CDoC EPts
'Purple Splendour' (d)	CDoC
'Pussy Cat' (T)	CLoc CWVF EBak SVic WOth
'Putney Pride'	EPts
'Put's Folly' ♀^{H2}	CWVF EBak MJac WOth
putumayensis	EBak
'Quasar' (d)	CDoC CLoc CWVF EPts LAst MJac SLBF SVic
'Queen Elizabeth' Garson **new**	WOth
'Queen Esther'	WOth
'Queen Mary'	CLoc EBak
'Queen of Bath' (d)	SVic
'Queen of Derby' (d)	CWVF
'Queen of Hearts' Kennett (d)	SVic
'Queen of Mercia'	MJac
'Queen's Park' (d)	EBak
'Query'	SVic WOth
'R.A.F.' (d)	CLoc CWVF EBak EPts SVic
'Radings Gerda' (E)	LCla SLBF
'Radings Karin'	CDoC
'Radings Mia' (T)	SLBF
'Radings Michelle'	CWVF WOth
'Ragtime' **new**	MSmi
'Rahnee'	CWVF
'Rainbow'	CWVF MSmi
'Ralph Storey'	CDoC
'Ralph's Delight' (d)	CWVF
'Rambling Rose' (d)	CLoc CWVF MJac
'Rams Royal' (d)	CDoC CWVF
'Raspberry' (d)	CLoc CWVF EBak SVic
'Raspberry Ripple' (d)	WOth
'Raspberry Sweet' (d)	CWVF
'Raspberry Twist' (d) **new**	WOth
'Ratae Beauty'	CWVF
'Ratatouille' (d)	WOth
ravenii	WOth
'Ray Redfern'	CWVF
'Reading Show' (d)	CWVF EPts SLBF
'Rebecca Williamson' (d)	CWVF MJac
'Rebeka Sinton' (v)	CLoc EBak
'Red Ace' (d)	WOth
'Red Jacket' (d)	CWVF EBak
'Red Petticoat'	CWVF
'Red Rain'	CWVF WOth
'Red Shadows' (d)	CLoc CWVF EBak
'Red Spider'	CLoc CWVF EBak LAst SCoo SVic WOth
'Red Sunlight'	CDoC
'Red Wing'	CLoc
'Reflexa'	see *F.* × *bacillaris* 'Reflexa'
'Reg Gubler'	SLBF
'Regal'	CLoc WOth
'Regal Robe' (d)	CDoC
regia subsp. ***regia***	LCla
- subsp. ***reitzii***	CDoC CDul LCla XLum
- subsp. ***serrae***	CBcs WOth
'Reji' **new**	CDoC
'Remember Carole Anne' (d)	SLBF WOth
'Remember Eric'	CDoC WOth
'Remember Tommy Struck'	CDoC
'Remembering Claire'	EPts WOth
'Remembrance' (d)	EPts LCla SLBF
'Remus' (d)	SVic
'Rene Schwab'	LCla
'Renée-Madeleine'	WOth
'Requiem'	CLoc
'Reverend Frank Pagden'	WOth
'Rhapsody' ambig.	SVic
I 'Rhapsody' Blackwell (d)	CLoc
'Rhona Foster'	CDoC
'Riccartonii' ♀^{H6}	Widely available
'Richard John' (v)	SVic
'Ridestar' (d)	CLoc CWVF
'Rigoletto'	SVic
'Rijs 2001' (E)	CDoC SLBF WOth
'Rina Felix'	WOth
'Ringwood Gold'	SVic
'Ringwood Market' (d)	CWVF EPts MJac SCoo SVic
'Rivendell'	EPts
'Riverdancer Claire'	WOth
'Robert Lutters'	SVic
'Rocket Fire' (California Dreamers Series) (d)	CDoC SVic
'Roesse Aristilius' **new**	WOth
'Roesse Belinda' (d)	CDoC
'Roesse Callisto'	CDoC
'Roesse Duck'	WOth
'Roesse Juliet'	CDoC
'Roesse Meton'	WOth
'Roesse Peacock' (d)	CDoC
'Roesse Sextans'	CDoC
'Roesse Tricolor'	CDoC
'Roger de Cooker' (T)	CDoC CLoc EPts LCla SVic WOth
'Rohees Lava'	SLBF
'Rohees Leada' (d)	SLBF
'Rohees Matar' (d) **new**	WOth
'Rohees New Millennium' (d)	SLBF
'Rolla' (d)	CWVF EBak
'Rolt's Ruby' (d)	CWVF SVic
'Roman City' (d)	CLoc SVic
'Romance' (d)	CWVF
'Romany Rose'	CLoc
'Ronald L. Lockerbie' (d)	CLoc CWVF SVic
'Rondo'	MJac
'Ron's Pet'	WOth
'Roos Breytenbach' (T)	CDoC LAst LCla MJac WOth
'Rosamunda' (d)	CLoc
'Rose Aylett' (d)	EBak
'Rose Bradwardine' (d)	EBak
'Rose Churchill' (d)	MJac
'Rose Fantasia' ♀^{H2}	CLoc CWVF EPts LAst MJac SLBF
'Rose of Castile'	CLoc EBak EPts LCla MJac SLBF SVic
'Rose of Castile Improved' ♀^{H4}	CWVF LCla MJac WOth
'Rose of Denmark'	CLoc CWVF EBak MJac SCoo SLBF WOth
'Rose Winston' (d)	SCoo
rosea misapplied	see *F.* 'Globosa'
rosea Ruíz & Pav.	see *F. lycioides* Andrews
'Rosecroft Beauty' (d)	CWVF EBak SVic WOth
Rosella = 'Goetzrose'[PBR] (Shadowdancer Series)	LAst
'Roselynne'	WOth
'Rosemarie Higham'	MJac SCoo WOth
'Rosemary Day'	CLoc
'Roswitha'	SLBF
'Rosy Bows'	CWVF
'Rosy Frills' (d)	CWVF MJac SVic

Cultivar	Suppliers
'Rosy Morn' (d)	CLoc
'Roualeyn's White Gold' (d)	SLBF
'Rough Silk'	CLoc CWVF EBak
'Roy Castle' (d)	CWVF
'Roy Walker' (d)	CWVF
'Royal Academy' (d)	EPts
'Royal and Ancient'	CWVF
'Royal Mosaic' (California Dreamers Series) (d)	MJac
'Royal Purple' (d)	EBak
'Royal Serenade' (d)	CWVF
'Royal Velvet' (d) $\mathbb{Y}^{H2}$	CDoC CLoc CWVF EBak EPts LAst LRHS MJac SLBF SVic
'Rubra Grandiflora'	CWVF LCla SLBF WOth
'Ruby Wedding' (d)	CWVF SLBF
'Ruddigore'	CWVF
'Ruffles' (d)	CWVF
'Rufus' $\mathbb{Y}^{H4}$	CDoC CLoc CMac CWVF EBak ELan EPts LCla MJac MRav SLBF SVic
'Ruth'	SVic WOth
'Ruth King' (d)	CWVF EBak WOth
'S'Wonderful' (d)	CLoc EBak
'Sailor'	EPts SVic
'Salmon Cascade'	CWVF EPts LCla MJac SLBF
'Salmon Glow'	CWVF SVic
'Sam Sheppard'	SLBF
'Samantha Reynolds'	WOth
'San Diego' (d)	CWVF
'San Mateo' (d)	EBak
§ ***sanctae-rosae***	CDoC LCla
'Sandboy'	CWVF EBak
'Sanrina'	CDoC
'Santa Cruz' (d)	CDoC CMac CWVF SLBF SVic WOth
'Santa Lucia' (d)	CLoc
'Santa Monica' (d)	EBak
'Sapphire' (d)	EBak
'Sappho Phaoon' (T)	EPts WOth
'Sara Helen' (d)	CLoc EBak
'Sarah Brightman' (d)	CDoC CLoc
'Sarah Eliza' (d)	EShb MSmi SCoo
'Sarah Jane' (d)	EBak SVic
'Sarah Louise'	CWVF
'Satellite'	CLoc CWVF EBak SVic
'Saturnus' $\mathbb{Y}^{H4}$	CDoC CWVF EBak LRHS SPoG
'Saxondale Sue'	SVic
scabriuscula	CDoC LCla
'Scarcity'	CWVF EBak SVic WOth
'Scarisbrick'	WOth
'Scarlet Jester'	EPts
'Schneeball' (d)	EBak SVic
'Schneewitcher'	CDoC EPts
'Schöne Hanaurin'	SLBF
'Schöne Wilhelmine'	see *F.* 'Die Schöne Wilhelmine'
'Scotch Heather' (d)	CWVF
'Sea Shell' (d)	CWVF
'Sealand Prince'	CDoC CWVF LCla SVic WOth
'Seattle Blue' (T/d)	SLBF
'Sebastopol' (d)	CLoc
'Selma Lavrijsen'	WOth
'Sensation'	WOth
serratifolia Ruíz & Pav.	see *F. denticulata*
'Seventh Heaven' (d)	CDoC CLoc CWVF LAst MJac SCoo
'Shady Blue'	CWVF
'Shanley'	CWVF SVic
'Sharon' (d)	WOth
'Sharpitor'	see *F. magellanica* var. *molinae* 'Sharpitor'
'Shawna Ree' (E)	WOth
'Sheila Crooks' (d)	CWVF EBak
'Sheila Kirby'	CWVF
'Sheila Steele' (d)	CWVF
'Shelford'	CDoC CLoc CWVF EBak EPts MJac SLBF SVic WOth
'Shell Pink'	SVic
'She's a Beauty'	MJac
'Shirley' PBR (Shadowdancer Series)	LAst SCoo
'Shirley Halladay' (d)	LCla
'Shirley Teece'	EPts
'Showfire'	EBak
'Showtime' (d)	CWVF
'Shrimp Cocktail'	CLoc LRHS
'Shuna Lindsay'	CDoC LCla WOth
'Siberoet' (E)	CDoC LCla SLBF WOth
'Sierra Blue' (d)	CLoc CWVF EBak
'Silver Anniversary' (d)	SVic
'Silver Dawn' (d)	WOth
'Silver Dollar'	SVic
'Silverdale'	CDoC EPts
'Simon J. Rowell'	LCla
simplicicaulis	CDoC EBak LCla
'Sincerity' (d)	CLoc SVic
'Siobhan'	CWVF
'Siobhan Evans' (d)	SLBF
'Sir Alfred Ramsey'	CWVF EBak
'Sir David Jason'	MJac
'Sir Matt Busby' (d)	CDoC EPts LAst MJac
'Sister Ann Haley'	EPts
'Sister Sister' (d)	SLBF
'Sleepy'	EPts SVic
'Sleigh Bells'	CLoc CWVF EBak SVic WOth
'Small Pipes'	CWVF
'Smokey Mountain' (d)	SVic
'Sneezy'	CDoC EPts SVic
'Snow Burner' (California Dreamers Series) (d)	CLoc LAst
'Snow White' (d)	SVic
'Snowbird' (d)	SLBF
§ 'Snowcap' (d) $\mathbb{Y}^{H4}$	CDoC CLoc CWVF EBak ELon EPfP EPts GKin LAst LCla LRHS MAsh MGos MJac MLHP MSmi NPer SCoo SHil SLBF SLim SPoG SVic WFar
'Snowdon' (d)	CWVF
'Snowdrift' Colville (d)	CLoc
'Snowdrift' Kennett (d)	EBak
'Snowfall'	CWVF
'Snowfire' (d)	CLoc CWVF SCoo SVic
'Snowflake' (E)	CDoC EPts LCla SLBF WBor WOth
'Softpink Jubelteen'	WOth
'Son of Thumb' $\mathbb{Y}^{H4}$	CDoC CLoc CWVF EPts LAst LRHS MAsh MJac MRav SCob SLBF SLim SPer SVic
'Sonata' (d)	CLoc CWVF SVic
'Sophie Grace'	WOth
'Sophie Louise'	CWVF EPts SLBF WOth
'Sophisticated Lady' (d)	CWVF EBak EPts SVic
'South Crofty'	CDoC
'South Gate' (d)	CLoc CWVF EBak EPts LAst MSmi SVic
'Space Shuttle'	CLoc LCla
'Sparky' (T)	CLoc CWVF EPts LCla WOth
'Speciana' **new**	EPts
§ 'Speciosa'	CDoC EBak LCla
'Spion Kop' (d)	CWVF LAst
§ ***splendens*** $\mathbb{Y}^{H2}$	CBot CDoC CLoc EBak IDee LCla MCot NPer SLBF
- B&SWJ 10469	WCru
'Spring Bells' (d)	LRHS

	'Squadron Leader' (d)	CWVF EBak EPts
	'Squirtie'	SLBF
	'St Ives Bay'	CDoC
	'Stan'	WOth
	'Stanley Cash' (d)	CLoc CWVF SVic
	'Star Wars'	CDoC CLoc EPts MJac WOth
	'Stardust'	CDoC CWVF WOth
	'Starlight'	WOth
	'Steeley' (d)	SVic
	'Stella Ann' (T)	CWVF EPts LCla
	'Straat Cumberland'	LCla
	'Straat Futami' (E)	EPts LCla
	'Straat Kobe' (T)	CDoC LCla
	'Straat La Plata'	LCla
	'Straat Magelhaen'	LCla WOth
	'Straat of Plenty'	CDoC LCla WOth
	'Strawberry Daiquiri' (d)	WOth
	'Strawberry Delight' (d)	CLoc CWVF MJac SVic
	'Strawberry Sundae' (d)	CLoc CWVF EBak
	'Strike the Viol' (T) **new**	WOth
	'String of Pearls'	CLoc CWVF MJac SLBF SVic
	'Stuart Joe'	CWVF
	'Stuart Lockyer' (d) **new**	CLoc
	'Sue'	SLBF WOth
	'Suffolk Splendour' (d)	EPts
	'Sugar Almond' (d)	CWVF
	'Summerdaffodil'	CDoC WOth
	'Sunbeam Hillary' (Sunbeam Series)	WOth
	'Sunny Jim'	SVic
	'Sunny Smiles'	CWVF
	'Sunray' (v)	CLoc CWVF EBak ELon LBuc LRHS MAsh MGos NEgg SCoo SHil SLim SPoG SPtp SVen WCot WOth
	'Sunset'	CLoc CWVF WOth
	'Sunshine' **new**	WOth
	'Supersport' (d)	SVic
	'Superstar'	CWVF SVic
	'Susan Ford' (d)	CWVF
	'Susan Green'	CWVF EBak MJac SLBF WOth
	'Susan McMaster'	CLoc
	'Susan Olcese' (d)	CWVF EBak
	'Susan Travis'	CLoc CWVF EBak SVic
	'Swanley Beauty' **new**	WOth
	'Swanley Gem' ♀H2	CLoc CWVF EBak SVic
	'Swanley Pendula'	CLoc
	'Swanley Yellow'	CWVF EBak SVic WOth
	'Sweet Hollie'	SLBF
	'Sweet Sarah' (E)	EPts WOth
I	'Sweetheart' van Wieringen	EBak
	'Swingtime' (d) ♀H2	CLoc CWVF EBak EPts LAst LCla MJac SLBF SVic
	sylvatica misapplied	see *F. nigricans*
	sylvatica Benth.	CDoC
	'Sylvia Barker' ♀H2	CWVF LCla SLBF WOth
	'Sylvia Rose' (d)	CWVF
	'Sylvia's Choice'	EBak
	'Symphony'	CLoc CWVF
	'Syreme' (d) **new**	SLBF
	'Szilvia Ócsai' (d) **new**	WOth
	''t Binnenland' **new**	WOth
	'T.S.J.' (E)	CDoC LCla
	'Taco'	CDoC LCla WOth
	'Taddle'	CWVF SLBF
	'Taffeta Bow' (d)	CLoc SLBF SVic
	'Tamworth'	CLoc CWVF EBak MJac SVic
	'Tangerine'	CLoc CWVF SVic WCot
	'Tanya Bridger' (d)	EBak WOth
	'Tarra Valley'	CDoC LCla SVic WOth
	'Task Force'	CWVF SVic
	'Taudens Heil'	WOth
	'Tausendschön' (d)	CLoc WOth
	'Ted Perry' (d)	CWVF
	'Temptation' ambig.	CWVF
	'Temptation' Peterson	CLoc EBak WOth
	'Tennessee Waltz' (d) ♀H2	CDoC CLoc CWVF EBak EPts SLBF SPer SVic
	'Tess'	SLBF
	tetradactyla misapplied	see *F.* × *bacillaris*
	'Texas Longhorn' (d)	CLoc CWVF EBak MSmi SVic
	'Thalia' (T) ♀H1c	CBot CDoC CLoc CWVF EBak EPts EUJe LAst LCla LSRN MBri MCot MHer MJac MSmi NEgg SLBF SPer SPlb SPoG SVic WBod WOth
	'Thamar'	CDoC CLoc CWVF EPts SVic WOth
	'That's It' (d)	SVic
	'The Aristocrat' (d)	CLoc EBak
§	'The Doctor'	CLoc CWVF EBak WOth
	'The Jester' (d)	EBak
	'The Madame' (d)	CWVF
	'The Tarns'	CWVF EBak SVic WOth
	'Thilco'	CDoC
	'Think Pink'	WOth
	'Thistle Hill' (d)	WOth
	'Thomas' (d)	EPts
	'Thompsonii'	see *F. magellanica* 'Thompsonii'
	'Thornley's Hardy'	SVic
	'Three Cheers'	CLoc
	'Three Counties'	EBak
	'Thumbelina'	CDoC LRHS
	'Thunderbird' (d)	CLoc CWVF
	thymifolia (E)	CWVF GCra LRHS MHer SDys SEND SMHy WKif WOth
	- subsp. ***minimiflora*** (E)	CBot
	- subsp. ***thymifolia*** (E)	CDoC WOth
	'Tiara' (d)	EBak
	'Tillingbourne' (d)	SLBF
	'Time After Time'	CLoc EShb
	'Timlin Brened' (T)	CWVF EBak
	'Timothy Titus' (T) ♀H1c	LCla
	'Ting-a-ling'	CLoc CWVF EBak SVic
	'Tinker Bell' Hodges	EBak SVic
	'Tintern Abbey'	CWVF
	'Tjinegara'	CDoC LCla
	'Toby Bridger' (d)	CLoc EBak
	'Toby Foreman'	SLBF
	'Toby S' (d) **new**	SLBF
	'Tolling Bell'	CWVF EBak
	'Tom Goedeman'	LCla
	'Tom Knights'	EBak WOth
	'Tom Thumb' ♀H4	Widely available
	'Tom West' misapplied	see *F.* 'Mr West'
	'Tom West' Meillez (v)	CDoC CLet CLoc CMHG COtt CSBt CWVF CWib EBak EHoe EPts LAst LCla MHer MJac MRav MSCN SLBF SLim SPtp WFar WOth
	'Tom Woods'	CWVF
	'Tomarama' (E)	WOth
	'Ton Ten Hove'	CDoC LCla
	'Tony Talbot'	MJac
	'Tony's Treat' (d)	EPts
	'Toos'	SVic
	'Toosje Vantveer' **new**	WOth
	'Topaz' (d)	CLoc
	'Topper' (d)	CWVF
	'Torch' (d)	CLoc CWVF EBak SVic
	'Torchlight'	CWVF EPts LCla
	'Torvill and Dean' (d)	CLoc CWVF EPts LAst MJac SLBF
	'Tosca'	CWVF
	'Town Crier'	SLBF

'Tracid' (d)	SVic
'Trail Blazer' (d)	CLoc CWVF MJac
'Trailing King'	WOth
'Trailing Queen'	MJac
'Trase' (d)	CDoC CWVF CWib EBak SVic
'Traudchen Bonstedt' (T) ♀H1c	CLoc CWVF LCla SVic
'Traviata'	see *F.* 'La Traviata' Blackwell
'Treasure' (d)	EBak
'Treslong'	WOth
'Tricolor'	see *F. magellanica* var. *gracilis* 'Versicolor'
'Trientje'	LCla SLBF
triphylla (T)	EBak MHer
'Trish's Triumph'	EPts WOth
'Tristesse' (d)	CLoc CWVF EBak
'Troon'	CWVF
'Tropic Sunset' (d)	CDoC
'Tropicana' (d)	CLoc CWVF SVic
'Troubador' Waltz (d)	CLoc
'Trudi Davro'	LAst MJac SCoo
'Trudy'	CDoC CWVF EPts SVic WOth
'Truly Treena' (d)	SLBF
'Trumpeter' ambig.	CWVF
'Trumpeter' Fry	SVic
'Trumpeter' Reiter (T)	CLoc EPts LCla MJac MSmi
'Tubular Bells' (T)	LCla
'Tuonela' (d)	CLoc CWVF
'Turkish Delight'	WOth
'Tutti-frutti' (d)	CLoc
'Twinkling Stars'	CWVF MJac SVic WOth
'Twinny'	CWVF EPts
'Two Tiers' (d)	CWVF
'Tycha' **new**	WOth
'U.F.O.'	CWVF SVic
'Ullswater' (d)	CWVF EBak WOth
'Uncle Charley' (d)	EBak MSmi SVic
'Uncle Steve' (d)	SVic
'University of Liverpool'	CLoc MJac
'Upward Look'	EBak
'Valda May' (d)	CWVF
'Vale of Belvoir'	SVic
'Valerie Ann' (d)	EBak SVic
'Valerie Bradley'	EPts
'Vanessa Jackson'	CLoc CWVF MJac SVic
'Vanessa Wright'	CDoC LRHS
'Vanity Fair' (d)	CLoc EBak
'Variegated Lottie Hobby' (E/v)	CDoC WOth
'Variegated Procumbens'	see *F. procumbens* 'Wirral'
'Variegated Swingtime' (v)	LAst
'Veenlust'	EBak MJac
'Velvet Crush'	EPts LAst
'Vendeta'	CDoC LCla WOth
'Venus Victrix'	EBak WOth
venusta	CDoC EBak LCla WOth
'Vera Garcia'	CDoC EPts SLBF
'Versicolor'	see *F. magellanica* var. *gracilis* 'Versicolor'
'Ville de Paris'	WOth
'Vincent van Gogh' (T)	WOth
'Vintage Dovercourt'	LCla
'Violet Bassett-Burr' (d)	CLoc EBak
'Violet Gem' (d)	CLoc
'Violet Rosette' (d)	CWVF SVic
Violetta = 'Goetzviol' (Shadowdancer Series)	CDoC LAst LSou SCoo
'Viva Ireland'	EBak
'Vivien Colville'	CLoc SVic
'Vivien Harris'	CDoC
'Vobeglo'	CWVF
'Voodoo' (d)	CDoC CLoc CWVF EBak EPts EShb LAst LCla SCoo SVic
vulcanica André	LCla
'Vyvian Miller'	CWVF
'W.P. Wood'	CDoC
'Wagtails White Pixie'	EBak
'Waldfee' (E)	CDoC LCla
'Waldis Grafin'	WOth
'Waldis Spezi'	CDoC LCla
'Walsingham' (d)	CWVF WOth
'Walton Jewel'	EBak
'Walz Banjo'	WOth
'Walz Bella'	LCla
'Walz Blauwkous' (d)	CWVF
'Walz Doedelzak'	WOth
'Walz Estafette' (d)	SVic
'Walz Fluit'	MJac
'Walz Freule'	CWVF MJac WOth
'Walz Harp'	CWVF WOth
'Walz Hoorn'	WOth
'Walz Jubelteen' ♀H2	CDoC CLoc CWVF ELon EPts LCla MJac SAdn SLBF SVen SVic WOth
'Walz Lucifer'	CWVF LCla SLBF WOth
'Walz Mandoline' (d)	CWVF SVic WOth
'Walz Nugget'	CDoC
'Walz Panfluit'	LCla
'Walz Parasol'	WOth
'Walz Polka'	CDoC LCla
'Walz Sitar'	CDoC WOth
'Walz Toeter'	WOth
'Walz Triangel' (d)	SVic
'Walz Trompet'	CDoC WOth
'Walz Tuba'	CDoC WOth
'Wapenveld 150'	LCla
'Wapenveld's Bloei'	CDoC EPts LCla SLBF
'War Paint' (d)	CLoc
'Warm Night'	CDoC
'Warton Crag'	CWVF SVic
'Water Color'	SLBF
'Water Nymph'	CLoc LAst MHer SLBF SVic WOth
'Wattenpost'	SLBF WOth
'Wave of Life'	CWVF
'Waveney Gem'	CLoc CWVF EBak LCla MJac SLBF WOth
'Waveney Queen'	CWVF SVic WOth
'Waveney Sunrise'	CWVF MJac SVic WOth
'Waveney Unique'	CWVF
'Waveney Valley'	CWVF WOth
'Waveney Waltz'	CWVF EBak WOth
'Wedding Bells' ambig.	SVic
'Welsh Dragon' (d)	CLoc CWVF EBak WOth
'Wendy' Catt	see *F.* 'Snowcap'
'Wendy Bendy'	EPts SLBF
'Wendy Jane Webster' **new**	EPts
'Wendy's Beauty' (d)	CLoc EBak EPts MJac
'Wentworth'	CWVF SVic WOth
'Wessex Belle' (d/v)	CWVF
'Westham'	LCla
'Westminster Chimes' (d)	CLoc CWVF
'Wharfedale' ♀H4	ELon EPts EWTr MJac SLBF SVic WOth
'What's-it' (E)	LCla SLBF
'Whickham Blue'	CWVF
'Whirlaway' (d)	CLoc CWVF SVic
'White Academy'	EPts
'White Ann'	see *F.* 'Heidi Weiss'
'White Bride' (d)	SVic
'White Clove'	CDoC SVic WOth
'White Galore' (d)	CWVF SVic

'White Général Monk' (d) CDoC
'White Joy' EBak WOth
'White King' (d) CLoc CWVF EBak LAst SVic
'White Pixie' ♀H4 CDoC EPts MJac SLBF SVic
'White Queen' ambig. CWVF
'White Queen' Doyle WOth
'White Spider' CLoc CWVF EBak SVic WOth
'White Veil' (d) CWVF
'Whiteknights Amethyst' CDoC WOth
'Whiteknights Blush' CCse CDoC CExl EWes GCal GQui LHop LRHS
'Whiteknights Cheeky' (T) CWVF EBak EPts LCla SVic
'Whiteknights Pearl' ♀H3 CBot CDoC CLet CTsd CWVF ECha EPfP EPts LAst LCla LCro MLHP MMuc SDys SEND SLBF SMHy SVic WHar WOth WPnn
'Whiteknights Ruby' (T) WOth
'Whitton Starburst' LCla
'Wicked Queen' (d) SVic
'Widnes Wonder' SLBF WOth
'Widow Twanky' (d) CWVF
'Wigan Peer' (d) CDoC EPts MJac SLBF WOth
'Wight Magic' (d) MJac
'Wild and Beautiful' (d) CWVF SVic
'Wilf Langton' WOth
'Wilhelmina Schwab' LCla
'Willow Tinsdale' CDoC LSou
'Willy Nijhuis' (T) WOth
'Wilma van Druten' CDoC LCla
'Wilson's Colours' EPts LCla
'Wilson's Joy' MJac
'Wilson's Pearls' (d) CWVF SLBF
'Wilson's Sugar Pink' EPts LCla MJac WOth
'Win Oxtoby' (d) CWVF
'Windhapper' LCla SLBF WOth
'Windmill' CWVF
'Wine and Roses' (d) EBak
'Wingrove's Mammoth' (d) SVic
'Wings of Song' (d) CWVF
'Winston Churchill' (d) ♀H2 CDoC CLoc CWVF EBak LAst MJac SCoo SVic
'Winter's Touch' WOth
'Witchipoo' SLBF
'Woodnook' (d) CWVF
'Woodside' (d) SVic
'Wyre Light' (E) SLBF
'Yattendon Lady' SLBF
'Ymkje' CDoC
'Yolanda Franck' LAst
'York Manor' EShb
'Yvonne Schwab' CDoC LCla
'Zeebrook' SVic
'Zeeuwse Parel' WOth
'Zellertal' CDoC WOth
'Zeta' CDoC
'Zets Bravo' CDoC
'Ziegfield Girl' (d) SVic
'Zifi' SLBF
'Zulu King' CDoC SVic WOth
'Zulu Queen' WOth
'Zus Liebregts' (d) WOth
'Zwarte Snor' (d) CWVF

Fumaria (*Papaveraceae*)

capreolata WSFF
lutea see *Corydalis lutea*

Furcraea (*Asparagaceae*)

bedinghausii see *F. parmentieri*
§ ***foetida*** WCot
gigantea see *F. foetida*
longaeva misapplied see *F. parmentieri*
macdougalii SPlb
§ ***parmentieri*** CBcs CCon CDTJ CExl CHGN CHII CPne CTsd EAla EBee GBin LEdu NLos SMad SPlb SVen
selloa var. ***marginata*** (v) CDoC MHin

G

Gahnia (*Cyperaceae*)

sieberiana SPlb

Gaillardia (*Asteraceae*)

aristata 'Maxima Aurea' EBee EPfP MSpe NBre SPhx
'Arizona Sun' EAJP LPal LRHS MHer MMuc NPri SCob SHil SPad SVic
'Bijou' EBee ELon LSun SWvt
'Celebration' **new** LRHS
'Dwarf Goblin' NGBl
§ 'Fackelschein' IBoy MSpe XLum
'Fanfare' PBR CWGN EBee ECtt LAst LHop LRHS MGos SCoo
Goblin see *G.* × *grandiflora* 'Kobold'
'Golden Queen' XLum
× ***grandiflora*** 'Amber Wheels' EPfP MSpe NCGa SPhx
- 'Arizona Apricot' LRHS NPri
- 'Arizona Red Shades' LRHS NPri SPad
- 'Bremen' XLum
- 'Burgunder' CSBt CSpe EAJP ELan ELon EPfP EWoo LAst LHop LRHS LSou LSun MBri MPie MSpe NGBl SCob SPer SPhx SPoG SWvt WHar XLum
- 'Dazzler' CSBt EAEE EBee ELan EPfP LAst LRHS SPer SPoG WMoo XLum
- 'Fanfare Blaze' **new** LRHS
- (Gallo Series) 'Gallo Dark Bicolor' LRHS
- - 'Gallo Fire' LRHS
- - 'Gallo Peach' LRHS
- - 'Gallo Yellow' LRHS
- - 'Gallo Yellow Trumpet' LRHS
§ - 'Goldkobold' XLum
§ - 'Kobold' CBcs CMac COtt CSBt CTsd EBee ELan ELon EPfP GMaP IBoy LAst LRHS LSun MBri NLar SPer SPlb SPoG SWvt WHar XLum
- 'Mesa Yellow' CBod NPri
- 'Sun Devil' **new** SPad
- 'Sun Flare' **new** LBMP
- (Sunburst Series) Sunburst Burgundy Picotee = 'Granretip' PBR LRHS
- - Sunburst Burgundy LRHS SHil
- - Sunburst Orange = 'Granoran' PBR LRHS SHil
- - Sunburst Yellow = 'Granyel' PBR LRHS SHil
- 'Tokajer' EAJP EBee ELan EPfP LRHS MSpe NBre SPhx WCAu XLum
'Naomi Sunshine' SHar
§ 'Oranges and Lemons' PBR EBee ECtt LSou SCob SHar
'Red Sun' CWGN NLar
Saint Clements see *G.* 'Oranges and Lemons'
'Solar Flare' SCob
Torchlight see *G.* 'Fackelschein'

Yellow Goblin	see *G.* × *grandiflora* 'Goldkobold'

Galactites (*Asteraceae*)

tomentosa	EHoe ELan EWTr SPav
- white-flowered	CPla

Galanthus ✿ (*Amaryllidaceae*)

'Acton Pigot No. 3'	CAvo
'Ailwyn'	CAvo GEdr
'Alan's Treat'	CAvo
'Alison Hilary'	EHrv GEdr MAsh
× ***allenii***	CBro EHrv GKev
alpinus var. ***alpinus*** late-flowering	GKev
- var. ***bortkewitschianus***	GKev
'Anglesey Not Galatea' **new**	EHrv
'Anne of Geierstein'	IFoB WCot
'Annette'	LAma NMyG
'Ann's Millenium Giant'	CBro
'Armine'	CElw CTal EPfP GKev IFoB LRHS WCot
'Art Nouveau'	CAvo EHrv
'Atkinsii' ♀H5	CAvo CBro CElw CLAP CRos ECho EHrv EPot EWoo GAbr GEdr GKev IFoB LAma LRHS MAsh MRav MWat NBir NMyG SDix WCot WFar WHoo WShi
'Autumn Beauty'	CBro LRHS
'Babraham Scented'	GEdr
'Backhouse Spectacles'	GEdr ITim
'Bankside' **new**	CAvo
'Barbara's Double' (d)	CAvo EWes MAsh NHar
'Barbara's Hybrid' **new**	EHrv
'Benhall Beauty'	CElw EHrv EWes GEdr
'Bertram Anderson' ♀H5	EHrv GEdr MAsh WCot
'Bess'	CAvo CElw CSna CTal EHrv GEdr IFoB
'Bill Bishop'	CBro CTal EHrv EWoo GEdr IFoB MAsh WCot
'Bitton' ambig.	NPol
'Blewbury'	EHrv IFoB
'Brenda Troyle'	CBro CElw CLAP ECho EPot GBin GEdr GKev LRHS MAsh MHom NMyG NPol WCot WFar
'Brigadier Mathias' **new**	EHrv
'Byfield Special'	CAvo EHrv IFoB
byzantinus	see *G. plicatus* subsp. *byzantinus*
'Castlegar'	IFoB
caucasicus (Bak.) Grossh.	see *G. alpinus* var. *alpinus*
caucasicus misapplied	see *G. elwesii* var. *monostictus*
caucasicus ambig.	IFoB NPol
- 'Comet'	see *G. elwesii* 'Comet'
- var. ***hiemalis*** Stern	see *G. elwesii* Hiemalis Group
'Charlotte'	GKev LRHS
'Cicely Hall'	CDes IFoB
'Clare Blakeway-Phillips'	CAvo
corcyrensis spring-flowering	see *G. reginae-olgae* subsp. *vernalis*
- winter-flowering	see *G. reginae-olgae* subsp. *reginae-olgae* Winter-flowering Group
'Cordelia' (d)	CDes CElw CLAP IFoB MAsh NMyG
'Cornwood Gem'	CAvo IFoB
'Cowhouse Green'	CAvo EHrv GEdr
'Curly'	CAvo CDes EHrv EWes GEdr IFoB MAsh
'Daglingworth'	GEdr
'David Baker'	GEdr
'Desdemona' (d)	CBro CLAP EHrv EPot GKev LLHF NMyG WCot WFar
'Ding Dong'	CAvo EHrv GEdr IFoB
'Dionysus' (d)	CBro CExl CLAP EHrv EPot EWes EWoo GEdr GKev LLHF MHom NBir NMyG WBrk WFar WShi
'Drummond's Giant'	IFoB
'Ecusson d'Or'	CAvo
§ ***elwesii*** ♀H5	CBro CTri ECho ELan EPfP EPot ERCP IFoB LAma LCro LPfy LRHS MMuc MWat NBir NPol SCob SDeJ SEND SPoG SRms WCot WFar WHoo WShi
- 'Abington Green'	CSna
- 'Bo Bette' **new**	GEdr
- 'Broadleigh Gardens'	EHrv
- 'Cedric's Prolific'	ECha EHrv EWoo GEdr IFoB NMyG WFar
§ - 'Comet' ♀H5	CDes CElw EHrv GBuc GEdr IFoB MAsh WFar
- 'Daphne's Scissors'	CElw CSna GEdr
- 'David Shackleton'	CElw EHrv IFoB MAsh
- 'December Green Tip' **new**	WCot
- 'Early Twin'	WCot
- 'Echoes'	WCot
- Edward Whittall Group	CLAP
- - 'Two Eyes' **new**	EHrv
- 'Elmley Lovett'	CAvo CDes CElw
- var. ***elwesii*** **new**	EHrv
- - 'Fenstead End'	CAvo GEdr
- - 'Fred's Giant'	GMaP
- - 'Kite'	EHrv GEdr
- - 'Magnus'	NBir
- - 'Maidwell L'	CBro CSna CTal EHrv
- - 'Sibbertoft Magnet'	CAvo CDes IFoB
* - 'Flore Pleno' (d)	NPol
- 'Godfrey Owen'	CDes GEdr IFoB
- 'Green Brush'	EWes GKev IFoB LAma LRHS
- 'Grumpy'	EHrv GEdr MAsh
§ - Hiemalis Group	CBro EHrv EPot GKev MHom WCot
- - 'Barnes'	EHrv WCot
- - 'Donald Sims' **new**	EHrv
- - 'Earliest of All'	CDes
- - 'Rainbow Farm Early' **new**	EHrv
- 'J. Haydn'	CDes ECho LAma NMyG
- 'Jessica'	IFoB
- 'Kyre Park'	GEdr MAsh
- 'Long 'drop'	CAvo GEdr IFoB
- 'Mandarin'	CElw EWes
- 'Marielle'	EPPr
- 'Marjorie Brown'	CFis EHrv GEdr ITim NMyG
- var. ***maximus***	see *G. elwesii* 'Yvonne Hay'
- 'Milkwood'	see *G. elwesii* 'Mrs Macnamara'
- 'Miss Mowcher' **new**	WCot
§ - var. ***monostictus*** ♀H5	CAvo CBro ECha ECho EHrv GKev IFoB LLHF WBrk WFar WShi
- - 'B. Britten' **new**	LAma LRHS
- - 'G. Handel'	ECho IFoB LAma LLHF LRHS NMyG
- - 'Grayswood'	GEdr
- - 'Green Tips'	CAvo
- - 'H. Purcell'	ECho GEdr LAma LLHF LRHS
- - late-flowering	ECho
- - 'Lord Monostictus'	CAvo
- - 'Miller's Late'	EHrv
- - 'Mozart' **new**	LAma LRHS
- - 'Rogers Rough'	SDys
- - 'Warwickshire Gemini'	CDes MHCG
- aff. var. ***monostictus***	WFar
- 'Mr Omer' **new**	WCot
- 'Mr Peggotty' **new**	WCot

	Name	Suppliers
§	- 'Mrs Macnamara'	CDes CTal EHrv EWoo GEdr IFoB MAsh WFar
	- November-flowering	WCot
	- 'Penelope Ann'	EHrv GEdr
	- 'Peter Gatehouse'	CAvo CDes EHrv
§	- 'Ransom's Dwarf'	CDes GEdr
*	- 'Robustus Praecox' **new**	GKev
	- 'Selborne Green Tips'	EHrv
	- 'Sickle'	CDes CSna EHrv NHar
	- 'Sir Edward Elgar'	LAma LLHF LRHS
	- 'Three Leaves'	CAvo IFoB
	- 'Washfield Colesbourne'	see *G.* 'Washfield Colesbourne'
§	- 'Yvonne Hay'	EHrv
	- 'Zwanenburg'	EHrv
	'Epiphany' **new**	CAvo EHrv
	'Ermine House' (d) **new**	EHrv
	'Erway'	CDes MHom
I	'Excelsis'	CAvo
	'F63'	IFoB
	'Falkland House'	CElw GEdr
	'Fanny' **new**	CAvo
	'Faringdon Double' (d)	CAvo EHrv MAsh
	'Fieldgate Prelude'	CAvo EHrv GEdr
	'Fieldgate Superb'	EHrv IFoB
	'Fieldgate Tiffany'	CAvo
	'Fly Fishing'	CAvo
	fosteri	CBro ECho EHrv GEdr GKev
	'Framlingham Double' (d) **new**	EHrv
	'G71' (d)	IFoB
	'Gabriel' **new**	CAvo
	'Galadriel'	CAvo GEdr
	'Galatea'	CAvo CBro CSna EHrv EPot EWes EWoo GAbr GKev MAsh MHom SDys WFar
	'Ginns'	CLAP EHrv EWoo IFoB
	'Gloria'	MAsh
§	***gracilis***	CBre CBro CExl ECho GKev NPol
	- 'Highdown'	CElw EHrv GKev IFoB MAsh MHom
	- Kew	CElw
	- 'Vic Horton'	CElw EHrv WThu
	graecus misapplied	see *G. gracilis*
	graecus Orph. ex Boiss.	see *G. elwesii*
	'Grande Juge'	IFoB
	'Grayling'	see *G. plicatus* 'Percy Picton'
	Greatorex double (d)	CLAP
	'Green Arrow'	CAvo
	'Green Man'	CAvo EHrv GEdr IFoB
	'Green Necklace'	CAvo EWes
	'Green Ribbon' **new**	CAvo
	'Greenfields'	CSna IFoB MAsh
	'Heffalump' (d)	CAvo EHrv IFoB MAsh
	'Hill Poë' (d)	CBro CElw CLAP EHrv EPot GEdr GKev IFoB LLHF MAsh MHom MWat NMyG
	'Hippolyta' (d)	CAvo CBro CElw CLAP ECha EHrv EPot EWoo GEdr GKev IFoB LAma LRHS MAsh MHom NMyG NPol SKHP WCot WShi
	'Hobson's Choice'	EHrv
	'Homersfield' **new**	EHrv
	'Honeysuckle Cottage'	CAvo
	× ***hybridus*** 'Merlin' ♀H5	CBro CDes CElw EHrv IFoB NMyG WCot WFar WHoo
	- 'Robin Hood'	CDes EHrv GEdr GKev IFoB
	'Icicle'	CAvo GEdr
§	***ikariae*** Bak.	EPfP GEdr
	- subsp. ***ikariae*** Butt's form	NPol
	- Latifolius Group	see *G. platyphyllus*

	Name	Suppliers
	- subsp. ***snogerupii***	see *G. ikariae*
	'Imbolc'	CAvo EHrv GEdr IFoB
	'Irish Green'	CAvo IFoB
	'Ivy Cottage Corporal' **new**	EHrv
	'Ivy Cottage Green Tip' **new**	EHrv
	'Jacquenetta' (d)	CAvo CBro CElw CLAP CSna EHrv EWes GEdr IFoB ITim LAma LRHS MCot MHom NMyG
	'James Backhouse'	EHrv WHoo WShi
	'John Gray'	CAvo CBro CSna EHrv EWes GEdr IFoB MAsh
	'June Boardman'	CAvo
	'Ketton'	CBro CElw CSna CTal EHrv EWoo GEdr GKev IFoB LLHF NRya
	'Kildare'	CAvo IFoB
	'Kingston Double' (d)	CLAP EHrv
	krasnovii	GKev
	'Lady Beatrix Stanley' (d) ♀H5	CAvo CBro CElw CLAP ECha EHrv EPot GEdr GKev IFoB LLWP MAsh MHom NMyG WCot WFar
	lagodechianus	CBro GKev MPhe
	'Lapwing'	CDes EHrv GEdr IFoB MAsh
	latifolius Rupr.	see *G. platyphyllus*
	'Lavinia' (d)	CElw EHrv EWes GEdr MAsh MHom WFar
	'Lerinda'	EHrv IFoB
	'Limetree'	CElw CLAP EHrv EPri EWes EWoo GKev ITim MHom NPol WFar
	'Little Ben'	EHrv GKev GMaP
	'Little Dorrit'	GEdr
	'Little John'	EHrv GEdr WBrk
	'Little Magnet'	CAvo
	'Longstowe'	MAsh
	'Louise Ann Bromley'	CAvo
	lutescens	see *G. nivalis* Sandersii Group
	'Lyn'	CBro EHrv GEdr NBir
	'Magnet' ♀H5	CAvo CBro CElw CLAP CTal ECho EHrv ELon EPfP EPot EWoo GAbr GEdr GKev LAma LRHS MAsh MHom MWat NBir NMyG NPol SKHP WBrk WCot WFar WHoo WShi
	aff. 'Magnet'	GMaP
	'Maidwell'	IFoB
	'Melanie Broughton'	CAvo CDes IFoB
	'Midwinter' **new**	CAvo
	'Mighty Atom'	CBro CDes CLAP WBrk
	'Mill House' **new**	EHrv
	'Moccas'	CElw CSna MHom
	'Modern Art'	CAvo GEdr IFoB MAsh
	'Mrs Backhouse No 12'	EHrv IFoB
	'Mrs Thompson'	CAvo CDes CElw EHrv GEdr GKev IFoB MAsh
	'Mrs Wrightson's Double' (d)	CDes
	'Natalie Garton'	CAvo EHrv IFoB
	'Neill Fraser'	EHrv GEdr MHom
	'Nerissa' (d)	GEdr
	nivalis ♀H5	Widely available
	- 'Anglesey Abbey'	CAvo CElw EHrv EWes GEdr IFoB MHom
	- 'April Fool'	MHom
	- 'Ballynahinch'	ITim
	- 'Bitton'	EHrv GEdr
	- 'Blonde Inge'	CAvo GEdr IFoB MAsh
	- 'Chedworth'	CElw GEdr WBrk
	- 'Cornwood'	CAvo
	- 'Dreycott Greentip'	IFoB
	- 'Elfin'	CAvo CElw EHrv EWes GKev IFoB MAsh

Name	Suppliers
- 'Fluff' **new**	EHrv
- 'Fuzz'	CAvo
- 'Gloucester Old Spot'	GEdr
- subsp. ***imperati***	CExl
- 'Lutescens'	see *G. nivalis* Sandersii Group
- 'Major Pam'	IFoB
- 'Maximus'	WShi
- 'Melvillei'	MAsh
- f. ***pleniflorus*** (d)	CTca ECho GKev MAsh SPoG
- - 'Blewbury Tart' (d)	CAvo CBro CDes CElw CLAP CSna EHrv EWes EWoo GEdr GKev IFoB WBrk
- - 'Flore Pleno' (d) ♀H5	CBro CExl CWCL EPfP EPot ERCP IFoB LAma LCro LHop LLWP LOPS LRHS MMuc NCot NRya SCob SDeJ SEND SPer SRms WBrk WCot WHoo WShi
- - 'Lady Elphinstone' (d)	CAvo CBro CDes CLAP CSna EHrv IFoB LLHF MAsh MHom NMyG NPol NRya WCot
- - 'Pusey Green Tips' (d)	CAvo CBro CElw CLAP EPot GKev IFoB NMyG NPol WCot
- - Scharlockii Group double (d) **new**	GKev
- - 'Walrus' (d)	EHrv GEdr MAsh NHar
§ - - 'Wonston Double' (d)	CAvo EHrv IFoB
- Poculiformis Group	CElw CLAP EHrv MAsh
- cf. Poculiformis Group	CElw
- - 'Henry's White Lady' **new**	GEdr
§ - Sandersii Group	GMaP IFoB
§ - Scharlockii Group	CElw MAsh MHom WBrk
- 'Sibbertoft White'	MAsh
- 'Tiny'	IFoB MHom WFar
- 'Tiny Tim'	MAsh
- 'Virescens'	CLAP IFoB
- 'Viridapice'	CAvo CBro CElw CExl ECha ECho EPfP EPot ERCP GAbr GKev GMaP IFoB LAma LRHS MAsh MWat NBir NPol SDeJ SKHP WCot WFar WHoo WShi
- 'Warei'	EHrv
- 'White Dream'	GEdr IFoB WShi
'Nothing Special'	CDes MAsh
'Ophelia' (d)	CAvo CBro EHrv EPot EWoo GEdr GKev MAsh MHom MWat NMyG NPol SKHP WBrk WFar WHoo
'Orion'	CDes
'Orleton'	CDes
'Peardrop'	EHrv GEdr NHar
'Peg Sharples'	EHrv GEdr IFoB MHom
peshmenii	CDes CEvo ECho LEdu
§ ***platyphyllus***	CExl LLWP LRHS
plicatus ♀H5	CAvo CBro CElw EHrv GKev LRHS MCot MHom NMyG NPol WBrk WCot WHoo WShi
- from Coton Manor	EHrv MCot
- 'Augustus'	CAvo CBro CElw EHrv EPot EWes GEdr GKev IFoB MAsh MHom NMyG WCot WHoo
- 'Babraham Dwarf' **new**	EHrv
- 'Baxendale's Late'	CAvo CLAP GEdr
- 'Beth Chatto'	EHrv
- 'Bill Clark'	IFoB
- 'Bolu Shades'	IFoB
- 'Bowles's Large'	EHrv
§ - subsp. ***byzantinus***	CBro EHrv MHom WThu
- - 'Fox Farm' **new**	EHrv
- 'Colossus'	CBro ECho EHrv EWes GKev IFoB WCot
- 'Diggory'	CAvo CDes EHrv GEdr IFoB MAsh
- 'Duckie'	GEdr
- 'E.A. Bowles' **new**	GEdr
- 'Edinburgh Ketton'	EHrv
- 'Florence Baker'	EHrv GEdr
- 'Gerard Parker'	CAvo EHrv IFoB
- 'Green Hayes'	EHrv
- 'Green Teeth'	MAsh
- 'Greenpeace'	CSna
- 'Henham No. 1'	EHrv
- 'John Long'	CAvo GEdr
- late flowering	GKev
- 'Limey'	EWoo
- 'Madelaine'	MAsh
§ - 'Percy Picton'	CAvo
- 'Sally Pasmore'	CAvo GKev
- 'Sophie North'	CDes CElw IFoB LLHF NPol
- 'The Pearl'	EHrv GEdr IFoB
- 'Three Ships' ♀H5	CAvo EHrv GEdr IFoB MHom NHar
- 'Trym'	CDes EHrv GEdr IFoB NPol
- 'Wandlebury Ring' **new**	EHrv
- 'Warham'	CBro CElw EPot GKev IFoB MHom NMyG WCot
- 'Warham Rectory'	EHrv
- 'Wendy's Gold' ♀H5	CAvo CBro CSna EHrv IFoB MAsh
- 'Woodtown'	IMou
'Pom-pom' **new**	CAvo
'Porlock No 2' **new**	EHrv
'Pride o' the Mill'	CAvo GEdr
'Primrose Warburg'	CAvo CDes EHrv GEdr IFoB MAsh
'Ransom's Dwarf'	see *G. elwesii* 'Ransom's Dwarf'
reginae-olgae	ECho EHrv GKev IFoB MHom
- subsp. ***reginae-olgae*** ♀H3	EPot GKev
- - 'Cambridge'	EHrv MHom
- - 'Tilebarn Jamie' **new**	MHom
§ - - Winter-flowering Group	CBro
§ - subsp. ***vernalis***	EPot GKev IFoB LEdu NMyG WCot
- - 'Miss Adventure' **new**	EHrv
'Reverend Hailstone'	CAvo EHrv GEdr IFoB
'Richard Ayres' (d)	CAvo EHrv GEdr IFoB
rizehensis	CDes CLAP GKev IFoB MHom NMyG
- Baytop 34474	EHrv IFoB
'Rodmarton'	EHrv GEdr IFoB
'Ruth Birchall' **new**	EHrv
'S. Arnott' ♀H5	CAvo CBro CElw CExl CLAP ECha ECho EHrv EPfP EPot ERCP EWoo GBuc GKev IFoB LAma LCro LOPS LRHS MAsh MWat NBir NPol NRya SDeJ WBrk WCot WFar WHoo
'Saint Anne's'	CElw CSna GEdr IFoB MHom
'Scharlockii'	see *G. nivalis* Scharlockii Group
'Seagull'	CAvo CElw EHrv GEdr
'Sentinel'	CAvo CElw EHrv
'Silverwells'	CSna EHrv GEdr IFoB
'Sir Herbert Maxwell'	ITim MAsh
'Spindlestone Surprise'	CAvo EHrv EWoo GEdr NHar
'Sprite'	CAvo
'St Pancras' **new**	CAvo EHrv
§ 'Straffan' ♀H5	CAvo CBro CElw ECho EHrv EPot GEdr GKev IFoB MHom NMyG NPol WBrk WCot
'Sutton Courtenay'	CAvo CDes CSna
'The Apothecary'	EHrv
'The O'Mahoney'	see *G.* 'Straffan'
'The Wizard' **new**	CAvo
'Titania' (d)	CBro EHrv GEdr GKev IFoB MAsh MHom WShi
'Trotter's Merlin'	CElw

'Trumps' new	CAvo NHar
'Trymming'	CAvo
'Trymposter' new	CAvo EHrv
'Tubby Merlin'	CElw EHrv EWoo IFoB
× *valentinei* 'Compton Court'	CBro IFoB ITim
§ 'Washfield Colesbourne'	CElw EHrv EWoo
'Washfield Warham'	CElw ECha EHrv EWoo ITim MAsh NMyG
'Wasp'	CAvo GEdr MAsh NHar
'Welshway'	CAvo GEdr
'White Admiral'	SKHP
'White Dreams'	GEdr IFoB
'White Swan' Ballard (d)	CElw EWes ITim
'William Thomson'	CSna EWes
'Winifrede Mathias'	CElw EHrv MAsh
'Wisley Magnet'	EHrv
'Wonston Double'	see *G. nivalis* f. *pleniflorus* 'Wonston Double'
woronowii ♀H5	CBro CElw CLAP CTca CTri ECho EHrv EPfP EPot GKev IFoB LAma LCro LRHS MHom MWat NBir NMyG SCob SDeJ SDix SPer WBrk WCot WFar

Galax (*Diapensiaceae*)

aphylla	see *G. urceolata*
§ ***urceolata***	EBee ECho EPot IBlr MNrw

Galega (*Papilionaceae*)

bicolor	NBir SRms SWat
'Duchess of Bedford'	GBin
× ***hartlandii***	CExl
- 'Alba' ♀H7	ELon EWes GBin IBlr LRHS MArl MCot MRav SHar SMHy SWat WCot WHoo WSHC WWtn
- 'Lady Wilson' ♀H7	CWld ECtt ELon EWes GBin MArl MAvo MLHP SHar SRms WCot WHrl WOut
'Her Majesty'	see *G.* 'His Majesty'
§ 'His Majesty'	CDes EBee ECtt IFro MAvo MCot MLHP MRav WCot WPGP
officinalis	Widely available
- 'Alba'	CBod ECtt ELan EPfP GJos LEdu LPot MAvo MBel MBrN MHer MMuc MNHC SPer SRms WHer WHrl WKif WMoo
- Coconut Ice = 'Kelgal' (v)	SPer
- 'Lincoln Gold'	MTPN
orientalis	CDes EBee ECtt EWes LEdu MArl MAvo MCot MRav WCot WMoo WPGP WSHC

Galeobdolon see *Lamium*

Galeopsis (*Lamiaceae*)

tetrahit	WSFF

Galium (*Rubiaceae*)

aparine 'Nettleton Strangler' new	CNat
cruciata	see *Cruciata laevipes*
mollugo	CHab CWld
§ ***odoratum***	Widely available
verum	CArn CHab CWld ENfk GJos GPoy MCoo MHer MMuc MNHC NMir SEND SIde SRms

Galtonia (*Asparagaceae*)

candicans ♀H4	Widely available
- 'Moonbeam' (d)	EBee GKev
princeps	CSam CTca EBee ECha GBin GCra IMou LRHS WPGP
regalis	CExl CTca WPGP
viridiflora	CAvo CTca CWld EBee ECha ELan EPot ERCP GBin GCal GGal GKev IBoy LRHS MNrw NChi NWad SDeJ WCot WHil XLum

Galvezia (*Plantaginaceae*)

speciosa	CHll CSpe LRHS MCot

Gamblea (*Araliaceae*)

pseudoevodiifolia B&SWJ 11707	WCru

Gardenia (*Rubiaceae*)

augusta	see *G. jasminoides*
'Crown Jewel' PBR	EPfP LRHS MOWG SEle
florida L.	see *G. jasminoides*
grandiflora	see *G. jasminoides*
§ ***jasminoides*** ♀H1c	CArn CBcs EBak
- 'Kleim's Hardy'	Widely available
magnifica	MOWG
'Perfumed Petticoats'	WHlf

garlic see *Allium sativum*

garlic, elephant see *Allium ampeloprasum* 'Elephant'

Garrya ✿ (*Garryaceae*)

elliptica	CBcs CDul CMac COtt EBee EPfP EWTr GGal LPfy LRHS LSRN MAsh MBri MGos NPri NWea SCob SEND WFar WHar
- (f)	MJak MRav MSwo SWvt
- (m)	CDoC CTri ELon LAst MBlu NLar SGol SLim
- 'James Roof' (m) ♀H4	Widely available
× ***issaquahensis*** 'Glasnevin Wine' (m) ♀H4	CAbP CDul CJun ELan ELon EPfP IArd LRHS MAsh MBri MGos SCob SCoo SPer SPoG
- 'Pat Ballard' (m)	EPfP NLar
× ***thuretii***	CBcs CDul EBee EUJe LAst MBri NLar SEND SGol SPer

Gasteria ✿ (*Asphodelaceae*)

bicolor var. ***liliputana*** ♀H2	SPlb
carinata var. ***verrucosa***	EShb SPlb
ellaphieae	LToo
excelsa	LToo
gracilis variegated (v) new	WCot
nitida var. ***nitida*** variegated (v)	WCot
'Smokey'	EShb

× *Gaulnettya* see *Gaultheria*

Gaultheria ✿ (*Ericaceae*)

NJM 10.032	WPGP
antarctica	WThu
cardiosepala	WThu
crassa 'John Saxton'	WAbe
cuneata	ECho GEdr LRHS MAsh NHar WThu
forrestii	CExl
- BWJ 7809	WCru

hispida **new**	CPne
hispidula	ECho
itoana	ECho GEdr GJos NHar WThu
miqueliana	GEdr WThu
§ ***mucronata***	CDul EPfP LRHS MAsh MJak NWea WFar
- SDR 7051	GKev
- (m)	CMac CSBt CTri CWSG ELan EPfP MGos MMuc NEgg NWad SPer SRms WFar
- 'Alba' (f)	MJak
- 'Bell's Seedling' (f/m) ♀H6	CBcs CDoC CDul CLet CTri EBee ELan EPfP LRHS MAsh MMuc NBir NEgg NLar SCob SGbt SPer SPoG
- 'Cherry Ripe' (f)	CMac MMuc
- 'Crimsonia' (f) ♀H6	CBcs CLet CMac EPfP SRms
- 'Indian Lake'	NWad
- 'Lilacina' (f)	CMac MAsh
- 'Lilian' (f)	CSBt EPfP NWad
- Mother of Pearl	see *G. mucronata* 'Parelmoer'
- 'Mulberry Wine' (f) ♀H6	CBcs CSBt CTri ELan MHtn MMuc NEgg NHol SPer
§ - 'Parelmoer' (f)	CSBt
- 'Pink Pearl' (f) ♀H6	CLet SRms
- red-berried (f)	MJak
- 'Rosea' (f)	MJak
§ - 'Signaal' (f)	CBcs EBee ELan EPfP LRHS MAsh NEgg NLar NWad SCob SPer
- Signal	see *G. mucronata* 'Signaal'
§ - 'Sneeuwwitje' (f)	CBcs CDul ELan EPfP LRHS MAsh MMuc NBir SPer
- Snow White	see *G. mucronata* 'Sneeuwwitje'
- 'Thymifolia' (m)	EPfP
- 'Wintertime' (f) ♀H6	CMac SRms
§ ***myrsinoides***	WThu
'Pearls'	NHar NWad WAbe WThu
'Pink Champagne'	ITim
procumbens ♀H4	Widely available
- 'Very Berry'	CBod EShb NWad WFar
prostrata	see *G. myrsinoides*
pumila	LEdu NHar
schultesii	WThu
shallon	CAgr CBcs CSBt EPfP MJak MMuc NLar SPer SRms SWvt WFar
sinensis	NHar
- lilac-berried	GEdr
tetramera	CExl
thymifolia	NWad WThu
trichophylla	NHar
× ***wisleyensis***	LRHS SLon SRms
- 'Pink Pixie'	LRHS MAsh NLar
- 'Ruby'	CMac
- 'Wisley Pearl'	MMuc SCoo WFar
yunnanensis	CExl

Gaura (*Onagraceae*)

deep rose-flowered **new**	LRHS
lindheimeri ♀H4	CAby CMea CSBt CSpe CWib EBee ECha ELan EPfP LCro LHop LOPS LRHS MCot MGos MHer SBch SDix SPer SWvt WCAu WCFE WHar WHoo WMnd WOut XLum XSen
- Belleza Series	CRos CWCL EPau EPfP LRHS MBri SHil
- 'Blaze' PBR	LRHS
- Cherry Brandy = 'Gauchebra' PBR	CRos EAEE EBee ECtt ELan EPfP IPot LRHS LSun MBel MBri SHil SWvt WHar
- 'Chiffon'	SHar
- compact pink-flowered	CBod
- compact red	CBod
- 'Corrie's Gold' (v)	CAby CBod EAEE EBee ECha ECtt EHoe ELan EPfP LRHS MHer SPer WMnd
- 'Crimson Butterflies' PBR	EPfP
- 'Freefolk Rosy' **new**	SHar
- 'Gambit Rose' **new**	EBee
- 'Gambit White' **new**	EBee
- Gaudi Red **new**	LRHS
- Gaudi Pink = 'Gaudpin' PBR **new**	LRHS
- (Geyser Series) Geyser Pink = 'Gaudros' PBR	EBee LRHS
- - Geyser White = 'Gaudwwhi' PBR	EBee
§ - 'Heather's Delight'	MRav
- In the Pink	see *G. lindheimeri* 'Heather's Delight'
- 'Jo Adela' (v)	ECha EPfP
- Karalee Petite = 'Gauka'	CWCL EPfP
- Karalee Petite Improved	see *G. lindheimeri* Lillipop Pink
- Karalee Pink	MBri
- Karalee White = 'Nugauwhite' PBR	CRos CWCL EPfP LAst LHop LPfy LRHS MAvo MBri MCot NLar SCoo SHil SPer SPoG
§ - Lillipop Pink = 'Redgapi' PBR	CAby EPfP LRHS MBrN MBri NLar SCob SPoG
- 'My Melody' PBR (v)	WTor
- 'Occitania' (v)	XLum
- Papillon = 'Nugaupapil' PBR	ECtt SPer SPoG
- 'Passionate Blush' PBR	CBcs CChe EAEE ECtt EPfP LAst LRHS LSou MGos SLon SPad SPoG SRms WHil
- 'Passionate Pink'	LRHS
- 'Passionate Rainbow' PBR (v)	CRos CWCL EPfP LAst LBMP LRHS SHil SPad SPoG SRms
- 'Pink Dwarf'	EBee EPfP MGos SAdn
- Pink Fountain = 'Walgaupf'	LRHS
- 'Pink Gin'	EBee LRHS LSou SPoG
- 'Rosyjane'	Widely available
- 'Ruby Ruby'	SHar
- short	WSHC
- 'Siskiyou Pink'	CBcs CSBt CWCL EAEE EAJP EBee ECha ECtt EHoe ELan EPfP LCro LOPS LPal LRHS MMuc MWat SAdn SCob SMad SPer SWat SWvt WCFE WGwG WMnd XLum XSen
- Snow Fountain = 'Walsnofou'	LRHS
- 'Summer Breeze'	CSpe EAJP LRHS LSun NGBl SBea SPhx
- 'Summer Emotions' **new**	MNrw
- 'The Bride'	CTri EAEE EBee ECtt EPfP LRHS LSRN MBel MMuc MNHC MRav MWat NBFr SAdn SBod SGbt SPav SPer SWvt WGwG
- 'Tutti Frutti'	CMac LRHS LSou SCob SPoG
- 'Vanilla'	CKno CMac CWCL LRHS LSou SPoG
I - 'Variegata' (v)	CRos LRHS SHil SRms
- 'Whirling Butterflies'	CBod CKno CSpe CWCL ECGP ECtt ELan EPfP GMaP LCro LOPS LPfy LRHS MWat SCob SMad SPer SWat SWvt WWEG
- 'White Dove'	LRHS LSou
- 'White Heron'	MNrw
sinuata	CAby CFis SHar

Gaylussacia (*Ericaceae*)

baccata (F)	CMac

Gazania (*Asteraceae*)

sp.	SVic
'Bicton Orange'	CSam ECtt SCoo SVen
'Big Kiss White Flame' (Kiss Series)	LBuc
'Big Kiss Yellow Flame' (Kiss Series)	LBuc
'Blackberry Ripple'	EBee SCoo
'Blackcurrant Ice'	MCot
'Christopher'	SCoo
'Christopher Lloyd'	ECtt
'Cookei'	CSpe
'Cream Beauty'	MCot
Daybreak Series	LAst
- 'Daybreak Bronze'	LAst
'Kiss Bronze Star' (Kiss Series)	SVen
'Lemon Beauty'	ECtt
'Magic'	SCoo
'Orange Beauty'	ELan
rigens 'Variegata' (v)	ELan
'Talent'	SEND
Tiger Eye = 'Gazte' (v)	LAst LSou
Totonaca = 'Suga212' (Sunbathers Series)	LAst

Geissorhiza (*Iridaceae*)

aspera	CTre
tulbaghensis	CTre

Gelidocalamus (*Poaceae*)

fangianus	see *Ampelocalamus mocrophyllum*

Gelsemium (*Gelsemiaceae*)

rankinii	EBee LRHS
sempervirens ♀H1c	CArn CHll CRHN EBee LRHS LSRN MOWG SBrt SLim SPoG

Genista (*Papilionaceae*)

aetnensis ♀H5	CDul ELan EPfP LRHS MGil MMHG SBrt SEND SPer SRms WSHC
§ ***canariensis*** ♀H1c	CExl CSBt CWib
carinalis	GJos
cinerea	WCFE
decumbens	see *Cytisus decumbens*
'Emerald Spreader'	see *G. pilosa* 'Yellow Spreader'
fragrans	see *G. canariensis*
hispanica	CBcs CDul CSBt ELan EPfP GGal MGos NLar SCob SEND SPer SRms SWvt WCFE
humifusa	see *G. pulchella*
lydia ♀H5	Widely available
§ ***maderensis***	LRHS SHil
monosperma	see *Retama monosperma*
pilosa	EPot MAsh
- 'Goldilocks'	LRHS MMuc
- 'Lemon Spreader'	see *G. pilosa* 'Yellow Spreader'
- var. ***minor***	NLar WAbe
- 'Procumbens' ♀H5	CMea EPot GEdr SRot
- 'Vancouver Gold'	CBcs ELan EPfP MGos MRav SPer SRms
§ - 'Yellow Spreader'	CBcs MAsh MSwo
§ 'Porlock' ♀H3	CBcs CDoC CDul CExl CLet CMac CSBt CTri CWib EPfP GGal LBMP LRHS MAsh MBri MMuc MRav SEND SHil WHor
§ ***pulchella***	CTri GCrg
sagittalis	CTri GJos LRHS MMuc NBir SPer WWFP
§ × ***spachiana*** ♀H1c	CTri SPoG
subcapitata	WAbe
tinctoria	CArn CHab GJos GPoy MCot MHer WHer
§ - 'Flore Pleno' (d) ♀H6	CLet ECho
- 'Moesiaca'	WAbe
- 'Plena'	see *G. tinctoria* 'Flore Pleno'
- 'Royal Gold' ♀H6	CWib EBee MRav NWad SPer SPlb
villarsii	see *G. pulchella*

Gentiana ✿ (*Gentianaceae*)

sp.	LLWG
§ ***acaulis*** ♀H5	CMea CPla ECho EDAr EPfP EPot GKev LHop LRHS MAsh NGdn NHar NLar NSla SBch SPlb SRms WAbe
- SDR 1323 **new**	GKev
- f. ***alba***	WThu
- 'Belvedere'	EPot
- 'Coelestina'	WThu
- 'Dinarica'	see *G. dinarica*
- 'Holzmannii'	IVic WAbe
- 'Krumrey'	EPot GEdr
- 'Luna'PBR	NLar
- 'Max Frei'	NHar
I - 'Maxima Enzian'	EPot GEdr
- 'Rannoch'	EPot GEdr
- 'Stumpy'	GEdr
- 'Trotter's Variety'	EPot WAbe
- 'Undulatifolia'	EPot
- 'Velkokvensis'	EPot IVic
'Alex Duguid'	GEdr IVic LRHS NHar
'Amethyst'	EPot GEdr LRHS NHar SPer WAbe
angulosa misapplied	see *G. verna* 'Angulosa'
angustifolia	WAbe XEll
'Ann's Special'	GEdr
asclepiadea ♀H5	CLAP CSpe CTal CTri ECho ELan GCra GEdr GMaP LEdu LRHS MNrw NBid NBir NCGa NLar SGSe SPer SPoG SRms SSpi WBor WCFE WHoo WKif WSHC
- 'Alba'	CCon CLAP EBee GCal GEdr GKev GMaP LEdu LRHS NBid SGSe SPer SPoG SRms WCFE
- dark blue-flowered **new**	GCal WPGP
- 'Knightshayes'	CCon EBee GKev NLar
- pale blue-flowered	SGSe
- 'Phyllis'	GKev
- 'Pink Cascade'	SGSe
- 'Pink Swallow'	GEdr GQue NLar NMyG SGSe WWEG
- 'Rosea'	GEdr GKev MNrw
atuntsiensis	GKev
'Balmoral'PBR	GMaP NHar
'Barbara Lyle'	WAbe
bavarica var. ***subacaulis***	SPlb
× ***bernardii***	see *G.* × *stevenagensis* 'Bernardii'
'Berrybank Dome'	GEdr GMaP LRHS SPer
'Berrybank Sky'	GAbr GEdr GMaP LRHS
'Berrybank Snowflakes'	GMaP
'Berrybank Star'	GEdr GMaP
bisetaea	SRms
'Blauer Diamant'	GEdr
'Blauer Kobold' **new**	GEdr

	'Blauer Stern'	IVic
	'Blauer Zwerg'	GEdr
	'Blue Flame'	GEdr
	'Blue Heaven'	EPot GEdr
	'Blue Magic'[PBR]	EBee LRHS
	'Blue Sea'	LRHS
	'Blue Silk' ♀[H5]	CSma EPot EWes GEdr GKev IVic LRHS NHar SPoG WAbe
	brachyphylla	WAbe
	'Braemar'[PBR]	GMaP NHar
*	***burrowthii*** **new**	GEdr
	cachemirica **new**	GAbr
	'Cairngorm'	GEdr LRHS NHar
	'Carmen'	GEdr
	× ***caroli***	WAbe
	clusii	WAbe
*	- ***alboviolacea***	LLHF
	'Compact Gem'	EPot GEdr NHar WAbe
§	***cruciata***	GEdr MMHG NLar NPri
§	***dahurica***	ECho GEdr NGdn NLar NSla XLum
	'Dark Hedgehog'	GEdr
	decumbens	GKev
	depressa	EPot GEdr GKev WAbe
	'Devonhall'	GEdr IVic NHar NWad
	'Diana'[PBR]	LRHS NLar
§	***dinarica***	ECho EPot NHar SIgm
	- 'Colonel Stitt'	GEdr WThu
	- 'Frocheneite'	EPot
	'Dumpy'	GEdr
	'Elehn'	GEdr NHar
	'Elizabeth'	GEdr
	'Ettrick'	GEdr IVic
	'Eugen's Allerbester' (d)	CSma GEdr GKev GMaP IVic LRHS NHar NHol NLar NRya NWad SPer WAbe
	'Eugen's Bester'	NHar
	farreri	WAbe
	- Silken Star Group	WAbe
	'Faszination' **new**	GEdr
	fetissowii	see *G. macrophylla* var. *fetissowii*
	'Gellerhard'	GEdr
	georgei	EPot
	'Gewahn'	GEdr IVic NHar
I	'Glamis Strain'	GEdr LRHS NHar
	'Glen Moy'	GEdr
	'Glendevon'	GEdr WAbe
§	***gracilipes***	GEdr GKev LLHF NSla SPlb SRms XLum
	- 'Yuatensis'	see *G. macrophylla* var. *fetissowii*
	'Henry'	GEdr WAbe
	hexaphylla	EPot GEdr
	Inshriach hybrids	LRHS
	'Inverleith'	GEdr LRHS NHol SPlb
	'Iona'[PBR]	GMaP NHar
	'Joan Ward'	LRHS SPer
	'John Aitken'	GEdr
	'John Ward'	LRHS
	'Juwel'	GEdr
	'Kobold'	GEdr
	kochiana	see *G. acaulis*
	kurroo var. ***brevidens***	see *G. dahurica*
	lagodechiana	see *G. septemfida* var. *lagodechiana*
	ligustica	EPot
	'Little Diamond'[PBR]	LRHS NLar
	'Lucerna'	EPfP GEdr GKev LRHS
	lutea	EBee GAbr GCal GPoy LLHF SRms
	- SDR 6302 **new**	GKev
	× ***macaulayi***	CPla
	- 'Blue Bonnets'	GEdr
	- 'Elata'	IVic NWad
	- 'Kidbrooke Seedling'	EWes GEdr GMaP LRHS WAbe
	- 'Kingfisher'	CPla GEdr IVic LRHS NBir WAbe
§	- 'Wells's Variety'	LRHS
§	***macrophylla*** var. ***fetissowii***	LLHF
	makinoi 'Marsha'[PBR]	CHll GEdr LRHS MMHG NLar SPoG
	- 'White Magic'[PBR] **new**	GEdr
	'Margaret'	GEdr WAbe
	'Maryfield'	GEdr
	'Melanie'	GEdr NHar
	'Multiflora'	LRHS
	'Mystic'[PBR]	NLar
	occidentalis	EPot
	ornata	LRHS
	paradoxa ♀[H5]	GKev LLHF NSla SBrt WAbe
	paradoxa × ***septemfida***	GKev
	phlogifolia	see *G. cruciata*
	pneumonanthe	LRHS NLar SPlb
	pumila subsp. ***delphinensis***	WAbe
	purdomii	see *G. gracilipes*
	'Sapphire Blue'	GEdr
	saxosa	GCrg GKev ITim LRHS NBir NSla WAbe WIce
	scabra	LRHS
	- 'Royal Stripe' **new**	EBee
	- 'Zuikorindo'	NLar
	'Selektra'	GEdr IVic
	septemfida ♀[H5]	LHop LRHS MAsh MBri MJak NBir NPri NSla SPlb SRms WHoo WKif
	- 'Alba'	LLHF
	- var. ***kolakovskyi***	LLHF
§	- var. ***lagodechiana*** ♀[H5]	LLHF LRHS NPri SRms XLum
	'Serenity'	CSma GEdr IVic LRHS NHar NLar NWad WAbe
	'Shot Silk' ♀[H5]	EWes GAbr GEdr GJos GMaP LRHS MGos NBir NHar NHol SPoG WAbe WIce
	'Silken Giant'	GEdr WAbe
	'Silken Night'	GEdr NHar WAbe
	'Silken Seas'	CSma GEdr NHar NWad WAbe
	'Silken Skies' ♀[H5]	GEdr NHar WAbe
	'Silken Surprise'	WAbe
	sino-ornata ♀[H5]	CPla CSma CTri ECho GAbr GMaP LSRN MAsh MBri NCGa SRms WAbe WIce
	- SDR 5127	MGos
	- 'Alba'	CPla
	- 'Angel's Wings'	GEdr LRHS
	- 'Bellatrix'	GEdr IVic NHar
	- 'Blautopf'	GEdr IVic
	- 'Brin Form'	SRms
	- 'Downfield'	GKev LRHS
	- 'Edith Sarah'	GEdr IVic
	- 'Gorau Glas'	WAbe
	- 'Mary Lyle'	GEdr
	- 'Oha'	GEdr IVic
	- 'Purity'	GEdr LRHS NHar WAbe
	- 'Starlight'	GEdr NHar
	- 'Weisser Traum'	GEdr IVic LRHS NHar NHol NLar SPer
	- 'White Wings'	GEdr
	'Sir Rupert'	GEdr IVic NHar
	'Sternschuppe'	GKev
	× ***stevenagensis***	CPla LRHS

§ - 'Bernardii'	GEdr NHar WAbe
- dark-flowered	WAbe
straminea	EPot LLHF
'Strathmore' ♀H5	CSma EWes GAbr GEdr GKev GMaP LRHS NBir NHar SPer SPlb WAbe
'Surprise' **new**	GEdr
syringea	WAbe
szechenyii	LLHF
ternifolia 'Cangshan'	GEdr WAbe
- 'Dali'	GEdr NHar
'The Caley'	GEdr GMaP NHar
tibetica	CArn CCon GCal GPoy XLum
- PAB 2357	LEdu WPGP
Tough's form **new**	GEdr
triflora var. ***japonica***	NLar WWEG
'True Blue'	SPad
veitchiorum	EPot LLHF WAbe
verna	CSma ECho EDAr EPfP EPot EWes LCro LHop LOPS LRHS LSRN NPri NSla SPlb SPoG WAbe WHoo
- 'Alba'	GEdr WAbe
§ - 'Angulosa' ♀H5	MAsh
- subsp. ***angulosa*** (Bieb.) V.E.Avet.	WIce
- subsp. ***oschtenica***	WAbe
- subsp. ***tergestina***	GKev WAbe
'Violette'	GEdr LRHS NWad
waltonii	EWes
wellsii	see *G.* × *macaulayi* 'Wells's Variety'
wilsonii	GKev ITim
wutaiensis	see *G. macrophylla* var. *fetissowii*

Geranium ✿ (*Geraniaceae*)

aconitifolium misapplied	see *G. palmatum*
aconitifolium L'Hér.	see *G. rivulare*
'Adam Moreland'	WOut
'Adi'	WCot
'Alan Mayes'	CBod CElw CMac CNec ECtt EPPr EWoo GBin GBuc GKin LRHS LSou NGdn SBod SRGP WCra WFar WPnP WPtf
'Alan's Blue'	NChi
albanum	CElw EPPr GLog LLWP MMuc NCot SDix SRGP WMoo
anemonifolium	see *G. palmatum*
'Ann Folkard' ♀H7	Widely available
'Ann Folkard' × ***psilostemon***	LSRN
'Anne Thomson' ♀H7	Widely available
× ***antipodeum*** 'Chocolate Candy'[PBR]	LBuc LRHS MGos
- 'Pink Spice'[PBR]	CWGN EWoo GKin LBuc LRHS MGos SRms
- 'Purple Passion'[PBR] **new**	LBuc LRHS
- 'Sea Spray'	CMHG NBro WMnd
- 'Stanhoe'	LEdu MHCG
- (*G. sessiliflorum* subsp. *novae-zelandiae* 'Nigricans' × *G. traversii* var. *elegans*)	SRms
aristatum	ECGP EPPr EWes GCal MNrw MRav NBir SGbt SRGP WCru WMoo
armenum	see *G. psilostemon*
asphodeloides	CBod CElw IFro LRHS MBNS MNrw MWhi NBid NBir NCot SGbt SPav SRGP WBrk WFar WMnd WMoo WPnP
- subsp. ***asphodeloides*** white-flowered	CElw SRGP WMoo
- 'Starlight'	NBid
atlanticum Hook. f.	see *G. malviflorum*
'Azure Rush'	CMos EBee ECtt EWTr ILea IPot LBMP LRHS LSqH MWhi NCot SPoG SRms WCAu WCra WPnP
'Azzurro'	EBee LRHS MAsh NCot
'Baby Blue'	see *G. himalayense* 'Baby Blue'
'Benjamin Browne'	NCot
'Bertie Crûg'	CBod CWld ECtt ELon LLHF NBir NLar SPer SRms SRot SWat SWvt
'Bill Tucker' **new**	MAvo
biuncinatum	IFro
'Blue Boy'	NLar
'Blue Cloud' ♀H7	Widely available
'Blue Pearl'	EPPr MAvo NBir NSti SRGP WMoo
§ Blue Sunrise = 'Blogold'[PBR] ♀H7	Widely available
'Blushing Turtle'[PBR]	CBod CMos EBee LBuc NCot NLar NSti WCAu WCra
'Bob's Blunder'	ECtt EPfP LHop LLWG LRHS MBNS MBel MHol MNrw MSCN SAko SPoG SRGP SRms SWvt WCot WCra WFar WHoo
bohemicum	SRGP WHer
- 'Orchid Blue'	CSpe SWvt
'Brookside' ♀H7	Widely available
'Buckland Beauty'	CExl EBee EWes SBch
'Buxton's Blue'	see *G. wallichianum* 'Buxton's Variety'
caeruleatum	EBee EPPr GCal NLar SBrt
caffrum	CPla SPlb SRGP
canariense	see *G. reuteri*
candicans misapplied	see *G. lambertii*
§ × ***cantabrigiense***	CMac CRos CSBt ECtt LRHS MHer MNrw NBir NBro NLar NPer NSti SBod SRms WBrk WCru WHea WMoo
- 'Berggarten'	EBee EPPr GBin NLar SAko SRGP WBrk WCra WPtf
- 'Biokovo'	Widely available
- 'Cambridge'	Widely available
- Crystal Rose = 'Abpp' **new**	EPPr
- 'Hanne'	EBee EPPr EWes WCra
- 'Harz'	EPPr SAko WBrk WCra
- 'Hilary Rendall'	EPPr
- 'Karmina'	CBod CFis CRos EBee EPPr EPfP GCal LRHS MWhi NPri SBod SHil SRGP SWat WCra WHoo WMoo WPnP WWEG XEll XLum
- 'Rosalina'	EPPr WBrk
- 'Show Time'	EPPr WBrk
- 'St Ola'	Widely available
- 'Vorjura'	EBee EPPr SAko WBrk WCra
- 'Westray'[PBR]	Widely available
'Chantilly'	CBod CFis CLAP EBee ECtt EPPr EPfP EWTr LRHS MAvo MNrw NBir WCra WCru WFib WGwG WMoo WPtf
'Chipchase Castle'	NChi
christensenianum B&SWJ 8022	WCru
cinereum	CNec ECho
- 'Apple Blossom'	see *G.* × *lindavicum* 'Apple Blossom'

- 'Elizabeth'	ECtt GBuc LSRN
- 'Sateene'[PBR]	CSma ECtt EPPr GMaP SRms SRot WCra WFib
(Cinereum Group) 'Alice'[PBR]	CMos CSma EBee EPPr GMaP LLHF LSRN MBNS NHar NLar NSti SRms SRot WCra
- 'Ballerina' ♀[H5]	Widely available
- 'Carol'	CSma CWGN EAEE ECtt EPPr EWes GKin LRHS LSRN LSou MBNS MRav NHar NLar NSti SWvt WFar WFib
- 'Lambrook Helen'	CExl CFis MHer
- 'Laurence Flatman'	CExl CKno CLet CPla CSpe ECtt ELan EPfP EPri EWoo GBuc GMaP IPot LAst LBMP LRHS LSou MAsh NBid NEgg NHar NQui NRya NSla SRms SRot SWat WCra WHoo WMnd
- 'Lizabeth'[PBR]	EBee ECtt EPPr GBin LSou NHar NLar NPri WCot WCra
- 'Penny Lane'[PBR]	CMos WCra
- 'Purple Pillow'	CMos CWGN CWib ECtt ELan EPPr EPot EWoo IPot LAst LLHF LSRN LSou MCot MRav MSCN NHar NSti SCob SGol SPer SRms SRot STPC SWvt WCra WFar
- René Macé = 'Progera'	SRkn
- Rothbury Gem = 'Gerfos'[PBR] ♀[H5]	ECtt ELon MAsh MRav MSCN NChi SKHP SPer SWvt WCra
- 'Signal'	ECtt EPPr EPot MAsh NHar NPri WCra
§ - 'Thumbling Hearts'	CMos CWGN EBee MHol MSCN MTis NSti SCob WCot WHoo
- Thumping Heart	see *G.* 'Thumbling Hearts'
'Claridge Druce'	see *G.* × *oxonianum* 'Claridge Druce'
clarkei 'Kashmir Pink'	Widely available
§ - 'Kashmir White'	Widely available
- 'Mount Stewart'	CExl CHid EBee EPfP WCra WCru WPGP
- (Purple-flowered Group) 'Kashmir Purple'	Widely available
- Raina 82.83	MNrw
clarum B&SWJ 10246	WCru
collinum	EPPr NBir NCot SRGP WCra WCru
'Colour Carousel'	EBee GBin
'Coombland White'	CBod CCon CExl CHid ECtt GBuc LRHS LSou MAvo MMuc NLar NSti SBea SKHP SPer SRGP WCot WCra WMoo WPnP
'Coquet Island'	EBee EPPr
'Criss Canning'	EBee EPPr
'Cyril's Blue'	EBee NChi
'Cyril's Fancy'	EBee EPPr
dahuricum	WCru
dalmaticum ♀[H5]	Widely available
- 'Album'	EBee ECho ECtt ELan EPPr EPfP EPot GBuc LRHS MRav NRya SBch SRGP SRms SWat WAbe WCru
- 'Bressingham Pink'	EBee ECtt EPPr
- 'Bridal Bouquet'	ECtt EPot LLHF NChi NCot NSla
- 'Croftlea'	GBuc
- 'Stades Hellrosa'	EPPr
dalmaticum* × *macrorrhizum	see *G.* × *cantabrigiense*
'Danny Boy' ♀[H7]	EBee NCot
delavayi misapplied	see *G. sinense*
'Deux Fleurs'	MAvo
'Devon Pride'	CElw EBee EPPr SRGP
'Dilys' ♀[H7]	CBod CElw CFis CMos CPrp EBee ELan EPPr GBuc MAvo MLHP MNrw MTis NBir NChi NCot NDov NGdn NLar SRGP WCra WCru WHal WMoo WPnP
'Distant Hills'	CDes EBee EPPr SRGP WCra
'Diva'	EBee ELan EPPr EPfP LLHF NCot
'Double Jewel'	see *G. pratense* 'Double Jewel'
Dragon Heart = 'Bremdra'[PBR]	CLAP CMos ECtt EWTr EWoo IPot LSRN MAvo MNrw MPnt NLar NSti SCob SKHP SPoG STPC WCAu WCra WHil WPnP
Dreamland = 'Bremdream'[PBR]	CPou EBee EWoo LCro LSou MHol STPC WCot WCra
'Dusky Crûg'	CSBt CSam ECtt EHoe ELan ELon EPPr EPfP EWTr GBBs GKin LAst MAsh MHol MPie NEgg NLar NSti SPoG SWvt WCot WCra WCru WFar WGwG WMnd
'Dusky Rose'	CAby CMos CPrp CSpe ECtt ELan EWoo GKev LBuc NLar SHar SRot WCra WFar
'Edith May'	EBee WCra
'Elke'	Widely available
'Ella'	CWGN
'Elworthy Eyecatcher'	CDes CElw MNrw NCot SRGP WPGP
'Elworthy Tiger'	CElw MAvo WCra
'Emily'	SRGP
endressii ♀[H7]	CBod CBre CElw CNec ECha ECho EPfP GBBs GLog GMaP LPot MBNS MCot MHer MMuc NBro NCot NPer NPol SCob SEND SPlb SRGP SRms SWvt WCra WHar WMoo WPtf XLum
- 'Album'	see *G.* 'Mary Mottram'
- 'Castle Drogo' ♀[H7]	EPPr
- 'Prestbury White'	see *G.* × *oxonianum* 'Prestbury Blush'
- 'Rose'	MAvo
- 'Wargrave Pink'	see *G.* × *oxonianum* 'Wargrave Pink'
erianthum	GMaP IMou MLHP NLar SRGP WCru WMoo
- 'Axeltree'	WCot
- 'Cally Pearl'	GCal
- 'Calm Sea'	CDes WCru WMoo
- 'Neptune'	WCru
- 'Pale Blue Yonder'	EBee EWes WCra
eriostemon Fischer	see *G. platyanthum*
'Eureka Blue'	CPou ECtt LRHS MHol MTis NCot NLar NSti SPoG WCot WCra WPnP
'Eva'	WCra WPnP
'Expression'	see *G.* 'Tanya Rendall'
'Extravaganza'	EBee EWes
'Farncombe Cerise Star'	CElw WCra
§ ***farreri***	CExl ECho EPot LHop LLHF LRHS NBir WOut
'Fay Anna'	NCot WFar
'Foundling'	MAvo
fremontii	EWld
goldmannii	SKHP
gracile	CFis EBee GMaP LRHS LSou MNrw NBir NCot SRGP WBrk WCru WMoo WPtf
- 'Blanche'	EPPr LRHS MNrw
- 'Blush'	CElw EPPr EWes LPla WCra
- 'Golden Gracile'	see *G.* 'Mrs Judith Bradshaw'

Name	Suppliers
grandiflorum	see *G. himalayense*
'Grasmere'	ECtt
'Gwen Thompson'	WOut
gymnocaulon	CMac GKin SRGP WCru
- from Lagonaki, Caucasus **new**	SBrt
gymnocaulon* × *platypetalum	EBee NCot
'Harmony'	EBee EPPr
harveyi	CMea EWes NChi SPhx SRGP WKif
§ ***hayatanum***	LRHS
- B&SWJ 164	NLar WCru WMoo
'Hilary'	WWtn
§ ***himalayense***	CBcs CMHG CNec ECha ELan EPfP LAst LRHS MBNS MLHP MMuc MRav MWat NBir NBro SEND SPlb SRGP SRms SRot SWat WCra WFar WFib WMoo WPnP WWEG XLum
- CC 1957 from Tibetan border	CExl EPPr
- ***alpinum***	see *G. himalayense* 'Gravetye'
§ - 'Baby Blue'	CElw CMos EBee ECtt ELon EPPr GBuc GCal GCra LRHS MAvo MNrw MTis NCot NGdn NLar NSti SRGP WBrk WCAu WCra WCru WFib WMoo WPnP WPtf
- 'Birch Double'	see *G. himalayense* 'Plenum'
- 'Derrick Cook'	CBod CCon CDes CElw CLAP CPrp EBee ECtt EPPr EPfP EWTr GBuc MAvo MSpe MTis MWhi NCot NSti SPoG STPC WBrk WCAu WCra WHal WHoo
- 'Devil's Blue'	EPPr SRGP WCra WPtf
§ - 'Gravetye'	Widely available
- 'Irish Blue'	CElw EBee EPPr EWTr EWoo GBee GBuc GCal GCra LRHS MSpe NCot NLar NPol NSti SRGP WCra WCru WFib WMoo WPnP WPtf
- ***meeboldii***	see *G. himalayense*
- 'Pale Irish Blue'	EBee EPPr GCal NCot
§ - 'Plenum' (d)	Widely available
- 'Spiti Valley'	WPtf
himalayense* × *pratense	WFib
ibericum misapplied	see *G.* × *magnificum*
ibericum ambig.	SRms
ibericum Cav.	CSBt CTri LRHS NBre SPav SRGP SRms
- 'Blue Springs'	ECtt LAll
- subsp. ***ibericum***	CMac EPPr
- subsp. ***jubatum***	EPPr MNrw SGbt SRms WCru
- - 'White Zigana'	CAby CBod CFis EBee ECtt EPPr EWTr EWoo LRHS LSRN MTis MWhi NCot NLar NSti SBea SRms WCra WFar WPnP WWtn
- subsp. ***jubatum* × *renardii***	SWvt
- var. ***platypetalum*** misapplied	see *G.* × *magnificum*
- var. ***platypetalum*** Boiss.	see *G. platypetalum* Fisch. & C.A.Mey.
§ - 'Ushguli Grijs'	EBee EPPr IMou NCot NLar WCot
ibericum* × *libani	CDes EBee
incanum	CAbP EBee ELon EWes GCal NBir SRGP SVen
- var. ***incanum***	SBch
- white-flowered	SRGP
'Ivan' ♀H7	CElw CLAP CMos CPrp EBee ECtt EPPr GBuc LPla LRHS NChi NLar SRGP WCra WCru WFib WHoo WMoo
'Ivybridge Eyeful'	CDes
'Jean Armour'	CBod CDes CPrp ECtt GBuc LRHS NDov NLar SPoG SRGP WCra WFar WGwG WPGP
'Johnson's Blue'	Widely available
'Jolly Bee'	see *G.* Rozanne
'Joy'	CBod CLAP CPrp EBee ECtt EPPr GBin GBuc LRHS LSou LSun MAvo MCot MRav NBir NCGa NChi NEgg NLar NSti NWad SBch SRGP SRms WCot WCra WFib WGwG WMoo WPnP
§ 'Kanahitobanawa'	CDes EBee MAvo WCra WSHC
'Karen Wouters'	EPPr NCot WPtf
'Kashmir Blue'	CExl ECtt ELan EPPr EPfP EWTr GMaP LRHS MAvo MTis NCot NLar SWat SWvt WCra WFar WKif WMoo WPtf
'Kashmir Green'	CLAP ECtt EPfP LLHF NSti WCra WMoo
§ 'Khan'	CElw CFis EPPr EWes IFro LRHS MAvo NCot NEoE SDys SMHy SRGP WCra WCru
'Kirsty'	EBee EWes WCra
kishtvariense	GCal IMou MNrw MRav NSti WCra WCru
koraiense	CFis WCra WMoo
- B&SWJ 797	WCru
- B&SWJ 878	CExl EBee WCru
koreanum misapplied	see *G. hayatanum*
koreanum ambig.	CPla NLar WMoo
- B&SWJ 602	CExl WCru
krameri	IMou NLar
- B&SWJ 1142	CExl WCru
'Lakwijk Star'	CBod ECtt ILea IPot LHop NCot NLar WCra
§ ***lambertii***	EWes GBuc NBir
- 'Swansdown'	GBuc GCal
'Larch Cottage Velvet' **new**	MAvo
I ***libani***	ELon EPPr LLWP MCot NBid NSti WBrk WCot WSHC
- RCB RL B-2	CDes WCot WCra
libani* × *peloponnesiacum	WPGP
'Light Dilys'	CMos EBee EPPr NDov WCra
'Lilac Ice'	CMos ECtt EPfP GMaP LRHS MAsh NLar NSti SCob SPoG WCAu WCra
§ × ***lindavicum*** 'Apple Blossom'	EBee EPot MAsh NSla WFar
linearilobum* subsp. *transversale	SRot WPnP
I - - 'Laciniatum'	SBrt WCot
- - 'Rose Foundling'	SBrt
§ 'Little David'	CElw EBee NLar WCra
'Little Devil'	see *G.* 'Little David'
'Little Gem'	CElw EBee ECtt EPPr LRHS NChi NDov SBch WFar WHoo WMoo
lucidum	NCot WOut WPtf WSFF
'Luscious Linda'	MAvo
'Lydia'	EBee SRGP
§ ***macrorrhizum***	CArn CBod CSBt ECrN EPfP GKev GKin IFro LEdu LOPS LSun MCot MLHP MRav MWat MWhi NBro

	Plant	Suppliers
		NCGa SRms SWat WCAu WCra WFar WHar WHil XLum
	- AL & JS 90179YU	CHid EPPr
	- 'Album'	CBre CElw CPrp ECha ELan EPPr EWTr GMaP LRHS MAsh MBel MSpe MSwo MWat NBid NBro NChi SAko SWat WBrk WCot WCra WCru WFib WMoo WWEG
	- 'Bevan's Variety'	Widely available
	- 'Bulgaria'	EPPr WBrk WCra
	- 'Cham-ce'	ECtt EPPr WBrk WCra
	- 'Czakor'	Widely available
I	- 'De Bilt'	EPPr EWes WBrk
	- 'Freundorf'	EBee EPPr EWes GCal LPla SAko WBrk WCra WOut
	- 'Frohenleiten' **new**	WFib
	- 'Glacier'	EPPr EWes
	- 'Ingwersen's Variety' ♀H7	Widely available
	- 'Lohfelden'	CLAP EPPr EWes GBuc GCal SRGP WBrk WCra WCru
	- 'Mount Olympus'	see *G. macrorrhizum* 'White-Ness'
	- 'Mytikas'	EPPr WBrk WPtf
	- 'Olympos' **new**	EPPr
	- 'Pindus'	CBod CLAP CPrp EBee EPPr GAbr GBuc LRHS MHer NLar NSti SPoG SRGP WBrk WCra WCru WFar WPnP WPtf
	- 'Prionia'	EPPr GCal SAko WBrk
	- 'Purpurrot'	WBrk
	- 'Ridsko'	EPPr GCal LPla NBro SRGP WBrk WCra WCru
	- ***roseum***	see *G. macrorrhizum*
	- 'Rotblut'	EPPr SRGP WBrk
	- 'Sandwijck'	EBee EPPr MAvo MWhi SBch WCra
	- 'Snow Sprite'	CMea CPla EPPr LLHF MHer NEoE NLar WBrk WHrl WPtf XLum
	- 'Spessart'	CBar EBee ELan ELon EPPr EPfP EWoo GMaP LBMP LHop LPal LRHS MMuc NBid NLar SCob SEND SGbt SPer SPhx SPoG SWvt WBrk WCra WFib WHar WRHF XLum
	- 'Variegatum' (v)	CFis CNec EBee ELan GMaP LEdu LPot NBir SRGP SRms WBrk WCot WMnd WWEG
	- 'Velebit'	EPPr SRGP WBrk WCru XLum
§	- 'White-Ness' ♀H7	Widely available
	macrostylum	WCot WCru
I	- 'Caeruleum'	WPtf
	- 'Leonidas'	EPPr WPnP
	- 'Talish'	EPPr
	- 'Uln Oag Triag'	EPPr
	maculatum	CFis LRHS MAvo MCot MMHG MNrw MRav NLar NSti SRGP SWat WCru WHal
	- from Kath Dryden	EPPr
	- f. ***albiflorum***	CElw CLAP EBee ELan ELon EPPr EPfP EWoo LRHS MBel MNrw MWhi NChi NLar NSti SRGP WBrk WCra WCru WMoo WPnP
	- 'Beth Chatto'	Widely available
	- 'Elizabeth Ann'PBR ♀H7	CElw CLAP CSam CWGN EBee ECtt EPPr EWoo GAbr LHop LRHS LSou MHol MNrw MTis NGdn NLar NSti NWad WCot WCra WFar WFib WHil WMoo WPGP WPnP
	- 'Espresso'	Widely available
	- purple-flowered	EPPr
	- 'Putnam County'	EBee EPPr WCra
	- 'Shameface'	EPPr WMoo
	- 'Silver Buttons'	CDes EBee
	- 'Smoky Mountain'	EPPr
	- 'Spring Purple'	CDes CElw EBee EPPr MAvo NChi NLar WCra
	- 'Sweetwater'	EPPr
	- 'Vickie Lynn'	EBee EPPr NChi WCra
	maderense ♀H3	CAbb CAby CBcs CCon CPla CSpe CTre ECre ELan EShb EUJe EWes IBoy LRHS NBir NLos NPer SChr SDix SPav SPhx SRGP SRkn SVen SWvt WCru
	- 'Guernsey White'	CBod CCon NLos WOut
	- white-flowered	CSpe EBee
§	× ***magnificum*** ♀H7	Widely available
	- 'Blue Blood'	CAbP CAby CBod CElw CLAP COtt EBee ECtt EPPr EPfP GAbr GCal LPfy LRHS LSou MBNS MCot MHol NGdn NSti SWvt WCot WCra WPtf WRHF
	- 'Ernst Pagels'	MHol NCot WOut
	- 'Hylander'	EPPr
	- 'Peter Yeo'	EBee EPPr SRGP WCra WPtf
	- 'Rosemoor'	CBod CElw CHid CNec COtt ECtt ELan EPPr EPfP GBin GBuc GCal IKil LCro LOPS LRHS MBel MWhi NEoE SPer SPtp WCra WFib WHoo WMnd WPtf XLum
	- 'Vital'	XLum
	magniflorum	ELan EWes GKev NBid NGdn
	'Maître Hugo'	EBee
§	***malviflorum***	CFis ECha ELan EPPr LLWP SBrt WCot WCru WHea WHoo
	- from Spain	EWes
	- pink-flowered	EPPr
§	'Mary Mottram'	CElw EPPr WCra
	'Mavis Simpson' ♀H4	Widely available
	maximowiczii	WPtf
	'Maxwelton'	EBee
	'Melinda'PBR	CBod CMos EBee ECtt EPPr EWTr EWoo LCro LHop LOPS LPla MNrw MTis NLar NMir WCot WCra WFib WPtf WRHF
	'Memories'PBR	ECtt LSRN MBNS SRms
	'Menna Bach'	MAvo WCra
	'Meryl Anne'	SRGP WPtf
	microphyllum	see *G. potentilloides*
	'Midnight Clouds'	CMos CWGN EBee ECtt EPfP EWTr LBuc MAvo NCGa NSti SCob WCra WFar
	molle	WSFF
	× ***monacense***	CBod EBee ELan IFoB IMou LEdu LRHS MBNS MWat SHar SRGP SWat WCra WCru WGwG WMoo WOut WPnP WWtn
	- var. ***anglicum***	CCon ECtt EPPr EPfP GMaP LRHS NLar WCra WMoo
	- - 'Eric Clement'	EBee
	- 'Anne Stevens'	EBee WPtf
	- 'Claudine Dupont'	CElw EBee EPPr IFro NCot NWad WCot WCra WFib WPtf
	- dark-flowered	WMoo
	- 'Emma White'	EBee EPPr
	- var. ***monacense*** 'Breckland Fever'	EBee EPPr NCot SRGP WCra

§	- - 'Muldoon'	EPPr EPfP NBir SRGP WMoo WPnP
*	'Money Peniche'	XEll
	'Mourning Widow'	see *G. phaeum* 'Lady in Mourning'
	'Mrs Jean Moss'	EBee EPPr EWes MAvo NCot SRGP
§	'Mrs Judith Bradshaw'	CDes EBee NChi NCot
	napuligerum misapplied	see *G. farreri*
	'Natalie'	EBee EPPr LRHS LSRN WCra
	nepalense	SRGP SRms
	'Nicola'	CElw EPPr IFro LRHS NLar SRGP WCra
	'Nimbus' ♀H7	Widely available
	nodosum	Widely available
	- 'Blueberry Ice'	CElw CLAP MAvo
	- 'Clos du Coudray'	EBee EPPr EWTr EWoo ILea MAvo NCot NLar WCAu WCra
	- 'Dark Heart'	MCot WCra
	- dark-flowered	see *G. nodosum* 'Swish Purple'
	- 'Darkleaf'	EBee
	- 'Hexham Big Eyes'	CElw CLAP EWes MAvo
	- 'Hexham Face Paint'	EPPr
	- 'Hexham Feathers'	CElw
	- 'Hexham Freckles'	EPPr
	- 'Hexham Lace'	CElw EPPr
	- 'Julie's Velvet'	CElw LEdu MAvo SBch WBor WHoo WPGP
	- pale-flowered	see *G. nodosum* 'Svelte Lilac'
	- 'Pascal'	EPPr
	- 'Saucy Charlie'	SBch
	- 'Silverwood'	CElw CLAP EBee ECtt EPPr EWoo GCal LSou MBel MTis NChi NSti SAko SBch SPoG SRGP WCot WCra WHoo WWFP
	- 'Simon'	SRGP
§	- 'Svelte Lilac'	CBod CElw EAEE EPPr EWTr LAst LRHS LSou NBro NDov NHol SRGP SWat WBrk WCra WCru WFib WMoo WPnP
§	- 'Swish Purple'	CElw ELon EPPr LRHS MAvo NLar SRGP WCru WMoo WPGP WPnP
	- 'Tony's Talisman'	EBee
	- 'Whiteleaf'	CElw CFis CMac CMea EPPr GCal NChi SRGP WCru WFar WHal WMoo WPGP WPnP
	- 'Wreighburn House White'	EBee MAvo
	'Northumberland Lavender Queen'	EBee
	'Nunwood Purple'	EBee EPPr EWes MAvo WCra WPtf
	ocellatum	IFro
	'Old Rose'	LRHS SRGP WCru
§	***orientalitibeticum***	CCon CExl CMHG CPrp CSpe ECtt EPPr EWTr GAbr GKev IFro MCot MHer MMuc NBid NLar SEND SKHP SMad SRGP WCot WMoo WWEG
	'Orion' ♀H7	Widely available
	'Orkney Blue'	CElw EPPr WCru
	Orkney Cherry = 'Bremerry'[PBR]	CMac EBee ECtt EPfP GBin LLHF MBel NSti SCob SRkn SRms WCra
	'Orkney Dawn'	WPnP
	'Orkney Mist'	EBee
	'Orkney Pink'	ECtt EPPr EPfP LEdu LHop LSRN NSti SRGP SWat
	'Out of the Blue'	WOut

	× ***oxonianum***	CNec NCot WMoo
	- 'A.T. Johnson' ♀H7	CAby CBcs EBee ECtt ELan EPPr EPfP GKin LAst LHop LRHS MRav MWat MWhi NBir NEgg NGdn NSti SCob SPer SRGP SRms SWat SWvt WCra WCru WMnd WMoo WWtn
	- 'Andy's Star'	EBee
	- 'Ankum's White'	CLAP EBee EPPr EWes
	- 'Anmore'	SRGP
	- 'Beholder's Eye' ♀H7	CPrp EPPr MMuc NLar SRGP WPnP WPtf
	- 'Breckland Sunset'	EBee EPPr NLar SRGP
	- 'Bregover Pearl'	CBre CElw EPPr SRGP WMoo
	- 'Bressingham's Delight'	LRHS SRGP WCra
	- 'Buttercup'	EPPr SRGP
	- Caborn hybrids	LLWP
I	- 'Cally Seedling'	EBee EWes GCal
	- 'Chocolate Strawberry'	EBee EPPr EWes WCra
§	- 'Claridge Druce'	Widely available
	- 'Coronet'	CCon GCal SRGP WCra WMoo
	- 'Cream Chocolate'	EBee EPPr
	- 'David Rowlinson'	EBee EPPr WCra
	- 'Diane's Treasure'	EBee NCot
	- 'Elworthy Misty'	CElw CFis EPPr SRGP WCra
	- 'Frank Lawley'	CPrp LLWP NBid SRGP WMoo
§	- 'Fran's Star' (d)	SRGP WCru
	- 'Frilly Gilly'	WCra
	- 'Hexham Pink'	EBee EPPr EWes NChi SRGP
	- 'Hollywood'	EBee ELan EPPr NLar NPer SAko SRGP SRms WCra WMoo WPtf
	- 'Julie Brennan'	EBee LRHS
	- 'Kate Moss'	EPPr EWes NSti SRGP
	- 'Katherine Adele'	CMos CSpe EBee ECha ECtt EPPr EPfP EWes GCal LLWP LPla LSou MAvo MMuc MSpe NLar NSti SEND SPoG SRGP SRms WCra WFar WFib
§	- 'Kingston'	CElw EBee EPPr
	- 'Königshof'	EPPr EWes
	- 'Kurt's Variegated'	see *G.* × *oxonianum* 'Spring Fling'
	- 'Lace Time'	CAby CBod CBre CCon CPrp EBee ECtt EPPr GBuc GKin LBMP LRHS LSRN MSpe NEgg SPer SPoG SRGP SRms WCAu WCra WGwG WMnd WMoo WPnP
	- 'Lady Moore'	SRGP WMoo WPtf
	- 'Lambrook Gillian'	CFis EPPr SRGP WBrk
	- 'Lasting Impression'	EPPr SRGP
	- 'Laura Skelton'	CElw EBee NCot SBch
	- 'Little John'	EPPr EWes
	- 'Maid Marion'	EWes
	- 'Maurice Moka'	EBee ECtt MAsh NLar WCra
	- 'Miriam Rundle'	EPPr SRGP WCru WMoo
	- 'Moorland Jenny'	WMoo
	- 'Moorland Star'	WMoo
	- 'Mrs Molly Kisby'	EBee
	- 'Music from Big Pink'	EBee EPPr EWes WCra
	- 'Pat Smallacombe'	EBee EPPr SRGP WMoo
	- 'Pearl Boland'	EBee EPPr SRGP
	- 'Phantom'	EBee EPPr WCra
	- 'Phoebe Noble'	CBre EBee EPPr LRHS MNrw NLar SRGP WCra WFib WMoo
	- 'Phoebe's Blush'	EPPr GCal GQue SRGP
	- 'Pink Cluster'	CLAP
§	- 'Prestbury Blush'	CElw EPPr SRGP
	- 'Prestbury White'	see *G.* × *oxonianum* 'Prestbury Blush'

- 'Raspberry Ice'	EBee EWes WCra
- 'Rebecca Moss'	CPrp ECha ECtt ELan EPPr GAbr GCra LRHS LSRN NSti SAko SRGP WCra WCru WFib WOut WPtf WWEG
- 'Robin's Ginger Nut'	EBee EWes WCra
- 'Robin's Red Eye'	EPPr
- 'Rose Clair'	CCon CNec ELan EPPr LRHS MBri MWhi NBir NLar SRGP WCAu WCra WCru WHlf WMnd WMoo
- 'Rosenlicht'	EAEE EBee EPPr EWoo GKin LRHS MRav SRGP WCra WCru WHoo WMnd WMoo WPtf XLum
- 'Rothbury Sarah'	EBee EPPr
- 'Sandy'	EBee EPPr EWes
§ - 'Spring Fling' (v)	ECtt EWes LPla MHer MSpe NWad SRGP WCra
- 'Stillingfleet Keira'	EBee EPPr NSti SRGP
- 'Summer Surprise'	EBee EPPr EWes SBch WCra WCru
- 'Susan'	EPPr EWes
- 'Susie White'	EPPr SRGP WCru
§ - f. ***thurstonianum***	Widely available
- - 'Armitageae'	EPPr SRGP
- - 'Breckland Brownie'	CElw EBee EPPr EWes MAvo SRGP WCra
- - 'Crûg Star'	WCru
- - 'David McClintock'	EBee SRGP WMoo
- - 'Red Sputnik'	EBee EPPr SRGP
- - 'Sherwood'	CSde EPPr GCal GQue MSpe NBro NSti SRGP WCra WMoo
- - 'Southcombe Double' (d)	CBod CLAP CMos CNec CPla ECtt ELan EPPr EWTr GCra LOPS LRHS LSou MHol SPer SPoG SRGP SRms WCra WCru WGwG WMoo WPtf
§ - - 'Southcombe Star'	EBee EPPr GAbr GCal NBro NGdn SRGP WCru WMoo WPtf WWEG
- - 'Sue Cox' (d)	EPPr NLar
- - 'White Stripes'	EBee EPPr
- 'Trevor's White'	CLAP EBee EPPr LLWP LRHS SRGP WCra WCru
- 'Wageningen' ♀H7	CBod CBre CNec EBee EPPr GCal LPla LRHS LSou NDov NGdn NLar SEND SRGP SRms WCot WCra WCru WHoo WMoo
- 'Walter's Gift'	CBod CNec ECtt EPPr EPri EShb EWoo LLWP LRHS LSou MAvo MHer MRav MWhi NBir NBro NChi NDov NLar NPer SAko SDix SPoG WCra WCru WHoo WMoo WPnP WWtn
§ - 'Wargrave Pink'	Widely available
- 'Waystrode'	EBee EPPr SRGP
- 'Westacre White'	EPPr EWes WCra
- 'Whitehaven'	SRGP
- 'Whiter Shade of Pale'	EBee EPPr
- 'Winscombe'	EPfP GCal SRGP WMoo
§ ***palmatum*** ♀H4	Widely available
palustre	EBee EPPr GLog MMuc MNrw NCot NLar SRGP WCot WMoo WPtf
'Pastel Clouds'	NCot WFar
Patricia = 'Brempat' ♀H7	Widely available
peloponnesiacum	CElw EAEE EPPr EWes GQue MAsh NWad WMoo WPtf
'Perfect Storm'	CLAP ECtt LLHF
phaeum	Widely available
- from Ploeger	NCot
- 'Acorn Bank'	EBee NCot WCra
- 'Advendo'	EBee EPPr NCot WCra
- 'Album'	Widely available
- 'Alec's Pink'	EBee EPPr LLWP NCot SHar WCra WPtf
- 'All Saints'	EBee EPPr LEdu SRGP WCra WPtf
- 'Angelina'	EBee EPPr NCot WCra WPtf
- 'Aureum'	see *G. phaeum* 'Golden Spring'
- 'Basket of Lavender'	EBee
- 'Blauwvoet'	EPPr LBMP NChi NCot WPtf
- 'Blue Shadow'	CElw CLAP EBee EPPr LEdu MAvo NCot SRGP WPtf
- 'Caborn Lilac'	LLWP
- 'Calligrapher'	CElw EPPr LLHF NChi NCot SRGP WCra WMoo
- 'Chocolate Chip'	EPPr NCot
- 'Conny Broe' (v)	CLAP EShb MAvo
- 'Dark Angel'	EBee
- 'Dark Dream'	EBee
- dark-flowered	NCot
- 'David Bromley'	WCru
- 'David Martin'	EBee EPPr NCot SRGP
- 'Enid'	EPPr
- 'George Stone'	EPPr NCot
- 'Golden Samobor'	CElw EPPr
§ - 'Golden Spring'	EBee EPPr MAvo NCot NEoE SRGP WOut
- 'Green Ghost'	EBee EPPr MAvo NCot
- 'Hector's Lavender'	EBee NCot SRGP WOut
- var. ***hungaricum***	EBee EPPr SRGP WCra WPtf
- 'James Haunch'	EPPr WCra
- 'Judith's Blue'	EBee EPPr NChi NCot
- 'Klepper'	EPPr GBin
§ - 'Lady in Mourning'	CExl EBee EPPr GCal LPla NChi SRGP SRms SWat WCru WMoo WPnP
- 'Lavender Pinwheel'	CBod CMos EBee EPfP MSpe MTis NCot SPer WCot WCra WHil
- 'Lilacina'	ECha WPtf
- 'Lily Lovell'	Widely available
- 'Lisa' (v)	CFis CLAP EPPr MAvo MNrw NCot SMHy WCot WCra
- 'Little Boy'	EPPr
- var. ***lividum***	CBre EPfP GMaP LLWP MRav NCot SRGP SRms WFar WPnP XLum
- - 'Joan Baker'	CFis CSam EBee EPPr LPla NChi NCot NGdn NSti SDys SRGP WCru WFib WMoo WOut WPnP
- - 'Majus'	EBee ECtt ELan EPPr EPfP LLWP LPla LRHS WFar WMoo WWFP
- 'Lustige Witwe' (v)	WCot
- 'Marchant's Ghost'	IFro LPla
- 'Margaret Wilson' (v)	CCon CDes CMos CWGN EBee ECtt EPPr EWes GAbr GCal LBMP LEdu LRHS MAvo MNrw MSpe NEgg NGdn NLar NSti SPoG SRGP WCot WMoo WSHC
- 'Mierhausen'	EBee EPPr NCot WPtf
- 'Mojito' (v)	WCot
- 'Moorland Dylan'	WMoo WOut
- 'Mottisfont Rose'	CLAP SBch
- 'Mourning Widow'	see *G. phaeum* 'Lady in Mourning'
- 'Mrs Charles Perrin'	CElw CFis WPtf
- 'Night Time'	EBee EPPr LLWP NCot WPtf
- 'Nightshade'	EBee EPPr NCot
- 'Our Pat' ♀H7	CDes CLAP EBee EPPr MAvo NChi WCot
- var. ***phaeum***	WPtf
- - 'Langthorns Blue'	CWCL EBee ELan EPPr EPfP EWes LEdu LRHS MNrw SRGP SWvt WCra WPGP

	Name	Suppliers
	- - 'Samobor'	Widely available
	- 'Phantom of the Opera' (v)	EBee EPPr NCot
I	- 'Ploeger de Bilt'	EBee EPPr WPtf
	- 'Rachel's Rhapsody'	CElw EBee EPPr MAvo MSpe NCot SRGP
	- 'Raven'	CBod CLAP CMos EBee ECtt EPPr EWoo LRHS MAvo NChi NCot NLar SCob WCAu WCra WPtf
	- 'Ray of Light'	EPPr
	- 'Rise Top Lilac'	EBee NCot WPGP WPtf
	- 'Robin's Angel Eyes'	EBee
	- 'Rose Air'	EPPr MAvo NCot SRGP WMoo WPnP
	- 'Rose Madder'	CCon CElw CPrp EPPr GBuc GCal LEdu LLWP LPla MNrw NChi NCot SPhx SRGP WCru WGwG WMoo WPnP
	- 'Rothbury Ruby'	EBee EPPr
	- 'Saturn'	EPPr WPtf
	- 'Séricourt'	CDes WCot WCra WFib
	- 'Shadowlight'	CBod EBee ECtt EPPr NCot NLar NSti SPoG WCra WFar
	- 'Slatina'	EPPr WPtf
	- 'Springtime'[PBR]	CMos EBee EPPr LBMP LLHF LPla MBNS MSpe NCot NGdn NLar WCra WFib
	- 'Stillingfleet Ghost'	EBee EPPr LEdu MNrw NChi NCot NSti
	- 'Taff's Jester' (v)	LPla MSpe NHol SRGP WCot
	- 'Trevor's Recall'	EBee NCot
	- 'Tyne Mist'	EPPr NCot
§	- 'Variegatum' (v)	CBre CFis CMac EBee EHoe ELan EPPr GMaP IFro MSpe NBir NBro NCot SGSe SRGP WCru WHer WMoo
	- 'Vintage Dave'	WOut
	- 'Walküre'	EPPr EWTr EWes EWoo MTis NCot NLar
	'Philippe Vapelle'	Widely available
	'Pink Delight'	CElw SBch
	'Pink Ghost'	WPtf
	'Pink Penny'	CBod CLAP EBee ECtt EPPr EPfP LRHS MNrw NLar SRGP WCra WMoo
§	***platyanthum***	EPPr MNrw SRGP WCru WPtf
	- var. ***reinii***	GCal LSun WCru
	- 'Russian Giant'	EPPr
	platypetalum misapplied	see *G.* × *magnificum*
	platypetalum Franch.	see *G. sinense*
§	***platypetalum*** Fisch. & C.A. Mey.	EBee EPPr LRHS NBir SRGP WCru XLum
	- 'Dark Side of the Moon'	EBee
	- 'Genyell'	EBee EPPr MAvo WCra
	- 'Georgia Blue'	WCru
	- 'Turco'	EBee EPPr NLar WCra
§	***pogonanthum***	CHid GLog NBir
	polyanthes	EWTr EWes NChi
§	***potentilloides***	EBee GCal NBir SRGP WMoo
	pratense	CArn CBre CHab CMac CNec CWld EBee ECtt ELan EPPr GJos GMaP MHer MLHP MNHC NCot NMir SCob SPer SPlb SPoG SRGP SRms SWat WCot WMoo WPnP WSFF XLum
	- 'Akaton'	NLar WCra
I	- 'Alboroseum'	EBee
	- 'Algera Double'	GBin MHol MSCN WCot WCra
	- 'Bittersweet'	EPPr
	- Black Beauty = 'Nodbeauty'[PBR]	CAby CBcs CExl CMea CSBt CWCL CWGN CWld EBee ECtt EPfP EWes LBuc LOPS LRHS LSRN MGos MHol MPnt NLar NPri SPer SPoG SRkn SRot SWat WFar WHoo
	- 'Blue Lagoon'	EBee EPPr MAsh WCra
*	- 'Blue Skies'	LSou WFar
	- 'Cluden Sapphire'	EBee EPPr EWTr GQue NEoE NHol WCra WCru
§	- 'Double Jewel' (d)	CMos CWGN EBee EPfP LLHF LRHS MAsh MAvo MBNS MHol NLar SPoG WBor WCra WFar
	- 'Else Lacey' (d)	CDes CElw EBee WCra
	- 'Flore Pleno'	see *G. pratense* 'Plenum Violaceum'
I	- 'Himalayanum'	NLar
	- 'Hocus Pocus'	CBod CMos CWGN ECtt ELan EWTr EWoo LRHS MAsh MAvo MBNS MHol MSCN NBro NLar NSti SCob WCAu WCra
	- 'Ilja'	EBee
	- 'Janet's Special'	WHoo
	- 'Midnight Blues'	CMos CWGN EBee GBin MAsh NCGa NSti SCob WCra
	- Midnight Reiter strain	CBct CExl CWGN CWld ECtt ELan EWTr GBuc IBoy IFoB MAvo MBel MHol MLHP NBro NChi NGdn NLar NQui SCob SDys SGSe SWat SWvt WCra WCru WFar WPnP
	- 'Milk Cow Blues'	EBee
	- 'Mrs Kendall Clark' ♀[H7]	Widely available
	- 'New Dimension'	CBcs EBee ELan MAsh WCra WFib
	- 'Okey Dokey'	EBee
	- 'Painter's Palette' (v) **new**	NBFr
	- 'Pink Splash'	EPPr WMoo
	- 'Plenum Caeruleum' (d)	CMHG ECtt EPPr GCra MRav NBid NEgg NLar SWat WSHC
§	- 'Plenum Violaceum' (d) ♀[H7]	Widely available
	- var. ***pratense*** f. ***albiflorum***	CElw CSam EPPr EPfP EWTr EWoo GCra GMaP IFro LRHS MLHP MNrw NBid SCob SGbt SPer WCra WMnd WMoo WPtf
	- - - 'Galactic'	CBod CLAP CMea ECtt EPPr LRHS MHol NBir NEgg NLar WCot WCra WCru WFib WMoo WPGP WPnP
	- - - 'Laura'[PBR] (d)	CBod CExl EBee EPfP EWTr EWes LSRN LSou NLar NSti SCob SKHP WCra WPnP
	- - - 'Plenum Album' (d)	CBot CDes CLAP EBee ECtt ELan EPPr EPfP EWTr EWes GBin LLHF LRHS MBel MNrw MRav NEgg NGdn NLar SGbt SPer SWvt WBor WCot WCra WFar WPnP
	- - - 'Silver Queen'	CAby CNec EBee ECtt EPPr GQue LRHS LSou NBir SRGP WCra WGwG WMoo WPGP
	- 'Purple Heron'	CDes LSRN
*	- 'Purple-haze'	CPla CTca WMoo WTou
	- 'Rectum Album'	see *G. clarkei* 'Kashmir White'
	- 'Robin's Grey Beard'	EBee
§	- 'Rose Queen'	EPPr NBir SGbt SRGP WCru
	- 'Roseum'	see *G. pratense* 'Rose Queen'
	- 'Splish-splash'	see *G. pratense* 'Striatum'
	- 'Stanton Mill'	NBid
	- var. ***stewartianum***	MRav

- - 'Elizabeth Yeo'	CBod CLAP CNec ECtt EPPr EWoo LRHS MAsh NCot NLar NWad SPoG WCra WCru WFib
- - 'Raina'	EBee EPPr
§ - 'Striatum'	Widely available
- 'Striatum' dwarf	WCru
- variegated, white-flowered (v)	WCot
§ - Victor Reiter Junior strain	CSpe ELan LEdu MLHP NBir NGdn SPoG SRot WCot
- 'Wisley Blue'	EPPr SRGP WCra WHal
- 'Yorkshire Queen'	EBee EPPr NGdn NSti WCru
'Prelude'	CBre CElw EBee ELon EPPr NBir NCot NEoE NLar SRGP WFib WPtf
procurrens	CBre CElw CTri EPPr GAbr GCal GCra WBor WBrk WCru WMoo WPtf
§ ***psilostemon*** ♀H7	Widely available
- 'Bressingham Flair'	CCon CKno CLAP ECtt GBuc GCra MRav NBid NChi NLar SRms WCra WCru WFar WMoo WPnP
- 'Catherine Deneuve'[PBR]	EBee EWTr EWes SCob STPC WCra
- 'Coton Goliath'	EPPr EWes NCot
- 'Jason Bloom'	EPPr LRHS
- 'Madelon'	CElw MAvo NCot NLar
- 'Moorland Jack'	WMoo
'Midnight Star'	EWes WFar
pulchrum	CFil CSpe EBee EWes SRGP WPGP
punctatum hort.	see *G.* × *monacense* var. *monacense* 'Muldoon'
- 'Variegatum'	see *G. phaeum* 'Variegatum'
'Purple Rain'	EBee EPPr
pylzowianum	NBid NRya WMoo
pyrenaicum	GAbr NCot NSti WTou
- f. ***albiflorum***	EPPr GAbr IFro MNrw NBir SRGP WBrk WCot WCra WFar WTou
- 'Barney Brighteye'	SRGP
- 'Bill Wallis'	Widely available
- 'Bright Eyes'	LLWP NCot
- 'Isparta'	EPPr IFro LPla MNrw NCot SBch SHar SPhx SRGP WBrk
- 'Summer Sky'	CBod GBin SPav SRGP SWvt
- 'Summer Snow'	CBod CCon
'Rainbow'[PBR]	EWoo MBNS WCra
Rambling Robin Group	CSpe ECre EPri EWes LLHF
'Ray's Pink'	CPla WFib
rectum	EPPr NBre NLar WCra WCru
- 'Album'	see *G. clarkei* 'Kashmir White'
'Red Admiral'	CNec ECtt EPPr GBin GBuc GCal LAst LRHS MAvo MWhi NCGa NCot NDov NGdn NLar NQui NSti SRGP WCra WFar WGwG WHoo WPnP WPtf
'Red Propellers'	CElw WSHC
reflexum	CFis EPPr EPfP LRHS WCru
- 'Katara Pass'	EPPr
refractoides	WCot
refractum	CExl
regelii	EPPr WCru WMoo WPtf
renardii ♀H5	Widely available
- 'Beldo'	MAvo
- blue-flowered	see *G. renardii* 'Whiteknights'
- 'Rothbury Hills'	EBee EPPr
- 'Sarah Comish'	EBee
- 'Tcschelda'	CBod CMHG EAEE ECha ECtt EPPr EShb GBuc LRHS NBir NLar SRms WCra WMoo
§ - 'Whiteknights'	EBee NBir WCru
- 'Zetterlund'	CBod CFis CMos EAEE EBee ELan EPPr EPri LHop LRHS NEgg NQui WCra WMnd WMoo
§ ***reuteri***	CHid CPla CTsd NCot NLos SChr SRGP WCru WOut
'Richard Nutt'	EBee
richardsonii	CBod CFis EBee EPPr GCal LRHS MCot NBir NWad SBod SRGP WCra WCru WPnP
- pink-flowered	MAvo
- white-flowered	NChi
× ***riversleaianum*** 'Russell Prichard' ♀H4	Widely available
§ ***rivulare***	GLog NLar
robertianum	ENfk EPPr LLHF MHer SRms WSFF
§ - 'Album'	CBod EPPr SHar SRGP SRms WHer
- f. ***bernettii***	see *G. robertianum* 'Album'
- 'Celtic White'	CBre EPPr GCal IFro MMuc SEND SPav SRGP WTou
robustum	EPri NBir SKHP SPav SPlb SRGP WHrl WKif
'Rosetta'[PBR]	GBin NDov NLar WCra
'Rosie Crûg'	SWvt
rosthornii	WCru
'Rothbury Red'	EBee NChi SBch
§ Rozanne = 'Gerwat'[PBR] ♀H7	Widely available
rubescens	see *G. yeoi*
rubifolium	WCru
ruprechtii (Grossh.) Woronow	EPPr MNrw SRGP
Sabani Blue = 'Bremigo'[PBR]	CAbP CLAP CMac CMos CSpe EBee ECtt EPPr EWes EWoo LCro LOPS LPla MHol NLar NSti SMHy SPer WCot WCra WSHC
'Salome'	CAby CBcs CBod CLAP EBee ECtt ELan GAbr ILea LHop MCot NBir NLar NSti SCob SPoG SRms SRot SWat SWvt WCot WCra WGwG WHoo WMoo WPnP WPtf WWEG
'Sandrine'[PBR]	CBcs CLAP CWGN EBee GBin IMou IPot LHop LLHF LRHS LSou MHol MNrw NSti SAko SCob SGol SPoG SRms WCot WCra WHil WPnP
sanguineum	Widely available
- Alan Bloom = 'Bloger'[PBR]	EBee EPPr LHop LRHS WCra WFib
- 'Album' ♀H5	Widely available
- 'Alpenglow'	EBee EPPr NCot SRGP WBrk WCra
- 'Ankum's Pride' ♀H7	CElw CPrp EPPr EPfP EWoo LHop LRHS LSou MTis NCGa NDov NGdn NHar NLar NSti SBch SRGP SWat WBrk WCra WCru WFib WMoo WPnP WPtf
- 'Apfelblüte'	ELon EPPr EWTr GJos IPot NLar WCAu WCra
- 'Aviemore' ♀H7	CElw CFis EPPr GCal
- 'Barnsley'	CPrp EPPr NBro NEoE WCra WHrl
- 'Belle of Herterton'	CElw EPPr MAvo NBid NEoE WBrk WCra WCru
- 'Bloody Graham'	EPPr LRHS MAvo WBrk WCra WMoo
- 'Canon Miles'	CElw ECtt EPPr LRHS NLar SRGP SRms WCra

	- 'Catforth Carnival'	EBee EPPr MAvo
	- 'Cedric Morris'	CElw ECha ELon EPPr GCra MAvo NBid SBch SRGP WBrk WCra WCru
	- 'Compactum'	WCra WMoo XLum
	- 'Connie Hansen'	WCra
§	- 'Droplet'	SRGP
	- 'Elsbeth'	CElw CNec CPrp EBee ECha ECtt ELan ELon EPPr EWes GCal LRHS MSpe NGdn NLar NSti SPoG SRGP WBrk WCra WCru WFar WFib WHal WMoo WPnP WWEG XLum
	- 'Feu d'Automne'	EBee EPPr WBrk WCra
	- 'Fran's Star'	see *G.* × *oxonianum* 'Fran's Star'
	- 'Glenluce'	CElw CPrp ECtt ELon EPPr EPfP EShb GBuc GCal LHop LRHS MRav MSpe MTis NChi NDov NLar NWad SRGP SRms SWat WBrk WCra WHal WMnd WPnP
	- 'Hampshire Purple'	see *G. sanguineum* 'New Hampshire Purple'
	- 'Holden'	CElw EBee EPPr WBrk
	- 'Inverness'	EBee EPPr NCot XLum
	- 'Joanna'	CFis MAvo WBrk WCra
	- 'John Elsley'	EAEE EBee ECtt EHoe EPPr LAst LLWP LRHS LSou MAsh MSpe NBro NGdn SRGP SWat WCra WMnd WPnP
	- 'John Innes'	EPPr
	- 'Jubilee Pink'	GCal WCru
	- 'Kristin Jacob'	EPPr
	- var. ***lancastrense***	see *G. sanguineum* var. *striatum*
	- 'Leeds Variety'	see *G. sanguineum* 'Rod Leeds'
§	- 'Little Bead' ♀H5	ECho NWad WBrk WCra XLum
	- 'Max Frei'	Widely available
	- 'Minutum'	see *G. sanguineum* 'Droplet'
	- 'Nanum'	see *G. sanguineum* 'Little Bead'
§	- 'New Hampshire Purple'	CBod CLAP CPrp EBee ECtt ELon EPPr EPfP GLog IPot LAst LRHS MAvo MWhi NBro NGdn NLar WBrk WCra WFib WHil
	- 'Nyewood'	CNec CPrp EAEE EBee ECGP ECtt EPPr LRHS MSpe SEND SRGP WBrk WCra WCru WFib
	- 'Pink Pouffe' **new**	EBee
I	- 'Plenum' (d)	EPPr
	- 'Prado'	XLum
	- var. ***prostratum***	see *G. sanguineum* var. *striatum*
	- 'Purple Flame'	see *G. sanguineum* 'New Hampshire Purple'
§	- 'Rod Leeds'	CFis CLAP EBee SRGP WFar
	- 'Sandra'	SRGP
	- 'Sara'	LLWP
§	- 'Shepherd's Delight'	ECtt EPPr
	- 'Shepherd's Warning' misapplied	see *G. sanguineum* 'Shepherd's Delight'
	- 'Shepherd's Warning' ♀H7	CMea CTri ECtt GCal MMuc MRav NBir NLar SEND SRGP SWat WCru WFib WHoo WIce WPnP
	- 'South Nutfield'	CElw
§	- var. ***striatum*** ♀H5	Widely available
	- - deep pink-flowered	CSBt MSwo SWvt
	- - 'Mottisfont'	SBch
	- - 'Reginald Farrer'	WCru
	- - 'Splendens' ♀H7	CWib EBee EPPr GCal LHop LRHS NBid SAko WCru
	- 'Tirol'	EBee NCot
	- 'Vision Light Pink'	CBod CNec EPPr NPri WCra
	- 'Vision Violet'	CBod CNec EBee IFoB LSqH MAvo MSpe NPri SWvt WBrk WCra XLum
	- 'Westacre Poppet'	EWes WCra
	'Sanne'	CBod EPPr EWes EWoo LRHS MHol NLar SCob STPC WCot WCra WFib WPGP WRHF
	saxatile	EBee EPPr
	'Scapa Flow'	EBee EPPr GCal MAvo WCra WHea WSHC
	schlechteri	CFis EWes MMuc SEND WKif
I	***sessiliflorum*** subsp. ***novae-zelandiae*** 'Nigricans'	CFis ECha ECho ELan GAbr MHer SBch SCob SRGP WFar
§	- - 'Porters Pass'	ECho EHoe EWes SBch SPlb WFar WHoo
	- - red-leaved	see *G. sessiliflorum* subsp. *novae-zelandiae* 'Porters Pass'
	shikokianum	EBee NLar SRGP WCra WHrl WPtf
	- var. ***kaimontanum***	WCru
	- var. ***quelpaertense***	CDes CFis EBee MAvo WPtf
	- - 'Crûg's Cloak'	WCru
	- var. ***yoshiianum*** B&SWJ 6147	WCru
	'Shocking Blue'	NLar NSti WCra WFib
	'Shouting Star'	see *G.* 'Kanahitobanawa'
	'Silva'	CElw EPPr MRav SWat WCru
*	'Silver Shadow'	SPhx
	'Simonside'	EBee
§	***sinense***	CBod CCon CExl CMos EBee ECtt GBuc GCal LRHS MCot MNrw NGdn WCra WGwG XLum
	'Sirak' ♀H7	Widely available
	'Slack's Purple Stargazer' **new**	NSla
	soboliferum	ELan EPPr NBir NLar SPer SRGP WCru WMoo
	- Cally strain	CDes EBee EPPr GCal MAvo NSti
	- var. ***kiusianum***	CElw
	- 'Rothbury Star'	EBee
	- 'Starman'	CMos EBee ECtt EPPr EWoo NLar SCob SKHP STPC WCra WFib WMoo
	'Solitaire'	CDes CFil EBee WCot
	'Southcombe Star'	see *G.* × *oxonianum* f. *thurstonianum* 'Southcombe Star'
	'Southease Celestial'	LPla SMHy
	'Spinners'	Widely available
	stapfianum var. ***roseum***	see *G. orientalitibeticum*
	'Stephanie'	CBod CDes CElw CNec EPPr EPfP EWes GBuc LRHS LSRN MAvo MBNS MNrw MRav MSpe MTis NChi NCot NDov NGdn NLar NSti SBea WCAu WCra WPnP WSHC
	'Storm Chaser'	CLAP EBee GBin LOPS LRHS MGos SCob
	'Strawberry Frost'	LLHF
	subcaulescens ♀H4	Widely available
	- 'Giuseppii' ♀H5	CExl EAEE ECtt ELon EPPr EPot GAbr GBuc LRHS LSou MAsh MRav NDov NFav NPri SRGP SRot SWvt WCra
	- 'Splendens' ♀H5	CTri EAEE ECtt EPPr GBuc GCrg LAst LHop LRHS LSou MAsh MHer NEgg NSla SRms SWat WFar WGwG
	'Sue Crûg'	EBee ECtt ELan EPfP GCra LAst LLWP LRHS LSou NEgg SBch SRGP WCra WCru WMoo WSHC

Name	Suppliers
'Sue's Sister'	WCru
'Summer Cloud'	EPPr SRGP WOut
Summer Skies = 'Gernic'PBR (d)	Widely available
suzukii B&SWJ 016	CExl WCru
'Sweet Heidy'PBR	CBod CMos EBee ECtt EPPr EPfP LBMP LLHF MBri MNrw MSwo NLar NSti SCob SPoG WBor WCra WFar
sylvaticum	NBid NGdn NMir WFar WMoo WShi
- 'Afrodite'	EPPr
- f. ***albiflorum***	CBre ELan EWoo NSti WCru
- - 'Cyril's Superb White'	EBee
- 'Album' ♀H7	Widely available
- 'Amanda'	EBee EPPr
- 'Amy Doncaster'	Widely available
- 'Angulatum'	CElw EPPr WMoo WPtf
- 'Birch Lilac'	CElw CLAP EBee EPPr EPri GBuc GCal LRHS NLar WCAu WCra WFib WMoo
- 'Coquetdale Lilac'	EBee EPPr WCra
- 'Greek Fire'	EBee EPPr MAvo
- 'Ice Blue'	EBee EPPr NChi
- 'Immaculée'	EPPr MRav
- 'Kanzlersgrund'	CElw EPPr
- 'Lilac Time'	EPPr
- 'Mayflower' ♀H7	Widely available
- 'Meran'	EPPr
- 'Miss Connie Wilson'	EBee EPPr MAvo
- 'Nikita'	CLAP EPPr
- f. ***roseum***	CFis NLar WPtf
- - 'Baker's Pink'	CLAP EBee EPPr GCra MNrw MRav NBir NCot SBch SRGP WCru WMoo WPtf
- subsp. ***sylvaticum*** var. ***wanneri***	EPPr WCru
§ 'Tanya Rendall'PBR	CMHG EBee ECtt ELan ELon EPPr GBin IPot LHop LRHS MHer NLar SPer SRms WCot WCra WFar WFib WPnP
'Terre Franche'	EPPr NLar SPhx WCra WWEG
§ ***thunbergii***	CCon CHid EWes LSou SRGP WMoo XLum
- 'Jester's Jacket' (v)	CPla EPPr MNrw NWad SRGP WFar WMoo WOut
- pink-flowered	EPPr SRGP
- white-flowered	EPPr SRGP
thurstonianum	see *G.* × *oxonianum* f. *thurstonianum*
'Tinpenny Mauve'	MAvo WCra WHoo
'Tiny Monster'	Widely available
transbaicalicum	CFis EPPr XLum
traversii	CWib
- var. ***elegans***	CWib ECho LRHS
tuberosum	CElw CHid ECha ECho ELan EPfP IMou MRav NBir NBro NGdn NQui SKHP SPhx WCra
- subsp. ***linearifolium***	EPPr
- pink-flowered	IFro
- 'Richard Hobbs'	EPPr
'Ushguli Grijs'	see *G. ibericum* Cav. 'Ushguli Grijs'
'Verguld Saffier'	see *G.* Blue Sunrise
versicolor	CMac CMea EBee EPPr EPfP GAbr GCal MHer MMuc NCot NLar SRms WCra WHea WMoo WPnP XEll
- 'Kingston'	see *G.* × *oxonianum* 'Kingston'
§ - 'Snow White'	EPPr SEND SRGP WCru WFib WMoo
- 'White Lady'	see *G. versicolor* 'Snow White'
'Victor Reiter'	see *G. pratense* Victor Reiter Junior strain
violareum	see *Pelargonium* 'Splendide'
viscosissimum	WFib WMnd
wallichianum	CFis CMac CPou EBee IFro NBir NChi NSti WMoo
§ - 'Buxton's Variety'	Widely available
- 'Chris'	EWes SRGP
- 'Crystal Lake'PBR	CBod CWGN EBee ECtt EPfP EWoo IPot LAst MBNS NBir NLar NSti SCob WCra WFar WHil WPnP WPtf
- 'Havana Blues'	CMos EBee ECtt EWoo GBin LCro LHop LPla LRHS MAvo MHol NCot NLar NSti SCob STPC WBrk WCot WCra WFar WPtf
- magenta-flowered	GBuc
- pale blue-flowered	CElw
- 'Pink Buxton'	EWes NLar
- pink-flowered	CLAP GBuc GCal WCru
- 'Rise and Shine'PBR	EBee EWoo LCro STPC WCot WCra
- 'Rosetta'	IMou
- 'Rosie'	SRGP
- 'Syabru'	CElw CMea MNrw SMHy WMoo
- 'Sylvia's Surprise'PBR	CLAP CMos IMou SCob SPoG WCra
'Wednesday's Child'	WFar
'White Doves'	NDov
wilfordii misapplied	see *G. thunbergii*
Wisley hybrid	see *G.* 'Khan'
wlassovianum	Widely available
- 'Blue Star'	EBee MRav NEoE SRGP WCra WFar
§ ***yeoi***	CSpe NBir NBro NSti SEND WCru WOut
yesoense	EBee IFro NSti
- var. ***nipponicum***	WCru
yoshinoi misapplied	see *G. thunbergii*
yunnanense misapplied	see *G. pogonanthum*
yunnanense ambig.	CCon

Gerbera (*Asteraceae*)

Name	Suppliers
(Everlast Series) Everlast Carmine = 'Amgerbcar'	EUJe MBNS
- Everlast Honey	MBNS
- Everlast Pink = 'Amgerbpink'	MBNS
(Garvinea Series) 'Fleurie'PBR	EUJe LAst LRHS MBNS WHil
- Garvinea Crista = 'Garcrista'	LRHS
- Garvinea Jilly	LRHS SPoG
- Garvinea Lisa = 'Garlisa'PBR	MHol
- Garvinea Madeleine **new**	LAst
- Garvinea Nikki = 'Garnikki'	LRHS SPoG
- Garvinea Orangina = 'Orangina'PBR	LAst WHlf
- Garvinea Pam = 'Pam'PBR	EUJe LRHS SPoG
- Garvinea Rachel = 'Garrachel'PBR	MHol MNrw MPie WHlf
- Garvinea Romy = 'Garromy' **new**	LRHS
- Garvinea Sunny	see *G.* 'Sunny'
- Garvinea Sylvana = 'Garsylvana'PBR	CAbP MHol MPie WCot
- Garvinea Valerie = 'Garvalerie'	LRHS
- Garvinea Vivian = 'Garvivian'	LRHS

§ – 'Sunny'PBR	LRHS SPoG
'La Lisa' **new**	LAst

Gesneria (*Gesneriaceae*)

cardinalis	see *Sinningia cardinalis*

Geum ✿ (*Rosaceae*)

'Abendsonne'	CElw EBee MAvo MRav MSpe NEoE WOut WWEG
'Alabama Slammer' (Cocktails Series)	EBee ECtt GBin MSCN MSpe NDov NEgg NLar SBri SCob SPad WHlf
alpinum	see *G. montanum*
'Apricot Beauty'	CWCL
'Apricot Delight'	LLHF NEoE
'Baked Beans' **new**	NEoE
'Banana Daiquiri' (Cocktail Series) **new**	CMos EBee LLWG MSpe NDov NLar
'Beech House Apricot'	CElw CLAP EAJP ECtt EPri GCra ILea LRHS MAvo MLHP MNrw MRav NChi NEoE NHol SBri SPoG WMoo WPnP WWEG XEll
'Bell Bank'	Widely available
'Birkhead's Creamy Lemon'	CElw EBee NBir
'Blazing Sunset' (d)	Widely available
'Blood Orange'	MAvo NEoE
'Borisii'	Widely available
'Bremner's Gold'	NEoE SBri
'Bremner's Nectarine'	CElw MNrw MSpe NChi NEoE SHar WWEG
'Broomrigg Beauty'	NEoE
'Brown Sugar'	NEoE
bulgaricum	CElw EBee MRav NBir NEoE NLar NRya WWEG XLum
'Butterscotch'	EBee
calthifolium	EPPr NBro
'Can-can' (d) **new**	MAvo
'Cantamos'	NEoE
capense	NBre NEoE SPlb
'Carlotta'	WWEG
§ ***chiloense***	SBri
– 'Red Dragon'	CBre CWld LLHF LSRN MMuc SEND SGSe SWvt WOut WWEG
'Chipchase'	CElw MAvo NChi WHoo WWEG
coccineum misapplied	see *G. chiloense*
coccineum ambig.	NCGa
coccineum Sibth. & Sm.	GLog WHoo
– 'Ann'	EPri MSpe SHar
– 'Cooky'	CElw CRos EBee EPfP GJos LRHS LSqH MMuc NEoE NLar SHil SPhx SPoG SRms SWvt WFar WRHF WWEG WWtn
– 'Eos'	CDes CElw CSpe CWCL EBee ECtt ELon EPPr EWes GQue LEdu LHop LRHS MAvo MHol MNrw MPnt MRav NEoE NGdn NLar NPri SCob SPoG SRms WGwG WHrl WMoo WWEG
– 'Koi'	EAJP EBee LEdu NEoE SPad WMoo
– 'Queen of Orange'	CBre CElw GBin GJos LAst NEoE NPri SRms SRot
– 'Werner Arends'	CElw CMHG ECtt GAbr GCal LRHS MAvo MNrw MRav SBri WFar WMoo WWEG
'Copper Pennies'	CElw NEoE WWEG
'Coppertone'	CElw CLAP CPla CWCL ELan EPri MRav NBir NBro NCGa NChi NRya SCob XEll
'Cosmopolitan' (Cocktails Series) **new**	EBee LLWG MSCN NDov NLar SCob SPad WHlf
'Cotton Candy'	NEoE WWEG
'Country Rock Star'	NEoE
'Cream Crackers'	NEoE
'Cumbrian Candy'	NEoE
'Cumbrian Cheddar'	NEoE
'Cumbrian Cherrypie' **new**	NEoE
'Cumbrian Cream'	NEoE
'Custard Pie'	NEoE WWEG
'Custard Tart'	NEoE
'Dawn'	NEoE SBri WWEG
'Deano's Delight'	NEoE WWEG
'Diamond White'	WWEG
'Diana'	MAvo MNrw NEoE NLar WWEG
'Dingle Apricot'	ECtt GAbr GBin GCal MNrw MRav NBir WWEG
'Dolly North' (d)	CElw EBee EWoo MArl MCot MRav MSpe MTis NBro NGdn SHar WCAu WHal WWEG XEll
'Double Sunrise' (d)	EBee
'Dusky Yellow'	WWEG
'East of Eden'	NEoE
'Eden Valley Angel'	NEoE WWEG
'Eden Valley Elf'	NEoE
'El Wano'	NEoE
'Elworthy Amber'	CElw WOut
'Emory Quinn'	ECtt LLHF LRHS NDov NEoE WWEG
'Fancy Frills'	CElw ECtt MAvo WHoo WWEG
'Farmer John Cross'	CAby CBre CElw CLAP EBee ECtt ELon EPri GJos LPla MAvo MNrw MSpe MTis NLar WHal WMoo WOut WWEG WWtn
'Feuermeer'	CElw MAvo NEoE NLar
'Fire Opal' (d) ♀H7	CDes CElw CWCL EAJP LPla MAvo MNrw NBir NEoE SBri WMoo WWEG
'Fire Storm'	CBre CMea CMos CWGN EBee ECtt GBin IKil LBMP LBrs LRHS MAvo MBel MNrw MPnt MTis NEgg NLar SBri SMad SPoG WCot WWFP
'Fireball'	CBod CHVG ECtt EShb LRHS LSou NDov NLar SBea SPoG
'Flame'	MAvo NEoE NLar WWEG
'Flames of Passion'PBR	Widely available
'Flower of Darkness'	NEoE
'Fresh Woods'	WWEG
'Georgeham'	CPla
'Georgenberg'	CBod CElw CLAP CSam ECtt EPfP EPri GMaP LAst LRHS MBel MCot MNrw MRav NBir NDov NGdn NHol NLar NWad SBea SBod SPoG SRms SWvt WCAu WGwG WMoo WWEG
'Gimlet' (Cocktail Series) **new**	NLar SCob WHlf
'Glencoe'	CElw
'Golden Joy'	LLHF MAvo NEoE WHoo WWEG
'Hannay's'	EBee MAvo MNrw MSpe NEoE SHar SPtp WWEG
'Harvest Moon'	NEoE
'Hearts in Amber' **new**	NEoE
'Herterton Lemon'	CElw WCot
'Herterton Primrose'	CCon CDes CElw CLAP CWCL ECtt EPPr GBuc GCal LLHF LLWG MAvo MSpe NCGa NSti WBor WHal WHoo WOut WWEG
'Hilltop Beacon' (d)	CDes CElw LLHF NEoE SBri WHoo WPnn

	Name	Suppliers
	'Honeydew'	NEoE
*	***hybridum luteum***	NSti SBri
	× ***intermedium***	CBre EPPr MAvo NEoE NGdn NLar SBri WMoo WWEG
	- 'Diane'	NChi SBri
	- 'Hofrennydd'	NWad
	'Jolly Roger'	EBee NEoE NWad WWEG
	'Karlskaer'	CCon CElw CWCL ECtt EPri EWTr EWes EWoo GBin GBuc GQue LHop LRHS LSun MBel MCot MNrw NGdn NLar SBea SBri SPtp WCAu WFar WGwG WMoo WPtf WWEG WWtn
	'Kath Inman'	WWEG
	'Kathryn'	MAvo
	'Lady Stratheden' (d) ♀H7	Widely available
	'Lemon Delight'	CDes CElw
	'Lemon Drops'	Widely available
	'Limoncello' **new**	NDov
	'Lionel Cox'	CPla CWCL ECtt ELan EPPr GAbr GCal GCra GMaP LAst LBMP MBNS MBel MCot MRav NBir NBro NChi NGdn NLar SRGP SRms WFar WWEG
	'Lipstick Sunset'	NEoE
	'Lisanne'	CBod CElw CSam CWCL GKev IPot MAvo MNrw MSpe NCGa NDov SBri SHar SMHy SPtp WWEG
	'Little Lottie'	NEoE
	'Little Twister'	NEoE WWEG
	macrophyllum	EBee
	'Maddy Prior'	NEoE
	magellanicum	EWes LEdu NBre NLar
	- PAB 237 **new**	LEdu
	'Magic Toybox'	NEoE WWEG
	'Mai Tai'PBR	Widely available
	'Mandarin' (d)	CCse CDes GAbr GCal SHar
	'Mango'	CDes NDov
	'Mango Lassi'	CElw GBin MTis NEoE SBri SHar WCAu
	'Marchant's Apricot Sundae' **new**	SBri
	'Marmalade'	ECtt EPri EWTr GAbr GJos LCro LLWG MAvo MNrw MRav MSpe NCGa NEoE NLar SMHy WCAu WFar WHrl WKif WMoo WOut WWEG
	'McClure's Magic'	NEoE
§	***montanum*** ♀H5	EBee ECho EDAr GBin GCra GLog LRHS MMuc NBir NBro NRya SEND SRms WWEG XLum
	'Moonlight Serenade'	EBee ECtt GCal LLHF LRHS LSou MAvo NDov NEoE WWEG
	'Moorland Sorbet'	NEoE SBri WMoo WPtf WWEG
	'Morning Sun'	SBri
	'Mrs J. Bradshaw' (d) ♀H7	Widely available
	'Mrs W. Moore'	CBre CDes CElw CLAP CWCL EBee ECtt EPPr EShb GAbr GJos MHer MNrw MRav MSpe NBir NChi NEoE NLar NQui SBri SCob SRGP WMoo WWEG
	'Nordek'	CBod CElw CMos ECha ECtt GAbr GBuc GCal GQue LAst MNrw MRav NEgg NGdn SBri WPtf WWEG
	'Norwell Yellow Lamp'	MAvo
	'Octavie'	MAvo WWEG

	Name	Suppliers
	'Orangeman'	MNrw
	'Peachy Proud'	NEoE WWEG
	'Pear Drops'	NEoE
	pentapetalum	see *Sieversia pentapetala*
	'Pink Frills'	CElw CWCL ECtt EPPr EPri EWTr EWes GBin GBuc GCra GQue LLWG LPla MAvo MPnt MRav MSpe MTis NCGa NLar SGbt SMHy SPtp WCAu WWEG
	'Poco'	CMos EBee ECtt GCal LLHF LRHS MAvo NDov NEoE SBea
	'Prairie Dancer' **new**	NEoE
	'Present'	ECtt NBre NCGa NChi NEoE WWEG
	'Primrose'	GAbr GJos GQue NEoE NGdn NLar
	'Primrose Cottage'	EBee
	'Prince of Orange' (d)	CElw GAbr LRHS MNrw MRav NBre SBri SWvt WFar WHrl WWEG
	'Prinses Juliana'	Widely available
	'Proud's Popcorn' **new**	NEoE
	pseudococcineum	LRHS
	pyrenaicum	EBee NBre NCGa
	quellyon	see *G. chiloense*
I	'Rearsby Hybrid'	CElw LLHF MRav NEoE SPlb WHoo WWEG
	'Red Wings' (d)	GBin GBuc GCal GMaP GQue MCot MNrw MRav NBir SBri WWEG
§	***reptans***	GBin LLHF
	rhodopeum	EBee
	'Rijnstroom'	EPPr MNrw SBri SHar WPtf
	rivale	CArn CBen CBod CHab CWld EAJP EHon EPfP MCot MHer MHol MMuc MNHC MWts NBro NMir NPer SPlb SRms SWat WFar WMAq WMoo WOut WWEG
	- 'Album'	Widely available
	- 'Apricot'	SBri
	- 'Barbra Lawton'	MSpe SBri WWEG
	- 'Cream Drop'	CElw GJos LLWG MCot MSpe NCGa NChi NEoE SHar WWEG
	- 'Elfenbein'	WWEG
	- subsp. ***islandicum***	SBrt
	- 'Leonard's Double' (d)	WWEG
	- 'Leonard's Variety'	Widely available
	- 'Marika'	CAby CHid EBee EPri NCGa SRGP WMoo WWEG WWtn
	- 'Marmalade'	CAby CBre CElw CWCL EBee IPot MPnt NChi NEoE SBri WPtf WWEG
	- 'Snowflake'	CElw GJos MAvo MSpe NChi NEoE SBri WWEG
	'Roger's Rebellion' **new**	NEoE
	'Rubin'	EBee ECtt EPPr GCra IPot NBro NDov WCAu
	'Rusty Young'	CBod CMos ECtt EWes GCal LLHF LSou MAvo MBel NDov NEoE SBea
	'Savanna Sunset'	CMos ECtt EWes GCal LAst LLHF LRHS MCot NDov NEoE SBea WHrl WWEG
	'Sigiswang'	EWes GJos LEdu MNrw MRav NEoE WCAu WWEG
	'Spider Muffin'	NEoE WWEG
	'Stacey's Sunrise'	CMos ECtt EWes GCal LLHF LRHS MAvo MHCG NDov NEoE
	'Star of Bethlehem'	NEoE WWEG
I	'Starker's Magnificum'	MAvo WCot WWEG
	'Stevie Nicks' **new**	NEoE

'Strawberries and Cream'	NEoE
'Sundrud Star'	NEoE
'Sunrise' (d)	CRos LRHS SHil
'Sweet Angel Dar'	NEoE WWEG
'Tangerine'	EPri GJos MRav MSpe NEoE WWEG
'Tango Dream'	CBod LRHS NEoE WWEG
'Tequila Sunrise'	EBee ECtt LLWG MHol MSpe NDov SBri SCob SPad
'Tinkerbell'	NEoE
'Tinpenny Orange'	CElw MAvo NEoE WHoo WWEG
× ***tirolense***	EBee NBre NCGa NEoE
'Toast of Cumbria' **new**	NEoE
'Toffee Apples' **new**	NEoE
'Totally Tangerine' PBR	CMea CSpe CWCL EBee ECtt EPfP EWTr GBin GMaP LBuc LHop LRHS LSou MBri MTis NDov NLar NPri SBri SCob SDys SHar SHil SPoG SWvt WCAu
'Trevor's Lemon'	MAvo
triflorum	CBod CElw CWCL EShb EWes GEdr LEdu MNrw SHar WOut
- var. ***campanulatum***	CCon GJos NEoE WWEG
'Turbango'	NEoE
'Turbango Twister' **new**	NEoE
'Turnpike Tales' **new**	NEoE
'Turnpike Troubadour'	NEoE
urbanum	CArn ENfk GJos SWat WHer WHfH WMoo
'Wallace's Peach'	WWEG
'Wyn's Wish' **new**	NEoE

Gevuina (*Proteaceae*)

avellana	CBcs WPGP

Gilia (*Polemoniaceae*)

achilleifolia	SPhx
californica	see *Leptodactylon californicum*
tricolor	NPol

Gillenia (*Rosaceae*)

stipulata	CLAP GBin IPot LEdu MNrw SHar SPhx WPGP
trifoliata ♀H7	Widely available
- 'Pink Profusion'	CBot CMos CSpe EBee ECtt IPot MBel MHol MSCN NDov NLar SCob SPad STPC WCot WHlf

Ginkgo (*Ginkgoaceae*)

biloba	Widely available
- B&SWJ 8753	WCru
- 'Anny's Dwarf'	MAsh MBlu NLar SBig
- 'Autumn Gold' (m) ♀H6	CBcs CDul CMCN EBee ECrN LAst LLHF MBlu MGos MPkF SBig SLim WMat
- 'Barabits' Fastigiata'	ESwi MBlu SAko SMad
- 'Barabits' Nana'	MBlu SBig
- 'Beijing Gold'	IVic MBlu MPkF NLar SAko SBig SMad WPGP
- 'Broom with Tubes'	SMad
- 'California Sunset'	MBlu SBig
- 'Chase Manhattan'	MPkF
- 'Chotek'	SBig
- 'Chris' Dwarf'	NLar
- 'David'	SAko SBig
- 'Eastern Star' (f)	CAgr
- 'Elsie'	SBig
- 'Everton Broom'	CMac CMen NEgg NLar SBig SBod
- 'Fairmount' (m)	MBlu SBig
- 'Fastigiata' (m)	CMCN EBee EPfP ESwi MBlu MGos SBig
- 'Finger' **new**	SLim
- 'Girard's Spreader' **new**	EBee
- 'Globosa'	MBlu SBig
- 'Gnome'	ESwi LSRN MGos MPkF SCob
- 'Golden Dragon'	MBlu
- 'Golden Globe'	ESwi MPkF SBig
- 'Gresham'	MPkF
- 'Horizontalis'	MBlu SBig
- 'Jade Butterflies' ♀H6	MBlu MPkF NLar SBig SLim SMad
- 'Jehosaphat'	NLar SBig
- 'Jerry Vercade'	MPkF
- 'King of Dongting' (f)	CAgr ESwi MBlu SBig
- 'Lakeview' (m)	MPkF SBig SCob
- 'Long March'	CAgr
- 'Mariken' ♀H6	ELan EPfP ESwi MPkF NLar SAko SBig SCob SLim SPoG
- 'Mayfield' (m)	NLar SBig SMad
- 'McFarland'	CAgr
- 'Menhir'	CBcs EBee ELan EPfP MPkF
- 'Montezuma'	SBig
- 'Obelisk'	NLar
- Ohazuki Group (f)	CAgr SBig
- Pendula Group	CMCN EBee ESwi MBlu MPkF SBig SGol WMat
- 'Pendula Gruga'	SBig
- 'Pixie'	SBig
- 'Princeton Sentry' (m) ♀H6	EBee IVic LLHF LRHS MBlu NLar SAko SBig
- 'Robbie's Twist'	MPkF SBig
- 'Santa Cruz'	SBig
- 'Saratoga' (m) ♀H6	CAgr CBcs CMCN EBee EPfP ESwi MBlu MBri MPkF NLar SAko SBig SCob SLim SMad SSpi WMat
- 'Shangri-La' (m)	MBlu SMad
- 'Sinclair'	MPkF
- 'Survivor'	SMad
- 'Thelma' **new**	SLim
- 'Tit'	CMCN EPfP ESwi MBlu MPkF NLar SBig
- 'Tremonia'	CMCN EPfP MBlu MPkF SAko SBig
- 'Troll' ♀H6	LRHS MAsh MBlu SBig SCoo SLim SMad
- 'Tubifolia'	CMCN ESwi MBlu MPkF NLar SBig SCob SLim
- 'Umbrella'	SBig
- Variegata Group (v)	CBcs ESwi MGos MPkF NLar SBig
- 'W.B.'	MPkF SBig
- 'Weeping Wonder' (f)	SBig

ginseng see *Panax ginseng*

Gladiolus (*Iridaceae*)

sp.	MNrw
abyssinucus	CEvo
acuminatus	WCot
'Adi' **new**	WCot
'Ajax'	WPhe
'Akuta' (M/E)	CGrW
alatus	ECho NRog WPhe
'Alba' (N)	LRHS WPhe
'Alice' (Min)	ERCP
'Amanda Mahy' (N)	GKev LAma NRog WPhe
'Amsterdam' (G)	CGrW WPhe
angustus L.	CDes CGrW CTal NRog WPhe

	antakiensis	CPou
	'Antica' (L)	WPhe
	'Astarte'	WPhe
	'Atom' (S/P)	CAvo CBro CGrW ECho GKev LAma NRog WPhe
	aureus	WCot WPhe
	'Bangladesh'[PBR]	WPhe
	Barnard hybrids	CGrW
	'Beautiful Angel'	CGrW WPhe
	'Beauty Bride' (L)	CGrW
	'Big Boss' (G)	CGrW
	'Black Star'	EPfP ERCP SPer
	'Black Surprise'	WPhe
	'Blackbird' (S)	CGrW
	'Blue Frost' (L)	ERCP SDeJ WPhe
	'Blue Mountain'	WPhe
	'Bonfire' (G)	CGrW WPhe
	'Boone'	GBin
	'Break of Dawn'	SDeJ
	'Brown Sugar'	WPhe
	byzantinus	see *G. communis* subsp. *byzantinus*
	caeruleus	WCot WPhe
	callianthus	see *G. murielae*
	'Cardinal'	WPhe
	cardinalis	CPrp EWoo GCal IBlr LEdu SBrt SKHP WCru WPhe
	carinatus	CDes CGrW NRog WCot
	carinatus* × *huttonii 'Purple Spray'	WCot
	carinatus* × *orchidiflorus	WCot
	'Carine' (N)	GKev MPie NRog SDeJ WPhe
	carmineus	CGrW WCot
	carneus	CDes CGrW ECho EPot GCal IPot NRog SDeJ WPhe
	- 'Georgina'	CGrW
	caryophyllaceus	CGrW
	'Charm' (N/Tub)	CBro GKev LEdu NRog SDeJ WPhe
	'Charming Beauty' (Tub)	GKev LAma LRHS NRog SDeJ WPhe
	'Charming Henry' (Tub) **new**	GKev
	'Charming Lady' (Tub)	GKev NRog WPhe
	'Cindy' (B)	WPhe
	citrinus	see *G. trichonemifolius*
	'Claudia' (N)	CGrW GKev WPhe
	'Columbine' (P)	SDeJ WPhe
	× ***colvillii***	CDes CMea IBlr WPhe
	- 'Albus'	ERCP GKev
	- 'The Bride'	CAvo CBro EBee GKev ITim LAma LCro LEdu LOPS LSRN SBod SDeJ WPhe
§	***communis*** subsp. ***byzantinus*** ♀H5	Widely available
	'Coral Lace' (L)	SDeJ WPhe
	'Côte d'Azur' (G)	CGrW WPhe
	crassifolius	CTre
	'Cream Perfection' (L)	CGrW SDeJ WPhe
	'Creamy Yellow' (S)	CGrW
	'Crispy Ruffle' **new**	ERCP
	cruentus **new**	CGrW WCot
§	***dalenii***	CExl CPou CSam CSde CTre GCal IBlr LEdu SMad WCot WPhe
	- 'Apricot Delight' (v)	IBlr
	- 'Boone'	WCot
	- 'Citrone Spectrum' (v)	IBlr
§	- subsp. ***dalenii***	CPrp IBlr WCot
	- - 'Spinners'	CDes EBee IBlr
	- green-flowered	IBlr

	- 'Guardsman' (v)	IBlr
	- red-flowered **new**	GCal
*	- f. ***rubra***	IBlr
	- yellow-flowered	CDes
	'David Hills' (*papilio* hybrid)	CDes CMea NCGa SDys WCot WHal
	'Debbieanne'	WPhe
	'Decadent'	WPhe
	'Delirium'	CGrW
	'Dion' (M)	CGrW WPhe
	'Dixon' (L)	CGrW WPhe
	'Domenica'	WPhe
	'Dusted Red'	GKev
	'Elegance' (G)	WPhe
	'Elvira' (N)	CSut GKev LAma NRog WPhe
	'Emerald Spring' (S)	WCot
	'Esta Bonita' (G)	CGrW WPhe
	'Excel' (L)	CGrW
	'Extasy'[PBR] (L)	CGrW WPhe
	'Farondole'	SDeJ
	'Felicita' (L)	CGrW WPhe
	'Fidelio' (L)	SDeJ
	'Finishing Touch'[PBR] (L)	CGrW WPhe
	'Fiona'	CGrW GKev
	flanaganii	CBro CExl CMea CPBP CSpe CTre ECho GCal GEdr GKev LLHF NSla SBrt SChr WAbe WCot WPhe
	- JCA 261.000	SKHP
	'Flevo Cosmic' (Min)	CGrW WPhe
	'Flevo Dancer' (S)	CGrW WPhe
	'Flevo Eclips'[PBR] (G)	CGrW WPhe
	'Flevo Junior' (S)	CGrW
	'Flevo Laguna' (S)	CAvo
	'Flevo Shine' (M)	CGrW
	'Flevo Smile' (S)	WPhe
	'Flevo Souvenir'[PBR] (L)	CGrW
	'Flevo Spirit'	CGrW
	'Flevo Sunset'[PBR] (L)	CGrW
	floribundus Jacq.	NRog
	- subsp. ***fasciatus***	CGrW WPhe
	'Fortarosa'	WPhe
	fourcadei	CGrW
	'French Silk' (L)	CGrW
	'Frizzled Coral Lace' (E)	CSut
	'Galaxian' **new**	GKev
	× ***gandavensis*** hort.	GBin WPhe
	garnieri	see *G. dalenii* subsp. *dalenii*
	geardii	WCot
	'Gold Struck' (L)	CGrW
	'Good Luck' (N)	CBro
	gracilis	CGrW WCot WPhe
	grandis	see *G. liliaceus*
	'Green Star' (L)	CGrW ERCP LCro SDeJ WPhe
	griseus	NRog
	gueinzii	CGrW
	'Guernsey Glory' (N)	GKev
	'Halley' (N)	GKev LAma NRog WPhe
	'Hansnett'	WCot
	'Happy Weekend' (L)	SDeJ
	'Holland Pearl' (B)	ERCP SDeJ WPhe
	'Huron Silk' (L)	CGrW
	huttonii	CGrW ECho NRog WCot
	huttonii* × *liliaceus	WPhe
	huttonii* × *tristis	CDes CPou WPhe
	huttonii* × *tristis var. ***concolor***	WCot
	hyalinus	WCot
	'Ibadan'[PBR] (L)	CGrW
	illyricus	GCal GKev SPlb WShi

Name	Suppliers
imbricatus	MHer
'Imperialis'	IBlr
'Impressive' (N)	CBro GKev IPot LAma NRog SBod SDeJ WPhe
'Indian Summer'PBR	ERCP
inflatus	WPhe
'Internet'	WPhe
involutus	CGrW
§ ***italicus***	CGrW CHid GKev LCro LOPS SKHP XLum
'Jacksonville Gold' (L)	SDeJ
'Jester' (L)	SDeJ WPhe
'Kazimir'	WPhe
'Kings Lynn'	WPhe
'Kissy Ruffle' (L)	ERCP
'Lady Lucille' (M)	WPhe
'Las Vegas'	CGrW GKev NRog WPhe
'Lavy Linda' (L)	CGrW WPhe
'Lemon Drop' (S)	CGrW WPhe
leptosiphon	CGrW
§ ***liliaceus***	CGrW NRog WCot
'Little Vintage' **new**	GKev
'Loulou' (G)	CGrW
'Lucifer'PBR	WPhe
'Mademoiselle de Paris'	ERCP WPhe
'Magma'	WPhe
'Mamma Mia'	WPhe
'Marj S' (L)	WPhe
'Marvinka' (M)	CSut
'Match Point' (L)	SDeJ
meliusculus	NRog
'Mexico'	CSut SDeJ WPhe
'Millennium' (L)	WPhe
miniatus	CDes NRog WCot WPhe
'Mirella' (N)	CAvo GKev LAma NRog WPhe
'Mon Amour'PBR	CGrW SDeJ WPhe
'Monsieur Piquet' (P) **new**	WCot
'Mr Chris' (S)	WPhe
§ ***murielae*** ♀H3	CAby CAvo CBod CBro CGrW CMea CWld EAJP EPfP ERCP GKev LCro LOPS LRHS MCot MPie NChi SCoo SDeJ SHil SPer SPlb SRms WHal WPhe
natalensis	see *G. dalenii*
'Natan' **new**	WCot
'Nathalie' (N)	CGrW GKev NRog SDeJ WPhe
'Nori' (M)	ERCP WPhe
'Nova Lux' (L)	SDeJ WPhe
'Nymph' (N)	CAvo CGrW GKev LAma LCro LEdu LOPS NRog SDeJ WPhe
'Oasis'PBR (G)	CGrW WPhe
ochroleucus	WHil
'Odysee'	WPhe
§ ***oppositiflorus***	CDes CEvo CTre EBee IBlr LEdu SChr SPlb
- subsp. ***salmoneus***	see *G. oppositiflorus*
'Orange King'	WPhe
orchidiflorus	CGrW
'Oscar' (G)	ERCP
'Pandora'	WPhe
papilio	Widely available
§ - Purpureoauratus Group	CBro CSam IBlr SRms WSHC
- yellow-flowered	CMea
'Passos'PBR	ERCP
'Peach Blossom' (N)	IBlr WCot
'Peach Melba' (L)	CGrW WPhe
'Perseus' (P/Min)	ERCP WPhe
'Perth Pearl' (M)	CGrW
'Peter Pears' (L)	ERCP SDeJ WPhe
'Phyllis M' (L)	CGrW
Pilbeam hybrids	CGrW WCot
'Platini'	WPhe
'Plum Tart' (L)	CBro ERCP LCro LOPS WPhe
'Pop Art'	SDeJ
primulinus	see *G. dalenii*
'Prins Claus' (N)	CBro CTca GKev LAma NRog WPhe
'Prinses Margaret Rose' (Min)	SDeJ WPhe
'Priscilla' (L)	MLHP SDeJ WPhe
'Purple Flora'	ERCP WPhe
'Purple Mate' **new**	LCro
'Purple Prince' (M)	CGrW
purpureoauratus	see *G. papilio* Purpureoauratus Group
quadrangularis	CGrW
'Raspberry Swirl' (L/E)	CGrW
recurvus	CGrW
'Red Shadow'	WPhe
'Robinetta' (*recurvus* hybrid) ♀H3	CWCL GKev LAma LCro LOPS LRHS NRog SDeJ WPhe
'Roma' (L)	WPhe
'Rosario'	WPhe
'Rotary'	WPhe
'Roxy'	WPhe
'Ruby' (*papilio* hybrid)	CAby CAvo CBro CDes CElw CExl CMea CPou CPrp CSde CTal CTca ECha EPri GKev IMou LEdu LSRN MHer NChi SMad WAul WCot WHoo WPGP WPhe
'Ruth Ann'	CGrW WPhe
saundersii	GCal
scullyi from Ceres Karoo, South Africa	NRog
segetum	see *G. italicus*
sericeovillosus	IBlr
'Slick Chick' (S)	CGrW
'Smoke 'n' Mirrors'	CGrW
'Solferino'	WPhe
'Solveiga' (L/E)	CGrW WPhe
'Sophie'PBR	CGrW WPhe
'Spic and Span' (L)	SDeJ WPhe
splendens	CDes CGrW NRog WCot WPGP
stefaniae	CGrW
'Stiena' (L)	CGrW WPhe
'Sweet Blue'	WPhe
'Terry' (G)	CGrW WPhe
'Thalia'	WPhe
'That's Love' (L)	CSut SDeJ
'Trader Horn' (G)	CGrW SDeJ WPhe
§ ***trichonemifolius***	CGrW
tristis	CAvo CBro CDes CElw CGrW CPne CPou CPrp ECho ELon EWoo NRog WPGP WPhe
- var. ***concolor***	CGrW CPou CPrp CTre WCot
undulatus	CDes CGrW EBee ECho NRog WCot WPhe
uysiae	CGrW ECho
vandermerwei	CGrW
'Velvet Eyes' (M)	SDeJ WPhe
venustus	CGrW NRog
'Video' (L)	WPhe
'Violetta' (M)	CGrW SDeJ WPhe
virescens	NRog
'Volcano'	GKev
watsonioides	SKHP
watsonius	NRog
'Wax Ruffles' (L/E)	CGrW

'White Prosperity' (L)	CSut ERCP LCro LOPS SDeJ
woodii **new**	WCot
'Yellow Gem'	SDeJ
'Zamora' (L)	CGrW
'Zizane'	CSut
'Zorro' **new**	WCot

Glandularia see *Verbena*

Glaucidium (*Ranunculaceae*)

palmatum 🏆H5	CExl EFEx EPot EWld GBuc GEdr GKev NSla WCru
- 'Album'	see *G. palmatum* var. *leucanthum*
§ - var. ***leucanthum***	EFEx GEdr

Glaucium (*Papaveraceae*)

§ ***corniculatum***	CAbP CAby CArn CCon CSpe EBee LRHS SPhx
flavum	CCon CSpe EBee ECha ELan LRHS MHer MMuc NFav SEND SPav XSen
- ***aurantiacum***	see *G. flavum* f. *fulvum*
§ - f. ***fulvum***	ECha EWTr MMuc SDix SEND WCot XSen
- orange-flowered	see *G. flavum* f. *fulvum*
- red-flowered	see *G. corniculatum*
phoenicium	see *G. corniculatum*

Glaucosciadium (*Apiaceae*)

cordifolium	CSpe EBee WCot
- PAB 9003 **new**	LEdu

Glebionis (*Asteraceae*)

coronaria	MNHC SRms
§ ***segetum***	CHab

Glechoma (*Lamiaceae*)

hederacea	GPoy MHer NMir WHer
§ - 'Variegata' (v)	EShb SPer XLum

Gleditsia (*Caesalpiniaceae*)

caspia	CArn LEdu
japonica	ITim NLar
koraiensis	LEdu
- B&SWJ 12569	WCru
triacanthos	CDul CWib IDee LEdu SCob SPlb
- 'Calhoun'	CAgr
- 'Emerald Cascade'	CBcs EBee
- 'Goofy'	SMad
- f. ***inermis*** Spectrum = 'Speczam'	MAsh MBri WHar
- - 'Sunburst'	Widely available
- 'Millwood'	CAgr
- 'Rubylace'	CBcs CCVT CDul CLnd CMCN CSBt EBee ECrN ELan EPfP EWTr IVic LAst LSRN MBlu MBri MGos MRav MSwo NLar SCob SGol SKHP SLim SPer WHar WMat

Globba ✿ (*Zingiberaceae*)

marantina	LAma
racemosa var. ***hookeri*** HWJCM 471	WCru
winitii 'Mount Everest'	LAma

Globularia (*Plantaginaceae*)

albiflora	EPot
alypum	SBrt
bellidifolia	see *G. meridionalis*
cordifolia 🏆H5	ECho EDAr EPot GCrg GEdr LRHS NBir NSla SBch
- RCB UA 30 **new**	WCot
- 'Alba'	NHar
incanescens	CPBP NSla
§ ***meridionalis***	CBod ECho EPot EWes GMaP MWat SIgm WOld
- 'Blue Bonnets'	GEdr NHar
- 'Hort's Variety'	NSla WAbe
nana	see *G. repens*
nudicaulis	ECho GEdr GKev IMou
orientalis **new**	XSen
punctata	CCon SRms
pygmaea	see *G. meridionalis*
§ ***repens***	CPBP ECho EPot GEdr LLHF SIgm WAbe
stygia	XSen
trichosantha	GEdr SRms XSen
valentina	EPot GEdr GKev LLHF
vulgaris	XSen

Gloriosa (*Colchicaceae*)

lutea	see *G. superba* 'Lutea'
modesta **new**	GKev
rothschildiana	see *G. superba* 'Rothschildiana'
superba 🏆H1c	GKev SDeJ
- 'Carsonii'	GKev LAma SDeJ
- 'Greenii'	GKev LAma SDeJ
§ - 'Lutea'	GKev LAma SDeJ
§ - 'Rothschildiana'	CBcs CGrW GKev LAma LCro LOPS SDeJ SRms WCot
- 'Rothschildiana Orange'	GKev
- 'Rothschildiana Salmon'	GKev
- 'Simplex'	CLak
- 'Sparkling Jip'	GKev
- 'Sparkling Orange'	GKev
- 'Sparkling Striped'	GKev
- 'Tricolor' **new**	GKev
- 'Verschuurii'	CLak

Gloxinia (*Gesneriaceae*)

sp.	EABi
nematanthodes	SBrt
- 'Evita'	EShb WCot
sylvatica 'Bolivian Sunset'	WDib

Glumicalyx (*Scrophulariaceae*)

flanaganii	SBrt SPlb

Glyceria (*Poaceae*)

aquatica variegata	see *G. maxima* var. *variegata*
maxima	MMuc MSKA MWLS NPer SEND SPlb
§ - var. ***variegata*** (v)	CLet CWat ECha EHoe EHon ELan EPfP EShb EWay GCra GMaP IBoy LRHS MMuc MWhi NGdn NWsh SCob SEND SPer SRms SVic SWat WMAq WMoo WWEG XLum
notata	SVic
spectabilis 'Variegata'	see *G. maxima* var. *variegata*

Glycyrrhiza (*Papilionaceae*)

echinata	CAgr
§ ***glabra***	CAgr CArn CBod CHby CLau ENfk GPoy MHer MNHC NLar SDix SPlb SRms WHfH WJek
glandulifera	see *G. glabra*
uralensis	CArn CLau GPoy MHer NLar SPhx

yunnanensis	CSpe LPla

Glyptostrobus (*Cupressaceae*)

pensilis	CExl CFil IDee SLim WPGP

Gnaphalium (*Asteraceae*)

'Fairy Gold'	see *Helichrysum thianschanicum* 'Goldkind'
trinerve	see *Anaphalis trinervis*

Gomphocarpus ✿ (*Apocynaceae*)

§	***fruticosus***	SVen
§	***physocarpus***	CArn

Gompholobium (*Papilionaceae*)

scabrum new	SPlb

Gomphostigma (*Scrophulariaceae*)

virgatum	CAbP CExl CFis CSpe EPPr EPfP EWld ITim LLWG MHol MPie SEND SMad SPlb WBod WCFE WCot WPtf WRHF WTor
- 'White Candy'	NLar SVen

Gomphrena (*Amaranthaceae*)

pulchella new	CSpe

Goniolimon (*Plumbaginaceae*)

	incanum 'Blue Diamond'	LSun
§	***tataricum***	MMuc
§	- var. ***angustifolium***	SRms

Goodyera (*Orchidaceae*)

biflora	EFEx
pubescens	EFEx
schlechtendaliana	EFEx

gooseberry see *Ribes uva-crispa*

Gordonia (*Theaceae*)

axillaris	see *Polyspora axillaris*

Gorgonidium (*Araceae*)

intermedium	WCot

granadilla see *Passiflora quadrangularis*

granadilla, purple see *Passiflora edulis*

granadilla, sweet see *Passiflora ligularis*

granadilla, yellow see *Passiflora laurifolia*

grape see *Vitis*

grapefruit see *Citrus* × *aurantium* Grapefruit Group

Graptopetalum (*Crassulaceae*)

	bellum ♀H2	CDoC
	filiferum	CDoC EUJe SPlb
	pachyphyllum	CDoC
§	***paraguayense***	CDoC SVen

× *Graptoveria* (*Crassulaceae*)

'Caerulescens'	CDoC
'Ghostly'	WCot
'Mrs Richards'	CSuc
'Titubans'	CDoC

Gratiola (*Plantaginaceae*)

officinalis	CArn CBod EHon LLWG LRHS MHer MSKA

Greenovia (*Crassulaceae*)

	aizoon	CSuc
§	***aurea***	CSuc NMen SPlb
	diplocycla 'Gigantea'	SPlb
	dodrentalis new	SChr

Grevillea (*Proteaceae*)

	aquifolium	MOWG
	banksii 'Canberra Hybrid'	see *G.* 'Canberra Gem'
	- var. ***forsteri***	SPlb
	barklyana	MOWG
	'Bronze Rambler'	MOWG
§	'Canberra Gem' ♀H4	Widely available
	'Clearview David'	LRHS LSRN MMuc MOWG SAko SLim SSpi SVen
	crithmifolia	SPlb
	'Desert Flame'	see *G. rosmarinifolia*
	'Evelyn's Coronet'	MOWG
	iaspicula	MOWG
	johnsonii	CMac MOWG
	juniperina	CBcs CExl CLet CMac EPfP LPar SEle SLim SVen
	- 'Molonglo'	CTsd
	- f. ***sulphurea***	CExl CTsd ELon EPfP MGil MMuc MOWG SEle SPer SPlb SPoG WSHC
	- - prostrate	MOWG
	lanigera	EUJe
I	- 'Lutea'	MOWG
	- 'Mount Tamboritha'	CBcs CDoC CExl CMac CSde EBee ECou EPfP IDee LRHS SEle SLim SPoG SVen
	- prostrate	MOWG WGrn WPat
	leucopteris	SPlb
	'Long John'	MOWG
	'Mason's Hybrid'	MOWG
	olivacea 'Apricot Glow'	MOWG
	'Olympic Flame'	CBcs CDoC CExl CSBt CTsd CWib LEdu LRHS LSou MGos MMuc MOWG SAko SBod SPoG SVen WBor WGrn
	paniculata	SPlb
	'Pink Lady'	ECou ELon EPfP LRHS MOWG SAko
	'Poorinda Constance'	MOWG
	'Red Dragon' (v)	LRHS
	'Red Hooks'	MOWG
	rhyolitica	MOWG
	robusta ♀H1c	MOWG SPlb
	'Robyn Gordon'	MOWG
	rosmarinifolia ♀H4	CBcs CDoC CExl CLet CMac CSBt CTri CTsd CWib ELan EPfP GKin MOWG SEle SIgm SLim SLon SPlb WFar
	- 'Desert Flame'	CBcs CExl
	- 'Jenkinsii'	CExl CMac CSBt EBee EPfP EUJe LSou MOWG SEle SLim
	'Scarlet Sprite'	MOWG
§	× ***semperflorens***	CSde CWib EBee LRHS MOWG SPlb WGrn
	'Splendour'	MOWG
	thelemanniana Spriggs' form	MOWG
	thyrsoides	GGal

tolminsis	see *G.* × *semperflorens*
victoriae	CBcs CDoC CJun CTsd EBee ECre EPfP IVic LRHS MOWG SAko SChF SEle SSpi WCot WGrn WPGP
- 'Mount Annan'	MOWG
- subsp. ***victoriae***	CExl
- yellow-flowered	LRHS
williamsonii	LRHS

Grewia (*Malvaceae*)

occidentalis	CDoC MOWG

Greyia (*Melianthaceae*)

sutherlandii	MOWG SPlb

Grindelia (*Asteraceae*)

§ ***camporum***	CCon IMou SPlb
chiloensis	CAbb
- F&W 9390	WCot
integrifolia	XLum
robusta	see *G. camporum*
squarrosa	WHil

Griselinia ✿ (*Griseliniaceae*)

littoralis ♀H4	Widely available
- 'Bantry Bay' (v)	CAbP CBcs CSde CTsd EHoe ELan ESwi LRHS MAsh NWad SPer SPoG SWvt WFar
- 'Brodick Gold'	CExl ELon GKin
- 'Dixon's Cream' (v)	CBcs CDul CMac CSBt EBee EPfP LRHS MRav SGol SLon SVen
- Green Horizon = 'Whenuapai'PBR	CDoC LRHS MGos SLim SPer SPoG STPC
- 'Green Jewel' (v)	CWib ESwi
- 'Variegata' (v) ♀H4	Widely available
ruscifolia	LEdu
scandens	SEND

guava, common see *Psidium guajava*

guava, purple or strawberry see *Psidium littorale* var. *longipes*

Guichenotia (*Sterculiaceae*)

macrantha	SPlb

Gunnera ✿ (*Gunneraceae*)

chilensis	see *G. tinctoria*
cordifolia	LLWG
densiflora	GEdr
dentata	CPla
flavida	CPla
hamiltonii	CPla ECha GAbr MMuc NBir
killipiana B&SWJ 9009	WCru
magellanica	Widely available
manicata	Widely available
monoica	GAbr LLWG
perpensa	CBcs CBen CCon CDes EBee EWTr IMou LLWG
prorepens	CExl CMac CPla ECha GAbr LLWG NBir
scabra	see *G. tinctoria*
§ ***tinctoria***	CBod CExl CMac CWib ECha ELan EPfP EWoo GBin IBoy IVic LLWG LRHS MMuc NLar SDix SEND SWat SWvt WFar WPGP

Guzmania (*Bromeliaceae*)

'Tempo'PBR	LAir NEve
'Torch'PBR	LAir NEve

Gymnadenia (*Orchidaceae*)

conopsea	ECho EFEx NLAp

Gymnocarpium (*Woodsiaceae*)

dryopteris ♀H5	CLAP EFer EShb EWld GKev GMaP ISha SGSe WAbe WFib WOut WShi
- PAB 1757	LEdu
- 'Plumosum' ♀H7	CDoC CKel CLAP CLet CWCL ERod GEdr LEdu LRHS NHar NLar WFib WHal WMoo
oyamense ♀H5	SKHP
robertianum	EFer EWld

Gymnocladus (*Caesalpiniaceae*)

chinensis	WPGP
dioica	CBcs CDul CLnd CMCN EBee EBtc ELan EPfP EUJe LEdu MBlu SMad SPer SSpi WPGP

Gymnocoronis (*Asteraceae*)

spilanthoides	LLWG

Gymnospermium (*Berberidaceae*)

§ ***albertii***	ECho
altaicum	ECho

Gynandriris see *Moraea*

Gynerium (*Poaceae*)

argenteum	see *Cortaderia selloana*

Gynostemma (*Cucurbitaceae*)

pentaphyllum	CAgr LEdu
- B&SWJ 570	WCru

Gypsophila (*Caryophyllaceae*)

aretioides	ECho EPot LHop LRHS
§ - 'Caucasica'	ECho LLHF
- 'Compacta'	see *G. aretioides* 'Caucasica'
cerastioides	CMea CTri ECho ECtt EDAr EPfP EPot GBin GCrg LBMP LHop LRHS MMuc NGdn NLar NPri SEND SPlb SRms SWvt WAbe WHoo WIce XLum
- silver variegated (v)	MHol
dubia	see *G. repens* 'Dubia'
elegans	SVic
fastigiata 'Silverstar'	LRHS
'Festival' (Festival Series)	SGbt
gracilescens	see *G. tenuifolia*
'Jolien' (v)	ELan WIce
muralis 'Garden Bride'	SWvt
- 'Gypsy Deep Rose'	ELan EPfP LRHS
- 'Gypsy Pink' (d)	EPfP SWvt
nana 'Compacta'	CPBP ECho
'Pacific Rose'	MRav
paniculata	MHol MRav SRms XLum
- 'Bristol Fairy' (d)	CSBt ECha ELan EPfP EWoo GMaP LRHS MJak NLar SCob SHar SPoG SWvt WFar WWEG XLum
- 'Compacta Plena' (d)	ECtt ELan EPfP GMaP LHop MPie MRav NGdn SRms
- double white-flowered (d)	XLum
- 'Festival Snow' (Festival Series)	LRHS
- 'Flamingo' (d)	CBcs ECha LHop LRHS NLar SHar SWvt XLum

	- 'Magic Golan' (d)	COtt
	- My Pink = 'Dangypink'	EBee
	- 'Pacific Pink'	EBee
	- 'Perfect Alba'	LRHS
	- 'Perfekta'	CBcs SPer
	- 'Pink Star' (d)	ECtt
§	- 'Schneeflocke' (d)	CBod ELan EPfP GMaP LRHS MBel SHar SRms WWEG
	- Snowflake	see *G. paniculata* 'Schneeflocke'
	- Summer Sparkles = 'Esm Chispa'PBR	EBee
	- White Fire = 'Dangypwhifa' **new**	EBee
§	***petraea***	NSla
	'Pink Festival' (Festival Series) (d)	ECtt GBee LRHS SPoG WFar
	repens ♀H5	ECtt EWTr GBin GJos MAsh NBFr SBch SCob SIgm SPlb SWvt WFar XLum
	- 'Dorothy Teacher'	CMea CSma CTal ECho ECtt MAsh SBch WTor
§	- 'Dubia'	ECha ECho ECtt EPot MHer NLar SRms
	- 'Fratensis'	ECho ECtt LLHF WIce
	- Pink Beauty	see *G. repens* 'Rosa Schönheit'
§	- 'Rosa Schönheit'	CMea ECha ECtt EPot NDov SPer XLum
	- 'Rosea'	CTri CWib EAJP EBee ECho ECtt EDAr ELan EPfP GJos GMaP ITim MHol MMuc NGdn NPri SBch SCob SEND SPoG SRms SWvt WFar WHoo WIce XLum
	- 'Silver Carpet' (v)	EBee
	- white-flowered	CMea CWib ECho ELan NGdn SWvt
§	'Rosenschleier' (d) ♀H6	CMea EBee ECha ECtt ELan EPfP LCro LHop LOPS MBel MRav NCGa NDov NGdn SRms SRot SWvt WHoo WSHC WWEG XLum
I	'Rosenschleier Variegata' (v)	EBee LHop WWEG
	'Rosy Veil'	see *G.* 'Rosenschleier'
§	***tenuifolia***	ECho EPot GMaP ITim
	transylvanica	see *G. petraea*
	Veil of Roses	see *G.* 'Rosenschleier'
	'White Festival'PBR (Festival Series) (d)	COtt LRHS SPoG

Gyptis (*Asteraceae*)

	commersonii	LHop

Haberlea (*Gesneriaceae*)

	ferdinandi-coburgii	CLAP ECho
	- 'Connie Davidson'	EBee GEdr GKev
	rhodopensis ♀H5	CElw EBee ECho EPPr GEdr NSla SRms WAbe WPGP WThu XLum
	- 'Virginalis'	CElw CLAP ECho NSla WAbe WThu

Hablitzia (*Chenopodiaceae*)

	tamnoides	CAgr LEdu MCoo

Habranthus (*Amaryllidaceae*)

	'Amazing Jumbo'	NRog
	andersonii	see *H. tubispathus*
	brachyandrus	CTal GCal GKev NRog SRms
	caeruleus	NRog
	gracilifolius	ECho NRog
	howardii	ECho
	magnoi	NRog
	martinezii ♀H2	CTal ECho GKev NRog
	mexicanus	ECho
§	***robustus*** ♀H2	CAby CExl CTal ECho EPot GKev LAma LHop NRog WPGP
	- 'Russell Manning'	NRog
§	***tubispathus*** ♀H2	CTal ECho GCal GKev NRog WCot WHil
	- var. ***roseus***	NRog

Hacquetia (*Apiaceae*)

	epipactis ♀H5	Widely available
	- 'Harry Foley' (v) **new**	NWad
§	- 'Thor' (v)	EBee ECha ECho EWes GEdr LLHF NBir NChi SIgm WPGP
	- 'Variegata'	see *H. epipactis* 'Thor'

Haemanthus (*Amaryllidaceae*)

	albiflos ♀H2	CEvo CPne CPrp CTca ECho EOHP EPri EShb GKev LAma LToo SRms WCot
	amarylloides **new**	WCot
	- subsp. ***polyanthes***	ECho
	barkerae	ECho WCot
	carneus	ECho WCot
	coccineus ♀H2	CLak ECho GKev WCot
	crispus	ECho
	deformis	GKev
	humilis	ECho WCot
	- subsp. ***hirsutus***	WCot
	- subsp. ***humilis*** 'Magaliesberg' **new**	GKev
	- - 'Piet Retief' **new**	GKev
	kalbreyeri	see *Scadoxus multiflorus* subsp. *multiflorus*
	katherinae	see *Scadoxus multiflorus* subsp. *katherinae*
	montanus	GKev
	natalensis	see *Scadoxus puniceus*
	nortieri **new**	WCot
	pauculifolius	GKev
	pubescens **new**	WCot
	sanguineus	ECho WCot

Hagenia (*Rosaceae*)

	abyssinica	WPGP

Hakea (*Proteaceae*)

	baxteri	SPlb
§	***drupacea***	CTre ECou
	epiglottis	ECou
	florida 'Summer Snow' **new**	ECou
	francisiana **new**	ECou
	laurina	CTre ECou SPlb
§	***lissosperma***	CDoC ECou EPfP SPlb WPGP
	oleifolia	CTre
	platysperma	SPlb
§	***salicifolia***	CBcs SPlb WCot
	saligna	see *H. salicifolia*
	sericea misapplied	see *H. lissosperma*
	sericea Schrad. & J.C.Wendl.	WCot
	- pink-flowered	SPlb WCot

suaveolens	see *H. drupacea*
victoriae	SPlb

Hakonechloa ✿ (*Poaceae*)

macra 🏆H7	Widely available
§ - 'Alboaurea' (v) 🏆H7	CBcs CExl CKno COtt CTsd ELan EPfP LAst LCro LRHS LSRN MGos MMuc NPla SEND SHil WOld
- 'Albovariegata' (v)	CKno EBee EPPr GCal LEdu MAvo SCob SPoG WBor
§ - 'All Gold'	CBod CDoC CExl CFil CKno CWCL EBee ECha ECtt EPPr EShb EWes GQue IBoy IKil ITim LBMP LEdu LRHS MAsh MBri MGos MJak SCob SMad SPad SPoG WCot WPGP
- 'Aureola' 🏆H7	Widely available
- 'Beni-kaze'	SCob
- 'Mediovariegata' (v)	CDoC EBee ECha EPPr WPGP
- 'Naomi' (v)	EBee SCob
- 'Nicolas'	CDoC CExl CKno CSam EBee ECtt EHoe ELan EPfP EWes GBin LEdu LLHF LPla LSRN LSou MBel MSCN NQui NSti SCob
- 'Ogon'	see *H. macra* 'All Gold'
- 'Samurai' (v)	CKno LRHS
- 'Stripe It Rich' (v)	CDoC CWCL EBee ECtt ESwi EWes SGol WGrn
- 'Variegata'	see *H. macra* 'Alboaurea'

Halenia (*Gentianaceae*)

elliptica	GKev
- SDR 7809 **new**	GKev

Halesia (*Styracaceae*)

§ ***carolina***	Widely available
- Monticola Group	CBcs CCVT CDul CMCN EBee ELan EPfP IVic LRHS MMuc NLar SPer SSpi SWvt WHar WMou
I - - 'Variegata' (v)	MBlu NLar SSta
- 'Uconn Wedding Bells'	CJun MBlu SKHP
- Vestita Group 🏆H5	CDoC CJun CTho EPfP LRHS MAsh MBlu MGos MRav NLar SPer SSpi SSta
- - 'Rosea'	CJun EPfP MBlu NLar SKHP
diptera	CBcs MBlu SKHP
- Magniflora Group	CJun EPfP MBlu
macgregorii **new**	CMCN
tetraptera	see *H. carolina*

× *Halimiocistus* (*Cistaceae*)

algarvensis	see *Halimium ocymoides*
§ 'Ingwersenii' 🏆H4	ECho EDAr ELan EWes SPer SPoG SRms XLum
revolii misapplied	see × *H. sahucii*
§ ***sahucii*** 🏆H4	CBcs CBod CDoC CSBt CTri ECha ELan EPfP LBMP LPmr LRHS MAsh MBNS MBri MRav MSwo NPri SBod SCob SPer SPoG SRms SWvt WHea XLum
- Ice Dancer = 'Ebhals'PBR (v)	EBee EPfP LAst MAsh SCob SPer SWvt
'Susan'	see *Halimium* 'Susan'
§ ***wintonensis*** 🏆H4	CBcs ELan EPfP LRHS MAsh MMuc SCob SLon SPer SRms WHar WSHC
§ - 'Merrist Wood Cream' 🏆H4	CBcs CBod CBot CDoC CMac COtt CSBt EBee ELan EPfP LAst LBrs LRHS LSRN MAsh MGil MMuc MRav MSwo NBir SEle SLim SPer SPoG SWvt WGrn WSHC

Halimium (*Cistaceae*)

§ ***atriplicifolium***	CAby
§ ***calycinum***	CBcs CBod CDoC ELan EPfP IVic LRHS MAsh MBri MHtn MMuc SCoo SEND SHil SLim SPer SPoG SWvt WCFE
commutatum	see *H. calycinum*
halimifolium misapplied	see *H.* × *pauanum*
§ ***lasianthum***	CBcs CMac CSBt CWib ELan EPfP LRHS MRav SLim
- 'Concolor' 🏆H4	CWib LRHS MAsh MSwo SWvt
- subsp. ***formosum*** 'Sandling' 🏆H4	ELan EPfP LRHS MAsh MMuc SLon SPoG SRms
libanotis misapplied	see *H. calycinum*
§ ***ocymoides***	CBcs CWib ELan IVic LRHS MSwo WHar WKif
§ × ***pauanum***	LRHS MMuc
§ 'Susan' 🏆H4	EBee ELan EPfP LBrs LRHS MMHG SCoo SLim SPer WAbe
§ ***umbellatum***	EPfP
wintonense	see × *Halimiocistus wintonensis*

Halimodendron (*Papilionaceae*)

halodendron	CArn CBcs CDul MBlu SPer

Halleria (*Stilbaceae*)

lucida	SEle SPlb SVen

Halocarpus (*Podocarpaceae*)

§ ***bidwillii***	CDoC

Haloragis (*Haloragaceae*)

erecta	SPlb SVen XLum
- 'Rubra'	WCot
- 'Wellington Bronze'	CBod CExl CSpe ECou EHoe ELan EUJe GEdr LEdu LHop SPtp WHer WMoo XLum

Hamamelis ✿ (*Hamamelidaceae*)

'Amethyst'	CJun MBlu SGol
'Brevipetala'	CJun
'Danny'	CJun
'Dishi'	CJun
'Doerak'	CJun NLar
'Fire Blaze'	CJun MBlu NLar
× ***intermedia***	CDul
- 'Advent'	CJun NLar
- 'Andrea' **new**	NLar
- 'Angelly' 🏆H5	CJun MBlu NLar
- 'Anne'	LRHS NLar
- 'Aphrodite' 🏆H5	CDoC CDul CJun EPfP LRHS MAsh MBlu MBri MGos MMuc MRav NCGa NLar SCob SHil SPer
- 'Arnhem'	NLar
- 'Arnold Promise' 🏆H5	Widely available
- 'Aurora' 🏆H5	CJun EPfP LRHS MBlu MBri MGos NLar SHil SPoG
- 'Barmstedt Gold' 🏆H5	CJun CRos EPfP IArd LRHS LSRN MAsh MGos NLar SAko SCob SHil SPer SPoG WPat
- 'Bernstein'	CJun
- 'Birgit'	NLar
- 'Carmine Red'	CJun CMac MGos
- 'Copper Beauty'	see *H.* × *intermedia* 'Jelena'
- 'Cyrille'	IArd SAko

- 'Diane' ♀H5	Widely available
§ - 'Feuerzauber'	CMac CSBt CTri LBuc MGos NLar NOrn SCob SPer SWvt
- Fire Cracker	see *H.* × *intermedia* 'Feuerzauber'
- 'Foxy Lady'	CRos LRHS MAsh SPoG
- 'Frederic' ♀H5	CJun EPfP LRHS MAsh
- 'Georges'	NLar
- 'Gimborn's Perfume'	NLar
- 'Gingerbread'	CJun EPfP LLHF LRHS MAsh
- 'Glowing Embers'	CJun LRHS MAsh
- 'Harlow Carr'	LRHS MAsh NLar
- 'Harry' ♀H5	CJun LRHS LSRN MAsh NLar
- 'Heinrich Bruns'	CJun
§ - 'Jelena' ♀H5	Widely available
- 'John'	LRHS LSRN MAsh
- 'Kew Sunshine' new	LRHS
- 'Limelight'	CJun MBlu NLar
- 'Livia'	CJun EPfP LRHS MAsh NLar SCoo SHil SPoG SSpi
- Magic Fire	see *H.* × *intermedia* 'Feuerzauber'
- 'Moonlight'	CJun
- 'Nina'	CRos EPfP LRHS MAsh MGos WPat
- 'Ninotchka'	CJun
- 'Old Copper'	NLar
- 'Orange Beauty'	CBcs LRHS MBlu MGos NOrn SAko SCoo SGol SHil WPGP WPat
- 'Orange Peel'	CJun CRos EPfP LCro LLHF LRHS MAsh NLar SHil WPat
- 'Ostergold'	CJun NLar
- 'Pallida' ♀H5	Widely available
- 'Primavera'	CJun CLnd LRHS MGos WPat
- 'Ripe Corn'	CJun EPfP LRHS MAsh
- 'Robert' ♀H5	CJun CRos EPfP LRHS LSRN MAsh SHil SPoG WPat
- 'Rubin' ♀H5	CJun EPfP LRHS MAsh MBri MGos NLar SCoo SHil SPer SPoG
- 'Rubinstar'	CJun
- 'Ruby Glow'	CBcs CMac CWGN CWib LSRN MGos NEgg NLar NWea SCoo SPer SWvt
- 'Savill Starlight'	CJun
- 'Spanish Spider'	CJun MBlu NLar
- 'Strawberries and Cream'	CJun MAsh
- 'Sunburst'	CJun LRHS MBlu MGos NLar SGol SHil WPat
- 'Twilight'	CJun NLar
- 'Vesna' ♀H5	CJun CMac CRos EPfP LRHS MAsh MBlu NLar SCoo SHil SPoG WPat
- 'Westerstede'	CJun LSRN MGos NHol NLar NPla NWea SCob SCoo SEWo SGol SLim WHor
- 'Wiero'	CJun NLar
- 'Zitronenjette'	CJun
japonica 'Pendula'	CJun MBlu
mollis	CBcs CCVT CDul CHab CMac CNWT CPne CSBt CTri CWSG ELan EPfP GKin LCro LRHS MBlu MBri MGos MRav MSwo NEgg NWea SCob SGol SLim SPer SRms SWvt
- 'Boskoop'	CJun
- 'Coombe Wood'	CJun LRHS MGos
- 'Emily'	LRHS MAsh
- 'Goldcrest'	CJun
- 'Imperialis'	CJun LRHS MAsh
- 'Iwado'	CJun
- 'Jermyns Gold' ♀H5	CJun EPfP LRHS MAsh SHil SPoG
- 'Kort's Yellow'	CJun
- var. ***pallida***	CRos SEWo SWvt
- 'Wisley Supreme' ♀H5	CJun ELan EPfP LLHF LRHS MAsh MGos SGol SHil SPoG WPat
'Rochester'	CJun NLar
vernalis 'Lombarts' Weeping'	NLar
- purple-flowered	MBlu
- 'Quasimodo'	NLar
- 'Sandra'	CMCN ELan EPfP LRHS MAsh MBlu MGos MRav NLar SLon SPer WPat
virginiana	CAgr GPoy IDee MMuc NWea WBod
- 'Green Thumb' (v) new	NLar
- 'Mohonk Red'	CJun
'Yamina'	NLar SGol

Hanabusaya (*Campanulaceae*)

§ ***asiatica***	NCGa NChi SBrt WHil

Haplocarpha (*Asteraceae*)

rueppellii	SRms SRot

Haplopappus (*Asteraceae*)

coronopifolius	see *H. glutinosus*
§ ***glutinosus***	ECha ECho ECtt EDAr EPot MMuc NLar SEND SPlb SRms
prunelloides var. ***mustersii*** F&W 9384	WCot

Hardenbergia (*Papilionaceae*)

comptoniana ♀H3	CExl WCot
violacea ♀H3	CDoC CHll CRHN ELan MHer SEND SLim SPer WCot
- f. ***alba***	CHll ECou
- dwarf	ECou
- 'Happy Wanderer'	MOWG SChF

Harpephyllum (*Anacardiaceae*)

caffrum (F)	XBlo

Hastingsia (*Asparagaceae*)

alba	WSHC

Haworthia ✿ (*Asphodelaceae*)

attenuata	EShb
'Black Major'	LToo
'Black Prince'	EShb SBch
'Chocolate'	LToo
* ***conigra***	LToo
cooperii var. ***pilifera***	LToo
fasciata	SEND
glabrata var. ***concolor***	EShb
'Kermit'	LToo
limifolia new	EShb LToo
mirabilis var. ***sublineata***	LToo
- var. ***triebneriana***	LToo
pumila ♀H2	SEND
tesselata	see *H. venosa* subsp. *tesselata*
truncata ♀H2	LToo
§ ***venosa*** subsp. ***tesselata*** ♀H2	SEND

hazelnut see *Corylus*

Hebe ✿ (*Plantaginaceae*)

sp.	SCob

albicans ♀H4	CBcs ELan EPfP GKin LAst LPot LRHS LSRN MAsh MBri MGos MJak MRav NPri NWea SCob SCoo SHil SLim SPer SRms SWvt WHar XLum
- prostrate	see *H. albicans* 'Snow Cover'
* - 'Snow Carpet'	LRHS
§ - 'Snow Cover'	EWes
- 'Snow Drift'	see *H. albicans* 'Snow Cover'
§ 'Alicia Amherst'	LRHS
'Amanda Cook' (v)	NPer SGol SPoG
§ 'Amy'	ELon LRHS NPer SPer SWvt
× ***andersonii***	LRHS
§ - 'Andersonii Variegata' (v)	CWib LRHS SRms
- 'Argenteovariegata'	see *H.* × *andersonii* 'Andersonii Variegata'
'Andressa Paula'	LRHS
anomala misapplied	see *H.* 'Imposter'
'Aoira'	see *H. recurva* 'Aoira'
§ ***armstrongii***	ECho SCob SEND
'Arthur'	ECou
'Autumn Beauty'	CMac
'Autumn Glory'	CSBt ELan EPfP LAst LOPS LRHS LSRN MAsh MBri MGos MJak MRav MSwo NBir NPri SCob SGol SPer SPlb SPoG SVen SWvt XLum
'Autumn Joy'	SWvt
azurea	see *H. venustula*
'Azurens'	see *H.* 'Maori Gem'
'Baby Blush'PBR	LRHS SLim
'Baby Boo' (v)	LRHS SCob SLon
'Baby Marie'	CAbP CSBt EBee ECho ELan EPfP GKin LBMP LBuc LRHS LSRN MBri MSwo NLar NPer SCob SCoo SLim SPoG SRGP SRms SRot SWvt
'Beverley Hills'PBR	CSBt LRHS SCob
'Bicolor Wand'	CTsd LRHS
bishopiana	SCob
'Black Beauty'	EPfP LBMP LBuc LRHS MJak NLar SCob
'Black Panther'	ELon LSou
'Blue Clouds' ♀H4	EBee EPfP LAst LLHF LRHS MBri MSwo NWad SBod SCob SPer WCFE
Blue Elegance = 'Lowgeko'PBR (Garden Beauty Series)	LRHS SLim
§ 'Blue Gem'	CMac SCob SLim WHil
Blue Haze = 'Lowchi' (Garden Beauty Series) **new**	LRHS
Blue Ice = 'Lowapb' (Garden Beauty Series) **new**	LRHS
'Blue Shamrock'	SWvt
Blue Star = 'Vergeer 1'PBR	EPfP LBuc LRHS MBri NLar SLon SPoG SRms
bollonsii	ECou
'Boscawenii'	WHer
'Bouquet'PBR	LLHF
§ 'Bowles's Hybrid'	LRHS MRav MSwo SCob SRms
brachysiphon	CTri ECou LRHS SCob SEND SPer SRms SVen
brevifolia	LRHS SLim
Bronze Glow = 'Lowglo' (Garden Beauty Series)	LBuc LRHS
'Bronzy Baby'PBR (v)	SPoG
buchananii	ECho MHer NPer SIgm
§ - 'Fenwickii'	ECho WHoo
- 'Minima'	ECho EPot
- 'Minor' Hort. NZ	ECho GBin GCrg
'Bullfinch' **new**	LRHS
buxifolia	see *H. odora*
§ 'Caledonia' ♀H4	CPBP CSBt CWib EPfP LBMP LCro LRHS LSRN MAsh MBri MGos NPer NPri SCob SCoo SLim SPoG SRms SWvt WHoo XLum
§ ***canterburiensis***	EAEE ECou
'Carl Teschner'	see *H.* 'Youngii'
'Carnea Variegata' (v)	EShb LRHS SLim SPer SRms WOut
carnosula	SPer
catarractae	see *Parahebe catarractae*
'Celine'	EPfP LBuc LRHS
'Champagne'	EBee EPfP LAst LCro LPot LRHS LSRN MBlu MBri MJak SCob SCoo SLim SRms XLum
Champion = 'Champseiont'PBR	EAEE EBee LRHS MSwo SCob SCoo
'Charming White'	CChe EAEE LRHS LSRN SCob
chathamica	ECou LRHS
cheesemanii	WAbe
'Christabel'	LRHS
'Clear Skies'PBR	CSBt ECou LBuc LLHF LRHS SLim SRms
'Colwall'	ECho
'Conwy Knight'	SRms WAbe
corstorphinensis	LRHS
'County Park'	ECou EWes
'Cranleighensis'	CTsd LRHS
cupressoides	CFis LRHS MSCN
- 'Boughton Dome'	CTri ECho MHer WAbe WCFE WHoo WOld
'Dazzler' (v)	CAbP
decumbens	EWes
'Denise'	LRHS
'Diamond'	LRHS LSRN SLon SRms
diosmifolia	CDoC EPfP LRHS SLim
- 'Wairua Beauty'	SLim
divaricata	ECou
'Dorothy Peach'	see *H.* 'Watson's Pink'
'E.B. Anderson'	see *H.* 'Caledonia'
'Eclipse'	LAst
'Edington'	SPer WCFE
'Ellie'	LRHS
elliptica	ECou
- 'Kapiti'	ECou
- 'Variegata'	see *H.* 'Silver Queen'
'Emerald Dome'	see *H.* 'Emerald Gem'
§ 'Emerald Gem' ♀H4	CDul CMac CTri EAEE ECho EPfP EShb LPfy LRHS LSRN MAsh MBri MGos MHer MJak MMuc MSwo NLar NPri SCob SHil SPer SPlb SPoG WFar WHar
'Emerald Green'	see *H.* 'Emerald Gem'
epacridea	EWes
§ 'Eveline'	CSBt CTri LRHS MJak NBir SBod SLim SPer
'Eversley Seedling'	see *H.* 'Bowles's Hybrid'
'Fairfieldii'	WPat
'First Light'PBR	LRHS SCob SGol SRms
'Fragrant Jewel'	CAbP CWib LRHS SEND SLim SPhx
× ***franciscana***	SBod
- 'Blue Gem' ambig.	CDul CTsd ELan EPfP LRHS MMuc MRav NBir NPer SCob SEND SGol SPer SPlb SPoG SRms

	Plant	Suppliers
	- 'Foreness Pink'	SEND
	- 'Lavender Queen'	LRHS
	- lime variegated (v)	SEND
	- 'Purple Tips' misapplied	see *H. speciosa* 'Variegata'
	- 'Variegata'	see *H.* 'Silver Queen'
I	- 'White Gem'	SRms
	- yellow variegated (v)	SPer
	'Frozen Flame' (v)	ELan LBuc LRHS SPoG
	'Galway Bay'	LSou
	(Garden Beauty Series) Garden Beauty Blue = 'Cliv'PBR	LBuc LRHS SLim SRms
	- Garden Beauty Pink = 'Lowink'	SLim SRms
	- Garden Beauty Purple = 'Nold'PBR	LBuc LRHS SLim
	(Garden Elegance Series) 'Garden Elegance Blush'	LRHS
	- 'Garden Elegance Pink'	SLim
	- 'Garden Elegance Purple'	SLim SPoG
	- 'Garden Elegance Rose'	SLim
	'Gauntlettii'	see *H.* 'Eveline'
	'Gibby'	LRHS
	glaucophylla 'Clarence'	ECou
	- 'Joan Hunwick'	LRHS
I	- 'Variegata' (v)	CTri LBuc LRHS SCoo SLim SPer
	'Gnome'	LRHS
	'Goethe'	SEND
	'Gold Beauty' (v)	SRms
	'Gold Pixie' **new**	LBuc
	'Golden Glow' (v) **new**	EPfP LRHS
	'Golden Nugget'	LRHS
	'Goldrush'PBR (v)	SPoG
	gracillima	ECou SCob SEle
	'Gran's Favourite'	LRHS LSRN
	'Great Orme' ♀H4	CDul CWib ECou ELan EPfP GBin GGal LAst LPfy LRHS LSRN MAsh MGos MJak MMuc MRav MSCN MSwo NPer SBod SCob SEND SLim SPer SPlb SPoG SRms SWvt WBod WSFF
	'Green Globe'	see *H.* 'Emerald Gem'
	'Greensleeves'	LRHS
	'Hadspen Pink'	LRHS
	'Hagley Park'	LRHS
§	'Hartii'	LRHS MRav SCob SLim
	'Heartbreaker'PBR (v)	ELan LAst LBuc LCro LOPS LRHS MAsh MGos MJak NPri SCob SCoo SLim SPoG SWvt
	HebeDonna Diana = 'Zenia'PBR	ELan
	HebeDonna Emma = 'Zassa'PBR **new**	EBee
	'Hielan Lassie'	LRHS
	'High Voltage' **new**	MJak
	'Highdownensis'	LRHS
	'Hinderwell'	NPer
	hookeriana	see *Parahebe hookeriana*
	hulkeana	LLHF LRHS MHer SCob WKif
§	'Imposter'	SRms
	'Inspiration'	LRHS SCob
	'James Stirling'	see *H. ochracea* 'James Stirling'
	'Jane Holden'	LRHS
	'Joanna'	ECou
	'John Collier'	SEND
§	'Johny Day'	LRHS SCob
	'Judy'	LRHS
	'Karna'	LPot
	'Karo Golden Esk'	EPfP LRHS
	'Kirkii'	EPfP LAst MSwo NLar SBod SCob XLum
	'Knightshayes'	see *H.* 'Caledonia'
	'La Favorite'	CTsd
	'Lady Ann'PBR (v)	CSBt EPfP LBuc LRHS LSou MJak NLar SPoG
	'Lady Ardilaun'	see *H.* 'Amy'
	laevis	see *H. venustula*
	laingii	GCrg
	latifolia	see *H.* 'Blue Gem'
	'Lavender Spray'	see *H.* 'Hartii'
	leiophylla	SVen
	Leopard = 'Lowand' (Garden Beauty Series)	LRHS
	'Lilac Wand'	CTsd
	'Linda'	SEND
	'Lindsayi'	ECou LRHS
	'Liz' **new**	LBuc LRHS
	lyallii	see *Parahebe lyallii*
	lycopodioides 'Aurea'	see *H. armstrongii*
	'Lynash'	LRHS
	mackenii	see *H.* 'Emerald Gem'
	macrantha ♀H4	CBod GBin LRHS SDix SPer SRms WAbe
	macrocarpa	LRHS
	- var. ***latisepala***	LBuc LRHS SLim
	- var. ***macrocarpa***	SLim
	'Magic Summer'PBR	LBuc LRHS MBri SPoG
§	'Maori Gem'	MRav
	'Margery Fish'	see *H.* 'Primley Gem'
	'Margret' ♀H4	CSBt EPfP LAst LRHS LSRN MAsh MBrN MBri MGos MRav NPri SCob SCoo SLim SPer SPoG SRms
	'Marie Antoinette'	LRHS
	'Marilyn Monroe'PBR	LRHS
	'Marjorie'	CDul CMac EAEE ELan EPfP GBin LAst LRHS LSRN MJak MSwo NLar NPer NWea SCob SPer SPoG SRms SWvt
	'Mauve Queen'	LRHS
	'McKean'	see *H.* 'Emerald Gem'
	'Megan'	ECou
	'Mette'	EAEE
	Midnight Sky = 'Lowten'PBR (Garden Beauty Series)	LBuc LRHS NPri SCoo SLim SPoG
	'Midsummer Beauty' ♀H4	CWCL ECrN EPfP LAst LPfy LRHS LSRN MBri MGos MJak MMuc MRav NBir SCob SEND SLim SPer SPlb SPoG SRms SWvt WOut WSFF XLum
	'Milmont Emerald'	see *H.* 'Emerald Gem'
§	'Mohawk'PBR	LRHS
*	'Moppets Hardy'	SPer
§	'Mrs Winder' ♀H4	CDul CMac EAEE EHoe ELan EPfP EUJe LAst LCro LRHS LSRN MAsh MCot MGos MJak MRav MSwo NBes NLar NPer NPri SCob SCoo SGbt SGol SLim SPer SPoG SWvt WFar
	'Nantyderry'	LRHS
§	'Neil's Choice' ♀H4	ECou ELon LRHS
	'Neopolitan'	SPoG
	'New Zealand'	XLum
	'Nicola's Blush' ♀H4	CDul CMac CSBt ECou ELon EPfP EShb LAst LRHS LSRN MCot MMuc MRav NBir NCot NLar SCob SEND SGol SPer SPoG SRGP SRms SWvt WKif

	Name	Suppliers
	ochracea	LRHS
§	- 'James Stirling' 🏆^{H4}	CBcs CMac CSBt ECho ELan EPfP EShb GKin LRHS LSRN MAsh MGos MJak MSwo NLar NWad SCob SCoo SLim SPlb SPoG SWvt WFar WHar
	'Oddity'	LRHS
§	***odora***	CMac CSde ELan LHop LRHS MJak MMuc NWea SCob
	- 'New Zealand Gold'	CLet LRHS MAsh MMuc SEND SHil
	- 'Summer Frost'	CSde LRHS
	'Oratia Beauty' 🏆^{H4}	LRHS LSRN MMuc MRav NFav NLar SCob SEND SLim
	'Orphan Annie' (v)	LSRN NLar
	parviflora misapplied	see *H.* 'Bowles's Hybrid'
	parviflora (Vahl) Cockayne & Allan var. ***angustifolia***	see *H. stenophylla*
	- 'Holdsworth'	CBod LRHS
	'Pascal' 🏆^{H4}	ELan EPfP LRHS LSRN MAsh MBri MGos SCoo SLim SLon SPer SPoG SRms SWvt
	Pastel Elegance = 'Lowjap'^{PBR} (Garden Beauty Series)	SLim
	'Patti Dossett'	see *H. speciosa* 'Patti Dossett'
	pauciramosa	GCal SRms
	'Pearl of Paradise'^{PBR}	SPoG
	perfoliata	see *Parahebe perfoliata*
	'Perry's Rubyleaf'	NPer
	'Petra's Pink'	LRHS SLim
	'Pewter Dome' 🏆^{H4}	CMac CSBt EHoe EPfP LHop LRHS MGos MRav SCob SDix SRms SWvt
	pimeleoides	SCob
	- 'Glauca'	NPer SGol
	- 'Glaucocaerulea'	ECou
	- 'Quicksilver' 🏆^{H4}	CLet CSBt CTri ECou ELan EPfP LAst LRHS LSRN MGos MMuc MRav NBir NPer SBod SCob SCoo SLim SPer SRms WHar
	pinguifolia	NLar SPlb
	- 'Dobson'	LRHS
	- 'Pagei' 🏆^{H5}	Widely available
	- 'Sutherlandii'	CBcs CDoC CDul EAEE ECho LRHS LSRN MGos MJak NBes NWea SCob SCoo SWvt WFar
	'Pink Elegance'	LRHS
	'Pink Elephant' (v) 🏆^{H4}	LBMP LBuc LRHS MAsh MJak NLar NPri SLim SPoG
	'Pink Fantasy'	LRHS SCob
	'Pink Goddess'	LRHS
	'Pink Lady'^{PBR}	SGol SPoG
	'Pink Paradise'^{PBR}	CAbP ELan EPfP LBuc LRHS MJak SPoG SRms
	'Pink Payne'	see *H.* 'Eveline'
	'Pink Pixie'	LBuc LRHS MAsh MBri SCoo SRms
	'Pink Wand'	CTsd
	poppelwellii	GBin
	'Porlock Purple'	see *Parahebe catarractae* 'Delight'
§	'Primley Gem'	CFis LRHS
I	'Prostrata'	CSBt
	'Purple Emperor'	see *H.* 'Neil's Choice'
	'Purple Paradise'^{PBR}	MBri SPoG
	'Purple Picture'	ELon
	'Purple Pixie'	see *H.* 'Mohawk'
	'Purple Princess'	LRHS SGol
	'Purple Queen'	EPfP EShb LRHS MJak SCob SPoG
	Purple Shamrock = 'Neprock'^{PBR} (v)	EPfP EUJe LAst LRHS MAsh MBri MGos NEgg SCoo SLim SPer SPoG SRms SWvt
	'Purple Tips' misapplied	see *H. speciosa* 'Variegata'
	'Rachel'	LRHS LSRN SLon
§	***rakaiensis*** 🏆^{H4}	Widely available
	- 'Golden Dome'	see *H. rakaiensis*
	raoulii	SRms WAbe
	Raspberry Ripple = 'Tullyraspb'^{PBR}	ECtt LBuc
	'Raven'	LRHS
	recurva	CSam CTri LPot LRHS MCot SCob SRms
§	- 'Aoira'	ECou
	- 'Boughton Silver' 🏆^{H5}	LRHS LSRN MMuc SLim
	- 'White Torrent'	ECou
	'Red Edge' 🏆^{H4}	Widely available
	'Red Moon' **new**	EBee SCob
	'Red Rum'	LBuc
	'Red Ruth'	see *H.* 'Eveline'
	'Rhubarb and Custard'	LBuc LRHS SCob
	rigidula	LRHS MMuc SEND
	'Ronda'	ECou
	'Rosie'^{PBR}	LBuc LRHS LSRN SCoo SPer SWvt
	'Royal Blue'	LRHS SLim
	'Royal Purple'	see *H.* 'Alicia Amherst'
	salicifolia	CMac CTca ELan EPfP LAst LRHS MGos MMuc MRav NWad SCob SEND SPer SPlb SRms XLum
	- pale blue-flowered	SEND
	'Sandra Joy'	LRHS
	'Sapphire' 🏆^{H4}	ECou EPfP LRHS MAsh MJak NPri SCob SCoo SLim SRms SWvt
	'Sarana'	LRHS LSRN
	'Shiraz'	LRHS
	'Silver Dollar' (v)	CAbP CMac CSBt ELan LRHS MJak NEgg NWad SLim SPer SPoG SRms
§	'Silver Queen' (v) 🏆^{H3}	CSBt ECrN ELan EShb GBin LRHS MAsh MMuc NLar NPer SCob SEND SPer SPoG SRms WOut
	'Silver Swallow'	LRHS
	'Simon Délaux'	LRHS SEND SPer
I	'Southlandii'	SGol
	'Sparkling Sapphires'	LBuc LRHS
	speciosa 'Johny Day'	see *H.* 'Johny Day'
	- 'La Séduisante'	CTri LRHS SEND SRms
§	- 'Patti Dossett'	LRHS
	- 'Rangatira'	ECou
§	- 'Variegata' (v)	LRHS NPer
	'Spender's Seedling' misapplied	see *H. stenophylla*
	'Spender's Seedling' ambig.	MCot MMuc MSCN SCob
	'Spender's Seedling' Hort.	ECou LRHS MRav SEND SPoG SRms
	'Spring Glory'	LRHS
§	***stenophylla***	EShb EUJe GGal LRHS LSRN NLar SPer SPlb
	stricta	ECou LRHS SEND
	- var. ***egmontiana***	LRHS
	subalpina	CSBt CWib
	'Summer Blue'	LRHS MBlu
	'Sunset Boulevard'^{PBR} **new**	LLHF
	'Super Red'	CSBt EAEE MBri SLim SPoG
	'Sweet Kim' (v)	CMac LBuc LRHS MBri SLim SPoG
	'Tina'	ECou
	'Tom Marshall'	see *H. canterburiensis*
	topiaria 🏆^{H4}	CAbP CLet CSBt CSam LHop LRHS MBrN MMuc MRav MSwo NBir NFav NLar NWad SCob

	SCoo SEND SEle SGbt SPer SPoG WHoo WRHF
- 'Doctor Favier'	LRHS SRms
townsonii	ECou LRHS SCob
treadwellii new	ECou
'Tricolor'	see *H. speciosa* 'Variegata'
'Twisty'	LRHS
'Valentino'PBR	CSBt SCoo SLim
'Veitchii'	see *H.* 'Alicia Amherst'
§ ***venustula***	ECou LRHS MMuc
- 'Patricia Davies'	ECou
vernicosa 🏆H4	CDul CLet EAEE LRHS MGos MHer NFav NWad SCob SCoo SEle SPer SPlb SRot SVen SWvt
'Violet Wand'	LRHS
'Vogue'	LRHS
'Waikiki'	see *H.* 'Mrs Winder'
§ 'Warley'	LRHS
'Warley Pink'	LRHS
'Warleyensis'	see *H.* 'Warley'
§ 'Watson's Pink'	LRHS SPer WBod WKif WSHC
'White Gem' (*brachysiphon* hybrid) 🏆H4	LRHS NPer SEND SPer
'White Heather'	EPfP LRHS SCob
'White Paradise'PBR	SPoG
'Wild Romance'	LBuc LRHS
'Willcoxii'	see *H. buchananii* 'Fenwickii'
'Wingletye' 🏆H4	ECou LRHS
'Winter Glow'	LRHS
'Wiri Blush'	LRHS SLim SWvt
'Wiri Charm'	CAbP CBcs CMac CSBt EBee EPfP LRHS MGos MSwo SCob SEND SLim
'Wiri Cloud' 🏆H4	CBcs CMac EPfP LRHS MGos MMuc MSwo SCob SEND SEle SRms
'Wiri Dawn' 🏆H4	ELan EPfP EWes LBuc LRHS SLim SRms SWvt
'Wiri Desire'	LRHS
'Wiri Gem'	SCob
'Wiri Image'	CBcs CSBt EAEE EPfP LRHS MRav SEND
'Wiri Joy'	LRHS SGol
'Wiri Mist'	CBcs ELan EPfP LRHS MJak SCob
'Wiri Prince'	LRHS
'Wiri Splash'	EPfP LRHS SGol
'Wiri Vision'	CSBt LRHS SEND
'Wiri Vogue'	LRHS SLim
§ 'Youngii' 🏆H4	CMac CSBt CTri ECrN ELan EPfP GKin LAst LOPS LPot LRHS MAsh MHer MJak MLHP MMuc MRav NBir NPri SEND SGol SLim SPer SPlb SPoG SRms SWvt WCFE WHoo WSHC

Hechtia (*Bromeliaceae*)

sp.	WCot
texensis	EAla

Hedeoma (*Lamiaceae*)

ciliolata	WAbe
hyssopifolia	SPhx

Hedera ✿ (*Araliaceae*)

sp.	LPar SCob
§ ***algeriensis***	CDoC WFib
- 'Bellecour'	WFib XLum
§ - 'Gloire de Marengo' (v) 🏆H5	Widely available
- 'Gloire de Marengo' arborescent (v)	SDix SPer
- 'Marginomaculata' (v)	CDoC EPfP EShb LRHS MAsh SMad WFib
- 'Montgomery'	EAEE LRHS LSRN
- 'Ravensholst' 🏆H4	CMac EShb MRav SCob SGol WFib
§ ***azorica***	EShb WFib
- 'Pico'	WFib
canariensis misapplied	see *H. algeriensis*
- 'Variegata'	see *H. algeriensis* 'Gloire de Marengo'
canariensis Willd. var. ***azorica***	see *H. azorica*
- 'Cantabrian'	see *H. maroccana* 'Spanish Canary'
chinensis	see *H. nepalensis* var. *sinensis*
- typica	see *H. nepalensis* var. *sinensis*
§ ***colchica***	CDul NWea SPer WCFE WFib
- 'Arborescens'	see *H. colchica* 'Dendroides'
- 'Batumi'	MBNS WFib
§ - 'Dendroides'	NWea
- 'Dentata' 🏆H5	MRav MWhi SGol WFar WFib
- 'Dentata Aurea'	see *H. colchica* 'Dentata Variegata'
§ - 'Dentata Variegata' (v) 🏆H5	Widely available
- 'My Heart'	see *H. colchica*
- 'Paddy's Pride'	see *H. colchica* 'Sulphur Heart'
§ - 'Sulphur Heart' (v) 🏆H5	Widely available
- 'Variegata'	see *H. colchica* 'Dentata Variegata'
cristata	see *H. helix* 'Parsley Crested'
§ ***cypria***	WFib
helix	CCVT CMac CTri LPar NWea SCob WSFF XLum
- 'Adam' (v)	CWib LSRN MBri NFav WFib
- 'Amberwaves'	MBri WFib
- 'Angularis Aurea' 🏆H5	WFib
- 'Anita'	GBin NFav WFib
§ - 'Anna Marie' (v)	MBri SRms WFib
- 'Anne Borch'	see *H. helix* 'Anna Marie'
- 'Arborescens'	WSFF XLum
- 'Ardingly' (v)	MWhi WFib
- 'Atropurpurea'	ELan EPPr GBin MMuc WFib
- var. ***baltica***	WFib
- 'Bill Archer'	GBin WFib
- 'Bird's Foot'	see *H. helix* 'Pedata'
- 'Boskoop'	WFib
- 'Bredon'	MRav
- 'Brimstone' (v)	WFib
§ - 'Brokamp'	WFib
- 'Buttercup' 🏆H5	CBcs CDul CMac CTri EHoe ELan EPfP LAst LRHS LSRN MAsh MBri MGos MWhi NBid NLar NPri SLim SPer SPoG SRms SWvt WCFE WFib
- 'Caecilia' (v) 🏆H5	EPfP MSwo SWvt WFib
- 'Caenwoodiana'	see *H. helix* 'Pedata'
- 'Caenwoodiana Aurea'	WFib
- 'Calico' (v)	WFib
- 'Calypso'	WFib
- 'Carolina Crinkle'	MWhi
- 'Cathedral Wall'	WFib
§ - 'Cavendishii' (v)	SRms WFib
- 'Cavendishii Latina' (v)	WCot
§ - 'Ceridwen' (v) 🏆H5	CSde MBri SPlb WFib
- 'Cheeky'	WFib
- 'Cheltenham Blizzard' (v)	CNat

	Name	Suppliers
	- 'Chester' (v)	CKel LRHS WFib
	- 'Chicago'	CWib WFib
	- 'Chicago Variegated' (v)	WFib
	- 'Chrysophylla'	MSwo
	- 'Clotted Cream' (v)	ECGP ECrN ELon LRHS MAsh SPoG WFib
	- 'Cockle Shell'	WFib
	- 'Colin'	GBin
§	- 'Congesta' 🏆H5	CMac GCra MLHP NBir SRms WFib
	- 'Conglomerata'	CBcs ELan NBir SRms WFib
	- 'Courage'	WFib
	- 'Crenata'	WFib
	- 'Crispa'	MRav
	- 'Cristata'	see *H. helix* 'Parsley Crested'
	- 'Curleylocks'	see *H. helix* 'Manda's Crested'
	- 'Curley-Q'	see *H. helix* 'Dragon Claw'
	- 'Curvaceous' (v)	WFib
	- 'Cyprus'	see *H. cypria*
	- 'Dainty Bess'	CWib
§	- 'Dealbata' (v)	CMac WFib
	- 'Deltoidea'	see *H. hibernica* 'Deltoidea'
	- 'Discolor'	see *H. helix* 'Minor Marmorata', *H. helix* 'Dealbata'
§	- 'Donerailensis'	MBlu WFib
	- 'Don's Papillon'	CNat
§	- 'Dragon Claw'	WFib
	- 'Duckfoot' 🏆H5	CDoC EShb MWhi WCot WFib
	- 'Eileen' (v)	WFib
	- 'Elfenbein' (v)	WFib
	- 'Erecta'	CDul CTca EPPr EPfP GCal IDee LAst LRHS MBlu MGos NHol SDix SHil SPer SPlb WCFE WFib XLum
	- 'Ester' (v)	CBar LAst SRGP WHar
§	- 'Eva' (v)	WFib
	- 'Fantasia' (v)	MBri WFib
	- 'Feenfinger'	WFib
	- 'Filigran'	WFib
	- 'Flashback' (v)	WFib
	- 'Flavescens'	WFib
	- 'Fluffy Ruffles'	WFib
I	- 'Francis Ivy'	WFib
	- 'Frosty' (v)	WFib
	- 'Garland'	WFib
	- 'Gavotte'	WFib
	- 'Gilded Hawke'	WFib
	- 'Glache' (v)	MRav WFib
	- 'Glacier' (v) 🏆H5	CBar CBcs CDoC CDul CTri CWib ELan EPfP LCro LHop LPal LRHS MAsh MBri MGos MJak MMuc MRav MSwo MWhi NHol NWea SCob SEND SLim SPer SPoG SRms SWvt WFib
	- 'Glymii'	ELan GCal WFib
	- 'Gold Harald'	see *H. helix* 'Goldchild'
	- 'Gold Ripple'	NLar SEND
§	- 'Goldchild' (v) 🏆H5	CBar CBcs CDoC CKel CMac EBee ELon EPfP EShb LAst LCro LRHS MAsh MGos MJak MMuc MRav MSwo NBir NHol SCob SLim SPer SPoG SWvt WFib WHar
	- 'Golden Ann'	see *H. helix* 'Ceridwen'
*	- 'Golden Arrow'	LRHS MAsh
	- 'Golden Curl' (v)	CMac EPfP LRHS
	- 'Golden Ester'	see *H. helix* 'Ceridwen'
	- 'Golden Girl'	WFib
	- 'Golden Ingot' (v) 🏆H5	ELan MWhi WFib
	- 'Golden Jytte' (v)	WFib
	- 'Golden Kolibri'	see *H. helix* 'Midas Touch'
	- 'Golden Mathilde' (v)	GBin
	- 'Goldfinch'	MBri WFib
	- 'Goldfinger'	MBri WFib
	- 'Goldheart'	see *H. helix* 'Oro di Bogliasco'
	- 'Goldstern' (v)	MRav MWhi WFib
	- 'Gracilis'	see *H. hibernica* 'Gracilis'
	- 'Green Finger'	see *H. helix* 'Très Coupé'
	- 'Green Ripple'	CBcs CTri EAEE ELan EPfP LRHS MBlu MGos MJak MMuc MSwo MWht SCob SEND SLim SPer SPlb SRms SWvt WFib
	- 'Greenman'	WFib
	- 'Halebob'	MBri WFib
	- 'Hamilton'	see *H. hibernica* 'Hamilton'
	- 'Harald' (v)	CTri CWib WFib
	- 'Harry Wood'	see *H. helix* 'Modern Times'
*	- 'Hazel' (v)	WFib
	- 'Heise' (v)	WFib
	- 'Heise Denmark' (v)	WFib
	- 'Helvig'	see *H. helix* 'White Knight'
	- 'Henrietta'	WFib
	- 'Hispanica'	see *H. iberica*
	- 'Hite's Miniature'	see *H. helix* 'Merion Beauty'
	- 'Holly'	see *H. helix* 'Parsley Crested'
	- 'Hullavington'	CNat
	- 'Humpty Dumpty'	CExl
	- 'Imp'	see *H. helix* 'Brokamp'
	- 'Ivalace'	CBcs EAEE EShb MGos MSwo MWhi SRms WFib XLum
	- 'Jake'	MBri WFib
	- 'Jasper'	WFib
	- 'Jersey Doris' (v)	WFib
	- 'Jerusalem'	see *H. helix* 'Schäfer Three'
	- 'Jester's Gold'	MBri
	- 'Jubilee' (v)	WFib
	- 'Kaleidoscope'	WFib
	- 'Kevin'	WFib
	- 'Kolibri' (v)	CDoC LAst MBri WFib
	- 'Königer's Auslese'	WFib
	- 'Lalla Rookh'	MRav WFib WRHF
	- 'Leo Swicegood'	MWhi WFib
	- 'Light Fingers'	ELon EPfP LRHS WFib
	- 'Little Diamond' (v)	CDoC CMac CTri ELan LRHS MBri SLon SWvt WFib
	- 'Little Luzii'	WFib
	- 'Liz'	see *H. helix* 'Eva'
	- 'Luzii' (v)	WFib
	- 'Maculata'	see *H. helix* 'Minor Marmorata'
§	- 'Manda's Crested' 🏆H5	ELan NLar WFib
	- 'Maple Leaf' 🏆H5	EShb WFib
	- 'Maple Queen'	MBri
	- 'Marginata Elegantissima'	see *H. helix* 'Tricolor'
	- 'Marginata Minor'	see *H. helix* 'Cavendishii'
I	- 'Marmorata' Fibrex	WFib
	- 'Mathilde' (v)	CKel WFib
	- 'Melanie'	WFib
	- 'Meon'	WFib
§	- 'Merion Beauty'	WFib
§	- 'Midas Touch' (v) 🏆H5	CWib EPPr EPfP MBri WFib
	- 'Mini Ester' (v)	MBri
	- 'Mini Heron'	MBri
	- 'Minikin' (v)	WCot
	- 'Minima' misapplied	see *H. helix* 'Spetchley'
	- 'Minima' Hibberd	see *H. helix* 'Donerailensis'
	- 'Minima' M. Young	see *H. helix* 'Congesta'
§	- 'Minor Marmorata' (v)	XLum
	- 'Mint Kolibri'	MBri
	- 'Minty' (v)	WFib

	- 'Misty' (v)	WFib
§	- 'Modern Times'	LPal
	- 'Needlepoint'	XLum
	- 'Niagara Falls'	LRHS
	- 'Nigra Aurea' (v)	WFib
	- 'Obovata'	WFib
	- 'Oro di Bogliasco' (v)	CDul CMac CTri EBee EPfP LRHS MBri MMuc MRav MSwo NLar NWad NWea SCob SEND SLim SPer SPlb SRms SWvt WFar WFib
	- 'Ovata'	WFib
§	- 'Parsley Crested' ♀H5	ELan EPfP SGol WFib
	- 'Patent Leather'	WFib
	- 'Pedata'	CDul MSwo WFib
	- 'Perkeo'	WFib
	- 'Peter' (v)	WFib
	- 'Pink 'n' Curly'	WCot WFib
	- 'Pink 'n' Very Curly'	WCot
§	- 'Pittsburgh'	WFib
	- 'Plume d'Or'	WFib
§	- f. ***poetarum***	GCal MBlu WCot WFib
	- - 'Poetica Arborea'	SDix
	- 'Poetica'	see *H. helix* f. *poetarum*
	- 'Raleigh Delight' (v)	WCot
	- 'Ray's Supreme'	see *H. helix* 'Pittsburgh'
	- subsp. ***rhizomatifera***	WFib
	- 'Richard John'	WFib
	- 'Ritterkreuz'	WFib
	- 'Romanze' (v)	WFib
	- 'Russelliana'	WFib
	- 'Sagittifolia' ambig.	ECrN LRHS MAsh MBlu
	- 'Sagittifolia' misapplied	see *H. helix* 'Pedata'
	- 'Sagittifolia' Hibberd	CTri EPfP
	- 'Sagittifolia Variegata' (v)	MBri WFib WRHF
	- 'Saint Agnes'	LRHS
	- 'Sally' (v)	WFib
	- 'Salt and Pepper'	see *H. helix* 'Minor Marmorata'
§	- 'Schäfer Three' (v)	CWib WFib
	- 'Seabreeze'	WFib
	- 'Shamrock' ♀H5	EPfP WFib
	- 'Shannon'	WFib
	- 'Silver Ferny'	WFib
	- 'Silver King' (v)	WFib
	- 'Silver Queen'	see *H. helix* 'Tricolor'
§	- 'Spetchley' ♀H5	CMac GEdr GKev MRav MWhi NLar NPer NWad WCot WFib WHea
	- 'Splashes'	WFib
	- 'Sunrise'	WFib
	- 'Suzanne'	see *H. nepalensis* 'Suzanne'
	- 'Tanja'	WFib
	- 'Teardrop'	WFib
	- 'Telecurl'	WFib
	- 'Temptation' (v)	WFib
	- 'Tenerife' (v)	WFib
	- 'Topazolite' (v)	WFib
§	- 'Très Coupé'	CDoC LRHS MMuc SEND
§	- 'Tricolor' (v)	CTri EPfP LRHS WCFE WFib
	- 'Trinity' (v)	WFib
	- 'Tripod'	WFib
	- 'Triton'	EPfP WFib
	- 'Troll'	WFib
	- 'Ursula' (v)	WFib
	- 'Very Merry'	WFib
*	- 'Vitifolium'	WFib
§	- 'White Knight' (v) ♀H5	WFib
	- 'White Mein Herz' (v)	WFib
	- 'White Ripple' (v)	WFib
	- 'White Wonder'	LBuc
	- 'Williamsiana' (v)	WFib
	- 'Winter Purple Vein'	CNat
	- 'Woerneri'	NLar WFib
	- 'Woodsii'	see *H. helix* 'Modern Times'
	- 'Yellow Ripple'	EShb MBri WFib
	- 'Zebra' (v)	WFib
	hibernica	CCVT CDul CSBt CSde EAEE EPfP LBuc LPal LRHS MJak MRav MSwo MWhi NWea SCob SEWo SGol SPer SWvt WFib
	- 'Anna Marie'	see *H. helix* 'Anna Marie'
I	- 'Arbori Compact'	WBor
	- 'Betty Allen'	WFib
§	- 'Deltoidea' ♀H5	MWht WCFE WFib
I	- 'Digitata Crûg Gold'	WCru
	- 'Ebony'	WFib
	- 'Glengariff'	WFib
§	- 'Gracilis'	WFib
§	- 'Hamilton'	WFib
	- 'Lobata Major'	SRms
	- 'Palmata'	WFib
	- 'Rona'	WFib
	- 'Sulphurea' (v)	WFib
	- 'Variegata' (v)	WFib
§	***iberica***	WFib
	maderensis	WFib
	maroccana 'Morocco'	WFib
§	- 'Spanish Canary'	WFib
	nepalensis	WFib
§	- var. ***sinensis***	WFib
	- - KWJ 12345	WCru
	- - 'Marble Dragon'	WFib
§	- 'Suzanne'	WFib
	pastuchovii	CDoC EShb WFib
	- from Troödos, Cyprus	see *H. cypria*
	- 'Ann Ala' ♀H5	CDoC CFil GBin MBlu WCot WFib WGwG
	- 'Lagocetti'	WFib
§	***rhombea***	WCot WFib
	- 'Japonica'	see *H. rhombea*
I	- f. ***pedunculata*** 'Maculata'	CWib
	- var. ***rhombea*** 'Variegata' (v)	WFib

Hedychium ✿ (*Zingiberaceae*)

	'Anne Bishop'	NLos SEND
	aurantiacum	CBcs CBct CTsd GKev LAma LEdu SBig XLum
	brevicaule B&SWJ 7171	WCru
	'C.P. Raffill'	see *H.* × *moorei* 'Raffillii'
*	'Clarkei'	CTsd
	coccineum	CDTJ CTsd EUJe GKev IKil LPal LTro MNrw SBig XLum
	- B&SWJ 5238	WCru
	- var. ***angustifolium***	CFil WPGP
	- 'Disney'	CDTJ
	- 'Shillong Ghost'	LEdu WPGP
	coronarium ♀H1c	CAbb CAvo CBct CDTJ CExl CFil CHll CTsd EUJe GKev IKil LLWG LTro NLos SBig SPer WPGP XBlo XLum
	- B&SWJ 3745	WCru
	- 'Gold Spot'	CBct CTsd EUJe GKev NLos SKHP
	- var. ***urophyllum***	see *H. flavum* Roxb.
	densiflorum	CAbb CDTJ CExl CHll CTsd ECha EUJe GKev IBlr LCro LEdu LOPS NLos SDix SSpi WCot WCru WPGP XLum

- EN 562	CExl CFil
- LS&H 17393	CExl CFil WPGP
- Sch 582	CDes
- 'Assam Orange'	CAvo CDes CExl CPne CSam CTsd EBee GCal IBlr IDee LEdu LRHS MNrw SBig SChr SDix SEND SMad SPlb WCru WPGP
- pale-flowered	GCal
- 'Sorung'	CCon CExl CFil LEdu SChr WPGP
- 'Stephen'	CAvo CBct CDTJ CDes CExl CFil CPne EBee EUJe LEdu LRHS MNrw SChr SPlb WPGP
'Devon Cream'	CDTJ CExl CHll LRHS SChr
'Doctor Moy' (v)	CDTJ EUJe
'Elizabeth'	CCon
ellipticum	CAbb CDTJ CTsd EUJe GKev LAma LTro NLos SBig XLum
- B&SWJ 8354	WCru
'Filigree'	CExl
§ ***flavescens***	CBct CDTJ CTsd EBee EUJe GKev LAma LCro LOPS NLos SChr
flavum misapplied	see *H. flavescens*
flavum Roxb.	CAbb CBcs IBlr XLum
- HWJ 604 **new**	WCru
forrestii misapplied	see *H.* 'Helen Dillon'
gardnerianum ♀H2	CAbb CCon CExl CHll CPne CTsd EAla EUJe GKev IKil LAma LCro LEdu LOPS LPal LRHS MNrw NLos SChr SDeJ SPer WCru WPGP XLum
'Gold Flame'	EBee
gracile	EUJe NLos WCru
greenii	CBcs CBct CCon CHll CPne CTsd EUJe GKev LEdu LPal LTro MNrw NLos SBig SDix SPlb WBor WCru XLum
griffithianum	CTsd EBee IKil SBig XLum
§ 'Helen Dillon'	CCon CDes CEvo CExl EUJe GCal IBlr IDee SPlb WCru WPGP
'Keneggy' **new**	SVen
'Luna Moth'	CDes CFil NLos WPGP
luteum	CTsd
maximum	CFil NLos SChr SKHP WPGP
- B&SWJ 8261A	WCru
- HWJ 810	WCru
§ × ***moorei*** 'Raffillii'	SBig WCru
'Orange Glow'	CPne
'Pink Princess'	CBct
'Pink V'	CCon NLos
'Samsheri'	CHll SChr
spicatum	CAbb CAvo CCon CDTJ CExl CPne CTsd EUJe GCal GKev GPoy IBlr LEdu LTro MNrw MRav NLos WPGP
- B&SWJ 7231	WCru
- BWJ 8116 from Sichuan, China	WCru
- CC 1705	CExl
- P. Bon. 57188	CExl CFil WPGP
- from Ciaojiang	SBrt
- from Salween Valley, China	CExl
- 'Himalayan Lipstick'	GKev
- 'Huani'	LEdu
- 'Liberty'	WCru
- 'Singalila'	WCru
stenopetalum B&SWJ 7155	WCru
'Tahitian Flame' (v)	EUJe
'Tai Pink Princess' (Tai Series)	CTsd
'Tara' ♀H4	CAbb CAvo CBct CDes CExl CHll CPne CSam EAla EBee EUJe IBlr IDee LEdu LRHS MNrw SChr SPlb SPoG WCru WPGP
thyrsiforme	CTsd EUJe GKev SBig WCru XLum
villosum	CDTJ GCal
- var. ***tenuiflorum*** KWJ 12305	WCru
wardii	CExl CFil CTsd EUJe WPGP
yunnanense	CDes CHll LEdu SBig SBrt SPlb WPGP
- B&SWJ 9717	WCru
- BWJ 7900	WCru
- L 633	CExl IBlr
- from Cally Gardens	GCal

Hedysarum (*Papilionaceae*)

coronarium	CSpe ELan SPoG WKif
hedysaroides	IKil SPhx
multijugum	MBlu WSHC
tauricum	SPhx

Heimia (*Lythraceae*)

salicifolia	CArn IDee IMou

Helenium ✿ (*Asteraceae*)

sp.	NBFr
'Adios'	MAvo
'Amber'	EBee ECtt ILea MAvo MSpe
autumnale	CBod CExl CSBt CTri LPot LSRN MLHP MMuc NChi SWvt WFar WHar WMoo WPtf WWtn XLum
- 'All Gold'	SWvt
I - 'Cupreum'	SBch
- 'Fuego' (Mariachi Series) **new**	WHil
§ - Helena Series	SWvt
§ - - 'Helena Gold'	EPfP NBre
- - 'Helena Rote Töne'	CBod CNec EAJP EPfP LRHS LSun MWhi SPad
- - 'Helena Yellow'	LRHS
- 'Salsa' (Mariachi Series) **new**	WHil
'Baronin Linden'	MAvo MSpe
'Baudirektor Linne' ♀H7	CSam ILea LEdu LRHS MAvo MSpe MTis
'Biedermeier'	CWCL ECtt LOPS MSpe SAko
bigelovii	XLum
'Blanche Royale'	MSpe
'Blütentisch' misapplied	see *H.* 'Riverton Beauty'
'Blütentisch' Foerster ♀H7	CHVG CMea CPrp GMaP LRHS MAvo MTis NLar WMnd WWEG
'Bressingham Gold'	LRHS MHCG MNrw MSpe WHrl
'Bruno'	ELon LRHS MArl
'Butterpat' ♀H7	ECtt GCra GMaP LRHS MArl MNrw MRav WBod
'Can Can'	CBod ECtt ELon LSou MAsh MAvo MBri MSpe MTis NGdn SPer WFar
'Chelsey'	CMos CPrp CTsd ECtt ELan EPfP GQue LHop LOPS LRHS LSRN LSou MBri MNrw MRav MSpe NLar NSti SGSe WBor WHil
'Chipperfield Orange'	CSam EBee ECtt GMaP MArl MNrw NGdn WOld WWEG
'Coppelia'	CBod ECtt LRHS MTis NBir NGdn
Copper Spray	see *H.* 'Kupfersprudel'
Dark Beauty	see *H.* 'Dunkle Pracht'
'Dauerbrenner'	LEdu MAvo MTis

	Name	Suppliers
	'Die Blonde'	MAvo SMHy
	'Doktor Hartmann'	MSpe
	'Double Trouble' PBR	CBod CMos COtt EBee ECtt IBoy IKil LHop LLHF LRHS MBNS MBri NGdn SGSe SGbt SPer SPoG WCAu WCot WFar
§	'Dunkle Pracht' ♀H7	CHVG CSam EBee ECtt LSRN NLar WCot WFar WOld
	'El Dorado'	CSam EBee ECtt EWoo LEdu MAsh MAvo MBel MSpe MTis NSti WCot WFar
	'Fata Morgana'	CBod ECtt LLHF MTis NBre WCAu
	'Festival' **new**	ECtt
	'Feuersiegel' ♀H7	CSam ECtt LRHS MAvo MSpe SAko SMad WOld
	'Fiesta'	CSam ECtt MAvo MBri MTis NDov
	'Flammendes Käthchen'	CSam EBee ECtt EHoe LRHS MAvo NCGa NDov SHar SPhx
	'Flammenrad'	CAby CSam EBee SAko
	'Flammenspiel'	ECtt LRHS MCot MNrw NLar
	flexuosum	NBFr SPhx
	'Gartensonne' ♀H7	CSam WWEG
	'Gay-go-round'	CSam MAvo MSpe
	'Gelbe Waltraut'	MSpe
	Gold Fox	see *H.* 'Goldfuchs'
	'Gold Intoxication'	see *H.* 'Goldrausch'
	Golden Youth	see *H.* 'Goldene Jugend'
§	'Goldene Jugend'	CMea ELan MSpe MTis WCot
§	'Goldfuchs'	MSpe WCot
	'Goldkogel'	EBee MSpe
§	'Goldlackzwerg'	LRHS MTis
§	'Goldrausch'	CAby CSam CWCL EBee ECtt EPfP GCra LSou MNrw MSpe MTis MWat NGdn SAko WFar WMoo WOld WWEG
	'Goldreif'	MSpe
	'Goldriese'	MSpe
	'Hartmut Rieger'	CSam MSpe
	'Helena' misapplied	see *H. autumnale* 'Helena Gold'
	'Herbstgold'	MSpe
	hoopesii	see *Hymenoxys hoopesii*
	'Hot Lava'	EBee ECtt MAsh MBel MSpe SCob
	'Hot Luv'	MSpe WCot
	'Indianersommer'	CElw CWCL ECtt GMaP ILea LRHS MNrw MSpe NLar SGSe SPer SPtp WWEG
	'Jam Tarts'	WCot
	'Julisamt'	LEdu
	'July Sun'	NBir
	'Kanaria'	CAby CHVG CPrp EBee ECtt GBin GQue LHop LRHS MAvo MRav MSpe MTis NDov NEgg NLar WHil WMnd
	'Kleine Aprikose'	MSpe MTis
	'Kleiner Fuchs'	MHer MSpe NLar WWEG
	'Kokarde'	MAvo WWEG
	'Königstiger'	CSam ECtt GBin LRHS MAvo MHCG MNrw MSpe MTis NDov SAko WFar
	'Kugelsonne'	CSam MSpe NBre SAko
§	'Kupfersprudel'	MAvo MTis SAko
	'Kupferzwerg'	CWCL EAJP ELan IPot MAvo NBre NDov SAko
	'Lambada'	EBee MTis
	'Louise Beacock'	MSpe
	'Loysder Wieck'	EBee ECtt LCro LOPS MAvo MSpe MTis NGdn SHil WWEG
	'Luc'	MAvo MSpe MTis WCot
§	'Mahagoni'	LEdu MSpe WBod
	'Mahogany'	see *H.* 'Goldlackzwerg'
	Mahogany	see *H.* 'Mahagoni'
	'Mardi Gras'	CMos ECtt LRHS LSou MBri MSpe MTis SLon SPoG
	'Margot'	CAby CSam MSpe MTis NBre
	'Meranti'	CMea MAvo SAko WCot
	'Moerheim Beauty' ♀H7	Widely available
	'Moth'	MSpe MTis NEgg
	'Oldenburg'	MSpe WCot
	Pipsqueak = 'Blopip'	LLHF LRHS NBre SPoG
	'Potter's Wheel'	EBee ECtt LCro LOPS MAvo WCot WWEG
	puberulum	CBod EBee LRHS NBir
	'Puck'	MSpe
	'Pumilum Magnificum'	ELan EPfP GQue IBoy LEdu LHop LRHS MSpe MTis SMad WFar WPGP XLum
	'Ragamuffin'	CSam ECtt MTis WCot
	'Rauchtopas'	CAby CSam EBee GQue ILea LCro LEdu LOPS MAvo MSpe MTis NCGa NDov SAko SDix WPGP
	Red and Gold	see *H.* 'Rotgold' Foerster
	'Red Army'	CHVG CPrp ECtt ELan ELon IPot LEdu LRHS LSou MAvo MNrw MSpe NCGa NGdn NLar SAko SWvt
	'Red Glory'	MTis
	'Red Jewel'	Widely available
	'Ring of Fire' ♀H7	SMHy
§	'Riverton Beauty'	CSam ECtt LLHF MNrw MSpe SDix WCot WHoo
	'Riverton Gem'	CSam ECtt LLHF MHCG MNrw NChi WHoo
	'Rotgold' misapplied	see *H. autumnale* Helena Series
§	'Rotgold' Foerster	CBod ECtt LSRN NChi SRms WMoo
	'Rouge Foncé'	WCot
	'Rubinzwerg' ♀H7	Widely available
	'Ruby Charm'	EBee ECtt EPfP MAsh MSpe WCot WFar
§	'Ruby Thuesday'	CAby CMos CTsd ECtt ELan EPfP IBoy IKil IPot LCro LHop LLHF LRHS LSRN MAvo MBNS MNrw MSpe MTis NGdn NHol NLar NWsh SCob SGSe SMad SPoG SWvt WCAu WCot
	'Ruby Tuesday'	see *H.* 'Ruby Thuesday'
	'Sahin's Early Flowerer' ♀H7	Widely available
	'Samtjuwel'	MTis
	'Schokoladenkönigin'	MSpe
	'Septemberfuchs'	LEdu LPla MCot MTis SPhx
	'Sonnenwunder'	CSam MLHP MSpe NBre
	'Sophie zur Linden'	ECtt MSpe MTis WCot
	'Sunshine Superman'	MSpe
	'The Bishop'	CBod EBee ECtt ELon EPfP GCra LAst LBMP LHop LOPS LRHS MBri MRav MSpe NHol SCob SGSe SGbt SGol SPer SWvt WFar WMnd
	'Tie Dye'	EBee MSpe SPoG WFar
	'Tijuana Brass'	ECtt NLar SAko
	'Tip Top'	NBFr
	'Tura'	MSpe
	'Two Faced Fan'	MSpe MTis
	'Vicky'	MSpe
	'Vivace'	LEdu MAvo MSpe WCot
	'Wagon Wheel'	WCot WWEG
	'Waldhorn'	MTis
	'Waltraut' ♀H7	CBod CElw CKno EBee ECtt ELan EPfP LBMP LCro LEdu LHop

		LOPS LRHS MAvo MBri MCot MPie MRav MSpe MTis NBir NLar SCob SDix SGSe SPer SWvt WCAu WMoo
	'Wesergold' ♀H7	EBee LLHF LPfy LRHS LSou MAvo MHer MSpe NDov NLar NSti SGSe
	'Westerstede'	MSpe MTis
	'Wonnadonga'	GBin MTis
	'Wyndley'	CBcs CHVG CMea ECtt EHoe ELan EPfP GMaP LRHS MHer MRav MSpe MTis NGdn NLar NPri SCob SGSe SPer WCAu WFar WHoo WMnd WWEG
	'Zimbelstern'	CCse ECtt EWTr IPot LHop MAvo MCot MPie MSpe MTis NLar SPhx WCot WFar WPGP WWEG
	'Zonnedam'	ECtt

Helianthella (*Asteraceae*)

§	***quinquenervis***	CEvo EBee ELon GCal LLHF MHer NLar SMad SPer

Helianthemum (*Cistaceae*)

	sp.	SCob SVic
	'Alice Howorth'	NPri WIce
	'Amabile Plenum' (d)	GCal
	'Amy Baring' ♀H4	CTri ECho ECtt GAbr GCrg LRHS NWad
	'Annabel' (d)	ECho ECtt GAbr LRHS NPri NSla
	apenninum	LLHF SRms XLum XSen
	'Apricot'	CTri ECtt
	'Apricot Blush'	WAbe
	'Baby Buttercup'	CMea GAbr
	'Beech Park Red'	CSma CTri EPot GCrg MHer WAbe WHoo WIce WKif
	'Ben Afflick'	ECho ECtt LHop LRHS SRms
	'Ben Alder'	ECtt GAbr MHer
	'Ben Dearg'	CMea ECho ECtt SRms
	'Ben Fhada'	CBcs CBod CMea CTri ECho ECtt ELan ELon EPfP GAbr GCrg GJos GMaP LBMP LBee LHop LRHS MAsh MHer MLHP NEgg SEND SPoG SRGP SRms WAbe WHoo XLum XSen
	'Ben Heckla'	CTal ECho ECtt GAbr LHop LRHS SRms XLum
	'Ben Hope'	CTri ECho ECtt ELan EPfP EWTr EWoo LAst MJak NPri SGol SRGP SRms XLum
§	'Ben Ledi'	CBcs CBod ECho ECtt ELan ELon GAbr GCrg GMaP LHop MAsh MHer MSCN NHol NSla SEND SGbt SPoG SRms SRot WAbe
	'Ben Lomond'	ECho GAbr
	'Ben More'	CBcs CBod CMea CTal ECho ECtt ELan EPfP GAbr GJos GMaP LHop LRHS MAsh MRav MSwo NBir SEND SIgm SPoG SRGP SRms SRot WHoo WIce
	'Ben Nevis'	CTri ECho ECtt GAbr SRms
	'Ben Vane'	ECho ECtt LRHS
	'Boughton Double Primrose' (d)	CTal ECho ECtt WAbe WHoo WSHC
	'Bronzeteppich'	EAJP
	'Broughty Beacon'	ECtt
	'Broughty Sunset'	ECtt GAbr
	'Bunbury'	ECtt ELon GAbr GCrg GJos LRHS NBir SDix SPoG SRms WIce WRHF
	canum subsp. ***balcanicum***	WAbe
	'Captivation'	ECtt GAbr NHol
	'Cerise Queen' (d)	CTri ECha ECho ECtt EPfP GKev LAst LHop MCot MHol MSwo NPri SEND SRms XSen
	chamaecistus	see *H. nummularium*
	'Cheviot'	NBir SMHy WHoo WSHC XLum
I	'Chloe's Variegata' (v)	EWes
	'Chocolate Blotch'	ECho ECtt GCra LHop LRHS NWad SEND SRms XSen
	'Cornish Cream'	ECtt GAbr LBee NHol NPri SRms
	croceum	LLHF
	cupreum	ECtt GAbr
	'David'	NHol
	'David Ritchie'	WHoo
	'Diana'	CMea ECtt
	double apricot-flowered (d)	GAbr
	double orange-flowered (d)	LHop
	double primrose-flowered (d)	GAbr
	'Dunwich'	GGal
	'Eisbar'	SAko
	'Everton Ruby'	see *H.* 'Ben Ledi'
	'Fairy'	ELan EPfP GAbr LLHF
§	'Fire Dragon' ♀H4	CMea ECho ECtt ELan EPfP EWoo GAbr GCrg GMaP GQue LRHS NBir NPri SGbt SIgm SRms WAbe WRHF XLum XSen
	'Fireball'	see *H.* 'Mrs C.W. Earle'
	'Firegold' (v)	WAbe
	'Georgeham'	CMea CSam CSma CTal EAJP ECtt ELon GCrg NBir NHol SRms WHoo WRHF XLum
§	'Golden Queen'	ECho ECtt EPfP GAbr LAst MAsh MCot MHol MSwo NPri
	'Hampstead Orange'	CTri
	'Hartswood'[PBR] **new**	NPri
	'Hartswood Ruby'	GMaP MBNS NPri SAko SRms
	'Henfield Brilliant' ♀H4	CExl CHVG CSam CTal ECho ECtt ELan EPfP EWoo GAbr GCrg LHop LRHS MHol MRav NBir NHol NSla SDix SIgm SMad SPoG SRms WCot WHoo WSHC XLum
	'Highdown'	SRms
	'Highdown Apricot'	EAJP ECho ECtt GCrg GJos LHop LLHF LRHS SPoG SRms
	'Honeymoon'	ECtt EPfP GAbr NWad
	'Jeanie' (d)	ECho
	'Jubilee' (d) ♀H4	CHVG CSma CTal CTri ECho ECtt ELan ELon EShb GJos LHop MAsh MBNS NBir NChi NHol SPoG SRms WHil WKif
	'Karen's Silver'	WAbe
	'Kathleen Druce' (d)	CTal ECho ECtt EWes NWad WHoo
	'Kathleen Mary'	CMea
	'Lawrenson's Pink'	CSma ECho ECtt GAbr GCrg LHop LPot LRHS MHol MLHP NPri SAko SRGP SRms
	'Lemon Queen'	ECtt GCrg
	'Lucy Elizabeth'	ECtt
	lunulatum	CMea ECho LLHF LRHS NWad SIgm WAbe
	'Mead Sunset'	CMea ECtt
§	'Mrs C.W. Earle' (d) ♀H4	CTri ECho ECtt ELan EPfP GCra LRHS MBNS NSla SRms
	'Mrs Clay'	see *H.* 'Fire Dragon'
	'Mrs Hays'	ECtt GAbr

'Mrs Lake' GAbr
'Mrs Moules' SRms
mutabile NPri SPlb
'New Moon' CSma CTal
§ ***nummularium*** ECho ENfk GPoy MHer MNHC NMir SRms WAbe WIce WSFF XSen
oelandicum NSla NWad SRms WAbe
- subsp. ***piloselloides*** WAbe
'Old Gold' ECtt GAbr SRms WAbe
'Orange Phoenix' (d) ECtt MBNS NWad
'Ovum Supreme' NHol
'Pink Angel' (d) CSma CTal ECtt ELon GCrg MBNS WAbe
'Praecox' CMea CTri ECho ECtt GAbr SRms WHoo
'Prima Donna' ELan EPfP
'Prostrate Orange' SRms
'Raspberry Ripple' CSma ECho ECtt ELan EPfP EPot GCrg LRHS NPri SPoG SRms XSen
'Razzle Dazzle' (v) ECtt LLHF NLar SLon SRms
'Red Dragon' EPot GCrg MLHP WAbe
'Red Orient' see *H.* 'Supreme'
'Regenbogen' (d) CPBP GCal SEND
§ 'Rhodanthe Carneum' ♀H4 Widely available
§ 'Rosakönigin' ECtt GAbr MHer NHol WAbe WRHF
'Rose of Leeswood' (d) CTri ECtt LBee NEgg SPoG SRms WHoo WKif WSHC XLum
Rose Queen see *H.* 'Rosakönigin'
'Roxburgh Gold' SRms
'Saint John's College Yellow' CSam ECho LRHS
'Salmon Queen' ECho ECtt GAbr LHop LRHS SEND SRms
* ***scardicum*** CMea
'Shot Silk' CSma ECtt EWes SRms
'Snow Queen' see *H.* 'The Bride'
'Sterntaler' GAbr LLHF SAko SRms
'Sudbury Gem' CTri ECha ECho ECtt GAbr LRHS NPri SGol
'Sulphur Moon' ECho LLHF LRHS
'Sulphureum Plenum' (d) ECtt SGol
'Sunbeam' ECho ECtt SRms
§ 'Supreme' ECho ELan EPfP EWes LHop MHol SAko SRms WCot XLum XSen
'Tangerine' ECtt
§ 'The Bride' ♀H4 Widely available
'Tigrinum Plenum' (d) ECho EWes
'Tomato Red' NSla XLum
umbellatum see *Halimium umbellatum*
'Voltaire' ECtt LLHF NWad XLum
'Watergate Rose' MWat
'Welsh Flame' ECtt NHol WAbe
'Whenday' CMea
'Wisley Pink' see *H.* 'Rhodanthe Carneum'
'Wisley Primrose' ♀H4 Widely available
'Wisley Rose' LRHS
'Wisley White' CTri ECha ECho ECtt ELan EPfP
'Wisley Yellow' ECtt ELan
'Yellow Queen' see *H.* 'Golden Queen'

Helianthus (*Asteraceae*)

sp. SVic
angustifolius SDix
atrorubens LHop MRav MSpe NBro
'Bitter Chocolate' LEdu MAvo MSpe WBor WCot WPGP
'Capenoch Star' ♀H7 CElw CPrp ECtt GMaP IBoy LEdu LRHS MAvo MBel MRav MSpe MTis NBro NLar SDix SWvt WMoo
'Capenoch Supreme' ECtt LRHS
'Carine' MLHP MNrw MTis WCot
decapetalus Morning Sun see *H.* 'Morgensonne'
'Dorian Roxburgh' ECtt MAvo MTis WCot
'Double Whammy' (d) ECtt MTis
giganteus SHar
- 'Sheila's Sunshine' CElw EWes GBin LHop LRHS MNrw NDov SAko SHar SMHy SPhx WOld WWEG
grosseserratus MPie
'Gullick's Variety' ♀H7 CBre ECtt LLWP NBro NChi NLar SAko SPhx SWvt WOld WWEG XLum
'Happy Days' CAby CBre CElw EBee ECtt ELon EWes LBMP LSou MHol MPie MSpe MTis NCGa NGBl NSti WCot WHoo WMoo WOld
'Hazel's Gold' LRHS
× ***kellermanii*** EBee MAvo MTis SPhx
§ × ***laetiflorus*** MWhi NLar
- 'Daniel Dewar' MMuc
§ 'Lemon Queen' ♀H7 Widely available
'Limelight' see *H.* 'Lemon Queen'
'Loddon Gold' ♀H7 ECtt ELan EPfP LRHS MBel MRav MSpe MTis NBir SWvt WBor WWEG
§ ***maximiliani*** CEvo ELan ELon LHop MMuc SPhx SPtp
microcephalus CSam EBee ELon MMuc NDov WPtf
- 'JS Straffe Prairie Gast' EBee
'Miss Mellish' ♀H7 EBee ECtt GCal LEdu MSCN MSpe SPhx WBor WBrk WCot WHoo WWEG
mollis CSam SBrt SPav SPhx
'Monarch' ♀H4 CMea CSam ECtt GBee MBel MMuc MRav MSpe NCGa NLar WCot WHal WHil WOld WTcb WWEG
§ 'Morgensonne' MTis MWat WBor WCot
× ***multiflorus*** 'Meteor' LRHS NBre SAko WWEG
'O Sole Mio' WCot
occidentalis SMad
orgyalis see *H. salicifolius*
petiolaris COtt
quinquenervis see *Helianthella quinquenervis*
'Razzmatazz' **new** SAko
rigidus misapplied see *H.* × *laetiflorus*
§ ***salicifolius*** Widely available
- 'Low Down'PBR SWvt
- 'Table Mountain'PBR GBin LRHS SAko SWvt WCot
scaberrimus see *H.* × *laetiflorus*
'Soleil d'Or' ECtt WHal
strumosus WCot
'Triomphe de Gand' LEdu MTis MWat NDov
tuberosus CArn EBee GPoy SVic
- 'Fuseau' LCro LOPS SVic
- 'Garnet' LEdu
- 'Sugarball' LEdu
× ***verticillatus*** **new** CEvo

Helichrysum (*Asteraceae*)

from Drakensberg Mountains, South Africa GAbr
adenocarpum SPlb

	alveolatum	see *H. splendidum*
	amorginum 'Pink Bud'	MMuc
	- Ruby Cluster = 'Blorub'PBR	LRHS
	angustifolium from Crete	see *H. microphyllum* (Willd.) Cambess.
§	***arwae***	EPot WAbe
	bellidioides	see *Anaphalioides bellidioides*
	bracteatum	see *Xerochrysum bracteatum*
	'Coco'	see *Xerochrysum bracteatum* 'Coco'
	confertum	SPlb
	coralloides	see *Ozothamnus coralloides*
	'County Park Silver'	see *Ozothamnus* 'County Park Silver'
	'Dargan Hill Monarch'	see *Xerochrysum bracteatum* 'Dargan Hill Monarch'
	depressum	EPot
	'Elmstead'	see *H. stoechas* 'White Barn'
	frigidum	WAbe
	hookeri	see *Ozothamnus hookeri*
§	***hypoleucum***	SDix
	'Icicles'	EBee GBin
	italicum	CArn ECha ECrN ENfk EPfP GBin GMaP GPoy LPot MHer MMuc MNHC NPri SEND SPoG SRms SVen WHer WHfH WJek XLum XSen
	- 'Dartington'	CBod ENfk GBin SRms WJek
I	- 'Glaucum'	CWib
	- 'Korma'PBR	ECGP EHoe ELan EPfP GBin LRHS LSou MGos SLon SPoG SRms
	- subsp. ***microphyllum***	see *H. microphyllum* (Willd.) Cambess.
	- 'Nanum'	see *H. microphyllum* (Willd.) Cambess.
§	- subsp. ***serotinum***	CBcs ECrN EHoe EPfP GPoy LRHS MRav SLim SPer SRms SWvt WRHF XSen
	lanatum	see *H. thianschanicum*
	ledifolium	see *Ozothamnus ledifolius*
	marginatum misapplied	see *H. milfordiae*
	marginatum DC.	GKev
	microphyllum misapplied	see *Plecostachys serpyllifolia*
	microphyllum ambig.	MMuc SPer SRms
§	***microphyllum*** (Willd.) Cambess.	ENfk MNHC SEND WJek
§	***milfordiae*** ♀H4	EPot NSla SRms WAbe
	montanum	GKev
	orientale	EPot XSen
	pagophilum	EPot WAbe
	petiolare ♀H3	EBak ECtt LAst MCot SPer SPoG WHea
	- 'Aureum'	see *H. petiolare* 'Limelight'
	- 'Goring Silver' ♀H3	NPri SPoG
§	- 'Limelight' ♀H3	ECtt LAst MCot NPri SPer SPoG
	- 'Variegatum' (v) ♀H3	ECtt LAst MCot SPoG
	plicatum	WCot
	populifolium misapplied	see *H. hypoleucum*
	rosmarinifolium	see *Ozothamnus rosmarinifolius*
§	'Schwefellicht'	EBee ECha EPfP MLHP MRav SPer WKif WSHC
	selago	see *Ozothamnus selago*
	serotinum	see *H. italicum* subsp. *serotinum*
	serpyllifolium	see *Plecostachys serpyllifolia*
	sessilioides	EPot WAbe
§	***sibthorpii***	WAbe
§	***splendidum*** ♀H5	LRHS NBro SKHP SLon XSen
	stoechas	CArn XSen
§	- 'White Barn'	CSpe WCot XLum
	Sulphur Light	see *H.* 'Schwefellicht'
§	***thianschanicum***	LRHS SRms XLum XSen
	- Golden Baby	see *H. thianschanicum* 'Goldkind'
§	- 'Goldkind'	NBir XLum
	- 'White Wonder' **new**	LRHS
	trilineatum misapplied	see *H. splendidum*
	tumidum	see *Ozothamnus selago* var. *tumidus*
	virgineum	see *H. sibthorpii*
	witbergense	WAbe
	woodii	see *H. arwae*

Helicodiceros (*Araceae*)

§	***muscivorus***	CHid WCot

Heliconia ✿ (*Heliconiaceae*)

	caribaea 'Burgundy'	see *H. caribaea* 'Purpurea'
§	- 'Purpurea'	XBlo
	'Golden Torch'	XBlo
	indica 'Spectabilis'	XBlo
	latispatha 'Orange Gyro'	XBlo
*	- 'Red Gyro'	XBlo
	metallica	XBlo
	rostrata	XBlo
	schiedeana	CHll

Helictotrichon (*Poaceae*)

	pratense	CHab EHoe
§	***sempervirens*** ♀H7	Widely available
I	- 'Pendulum'	CBod CLet EBee GBin MAvo MSpe
	- 'Saphirsprudel'	CCse EBee EPfP LRHS MJak SHil WCot WPGP WWEG

Heliophila (*Brassicaceae*)

	coronopifolia	CSpe

Heliopsis (*Asteraceae*)

	Golden Plume	see *H. helianthoides* var. *scabra* 'Goldgefieder'
	helianthoides	LRHS MLHP NBre WFar WWtn
	- 'Limelight'	see *Helianthus* 'Lemon Queen'
	- Loraine Sunshine = 'Helhan'PBR (v)	CWGN IKil LSou MHol MMHG MSCN NWsh SMad SPad SPer SPoG WCot WFar WHlf
	- var. ***scabra***	NHol SRot WMnd XLum
	- - 'Asahi'	CBod ECtt ELan GMaP SAko SMad WHoo
	- - Ballerina	see *H. helianthoides* var. *scabra* 'Spitzentänzerin'
	- - 'Benzinggold' ♀H5	LRHS LSou MRav
	- - 'Bressingham Doubloon' (d)	ECtt
	- - Golden Plume	see *H. helianthoides* var. *scabra* 'Goldgefieder'
§	- - 'Goldgefieder' ♀H5	EBee NBre SAko WFar
	- - Goldgreenheart	see *H. helianthoides* var. *scabra* 'Goldgrünherz'
§	- - 'Goldgrünherz'	LCro
	- - 'Light of Loddon' ♀H5	LRHS
	- - 'Patula'	EBee ECtt
	- - 'Prairie Sunset'PBR	EBee ECtt MSCN SAko
§	- - 'Sommersonne'	CSBt ECtt EPfP LRHS MWhi NBFr NGBl NPer SCob SPer SRms WMnd
§	- - 'Spitzentänzerin' ♀H5	ECtt SAko
	- - 'Summer Nights'	EBee EPfP EWTr LCro LOPS MNrw MPie MRav MSpe SBea SPhx WCot WWEG

- - Summer Sun	see *H. helianthoides* var. *scabra* 'Sommersonne'
- - 'Sunburst' (v)	SPav
- - 'Venus'	CBod ECtt LRHS LSou
- - 'Waterperry Gold'	MWat
- 'Summer Pink'	MHol SPad SPoG WCot WRHF
- 'Tuscan Sun'PBR	EBee ECtt LRHS SCob

Heliotropium ✿ (*Boraginaceae*)

§ ***amplexicaule***	SDys
anchusifolium	see *H. amplexicaule*
§ ***arborescens***	CArn ENfk EPfP EShb MCot MHom
- 'Chatsworth' ♀H1c	CAby CSpe ECre ECtt MHom
- 'Dame Alice de Hales'	ECtt MHom
- 'Gatton Park'	MHom
- 'Lord Roberts'	ECtt MHom
- 'Marine'	CSam
- 'Mary Fox'	MHom
- 'Mrs J.W. Lowther'	MHom
- 'Netherhall Lilac' **new**	EBee
- pale lilac-flowered	CSam
- 'President Garfield'	MHom
- 'Princess Marina' ♀H1c	EPfP LAst NLar
- 'Reva'	ECtt MHom
- 'The Queen'	ECtt
- 'The Speaker'	MHom
- 'White Lady'	CSpe ECtt MHom
- 'White Queen'	ECtt MHom
- 'Woodcote'	MHom
'Butterfly Kisses'	LBuc
peruvianum	see *H. arborescens*

Helipterum see *Syncarpha*

Helleborus ✿ (*Ranunculaceae*)

abruzzicus	CEvo
- WM 0227	MPhe
abschasicus	see *H. orientalis* Lam. subsp. *abchasicus*
'Angel Glow'	CBcs EBee LRHS SCob WHil
§ ***argutifolius*** ♀H5	Widely available
- mottled-leaved	see *H. argutifolius* 'Pacific Frost'
§ - 'Pacific Frost' (v)	CPla MMHG
- 'Red Riding Hood'	LRHS
- 'Silver Lace'	CCon EAEE ELan EPfP GKev IBoy LHop LRHS LSRN MHol NBir NLar NWad SKHP SPer SPoG SPtp WMoo
atrorubens misapplied	see *H. orientalis* Lam. subsp. *abchasicus* Early Purple Group
atrorubens ambig.	MAsh SCob
atrorubens Waldst. & Kit.	CEvo LOPS MRav XEll
- WM 9028 from Slovenia	MPhe
- WM 9805 from Croatia	GBuc MPhe
- spotted form	MPhe
× ***ballardiae***	CLAP
- 'Candy Love'PBR	EBee GBin LRHS MBri MHol NLar SCob SHil
- HGC Camelot **new**	LRHS
- HGC Champion ='Coseh 730'PBR **new**	LRHS
- HGC Maestro ='Coseh 890'PBR **new**	CRos LRHS
- HGC Merlin ='Coseh 810'PBR **new**	LRHS
- HGC Snow Dance ='Coseh 800'PBR **new**	CRos LRHS
'Blue Moon'	IBoy
§ ***bocconei***	CEvo MAsh
- WM 1332 from Sicily	MPhe
- WM 1334 from Calabria, Italy **new**	MPhe
- WM 9719 from Italy	MPhe
- WM 9905 from Sicily	MPhe
- subsp. ***bocconei***	see *H. bocconei*
colchicus	see *H. orientalis* Lam. subsp. *abchasicus*
corsicus	see *H. argutifolius*
croaticus	CEvo MAsh
- WM 9810	MPhe
cyclophyllus	GKev MAsh MPhe SCob SPer
dumetorum	CEvo GBuc GCal
- WM 1306 from Hungary **new**	MPhe
- WM 1309 from Slovenia **new**	MPhe
- WM 9209	MPhe
- WM 9627 from Croatia	GBuc MPhe
§ × ***ericsmithii***	CDes CExl CLAP CMHG ECha ELon EPfP GBuc LAst LHop LLHF LRHS LSRN LSou MAsh NBir NGdn NLar SCob WHoo WPGP
- 'Bob's Best'	CExl CHid CLAP ECtt EPfP ESwi GBin LPla LRHS MBNS MHol MNrw SEND SKHP SWvt
- HGC Shooting Star ='Coseh 790'PBR **new**	CRos ECre LRHS
- 'HGC Silvermoon'PBR	IBoy LRHS NLar
- HGC Marlon Cream ='Coseh 980' **new**	LRHS
- HGC Monte Cristo ='Coseh 860' **new**	CRos LRHS
- 'Pirouette'PBR	CLAP ECre EPfP LRHS MAsh MBri SCob
- 'Ruby Glow'	CBcs ECre LAst LRHS MAsh SCob WHil
- 'Snow Love'PBR	EBee LBuc LRHS MAsh MBri NLar SCob SHil WCot
- 'Winter Moonbeam'PBR	CBod CLAP EPfP LBuc LRHS LSRN LSun MBri MCot MHol NCGa SCob SKHP SLon SPoG WCot WHil
- 'Winter Sunshine'PBR	CLAP EPfP LBuc LRHS MBri SCob SKHP SPoG WHil
foetidus ♀H7	Widely available
- from Italy	IFoB
- 'Chedglow'	CNat
- 'Gold Bullion'	CPla ECtt GBuc MAsh
- 'Harvington Pewter'	CLAP ENun LRHS SPoG
- 'Miss Jekyll'	SVic
- 'Ruth'	EWoo MAsh SCob
- 'Sienna'	SCob
- sweet-scented	MHom
- 'Vogezen'	SCob
- Wester Flisk Group	CExl ECtt EPfP GBuc IFoB LHop MAsh NHol NPer SCob SEND WHar WPGP
- Wilgenbroek selection	SCob
- 'Yellow Wilgenbroek'	SCob
- 'Yorkley'	LSRN
Gold Collection	see *H.* cultivars with names starting HGC
HGC Cinnamon Snow ='Coseh 700'PBR	ECre ESwi LRHS NLar
'HGC Jericho'PBR	IVic
HGC Pink Frost ='Coseh 710'PBR	LRHS
Hillier hybrids anemone-centred, spotted pink	CRos LRHS SHil

Hillier hybrids anemone-centred, yellow	CRos LRHS SHil
× ***hybridus***	Widely available
- anemone-centred	CHid CLAP GBin IFoB LHel MNrw WFar
- 'Apple Blossom'	IFoB WFar
- 'Apricot Blush' (Winter Jewels Series)	CWGN NCGa
- apricot-flowered	CLAP CTal GBuc IFoB WFar
- 'Ashwood Elegance Pearl'	MAsh
- 'Ashwood Elegance Snow'	MAsh
- 'Ashwood Fascination'	MAsh
- Ashwood Garden hybrids	ELan EPfP LRHS MAsh MRav SRms
- - anemone-centred	MAsh
- - double-flowered (d)	MAsh
- 'Ashwood Glade'	MAsh
- 'Ashwood Meadow'	MAsh
- Ballard's Group	CLAP IBoy LRHS SPer WFar WPnP
- Barnhaven hybrids, anemone-centred **new**	XBar
- - apricot **new**	XBar
- - picotee **new**	XBar
- - red and green **new**	XBar
- - slate **new**	XBar
- - spotted **new**	XBar
- - white **new**	XBar
- - yellow **new**	XBar
- 'Black Beauty'	IFoB
- 'Black Diamond' (Winter Jewels Series)	NCGa
- 'Black Knight'	IFoB
- black-flowered	CLAP GBuc GMaP IFoB NChi WFar
- 'Blue Lady' (Lady Series)	CBcs GAbr GBin GKev IFoB LRHS MBNS NGdn SPer
- 'Blue Metallic Lady' (Lady Series)	CBod CExl CTsd EPfP GKev IBoy IFoB LAst LCro LRHS LSun MBNS MHol NEgg NGdn SPer
- Bradfield hybrids	MCot
- - anemone-centred	MCot
- - double-flowered (d)	MCot
- - picotee	MCot
- Caborn hybrids	LLWP
- 'Cherry Blossom' (Winter Jewels Series)	CWGN MPnt NCGa
- 'Cherry Frost'	MAsh
- 'Cinderella'[PBR] (d)	LRHS
- 'Clare's Purple'	CBod LSRN
- 'Cosmos'	CTal MBNS
- cream-flowered	CLAP IFro WFar
- dark picotee	WFar
- dark purple-flowered	IFoB LHel WFar
- dark red-flowered	IFoB LHel WFar
- dark-flowered	WFar
- deep red-flowered	CLAP GBuc MHol NChi WFar
- double (d)	CLAP GBuc IFoB LHop MNrw WFar
- - black-flowered (d)	CExl IFoB WFar
- - pink-flowered (d)	IFoB LHel WFar
- - dark purple-flowered (d)	WFar
- - green-flowered (d)	IFoB LHel WFar
- - purple-flowered (d)	LHel WFar
- - red-flowered (d)	CExl LRHS WFar
- - white-flowered (d)	CExl IFoB LHel WFar
- - yellow-flowered (d)	CExl IFoB IFro LHel WFar
- 'Double Ellen Picotee' (d)	CWGN GBin LCro LOPS WHlf
- 'Double Ellen Pink' (d) **new**	LCro LRHS
- 'Double Ellen Purple' (d) **new**	LRHS
- 'Double Ellen Red' (d)	GBin LCro LOPS LRHS WHlf
- 'Double Ellen White' (d)	CWGN EPfP GBin LCro LOPS LRHS WHlf
- Double Ladies, mixed (d)	GAbr WCot
- Elizabeth Town anemone-centred	IFro
- - double-centred (d)	IFro
- - picotee-centred	IFro
- - red-centred	IFro
- 'Emerald Queen' (Queen Series)	ELan GBin GQue
- 'Enchantment'	MAsh
- 'Farmyard' Appleblossom	WFar
- Farmyard anemone-centred	WFar
- - apricot	WFar
- - black	WFar
- - cream	WFar
- - cream, spotted	WFar
- - dark pink	WFar
- - double apricot (d)	WFar
- - - black (d)	WFar
- - - cream (d)	WFar
- - - - spotted (d)	WFar
- - - pink (d)	WFar
- - - - spotted (d)	WFar
- - - primrose (d)	WFar
- - - - spotted (d)	WFar
- - - red (d)	WFar
- - - slate-grey (d)	WFar
- - - white (d)	WFar
- - - - spotted (d)	WFar
- - green	WFar
- - - spotted	WFar
- - picotee	WFar
- - pink	WFar
- - pink spotted	WFar
- - plum	WFar
- - primrose	WFar
- - - dark-eyed	WFar
- - - spotted	WFar
- - red	WFar
- - slate spotted	WFar
- - slate-grey	WFar
- - white	WFar
- - - dark-eyed	WFar
- - - splash	WFar
- - - spotted	WFar
- 'Farmyard Woodland'	WFar
- Field of Blooms hybrids	IFoB
- - anemone-centred	IFoB
- - double-flowered (d)	IFoB
- - picotee	IFoB
- 'Gala Queen' (Queen Series)	ELon
- 'Golden Discovery' mixed (d)	CBod
- 'Golden Lotus' (d)	CWGN MPnt
- 'Golden Sunrise' (Winter Jewels Series)	MPnt NCGa
- 'Green Ripple'	WFar
- green-flowered	IFoB WFar
- 'Harlequin Gem' (Winter Jewels Series) (d)	MPnt
- Harvington apricot	CRos ENun LCro LRHS NBir NLar NPri SKHP SLon
- - double apricot (d)	CRos ENun LRHS NPri SHeu

- - - blush (d) **new**	ENun
- - - chocolate (d)	CLAP CRos ENun LCro LRHS NPri SHeu SPoG
- - - cream speckled (d) **new**	ENun
- - - dark purple (d)	LRHS NPri
- - - green (d) **new**	ENun
- - - pink (d)	CLAP CRos ENun LCro LOPS LRHS NPri SHeu SKHP SLon SPoG
- - - - speckled (d)	CRos ENun LCro LRHS NPri SHeu SPoG
- - - purple (d)	CLAP CRos ENun LCro LRHS NBir NLar NPri SHeu SKHP SPoG
- - - - cascade (d)	ENun LRHS SHeu SPoG
- - - red (d)	CLAP CRos ENun LCro LOPS LRHS NBir NLar NPri SLon SPoG
- - - speckled (d)	CRos ENun LCro LRHS NPri SPoG
- - - white (d)	CLAP CRos ENun LCro LRHS NBir NLar NPri SHeu SKHP SLon SPoG
- - - yellow (d)	CLAP CRos ENun LRHS NBir NLar NPri SHeu SKHP SLon SPoG
- - - - speckled (d)	CRos ENun SHeu SPoG
- - - lime-green (d)	CLAP LOPS LRHS NPri SHeu SPoG
- - dusky	ENun LRHS
- - picotee	CLAP CRos ENun LCro LRHS NBir NLar NPri SHeu SKHP SLon SPoG
- - pink	CRos ENun LRHS NLar NPri SHeu SLon SPoG
- - - speckled	CRos ENun LCro NLar NPri SHeu SLon SPoG
- - red	CRos ENun LCro LOPS LRHS MHer NLar NPri SLon SPoG
- - single **new**	LRHS
- - smokey **new**	ENun
- - speckled	CRos MHer NPri SHeu SLon
- - white	CRos ENun LCro LOPS LRHS MHer NLar NPri SKHP SLon SPoG
- - - speckled	ENun LCro LOPS NPri SHeu SKHP SLon SPoG
- - yellow	CRos ENun LCro LRHS MHer NLar NPri SHeu SKHP SLon SPoG
- - - speckled	CRos ENun LCro LRHS MHer NLar NPri SHeu SLon SPoG
- - - with maroon eye **new**	ENun
- - lime **new**	LCro LRHS SPoG
- 'Harvington Shades of the Night'	CRos ENun LCro LRHS MHer NLar NPri SHeu SKHP SLon SPoG
- 'Harvington Smokey Blues'	CRos LCro NPri SHeu SKHP SLon SPoG
- 'Harvington Smokey Double' (d)	NPri SHeu
- 'Helen Ballard'	SVic
- Hillier hybrids clear white	CRos LRHS SHil
- - double pink (d)	CRos LRHS
- - - white (d)	LRHS
- - pink and white	LRHS
- - slate	LRHS SHil
- - spotted, double yellow (d)	CRos EPfP LRHS SHil
- - - double-pink (d)	EPfP LRHS SHil
- - - green	LRHS
- - - pink	CRos LRHS MBri
- - - white	CRos LRHS MBri
- - yellow	MBri
- - anemone-centred	CRos
- - burgundy	CBod CRos LRHS MBri SHil
- 'Ice Queen' (Queen Series)	ELan
- 'Kingston Cardinal'	MAsh
- 'Lady in Red'	IBoy
- Lady Series	IFoB NSum
- large, pink-flowered	IFoB IFro
- maroon-flowered	WFar
- mauve freckled, double (d)	IFro WFar
- 'Mrs Betty Ranicar' (d)	CBro EPfP GKev IFoB ILea LRHS MBri SCob
- nearly black-flowered	WFar
- 'Onyx Odyssey'	CWGN MPnt NCGa
- 'Orion'	CTal
- 'Pale Picotee'	GBuc
- pale pink-flowered	GBuc WFar
- 'Pamina'	IFoB
§ - Party Dress Group (d)	CBod CHid ELan ELon GBin IFoB LRHS LSRN NLar SCob WBor WFar
- - 'Party Dress Pink' (d)	CBod CWCL
- - 'Party Dress Primrose' (d)	CBod
- 'Pebworth White'	CTal
- 'Philip Ballard'	CTal
- Picotee Group	NLar WFar
- 'Picotee'	CLAP GBuc IFoB LHel WFar
- 'Picotee' double-flowered (d)	LHel WFar
- pink freckled, double (d)	IFro WFar
- 'Pink Lady' (Lady Series)	CBcs CBod GKev GQue IFoB LCro LOPS LRHS NEgg NGdn NPri SPer
- 'Pink Upstart'	IFoB
- pink-flowered	CLAP CLet GBuc LHel MBNS SDeJ WHoo
- pink-red-flowered	LHel WFar
- plum-flowered	CLAP GBuc MMuc SEND
- 'Pluto'	CTal WFar
- 'Pretty Ellen Pink' **new**	LCro LRHS
- 'Pretty Ellen Purple' **new**	LRHS
- 'Pretty Ellen Red' **new**	LCro
- 'Pretty Ellen White' **new**	LCro
- 'Primrose Picotee'	WFar
- primrose-flowered	CLAP ECGP ELan GBuc MCot
- 'Purity'	MAsh
- purple-flowered	CLAP SGSe WFar WHoo
- (Queen Series) 'Queen of Hearts'	ELan
- - 'Queen of Spades'	ELan
- - 'Queen of the Night'	CExl CLAP ELan EPfP IBal
- - red and purple	CBod
- 'Red Lady' (Lady Series)	CBcs CBod CExl EPfP EPot GAbr GKev IBal IFoB LCro LOPS LPfy LRHS LSRN MBNS NEgg NHol SPer
- 'Red Upstart'	IFoB
- red-flowered	CBod GBuc WFar
- 'Sirius'	CTal
- slaty blue-flowered	CBod CLAP GBuc IFoB LEdu LHel SEND
- slaty purple-flowered	GBuc
- 'Smokey Blue'	IFoB LRHS
- smokey purple-flowered	ELan LSRN MAsh SGbt
- (Spring Promise Series) SP Charlotte = 'Hlr 140' PBR **new**	LRHS

	- - SP Elly = 'Hlr 190' **new**	LRHS
	- 'Speckled Draco'	CExl
§	- spotted	CLAP EPfP GBuc GMaP IFoB NEgg WCot WFar WHoo
	- - cream	CBod CLAP IFoB NBir WFar
	- - - pink (d)	LHel WFar
	- - - white (d)	IFoB LHel WFar
	- - - yellow (d)	IFoB WFar
	- - green	CLAP WFar
	- - ivory	CLAP WFar
	- - light purple	WFar
	- - pink	CLAP CWld IFro LHel LRHS MBNS NBir SEND SHil WFar WHoo
	- - primrose	CLAP ELan SGbt WFar
	- - white	GBuc IFro LHel MMuc NBir SEND SHil WBor WFar
	- - yellow	LHel SHil WFar
	- 'Spotted Lady'	GBin
	- 'Stained Glass'	MAsh
	- Sunshine selections	IBal
	- 'Swirling Skirts'	GBin
	- 'Titania'	CTal
	- 'Tricastin'	IBoy
	- 'Tutu'PBR	EPfP GKev LBuc LRHS MBri SCob SPer SPoG SRms WHil
	- 'Ushba'	CLAP IFoB
	- Washfield double-flowered (d)	CWld EPfP SPer SRkn WRHF
	- - - white (d)	IFoB
	- 'White Lady' (Lady Series)	CBcs CBod CExl EPot IFoB MBNS NEgg NPri SPer
	- 'White Lady Spotted' (Lady Series)	CBod CHVG CLet ELon GBin GKev GQue LCro LOPS LRHS MHol NEgg NHol SPer
	- white-flowered	GBuc IFoB LHel WCFE WFar WHoo
	- white-veined	WFar
	- Wilgenbroek hybrids anemone-centred, red	SCob
	- - - white freckled	SCob
	- - apricot	SCob
	- - aubergine with white edge	SCob
	- - black	SCob
	- - dark	SCob
	- - double red (d)	SCob
	- - - slaty blue (d)	SCob
	- - - white (d)	SCob
	- - - picotee (d)	SCob
	- - - white-spotted (d)	SCob
	- - green	SCob
	- - picotee	SCob
	- - red	SCob
	- - slaty blue	SCob
	- - spotted, apricot	SCob
	- - - aubergine	SCob
	- - - pink	SCob
	- - - red	SCob
	- - - yellow	SCob
	- - white	SCob
	- - - with pink edge	SCob
	- yellow freckled, double (d)	IFro
	- 'Yellow Lady' (Lady Series)	CBcs CBod CBro CCon CTsd EPot LCro LOPS LRHS MBNS NEgg SPer
	- yellow-flowered	GMaP IFoB LHel SEND WFar WHoo
	- Zodiac Group	MBNS
	'Ice Dance' **new**	LRHS
§	'Ivory Prince'PBR	EPfP LBuc LRHS MAsh SPoG
	'Jade Star' (Winter Jewels Series)	MPnt
	'Kiwi Black Velvet'	IBal
	liguricus	CEvo MAsh
	- WM 0230	MPhe
	lividus	CBro CLAP EBee EPfP EWes GKev IFoB LHop LRHS NBir SDeJ SKHP SRms SWat
	- subsp. ***corsicus***	see *H. argutifolius*
	- 'Pink Marble' **new**	EBee
	- 'Purple Ear' **new**	EBee
	- 'Silver Edge'	EPfP
	- 'White Marble'	EBee LRHS MAsh SKHP
	- white-flowered **new**	GKev
	'Lucy Black' **new**	LRHS
	'Marlon Cream' **new**	LRHS
	'Moonshine'PBR	CLAP EBee ELon MHol NHol NLar NWad SLon WMoo
	multifidus	EPPr IFoB NBir
	- WM 1316 **new**	MPhe
	- subsp. ***hercegovinus***	CEvo SCob
	- - WM 0020	MPhe
	- - WM 0622	MPhe
	- subsp. ***istriacus***	CBro CEvo MAsh WCot
	- - WM 9322	MPhe
	- - WM 9324	MPhe
	- subsp. ***multifidus***	CEvo MAsh
	- - WM 9529	MPhe
	- - WM 9833 from Croatia	MPhe
	niger	Widely available
	- Ashwood marble leaf	MAsh
	- Ashwood strain	CLAP MAsh
	- Blackthorn Group	CLAP NLar
	- 'Christmas Carol'	LRHS
	- 'David'	IVic
	- 'Double Fashion'PBR (d)	EBee EPfP LRHS SCob
	- double-flowered (d)	MAsh
	- 'Eifelturm'	IVic
	- 'Harvington Double Petticoat' (d) **new**	ENun
	- Harvington hybrids	CLAP CRos ENun LCro LOPS LRHS MAsh MHer NPri SPoG
	- - double-flowered (d)	CRos LCro LOPS SPoG
	- 'HGC Jacob'PBR	IVic LBuc LSRN SRms
	- HGC Jacob Royal **new**	LRHS
	- HGC Joel = 'Coseh 210'PBR **new**	CRos LRHS
	- HGC Jonas = 'Coseh 220'PBR **new**	CRos LRHS
	- 'HGC Josef Lemper'PBR	IVic LRHS LSRN NLar SRms
	- 'HGC Joshua'PBR	CRos IVic LRHS
	- HGC Wintergold = 'Coseh 2010'PBR **new**	CRos LRHS
	- 'Ivory Prince'	see *H.* 'Ivory Prince'
	- marbled leaves	SCob
	- 'Marion' (d)	IFoB
	- 'Maximus'	CLAP
	- pink-flowered	MAsh
	- 'Potter's Wheel'	CLAP LRHS NBir SCob
	- 'Praecox'	EWes LRHS
	- 'Schneeball'	IVic
	- Sunset Group	SCob
	- 'White Christmas'	LRHS
	- 'Wilgenbroek Select'	SCob
	× ***nigercors***	ECha ECtt GBin GMaP LHop LPla MAsh SCob WPGP
	- double-flowered (d)	GBin LSou

- 'Emma'PBR	CBod CMea ECtt LRHS LSun MAvo MHol SCob WCot
- 'HGC Green Corsican'PBR	EBee LRHS
- HGC Ice Breaker Fancy = 'Hlr 820'PBR new	LRHS
- HGC Ice Breaker Max = 'Coseh 750'PBR new	LRHS
- HGC Ice Breaker Pico = 'Coseh 840' new	ECre
- 'Morning's Pride'PBR	EBee LRHS MMHG
- 'Pink Beauty'	NLar SCob
× ***nigristern***	see *H.* × *ericsmithii*
odorus	CEvo GCal IFoB MAsh MPhe SCob SPer XLum
- WM 0312 from Bosnia	MPhe
- WM 9415	MPhe
- WM 9728 from Hungary	MPhe
orientalis misapplied	see *H.* × *hybridus*
orientalis ambig.	CBar CTsd CWCL ECho EWTr GKev LAst MSCN MWat NPri SCob WCAu WHar WPtf
orientalis Lam.	CBcs CEvo EWes LPal LRHS LSun MPhe MSwo XLum
§ - subsp. ***abchasicus***	MAsh
§ - - Early Purple Group	CTri GCal MRav SRms
- subsp. ***guttatus*** misapplied	see *H.* × *hybridus* spotted
- subsp. ***guttatus*** (A. Braun & Sauer) B. Mathew	NChi SRkn
'Pink Beauty'PBR	CBcs EPfP LRHS MBri NLar SLon SPoG WCot
purpurascens	CEvo EPPr GBuc GMaP IFoB MAsh MRav NBir XEll
- WM 0815 from Romania	MPhe
- WM 9211 from Hungary	MPhe
- WM 9412	MPhe
(Rodney Davey Marbled Group) 'Anna's Red'	CBcs LOPS LRHS MAsh MBri SPoG WCot
- 'Penny's Pink'	CBcs CMea CMil EPfP LOPS LRHS LSRN MAsh MBri MHol SCob SPoG WCot WHil
× ***sahinii*** 'Winterbells' new	EBee WHlf
'Silver Dollar'	CBod EBee EPfP EWes LPla LRHS LSRN SHil SPer SPoG
'Snow White'	MAsh
(Spring Promise Series) 'SP Bridget' new	LRHS
- 'SP Conny' new	EPfP
- SP Mary Lou = 'Hlr 150'PBR new	LRHS
- 'SP Roxanne' new	LRHS
× ***sternii***	CBcs CRos CSpe CTri ELan ENun EPfP GKev GMaP IFro LCro LRHS MBel MNrw MWat NEgg NLar NPri SCob SPer SPoG WBrk WMoo WWtn
- Ashwood strain	MAsh NLar
- 'Beatrice le Blanc'	MAsh
- Blackthorn Group	ECre ELon EPfP EUJe IFoB LHop LRHS SWvt
- Blackthorn dwarf strain	EWTr
- 'Boughton Beauty'	CLAP ELan GBuc MAsh SCob
- pewter-flowered	CSpe ECho
- 'Tom'	SCob
- 'Wilgenbroek'	SCob
thibetanus	CCon CExl EFEx EWes GKev LAma MAsh MPhe
torquatus	CBro CEvo CTal GBuc MAsh MPhe XEll
- WM 0609 from Montenegro	MPhe
- WM 0617 from Serbia	MPhe
- WM 0620 new	MPhe
- WM 9106	GBuc MPhe
- WM 9820 from Bosnia	MPhe
- Caborn hybrids	LLWP
- 'Dido' (d)	CExl WFar
- double-flowered, from Montenegro (d) WM 0620	MPhe
- - - WM 0621 (d) new	MPhe
- hybrids	CTal IFoB
- Party Dress Group	see *H.* × *hybridus* Party Dress Group
'Verboom Beauty'	LRHS
vesicarius	MAsh
viridis	CEvo GCal GPoy IFoB LRHS MHer SCob SRms XEll XLum
- WM 0444 from Italy new	MPhe
- WM 1303 from Slovenia new	MPhe
- WM 9723 from Italy	MPhe
- subsp. ***occidentalis***	CBro CEvo
- - WM 1340 from Germany new	MPhe
- - WM 1344 from Spain new	MPhe
- - WM 9501 from Wales new	MPhe
Walberton's Rosemary = 'Walhero'PBR	CRos EPfP LRHS MAsh SPoG
'Washfield Queen' (Queen Series)	CWCL
'White Beauty'PBR	EPfP LRHS MBri NCGa NLar SCob SPer SPoG WHil

Helminthotheca (*Asteraceae*)

§ ***echioides***	WHer

Helonias (*Melanthiaceae*)

bullata	EBee GKev WCot

Heloniopsis (*Melanthiaceae*)

acutifolia	CDes
- B&SWJ 218	WCru
- B&SWJ 6817	WCru
- B&SWJ 6836	WCru
japonica	see *H. orientalis*
§ ***kawanoi***	CDes EBee GKev SKHP WCot WCru
koreana B&SWJ 4173	WCru
leucantha B&SWJ 11148	WCru
§ ***orientalis***	CBro CLAP CTal ECho GBuc GCal LLHF WCru
- B&SWJ 6278	WCru
- B&SWJ 6327	WCru
- B&SWJ 6380 from Japan	WCru
- from Japan	EBee
- from Korea	EPfP SChF SKHP
- var. ***breviscapa***	EBee EPfP LEdu SChF SMad WCru
- - B&SWJ 5635	WCru
- - B&SWJ 5873	WCru
- - B&SWJ 5938	WCru
- - 'A-so'	LEdu WCru
- 'Dark Single' new	GEdr
- var. ***flavida*** B&SWJ 11400	CTal WCru

- - 'Snow White' **new**	GEdr
- variegated (v)	WCru
- var. ***yakusimensis***	see *H. kawanoi*
tubiflora B&SWJ 822	WCot WCru
- 'Temple Blue'	CDes CLAP WCru
umbellata	CTal EBee EPfP LHop SKHP WMoo WSHC
- B&SWJ 1839	CLAP WCru
- B&SWJ 3732	CBct WCru
- B&SWJ 6836	WCru
- B&SWJ 6846	WCru
- B&SWJ 7117	WCru

Helwingia (*Helwingiaceae*)

chinensis	EBee ESwi EWld NLar SBrt SSpi WBor WPGP
- broad-leaved	EBee NLar SChF WPGP
- narrow-leaved	EBee ESwi
himalaica	CExl CFil ESwi SBrt WPGP
- broad-leaved	WPGP
- narrow-leaved	WPGP
japonica	CHGN EFEx NLar
- broad-leaved	WPGP
- narrow-leaved	WPGP

Helxine see *Soleirolia*

Hemerocallis ✿ (*Hemerocallidaceae*)

from Gansu	MPhe
'A Special Lady'	EStr
'Aabaa'	EWoo
'Aabachee'	CBgR
'Above the Clouds'	EWoo
'Absolute Treasure'	CFwr EStr
'Absolute Zero'	SDay SPol
'Adah'	SDay
'Adamas'	CFwr
'Addie Branch Smith'	SDay
'Adeline Goldner'	CFwr
'Adirondack Trust' **new**	CFwr
'Admiral's Braid'	EWoo
'Adorable Tiger'	CFwr
'Adoration'	SPer
'Africa'	SPol
'African Chant'	ELan
'Age of Miracles'	SPol
'Ageless Beauty'	EStr
'Agnes Elpers'	WAul
'Ahoya'	CBgR SPol
'Airs and Graces'	SDay
'Alabama Jubilee'	WNHG
'Alabama Wildfire'	CFwr
'Alakazam'	EWoo
'Alan'	EAEE ECtt LRHS MRav
'Alan Adair'	SDay
'Alaqua'	CCon GBuc MBNS
'Alberene'	CFwr
'Alec Allen'	SDay
'Alexander the Great'	WHrl
'Alien Encounter'	SPol
'All American Baby'	CWat MBNS MSpe SPol
'All American Chief' 🏆H6	EStr
'All American Eagle'	SPol
'All American Magic'	SPol
'All American Plum'	CWCL IBoy MBNS MSpe SPol WAul WHrl
'All American Tiger'	EStr MSpe SDay
'All American Windmill'	CBgR CFwr EStr EWoo
'All Creation Sings'	CFwr
'All Fired Up'	EStr SDay SPol
'All I Want for Christmas'	CFwr
'Allegiance'	WNHG
'Alli Sheldon'	ECha
'Alluring Peach' **new**	EStr
'Almost Paradise'	SPol
'Alpine Mist'	SDay
'Alpine Rhapsody'	SPol
'Alternate Universe'	CFwr
altissima	LPla MNrw SDix SPhx XSen
'Always Afternoon' 🏆H6	CBgR CKel EStr EWoo GBuc MBNS MNrw SGSe SPol WCAu WHrl WWEG XSen
'Amadeus'	EStr GBuc SCob
'Amazon Amethyst'	WCAu
'Ambassador'	CBgR
'Amber Classic'	ELon
'American Freedom'	EWoo
'American Revolution'	CBgR CBod CPar ELon EStr EWoo GBin IPot MBNS MHol MWat MWhi NChi SDys SPol WAul WCot WHrl WMoo WPnP XLum XSen
'America's Most Wanted'	EStr
'Amerstone Amethyst Jewel'	SPol
'Amethyst Island'	CFwr
'Amethyst Squid'	EWoo
'Among Us'	CFwr
'Amy'	WWEG
'Amy Michelle' (d) **new**	EStr
'Anatomically Correct'	EWoo
'Andrew Christian'	SPol
'Android'	CFwr
'Andy Warhol's Hair' **new**	CFwr
'Angel Artistry'	SDay
'Angel Rodgers'	EStr
'Aniakchak'	EWoo
'Anna Warner'	ELon MMuc SEND
'Annabelle's Ghost'	CBgR SPol
'Annie Welch'	ELon EPfP MBNS NBre
'Answering Angels'	CFwr
'Antarctica'	SPol
'Antique Lavender' **new**	WCAu
'Antique Rose'	CKel EStr
'Anzac'	CTsd ECha ECtt EStr IBoy LRHS MBNS NGdn SGol SWvt WMoo
'Apache Bandana'	EWoo
'Apache Beacon'	EWoo
'Apollo'	XSen
'Apple Court Chablis'	EStr SPol
'Apple Court Champagne'	SPol
'Apple Court Damson'	EStr SPol
'Apple Court Ruby'	SPol
'Apple Of My Eye'	EWoo
'Apple Swirl'	CFwr EStr SPol
'Apple Tart'	SDay
'Applique'	CFwr
'Après Moi'	MBNS NLar
'Apricot Beauty' (d)	MBNS SGol
'Apricot Velvet'	CBgR
'Apricotta'	WCot WPnP
'April Fools' **new**	EStr
'Apron Strings'	CFwr
'Aquamarine'	SDay
'Aquarelle' **new**	EStr
'Arachnephobia'	EWoo
'Arctic Snow' 🏆H6	CBgR CBro CMac ECrc ECtt ELon EStr EWoo GKev LRHS MBNS MNrw SCob SPol WAul WPnP
'Armed and Dangerous'	CFwr

'Arms to Heaven'	EWoo
'Arpeggio'	EStr SDay
'Arriba'	NBro
'Art Gallery Quilling' **new**	EStr
'Arthur Moore'	SDay
'As You Wish'	CFwr
'Asian Artistry'	WNHG
'Asiatic Pheasant'	SPol
'Asterisk' ♀H6	EStr SDay
'Astolat'	EBee
'Astral Voyager'	CFwr
'Aten'	CBgR SDay
'Athlone'	EWoo
'Atlanta Bouquet'	SDay
'Atlanta Cover Girl'	SDay
'Atlanta Fringe Benefit'	SDay
'August Frost' ♀H6	EStr SDay SPol
'August Morn'	CBgR
'Aunt Wimp'	EWoo
'Authur Vincent'	SPol
'Autumn Jewels'	CFwr EWoo SPol
'Autumn Minaret'	EStr EWoo SGSe
'Autumn Prince'	EWoo
'Autumn Red'	CBcs CBgR EStr GKin MBNS MBri MMuc MNrw NBir SEND SPol WCot
'Autumn Wood'	CFwr
'Ava Michelle'	SDay
'Avant Garde'	EStr SPol WCAu
'Avon Crystal Rose'	WNHG
'Awakening Spirit' **new**	CFwr
'Awash With Color'	EStr
'Awesome Blossom'	EStr LSou MBNS MNrw SPol
'Awesome Candy'	EStr EWoo LSRN
'Aztec Firebird'	CFwr EStr EWoo
'Aztec Furnace'	CBro EStr SDay
'Aztec Gold' **new**	EStr
'Baby Betsy'	EStr
'Baby Blues'	SDay SPol
'Baby Darling'	SDay
'Baby Red Eyes'	WFar
'Baby Talk'	CCon
'Baja'	WFar
'Bald Eagle'	EStr MNrw WWEG
'Bali Hai'	EStr MBNS SRms WHrl
'Ballerina Girl'	EStr
'Bam'	EStr
'Bama Bound' **new**	EStr
'Bamboo Blackie'	CBgR EWoo SPol XSen
'Banana Cream Beauty'	SDeJ
'Banana Glow' **new**	SGSe
'Banana Man'	EStr
'Banbury Cinnamon'	MBNS
'Bandit Man' **new**	EStr
'Bangkok Belle'	CWat
'Banned in Boston'	EWoo
'Baracuda Bay' **new**	EStr
'Barbara Dittmer'	SPol
'Barbara Mitchell'	EStr EWoo GBuc MBNS SDay SDeJ WCAu WNHG XSen
'Barbaresco'	SPol
'Barbarian Princess'	CFwr
'Barbary Corsair'	EStr SDay
'Bark At Me'	CFwr
'Barnegat Orange Twister'	CFwr
'Baronet's Badge'	SPol
'Baroni'	ECha
'Bat Signal'	EWoo SPol
'Bathsheba'	SPol
'Bea'	EStr
'Beat the Barons'	SPol
'Beautiful Edgings'	EStr SPol
'Beauty to Behold' ♀H6	SDay
'Becky Lynn'	ECtt EStr MBNS
'Before Night Falls'	CFwr
'Beijing'	SDay
'Bela Lugosi'	CBgR CMac CWat ECrc ELon EPfP EStr EWoo GQue LRHS LSRN LSun MBNS MCot MNrw MWat MWhi NBro NEgg NQui SCob SDay SMad SPer SPol WCAu WCot WHrl WNHG
'Believe It'	WNHG
'Ben Adams'	SDay
'Ben Webster'	CFwr
'Benchmark'	SDay WHrl
'Bengal Bay'	EWoo
'Bengal Fire'	WNHG
'Berlin Oxblood'	WAul
'Berlin Red'	CBod CWCL ECha GBee GKin MNrw SDay WFar
'Berlin Tallboy'	SDay WAul
'Berlin Watermelon'	MBNS
'Berliner Premiere'	EStr
'Berry Blitz'	EStr
'Berrylicious'	EPfP
'Bertie Ferris'	EStr EWoo NLar SDay
'Beside Myself'	CFwr
'Bess Ross'	CMHG XSen
'Bess Vestal'	MWat
'Best Kept Secret'	EWoo SPol
'Best Seller' **new**	EStr WCAu
'Bette Davis Eyes'	CBgR CWat EStr SDay SPol
'Betts Allen' **new**	EStr
'Betty Jenkins'	EStr
'Betty Warren Woods'	SDay
'Betty Woods' (d)	SDay
'Bettylen' **new**	EStr
'Betty's Pick'	EWoo
'Beware the Wizard'	CFwr
'Bicolor Beautiful' **new**	CFwr
'Big Apple'	SDay SPol
'Big Bird'	EStr EWoo LSRN MBNS SDay
'Big Blue'	EStr
'Big City Eye'	MBNS
'Big Golden'	WWEG
'Big Kiss' (d)	SPol
'Big Ross'	CFwr
'Big Smile'	CWGN MBNS MNrw NBro SDeJ WFar
'Big Snowbird'	SDay
'Big Time Happy'	LRHS MBNS SPoG STPC
'Big World'	CBgR
'Bigcabin Neon Beacon'	CFwr
'Bill Norris'	SDay SPol
'Bird Bath Pink'	SPol
'Birdwing Butterfly'	SPol
'Bite the Bullet'	CFwr
'Bitsy'	ELon SCob WCot WMnd WRHF WWEG
'Black Adder'	SDay
'Black Ambrosia'	EStr SDay SPol
'Black Arrowhead'	CFwr EStr SPol WCAu
'Black Emanuelle'	CExl IKil LAst LSun MBNS MNrw NLar
'Black Eye'	SDay WNHG
'Black Eyed Stella'	CKel MBNS WCot
'Black Eyed Susan'	ECtt EStr MBNS
'Black Falcon'	SGSe

'Black Falcon Ritual'	CFwr
'Black Friar'	EWoo
'Black Ice'	EWoo SPol
'Black Knight'	EWoo NLar SRms
'Black Magic'	CBod CBro CTri CWat EAEE ELan EPfP EStr GKin GMaP LHop LRHS LSRN MHer MRav MWhi NBir NEgg NGdn SGSe SPer WHer WHrl WMoo WNHG
'Black Plush'	EStr EWoo SGSe SPol
'Black Prince'	CBgR CCon EShb EStr EWoo IBoy MBNS NBre NBro WAul
'Black Stockings'	EBee EStr EWes IPot MWhi SCob SDeJ
'Blackberries and Cream'	EStr
'Blackberry Candy'	CSam EAEE ECtt EStr GKin MBNS MNrw MSpe NHol NWad SDay
'Blackberry Sherbert'	WFar
'Blackeye Belle'	EWoo
'Blessed Again'	SDay
'Blessing'	EStr SPol
'Blizzard Bay'	EStr SDay SPol
'Blonde is Beautiful'	SDay
'Blue Beat'	CFwr
'Blue Diana'	EStr
'Blue Happiness'	SDay
'Blue Sheen'	CBgR CCon CMac ECtt GMaP MBNS WFar WMoo WRHF
'Blueberries and Cream' **new**	EStr
'Blueberry Candy'	ECtt EStr IBoy ILea MBNS
'Blueberry Cream'	ELon EStr MBNS MMHG MNrw
'Blueberry Frost'	CBgR
'Blueberry Sundae'	CWat EBee ELon SGol
'Blue-eyed Butterfly'	SPol
'Blushing Angel'	SDay
'Blushing Belle'	MBNS NBro NEgg
'Blutorange'	CFwr
'Bobby Martin'	CFwr
'Bobby's Lavender Eyes'	EStr
'Bobo Anne'	CWat EStr
'Body Rub'	CFwr
'Bogie and Becall'	SPol
'Bold Courtier'	CBgR EStr
'Bold One'	CMHG SPol
'Bold Ruler'	SPol
'Bonanza'	Widely available
'Bone China' **new**	WNHG
'Boney Maroney'	CBgR CFwr EWoo
'Bonnie Boy'	XLum XSen
'Bonnie Holley'	CFwr
'Booger'	SDay
'Boogie my Woogie Baby'	CFwr EWoo
'Booroobin Magic'	EStr EWoo
'Border Baby'	ECtt
'Border Lord'	EStr EWoo
'Border Music' **new**	EStr
'Borgia Queen' **new**	EStr
'Both Sides Now'	ECtt
'Boulderbrook Serenity'	SDay
'Bourbon Kings'	EStr MBNS MSpe SDeJ WHrl WWtn
'Bowl of Roses'	EStr
'Bradley Bernard'	SPol
'Brand New Lover'	SDay
'Brass Buckles'	see *H.* 'Puddin'
'Brasstown'	SPol
'Brazilian Orange'	XSen
'Breed Apart'	CFwr SPol
'Brenda Newbold'	EStr SDay SPol
'Brer Rabbit's Baby'	EWoo
'Bridget'	ELan
'Bright Beacon'	SDay SPol
'Bright Island'	XSen
'Bright Side'	CBgR
'Bright Spangles'	MSpe SDay SGSe WAul
'Brilliant Circle'	ECtt
'Bring It On'	CFwr
'Broadway Bold Eyes'	SPol
'Broadway Valentine'	XSen
'Brocaded Gown'	ELan SDay
'Brooklyn Twist'	EStr
'Brother Cal'	CFwr
'Brown Billows'	EWoo
'Brown Exotica'	CFwr
'Brown Witch'	EWoo
'Brown-Eyed Girl'	SPol
'Bruce'	EStr
'Brushed with Bronze'	SPol
'Brutus'	WHrl
'Bubbling Brown Sugar'	EStr MSpe
'Bubbly'	SDay
'Bud Producer'	CBgR SPol
'Buenos Aires'	XSen
'Buffys Doll'	EStr MBNS SDay
'Bugs Ear'	SDay
'Bug's Hug'	EStr
'Bumble Bee'	CWat ECtt EStr MBNS NBre SDay
'Bumble Bee Boogie'	CFwr
'Bunny Puff'	EStr
'Burgundy Baroness'	EStr
'Burlesque'	SDay SPol WCot
'Burning Daylight' ℽH7	CAby CBgR EAEE EBee ECtt EPfP EStr LRHS MNrw MRav NEgg SCob SGol SPer SRms WAul WCAu WCFE WCot WFar WPtf
'Burnished Ruffles' **new**	EStr
'Bus Stop'	SPol
'Buster Ruster'	CFwr
'Buttercup Parade'	EStr
'Butterfly Charm'	CWat SDay
'Butterpat'	SDay
'Butterscotch'	WFar
'Butterscotch Ruffles'	SDay
'Buzz Bomb'	ECGP ECrc ECtt EStr GBee GKin LRHS LSRN MBNS MCot NEgg NGdn SPer WFar WWEG
'By Myself'	XSen
'Caballero'	EStr
'Cabbage Flower'	SDay XSen
'Cabriolet'	XSen
'Cajun Gambler' **new**	EStr
'Cake Plate'	CFwr
'Calgary Stampede' **new**	EStr
'Calico Jack'	EStr SPad
'Calico Spider'	EStr SPol XSen
'California Sunshine'	SPol
'Caliph's Robes' **new**	SDay
'Call Girl'	SDay
'Calypso'	EWoo
'Camden Ballerina'	SDay
'Camden Gold Dollar'	SDay
'Camelot Green'	WNHG
'Cameroons'	SGSe SPol
'Campfire Embers'	EStr

'Canadian Border Patrol'	EStr IPot MBNS MNrw NLar SPer SPol WHrl
'Canary Chaos' **new**	EStr
'Canary Glow'	CTri IBoy
'Canary Wings'	CBgR
'Candide'	SDay
'Candied Popcorn Perfection'	CFwr
'Candor'	SDay
'Candy Cane Dreams'	CFwr
'Candy Gram'	EStr
'Canopy of Heaven' **new**	SPol
'Cantique'	SDay SPol
'Cape Breton' **new**	EBee EStr
'Capernaum Cocktail'	SPol
'Capulina'	EWoo
'Cara Mia'	CBgR EStr MBNS NBir SPol
'Caramba'	CBgR
'Cardinal Explosion' **new**	CFwr
'Caribbean Jack Dolan'	EWoo
'Caribbean Purple Spires' **new**	EStr
'Carlotta'	SDay
'Carmen Marie'	XSen
'Carmine Monarch'	EStr
'Carnival in Mexico'	CFwr
'Carnival Mask'	CFwr
'Carolicolossal'	ELon SDay SPol
'Carolina Cranberry'	ELan
'Carolina Dynamite'	CFwr
'Carolina Low Country'	CFwr
'Carolina Red Bug'	CFwr
'Caroline Taylor'	WHrl
'Carousel Princess'	LRHS
'Carrick Wildon'	CFwr EBee
'Carrot'	SDay
'Cartwheels'	EAEE ECha EPfP EShb EStr GBuc GKin GMaP LRHS MBNS MBel MRav MSpe NBro SPer WCAu WMoo
'Carved Initials'	CFwr
'Carved Pumpkin Pie'	CFwr
'Casa des Juan'	CFwr
'Castile'	SDay
'Castle Pinkney'	CFwr
'Castle Strawberry Delight'	SPol
'Cat Dancer' ♀H6 **new**	EStr
'Catapult Sam'	CFwr
'Catch a Falling Star'	CFwr
'Catherine Neal'	EStr SDay SPol
'Catherine Woodbery'	Widely available
'Cathy Cute Legs'	CFwr
'Cathy's Sunset'	CKel CSam ECtt GKin LRHS LSRN MBNS MSpe MWat NBro NGdn NWad SRGP
'Cat's Cradle'	SDay
'Cause for Pause'	EStr
'Caviar'	SDay
'Cayenne' ♀H6	SPol
'Cedar Waxwing'	MNrw
'Celery Plate'	CFwr
'Celestial City'	SDay
'Celtic Christmas'	CFwr SPol
'Cenla Crepe Myrtle'	EWoo
'Cerulean Star'	EWoo SPol
'Cerulean Warbler' **new**	EStr
'Challenger'	EWoo
'Chamonix'	XSen
'Chance Encounter'	EStr MBNS NHol SPol WCAu
'Chang Dynasty'	CFwr
'Changing Latitudes'	SPol WHrl
'Chantilly' **new**	EStr
'Charlene Moore'	SPol
'Charles Johnston'	CBgR CKel EPfP EStr EWoo MBNS SDay
'Charlie Pierce Memorial'	EStr SDay SPol
'Charon the Ferryman'	CFwr SPol
'Chartreuse Magic'	CMHG
'Chartwell'	EWoo
'Chasing the Sun'	CFwr
'Château Lafite'	SPol
'Checkerboard Curls'	CFwr
'Cheerful Note'	WNHG
'Cherokee Mary' (d)	EStr
'Cherokee Patterns'	SPol
'Cherokee Star' **new**	EStr
'Cherokee Vision'	CFwr
'Cherry Candy'	MSpe
'Cherry Cheeks'	CCon ECtt ELan ELon EStr LRHS MBNS MHol MNrw MRav SPol WCAu WCot WMoo WWEG WWtn
'Cherry Eyed Pumpkin' ♀H6	EStr EWoo SDay SPol WCAu
'Cherry Kiss'	IVic
'Cherry Lace'	XSen
'Cherry Tiger'	EStr MBNS
'Cherry Valentine'	CBcs MBNS SPad
'Cherrystone' **new**	EStr
'Chesapeake Crablegs'	CFwr
'Chesières Lunar Moth'	CBgR ELon SPol
'Chesnut Lane'	SDay
'Chester Cyclone'	SDay
'Chevron Spider'	EStr
'Chicago Antique Tapestry'	SDay
'Chicago Apache'	CCon EBee ELon EPfP EWoo MBNS NBir SPer SPol WWEG
'Chicago Aztec'	ELon
'Chicago Blackout'	CCon CWat ECtt EStr WAul WCot
'Chicago Cardinal'	EStr
'Chicago Cattleya'	CCon
'Chicago Cherry'	WNHG
'Chicago Fire'	EBee EPfP MBNS SDay
'Chicago Firecracker'	XLum XSen
'Chicago Heirloom'	CCon MBNS WCAu
'Chicago Jewel'	CCon ELon NSti
'Chicago Knobby'	EBee EStr MBNS MNrw SDay
'Chicago Knockout'	CCon ELan EPfP EWoo SPer WAul WWEG
'Chicago Mist'	WNHG
'Chicago Peach'	NBir WCAu
'Chicago Picotee Lace'	WWEG
'Chicago Picotee Memories'	EBee MBNS
'Chicago Picotee Promise'	WNHG
'Chicago Princess'	EWoo
'Chicago Queen'	SDay WMnd WNHG
'Chicago Rainbow'	CBgR MBNS
'Chicago Royal Crown'	EAEE ECtt
'Chicago Royal Robe'	CWCL CWat ELon MBNS NBid SPer SRms SWat WCot WWtn
'Chicago Silver'	CCon MBNS WAul
'Chicago Star'	WNHG
'Chicago Sugarplum'	SDay
'Chicago Sunrise'	CBgR EAEE GMaP IBoy LRHS MBNS MRav NGdn SDay SPol SWvt WCot WWEG

'Chief Four Fingers'	EWoo
'Chief Sequoia'	EStr
'Children's Festival'	CMac EAEE ECtt EStr GMaP LRHS MBNS MRav NLar SGSe SWvt WMoo
'China Bride'	EStr EWoo SCob SPol
'Chinese Autumn'	EStr
'Chinese Cloisonne'	EStr
'Chinese Coral'	EWoo
'Chinese Imp'	NLar SDay
'Chinese New Year' **new**	EStr
'Chinese Temple Flower' **new**	SDay
'Chireno'	EStr
'Chocolate Candy'	CWGN EPfP IPot MBNS
'Choctaw Chick'	CFwr
'Chokecherry Mountain'	EStr EWoo
'Chorus Line'	EStr SDay SPol WNHG
'Chorus Line Kid'	SPol
'Christina's Pink Parasol'	EStr
'Christine Lynn'	WNHG
'Christine Walser-Hite'	CFwr
'Christmas in Oz' **new**	CFwr
'Christmas Is'	CBgR CMac CWGN EAEE EBee ECtt ELon EStr GBin GKin LPot LRHS LSou MBNS MBel MNrw NCGa NHol SDay SPol WAul WCot WHrl WWEG XSen
'Christmas Wishes' **new**	EStr
'Church and Wellesley' (d)	CFwr
'Ciara Marie'	CFwr
'Ciarra Vonnie'	SDay
'Cimarron Knight'	CBgR EWoo SPol WCAu
'Cinderella Sue'	CFwr
'Cindy's Eye'	WCot
'Cinnamon Sunrise' **new**	EStr
'Circle of Beauty'	SPol
'Circle of Friends' **new**	CFwr
citrina ♀H6	CBgR CExl CHid CMac EBee EWoo GKev GQue IBoy IMou LRHS MCot WCot WHrl WRHF XLum XSen
citrina × (× ***ochroleuca***)	WCot
'Civil Law'	SDay
'Civil Rights'	SDay
'Classic Caper'	WNHG
'Claudine'	ELon
'Cleo'	EWoo
'Cleopatra'	ELon EWoo SDay SPol
'Clothed in Glory'	EStr EWoo MBNS WCot WWEG
'Coach's Hot Lips'	CFwr
'Coburg Fright Wig'	EWoo
'Cocktail Party'	EStr
'Colonel Joe'	EWoo
'Color Flash' **new**	CFwr
'Color Stick'	EStr
'Comanche Eyes'	SDay
'Comet Flash'	SPol
'Coming Up Roses'	ELon
'Concorde Nelson'	CFwr
'Condilla' (d) ♀H6	EStr SDay SPol
'Connie Abel'	CFwr
'Connie Can't Have It'	CFwr
'Conspicua'	CBgR SMHy SPol
'Contessa'	CBro EAEE GBin LRHS
'Cool and Crepy'	EStr
'Cool It'	CKel LHop MBNS MPie NLar SCob SDeJ WHrl
'Cool Jazz'	SDay SPol
'Cool Summer Breeze'	SPol
'Copper Dawn'	EStr NChi SPol
'Copper Windmill'	CBgR ELon EStr SDay SPol
'Copperhead'	EStr SPol
'Copperhead Road'	CFwr
'Coral Crab'	EWoo
'Coral Eye Shadow'	EWoo
'Coral Mist'	ECrc MBNS NBre
'Coral Sparkler'	WNHG
'Coral Spider'	SPol
'Corky'	Widely available
'Corolla Light'	CFwr
'Corryton Pink'	SPol
'Cosmic Hummingbird'	ECtt EStr LRHS SDay
'Cosmopolitan'	ILea MBNS
'Country Club'	EBee GMaP MBNS SPol WWEG
'Country Melody'	SDay
'Court Magician'	EStr EWoo
'Court Troubadour'	SPol
'Coyote Moon'	EStr SDay
'Craig Green'	CFwr
'Cranberry Baby'	ECtt EStr LRHS WHoo WNHG
'Cranberry Coulis'	CWat MBNS
'Crawleycrow'	XSen
'Crazy Crane'	CFwr
'Crazy Larry'	EStr
'Crazy Pierre'	EWoo SPol WHrl XSen
'Cream Drop'	COtt CPrp ECtt EPPr GBuc GMaP IBoy LRHS MCot MHer MRav NBro NGdn NLar NSti SCob WAul WCot WHrl WMoo
'Cream Sundae' **new**	SGSe
'Creation'	CFwr EWoo
'Cricket Call'	CFwr
'Crimson Flood'	EWoo
'Crimson Icon'	SDay
'Crimson Pirate'	Widely available
'Crimson Wind'	EStr
'Crintonic Shadowlands'	SPol
'Cripple Creek'	CFwr EStr EWoo
'Croesus'	SRms
'Crooked House'	CFwr
'Cruise Control' **new**	SPol
'Crystal Cupid'	XSen
'Crystal Pinot'	ELon EStr
'Cupid's Gold'	SDay
'Curls'	CBgR MBNS SDay
'Curly Brick Road'	SPol
'Curly Cinnamon Windmill' ♀H6	EStr SDay SPol
'Curly Rosy Posy'	EStr SDay
'Custard Candy' ♀H6	CWCL CWGN ECtt EStr EWoo GKin MBNS NHol WCAu WNHG
'Cute As Can Be'	EStr
'Cynthia Mary'	ECtt GKin LHop MBNS NBro SRGP
'Cypriana'	EBee XSen
'D.R. McKeithan'	CFwr
'Daddeeo Segrest' **new**	EStr
'Dad's Best White'	EStr
'Daily Dollar'	MBNS MSpe NGdn
'Dainty Pink'	WWtn
'Dallas Spider Time'	SDay
'Dallas Star'	EStr SDay SPol WHrl
'Dan Mahony'	EStr MBNS
'Dan Tau'	CKel SDay
'Dance Among the Stars'	CFwr
'Dance Ballerina Dance'	EBee SDay
'Dancing Crab'	CBgR EWoo SPol
'Dancing Lions'	SDay

'Dancing Shiva'	SDay SPol
'Dancing Summerbird'	ELon SPol
'Daring Deception'	CCon CKel ECtt ELon EPfP EStr IPot MBNS MNrw SCob SPad
'Daring Dilemma'	EStr SPol
'Daring Reflection'	SDay
'Darius'	WNHG
'Dark and Handsome'	MBNS
'Dark Avenger'	MBNS
'Dark Elf'	SDay
'Dark Magician' **new**	EStr
'Dark Monkey'	CFwr
'Darker Shade'	EStr
'Darrell'	SDay
'Date Book'	EWoo
'David Holman'	WNHG
'David Kirchhoff'	EStr
'Davidson Update'	WNHG
'Dazzling Spider'	CFwr
'De Colores'	EStr
'Dean Corey'	CFwr
'Debary Canary'	EWoo
'Debussy'	EStr EWoo
'Decatur Ballerina'	WNHG
'Decatur Captivation'	WNHG
'Decatur Dictator'	WNHG
'Decatur Elevator'	EWoo
'Decatur Imp'	SDay WHrl
'Decatur Jewel'	WNHG
'Decatur Piecrust' **new**	EStr
'Decatur Rhythm'	WNHG
'Decatur Supreme'	WNHG
'Decatur Treasure Chest'	WNHG
'Deep in My Heart'	CFwr
'Delayed Arrival' **new**	CFwr
'Delicate Design'	SPol
'Delightsome'	SDay
'Deloris Gould'	SDay
'Demetrius'	CWat EStr
'Derrick Cane'	SPol
'Desdemona'	EStr SPol XLum
'Desert Dreams'	WCot
'Desert Icicle'	EStr EWoo SPol
'Designer Gown'	EStr SDay
'Designer Jeans'	EStr SDay SPol
'Designer Rhythm' **new**	EStr
'Desirable Duchess' **new**	EStr
'Destination Y'	XSen
'Destined to See'	CBcs CBro CCon CPar ECtt ELon EStr IPot LHop LRHS LSRN LSou MBNS MHol MNrw NBir NBro NEgg SPad SPer SPol WCot WHrl
'Devil's Footprint'	SPol
'Devon Cream'	SPer
'Devonshire'	EStr SDay
'Diabolique'	EWoo
'Diamond Dust'	CKel ECtt MBNS NLar SPer
'Diamonds and Ringlets'	CFwr
'Diana Grenfell'	CBgR
'Dick Kitchingman'	CBgR SPol
'Dido'	CTri
'Dipped in Ink'	EStr SPol
'Distant Galaxy' **new**	WCAu
'Distant Star'	EWoo
'Diva's Choice' **new**	SCob
'Divertissment'	CBgR ELon EWoo SDay WHrl
'Dixie Rooster'	CFwr
'Dizzy Miss Lizzy'	CFwr
'Do the Twist'	EWoo
'Do You Know Doris'	SDay
'Doc Holliday'	EStr
'Dominic'	CBgR CPar EWoo IBoy MSpe SDay SGSe SPol WCot WMoo
'Don Stevens'	WHrl
'Don's Wild Heather'	EStr
'Don't Know Jack'	CFwr
'Don't Mess with Me'	CFwr
'Dooty Owl'	CFwr
'Dorethe Louise'	CBgR SDay SPol
'Dorothy McDade'	EWoo MNrw
'Dot Paul'	ELan
'Double Action' (d)	SDay SPol
'Double Bold One' (d)	SPol
'Double Charm' (d)	XSen
'Double Coffee' (d)	SPol
'Double Corsage' (d)	SPol
'Double Cream' (d)	WCot
'Double Cutie' (d)	EStr NLar SDay SRms
'Double Delicious' (d)	WCot
'Double Doubloon' (d)	XLum
'Double Dream' (d)	CWld EStr WHrl
'Double Firecracker' (d)	EBee MBNS MSpe NBro NLar XSen
'Double Glitter' (d)	XSen
'Double Oh Seven' (d)	ELon SPol
'Double Passion' (d)	MBNS
'Double Pompon' (d)	EStr
'Double Pop Art' (d)	XSen
'Double Red Royal' (d)	EPfP XSen
'Double River Wye' (d)	CBgR CCon CWat ECtt EShb EStr GBin IBoy LRHS MBNS MHer MNrw NGdn SPol SWat WAul WBrk WCot WHoo WHrl WMnd WWEG
§ 'Doubloon' (d)	SGSe
'Dowager Queen'	WNHG
'Dragon Dreams'	SPol
'Dragon Heart'	EWoo
'Dragon King'	SDay SPol
'Dragon Lore'	EPfP MBNS
'Dragon's Eye'	CWat EWoo SDay SPol WNHG
'Dragon's Orb'	CKel SDay
'Dream Baby'	NBre
'Dream Catcher'	CFwr EWoo
'Dream Keeper'	CFwr EWoo
'Dream Legacy'	EStr
'Dresden Doll'	SPer
'Droopy Drawers'	SPol
'Drop Cloth'	EStr
'Druid's Chant'	EWoo
'Drunken Sailor' **new**	CFwr
'Duke of Durham'	EWoo MBNS MSpe
'Duke of Earl'	CBgR
dumortieri	CAgr CBro EBee ECha ELan MCoo MCot MMuc MRav NBid NBir NSti SEND SPer WCot WHrl WWEG WWtn XSen
- B&SWJ 1283	WCru
'Dumpy'	EStr
'Dune Buggy'	XSen
'Dune Needlepoint'	SPol WHrl
'Duplex' (d)	XSen
'Dutch Art'	SDay
'Dutch Gold'	MNrw
'Earl of Warwick'	CBgR SPol
'Earlianna'	EStr SPol
'Earnest Yearwood'	SDay
'Earth Angel'	SPol
'Earth Fire'	SDay

'Easter Star'	CFwr
'Easy Ned'	ELon EWoo SPol
'Easy Street'	SDay
'Eat Our Wake Pintaheads'	CFwr
'Ed Kirchhoff'	XLum
'Ed Murray'	EStr SDay WAul WCAu WHrl
'Edgar Brown'	MBNS SPol WCot
'Edge Ahead'	CMac EAEE ECtt EStr GKin LRHS MBNS NHol SDay WCAu WHrl
'Edge of Darkness'	CKel CWGN EPfP MBNS NBro NLar NSti
'Edge of Frenzy'	CFwr
'Edge of Heaven'	EStr
'Edith Vaughan'	EStr
'Edna Selman'	CFwr
'Edna Spalding'	EAEE LRHS SDay
'Eenie Allegro'	CBro ECtt MBNS SPer WMnd
'Eenie Fanfare'	MBNS NBir WWEG
'Eenie Weenie'	CBro ECtt ELon GKev IBoy MBNS NBro SRms WOut WWEG WWtn
'Eenie Weenie Non-stop'	ECha EPPr
'Eggplant Electricity'	EWoo
'Eggplant Escapade' ♀H6	CBgR EStr MSpe SDay SPol
'Egyptian Ibis'	EStr EWoo MSpe SPol WMnd WNHG
'Egyptian Queen'	CBgR
'Eight Miles High'	EStr
'Eighteen Karat'	EStr
'Einstein'	CFwr
'El Desperado'	CBgR CPar CSam ECtt ELon EPfP EStr EWoo GBin GBuc IPot LRHS LSRN LSun MBNS MHol MLHP MNrw NEgg SPav SPol WCAu WCFE WCot WWEG
'El Glorioso'	CWat EStr
'Elaine Farrant'	SDay
'Elaine Strutt'	MBNS MNrw SDay SWvt WCot
'Electric Shocker' **new**	CFwr
'Elegant Candy' ♀H6	CBgR CKel CMac EStr EWoo MBNS
I 'Elegantissima'	SPol
'Eleonor'	EBee EPfP MBNS
'Elfin Daydream'	SPol
'Elf's Cap'	SDay
'Elijah Sain'	SPol
'Elizabeth Anne Hudson'	SDay
'Elizabeth Case' **new**	EStr
'Elizabeth Salter'	CWCL EStr MBNS NLar SPol
'Elmore James'	EWoo
'Eloquent Cay'	CFwr
'Eloquent Silence'	SDay
'Elva White Grow'	SDay
'Elves' Watermark'	SPol
'Emerald Dew'	SDay
'Emerald Eye'	EStr SDay
'Emerald Lady'	SPol
'Emily Anne'	SPol
'Emily's Fiery Horse'	CFwr
'Emperor's Choice'	SDay
'Emperor's Dragon'	EStr SDay
'Enchanted April'	SPol
'Enchanted Forest'	EStr WCAu
'Enchanter's Spell'	SDay
'Enchanting Blessing'	EStr SDay
'Energizer Ty Howard'	CFwr
'English Cameo'	SPol
'Enigma Variations'	SPol
'Entransette'	SDay
'Entrapment'	ECtt EStr IBoy MBNS SDeJ
'Envoyé Spécial'	XSen
'Envy Me'	SPol
'Erica Nichole Gonzales'	SDay
'Erin Prairie'	EStr SPol
'Etched Eyes'	EWoo SPol
'Eternal Blessing'	SPol
'Eternity Road'	EStr
'Etruscan Tomb'	EStr SPol
'Evelyn Claar'	CMac
'Evelyn Lela Stout'	SDay
'Even Stephen'	SPol
'Evening Enchantment'	EStr
'Evening Gown'	SPol
'Ever So Ruffled'	EStr SDay
'Exotic Candy'	SPol
'Exotic Design'	CFwr
'Exotic Love'	SDay
'Exotic Treasure'	EStr
'Exploded Pumpkin'	EBee
'Eye Catching'	EWoo
'Eye of Round'	CFwr
'Eye of the Hurricane' **new**	EStr
'Eye on America'	EBee EStr
'Eyelashes' **new**	CFwr
'Eyes Right Jones'	CFwr
'Eyes Wide Shut'	CFwr
'Eye-yi-yi'	SPol
'Ezekiel'	SPol XSen
'Fabergé'	SDay
'Fairest Love'	EBee MBNS MNrw
'Fairest of Them'	CBgR
'Fairy Charm'	SDay
'Fairy Firecracker'	SPol
'Fairy Frosting'	SDay
'Fairy Summerbird'	SPol
'Fairy Tale Pink'	EStr SDay SPol
'Fairy Wings'	EStr SPer
'Faith Nabor'	SPol
'Falcon'	SPol
'Fall Farewell'	WNHG
'Fama'	EStr
'Fandango'	LPla SPer
'Fantasia'	EWoo
'Farmer's Daughter'	CBgR EWoo
'Fashion Police'	CFwr
'Fat Lady Sings'	SPol
'Father James Foster' **new**	EStr
'Father's Day Gift'	CFwr
'Feather Down'	SPol
'Fee Fi Fo Fum' **new**	CFwr
'Fellow'	EStr SPol
'Femme Fatale'	SDay
'Femme Osage'	EStr SDay
'Feria'	XSen
'Festive Art'	SPol
'Fiestaville'	EStr
'Final Exams' **new**	CFwr
'Final Touch'	CBgR EAEE EBee EStr MBNS MSwo NBro SGol SPol
'Finders Keepers'	EBee EStr
'Fire and Fog'	EStr MBNS
'Fire and Wind'	CFwr
'Fire Dance'	ELon
'Fire from Heaven'	WHrl
'Fire on the Mountain' **new**	CFwr
'Fire Tree'	CBgR ELon EStr SPol

'Firestorm'	EWoo SPol
'First Formal'	SPer
'First Knight'	EStr SDay
'Fitzasaurus'	CFwr
'Flaming Firebird'	EStr
'Flaming Frolic'	SPol
'Flaming Sword'	WBrk WRHF
'Flamingo Dance' new	CFwr
'Flamingo Lipstick' new	CFwr
flava	see *H. lilioasphodelus*
'Florida Sunshine' (d)	XSen
'Florissant Miss'	EStr
'Flower Basket' (d)	EStr
'Flower Pavilion'	SDay SPol
'Floyd Cove'	SDay
'Fly Catcher'	CBgR SDay
'Flyaway Home'	SPol
'Flying Frisbee'	CFwr
'Flying Saucer'	EWoo
'Fol de Rol'	EWoo
'Fooled Me' ♀H6	EBee ECtt EStr MBNS MSpe SDay SPad SPol
'Foolscap'	EWoo
'For the Good Times'	CFwr EWoo
'Forbidden Desires'	EStr
'Forbidden Dreams'	EWoo
'Forest Phantom' new	EStr
'Forestlake Ragamuffin'	SPol
'Forever Red'	EStr
'Forgotten Dreams'	EBee MBNS MSpe
forrestii	CExl GKev
'Forsooth'	CBgR
'Forsyth Ace of Hearts'	CBgR
'Forsyth Evening Glow'	EStr
'Forsyth Flamboyant'	CFwr
'Forsyth Frostbound'	SPol
'Forsyth Lemon Drop'	SDay
'Forsyth Myra Dolores'	CFwr
'Forsyth White Buds' new	EStr
'Forsyth White Sentinel'	CFwr
'Forsyth Wrinkles and Crinkles'	CFwr
'Forty Second Street'	CCon MBNS
'Fox Ears'	EWoo
'Foxhaven Enigma'	CFwr
'Fragrant Bouquet'	EStr
'Fragrant Pastel Cheers'	SDay
'Fragrant Treasure'	CWld
'Frances Busby'	CFwr
'Frances Fay'	SPol
'Frances Joiner'	EWoo
'Francis of Assisi'	EWoo
'Francois Verhaert'	EWoo
'Frank Gladney'	SPol XSen
'Frans Hals'	Widely available
'Fred Ham'	XSen
'Fred Manning'	CFwr
'Free Wheelin''	CWGN EPfP EStr MSCN
'French Connection'	SDay
'French Lingerie'	EStr
'French Pavilion' new	SDay
'French Porcelain'	SDay
'Fresh Air'	MNrw
'Frilly Bliss'	CFwr
'Fritz Schroer'	CBgR
'Frosted Encore'	SDay
'Frosted Pink Ice'	SPol
'Frosted Vintage Ruffles'	EBee EStr WCAu
'Frosty White'	SDay
'Frozen Jade'	SDay

'Fuchsia Beauty'	SPol
'Fuchsia Cockatoo'	CFwr
'Fuchsia Four'	SPol
'Full Grown'	EStr
fulva	CTri ELan LPot MMuc NBir SCob SEND SPol SRms WBrk WHrl XSen
- B&SWJ 8647	WCru
- 'Flore Pleno' (d)	CAvo CMHG CMac COtt ECtt EHon ELan LHop MHer MJak MRav MSpe NBir NBro NGdn NSti SMad SPav SPer SRms SWat WBrk WCAu WMoo WWEG XSen
- 'Green Kwanso' (d)	CBgR CExl CWCL EBee ECGP ECha ITim WPnP
- var. ***kwanso*** B&SWJ 6328	WCru
- 'Kwanso' ambig. (d)	EAEE LRHS
- var. ***littorea***	CMac XLum XSen
- var. ***rosea***	SPol WCot XSen
§ - 'Variegated Kwanso' (d/v)	CBro EBee EWoo GCra MRav NBir SCob SMad WBor WCot WHer WHoo WHrl
- yellow-variegated (v)	WCot
'Fun Fling'	EStr SPol
'Funky Fuchsia'	SPol
'Future Whispers'	CFwr
'Gadsden Firefly'	CFwr
'Gadsden Goliath'	SGSe SPol
'Gadsden Light'	EStr SDay SPol
'Gala Greetings'	XSen
'Galaxy Ranger'	CFwr
'Gale Storm'	SPol WNHG
'Garden Crawler'	CBgR
'Garden Portrait'	EWoo SDay SPol
'Gay Music'	MBNS
'Gay Octopus'	CBgR EStr SPol WHrl
'Gay Rapture'	SPer
'Gay Troubadour'	EWoo
'Gemini'	SDay
'Gentle Country Breeze'	SDay SPol
'Gentle Rose'	EStr SDay
'Gentle Shepherd'	Widely available
'George Cunningham'	EAEE ECtt ELan EStr LRHS MRav NBir SDay SPol
'George David'	WHrl
'George Jets On' new	SPol
'Georgette Belden'	EAEE ECGP ECtt GKin LRHS MBNS MSpe MWat NHol SGSe SPol WWEG
'Georgia Cream' (d)	NLar
'Gerard Deschenes'	CFwr
'German Ballerina'	SPol
'Get All Excited'	ELon SPol
'Ghost Fingers' new	EStr
'Giant Moon'	CBgR CCon CMHG EAEE ECtt ELan LRHS MBNS SRms WHal
'Giant on the Mountain'	CFwr
'Giddy Go Round'	EWoo SDay SPol
'Ginger Twist'	CFwr EStr
'Gingerbread Man'	MSpe
'Girouette'	XSen
'Give Me Eight'	SPol
'Glacier Bay'	CBgR CWat EWoo MBNS
'Gladys Campbell' (d)	CFwr
'Glass Menagerie'	CFwr
'Glazed Heather Plum'	EStr
'Gleber's Top Cream'	EStr
'Gleeman Song'	CBgR
'Glendevon' new	EStr

'Glittering Treasure'	XLum
'Glory in the Sunset' **new**	CFwr
'Glowing Heart'	SDay
'Go Seminoles'	CFwr
'God's Handicraft' **new**	EStr
'Going Bananas'PBR	WCot
'Gold Dust'	CMea
'Gold Elephant'	SDay
'Gold Imperial'	NBre
'Golden Bell'	NGdn
'Golden Change'	CFwr
'Golden Chimes'	Widely available
'Golden Compass' **new**	EStr
'Golden Marvel'	EWoo
'Golden Orchid'	see *H.* 'Doubloon'
'Golden Prize'	EWoo GQue NGdn SDay WCot XSen
'Golden Scroll'	SDay
Golden Zebra = 'Malja'PBR (v)	CLet CWGN ELan EPfP IBoy MRav NLar NSti SRms
'Golliwog'	CBgR EStr
'Graal'	XSen
'Grace and Favour'	SDay SPol
'Grace and Grandeur'	EWoo
'Graceful Eye'	SDay
'Graceland'	SDay WHrl
'Grand Masterpiece'	EStr NGdn SDay
'Grand Palais'	SDay
'Grandma Kissed Me'	SPol
'Granite City Towhead'	ELon
'Granny Coot'	EStr
'Grape Arbor'	WNHG
'Grape Harvest'	WNHG
'Grape Magic'	MSpe WCot
'Grape Velvet'	CSpe EStr EWoo ILea MHer NSti SBch SDay SPol SRms WCAu WMnd WNHG WWEG WWtn
'Grapes of Wrath' **new**	EStr
'Green Canary'	SPol
'Green Dolphin Street'	SDay SPol
'Green Dragon'	SDay SPol
'Green Eyed Lady'	SDay
'Green Eyes' **new**	SGSe
'Green Eyes Wink'	MHol MLHP
'Green Flutter'	CBgR EBee EStr EWoo GCal GQue IMou LPla LSRN MBNS NBir NGdn NSti SDay SPhx SPol WWEG
'Green Fringe' **new**	SDay
'Green Goddess'	XLum
'Green Gold'	CMHG
'Green Lines' **new**	EStr
'Green Mystique'	EBee EStr
'Green Nautilus'	EStr
'Green Puff'	NBir SDay
'Green Spider'	CBgR SDay
'Green Warrior'	EWoo
'Green Widow'	EWoo SDay
'Greenland' **new**	ECtt EStr
'Grey Witch' ♀H6	SPol
'Greywoods Nautical Nellie'	CFwr
'Groovy Green'	SDay
'Grumbly'	ELan WPnP
'Guadalajara' (d)	CFwr
'Guardian Angel'	WCFE
'Gwen Leman' **new**	EStr
'Gypsy Cranberry'	SPol
'Hail Mary'	SDay
'Halloween Costume'	CFwr
'Hamlet'	SDay WNHG
'Happy Apache' **new**	EStr
'Happy Hopi'	EStr
'Happy Returns'	CBgR CBod CHid CSBt CTri EAEE ECha ELan EPfP EStr EWoo GBin GBuc LPot LRHS LSRN MBNS MBel MSpe NGdn NHol SGol SRGP SRms WCAu WWEG XLum
'Harbor Blue'	MSpe SDay
'Harrods'	EStr
'Harry Barras'	XLum
'Having Fun' **new**	EStr
'Hawaiian Nights'	EWoo
'Hawk'	ELon SDay SPol
'Hazel'	EStr
'Heady Wine'	EStr SDay
'Heartbreak Ridge'	CFwr
'Heart's Glee'	XSen
'Heat Wave'	CFwr
'Heavenly Angel Ice'	CFwr EStr
'Heavenly Beginnings'	CFwr
'Heavenly Curls'	SDay SPol
'Heavenly Dragon Fire'	CFwr
'Heavenly Fire Arrow'	CFwr
'Heavenly Flight of Angels'	CFwr EStr
'Heavenly Pink Butterfly' **new**	EStr
'Heavenly Pink Fang' **new**	EStr
'Heavenly Starfire'	CFwr EWoo SPol
'Heavenly Treasure'	SPol
'Heidi Eidelweiss'	CExl
'Heirloom Lace'	SDay WCAu
'Helen Shooter' **new**	EStr
'Helena Seabird'	EStr
'Helix'	EStr
'Helle Berlinerin'	SDay SPol
'Hello Screamer'	CFwr EStr
'Helter Skelter'	SDay SPol
'Hen's Teeth'	CFwr
'Her Majesty's Wizard'	CBgR ELan ELon EWoo IMou MBNS SPol
'Hermitage Newton'	SDay
'Heron's Cove'	EWoo
'Hesperus'	EWoo
'Hexagon'	EStr
'Hey There'	SDay
'High Profile' **new**	EStr
'High Tor'	ELon EStr GQui SDay SPol WHrl
'Highland Lord' (d)	EBee MBNS SDay WCAu XSen
'Hint of Blue'	SPol
'Hippie Chic'	CFwr
'Holiday Delight'	MBNS
'Holiday Mood'	ELan
'Holly Dancer' ♀H6	EStr EWoo SPol
'Homeward Bound'	SDay
'Honey Jubilee'	SPol
'Honey Redhead'	SPol
'Hope Diamond'	SDay
'Hornby Castle'	CBro EAEE LRHS SGSe
'Hot Chocolate'PBR	EBee GKev
'Hot Pink Fury' **new**	EStr
'Hot Tamales and Red Hots' **new**	EStr
'Hot Town'	ELan
'Hot Wheels'	CBgR
'Hot Wire'	SDay
'Hotter than the Fourth of July'	CFwr

	Name	Suppliers
	'Houdini'	MSpe WCAu WMnd
	'House Music'	XSen
	'House of Bluelights'	SPol
	'House of Orange'	SPol
	'Howlin' Wolf'	CFwr
I	'How's the Weather up There?'	CFwr EWoo
	'Hubbles Buddy'	EWoo
	'Huckleberry Candy' **new**	SPol
	'Humdinger'	EStr SDay WCot
	'Hummingbird'	EStr
	'Hymn'	EStr SDay
	'Hyperion'	CBgR CBod CCon CMac CPrp CTri ECha ECtt ELon EShb EStr EWoo GKin LAst LEdu MHol MMuc MRav MSpe NBid NGdn SDay SEND SPer SPoG SWvt WCot WWEG WWtn
	'I Luv Lucy'	CFwr
	'Ice Carnival'	CKel EBee ELon EStr MBNS NGdn NLar SCob SPol SWvt
	'Ice Castles'	CTri SDay
	'Ice Cream Dream'	SGSe
	'Icecap'	CBgR WMoo
	'Icy Lemon'	EStr SDay
	'Ida Duke Miles'	SDay
	'Ida's Magic'	EStr
	'Iditarod'	EStr
	'Ikebana Star' **new**	EStr
	'Illini Jackpot'	SDay
	'Impromptu'	SDay
	'In Depth' (d)	EWoo MBNS NBro NLar WCot WHrl
	'In Search of Angels'	CFwr
	'In Strawberry Time'	WNHG
	'Inca Secret'	EStr
	'Indian Fandango'	EWoo
	'Indian Fires'	CFwr
	'Indian Giver'	SPol
	'Indian Paintbrush'	ELon EWoo NBir SPol
	'Indigo Moon'	SPol XSen
	'Inimitable'	CFwr
	'Inky Fingers'	SPol
	'Inner View'	ECtt EWoo MBNS NLar SDay WMnd
	'Innocent Blush'	EStr
	'Inspired Edge'	EStr
	'Inspired Word'	SDay
	'Instant Zéro'	XSen
	'Intelligent Design'	CFwr
	'Intertwined Entity'	CFwr
	'Invitation to Immortality'	EStr EWoo
	'Iowa Greenery'	SPol
	'Iowa Sunrise' **new**	EStr
	'Iridescent Jewel'	SDay
	'Irish Elf'	EBee ELon SDay SHar
	'Irish Handshake'	CFwr
	'Iron Gate Glacier'	EBee EStr MBNS SDay XLum
	'Irresistible Charm'	EPfP
	'Isaac'	EStr
	'Isabelle Rose' **new**	SDay
	'Isle of Dreams'	SPol
	'Isleworth'	EWoo
	'Isolde'	CBgR
	'Itsy Bitsy Spider'	CBgR CFwr EWoo
	'Ivelyn Brown'	SDay SPol
	'Ivory Cloud' (d)	EStr
	'Ivory Coast'	SDay
	'Jabo'	SPol
	'Jack Sprat'	CFwr
	'Jake Russell'	MBNS
	'Jalapeno Pepper' **new**	CFwr
	'Jam All Night'	CFwr
	'Jamaican Jammin''	SPol
	'Jamaican Magic'	CFwr
	'James Clark'	EWoo
	'James Marsh'	CBgR EWes EWoo GBin MBNS MNrw MSpe NSti WCAu WCot WMnd WNHG
	'Jammin' with Jane'	CFwr
	'Janet Gordon'	SPol
	'Janice Brown'	CKel CWCL ECtt EStr EWoo LAst LSou MBNS NHol NLar SDay SPol WHrl
	'Jan's Twister'	MNrw SDay SPol WHrl
	'Jason Salter'	EStr SDay WAul
	'Jay Turman'	SDay
	'Jazz at the Wool Club'	CFwr
	'Jean'	SDay
	'Jean Swann'	EStr MBNS
	'Jedi Dot Pierce'	EStr SDay
	'Jelly Dancer' **new**	SPol
	'Jellyfish Jealousy' ♀H6	EWoo
	'Jenny Wren'	EPPr EWoo MBNS NBro SRGP WAul WWEG
	'Jersey Breeze' **new**	EStr
	'Jersey Jim'	SPol
	'Jersey Spider'	EWoo SDay SPol
	'Jerusalem'	SDay
	'Jesse James'	SPol
	'Jeu de Piste'	XSen
	'Jeune Tom'	CBgR
	'Jewel Case'	WNHG
	'Jim McKinney' **new**	EStr
	'Joan Derifield' **new**	EStr
	'Joan Senior'	Widely available
	'Jockey Club' (d)	ECtt EStr MBNS WHrl
	'Joe Marinello'	SPol
	'Johanna Klein Strack'	CFwr
	'Johnny Come Lately'	EStr SPol
	'Joie de Vivre'	EWoo
	'Jolly Red Giant'	EWoo
	'Jolyene Nichole'	SDay
	'Jordan'	LSRN SWvt
	'Josephine Marina'	EStr
	'Journey to Oz'	EWoo
	'Journey's End'	SDay
	'Jovial'	EStr
	'Joy of Life' **new**	CFwr
	'Joyful Participation'	EStr
	'Judah'	SPol
	'Judge Roy Bean'	EStr EWoo SPol
	'Julie Newmar' ♀H6	IPot
	'June Explosion'	CFwr
	'June Melody'	WNHG
	'June Rose'	EStr
	'Jungle Beauty'	CBgR SDay SPol
	'Just Celebrate' **new**	SDay
	'Just Kiss Me'	SPol
	'Just My Size'	EBee
	'Just Whistle' **new**	EStr
	'Justin Brent'	XSen
	'Justin George'	SDay SPol
	'Kachina Firecracker'	CFwr EWoo
	'Kamadeva'	CFwr
	'Kansas Kitten'	EWoo
	'Karateake'	CFwr
	'Karen's Curls' ♀H6	EWoo SPol
	'Kasia'	Hrl

'Katahdin'	EWoo
'Kate Carpenter'	EStr SDay SPol
'Katherine Harris'	CFwr
'Kathleen Salter'	EStr EWoo
'Kathryn June Wood'	EWoo
'Kathy Macartney'	EWoo
'Kathy's Cat Spooky'	CFwr
'Katie Elizabeth Miller'	SDay
'Kazuq'	SDay
'Keene'	EWoo
'Kelly's Girl'	SPol
'Kempion'	CBgR
'Kenyan Sun'	EWoo
'Kevin Michael Coyne'	SPol
'Key to my Heart'	CBgR
'Killarney Castle'	CFwr
'Killer Purple'	EStr
'Kimberly Sue' **new**	EStr
'Kindly Light'	EWoo SPol
'King George' **new**	EStr
'King Kahuna' (d)	EStr
'King's Gold'	EStr
'King's Throne'	WNHG
'Kipling'	CFwr
'Kirsten My Love' **new**	EStr
'Kiss Me Softly' **new**	EStr
'Kisses for Cinderella'	CFwr
'Klaatu Barada Nikto'	CFwr
'Knights in White Satin'	EStr SPol
'Kokopelli'	CFwr
'Krakatoa Lava' **new**	CFwr
'Kristal Sunset'	CFwr
'Kwanso Flore Pleno'	see *H. fulva* 'Green Kwanso'
'Kwanso Flore Pleno Variegata'	see *H. fulva* 'Variegated Kwanso'
'La Fenice'	EStr
'La Peche'	SDay
'Lacy Doily'	EStr LLHF WCAu
'Lacy Marionette'	ELon EWoo SDay SPol
'Lady Betty Fretz'	EBee EStr
'Lady Blue Eyes'	EStr
'Lady Cynthia'	CKel
'Lady Fermor-Hesketh'	EStr
'Lady Fingers'	CBgR EStr SPol
'Lady Liz'	SDay SPol
'Lady Mischief'	EStr SDay
'Lady Neva' ♀H6	CBgR ELon EWoo SDay SGSe
'Lady Tiger'	WNHG
'Ladybug's Two Moons' (d)	EStr
'Ladykin'	ELon SDay SPol
'Lake Effect'	EWoo
'Lake Norman Spider'	EWoo SPol
'Lamar'	CFwr
'Lambada'	EStr
'Land of Cotton'	XSen
'Land of Enchantment'	CFwr
'Land's End'	EStr
'Lark Song'	EAEE LRHS WHrl
'Last Song'	CFwr
'Laughing Feather'	CFwr EWoo
'Laughing Giraffe'	EStr WCot
'Laughton Tower'	SMHy
'Laura Lambert'	SPol
'Lauradell'	SDay
'Lauren Leah'	SDay
'Laurena'	SPol
'Lavender Blue Baby'	EPfP LRHS
'Lavender Cascades'	CFwr
'Lavender Deal'	MNrw WNHG
'Lavender Light'	EWoo
'Lavender Lion'	EStr
'Lavender Memories'	SDay
'Lavender Plicata'	SPol
'Lavender Showstopper'	WCAu
'Lavender Silver Cords'	SPol
'Lavender Spider'	CBgR SPol
'Lavender Tonic'	SPol
'Lavender Tutu'	EStr
'Layers of Gold' (d)	XSen
'Ledgewood's Cinnamon Lace'	CFwr
'Ledgewood's Firecracker'	CFwr
'Lee Reinke'	EStr SPol
'Legs Limmer'	CFwr EWoo
'Leila Mantle'	CBgR
'Lemon Bells'	CWat EAEE ECGP ECha EPfP EStr EWoo GKin GMaP LEdu LRHS MBNS NBro NCGa SDay SHar WCAu
'Lemon Custard'	EStr
'Lemon Dessert'	ELon
'Lemon Fellow'	EWoo
'Lemon Fringed Pastel'	CFwr
'Lemon Madeline'	EStr EWoo
'Lemon Meringue Twist'	EWoo
'Lemon Mint'	ELon
'Lemonora'	SDay
'Lenox'	SDay
'Leonard Bernstein'	EStr EWoo SPol
'Leslie Renee'	CFwr
'Let it Rip'	EWoo SPol
'Let Loose'	CFwr EStr
'Lexington Avenue'	SPol
'Licorice Candy'	SPol
'Licorice Twist'	CFwr
'Life on Mars'	EStr
'Light of the World'	CFwr
'Light the Way'	GBin MHol WCot
'Light Years Away'	ELon MBNS MNrw
'Lilac Lady'	EStr
'Lilac Wine'	SCob
§ ***lilioasphodelus***	Widely available
'Lilly Dache'	EStr EWoo
'Lilting Belle'	SPol
'Lilting Lady'	SDay SPol
'Lilting Lavender'	ELon SPol WCAu
'Lime Frost' ♀H6	CBgR EStr SPol
'Lime Painted Lady'	CBgR
'Limetree'	CBgR EStr
'Limited Edition'	EWoo
'Lin Wright'	EWoo
'Linda'	MRav
'Linda Agin'	EWoo
'Lines of Splendor'	EWoo
'Lipstick'	EStr
'Little Bee'	NBre
'Little Big Man'	SDay
'Little Bugger'	ELon NLar WWEG
'Little Bumble Bee'	CCon LRHS MBNS WWEG WWtn
'Little Business'	MBNS SDay SPol
'Little Cadet'	XLum
'Little Carpet'	MBNS
'Little Dart'	ECha
'Little Deeke'	SDay WHrl
'Little Dream Red'	SDay
'Little Fantastic'	ELon LRHS SDay WWtn
'Little Fat Cat'	EStr

'Little Fat Dazzler'	ELon SDay SPol
'Little Fellow'	EStr MBNS
'Little Girl' **new**	ELon
'Little Grapette'	CPrp ELon EPfP ERCP EStr GCra GQue LPla MBNS NLar NSti WAul WCAu WWEG
'Little Greenie'	SDay
'Little Gypsy Vagabond'	CBgR CWat EStr SDay SPol
'Little Heavenly Angel'	EStr SPol
'Little Isaac' **new**	EStr
'Little Judy'	SPol
'Little Kiki'	SDay
'Little Lassie'	CBgR
'Little Maggie'	SDay SPol
'Little Men'	WCAu
'Little Miss Manners'	EStr NLar
'Little Missy'	CBgR CWat EPfP MBNS SDay SGSe WHoo WNHG
'Little Monica'	SDay
'Little Music Maker' (d)	EStr
'Little Rainbow'	WWEG
'Little Red Hen'	CSam EAEE ECGP GKin LRHS MBNS MSpe NBir NBro NEgg NGdn SDay
'Little Show Stopper'	EWoo MBNS NBro NLar
'Little Showoff'	SDay
'Little Swain'	SDay
'Little Sweet Talk'	ELon
'Little Tawny'	ELon LRHS
'Little Toddler'	SDay
'Little Violet Lace'	SDay
'Little Wart'	CBgR SDay WHrl
'Little Wine Cup'	CBod CMHG CMac COtt CSam CWat EAEE ECrc ECtt ELon EPfP EStr GKin GMaP LBMP LRHS MRav MWat MWhi NBir NEgg NGdn SEND SPer SPol SRms WAul WMoo WWEG
'Little Women'	MBNS SDay
'Little Zinger'	SDay
'Littlest Angel'	SDay
'Littlest Clown'	SDay
'Living in Amsterdam'	EBee EStr
'Liz Schreiner'	CFwr
'Lizard's Purple Fashion'	CFwr
'Lobo Lucy'	ELon EStr
'Lochinvar'	CSam GBuc MRav
'Loco Bo'	EStr
'Lois Burns'	EWoo SDay SPol
'Lonesome Dove'	SPol
'Long John Silver'	ELon EStr
'Long Legged Lap Dancer'	CFwr
'Long Stocking'	EStr EWoo SPol WCot
'Long Tall Sally' **new**	EStr
'Longfields Anwar'	EWoo
'Longfields Bandit'	EWoo
'Longfields Beauty'	EWoo MBNS
'Longfields X Factor' **new**	EStr
'Longfields Glory'	MBNS MSpe NBre
'Longfields Maxim' (d)	EStr MBNS SDeJ
'Longfields Pride'	EStr IBoy MBNS SRms WBor
'Longfields Purple Eye'	NLar
'Longfields Think Pink' **new**	EStr
'Longfields Tropica'	MBNS
'Longfields Twins'	MBNS WCot
'Longfields Whoopy' **new**	EPfP SCob
longituba AIK 284	WCot
- B&SWJ 4576	WCru
'Look at Me'	ELan
'Look Lucky'	CFwr
'Loose as a Goose'	CFwr
'Loose Reins'	CFwr
'Lori Goldston'	EWoo MBNS
'Lorita Wadsworth'	CFwr
'Loth Lorien'	CFwr
'Lots of Hoopla' **new**	EStr
'Lotsa Dots' **new**	CFwr
'Lotus Land'	SDay
'Louie the Lip'	CFwr
'Louis Burnes'	SPol
'Louis McHargue'	SDay
'Love Glow'	CCon
'Love Those Eyes'	EStr
'Lovin Up a Storm'	CFwr
'Loving Memories'	SDay
'Lowcountry Gem'	EStr
'Lucille Ball'	EStr
'Lucille Lennington'	WNHG
'Lucky Streak' **new**	CFwr
'Lullaby Baby'	CWat ELan GCal MBNS NLar SDay SPol
'Luna'	SPol
'Lunar Sea'	EStr
'Luscious Honeydew'	WNHG
'Lusty Lealand'	MBNS SDay
'Luxury Lace'	CAgr CPrp CWat EAEE EBee ECtt ELan EPfP EStr GBin GKin LSRN NBir NGdn NHol NWad SPer SPol WHrl WMoo WWtn XLum XSen
'Lydia Bechtold'	EStr
'Lyndell's First' **new**	CFwr
'Lyndell's Peach Craze' **new**	CFwr
'Lyndell's Purple Lady' **new**	CFwr
'Lynn Hall'	EMil MBNS NLar
'Lynn's Delight' **new**	EStr
'Lyric Opera'	SDay
'Mabel Fuller'	CBgR MRav SPer WHrl
'Mable Lewis Nelson' **new**	EStr
'Macbeth'	EStr MBNS
'Mad Max'	EStr EWoo MSpe SPol
'Made from Scratch'	CFwr
'Madeline Nettles Eyes'	EBee
'Madge Cayse'	CFwr
'Maestro Puccini'	SDay
'Maggie Fynboe'	CBgR SPol
'Magic Amethyst'	CBgR
'Magic Attraction'	CFwr
'Magic Carpet Ride'	EStr SPol
'Magic Dancer' **new**	EStr
'Magic Lace'	EStr EWoo
'Magic Masquerade'	SDay
'Magical Messenger' **new**	EStr
'Magnificent Eyes'	SPol
'Magnificent Rainbow'	CBcs
'Mahdi' **new**	CFwr
'Mahogany Magic' ♀H6	ELon EStr
'Majestic Dark Eyes' **new**	EStr
'Malachite Prism'	CWGN EStr
'Malaysian Monarch'	EStr SDay WMnd WNHG
'Malaysian Spice'	WNHG
'Maleny Chantilly Lace'	EStr
'Maleny Debutante'	EStr
'Maleny Mite'	EWoo

'Maleny Piecrust'	EWoo
'Maleny Think Big'	EWoo
'Mallard'	CAby CBgR CWat EAEE ECGP ECtt EStr LLWP LRHS MBNS MRav NBir SPer SWat WCot
'Malmaison Plum'	EStr
'Mama Joe'	EStr
'Mama Sohpia' **new**	EStr
'Mambo Maid'	XSen
'Man on Fire'	MBNS WNHG
'Manchurian Apricot'	SDay
'Mandalay Bay Music'	EWoo
'Mansfield Plantation'	CFwr
'Marble Faun'	SDay
'Margaret McWhorter'	SPol
'Margaret Perry'	CPrp ECrc MNrw NLar
'Margaret Seawright'	EStr
'Margo Reed Indeed'	SPol
'Marietta Charmer'	SDay SPol
'Marietta Delight'	EStr
'Marilyn Siwik'	EWoo
'Marion Caldwell'	SPol
'Marion Vaughn'	ECtt ELan EPfP EWoo GBuc GKin GMaP LHop LRHS MBel MLHP MRav MSpe NSti SDix SPer SRGP SSpi SWvt WCAu WCot WHar WHoo WPtf WWEG
'Mariska'	EStr EWoo SDay WNHG
'Marked by Lydia'	CFwr ELon SPol
'Marmalade'	EBee EPfP
'Marse Connell'	MSpe
'Martha Adams'	SDay
'Martie Everest'	EWoo
'Martina Verhaert'	CWGN EBee EStr
'Mary Alice Stokes'	EStr
'Mary Ethel Anderson'	EStr EWoo
'Mary Todd'	EBee MBNS WMnd XSen
'Mary's Gold' ♀^{H6}	MBri SDay SPol
'Mask of Time' **new**	EStr
'Masquerade Show'	CFwr
'Mata Hari'	SDay SPol
'Matisse'	SPol
'Mauna Loa'	CSBt EStr GQue MBNS MNrw NLar SDeJ SWvt WAul WCot
'May May'	CBgR SPol
'Maya Cha Cha'	CFwr
'Mayan Poppy'	EStr
'Meadow Mist'	CBgR ELon WWtn
'Meadow Sprite'	WCot
'Meadowsweet'	EStr
'Medicine Feather'	EWoo
'Medieval Guild'	EStr
'Medusa's Glance'	EWoo
'Meerkat Manor'	CFwr
'Megatrend'	CFwr
'Mema's Dingaling' **new**	EStr
'Mema's Dingbat'	CFwr
'Memories of Oz' **new**	CFwr
'Mephistopheles'	EWoo
'Merry Moppet'	EWoo
'Merry Witch' **new**	EStr
'Metaphor'	SDay XSen
'Michele Coe'	ECtt GKin LPla MBNS NBro NEgg NGdn SDay SRGP WCAu WHrl WMoo
'Mico'	ELon
middendorffii	CMac EBee GMaP LPla MCoo NSti WHrl WThu
'Midnight Dynamite'	MBNS
'Midnight Love'	EWoo
'Midnight Magic'	EWoo SDay
'Midnight Mantis'	SDay SPol
'Midnight Raider'	EWoo
'Midnight Rendezvous' **new**	EStr
'Mighty Highty Tighty'	CFwr
'Mikado'	CBgR CMac
'Mike Reed' **new**	EStr
'Milady Greensleeves'	EStr EWoo SDay SPol WHrl
'Milanese Mango'	EStr EWoo
'Mildred Mitchell'	CBgR CWat ELon EStr MBNS NLar SPol WCAu
'Military School' **new**	EStr
'Millie Schlumpf'	SPol
'Mimosa Umbrella'	EStr SPol
'Ming Lo'	SDay
'Ming Porcelain'	EStr SPol WCAu
'Mini Pearl'	ECtt ELon EStr LRHS MBNS SDay SPer
'Mini Stella'	CBro ECtt GJos MBNS SDay
miniature hybrids	SRms
'Minnie Wildfire'	EStr SPol
minor	CBro EBee EDAr EPPr GKev LRHS SRms XSen
- B&SWJ 8841	WCru
'Minstrel's Fire'	CFwr
'Miracle Maid'	WNHG
'Miss Jessie'	EStr EWoo SPol WHrl
'Missenden'	CBgR MNrw
'Missouri Beauty'	IBoy MBNS SPol SWvt
'Missouri Memories'	SPol
'Misty Twisty'	CFwr
'Moment in the Sun'	CFwr
'Moment of Truth'	EAEE NBre
'Monica Marie'	EStr SDay
'Mont Royal Demitasse'	ELon SPol
'Montserrat's Revenge'	EStr
'Moon Snow'	SDay
'Moon Witch'	EStr SDay SPol
'Moonlight Masquerade'	CBgR CWat ECtt GBuc MMuc NLar SRms WOut
'Moonlight Mist'	SDay SPol
'Moonlight Orchid'	WHrl
'Moonlit Caress'	CBgR EBee ECtt MBNS NBro
'Moonlit Crystal'	EStr SPol
'Moonlit Masquerade' ♀^{H6}	CPar CWGN EStr EWoo GBin MBNS MBel MNrw SEND SPer SPol WCAu WHrl
'Moonlit Summerbird'	SDay SPol
'Moontraveller'	WCot
'Moose Man'	CFwr
'Morgan le Fay' **new**	EStr SPol
'Mormon Spider'	EStr SPol
'Morning Dawn'	WWEG
'Morning Sun'	MBNS WCot
'Morocco'	SPol
'Morocco Red'	CBro CCse CTri ELan MHCG WWEG
'Morrie Otte'	SPol
'Mosel'	SDay
'Moses' Fire'	ECtt EPfP EStr MBNS NLar
'Mossy Glade'	CBgR
'Mount Echo Sunrise'	EWoo
'Mount Joy'	EStr SPer
'Mountain Lace' **new**	CFwr
'Mountain Laurel'	EAEE ECGP ECtt ELon EStr GKin LRHS LSRN MBNS MRav NEgg SPol
'Moussaka'	EStr WCAu WFar
'Move Over Moon'	EStr SDay
'Moving Forward'	CFwr

'Mrs David Hall'	CCse
'Mrs Hugh Johnson'	CChe GCra WHrl
* 'Mrs Lester'	SDay
'Muddy Waters'	CFwr
'Muffet's Little Friend'	SPol
'Mulberry Charm' **new**	CFwr
'Mulberry Frosted Edge'	EWoo
multiflora	XSen
'Muscle Man'	EStr XSen
'Music of the Master' (d)	CFwr
'My Belle'	SDay
'My Darling Clementine'	EStr SDay
'My Friend Floyd'	CFwr
'My Heart Belongs to Daddy'	CFwr
'My Hope'	SPol
'My Melinda'	SDay
'Mynelle's Starfish'	CPar SPol WHrl
'Mystical Rainbow' **new**	SDay
'Nabis'	SDay
'Nacogdoches Lady'	SWvt
nana	CCon GKev
'Nanuq'	ELon SDay
'Naomi Ruth'	EStr MBNS
'Nashville'	CBro ELan WHrl
'Nashville Lights'	CBgR EStr SPol
'Nathan Sommers'	EWoo
'Natural Veil'	SPol
'Nature's Crown' (d)	CFwr
'Navajo Jewel' **new**	EStr
'Navajo Princess'	CWat EBee MBNS MNrw SPol
'Neal Berrey'	EStr SDay SPol
'Ned Cricket'	CFwr
'Ned's Elena'	CFwr
'Nefertiti'	CBgR ELon MBNS NBir SPer WAul WCAu
'Neon Rose'	GKin MWat
'Neon Yellow'	EStr
'Never Ending Fantasy'	EStr
'Never Get Away'	EStr
'New Direction'	CFwr EWoo
'Neyron Rose'	EAEE GBuc GKin GQue LRHS MBNS NEgg NGdn WMoo WWtn XLum
'Nick's Faith'	WHrl
'Nicole Ashley Scott'	EStr
'Nicole Joyce'	SPol
'Night Beacon'	CBgR ECtt ELon EStr EWes EWoo GBuc GKin LPot MBNS MNrw MPie MSpe NLar SCob SDay SDeJ SPol WCAu WHrl
'Night Embers'	ECtt EWoo NLar SGSe WCAu
'Night Raider'	CBgR SDay
'Night Wings'	EWoo
'Nile Crane'	CBgR ELon EStr MBNS MNrw SDay SPer WAul
'Nile Plum'	EStr EWoo SDay SPol
'Ninja Throwing Star'	CFwr
'Ninth Millennium'	CFwr
'Nob Hill'	CCse ELon SPol WHrl XLum
'Nona's Garnet Spider'	ELon SPol
'Noonday Dreams'	CFwr
'Nordic Night'	CBgR SDay SPol
'North Star'	LPla
'North Wind Dancer' ♀H6	EWoo
'Norton Beauté'	WCot
'Norton Eyed Seedling'	WNHG
'Norton Orange'	EStr
'Nosferatu'	SDay SPol
'Not Forgotten'	WNHG
'Nouveau Riche'	SPol
'Nova'	ELon SDay
'Novarlis'	CFwr
'Nowhere to Hide' **new**	EStr
'Nuclear Meltdown'	EWoo
'Nuit Parisienne'	EStr
'Nuka'	XLum
'Nutmeg Elf'	CBgR EWoo SDay SPol
'Nuttin Bugs Me'	CFwr
'Oakes Love'	MNrw
'Ocean Rain'	EStr SDay SPol WNHG
'Octopus Hugs'	EStr SPol
'Official Curse'	SPol
'Ojo de Dios'	EWoo
'Oklahoma Kicking Bird'	SDay
'Olallie Lad'	EStr
'Old San Juan' **new**	EStr
'Old Tangiers' ♀H6	EStr EWoo
'Old Time Memories'	CFwr
'Olive Bailey Langdon'	EStr SDay SPol WCot
'Oliver Billingslea'	EWoo
'Olive's Odd One'	EStr
'Olly Olly Oxen Free'	CFwr
'Oloroso'	CBgR
'Olympic Gold'	XSen
'Olympic Showcase'	EStr
'Omomuki'	SDay
'On and On'	GQue LHop MBNS NCGa
'On Pointe'	CFwr EWoo
'On Silken Thread'	SPol
'On the Border'	CFwr
'On the Fringe'	CFwr
'On the Web'	CFwr
'Once upon a Time' **new**	CFwr
'One Fire'	XSen
'Oodles'	WHrl
'Open Hearth'	EStr SPol WHrl
'Open my Eyes'	EStr EWoo
'Orange Clown'	CFwr
'Orange Dream'	SDay
'Orange Exotica'	CBgR EStr
'Orange Nassau' **new**	WCAu
'Orange Prelude'	XSen
'Orange Splash'	CFwr
'Orange Velvet'	CFwr SPol
'Orangeman' misapplied	MBNS NGdn
'Orchid Beauty'	MLHP WMoo
'Orchid Candy'	EWoo MBNS NBir SPol
'Orchid Corsage'	ELon EStr SPol
'Orchid Lady Slipper'	EWoo
'Orchid Moonrise'	EWoo
'Oriental Ruby'	SDay
'Orion's Band'	EWoo
'Orphée'	XSen
'Osterized' **new**	EStr
'Ostrich Plume'	SDay
'Ouachita Beauty'	CBgR SPol
'Our Kirsten'	EStr SDay
'Out of Darkness'	EWoo
'Outrageous'	CBgR EStr SDay SPol WNHG
'Outrageous Ramona'	WNHG
'Over the Top'	MBNS
'Paige's Pinata'	EBee EStr MBNS
'Painted Peach'	SPol
'Painted Pink'	SDay
'Painting the Roses Red'	CFwr
'Palace Garden Beauty'	EWoo
'Pale Moon Windmill'	CFwr

'Pandora's Box'	CExl CMHG CTri CWat EAEE EAJP ECtt ELan EStr LRHS MBNS MMuc MNrw MWat NBir NGdn NLar SDay SDeJ SEND SPol SWvt WBor WCAu WHoo WMoo WWEG
'Panic in Detroit'	CFwr
'Pantherette'	SPol
'Paper Butterfly'	EStr SDay SPol
'Papilion' **new**	EStr
'Papoose'	XLum
'Paprika Flame' **new**	EStr
'Parade of Peacocks'	CBgR
'Pardon Me'	CBro CMHG CPrp CWld EAEE ECtt ELan ELon EStr EWoo GKin GMaP LRHS MBNS MBel NCGa NGdn SDay SDeJ SPol SRGP SWvt WAul WBor WCAu
'Pardon Me Boy'	SPol
'Parfait'	CBgR EStr EWoo SPol
'Parson's Robe'	SDay
'Party Queen'	SDay
'Passion for Red'	SDay
'Pastel Ballerina'	SDay
'Pastel Classic'	SPol
'Pastilline'	SPol
'Pat Mercer'	SDay XSen
'Patchwork Puzzle'	EWoo SPol
'Patricia'	MBNS
'Patricia Fay'	XSen
'Patricia Gentzel Wright'	EWoo
'Patricia Snider Memorial'	CFwr
'Patriotic Flavor'	EStr
'Patsy Bickers'	EWoo SGSe
'Patsy Jane'	SPol
'Patterns'	SPol
'Patti Neyland' **new**	EStr
'Paula Nettles' **new**	EStr
'Peace be Still'	EWoo
'Peach Float'	EWoo
'Peach Jubilee'	EStr SPol
'Peach Magnolia' (d)	EStr
'Peach Wisper' **new**	EStr
'Peach Yum Yum'	CFwr
'Peacock Curls'	EWoo
'Peacock Maiden'	EStr EWoo SDay SPol WHrl XSen
'Pear Ornament'	SDay
'Pearl Jam' **new**	SDay
'Pearl Lewis'	EStr SDay SPol
'Pearl Sherwood'	EWoo
'Penelope Vestey'	CBgR EStr GBuc MBNS NBir SDay SPol SRGP
'Penny Pinsley' (d)	CFwr
'Penny's Worth'	LEdu LRHS MBNS WAul WCot WHoo XLum
'Penthouse' **new**	CFwr
'Perfect Pleasure'	MBNS
'Persian Melon Plus'	WCAu
'Persian Ruby'	EStr SPol
'Persian Shrine'	SPol
'Persimmone'	SPol
'Persimmons Cinnamon and Marmalade'	CFwr
'Petite Ballerina'	SDay
'Photon Torpedo'	CFwr
'Phyllis Cantini'	SPol
'Piano Man'	MBNS WAul WNHG

'Piccadilly Princess'	EStr SDay
'Picket Fences'	CFwr
'Picotee Rippled Ruffles'	CFwr
'Pinebelt Darkeyes'	CFwr
'Pink Ambrosia'	ECtt EStr EWoo
'Pink Ballerina'	WWtn
'Pink Charm'	CBen CMac EAEE ECha ECtt EPPr GKin GMaP LRHS MBNS NBro SPol
'Pink Circle'	SDay
'Pink Cotton Candy'	EWoo SDay SPol
'Pink Damask' 🏆H7	Widely available
'Pink Dazzler'	WNHG
'Pink Delight' **new**	MPie
'Pink Dream'	CBgR MBNS NBir NBre SPol
'Pink Flirt'	SDay
'Pink Grace'	SPol
'Pink Lady'	MNrw MRav SRms
'Pink Monday'	SDay WNHG
'Pink Pajamas'	CFwr
'Pink Prelude'	CCon GBee MBNS MSpe MWat NBro
'Pink Puff'	MBNS NBir NBre NLar
'Pink Rain Dance'	SPol
'Pink Scintillation'	SDay
'Pink Spider'	SDay
'Pink Stripes'	CFwr
'Pink Sundae'	WHrl
'Pink Super Spider'	EWoo SDay SPol
'Pink Whip Tips'	CFwr
'Pink Windmill'	ELon EWoo SPol
'Pinocchio'	SMHy
'Piping Rock'	CFwr
'Piquante'	SCob
'Pirate Treasure'	EStr MBNS
'Pirate's Patch'	EWoo SPol WCot
'Pixie Parasol'	WMnd WNHG
'Pixie Pipestone'	SPol
'Pixie Princess'	EStr
'Pizza'	SDay
'Planet Golden Orange Ruffy'	CFwr
'Planet Sunshine'	CFwr
'Plum Beauty'	NLar
'Plum Candy'	EWoo
'Plumburst'	EPfP
'Poetic Dance'	EWoo
'Poinsettia'	EStr
'Point of Honor'	EWoo
'Point of View' **new**	EStr
'Pojo'	EStr SDay
'Pony'	CWat SDay SPol
'Possum in a Sack'	CBgR
'Prague Spring'	EStr MSpe SDay SPol WHrl
'Prairie Belle'	MBNS NLar SGSe SPol
'Prairie Blue Eyes'	ECtt EStr IBoy ILea MBNS NPri SDay SPlb SPol WCot WHrl WMnd WWEG WWtn
'Prairie Charmer'	MMuc SEND WHrl
'Prairie Moonlight'	EWTr
'Precious d'Oro'	EBee GQue
'Pretty Miss'	EAEE ECtt
'Preview Party'	WNHG
'Primal Scream' 🏆H6	EStr SPol WCot
'Primrose Mascotte'	NBir
'Prince of Midnight'	SDay
'Prince of Purple'	ELon
'Prince Redbird'	SDay
'Princess Blue Eyes'	SPol
'Princess Lilli'	MBNS

'Princeton Eye Glow' MSpe SDay
'Priscilla's Wish' **new** SPol
'Prissy Frills' SPol
'Prize Picotee Deluxe' SPol
'Prize Picotee Elite' SDay SPol
'Promising Future' CFwr
'Protocol' MSpe SDay SPol
'Proud Mary' SDay
'Ptarmigan' CBgR EStr
'Pterodactyl Eye' EStr
§ 'Puddin' CWat SDay
'Pueblo Dancer' EStr
'Pueblo Dreamer' CFwr EWoo
'Puff the Magic Dragon' CFwr
'Pug Yarborough' EStr SPol
'Pumpkin Kid' SPol
'Pumpkin Pie Spice' SPol
'Pumpkin Prince' CFwr EStr
'Pumpkins Gone Wild' CFwr
'Puppet Show' SDay
'Pure and Simple' SDay SPol
'Purple Arachne' SPol
'Purple Bicolor' WHrl
'Purple Corn Dancer' **new** WCot
'Purple Grasshopper' EWoo
'Purple Many Faces' SPol
'Purple Oddity' EWoo SPol
'Purple Pinwheel' EWoo SPol
'Purple Rain' CWat MBNS SDay SPol SWvt
'Purple Rain Dance' SPol
'Purple Waters' EStr MBNS MJak SPol WPnP
'Purpleicious' NLar
'Pyewacket' SDay
'Pygmy Plum' SDay XSen
'Pyrotechnics' **new** EStr
'Quality of Mercy' **new** SDay
'Queen Charlotte' **new** EStr
'Queen Empress' WNHG
'Queen Kathleen' CFwr
'Queen Lily' WNHG
'Queen of Can Do' CFwr
'Queen of May' MNrw WCot
'Quick Results' SDay
'Quietly Awesome' SDay
'Quilt Patch' EStr SPol
'Quinn Buck' SDay
'Ra Hansen' EStr SDay
'Rachael My Love' (d) XSen
'Racing Stripes' CFwr
'Radiant' CBcs
'Radiant Greetings' XSen
'Radiant Moonbeam' ♀H6 CBgR
'Radiation Biohazard' CFwr SPol
'Raging Tiger' WHrl
'Rags to Riches' CFwr
'Rain Dance' **new** EStr
'Rainbow Candy' CWGN LLHF MBNS
'Rainbow Drive' CFwr
'Rainbow Gold' XSen
'Rainbow Serpent' CFwr
'Raining Violets' EWoo
'Rajah' CBgR CMac EStr MBNS MSpe NBro SCob WHrl
'Randall Moore' SPol
'Rander's Pride' EWoo
'Raspberry Beret' **new** CFwr
'Raspberry Butterflies' EWoo
'Raspberry Candy' CBro EStr GCra IBoy MBNS MNrw SRms WHrl
'Raspberry Fields Forever' EStr
'Raspberry Griffin' CFwr
'Raspberry Masquerade' CFwr
'Raspberry Pixie' SPol
'Raspberry Wine' ECha
'Raspberry Winter' **new** EStr
'Raven Woodsong' EWoo
'Razzle' **new** EStr
'Real Life Drama' **new** EStr
'Real Wind' EStr SPol
'Red Admiral' EAEE LRHS
'Red Butterfly' SPol
'Red Eyed Fantasy' CFwr
'Red Eyed Shocker' CFwr
'Red Flag' SGSe
'Red Grace' **new** EStr
'Red Hill' EWoo
'Red Precious' ♀H7 MNrw SMHy WCot
'Red Rain' EStr EWoo WHrl XSen
'Red Resplendence' EWoo
'Red Ribbons' ELon EWoo SDay SGSe SPol
'Red Ruby' ERCP
'Red Rum' CBgR LRHS MSpe MSwo NBro WMoo
'Red Squirrel' CFwr
'Red Suspenders' ECtt EStr MBNS
'Red Thrill' WHrl
'Red Twister' ELon EStr SDay SPol
'Red Volunteer' EStr SDay SGSe SPol
'Red Vortex' EStr
'Redheaded Hussy' CFwr EStr
'Redneck Red' CFwr
'Reflections in Time' EWoo
'Regal Giant' EStr EWoo
'Regency Dandy' SDay SPol XSen
'Regency Heights' EStr
'Reigning Sunshine' CFwr
'Renee' MNrw
'Respighi' EStr
'Return to Oz' **new** CFwr
'Return Trip' SPol
'Revolute' SDay
'Rhode Island Red' CFwr
'Ribbonette' EBee EStr MBNS
'Ricky Rose' SDay XSen
'Rigamarole' SPol
'Rise of the Phoenix' **new** EStr
'River Wye' MWat
'Roaring Jellyfish' CFwr
'Robespierre' SDay
'Rocket Booster' EStr
'Rocket City' ELan EStr SPol WNHG
'Rocky Mountain Pals' CFwr
'Rodeo Sweetheart' CFwr
'Roger Grounds' CBgR SPol
'Roll Up Candy' CFwr
'Rolling Hill' CFwr
'Rolling Raven' CFwr
'Roman Toga' CBgR SDay
'Romanian Rendevous' CFwr
* 'Romantic Rose' ELon MBNS NLar WHrl
'Romeo is Bleeding' **new** EStr
'Ron Rousseau' SPol
'Root Beer' WCAu WHrl
'Rose Claire' LPla
'Rose Corsage' EWoo
'Rose Emily' CBgR EStr SDay SPol

'Rose Fever'	EWoo
'Rose for Charlotte'	SPol
'Rose Tattoo' **new**	EStr
'Rose Victorious'	CFwr
'Roseate Spoonbill'	EWoo
'Roses in Snow'	IBoy MBNS SPol
'Roswitha'	CWat SPol
'Rosy Lights'	EWoo SPol
'Rosy Polyphemus'	EStr
'Rosy Returns'	EPfP LRHS MBNS NLar WHoo
'Round Midnight'	SPol
'Royal Bird'	EStr
'Royal Braid'	EStr MBNS NLar SPer WCot
'Royal Butterfly'	CFwr
'Royal Celebration'	WCot
'Royal Elk'	EWoo
'Royal Emperor'	CFwr
'Royal Eventide'	CFwr XSen
'Royal Flycatcher'	CFwr
'Royal Heritage'	EStr SDay
'Royal Hunter'	CFwr
'Royal Pink Twist' **new**	CFwr
'Royal Robe'	CTri
'Royal Russian Rendezvous'	CFwr
'Royal Saracen'	SDay
'Royal Thornbird'	CBgR
'Royal Trophy'	WNHG
'Royalty'	GCra
'Ruby Corsage' **new**	EStr
'Ruby Sentinel'	SDay
'Ruby Spider' ♀H6	ELon EWoo SPol
'Ruby Storm'	CFwr
'Rue Madelaine'	SPol
'Ruffled Apricot'	CKel MBNS SDay WNHG
'Ruffled Carousel'	WNHG
'Ruffled Dude' **new**	EStr
'Ruffled Ivory'	SDay
'Ruffled Lemon Lace' **new**	EStr
'Ruffled Magic' **new**	SDay
'Ruffled Perfection' **new**	EStr
'Rumble Seat Romance'	WNHG
'Russian Easter'	EStr
'Russian Ragtime'	EStr
'Russian Rhapsody' ♀H6	CKel SDay SPol
'Ruth Oliver'	EStr
'Sabie'	EStr
'Sabine Baur'	CWat EStr IPot LRHS MBNS MNrw NLar WFar
'Sabra Salina'	EStr EWoo SDay SPol
'Sacred Drummer'	SDay
'Saffron Glow'	SDay
'Sahara Sand Storm'	EStr
'Saintly'	EWoo
'Sallie Brown'	EStr SDay
'Salmon Pagoda'	EWoo
'Salmon Sheen'	SDay SPer
'Sammy'	EStr SDay
'Sammy Russell'	Widely available
'Samuel Bell'	EWoo
'San Luis Halloween'	CFwr
'Sandra Elizabeth'	SDay
'Sandra Walker'	WWtn
'Sanford Code Red'	CFwr
'Sanford Star Search'	CFwr
'Santa's Little Helper'	CFwr
'Santiago'	SPol
'Saratoga Pinwheel'	SPol
'Sariah'	SDay
'Satan's Curls' **new**	SGSe
'Satin Glass'	EAEE EBee LRHS
'Satin Glow'	ECha MLHP
'Scapes from Hell'	EWoo
'Scarlet Butterfly'	SPol
'Scarlet Flame'	ECha WMoo
'Scarlet Oak'	SDay
'Scarlet Orbit'	EWoo SDay SPol
'Scarlet Pimpernel'	CFwr
'Scarlet Prince'	WNHG
'Scarlet Ribbons'	EStr SPol
'Scatterbrain'	CFwr CKel SPol
'Schnickel Fritz'	EBee
'School Girl'	EAEE EBee LRHS
'Scorpio'	CBgR MSpe SDay SGSe SPol WHrl
'Scout's Honor' (d)	CFwr
'Screaming Demon'	EStr SPol WCot
'Sea Siren'	CWat
'Sea Swept Dreams'	SDay
'Seabiscuit'	CFwr
'Seal of Approval'	EBee EStr
'Sebastian'	SDay
'Secret Splendor'	SPol
'Secretary's Sand'	EWoo
'Seductive Fairy Tale' **new**	EStr
'Selma Longlegs' ♀H6	EStr SPol
'Seminole Blood'	SPol
'Seminole Princess'	CFwr
'Seminole Wind'	EWoo SPol
'Semiramide'	CBgR
'Sentinel Solar Burst' (d)	CFwr
'Serena Lady'	SDay
'Serena Sunburst' ♀H6	EStr SPol
'Serenade'	EWoo
'Serene Madonna'	CCon ELan GBin
'Serenity Bay'	CFwr
'Serenity Morgan'	CBgR MBNS
'Serge Rigaud'	WHrl
'Sergeant Major'	EStr EWoo
'Shadowed Pink'	WNHG
'Shady Lady'	SDay SPol
'Shaman'	SDay SPol
'Shangri La Truffle'	CFwr
'She Devil'	CFwr EStr
'Shelly Victoria'	SDay
'Sherry Lane Carr'	EStr SDay SPol
'Sherwood Gladiator'	WNHG
'Shibui Splendor'	SPol
'Shimek September Morning'	EStr SPol
'Shinto Etching' **new**	EStr
* 'Shocker'	EWoo
'Shogun'	MBNS
'Shotgun'	EStr SPol
'Shuffle the Deck'	CFwr EWoo
'Sidewinder Oh Seven'	CFwr
'Signature Truffle' (d)	CFwr
'Sigudilla'	WNHG
'Silent Thunder' **new**	EStr
'Silken Fairy'	CBgR SDay WWtn
'Silken Touch'	CBgR EStr SPol
'Siloam Amazing Grace'	SDay
'Siloam Angel Blush'	SDay
'Siloam Baby Doll'	SDay
'Siloam Baby Talk'	ELon EStr GBuc NBir SDay WAul WMoo WPnP
'Siloam Bertie Ferris'	MBNS
'Siloam Bo Peep'	SDay

'Siloam Button Box'	MBNS WHrl
'Siloam Bye Lo'	EWoo SDay
'Siloam Cinderella'	SDay SPol
'Siloam David Kirchhoff'	EBee MBNS SDay XSen
'Siloam Doodlebug'	CBgR CWat
'Siloam Double Classic' (d)	EStr SDay SPol
'Siloam Dream Baby'	ELon MBNS
'Siloam Ethel Smith'	SDay SPol
'Siloam Fairy Tale'	CWat SDay
'Siloam Flower Girl'	SDay
'Siloam French Doll'	MBNS NLar
'Siloam French Marble'	SDay
'Siloam Frosted Mint'	SDay SPol
'Siloam Gold Coin'	SDay
'Siloam Grace Stamile'	CCon MBNS SDay
'Siloam Helpmate'	WNHG
'Siloam Joan Senior'	MBNS
'Siloam John Yonski'	SDay
'Siloam June Bug'	CBgR ELan WCot
'Siloam Justine Lee'	MBNS
'Siloam Little Angel'	SPol
'Siloam Little Girl'	ECtt EStr SDay
'Siloam Mama'	SDay
'Siloam Merle Kent'	EWoo SDay SPol WAul
'Siloam Nugget'	EStr
'Siloam Orchid Jewel'	SDay
'Siloam Paul Watts'	SPol
'Siloam Peewee'	ELon LRHS
'Siloam Pink Glow'	SDay SWat
'Siloam Plum Tree'	SPol
'Siloam Pocket Size'	SDay
'Siloam Queen's Toy'	SPol
'Siloam Red Toy'	SMHy
'Siloam Ribbon Candy'	SDay WNHG
'Siloam Rose Dawn'	SPol
'Siloam Rose Queen'	SDay
'Siloam Royal Prince'	SDay
'Siloam Ruffled Infant'	SDay
'Siloam Shocker'	EStr
'Siloam Show Girl'	CWGN EWoo GKin MBNS NLar SDay
'Siloam Space Age' **new**	WNHG
'Siloam Spizz'	EStr SDay
'Siloam Sugar Time'	ELon
'Siloam Tee Tiny'	WAul WWtn
'Siloam Tiny Mite'	SDay WHrl
'Siloam Toddler'	EStr
'Siloam Tom Thumb'	CBgR EStr MBNS
'Siloam Ury Winniford'	CBro CMac MBNS NLar WHoo WPnP
'Siloam Virginia Henson'	EStr EWoo WWEG WWtn
'Silver Ice'	SDay SPol
'Silver Lance'	EStr SDay SPol
'Silver Quasar'	SDay SPol
'Silver Trumpet'	WWEG
'Silver Veil'	SDay
'Simmering Elephants'	CFwr
'Simmons Overture'	ECtt
'Simplicity in Motion'	CFwr
'Sinbad Sailor'	NLar
'Singing in the Sunshine'	EWoo
'Sink Into Your Eyes'	EStr WHrl
'Sir Blackstem'	ELon GCal SDay
'Sir Knight'	SPol
'Sir Modred' ♀H6	EStr SPol WNHG
'Sitting on a Rainbow'	EStr
'Sixth Sense'	ELon MBNS
'Skeezix' (d)	CFwr
'Skeleton Man'	CFwr
'Skinny Dipping'	CFwr
'Skinwalker'	EWoo
'Slapstick'	ELon EStr SDay SPol
'Sleepy'	ECha
'Sleepy Hollow'	EStr
'Slender Lady'	CFwr ELon SDay XSen
'Slipping Into the Abyss' **new**	EStr
'Small Town'	EWoo
'Small World Tornado'	EWoo
'Small World Twister' **new**	CFwr
'Smith Brothers'	SPol
'Smoke Scream'	CFwr
'Smokestack Lightning'	CFwr
'Smoky Mountain Autumn'	EWoo SDay SPol
'Smooch Hollow'	CBgR EStr
'Smuggler's Gold'	ECtt
'Smuggler's Temptation'	SPol
'Snowed In'	EWoo
'Snowy Apparition'	EAEE EBee ECrc ECtt EWTr GKin LHop LRHS MBNS MWhi NWad SPol SWvt WCAu
'Snowy Eyes'	CHid GKin MBNS SWat
'So Excited'	SDay
'So Lovely'	EWoo XLum
'So Many Stars'	CFwr SPol
'Soft Cashmere'	XLum
'Soho Style'	CFwr
'Solano Bull's Eye'	MLHP
'Solid Scarlet'	EStr
'Sombrero Way'	SDay
'Someone Special'	EStr SDay SPol
'Somerset Fandango'	CBgR
'Song In My Heart'	EWoo
'Song Sparrow'	CBro
'Soraya Seline'	CBgR
'Sorcerer's Song'	SDay
'South Seas'	EStr
'Southern Prize'	SDay
'Sovereign Queen'	WNHG
'Spacecoast Dragon Prince'	EWoo
'Spacecoast Freaky Tiki'	EStr
'Spacecoast Scrambled'	MBNS NLar
'Spacecoast Starburst'	CBcs EStr MBNS WCot
'Spanish Fandango'	EStr SPol
'Spanish Glow'	SPol
'Sparkling Dawn'	EStr
'Spice Hunter'	CFwr
'Spider Breeder'	CBgR ELon EStr
'Spider Man' ♀H6	ELon EStr SDay SPol WCAu XSen
'Spider Miracle'	SDay SPol
'Spider Red'	CWGN EWoo
'Spider Web'	EStr
'Spilled Milk'	SPol
'Spin Master'	EStr
'Spindazzle'	CBgR SDay SPol
'Spinne in Lachs'	EStr SPol
'Spiral Charmer'	SPol
'Spiral Nebula' **new**	EStr
'Spirit of Sapelo'	EWoo
'Spock's Ears'	CFwr
'Spooner'	CBgR
'Spoons for Escargot' **new**	EStr
'Spring Willow Song'	SDay
'Springfield Clan' **new**	EStr
'Square Dancer's Curtsy'	CFwr

	Name	Suppliers
	'Squash Dolly'	EWoo
	'Stafford' 🏆H7	Widely available
	'Staghorn Sumac'	GKin LEdu MBNS NHol WCAu
	'Star Asterisk'	CFwr SPol
	'Star of Fantasy'	CFwr EStr
	'Star of India'	SPol
	'Star Poly' **new**	EStr
	'Star Spangled' **new**	SPol
	'Star Twister'	CFwr
	'Stargate Corridor'	SPol
	'Starling'	CPar WWEG WWtn
	'Starman's Gift'	EStr
	'Starman's Quest'	SPol
	'Starstruck'	WNHG
	'Startle'	ELon MBNS MNrw WCot WHrl
	'Startling Creation'	CFwr
	'Statuesque'	EWoo
	'Stella de Oro'	Widely available
	'Stella in Red'	EPfP
	'Steve Trimmer'	SPol
	'Stinnette'	WCot
	'Stippled Starlight'	CFwr
	'Stoke Poges'	CBgR CBro EAEE EBee ELon EPPr EPfP EShb GBin LAst LHop LPot LSRN MBNS MMuc SPer SWat WHrl WWEG
	'Stone Beacon'	CFwr
	'Stone Island'	CFwr
	'Stoplight'	CBgR ELon SDay SGSe SMHy SPol WHrl
	'Storm of the Century'	EStr MNrw
	'Storm Over Toledo'	CFwr
	'Strasbourg'	CMac
	'Strawberry Candy' 🏆H6	CBgR CMac CSBt ECtt ELon EPfP EStr EWoo IBoy ILea LSRN MBNS NGdn NLar SCob SDay SPer WAul WCAu WHoo WHrl WMoo WNHG WWEG
	'Strawberry Fields Forever'	EWoo MBNS NLar SPol
I	'Streaker' B. Brown (v)	XSen
	'Street Urchin'	SPol
	'Streets of Heaven'	EWoo
	'String Bikini'	EStr
	'String Theory'	CFwr
	'Strutter's Ball'	CBod EStr EWoo LPla MBNS MJak NGdn SPer SPol SWat WAul WCAu WHrl WMnd
	'Stupidville USA' **new**	EStr
	'Stu's Old Pink Spider'	CBgR
	'Suburban Golden Eagle'	EStr
	'Sugar Cookie'	EWoo SDay SPol
	'Sugar Plum Jam' **new**	CFwr
	'Summer Dragon'	EStr MBNS
	'Summer Fireworks'	EWoo
	'Summer Interlude'	WMoo
	'Summer Star' **new**	EStr
	'Summer Wine'	Widely available
	'Sunday Gloves'	SPol WNHG
	'Sunday Morning'	EStr SDay
	'Sungold Candy'	EStr
	'Sunray Brilliance'	EWoo
	'Sunrise Sunset Beautiful' **new**	CFwr
	'Sunset Lagoon'	EStr SPol
	'Sunshine Junkie'	CFwr
	'Super Purple'	CKel
	'Superlative'	EStr SPol
	'Susan Weber'	SPol
	'Suzy Cream Cheese'	CFwr SPol
	'Svengali'	SDay SPol
	'Swallow Tail Kite'	SPol
	'Swan Dance'	SDay
	'Swashbuckler Bay Boy'	CFwr
	'Sweet Charlotte'	SPol
	'Sweet Country Luvin''	EStr
	'Sweet Hot Chocolate'	LRHS MBNS WCAu
	'Sweet Pea'	EStr SDay
	'Sweet Sugar Candy'	ECtt EWoo SDeJ
	'Swirling Spider'	CBgR EWoo SPol
	'Tail Feathers'	CFwr
	'Taj Mahal'	ELon EWoo
	'Tammy Faye Eyes'	CFwr
	'Tang'	CHid MBNS
	'Tangerine Tango'	EWoo
	'Tangerine Twist'	EStr SPol
	'Tango Noturno'	SPol
	'Tani'	SDay
	'Taos'	EStr
	'Tarantula'	ELon SPol
	'Taruga'	EWoo SDay
	'Tasmania'	SPer
	'Tchao Pantin'	XSen
	'Teacup Fingers'	CFwr
	'Technical Knockout'	EWoo
	'Techny Peach Lace'	EStr SPol
	'Techny Spider'	EStr SPol
	'Teenie Girl' **new**	EStr
	'Tejas'	CElw ELon LTro SPer
	'Témoin'	XSen
	'Tennessee Flycatcher'	EStr EWoo SPol
	'Tennessee Williams'	SPol
	'Tennyson'	CFwr
	'Tequila Mockingbird'	CFwr
	'Tet Set'	WNHG
	'Tetraploid Siloam Red Toy' **new**	SDay
	'Tetraploid Stella de Oro'	SDay
	'Tetrina's Daughter'	CBgR EPfP LRHS SGSe
	'Thanks a Bunch'	SPol
	'The Tingler'	CFwr EWoo
	'Thelma Perry'	LEdu
	'Thin Man'	CFwr
	'Think Pink'	EBee EPfP
	'Third Witch'	CFwr EWoo
	'Thomas Tew'	CFwr
	'Three Diamonds'	SPol
	'Three Times a Lady'	CFwr
	'Thrill Ride'	SPol
	'Thumbelina'	ECha WMoo XLum
§	***thunbergii***	ECha GCal MCoo
	- 'Ovation'	MBNS
	'Thunder and Lightning' **new**	EStr
	'Thundering Ovation'	CWGN
	'Thy True Love'	SDay
	'Tierra Del Fuego'	EStr
	'Tiger Prince'	CFwr
	'Tiger Swirl'	CFwr
	'Tigereye Spider'	EStr EWoo
	'Tigerling'	EStr EWoo MSpe SPol
	'Tigger'	EStr SPad SPol WCAu
	'Time Lord'	SDay XSen
	'Time to Believe'	SPol
	'Time Together'	EStr
	'Time Window'	EStr
	'Tiny Talisman'	SDay
	'Tiny Temptress'	SDay
	'Tis Midnight'	WNHG
	'Titanic Tower'	CFwr

'Tom Collins'	SDay
'Tom Wise'	EStr SPol
'Tomorrow's Song'	SPol
'Tone Poem'	WNHG
'Tonia Gay'	SDay SPol
'Toodleloo Kangaroo'	EWoo
'Tooth'	EStr
'Toothpick'	EWoo SPol WHrl
'Tootsie'	SDay
'Tootsie Rose'	SDay SPol
'Top Honors'	SPol
'Topaz Gem'	SPol
'Topguns Aleah Kaye'	CFwr
'Topguns Anita Causey' (d)	CFwr
'Topguns Bandit's Bandana'	CFwr
'Topguns Butterball' (d)	CFwr
'Topguns Cactus Jack'	CFwr
'Topguns Cherokee Dancer'	CFwr
'Topguns Cherry Limeade'	CFwr
'Topguns Citrine Dream' (d)	CFwr
'Topguns Copper Butterflies' (d)	CFwr
'Topguns Dragonfly Sunset' (d)	CFwr
'Topguns Dream Catcher' (d)	CFwr
'Topguns Eye Popper'	CFwr
'Topguns Grim Reaper'	CFwr
'Topguns Harlequin Ruffles'	CFwr
'Topguns Jennifer Hankins'	CFwr
'Topguns Lemon Ruffles'	CFwr
'Topguns Linda Farris' (d)	CFwr
'Topguns Molten Lava' (d)	CFwr
'Topguns Okie Twister'	CFwr
'Topguns Orange Fizz' (d)	CFwr
'Topguns Orange Marmalade'	CFwr
'Topguns Pawnee Princess'	CFwr
'Topguns Pinwheel'	CFwr
'Topguns Rising Sun' (d)	CFwr
'Topguns Ruffled Amazement' (d)	CFwr
'Topguns Stop 'n' Go'	CFwr
'Topguns Tilt-A-Whirl'	CFwr
'Torpoint'	CBgR GBee MBNS MRav NEgg
'Total Eclipse'	EStr
'Touch of Magic' **new**	EStr
'Towhead'	MRav SDay WCot
'Toyland'	MBNS NBir NGdn NLar SPol
'Trahlyta'	CBgR EWoo MSpe SDay SPol WHrl
'Treasure of Love'	EWoo
'Tremor'	EStr
'Trevi Fountain'	EWoo
'Trond'	SDay
'Tropical Breeze'	CFwr
'Tropical Depression'	CFwr EWoo
'Tropical Toy'	SDay
'Troubled Sleep'	EWoo
'Truchas Sunrise'	CFwr EWoo
'True Gertrude Demarest'	WHrl
'True North'	CFwr
'True Pink Beauty'	EWoo
'Truffle Heritage'	CFwr
'Tune the Harp'	EStr SPol
'Tuolumne Fairy Tale'	SPol
'Turkish Tapestry'	CBgR
'Turkish Turban'	SDay SPol
'Turn the Other Cheek' **new**	EStr
'Turtle Island' **new**	EStr
'Tuscawilla Blackout'	SPol XSen
'Tuscawilla Princess' **new**	EStr
'Tuscawilla Tigress'	EStr GKin IKil MBNS MNrw MSpe SDay SPol WAul WHrl
'Tutankhamun'	EStr
'Tutti Frutti Truffle'	CFwr
'Tuxedo'	SPol
'Tuxedo Junction' ♀H6 **new**	EStr
'Tuxedo Whiskers' **new**	EStr
'Twenty Third Psalm'	WHal
'Twilight Secrets'	MBNS SGol
'Twilight Swan'	WNHG
'Twirling Wings'	CFwr
'Twist and Shout'	CFwr
'Twist and Spin'	CFwr
'Twist of Lemon'	EWoo SDay
'Two Faces of Love'	SPol
'Tylwyth Teg'	CFwr SPol
'Ultimate Destiny'	CWat
'Unchartered Waters'	MBNS
'Unending Melody' **new**	CFwr
'Unforgetable Fire'	EWoo
'Unique Purple'	SPol
'Uniquely Different'	SPol
'Upper Class Peach'	EStr
'Uptown Girl'	EStr
'Valiant'	EWoo MBNS WHrl
'Valley Monster'	SPol
'Vanessa Arden'	SPol
'Vanilla Fluff'	EStr
'Variegated Woottens' (v)	EWoo
'Varsity'	CExl CWat LRHS NBir SPer
'Veins of Truth'	CBgR EBee WCAu
'Velvet Eyes'	EStr
'Velvet Ribbons'	CFwr
'Velvet Shadows'	CBgR SDay
'Vendetta'	WNHG
'Venusian Heat'	CFwr
'Venusian Mirage'	EStr
'Venus's Fire'	CFwr
'Vera Biaglow'	MSpe SDay SPol
'Very Berry Ice'	SPol
'Vespers'	WPnP
vespertina	see *H. thunbergii*
'Veuve Joyeuse'	XSen
'Vicountess Byng'	WWtn
'Victoria Aden'	CBro
'Victoria Elizabeth Barnes'	WNHG
'Victorian Lace'	EWoo
'Victorian Ribbons'	SPol
'Victorian Violet'	SDay
'Video'	SDay
'Vie en Rose' **new**	EStr
'Viewpoint' **new**	SDay
'Vino di Notte'	EStr
'Vintage Bordeaux'	ELan
'Vintage Burgundy'	CBgR WNHG
'Violent Thunder'	CFwr EStr
'Violet Hour'	EStr SDay
'Viracocha'	WMnd WNHG

'Virgin's Blush'	SPer
'Vohann'	SDay
'Volcano Queen'	CFwr
'Voodoo Dancer' new	EBee EStr SCob
'Walking on Sunshine'	EStr WCot
'Wally Nance'	CFwr
'Walnut Hill'	EStr
'Walt Disney'	GKin
'War Paint'	EStr SDay
'Warp Drive' new	SDay
'Warrior Victorious'	CFwr
'Watch Tower'	CBgR
'Watchyl Christmas Widow'	CFwr
'Watchyl Dancing Spider'	EStr SPol
'Water Bird'	EStr
'Water Witch'	CWat SDay
'Watermelon Man'	CBgR EWoo
'Watership Down'	EWoo
'Watson Park Tempest'	CFwr
'Wayne Johnson' new	WNHG
'Wayside Green Imp'	MNrw
'We Love'	EWoo
'Weaver's Art'	SPol
'Web Browser'	CFwr EStr
'Web Dancer'	SPol
'Webster's Pink Wonder' new	EStr SPol
'Wee Willie Wonka'	WNHG
'Wekiwa'	EWoo
'Welchkins'	SDay WAul
'Welfo White Diamond'	SPol
'Westward Wind'	EWoo
'Whammer Jammer'	CFwr
'What a Day for a Daydream'	CFwr
'When I Dream'	EStr
'Which Way Jim' new	SDay
'Whichford'	CAby CBgR CBod CBro CSam ECha ECrc ECtt ELan EPfP EWoo GBuc GCal GKin LRHS MBNS SPer SPhx WGwG WHrl WPtf
'Whirling Fury'	ELon EWoo
'White Coral'	EAEE LRHS LSRN MBNS NBro
'White Edged Madonna'	WHrl
'White Ensign' new	SDay
'White Magician' new	EStr
'White Temptation'	CCon EPfP IBoy LRHS NGdn SDay WAul WHoo WMnd WNHG WWEG XSen
'White Tie Affair'	EWoo
'White Zone'	EWoo SDay
'Whooperee'	SDay
'Whoopie'	CHid CWld SPad
'Wideyed'	XLum
'Wild about Sherry'	CFwr SPol
'Wild and Wonderful'	EPfP EStr EWoo LSun
'Wild Child'	CFwr
'Wild Horses'	CWGN EPfP EWes LRHS MNrw NLar SCob SMad SPad SPol WHrl
'Wild Mustang'	EStr MBNS MSpe
'Wild Rose Fandango'	CFwr EWoo
'Wild Winter Wine'	CFwr
'Wildest Dreams'	EWoo SDay
'William Milo Spalding' new	EStr
'Willy Nilly'	SPol
'Wilson Spider'	EStr SPol
'Wind Beneath My Sails'	EWoo
'Wind Frills'	EStr NQui SDay SPol XSen
'Wind Master'	CFwr
'Wind Song'	ELon SDay
'Windmill Yellow'	EWoo SDay
'Window Dressing'	EWoo
'Winds of Love'	EWoo
'Wineberry Candy'	EStr EWoo MBNS NLar SDay
'Winged Migration'	CFwr EWoo
'Wings of Chance' new	SPol
'Wings on High'	EWoo SPol
'Winnie the Pooh'	SDay
'Winsome Lady'	ECGP ECha ECtt GKin MBNS WHrl
'Winter Wolf' new	EStr
'Wisest of Wizards'	MBNS SPol WHrl
'Wishing Well'	WCot
'Witch Hazel'	WCAu WWtn
'Witch Stitchery'	EStr SDay
'Witches Brew'	CBgR
'Witches Wink'	EWoo
'Witch's Stick'	CFwr
'Without Warning'	CBgR
'Woodland Spider'	SDay
'Woodside Ruby'	WNHG
'Worth it All' new	CFwr
'Wyoming Wildfire'	CBgR
'Xia Xiang'	EWoo SDay
'Xochimilco'	WNHG
'Ya Ya Girl'	EWoo
'Yabba Dabba Doo'	EStr SPol
'Yazoo Green Octopus'	EWoo
'Yazoo Wild Violet'	EStr
'Yellow Angel'	ELon SPol WCot
'Yellow Finch'	CFwr
'Yellow Lollipop'	SDay
'Yellow Rain'	WCot
'Yellow Ribbon'	SPol
'Yellow Submarine'	EPfP MBNS
'Yesterday Memories'	SDay
yezoensis	EBtc
'Yo-rick Yost'	CFwr
'You Angel You'	MBNS MSpe
'You Are My Sunshine' new	CFwr
'Yum Yum Plum' new	EStr
'Yuma'	WNHG
'Zagora'	EStr WCAu
'Zampa'	CBgR EStr SDay
'Zara'	SPer
'Zenobia'	EStr
'Zip Boom Bah' new	EStr
'Zuni Mountains' new	WNHG
'Zuni Thunderbird'	EWoo

Hepatica ✿ (*Ranunculaceae*)

acutiloba	CBro CEvo ECho GBuc GEdr GKev NBir NLar WPnP XEll
- blue-flowered	MAsh
- white-flowered	MAsh NLar
americana	ECho ELan GKev MAsh NBir
angulosa	see *H. transsilvanica*
(Forest Series) 'Forest Blue' new	EBee LCro
- 'Forest Pink'	EBee ELan LCro XEll
- 'Forest Purple'	EBee ELan LCro XEll
- 'Forest Red'	CWCL EBee ELan GEdr LCro XEll
- 'Forest White'	EBee ELan LCro XEll
henryi	EBee ECho GEdr GKev MAsh NSla
insularis	GBuc MAsh

maxima	ECho GBuc GEdr MAsh
× ***media*** 'Ballardii'	GBuc GEdr IBlr LLHF
- 'Harvington Beauty'	CLAP GEdr IBlr IFoB MAsh MHom NBir WSHC
- 'Millstream Merlin'	GEdr
'Miyoshino'	GEdr
§ ***nobilis*** ♀H5	Widely available
- var. ***asiatica***	MAsh
- - pink-flowered	MAsh
- - purple-flowered	MAsh
- - white-flowered	MAsh
- blue-flowered	ECho IFoB MAsh NSla WAbe
- 'Cobalt'	CLAP ECho GEdr NSla
- compact evergreen	MAsh
- 'Cremar'	GEdr MAsh
- dark-blue-flowered	CLAP
- dwarf white-flowered	IFoB
- 'Elkofener Heidi'	GEdr
- 'Gold Band' (v) new	GEdr
- var. ***japonica***	EPfP EWes IFoB LHop MAsh NBir NSla
- - 'Akabuku' (1)	GEdr
- - 'Akafuku' (1)	GEdr
- - 'Akane' (1)	GEdr
- - 'Akanezora' (6/d)	GEdr
- - 'Akebono' (9/d)	GEdr
- - 'Anjyu' (9/d)	GEdr
- - 'Asahi' (7/d)	GEdr
- - 'Asahizuru' (6/d)	GEdr
- - 'Benikanzan' (1)	GEdr
- - 'Benikujyaku' (7/d)	GEdr
- - 'Benioiran' (3)	GEdr
- - 'Beniokesa' (9/d)	GEdr
- - 'Benishinjyu' (6/d)	GEdr
- - 'Benisuzume' (1)	GEdr
- - 'Benitaiko' (9/d)	GEdr
- - 'Bojyou' (5A/d)	GEdr
- - 'Daishihou' (9/d)	GEdr
- - 'Dewa' (9/d)	GEdr
- - 'Echigobijin' (1)	GEdr
- - 'Fukujyu' (9/d)	GEdr
- - 'Getsurin' (5A/d)	GEdr
- - 'Gosho-zakura' (5A/d)	GEdr
- - 'Gyousei' (1)	GBuc GEdr
- - 'Hakuji' (1)	GEdr
- - 'Hakurin' (6/d)	GEdr
- - 'Hakusetsu' (9/d)	GEdr
- - 'Haruka' (2)	GEdr
- - 'Harukaze' (5A/d)	GEdr
- - 'Haruno-awajuki' (9/d)	GEdr
- - 'Hatsune' (5/d)	GEdr
- - Herashibe Group (5/d)	GBuc
- - 'Hohobeni' (9/d)	GEdr
- - 'Hokutosei' (7/d)	GEdr
- - 'Hosyun' (1)	GEdr
- - 'Houkan' (9/d)	GEdr
- - 'Isaribi' (1)	GEdr
- - 'Junissen' (6/d)	GEdr
- - 'Kagura' (5A/d)	GEdr
- - 'Kasumino'	GEdr
- - 'Kiko' (9/d)	GEdr
- - 'Kimon' (9/d)	GEdr
- - 'Koshi-no-maboroshi' (7/d)	GEdr
- - 'Kougyoku' (9/d)	GEdr
- - 'Kousei' (9/d)	GEdr
- - 'Kuetsu' (9/d)	GEdr
- - 'Kuukai' (8/d)	GEdr
- - f. ***magna***	MAsh
- - - 'Murasaki-shikibu' (9/d)	GEdr
- - - 'Seizan' (9/d)	GEdr
- - 'Manazuru' (9/d)	GEdr
- - 'Miwaku' (1)	GEdr
- - 'Miyuki' (9/d)	GEdr
- - 'Murasaki-sakama' (9/d)	GEdr
- - 'Odoriko' (9/d)	GEdr
- - 'Okina' (9/d)	GEdr
- - 'Ō-murasaki' (1)	GEdr
- - 'Orihime' (9/d)	GEdr
- - 'Reeka' (1)	GEdr
- - 'Ryokurei' (5A/d)	GEdr
- - 'Ryokusetsu' (9/d)	GEdr
- - 'Ryokuun' (9/d)	GEdr
- - 'Ryougetsu' (1)	GEdr
- - 'Sadobeni' (1)	GEdr
- - 'Saichou' (7/d)	GEdr
- - Sandan Group (7/d)	GEdr
- - 'Sawanemidori' (6/d)	GEdr
- - 'Sayaka' (1)	GEdr
- - 'Seikai' (5A/d)	GEdr
- - 'Senhime' (9/d)	GEdr
- - 'Setsudu' (7/d)	GEdr
- - 'Shihou' (9/d)	GEdr
- - 'Shikouden' (9/d)	GEdr
- - 'Shikouryuu' (9/d)	GEdr
- - 'Shirayuki' (9/d)	GEdr
- - 'Shirin' (9/d)	GEdr
- - 'Shiun' (9/d)	GEdr
- - 'Shoujyouno-homare' (9/d)	GEdr
- - 'Sougetsu' (6/d)	GEdr
- - 'Soushyunka' (9/d)	GEdr
- - 'Subaru' (9/d)	GEdr
- - 'Suien' (9/d)	GEdr
- - 'Syoujyouno-Homare' (9/d)	GEdr
- - 'Tae' (5A/d)	GEdr
- - 'Taeka' (9/d)	GEdr
- - 'Takumi' (9/d)	GEdr
- - 'Tamahime' (8/d)	GEdr
- - 'Tamakujyaku' (6/d)	GEdr
- - 'Tamamushi' (9/d)	GEdr
- - 'Tamao' (1)	GEdr
- - 'Tamasaburou' (1)	GEdr
- - 'Tenjinbai' (1)	GEdr
- - 'Tennyonomai' (6A/d)	GEdr
- - 'Tenzan' (7/d)	GEdr
- - 'Toki' (9/d)	GEdr
- - 'Touen' (9/d)	GEdr
- - 'Touhou' (9/d)	GEdr
- - 'Touryoku' (9/d)	GEdr
- - 'Toyama-chiyoiwai'	GEdr
- - 'Unabara' (9/d)	GEdr
- - 'Usugesyou' (9/d)	GEdr
- - 'Utyuu' (1)	GEdr
- - 'Wakakusa' (9/d)	GEdr
- - 'Yaegoromo' (6/d)	GEdr
- - 'Yahiko' (5/d)	GEdr
- - 'Yahikomurasaki' (1)	GEdr
- - 'Yamahibiki' (9/d)	GEdr
- - 'Yukishino' (2)	GEdr
- - 'Yuunagi' (9/d)	GEdr
- - 'Yuunami' (1)	GEdr
- - 'Yuzuru' (9/d)	GEdr
- large, pale blue-flowered	NSla
- 'Lilac Picotee'	NSla

	- 'Marble Leaf' new	CElw
	- mottled leaf	ECho
	- patterned leaf	NSla
	- pink-flowered	CLAP ECho GAbr MAsh WCot
	- var. ***pubescens***	MAsh
*	- var. ***pyrenaica***	GBuc LEdu MAsh NSla WThu
*	- - 'Apple Blossom'	GBuc NBir WAbe
	- 'Pyrenean Marbles'	CLAP GBin
	- red-flowered	ECho
	- var. ***rubra***	CLAP ECho NSla
	- 'Rubra Plena' (d)	CElw GEdr NHar NSla
	- violet-flowered	GAbr MAsh
	- 'White Sands' new	ELan GEdr
	- white-flowered	CLAP ECho GAbr MAsh
	'Noubeni'	GEdr
	'Oboroyo'	GEdr
	'Sakaya'	GEdr
	× ***schlyteri*** 'Ashwood Hybrids'	MAsh
§	***transsilvanica*** ♀H5	CBro CLAP ECho GAbr GBin MAsh MCot WCot WThu
	- 'Ada Scott'	GEdr
	- 'Blue Eyes'	ECho GEdr GKev NCGa
	- 'Blue Jewel'	CCon CLAP CWCL EBee ECho ELan EPot GEdr LHop MCot MHol NCGa WCot WPnP
	- blue-flowered	IBlr IFoB MAsh
	- 'Buis'	CLAP ECha ECho GEdr IFoB ILea MHom NLar WPnP
	- 'Eisvogel'	ECho GEdr
	- 'Elison Spence' (d)	GEdr IBlr LLHF MCot
	- 'Lilacina'	GEdr MAsh NSla
	- 'Loddon Blue'	GEdr IBlr
	- pink-flowered	ECho MAsh
	- 'Sieben Bergen'	IBlr
	- white-flowered	ECho GEdr MAsh
	triloba	see *H. nobilis*
	'Umezono'	GEdr
	'Wakana'	GEdr
	yamatutai	GBuc GEdr GKev
	aff. ***yamatutai***	MAsh

Heptacodium (*Caprifoliaceae*)

	jasminoides	see *H. miconioides*
§	***miconioides*** ♀H5	Widely available

Heptapleurum see *Schefflera*

Heptaptera (*Apiaceae*)

triquetra W&B BGA-2	WCot

Heracleum (*Apiaceae*)

dulce	EBee
sphondylium	WHil WSFF
- 'You're so Vein'	CNat
stevenii	MHol MSCN NSti SDix WCot

Herbertia (*Iridaceae*)

§	***lahue***	CDes ECho
	platensis hort. ex L. H. Bailey	GKev

Hereroa (*Aizoaceae*)

glenensis	CSma EDAr LRHS SPlb

Hermannia (*Malvaceae*)

flammea	SPlb
stricta	CPBP WAbe

Hermodactylus see *Iris*

Herniaria (*Caryophyllaceae*)

glabra	CArn GPoy WHfH

Hertia see *Othonna*

Hesperaloe (*Asparagaceae*)

F&M 311.1	WPGP
campanulata new	WCot
engelmannii new	WCot
'Lynn's Pink' new	WCot
malacophylla	CFil EBee
'Mamulique'	WCot
'New Blue'	WCot
parviflora	EBee LEdu LTro SBig SIgm SPlb XSen
- creamy yellow-flowered	WCot

Hesperantha ✿ (*Iridaceae*)

§	***baurii***	CTre ECho GBuc LLHF WThu
	coccinea	Widely available
	- from Giants Castle	CTca
	- f. ***alba***	Widely available
	- 'Anne'	NLar
	- 'Ballyrogan Giant'	CCon CPrp CTca ECtt GBuc IBlr WFar WHer WPGP WSHC
	- 'Big Moma'	CPrp
	- 'Cardinal'	NHol WMoo
	- 'Caroline'	CPrp
	- 'Cindy Towe'	CYeo EAJP
	- 'Countesse de Vere'	EBee
	- 'Elburton Glow'	WFar
	- 'Fenland Daybreak'	Widely available
	- 'Good White'	NBir NCGa
	- 'Hilary Gould'	CMea CPrp ECtt GBuc WHal
	- 'Jack Frost'	EBee WMoo
	- 'Jazz' new	CYeo
	- 'Jennifer' ♀H4	CBro CPrp CTca CTri EBee ECha ECtt ELon EPfP GAbr GBin GBuc LPot LRHS LSou MCot MMuc MRav NLar SEND SRms SWvt WFar WMoo WPnP XLum
	- 'Maiden's Blush'	ECtt ELan LEdu LRHS LSou MCot NLar SRms WFar
§	- 'Major' ♀H4	Widely available
	- 'Marietta'	CYeo NWad
	- 'Mollie Gould'	CPrp CTca CYeo ECtt EHrv ELon GBuc GCra LHop LLWG LRHS LSou MAvo MHer MPie NCGa NHol SCoo SRms WMoo
	- 'Mrs Hegarty'	Widely available
	- 'November Cheer'	CMac IBlr NBir NLar WWEG XLum
	- 'Oregon Sunset'	CPrp
	- 'Pallida'	CPrp CSam ECtt EHrv ELan MLHP MRav NBir WFar
	- 'Pink Marg'	CPrp ITim
	- 'Pink Princess'	see *H. coccinea* 'Wilfred H. Bryant'
	- pink-flowered	MBel
	- 'Professor Barnard'	CSpe CTca EBee ECtt ELon EPfP EPri GAbr LBrs MBNS NBir NLar SRot WMoo WRHF
	- 'Red Arrow'	EWes
	- 'Red Dragon'	CYeo ECtt GBuc LLHF NHol
I	- 'Rosea'	GKev SDeJ
	- 'Salmon Charm'	ECtt GBuc LRHS WFar WMoo
	- 'Salome'	CPrp
	- 'Silver Pink'	IBlr
	- 'Snow Maiden'	CWCL CYeo EBee EWTr GAbr LRHS

- 'Strawberry'	CPrp EBee
§ - 'Sunrise' ♀H4	Widely available
- 'Tambara'	CCse CPou CPrp CSam ECtt EHrv GAbr GBuc XLum
- 'Viscountess Byng'	CBcs CFis CTca CTri CWCL EBee NBir SPer
§ - 'Wilfred H. Bryant' ♀H4	Widely available
- 'Zeal Salmon'	CBro CCon CElw CPou CYeo ECha ECtt GAbr NBir NCGa
cucullata	CTre ECho NRog
falcata	ECho
grandiflora	ECho
huttonii	ECho GEdr ITim LLHF MHer MSCN NBir
mossii	see *H. baurii*
oligantha new	CDes
pauciflora	CTre
vaginata	CTre

Hesperis (*Brassicaceae*)

lutea	see *Sisymbrium luteum*
matronalis	Widely available
- ***alba***	see *H. matronalis* var. *albiflora*
§ - var. ***albiflora***	CLau CSpe CTri CWld EPfP EWoo GMaP LCro LOPS LRHS LSun MCot MNHC NGdn SIde SPer SPhx SPoG SWat WBrk WMoo
- - 'Alba Plena' (d)	CAbP ELan ELon IBoy LRHS MCot NBir SBod
- 'Cally Dwarf' (d)	GCal
- 'Lilacina'	SWat
I - 'Variegata' (v)	WBor
nivea	LEdu

× *Hesperotropsis* see × *Cuprocyparis*

Heteromeles (*Rosaceae*)

arbutifolia	see *H. salicifolia*
§ ***salicifolia***	LEdu

Heteromorpha (*Apiaceae*)

arborescens	CExl SPlb SVen

Heteropolygonatum (*Convallariaceae*)

'Mikinori Ogisu' new	GKev
roseolum	CAby

Heterotheca (*Asteraceae*)

mariana	see *Chrysopsis mariana*
subaxillaris	WCot
§ ***villosa***	EPPr
- 'Golden Sunshine'	CPrp

Heuchera ✿ (*Saxifragaceae*)

sp.	ETod
'Alan Davidson'	MPnt
'Alison'	MPnt
'Amber Waves'PBR	CExl CNor ELan LRHS LSRN MJak MPnt NBir SCob SGol SPtp SWvt
§ ***americana***	CEvo EAEE MRav NBir SHeu SWvt
- var. ***americana***	MPnt
- Dale's strain	IFoB LBuc LSun MPnt NLar SHeu SPlb SWvt WRHF WWtn
- 'Harry Hay'	CDes EBee EPPr EPri LPla MPnt SHeu WPGP WSHC WWEG
- 'Ring of Fire'	MPnt SHeu SWvt
'Amethyst Myst'	CLAP ECtt EPfP LHop LRHS LSRN MAvo MPnt NPla SCob SGol SHeu SLim SPer
'Apple Crisp'	ECtt LBMP LSou MPnt SCob SHeu SWvt WNPC
'Apple Souffle'	MPnt SHeu
'Apricot' new	LBrs MHol MPnt WCot
'Autumn Haze'PBR	MPnt SHeu
'Autumn Leaves'	CAbP CBod CLAP ECtt ELan ELon EWoo LRHS MHol MPnt MWhi SHeu SPoG SRot SWvt WCot
'Baby's Breath'	ECho MPnt
'Bardot'	MPnt
'Beaujolais'PBR	CAbP CLAP ECtt LBrs LRHS MBNS MBri MHol MNrw MPnt NBir SHeu WCot WNPC
'Beauty Colour'	CAbP CLAP CRos ECha ECtt ELan ELon EPfP GMaP LHop LPfy LRHS LSRN MBri MJak MRav NGdn NWad SHeu SHil SWvt
'Belle Notte'	ECtt MPnt SHeu WNPC
'Berry Marmalade'	ECtt EPfP GBin LSou MAsh MPnt NWad SCob SHeu SWvt WHar WNPC
'Berry Smoothie'PBR	Widely available
'Big Top Bronze' new	SHeu
'Big Top Burgundy'	SHeu
'Big Top Gold' (Big Top Series)	MNrw SHeu
'Binoche'PBR	EBee ECtt LRHS MHol MPnt SCob SHeu SHil WCot WTor
'Birkin'	LRHS MPnt SHeu
'Black Taffeta' new	LBMP MPnt SHeu SPad
'Blackberry Crisp'PBR	EBee ECtt LSou MPnt SHeu WNPC
'Blackberry Jam'	CLAP CRos CSpe ECha ECtt ELan ELon GBin GKev LAst LBMP LRHS MGos MPnt NBir NHol NPri SHeu SWvt
'Blackbird'	CLAP MPnt SHeu SWvt WMnd
'Blackout'	CAbP CLet ECtt MNrw MPnt NLar SHeu
'Blondie' (Little Cutie Series)	EBee ECtt MHol MPnt SHeu WCot
'Blood Red'	CLAP LSou MPnt SHeu SLim WNPC
'Blood Vein'	MPnt SHeu
'Blushing Down'	MPnt
'Bouquet'	MPnt SHeu
bracteata	MPnt XLum
'Bressingham Glow'	MPnt SHeu
Bressingham hybrids	CWib GJos IFoB MLHP NBir SRms
'Bressingham Spire'	MPnt
'Bright and Breezy' (Seasonal Selection Series) new	SCob
'Bronze Beauty'	CMil ECtt MHol MPnt SAko SHeu WBrk WCot
'Brown Sugar'	ECtt MPnt SHeu WCot WNPC
'Brownfinch'	CElw LPla MPnt SHeu
'Brownies'	CAbP CBod CLAP ECtt LPla MPie MPnt SHeu WHrl WPtf WWtn
'Burgundy Frost'	MPnt SHeu
'Café Olé'	ECtt MAsh MPnt NLar SCob SHeu WHer WNPC
'Cajun Fire'	CWGN ECtt MPnt SCob SHeu WNPC
'Can-can' ♀H6	CLet CRos CTri ECtt ELon EPfP EWoo ITim LRHS LSRN MNrw MPnt NBir NGdn NLar NPri SCob SHeu SHil SPer SRot SWvt
'Canyon Duet'	MPnt SHeu

Name	Suppliers
'Cappuccino'	EBee ELan EPfP IBoy MPnt MRav SCob SGol SHeu SWvt
'Caramel'PBR	CKno CLAP CMac CWGN EBee ECtt ELan ELon EUJe EWoo GMaP LLHF LPal LRHS LSRN LSou MHol MNrw MSpe NSti SCob SGbt SGol SHeu SPer SPoG SWvt WBrk WCot WMnd
'Carmen'	MPnt SHeu
'Cascade Dawn'	CLAP EAEE EBee ECtt LSRN MPnt NBir SWvt
'Cassis' **new**	LBrs MHol MPnt SCob WCot
'Cézanne' (Master Painters Series) **new**	MPnt
'Champagne Bubbles'	MLHP MPnt SHeu
Charles Bloom = 'Chablo'	LRHS MPnt SHeu
'Chatterbox'	MPnt SHeu
'Checkers'	see *H.* 'Quilter's Joy'
'Cherries Jubilee'PBR	CAbP CLAP ELon EPfP GMaP LSRN MPnt SLim WNPC
'Cherry Cola'PBR	CBcs EBee ECtt EPfP LBMP LBrs LRHS LSou MAsh MPnt NLar NSti SCob SHeu WGor WNPC
'Chiqui'	MPnt
chlorantha	MPnt
- 'Burnt Sienna'	GCal
'Chocolate Ruffles'PBR	Widely available
'Chocolate Veil'	LSRN MPnt
'Christa'	MPnt SHeu
'Cinnabar Silver'PBR	CLAP ECtt LBMP LRHS MPnt NBir SCob SHeu WNPC
'Circus'	ECtt MPnt SCob SHeu
'Citronelle'	CBod CWGN ECtt EPfP MHol MPnt SCob SHeu SPer SWvt WCot
'City Lights'	SHeu
'Coco' (Little Cutie Series)	ECtt LSou MAsh MPnt SHeu WNPC
'Color Dream'PBR	MPnt SHeu
coral bells	see *H. sanguinea*
'Coral Bouquet'	MPnt SHeu
'Coral Cloud'	MPnt SHeu
'Corallion'	MPnt
Crème Brûlée = 'Tnheu041' (Dolce Series)	CBcs CExl ECtt EHoe ELan EPfP EShb EUJe GMaP LLHF LRHS LSRN MBri MGos NBir NBro NLar NPla SCob SHeu SHil SLim SPer SPoG SRot SWvt
'Crème Caramel'	CExl IFoB MPnt
'Creole Nights'	ECtt MPnt SHeu WNPC
'Crimson Curls'	CLAP ECtt EPfP LBuc LRHS LSou MGos MPnt SCob SHeu SRms SWvt
'Crispy Curly'	MPnt SHeu
cylindrica	EPfP MLHP MPnt SHeu
- var. ***alpina***	GKev LLHF
- 'Cream'	MPnt
- 'Francis'	MPnt
- 'Greenfinch'	CFis ELan EWTr GKev GMaP LRHS LSRN MPnt MRav NBir SHeu SWat SWvt WHea WMnd XLum
- 'Hyperion'	LRHS MPnt SHeu
'Da Vinci' (Master Painters Series) **new**	MPnt
'Damask'	MPnt SHeu
'Dark Beauty'PBR	CLAP EAEE ECtt ELon LBMP LRHS LSRN NPri NWad SCob SHeu SRot WNPC
'Dark Secret'PBR	EBee MPnt SHeu
'Dark Storm' (Seasonal Selection Series) **new**	SCob
'David'	MPnt SHeu WBrk
'Delta Dawn'PBR	CBod EBee ECtt LAst LBMP LBrs LRHS LSou MAvo MPnt SCob SHeu SPoG SWvt WHlf WNPC
'Dennis Davidson'	see *H.* 'Huntsman'
'Earth Angel' **new**	MPnt
Ebony and Ivory = 'E and I'PBR	CAbP CBcs CLAP EBee ECtt EHoe EShb GMaP LHop LRHS LSRN MBri MPnt NBir NWad SCob SHil SRms SRot SWvt
'Eden's Aurora'	MPnt
'Eden's Mystery'	NLar
'Electra'PBR	CBcs CLAP CMea ECtt EUJe LBMP LHop LRHS LSou MBNS MBri MPnt SCob SHeu SRot SWvt
'Electric Lime'	CLAP ECtt EHoe ELan GBin LHop MAvo MPnt NLar NPri SHeu SPer WNPC
'Elworthy Rusty'	CElw
'Emperor's Cloak'	GLog LEdu SHeu SPad SWvt WHrl WMoo
'Encore'PBR	ECtt MNrw MPnt SHeu
'Fairy Dance'	MPnt
'Fantasia'	SHeu
'Fire Alarm'	EBee ECtt MAsh MHol MPnt SHeu WNPC WTor
'Fire Chief'PBR	Widely available
'Firebird'	LRHS MPnt
Firefly	see *H.* 'Leuchtkäfer'
'Fireworks'PBR ♀H6	CAbP ECtt LRHS MBNS MPnt MRav NLar NPri SHil SLim SPer SRot
'Florist's Choice'	SHeu
'French Quarter'	MPnt SHeu
'Frost' (Little Cutie Series)	ECtt MPnt SHeu WNPC
'Frosted Violet'	see *H.* 'Frosted Violet Dream'
§ 'Frosted Violet Dream'PBR	CLAP ECtt LBMP LSRN LSou MPnt SCob SHeu SWvt WNPC
'Galaxy'	CWGN ECtt MPnt SHeu WNPC
'Gauguin' (Master Painters Series)	ECtt MAsh MPnt SCob SHeu
'Georgia Peach'PBR	CAbP CBod CLAP CRos CWGN EBee ECtt ELan EPfP LBMP LBrs LHop LSou MBri MHol MNrw MPnt NBir NLar NPla NPri SGol SHeu SRot SWvt WCot WHar WMnd
'Georgia Plum'	CWGN ECtt LRHS MPnt SHeu WNPC
'Ginger Ale'PBR	CLAP CWGN EBee ECha ECtt ELan ELon EPfP EWes LHop LRHS LSou MBNS MJak MPnt NBir NHol NLar NPri NSti NWad SCob SHeu SPer SPoG SWvt WCot WHar
'Ginger Peach'PBR	CLAP ECtt LRHS LSou MPnt SCob SHeu WNPC
'Ginger Snap' (Little Cutie Series)	LSou MPnt SHeu
glabra	MPnt SHeu
glauca	see *H. americana*
'Glitter' **new**	MPnt SHeu WNPC
'Gloire d'Orléans'	MPnt XLum
'Gotham'	ECtt MPnt SHeu WNPC
'Green Ivory'	EAEE MPnt SHeu XLum
'Green Sashay'	MPnt SHeu
'Green Spice'	CLAP EAEE EBee ECtt EHoe ELan ELon EPfP EShb EUJe LBMP LCro LHop LRHS MBri MJak MPnt NBir NCGa NHol NPla NPri SCob SHeu SPer SPoG SWvt

grossulariifolia	GMaP
'Guardian Angel'	MPnt SHeu SRGP
'Gypsy Dancer'PBR (Dancer Series)	CLAP EBee MPnt SHeu WNPC
'Hailstorm' (v)	MPnt
hallii	CPBP MPnt
Harvest Burgundy = 'Balheubur'	MPnt
Harvest Silver = 'Balheusil'	MPnt
'Havana'PBR	ECtt MPnt SHeu
'Helen Dillon' (v)	GMaP LAst MPnt NBir SHeu SRGP SWvt WWEG
'Hercules'PBR	ECtt LRHS MPnt SHeu
hispida	MPnt
'Hollywood'PBR	CMea EBee ECtt ELon EPfP LAst LBMP LSRN MBri MGos MPnt NBir NHol NLar NPri SCob SHeu SPoG SRot
§ 'Huntsman'	MPnt MRav
'Jade Gloss'PBR	CLAP EPfP GBin LRHS MBri MPnt SHeu SWvt WNPC
'June Bride'	MPnt
'Kadastra'	MPnt SHeu
'Kassandra'PBR	EBee ECtt MPnt SCob SGol SHeu STPC SWvt
Key Lime Pie = 'Tnheu042'PBR (Dolce Series)	CBcs CExl CMea CWGN ECtt EPfP GMaP LHop LRHS LSRN MBri MGos NBir NBro NHol SCob SHeu SRms SRot SWvt
Kira Series	MPnt
'Lady in Red'	NBre
'Lady Romney'	GCal XLum
'Lemon Chiffon'PBR	ECtt MPnt SHeu
§ 'Leuchtkäfer'	CWat ECtt EPfP EShb EWTr GMaP LAst LHop LPot LRHS MBel MHer MMuc MPnt MRav MWhi NBir NMir SGol SPlb SRms WMnd WMoo WPtf XLum
Licorice = 'Tnheu044'PBR (Dolce Series)	CBod CRos ECtt ELon EUJe GBin LRHS MBNS MBri MGos MPnt NBir NLar NPri SHeu SHil SLim SPoG SRot SWvt WHoo
'Lime Marmalade'	CBcs CLAP CWGN EAEE EBee ECtt ELan ELon EPfP LBMP LRHS LSou MAsh MBNS MBri MGos MJak MPnt NHol NLar NPri NWad SCob SHeu SHil SPad SPoG SRot
'Lime Rickey'PBR	CBod CWGN ECtt EPfP ETod EUJe LBrs LRHS LSRN MBri MGos MHol NBir NSti SCob SGol SHeu SWvt WCot WHer
'Lime Ruffles' **new**	LBMP MPnt SHeu WNPC
'Lipstick'PBR	CWGN ELon MPnt NDov SHeu SWvt WNPC
'Little Tinker'	MPnt SHeu
longiflora **new**	CEvo
'Lune Rousse'	MPnt SHeu
'Magic Wand' ♀H6	CAbP ELon SHeu
'Magnum'	CMil CWGN EBee ECtt IBoy LHop MHol MPnt SHeu WCot
'Mahogany'PBR	CLAP CRos ELon EPfP EUJe GBin LRHS LSou MJak MPnt NBir NPri SCob SHeu SLim SWvt WHoo
'Malachite'	MPnt SHeu
'Mango'	MPnt SHeu
'Marmalade'PBR	Widely available
'Mars'	EPfP LRHS MPnt SHeu
'Mary Rose'	MPnt SHeu
maxima **new**	MPnt
'Melting Fire'	CBod GJos LRHS MPnt SGol SHeu WHar WNPC
'Mercury'	SHeu
'Metallic Shimmer' (Fox Series)	MPnt
'Metallica'	SHeu WMoo
micans	see *H. rubescens*
micrantha	CEvo GCal MLHP MPnt SHeu SRms
- var. ***diversifolia*** misapplied	see *H. villosa*
- 'Martha's Compact'	MPnt WCot
§ - 'Ruffles'	ECha MPnt SHeu
'Midas Touch'	CLAP CWGN EBee MPnt NLar SHeu WNPC
'Midnight Bayou'	EBee ECtt ELan ELon EPfP GBin LHop LRHS MBri MPnt NLar NPer NPri SHeu SRot SWvt WNPC
'Midnight Rose'	Widely available
'Midnight Rose Select'	ECtt MPnt NWad
'Midnight Ruffles' **new**	MPnt SHeu WNPC
'Milan'PBR	ECtt MPnt SHeu WNPC
'Mini Mouse'	MPnt SHeu
'Mint Frost'PBR	EAEE ECtt ELan LHop LPot LRHS MPnt NBir SHeu SWvt
'Mint Julep'PBR	CWGN ECtt MBri MPnt SHeu WNPC
'Miracle'PBR	CLAP CMos ECtt EPfP EWoo MPnt SHeu WNPC
'Mocha'PBR	CLAP ECtt MNrw MPnt SHeu SWvt WCot
'Molly Bush' ♀H6	EAEE EBee MBri MPnt MWhi SHeu
'Morello' **new**	MPnt SCob SHeu WNPC
'Mother of Pearl'	MPnt SHeu
'Muscat'	ECtt MPnt SHeu
'Mysteria'PBR	LBMP MPnt SHeu WNPC
'Mystic Angel'	MPnt SHeu
'Neptune'	EAEE ECtt EShb LRHS MBel MPnt SHeu
'Oakington Jewel'	MPnt
'Obsidian'PBR	Widely available
'Orphée'	MPnt
'Paprika'	CWGN EBee ECtt LBMP LLWG LSun MPnt SHeu WCot WNPC
'Paris'PBR	CLAP CRos EBee ECtt EPfP GBin LRHS LSRN LSou MBri MGos MPnt NDov NHol NPri SHeu SHil SPoG WNPC
parishii NNS 93384	MPnt
parvifolia var. ***nivalis***	MPnt
- var. ***utahensis***	MPnt
'Peach Crisp'PBR	CMos CWGN EBee ECtt LBMP LSou SCob SHeu SPoG SRkn WNPC
'Peach Flambé'PBR	Widely available
'Peach Pie'	MPnt
'Peachy Keen'	SHeu
'Pear Crisp'	CWGN ECtt LSou MPnt SCob SHeu WNPC
'Penelope'	MPnt SHeu
'Peppermint' (Little Cutie Series)	ECtt MPnt SHeu
'Peppermint Spice'PBR (21st Century Collection Series)	MPnt SGol SHeu
'Persian Carpet'	GMaP LRHS MPnt NBir SHeu SWvt WPtf
(Petite Series) 'Petite Marbled Burgundy'	ECtt EHoe LLHF MPnt SHeu SWvt

Plant	Suppliers
- 'Petite Pearl Fairy'	CAbP EHoe EWTr MPnt SHeu SWvt
- 'Petite Pink Bouquet'	MPnt SHeu
'Pewter Moon'	ELan EWTr GMaP MGos MPnt NBir SHeu XLum
'Pewter Veil'	MPnt SHeu WMnd
'Phoebe's Blush' (Fox Series)	MPnt WNPC
'Picasso' (Master Painters Series)	ECtt MPnt SHeu
'Pilley Pink' (Heucheraholics Series) **new**	SHeu
'Pilley Pumpkin' (Heucheraholics Series) **new**	SHeu
pilosissima	XLum
'Pink Pearls' **new**	MHol MPnt SCob WCot
'Pinot Bianco'	MAsh MPnt SHeu
'Pinot Gris'PBR	CLAP CWGN EBee ECtt MAsh MHol MNrw MPnt SHeu WCot WNPC
'Pinot Noir'	MPnt SHeu WNPC WOut
'Pistache'	CAbP ECtt MHol MPnt SHeu WCot WNPC
§ 'Pluie de Feu'	CCon EPPr GBuc LRHS MPnt MRav XLum
'Plum Pudding'PBR	Widely available
'Plum Royale'PBR	CLAP CWGN ELan ELon EPfP LRHS MBri MCot MGos MHol MPnt MSCN NPri NSti NWad SHeu SHil SPer SRkn SWvt WCot
'Pretty Perinne'	EBee MPnt SHeu
'Pretty Polly'	MPnt SHeu
'Pride of Pilley' (Heucheraholics Series) **new**	SHeu
'Prince'	ELan LRHS LSRN MBNS MPnt SHeu SWvt
'Prince of Orange'	SHeu
'Prince of Silver'	LRHS MPnt MWhi SHeu
pringlei	see *H. rubescens*
pubescens	ECho MPnt SHeu XLum
- 'Alba'	MPnt
pulchella	CPBP EDAr GCal LLHF MHer MPnt NLar SHeu SRms
'Purple Petticoats' ♀H6	CBcs ELan EPfP GBin LRHS LSou MGos MHtn MLHP MPnt NLar NPri SHeu SLim SPoG SRot
'Purple Rain Forest' (Kira Series) **new**	SHeu
'Quick Silver'	LRHS MPnt NBir SHeu SWvt
§ 'Quilter's Joy'	MPnt
'Rachel'	CAbP CLet EAEE EBee ECGP ELan EPfP GBuc GMaP IFoB LRHS LSRN MPnt MRav NBir NGdn SRGP SWvt XLum
Rain of Fire	see *H.* 'Pluie de Feu'
'Raspberry' (Fox Series)	MPnt
'Raspberry Ice'PBR	MPnt SHeu
'Raspberry Regal' ♀H6	MPnt MRav NBir SHeu SWvt WCot WSHC
'Rave On'PBR	CAbP CHVG CWGN EBee ECtt ELan ELon GBin LHop LRHS LSRN LSou MBri MPnt NEgg NHol NLar NWad SCob SHeu SHil SPer SRkn SRot SWvt
'Red Dress'	MPnt SHeu
'Red Spangles'	LRHS MPnt NBir SHeu
'Regina' ♀H6	CAbP ECtt EPfP LSRN MPnt SCob SHeu SWvt
'Renoir' (Master Painters Series)	MPnt SHeu
'Rhapsody'	LRHS
richardsonii	EBee MPnt XLum
'Rickard'	MPnt
'Rio'	ECtt LSou MPnt SCob SHeu WBor WNPC
'Robert'	MPnt
'Root Beer'PBR	EBee ECtt EPfP LRHS LSou MPnt SHeu SRkn WNPC
Rosemary Bloom = 'Heuros'PBR	EBee LRHS SHeu
§ ***rubescens***	CAbP ECho GKev NBro WThu
'Ruffles'	see *H. micrantha* 'Ruffles'
'Sanbrot'	MPnt
§ ***sanguinea***	CMac CSBt IMou MPnt MRav NBir
- 'Alba'	EPPr LPla MPnt SMHy
- 'Geisha's Fan'	CHid ECtt MPnt SHeu SPer SWvt WNPC
- 'Monet' (v)	EBee ECtt MLHP MPnt SHeu
- 'Ruby Bells'	CBod EPPr LRHS LSRN MAsh MPnt MSpe NLar SHeu WHoo
- 'Sioux Falls'	SHeu
- 'Snow Storm' (v)	ELan MPnt SHeu WMnd WNPC
- 'Splendens'	MPnt XLum
- 'Taff's Joy' (v)	MPnt
- 'White Cloud' (v)	EBee EPfP EShb LCro MPnt NBre NDov SHeu SRms XLum
'Sashay' ♀H6	CLAP ELon IBoy LSou MPnt SGol SHeu WNPC
'Saturn'	MPnt SHeu SWvt WNPC
'Schneewittchen'	MPnt MRav
'Scintillation' ♀H6	MPnt
'Shanghai'PBR	CMos ECtt EPfP GBin LHop LRHS LSRN MAsh MPnt MWhi NCGa NWad SHeu SWvt WNPC WTor
'Shenandoah Mountain'	MPnt
'Shere Variety'	MPnt
'Silver Blush'	MAsh
'Silver Dollar' **new**	MPnt SPoG WCot
'Silver Heart'	MPnt
'Silver Indiana'	LSRN MPnt SHeu
'Silver Light'PBR	MPnt SHeu
'Silver Lode'PBR	MPnt SHeu
'Silver Scrolls'PBR	Widely available
'Silver Shadows'	MPnt SHeu
'Silver Streak'	see × *Heucherella* 'Silver Streak'
'Silvery Sheen' **new**	WCot
'Sioux Falls'	CFis MPnt
'Slater's Pink' (Fox Series)	MPnt
'Snow Angel'	CWGN ECtt LRHS LSou MPnt SHeu SPoG WCot WRHF
'Snowfire' (v)	MPnt SHeu
'Southern Comfort'PBR	CLAP CWGN EBee ECtt LBrs LRHS MAvo MBNS MHol MPnt NHol NLar NPer NPri SGol SHeu SLim SPoG SRot SWvt WCot
'Sparkler'	MPnt
'Sparkling Burgundy'	ECtt ELan ELon LPal LRHS MPnt NPri SHeu SWvt
'Spellbound'	CWGN EBee ECtt LBMP LRHS MPnt SCob SHeu SPoG SRkn WNPC
'Starry Night'	MPnt
'Steel City'	MPnt SHeu
'Stormy Seas'	CBod EAEE EBee ELan EPfP EWTr GCra LRHS MLHP MPnt MRav NBir SCob SHeu SWvt WPtf

'Strawberries and Cream' (v)	MPnt SHeu
'Strawberry Candy'PBR	CBcs CWGN ELon GBin GJos LAst LSRN MPnt NBir NLar NWad SHeu SLim WNPC WWtn
'Strawberry Swirl'	CElw EPfP GMaP MGos MPnt MRav NBir SCob SHeu SWvt WNPC
'Sugar Berry' (Little Cutie Series)	ECtt LSou MAsh MPnt SCob SHeu
Sugar Frosting ='Pwheu0104'PBR	CBod CRos EAEE EHoe GBin LRHS MBri MGos MPnt NHol NPri SHeu SHil SRot SWvt
'Sugar Plum'PBR	CAby CSpe ECtt ELon EPfP EUJe LBMP LRHS MBNS MPnt NPri SCob SHeu SRot WCot WHoo WNPC
'Sunrise' (Seasonal Selection Series) **new**	SCob
'Sweet Berry'	MPnt
'Sweet Tart' (Little Cutie Series)	LSou MPnt SHeu
'Swirling Fantasy'PBR	COtt EShb GJos MPnt SHeu
'Tangerine Wave' (Fox Series)	MPnt WNPC
'Tara'	ECtt MPnt SHeu
'Thomas' (Fox Series)	MPnt WNPC
'Tiramisu'PBR	CAbP CLAP CWGN ECtt IBoy LHop LRHS MBNS MHol MPnt NBir NSti SHeu SPer SPoG SWvt WCot WRHF
'Tresahor White'	MPnt
'Van Gogh' (Master Painters Series)	ECtt MPnt SCob SHeu
'Vanilla Spice'	MPnt SHeu
'Veil of Passion'	NBre
'Velvet Night'	EPfP LSou MPnt NBir SHeu SPlb WMnd
'Venus'	CWGN ECtt LPal LSun MBel MGos MHol MMuc MNrw MPie MPnt NSti SHeu SPer WBrk WCot WHoo WHrl
'Vesuvius'	MPnt SHeu WNPC
'Vienna'PBR (City Series)	MPnt SHeu WNPC
§ ***villosa***	CEvo CSam GKev MPnt MRav SVic XLum
- 'Autumn Bride'	MPnt SHeu SMHy
- Bressingham Bronze ='Absi'PBR	EAEE ECtt LRHS MPnt SHeu
- 'Chantilly'	MPnt SHeu
- var. ***macrorhiza***	CEvo EShb MPnt NBre XLum
- 'Palace Purple'	Widely available
- 'Palace Purple Select'	CMac CTri CWat CWib ETod EUJe LAst LPfy LSun MCot MJak SLim SWvt WHar
'Virginale'	MPnt
'Vulcano'	EBee ECtt MHol WCot
'Walnut' (Fox Series)	MPnt WNPC
'White Marble'	MPnt
'White Spires'	EAEE LRHS MPnt SHeu
'White Swirls'	MPnt
'William How'	MPnt
'Winter Joy' (Seasonal Selection Series) **new**	SCob
'Winter Red'	EAEE LRHS MPnt SHeu
'XXL' **new**	MPnt SCob
'Zabeliana'	MPnt
'Zipper' **new**	MPnt SHeu WHlf WNPC

× *Heucherella* ✿ (*Saxifragaceae*)

'Alabama Sunrise'PBR	CHid CLAP CRos ECtt ELan GBin LBMP LRHS MBri MPnt NPer NPri SCob SGol SHeu SPoG SRot SWvt
alba 'Bridget Bloom'	ECha ELan EPfP GMaP LPot LRHS MPnt MRav SHeu SPer SRms XLum
§ - 'Rosalie'	EAEE ECha EWoo LRHS MPnt MRav NBir NBro SHeu SPlb WSHC
'Art Deco'	MPnt SHeu
'Berry Fizz'	LBuc MPnt SHeu STPC SWvt WNPC
'Birthday Cake'	MPnt SHeu
'Blue Ridge'	MPnt
'Brass Lantern'PBR	CRos CSpe CWGN ECtt EPfP GBin LBMP LRHS LSou MBel MBri MJak MPnt NCGa NHol NLar NSti NWad SCob SHeu SRot STPC SWvt WNPC
'Burnished Bronze'PBR	EAEE ECtt ELon EPfP GBin LRHS MBri MPnt NBro NLar NPla NWad SCob SHeu SPer SRot SWvt
'Buttered Rum'	EBee MPnt SHeu WNPC
'Chocolate Lace'PBR	MPnt SHeu
'Cinnamon Bear'	MPnt SHeu
'Citrus Shock'	MPnt SHeu
'Copper Cascade' (Cascade Series) **new**	MPnt SHeu WNPC
'Cracked Ice'	EBee MPnt SHeu
'Dayglow Pink'PBR	CLAP ECtt GBin GMaP LBMP LSRN MPnt NBro NLar SCob SHeu WBor WNPC
'Fan Dancer'	CLAP MPnt SHeu
'Fire Frost' **new**	MPnt SHeu WNPC
'Glacier Falls' (Falls Series) **new**	SHeu WNPC
'Gold Cascade' (Cascade Series) **new**	MPnt
Gold Strike ='Hertn041'PBR	CLAP ECtt MBNS MPnt SHeu
'Golden Zebra'PBR	CBod CLAP CRos CWGN EBee ECtt ELan LRHS MBNS MBri MNrw MPnt MWhi NLar SHeu SWvt WCot
'Great Smokies'	ECtt MPnt SHeu
'Gunsmoke'PBR	CLAP ECtt GBin LBMP LRHS LSou MBel MBri MPnt NWad SCob SHeu SWvt WGor WNPC
'Heart of Darkness'PBR	MPnt SHeu
'Honey Rose' **new**	MPnt SHeu WNPC
'Kimono'PBR ♀H6	CLAP CMac EAEE ECtt EHoe ELan EPfP EShb EUJe GKev GMaP LAst LPla LPot LRHS LSRN LSou MBel MBri MJak MPnt MWhi NBro NLar NPri NWad SCob SHeu
'Ninja'	see *Tiarella* 'Ninja'
'Party Time'PBR	SHeu
Pink Whispers ='Hertn042'PBR	MPnt SHeu
'Quicksilver'	CBcs GMaP MBri MPnt SHeu SWvt
'Redstone Falls'PBR	CWGN ECtt LBMP LRHS LSou MJak MNrw MPnt NCGa NLar NPri NWad SHeu SPer SPoG STPC SWvt WCot WGor WNPC
'Ring of Fire'	SWvt
§ 'Silver Streak'	MPnt NBro SHeu SWvt
'Solar Eclipse'	CBod EAEE ECtt EShb IBoy LRHS MAsh MHol MPnt NCGa NLar NWad SCob SHeu SPer SPoG SWvt WCot WGor WNPC
'Solar Power'PBR	CRos CWGN ECtt LRHS LSou MPnt NLar NWad SCob SHeu SHil SWvt WNPC

'Stoplight'[PBR]	Widely available
'Sunrise Falls' (Falls Series)	CWGN EBee LLWG MJak MNrw MPnt NWad SHeu SPer SWvt WCot WGor WNPC
'Sunspot'[PBR] (v)	CLAP EAEE EPfP MGos NBro NSti SGol SHeu WHer
'Sweet Tea'[PBR]	Widely available
'Tapestry'[PBR]	CHid CLAP CMos CRos CWCL ECtt ELan EPfP GMaP LAst LBMP LRHS LSou MBNS MBri MPnt NHol NSti NWad SCob SHeu SHil SPer SPoG SRkn SRot SWvt
tiarelloides ♀H6	CMac EPfP
'Twilight' **new**	MPnt SHeu WNPC
§ 'Viking Ship'	EAEE ECtt MPnt MTPN NBir SHeu
'Yellowstone Falls'[PBR]	CBod CWGN LBMP LRHS LSou MJak MPnt NWad SCob SHeu SPoG SRot STPC SWvt WGor WNPC

Hexastylis see *Asarum*

Hibanobambusa (*Poaceae*)

tranquillans	CEnt ERod MBrN MMuc MWht SEND WJun
- 'Shiroshima' (v)	CAbb CBod CDTJ CDoC CEnt ENBC EPfP ERod EUJe LPal MBrN MMuc MWhi MWht SBig SEND WJun

Hibbertia (*Dilleniaceae*)

aspera	CAbb CBcs CTsd EBee ECou IVic LRHS MOWG WCFE WCot WSHC
pedunculata	WAbe
procumbens	GEdr WAbe
§ ***scandens*** ♀H1c	CBcs CHII CRHN ECou ELan MOWG
'Spring Sunshine'	ESwi LHop SEle
volubilis	see *H. scandens*

Hibiscus ✿ (*Malvaceae*)

coccineus	SBrt SMad SPlb
coccineus* × *moscheutos	SBrt
'Eruption'	ELon EPfP
'Fireball'[PBR]	EUJe SMad SPoG
Full Blast	see *H.* 'Resi'
huegelii	see *Alyogyne huegelii*
'Kopper King'[PBR]	EUJe MBNS SMad SPad SPoG
leopoldii	SRms
militaris	SBrt
moscheutos	CSpe EBee SBrt SVic XLum
- 'Galaxy'	XLum
- 'Old Yella'[PBR]	SMad
- 'Robert Fleming'[PBR]	EUJe
mutabilis ♀H1b	MOWG
paramutabilis	EWes
§ 'Resi'[PBR]	LRHS NPri WMat
rosa-sinensis	EBak MOWG SPre
- 'Arcadian Spring'	MOWG
- 'Big Tango'	MOWG
- 'Blues Man'	MOWG
- 'Byron Metts'	MOWG
- 'Cajun Cocktail'	see *H. rosa-sinensis* 'Jambalaya'
- 'Candy Floss' (d)	MOWG
- 'Carmen Keene'	MOWG
- 'China Town' **new**	MOWG
- 'Cloud Nine'[PBR]	MOWG
- 'Cockatoo'	MOWG
- 'Cooperi' (v) ♀H1b	MOWG
- 'Cosmic Dancer' **new**	MOWG
- 'Courier Mail'	MOWG
- 'Dorothy Brady'	MOWG
- 'Enid Lewis' (d)	MOWG
- 'Erin Rachael'	MOWG
- 'Expo'	MOWG
- 'Fifth Dimension' **new**	MOWG
- 'Gabriel' **new**	MOWG
- 'Georgia Peach' **new**	MOWG
- 'Gwen Mary'	MOWG
- 'Helene'	LSRN
- 'Holly's Pride'	MOWG
- 'Hot Bikini'	MOWG
§ - 'Jambalaya'	MOWG
- 'Jayella' **new**	MOWG
- 'June's Joy'	MOWG
- 'Key West Thunderhead' (d)	MOWG
- 'Lady Bug'	MOWG
- 'Lady Flo'	MOWG
- 'Lemon Chiffon'	MOWG
- 'Linda Pear' (d)	MOWG
- 'Madame Dupont'	MOWG
- 'Me Oh My Oh' **new**	MOWG
- 'Mrs Andreasen' (d)	MOWG
- 'Rhinestone'	MOWG
- 'Roman Candle' **new**	MOWG
- 'Rum Runner' **new**	MOWG
- 'Soft Shoulders'	MOWG
- 'Spanish Lady'	MOWG
- 'Sprinkle Rain'	MOWG
- 'Susan Schlueter' **new**	MOWG
- 'Tahitian Burning Sands' **new**	MOWG
- 'Tahitian Christmas' **new**	MOWG
- 'Tarantella'	MOWG
- 'The Path'	MOWG
- 'Vermillion Queen'	MOWG
- 'Weekend'	MOWG
- 'White Swan'	MOWG
schizopetalus ♀H1b	MOWG
sinosyriacus 'Lilac Queen'	CExl LRHS SKHP WPGP
- 'Ruby Glow'	CExl LRHS LSRN SKHP WPGP
surattensis **new**	EBee
syriacus	LPal
- 'Aphrodite'	LRHS MAsh
- 'Ardens' (d)	SPer SPoG
- Blue Bird	see *H. syriacus* 'Oiseau Bleu'
- Blue Chiffon = 'Notwood3'[PBR] ♀H5	CSBt LRHS MBri MGos SPoG
- China Chiffon = 'Bricutts'	LRHS MAsh MBri MGos MMuc SEND SHil SPoG
- 'Coelestis'	SPer
- 'Diana' ♀H5	CDul EBee EPfP LRHS LSRN MAsh MGos SCoo SKHP SLon SPer
- 'Dorothy Crane'	EMil LRHS SKHP
- 'Duc de Brabant' (d)	CSBt ELon MBlu SPer
- 'Elegantissimus'	see *H. syriacus* 'Lady Stanley'
- 'Hamabo' ♀H5	CDul CSBt CTri EBee ELan ELon EPfP LAst LRHS LSRN MBri MGos MMuc NLar NPri SBod SCoo SEND SGol SHil SLim SPer SPoG SWvt WHar
- 'Helene'	ELan LSRN MBlu
- 'Jeanne d'Arc' (d)	SGol
§ - 'Lady Stanley' (d)	CMac CSBt LSou SCoo SPer
- Lavender Chiffon = 'Notwoodone'[PBR] ♀H5	CSBt EBee ELan ELon EPfP EWes LRHS LSRN MBri MGos MMuc SCoo SEND SHil SPer SPoG

- 'Leopoldii'	SKHP
- 'Marina'	ELon EPfP LSou MBlu MRav SGol
- 'Meehanii' misapplied	see *H. syriacus* 'Purpureus Variegatus'
- 'Meehanii' (v) 𝕐H5	EMil EPfP LRHS SCoo SKHP SPer SPoG
- 'Monstrosus'	NLar
§ - 'Oiseau Bleu' 𝕐H5	Widely available
- Pink Chiffon = 'Jwnfour'	LRHS SLon WCot
- Pink Giant = 'Flogi'	CDul CMac ELan EPfP LRHS MGos SPad SPer
- 'Pinky Spot'	LRHS
- Purple Pillar = 'Gandini Santiago' **new**	SGol
- Purple Ruffles = 'Sanchoyo' (d)	EPfP LCro LRHS MBri SHil SPoG
§ - 'Purpureus Variegatus' (v)	CMac LRHS
- 'Red Heart' 𝕐H5	CDul CLet CMac CSBt CTri ELan EPfP LRHS MAsh MBri MGos MMuc NLar SEND SHil SKHP SLim SPad SPer SPoG SRms SWvt WCFE
- Rosalbane = 'Minrosa'	SGol
- Russian Violet = 'Floru'	EPfP LRHS SKHP
- 'Shintaeyang'	MBri
- 'Speciosus'	SPoG
- 'Totus Albus'	CMac
- Ultramarine = 'Minultra'PBR	EPfP LRHS SKHP
- 'Variegatus'	see *H. syriacus* 'Purpureus Variegatus'
- 'Violet Clair Double' (d)	CMac
- White Chiffon = 'Notwoodtwo'PBR (d) 𝕐H5	CSBt EPfP EWes LCro LRHS LSRN MAsh MBri MGos MRav SCoo SHil SPer SPoG
- 'William R. Smith' 𝕐H5	LRHS MBri MSwo SPer
- 'Woodbridge' 𝕐H5	Widely available
trionum	CSpe WKif
- 'Sunny Day'	ELan

hickory, shagbark see *Carya ovata*

Hieracium (*Asteraceae*)

aurantiacum	see *Pilosella aurantiaca*
brunneocroceum	see *Pilosella aurantiaca* subsp. *carpathicola*
laevigatum subsp. ***nivale*** **new**	MMuc
§ ***lanatum***	ECho NBir
maculatum Sm.	see *H. spilophaeum*
pilosella	see *Pilosella officinarum*
scullyi	EPPr
§ ***spilophaeum***	EHoe MMuc NBid NPer NSti WOut
- 'Blue Leaf'	WCot
umbellatum	WOut
villosum	ECho EHoe WHer
welwitschii	see *H. lanatum*

Hierochloe (*Poaceae*)

odorata	ELon EPPr GPoy MBNS XLum

hildaberry see *Rubus* 'Hildaberry'

Himalayacalamus (*Poaceae*)

asper	CDTJ ERod
§ ***falconeri***	CEnt SDix
§ - 'Damarapa'	CEnt EPfP WJun
§ ***hookerianus***	CExl EPfP IMou WJun
- 'Himalaya Blue'	CDTJ
porcatus	WJun WPGP

Himantoglossum (*Orchidaceae*)

hircinum	NLAp

× *Hippeasprekelia* (*Amaryllidaceae*)

sp.	CDes
'Durga Pradhan'	WCot
'Red Beauty'	WCot

Hippeastrum ✿ (*Amaryllidaceae*)

× ***acramannii*** 𝕐H2	CDes CPne GCal WCot
advenum	see *Rhodophiala advena*
'Alfresco'PBR	LAma
'Amputo'	LAma
'Apple Blossom' 𝕐H2	LAma SDeJ
'Baby Star'	SDeJ
'Benfica' 𝕐H2	CSpe LCro
bifidum	see *Rhodophiala bifida*
'Black Beauty'	LAma
'Black Pearl'	EPfP LCro LOPS
'Blossom Peacock' (d)	LAma
'Bogota'	LCro LOPS
'Bolero'	LAma
'Charisma' 𝕐H2	LAma SDeJ
Cherry Nymph = 'Chernym'PBR **new**	LAma
'Christmas Gift'	LAma LCro LOPS
'Clown'	LAma
'Dancing Queen'	LAma LCro
(Double Galaxy Group) 'Double Dragon'PBR (d) **new**	LAma
'Double Record' (d)	SDeJ
'Emerald'	LAma WCot
'Estella'	LCro LOPS
'Evergreen' 𝕐H2 **new**	EPfP
'Fairytale'	SDeJ
'Fantasy' **new**	LAma
'Ferrari'	LAma
'Flamenco Queen' **new**	LAma
'Flaming Peacock'	LAma
'Grand Diva' **new**	LAma
'Grandeur'	LAma
'Green Goddess'	LAma
'Inca'	LAma
'Jewel' (d)	LAma
× ***johnsonii*** hort. 𝕐H2	CExl WCot
'La Paz'	LAma
'Lady Jane'	LAma SDeJ
'Lemon Lime'	LAma
'Liberty'	SDeJ
'Lima'	LAma
'Limona'PBR	LCro LOPS
'Magic Green' 𝕐H2	LAma
'Marilyn' (d) **new**	LAma
'Misty'	LAma
'Mont Blanc'	SDeJ
'Mrs Garfield'	LAma
'Naughty Lady'	LAma
papilio 𝕐H1c	LAma LCro MMHG SDeJ
'Picotee'	LAma SDeJ
'Pink Floyd'	LAma
puniceum	LAma
'Red Lion' 𝕐H2	LAma
'Red Peacock' (d)	LAma SDeJ
'Rembrandt van Rijn'	LAma

'Rilona' LAma SDeJ
'Rosario' LAma
'Royal Velvet' LAma
'Ruby Meyer' LAma
'San Antonio Rose' WCot
'Santiago' LAma
'Snow Queen' **new** LCro LOPS
striatum WCot
'Sumatra'PBR LCro LOPS
'Sweet Surrender' LAma
'Toughie' CTal EBee
vittatum LAma
'White Dazzler' LAma
yungacense 'Kiara' XTur

Hippocrepis (*Papilionaceae*)

§ ***comosa*** EDAr SPhx
§ ***emerus*** CBcs CExl CMHG CMac ELan EPfP MGil MGos MMuc NLar SBod SEND SVen WSHC

Hippophae (*Elaeagnaceae*)

rhamnoides CArg CArn CBcs CCVT CDul CHab CLnd CMac CSpe CTri ECrN EHoe ELan EPfP EPom EShb LBuc LEdu MBlu MCoo MMuc NWea SCob SEND SEWo SGol SPlb
- (m) EPom
- 'Askola' (f) CAgr
- 'Dorana' (f) CAgr
- 'Frugna' (f) CAgr NLar
- 'Hergo' (f) CAgr MCoo NLar
- 'Hikul' (m) CAgr NLar WHor
- 'Juliet' (f) CAgr
- 'Leikora' (f) ♀H7 CAgr CDoC ELan IVic MBlu MCoo MGos NLar SPer
- 'Orange Energy' (f/F) CAgr EPfP MCoo
- 'Pollmix' (m) ♀H7 CAgr CDoC ELan EPfP IVic MBlu MCoo MGos NLar SPer
- 'Pollmix 3' (m) MCoo
- 'Sirola' (f) CAgr MCoo
salicifolia CAgr
- GWJ 9221 WCru

Hippuris (*Plantaginaceae*)

vulgaris CBen CWat EHon EWay MSKA NPer WMAq XLum

Hirpicium (*Asteraceae*)

armerioides SPlb

Histiopteris (*Dennstaedtiaceae*)

incisa SGSe

Hoheria ✿ (*Malvaceae*)

'Ace of Spades' CAbb CDoC CMHG EBee ELon EPfP EWTr LRHS NLar SKHP SMad SPer SWvt WPGP
§ ***angustifolia*** EBee ECou EPfP SVen WPGP
angustifolia* × *sexstylosa WPGP
'Borde Hill' CAbb CDoC CDul CJun CMHG CMac CTho EBee ECou ELan ELon EPfP EWoo IVic LHop LRHS MAsh SEND SKHP SLim SPer SSpi SWvt WCFE WPGP
'County Park' ECou
glabrata CMac ECou EPfP GGGa GGal IDee NBir SKHP WPGP
'Glory of Amlwch' ♀H4 CAbb CBcs CDoC CDul CJun CSam CTho ECou ELan EPfP GGGa GQui LRHS LSRN SChF SKHP SPer SSpi SWvt WPGP
'Hill House' CHll
§ ***lyallii*** ♀H4 CDoC CDul CExl CTho ECou ELan GCra LRHS LSRN SPer SVen
- 'Chalk Hills' ECou
- 'Swale Stream' ECou
microphylla see *H. angustifolia*
populnea CBcs CTsd IDee
- 'Alba Variegata' (v) ♀H3 ECou
- 'Holbrook' CSam
- 'Purple Shadow' ECou
- 'Variegata' (v) ECou
'Purple Delta' ECou
sexstylosa CAbb CBot CDul CHid CTho CTri ECou ELan EPfP IDee LHop LRHS LSRN MGos NEgg SKHP SPer SPlb SVen SWvt
- 'Crataegifolia' CAbb EBee EWTr NLar
- 'Pendula' CBcs CMac
- 'Stardust' ♀H4 CAbP CBcs CDoC CDul CJun CMCN CMHG CSBt CTho ECou ELan ELon EPfP EWoo IVic LRHS LSRN MAsh MBlu MGos NLar SEND SMad SPer SPoG SSpi SWvt WBod WPGP WSHC
'Snow White' **new** LRHS MGos SPoG WMat

Holboellia (*Lardizabalaceae*)

angustifolia NLar WCru
- subsp. ***angustifolia*** LRHS SKHP WCot WCru
- subsp. ***linearifolia*** BWJ 8004 WCru
- subsp. ***obtusa*** DJHC 506 WCru
brachyandra HWJ 1023 WCru
aff. ***chapaensis*** B&SWJ 7250 WCru
coriacea CBcs CHll CKel CRHN CSde CTsd ELan EPfP EShb IDee LRHS MGos MRav NLar SEND SKHP SPer WCFE WCru
- B&SWJ 2818 WCru
latifolia CBcs CBot CHll CMac CRHN CTri EBee ELan EPfP GCal LEdu LRHS NLar SAdn SEND SEle SHil SKHP SLim SPer SPoG SWvt WBor WCru WPGP
- HWJCM 008 WCru
- HWJK 2014 WCru
- HWJK 2213 WCru
- SF 95134 EPfP
- subsp. ***chartacea*** DJHC 98442 **new** WCru
- dark-flowered HWJK 2213 WCru
- lanceolate-leaved HWJK 2419 **new** WCru
- pale-flowered HWJK 2213C WCru

Holcus (*Poaceae*)

lanatus WSFF
mollis 'Albovariegatus' (v) CWCL ECha EHoe ELan EPPr EPfP GMaP LBMP MWhi NBid NBro NPer NSti SPlb SRms XLum

- 'Jackdaw's Cream' (v) EPPr
- 'White Fog' (v) CBod EAJP EBee EPPr MMuc NWad

Holodiscus (*Rosaceae*)

discolor CBcs CDul CWld ELan EPfP EWes GCal IDee LEdu LRHS MBlu MBri MMuc MRav NLar SHil SKHP SLon SPer SPlb SSpi WBor
- var. ***ariifolius*** WSHC

Homalocladium (*Polygonaceae*)

§ ***platycladum*** EShb

Homeria (*Iridaceae*)

breyniana var. ***aurantiaca*** see *Moraea collina*

Homoglossum see *Gladiolus*

Hordeum (*Poaceae*)

jubatum CKno CSpe CWCL EAJP EHoe EWes MSCN MWhi NChi NGdn SEND SPhx
- 'Early Pink' NDov
secalinum CHab

Horminum (*Lamiaceae*)

pyrenaicum ECho MMuc SEND SRms WMoo WPtf
- dark-flowered ECho GCal SBrt

Hornungia (*Brassicaceae*)

alpina XLum

horseradish see *Armoracia rusticana*

Hosta ✿ (*Asparagaceae*)

AGSJ 302 CDes WCot WPGP
'A Many-Splendored Thing' EMic IBal
'Abana' (v) **new** IBal
'Abba Dabba Do' (v) ECtt ELon EMic IBal LPla NEgg NSue
'Abba Showtime' IBal
'Abby' (v) EMic IBal NSue WWEG
'Abiqua Ariel' EMic
'Abiqua Blue Crinkles' IBal NBir
'Abiqua Blue Edger' EMic IBal
'Abiqua Drinking Gourd' 🏆H7 EMic GMaP IBal IFoB MHom NEgg NMyG NSue WWEG
'Abiqua Elephant Ears' IBal
'Abiqua Ground Cover' IBal
'Abiqua Moonbeam' (v) CCon EMic IBal NGdn NSue
'Abiqua Recluse' EMic IBal
'Abiqua Trumpet' EMic IBal LRHS NGdn NLar NNor
'Abraham Lincoln' IBal
'Ada Reed' IBal
'Adorable' IBal
aequinoctiiantha IBal
'Alakazaam' (v) EMic IBal NSue
'Alan Titchmarsh' IBal
albomarginata see *H.* 'Paxton's Original' (*sieboldii*)
§ 'Albomarginata' (*fortunei*) (v) CBcs CMac IFoB LRHS MNrw NBir NGdn SPoG SWvt WMoo
'Alex Summers' EMic IBal NMyG WFar
'All That Jazz' (v) EMic IBal
'Allan P. McConnell' (v) EMic GCra IBal LRHS MHom NSue WHal WWEG
'Allegan Emperor' (v) IBal
'Allegan Fog' (v) 🏆H7 EMic EShb IBal IFoB LRHS NSue
'Alligator Alley' (v) **new** IBal
'Alligator Shoes' (v) 🏆H7 EMic IBal
'Alpine Aire' EMic IBal
'Alpine Dream' IBal
'Alvatine Taylor' (v) EMic IBal NGdn NSue
'Amanuma' EMic IBal MHom
'Amazing Grace' (v) IBal
'Amber Tiara' EMic IBal
'American Dream' (v) EMic IBal LRHS
'American Gothic' (v) IBal
'American Great Expectations' (v) IFoB
'American Halo' EMic IBal NEgg NLar NSti
'American Icon' EMic IBal
'American Sweetheart'^{PBR} EMic IBal
'Americana' (v) IBal
'Amethyst Gem' IBal NSue
'Amy Elizabeth' (v) EMic IBal
'Andorian' IBal NSue
'Andrew' EMic NSue
'Angel Feathers' (v) IBal
'Anglo Saxon' (v) IBal
'Ani Machi' (v) 🏆H7 **new** NSue
'Ann Kulpa' (v) EMic IBal NGdn
'Annabel Lee' IBal
'Anne' (v) IBal LRHS LSRN NSue
'Ansly' (v) IBal
'Antioch' (*fortunei*) (v) EMic GLog IBal MRav NLar NSue
'Aoba Tsugaru' IBal
'Aoki' (*fortunei*) EMic IBal
'Aphrodite' (*plantaginea*) (d) EPfP EWTr IBal MBNS MBel NGdn NLar WCot WWEG
'Apollo' NNor
'Apple Green' EMic GKev IBal
'Apple Pie' IBal
'Aqua Velva' IBal
'Arc de Triomphe' EMic IBal
'Arch Duke' **new** IBal
'Arctic Blast' EMic IBal
'Argentea Variegata' (*undulata*) see *H. undulata* var. *undulata*
'Aristocrat' (Tardiana Group) (v) EBee EMic IBal LRHS MBri NEgg NGdn NSue WFar
'Asian Pearl' (v) IBal
'Aspen Gold' (*tokudama* hybrid) EMic
'Astral Bliss' IBal
'Atlantis'^{PBR} (v) 🏆H7 EMic IBal NGdn NSue
'Atomic Elvis' IBal
'August Beauty' EMic IBal
'August Moon' Widely available
'Aureafolia' see *H.* 'Starker Yellow Leaf'
'Aureoalba' (*fortunei*) see *H.* 'Spinners'
'Aureomaculata' (*fortunei*) see *H. fortunei* var. *albopicta*
'Aureomarginata' ambig. (v) CLet SCoo
'Aureomarginata' (*montana*) (v) 🏆H7 CMac EHoe ELan EMic GCal GMaP IBal MMuc NEgg NGdn NLar NSue WFar
§ 'Aureomarginata' (*ventricosa*) (v) 🏆H7 EMic IBal NGdn WFar
'Aureostriata' (*tardiva*) see *H.* 'Inaho'
'Austin Dickinson' (v) ECtt EMic IBal LRHS NEgg
'Autumn Frost' (v) IBal NSue
'Avocado' ELon EMic EWTr IBal NSue
'Azure Snow' IBal
'Azuretini' IBal
'Babbling Brook' IBal NSue

'Baby Blue' (Tardiana Group)	EMic
'Baby Blue Eyes'	IBal NSue
'Baby Booties' (v) **new**	NSue
'Baby Bunting' ♀H7	EMic IBal IFoB NBro NLar NNor NSue
'Baby Doll' (v)	IBal
'Bailey's Cream' (v)	IBal
'Baja White' **new**	IBal
'Bali-Hai'	IBal
'Ballerina'	IBal LRHS NSue
'Bam Bam Blue' **new**	IBal
'Banana Muffins'	IBal
'Band of Gold'	EMic IBal
'Banyai's Dancing Girl'	EMic IBal
'Barbara Ann' (v) ♀H7	EBee EMic IBal MHom NGdn WWEG
'Barbara May'	IBal
'Barbara White'	IBal
'Barney Fife'	IBal
'Battle Star' (v)	EMic IBal
'Beach Boy' (v)	IBal NSue
'Bea's Colossus'	IBal
'Beauty Little Blue'	IBal NSue
'Beauty Substance'	EMic IBal NNor
'Beckoning'	IBal NSue
'Bedazzled' (v)	IBal WBla
'Bedford Blue'	EMic IBal
'Bedford Rise and Shine' (v)	IBal
'Bedford Wakey-Wakey'	IBal
'Behemoth'	IBal NSue
'Bell Bottom Blues'	IBal
bella	see *H. crassifolia*
'Bells of Edinburgh'	IBal
'Ben Vernooij' (v) **new**	IBal
'Bennie McRae'	IBal
'Best of Twenty'	IBal NSue
'Betcher's Blue'	EMic IBal
'Betsy King'	CMac MRav NLar
'Bette Davis Eyes'	IBal
'Betty'	IBal NSue
'Biddy's Blue'	IBal
'Big Boy' (*montana*)	IBal LRHS
'Big Daddy' (*sieboldiana* hybrid) (v) ♀H7	Widely available
'Big John' (*sieboldiana*)	IBal
'Big Mama'	EMic IBal MBNS MNrw NGdn NSue
'Big Top'	IBal
'Bigfoot'	IBal
'Biggie'	IBal
'Bill Brinka' (v)	EMic IBal LRHS
'Birchwood Blue Beauty'	IBal
'Birchwood Gem'	IBal
§ 'Birchwood Parky's Gold'	EBee ECtt EMic EPfP GMaP IBal MBNS NGdn NHol NNor SCob
'Birchwood Ruffled Queen'	EMic
'Bitsy Gold'	EMic
'Bix Blues'	IBal
'Bizarre'	EMic IBal
'Black Beauty'	IBal
'Black Hills'	EMic IBal NSue
'Blackfoot'	EMic IBal
'Blackjack' (*sieboldiana*)	IBal WFar
'Blarney Stone' **new**	IBal
'Blaue Venus'	IBal
'Blaze of Glory'	IBal
'Blazing Saddles' (v)	EMic IBal

'Blonde Elf'	EMic IBal MPnt NEgg NGdn NHol NNor WWEG
'Blue Angel' misapplied	see *H. sieboldiana* var. *elegans*
'Blue Angel' (*sieboldiana*) ♀H7	Widely available
'Blue Arrow' ♀H7	IBal LRHS MHol NNor NSue
'Blue Baron'	EMic IBal
'Blue Beard'	IBal
'Blue Belle' (Tardiana Group)	EMic IBal NEoE NGdn WWEG
'Blue Blush' (Tardiana Group)	EMic IBal NGdn
'Blue Boy'	EMic EWes IBal NNor
'Blue Cadet'	CMac COtt EBee EHoe EMic EShb GQue IBoy IFoB LRHS MLHP MWhi NBir NGdn NLar NSue NWad SBod SPoG WBla WFar WMnd WWEG
'Blue Canoe'	IBal
'Blue Cascade'	EMic IBal
'Blue Chip'	EMic IBal
'Blue Circle' PBR	IBal
'Blue Clown'	IBal
'Blue Cup' (*sieboldiana*)	EMic MRav SRms
'Blue Danube' (Tardiana Group)	EMic IBal MHom NEgg
'Blue Diamond' (Tardiana Group)	EMic LRHS NNor WFar WWEG
'Blue Dimples' (Tardiana Group)	ECtt EMic IBal
'Blue Dolphin'	IBal
'Blue Edger'	EMic IBal NBir
'Blue Eyes'	NSue
'Blue Flame'	EMic IBal
'Blue Frost'	IBal
'Blue Haired Lady'	IBal
'Blue Hawaii'	EMic IBal
'Blue Heart' (*sieboldiana*)	ECha EMic IBal
'Blue Impression'	EMic
'Blue Ivory' (v)	CBcs CBod EBee ECtt IBal LRHS MAsh NSue SGol
'Blue Jay' (Tardiana Group)	EMic
'Blue Lady'	EMic IBal
'Blue Lollipop'	NSue
'Blue Mammoth' (*sieboldiana*)	EMic IBal NEgg NSue WWEG
'Blue Maui'	IBal
'Blue Monday'	EMic
'Blue Moon' (Tardiana Group)	EMic GKev IBal NGdn NLar NNor
'Blue Mountains'	IBal LBuc
'Blue Mouse Ears' ♀H7	Widely available
'Blue River' (v)	EMic IBal
'Blue Seer' (*sieboldiana*)	EMic
'Blue Shadows' (*tokudama*) (v)	EMic ESwi IBal WFar
'Blue Skies' (Tardiana Group)	IBal MHom
'Blue Splendor' (Tardiana Group)	IBal
'Blue Umbrellas' (*sieboldiana* hybrid)	ELan EMic EPfP GMaP IBal LRHS MHom NGdn NLar NNor
'Blue Vision'	IBal MWhi
'Blue Wedgwood' (Tardiana Group)	ELan EMic GQue IBal LRHS MHol NGdn WWEG
'Blue Wonder'	IBal
'Blue Wu'	IBal
'Blueberry à la Mode'	IBal
'Blueberry Cobbler'	IBal

	Name	Suppliers
	'Blueberry Muffin'	EMic NSue
	'Blueberry Tart'	IBal
	'Bluetooth'	IBal
	'Bob Deane' (v)	EMic IBal
	'Bob Olson' (v)	IBal WBla
	'Bobbie Sue' (v)	IBal
	'Bobcat'	IBal
	'Bogie and Bacall' (v)	IBal
	'Bold Edger' (v)	EMic IBal
	'Bold Intrigue' (v)	IBal
	'Bold Ribbons' (v)	EMic GAbr
	'Bolt out of the Blue'	EMic
	'Bonanza'	EMic
	'Boracay'	IBal
	'Border Bandit' (v)	IBal LRHS
	'Border Favorite'	EMic
§	'Borwick Beauty' (*sieboldiana*) (v)	ELon EMic IBal LSou NGdn NLar SPer WWEG
	'Bottom Line' (v)	IBal
	'Bountiful'	EMic IBal
	'Boyz Toy'	IBal NSue WBla
	'Brandywine'	IBal
	'Brave Amherst' (v)	IBal
	'Brenda's Beauty' (v)	EMic IBal
	'Bressingham Blue'	CAby EBee ECtt GQue IBal LRHS MRav NLar NNor SPer SWvt WFar WMnd WMoo
	'Bridal Veil'	EMic IBal
	'Bridegroom'	EMic IBal
	'Bridgeville'	IBal
	'Brigadier'	IBal
	'Brigham Blue'	IBal
	'Bright Glow' (Tardiana Group)	EMic IBal
	'Bright Lights' (*tokudama*) (v)	EMic IBal NGdn WFar
	'Brim Cup' (v)	CAby CCon CRos EBee ECtt ELon GAbr GBuc IBal LAst LRHS LSou MBNS NBro NGdn NMyG NNor SPer WBla WWEG
	'Broadway' (v) **new**	EMic IBal
	'Brooke'	EMic IBal NMyG WWEG
	'Brother Ronald' (Tardiana Group)	EMic IBal NEgg
	'Brother Stefan'	EMic IBal
	'Brutus'	IBal
	'Buckshaw Blue'	IBal NBir NEoE NGdn WHrl
	'Bulletproof'	IBal
	'Bunchoko'	IBal NNor
	'Burke's Dwarf'	IBal
	'Cadillac' (v)	EMic
*	'Caerula' (*ventricosa*)	IFoB
	'Cally Atom'	EBee GCal IBal
	'Cally Colossus'	GCal IBal
I	'Cally Strain' (*nigrescens*)	MHer
	'Cally White' (*nigrescens*)	EBee GCal IBal
	'Calypso' (v)	EMic IBal NGdn WBla WWEG
	'Camelot' (Tardiana Group)	IBal LRHS NGdn
	'Cameo'	NSue
	'Camouflage'	EMic IBal
	'Canadian Blue'	EMic IBal MWhi NLar NSue
	'Candle Wax' **new**	IBal
	'Candy Dish'	IBal NSue
	'Candy Hearts'	CSam EMic IBal MHom NNor
	capitata	NNor
	- B&SWJ 588	WCru
	'Captain Kirk' (v) ♀H7	EMic IBal NGdn NMyG NSue
	'Captain's Adventure' (v)	EMic IBal NGdn NSue WFar
	caput-avis	see *H. kikutii* var. *caput-avis*
	'Carder Blue'	EMic IBal
	'Carnival' (v)	EMic IBal IFoB LRHS NEgg NGdn
	'Carol' (*fortunei*) (v)	IBal MBel NEgg NGdn NLar NMyG NNor NSue
	'Carolina Blue'	IBal
	'Carousel' (v)	IBal
	'Carrie' (*sieboldii*) (v)	EMic
	'Cascades' (v)	IBal NGdn
	'Cathedral Windows' (v) ♀H7	EMic IBal NSue
	'Catherine'	ELon IBal LSun NSue WFar
	'Cat's Eyes' (*venusta*) (v)	IBal NNor NSue
	'Cavalcade' (v)	EMic
	'Celebration' (v)	ELan EMic IBal WWEG
	'Celestial'	IBal
	'Celtic Dancer'	EMic IBal
	'Celtic Uplands'	EMic IBal
	'Center of Attention'	EMic IBal NGdn
	'Centerfold'	NSue
	'Cha Cha Cha'	IBal
	'Chain Lightning' (v)	EMic IBal
	'Challenger'	EMic
	'Chameleon' (v)	EMic
	'Change of Tradition' (*lancifolia*) (v)	EMic
	'Chantilly Lace' (v)	EMic IBal WWEG
	'Chariots of Fire' (v)	IBal
	'Chartreuse Waves'	IBal
	'Chartreuse Wiggles' (*sieboldii*)	IBal NSue
	'Cheatin' Heart'	EMic IBal NMyG NSue WWEG
	'Chelsea Babe' (*fortunei*) (v)	IBal
	'Cherish' ♀H7	IBal NGdn NSue
	'Cherry Berry' (v)	CBod CWGN EMic GBin IBal IFoB LRHS MBNS MHol MNrw MPie NBro NEgg NEoE NGdn NLar NWad SCob SHar SPoG WBla WFar WWEG
	'Cherry Tart'	IBal NSue
	'Cherub' (v)	EMic IBal LRHS
	'Chesapeake Bay'	EMic IBal NSue
	'Chesterland Gold'	IBal
	'Chief Sitting Bull' **new**	NSue
	'Childhood Sweetheart' (v)	IBal
	'China Girl'	EMic IBal
	'Chinese Gold'	IBal
	'Chinese Sunrise' (v) ♀H7	CWCL EMic GBin IBal MHom NNor SRms
	'Chionea' (v)	IBal
	'Chiquita'	IBal
	'Chi-town Classic' (v)	IBal
	'Chodai Ginba'	IBal
§	'Chōkō-nishiki' (*montana*) (v)	IBal LRHS NGdn NNor
	'Choo Choo Train'	EMic
	'Chopsticks'	EMic
	'Christmas Candy'PBR	EMic IBal LRHS MBri
	'Christmas Charm' (v)	IBal
	'Christmas Cookies'	IBal
	'Christmas Pageant' (v)	EMic IBal
	'Christmas Tree' (v) ♀H7	CBod EBee EMic IBal IFoB LPla LRHS NEgg NGdn NLar NSue WMoo WWEG
	'Church Mouse' **new**	IBal NSue
	'Cinderella'	IBal
	'Cinnamon Sticks'	IBal
	'Citation' (v)	IBal
	'City Lights'	ECtt EMic MHtn NEgg
	'City Slicker' (v)	IBal

'Claudia'	IBal
clausa	EMic
- var. ***normalis***	GQui IBal NBir NGdn NLar
'Clear Fork River Valley'	EMic IBal
'Clifford's Forest Fire'	ECtt EMic IBal LRHS NLar WFar
'Clifford's Stingray' (v)	EMic IBal NSue
'Climax' (v) ♀H7	EMic IBal IBoy NSue
'Cloud Lime' **new**	IBal
'Cloudburst'	EMic IBal
'Clovelly'	IBal
'Clown's Collar' (v)	EMic IBal
'Coal Miner'	IBal
'Coconut Custard'	NSue
'Cody'	IBal
'Cold Heart'	EMic IBal
'Collector's Banner'	IBal
'Collector's Choice'	IBal NSue
'Color Festival' (v)	EMic IBal LLWG NSue
'Color Glory'	see *H.* 'Borwick Beauty'
'Colored Hulk' (v) **new**	IBal
'Colossal'	EMic IBal
'Columbus Circle' (v)	EMic IBal
'Con Te Partiro' (v)	NSue
'Confused Angel' (v)	IBal
'Cookie Crumbs' (v)	EMic IBal
'Coquette' (v)	EMic GAbr IBal
'Corkscrew'	EMic NSue
'Corn Belt' (v)	EMic IBal
'Corn Muffins'	EMic
'Corryvreckan'	IBal
'Cotillion' (v)	EMic IBal NSue
'Cotton Candy' (v) **new**	NSue
'Count Your Blessings' (v)	EMic IBal
'Country Mouse' (v)	EMic IBal NSue
'County Park'	EMic IBal
'Cowrie' (v)	IBal
'Cracker Crumbs' (v) ♀H7	EMic GEdr GKev IBal MHom NHar NMyG NNor NSla NSue WBla WWEG
'Craig's Temptation'	IBal
'Cranberry Wine'	IBal
§ ***crassifolia***	EMic IBal LRHS XLum
'Cream Cheese' (v)	IBal
'Cream Delight' (*undulata*)	see *H. undulata* var. *undulata*
'Crepe Soul' (v)	IBal
'Crepe Suzette' (v)	IBal NNor
'Crested Reef'	EMic
'Crested Surf' (v)	EMic
'Crinoline Petticoats'	IBal
§ ***crispula*** (v)	EMic EPfP IBal MCot MHom MRav NChi
'Crown Prince' (v)	IBal NGdn
'Crown Royalty'	EMic IBal
§ 'Crowned Imperial' (*fortunei*) (v)	EMic IBal
'Crumb Cake'	NSue
'Crumples' (*sieboldiana*)	IBal
'Crusader' (v) ♀H7	ELon EMic IBal LRHS WFar WWEG
'Crystal Chimes'	IBal
'Crystal Dixie'	EMic IBal NSue WBla
'Cumulonimbus'	IBal
'Curlew' (Tardiana Group)	IBal
'Curls'	EMic IBal
'Curly Fries'	EMic IBal NSue
'Curtain Call'	IBal
'Cutting Edge'	EMic IBal
'Cuyahoga' (v)	IBal
'Dab a Green'	IBal
'Dance with Me' (v)	EMic IBal
'Dancing in the Rain' (v)	CWGN EMic LLWG MBri NBro NSue WFar
'Dancing Mouse' (v)	IBal NSue
'Dancing Queen'	EMic IBal
'Dark Shadows'	EBee EMic IBal NGdn NSti WFar
'Dark Star' (v)	EMic IBal NGdn NSue
'Dartmoor Forest'	IBal
'Dawn'	EMic IBal NSue
'Dawn's Early Light'	EMic IBal
'Dax'	IBal
'Daybreak' ♀H7	EMic IBal MBri NBro
'Day's End' (v)	EMic IBal
'Deane's Dream'	EMic IBal NSue
decorata	EMic
'Deep Blue Sea' ♀H7	EMic IBal NSue
'Deep Pockets'	IBal
'Dee's Golden Jewel'	EMic
'Déjà Blu' (v)	EMic IBal
'Deliverance'	IBal NSue
'Delta Dawn' (v)	EMic IBal NGdn
'Delta Desire'	IBal
'Desert Mouse'[PBR] (v)	IBal NSue
'Designer Genes'	EMic IBal NSue
'Devil's Advocate' **new**	IBal
'Devon Blue' (Tardiana Group)	IBal NNor
'Devon Desire' (*montana*)	IBal NLar
'Devon Discovery'	IBal
'Devon Giant'	EMic NNor
'Devon Gold'	EMic GAbr IBal
'Devon Green' ♀H7	CLet CRos EAEE ELan EMic EWoo GBin IBal IPot LCro LOPS LRHS MBel MHom MMuc NBro NEgg NEoE NGdn NLar NMyG NRya NSue SEND WAul WCot WFar WHal WHoo WWEG
'Devon Mist'	IBal NNor
'Devon Tor'	IBal
'Dew Drop' (v)	EMic WWEG
'Dewed Steel'	IBal
'Diamond Tiara' (v)	EMic IBal LRHS NBir NGdn WWEG WWtn
'Diamonds are Forever' (v) **new**	IBal
'Diana Remembered'	EMic IBal NGdn NSue
'Dick Ward'	EMic IBal
'Dilithium Crystal'	IBal NSue
'Dillie Perkeo'	IBal
'Dilys'	EMic MNrw
'Dimple'	EMic
'Dinky Donna' (v)	EMic IBal NSue
'Dinner Jacket'	ELan IBal LRHS
'Dixie Chick' (v)	EMic IBal NNor NSue WBla
'Dixie Chickadee' (v)	WBla
'Dixieland Heat'	IBal
'Doctor Fu Manchu'	IBal
'Domaine de Courson'	EMic IBal NSue WFar
'Don Stevens' (v)	IBal LRHS
'Dorothy'	EMic
'Dorset Blue' (Tardiana Group)	EMic IBal LRHS
'Dorset Charm' (Tardiana Group)	EMic
'Dorset Flair' (Tardiana Group)	EMic IBal
'Doubled Up'	IBal
'Doubloons'	EMic

Name	Suppliers
'Dragon Tails' ♀H7	EMic IBal NHar NSue
'Dragon Warrior' (v)	IBal
'Drake's Tail' **new**	IBal
'Dream Queen' (v)	ECtt EMic EWTr IBal SPoG
'Dream Weaver' (v) ♀H7	CBod ELon EMic IBal IFoB IPot LRHS MHom MNrw NBro NEgg NGdn NSue SPer WFar WWEG
'Dress Blues'	CMac EMic IBal
'Drummer Boy'	EMic IBal WBla WWEG
'Duke of Cornwall' (v)	IBal
'DuPage Delight' (*sieboldiana*) (v)	EMic IBal NGdn NLar
'Dust Devil' (*fortunei*) (v)	IBal
'Dusty Waters'	IBal
'Eagle's Nest' (v)	IBal
'Early Times'	IBal
'Earth Angel'[PBR] (v) ♀H7	EBee EMic IBal NGdn NSue
'Ebony Towers'	EMic IBal
'Edge of Night'	EMic IBal
'Edwin Bibby'	EMic
'El Capitan' (v)	EMic IBal IFoB LRHS
'El Niño'[PBR] (Tardiana Group) (v) ♀H7	CWGN EMic IBal LRHS MHom MNrw NBro NGdn SPoG WBla WFar WHoo WWEG
§ 'Elata'	EMic
'Elatior' (*nigrescens*)	IBal LRHS
'Elbridge Gerry' (v)	IBal
'Eldorado'	see *H.* 'Frances Williams'
'Eleanor Lachman' (v)	EMic IBal NSue
'Eleanor Roosevelt'	IBal
'Electrocution' (v)	IBal NSue
'Elegans'	see *H. sieboldiana* var. *elegans*
'Elisabeth'	EMic IBal LSRN
'Elizabeth Campbell' (*fortunei*) (v)	EMic
'Elkheart Lake'	EMic IBal
'Ellen'	EMic
'Ellerbroek' (*fortunei*) (v)	EMic
'Elsley Runner'	IBal NSue WWEG
'Elvis Lives'	EMic IBal NEgg NEoE NGdn NLar NNor NSue
'Emerald Carpet'	IBal NSue
'Emerald Charger' (v) **new**	IBal
'Emerald Crown'	IBal
'Emerald Emperor' **new**	IBal
'Emerald Necklace' (v)	EMic IBal
'Emerald Ruff Cut'	EMic
'Emerald Tiara' (v)	EMic IBal LRHS MLHP NLar SHil WBla WWEG
'Emeralds and Rubies'	EMic IBal NSue WBla
'Emily Dickinson' (v)	EMic IBal LRHS NNor WWEG
'Empress Wu'[PBR]	CAby CCon EBee ECtt EMic ESwi EUJe GAbr GBin IBal IBoy ITim LBrs LRHS LSun MHol MSCN NGdn NSue SMad SPoG WCot
'Encore'	IBal
'English Sunrise' (Tardiana Group)	IBal
'Enterprise' (v)	EBee EMic IBal NGdn NSue
'Eola Sapphire'	EMic IBal
'Eos'	IBal NLar
'Eric Smith' (Tardiana Group)	EMic IBal MHom SHar WFar
'Eric Smith Gold'	GKev
'Eric's Gold'	IBal
'Erie Magic' (v)	IBal
'Eskimo Pie' (v)	MBri NSue WFar
'Essence of Summer'	EMic IBal
'Eternal Flame'	EMic IBal
'Everlasting Love' (v)	IBal
'Excitation'	EMic IBal
'Exotic Presentation' (v)	EMic IBal
'Extasy' (v)	EMic IBal NGdn NSue
'Eye Candy' (v)	IBal
'Eye Catcher'	EMic
'Eye Declare' (v)	IBal
'Faith'	EMic
'Faithful Heart' (v)	IBal NSue
'Fall Dazzler' (v) **new**	IBal
'Fall Emerald'	EMic
'Fan Dance' (v)	IBal
'Fantabulous' (v)	IBal
'Fantasy Island' (v)	EMic IBal NSue
'Fat Boy'	IBal
'Fatal Attraction'	IBal
'Feather Boa'	EMic IBal IFoB LRHS NHar NSue WBla WWEG
'Feng Shui' **new**	IBal
'Fenman's Fascination'	EMic
'Fiesta' (v)	IBal
'Final Summation' (v)	EMic IBal NSue
'Finlandia'	IBal
'Fire and Ice' (v) ♀H7	Widely available
'Fire Island' ♀H7	EBee ECtt ELan EMic EPfP GBin IBal LRHS MHom MNrw NGdn NSue SPoG WCot
'Fire Opal' (v)	IBal
'Fireworks' (v) ♀H7	EMic EPfP GBin IBal LRHS MBNS MBri MHol NBro NGdn WCot
'Firn Line' (v) **new**	IBal
'First Frost' (v) ♀H7	EBee EMic IBal LRHS MAsh MBri NGdn NLar NMyG NSue WWEG
'First Love' (*montana*)	EMic IBal
'First Mate' (v)	EMic IBal NSue
'Five O'Clock Shadow' (v)	IBal
'Five O'Clock Somewhere' (v)	IBal
'Flapjack' (v)	IBal
'Fleet Week'	EMic IBal
'Flemish Angel' (v)	IBal NSue
'Flemish Gold'	IBal
'Flemish Sky'	EMic IBal IFoB MBri NGdn
'Floradora'	EMic IBal NSue
'Flower Power'	IBal NNor
'Fluted Fountain'	EMic
'Fog Light' **new**	IBal
'Fool's Gold' (*fortunei*)	EMic IBal
'Forbidden Fruit' (v) **new**	IBal
'Forest Fireworks' (v)	IBal
'Forest Shadows'	IBal
'Formal Attire' (*sieboldiana* hybrid) (v) ♀H7	EMic IBal LRHS
'Forncett Frances' (v)	IBal
'Fortis'	see *H. undulata* var. *erromena*
fortunei	EMic GKev NNor WFar
§ - var. ***albopicta*** (v)	CSam ECha EHoe ELan EMic EPfP EUJe GMaP IFoB LEdu LOPS LPot LRHS MJak MRav NEgg NGdn NLar NMyG NNor SPer SRms WBrk WHoo WMnd WMoo WWEG
- - f. ***aurea***	CMac ECha EHoe EMic MMuc NEgg NLar SRms WFar WHal
- - - dwarf	EMic
- - f. ***viridis***	NNor
§ - var. ***aureomarginata*** (v) ♀H7	CSam CTri ECha EHoe ELan ELon EMic EPfP EShb GMaP IBal LPot

	LRHS MLHP MMuc NGdn NLar
	NNor SEND SPer SPlb SPoG WFar
	WMnd WWEG
- var. ***gigantea***	see *H. montana*
- var. ***hyacinthina***	EMic EPfP IBal LRHS MRav NGdn NLar WFar XLum
- - variegated	see *H.* 'Crowned Imperial'
- var. ***stenantha***	EMic
'Fountain of Youth' (*kikutii*)	IBal
'Fourteen Carats'	EMic IBal
'Fourth of July'	NSue
'Foxfire Palm Sunday' (v) **new**	IBal
'Fragrant Blue'	EMic IBal LRHS NBro NGdn NSue SPoG XLum
'Fragrant Blue Ribbons' (v)	EMic IBal
'Fragrant Bouquet' (v) 🏆H7	ECtt ELan EMic IBal LAst LRHS LSRN NEgg NGdn NHol NLar NMyG NSue SEND WBla WFar WWEG
'Fragrant Dream'	EBee EMic IBal LRHS NLar WWEG
'Fragrant Fire'	EMic IBal
'Fragrant Gold'	EMic
'Fragrant King'	IBal
'Fragrant Queen'[PBR] (v)	IBal NSue
'Fragrant Star'	EMic IBal
'Fran Godfrey'	EMic IBal NMyG
'Francee' (*fortunei*) (v) 🏆H7	Widely available
§ 'Frances Williams' (*sieboldiana*) (v) 🏆H7	Widely available
'Frances Williams Improved' (*sieboldiana*) (v)	EPfP GBuc IFoB MWat
'Francheska' (v)	EMic IBal
'Frank Lloyd Wright' **new**	IBal
'Free Jazz' (v) **new**	IBal
'Fresh' (v)	EMic IBal
'Fried Bananas'	EMic IBal ITim WWEG
'Fried Green Tomatoes'	EMic IBal NLar NNor
'Friends' (v)	EMic
'Fringe Benefit' (v)	EMic WWEG
'Frisian Pride' **new**	IBal
'Frisian Waving Steel' **new**	IBal
'Frosted Dimples'	EMic IBal
'Frosted Frolic' (v)	EMic IBal WBla
'Frosted Jade' (v) 🏆H7	EBee EMic EPfP IBal MMuc NEgg NLar
'Frosted June'	EMic IBal
'Frosted Mini Hearts' **new**	NSue
'Frosted Mouse Ears'[PBR]	EMic IBal MAsh NSue WBla
'Frozen Margarita'	EMic IBal
'Frühlingsgold' (v)	IBal
'Fruit Punch'	EMic IBal IFoB
'Fujibotan' (v)	EMic IBal IFoB
'Fulda'	EMic IBal
'Funky Monkey'	EMic IBal
'Funny Mouse' (v)	EMic IBal NSue WBla
'Futura' (v) **new**	IBal
'Gaiety' (v)	ECtt EMic IBal LRHS
'Gaijin' (v)	IBal NSue
'Garden Party' (v)	IBal
'Garnet Prince'	IBal
'Gay Blade' (v)	IBal
'Gay Feather' (v)	EMic IFoB

'Gay Search' (v)	IBal
'Geisha' (v)	IBal LBMP LRHS NEoE NGdn NNor NSue WBla WWEG
'Geisha Satin Ripples'	IBal
'Gemstone'	NSue
'Gentle Giant'	IBal
'Gentle Spirit' (v)	IBal
'George M. Dallas' (v)	IBal
'George Smith' (*sieboldiana*)	EMic IBal
'Georgia Sweetheart' (v) **new**	IBal
'Ghost Spirit'	IBal NSue WFar
'Ghostmaster' (v)	IBal
'Giantland Mouse Cheese' **new**	NSue
'Giantland Sunny Mouse Ears' **new**	NSue
'Gig Harbor'	IBal
'Gigantea' (*sieboldiana*)	see *H.* 'Elata'
'Gilt by Association'	IBal
'Gilt Edge' (*sieboldiana*) (v)	EMic WWEG
'Gingee'	IBal
'Ginko Craig' (v) 🏆H7	CMac ECha EHoe ELan EMic EPfP GKev GMaP IBal IFoB LRHS MRav MWhi NBir NEgg NGdn NLar NNor NSti SPer SPoG WBla WFar WMnd
'Ginrei'	IBal
'Ginsu Knife' (v)	EMic IBal
'Glacial Towers' (v) **new**	IBal
'Glad Rags' (v)	IBal
'Glad Tidings'	IBal
'Glamour'	EMic IBal NSue
'Glass Hearts'	EMic IBal
glauca	see *H. sieboldiana* var. *elegans*
'Glitter'	EMic IBal
'Glockenspiel'	EMic IBal
I 'Gloriosa' (*fortunei*) (v)	IBal IFoB LRHS NSue WFar
'Glory'	IBal
'Glory Hallelujah'	EMic IBal
'Goddess of Athena' (*decorata*) (v)	IBal
'Gold Drop' (*venusta* hybrid)	EMic IBal NHol NSue WWEG
'Gold Edger'	CBcs CBod CMac EBee EHoe ELan EMic EPfP EShb GCal GKev GMaP IBal LRHS MMuc MRav NBir NGdn NLar NNor NSti WBla WFar WWEG
'Gold Edger Surprise' (v)	EMic
'Gold Flush' (*ventricosa*)	EMic
§ 'Gold Haze' (*fortunei*)	EMic IBal MHom NBir NMyG WWEG
'Gold Leaf' (*fortunei*)	IBal
'Gold Pressed Latinum'	IBal
'Gold Regal'	EBee EMic GBin IBal IFoB MHom NMyG WFar WMnd
'Gold Rush'	IBal
'Gold Standard' (*fortunei*) (v) 🏆H7	Widely available
'Goldbrook' (v)	EMic IBal
'Goldbrook Galleon'	IBal
'Goldbrook Gaynor'	IBal
'Goldbrook Genie'	IBal
'Goldbrook Glamour' (v)	IBal
'Goldbrook Gleam' (v)	IBal
'Goldbrook Glimmer' (Tardiana Group) (v)	IBal LRHS

‘Goldbrook Glory’	EMic IBal
‘Goldbrook Gold’	IBal
‘Goldbrook Good Gracious’ (v)	IBal
‘Goldbrook Grace’	IBal
‘Goldbrook Gratis’ (v)	IBal
‘Goldbrook Grayling’	EMic IBal NSue
‘Goldbrook Grebe’	IBal
‘Goldbrook Greengage’ (v)	IBal
‘Goldbrook Greenheart’	IBal
‘Golden Age’	see *H.* ‘Gold Haze’
‘Golden Fountain’	EMic
‘Golden Gate’	IBal
‘Golden Goal’	IBal
‘Golden Guernsey’ (v)	EMic
‘Golden Isle’	IBal
‘Golden Meadows’[PBR] (*sieboldiana*)	ECtt EMic IBal NGdn NSue SGol WFar
‘Golden Medallion’ (*tokudama*)	ECtt EMic LRHS NEgg NGdn WFar
‘Golden Nakaiana’	see *H.* ‘Birchwood Parky’s Gold’
‘Golden’ (*nakaiana*)	see *H.* ‘Birchwood Parky’s Gold’
‘Golden Needles’ (v) **new**	NSue
‘Golden Oriole’	EMic IBal LRHS NNor WWEG
‘Golden Prayers’ (*tokudama*)	EBee ECtt EHoe ELan MRav NBir NBro NEgg NGdn NLar WFar WHal WSHC
‘Golden Scepter’	CBod EMic IBal LRHS NNor WBla WFar
‘Golden Sculpture’ (*sieboldiana*)	EMic
‘Golden Spades’	NSue
‘Golden Spider’	EMic WWEG
‘Golden Sunburst’ (*sieboldiana*)	NEgg NGdn NLar WFar XLum
‘Golden Tiara’ (v) ♀H7	Widely available
‘Golden Tusk’	IBal
‘Golden Waffles’	EMic NEgg
‘Gone Fishin’’ (v)	IBal
‘Gone with the Wind’ (v) **new**	IBal
‘Goober’	IBal
‘Good as Gold’	EMic
‘Goodness Gracious’ (v)	IBal NSue
‘Gorgeous George’	IBal
‘Gosan Leather Strap’	IBal
gracillima	IBal NRya WWEG
‘Granary Gold’ (*fortunei*)	MHom
‘Grand Canyon’	EMic
‘Grand Finale’	IBal
‘Grand Marquee’ (v)	EMic IBal NGdn NLar SGol WFar WWEG
‘Grand Master’	IBal
‘Grand Prize’ (v)	EMic IBal
‘Grand Rapids’	IBal
‘Grand Slam’	IBal
‘Grand Tiara’ (v)	EMic IBal LRHS NGdn WBla
‘Grand Total’	IBal
‘Grant Park’	IBal
‘Grape Fizz’	IBal
‘Gray Cole’ (*sieboldiana*)	EMic IBal ITim
‘Great Arrival’	EMic IBal
‘Great Escape’[PBR] (v)	EBee IBal LLWG
‘Great Expectations’ (*sieboldiana*) (v)	CHid CMac CNor EAEE EMic EPfP IBal IBoy IFoB IVic LRHS LSRN MBNS MHer MNrw MWhi NBro NGdn NNor NSti SPoG WWEG
‘Great Lakes Gold’	IBal
‘Green Acres’ (*montana*)	EMic IBal LEdu WFar
‘Green Angel’ (*sieboldiana*)	IBal
‘Green Dwarf’	WBla
‘Green Eyes’ (*sieboldii*) (v)	IBal NSue
‘Green Fountain’ (*kikutii*)	EMic IBal WWEG
‘Green Lama’	IBal
‘Green Mouse Ears’	EMic IBal MAsh NSue WBla
‘Green Piecrust’	NNor
‘Green Sheen’	EMic
‘Green Velveteen’	IBal
‘Green with Envy’ (v) ♀H7	EMic IBal LLHF NNor NSue WWEG
‘Greensleeves’ (v)	IBal
‘Grey Ghost’	EMic IBal
‘Grey Goose’ (Tardiana Group)	EMic
‘Ground Master’ (v)	CMac EBee ECtt ELan EPfP GCra GMaP IBal IFoB MRav NBro NGdn NLar NNor NSti WBla WFar WMoo WWEG
‘Ground Sulphur’	EMic IBal NSue
‘Grover Cleveland’	IBal
‘Grünherz’	IBal
‘Grunspecht’ (Tardiana Group)	IBal
‘Guacamole’ (v) ♀H7	CAby CBcs ECha ECtt EHoe ELon EMic EPfP IBal LRHS NGdn NLar NNor SBod SPoG WBla WWEG
‘Guardian Angel’ (*sieboldiana*) ♀H7	EMic IBal NSue
‘Gum Drop’	EMic NNor
‘Gun Metal Blue’	IBal
‘Gunther’s Prize’ (v) **new**	IBal
‘Gunther’s Rim’ (v)	IBal
‘Gypsy Rose’ ♀H7	IBal NGdn NMyG NSue WFar
‘Hacksaw’	EMic IBal NSue
‘Hadspen Blue’ (Tardiana Group) ♀H7	CAby CSBt CWCL EBee ELan EMic EPfP GBin GMaP IBal IBoy LOPS LRHS MBrN MGos MRav NBir NBro NEgg NGdn NHol NLar NNor SHil SPer SPoG WMnd WWEG
‘Hadspen Hawk’ (Tardiana Group)	IBal
‘Hadspen Heron’ (Tardiana Group)	EMic IBal MHom MWat XLum
‘Hadspen Honey’	LRHS
‘Hadspen Nymphaea’	IBal
‘Hadspen Rainbow’	EMic IBal
‘Hadspen Samphire’	CRos EMic IBal LRHS MHom NBir NBro NMyG
‘Hadspen White’ (*fortunei*)	EMic IBal NLar
‘Hakujima’ (*sieboldii*)	IBal NSue
‘Hakumuo’ (v)	IBal
§ ‘Halcyon’ (Tardiana Group) ♀H7	Widely available
‘Halcyon Gold’	SGol
‘Half and Half’	EMic IBal NSue
‘Hampshire County’ (v)	EMic IBal
‘Hands Up’ (v)	IBal NSue
‘Hanky Panky’ (v)	EMic IBal LRHS NGdn NSti NSue WFar
‘Hannibal Hamlin’ (v)	IBal
‘Happily Ever After’ (v)	IBal
‘Happiness’ (Tardiana Group)	EHoe EMic IBal MHom MRav
‘Happy Camper’ (v)	IBal
‘Happy Dayz’ (v) **new**	IBal
‘Happy Hearts’	EMic
‘Happy Valley’ (v)	IBal

'Harmony' (Tardiana Group)	EMic
'Harpoon' (v)	EMic
'Harriette Ward'	IBal
'Harry van de Laar'	EMic IBal
'Harry van Trier'	EMic GBin WBla
'Hart's Tongue'	IBal
'Harvest Delight'	EMic
'Harvest Glow'	IBal
'Hawkeye' (v)	IBal
'Hazel'	EMic IBal
'Heart and Soul' (v)	EMic IBal
'Heart Broken'	IBal
'Heart of Chan'	IBal
'Heart Throb'	EMic
'Heartache' **new**	IBal
'Heartleaf'	EMic
'Heart's Content' (v)	IBal
'Heartsong' (v)	EMic IBal LRHS NMyG
'Heat Wave'PBR (v)	EMic IBal
'Heavenly Beginnings' (v)	IBal
'Heavy Duty'	IBal
'Heideturm'	IBal
'Helen Doriot' (*sieboldiana*)	EMic
'Helen Field Fischer' (*fortunei*)	IBal NLar
helonioides f. ***albopicta*** misapplied	see *H. rohdeifolia*
'Herifu' (v)	EMic
'Hertha' (v)	EMic
'Hidden Cove' (v)	IBal NSue
'Hidden Treasure' (v)	IBal
'Hideout' (v)	IBal NSue
'High Kicker'	IBal
'High Society' (v)	CBcs ELan EPfP IBal IFoB MHom MNrw NGdn NNor NSue WBla
'High Tide'	IBal
'Hi-ho Silver' (v)	EMic IBal NSue WBla WWEG
'Hilda Wassman' (v)	IBal
'Hillbilly Blues' (v)	NSue
'Hippodrome' (v)	EMic IBal
'Hirao Elite'	EMic IBal
'Hirao Majesty'	IBal
'Hirao Supreme'	EMic IBal
'His Honor' (v)	EMic IBal
'Holly's Dazzler'	IBal
'Hollywood Lights' (v)	EMic EPfP IBal NGdn NSue
'Holstein'	see *H.* 'Halcyon'
'Holy Molé' (v)	EMic IBal
'Holy Mouse Ears'PBR	EMic IBal NSue WBla
'Honey Moon'	IBal NNor
'Honeybells'	CBcs CMac CTri EBee ECha ELan EMic EPfP IBal LEdu LHop MCot MRav NBid NGdn NNor NSti SBod SPer WFar WWEG XLum
'Honeysong' (v)	EMic IBal NNor
'Hoosier Dome'	EMic
'Hoosier Harmony' (v)	EMic
'Hope' (v)	IBal
'Hot Air Balloon' **new**	IBal
'Hotcakes'	IBal
'Hotspur' (v)	EMic
'Hudson Bay' (v) **new**	IBal
'Humpback Whale' **new**	IBal
'Hush Puppie'	EMic IBal NSue
'Hyacintha Variegata' (*fortunei*) (v)	CMac NNor
'Hydon Gleam'	EMic IBal NSue
'Hydon Sunset'	CNor EBee ECtt EMic GCra GEdr IBal LRHS NBir NLar NNor NRya NSti NSue WBla WHal WMnd WWEG
hypoleuca	EMic IBal
'Hyuga-urajiro' (v)	EMic IBal
'Ice Cream' (*cathayana*) (v)	IBal NGdn
'Ice Cube' (v)	IBal NSue WBla
'Ice Prancer'	EMic IBal
'Iced Lemon' (v)	EMic IBal NNor NSue WBla
'Illicit Affair'	EMic IBal NSue
'Imp' (v)	EMic IBal
§ 'Inaho'	LRHS NSue
'Inca Gold'	IBal NSue WBla
'Incoming' **new**	IBal
'Independence' (v)	EBee EMic IBal MBri NBro NMyG NSue SPoG WFar
'Independence Day' (v)	EMic
'Inniswood' (v)	CCon CWCL ECtt EMic IBal LRHS MBNS NBro NGdn NLar NSti WBla WFar WMnd WWEG
'Invincible'	ECtt EMic IBal LAst NBid NEgg NGdn NLar NMyG NNor WWEG
'Invincible Spirit'	IBal
'Iona' (*fortunei*)	EMic IBal NNor
'Irische See' (Tardiana Group)	IBal
'Irish Eyes' (v)	EMic IBal
'Irish Luck'	EMic IBal NSue
'Iron Gate Delight' (v)	NNor
'Iron Gate Special' (v)	EMic
'Iron Gate Supreme' (v)	EMic
'Island Charm' (v) ♀H7	EMic IBal LRHS NHar NLar NMyG SCob
'Itty Bitty' (v) **new**	NSue
'Ivory Coast' (v)	EMic IBal MHol
'Ivory Necklace' (v)	IBal
'Ivory Queen' (v) **new**	EMic IBal
'Iwa Yara Moto'	IBal
'Jack of Diamonds'	IBal
'Jade Cascade'	EMic GBin IBal NBir NEgg NLar WHal WWEG
'Jade Scepter' (*nakaiana*)	EMic
'Janet Day' (v)	EMic
'Janet' (*fortunei*) (v)	EMic NGdn NNor
'Jason and Katie' (v)	IBal
'Jaws'	EMic IBal NSue
'Jaz'	IBal
'Jennifer Bailey' (v)	IBal
'Jerry Landwehr'	IBal
'Jewel of the Nile' (v)	EMic IBal
'Jimmy Crack Corn'	EMic IBal NEgg NGdn
'Jingle Bells'	IBal
'John Wargo'	IBal
'Johnny Angel'	EMic
'Joker' (*fortunei*) (v)	NNor
'Jolly Green Giant' (*sieboldiana* hybrid)	EMic
jonesii	EMic
'Joseph'	IBal
'Josephine' (v)	NNor
'Journeyman'	EMic IBal
'Journey's End' (v)	EMic IBal
'Joyce Trott' (v)	EMic
'Joyful' (v)	IBal
'Jubilee' (v)	EMic IBal
'Judy Rocco'	IBal
'Juha' (v)	EMic

	'Jules'	IBal
	'Julia' (v)	EMic IBal NSue
	'Julie Morss'	EMic GMaP IBal MHom NEgg WWEG
	'June'PBR (Tardiana Group) (v) ♀H7	Widely available
	'June Fever'PBR (Tardiana Group)	EMic ESwi IBal LLWG MBri NBro NGdn NLar NSue WFar
	'June Spirit' (v) **new**	IBal
	'Junka' **new**	SMHy
	'Jurassic Park'	EBee EMic GBin IBal LLWG MNrw NLar
	'Just June' (Tardiana Group) (v)	MAsh
	'Just So' (v)	EMic IBal
	'Justine'PBR	EMic IBal NSue
	'Kabitan'	see *H. sieboldii* var. *sieboldii* f. *kabitan*
	'Kabuki'	IBal
	'Kalamazoo' (v)	EMic IBal
	'Kaleidochrome' (v)	IBal NSue
	'Karin'	EMic IBal
	'Katherine Lewis' (Tardiana Group) (v)	ECtt EMic IBal LRHS LSRN NHol
	'Kath's Gold'	EMic
	'Katie Q' (v)	EMic IBal
	'Katsuragawa-beni' (v)	EMic IBal
	'Kelsey'	EMic
	'Kenzie' (v)	EMic IBal
	'Key Lime Pie'	EMic IBal
	'Key West'	EMic
	'Kifukurin' (*kikutii*)	see *H.* 'Kifukurin-hyuga'
	'Kifukurin' (*venusta*) (v)	EMic WBla
§	'Kifukurin-hyuga' (v)	IBal
	'Kifukurin-kiyosumi' **new**	IBal
	'Kifukurin-ko-mame' (*gracillima*) (v)	EMic NSue
	'Kifukurin-otome' (*venusta*) (v)	EMic NSue
	'Kifukurin-ubatake' (*pulchella*) (v)	EMic IBal
	kikutii	EMic IBal IMou LRHS
§	- var. ***caput-avis***	EMic
§	- var. ***yakusimensis***	EMic IBal NHar SMad
	'Ki-nakafu-otome' (*venusta*)	IBal WBla
	'Kinbotan' (v)	EMic
	'Kinbuchi Tachi' (*rectifolia*) (v)	IBal
	'King James'	IBal
	'King of Spades'	IBal
	'King Tut'	EMic
	'Kingfisher' (Tardiana Group)	LRHS
	'Kingsize' **new**	IBal
§	'Kirishima'	EMic NSla NSue
	'Kisuji'	see *H.* 'Mediopicta'
	'Kitty Cat'	EMic IBal NSue
	'Kiwi Black Magic'	IBal
	'Kiwi Blue Baby'	EMic IBal
	'Kiwi Blue Ruffles'	IBal
	'Kiwi Blue Sky'	IBal
	'Kiwi Canoe'	IBal
	'Kiwi Cream Edge' (v)	EMic
	'Kiwi Forest'	IBal
	'Kiwi Full Monty' (v)	EBee EMic IBal LRHS NSue
	'Kiwi Gold Rush'	IBal
	'Kiwi Hippo'	IBal
	'Kiwi Jordan'	IBal
	'Kiwi Kaniere Gold'	IBal
	'Kiwi Minnie Gold'	IBal ITim
	'Kiwi Parasol'	IBal
	'Kiwi Skyscraper'	IBal
	'Kiwi Sunshine'	IBal
	kiyosumiensis	IBal
	'Klopping Variegated' (v)	EMic
	'Knight's Journey'	IBal
	'Knockout' (v)	MBNS MNrw MRav NBro NEgg NGdn NLar NMyG NNor
	'Komodo Dragon'	EMic IBal SKHP
	'Konkubine'	EMic
	'Korean Snow'	IBal
	'Koriyama' (*sieboldiana*) (v)	EMic
	'Krossa Cream Edge' (*sieboldii*) (v)	IBal
	'Krossa Regal' ♀H7	Widely available
	'Krugerrand'	IBal
	'La Donna'	IBal
	'Lacy Belle' (v)	CSBt EBee EMic EPfP IBal NBro NEoE NGdn NSue WRHF
	'Lady Godiva'	IBal
	'Lady Guineverre'	EMic IBal
	'Lady Helen'	EMic
	'Lady in Red'	IBal
	'Lady Isobel Barnett' (v) ♀H7	IBal
	laevigata	IBal NSue
	'Lake Hitchock'	IBal
	'Lake Superior'	IBal
	'Lakeside Alex Andra' (v)	IBal
	'Lakeside April Snow' (v)	EMic IBal NGdn
	'Lakeside Baby Face' (v)	EMic IBal NSue WBla
	'Lakeside Banana Bay' (v)	IBal NGdn WBla
	'Lakeside Beach Bum'	IBal NSue
	'Lakeside Beach Captain' (v)	EMic
	'Lakeside Black Satin'	EMic WFar
	'Lakeside Blue Cherub'	EMic IBal
	'Lakeside Breaking News' (v)	EMic IBal
	'Lakeside Butter Ball'	IBal
	'Lakeside Cha Cha' (v)	EMic IBal LRHS MWhi WBla
	'Lakeside Cindy Cee' (v)	IBal
	'Lakeside Coal Miner'	EMic IBal NGdn
	'Lakeside Color Blue'	IBal
	'Lakeside Contender'	IBal
	'Lakeside Cupcake' (v)	EMic IBal LRHS NGdn NSue WBla
	'Lakeside Cupid's Cup' (v)	IBal
	'Lakeside Dividing Line' (v)	IBal
	'Lakeside Doodad' (v)	IBal WBla
	'Lakeside Down Sized' (v)	EMic IBal MHom NSue WBla
	'Lakeside Dragonfly' (v)	EBee EMic EPfP IBal LLWG LRHS NGdn NSue WBla WFar
	'Lakeside Elfin Fire'	EMic WBla
	'Lakeside Fancy Pants' (v)	IBal
	'Lakeside Feather Light' (v)	IBal
	'Lakeside Foaming Sea'	IBal
	'Lakeside Full Tide'	IBal
	'Lakeside Hazy Morn' (v)	IBal
	'Lakeside Hoola Hoop' (v)	IBal
	'Lakeside Iron Man'	IBal
	'Lakeside Jazzy Jane' (v)	IBal
	'Lakeside Kaleidoscope'	EMic IBal NGdn
	'Lakeside Keepsake' (v)	IBal
	'Lakeside Legal Tender'	IBal

'Lakeside Lime Time'	IBal
'Lakeside Little Gem'	IBal NSue WBla
'Lakeside Little Tuft' (v)	EMic IBal NSue
'Lakeside Lollipop'	EMic IBal
'Lakeside Looking Glass'	EMic
'Lakeside Love Affaire'	EMic IBal WFar
'Lakeside Maestro'	IBal NLar
'Lakeside Maverick'	IBal
'Lakeside Meadow Ice' (v)	IBal
'Lakeside Meter Maid' (v)	IBal
'Lakeside Midnight Miss'	IBal
'Lakeside Miss Muffett' (v)	NSue WBla
'Lakeside Missy Little' (v)	IBal
'Lakeside Neat Petite'	IBal NSue
'Lakeside Ninita' (v)	EMic IBal LRHS NSue
'Lakeside Old Smokey'	IBal
'Lakeside Paisley Print' (v)	EMic IBal NSue
'Lakeside Pebbles'	IBal
'Lakeside Premier'	EMic IBal
'Lakeside Prophecy'	IBal
'Lakeside Prophecy Fulfilled' (v)	IBal
'Lakeside Rhapsody' (v)	EMic IBal
'Lakeside Ring Master' (v)	IBal
'Lakeside Ripples'	IBal
'Lakeside Rocky Top' (v)	IBal
'Lakeside Roy El' (v)	IBal
'Lakeside Sapphire Pleats'	EMic
'Lakeside Sassy Sally'	IBal
'Lakeside Scamp' (v)	EMic NSue
'Lakeside Shadows' (v)	IBal
'Lakeside Shoremaster' (v)	IBal
'Lakeside Slick Chick' (v)	IBal
'Lakeside Sophistication' (v)	IBal
'Lakeside Sparkle Plenty' (v)	IBal
'Lakeside Spellbinder' (v)	IBal LRHS
'Lakeside Spruce Goose' (v)	EMic IBal
'Lakeside Storm Watch'	EMic IBal NSue
'Lakeside Swan Pon' (v) **new**	IBal
'Lakeside Symphony' (v)	EMic
'Lakeside Tee Ki' (v)	IBal
'Lakeside Whizzit' (v)	IBal
'Lakeside Zesty Zeno' (v)	IBal
'Lakeside Zinger' (v)	EMic IBal NSue WBla
lancifolia	CMac EBee ELan EMic GMaP IBal MRav NGdn NSti SBod SPer SRms WKif WSHC WThu
'Last Dance' (v)	IBal
'Laura Lanier'	EMic IBal
'Laura Z'	IBal
'Lavender Doll'	IBal
'Leading Lady' ♀[H7]	IBal
'Leather Sheen'	EMic
'Leatherneck'	IBal
'Lederhosen'	EMic
'Lemon Delight'	EMic IBal LRHS NNor NSue WWEG
'Lemon Frost'	EMic IBal
'Lemon Juice'	EBee NMyG
'Lemon Lime'	EMic EWld IBal MHom MNrw NEgg NEoE NNor NSue WBla WCot WWEG
'Lemon Twist'	IBal
'Lemonade'	GBin IBal
'Leola Fraim' (v)	IBal LRHS
'Let Me Entertain You'	EMic
'Leviathan'	EMic
'Lewis and Clark'	IBal
'Libby'	EMic IBal
'Liberty'[PBR] (v) ♀[H7]	CBod CWGN EMic EPfP IBal LRHS MBri NBro NGdn NNor NSue WFar
'Li'l Abner' (v)	IBal
* ***lilacina***	WFar
'Lily Blue Eyes'	EMic
'Lime Fizz'	EMic IBal NSue
'Lime Shag' (*sieboldii* f. *spathulata*)	IBal NSue
'Limey Lisa'	EMic IBal NSue WBla WWEG
'Linda Sue' (v)	IBal
'Lionheart' (v)	IBal NSue
'Little Aurora' (*tokudama* hybrid)	EMic IBal NSue WFar WWEG
'Little Bit'	IBal NSue
'Little Black Scape'	EMic IBal LSRN MHom NEgg NGdn NLar
'Little Blue' (*ventricosa*)	EMic
'Little Bo Beep' (v)	IBal NSue WBla WWEG
'Little Boy'	IBal
'Little Caesar' (v)	EMic IBal NGdn NSue
'Little Devil'	EMic NSue
'Little Doll' (v)	IBal
'Little Jay' (v)	IBal NSue
'Little Maddie'	EMic NSue
'Little Miss Magic'	IBal
'Little Miss Sunshine' **new**	IBal
'Little Razor'	IBal NSue
'Little Red Joy'	EMic IBal NSue WBla
'Little Red Rooster'	EMic IBal NGdn NMyG NNor NSue WBla WFar WWEG
'Little Stiffy'	IBal NSue WBla
'Little Sunspot' (v)	EMic IBal NHar NSue
'Little Treasure' (v)	IBal NSue
'Little White Lines' (v)	EMic GKev IBal LRHS NSue
'Little Willie' (v)	NSue
'Little Wonder' (v) ♀[H7]	EMic NSue WWEG
'Living Water'	EMic
'Lizard Lick'	IBal NSue
'Lollapalooza' (v)	IBal
'London Fog' (v)	IBal
'Long Fellow' (v) **new**	IBal
longipes B&SWJ 10806	WCru
longissima	NSue
var. ***brevifolia***	
'Lost World'	IBal
'Lothar the Giant'	IBal
'Love Pat' ♀[H7]	CCon ECtt EMic EPfP GAbr IBal LRHS LSRN MRav NGdn NLar NNor NSue
'Love Song' **new**	IBal
'Loyalist'[PBR] (v)	EMic IBal LRHS NGdn NLar SPoG WFar WWEG
'Lucky Mouse'[PBR] (v)	IBal NSue WBla
'Lucy Vitols' (v)	EMic IBal
'Lullabye'	EMic
'Luna Moth' **new**	IBal
'Lunar Eclipse' (v)	EMic NEgg WWEG
'Machete'	IBal
'Mack the Knife'	EMic IBal WBla
'Maekawa'	EMic IBal
'Magic Fire'[PBR] (v)	EMic EPfP IBal MNrw
'Magic Island'	IBal NSue
'Majesty'	EMic IBal MBri NGdn
'Major Tom'	IBal

	'Malabar' (v)	EMic IBal
	'Mama Mia' (v)	EMic EPfP IBal LRHS MBNS NBro NGdn NHol NWad
	'Mango Salsa' **new**	IBal
	'Mango Tango' (v) **new**	IBal
	'Manhattan'	EMic
	'Maraschino Cherry'	EMic IBal NEgg NGdn
	'Mardi Gras' (v)	EMic IBal
	'Marge' (*sieboldiana* hybrid)	EMic
	'Margie's Angel' (v)	NSue
	'Margin of Error' (v)	IBal
	'Marginata Alba' misapplied	see *H.* 'Albomarginata' (*fortunei*), *H. crispula*
	'Marginata Alba' ambig. (v)	NNor
	'Marilyn'	EMic IBal NSue
	'Marilyn Monroe'	EMic IBal NSue
	'Marmalade on Toast'	EMic
	'Marquis' (*nakaiana* hybrid)	IBal
	'Marrakech'	EMic IBal LRHS NSue
	'Mary Joe'	EMic
	'Mary Marie Ann' (*fortunei*) (v)	EMic IBal
	'Masquerade' (v)	EMic LLHF NHar NRya NSue SMHy WFar WHal WThu
	'May'	EMic IBal
	'Maya' (*fortunei*) (v)	EMic IBal
	'Medieval Age' (v)	IBal
§	'Mediopicta' (*sieboldii*)	EMic IBal
	'Mediovariegata' (*undulata*)	see *H. undulata* var. *undulata*
	'Medusa' (v)	IBal NGdn NSue
	'Memories of Dorothy'	EMic IBal
	'Mesa Fringe' (*montana*)	EMic IBal NLar
	'Mid Afternoon'	IBal
	'Midas Touch'	NEgg NLar NNor
	'Middle Ridge'	EMic
	'Midnight at the Oasis' (v)	EMic IBal
	'Midnight Ride'	IBal
	'Midwest Gold'	MHom
	'Midwest Magic' (v)	EMic IBal NLar
	'Mighty Mite'	IBal
	'Mikawa-no-yuki'	IBal
	'Mike Shadrack' (v)	EMic IBal
	'Miki'	IBal
	'Mildred Seaver' (v)	EMic IBal LRHS MHom
	'Millennium'	EMic IBal
I	'Minima Aurea' **new**	IBal
	'Minnesota Wild' (v) **new**	IBal
	'Minnie Bell' (v)	IBal
	'Minnie Klopping'	EMic
	minor misapplied f. ***alba***	see *H. sieboldii* var. *alba*
§	***minor*** Maekawa	EBee GEdr ITim WCot WFar XLum
	- B&SWJ 11103 from Japan	WCru
	- B&SWJ 1209 from Korea	WCru
	- B&SWJ 8775 from Korea	WCru
	- from Korea	IBal NSue
	'Minor' (*ventricosa*)	see *H. minor* Maekawa
	'Mint Julep' (v)	IBal
	'Minuet' (v)	IBal
	'Minuta' (*venusta*)	NSue
	'Minuteman' (*fortunei*) (v) ♀H7	CCon ECtt EMic EPfP EWoo GBin IBal LRHS MAvo MBNS MMuc NFav NGdn NLar NMyG NNor SEND WFar WWEG
	'Minutini' **new**	NSue
	'Miss Linda Smith'	IBal
	'Miss Ruby'	EMic IBal
	'Miss Saigon' (v)	IBal
	'Miss Susie'	IBal
	'Miss Tokyo' (v)	EMic IBal
	'Mississippi Delta'	EMic
	'Mister Watson'	EMic IBal
	'Misty Waters' (*sieboldiana*)	EMic
	'Moerheim' (*fortunei*) (v)	EMic IBal LRHS WHal WWEG
	'Mohegan'	EMic
	'Monster Ears' **new**	IBal
	montana	EMic
	- B&SWJ 4796	WCru
	- B&SWJ 5585	WCru
	- 'Hida-no-hana' (v)	IBal
	- f. ***macrophylla***	IBal NSue
	'Moody Blues' (Tardiana Group)	EMic
	'Moon Dance' (v) **new**	IBal
	'Moon Lily'	EMic
	'Moon River' (v)	EMic IBal
	'Moon Split' (v)	EPfP NGdn
	'Moonbeam'	EShb
	'Moongate Flying Saucer'	EMic
	'Moonlight' (*fortunei*) (v)	EMic GMaP IBal LRHS NEgg NNor
	'Moonlight Sonata'	EMic IBal
	'Moonstruck'PBR (v)	ECtt EMic IBal NSue
	'Morning Light'	ECtt EMic EPfP GBin IBal MAvo MBNS MBri NBro NGdn NLar NMyG SRkn WFar
	'Morning Star' (v)	EMic IBal NSue
	'Moscow Blue'	EMic
	'Moulin Rouge'	IBal NSue
	'Mount Everest'	EMic IBal
	'Mount Fuji' (*montana*)	IBal
	'Mount Kirishima' (*sieboldii*)	see *H.* 'Kirishima'
	'Mount Tom' (v)	EMic IBal
	'Mountain Snow' (*montana*) (v)	EMic LRHS
	'Mourning Dove' (v)	EMic IBal
	'Mr Big'	IBal NGdn WCot
	'Mrs Minky'	EBee EMic LRHS
	'Muffie' (v)	EMic
	'Munchkin' (*sieboldii*)	LLHF NSue
	'My Claire' (v)	IBal
	'My Cup of Tea'	IBal
	'Mystic Mouse' **new**	IBal
	'Mystic Star'	IBal NSue
	nakaiana	EBee EMic
	'Nakaimo'	IBal
	'Nana' (*ventricosa*)	see *H. minor* Maekawa
	'Nancy'	EMic
§	'Nancy Lindsay' (*fortunei*)	CTri EMic IBal NGdn NLar
	'Nancy Minks'	IBal
	'Neat and Tidy'	IBal
	'Neat Splash' (v)	CWCL NBir WBla WWEG
	'Neelix'	IBal
	'Nemesis' (v)	IBal
	'Neptune'	EMic IBal
	'Niagara Falls' ♀H7	CCon EMic IBal NEgg NGdn NSue
	'Nicola'	EMic IBal MHom NSue
	'Night before Christmas' (v) ♀H7	CHid EMic IBal LRHS MBNS MNrw NBro NEgg NGdn NHol NMyG NNor WHoo WWEG
	'Night Life'	EMic IBal
	nigrescens	EMic GGal IBal LRHS NChi NEgg
	'Niko' (v)	IBal
	'Nippers'	IBal NSue
	'Nokogiryama'	EMic

Name	Suppliers
'None Lovelier' (v)	EMic IBal
'North Hills' (*fortunei*) (v)	EMic IBal MHom NBir NGdn SWvt WFar WWEG
'Northern Exposure' (*sieboldiana*) (v)	EMic NGdn NLar NSti SPoG
'Norwalk Chartreuse'	IBal
'Nutty Professor' (v)	IBal
'Oberon'	NSue
'Obscura Marginata' (*fortunei*)	see *H. fortunei* var. *aureomarginata*
'Ocean Isle' (v)	IBal
'October Sky'	EMic IBal
'Oder'	IBal
'Ogon Tachi' (*rectifolia*) (v)	EMic IBal
'Ogon-chirifu-hime'	IBal
'Ogon-hime-tokudama'	IBal
'Ogon-koba'	IBal
'Oh Cindy' (v)	EMic IBal
'O'Harra'	EMic NSue
'Old Faithful'	EMic IBal LRHS
'Old Glory'^{PBR} (v)	ECtt EMic IBal
'Olga's Shiny Leaf'	EMic
'Olive Bailey Langdon' (*sieboldiana*) (v)	EMic IBal
'Olive Branch' (v)	EMic IBal
'Olympic Edger'	EMic IBal
'Olympic Glacier' (v)	EMic IBal
'Olympic Gold Medal'	EMic IBal
'Olympic Silver Medal'	EMic IBal
'Olympic Sunrise' (v)	EMic IBal
'Olympic Twilight'	EMic IBal
'On Stage'	see *H.* 'Chōkō-nishiki'
'On the Border' (v)	IBal
'One Man's Treasure' 🏆^{H7}	EMic IBal MBel NEgg NGdn
'Ooh La La' (v)	IBal
'Ophir'	EMic IBal
opipara	NEgg
'Ops' (v)	EMic IBal NSue
'Orange Crush' (v)	IBal
'Orange Marmalade' (v) 🏆^{H7}	ECtt EMic GBin IBal LRHS MNrw NGdn NSue SCob SGol SPoG
'Orange Star' (v) **new**	IBal
'Oriana' (*fortunei*)	EMic
'Orion's Belt' (v)	IBal
'Oxheart'	EMic IBal
'Oze' (v)	EMic IBal NSue
pachyscapa	EMic
'Pacific Blue Edger'	CCon EMic NGdn NNor WAul WFar WWEG
'Painted Lady' (*sieboldii*) (v)	GKev
'Pamela Lee' (v)	IBal NGdn NSue
'Pandora's Box' (v)	GEdr NHar NSue WCot
'Paradigm' (v)	EBee EMic IBal LRHS NGdn
'Paradise Backstage' (v)	EMic IBal
'Paradise Beach'	EMic IBal
'Paradise Blue Sky'	IBal
'Paradise Expectations' (*sieboldiana*) (v)	EMic IBal
'Paradise Glory'	EMic IBal
'Paradise Gold Line' (*ventricosa*) (v)	IBal
'Paradise Island'^{PBR} (*sieboldiana*) (v)	EMic EPfP IBal NGdn NSue
'Paradise Joyce'^{PBR}	EMic IBal LRHS NEgg NNor WBla WWEG
'Paradise Ocean'	EMic IBal WBla
'Paradise on Fire' (v)	EMic IBal
'Paradise Parade' (v)	IBal
'Paradise Passion' (v)	IBal
'Paradise Power'^{PBR}	EMic
'Paradise Puppet' (*venusta*) 🏆^{H7}	EMic GKev IBal NNor NSue WWEG
'Paradise Red Delight' (*pycnophylla*)	EMic IBal
'Paradise Sandstorm'	IBal
'Paradise Standard' (d)	EMic IBal
'Paradise Sunset'	EMic IBal NSue
'Paradise Sunshine'	EMic IBal
'Paradise Surprise' (v)	IBal
'Paradise Tritone' (v)	EMic IBal
'Parhelion'	EMic
'Parky's Prize' (v)	IBal
'Pastures Green'	IBal
'Pastures New'	EMic MHom NEgg WWEG
'Pathfinder' (v)	EMic IBal
'Patricia'	EMic
'Patrician' (v)	EMic IBal
'Patriot' (v) 🏆^{H7}	Widely available
'Patriot's Fire' (v)	IBal LRHS
'Patriot's Green Pride'	IBal
'Paul's Glory' (v) 🏆^{H7}	EMic EPfP GLog GMaP IBal LLWG LRHS MAvo MBri NBir NGdn NNor NSue SPoG WFar WWEG
§ 'Paxton's Original' (*sieboldii*) (v)	IFoB WWEG
'Peace' (v)	EMic IBal LRHS
'Peacock Strut'	IBal
'Peanut'	IBal NSue
'Pearl Lake'	EMic IBal MHom NBir NEgg NGdn NHol NLar NMyG NNor
'Peedee Absinth'	EMic
'Pelham Blue Tump'	EMic
'Peppermint Ice' (v)	EMic IBal NGdn
'Percy'	EMic
'Permanent Wave'	IBal
'Perry's True Blue'	EMic IBal
'Peter Pan'	EMic IBal NEgg
'Pete's Dark Satellite'	EMic IBal NSue
'Pewterware'	EMic IBal
'Phantom'	IBal
'Philadelphia'	EMic IBal
'Phoenix'	EMic IBal NLar
'Photo Finish' (v)	IBal
'Phyllis Campbell' (*fortunei*)	see *H.* 'Sharmon'
'Picta' (*fortunei*)	see *H. fortunei* var. *albopicta*
'Piecrust Power'	IBal
'Piedmont Gold'	CBod CHid EHoe EMic GBin IBal LHop LRHS WPtf
'Pilgrim' (v)	EMic IBal LRHS MMuc NBro NEgg NGdn NSue SEND WFar
'Pineapple Poll'	EMic MHom NNor NSue WHoo WWEG
'Pineapple Upside Down Cake' (v)	EMic IBal NBro NLar NSue
'Pinky'	IBal
'Pin-up' (v) **new**	IBal
'Pistache' (v)	EMic IBal NSue
'Pixie Vamp' (v)	EMic IBal
'Pizzazz' (v)	EMic IBal LRHS MHom NGdn NHol NLar WFar WWEG
plantaginea	EMic LEdu LPla LRHS SSpi WFar WWtn
- var. ***grandiflora***	see *H. plantaginea* var. *japonica*
§ - var. ***japonica*** 🏆^{H7}	CAby CBot EBee ECha LRHS MNrw MRav SMHy SMad WCFE WFar WPGP WWEG

Name	Suppliers
'Platinum Tiara' (v)	EMic IBal NBir
'Plug Nickel'	EMic IBal NSue
'Pocketful of Sunshine' (v) **new**	IBal
'Poker'	IBal
'Polar Moon' (v)	IBal
'Pole Cat' (v)	IBal
'Pooh Bear' (v)	EMic IBal NSue
'Popcorn'	EMic IBal NSue
'Popo' ♀H7	EMic IBal NSue
'Porter' (*venusta*)	IBal
'Pot of Gold'	EMic
'Potomac Pride'	EMic LRHS NEgg
'Powder Blue' (v)	IBal
'Prairie Moon'	NSue
'Prairie Sky'	EMic IBal MBri NGdn NLar WBla WFar
'Prairie Sunset' (v) **new**	NSue
'Praying Hands' (v) ♀H7	EBee ECha ECtt ELan EMic EPfP GBin GEdr GKev IBal IBoy IFoB IPot LRHS LSou MBNS NEgg NGdn NLar NMyG NSue SCob SPoG WFar WWEG
'Precious Metal' **new**	IBal
'Prestige and Promise' (v)	IBal
'Pretty Flamingo'	EMic IBal
'Prima Donna'	EMic
'Prince of Wales'	EMic IBal LRHS NNor SPoG
'Princess Anastasia' (v)	IBal
'Private Dancer'	IBal
'Prom Queen' (v) **new**	IBal
'Proud Sentry'	EMic IBal NSue
'Punk Rock' **new**	IBal
'Punky' (v)	EMic IBal
'Purple Boots'	EMic IBal
'Purple Dwarf'	EMic IBal NLar NSue WCru WHal WWEG
'Purple Glory'	EMic
'Purple Haze'	EMic IBal LRHS NGdn NSue SHar
'Purple Heart'	CAby EBee ECtt GBin IBal LCro NMyG NSti NSue NWad SCob SHar SPoG WCot WNPC
'Purple Lady Finger'	WBla WWEG
'Purple Passion'	EMic IBal NSue
'Purple Profusion'	EMic IBal
'Purple Python' **new**	IBal
'Quarter Note' (v)	IBal
'Queen Josephine' (v)	EMic EPfP IBal LRHS MBNS MHom NEgg NGdn SRGP WFar
'Queen of the Seas'	EMic IBal NSue
'Quill'	EMic IBal NSue
'Quilting Bee'	EMic IBal NSue
'Radiant Edger' (v)	EMic GCra IBal LRHS NHol NSue WWEG
'Rain Dancer'	EMic IBal
'Rain Forest'	EMic IBal
'Rainbow's End' (v)	EMic IBal LLWG NSue
'Rainforest Sunrise' (v)	ELon EMic IBal LSou NGdn NSue
'Randy Rachel' (v) **new**	LRHS
'Rare Breed' (v) **new**	IBal
'Rascal' (v)	EMic
'Raspberries and Cream' (v)	IBal
'Raspberry Sorbet'	EMic IBal LRHS NSue
'Raspberry Sundae' (v)	CMil CWGN EBee IBal MHol NGdn NSue NWad SCob WNPC
rectifolia	NNor
'Red Cadet'	EMic IBal WBla
'Red Dog'	EMic NSue
'Red Dragon'	IBal
'Red Hot Flash' (v)	EMic IBal
'Red Hot Poker'	IBal
'Red Neck Heaven' (*kikutii* var. *caput-avis*)	IBal
'Red October'	ECtt EMic EPfP EUJe EWTr EWoo GAbr IBal IBoy LEdu LPal LRHS LSou MBNS MHol MPie NEgg NGdn NLar NSue SMad SPoG WCot WFar WWEG
'Red Salamander'	EMic IBal
'Red Sox'	IBal
'Red Stepper'	EMic IBal
'Red Tubes' (*venusta*)	IBal
'Regal Rhubarb'	EMic IBal
'Regal Splendor' (v) ♀H7	ELan ELon EMic IBal LRHS MHom NBro NGdn NNor NSue WFar WHoo WMnd
'Regal Supreme' (v)	IBal NSue
'Regal Tot' **new**	NSue
'Reginald Kaye'	EMic
'Rembrandt Blue'	EMic IBal
'Remember Me'PBR ♀H7	CWCL ELan ELon GBin IBal LSRN MBNS MBri MPnt NEgg NGdn NHol NLar NNor NSue NWad WFar WWEG
'Reptilian'	EMic IBal
'Resonance' (v)	IBal NGdn NLar
'Restless Sea'	EMic
'Reverend Mac'	IBal
'Reversed' (*sieboldiana*) (v)	EMic IBal LRHS NBro NGdn NNor WFar WHal
'Revolution'PBR (v) ♀H7	EMic IBal LRHS LSRN NBro NEgg NGdn NLar NSue SPoG WFar WWEG
'Rhapsody' (*fortunei*) (v)	EMic IBal
'Rhein' (*tardiana*)	IBal
'Rhinestone Cowboy' (v)	IBal
'Rhino Hide' (v)	EMic IBal NSue
'Rhythm and Blues'	IBal NSue
'Rich Uncle'	IBal
'Richland Gold' (*fortunei*)	EMic
'Rim Rock'	EMic IBal
'Ringtail'	EMic IBal
'Ripple Effect' (v)	IBal NSue
'Rippled Honey'	ELan EMic IBal NEoE NMyG
'Rippling Waves'	EMic
'Riptide'	NGdn
'Risa'	IBal
'Risky Business'PBR (v)	CWGN EBee EMic IBal NSue
'Robert Frost' (v)	EMic IBal
'Robin Hood'	EMic IBal
'Robin of Loxley'	EMic IBal
'Robusta' (*fortunei*)	see *H. sieboldiana* var. *elegans*
'Robyn's Choice' (v)	IBal
'Rock and Roll'	EMic IBal
'Rock Island Line' (v)	EMic IBal NSue WBla
'Rock Princess'	IBal LLHF
'Rocket's Red Glare' **new**	IBal
§ ***rohdeifolia*** (v) B&SWJ 10862	WCru
- f. ***albopicta***	ELan
'Roller Coaster Ride'	IBal NSue
'Ron Damant'	IBal
'Rootin'-Tootin'' (v)	IBal
'Roseann Walter' (v)	EMic IBal
'Rosedale Knox'	IBal
'Rosedale Lost Dutchman'	IBal
'Rosedale Melody of Summer' (v)	IBal

	Name	Suppliers
	'Rosedale Misty Magic' (v)	IBal
	'Rosedale Richie Valens'	IBal
	'Rosedale Tractor Seat' **new**	IBal
	'Rosemoor'	IBal
	'Roxsanne'	EMic
	'Roy Klehm' (v)	EMic IBal
	'Royal Charm'	IBal
	'Royal Flush' (v)	IBal
	'Royal Golden Jubilee'	EMic IBal
§	'Royal Standard' 🏆H7	Widely available
	'Royal Tapestry' (v)	IBal
	'Royal Tiara' (*nakaiana*) (v)	IBal
	'Royalty'	IBal
	'Rubies and Ruffles' (v) **new**	IBal
	'Ruffled Mouse Ears' **new**	NSue
	'Rufus Rider'	IBal
	rupifraga	IBal
	'Rusty Bee'	IBal
	'Ryan's Big One'	EBee IBal
§	'Sagae' (v) 🏆H7	EMic IBal LRHS MBri MHom MNrw NGdn NNor SDix WAul WFar WHoo WWEG
	'Saint Elmo's Fire' (v)	EMic IBal LRHS
	'Saint John' **new**	IBal
	'Saint Paul'	EMic IBal MNrw NSue
	'Saishu-jima' (*sieboldii* f. *spathulata*)	EMic GEdr ITim WCru
	'Saishu-yahato-sito' (v)	IBal
	'Salute' (Tardiana Group)	EMic
	'Samurai' (*sieboldiana*) (v)	EMic IBal MRav NBir NBro NEgg NGdn NLar NNor NSue
	'Sandhill Crane' (v)	IBal
	'Sarah Kennedy' (v)	IBal
	'Sara's Sensation' (v)	IBal
	'Satisfaction' (v) 🏆H7	EMic IBal
	'Sazanami' (*crispula*)	see *H. crispula*
	'Scallion Pancakes'	EMic
	'Scarlet Ribbons' (v)	IBal
	'Schwan'	GBin
	'Scooter' (v)	IBal
	'Sea Current'	IBal
	'Sea Dream' (v)	EMic LRHS NEgg NGdn NNor
	'Sea Fire'	IBal NGdn
	'Sea Gulf Stream'	EMic NSue
	'Sea Lotus Leaf'	LLWP NLar NNor
	'Sea Monster'	IBal
	'Sea Sapphire'	IBal
	'Sea Thunder' (v)	EMic IBal LRHS
	'Sea Yellow Sunrise'	EMic IBal
	'Searing Flame' (v)	IBal
	'Second Wind' (*fortunei*) (v)	EMic NMyG
	'Secret Ambition'PBR (v)	EMic IBal
	'Secret Love'	EMic IBal
	'Secret Treasure' (v) **new**	IBal
	'Seducer' (v)	EMic IBal
	'See Saw' (*undulata*)	EMic IBal
	'Semperaurea' (*sieboldiana*)	IBal
	'September Sun' (v)	EMic IBal LRHS NNor
	'Serena' (Tardiana Group)	IBal
	'Serendipity'	EMic GAbr IBal MHom
	'Shade Beauty' (v)	IBal
	'Shade Fanfare' (v)	ECtt EHoe ELan ELon EMic EPfP IBal LAst LPla LRHS MBNS MRav MWhi NBir NGdn NLar NSti SPer WFar WMnd WWEG
	'Shade Finale' (v)	IBal
	'Shade Master'	EMic
	'Shade Parade' (v)	EMic IBal
§	'Sharmon' (*fortunei*) (v)	ELon EMic IBal MBNS NEgg NLar
	'Sharp Dressed Man'	IBal NGdn
	'Shazaam'	IBal WBla
	'Sheila West'	EMic IBal
	'Shelleys' (v)	IBal
	'Sherborne Profusion' (Tardiana Group)	EMic IBal
	'Sherborne Songbird' (Tardiana Group)	IBal
	'Sherborne Swallow' (Tardiana Group)	IBal
	'Sherborne Swan' (Tardiana Group)	IBal
	'Sherborne Swift' (Tardiana Group)	EMic IBal LRHS
	'Shimmy Shake'	EMic
	'Shining Tot' 🏆H7	IBal LLHF
	'Shiny Penny' (v)	EMic IBal NSue WBla WWEG
	'Shirley Levy'	IBal
	'Shirley Vaughn' (v)	IBal
	'Showboat' (v)	EMic IBal LRHS
	sieboldiana	CAgr CMac CSBt CWat ECha ELan EMic GCra GMaP LLWP MRav MSwo NChi SPlb SRms WMoo WWEG XLum
§	- var. ***elegans*** 🏆H7	Widely available
	- var. ***mira***	EMic
	- var. ***sieboldiana***	NGdn
	sieboldiana* × *venusta	NGdn
	sieboldii	GBin MRav
§	- var. ***alba***	IBal
§	- var. ***sieboldii*** f. ***kabitan*** (v)	EMic IBal NGdn NHar NSue WBla WWEG
	- - f. ***shiro-kabitan*** (v)	EMic LRHS
	- f. ***spathulata***	EMic
	'Silberpfeil'	EMic NSue
	'Silk Road' (v) **new**	IBal
	'Silver Bay' 🏆H7	EMic
	'Silver Crown'	see *H.* 'Albomarginata'
	'Silver Lance' (v)	EMic IBal
	'Silver Lode' (v)	IBal
	'Silver Moon'	EMic IBal
	'Silver Serenity' **new**	IBal
	'Silver Shadow' (v)	CHid EMic GBin IBal NBir NGdn NNor NWad WHoo
	'Silver Spray' (v)	IBal
	'Silver Star' (v)	IBal
	'Silver Threads and Gold Needles' (v)	IBal NSue
	'Silverado' (v)	IBal
	'Silvery Slugproof' (Tardiana Group)	LRHS WWEG
	'Simply Sharon' (v) **new**	IBal
	'Singin' the Blues'	IBal
	'Singing in the Rain' (v)	IBal
	'Sitting Pretty' (v)	IBal
	'Sizzle' **new**	IBal
	'Sky Dancer'	EMic IBal MBri NSue
	'Sleeping Beauty'	CWGN EMic IBal NGdn NMyG NSue
	'Sleeping Star' (v) **new**	IBal
	'Slim and Trim'	EMic IBal MHom NSue
	'Small Parts'	EMic IBal NSue
	'Small Sum'	IBal
	'Smiley Face' **new**	NSue
	'Smoke Signals'	IBal

'Snake Eyes' (v) **new**	CBod SCob
'Snow Boy' (v)	IBal NSue
'Snow Cap' (v)	ECtt EMic IBal NEoE NGdn NLar NNor SPoG WFar WWEG
'Snow Crust' (v)	EMic
'Snow Flakes' (*sieboldii*)	CMac NBro NEoE NGdn NLar WFar WWEG
'Snow Mouse' (v)	EMic IBal NSue
'Snowden' ♀H7	ECha EMic GMaP IBal LPla LRHS MWat NBir NGdn NNor SSpi WCru WWEG
'Snowy Lake' (v)	IBal
'So Sweet' (v)	EBee ECtt EHoe ELan EMic EPfP EWoo GBin IBal LRHS LSun MHom MSwo NBro NGdn NHol NMyG NNor SHil SPad SPoG WFar WWEG
'Solar Flare'	EMic
'Something Blue'	EMic IBal
'Something Different' (*fortunei*) (v)	IBal
'Something Else'	EMic
'Southern Gold'	EMic
'Space Odyssey'	IBal
'Sparkler' (v) **new**	IBal
'Sparkling Burgundy'	EMic LRHS
'Sparky' (v)	IBal
'Spartacus' (v)	EMic IBal NSue
'Spartan Arrow'	NSue
'Spartan Glory' (v)	IBal
'Special Gift'	EMic WWEG
'Spellbound' (v)	IBal
'Spilt Milk' (*tokudama*) (v) ♀H7	EBee EMic IBal LRHS SPoG WHoo
'Spinach Souffle' (v) **new**	IBal
§ 'Spinners' (*fortunei*) (v)	ECha EMic IBal NNor SSpi
'Spock's Ears'	IBal
'Spring Break' (v)	EMic
'Spring Fling'	EMic IBal
'Spritzer' (v)	EMic MNrw NSue
'Squash Casserole'	IBal NSue
'Stained Glass' (v) ♀H7	CAby CBcs ECtt ELon EMic EPfP IBal LRHS NEgg NGdn NNor NSue WBla WFar WHlf
'Stand by Me' (v)	EMic IBal NSue
'Stand Corrected' (v) **new**	IBal
'Star Kissed'	IBal
'Star Light Star Bright'	IBal
'Starburst' stable (v)	IBal
'Stardust'	IBal
'Stargate'	IBal
§ 'Starker Yellow Leaf'	EMic
'Starship' (v)	EMic IBal
'Steffi' (v)	IBal
'Step Sister'	EMic IBal
'Stepping Out' (v)	EMic IBal
'Stetson' (v)	EMic IBal
'Stiletto' (v)	EHoe ELon EMic GAbr GCra GEdr GKev IBal LBMP LRHS MBNS MHom MNrw NBro NEoE NGdn NLar NMyG NNor NSue SPoG SWvt WSHC WWEG
'Stimulation'	IBal
'Stirfry'	EMic SCob
'Stitch in Time' (v)	IBal
'Stonewall'	IBal
'Strawberry Surprise' (v)	IBal
'Striker' (v)	IBal NSue
'Striptease' (*fortunei*) (v) ♀H7	CMac EMic EPfP IBal LRHS MBNS MBri MNrw NEgg NGdn NHol NLar NSue WFar WWEG
'Stuck in Time' **new**	IBal
'Sugar and Cream' (v)	EMic IBal LRHS NGdn NNor
'Sugar and Spice' (v)	ELon EMic IBal
'Sugar Daddy'	EMic IBal
'Sultana' (v)	EMic IBal WWEG
'Sum and Substance' ♀H7	Widely available
'Sum and Subtle' (v)	EMic IBal
'Sum Cup-o-Joe' (v)	EMic
'Sum it Up' (v)	EMic
'Sum of All' (v)	NSue
'Summer Breeze' (v)	EMic IBal NGdn NSue
'Summer Fragrance'	EBee ECtt EMic GBin IBal LRHS
'Summer Lovin'' (v)	IBal
'Summer Music' (v) ♀H7	EMic IBal WWEG
'Summer Serenade' (v)	EMic IBal NGdn
'Summer Squall'	IBal
'Sumsational' **new**	IBal
'Sun Catcher'	EMic
'Sun Power'	EBee ELon EMic LRHS MBNS MBri NBro NGdn NLar NSti
'Sun Worshipper'	IBal
'Sundance' (v) **new**	IBal
'Sunlight Child'	IBal NSue
'Sunny Smiles' (v)	EMic
'Sunset Grooves' (v) **new**	IBal
'Sunshine Glory'	EMic IBal
'Super Bowl'	IBal
'Super Nova' (v)	EMic IBal
'Super Sagae'	EMic IBal WFar
'Surfer Girl' **new**	NSue
'Surprised by Joy' (v)	EMic IBal NNor NSue WBla WWEG
'Susy'	IBal
'Sutter's Mill'	IBal
'Suzuki Thumbnail'	EMic
'Swamp Thing' (v)	IBal
'Sweet Bo Beep'	IBal LRHS
'Sweet Bouquet'	EMic
'Sweet Home Chicago' (v)	EBee EMic IBal LRHS
'Sweet Innocence' (v)	EMic IBal
'Sweet Marjorie'	IBal
'Sweet Susan'	EMic LSRN MBNS SPer SWvt
'Sweet Tater Pie'	EMic IBal
'Sweetheart'	EMic
'Sweetie' (v)	EMic IBal LRHS NSue WWEG
'Sweetness'	IBal
'Swirling Hearts'	IBal NSue
'T. Rex'	CCon ELon EMic IBal NSue WFar
'Tall Boy'	GBin IBal NBir NNor
'Tamborine' (v)	IBal LRHS
'Tango'	EMic IBal NSue
'Tappen Zee' (v)	EMic IBal
Tardiana Group	MHom NGdn
tardiflora	CExl CFil IBal LRHS WPGP
tardiva	NLar
'Tattle Tails'	EMic IBal NSue
'Tattoo'[PBR] (v)	CWGN LSRN MBNS NLar WWEG
'Tea at Bettys' ♀H7	IBal
'Tears of Joy'	NSue
'Teaspoon'	EMic IBal NNor NSue WBla
'Teatime' (v)	EMic IBal
'Teeny-weeny Bikini' (v)	NSue WBla
'Templar Gold'	IBal
'Temple Bells'	IBal
'Temptation'	EMic IBal
'Tequila Sunrise'	IBal
'Terpsichore'	EMic

'Terracotta'	MCri
'Terry Wogan'	IBal NNor
'Tet-a-Poo'	IBal
'The King' (v)	IBal
'The Leading Edge' (v)	IBal
'The Queen' (v)	IBal
'The Razor's Edge'	IBal
'The Right One' (v)	IBal
'The Shining'	IBal
'Theo's Blue'	EMic IBal
'Theo's Red' **new**	IBal
'Thomas Hogg'	see *H. undulata* var. *albomarginata*
'Thumb Nail'	EMic IBal NNor NSue
'Thumbelina'	EMic IBal NGdn
'Thunderbolt'[PBR] (*sieboldiana*)	EMic IBal MBNS NGdn NLar WFar
tibae	IBal
'Tick Tock' (v)	EMic IBal NSue
'Tickle Me Pink'	EMic IBal NSue
'Tidewater'	IBal
'Time Tunnel' (*sieboldiana*) (v)	EMic IBal
'Timeless Beauty' (v)	IBal WFar
'Tiny Tears'	GAbr IFoB NSue
'Titanic'[PBR]	IBal
'Titanium'	IBal
tokudama	EMic IBal LRHS MHom NBir NGdn NNor NSti WFar XLum
§ - f. ***aureo-nebulosa*** (v)	EMic IBal NGdn SRms WMnd
- f. ***flavocircinalis*** (v) 🏆H7	EBee ELon EMic EPfP GMaP IBal MWhi NBro WFar WHoo WMnd
'Tokudama Blue'	IBoy
'Tokyo Smog' (v) **new**	NSue
'Toledo'	IBal
'Tom Schmid' (v)	EMic IBal LBMP LRHS NMyG NSue WBla
'Tom Thumb'	EMic IBal NSue
'Tongue Twister' **new**	IBal
'Topaz'	IBal
'Topscore'	NNor
'Torchlight' (v) 🏆H7	IBal LRHS MHom NSue
tortifrons	EMic IBal
'Tortilla Chip'	IBal NSue
'Tot Tot'	EMic IBal NSue
'Totally Twisted' **new**	IBal
'Touch of Class'[PBR] (v) 🏆H7	ECtt EMic GBin IBal LRHS NGdn NHol NMyG NNor NSue WFar WWEG
'Touchstone' (v)	SWvt WWEG
'Toy Soldier'	EMic IBal NGdn NSue
'Tranquility' (v)	EMic
'Tremors'	EMic IBal
'Trixi' (v)	IBal
'Tropical Dancer'	IBal
'Tropical Storm' (v) **new**	IBal
'True Blue'	EBee ECtt IBal WWEG
'Tsugaru Komachi'	EMic
'Tsugaru Komachi Kifukurin' (v)	IBal
'Turnabout' (v)	IBal
'Turning Point'	IBal LRHS
'Twiggie'	EMic
'Twilight' (*fortunei*) (v)	CAby EAEE ECtt ELon EMic EShb IBal LRHS MBNS MHol NEgg NGdn NLar SWvt WHar WWEG
'Twilight Time'	IBal LRHS
'Twinkle Toes'	EMic IBal NSue
'Twist of Lemon'	NEgg
'Twist of Lime' (v)	EMic GKev IBal LRHS NGdn NNor NSue WBla WCot WWEG
'Twitter'	IBal
'UFO'	EMic IBal NSue
'Ultramarine'	IBal
'Ultraviolet Light'	IBal
'Ulysses S. Grant'	IBal
'Unchained Melody'	IBal
undulata (v)	NNor WFar
§ - var. ***albomarginata*** (v)	CBcs CMac CSam EMic EPfP GMaP IBoy LRHS LSRN MRav MWat NBid NBir NGdn NLar SCob SPer SRms SWvt WFar WMnd WWEG XLum
§ - var. ***erromena***	EMic GMaP LRHS NNor WHrl XLum
§ - var. ***undulata*** (v) 🏆H7	CBod COtt EBee GMaP IBal LPot LRHS MCot MRav NEgg NGdn NLar NNor SCob SPer WWEG
- var. ***univittata*** (v)	ECha EMic GKev LAst MHom MWhi NBir NEoE WFar WMoo
'Unforgettable'	EMic IBal
'Upper Crust' (v)	IBal
'Uprising' (v)	IBal
'Urajiro' (*hypoleuca*)	IBal
'Urajiro-hachijo' (*longipes* var. *latifolia*)	IBal
'Valentine Lace'	EMic GKev IBal
'Valley's Cathedral'	IBal
'Valley's Chute the Chute'	EMic IBal
'Valley's Glacier' (v)	EMic IBal WFar
'Valley's Vanilla Sticks'	EMic IBal
'Van Wade' (v)	IBal
'Vanilla Cream' (*cathayana*)	EMic IBal LRHS
'Variegata' (*gracillima*)	see *H.* 'Vera Verde'
'Variegata' (*tokudama*)	see *H. tokudama* f. *aureo-nebulosa*
'Variegata' (*undulata*)	see *H. undulata* var. *undulata*
'Variegata' (*ventricosa*)	see *H.* 'Aureomarginata' (*ventricosa*)
'Variegated' (*fluctuans*)	see *H.* 'Sagae'
'Velvet Moon' (v)	EMic IBal
ventricosa 🏆H7	CMac EMic GMaP IBal MWhi WBla WFar XLum
- BWJ 8160 from Sichuan	WCru
- var. ***aureomaculata***	EMic NBir NNor NSti WFar
'Venus' (d)	CAby ECtt EMic IBal ITim LRHS MHol NGdn NSue WCot WFar WPGP
'Venus Star'	EMic
venusta 🏆H7	CDes EAEE EBee ECho EMic EWld GCra GEdr IBal LRHS MHer MRav NBid NBir NNor NRya NSti SRot WBla WRHF WWEG
- B&SWJ 4389	WCru
- dwarf	IBal
- 'Kin Botan' (v)	GEdr
- ***yakusimensis***	see *H. kikutii* var. *yakusimensis*
§ 'Vera Verde' (v)	GCra GQui NBir NSue
'Verdi Valentine'	IBal
'Verkade's No 1'	IBal
'Vermont Frost' (v) **new**	NSue
'Verna Jean' (v)	EMic IBal LRHS
'Veronica Lake' (v)	ECtt EMic IBal LRHS NNor NSue WHal
'Victor' **new**	IBal
'Victory' 🏆H7	EMic IBal
'Viking Ship'	EMic IBal
'Vilmoriniana'	EMic
'Vim and Vigor'	EMic IBal
'Vina'	IBal
'Viridis Marginata'	see *H. sieboldii* var. *sieboldii* f. *kabitan*

'Volcano Island' (v) **new**	IBal
'Vulcan' (v)	EMic IBal
'Wagtail' (Tardiana Group)	EMic IBal
'Wahoo' (*tokudama*) (v)	IBal
'War Paint' 𝕐H7	CBod EMic IBal ITim NSue WFar
'Warwick Comet' (v)	EMic IBal
'Warwick Curtsey' (v)	EMic IBal
'Warwick Edge' (v)	EMic IBal NEgg
'Warwick Essence'	EMic IBal
'Warwick Sheen'	IBal
'Waukon Glass'	EMic IBal
'Waukon Thin Ice'	EMic IBal
'Waukon Water'	EMic IBal
'Waving Winds' (v)	IBal
'Waving Wuffles'	EMic
'Wayne' (v) **new**	EMic
'Wayside Blue'	EMic
'Wayside Perfection'	see *H.* 'Royal Standard'
'Weihenstephan' (*sieboldii*)	EMic IBal
'Well Shaked' (v)	IBal
'Wheaton Blue'	EMic LRHS
'Whee' (v) **new**	NSue
'Whirligig' (v)	EMic
'Whirling Dervish' (v)	IBal
'Whirlwind' (*fortunei*) (v) 𝕐H7	EBee EMic GBin GQue IBal LRHS MBri MNrw MRav NBro NEgg NGdn NMyG NNor NSue SPad SPtp WAul WBor WFar WHoo WMnd WWEG
'Whirlwind Tour' (v)	IBal
'Whiskey Sour'	IBal
'White Bikini' (v)	IBal NSue
'White Ceiling'	IBal
'White Christmas' (*fortunei*) (v)	NGdn
'White Christmas' (*undulata*) (v)	EMic
'White Dove' (v)	EMic IBal
'White Edger'	EMic
'White Elephant' (v)	IBal
'White Fairy' (*plantaginea*) (d)	EMic
'White Feather' (*undulata*)	CHid CWGN EBee ELan ELon EPfP LCro LOPS LRHS MNrw NBir NGdn NLar NMyG NNor SMad SPoG WFar
'White Knight'	IBal
'White On' (*montana*)	EMic
'White Triumphator' (*rectifolia*)	EMic GBin IBal
'White Trumpets'	EMic
'Wide Brim' (v) 𝕐H7	Widely available
'William Lachman' (v)	IBal NLar
'Wily Willy'	IBal
'Wind River Gold'	EMic IBal
'Windsor Gold'	see *H.* 'Nancy Lindsay'
'Winfield Blue'	EMic IBal
'Winfield Gold'	EMic
'Winfield Mist' (v)	IBal
'Winsome' (v)	IBal LRHS
'Winter Lightning' (v)	NNor
'Winter Snow' (v)	EMic IBal LRHS NGdn NSue
'Winter Warrior' (v)	EMic IBal
'Wogon' (*sieboldii*)	EMic GKev GMaP ITim NSti
'Wogon's Boy'	EMic LRHS WWEG
'Wolverine' (v) 𝕐H7	EBee ECtt EHoe EMic GAbr LRHS LSou MBNS MBel MHom NGdn NQui NSue SPoG SWvt WBla WFar WWEG
'Woodland Elf' (v)	IBal NSue WBla
'Woolly Mammoth' (v)	IBal
'Woop Woop' (v)	EMic IBal NSue
'World Cup'	IBal
'Worldly Treasure'	IBal
'Wrinkles and Crinkles'	EMic
'Wylde Green Cream'	IBal NGdn
'Xanadu' (v)	IBal
'X-ray' (v)	NSue
'Yakushima-mizu' (*gracillima*)	EMic IBal NMyG
'Yankee Blue'	IBal
'Yellow Boa'	EMic IBal NSue WBla
'Yellow Edge' (*fortunei*)	see *H. fortunei* var. *aureomarginata*
'Yellow Edge' (*sieboldiana*)	see *H.* 'Frances Williams'
'Yellow Polka Dot Bikini' (v)	EMic NSue WBla
'Yellow River' (v)	EMic IBal LRHS NGdn NNor NSue
'Yellow Splash' (v)	EMic LRHS MHom NNor
'Yellow Splash Rim' (v)	EMic
'Yesterday's Memories' (v)	EMic IBal
'Yin' (v)	EMic IBal
yingeri	WPGP WSHC
- B&SWJ 546	LEdu WCru
'Yucca Ducka Do' (v)	IBal
'Zager Blue'	EMic
'Zager Green'	EMic
'Zager White Edge' (*fortunei*) (v)	EMic IBal
'Zebra Stripes' (v)	IBal
'Zion's Hope'	EMic
'Zodiac' (*fortunei*) (v)	IBal
'Zounds'	EBee ECtt EMic EPfP EShb GKev IBal LRHS MRav NGdn NLar NSti NSue SRms WFar WWEG

Hottonia (*Primulaceae*)

palustris	MSKA MWts NPer SWat

Houstonia (*Rubiaceae*)

caerulea L.	ECho
- var. ***alba***	EWes SPlb
- 'Millard's Variety'	WIce
michauxii 'Fred Mullard'	EWes GCrg

Houttuynia (*Saururaceae*)

cordata	CAgr CBod COtt GKev GPoy LEdu LLWG LPot SDix SWat WFar WTcb WWEG XLum
§ - 'Boo-Boo' (v)	CMac WWEG
§ - 'Chameleon' (v)	Widely available
- 'Fantasy' (v)	EBee LLWG
- 'Flame' (v)	CMac CWCL EBee LBMP MBri MHol NPla SHil WFar WWEG
- 'Flore Pleno' (d)	CBen CMac CWat ECha EHon EPfP MRav MSCN NBir NPer SPer SPlb SRms SWat WPnP XLum
- 'Joker's Gold'	CMac EBee ECtt ELan EPPr EPfP WFar
- 'Pied Piper' (v)	CWCL ELan NBir SGol SPad SPtp
- 'Terry Clarke'	see *H. cordata* 'Boo-Boo'
- 'Tricolor'	see *H. cordata* 'Chameleon'
- Variegata Group (v)	NBro

Hovea (*Papilionaceae*)

celsii	see *H. elliptica*
§ ***elliptica***	SPlb
montana	SPlb

Hovenia (*Rhamnaceae*)

dulcis	CAgr CBcs CPne EBee EPfP ESwi LEdu MBlu NLar
- B&SWJ 11024	WCru
- NJM 11.003	WPGP

Howea (*Arecaceae*)

§ **belmoreana** ♀H1b	XBlo
§ **forsteriana** ♀H1b	ETod LPal NPla SPlb XBlo

Hoya (*Apocynaceae*)

§ **australis**	CBcs
bella	see *H. lanceolata* subsp. *bella*
carnosa ♀H2	CBcs EBak EOHP WWFP
- 'Compacta Regalis' (v)	NPer
- 'Krinkle 8'	NPer
- 'Tricolor' (v)	NPer
* **compacta** 'Tricolor'	NPer
darwinii misapplied	see *H. australis*
§ **lanceolata** subsp. **bella** ♀H1c	CBcs EShb
linearis	EShb

huckleberry, garden see *Solanum scabrum*

Huernia (*Apocynaceae*)

keniensis new	LToo
schneideriana	LToo

Hugueninia (*Brassicaceae*)

alpina	see *H. tanacetifolia*
§ **tanacetifolia**	WOut

Humata (*Davalliaceae*)

tyermannii	CMen EShb ISha SBrt SPlb WFib

Humea see *Calomeria*

elegans	see *Calomeria amaranthoides*

Humulus ✿ (*Cannabaceae*)

japonicus 'Variegatus' (v)	SGol
lupulus	CArn CBcs EPfP GPoy NLar NMir SCob SIde WHer
- 'Aureus' ♀H6	Widely available
- 'Aureus' (f)	CRHN ELon GCal GKev SPoG WCot WWFP
* - **compactus**	GPoy
- 'Fuggle'	CAgr GPoy SDea
- 'Golden Tassels' (f)	CKel ECrN ELon LBrs LRHS MCoo MGos MJak MMuc MNHC NLar SEND SGol SPer SPoG
- (Goldings Group) 'Cobbs'	SDea
- - 'Mathons'	CAgr SDea
- 'Hallertauer'	SDea
- 'Prima Donna'	CAgr CMac MCoo MMuc NLar SCoo SPer SPoG SWvt
- 'Taff's Variegated' (v)	EWes WSHC
- 'Wye Challenger'	CAgr GPoy MHer
- 'Wye Northdown'	CAgr SDea

Hunnemannia (*Papaveraceae*)

fumariifolia	CSpe

Huodendron (*Styracaceae*)

tibeticum	CFil

Hutchinsia see *Pritzelago*

rotundifolia	see *Thlaspi cepaeifolium* subsp. *rotundifolium*

Hyacinthella (*Asparagaceae*)

acutiloba	ECho
dalmatica	ECho
glabrescens	WCot
heldreichii	ECho
leucophaea	ECho
millingenii	ECho
pallens	ECho

Hyacinthoides (*Asparagaceae*)

aristidis	ECho WCot
- from Algeria	ECho
ciliolata	CBro ECho EPot NRog SBch
§ **hispanica**	ECho NBir SEND WCot
- 'Alba'	ECho LRHS
- subsp. **algeriensis**	WCot
- 'Dainty Maid'	ECho WCot
- 'Miss World'	WCot
- 'Queen of the Pinks'	WCot
- 'Rosea'	ECho
- 'White City'	ECho WCot
§ **italica** ♀H4	ECho WShi
mauritanica	ECho
§ **non-scripta**	CAvo CBro CHab CTca CTri CWld ECho EPot GKev ILea LAma LCro LEdu LOPS LPot LRHS MCot MMuc NBir NPri SCob SDeJ SEND SPad SPer SRms SVic WHer WShi XLum
- 'Alba'	ECho LRHS MMuc NBir SEND
- 'Bracteata'	CNat
- cleistogamous	CNat
- long-bracteate, white-flowered	CDes
- 'Rosea'	ECho
reverchonii	ECho
- from Spain	ECho WCot
§ **vincentina**	WCot

Hyacinthus ✿ (*Asparagaceae*)

amethystinus	see *Brimeura amethystina*
azureus	see *Muscari azureum*
comosus 'Plumosus'	see *Muscari comosum* 'Plumosum'
orientalis	MGib
'Aida' ♀H4 new	
- 'Aiolos'	MGib SDeJ SPer
- 'Amethyst'	MGib
- 'Anastasia'	CAvo
- 'Anna Liza'	MBri SDeJ
- 'Anna Marie' ♀H4	CBro LAma MBri SDeJ
- 'Apricot Passion'	ERCP SDeJ
- 'Blue Eyes'	SDeJ
- 'Blue Festival' ♀H4	MGib SDeJ
- 'Blue Giant'	LAma SDeJ
- 'Blue Jacket' ♀H4	CBro LAma MBri MGib SCob SDeJ
- 'Blue Magic'	SDeJ
- 'Blue Pearl'PBR	LCro LOPS SDeJ
- 'Blue Star'	LAma
- 'Blue Tango' new	MGib
- 'Carnegie'	CAvo CBro EPfP ERCP LAma LCro LOPS
- 'Chestnut Flower' (d)	SDeJ
- 'China Pink'	LRHS SDeJ SPer
- 'City of Haarlem' ♀H4	CBro EPfP LAma LOPS LRHS MBri SDeJ
- 'Crystal Palace' (d)	LAma SDeJ
- 'Delft Blue' ♀H4	CAvo CBro EPfP LAma LCro LOPS LRHS MBri SCob SDeJ SPer

- 'Fondant'	LAma LRHS SDeJ
- 'General Köhler' (d)	LAma SDeJ
- 'Gipsy Princess'	LAma
- 'Gipsy Queen' ♀H4	EPfP LAma MBri MGib SCob SDeJ WCot
- 'Hollyhock' (d) ♀H4	ERCP LAma SCob SDeJ
- 'Ibis' **new**	MGib SCob SPer
- 'Jan Bos' ♀H4	LAma LOPS LRHS MBri MGib SCob SDeJ
- 'Lady Derby'	SDeJ
- 'L'Innocence' ♀H4	CAvo CBro SCob
- 'Marie'	EPfP SPer
- 'Miss Saigon' ♀H4	ERCP SDeJ
- multi-flowered	CAvo ERCP SDeJ
- 'Odysseus'	LAma SDeJ
- 'Ostara' ♀H4	LAma MBri
- 'Paul Hermann' ♀H4	MGib SDeJ
- 'Peter Stuyvesant'	EPfP ERCP LAma LCro LOPS SDeJ
- 'Pink Festival' ♀H4	MGib SDeJ
- 'Pink Pearl'	EPfP LAma LCro LOPS LRHS MBri SDeJ
- 'Pink Royal' (d)	LAma
- 'Red Magic'	SDeJ
- 'Rosette' (d)	LAma SDeJ
- 'Royal Navy' (d) ♀H4 **new**	ERCP MGib
- 'Sky Jacket'	LCro LOPS SCob
- 'Snow Crystal' (d) **new**	ERCP
- 'Splendid Cornelia'	ERCP SDeJ
- 'Top Hit'	MGib
- 'White Festival' ♀H4	MGib SDeJ
- 'White Pearl'	EPfP LAma LCro LOPS LRHS MBri SCob SDeJ SPer
- 'Woodstock'	CAvo CBro EPfP ERCP LAma LCro LOPS MGib SCob SDeJ SPer
- 'Yellow Queen' ♀H4	MGib

Hydrangea ✿ (*Hydrangeaceae*)

	sp.	LPar
	angustipetala	see *H. scandens* subsp. *chinensis* f. *angustipetala*
	anomala	WCru
	subsp. ***anomala*** BWJ 8052 from China	
	- - HWJK 2065 from Nepal	WCru
§	- - 'Winter Glow'	CJun ESwi MRav MTPN WCot WCru WFar
	- subsp. ***glabra*** B&SWJ 6804	WCru
	- - 'Crûg Coral'	WCru
§	- subsp. ***petiolaris*** ♀H5	Widely available
	- - B&SWJ 5996 from Yakushima	WCru
	- - B&SWJ 6337	WCru
	- - from Yakushima	CFil
§	- - var. ***cordifolia***	NBro NLar
	- - - B&SWJ 6081	WCru
	- - - B&SWJ 11487	WCru
§	- - - 'Brookside Littleleaf'	GKin IDee NBro NLar WFar
	- - dwarf	see *H. anomala* subsp. *petiolaris* var. *cordifolia*
	- - 'Early Light' (v)	SGbt
	- - 'Firefly' (v)	WPat
	- - var. ***megaphylla*** B&SWJ 4400	WCru
	- - - B&SWJ 8497	WCru
*	- - var. ***minor*** B&SWJ 5991	GEdr WCru
	- - 'Mirranda' (v)	CBcs CDoC CRHN ELan EPfP ESwi GCal NBro NLar SGol SPoG SWvt WBor WGrn
§	- - var. ***ovalifolia***	CRHN ESwi GQui LRHS
	- - - B&SWJ 8799	WCru
	- - - B&SWJ 8846	WCru
	- - 'Silver Lining'	EBee EPfP LCro SPoG
	- - 'Summer Snow' (v)	LLHF LRHS SPoG
	- - var. ***tiliifolia***	see *H. anomala* subsp. *petiolaris* var. *ovalifolia*
	- - 'Yakushima'	WCru
	- subsp. ***quelpartensis***	see *H. anomala* subsp. *petiolaris* var. *ovalifolia*
	- 'Winter Surprise'	see *H. anomala* subsp. *anomala* 'Winter Glow'
§	***arborescens***	CArn CExl MRav WPGP
	- 'Annabelle' ♀H6	Widely available
	- 'Bounty'	MAsh WPat
§	- subsp. ***discolor***	LEdu WPat
	- - 'Sterilis'	CFil GBin GGGa SHyH WPGP WPat
	- 'Eco Pink Puff' **new**	WPGP
	- Endless Summer Bella Anna = 'Piiha-I'PBR (Endless Summer Series)	MBri
	- 'Grandiflora'	CBcs IBoy NBro NEgg WBod WPGP
	- 'Hayes Starburst'PBR	CBot CDoC CMil CRos CWGN EBee GGGa LEdu LHop LLHF LRHS SAko SHyH SKHP SPoG SSpi SWvt WPGP WPat
	- 'Hills of Snow'	IVic NLar
	- Incrediball = 'Abetwo'	CBcs CLet CRos ELan EPfP LCro LPfy LRHS MBlu NLar SGol SLon SPoG
§	- Invincibelle Spirit = 'Ncha1'	CBcs CBot CDoC CLet CRos ELan EPfP GBin LCro LHop LLHF LOPS LRHS MBlu SCob SGol SHyH SLon SMDP SMad SPer SPoG SWvt
	- 'Invincible Spirit'	see *H. arborescens* Invincibelle Spirit
	- 'Picadilly'	NLar
	- 'Pink Annabelle'	see *H. arborescens* Invincibelle Spirit
	- 'Pink Pincushion'	CJun NBro NLar SAko
	- 'Puffed Green'	NLar
	- subsp. ***radiata***	CRos EBee LRHS MRav WCru WPGP
	- - 'Samantha'	EPfP LLHF LRHS SCob SPoG WPGP
	- 'Ryan Gainey'	EUJe LEdu MPkF
	- 'Vasterival'	NLar
	- White Dome = 'Dardom'PBR	NBro
	aspera	CMac CTri EUJe SHyH SLon SSpi SSta WCru WKif WPGP
	- HWJCM 452	WCru
	- from Gongshan, China	CExl CFil CMil WPGP
	- 'Anthony Bullivant' ♀H5	CBot CDoC CDul IArd IDee LRHS MAsh NLar SAko SHyH SKHP SWvt WPat
	- 'Bellevue'	IVic WPGP
	- Farrell form	CFil
	- Hot Chocolate = 'Hpopr012'	CMil LCro LOPS MBlu MGos NLar SCob SGol SHyH WGrn WHlf
	- Kawakamii Group	CBot CExl CMil CSpe ESwi LRHS NLar SGol SKHP SWvt WCru WPGP WPat
	- - B&SWJ 3456	WCru
	- - B&SWJ 3527	WCru
	- - B&SWJ 6702	WCru

- - B&SWJ 6714	WCru
- - B&SWJ 6827	WCru
- - B&SWJ 6996	WCru
- - B&SWJ 7101	WCru
- - 'August Abundance'	WCru
- - 'Formosa'	WCru
- - 'Maurice Mason'	CExl CFil
- - 'September Splendour'	WCru
- Kawakamii Group × ***involucrata***	CFil WPGP
- 'Koki' **new**	LRHS
- 'Macrophylla' ♀H5	CBot CFil CWib EPfP EWTr GCal GKin IVic MBri MGos MRav NLar SHil SHyH SPer SWvt WCru WPGP
- 'Mauvette'	CBot CMil ECre EPfP GKin LRHS MBlu NBro NLar SCob SGol SHyH SPer WCru
- 'Peter Chappell' ♀H5	CExl CMac CMil LRHS NLar SAko SHyH SWvt WPat
- 'Pink Cloud'	CFil
§ - subsp. ***robusta***	CExl LRHS WPGP
- - GWJ 9430	WCru
- - WWJ 11888	WCru
- 'Rocklon'	CMil EBee ESwi NLar
- 'Rosthornii'	see *H. aspera* subsp. *robusta*
- 'Sam MacDonald'	CExl CMil EPfP LRHS NLar SKHP SSpi WPGP WPat
- 'Sapa' **new**	EBee
§ - subsp. ***sargentiana***	Widely available
- - 'La Fosse'	WPGP
- - large-leaved	CExl CFil WCru
- 'Spinners'	NLar
- subsp. ***strigosa***	CDul CExl CSde EPfP LRHS SSpi SWvt WCru WPGP
- - B&SWJ 8201	WCru
- - HWJ 653	WCru
- - HWJ 737	WCru
- - KWJ 12151 from northern Vietnam	WCru
- - from Gong Shan, China	CExl
- aff. subsp. ***strigosa***	CFil
- 'Taiwan Pink'	EPfP IArd NLar
- 'The Ditch'	ESwi NLar
- 'Trelissick Blue Skies'	CFil
§ - Villosa Group	Widely available
- - 'Trelissick'	CFil
- - 'Velvet and Lace' ♀H5	CJun CRos LRHS MBri MGos NLar SHil
asterolasia B&SWJ 10481	WCru
§ 'Blue Deckle' (L)	CAbb CMHG CMac GGal LRHS MAsh MGos MRav NBro NLar SDys
cinerea	see *H. arborescens* subsp. *discolor*
davidii B&SWJ 8307 **new**	WCru
- B&SWJ 11717	WCru
- B&SWJ 11692	WCru
- f. ***purpurascens*** KWJ 12233B	WCru
'Dharuma'	GKin LRHS SAko SGol
Early Sensation = 'Bulk'PBR ♀H5	CBot CLet EShb ESwi EThi GBin GKin LRHS MSwo SGol SHyH SKHP SMDP SSpi WFar WGrn WMoo
'Garden House Glory'	CExl CFil EBee WPGP
glabrifolia	see *H. scandens* subsp. *chinensis*
glandulosa B&SWJ 4031	WCru
'Glyn Church'	EBee SAko WPGP

aff. ***gracilis*** B&SWJ 3942	WCru
§ ***heteromalla***	CMHG CPne GGGa GGal NBro WPGP
- B&SWJ 2142 from India	WCru
- B&SWJ 2602 from Sikkim	WCru
- BWJ 7657 from China	WCru
- GWJ 9337 from Sikkim	WCru
- HWJ 526 from Vietnam	WCru
- HWJ 938 from Vietnam	WCru
- HWJCM 180	WCru
- HWJK 2127 from Nepal	WCru
- KR 9913 from India	WPGP
- SBEC	GGGa
- Bretschneideri Group	EBee EPfP GKin GQui SHyH WCru
- 'Fan Si Pan'	WCru
- 'June Pink'	NLar
- 'Long White'	NLar
- 'Morrey's Form'	NLar WCru WPGP
- 'Nepal Beauty'	CDoC EBee EPfP ESwi EUJe IVic MMHG SGol WPGP
- 'Snowcap'	EPfP GQui IArd LRHS NLar SHyH SKHP WPGP
- f. ***xanthoneura***	CBot
- - NJM 11.009	WPGP
- - 'Wilsonii'	WCru WKif
- 'Yalung Ridge'	WCru
hirta B&SWJ 5000	WCru
- B&SWJ 11022	WCru
indochinensis	CExl ESwi
- B&SWJ 8307	WCru
- WWJ 11609	WCru
integerrima	see *H. serratifolia*
integrifolia B&SWJ 022	WCru
- B&SWJ 6967	NLar WCru
involucrata	LLHF LRHS MMHG SBrt SHil SHyH
- B&SWJ 4790	WCru
- B&SWJ 11578 **new**	WCru
- dwarf	CExl CFil WCru
- 'Hortensis' (d)	CBot CMil MRav NLar SMad SSpi WBod WCru WKif WPGP WSHC
- var. ***idzuensis*** **new**	WCru
- 'Mihara-kokonoe'	WPGP
- 'Multiplex'	CBot WCru
- 'Oshima'	WPGP
- 'Plena' (d)	EBee LRHS MRav NLar SHyH WCru WPGP
- 'Plenissima' (d)	WCru
- 'Sterilis'	CMil WCru
- 'Tokada Yama'	CMil NLar
- 'Viridescens' ♀H4	EBee LLHF LRHS NLar SHyH WCru WPGP
- 'Yohraku-tama' ♀H4	CFil NLar WPGP
- 'Yokudanka' (d)	CBot CMil GQui NLar SAko WPGP
- 'Yoraku' (d)	EBee WCru
kawagoeana var. ***grosseserrata*** B&SWJ 11500	WCru
- - B&SWJ 11511 **new**	WCru
lobbii	see *H. scandens* subsp. *chinensis*
longifolia B&SWJ 6883	WCru
- CWJ 12413	WCru
longipes	CExl GQui WCru WPGP
- var. ***fulvescens*** B&SWJ 8188	WCru
- var. ***longipes***	CExl CFil
- - NJM 11.052	WPGP
luteovenosa	WCru

	Name	Suppliers
	- B&SWJ 5647	WCru
	- B&SWJ 5929	WCru
	- B&SWJ 6220	WCru
	- B&SWJ 6317	WCru
	macrophylla (H)	GGal LRHS
	- 'AB Green Shadow'PBR (H)	COtt EBee MAsh MMHG SCob
	- 'Adria' (H)	COtt NLar SGol SHyH
	- 'Aduarda'	see *H. macrophylla* 'Mousmée'
	- 'All Summer Beauty' (H)	CDoC ELon GBin GGGa MAsh SHyH
	- Alpen Glow	see *H. macrophylla* 'Alpenglühen'
§	- 'Alpenglühen' (H)	CBcs CExl CSBt IVic LRHS MJak SAko SHyH SLim
	- 'Altona' (H) ♀H5	CBcs CCVT EPfP GGGa IArd LCro LOPS LRHS MAsh MGos MRav NBir NLar SHyH SPer WBod
	- 'Amethyst' (H/d)	LRHS
	- 'Ami Pasquier' (H)	CBcs CDoC CMac CSBt CSde CTri ELan EPfP GGal IVic LRHS LSRN MAsh MMuc MRav MSwo NEgg SAko SCob SCoo SEND SHyH SLim SPoG SSpi SWvt
	- 'Amor' (H)	SCob SGol
*	- 'Aureomarginata' (v)	SHyH WCot
	- 'Ave Maria' (H)	GGGa MAsh
§	- 'Ayesha' (H)	Widely available
	- 'Bachstelze' (Teller Series) (L)	IVic MAsh WPGP
	- 'Bavaria' (H)	GKin SGol WFar
	- 'Beauté Vendômoise' (L)	CMil LRHS NLar SHyH SSpi WPGP
	- 'Bela'PBR (H)	COtt EBee LRHS SCob
	- 'Benelux' (H)	CBcs
	- 'Bergfink' (Teller Series) (L) **new**	NLar
	- Berlin = 'Rabe'PBR (City-line Series) (H) **new**	SGol
	- 'Bichon' (H) **new**	SGol
	- 'Bicolor'	see *H. macrophylla* 'Harlequin'
	- 'Black Steel Zambia' (H)	EBee EPfP LBuc NPri SLon
	- 'Black Steel Zebra' (H)	EBee EPfP LBuc LPfy NPri SLon
§	- 'Blauer Prinz' (H)	SHyH
§	- 'Bläuling' (Teller Series) (L) ♀H5	CDoC CRos EPfP GKin LRHS LSRN MBri SCob SGol SLim WHar
§	- 'Blaumeise' (Teller Series) (L) ♀H5	CDoC CFil CMHG COtt EAEE ELon GGGa LPfy LRHS MAsh MBri MGos MRav SCob SCoo SGol SHyH SLim SLon SSpi SWvt WFar WPGP
	- 'Blue Bonnet' (H)	CDul EPfP LRHS LSRN MRav SAko SHyH SPer
	- Blue Butterfly	see *H. macrophylla* 'Bläuling'
	- Blue Prince	see *H. macrophylla* 'Blauer Prinz'
	- Blue Sky	see *H. macrophylla* 'Blaumeise'
	- Blue Tit	see *H. macrophylla* 'Blaumeise'
	- 'Blue Wave'	see *H. macrophylla* 'Mariesii Perfecta'
	- Bluebird	see *H. macrophylla* 'Bläuling'
	- 'Bluebird' misapplied	see *H. serrata* 'Bluebird'
§	- 'Blushing Bride'PBR (H)	ELan LCro MAsh MBri NPri SLon
	- 'Bodensee' (H)	CCVT MBri MGos MJak MMuc SCob SEND SHyH
	- 'Bottstein' (H) **new**	CCVT
	- 'Bouquet Rose' (H)	CWib ECtt MJak MMuc NLar SEND SHyH
	- 'Brestenburg' (H)	MAsh
	- 'Brügg' (H)	LRHS MAsh SAko SGol SHyH SLim SPer WPGP
	- 'Camilla'PBR (H)	SGol WFar
	- 'Camino' (L)	EPfP
	- Cardinal	see *H. macrophylla* 'Kardinal' (Teller Series)
§	- 'Cardinal Red' (H)	ECre NPri WFar
	- 'Cendrillon' (H)	LLHF LRHS STPC
	- 'Choco Chic' (L) **new**	SGol
	- 'Cocktail' (H) **new**	SGol
	- 'Coco' (H) **new**	LRHS
	- 'Coco Blanc' (H/d)	SCob SGol
	- Color Fantasy (H)	MBrN
	- 'Cordata'	see *H. arborescens*
	- 'Dandenong' (L)	GQui
	- 'Dark Angel' (L)	LRHS WHlf
	- 'Dart's Romance' (L)	SHyH
	- 'Deutschland' (H)	CTri MBri
	- 'Doctor Jean Varnier' (L)	EMil EPfP SHyH
	- Dolce Farfalle = 'Dolfarf' (H) **new**	WCot
	- Dolce Gipsy = 'Dolgip'PBR (L)	CRos EPfP ESwi LRHS MGos SHil
	- Dolce Kiss = 'Dolkis'PBR (L)	CDoC CRos EPfP LRHS MGos MMHG SGol SHil
	- 'Domotoi'	see *H. macrophylla* 'Setsuka-yae'
	- 'Doris' (H)	SCob SGol
	- (Double Stars Expression Series) 'Double Stars Expresssion Blue' (d) (H) **new**	WHlf
	- - 'Double Stars Expresssion Pink' (d) (H) **new**	WHlf
	- - 'Double Stars Expresssion White' (d) (H) **new**	WHlf
	- Dragonfly	see *H. macrophylla* 'Libelle'
	- Early Blue = 'Hba 202911'PBR (H)	COtt LRHS SCob SGol
§	- 'Early Sensation' (Forever & Ever Series) (H)	CMac GKin LBuc LLHF MHol
	- 'Eldorado' (H)	SHyH
	- 'Elégance' (L) **new**	SGol
	- Endless Summer = 'Bailmer' (H)	ELan EPfP LCro MAsh MGos NPri SPoG
	- Endless Summer Blushing Bride	see *H. macrophylla* 'Blushing Bride'
	- Endless Summer Twist-n-Shout = 'Piihm-I' (L)	EPfP LCro MBri
§	- 'Enziandom' (H)	CBcs CExl CFil CSBt GGal MAsh WPGP
	- Eternity = 'Youmetwo'PBR (H/d)	WCot
	- 'Etoile Violette' (L)	ESwi LRHS
	- 'Europa' (H) ♀H5	CBcs CExl NLar SHyH
	- Expression = 'Youmesix' **new**	LCro SGol
§	- 'Fasan' (Teller Series) (L)	MAsh NBro SDix WHar
	- Firelight	see *H. macrophylla* 'Leuchtfeuer'
	- Fireworks	see *H. macrophylla* 'Hanabi'
	- Fireworks Blue	see *H. macrophylla* 'Jōgasaki'
	- Fireworks Pink	see *H. macrophylla* 'Jōgasaki'
	- Fireworks White	see *H. macrophylla* 'Hanabi'
	- Forever & Ever Together = 'Rie 05' (Forever & Ever Series) (H/d)	SGol SMDP
	- Forever and Ever	see *H. macrophylla* 'Early Sensation'
	- 'Forever Pink' (H)	GGGa MAsh NLar SGol
§	- 'Frau Fujiyo' (Lady Series) (H)	CExl

§ - 'Frau Katsuko' (Lady Series) (H) SPer
§ - 'Frau Mariko' (Lady Series) (H) MRav
§ - 'Frau Taiko' (Lady Series) (H) SPer
- 'Freudenstein' (H) ESwi
- 'Frillibet' (H) CAbP MRav NLar
- 'Ganku Bo Chokens' (H) WCot
- 'Gartenbaudirektor Kühnert' (H) SHyH
§ - 'Générale Vicomtesse de Vibraye' (H) ♀H5 CBcs CDoC CDul CSde CTri ELan ELon EPfP GGal LRHS MAsh SCob SHyH SLim SPer SPoG SSpi WBod
- Gentian Dome see *H. macrophylla* 'Enziandom'
- 'Geoffrey Chadbund' see *H. macrophylla* 'Möwe'
- 'Gerda Steiniger' (H) SHyH
- 'Gertrud Glahn' (H) SHyH
- 'Gimpel' (Teller Series) (L) MAsh
- 'Glowing Embers' (H) IArd
- Goldrush = 'Nehyosh' (L/v) CDul EBee LBMP LRHS NHol WCot
- 'Goliath' (H) ELon EPfP
- 'Gräfin Cosel' (H) **new** SGol
§ - 'Grant's Choice' (L) NBro SHyH
- Great Star = 'Blanc Bleu' (L) ♀H5 ECrN EPfP LRHS LSRN SLim WFar
- 'Grünes Gewölbe' (H) **new** SGol
- 'Hamburg' (H) CBcs CTri ECtt EPfP LRHS MGos SCob SDix SHyH SLim WFar
§ - 'Hanabi' (L/d) ♀H5 CAbP CDoC ECre GGal LRHS MBlu NLar SHyH
§ - 'Harlequin' (H) CMac GGGa WCot
- 'Harry's Red' (H) MAsh
- 'Hatsu-shime' (L) NLar
- 'Heinrich Seidel' (H) CBcs CTri WMoo
- 'Hobella'[PBR] (Hovaria Series) (L) CBcs WCot WFar
- 'Holehird Purple' (H) MAsh
- 'Hopcorn'[PBR] (H) **new** EBee
- Hot Red = 'Hba 206901'[PBR] (H) LRHS
- 'Hot Red Violet' **new** LCro LOPS MJak
- 'Izu-no-hana' (L/d) CAbb CBcs CFil CMil ELon EPfP ESwi GBin LHop MBlu NLar SBod SHyH SPoG WBor WPGP
- 'James Grant' see *H. macrophylla* 'Grant's Choice'
- 'Jofloma' (H) ESwi NLar
§ - 'Jōgasaki' (L/d) CBcs CExl CLAP CMil CSde LRHS MAsh MBlu NLar SDys SHyH WPGP
- 'Joseph Banks' (H) CBcs CTri SHyH
- 'Kardinal' see *H. macrophylla* 'Cardinal Red' (H)
§ - 'Kardinal' (Teller Series) (L) ♀H5 MAsh SCob SGol
- 'King George' (H) CBar CBcs CDoC CDul CSBt EBee ECtt EPfP LRHS MGos MMuc NEgg NHol SAdn SAko SCob SGol SHyH SLim SPer SPoG SWvt WFar WMoo
§ - 'Klaveren' (L) ♀H5 CMil GGGa LRHS MAsh NBro
- 'Kluis Superba' (H) CBcs CTri GGal SHyH
- 'Koria'[PBR] (L) **new** LRHS
- 'La France' (H) CTri IVic LRHS SCob SHyH SLim
- 'La Vie en Rose' (H) **new** SGol
- 'Lady Fujiyo' see *H. macrophylla* 'Frau Fujiyo'
- 'Lady in Red' (L) CMil CRos EBee EPfP LRHS SPoG
- Lady Katsuko see *H. macrophylla* 'Frau Katsuko'
- 'Lady Mariko' see *H. macrophylla* 'Frau Mariko'
- 'Lady Oshie' (Teller Series) (L) **new** SGol
- 'Lady Taiko Blue' see *H. macrophylla* 'Frau Taiko'
- 'Lady Taiko Pink' see *H. macrophylla* 'Frau Taiko'
- 'Lanarth White' (L) ♀H5 Widely available
- 'Lemon Wave' (L/v) NLar
§ - 'Leuchtfeuer' (H) ELon LRHS MBri SHyH WMoo
§ - 'Libelle' (Teller Series) (L) ♀H5 CBcs CMil ELon EPfP LRHS MGos MRav NLar SCob SGol SHyH SLim SPer SSpi
- 'Lilacina' see *H. macrophylla* 'Mariesii Lilacina'
- 'Little Lime' see *H. paniculata* 'Jane'
- 'Love You Kiss'[PBR] (Hovaria Series) (L) ♀H5 CBcs CMil COtt LRHS NLar SCoo SPoG STPC WCot
§ - 'Maculata' (L/v) GQui WGwG
- 'Madame A. Riverain' (H) EPfP NLar SHyH
- 'Madame Emile Mouillère' (H) ♀H5 Widely available
- 'Madame Plumecocq' (H) **new** LRHS
- Magical Amethyst = 'Hokomathyst'[PBR] (H) **new** LCro SGol
- Magical Harmony = 'Hortmahar'[PBR] (H) NLar
- Magical Jade = 'Hortmaja'[PBR] (H) EPfP MBlu NLar WCot
- Magical Noblesse = 'Hokomano'[PBR] (H) **new** SGol
- Magical Revolution = 'Hokomarevo' (H) **new** LCro SGol
- 'Maréchal Foch' (H) CTri GGal LRHS NLar
- 'Mariesii' (L) CMHG CTri ECrN ELan GGal LRHS MNHC MSwo NLar SHyH SPer
§ - 'Mariesii Grandiflora' (L) EPfP GGal LRHS MMuc NBro SEND SHyH SPer SRms WBod WMoo
§ - 'Mariesii Lilacina' (L) ♀H5 EPfP MMuc SEND SHyH SPer SSpi WMoo
§ - 'Mariesii Perfecta' (L) Widely available
- 'Mariesii Variegata' (L/v) CWib
- 'Masja' (H) CBcs CCVT ELon GKin IArd IVic LAst MAsh MGos MMuc MRav MSwo NBro NLar SAko SCob SEND SGol SHyH SLim WBor WMoo
- 'Mathilde Gütges' (H) CCVT CDoC GGal
- 'Max Löbner' (H) SHyH
- 'Merveille' (H) NBro
- 'Merveille Sanguine' (H) Widely available
- 'Messalina' (L) SCob SHyH
- 'Mini Penny' (H) **new** SGol
- 'Mirai'[PBR] (H) CBcs CDoC CMil ELan ESwi WCot WPGP
- 'Miss Belgium' (H) CMac CTri GKin MAsh
§ - 'Mousmée' (L) IArd SHyH SSpi
- 'Mousseline' (H) CFil CMil MAsh
§ - 'Möwe' (Teller Series) (L) ♀H5 CBcs CDoC CExl CMil ECtt ELon EPfP GBin GGal LSRN MAsh MBri MMuc SCob SCoo SDix SEND SGol SHyH SLim SPer SRms SSpi SSta WPat
- Mrs Kumico = 'Kumico' (H) **new** SGol
- 'Mrs W.J. Hepburn' (H) CSBt SHyH SPer
§ - 'Nachtigall' (Teller Series) (L) ♀H5 EPfP GGal IVic MAsh WPGP WPat

Name	Suppliers
- 'Nanping'PBR (Sturdy Series) (L)	EPfP
- 'Niedersachsen' (H)	CDoC CTri MRav SHyH
- Nightingale	see *H. macrophylla* 'Nachtigall'
- 'Nigra' (H)	Widely available
- 'Nikko Blue' (H)	CBcs EBee GKin LRHS MBri MJak NLar SHyH
- Nizza = 'Ranice'PBR (City-line Series) (H)	SCob
- var. ***normalis*** (L)	CExl
§ - 'Nymphe' (H)	MBri SCob SHyH
- 'Oregon Pride' (H)	CFil GGGa MAsh WFar WPGP
- 'Otaksa' (H)	NLar
- 'Papagei' (Teller Series) (L)	SPer
- 'Parzifal' (H) 🏆^{H5}	CDul
- Passion = 'Youmefour' (L)	WCot
- 'Pax'	see *H. macrophylla* 'Nymphe'
- 'Pfau' (Teller Series) (L) 🏆^{H5}	CMil ELon GBin MAsh SHyH
- Pheasant	see *H. macrophylla* 'Fasan'
- 'Pia' (H)	CDoC CExl CMac CMil CPla EShb LBMP LRHS MBri MGos MRav SCob SHyH SMad SPer SRms WGrn
- Pigeon	see *H. macrophylla* 'Taube'
- 'Pirate's Gold' (v)	EHoe WHar WMoo
- 'Prinses Beatrix' (H)	SHyH
- 'Quadricolor' (L/v) 🏆^{H5}	CExl CHII CMac CMil CTsd EHoe GCal GGal MAsh MGos MHol MRav SAdn SDix SHyH SLim SMDP SPer SPlb SRms WCot WSHC
- 'Queen Elizabeth' (H)	GKin
- 'R.F. Felton' (H)	CBcs SHyH
- 'Red Baron'	see *H. macrophylla* 'Schöne Bautznerin'
- 'Red Beauty'PBR (H) **new**	LRHS
- 'Red Red' (H)	MAsh
- 'Red Wonder' (H) **new**	SAko
- Redbreast	see *H. macrophylla* 'Rotkehlchen'
- 'Regula' (H)	SHyH
- 'Renate Steiniger' (H)	CDoC LRHS MBri MGos MMuc MRav SCob SHyH SLim WMoo
- 'Ripple'PBR (H) **new**	EBee
- 'Romance'	LRHS SCob SGol WCot
- 'Rosea'	MCri
- 'Rosita' (H)	COtt EBee MAsh MBri NBir SCob
- 'Rotdrossel' (Teller Series) (L)	GBin
§ - 'Rotkehlchen' (Teller Series) (L)	CDoC NLar SAko SGol SLim SPlb SWvt
- 'Rotschwanz' (Teller Series) (L) 🏆^{H5}	CFil CMil ESwi GBin LLHF LRHS MAsh NLar SHyH WPGP WPat
- 'Rouge Baiser' (H) **new**	SGol
- 'Royal Red' (H) **new**	LRHS
- 'Sabrina'PBR (H)	CBcs LLHF LRHS MAsh SCob SGol SHyH SRkn
- 'Saint Claire' (H)	CBcs
- 'Salsa'	LBMP LLHF MAsh MBri SGol SHyH
- 'Sandra' (Dutch Ladies Series) (L)	CBcs MAsh STPC
- 'Saskia' **new**	SGol
- 'Schloss Wackerbarth' (H) **new**	SGol
- 'Schneeball' (H)	CCVT MAsh MBri SCob SHyH
§ - 'Schöne Bautznerin'	CCVT EBee LRHS MBri SAdn SCob SHyH SLim
- 'Sea Foam' (L)	NLar
- 'Selina'	CBcs CDoC EBee EPfP LAst LBuc LLHF LSRN MAsh MBri SCoo
- 'Selma'PBR (Dutch Ladies Series) (L)	CBcs SGol SHyH
- 'Semperflorens' (H)	LRHS
§ - 'Setsuka-yae' (L/d)	CMil
- 'Shakira' (H)	CDoC LLHF SGol
- 'Sheila' (Dutch Ladies Series) (L)	CBcs CTsd EPfP LCro LOPS LSRN
- 'Shin-ozaki' (H)	NLar
- 'Shooting Star'PBR (L) **new**	LRHS
- 'Sibilla' (H)	MJak SGol SPlb
- 'Sindarella'	CDoC MGos
- Sister Therese	see *H. macrophylla* 'Soeur Thérèse'
- 'Sita' (L)	SHyH
§ - 'Soeur Thérèse' (H)	CBar CBcs EPfP MAsh MMuc NLar SGol SWvt WGwG
- 'Spike'PBR (H) **new**	LRHS
- subsp. ***stylosa***	WCru
- 'Sumida-no-hanabi' (L/d)	WPGP
* - 'Sunset' (L)	CBcs
- 'Superba' (H)	SCob
- 'Sweet Fantasy' (Hovaria Series) (H)	ELan EPfP
§ - 'Taube' (Teller Series) (L)	CBcs CDoC CDul CExl CMHG GGal GQui MAsh MGos SHyH SLim SWvt
- 'Teller Pink'	see *H. macrophylla* 'Taube'
- 'Teller Red'	see *H. macrophylla* 'Rotkehlchen'
- Teller variegated	see *H. macrophylla* 'Tricolor'
- Teller Weiss	see *H. macrophylla* 'Libelle'
- var. ***thunbergii***	see *H. serrata* var. *thunbergii*
- 'Tivoli' (H)	LRHS SCob WFar
- 'Tokyo Delight' (L) 🏆^{H5}	CExl CMac LRHS MAsh SDys SHyH WPGP
§ - 'Tricolor' (L/v)	CBcs CDoC CDul CTri CTsd EBee ELan ELon EShb ESwi LAst LRHS MGos MSCN NLar SHyH SLon SPer WFar WMoo
- 'Variegata'	see *H. macrophylla* 'Maculata'
- 'Veitchii' (L) 🏆^{H5}	CBcs CDul CExl CMHG CMil CSBt ECre EPfP EWTr GGal LPot LRHS MGos MRav MSwo SDix SHyH SPer SSpi WPGP
- 'Vicomte de Vibraye'	see *H. macrophylla* 'Générale Vicomtesse de Vibraye'
- 'Westfalen' (H) 🏆^{H5}	CMac IArd SDix
I - 'White Lace' (L)	GKin
- 'White Mop' (H)	CWib
- 'White Wave'	see *H. macrophylla* 'Mariesii Grandiflora'
- 'Wudu'PBR (H) **new**	SGol
- 'Yola' (H)	NBro SMDP
- 'Zaunkoenig' (L)	MAsh
- 'Zaza' (Black Steel Series) (H)	EPfP LCro LOPS
- 'Zebra'PBR (H)	ELan ESwi LBuc LCro MGos MHol SCob SMDP WCot WPtf
- 'Zhuni Hito' (L)	NLar
- 'Zorro'PBR (L) 🏆^{H5}	CBcs CDoC CMil CRos CTsd CWGN EPfP ESwi GGGa GKin LBMP LRHS MAsh MCri MGos SCob SCoo SLim SLon SPer SPoG SSpi WCot
- 'Zulu' (H)	ELan
aff. ***mangshanensis*** BWJ 8120	WCru
paniculata	CMCN LPar

- B&SWJ 3556 from Taiwan WCru WFar
- B&SWJ 5413 from Japan WCru
- B&SWJ 8894 from Japan WCru
- from Taiwan SKHP
- 'Ammarin' GQui NLar WPat
- Angel's Blush see *H. paniculata* 'Ruby'
- 'Big Ben' ♀H5 CMil EPfP GGGa GQui LRHS NLar SHyH SKHP
- Bobo = 'Ilvobo'PBR MPkF SCob SGol
- 'Bombshell'PBR LCro LOPS SCob
- 'Brussels Lace' CAbP CAbb CDul CLAP CMil CRos EPfP GBin LEdu LRHS LSRN MAsh MRav NLar SCob SGol SHyH SLon SSta WPat
- 'Burgundy Lace' CLAP MBlu NLar
- Candlelight = 'Hpopr013' **new** SGol
- 'Chantilly Lace' CMHG CMil EBee LRHS SCob SHyH
- Dart's Little Dot = 'Darlido'PBR GBin IVic LLHF LSRN NLar SLim WFar WPGP WPat
- Diamant Rouge = 'Rendia' LCro LOPS LRHS MPkF SGol
- Diamantino = 'Ren101' **new** SGol
- 'Dolly' GQui LRHS LSRN SHyH
- 'Everest' CAbP CLAP CMil EPfP LRHS MAsh NLar SHyH WPat
- 'Floribunda' CRos ELan EPfP LRHS SHyH WFar WPGP
- 'Grandiflora' Widely available
- 'Great Escape' NLar WPat
- 'Greenspire' EPfP LRHS MAsh MBlu MRav SHyH WFar WPat
- 'Harry's Souvenir' NLar

§ - 'Jane' **new** LRHS SGol
- 'Kyushu' Widely available
- 'Last Post' GQui
- 'Levana'PBR CMil SGol SHyH
- 'Limelight'PBR ♀H5 Widely available
- 'Little Lime' see *H. paniculata* 'Jane'
- Magical Candle = 'Bokraflame'PBR EPPr EPfP LPar SGol WCot
- Magical Fire = 'Bokraplume'PBR NLar SCob SGol
- 'Mathilde' NLar
- Mega Mindy = 'Ilvomindy'PBR CBcs ESwi SCob SGol SKHP
- 'Mega Pearl' LSRN NLar
- 'Melody' NLar
- 'Mount Aso' GQui NBro WPGP
- 'October Bride' GQui NLar WPGP
- 'Papillon' WPGP WPat
- 'Pee Wee' LLHF NLar
- 'Phantom' ♀H5 Widely available
- 'Pink Beauty'PBR (H) CTri LSRN
- Pink Diamond = 'Interhydia' ♀H5 Widely available
- 'Pink Jewel' CWib LLHF WPat
- 'Pink Lady' NBro SCob SHyH
- Pinky-Winky = 'Dvppinky'PBR ♀H5 Widely available
- 'Praecox' GQui MRav WCru
- Prim'White = 'Dolprim' CDoC LRHS
- 'Rosy Morn' LRHS

§ - 'Ruby' CBcs IArd LSRN NLar
- 'Saville Lace' **new** CMil
- 'Silver Dollar' ♀H5 CDoC CMil CRos EPfP ESwi IArd LCro LOPS LRHS LSRN MBri SCob SGol SHyH SWvt WFar
- Sundae Fraise = 'Rensun'PBR CDoC CMil CWGN EPfP EShb GGGa LRHS MAsh MGos MPkF SGol SHil WGrn
- 'Tardiva' CBcs EPfP GGal GKin GQui LCro LRHS MGos MRav NBro SCob SDix SHyH SPer SRms SWvt WFar WPGP WPat
- 'Tender Rose' NLar
- 'Unique' Widely available
- Vanille Fraise = 'Renhy'PBR Widely available
- 'White Goliath' GQui IArd NLar SAko
- 'White Lace' NLar
- 'White Lady' CBcs
- 'White Moth' CAbP CBcs EBee GGGa LLHF LRHS NBro NLar SAdn SHyH WPat
- 'Wim's Red'PBR CBcs CMil ELan ESwi MMHG NLar SCob SGol
- 'Yuan-Yang' WCru

peruviana* × *seemannii GKin IArd MJak SSta

peruviana* × *serratifolia WPGP

petiolaris see *H. anomala* subsp. *petiolaris*

'Preziosa' ♀H4 Widely available

quercifolia Widely available

- 'Alice' CJun CRos EBee ELan EMil EPfP ESwi LHop LRHS LSRN MAsh NLar SCob SGol SHyH SSpi WPGP
- 'Alison' SGol

I - 'Amethyst' Dirr CJun NLar SGol
- 'Applause' EPfP LCro LOPS LRHS NLar
- 'Back Porch' GBin MBri NLar SGol
- 'Bride' **new** SIgm
- 'Burgundy' CBcs CJun CMil EBee EPfP ESwi GBin IArd IVic LRHS NLar SAko SGol WPGP
- 'Flore Pleno' see *H. quercifolia* Snowflake
- 'Harmony' CDoC CJun CMil EBee ELan EMil EPfP ESwi IArd LRHS MBri NLar SAko SHil SHyH SKHP SSta WPGP WPat
- Ice Crystal = 'Hqopr010'PBR CMil EBee IVic LBMP NLar SCob SGol SHyH WHar WPGP
- 'Lady Anne' EPfP WPGP
- 'Little Honey'PBR CMil NLar SGol SSpi
- Little Honey = 'Brihon' CAbP IVic LPfy LRHS MAsh MPkF
- 'Pee Wee' CAbP CBcs CDoC CJun CMil ELan EMil LPfy LRHS MAsh MPkF SAko SGol SHyH SKHP SLon SMDP SPoG SSta SWvt WPGP
- 'Sike's Dwarf' CJun IVic MPkF MRav NLar SCob SGol WPat
- 'Snow Giant' CJun
- Snow Queen = 'Flemygea' ♀H5 Widely available
- 'Snowdrift' CJun CMil

§ - Snowflake = 'Brido' (d) ♀H5 CAbP CBcs CDoC CMac CMil CRos CSde CWGN ELan EPfP LCro LOPS LRHS MAsh MGos MRav NLar SAko SHyH SKHP SLon SPer SPoG SSpi WCFE WPGP WPat
- 'Stardust' MMHG
- 'Tennessee Clone' CJun ESwi LRHS NLar SKHP

sargentiana see *H. aspera* subsp. *sargentiana*

scandens CFil NBro

- B&SWJ 5448 WCru
- B&SWJ 5481 WCru
- B&SWJ 5496 WCru
- B&SWJ 5523 WCru

- B&SWJ 5602	WCru
- B&SWJ 5725	WCru
- B&SWJ 5893	WCru
- B&SWJ 6159	WCru
- B&SWJ 6317	WCru
§ - subsp. ***chinensis***	CExl
- - B&SWJ 1488	WCru
- - B&SWJ 3214	WCru
- - B&SWJ 3410 from Taiwan	WCru
- - B&SWJ 3420	WCru
- - B&SWJ 3423 from Taiwan	WCru
- - B&SWJ 3487 from Taiwan	WCru
- - B&SWJ 3869	WCru
- - BWJ 8000 from Sichuan	WCru
- - BWJ 8035	WCru
§ - - f. ***angustipetala*** B&SWJ 3454	WCru
- - - B&SWJ 3553	WCru
- - - B&SWJ 3667	WCru
- - - B&SWJ 3733	WCru
- - - B&SWJ 3814	WCru
- - - B&SWJ 6038 from Yakushima	WCru
- - - B&SWJ 6041 from Yakushima	WCru
- - - B&SWJ 6056 from Yakushima	WCru
- - - B&SWJ 6787	WCru
- - - B&SWJ 6802	WCru
- - - B&SWJ 7121	WCru
- - - B&SWJ 7128	WCru
§ - - - 'Golden Crane'	SCob WCru
- - - 'Monlongshou'	see *H. scandens* subsp. *chinensis* f. *angustipetala* 'Golden Crane'
- - f. ***formosana*** B&SWJ 1488	WCru
- - - B&SWJ 3271	WCru
- - - B&SWJ 7058	NLar WCru
- - - B&SWJ 7097	NLar WCru
- - f. ***macrosepala*** B&SWJ 3423	ESwi WCru
- - - B&SWJ 3476	WCru
- - - CWJ 12441	WCru
- - f. ***obovatifolia*** B&SWJ 3487b	WCru
- - - B&SWJ 3683	WCru
- - - B&SWJ 3869 from the Philippines	WCru
- - - B&SWJ 7121	WCru
- subsp. ***liukiuensis***	WCru
- - B&SWJ 6022	WCru
- - B&SWJ 11471	WCru
- 'Splash' (v)	CMil
seemannii	Widely available
- 'Roger Grounds' (v)	WCot
aff. ***seemannii***	GKin
Semiola = 'Inovalaur'^{PBR}	EPfP ESwi LLHF LRHS NLar SGol SKHP SLim WPGP
serrata	CExl CTri CWib WKif
- B&SWJ 6184	WCru
- B&SWJ 6241	WCru
- PAB 4757	LEdu
- 'Acuminata'	see *H. serrata* 'Bluebird'
- 'Aigaku' (L)	CExl CFil CMil
- 'Aka Beni-yama'	CLAP GQui
- 'Akabe-yama'	NBro NLar
- 'Akishino-temari'	EBee WPGP
- (Amacha Group) 'Amagi-amacha' (L)	CMil GQui NBro NLar
- - 'Ō-amacha' (L)	CMil EBee GQui WPGP

- 'Amagyana' (L)	CExl
- subsp. ***angustata***	WCru
- 'Ao-yama'	WPGP
- Avelroz = 'Dolmyf'^{PBR}	EPfP LRHS
- 'Belladonna'	GQui NBro
- 'Belle Deckle'	see *H.* 'Blue Deckle'
- 'Beni-gaku' (L)	CExl CFil CLAP CMil CRos ECre LRHS MAsh NBro NLar SCob
- 'Beni-temari'	NBro
- 'Beni-yama' (L) ♀H5	CFil CMil GQui
- 'Besshi-temari'	CFil
- 'Bleuet' **new**	LRHS
- 'Blue Billow' (L)	NBro NLar
- Blueberry Cheesecake	see *H. serrata* Tuff Stuff
§ - 'Bluebird' (L) ♀H5	Widely available
- 'Cap Sizun'	LRHS SChF WPGP
- 'Chiba Cherry-lips'	ESwi WCru
- 'Chiri-san Sue' (d)	CFil WCru
- 'Crûg Bicolor' (L)	WCru
- 'Crûg Cobalt' (L)	ESwi WCru
- 'Crûg Sō Cool' (L) **new**	WCru
- 'Diadem' (L) ♀H5	CAbb CBot CDoC CExl CLAP CMil EPfP GQui LRHS NBro SHyH
- dwarf white-flowered (L)	WCru
- 'Forget Me Not'	GQui NBro
- 'Fuji Snowstorm' (v)	CMil
- 'Fuji Waterfall'	see *H. serrata* 'Fuji-no-taki'
§ - 'Fuji-no-taki' (L/d) ♀H5	CAbP CBot CMil ELon ESwi LLHF NCGa WPGP WWFP
- 'Golden Showers' (L)	NBro
- 'Golden Sunlight'^{PBR} (L)	SGol SWvt
- 'Graciosa' (L)	LLHF LRHS WPat
- 'Grayswood' (L) ♀H5	CBcs CDul CExl CLAP CMac CRos CSBt EPfP GGal GQui LRHS MAsh MRav NBro SCob SDix SGol SHyH SLim SPer SSpi WKif WPGP
- 'Hakucho' (L/d)	EBee NBro WPGP
- 'Hallasan' misapplied	see *H. serrata* 'Maiko', 'Spreading Beauty'
- 'Hallasan' ambig.	CMil
- 'Hallasan' R. & J. de Belder (L)	CMil WPGP
- 'Hime-benigaku' (L)	CMil MAsh WFar
- 'Impératrice Eugénie' (L)	GQui NLar
- 'Intermedia' (L)	CExl NBro
- 'Isusai-jaku' (L)	GQui
- 'Kiyosumi' (L) ♀H5	CChe CDoC CExl CFil CLAP CMil ECre ELon EPfP GGal GQui LRHS NBir NLar SAko SBrt SHyH WBor WCot WCru WPGP WPat
- 'Klaveren'	see *H. macrophylla* 'Klaveren'
- 'Kurenai' (L)	CMil NBro NLar SChF WPGP
- 'Kurohime' (L)	CDoC CMil NBro WPGP
- 'Macrosepala' (L)	CDoC WPGP
§ - 'Maiko' (L)	IArd SAko
- 'Midori' (L)	CExl
- 'Mikata Yae'	CMil WPGP
- 'Miranda' (L) ♀H5	CDoC CExl CLAP CMil EPfP LRHS MAsh NBro NLar SAko SDys SHyH SSpi WFar
- 'Miyama-yae-murasaki' (L/d) ♀H5	CAbP CExl CFil CLAP CMil ESwi WPGP
- 'Momo-beni-yama'	CMil NBro
- 'Mont Aso'	CBot CMil NLar
- 'Niji' (L)	WPGP
- 'Odoriko-amacha'	EBee SChF WPGP
- 'Otsu-hime'	NLar
- 'Panachée' (L/v)	SHyH

- 'Pretty Maiden' see *H. serrata* 'Shichidanka'
§ - 'Prolifera' (L/d) CMil LLHF WPat
- 'Pulchella' see *H. serrata* 'Prolifera'
- 'Ramis Pictis' (L) CBcs GQui NBro NLar
- 'Rosalba' (L) ♀H5 CExl CLAP ECre GGal IVic NBro WSHC
- 'Santiago'PBR (L) CDoC EPfP WCot
- 'Sapphirine' (L) GQui
- 'Sekka' WPGP
§ - 'Shichidanka' (L/d) CBot CFil CLAP EBee EPfP LLHF LRHS NBro WPat
- 'Shichidanka-nishiki' (L/d/v) CDoC CExl CLAP ECre ESwi GQui SHyH
- 'Shinonome' (L/d) CExl CMil GQui
- 'Shirofuji' (L/d) ♀H5 CFil CLAP CMil EWld LLHF MAsh WPGP WPat
- 'Shiro-gaku' (L) CMil MAsh NBro NLar
- 'Shiro-maiko' WPGP
- 'Shirotae' (L/d) CExl CFil CMil WPGP
- 'Shōjō' ♀H5 CMil LRHS NBro WPGP WPat
§ - 'Spreading Beauty' (L) CMil WPGP
- 'Suzukayama-yama' EBee SChF WPGP
§ - var. ***thunbergii*** (L) GQui
* - - 'Plena' (L/d) GQui WCru
- 'Tiara' (L) ♀H5 CAbb CDoC CDul CExl CFil CLAP CMil EPfP GGGa GGal IVic LRHS LSRN MAsh NBir NBro NLar SDix SDys SHyH SLim WPGP WPat
- 'Tosa-no-akatsuki' CFil
§ - Tuff Stuff = 'Mak20' (L) LLHF LRHS SCob SPoG
- 'Veerle' (L) NBro NLar
- 'Woodlander' (L) WPat
- 'Yae-no-amacha' (L/d) CBcs CExl NBro NLar
- subsp. ***yezoensis*** CMil GQui NLar
- - 'Hime-gaku' CMil
§ ***serratifolia*** CExl EPfP IArd IDee SSpi SSta WPGP
- HCM 98056 WCru
sikokiana CLAP
- B&SWJ 5035 WCru
- B&SWJ 5855 WCru
- B&SWJ 11174 WCru
- B&SWJ 11381 WCru
'Silver Slipper' see *H. macrophylla* 'Ayesha'
tiliifolia see *H. anomala* subsp. *petiolaris* var. *ovalifolia*
villosa see *H. aspera* Villosa Group
xanthoneura see *H. heteromalla*
'Zambia' WCot
aff. ***zhewanensis*** MF 93117 WCru

Hydrangea × Dichroa see × *Didrangea*

Hydrastis (*Ranunculaceae*)

canadensis CArn CEvo GPoy LEdu

Hydrocharis (*Hydrocharitaceae*)

morsus-ranae CBen CHab CWat EHon EWay MSKA MWts NPer SWat WPnP

Hydrocleys (*Alismataceae*)

nymphoides LLWG XBlo

Hydrocotyle (*Araliaceae*)

asiatica see *Centella asiatica*
sibthorpioides 'Crystal Confetti' (v) LLWG
vulgaris CWat

Hydrophyllum (*Boraginaceae*)

canadense IMou
'Spring Silver' SKHP
virginianum LEdu WHal

Hylomecon (*Papaveraceae*)

hylomeconoides EWld WCru WWEG
§ ***japonica*** CAby CLAP EBee ECho ELan EWld GBuc GCra GEdr GKev IMou LEdu LRHS MAvo NBir NQui NRya WCru WPGP WThu

Hylotelephium see *Sedum*

Hymenanthera see *Melicytus*

Hymenocallis (*Amaryllidaceae*)

'Advance' LAma
× ***festalis*** ♀H1c LAma LCro LOPS LTro SDeJ SPav WCot
- 'Zwanenburg' CGrW
harrisiana CTca SDeJ
'Sulphur Queen' ♀H1c CGrW LTro SDeJ SPav

Hymenolepis (*Asteraceae*)

parviflora see *Athanasia parviflora*

Hymenosporum (*Pittosporaceae*)

flavum EShb EUJe MOWG

Hymenoxys (*Asteraceae*)

grandiflora see *Tetraneuris grandiflora*
§ ***hoopesii*** CBod CMac COtt EBee ELan EPfP GMaP LRHS MPie NBir NLar NPri SCob SDix SPer SRms WCot WFar WHar WMnd WWEG XLum

Hyophorbe (*Arecaceae*)

lagenicaulis LPal
verschaffeltii LPal

Hyoscyamus (*Solanaceae*)

niger GPoy MNHC SRms WSFF

Hypericum ✿ (*Hypericaceae*)

CC 4131 CExl
CC 4544 CExl
aegypticum ECho MHer SBrt SIgm SPlb WAbe WThu
androsaemum CArn ECha ELan GAbr MHer MMuc MSwo NPer SEND WFar WHfH WMoo WOut
§ - 'Albury Purple' ELan EShb NLar WMoo XLum
- 'Autumn Blaze' CBcs MBri
- 'Excellent Flair' MBri NLar
- 'Golden Flair' MMuc
§ - f. ***variegatum*** 'Mrs Gladis Brabazon' (v) EShb NBir WCot
athoum WIce WThu
balearicum SBrt SEND WAbe XSen
bellum EBee GCal SLon
buckleyi WAbe
calycinum CBcs CBod CDul CMac COtt CTri ECrN ELan ELon EPfP LAst LBuc MGos MRav NWea SCob SEND SGol SPer SWvt WFar WMoo XLum
- 'Brigadoon' ♀H5 LRHS MAsh SGol

- 'Senior'	LAst
cerastioides	CTri CWib ECho EDAr EWes GCrg MMuc NGdn SIgm SRms WAbe
coris	EWes SRms
cuneatum	see *H. pallens*
× ***cyathiflorum*** 'Gold Cup'	CMac LRHS MAsh
× ***dummeri*** 'Peter Dummer'	EAEE LAst NLar
'Eastleigh Gold'	CMac
'Elite Baby Green'	EPfP
'Elite Mayor'	EPfP
'Elite Sweet Lion'	EPfP
elodes	CWat LLWG MWLS
forrestii 🏆H5	MMuc SEND
fragile misapplied	see *H. olympicum* f. *minus*
Golden Beacon = 'Wilhyp' PBR 🏆H5	CBod CSpe EBee ESwi LHop LLWG LRHS LSou LSun MHer MNrw NEgg NLar NWad SBod SEND SPad SPoG WCot
grandiflorum	see *H. kouytchense*
grandifolium	EDAr
henryi L 753	SRms
- subsp. ***hancockii***	CEvo
- - NJM 10.092	WPGP
'Hidcote'	see *H.* × *hidcoteense* 'Hidcote'
§ × ***hidcoteense*** 'Hidcote' 🏆H5	Widely available
- 'Hidcote Variegated' (v)	LRHS MAsh SLim SRms
hirsutum	CHab NMir
(Hypearls Series) Hypearls Annelies	LRHS
- Hypearls Ella	LRHS
- Hypearls Jacqueline	LRHS
imbricatum **new**	LLHF
× ***inodorum*** 'Albury Purple'	see *H. androsaemum* 'Albury Purple'
- 'Autumn Surprise' PBR	ELon NEgg NWad
- 'Dream'	NLar
- 'Elstead'	ECtt ELan EPfP MRav NLar NWad NWea
- Magical Cherry = 'Kolmcherrip' PBR	ELan EPfP SCob
- Magical Limelight = 'Kolmalimeli' PBR	ELan
- Magical Pumpkin = 'Kolmapuki' **new**	LCro LOPS
- Magical Sunshine = 'Kolmasun' PBR	LRHS
- Magical Universe = 'Kolmuni' **new**	LCro SCob
- Magical White Fall = 'Kolmwhifa' PBR	SCob
- Magical White = 'Kolmawhi' PBR	ELan EPfP SCob SPoG
- 'Rheingold'	MAsh
- 'Ysella'	MRav
interior **new**	CEvo
japonicum	ECho
kalmianum	SBrt WCot
kamtschaticum	XLum
§ ***kouytchense*** 🏆H5	CDul EPfP EWes GQui LRHS MAsh MMuc MRav SEND SPoG SWvt WCFE WCot WPat
lancasteri	EPfP LRHS SPoG
leschenaultii misapplied	see *H.* 'Rowallane'
'Little Misstery'	LBuc SPoG
maclarenii	EWes
Magical Beauty = 'Kolmbeau' PBR	ELon EPfP LRHS MJak NLar SCob SPoG
Magical Pink = 'Kolmpin' **new**	SCob
Magical Red = 'Kolmred' PBR	EPfP MJak NLar SCob SPoG
Miracle Attraction = 'Alldiablo' PBR	EBee LRHS NLar SHil
Miracle Blizz = 'Allblizz' **new**	EBee LRHS
Miracle Blossom = 'Allblossom' PBR **new**	LRHS
Miracle Fantasy = 'Hymirfan'	NLar
Miracle Summer = 'Hymirsum'	EPfP LRHS NLar SHil
Miracle Wonder = 'Hymirwon'	LRHS NLar SHil
× ***moserianum*** 🏆H5	CDul CMac EAEE LRHS MGos MJak NPer SCob SHil SLon SPer SRms WFar
- 'Daybreak'	LBMP LRHS MAsh SPoG WRHF
§ - 'Tricolor' (v)	Widely available
- 'Variegatum'	see *H.* × *moserianum* 'Tricolor'
'Mrs Brabazon'	see *H. androsaemum* f. *variegatum* 'Mrs Gladis Brabazon'
oblongifolium	CExl NLar
olympicum 🏆H5	CArn CTri EBee ECha ECho ELan EPot GAbr GJos LRHS MAsh MWat SCob SEND SPer SRms SWvt WIce WSHC XLum XSen
- 'Grandiflorum'	see *H. olympicum* f. *uniflorum*
§ - f. ***minus***	CTri ECho ECtt NGdn SPlb SRms WHrl
§ - - 'Sulphureum'	CBod ECho ELon EWes LRHS MNHC NBir SPer SRms SWvt WCFE
- - 'Variegatum' (v)	EWes NBir SPoG SWvt
§ - f. ***uniflorum***	EAJP ECho NBro NRya
- - 'Citrinum' 🏆H5	CMea CSpe ECha ECtt EPfP GBuc MGil MMuc MRav NLar SEND SIgm SRot WAbe WCot WHoo WKif XSen
orientale	EWes GLog
§ ***pallens***	ECho WAbe
perforatum	CArn CBod CHab CHby ENfk EPfP GPoy IRos MHer MMuc MNHC NLar NMir SEND SIde SRms WHer WHfH WMoo WSFF
polyphyllum misapplied	see *H. olympicum* f. *minus*
- 'Citrinum'	see *H. olympicum* f. *minus* 'Sulphureum'
- 'Grandiflorum'	see *H. olympicum* f. *uniflorum*
prolificum	MMHG WCFE
pulchrum	SBrt
quadrangulum L.	see *H. tetrapterum*
reptans misapplied	see *H. olympicum* f. *minus*
reptans Hook.f. & Thomson ex Dyer	CMea EWes NWad SBrt
revolutum PAB 3861	LEdu WPGP
§ 'Rowallane' 🏆H4	CBot CTri GCal LRHS NLar SDix SSpi SWvt
subsessile	CExl
'Sungold'	see *H. kouytchense*
'Sweet Lion'	CMac
§ ***tetrapterum***	CBod CWld LLWG
trichocaulon	ECho EWes ITim
uralum	SLim
- HWJ 520	WCru
- KR 10691 **new**	WPGP

Hypocalyptus (*Papilionaceae*)

sophoroides	SPlb

Hypochaeris (*Asteraceae*)

radicata	CHab NMir

Hypocyrta see *Nematanthus*

Hypoestes (*Acanthaceae*)

aristata	CExl EShb SVen

Hypolepis (*Dennstaedtiaceae*)

millefolium	EBee LEdu

Hypoxis (*Hypoxidaceae*)

hemerocallidea from Bloemfontein	ECho
hirsuta	ECho GKev
hygrometrica	ECho ECou GKev IBal WThu
krebsii	ECho
obtusa from Harrismith, South Africa	ECho
parvula	XLum
- var. ***albiflora***	GKev
§ - - 'Hebron Farm Biscuit'	CBro CTal ECho EWes GEdr NWad WAbe WBla WFar
- pink-flowered	GKev
rigidula from Harrismith	ECho
villosa	ECho

Hypoxis × *Rhodohypoxis* see × *Rhodoxis*

H. parvula × ***R. baurii***	see × *Rhodoxis hybrida*

Hypsela (*Campanulaceae*)

longiflora	see *H. reniformis*
§ ***reniformis***	ECho GCrg ITim LLWG MSCN SBod

Hyssopus ✿ (*Lamiaceae*)

from Georgia	EWes
officinalis	Widely available
- f. ***albus***	CLau ECha ENfk EPfP GPoy MHer MNHC SPer SPlb SRms WHfH WJek XLum XSen
- subsp. ***aristatus***	CBod CLau EBee ELon ENfk EPfP GPoy IMou MHer MNHC SPoG WHoo WJek XLum XSen
- subsp. ***officinalis*** **new**	XSen
- 'Roseus'	CLau CWld ECha ENfk EPfP GPoy MHer MHol MNHC SIde SPer SPoG WJek XLum XSen
- white-flowered	CBod

Hystrix (*Poaceae*)

patula	CKno EHoe EPPr EShb GCal LLWP MBel MNrw SPlb XLum

I

Iberis (*Brassicaceae*)

Absolutely Amethyst = 'Ib2401'	ECtt ELon GBin LHop LRHS WHlf WIce
candolleana	see *I. pruitii* Candolleana Group
commutata	see *I. sempervirens*
gibraltarica	CSpe ECho SRms
- 'Betty Swainson' 🏆H4	CSpe EWTr SPhx
jordanii	see *I. pruitii*
'Masterpiece'PBR	ECtt WHlf
'Pink Ice'	ECtt MCot WHlf
§ ***pruitii***	CTal NSla WAbe
§ - Candolleana Group	ECho EPot
saxatilis	ECho ITim LHop LRHS SIgm WThu
semperflorens	WCFE
§ ***sempervirens***	CHVG CMea CTri CWib ECho ELan EPfP IFoB LAst MAsh MCot MSCN MWat NBro SEND SRms WBod WCFE WHar
- 'Appen-Etz' **new**	LRHS MAvo NWad
- 'Compacta'	ECho
- 'Elfenreigen'	GCal
- 'Fischbeck'	NPri SRot
- 'Golden Candy'	CTri EHoe GEdr MAvo SPoG WCot
- 'Little Gem'	see *I. sempervirens* 'Weisser Zwerg'
- 'Pygmaea'	CTal ECho
- Schneeflocke	see *I. sempervirens* 'Snowflake'
- 'Snow Cushion'	ECho EPfP LSun WHoo
§ - 'Snowflake' 🏆H5	CBar CWCL ECho EPfP EPot GBin GMaP IFoB LHop LPal MBel MWat NPri SPer SPoG SWvt WIce WRHF XLum
§ - 'Weisser Zwerg'	CMea ECha ECho ECtt ELan GCrg GMaP MRav SRms WThu
'Snowball' **new**	CBod MHol
umbellata	ECrN

Ichthyoselmis (*Papaveraceae*)

§ ***macrantha***	EPfP EPot GCra IMou LHop WCru WSHC

Idesia (*Salicaceae*)

polycarpa	CBcs CDul CMCN EBee EBtc EPfP IVic LHop NLar SChF WPGP
- CWJ 12837	WCru

Ilex ✿ (*Aquifoliaceae*)

sp.	ETod
NJM 10.072 **new**	WPGP
§ × ***altaclerensis*** 'Belgica Aurea' (f/v) 🏆H6	CBcs CDoC CJun CTho EPfP MBri MSwo NEgg NHol
- 'Camelliifolia' (f) 🏆H6	CBcs CTho MBlu NEgg SGol
- 'Camelliifolia Variegata' (f/v)	CMac
- 'Golden King' (f/v) 🏆H6	Widely available
- 'Hendersonii' (f)	NEgg
- 'Hodginsii' (m)	CTri
- 'James G. Esson' (f)	CRos LRHS SHil
- 'Lady Valerie' (f/v)	SAko
- 'Lawsoniana' (f/v) 🏆H6	CDoC CDul CJun CMac CRos CSBt CTri EHoe ELan EPfP LRHS MAsh MBlu MJak MMuc NEgg NHol NLar NWea SEND SGol SHil SLim SLon SPer SPoG SRms WHar WPat
- 'Maderensis' (m)	CBcs
- 'Purple Shaft' (f)	CMCN MRav
- 'Ripley Gold' (f/v)	CJun CLnd CMac LRHS MAsh MBri MRav NWea
- 'Silver Sentinel'	see *I.* × *altaclerensis* 'Belgica Aurea'
- 'W.J. Bean' (f)	CJun
- 'Wilsonii' (f)	NEgg NLar NWea
aquifolium 🏆H6	Widely available
- 'Alaska' (f) 🏆H6	CCVT CDoC CDul CJun CMCN CRos EPfP LBuc LPar LRHS MAsh MBri NLar NWea SAko SGol SHil SWvt WFar WMat
- 'Amber' (f) 🏆H6	CJun CTri NLar NWea
- 'Angustifolia' (f)	CJun CRos LRHS WCFE

- 'Angustifolia' (m or f) EPfP MAsh
§ - 'Argentea Marginata' (f/v) ♀H6 Widely available
§ - 'Argentea Marginata Pendula' (f/v) ♀H6 CDoC CMac CTri ELan EPfP LRHS MAsh SPer SRms WFar WPat
- 'Argentea Pendula' see *I. aquifolium* 'Argentea Marginata Pendula'
- 'Argentea Variegata' see *I. aquifolium* 'Argentea Marginata'
- 'Atlas' (m) CBcs LBuc SWvt
- 'Aurea Marginata' (f/v) CLnd CMac EPfP LBuc MGos NWea SCob SEWo WCFE WHar WMat WPat
- 'Aurea Marginata Pendula' (f/v) CDoC WPat
- 'Aurea Regina' see *I. aquifolium* 'Golden Queen'
- 'Aureomaculata' **new** NEgg
- 'Aureovariegata Pendula' see *I. aquifolium* 'Weeping Golden Milkmaid'
- 'Aurifodina' (f) CJun NEgg
- 'Bacciflava' (f) ♀H6 CBcs CDoC CDul CJun CMac CTho CTri CWib EBee ELan ELon EPfP IArd MBlu MGos MJak MRav NEgg NLar NWea SAko SLim SPer SRms SWvt WCFE WFar
- 'Crassifolia' (f) CWib SMad
- 'Elegantissima' (m/v) CJun
- 'Fastigiata Sartori' NLar
- 'Ferox' (m) CJun CRos ELan EPfP LRHS NEgg NLar
- 'Ferox Argentea' (m/v) ♀H6 Widely available
- 'Ferox Aurea' (m/v) CDoC CJun CRos CWib ELan ELon LRHS MAsh NEgg
§ - 'Flavescens' (f) MBlu NEgg
- 'Fructu Luteo' (f) WHar
- 'Glanzzwerg' **new** SAko
- 'Gold Flash' (f/v) LRHS NLar
- 'Golden Milkboy' (m/v) CLnd CMac ELan SGol WPat
§ - 'Golden Queen' (m/v) ♀H6 CDoC CWib MGos NBir SRms WPat
- 'Golden Tears' (f/v) CJun
- 'Golden van Tol' (f/v) CBcs CDoC CJun CSBt CTri ELan ELon EPfP ETod LRHS MAsh MBlu MGos MSwo NEgg NLar SCoo SGol SPer SRms WFar
- 'Green Minaret' IVic SAko
- 'Handsworth New Silver' (f/v) ♀H6 Widely available
- 'Harpune' (f) IArd SAko
§ - 'Hascombensis' CDoC LHop NWea
- 'Hastata' (m) CWib IArd IDee
- Heckenzwerg = 'Hachzwerg'PBR **new** SAko
- 'Ingramii' (m/v) CJun
- 'J.C. van Tol' (f) ♀H6 Widely available
- 'Latispina' (f) CJun
- 'Lichtenthalii' (f) CJun IArd IVic NEgg
- 'Madame Briot' (f/v) ♀H6 Widely available
- 'Marijo' LRHS SHil
- 'Monstrosa' (m) CJun
- moonlight holly see *I. aquifolium* 'Flavescens'
- 'Myrtifolia' (f) NEgg SWvt
- 'Myrtifolia' (m) CMac ELan EPfP MGos NLar SMad
- 'Myrtifolia Aurea' (m/v) NWea SWvt
- 'Myrtifolia Aurea Maculata' (m/v) CDoC CJun CTri ELan LRHS MAsh MBri MRav NEgg NWea SPoG SWvt WPat
- 'Northern Lights' (v) EPfP LRHS MSwo
- 'Pendula' (f) MRav NWea
- 'Pendula Mediopicta' see *I. aquifolium* 'Weeping Golden Milkmaid'
- 'Pyramidalis' (f) ♀H6 CBcs CDoC CDul CMac CRos CTri ELan LRHS MAsh MBri MGos MJak NLar NWea SCob SGol SHil SPer SRms WFar
- 'Pyramidalis Aureomarginata' (f/v) NLar
- 'Pyramidalis Fructu Luteo' (f) ♀H6 MAsh MBri
- 'Recurva' (m) CJun CMac
- 'Rubricaulis Aurea' (f/v) NEgg NLar
- 'Scotica' (f) NWea
- Siberia = 'Limsi'PBR (f) IVic NLar
- 'Silver King' see *I. aquifolium* 'Silver Queen'
- 'Silver Milkboy' (f/v) ELan EPfP MBlu WFar
- 'Silver Milkmaid' (f/v) CDoC CJun LRHS MAsh MJak MMuc NEgg SLim SWvt
§ - 'Silver Queen' (m/v) ♀H6 CBcs CCVT CDoC CDul CLnd CWSG CWib EHoe EPfP LRHS MAsh MBri MGos MJak MRav MSwo NBir NEgg NHol NLar NPri NWea SAko SLim SLon SPer SRGP SWvt WHar WMat
- 'Silver Sentinel' see *I.* × *altaclerensis* 'Belgica Aurea'
- 'Silver van Tol' (f/v) CDoC CJun CLnd CWSG EBee ELan EPfP MAsh NEgg NLar NPer NWea SPer
- 'Somerset Cream' (f/v) CJun CTri CWib
- 'Sterntaler' IVic SAko
§ - 'Weeping Golden Milkmaid' (f/v) WPat
- 'White Cream' (m/v) IVic SAko
- 'Wichtel' IVic
- 'Yellow Star' (f/v) IVic
× ***aquipernyi*** LPar
- Dragon Lady = 'Meschick' (f) ♀H6 CDoC CJun IArd LPar NEgg
- 'San Jose' (f) CJun
× ***attenuata*** 'Sunny Foster' (f/v) CDoC CMCN EPfP MAsh SAko
× ***beanii*** CJun
§ ***bioritsensis*** CMCN CTri
'Brilliant' (f) NEgg
cassine L. CMCN
'Clusterberry' (f) CJun NEgg
colchica CMCN IDee SAko
cornuta EPfP LPar
- B&SWJ 8756 WCru
- 'Anicet Delcambre' (f) CJun
- 'Burfordii' (f) NLar
§ - 'Dazzler' (f) CJun
- 'Ira S. Nelson' (f) CJun IArd SAko
- 'O. Spring' (f/v) CJun
crenata CMCN CTal CTri EPfP GCra LPar MGos NBes NHol NWea SCob STrG SVic WFar
* - 'Akagi' WFar
- 'Aureovariegata' see *I. crenata* 'Variegata'
- 'Convexa' (f) ♀H6 CDul CJun CTal EAEE EPfP LPar MAsh MRav NEgg NWea SCob SPer WMoo WPat
- 'Convexed Gold' (f/v) LRHS MBri NLar NWad SPoG WFar
- Dark Green = 'Icoprins11'PBR NWea SPer SVic
- 'Dwarf Pagoda' (f) IVic SAko
- Fastigiata Group CRos SCob

	- - 'Fastigiata' (f) 🏆H6	CDoC EPfP LRHS MAsh MBri MGos NLar SBod SPer SPoG
	- - 'Sky Pencil' (f)	CMCN
	- 'Fructu Luteo'	see *I. crenata* f. *watanabeana*
*	- 'Glory Gem' (f)	CBcs
	- 'Golden Gem' (f/v) 🏆H6	CDoC CJun CMac CRos CSBt CTri ELan ELon EPfP IVic LRHS MAsh MGos MSwo NWea SGol SHil SPer SPoG SWvt WFar WPat WThu
	- 'Green Hedger' 🏆H6	EPfP LBuc LHop LPar MGos
	- 'Helleri' (f)	WPat
	- 'Kinme'	LPal LPar
	- 'Korean Gem'	CTal
	- 'Luteovariegata'	see *I. crenata* 'Variegata'
	- 'Mariesii' (f)	CMac MBlu SAko
I	- 'Pyramidalis' (f)	CMac MRav NWea
	- 'Robert Culpepper' (m)	CTal
§	- 'Shiro-fukurin' (f/v)	CMCN CRos ELan EPfP LRHS SLon
	- 'Snowflake'	see *I. crenata* 'Shiro-fukurin'
	- 'Stokes' (m)	MSwo NLar
§	- 'Variegata' (v)	CMCN CMac CRos EPfP LRHS NLar
§	- f. ***watanabeana*** (f)	WGwG
	'Dazzler'	see *I. cornuta* 'Dazzler'
	dimorphophylla	CMac
	dipyrena	ESwi SAko
	'Doctor Kassab' (f)	CMCN
	'Elegance' (f)	MBlu WFar
	glabra	CJun
	- f. ***leucocarpa*** 'Snow White' (f)	CJun
	'Good Taste' (f)	CJun WFar
	hascombensis	see *I. aquifolium* 'Hascombensis'
	'Hohman' **new**	CJun
	'Indian Chief' (f)	CJun
	× ***koehneana***	CDul
	- 'Chestnut Leaf' (f) 🏆H5	CDoC CJun CLnd CMCN EBtc EWTr LRHS MRav NEgg NLar SSta WFar WGrn
	laevigata	CMCN
	latifolia	CJun CMCN NLar
*	'Little Diamond'	LSRN
	'Lydia Morris' (f)	CSam
	'Mary Nell' (f)	CJun
	× ***meserveae*** Blue Angel = 'Conang' (f)	CBcs CDoC CDul CMac CWib ELan EPfP IFoB LRHS MBri MMuc MRav NEgg NLar NWea SPer SPoG SRms WFar
	- Blue Bunny = 'Meseal' (f)	IVic SAko
	- 'Blue Girl' (f)	CTri
	- Blue Maid = 'Mesid' (f)	LPar MGos NEgg NLar STrG
	- Blue Prince = 'Conablu' (m) 🏆H6	CBcs CDoC CDul CLnd CMCN CMac ELan LBuc LRHS MBlu MJak NEgg NHol NLar NWea SCob SLim SPer SPoG WFar
	- Blue Princess = 'Conapri' (f) 🏆H6	CBcs CDul CMCN CMac ELan EPfP LBuc LRHS MBlu MGos MJak MRav NEgg NLar NWea SCob SCoo SLim SPer SPoG WFar
	- Castle Spire = 'Hachfee' ^{PBR}	SLim WFar
	- Castle Wall = 'Hecken Star' ^{PBR}	IVic LRHS SLim WFar
	- 'Heckenpracht' ^{PBR}	IVic WFar
	- 'Little Gloss' **new**	SAko
	- Little Rascal = 'Mondo' (m)	LRHS
	myrtifolia	MAsh MRav NHol
	'Nellie R. Stevens' (f)	CCVT CDoC CJun EBee ECrN ELan EPfP LPar NLar NWea SCob SEWo WMat
	opaca	CMCN
	perado **new**	NEgg
	- subsp. ***azorica***	CFil WPGP
	- - B&SWJ 12526	WCru
	- subsp. ***perado***	CBcs
	- subsp. ***platyphylla***	CBcs CMCN MBlu
	pernyi	CJun CMCN CMac CTri LPar LRHS MAsh
	- var. ***veitchii***	see *I. bioritsensis*
	rotunda	LEdu
	rugosa	CMCN
	'September Gem' (f)	CJun CMCN NEgg
	serrata	CMac CMen
	- 'Koshobai'	CMen
	- 'Leucocarpa'	CMac CMen
	suaveolens	CMCN
	sugerokii	WCru
	var. ***brevipedunculata*** B&SWJ 10856	
	'Tanager' (f) **new**	CJun
	triflora var. ***kanehirae***	CDul NLar
	verticillata	CMCN EBee LRHS WFar
	- (f)	CBcs EBtc ELon EPfP MMHG NLar NWea
	- (m)	EBtc ELon EPfP MMHG NLar NWea
	- f. ***chrysocarpa*** (f)	NLar
	- 'Maryland Beauty' (f)	CJun NLar
	- 'Southern Gentleman' (m)	CJun MBlu NLar
	- 'Winter Gold' (f)	CJun MBlu
	- 'Winter Red' (f)	CJun CMCN MBlu
	vomitoria	CMCN EBtc
	'William Cowgill' (f)	CJun
	yunnanensis	GQui IArd

Iliamna see *Sphaeralcea*

Illicium (*Schisandraceae*)

anisatum	CBcs CDoC CExl CFil CMac EBee EPfP NLar WPGP WPat WSHC
floridanum	CBcs CPne EPfP LEdu SBrt SSpi WPat
- f. ***album***	EPfP
- 'Halley's Comet'	CExl CFil NLar
aff. ***griffithii***	WCru
WWJ 11911 **new**	
- WWJ 11971 **new**	WCru
- WWJ 11974	WCru
henryi	CDoC CExl CWib EBee EPfP IVic NLar SSpi WPGP WSHC
aff. ***henryi***	CBcs
lanceolatum	CExl CFil
- KWJ 12245	WCru
majus	CFil
- WWJ 11919	WCru
aff. ***majus***	WCru
- WWJ 12017	WCru
mexicanum	CExl CFil
oligandrum	CExl NLar WPGP
parviflorum	CFil
simonsii	CExl CFil IVic MBlu WPGP
- BWJ 8024	WCru
'Woodland Ruby'	NLar WPGP

Ilysanthes see *Lindernia*

Impatiens ✿ (*Balsaminaceae*)

CC 4980	CExl
DJHC 98415	WCru WPGP

	apiculata	EBee GCal
	arguta	CCon CDes CExl CLAP CSam CSpe EShb EWld GCal SBrt WBor WPGP
	- 'Alba'	CExl CSpe
	auricoma × bicaudata	CDes CDoC MPie WDib
	balfourii	CPla
	bicaudata	CSpe SDix SPlb
	ernstii	CExl
	flanaganae	CFil WPGP
	forrestii	CDes CLAP
	gomphophylla	CCon CDes CFil
	hawkeri Divine Series **new**	LAst
	keilii	WDib
	kerriae B&SWJ 7219	WCru
	kilimanjari subsp. ***kilimanjari***	CCon CDoC CSpe MPie WCot
	kilimanjari* × *pseudoviola	CDes CDoC CSpe MPie WDib
	langbianensis HWJ 1054	WCru
	(LaTina Series) LaTina Appleblossum = 'Kleni10120'	LAst
	- LaTina Electric Purple = 'Kleni10119'^{PBR}	LAst
	- LaTina Red Orange = 'Kleni10123'	LAst
	'Linda's White'	WCot
	'Little Brother Montgomery'	CHll
	macrophylla B&SWJ 10157	WCru
	namchabarwensis	CSpe GCal WPGP
	niamniamensis 🏆H1b	CHll EBak EShb WDib
	- 'Congo Cockatoo'	CDTJ CDoC NPer SRms
	- 'Golden Cockatoo' (v)	CDTJ CHll EBak EShb
	noli-tangere	WSFF
	omeiana	CCon CDoC CLAP CMil CSam CSpe EBee EPPr ESwi EUJe EWld GCal GEdr LEdu MNrw MSCN NLar SBch WBod WCru WFar WPGP WPtf
	- DJHC 98492	CDes WCru
	- 'Ice Storm'	CDes EBee GCal GEdr LEdu NLar WCot WCru WPGP
	- 'Pink Nerves' **new**	CDes
	- variegated (v)	GEdr
	parasitica	WDib
	qingchengshanica 'Emei Dawn'	CDes CExl GCal WCru
	platypetala B&SWJ 9722	WCru
	puberula	CCon CDoC CSam
	- HWJK 2063	CDes EBee SBrt WCru WPGP
	repens 🏆H1c	CDoC WDib
	rothii	CCon CDes EBee GCal
	scabrida	CPla CSpe NSti
§	'Secret Love'	WDib
	sodenii 🏆H1c	CDTJ CDoC CHll CSpe EShb GCal SDix WDib
	- 'Madonna' **new**	CSpe
	- 'Robert the Red' **new**	CSpe
	stenantha	CCon CDes SBrt
	tinctoria	CAby CCon CDoC CExl CFil CHll CSpe EBee GCal GCra GGal SDix WBod
	- from Cherangani, Kenya	EBee GCal
	- subsp. ***tinctoria***	IFro
	tuberosa	CDoC WDib
	ugandensis	GCal
	uniflora	CCon EBee GCal SBrt WPGP
	Velvetea	see *I.* 'Secret Love'
	walleriana DeZire Series	NPri
	- - 'DeZire Lavender Splash'	LAst
	- (Musica Series) 'Musica Bicolor Cherry' (d)	LAst
	- - 'Musica Pink Aroma' (d)	LAst
	- - 'Musica Salmon' (d)	LAst

Imperata (*Poaceae*)

	cylindrica	CMen XLum
	- 'Red Baron'	see *I. cylindrica* 'Rubra'
§	- 'Rubra'	Widely available

Incarvillea (*Bignoniaceae*)

	arguta	LLHF SGSe XLum
	brevipes	see *I. mairei*
	compacta	EBee GKev LLHF
	- BWJ 7620	WCru
	delavayi	Widely available
	- 'Alba'	see *I. delavayi* 'Snowtop'
	- 'Bees' Pink'	CAby EPfP GBuc LRHS
§	- 'Snowtop'	CAby CBct COtt EBee ELan EPfP EPot GKev GMaP IBoy LRHS NBir SDeJ SGSe SGol SPer SWvt WCot
	grandiflora	EBee GKev
	himalayensis 'Frank Ludlow'	EBee GKev
	lutea	EBee GKev
§	***mairei***	CTsd ECho GKev LRHS NLar
	- var. ***mairei***	GBuc
	- - f. ***multifoliata***	see *I. zhongdianensis*
	- white-flowered **new**	GKev
	olgae	EBee EPfP
	przewalskii	GKev
	sinensis	EBee
	'Snowdrop' **new**	MSCN
	younghusbandii	EBee GKev
§	***zhongdianensis***	CFis EBee ECho EPot GKev LLHF SBrt SPhx
	- ACE 1600	GBuc
	- BWJ 7692	WCru
	- BWJ 7978	WCru
	- white-flowered	EBee

Indigofera (*Papilionaceae*)

	amblyantha	CBcs CExl CWSG EPfP EWTr LRHS MAsh MBlu MNHC NLar SEND SKHP SPlb SSpi WSHC
	aff. ***amblyantha***	LSou
	balfouriana BWJ 7851	WCru
	cassioides	WCru
	'Claret Cascade' 🏆H5 **new**	SKHP WSHC
	dielsiana	EBee ELan EPfP LRHS WPGP
	'Dosua'	SEND
	frutescens	CTre
	gerardiana	see *I. heterantha*
	hancockii	CExl EBee EPfP SChF SKHP WPGP WSHC
	hebepetala	CHid EBee EPfP SBrt SKHP WPGP WSHC
§	***heterantha*** 🏆H5	Widely available
	himalayensis	CExl CMHG EBee SKHP
	- Yu 10941	CExl WPGP
	- 'Silk Road'	ELan EPfP GKev LCro LRHS MBlu MBri MGos NLar SHil SKHP SPoG WSHC

howellii CExl CHid CMHG SChF SKHP WCru WPGP
kirilowii ELan EPfP IVic LRHS NLar SKHP WPGP WSHC
- var. ***alba*** EPfP
pendula CExl CMHG CSpe CWGN ELan EPfP GKev LRHS MOWG SBrt SKHP SPoG SSpi WKif WPGP WSHC
- B&SWJ 7741 WCru
- 'Shangri-La' ♀H5 **new** CBot
potaninii ambig. CBcs CExl CMac EPfP LHop LRHS MOWG SAko WHer
pseudotinctoria SRms
subverticillata WSHC
szechuensis SKHP

Indocalamus (*Poaceae*)

latifolius EPPr ERod EUJe MMuc MWht WJun
solidus see *Bonia solida*
§ ***tessellatus*** ♀H4 CAbb CBod CDoC CEnt ELon ENBC ERod GCal LPal MWht NGdn SMad WJun WMoo WPGP
- f. ***hamadae*** ERod MWht WJun

Indosasa (*Poaceae*)

gigantea ERod

Inula (*Asteraceae*)

acaulis WCot
barbata GCal
conyzae WHer
dysenterica see *Pulicaria dysenterica*
ensifolia CBcs EBee ELan EPfP GAbr GJos LRHS MNHC NBro WHoo XLum
- 'Compacta' ECho GCal
- 'Gold Star' EBee ECho MBNS MRav NBid NBir SPoG
'Finnish Feathers' EBee
glandulosa see *I. orientalis*
helenium CArn CBod CHab CHby CLau ENfk GAbr GPoy IBoy LEdu MHer NBid NBir NLar NMir SPoG SRms WGwG WHer WHfH WJek WMoo
hirta XLum
hookeri CBre CMea CSam ECha ELan GBin GCal GJos GMaP IFro ILea LEdu LLWG MBel MHol MLHP MMuc NBid NChi NDov NPer NSti SDix SEND WBrk WHil WOld WWEG WWtn
- GWJ 9033 CEvo WCru
macrocephala misapplied see *I. royleana*
magnifica Widely available
- 'Sonnenstrahl' ♀H7 GQue LEdu NLar SPhx
oculus-christi EBee EWes NBre WCot WMoo
§ ***orientalis*** EBee EPfP GAbr GJos LRHS LSun MBri NGBl NLar SGSe SPad SPer SRms WJek XLum
racemosa CTca EBee EPPr EWes GBin GCal LHop LRHS MNrw SPlb WBor
- 'Sonnenspeer' GBin NBid NLar WPtf
§ ***royleana*** GCal MNrw MRav
salicina EBee

Inulanthera (*Asteraceae*)

calva WCot

Iochroma (*Solanaceae*)

§ ***australe*** ♀H3 CExl CHll CNor CSpe EBee ELan EWld LSRN MOWG SEND SPlb SPtp SVen
§ - 'Andean Snow' CHll EShb MNai
§ - 'Bill Evans' EShb MNai
- purple-flowered MNai
- 'Rubin' MNai
- violet-flowered MNai SPlb
cyaneum CDoC CHll ECre MOWG SVen
- purple-flowered CHll
gesnerioides 'Coccineum' CDoC CHll WCot
§ ***grandiflorum*** CDoC CHll SEND
warscewiczii see *I. grandiflorum*

Ipheion (*Alliaceae*)

'Alberto Castillo' ♀H4 CAby CAvo CBro CDes CHid CMea ECho ELan ELon EPot ERCP EWes GBuc GKev LAma LHop LLHF LRHS MNrw SCob SDeJ SDys SPhx WCot WHoo WPGP WWFP
dialystemon ECho EPot LLHF WAbe
- JCA 2420010 WPGP
hirtellum CDes
'Jessie' CAby CBro CDes CMea CPrp EBee ECha ECho EPot EWes GBuc GKev LAma LHop LLHF LRHS SCob WBor WCot WRHF WTor
'Judy' **new** WCot
'Rolf Fiedler' ♀H3 CBro CPne CPrp CTri EBee ECho ELan EPPr EPfP EPot ERCP EWes GBuc GKev LAma LHop LRHS MNrw NRya SBch SCob SDeJ WHoo
sellowianum CAby CDes CPne WCot
sessile CDes EBee ECho
'Tessa'PBR EBee ECho EWes GKev LLHF
§ ***uniflorum*** CBro CPne CTri ECha ECho ITim LAma MNrw SBch SEND SGSe SRms WBrk WCot XLum
- f. ***album*** CBro CPrp EBee ECha ECho EPPr EWes GBuc GKev LEdu LRHS MNrw SCob WCot WHil
- 'Charlotte Bishop' CAvo CBro CCon CDes CMea CPne CPrp EBee ECha ECho ELon EPPr EPot ERCP EWes GBuc GKev LAma LHop LLHF LRHS MNrw NBir NRya SCob SDeJ WCot WHoo
- 'Froyle Mill' ♀H5 CBro CMea CPrp ECho ELon EPPr EPot ERCP EWes GKev LHop LLWP LRHS MNrw SBch SCob SDeJ WCot WHoo
- subsp. ***tandiliense*** CDes EBee
- f. ***violaceum*** **new** SCob
- 'Wisley Blue' ♀H5 CBro CCon CExl CMea CPrp CTri ECha ECho ELan ELon EPPr EPfP EPot ERCP GBuc GKev LAma LHop LLWP LRHS MRav NPri NRya SCob SDeJ SRms WCot WHea WHoo

Ipomoea (*Convolvulaceae*)

acuminata see *I. indica*
alba EShb
batatas 'Blackie' EShb ESwi
- 'Margarita' EShb ESwi
- (Sweet Caroline Series) 'Sweet Caroline Bronze'PBR ESwi EUJe

- - 'Sweet Caroline Light Green'PBR	EShb
- - 'Sweet Caroline Purple'PBR	EUJe
- - 'Sweet Caroline Sweetheart Light Green'PBR	ESwi
- - 'Sweet Caroline Sweetheart Purple'PBR	CSpe ESwi
§ ***indica*** 🏆H1c	CHll CRHN CSam EShb MOWG SPer
learii	see *I. indica*
§ ***lobata***	CSpe LSou
× ***multifida***	CSpe
purpurea 'Grandpa Otts'	CWCL
- 'Kniola's Black Night'	CSpe
quamoclit	CSpe
versicolor	see *I. lobata*

Iresine (*Amaranthaceae*)

Blazin' Lime	see *I.* 'Lime'
Blazin' Rose	see *I.* 'Rose'
herbstii 🏆H1c	EShb EUJe
- 'Brilliantissima'	CTsd
§ 'Lime'	EUJe
§ 'Rose'	EUJe

Iris ✿ (*Iridaceae*)

sp.	ETod
'Abbey Chant' (IB)	CIri WCAu XSen
'Abbondanza' (TB)	WCAu
'Abbracciami' (SDB) **new**	SIri
'About Town' (TB)	WCAu
'Acacia Rhumba' (La) **new**	LLWG
'Acoma' (TB)	WCAu
'Action Front' (TB)	CRos EAEE ECGP EIri EPfP ESgI EShb EWoo LRHS MGos MLHP SDeJ SHil WCAu WGwG WWEG
'Actress' (TB)	CKel CMac CRos EAEE EBee EPfP LBuc LRHS LSRN LSou MGos SHil WGwG
acutiloba subsp. ***lineolata***	CTal
'Adobe Rose' (TB)	SIri XSen
'Advanced Features' (TB) **new**	CIri
'Adventuress' (TB)	XSen
'Afternoon Delight' (TB)	EWoo WCAu
'Afternoon in Rio' (TB)	WCAu
'Again and Again' (TB)	EWoo
'Agatha Christie' (IB)	WCAu
'Aggressively Forward' (TB)	WCAu
'Aglow Again' (MTB)	SDys
'Agnes James' (CH)	CBro
'Agua Fresca' (TB/v)	WCAu
'Ahwahnee Princess' (SDB)	EWoo
'Aichi-no-kagayaki' (SpH)	EBee WCot XLum
'Alabaster Unicorn' (TB)	ESgI
albicans 🏆H5	CBro CMea CTal ECho GKev LEdu
- 'Blue Pygmy'	CAby CTal
albomarginata	ECho
'Alcazar' (TB)	EWoo LSRN SWat WMnd WWEG
'Aldo Ratti' (TB)	ESgI
'Alene's New Love' (SDB)	EWoo
'Alene's Other Love' (SDB)	WCAu
'Alenette' (TB)	WCAu
'Alexia' (TB)	CKel
'Alice Harding' (TB)	ESgI
'Alida' (Reticulata)	CBro ECho EPot ERCP GKev LAma LLHF SDeJ WBrk
'Alien Mist' (TB)	CIri
'Alizes' (TB) 🏆H7	CPar ESgI LRHS WCAu XSen
'All Night Long' (TB)	EWoo
'Allegiance' (TB)	WCAu
'Amadora' (TB)	EIri
'Amaryllis' (TB) **new**	CIri
'Amas' (TB)	EWoo
'Amazing Grace' (TB)	EWoo
'Ambassadeur' (TB)	EWoo
'Amber Beauty' (Dut)	GKev
'Amber Queen' (DB)	CTal ECtt ELan LRHS LSou NBir SBea SDeJ SPer
'Ambroisie' (TB) 🏆H7	ESgI EWoo
'Amelia Bedeila' (IB)	SIri
'American Patriot' (IB)	CKel WCAu
'Amethyst Dancer' (TB)	WCAu
'Amethyst Flame' (TB)	ECho SRms WCAu
'Amherst Blue' (IB)	EIri
'Amherst Bluebeard' (SDB)	ESgI
'Amherst Caper' (SDB)	EIri ESgI
'Amherst Glacier' (IB)	WCAu
'Amherst Jester' (BB)	SIri
'Amherst Purple Ribbon' (SDB)	WCAu
'Amphora' (SDB)	CBro
'Amy Remy' (TB)	CIri
'Ancient Echoes' (TB)	ESgI
'Andalou' (TB) 🏆H7	CWCL EWoo XSen
'Angel Heart' (IB)	EWoo
'Angel Unawares' (TB)	WCAu
'Angel Wings' (TB)	CIri
'Angel's Tears'	see *I. histrioides* 'Angel's Tears'
'Angel's Touch' (TB)	ESgI
anglica	see *I. latifolia*
'Ann Dasch' (Sib)	WAul WWEG
'Annabel Jane' (TB)	CKel ELon WCAu
'Anne Elizabeth' (SDB)	CBro
'Annemarie Troeger' (Sib) 🏆H7	ELon
'Annick' (Sib)	EBee LRHS
'Annikins' (IB)	CKel
'Anniversary' (Sib)	WWEG
'Antarctique' (IB)	ESgI
'Antigone' (TB)	EWoo
'Anvil of Darkness' (TB)	CIri EWoo
'Aphrodisiac' (TB)	XSen
aphylla	GBin SBrt WThu
- 'Slick'	SDys
'Apollo' (Dut)	CAvo
'Appointer' (SpH)	NChi
'Apricorange' (TB)	CKel WCot
'Apricot Blaze' (TB)	ESgI
'Apricot Drops' (MTB) 🏆H7	ESgI WCAu
'Apricot Frosty' (BB)	WCAu XSen
'Apricot Silk' (IB)	CKel IBoy NQui WCot WWEG
'Apricot Topping' (BB)	WCAu
'Aquamarine' **new**	MHol
'Arab Chief' (TB)	CKel
'Arabi Pasha' (TB)	WCAu
* 'Arabic Night' (IB)	WCAu
'Archie Owen' (Spuria)	WCAu

'Arcobaleno' (TB)	CIri
'Arctic Age' (TB)	WCAu
'Arctic Fancy' (IB)	CKel
'Arctic Fox' (TB)	WCAu
'Arctic Sunrise' (TB)	ESgI
'Arctic Wind' (IB)	WCAu
'Argus Pheasant' (TB)	ESgI
'Arms Wide Open' (TB)	CIri
'Around Midnight' (TB)	LRHS
'Arpège' (TB)	XSen
'Art Deco' (TB)	SIri XSen
'Art School Angel' (TB)	CIri
'As de Coeur' (TB)	XSen
'As You Were' (TB)	CIri
'Ascension Crown' (TB)	ESgI
'Ask Alma' (IB)	ESgI XSen
'Astrid Cayeux' (TB)	ESgI
'Astro Flash' (TB)	ESgI
'Athaenos' (IB)	CIri
'Atlantic Crossing' (Sib)	SIri WAul
'Atlantic Sky' (TB)	ESgI
'Attention Please' (TB)	CKel ELan WWEG
attica	CBro CPBP ECho GEdr LLHF WCot WThu
- lemon-flowered	WAbe WThu
'Attitude' (IB)	WCAu
§ ***aucheri*** ♀H4	ECho EPot GKev LLHF
- 'Snow White'	GKev
'Aunt Josephine' (TB)	ESgI
'Aurean' (IB)	CKel
'Austrian Sky' (SDB)	CAby CKel CMac ECtt EPfP LHop LRHS SDeJ WAul WCot
'Autumn Apricot' (TB)	EWoo
'Autumn Circus' (TB)	EWoo
'Autumn Echo' (TB)	ESgI XSen
'Autumn Encore' (TB)	EWoo MHer
'Autumn Leaves' (TB)	WCAu
'Autumn Princess' (Dut)	GKev
'Autumn Riesling' (TB)	WCAu
'Autumn Tryst' (TB)	ESgI WCAu
'Autumn Wind' **new**	WCAu
'Autumn Wine' (BB) **new**	CIri
'Avalon Sunset' (TB)	EIri
'Awesome Blossom' (TB)	ESgI
'Az Ap' (IB)	ELon WCAu
babadagica	WAbe
'Babbling Brook' (TB)	XSen
'Baboon Bottom' (BB)	CIri
'Baby Bengal' (BB)	XSen
'Baby Blessed' (SDB)	CBro WCAu
'Baby Prince' (SDB)	ESgI
'Baby Sister' (Sib)	CMHG EBee EWoo GBin GBuc LRHS LSRN NBro SRGP SWat
'Bach Toccata' (MTB)	SDys
'Back in Black' (TB)	CKel
'Badlands' (TB)	WCAu
'Bal Masqué' (TB)	ESgI XSen
'Ballerina Pink' (BB) **new**	WCAu
'Ballistic' (SDB)	WCAu
'Ballyhoo' (TB)	WCAu XSen
'Baltic Star' (TB)	EWoo WCAu
'Banbury Beauty' (CH) ♀H4	MAvo
'Banbury Melody' (CH)	MAvo
'Banbury Ruffles' (SDB)	ESgI LRHS WCAu
'Bandera Waltz' (TB)	WCAu
'Bang' (TB)	CKel
'Bangles' (MTB) ♀H7	SDys WCAu
'Banish Misfortune' (Sib)	WAul
'Banker Dave' (TB)	CIri
'Bar de Nuit' (TB)	ESgI EWoo
'Barbara May' (TB) **new**	WCAu
'Barbara My Love' (TB)	WCAu
barbatula BWJ 7663	WCru
'Baria' (SDB)	CTal
'Batik' (BB)	SIri WCot XSen
'Battle Star' (TB)	CIri
'Battlestar Atlantis' (TB)	CIri
'Bayberry Candle' (TB)	CIri WCAu
'Be Mine' (TB)	CIri
'Be My Baby' (BB)	WCAu
'Beach Girl' (TB)	EWoo
'Beacon of Light' (TB) **new**	CIri
'Bedtime Story' (IB)	SWat WWEG XSen
'Bee's Knees' (SDB) ♀H7	SIri
'Before the Storm' (TB)	CIri ELon ESgI GBin LRHS WCAu XSen
'Beguine' (TB)	ESgI
'Being Busy' (SDB)	ESgI
'Bel Azur' (IB)	ESgI LRHS
'Bel Esprit' (TB)	WCAu
'Belgian Princess' (TB)	WCAu
'Belle de Nuit' (TB)	EWoo
'Ben a Factor' (MTB)	ESgI
'Benbow' (TB)	WMil
'Benton Apollo' (TB) **new**	EMal
'Benton Arundel' (TB)	EMal EWoo
'Benton Bluejohn' (TB)	EMal
'Benton Caramel' (TB)	EMal EWoo
'Benton Cordelia' (TB)	EMal EWoo
'Benton Daphne' (TB)	EMal EWoo
'Benton Dierdre' (TB)	ELon EMal EWoo MNHC SRms
'Benton Evora' (TB)	EMal EWoo
'Benton Farewell' (TB)	EWoo
'Benton Lorna' (TB)	EMal EWoo
'Benton Menace' (TB) **new**	EMal
'Benton Nigel' (TB)	ECha EMal EWoo WCAu
'Benton Nutkin' (TB) **new**	EMal
'Benton Olive' (TB)	EMal EWoo
'Benton Opal' (TB)	EMal
'Benton Pearl' (TB)	EMal
'Benton Primrose' (TB)	EMal EWoo
'Benton Sheila' (TB)	ECha ELon EWoo
'Benton Susan' (TB)	EMal EWoo MMHG
'Beotie' (TB)	EWoo
'Berkeley Gold' (TB)	CKel CLet CSBt ECtt ELan EWes LRHS SCob SDeJ SPer SWat WGwG WWEG
'Berlin Bluebird' (Sib)	SMHy
'Berlin Purple Wine' (Sib)	EPri IMou
'Berlin Ruffles' (Sib) ♀H7	CKel EWes EWoo WAul
'Berlin Sky' (Sib)	ESgI EWes
'Berlin Tiger' (SpH) ♀H7	EPPr LLWG MSCN MWts NLar SCob SGol WHil WMoo
'Bermuda Triangle' (BB)	SDys
'Best Bet' (TB)	ESgI EWoo LCro WCAu
'Bête Noir' (MDB) **new**	CIri
'Bethany Claire' (TB)	ESgI WCAu
'Betty Cooper' (Spuria)	WCAu
'Betty Simon' (TB)	CWCL EWoo XSen
'Beverly Sills' (TB)	CAby CKel CRos CWld EAEE EPfP EWoo GBin LRHS LSou MRav SBea SCob SDeJ SRGP WCAu WGwG XSen
'Bewilderbeast' (TB)	XSen
'Bianco' (TB)	WCAu
'Bibury' (SDB) ♀H7	WCAu

'Bickley Cape' (Sib)	WWEG
'Big Blue' (Sib)	WFar
'Big Dipper' (TB)	ECtt
'Big Heart' (Sib) **new**	EIri
'Big Squeeze' (TB)	WCAu
biglumis	see *I. lactea*
biliottii	CBro
'Bishop's Robe' (TB)	ESgI EWoo
'Black as Night' (TB)	XSen
'Black Beauty' (Dut)	EPfP
'Black Cherry Delight' (SDB)	ESgI
'Black Dragon' (TB)	CBod LRHS NLar XSen
'Black Flag' (TB)	XSen
'Black Gamecock' (La)	CBod CCon CWCL EBee ECtt ELan MBNS MNrw MSCN MWts NBro NLar SKHP WMAq
'Black Hope' (TB)	CIri EWoo
'Black is Back' **new**	WCAu
'Black Knight' (TB)	MJak MRav NLar NQui WKif
'Black Magic' (IB)	EWoo
'Black Night' (IB)	NEgg SRGP WWEG
'Black Prince' (IB)	SCob
'Black Stallion' (MDB)	ESgI
'Black Swan' (TB)	CKel CLet CMac ECha ECtt ELan EPfP ESgI EShb EUJe EWoo GCal LAst LCro LRHS LSRN MAvo MNrw NQui SBea SCob SPer SPoG WCot XSen
'Black Tie Affair' (TB)	CAby EAEE ELan EPfP ESgI EWoo IPot LRHS MAsh WCAu WTor XSen
'Black Watch' (IB)	EBee
'Blackbeard' (BB) ♀H7	WCAu
'Blackbeard's Ghost' (AB) **new**	WCAu
'Blackberry Tease' (TB)	WCAu
'Blackberry Towers' (TB)	ESgI
'Blackcurrant' (IB)	WCAu
'Blackout' (TB)	ESgI EWoo
'Blast' (IB)	CKel
'Blatant' (TB)	ESgI EWoo WCAu XSen
'Blazing Light' (TB)	XSen
'Blenheim Royal' (TB)	ESgI WCAu XSen
'Blessed Again' (IB)	EBee
'Blitzen' (IB)	WCAu
'Blue Admiral' (TB)	GBin
'Blue Boy' (IB)	EWoo
'Blue Burgee' (Sib)	ECha
I 'Blue Butterfly' (Sib)	CBod EBee EPfP LAst NGdn
'Blue Denim' (SDB)	ECho ECtt EPfP GCal GMaP MRav NBir NLar WBor WCAu WCot WWEG
'Blue Eyed Blond' (IB)	MNrw
'Blue Eyed Brunette' (TB)	WCAu
'Blue Giant' (Dut)	LLWG
'Blue Gown' (TB)	EWoo
'Blue Hendred' (SDB)	NBir WCAu
'Blue Hill' (Reticulata) **new**	LAma
'Blue Hour' (TB) **new**	WCAu
'Blue King' (Sib)	CHid ELan EPfP GBin GKev GMaP ILea LCro MRav NBro NGdn SCob SPer WMnd WMoo WWEG
'Blue Lamp' (TB)	CKel
'Blue Line' (SDB)	CDes
'Blue Meadow Fly' (Sino-Sib)	LLHF
'Blue Mere' (Sib)	MCot
'Blue Moon' (Sib)	ELon GBuc GQue IMou LAst MJak MSCN WFar
'Blue Mystery' (J)	LLHF
'Blue Note Blues' (TB)	WCAu
'Blue Note' (Reticulata)	ECho EPot ERCP LAma LLHF
'Blue Pigmy' (SDB)	CBod CTal CWat ECtt EPfP LRHS LSou MBri MRav NLar SBea SDeJ SPer
'Blue Reverie' (Sib)	ELon EPPr ESgI
'Blue Rhythm' (TB)	CAby CKel ELan ELon EPfP EWoo GMaP LRHS MRav SCoo SDeJ SPer WCAu WMnd WWEG
'Blue Sapphire' (TB)	CKel ESgI WCAu
'Blue Sceptre' (Sib)	IBlr
'Blue Shimmer' (TB)	CMac CSBt EBee ECha ELan EPfP ESgI EShb EWoo LRHS LSRN LSou MBri SDeJ SPer SWat WCAu WGwG WWEG
'Blue Splash' (IB) **new**	WCAu
'Blue Staccato' (TB)	WCAu XSen
'Blue Suede Shoes' (TB)	ESgI EWoo LSRN XSen
'Blue Trill' (TB) **new**	WCAu
'Bluebeard's Ghost' (SDB) ♀H7	CIri WCAu
'Bluebird Wine' (TB)	CKel WCAu
'Blue-eyed Susan' (TB)	CIri
'Bob's Fancy'	SDeJ
'Bockingford' (MTB)	SIri
'Bohemian' (TB)	CWCL
'Bold Encounter' (TB)	WCAu
'Bold Pretender' (La)	ECtt ELan ELon EPfP LLWG MBNS MSCN NLar SKHP WHil
'Bold Print' (IB)	CAby CRos EAEE ELon IPot LRHS LSRN MBri MGos SBea SHil SPoG WCAu WWEG
'Bollinger'	see *I.* 'Hornpipe'
'Bonnie Davenport' (TB)	CIri
'Bonus Lite' (TB)	CIri
'Boo' (SDB)	CPBP CTal EAJP WCAu XSen
'Border Guard' (BB) **new**	WCAu
'Border Happy' (TB)	WCAu
'Bottled Sunshine' (IB)	LRHS
'Bound for Glory' (La)	LLWG
'Bournemouth Ball Gown' (Sib)	WAul
'Bournemouth Beauty' (Sib) ♀H7	CIri WAul
'Bouzy Bouzy' (TB)	ESgI XSen
'Bracknell' (Sib)	WAul
bracteata	EBee GBuc
- NNS 04-223	GBuc
'Braggin' Rights' (TB)	CIri
'Braithwaite' (TB)	CAby CKel CRos CWGN ECGP ELan EPfP ESgI EShb EWoo LRHS MBri SBea SDeJ SPer SRms SWat WCAu WGwG
'Brandaris' (TB)	ESgI
'Brannigan' (SDB)	NBir NSti
'Brasero' (TB)	CWCL EWoo
'Brasilia' (TB)	NBir
'Brassie' (SDB)	CBro MBNS WHil WWEG XSen
'Brave New World' (TB) ♀H7	CIri
'Breakers' (TB) ♀H7	CKel EWoo WCAu
'Breezy Blue' (SDB)	WCAu
'Brenchley' (IB)	SIri
'Bridal Icing' (TB)	WCAu
'Bride's Blush' (TB)	CIri
'Bride's Halo' (TB)	LSRN WCAu XSen
'Bright Button' (SDB)	CKel ESgI EWoo
'Bright Fire' (TB)	EIri
'Bright Vision' (SDB)	ESgI

Name	Suppliers
'Bright White' (MDB)	CBro CKel ECho
'Bright Yellow' (DB)	MRav
'Brighteyes' (IB)	SRms
'Brindisi' (TB)	XSen
'Brise de Mer' (TB)	XSen
'Bristo Magic' (TB)	XSen
'Bristol Gem' (TB)	XSen
'Broad Shoulders' (TB)	WCAu
'Broadleigh Angela' (CH)	CBro
'Broadleigh Ann' (CH)	CBro
'Broadleigh Carolyn' (CH) 🏆H5	CBro CElw
'Broadleigh Clare' (CH)	CBro
'Broadleigh Dorothy' (CH)	CBro MAvo
'Broadleigh Eleanor' (CH)	CBro
'Broadleigh Elizabeth' (CH)	CBro
'Broadleigh Emily' (CH)	CBro
'Broadleigh Fenella' (CH)	CBro
'Broadleigh Jean' (CH)	CBro
'Broadleigh Joan' (CH)	CBro
'Broadleigh Lavinia' (CH)	CBro MRav
'Broadleigh Mitre' (CH)	CBro
'Broadleigh Nancy' (CH)	CBro MAvo
'Broadleigh Peacock' (CH)	CBro CElw MAvo NLar WSHC
'Broadleigh Penny' (CH)	CBro MAvo
'Broadleigh Rose' (CH)	CBro CElw EPri MBrN MRav WSHC
'Broadway Baby' (IB)	ESgI SIri
'Broadway Star' (TB)	LRHS
'Broken Link' (BB)	CIri
'Bronzaire' (IB)	CKel EIri WCAu WGwG
'Bronze Beauty' (Dut)	ERCP GKev
'Bronze Beauty' (TB)	SDeJ
'Bronze Beauty' van Tubergen (*hoogiana* hybrid)	NBir SDeJ
'Brother Carl' (TB)	XSen
'Brown Chocolate' (TB)	WCAu
'Brown Lasso' (BB) 🏆H7	CKel
'Bruce' (TB)	WCAu
'Brummit's Mauve' (TB)	WCAu
'Bruno' (TB)	LSRN NLar WMil
'Brussels' (TB)	ESgI
bucharica misapplied	see *I. orchioides* Carrière
bucharica ambig.	ECho ELon LSun MNrw SDeJ
§ ***bucharica*** Foster 🏆H5	CBro ECho EPfP EPot GKev LAma
- 'Princess'	ECho
* - 'Top Gold'	ECho
bucharica* × *orchioides	ECho
'Buckwheat' (TB)	EWoo SIri
'Buisson de Roses' (TB)	XSen
bulleyana	CBro ECho GEdr GKev MMuc SRms
- BWJ 7912	WCru
- from Dali, Yunnan, China	SBrt
- black-flowered	CExl GKev
- - SDR 1792	EBee
'Bumblebee Deelite' (MTB) 🏆H7	CJun CKel CTal WCAu
'Bundle of Love' (BB) **new**	WCAu
'Burgermeister' (TB)	XSen
'Burgundy Party' (TB)	XSen
'Burka' (TB)	ESgI
'Burnt Toffee' (TB)	ESgI XSen
'Burst' (TB)	CKel WCAu
'Buto' (TB)	EWoo
'Butter and Cream' (Sib) **new**	MNrw
'Butter and Sugar' (Sib) 🏆H7	Widely available
'Buttercup Bower' (TB)	WCAu
'Buttermere' (TB)	SRms
'Butterpat' (IB)	ESgI
'Butterscotch Carpet' (SDB)	WCAu
'Butterscotch Kiss' (TB)	CKel CMac CRos ECGP ELan ELon EPfP GMaP LRHS MBNS MGos MRav NBir NLar SBea SHil SPer
'Buzzword' (SDB)	WCAu
'Bye Bye Blues' (TB)	ESgI XSen
'Byzantine Purple' (TB)	EWoo
'Cabaret Royale' (TB)	ESgI XSen
'Cable Car' (TB)	CKel CWCL ESgI EWoo
'Cache of Gold' (SDB)	EWoo
'Caesar' (Sib)	EWoo SDys SRms
'Caesar's Brother' (Sib)	CCon CHid CKel CPrp CRos ELan EPfP EWoo GAbr GBin GBuc LCro LOPS LRHS MGos MSpe NHol NLar SHil SPer SWat WFar WHoo WWEG
'Cajun Rhythm' (TB)	XSen
'Calgary' (TB)	WCAu
'Caliente' (TB)	EWoo MRav MWhi WCAu XSen
'California Dreamin'' (TB)	CIri
'California Gold' (TB)	WWEG
'California Style' (IB)	XSen
§ Californian hybrids	CElw CMac CPBP EPot GCra GKev NBir WCot
'Calm Stream' (TB)	WCAu
'Calypso Mood' (TB)	XSen
'Cambridge' (Sib) 🏆H7	CAvo CKel EHoe EIri GBuc IMou LRHS MLHP MWat NGdn SWat WAul WFar WHoo
'Cameliard' (TB)	EWoo
'Camelot Rose' (TB)	WCAu XSen
'Cameo Blush' (BB)	XSen
'Cameo Queen' (SDB) 🏆H7	CIri
'Cameo Wine' (TB)	ESgI MNrw XSen
'Cameroun' (TB)	ESgI EWoo
'Campbellii'	see *I. lutescens* 'Campbellii'
canadensis	see *I. hookeri*
'Canadian Kisses' (SDB)	ESgI
'Canadian Streaker' (TB/v)	WCot
'Canary Bird' (TB)	ESgI
'Candy Rock' (IB)	CIri EWoo WCAu
'Cannington Bluebird' (TB)	WCAu
'Cannington Ochre' (SDB)	CBro
'Canonbury Belle' (Sib)	WAul
'Can't Touch This' (TB)	WCAu
'Cantab' (Reticulata)	CBro ECho EPot ERCP EWTr GBin GKev LAma LRHS SCob SDeJ
'Caprice' (TB)	EWoo
'Capricious Candles' (TB)	CIri
'Captain Indigo' (IB)	ESgI WCAu
'Captive Sun' (SDB)	CKel CTal EAEE EPfP LRHS SIri WTor
'Caramel' (TB)	XSen
'Cardinal' (TB)	WMil
'Care to Dance' (TB) **new**	WCAu
'Careless Sally' (Sib)	WAul
'Carfax' (TB) **new**	WMil
'Caribbean Dream' (TB)	XSen
'Carnaby' (TB)	CBod CKel CWld ESgI EShb LRHS MRav SDeJ WCAu WGwG XSen

'Carnival Time' (TB)	CKel CMac CRos CWGN EBee ECtt EPfP LRHS MCot SBea SPer WHoo XSen
'Carol Lee' (TB)	EBee
'Carolina Gold' (TB)	XSen
* 'Caronte' (IB)	ESgI
'Carriage Trade' (TB)	LRHS
'Casbah' (TB)	XSen
'Cascade Rhythm' (TB)	WCAu
'Cascade Springs' (TB)	XSen
'Cascade Sprite' (SDB)	SRms
'Casino Cruiser' (TB) **new**	CIri
'Casual Joy' (TB)	CIri
'Catalyst' (TB)	XSen
'Cat's Eye' (SDB)	CIri ESgI SIri WCAu
'Catwalk Idol' (La)	LLWG
caucasica	CMac
'Cayenne Capers' (TB)	ESgI
* 'Cedric Morris'	EWes
'Cee Jay' (IB) ♀H7	EWoo
'Cee Tee'	EWoo XSen
'Celebration Song' (TB)	ESgI SIri WCAu XSen
'Celestial Glory' (TB)	XSen
'Cerdagne' (TB)	XSen
'Chalkhill' (SDB)	WCAu
chamaeiris	see *I. lutescens* subsp. *lutescens*
'Champagne Elegance' (TB)	EIri EPri NBir XSen
'Champagne Encore' (IB)	EWoo
'Champagne Frost' (TB)	XSen
'Champagne Waltz' (TB)	XSen
'Chandler's Choice' (Sib)	EWes
'Change of Pace' (TB)	ESgI WCAu XSen
'Chanted' (SDB)	EWoo WCAu XSen
'Chantilly' (TB)	CBod CHid CKel CLet EAJP EBee ELan EPfP EWoo LCro LOPS LRHS MRav NBir NGdn NLar SPer SWat
'Chapeau' (TB)	ESgI WCAu
'Charlotte's Tutu' (La) **new**	LLWG
'Charmaine' (TB)	XSen
'Chartreuse Bounty' (Sib)	EPri EWes GAbr NLar NSti
'Chasing Rainbows' (TB)	SDys WCAu
'Château d'Auvers-sur-Oise' (TB)	SIri
'Cheap Frills' (TB)	WCAu
'Cher' (TB)	LSRN
'Cherished' (TB)	MAvo WWEG
'Cherished One' (La)	LLWG
'Cherry Blossom Song' (TB) **new**	SIri
'Cherry Blossom Special' (TB)	CIri
'Cherry Garden' (SDB)	Widely available
'Cherry Twist' (La)	LLWG
'Cherrywood' (SDB)	CBro
'Cherub's Smile' (TB)	XSen
'Chicken Little' (MDB)	CBro
'Chief Moses' (TB)	WCAu
I 'Chieftain' (SDB)	MRav
'Childhood Sweetheart' (La)	LLWG
'Chilled Wine' (Sib)	ELon
'China Dragon' (TB)	SWat XSen
'Chinese Coral' (TB)	XSen
'Chinese Treasure' (TB)	XSen
'Chinook Winds' (TB)	ESgI WCAu
'Chivalry' (TB)	ESgI
'Christine Mullins' (Sib)	WBor
'Christmas Angel' (TB)	WCAu
Chrysofor Group	CAby
chrysographes ♀H7	CBro CHid CLet CMac CTsd CWCL EHoe EPfP EPri EWoo GBBs GJos GKev IBoy IKil LAst LLWG LRHS MBel MHer MLHP MMuc MRav NPri NSti SCob SRot
- BWJ 7930 **new**	WCru
I - 'Black Beauty'	CCon ECho EPfP EWoo
- 'Black Gold'	EPri MHol
I - 'Black Knight'	CBot CCse CExl ELon EPfP GBuc GCal GCra LHop MCot NChi NLar SWat WMnd WPnP
I - 'Black Velvet'	GEdr
- black-flowered	CAby CBod CDes CExl CFil EBee ELan GAbr GBin GBuc GCal GKev GKin LCro LRHS MNrw MWhi NGdn SCob SPer SPoG WCot WCru WFar WGwG WMoo WPGP WPnP WSHC WWEG
- dark-flowered	GKev MSCN WFar
- 'Goldvein'	CMac
- hybrid	WFar
- 'Inshriach'	IMou LEdu WAbe
- 'Kew Black'	CExl ECho GKev LEdu NBir WHer WWEG
- 'Kilmurry Black'	IKil
- 'Mandarin Purple'	GCal SWat
§ - 'Rubella'	CAby GCra GKev
- 'Rubra'	see *I. chrysographes* 'Rubella'
- yellow-flowered	WFar
chrysographes* × *forrestii	GBin NBir
'Chubby Cheeks' (SDB)	CKel WCAu
'Church Stoke' (SDB)	WCAu
'Ciaparat' (TB) **new**	CIri
'Cimarron Rose' (SDB)	ESgI
'Cimarron Strip' (TB)	CKel EPfP WCot WWEG XSen
'Cinque Terre' (TB) **new**	WCAu
'Circle of Light' (TB)	WCAu
'Circle Round' (Sib)	CSpe
'Circus Stripes' (TB)	XSen
'Cirrus Veil' (SDB)	WCAu
'Citoyen' (TB)	XSen
'Citronnade' (TB)	ESgI
'City' (SDB)	SIri
'City of Paradise' (TB)	ESgI
'Clairette' (Reticulata)	ECho EPot LAma LRHS MWat SCob SDeJ
'Clara Garland' (IB)	WCAu
'Clarence' (TB)	ESgI EWoo WCAu XSen
clarkei	ECho GBin GEdr
- B&SWJ 2122	WCru
- CC 2751	CExl
- SDR 3819	GKev
'Class Ring' (TB) **new**	WCAu
'Classic Look' (TB)	ESgI
'Classic Navy' (BB)	ESgI
'Clear Morning Sky' (TB)	GKev
'Clee Hills' (Sib)	WAul
'Cleedownton' (Sib)	WAul
'Clematis' (TB)	CIri WMil
'Cleo' (TB)	NSti
'Cleo Murrell' (TB)	ESgI EWoo
'Cleve Dodge' (Sib)	EPri ESgI EWoo SIri XLum
'Cliffs of Dover' (TB)	CKel EIri ESgI EWoo GCal MCot SCob SRms

'Cloudcap' (TB)	SRms
'Clown Around' (TB)	CIri
'Clownerie' (TB)	EWoo
'Clyde Redmond' (La) ♀H5	WMAq
'Coal Face' (TB) **new**	WCAu
'Coal Seams' (TB) **new**	WCAu
'Coalignition' (TB)	EWoo WCAu
'Codicil' (TB)	EIri EWoo XSen
'Coffee Boy' (SDB)	CBro
colchica	LEdu
'Colette Thurillet' (TB)	XSen
'Colin's Pale Blue' (Sib)	NCGa SMHy
collettii	ECho GKev
'Color Carnival' (TB)	ESgI
'Color Me Blue' (TB)	WCAu
'Color Splash' (TB)	XSen
'Color Strokes' (TB) **new**	WCAu
'Colorific' (La)	NLar
'Colortart' (TB)	XSen
'Come to Me' (TB)	CIri
'Coming Up Roses' (TB)	XSen
'Con Fuoco' (TB)	XSen
'Concertina' (IB)	CIri EWoo WCAu
'Concord Crush' (Sib)	LLWG
confusa ♀H4	CPla CPne EUJe GGal SBig SEND SGSe SMad XSen
§ - 'Martyn Rix'	CAbb CAby CBct CDes CHid CMac CPou ELon EPfP GCal IDee LRHS MLHP SBrt SEND SGSe WGwG WHer
confusa* × *japonica	WWFP
'Conjuration' (TB)	EWoo SIri
'Connection' (TB)	WCAu
'Constant Wattez' (IB)	CKel ESgI NLar
'Constantine Bay' (TB)	ESgI
'Consummation' (MTB)	SGol
'Contrast in Styles' (Sib)	CBod EPri LSou NQui WBor WFar
'Cool Satin' (SDB) **new**	CIri
'Cool Spring' (Sib)	MSpe
'Copatonic' (TB)	ESgI WCAu
'Copper Capers' (TB)	ESgI
'Copper Classic' (TB)	ELon ESgI LSRN SEND WCAu
'Coquet Waters' (Sib)	NBid WAul
'Coquetterie' (TB)	EWoo
'Coral Point' (TB)	WCAu
'Coral Splendor' (TB) **new**	WCAu
'Coral Sunset' (TB)	XSen
'Cordoba' (TB)	WCAu XSen
'Coronation Anthem' (Sib)	EPri EWoo WAul
'Côte d'Or' (TB)	XSen
'Counting Sheep' (SDB) **new**	SIri
'Country Kisses' (TB) **new**	WCAu
'County Town Red' (TB)	SIri
'Coup de Soleil' (TB)	EWoo
'Coyote Ugly' (TB) **new**	CIri
'Cozy Calico' (TB)	WCAu
'Cracklin' Burgundy' (TB)	XSen
'Craithie' (TB)	EMal EWoo
'Cranapple' (BB) ♀H7	ESgI WCAu
'Cranberry Ice' (TB)	ELon EWoo XSen
'Cranberry Sauce' (TB)	SIri WCAu
'Cranbrook' (IB) ♀H7	SIri
'Cream Beauty' (Dut)	GKev LCro LOPS SDeJ
'Cream Pixie' (SDB)	WCAu
'Creative Artistry' (La)	LLWG
cretensis	see *I. unguicularis* subsp. *cretensis*
'Crimson King' (IB)	EWoo
'Crinoline' (TB)	XSen
'Crispette' (TB)	WCAu
cristata	EPot GEdr GKev NHar NLar SRms
- 'Alba'	CPBP EBee GCal GEdr NHar NLar WThu
crocea ♀H7	EBee GKev
'Croftway Lemon' (TB)	ELon
'Cross Current' (TB)	WCAu
'Crowned Heads' (TB)	WCAu XSen
'Crow's Feet' (BB) **new**	WCAu
'Crushed Ice' (La)	LLWG
'Crystal Fountain' (TB)	CIri
'Crystal Gazer' (TB)	ESgI
'Crystal Glitters' (TB)	ESgI
'Cumulus' (TB)	EWoo SIri
cuniculiformis	ECho WCot
'Cup Race' (TB)	WCAu XSen
'Cupid's Arrow' (TB)	WCAu
'Curlew' (IB)	WCAu
'Cutie' (IB)	ESgI EWoo WCAu
'Cyanea' (DB)	ECho
'Cyclamint' (La)	LLWG
cycloglossa	ECho GKev
'Daemon Imp' (MTB) **new**	WCAu
'Dahdah' (TB) **new**	WCAu
'Dainty Lace' (La)	LLWG
'Dakota Smoke' (TB)	EWoo
'Dale Dennis' (DB)	XSen
'Dance Away' (TB)	ESgI
'Dance Ballerina Dance' (Sib)	CCon CHid CWCL EBee EPfP EPri LLWG MRav NLar WFar WTor
'Dance for Joy' (TB)	XSen
'Dance the Night Away' (TB)	WCAu
'Dancer's Veil' (TB)	CKel CMac EBee ECtt ELon ESgI LRHS MRav SPer WCAu
'Dancing Lilacs' (MTB)	ESgI
'Dancing Nanou' (Sib)	EBee ECtt SWat
danfordiae	CBro ECho EPfP EPot GKev LAma LCro LOPS LRHS SCob SDeJ SPer
'Dangerous Mood' (TB)	EWoo
'Dante's Inferno' (TB)	EWoo
'Dardanus' (Rc)	ECho EPot ERCP GKev SDeJ WCot
'Dark Crystal' (SDB)	ESgI EWoo
'Dark Desire' (Sib)	MRav
'Dark Drama' (TB) **new**	WCAu
'Dark Spark' (SDB)	WCAu
'Dark Vader' (SDB)	ESgI
'Darkness' (IB)	SIri
'Darkside' (TB)	XSen
'Darts' (IB)	CIri
'Dash Away' (SDB)	ESgI SIri
'Dashing' (TB)	EWoo
'Dauber's Delight'	CIri
'Dauber's Surprise' (TB)	CIri
'Daughter of Stars' (TB)	ESgI
'Dauntless' (TB)	ESgI EWoo
'Dawn of Fall' (TB)	ESgI
'Dawn Waltz' (Sib)	EBee LLWG WFar WHlf
'Dawning' (TB) ♀H7	ESgI EWoo
'Dazzle Time' (TB)	CIri
'Dazzling' (IB)	WCAu
'Dazzling Gold' (TB)	ESgI XSen
'Dear Currier' (Sib) **new**	WAul
'Dear Delight' (Sib)	EWTr ILea LLHF LLWG NLar WBor WFar

Name	Suppliers
'Death by Chocolate' (SDB)	ESgI
'Decadence' (TB)	WCAu
§ ***decora***	CTal LLHF
'Deep Black' (TB)	CKel CPar CRos CSpe CWGN CWld EAJP EBee ELan EPfP ESgI EUJe GBin GMaP IPot LRHS LSRN MBNS MBri MCot MRav MWat NLar NWad SDeJ SPer SPoG SWat WGwG WWEG
'Deep Pacific' (TB)	WCAu
'Deep Sea Quest' (La) **new**	LLWG
'Deepening Shadows' (CH) **new**	MAvo
'Deft Touch' (TB)	XSen
delavayi $\mathbb{Y}^{H7}$	ECho EWes GMaP WRHF
- SDR 50	CExl GKev
- 'Didcot'	LRHS
'Delirium' (IB)	WCAu
'Delta Blues' (TB)	EWoo SIri
'Delta Butterfly' (La)	WMAq
'Demi-Deuil' (TB)	EWoo
'Demon' (SDB)	CJun XSen
'Demure Illini' (Sib)	MNrw
'Denys Humphry' (TB)	WCAu
'Deputé Nomblot' (TB)	EWoo
'Derwentwater' (TB)	SRms WCAu
'Desert Echo' (TB)	MHer XSen
'Desert Jewel' (La) **new**	LLWG
'Desert Song' (TB)	WCAu
'Desi Brouwer' (IB) **new**	SIri
'Desiris' (TB)	WCAu
'Devil David' (TB)	CIri
'Devil May Care' (IB)	ESgI
'Devilry' (SDB)	EWoo
'Devil's Spoon' (TB)	CIri
'Devonshire Cream' (TB)	WCAu
'Devoted' (SDB)	WCAu
'Dewful' (Sib)	EBee WFar
'Diabolique' (TB) $\mathbb{Y}^{H7}$	XSen
'Diamond Ring' (TB)	SDys
§ ***dichotoma***	EWes SBrt
'Disco Jewel' (MTB)	ESgI
'Discovered Treasure' (TB)	WCAu
'Disguise' (TB) **new**	WCAu
'Distant Music' (La)	LLWG
'Ditzy' (SDB)	SIri
'Diversion' (TB)	ESgI
'Dividing Line' (MTB) **new**	WCAu
'Dixie Darling' (TB)	ESgI XSen
'Dixie Pixie' (SDB)	WCAu
'Doctor No' (TB)	CIri
'Dogrose' (TB)	EWoo
'Dolce' (SpH)	WCAu
'Doll Ribbons' (MTB)	EPfP
'Dolly Madison' (TB)	ESgI EWoo
§ ***domestica***	CArn CBro CHll ELan EPfP GKev LRHS SPav SPlb SRms WSHC
- B&SWJ 8692B	WCru
- 'Crûg Colossal'	WCru
- 'Freckle Face'	CWCL LSou
'Dominion' (TB)	WMil
'Don Juan' (TB)	EWoo
'Doohicky' (IB) **new**	CIri
'Dotted Swiss' (TB)	XSen
'Double Bubble' (TB)	EWoo
'Double Byte' (SDB)	XSen
'Double Click' (TB)	EWoo
'Double Espoir' (TB)	XSen
'Double Lament' (SDB)	CBro
'Double Mini'	EWoo
'Double Shot' (TB)	EWoo
'Double Standards' (Sib)	EBee EPri NLar WHil
'Double Vision' (TB)	EWoo XSen
douglasiana	ECho GCal GKev
- 'Cape Ferrelo'	SKHP
'Dover Beach' (TB)	SIri
'Dover Castle' (BB) $\mathbb{Y}^{H7}$	SIri
'Downtown Brown' (TB) **new**	WCAu
'Draco' (TB)	ESgI XSen
'Drake Carne' (TB)	CKel
'Drama Queen' (TB)	WCAu
'Dream Indigo' (IB)	EWoo WCAu XSen
'Dreaming Green' (Sib)	EBee
'Dreaming Orange' (Sib)	ECtt EPri
'Dreaming Rainbows' (TB) **new**	WCAu
'Dreaming Spires' (Sib)	ESgI SIri
'Dreaming Yellow' (Sib)	CAby CBre CKel CMHG CSam ECha EHon EPfP EPri EShb GBuc GKin LEdu LRHS MBri MLHP MMuc MRav NGdn SBod SPer WAul WMoo WWEG WWtn
'Dreamsicle' (TB)	EWoo
'Dresden Candleglow' (IB)	WCAu
'Drive Me Wild' (TB)	WCAu
'Dualtone' (TB)	CKel
'Dude Ranch' (TB)	WCAu
'Duded Up' (TB)	CIri
'Duke of Bedford' (TB)	WMil
'Dunkler Wein' (Sib)	EBee EWes
'Dunlin' (MDB)	CBro CTal ECho NBir
'Dural White Butterfly' (La)	CBod CHid
'Durham Dream' (TB)	CIri
'Dusky Challenger' (TB)	CKel EBee ESgI EWoo LCro WCAu XSen
'Dusky Evening' (TB)	XSen
'Dutch Chocolate' (TB)	CKel ESgI EWes EWoo LCro WCAu XSen
'Dynamite' (TB)	ESgI EWoo XSen
'Dyonisos' (TB)	SIri
'Eagle's Flight' (TB)	XSen
'Earl of Essex' (TB)	WCAu XSen
'Early Frost' (IB)	CKel
'Early Light' (TB) $\mathbb{Y}^{H7}$	ESgI LPot WCAu
'Easter' (SDB)	SIri
'Eastertime' (TB)	ESgI EWoo
'Eastman Winds' (La)	LLWG
'Easy' (MTB)	EIri SIri
'Ebony Echo' (TB)	EWoo
'Echo de France' (TB)	CKel ESgI EWoo XSen
'Eden's Paradise Blue' (Sib)	ELon
'Edge of Winter' (TB)	CKel XSen
'Edith Wolford' (TB)	CBod CKel EBee ESgI MMHG SCob SGol SHar SRGP XSen
'Edna Grace' (La)	LLWG
'Ed's Blue' (DB)	ELan
'Edward' (Reticulata)	CBro ECho EPfP EPot GKev LAma SDeJ
'Edward of Windsor' (TB)	ELan EWoo GMaP LRHS NLar SCob SRGP WMnd
'Ego' (Sib)	CAvo CHid ECha ELon EPfP EPri EWTr EWoo GBuc MGos SGSe SWat WMoo

	Name	Suppliers
	'Egyptian' (TB)	EWoo
	'Eileen Louise' (TB) ♀H7	WCAu
	'El Tovar' (TB)	EWoo
	'Eldorado' (TB)	EWoo
	'Eleanor Roosevelt' (IB)	EWoo
	'Eleanor's Pride' (TB)	ESgI WCAu
	'Electrique' (TB)	WCAu
	elegantissima	see *I. iberica* subsp. *elegantissima*
	'Eliminator' (TB) **new**	CIri
	'Elizabeth of England' (TB)	EWoo GKev MLHP WWEG
	'Elizabeth Poldark' (TB)	ESgI XSen
	'Ellenbank Sapphire' (Sib)	GBin
	'Ellesmere' (Sib)	EBee NGdn WAul
	'Elsa Sass' (TB)	ESgI
	'Elsie Petty' (IB)	SIri
	'Elvinhall'	CBro
	'Emperor' (Sib)	CWat NSti SWat
	'Empress of India' (TB)	EWoo
	'Encre Bleue' (IB)	ESgI
	'Endless Love' (TB)	EIri
	'English Charm' (TB)	ESgI WCAu XSen
	'English Cottage' (TB)	ELon GBin GCal LSRN MWat NLar WCAu XSen
	'Ennerdale' (TB)	SRms
	'Enriched' (MTB) ♀H7	SIri WCAu
§	***ensata***	CBcs CBod CBro ELan EPfP GKev LRHS MHer MJak MLHP MMuc MNrw NLar SEND SPlb SRms SWat WBor WPnP WWtn
	- 'Activity'	SHar WFar
	- 'Agrippine'	SKHP
	- 'Alba'	ECha
	- 'Alpine Majesty' ♀H7	CIri
	- 'Asian Warrior'	WFar
	- 'August Emperor'	MBel
	- 'Azuma-kagami'	CCon EBee ELan EPfP MNrw
	- 'Azure'	EBee WFar WMoo
	- 'Barnhawk Sybil'	SKHP
I	- 'Blue King'	NHol
I	- 'Blue Peter'	CBen
	- 'Blue Prince'	CBen
	- 'Caprician Butterfly' ♀H7	EPfP NLar
	- 'Carnival Prince'	CCon WFar WMoo
	- 'Cascade Crest'	SWat WFar
	- 'Center of Interest'	NBir
*	- 'Charm'	LRHS
	- 'Crepe Paper'	WFar
	- 'Cry of Rejoice'	EBee ECho ECtt SGol SWat
	- 'Crystal Halo' ♀H7	CIri EBee LSun
	- 'Dace'	GBin
I	- 'Darling'	ECho EPfP SWat WFar WMoo
	- 'Diamant'	GBin
	- 'Dramatic Moment'	GBuc WFar WWEG
	- 'Eden's Blush'	EBee MLHP
	- 'Eden's Charm'	EPfP GBin
	- 'Eden's Paintbrush'	EPfP SPer
	- 'Eden's Picasso'	CCon
	- 'Eden's Purple Glory'	CHid GBin
	- 'Eden's Starship'	CCon
	- 'Electric Rays'	EBee GAbr WFar
I	- 'Emotion'	CMac EBee WFar
	- 'Flying Tiger' ♀H7	CIri
I	- 'Fortune'	CBod EWTr GBin IKil MSCN
	- 'Freckled Geisha'	CIri CMac EBee ELon EPfP IPot NBir NQui SGol WFar
	- 'Frilled Enchantment' ♀H7	IPot WFar
I	- 'Galatea'	CBod CExl EBee LEdu WFar
	- 'Gipsy'	CMac EBee
	- 'Gold Bound'	GAbr SKHP
	- 'Gracieuse'	ELan GBin LRHS NLar SWat WCot
	- 'Gusto'	CMHG CMac EBee ELon EPfP IPot MNrw SWat WBor WFar
	- 'Harpswell Chantey' **new**	IPot
	- 'Hercule'	CExl CHid GAbr NBir
	- Higo white	SPer
	- 'Hoshi-akari'	WBor WFar
	- 'Hue and Cry' ♀H7	CIri
	- hybrids	EHon
	- 'Imperial Velvet'	WFar
*	- 'Innocence'	NLar SWat WFar WMoo
	- 'Iso-no-nami'	CDes EBee WFar
*	- 'Jitsugetsu'	CCon
	- 'Jocasta'	EPfP WFar
	- 'Jodlesong'	WFar
	- 'Kalamazoo'	WFar
	- 'Katy Mendez' ♀H7	IPot LLWG NLar
*	- 'Kiyo-zuru'	EPfP
	- 'Kogesho'	EBee EPfP GBuc NLar
	- 'Koh Dom'	SPer
	- 'Kongo San'	NLar WFar
	- 'Kuma-funjin'	CExl EBee
	- 'Kumo-no-obi'	CExl CMHG EBee GBin GBuc LRHS MCot NHol SPtp SWat WFar
	- 'Lady in Waiting'	CMHG EBee ECtt EPfP
	- 'Laughing Lion'	ECtt EWoo IKil WFar WMoo WWEG
	- 'Light at Dawn'	CMHG MBel WMoo
	- 'Lilac Blotch'	SPer
I	- 'Loyalty'	CExl ECho EWoo LRHS SHar WFar
	- 'Momogasumi'	LLWG NQui
	- 'Momozomo'	LLHF
§	- 'Moonlight Waves'	CExl CHid CMHG CMac CPrp EAEE EBee ELan EPfP GBuc GCra GKin GMaP IPot LRHS MBri MCot MRav MWts NGdn NHol SWat WFar
	- 'Oase'	ECtt
	- 'Ocean Mist'	CHid EBee ECtt GBuc IKil
	- 'Oku-banri'	CExl EBee WFar
	- 'Oriental Eyes'	NGdn NLar
	- pale mauve-flowered	NBir
	- 'Pin Stripe'	CDes EBee GAbr LSun NLar SWat WMoo
	- 'Pink Frost'	CPrp EBee ELan EPfP LHop WFar
	- 'Pinkerton'	CIri
	- 'Pleasant Earlybird'	WFar
	- 'Pleasant Journey'	EBee ECtt
	- 'Prairie Frost'	EBee NLar
	- 'Prairie Noble'	EBee
	- 'Praise' **new**	EBee
	- 'Purple Parasol' **new**	LLWG
	- 'Queen's Tiara'	ELon IPot LLWG
	- 'Rakka-no-utage'	EBee NLar
I	- 'Reveille'	SWat
	- 'Rivulets of Wine'	CIri
§	- 'Rose Queen' ♀H7	CExl CMac CPrp CSam ECha EHon ELan EPfP EWTr GBin GBuc GCra GKin GMaP LRHS MCot MRav MWts NBir NGdn NHol SPer WFar WMoo XLum
I	- 'Royal Banner'	EBee ECtt EWoo LRHS WFar WWEG
	- 'Royal Crown'	ECho XLum
I	- 'Ruby King'	LEdu LRHS
	- 'Ruffled Dimity'	EBee IPot
	- 'Sandsation'	CIri
I	- 'Sensation'	CWCL ECho ECtt EWoo GBin IKil IPot MWts NLar SWat WWEG

	- 'Snowy Hills'	XLum
	- 'Sorcerer's Triumph'	WFar
	- var. ***spontanea***	SWat
	- - B&SWJ 1103	WCru
	- - B&SWJ 8699	WCru
	- 'Stippled Ripples'	IPot MWts
	- 'Strut and Flourish'	EWoo
	- 'Taketori-hime' (v)	XLum
	- 'Umi-kaze'	NLar
	- 'Variegata' (v) ♀H7	CBod CHid CMac CPrp CSpe EBee ECha EHon ELon EPfP GBin GMaP IBoy LEdu LRHS MMuc MWts NLar NSti SEND SKHP SRms SWat WCot WFar WMoo WPnP WWEG
	- 'Velvety Queen'	ECtt
I	- 'White Ladies'	CSBt EWoo LRHS SWat
	- white-flowered	WFar
	- 'Wine Ruffles'	CMHG LSRN
	- 'Yako-no-tama'	WMoo
	- 'Yedo-yeman'	EBee IMou WFar
	'Épée Violette' (TB)	ESgI
	'Epicenter' (TB)	XSen
	'Eramosa Miss' (BB)	WCAu
	'Eramosa Skies' (SDB)	WCAu
	'Erect' (IB)	CKel
	'Eric the Red' (Sib)	ELon EWoo
	'Erste Sahne' (Sib)	GBin
	'Eternal Bliss' (TB)	SIri
	'Evadne' (TB)	WMil
	'Evening Drama' (TB)	WCAu
	'Evening Gown' (TB)	XSen
	'Ever After' (TB)	EWoo LCro XSen
	'Ever Again' (Sib)	ELon EWoo
	'Everything Plus' (TB)	ESgI WCAu XSen
	'Ewen' (Sib)	CHid CPou EWoo GBin GKin GLog GMaP ILea LEdu MNrw NGdn SGSe SWat WAul WCot WFar WWEG
	'Exotic Isle' (TB)	ESgI XSen
	'Expose' (TB)	WCAu
	'Extra' (BB)	CPBP LLHF
	'Extra Dazzle' (La)	LLWG
	'Extra Innings' (TB)	EWoo
	'Eye Magic' (IB)	CKel XSen
	'Eye of Tiger'	see *I.* 'Tigereye'
	'Eye Shadow' (SDB)	WCAu
	'Eyebright' (SDB) ♀H7	CBro WCAu
	'Fabuleux' (TB)	SIri
	'Face of an Angel' (TB) **new**	WCAu
	'Faenelia Hicks' (La)	WMAq
	'Falconeer' (TB)	CIri
	'Fall Empire' (TB)	EWoo
	'Fall Fiesta' (TB)	XSen
	'Fanciful Whimsy' (IB) **new**	WCAu
	'Fancy Brass' (TB)	SIri
	'Fancy Dress' (TB)	SIri
	'Fancy Woman' (TB)	WCAu
	'Fanfaron' (TB)	ESgI XSen
	'Farleigh Damson' (SDB)	SIri
	'Fashion Holiday' (IB)	SIri
	'Fashion Lady' (MDB)	CBro ECho
	'Fathom' (IB)	WCAu
	'Feather and Fan' (La) **new**	LLWG
	'Feminine Charm' (TB)	MRav WCAu
	'Festive Skirt' (TB)	CKel WCAu
	'Feu du Ciel' (TB) ♀H7	ESgI EWoo XSen
	'Few Are Chosen' (La)	LLWG
	'Fiddlin' Around' (TB) **new**	WCAu
	'Fiesta Time' (TB)	CWCL XSen
	'Film Festival' (TB)	ESgI
	'Finalist' (TB)	WCAu XSen
	'Fire in the Sky' (IB) **new**	WCAu
	'Firebeard' (TB)	CIri
	'Firebird' (TB) **new**	LRHS
	'Firebug' (IB)	ESgI XSen
	'Firecracker' (TB)	MRav WCAu
	'First Interstate' (TB)	CWCL ESgI XSen
	'First Movement' (TB)	ESgI
	'First Romance' (SDB)	LSRN
	'First Violet' (TB)	ESgI
	'Fit the Bill' (TB)	EWoo
	'Five Star Admiral' (TB)	XSen
	'Flaming Dragon' (TB)	XSen
	'Flaming Victory' (TB)	XSen
	flavescens	ESgI EWoo WCAu XSen
	'Flavours' (BB)	WCAu
	'Fleece of White' (BB)	WCAu
	'Fleur Collette Louise' (La)	CIri
	'Flight of Butterflies' (Sib)	Widely available
	'Flirting Again' (SDB) ♀H7	SIri
	'Floorshow' (TB)	XSen
	'Flopsy' (TB)	CIri
§	'Florentina' (IB/TB) ♀H7	CArn CBro CHby ECGP ESgI EWoo GCal GPoy LRHS MNHC MRav NBid NBir SEND WCAu WHer WHfH XSen
	'Florentine Silk' (TB)	WCAu
	'Floridor' (TB)	EWoo
	'Fluffy Pillows' (TB)	CIri
	'Flumadiddle' (IB)	CBro CTal
	'Flûte Enchantée' (TB)	CIri XSen
	'Flying Solo' (IB) **new**	CIri
	'Focus' (TB)	XSen
	foetidissima ♀H5	Widely available
	- 'Aurea'	EBee WCot
	- ***chinensis***	see *I. foetidissima* var. *citrina*
§	- var. ***citrina***	CBre CCon EPfP EPri GAbr GCra GKev LEdu NLar SChr WGwG
	- 'Fructu Albo'	GBin NSti
	- var. ***lutescens***	CHid
	- 'Variegata' (v) ♀H5	CElw EWoo NBir NPer
	'Fogbound' (TB)	WCAu
	'Foggy Dew' (TB)	EAEE LRHS MBri
	'Fondation Van Gogh' (TB)	XSen
	'Foolish Fancy' (TB)	SIri
	'Footloose' (TB)	SIri XSen
	'For Richard' (TB) **new**	CIri
	'Fordwich' (SDB)	SIri
	'Forecasting Rain' (SDB)	SIri
	'Foreign Legion' (TB)	EWoo WCAu
	'Foreigner' (TB)	WCAu
	'Forest Light' (SDB)	CBro ESgI
	'Forever Blue' (SDB)	WCAu
	'Forever Gold' (TB)	EWoo XSen
	'Forge Fire' (TB)	ESgI
	formosana	ECho
	- B&SWJ 3076	WCru
	'Forrest Hills' (TB)	CBod EPfP LRHS
	forrestii ♀H7	CAby CAvo CBro CCon CExl CHid CMac ECho EHoe EWoo GAbr GBin GCal GCra GKev GLog LRHS MMuc NBir SPtp SRot WAbe

- SDR 5802	GKev
- SDR 7871 **new**	GKev
'Fort Apache' (TB)	EWes EWoo
'Fortunata' (TB)	XSen
'Fortunate Son' (TB)	EWoo WCAu
'Fourfold Blue' (SpH)	GBin
'Fourfold Lavender' (Sib)	EWes NLar
'Fourfold White' (Sib)	ESgI
'Foxy Lady' (TB)	EWoo
'Framboise' (TB)	XSen
'Frances Iva' (TB)	EWoo
'Francheville' (TB)	EWoo
'Francina' (TB)	WMil
'Frank Elder' (Reticulata)	ECho EPot ERCP GKev LAma LLHF LRHS SDeJ WAbe
'Freedom Flight' (TB)	CIri
'French Can Can' (TB)	EWoo SIri
'French Horn' (TB)	CIri
'French Rose' (TB)	WCAu
'Fresno Calypso' (TB)	ESgI WCAu XSen
'Frison-roche' (TB)	CWCL
'Frisounette' (TB)	ESgI
'Fritillary Flight' (IB) ♀H7	CKel
'From this Moment' (La)	LLWG
'Frontier Lady' (TB)	CIri
'Frontier Marshall' (TB)	XSen
'Frost and Flame' (TB)	CKel EBee ECGP ECtt ELan EWoo GBin LCro LRHS MRav NBir NLar SDeJ SPer SPoG SWat WGwG
'Frost Echo' (TB)	EWoo
'Frosted Angel' (SDB)	CBro
'Frosted Velvet' (MTB)	WCAu
'Frosty Crown' (SDB)	CDes
'Frosty Jewels' (TB)	XSen
'Frosty Moonscape' (TB)	CIri
'Fruit Cocktail' (IB)	XSen
'Full Sun' (Spuria)	EWoo
fulva ♀H5	CSpe EBee EPri GBin GCal LPot MMHG MWts NBir NSti SBrt WBor WCot
- 'Marvell Gold' (La)	CDes EBee
× ***fulvala*** ♀H5	CCon EWes GBin NBir NSti
- 'Violacea'	LRHS
'Furnaceman' (SDB)	CBro CTal
'Futuriste' (TB)	SIri
'Fuzzy' (MDB)	EPot
'Gai Luron' (TB)	CKel WWEG
'Gallant Moment' (TB)	ECtt EWoo SIri XSen
'Galway' (IB)	SIri XSen
'Game Plan' (TB)	WCAu
'Gandalf the Grey' (TB)	ESgI
'Garnet Storm Dancer' (La) **new**	LLWG
'Gelbe Mantel' (Sino-Sib)	CHid GBin GKin MSpe NBir NSti
'Gemstone Walls' (TB)	ESgI
'Gentius' (TB)	EWoo WMnd
'George' (Reticulata) ♀H7	CAby CAvo CBro CWCL ECho EPfP EPot ERCP GKev LAma LRHS WBor WBrk WCot WHoo
'Gerald Darby'	see *I.* × *robusta* 'Gerald Darby'
'Germaine Perthuis' (TB)	EWoo
§ ***germanica***	MMuc SEND WCAu WCot WGwG
- var. ***florentina***	see *I.* 'Florentina'
§ - 'Nepalensis'	WCAu
- 'The King'	see *I. germanica* 'Nepalensis'
'Gertrude' (TB)	EWoo
'Ghost Train' (TB)	EWoo SIri
'Giacatollo' (TB)	CIri
'Gingerbread Castle' (TB)	WCAu
'Gingerbread Man' (SDB)	CBro CMea CTal ESgI EWoo MBrN WCAu
'Gingersnap' (TB)	EWoo
'Girly Girl' (TB) **new**	WCAu
'Glacier Gold' (TB)	XSen
'Glacier Point' (TB) **new**	CIri
'Glad Rags' (TB)	XSen
'Gladiator's Gift' (La)	LLWG
'Gladys Austin' (TB)	XSen
'Glowing Embers' (TB)	ESgI
'Gnu' (TB)	XSen
'Go Between' (TB)	WCAu
'Goddess of Green' (IB)	EWoo
'Godfrey Owen' (TB)	WCAu
'Godsend' (TB)	CIri
'Going Green' (TB)	CIri
'Going Home' (TB) ♀H7	SIri
'Going My Way' (TB)	ESgI EWoo LSou SIri WCAu WWEG XSen
'Gold Burst' (TB)	XSen
'Gold Country' (TB)	XSen
'Gold of Autumn' (TB)	CKel
'Goldberry' (IB)	WCAu
'Golden Alps' (TB)	SRms WCAu
'Golden Beauty'	SDeJ
'Golden Child' (SDB)	XSen
'Golden Crimping' (Sib)	EWoo
'Golden Ducat' (Spuria)	CIri
'Golden Edge' (Sib)	EWoo GQue LLWG MBel MWts NLar WFar WHil
'Golden Encore' (TB)	CKel WCAu
'Golden Fireworks' (La) **new**	LLWG
'Golden Folly' (SDB) **new**	CIri
'Golden Forest' (TB)	CBod GBin
'Golden Immortal' (TB)	EWoo
'Golden Panther' (TB)	WCAu
'Golden Violet' (SDB)	ESgI
'Good Looking' (TB)	ESgI WCAu
'Good Show' (TB)	ESgI EWoo WCAu XSen
'Good Vibrations' (TB)	SIri XSen
'Goodbye Heart' (TB)	EWoo LSRN
'Gordon' (Reticulata)	CAvo CBro ECho EPfP EPot ERCP GKev LAma LCro LOPS LRHS SCob
gormanii	see *I. tenax*
'Gossip' (SDB)	CBro
'Got the Melody' (TB)	EWoo WCAu
'Goudhurst' (SDB)	SIri
'Gracchus' (TB)	EWoo WCAu
'Grace Sturtevant' (TB) **new**	WMil
gracilipes	CEvo GEdr SBrt
- 'Alba'	CEvo GEdr
gracilipes × ***lacustris***	GEdr WAbe
graeberiana	ECho EPot GKev SDeJ
- yellow fall	ECho
graminea ♀H7	CAvo CBro CHid CMac ECho ELan EPfP EPri IFro LLWP MLHP NBir NSti WCot XEll
- 'Hort's Variety'	EBee
- var. ***pseudocyperus***	GCal SDys
graminifolia	see *I. kerneriana*
'Granaat' (Sib)	EBee
'Granada Gold' (TB)	SRms XSen
'Grand Circle' (TB)	EWoo
'Grand Illusion' (Spuria)	EWoo
'Grand Waltz' (TB)	XSen
'Granny Jean' (Sib) **new**	CKel

'Grapelet' (MDB)	CPBP WCAu
'Great Lakes' (TB)	ESgI EWoo
'Grecian Skies' (TB)	ESgI
'Green Eyed Lady' (TB)	ESgI
'Green Ice' (TB)	LRHS MRav
'Green Jungle' (TB)	EWoo
'Green Prophecy' (TB)	CKel
'Green Spot' (SDB) ♀H7	CBod CBro CKel CTal EAEE ECha ECho ECtt ELan GBuc LAst LHop LRHS MBri MRav NBir NLar SBea SDeJ SPer WAul WCAu
'Greenstuff' (SDB)	CTal
grey-flowered (Sib)	ELon
'Gringo' (TB)	WCAu
'Grooving' (BB)	ESgI
'Guatemala' (TB)	WCAu
'Gudrun' (TB)	EWoo
'Guess Who I Am' (TB)	WCAu
'Gull's Wing' (Sib)	LEdu LLWG NLar NSti
'Gurkha's Dance' (SDB)	SIri
'Gypsy Beauty' (Dut)	CAvo GKev LCro LOPS SDeJ
'Gypsy Jewels' (TB)	CKel ESgI XSen
'Gypsy Romance' (TB) ♀H7	EIri ESgI SIri WCAu
'Gypsy Tart' (SDB)	SIri
'Habit' (TB)	EWoo WCAu
'Hakuna Matata' (AB)	SDys
'Halloween Halo' (TB)	WCAu
halophila	see *I. spuria* subsp. *halophila*
'Happenstance' (TB)	EWoo WCAu
'Happy Mood' (IB)	WCAu
'Harbor Blue' (TB)	CKel CTsd EWoo MWat SWat WCAu WWEG
'Harlow Gold' (IB)	ESgI
'Harmony' ambig.	SCob SPer
'Harmony' (Reticulata)	CAby CAvo CBro ECho EPfP EPot GKev LAma LCro LOPS LRHS MBri SCob SDeJ WBrk
'Harpswell Hallelujah' (Sib)	EBee EWoo
'Harpswell Happiness' (Sib) ♀H7	CPrp EBee ELon EPfP EPri GAbr GBin GCra ILea MLHP SBch SWat WAul WMoo
'Harpswell Haze' (Sib)	ECha
'Harriette Halloway' (TB)	CBod CWGN ECGP EPfP EShb EWoo LHop LRHS LSRN NLar SHar SRGP WCot
hartwegii	ECho
'Harvest King' (TB)	XSen
'Harvest of Memories' (TB)	CKel ESgI EWoo WWEG
'Haut les Voiles' (TB)	CWCL
'Haute Couture' (TB)	XSen
'Haviland' (TB)	XSen
'Headcorn' (MTB) ♀H7	SIri
'Headline Banner' (BB)	EWoo WCAu
'Headway' (Spuria)	WCAu
'Heartbeat Away' (TB)	CIri
'Heartbreak Point' (TB)	EWoo
'Heart's Radiance' (MTB)	SDys
'Heather Carpet' (SDB)	WCAu
'Heather Stream' (La) **new**	ELon
'Heavenly Blue' (Sib)	LSun MWat SPer
'Heavenly Days' (TB)	WCAu
'Heavenly Horns' (TB)	CIri
'Helen Astor' (Sib)	CTri MRav SWat
'Helen Collingwood' (TB)	ESgI EWoo
'Helen Dawn' (TB) ♀H7	SIri
'Helen McGregor' (TB)	EWoo
'Helen Proctor' (IB)	ESgI WCot XSen
'Helen Traubel' (TB)	WCAu
'Helena Terry' (TB)	ESgI
'Helene C.' (TB)	EWoo XSen
'Helge' (IB)	ECho SWat
'Heliotrope Bouquet' (Sib)	EWoo
'Hellcat' (IB)	EWoo WCAu
'Hello Darkness' (TB) ♀H7	ESgI EWoo WCAu WCot XSen
'Hell's Fire' (TB)	ELan ELon EWoo WCAu
'Hemstitched' (TB)	EWoo MHol
'Her Majesty' (TB)	EWoo
'Hercules' (Reticulata)	ECho
'Here Comes The Night' (TB)	WCAu
'Here Comes The Sun' (TB)	WCAu
'Hever Castle' (Kent Castles Series) (BB)	SIri
'Hey True Blue' (TB) **new**	WCAu
'Hi' (IB)	CIri
'High Barbaree' (TB)	EWoo
'High Blue Sky' (TB)	WCAu
'High Command' (TB)	CKel WCAu
'High Impact' (TB)	CIri EWoo
'High Peak' (TB)	WCAu
'Highland Mist' (La)	LLWG
'Highline Amethyst' (Spuria)	EPri
'Hildegarde' (Dut)	SDeJ
'Himmel von Komi' (Sib)	GBin
'His Royal Highness' (TB)	WCAu
histrio	ECho EPot
- subsp. ***aintabensis***	ECho
histrioides	ECho GKev
§ - 'Angel's Tears' (Reticulata)	ECho
- 'Halkis' (Reticulata)	EPot ERCP GKev LAma SDeJ
- 'Lady Beatrix Stanley'	CAvo CBro ECho EPot ERCP GKev LAma LLHF LRHS SBch WBrk WHoo
- 'Major'	CDes ECho GKev LAma
- var. ***sophenensis***	ECho EPot LAma
'Hoar Edge' (Sib)	NChi WAul
'Hocus Pocus' (SDB)	CAby CBod CKel CTal CWGN EAEE ECho EPfP EWoo GBuc LRHS LSou MMHG SBea WAul
'Hohe Warte' (Sib) ♀H7	GBin WAul
'Höhenflug' (Sib)	GBin
'Holden Clough' (SpH) ♀H7	CExl ELan EPfP GBin GCra GMaP LEdu MMuc MNrw MRav MSpe NBir NChi NGdn NSti NWad WBrk WCAu WFar WHer WSHC WWEG
'Holden's Child'	CBod
'Holidaze' (IB) ♀H7	EIri
'Hollywood Nights' (TB)	EWoo
'Holtentol' **new**	WCAu
'Holy Night' (TB)	CKel
'Honey Glazed' (IB)	ESgI WCAu
'Honey Mocha Lotta' (Spuria)	EWoo
'Honey Stars' (La)	LLWG
'Honeylove' (SDB)	SDys
'Honeymoon Suite' (TB)	EWoo
'Honeyplic' (IB) ♀H7	ESgI SIri
'Honington' (SDB)	WCAu
'Honky Tonk Blues' (TB)	ESgI LSRN MAvo
'Honorabile' (MTB)	ESgI WCAu
hoogiana ♀H4	ECho EPot GKev

	- 'Purpurea'	ECho
§	***hookeri***	CFis CPBP CSma CTal ECho ELan GBin GKev GMaP SBrt SGSe WIce WThu WTor
	- SDR 2202	GKev
	'Hopelessly Devoted' (La)	LLWG
	'Hoptoit' (TB)	CIri
	'Horizon Bleu' (TB)	EWoo
	'Horned Rosyred' (TB)	EWoo
§	'Hornpipe' (TB)	WCAu
	'Hortensia Rose' (TB)	SIri
	'Hot and Spicy' (La) **new**	LLWG
	'Hot Gossip' (TB)	WCAu
	'Hot to Trot' (TB)	ESgI
	'Hottentot' (SDB)	WCAu
	'Howler' (TB) **new**	WCAu
	'Hubbard' (Sib)	EPri LLWG MBel MNrw WFar
	'Huckleberry Fudge' (TB)	XSen
	'Hugh Miller' (TB)	WCAu
	'Hula Hands' (IB)	CIri
	'Hula Moon' (TB)	ESgI
	'Hypnotizer' (TB)	CIri
	hyrcana	ECho
	'I Feel Good' (TB)	WCAu
	'I Pink I Can' (TB) **new**	WCAu
	'I Repeat' (TB)	XSen
	'I Seek You' (TB)	ESgI
	iberica	ECho
§	- subsp. ***elegantissima***	ECho
	'Ice' **new**	WCAu
	'Ice and Indigo' (SDB)	WCAu
	'Ice Cave' (TB)	WCAu
	'Ice Dancer' (TB) ♀H7	CKel
	'Ice Etching' (SDB)	WCAu
	'Ice for Brice' (TB)	CIri
	'Ice Wings' (BB)	WCAu
	'Ida' (Reticulata)	ECho LAma
	'Idol' (TB)	EWoo
	'Ila Crawford' (Spuria) ♀H7	XSen
	'Illini Charm' (Sib)	CHid EBee WFar WMoo
	illyrica	see *I. pallida*
	'I'm Back' (TB)	WCAu
	'Immortality' (TB)	CKel CWGN ESgI LRHS SCob WCAu WWEG XSen
	'Imperative' (IB)	EWoo SIri WCAu
I	'Imperial Velvet' (Sib)	EWoo WFar
	'Impersonator' (TB)	CIri
	'Imprimis' (TB)	EWoo XSen
	'In a Flash' (IB)	WCAu
	'In Love' (TB)	XSen
	'In Town' (TB)	EWoo XSen
	'In Your Dreams' (TB)	CIri
	'Incentive' (TB)	EWoo
	'Incognito Too' (TB)	CIri
*	'Incoscente' (TB)	ESgI
	'Indeed' (IB)	ESgI
	'Indian Chief' (TB)	CBod CWCL EPfP ESgI EWoo IBoy MCot MRav WCAu WWEG
	'Indian Hills' (TB)	EWoo
	'Indian Idyll' (IB)	CKel
	'Indian Jewel' (SDB)	ECho
	'Indiana Sunset' (TB)	CKel
	'Indigo Princess' (TB)	EWoo XSen
	'Infanta' (SDB)	WCAu
	'Inferno' (TB)	EWoo
	'Ink Patterns' (TB) **new**	WCAu
	'Inner Show' **new**	WCAu
	'Innocent Devil' (TB)	CIri
	'Innocent Pink' (TB)	ESgI
	innominata	ECho GKev LRHS NBir NBro SRms WWEG
	- hybrids	CPne
	- yellow-flowered	NRya
	'Inscription' (SDB)	ECho
	'Inside Job' (TB) **new**	WCAu
	'Inspired' (TB)	WCAu
	'Instant Hit' (TB)	WCAu
	'Intermediary' (IB)	WCAu
	'Interpol' (TB)	ESgI EWoo XSen
	'Invicta Daybreak' (IB)	SIri
	'Invicta Garnet' (SDB)	SIri
	'Invicta Gold' (SDB)	SIri
	'Invicta Reprieve' (IB)	SIri
	'Irene' (TB) **new**	WCAu
	'Iriade' (TB) **new**	WCAu
	'Iris Bohnsack' (BB) **new**	WCAu
	'Irisades' (TB)	WCAu
	'Irish Chant' (SDB)	WCAu
	'Irish Doll' (MDB)	WCAu
	'Irish Gold' (TB) **new**	WCAu
	'Irish Harp' (SDB)	ESgI
	'Irish Jig' (TB) **new**	WCAu
	'Irish Squire' (TB) **new**	WCAu
	'Irish Tune' (TB)	ESgI
	'Iron Eagle' (TB)	CIri
	'Isabelle' (Sib)	LSRN XSen
	'Island Sun' (SDB)	SIri
	'Island Sunset' (TB)	ESgI SIri
	'Isoline' (TB)	ESgI
	'It Happens' (TB)	WCAu
	'Italian Ice' (TB)	EIri
	'Italian Velvet' (TB)	EWoo WCAu
	'It's Amazing' (IB) **new**	WCAu
	'Ivory Queen' (Sib)	EWoo
	'J.S. Dijt' (Reticulata)	CAvo CBro ECho EPot ERCP GKev LAma LRHS MBri MGos SDeJ
	'Jack Attack' (La)	CBod CPrp LAst SPoG WMoo
	'Jac-y-do' (Sib)	EWes
	'Jade Mist' (SDB)	ECho
	'Jaguar Blue' (TB)	EWoo
	'Jane Phillips' (TB) ♀H7	Widely available
	'Janet Lane' (BB)	CKel
	'Japanesque' (MTB)	CIri
	japonica ♀H4	CExl ECho NLar NPer SPlb XLum XSen
	- B&SWJ 8921	WCru
	- 'Bourne Graceful'	CExl
	- 'Ledger'	CAby CAvo CExl CHll CMac ECha MRav SEND SGSe SMad
	- 'Monty'	WWFP
	- f. ***pallescens***	SGSe
I	- 'Purple Heart'	CAvo
	- 'Rudolph Spring'	EBee GCal WSHC WWFP
I	- 'Snowflake'	CAvo
§	- 'Variegata' (v) ♀H4	CBro CPrp CTsd ECha ECho ELan ESwi NPer NSti SEND WWFP XSen
	'Jasper Gem' (MDB)	ECho
	'Jazz Festival' (TB)	EWoo SIri WCAu XSen
	'Jazz Hot' (La) **new**	LLWG
	'Jazzed Up' (TB)	XSen
	'Je l'Adore' (TB)	EWoo
	'Jean Cayeux' (TB)	ESgI EWoo
	'Jean Guymer' (TB)	ESgI
	'Jeanne Price' (TB)	ESgI EWoo LSRN WCAu
	'Jelly Belly' (SDB)	EWoo
	'Jeremy Brian' (SDB)	WCAu
	'Jeremy Jets On' (TB)	CIri

	Name	Suppliers
	'Jesse's Song' (TB)	ESgI WCAu XSen
	'Jet Black' (TB)	EWoo
	'Jet-Setter' (TB)	CIri
	'Jeunesse' (TB)	ESgI
	'Jewel Baby' (SDB)	CBro
	'Jeweler's Art' (SDB)	ESgI EWoo
	'Jewelled Crown' (Sib)	WFar
	'Jiansada' (SDB)	CBro
	'Jigsaw' (TB)	ESgI XSen
	'Jitterbug' (TB)	WCAu
	'Joanna' (TB)	LSRN NLar WWEG
	'John' (IB)	CKel LSRN
	'Joli Coeur' (TB)	EWoo
	'Joyce' (Reticulata)	CBro ECho EPfP EPot GKev LAma LRHS MBri SDeJ
	'Joyful Skies' (TB)	WCAu
	'Jubilant Spirit' (Spuria)	EWes
	'Jubilation' (TB)	EWoo
	'Jubilee Gem' (TB)	CKel WCAu
	'Judy Mogil' (TB)	CIri
	'Juliet' (TB)	ESgI
	'Jump for Joy' (TB)	CIri
	'Jump Start' (IB)	EWoo WCAu
	'Jumping Jupiter' (TB)	CIri
	'Junaluska' (TB)	EWoo
	'June Prom' (IB)	EAEE LRHS SRGP WCAu
	'Jungle Fires' (TB)	WCAu
	'Jungle Shadows' (BB)	ESgI EWoo MRav NBir WCAu
	'Jurassic Park' (TB)	ESgI EWoo WCAu XSen
	'Just Before Midnight'	LRHS
	'Just Imagine' (La)	LLWG
	'Just Jennifer' (BB)	WCAu
	'Kabluey' (Sib)	IPot
	'Kaboom' (Sib) **new**	IPot
	kaempferi	see *I. ensata*
	'Kahuna' (IB)	WCAu
	'Kaint Hardly Believe' (TB) **new**	CIri
	'Karen' (TB)	LSRN
	'Katharine Hodgkin' (Reticulata) ♀H7	CAby CAvo CBro CTca EBee ECha ECho EPfP EPot ERCP GAbr GBuc GKev LAma LCro LOPS LRHS MNrw MRav MWat NBir NLar SCob SDeJ WAbe WBrk WCot WFar WHoo WSHC
	'Katharine Hodgkin' dark-flowered (Reticulata)	EPot
	'Kathleen Mary' (Sib)	WAul
	'Katie-Koo' (IB) ♀H7	CKel
	'Katy Petts' (SDB)	ESgI WCAu
	'Keeping up Appearances' (TB)	WCAu
	kemaonensis PAB 8473 **new**	LEdu
	'Kent Arrival' (Sib)	SIri
	'Kent Blackguard' (IB)	SIri
	'Kent Compote' (IB)	SIri
	'Kent Pride' (TB)	CAby CBod CKel COtt CSBt EAEE ECha ECtt EPfP ESgI EUJe EWoo GBin LRHS MBri MCot MRav MWhi SCob SPer SPoG SWat WBod WCAu
	Kenta No Se129 (Sib)	EPri
	'Kentish Icon' (SDB)	SIri
	'Kentish Lad' (IB)	SIri
	'Kentucky Derby' (TB)	XSen
§	***kerneriana*** ♀H4	CBro EHoe GBuc GKev NBir
	'Kęstutis Genys' (Sib)	WAul
	'Kharput' (IB)	EWoo
	'Kildonan' (TB)	WCAu

	Name	Suppliers
	'King of Kings' (Sib)	WFar
	'Kingfisher' (Sib)	WAul
	'King's Jester' (TB)	EWoo
	'Kirkstone' (TB)	WCAu
	kirkwoodii	ECho
	'Kiss of Summer' (TB) ♀H7	ESgI SDys
	'Kissing Circle' (TB)	ESgI EWoo
	'Kita-no-seiza' (Sib)	CIri EBee
	'Kiwi Slices' (SDB)	CWat ESgI
	'Knick Knack' (MDB)	CBro CPBP CTal ECho ELan ELon EPfP GMaP LRHS MBri MRav SDeJ SPoG
	korolkowii	CTal ECho
	'Kuh-e-Abr'	LAma LLHF
	'La Meije' (TB)	SIri
	'La Senda' (Spuria)	WCot
	'Lace Legacy' (TB)	EWoo LSRN
	'Laced Cotton' (TB)	WCAu XSen
§	***lactea***	SBrt XEll XSen
	- CC 7174 **new**	GKev
	lacustris	CPBP WAbe WCot XSen
	'Lacy Snowflake' (TB)	LHop LRHS
	'Lad'	WCAu
	'Lady Belle' (MTB)	ESgI
	'Lady Byng' (TB)	WMil
	'Lady Essex' (TB)	EWoo WCAu
	'Lady Friend' (TB)	WCAu XSen
	'Lady Gale' (IB)	CKel
	'Lady in Red' (SDB)	ESgI WCAu
	'Lady Mohr' (AB)	WCAu
	'Lady of the Night' (BB) **new**	WCAu
	'Lady R' (SDB)	ECho
	'Lady Vanessa' (Sib)	CPou EBee ELon EPPr MRav NSti
	laevigata	CWat ECho EHon ELan EPfP EWay ITim MRav NBro NPer SPer SWat WFar WMAq WMoo WShi WWEG
	- var. ***alba***	ECho LLWG SWat WAbe WMoo
	- 'Albopurpurea'	SGSe
	- 'Atropurpurea'	LLWG
	- 'Colchesterensis'	CWat EPri EWay NGdn NPer SWat WMAq WMoo
I	- 'Dorothy'	NGdn
	- 'Dorothy Robinson'	ELan EPfP MRav SWat
I	- 'Elegante'	EWay
*	- 'Elgar'	WMAq
	- 'Midnight'	see *I. laevigata* 'Weymouth Midnight'
	- 'Monstrosa'	CDes EWay
	- 'Richard Greaney'	EWay
	- 'Rose Queen'	see *I. ensata* 'Rose Queen'
I	- 'Snowdrift'	CWat EHon EWay MJak NBir NGdn NLar NPer SWat WFar WMAq WMoo
	- 'Variegata' (v) ♀H7	CBen CWat EAEE ECha ECho EHoe ELan ELon EPfP EWay LLWG MWts NBro NGdn NPer SWat WMAq WMoo WPnP WWtn
	- 'Violet Garth'	EWay
	- 'Weymouth'	see *I. laevigata* 'Weymouth Blue'
§	- 'Weymouth Blue'	CBen EWay
§	- 'Weymouth Midnight'	SWat
	- 'Weymouth Purity'	EWay
§	'Lake Niklas' (Sib)	EBee ELon GBin MHol NCGa
	'Lambourn Hills' (TB) **new**	WCAu
	'Lamia' (TB)	CIri
	'Langport Chapter' (IB)	CKel ESgI
	'Langport Chief' (IB)	CKel

'Langport Claret' (IB)	CKel ESgI
'Langport Curlew' (IB)	CKel ESgI
'Langport Duchess' (IB)	ESgI
'Langport Fairy' (IB)	CKel
'Langport Flame' (IB)	CKel ESgI
'Langport Hope' (IB)	CKel
'Langport Jane' (IB)	CKel
'Langport Lady' (IB)	CKel
'Langport Lord' (IB)	ESgI
'Langport Minstrel' (IB)	CKel ESgI
'Langport Pearl' (IB)	CKel
'Langport Pinnacle' (IB)	CKel
'Langport Smoke' (IB)	CKel
'Langport Star' (IB)	CKel ESgI
'Langport Storm' (IB)	CKel EPfP LRHS MBri MRav SBea SDeJ WHoo
'Langport Sun' (IB)	ESgI
'Langport Sylvia' (IB)	CKel
'Langport Violet' (IB)	CKel ESgI
'Langport Vista' (IB)	CKel
'Langport Wren' (IB) ♀H7	CAby CBod CBro CKel ECGP EPfP EPri ESgI EShb EWoo GBuc GCal LAst LHop LRHS MBri MWhi NBir NGdn SBea WAul WPtf WWEG
'Langthorns Pink' (Sib)	CCse ELan MRav WAul
'Lark Rise' (TB) ♀H7	CKel
'Larry Gaulter' (TB)	WCAu
'Last Hurrah' (TB)	EWoo
'Late Liftoff' (TB)	CIri
§ ***latifolia***	GKev MMuc SEND WShi
- ***alba***	WCot
- 'Duchess of York'	EBee ECho GKev
- 'Isabella'	GKev SDeJ
- 'King of the Blues'	CAvo EBee ECho EPot GKev SDeJ
- 'Mansfield'	ECho MNrw
- 'Montblanc'	CAvo EPot GKev SDeJ
- 'Queen of the Blues' (Eng)	ECho EPot SDeJ
- wild-collected	GCal
'Latin Lark' (TB)	ESgI
'Latin Rock' (TB)	WCAu
'Latino' (IB)	WCAu
'Laura Jean' (TB)	EWoo
'Laura Louise' (La)	LLWG SKHP
'Laurenbuhl' (Sib)	CExl
'Lavanesque' (TB)	WCAu
'Lavender Bounty' (Sib)	CHid
'Lavender Light' (Sib)	WAul
lazica ♀H5	CBct CBro CMac CPrp EPPr EPfP EPot EWoo GBin GKev IBlr LRHS MRav NBir NCGa NSti SBrt SEND SPlb WGwG WSHC
- 'Joy Bishop'	CJun
* - 'Richard Nutt'	CJun ELon WCot WSHC
- 'Turkish Blue'	CPrp IBlr
'Legato' (TB)	ESgI
* 'Lemon Beauty' (TB)	LHop
'Lemon Brocade' (TB)	EWoo WCAu
'Lemon Flare' (SDB)	EIri MRav SRms
'Lemon Ice' (TB)	CAby CBod CKel EAEE ECha EPfP GBin LRHS SDeJ SPer WHoo
'Lemon Lyric' (TB)	ESgI
'Lemon on Ice' (SDB)	WCAu
'Lemon Pop' (IB)	WCAu
'Lemon Puff' (MDB)	CBro LLHF WCAu
'Lemon Tree' (TB)	WCAu
'Lemon Whip' (IB)	EWoo
'Lena' (SDB)	CBro
'Lenna M' (SDB)	ECho
'Lenora Pearl' (BB)	XSen
'Lent A. Williamson' (TB)	EWoo GMaP WWEG
'Lenten Prayer' (TB)	EWoo WCAu
'Lenzschnee' (TB)	EWoo
'Leprechaun's Purse' (SDB)	WCAu
'Let's Elope' (IB)	ESgI WCAu
'Licorice Stick' (TB)	XSen
'Light Beam' (TB)	XSen
'Light Cavalry' (IB)	ESgI EWoo
'Light Laughter' (IB)	WCAu
'Light Rebuff' (TB)	EWoo
'Lilac Times'	EWoo
'Lilli-white' (SDB)	CAby CKel CWat ELan ELon EPfP GEdr LRHS MBNS MBri MRav SBea SPoG WCAu WWEG
'Lilting' (TB)	XSen
'Lime Fizz' (TB)	XSen
'Limeheart' (Sib)	CPou LLHF
'Limelight' (TB)	SRms
'Linda Mary' (Sib)	EWoo
'Linda's Child' (TB)	WCAu
'Line Dancing' (Spuria)	CIri
'Lingering Love' (TB)	WCAu
'Lion King' (Dut)	LCro LOPS
'Little Black Belt' (SDB)	EBee EWoo LRHS
'Little Blackfoot' (SDB)	CDes CTal ESgI WCAu WCot
'Little Blue-eyes' (SDB)	ESgI WCAu
'Little Bluets' (SDB)	ESgI
'Little Dandy' (SDB)	ECho
'Little Dogie' (SDB)	ECho
'Little Dream' (SDB)	WCAu
'Little Firecracker' (SDB)	WCAu
'Little Freak' (BB) **new**	CIri
'Little Nutkin' (La) **new**	LLWG
'Little Paul' (MTB)	ESgI
'Little Rosy Wings' (SDB)	CBro CPBP
'Little Shadow' (IB)	MRav SRms WWEG
'Little Sheba' (AB)	WCAu
'Little Showoff' (SDB)	ESgI
'Little Tilgates' (CH)	WCot WSHC
'Living Waters' (TB)	ESgI
'Local Color' (TB)	ESgI EWoo SIri XSen
'Local Hero' (IB)	WCAu
'Lodore' (TB)	SRms
'Logo' (IB)	WCAu
'Lohengrin' (TB)	EWoo
'Lollipop' (SDB)	EAJP ESgI SIri
'London Pride' (TB)	EWoo
longipetala	EPPr EWes NBir
'Looking Forward' (TB)	ESgI
'Loop the Loop' (TB)	CBod CMac CTsd EWoo SGol SPoG SWat
'Loose Valley' (MTB) ♀H7	SIri
'Lord Warden' (TB)	CAby CBod CKel ECtt EPfP LRHS WGwG
'Lorilee' (TB)	ESgI WCAu
'Lost in Love' (TB) **new**	WCAu
'Lost in Space' (BB)	CIri
'Lottie Lou' (TB)	SIri
'Lotus Land' (TB)	WCAu
'Louisa's Song' (TB)	WCAu
Louisiana hybrids	ELan
'Louvois' (TB)	CKel ESgI EWoo NLar
'Love Power' (BB)	WCAu
'Love the Sun' (TB)	ESgI XSen
'Lovely Again' (TB)	LRHS MRav WCAu
'Lovely Dawn' (TB)	WCAu
'Lovely Leilani' (TB)	ESgI
'Lovely Señorita' (TB)	WCAu

	Name	Suppliers
	'Love's Tune' (IB)	CRos EAEE EBee LRHS SRGP SWat
	'Low Ho Silver' (IB)	WCAu
	'Loyalist' (TB)	CPar EWoo SIri
	'Lucy's Gift' (MTB) ♀H7	EAJP SRGP
	'Lugano' (TB)	ESgI EWoo
	'Lula Marguerite' (TB)	EWoo
	'Luli-Ann' (SDB)	CKel
	'Lullaby of Spring' (TB)	CKel
	'Lullingstone Castle' (Kent Castles Series) (IB)	SIri
	'Lumarco' (TB)	EWoo
	'Lumière d'Automne' (TB)	ESgI XSen
	'Lunar Fire' (TB) **new**	LRHS
	'Lure of Gold' (IB)	WCAu
	'Lurline' (TB)	WMil
	lutescens ♀H7	ECho EPot GCra GKev WAbe
§	- 'Campbellii'	ECho
§	- subsp. ***lutescens***	XSen
	- subsp. ***subbiflora***	EPot
	'Ma Mie' (IB)	MMHG
	maackii	GEdr
	'Mabel Coday' (Sib)	EPri EWoo
	'Madame Lynn' (Spuria)	EWoo
	'Madeira Belle' (TB)	CKel EAEE EPfP ESgI LRHS WCAu WGwG WTor
	'Madeleine Frances' (SDB)	SIri
	'Magharee' (TB)	ESgI
	'Magic Man' (TB)	XSen
	'Magic Masquerade' (TB) **new**	WCAu
	'Magical Encounter' (TB)	EWoo LCro SIri
	magnifica ♀H5	ECho ELon GKev
	- 'Agalik'	ECho GKev
	- 'Alba'	ECho GKev
	'Maid of Orange' (BB)	WCAu
	'Maisie Lowe' (TB)	ESgI EWoo
	'Majestic' (TB) **new**	WMil
	'Majestic Ruler' (TB)	WCAu
	'Making Eyes' (SDB)	WCAu
	'Mambo Italiano' (TB) **new**	WCAu
	'Man About Town' (TB)	WCAu
	'Mandarin Purple' (Sino-Sib)	EBee NEgg
	mandshurica	CPBP
	'Mango Entree' (TB)	WCAu
	'Mango Smoothy' (BB)	ESgI
	'Marden Beech' (IB) **new**	SIri
	'Marden Meadow' (MTB)	SIri
	'Margrave' (TB)	EWoo XSen
	'Marguérite' (Reticulata/v)	ECho WCAu
	'Marilyn Holmes' (Sib)	GBin GLog GQue WCot
	'Mariposa Autumn' (TB)	EWoo SIri
	'Marmalade Skies' (BB)	WCAu
	'Marsh Marigold' (TB) **new**	WMil
	'Marshmallow Frosting' (Sib)	WFar
	'Martyn Rix'	see *I. confusa* 'Martyn Rix'
	'Mary Frances' (TB)	CKel ESgI LSRN WCAu XSen
	'Mary Geddes' (TB)	EWoo
	'Mary McIlroy' (SDB) ♀H7	CBro
	'Master Touch' (TB)	ELon XSen
	'Masterwork' (TB)	CIri
	'Material Girl' (TB)	WCAu
	'Matinata' (TB)	CKel EWoo XSen
	'Matt McNames' (TB)	EWoo
	'Maui Moonlight' (IB) ♀H7	CKel ESgI EWoo NLar WCAu
	'May Melody' (TB)	WCAu
	'Maya Mint' (MDB)	LLHF
	'Meadow Court' (SDB)	CBro CKel CTal WCAu WWEG
	'Medallion' (Spuria)	EWoo
	'Media Luz' (Spuria)	WCAu
	'Medici Prince' (TB)	EWoo WCAu
	'Medway Valley' (MTB) ♀H7	SIri WCAu
	'Megglethorp' (IB)	WCAu
	'Melbreak' (TB)	ESgI
	mellita	see *I. suaveolens*
	'Mellow Yellow' (TB) **new**	CLet
	'Melon Honey' (SDB)	CKel EBee ELon WCAu
	'Melted Butter' (TB)	WCAu
§	'Melton Red Flare' (Sib)	EAJP EBee EPPr LRHS LSou MBNS MSpe WWEG
	'Memphis Memory' (Sib)	ELan ELon GCra MHol NLar SPer WWEG
	'Men in Black' (TB)	EWoo WCAu
	'Mer du Sud' (TB) ♀H7	EBee EIri ESgI EWoo LCro LRHS XSen
*	'Merebrook Blue Lagoon' (La)	WMAq
	'Merebrook Jemma J' (La)	WMAq
*	'Merebrook Lemon Maid' (La)	WMAq
	'Merebrook Purpla' (La)	WMAq
	'Merebrook Rum 'n' Raisin' (La)	WMAq
*	'Merebrook Rusty Red' (La)	WMAq
*	'Merebrook Snowflake' (La)	WMAq
	'Merebrook Sunnyside Up' (La)	WMAq
	'Merebrook Symphony' (La)	WMAq
	'Mescal' (TB)	WCAu
	mesopotamica	see *I. germanica*
	'Messire Pierre' (BB)	CIri
	'Messy Jessi' (TB)	CIri
	'Metaphor' (TB)	WCAu
	'Mezza Cartuccia' (IB)	ESgI
	'Miami Beach' (TB)	WCAu
	'Midas Mite' (MDB)	LLHF
I	'Midnight Blue' (MDB)	CBro
	'Midnight Caller' (TB)	ESgI EWoo XSen
	'Midnight Majesty' (TB)	EWoo
	'Midnight Oil' (TB)	EWoo WCAu
	'Midnight Thunder' (TB)	CIri
	'Midnight Treat' (TB)	WCAu
	'Midsummer Night's Dream' (IB)	ESgI EWoo
	'Mighty Mouse' (MDB)	ELon EWoo
	'Mighty Warrior' (TB)	CIri
	'Milesaway' (TB) **new**	WCAu
	milesii ♀H3	CExl GKev NBir SBrt
	- CC 6839	GKev
	'Millennium Sunrise' (TB)	WCAu
	'Mini Big Horn' (IB)	CIri
	'Mini-Agnes' (SDB)	CBro
	'Minisa' (TB)	ESgI
	'Miss Nellie' (BB)	CKel
	'Miss Sunshine' (SDB)	CPBP
	'Missouri Streams' (Spuria)	EWoo
	missouriensis	CMac
	'Mist Arising' (TB)	CIri
	'Mister Roberts' (SDB)	ESgI

Name	Suppliers
'Mistress of Camelot' (TB)	SDys
'Mme Chéreau' (TB)	ESgI EWoo WCAu
'Moby Grape' (TB)	GKev
'Mon Prince' (BB)	CIri
'Monsieur-Monsieur' (TB)	ESgI
Monspur Group	WCot
'Moon Journey' (TB)	EWoo
'Moon Silk' (Sib)	ECtt ELon EPri GAbr GBuc LLHF SCob WCot WFar
'Moonlight Waves'	see *I. ensata* 'Moonlight Waves'
'Moonlit' (TB)	CIri
'Moonlit Water' (TB)	WCAu
'Morning Splendor' (TB)	EWoo
'Morwell' (TB)	WMil
'Morwenna' (TB) 🏆H7	ESgI
'Mother Earth' (TB)	ESgI
'Mountain Lake' (Sib)	EPfP EShb GBin LRHS SHar SPtp SWat WFar WPtf
'Mountain Violet' (TB)	EWoo
'Mrs Horace Darwin' (TB)	CCon EWoo SWat WMnd
'Mrs Nate Rudolph' (SDB)	WCAu
'Mrs Rowe' (Sib)	CCse CPou EIri EPri GBuc LLWP MRav MWat SWat WAul WFar
'Mrs Tait' (Spuria)	NChi
'Mrs Valerie West' (TB)	WMil
'Mrs Wright's Pink' **new**	WCAu
'Muggles' (SDB)	SIri
'Mukaddam' (TB)	CIri
'Murder Mystery' (TB)	WCAu
'Murmuring Morn' (TB)	WCAu
'Music' (SDB)	SIri
'Must Unite' (TB)	WCAu
'My First Kiss' (Sib) **new**	WAul
'My Kayla' (SDB)	ESgI
'My Love' (Sib)	GBin IMou WAul
'My Seedling' (MDB)	CBro
'Myra' (SDB)	XSen
'Mysterieux' (TB)	SIri
'Mystic' (TB)	WMil
'Mystic Beauty' (Dut)	GKev
'Mystic Dragon' (TB)	CIri SDys
'Nada' **new**	WCot
'Naivasha' (TB)	CKel
'Nancy Hardy' (MDB)	CBro
'Naples' (TB)	WCAu
'Nassak' (TB)	EWoo
'Natascha' (Reticulata)	ECho EPot LAma SCob SDeJ
'Natchez Trace' (TB)	CKel EPri WCot XSen
'Navajo Code' (TB)	CIri
'Navajo Jewel' (TB)	ESgI EWoo WCAu XSen
'Navy Brass' (Sib)	EPri WAul
'Needlecraft' (TB)	XSen
'Needlepoint' (TB)	ESgI
'Negro Modelo' (SDB)	WCAu
'Neige de Mai' (TB)	ESgI
* 'Nel Jupe' (TB)	LRHS NLar
nepalensis	see *I. decora*
nertschinskia	see *I. sanguinea*
'Neutron Dance' (TB)	WCAu
'New Argument' (J)	LLHF
'New Centurion' (TB)	EWoo XSen
'New Face' (TB)	WCAu
'New Flame' (TB)	ESgI
'New Idea' (MTB)	CBro ESgI WCAu
'New Leaf' (TB)	WCAu
'New Perspective' (TB) **new**	CIri
'New Snow' (TB)	WCAu
'Next in Line'	EWoo
'Nibelungen' (TB)	CBro CJun ESgI WCAu XSen
'Night Breeze' (Sib)	EPri SIri
'Night Edition' (TB)	ESgI EWoo XSen
'Night Game' (TB)	EWoo XSen
'Night Owl' (TB)	CKel ELan ELon ESgI MHer SPoG
'Night Ruler' (TB)	EWoo WCAu
'Nights of Gladness' (TB)	ESgI
'Nine Lives' (SDB) **new**	WCAu
'No Down Payment' (TB)	WCAu
'Noble Lady' (TB)	CIri
'Noctambule' (TB)	EWoo
'Noon Siesta' (TB)	ESgI
'Nordica' (TB)	ESgI
§ × ***norrisii***	EBee EWes MSCN
- 'Butterfly Magic'	EBee
- 'Dazzler'	NQui
'North Downs' (BB)	SIri
'Northern Jewel' (IB)	SIri
'Northumberland Piper' (TB)	SIri
'Nottingham Lace' (Sib)	GBin LLHF SWat
'Nouveau Riche' (TB) **new**	WCAu
'Now and Forever' (La) **new**	LLWG
'Now This' (Spuria)	EWoo
'Oasis Fuzzy Wuzzy' (TB)	CIri
'Oasis Sydney' (TB)	CIri
'Oban' (Sib)	ESgI GBuc
'Obligato' (IB) **new**	CKel
'Obsidian' (TB)	WCAu
'Ochre Doll' (SDB)	CBro CKel CTal
ochroleuca	see *I. orientalis* Mill.
'O'Cool' (IB)	CKel
'October' (TB)	ESgI
'October Storm' (IB)	CIri EWoo
'Oh Happy Day' (La) **new**	LLWG
'Oh Jamaica' (TB)	WCAu XSen
'Oh So Cool' (MTB)	ESgI
'Oklahoma' (TB)	EWoo
'Oklahoma Centennial' (TB) **new**	WCAu
'Oktoberfest' (TB)	XSen
'Ola Kalá' (TB)	CRos GMaP LRHS MCot MGos NLar SHil SPer WAul WCAu XSen
'Old Black Magic' (TB)	ESgI EWoo XSen
'Old Flame' (TB)	XSen
'Olympiad' (TB)	ESgI XSen
'Olympic Challenge' (TB)	ESgI MRav WCAu
'Olympic Torch' (TB)	WCAu
'Ominous Stranger' (TB)	ESgI MMHG WCAu
'Once Again' (TB)	EWoo XSen
'One Desire' (TB)	XSen
'Open Arms' (TB)	CIri
'Open Sky' (SDB)	EWoo LRHS SIri XSen
'Opposing Forces' (TB)	WCAu
'Orageux' (IB)	CWCL SIri
'Orange Caper' (SDB)	CBod CMac CPBP CTal EAEE ECtt EPfP ESgI GBuc LRHS LSou MBri MRav SBea WCot
'Orange Harvest' (TB)	ESgI XSen
'Orange Order' (TB)	WCAu
'Orbison' (TB) **new**	CIri
'Orchidarium' (TB)	CKel
'Orchidea Selvaggia' (TB)	ESgI
orchioides misapplied	see *I. bucharica* Foster
§ ***orchioides*** Carrière	CAby ECho ELan
'Oregon Skies' (TB)	ESgI EWoo
'Oriental Beauty' (Dut)	CAvo GKev LCro LOPS SPer

	Name	Suppliers
	'Oriental Beauty' (TB)	SDeJ
	orientalis Thunb.	see *I. sanguinea*
	orientalis ambig.	CAvo EWes MNrw
§	***orientalis*** Mill. ♀H7	CCon GBin GCal WCot WCru XSen
	'Orinoco Flow' (BB) ♀H7	ESgI WCAu
	'Orloff' (TB)	ESgI
	'Oro Antico' (TB)	CIri
	'Orville Fay' (Sib)	WBor WCot WFar
	'Osay Canuc' (TB)	CIri
	'Osborne's Grey' (Sib)	WAul
	'Ostrogoth' (TB)	CIri
	'Ottawa' (Sib)	CPou CWat LPot LRHS MMuc SWat WFar
	'Oulo' (TB)	ESgI XSen
	'Our House' (TB)	ESgI
	'Out of the Dark' (TB) **new**	WCAu
	'Out Yonder' (TB)	WCAu
	'Outrage' (SDB)	CIri
	'Outset' (Sib)	ELon WWEG
	'Over Easy' (SDB)	CKel
	'Overjoyed' (TB)	WCAu XSen
	'O'What' (SDB)	ESgI
	'Owyhee Desert' (TB)	WCAu
	'Ozark Maid' (MTB)	SDys
	Pacific Coast hybrids	see *I.* Californian hybrids
	'Pacific Mist' (TB)	WCAu
	'Pacific Panorama' (TB)	XSen
	'Pagan Dance' (TB)	EWoo WCAu
	'Pagan Goddess' (TB)	EWoo
	'Pagan Pink' (TB)	XSen
	'Pagan Princess' (TB)	WCAu
I	'Pageant' (Sib)	WCot
	'Paint It Black' (TB)	EWoo XSen
	'Pale Shades' (IB)	CBro CKel
§	***pallida***	CBro CMac ESgI EWoo GMaP MRav MWat SCob SEND SRms WCAu WMnd XSen
§	- 'Argentea Variegata' (TB/v)	Widely available
	- 'Aurea'	see *I. pallida* 'Variegata' Hort.
	- 'Aurea Variegata'	see *I. pallida* 'Variegata' Hort.
	- subsp. ***cengialtii***	XSen
	- var. ***dalmatica***	see *I. pallida* subsp. *pallida*
§	- subsp. ***pallida***	CArn CExl CKel EAEE ECha ELan EPfP GCal LRHS SDix SHar SPer
	- 'Variegata' misapplied	see *I. pallida* 'Argentea Variegata'
§	- 'Variegata' Hort. (v) ♀H7	CBcs CBro CKel CMac CWat ECha ELan EPfP ESgI LRHS MAsh MBri MRav MWat SPer SPlb SRot SWvt WAbe WWEG XSen
	'Palm Spring' (Reticulata) **new**	LAma
	'Palm Springs' (IB)	LLHF
	'Palomino' (TB)	WCAu
	'Pane e Vino' (TB)	ESgI
	'Panther' (SDB)	WCAu
	'Papillon' (Sib)	CTri ECtt ELan ELon EPri EWoo LHop LRHS MBel MWat NBir NGdn NSti SCob SDeJ SPer SWat WAul WFar WWEG
	'Paprika Fono's' (TB)	WCAu
	'Paradise' (TB)	CKel
	paradoxa	ECho
	'Paris Lights' (TB)	XSen
	'Parisian Dawn' (TB)	WCAu
	'Parisien' (TB)	EIri
	'Parts Plus' (IB)	CIri
	'Party Dress' (TB)	CBod CKel CMac EBee ELan EPfP EShb LRHS MRav MWhi NBir NLar NWad SPer SPoG SRms SWat WGwG
	'Party's Over' (TB)	WCAu
	'Passionate Embrace' (TB) **new**	WCAu
	'Pastel Charm' (SDB)	WMnd
	'Patina' (TB)	EIri EWoo LRHS WCAu
	'Patricia Elizabeth Linnegar' (TB) **new**	WCAu
	'Patterdale' (TB)	NBir
	'Paul Black' (TB) ♀H7	CIri WCAu
	'Pauline' (Reticulata)	CAvo CBro ECho EPfP EPot ERCP GKev LAma LCro LOPS LRHS MWat SCob
	'Pause' (SDB)	WCAu
	'Pay the Price' (TB)	WCAu
	'Peaceful Waters' (TB)	XSen
	'Peach Eyes' (SDB)	CBro CKel CTal
	'Peach Picotee' (TB)	ESgI XSen
	'Peach Spot' (TB)	WCAu
	'Peaches in Wine' (La) **new**	LLWG
	'Peachy Face' (IB)	ESgI XSen
	'Pearl Queen' (Sib)	MCot WFar
	'Pearls of Autumn' (TB)	WCAu
	'Pearly Dawn' (TB)	ECtt SRGP SWat WWEG
*	'Pêche Melba' (TB)	XSen
	'Peebee and Jay' (MTB) **new**	WCAu
	'Peg Edwards' (Sib)	EWoo
	'Pelion Hills'	LRHS
	'Penny a Pinch' (TB)	WWEG
	'Pepita' (SDB)	EWoo
	'Percheron' (Sib)	EBee EPri ESgI EWoo SIri
	'Peresh' (AB)	CTal
	'Perfect Interlude' (TB)	EIri XSen
	'Perfect Vision' (Sib) ♀H7	CIri
	'Performer' (MTB)	EIri
	'Perky' (MDB)	CPBP
	'Perry's Blue' (Sib)	CAby CBcs CMac CSBt EBee EHon EPfP EPri GKin GMaP IKil LCro LOPS LRHS MBel MBri MGos MRav MSpe NBir NGdn NPer SPer SRms SWat WFar WMnd WWtn
I	'Perry's Favourite' (Sib)	WAul
	'Persan' (TB)	EWoo
	'Persian Berry' (TB)	WCAu XSen
	'Persimmon' misapplied	see *I.* 'Tycoon'
	'Persimmon' ambig. (Sib)	CAby CCon CHid CKel CRos ECtt GCra GKin LRHS SHil SPtp SWat WFar WMoo WPtf
	'Petal Pushers' (TB)	CIri
	'Peter Hewitt' (Sib) ♀H7	EPri WAul
	'Pétillant' (TB)	EWoo
	'Petit Tigre' (IB)	EWoo SIri
	'Petite Monet' (MTB)	ESgI
	'Petite Polka' (SDB)	NLar
	'Pharaoh's Daughter' (IB)	EWoo
	'Picadee'	CDes CTal EBee EPfP
	'Picasso Moon' (TB)	WCAu
	'Pigeon' (SDB)	XSen
	'Pinewood Charmer' (CH)	CElw
	'Pinewood Sunshine' (CH)	MAvo
	'Pink Attraction' (TB)	ESgI XSen
	'Pink Bubbles' (BB)	XSen
	'Pink Charm' (TB)	CKel COtt EAEE EPfP LRHS SDeJ SPlb SPoG

	Name	Suppliers
	'Pink Confetti' (TB)	EWoo XSen
	'Pink Haze' (Sib)	EBee EPfP ESgI GBin WWEG
	'Pink Horizon' (TB)	XSen
	'Pink Kitten' (IB)	WCAu WGwG XSen
	'Pink Lavender' (TB)	ELon
	'Pink Pele' (IB)	ESgI
	'Pink Pinafore' (TB)	EWoo
	'Pink Quartz' (TB)	ESgI
	'Pink Reprise' (BB)	EWoo
	'Pink Swan' (TB)	XSen
	'Pink Taffeta' (TB)	EWoo XSen
	'Pinnacle' (TB)	CKel EWoo GCal SWat
	'Pioneer' (TB)	WMil
	'Pipes of Pan' (TB)	ESgI MRav WCAu
	'Pirate Prince' (Sib)	NPer
	'Pirate's Quest' (TB)	ESgI EWoo XSen
	'Piroska' (TB)	ESgI XSen
*	'Piu Blue' (TB)	ESgI
	'Pixie' (DB)	GKev
	'Pixie' (Reticulata) ♀^{H7}	ECho ELan EPot ERCP LAma LRHS SDeJ
	planifolia	ECho
	'Play With Fire' (TB) **new**	EWoo
	'Pleasures of May' (Sib)	EBee ELon LCro WBor
	'Pledge Allegiance' (TB)	ESgI EWoo WCAu
	'Plickadee' (SDB)	CBro
	'Plissée' (Sib) ♀^{H7}	GBin
	'Plum Lucky' (SDB)	SIri
	'Plum Wine' (SDB)	CKel
	'Poem of Ecstasy' (TB)	WCAu
	'Pogo' (SDB)	CMac CTal ECho ECtt ELan ELon EPfP EShb GBuc GMaP LRHS LSou MBri MRav NBir SBea SDeJ SRms
	'Pokemon' (MDB)	CIri
	'Polvere di Stelle' (TB)	ESgI
	'Popsicle' (SDB)	WCAu
	'Port of Call' (Spuria)	EWoo
	'Pounsley Purple' (Sib)	CPou EPri
	'Powder Blue Cadillac' (TB)	CKel WCAu
	'Power Point' (TB)	CIri WCAu
	'Praetorian Guard' (TB)	CIri
	'Prairie Sunset' (TB)	EWoo
	'Prairie Thunder' (AB)	WCAu
	'Presby's Crown Jewel' (TB)	WCAu
	'Presence' (TB)	SIri
	'Pretender' (TB)	WCAu
	'Pretty Please' (TB)	ESgI
	'Primrose Cream' (Sib)	WCot
	'Primrose Drift' (TB)	ESgI WCAu
	'Prince Indigo' (TB)	MRav
	'Prince of Burgundy' (IB)	WCAu
	'Princess Beatrice' (TB)	WCAu
	'Princess Bride' (BB) ♀^{H7}	WCAu
	'Princess Diana' (SDB) **new**	SIri
	'Princess Osra' (TB)	WMil
	'Princesse Caroline de Monaco' (TB)	ESgI EWoo
	prismatica	GKev
	'Private Eye' (TB) **new**	WCAu
	'Professor Blaauw' (Dut) ♀^{H5}	CAvo
	'Progressive Attitude' (TB)	EPri
	'Props' (SDB)	CIri
	'Prosper Laugier' (IB)	SEND WCAu
	'Prospero' (TB)	EWoo
	'Protocol' (IB)	CKel
	'Proud Tradition' (TB)	ESgI SIri WCAu XSen
	'Provençal' (TB)	CKel CPar CWCL ELon ESgI EWoo WCAu XSen
	'Prussian Blue' (Sib) ♀^{H7}	GBin
	pseudacorus	Widely available
	- B&SWJ 5018 from Japan	WCru
	- 'Alba'	CPrp GCal MRav MSKA MWts NGdn SWat
	- var. ***bastardii***	CBen CWat ECha ELon EPfP EWay LLWG MSKA NPer SLon SPer SWat WBrk WFar WMoo WPnP WWtn XLum
	- 'Come in Spinner'	LLWG
	- cream-flowered	NBir SWat
	- 'Crème de la Crème'	ELon EWoo GBin GQue LLWG NLar NSti NWad WFar
	- 'Dragonfly Dance' **new**	LLWG
	- 'Flore Pleno' (d)	CBen CPrp ECho GCra LLWG MSKA NLar NPer WBrk WCot WFar WPnP WWEG WWtn
I	- 'Golden Fleece'	SPer
	- 'Golden Queen'	EWay LLWG
	- 'Ivory'	LLWG
	- 'Kelis Choice' **new**	LLWG
	- 'Krill'	EBee LLWG WHil
	- 'Mandchurica'	XBlo
	- 'Mini Mart' **new**	LLWG
	- 'Roy Davidson' ♀^{H7}	CBro CPrp GBin GCal IBlr NLar WCot WFar WHil WWtn
	- 'Spartacus'	EBee
*	- 'Sulphur Queen'	NLar WCot WWEG
	- 'Sun Cascade'	GBin
	- 'Tiger Brother'	CBro LLWG WBrk
	- 'Turnipseed'	WCot
	- 'Variegata' (v) ♀^{H7}	Widely available
	pseudopumila	WWEG
	'Puddy Tat' (SDB)	WCAu
	'Pulse Rate' (SDB)	CBro
	pumila	CSpe EPot ITim LRHS MCot
	- f. ***atroviolacea***	CKel GEdr WAbe
*	- 'Gelber Mantel'	NBir WFar
	- 'Violacea' (DB)	SRms
	'Pumpin' Iron' (SDB) ♀^{H7}	CKel ESgI
	'Punk' (MDB)	CIri
	'Pure As Gold' (TB)	CWCL ESgI EWoo WCot XSen
	'Purple Gem' (Reticulata)	CAby ECho EPfP GKev LAma LRHS
	'Purple Hill' (Reticulata) **new**	LAma
	'Purple Mere' (Sib)	MHCG
	'Purple People Eater' (TB)	CIri
	'Purple Pepper' (TB)	WCAu
	'Purple Ritz' (TB)	WCAu
	'Purple Sensation' (Dut)	ECho SDeJ
	'Purple Study' (MTB)	WCAu
	'Purr for Mints' (TB)	CIri
	'Pussycat Pink' (SDB)	ESgI WCAu
	'Quaker Lady' (TB)	ESgI EWoo SIri WCAu
	'Qualified' (TB)	CIri
	'Quantum Leap' (TB)	CIri
	'Quark' (SDB)	CBro CKel
	'Quechee' (TB)	CKel COtt CWld EAEE EBee EPfP ESgI EWoo GMaP LBuc LRHS LSRN MBri MCot MNrw MRav MWat NLar NWad SBea SCob SDeJ SPer SWat WGwG
	'Queen in Calico' (TB)	ESgI WCAu
	'Queen of Angels' (TB)	WCAu
	'Queen of Hearts' (TB)	XSen
	'Queen of May' (TB)	EWoo
	'Queen's Circle' (TB) ♀^{H7}	WCAu

	Name	Suppliers
	'Queen's Prize' (SDB)	SIri
	'Rabbit's Foot' (SDB)	LSRN SIri
	'Radiant Apogee' (TB)	EIri
	'Radiant Burst' (IB)	SIri
	'Rain Dance' (SDB) ♀H7	ESgI
	'Rainbow Candy' (TB) **new**	WCAu
	'Rainbow Etude' (TB) **new**	WCAu
	Rainbow Grand Mixture	SDeJ
	'Rainbow High' (TB) **new**	WCAu
	'Rainbow Rim' (SDB)	ESgI WCAu
	'Rainbow Selection' (TB)	CIri WCAu
	'Rainbow Sky' (TB) **new**	WCAu
	'Rainbow Tour' (TB) **new**	WCAu
	'Rajah' (TB)	CAby CBod CKel ELan ELon EPfP EWoo GMaP LRHS LSRN MBri MLHP MRav SDeJ SPer SPoG WMnd
	'Rameses' (TB)	ESgI EWoo WCAu
	'Rancho Rose' (TB)	XSen
	'Rapture in Blue' (TB)	EWoo
	'Rare Edition' (IB)	CKel EWoo NBir XSen
	'Rare Quality' (TB)	XSen
	'Rare Treat' (TB)	XSen
	'Rarer than Rubies' (TB) **new**	WCAu
	'Raspberry Acres' (IB)	MRav WCAu
	'Raspberry Blush' (IB) ♀H7	CKel CPar EIri EPfP GBin LRHS LSou MBri MRav SBea SWat WAul WGwG WHoo WWFP XSen
	'Raspberry Tiger' (SDB) **new**	WCAu
	'Razoo' (SDB)	CKel CPBP
	'Re La Blanche' (TB)	SIri
	'Reach for the Sky' (TB)	CIri
	'Real Coquette' (SDB)	EWoo SIri
	'Rebecca Perret' (TB)	WCAu
	'Rebus' (SDB)	SIri
	'Recurring Delight' (TB) **new**	WCAu
	'Red Canyon Glow' (TB)	CIri
	'Red Dazzler' (La)	CIri
	'Red Echo' (La)	CIri
	'Red Ember' (Dut) **new**	LCro LOPS
	'Red Flare' (TB)	WFar
	'Red Flash' (TB)	ESgI
	'Red Hawk' (TB)	EWoo
	'Red Heart' (SDB)	ELon ESgI MRav WWEG XSen
	'Red Masterpiece' (TB) **new**	EWoo
	'Red Orchid' (IB)	ELan ESgI EWoo LHop LRHS SRms WBod WCAu
	'Red Revival' (TB)	MRav WCAu
	'Red Rum' (TB)	EWes
	'Red Zinger' (IB)	ESgI EWoo LRHS
	'Redelta' (TB)	XSen
	'Redondo' (IB)	EWoo
	'Reflets Safran' (TB)	SIri XSen
	'Regal Surprise' (SpH) ♀H7	LLWG
	'Regality' (Sib)	CWCL EBee MHer MMuc
	'Regards' (SDB)	CBro XSen
	'Regency Belle' (Sib) ♀H7	EWoo SIri
	'Regency Buck' (Sib)	EWoo
§	***reichenbachii***	GKev LLHF WAbe
	'Reincarnation' (TB)	CIri EWoo
	'Remembering Vic' (Spuria)	EWoo

	Name	Suppliers
	'Renewal' (TB)	EWoo
	'Renown' (TB)	EWoo
	'Repartee' (TB)	XSen
	'Repertoire' (TB) **new**	WCAu
	'Replicator' (SDB)	EWoo
	reticulata	ECho ELan EPfP LPfy SDeJ SEND SPer
	- var. ***bakeriana***	ECho LAma LLHF XEll
	- 'Carolina'	ECho LAma
	- 'Fabiola'	ECho LAma
*	- 'Violet Queen'	ECho
	'Return to Elegance' (TB)	WCAu
	'Réussite' (TB)	EWoo
	'Rhages' (TB)	EWoo
	'Rhapsody' (Reticulata)	ECho EPot ERCP LAma SDeJ
	'Rheinfels' (TB)	EWoo
	'Rheingauperle' (TB)	ESgI EWoo
	'Rhett' (La) **new**	CDes
	'Rhythm' (TB)	CIri
	'Rigamarole' (Sib)	LLWG MSCN MWts SCob WFar
	'Rikugi-sakura' (Sib)	EBee EPri GBin LLHF MWts NLar WCot
	'Ringo' (TB)	EWoo LSRN MRav WCAu
	'Rings of Saturn' (TB)	CIri
	'Rio Rojo' (TB)	EWoo WCAu
	'Rip City' (TB)	ESgI EWoo
	'Rising Moon' (TB)	EWoo SIri
	'Ritz' (SDB)	EAJP GEdr WWEG
	'Rive Gauche' (TB)	ESgI
	'River Avon' (TB)	WCAu
	'Riverbuds' (SDB)	SIri WCAu
	'Riverdance' (Sib)	EWoo
	'Roanoke's Choice' (Sib)	CBro CElw EBee ELon EWes GAbr GBin NCGa WFar
	'Roaring Jelly' (Sib)	EPri EWes NLar WCot
	'Rob Cornell' (TB)	ESgI
§	× ***robusta*** 'Dark Aura' ♀H7	MAvo MSCN WCot
§	- 'Gerald Darby'	Widely available
	- 'Mountain Brook'	LLWG
*	- 'Purple Fan'	LLWG
	'Rochester Castle' (Kent Castles Series) (IB)	SIri
§	'Rocket' (TB)	EPfP GMaP LBuc LRHS MBri MCot MRav NBir SDeJ SPer
	'Rocket Master' (TB)	ESgI
	'Rocket Randy' (TB)	CIri
	'Roku Oji' (Sib)	CIri
	'Roman Carnival' (TB)	EWoo
	'Romance' (TB)	EWoo
	'Romano' (Dut)	GKev
	'Romantic Evening' (TB)	EIri EWoo WCAu XSen
	'Romney Marsh' (IB)	SIri
	'Romola' (TB)	WMil
	'Rosace' (Sib)	EWoo
	'Rosalie Figge' (TB)	ESgI EWoo WCAu WCot
	'Rosé' (TB)	LSRN
	'Rose Queen'	see *I. ensata* 'Rose Queen'
	'Rose Unique' (IB)	EWoo
	'Rose Violet' (TB)	WCAu
	'Rose-Marie' (TB)	EWoo
	'Rosemohr' (TB)	EWoo
	rosenbachiana	ECho
*	- 'Harangon'	ECho
	'Roseplic' (TB)	EBee LRHS
	'Rosette Wine' (TB)	ESgI
	'Rosselline' (Sib)	WAul
	'Rosy Bows' (Sib)	WHlf
	'Rosy Veil' (TB)	EAJP ESgI EWoo

	Name	Suppliers
	'Rosy Wings' (TB)	ECho ESgI EWoo
	'Roucoulade' (TB)	SIri
	'Rouge Gorge' (TB)	SIri
	'Rowden Aurelius' (Sib)	WAul
	'Rowden Starlight'	LLWG
I	'Royal Blue' (Sib)	EBee ECha SWat
	'Royal Crusader' (TB)	CCse EWoo WCAu XSen
	'Royal Elegance' (TB)	SIri
	'Royal Intrigue' (TB)	SIri
	'Royal Satin' (TB)	CHid
	'Royal Summer' (TB)	EWoo
	'Royal Tapestry' (TB)	MAvo
	'Roy's Repeater' **new**	EBee
	'Rubacuori' (TB)	ESgI EWoo
	'Rubistar' (TB)	EWoo
	'Ruby Chimes' (IB)	ESgI WCAu
	'Ruby Contrast' (TB)	WCAu
	'Ruby Eruption' (SDB)	EIri WCAu
	'Ruby Morn' (TB)	WCAu
	'Ruby Wine' (Sib)	CCon EPri LEdu
	rudskyi	see *I. variegata*
	'Ruffled Velvet' (Sib) ♀H7	CBcs CElw CHid CKel ECho ECtt ELan EPfP EPri EWoo GBin GLog ILea IMou LRHS MBri MCot MHol MNHC MRav MSpe NLar SCob SGSe SPer SWat WAul WFar WWEG
	'Ruffles Plus' (Sib)	EPri
	'Russet Crown' (TB)	CKel
	'Rustic Cedar' (TB)	ESgI
	'Rustle of Spring' (TB)	WCAu
	'Rustler' (TB)	WCAu
	'Rusty Beauty' (Dut)	GKev SDeJ
	'Rusty Magnificence' (TB)	EWoo
	'Ruth Margaret' (TB)	CKel
	'Ruth Rowlands' (TB)	ESgI EWoo
	ruthenica	ECho WCot
	- var. ***nana***	CExl GEdr GKev
	'Sable' (TB)	CKel ELan EPfP ESgI EWoo GMaP LRHS LSRN MBri MCot MRav MWat NLar SCob SDeJ SEND SPer WAul WCAu WGwG WWEG
	'Sable Night' (TB)	CKel ESgI
	'Safari Sunset' (TB)	WCAu
	'Sailor' (IB)	WCAu
	'Sailor's Dream' (MTB) **new**	WCAu
	'Saint Crispin' (TB)	EBee EPfP EWoo GCra GMaP LRHS MBri MRav SPer SPoG WGwG
	'Salamander Crossing' (Sib) ♀H7	WAul
	'Sally Jane' (TB)	WCAu
	'Salmon Sunset' (Spuria)	EWoo
	'Salonique' (TB)	ESgI EWoo MMHG NLar WCAu
	'Saltwood' (SDB)	CBro ESgI
	'Saltwood Castle' (Kent Castles Series) (IB)	SIri
	'Salzburg Echo' (TB)	WCAu
	'Sam Carne' (TB)	WCAu
	'Samarcande' (TB)	ESgI
	× ***sambucina***	XSen
	'San Diego' (TB)	ESgI
	'San Francisco' (TB)	ESgI EWoo
	'San Gabriel' (TB)	EWoo
	'Sandling Sunset' (TB)	SIri
	'Sandy Caper' (IB)	WCAu
	'Sangone' (IB)	ESgI MNrw
	'Sangreal' (IB)	LRHS
§	***sanguinea*** ♀H7	CMCN
	- 'Nana Alba'	GBin
§	- 'Snow Queen'	CAvo CBcs EBee ELan ELon EPfP EPri EWTr EWoo GBin GKev IKil IMou LPot LRHS MMuc NLar NQui NSti SCob SEND SGSe SPer SWat WAul WCot WFar WHoo WMoo WWEG
	'Sapphire Beauty' (Dut)	GKev SDeJ
	'Sapphire Gem' (SDB)	CKel ESgI EWoo LSRN WCAu
	'Sapphire Hills' (TB)	LRHS WCAu XSen
	'Sarah Taylor' (SDB) ♀H7	ECho EWoo
	sari	ECho
	'Sasha Borisovich' (TB)	ESgI
	'Satyre' (SDB)	CIri
	'Savoir Faire' (Sib)	ECha
	'Scandinavian Girl' **new**	WCAu
	'Scented Wonder' (TB) **new**	WCAu
	schachtii	GKev
	- purple-flowered	WAbe
	'Scottish Warrior' (TB)	CIri
	'Scramble' (Sib)	NEgg WCot
	'Scribe' (MDB)	CBro NBir
	'Sea Double' (TB)	WWEG
	'Sea Fret' (SDB)	CBro
	'Sea of Joy' (TB)	XSen
	'Sea Shadows' (Sib)	EPri ESgI NBir
	'Sea Wisp' (La)	SKHP
	'Seafire' (SDB)	WCAu
	'Seakist' (TB)	WCAu
	'Season Ticket' (IB)	XSen
	'Seastone' (SDB)	WCAu
	'Second Look' (TB)	XSen
	'Second Wind' (TB)	EWoo WCAu
	'Secret Melody' (TB)	XSen
	'Secret Service' (TB)	EWoo
	'Self Evident' (MDB)	LLHF
	'Semola' (SDB)	ESgI
	'Senlac' (TB)	EWoo NLar WMil WMnd
	'Señor Frog' (SDB)	ESgI
	serbica	see *I. reichenbachii*
	'Serene Moment' (TB)	SIri
	'Serenity Prayer' (SDB)	WCAu
	setosa ♀H7	CBro CMac CTri CWCL EAJP ECho GCra GKev LRHS MNrw NCGa WOld
	- ***alba***	NLar
	- var. ***arctica***	GBuc GKev LEdu MHer
I	- 'Baby Blue'	EPfP LRHS MBNS MJak
	- subsp. ***canadensis***	see *I. hookeri*
	- dark violet-flowered	EPri
	- var. ***nana***	see *I. hookeri*
	'Seven Hills' (TB)	ESgI
	'Shaker's Prayer' (Sib) ♀H7	EWes GAbr MBrN SBch
	'Shakespeare's Sonnet' (SDB)	ESgI
	'Shall We Dance' (Sib) ♀H7	CIri EWes
	'Shampoo' (IB)	SIri WCAu
	'Share the Spirit' (TB)	WCAu
	'Sharp Dressed Man' (TB) **new**	WCAu
	'Shawano' (TB)	EWoo
	'Sheila Ann Germaney' (Reticulata)	CBro ECho EPot ERCP GKev LAma LLHF LRHS NWad SBch WBrk
	'Shelby Lynne' (TB)	CIri
	'Shelford Giant' (Spuria) ♀H7	NEgg
	'Sherbet Lemon' (IB) ♀H7	WCAu
	'Shifnal'	WCAu
	'Shirley Chandler' (IB) ♀H7	SIri
	'Shirley Pope' (Sib) ♀H7	EWes GBin GBuc LRHS NSti SMHy WFar WMoo WWEG

	Name	Suppliers
	'Shirley's Choice' (Sib)	EBee EPri SIri
	'Short Distance' (IB)	EWoo SIri
	'Showdown' (Sib)	ECtt GMaP LRHS SWat WWEG
	'Shrawley' (Sib)	EWoo WAul
	shrevei	see *I. virginica* var. *shrevei*
	'Shurton Brook' (TB)	CKel
	'Shurton Demon' (TB)	CKel
	'Shurton Inn' (TB)	CKel WCAu
	'Shurton Princess' (TB) **new**	CKel
	sibirica	CAvo CBod CMHG CTsd CWat EHon GAbr GBBs GKev LLWP MCot MLHP MMuc NChi SCob SEND SPlb SRot WBrk WCFE WFar WGwG WHer WMoo WShi
	- PAB 6119	LEdu
	- 'Niklas Sea'	see *I.* 'Lake Niklas'
	- 'Redflare'	see *I.* 'Melton Red Flare'
	- 'Snow Queen'	see *I. sanguinea* 'Snow Queen'
	'Sibirica Alba'	ECha EPfP EPri IBoy LLWP SWat WBrk WFar
	sichuanensis	CExl SPlb
	'Side Effect'	WCAu
	'Sidney Linnegar' (TB)	WCAu
	'Sidney Unknown' **new**	WCAu
	sieboldii	see *I. sanguinea*
	'Sierra Blue' (TB)	ESgI EWoo
	'Sierra Grande' (TB)	SIri XSen
	'Sierra Nevada' (Spuria)	XSen
	'Sign of Leo' (TB)	CKel EWoo XSen
	'Silence in Heaven' (Spuria)	CIri
	'Silkirim' (TB)	CKel
	'Silver Edge' (Sib) 🏆H7	Widely available
	'Silver Shower' (TB)	EWoo
	'Silverado' (TB)	CKel ESgI EWoo GBin LRHS MAvo WCAu
	'Silvery Beauty' (Dut)	GKev LOPS NBir SDeJ
	sindjarensis	see *I. aucheri*
	'Sinfonietta' (La)	LLWG WCot
	'Sing to Me' (TB)	WCAu
	'Sinister Desire' (IB)	EWoo SIri
	sintenisii 🏆H5	CBro CPBP ECho GKev SBrt WAbe XSen
	'Sir Michael' (TB)	ESgI EWoo
	'Siva Siva' (TB)	MRav
	'Sixteen Candles' (IB)	EWoo
	'Sixtine C' (TB)	SIri
	'Skating Party' (TB)	CKel ESgI XSen
	'Sky Beauty' (Dut)	GKev SDeJ
	'Sky Hooks' (TB)	XSen
	'Sky Tracery' (MTB)	SDys
	'Sky Wings' (Sib)	ECha EWoo GQue MArl WMoo
	'Skydancer' (SDB)	WCAu
	'Skyfire' (TB)	EBee ESgI WWEG
	'Skylark's Song' (TB)	EIri EWoo
	'Small Sky' (SDB)	CBro
	'Smart' (SDB)	WCAu
	'Smart Aleck' (TB)	ESgI EWoo
	'Smart Girl' (TB)	EIri
	'Smart Move' (TB)	ESgI
	'Smiling Faces' (TB)	WCAu
	'Smith Named Keith' (TB)	CIri
	'Smitten Kitten' (IB)	LSRN WCAu
	'Smokey Salmon' (TB)	CKel
	'Smooth' (SDB)	SDys
	'Snow Fiddler' (MTB)	EWoo
	'Snow Plum' (IB)	SIri
	'Snow Prince' (Sib)	EPri
	'Snow Season' (SDB)	ESgI
	'Snow Shoes' (TB)	CIri
	'Snow Tracery' (TB)	CBod EBee LRHS MBri
	'Snow Troll' (SDB)	WCAu
	'Snowcone' (IB)	EWoo
	'Snowcrest' (Sib)	CBre LRHS MRav MSpe WAul
	'Snowmound' (TB)	CKel ESgI EWoo WCAu
	'Snowy Owl' (TB)	CKel WCAu
	'Snugglebug' (SDB)	CPBP CTal EWoo WCAu
	'Soaring Kite' (TB)	WCAu
	'Social Event' (TB)	ESgI XSen
	'Soft Blue' (Sib) 🏆H7	EPri WAul
	'Soft Rain' (TB)	CIri
	'Soft Return' (TB)	EWoo
	'Solar Fire' (TB)	CIri
	'Solar Fusion' (Spuria)	EWoo
	'Solid Mahogany' (TB)	MRav
	'Soligo' (MDB)	ESgI
	'Solo Flight' (TB)	SDys
	'Somerset Blue' (TB)	CKel
	'Somerset Cider' (TB)	SIri
	'Somerton Dance' (SDB)	CKel
	'Song of Norway' (TB)	EIri EWoo XSen
	'Sonoran Sands' (IB)	SDys
	'Sopra il Vulcano' (BB)	ESgI EWoo
	'Sorbonne' (TB) **new**	WCAu
	'Sordid Lives' (TB)	WCAu
	'Sostenique' (TB)	ESgI
	'Southcombe White' (Sib)	WWEG
	'Southland' (IB)	EWoo
	'Souvenir de Madame Gaudichau' (TB)	ESgI EWoo
	'Spanish Angel' (TB) **new**	CIri
	'Sparkling Rose' (Sib)	Widely available
	'Sparkling Waters' (TB)	ESgI
	'Sparkplug' (SDB)	ESgI
	'Spartan' (TB)	EWoo
	'Special Feature' (TB)	CIri
	'Speck So' (MTB)	WCAu
I	'Speckles' (Sib)	EPPr
	'Spellbreaker' (TB)	EWoo SIri
	'Spice Lord' (TB)	WCAu
	'Spiced Custard' (TB)	EIri ESgI EWoo WCAu
	'Spiced Lemon' (TB) **new**	WCAu
	'Spiced Tiger' (TB)	ESgI
	'Spicy Cajun' (La)	WHil
	'Spinning Wheel' (TB)	SIri
	'Spirit of Memphis' (TB)	XSen
	'Splashacata' (TB)	WCAu XSen
	'Splashdown' (Sino-Sib)	SWat
	'Splat' (IB)	CIri
	'Spot of Tea' (MDB)	LLHF
	'Spreckles' (TB)	ESgI
	'Spree' (SDB)	WCAu
	'Spring Blush' (MTB) 🏆H7	SIri
	'Spring Festival' (TB)	WCAu
	'Spring Kiss' (TB)	SIri
	'Spring Madness' (TB)	WCAu
	'Spring Time' (Reticulata)	ECho GKev LAma LOPS SDeJ
	'Spun Gold' (TB)	EWoo
	spuria	CMac CPou
§	- subsp. ***halophila***	GBin GKev
	- subsp. ***notha*** CC 725	WCot
	- subsp. ***ochroleuca***	see *I. orientalis* Mill.
	'Spy' (BB)	WCAu
	'Square Dance Skirt' (TB)	SDys
	'St Louis Blues' (TB)	ESgI XSen
	'Stairway to Heaven' (TB)	ESgI WCAu

'Stapleford' (SDB)	CBro
'Staplehurst' (MTB) 🏆H7	SIri
'Star Cluster' (Sib)	WFar
'Star in the Night' (TB) **new**	WCAu
'Star Shine' (TB)	ESgI WCAu
'Starcrest' (TB)	EWoo
'Stardate' (SDB)	CKel
'Starheart' (IB)	WCAu
'Starlette Rose' (TB)	EWoo
'Starring' (TB)	EWoo
'Starship' (TB)	XSen
'Starwoman' (IB) 🏆H7	SDys WCAu
'Staten Island' (TB)	ESgI SRms WCAu
'Stella Polaris' (TB)	ELon
'Stellar Lights' (TB)	EIri EWoo WCAu
'Stephen Wilcox' (Sib)	CIri EPri WAul
'Stepping Out' (TB) 🏆H7	CKel CMac CPar EAEE EPfP ESgI GBin LRHS SCob SDeJ WCAu
'Steve' (Sib)	CPar EWes SWat
'Steve Varner' (Sib)	EPri EWoo IMou
'Stilo Libero' **new**	WCAu
'Stinger' (SDB) 🏆H7	CIri
'Stingray' (TB)	ESgI
'Stitch in Time' (TB)	EIri EWoo WCAu
'Stockholm' (SDB)	CKel
stolonifera	ECho
- 'Zwanenburg Beauty'	ECho
'Stop the Music' (TB)	XSen
'Storm Center' (TB)	EWoo
'Stormy Circle' (SDB)	WCAu
'Storrington' (TB)	EMal EWoo
'Strange Brew' (TB)	WCAu
'Strathmore' (TB)	EMal EWoo
'Strawberry Fair' (Sib) 🏆H7	CIri
'Strictly Jazz' (TB)	WCAu
'Strike it Rich' (TB)	ESgI
'Striking' (TB)	EWoo
'Strozzapreti' (TB)	ESgI
'Strut' (TB)	WCAu
'Strut your Stuff' (TB) **new**	WCAu
'Study In Black' (TB)	XSen
stylosa	see *I. unguicularis*
§ ***suaveolens***	CPBP CPou ECho GEdr NWad
- var. ***flavescens***	see *I. suaveolens* yellow-flowered
§ - purple-flowered	ECho GCrg GEdr WAbe
- var. ***violacea***	see *I. suaveolens* purple-flowered
§ - yellow-flowered	ECho GKev
'Succès Fou' (TB)	EWoo SIri
'Sugar' (IB)	NSti WCAu
'Sugar Magnolia' (TB)	EWoo
'Sultan's Palace' (TB)	CKel EBee ECho ESgI EWoo LCro LPot LRHS NLar WCAu XSen
'Summer Holidays' (TB)	XSen
'Summer Revels' (Sib)	EPri WHlf
'Summer Sky' (Sib)	CBre CSpe GBin LEdu MSCN NCGa SWat WAul WCot WWEG
'Summer's Smile' (TB)	EWoo
'Summertime Blues' (TB)	EWoo
'Sun Ada Beach' (TB)	CIri
'Sun Doll' (SDB) 🏆H7	CTal
'Sunblaze' (TB)	WCAu
'Sunlit Shores' (La) **new**	LLWG
'Sunny Dawn' (IB)	CKel
'Sunny Disposition' (TB)	XSen
'SunnySide Up' (TB)	ECho
'Sunnyside Delight' (TB)	WCAu
'Sunset Skies' (TB)	CWCL
'Super Model' (TB)	WCAu
'Superba' (Sib)	WWtn
'Superstition' (TB) 🏆H7	CKel EIri ELan ESgI EWes EWoo LAst LCro LOPS LRHS MRav SCob WCAu XSen
'Supreme Sultan' (TB)	CWCL ESgI EWoo SCob WCAu XSen
'Susan Bliss' (TB)	CKel ELan EPfP ESgI EWoo WCAu WMil
'Suspicion' (TB)	CIri
'Sutton Valence' (Sib)	SIri
'Swain' (TB)	ESgI
'Swan Ballet' (TB)	ESgI
'Swank' (Sib)	WAul
'Swazi Princess' (TB)	ELon ESgI
'Sweet Kate' (SDB)	WCAu
'Sweet Lavender' (TB)	WMil
'Sweet Lena' (TB)	ESgI
'Sweet Musette' (TB)	WCAu
'Sweet Surrender' (Sib)	EPri
'Sweeter than Wine' (TB)	EWoo MRav
'Swingtown' (TB)	EWoo WCAu
'Swirling Waters' (La)	LLWG
'Swiss Majesty' (TB)	WCAu
'Swizzle' (IB)	XSen
'Sybil' (TB)	GBin GCra
'Sylvan' (TB)	XSen
'Sylvia Murray' (TB)	WCAu
'Symphony' (Dut)	ECho NBir SDeJ
'Symphony of Light' (TB)	CIri
'Syncopation' (TB)	ESgI WCAu XSen
'Syrian Hills' (TB) **new**	WCAu
'Tabac Blond' (TB)	EWoo
'Tact' (IB)	SIri
'Take Me Away' (TB)	SDys
'Tall Chief' (TB)	WCAu
'Tamberg' (Sib)	CKel EBee EWoo
'Tamerlan' (TB)	EWoo
'Tan Tingo' (IB)	WCAu XSen
'Tanex'	ECho
'Tangerine Sky' (TB)	EWoo WCAu
'Tangfu' (IB)	ESgI
'Tantara' (SDB)	XSen
'Tantrum' (IB)	WCAu XSen
'Tanz Nochmal' (Sib)	GBin
'Tanzanian Tangerine' (TB)	WCAu
'Tarn Hows' (TB)	ESgI SRms
'Taubenblau' (Sib) **new**	SAko
'Teal Velvet' (Sib)	CKel ECha ELon EPfP EPri EWoo GLog LRHS MCot SCob WFar
'Teapot Tempest' (BB)	WCAu
'Teasaucer Hill' (MTB) 🏆H7	SIri
tectorum	CCse CEvo SChr SDix WCot XLum XSen
- BWJ 8191	WCru
- 'Alba'	CEvo WThu XSen
- 'Cruella'	EPfP
- 'Variegata' misapplied	see *I. japonica* 'Variegata'
- 'Variegata' (v)	CBod SGSe
'Tell Fibs' (SDB)	CBro CTal
'Teller of Tales' (La) **new**	LLWG
'Temper Tantrum' (Sib)	LRHS MBri
'Temple Gold' (TB)	CKel NPer
'Temple Meads' (IB)	ESgI WCAu
'Templecloud' (IB) 🏆H7	CKel
'Tempting Fate' (TB)	SIri WCAu
§ ***tenax***	EBee ECho GBuc LRHS

'Tenebrae' (TB) **new**	WMil
'Tennison Ridge' (TB)	WCAu
'Teverlae' (Sib)	EBee LRHS
'Thaïs' (TB)	ESgI
'The Black Douglas' (TB)	EWoo
'The Citadel' (TB)	ELon
'The Red Douglas' (TB)	ESgI
'The Rocket'	see *I.* 'Rocket'
'Theatre' (TB)	ESgI
'Thelma Perry' (Sib)	EPfP
'Theodolinda' (TB)	EWoo
'Third Charm' (SDB)	CBro
'Third World' (SDB)	CBro
'This and That' (IB)	WCAu
'Thornbird' (TB) ♀H7	CIri EIri ESgI EWoo WCAu
'Three Cherries' (MDB)	CBro CPBP ECho SIri
'Three Quarters' (Sib) **new**	ELon
'Thriller' (TB)	ESgI EWoo WCAu XSen
thunbergii	see *I. sanguinea*
'Thunder Echo' (TB)	ESgI SIri
'Thundering Ovation' (TB) **new**	WCAu
'Tickety Boo' (SDB)	CIri
'Tickle the Ivories' (IB)	CIri
§ 'Tigereye' (Dut)	ERCP GKev LCro SDeJ
tigridia	CExl
'Time to Shine' (SDB)	WCAu
'Time Traveler' (TB)	CIri
'Time Zone' (TB)	WCAu
'Tinkerbell' (SDB)	CPBP CTal EBee EPfP GMaP LRHS MBri NBir SBea SDeJ
'Tishomingo'	EWoo
'Titan's Glory' (TB) ♀H7	CKel ESgI EWoo LEdu MRav WCot WHoo
'To the Point' (TB)	CIri
'Tollong'	IKil ILea IMou
'Tom Johnson' (TB) ♀H7	EWoo
'Tom Tit' (TB)	WCAu WMil
'Toni Lynn' (MDB)	ECho
'Toots' (SDB)	ECho
'Top Flight' (TB)	CKel ELan LRHS SPer SRms
'Top Gun' (TB)	ESgI
'Topaz Jewel' (TB) **new**	MHol
'Topolino' (TB)	CKel
'Torero' (TB)	EWoo SIri
'Toro Blanco' (IB)	CIri
'Total Eclipse' (TB)	SRms
'Total Recall' (TB)	WCAu
'Totally Cool' (SDB)	LSRN SIri
'Touch of Mahogany' (TB)	WCAu
'Town Flirt' (TB) **new**	WCAu
'Toy Clown' (SDB)	EWoo
'Trails West' (TB)	EWoo
'Trajectory' (SDB)	WCAu
'Trapel' (TB)	ESgI
'Trencavel' (TB)	ESgI
'Trenwith' (TB)	ESgI
'Triffid' (TB)	CIri
'Trillion' (TB)	CIri
'Trim the Velvet' (Sib)	WAul
'Triple Whammy' (TB)	ESgI XSen
'Tripod' (IB)	CIri
'Tristan' **new**	CKel
'Tristram' (TB)	WMil
'Tropic Night' (Sib)	CCon CRos CSam CTri EBee ECtt EIri ELan EPfP EPri EWoo GBin GKin LCro LHop LRHS MBel MBri MCot MNHC MRav MWts NRya NSti SHil SPer SWat WAul WFar WWtn
'Tropical Delight' (TB) **new**	CIri
'True Charm' (TB)	EWoo
tuberosa	CAby CArn CAvo CBro CDes CHid CTri CWCL ECGP ECha ECho ERCP LAma MHer MPie SDeJ WCot WShi
- BS 348	WCot
- MS 76	WCot
- MS 729	WCot
- MS 731	WCot
- MS 821	CDes WCot
- MS 964	WCot
- PB	WCot
'Tulip Festival' (TB)	EBee SGol
'Tumultueux' (TB)	EWoo
'Tut's Gold' (TB)	ESgI WCAu
'Tuxedo' (TB)	XSen
'Twist of Twilight' (La) **new**	LLWG
'Two Sided Coin' (TB)	WCAu
§ 'Tycoon' (Sib)	EShb EWoo GQue LCro LRHS SPer
'Tyland Blue' (TB)	SIri
'Tyrian Dream' (IB)	WCAu
'UFO' (TB)	CIri
'Ultimate' (SDB)	CIri WCAu
'Uncle Charlie' (TB)	WCAu
'Undercurrent' (TB)	WCAu
'Unfinished Business' (TB)	CIri WCAu
§ ***unguicularis***	Widely available
- 'Abington Purple'	CJun EIri
- 'Alba'	CEvo CExl EWoo XSen
§ - subsp. ***cretensis***	ECho GKev SKHP
- 'Diana Clare'	CJun
- 'Kilbroney Marble'	EPri
- 'Marondera'	CAvo CJun
- 'Mary Barnard' ♀H5	CAvo CBro CJun CPou CTca EBee ECGP ECho EWoo LRHS NBir WHoo
- 'Oxford Dwarf'	ECho LLHF
- 'Stavendale Tiger'	MAvo
§ - 'Walter Butt'	CAvo CJun EBee ECGP EWoo NBir
'Unicorn' (TB)	CIri
'Vague à l'Ame' (TB)	ESgI EWoo
'Val de Loire'	EWoo
'Valda' (Sib)	EBee ELon
'Valerie Joyce'	WCAu
'Vamp' (IB)	CKel EWoo XSen
'Vanilla Mist' (La) **new**	LLWG
'Vanilla Skies' (TB)	WCAu
'Vanity' (TB)	XSen
'Vanity's Child' (TB)	WCAu XSen
§ ***variegata*** ♀H7	WCAu XSen
'Vegas Heat' (BB)	CIri
'Velvet Dusk' (TB)	EWoo
'Velvet King' (TB)	ESgI
'Velvet Purple'	XBlo
'Venita Faye' (TB)	WCAu
'Vera' (Rc)	GKev
'Verity Blamey' (TB)	CKel
verna	EPot
versicolor	CArn CBen CBod CWat GBin GKev GMaP GPoy MMuc MNHC MWts SPlb SRms SWat WBrk WFar WMAq WMoo WPnP WShi WWtn
- 'Algonquin'	LLWG
- 'Between the Lines'	LLWG
- 'China West Lake'	LLWG

- 'Claret Cup'	CPou ILea
- 'Kermesina'	CPrp CWat ECha ELan ESgI GBuc LLWG MWts NPer NSti SRms SWat WFar WMAq WMoo WPnP
- 'Mint Fresh'	LLWG
- 'Mysterious Monique'	CCse CDes CWat LLWG
- purple-flowered	EWay
- 'Rosea'	EWay
- 'Rowden Cadenza'	EWay LLWG
- 'Rowden Cantata'	LLWG
- 'Rowden Concerto'	LLWG
- 'Rowden Melody'	LLWG
- 'Rowden Pastorale'	LLWG
- 'Rowden Sonata'	LLWG
'Vi Luihn' (Sib)	ECha WMoo
'Vibrations' (TB)	ESgI WCAu
vicaria	ECho
'Victoria Falls' (TB)	ESgI EWoo MHol
'Victorian Secret' (Sib)	EBee ELon
'Viel Schnee' (Sib)	GBin
'Vigilante' (TB)	EWoo
'Vin Nouveau' (TB)	XSen
'Vinho Verde' (IB)	CKel
'Vino Rosso' (SDB)	ESgI
'Violet Beauty' (Reticulata)	ECho GKev LAma LRHS
'Violet Classic' (TB)	WCAu
'Violet Fusion' (Spuria)	EWoo
'Violet Harmony' (TB)	ESgI
'Violet Icing' (TB)	CKel
'Violet Rings' (TB)	WCAu
'Violet Skies' (Sib)	GBin
'Violet Turner' (TB) **new**	MHol
'Viper' (IB)	CIri EWoo
virginica	LLWG
- 'De Luxe'	see *I.* × *robusta* 'Dark Aura'
- 'Lavender Lustre'	LLWG
- 'Orchid Purple'	LLWG
- 'Pale Lavender'	LLWG
- 'Pink Perfection'	LLWG
§ - var. ***shrevei***	LLWG
- 'Slightly Daft'	LLWG
'Visual Intrigue' (TB)	EWoo
'Visual Treat' (Sib)	EWoo
'Vitafire' (TB)	ESgI EWoo LRHS
'Vitality' (IB)	ELon ESgI
'Viva Mexico' (TB)	EWoo
'Vizier' (TB)	WCAu
'Voilà' (IB)	CMea ESgI
'Volts' (SDB)	XSen
'Volute' (TB)	ESgI
'Voyage' (SDB)	EWoo XSen
'Wabash' (TB)	EWoo WCAu XSen
'Waihi Wedding' (La) **new**	LLWG
'Wall Street Blues' (Sib)	EWoo
'Walmer Castle' (Kent Castles Series) (IB)	SIri
'Walter Butt'	see *I. unguicularis* 'Walter Butt'
'War Chief' (TB)	ESgI EWoo MRav WCAu
'War Sails' (TB)	EWoo SIri WCAu
warleyensis	ECho EPot
'Warrior King' (TB)	EWoo
'Waters Of Miraba' (BB)	EWoo
wattii	CExl GCal IKil WGwG
'Way to Go' (TB)	CIri
'Wealden Butterfly' (Sib) ♀H7	SIri WAul
'Wealden Carousel' (Sib)	SIri WAul
'Wealden Mystery' (Sib)	EPri SIri WAul
'Wealden Skies' (Sib)	SIri WAul
'Wealden Spires' (Sib)	WAul
'Wealden Summer' (Sib)	WAul
'Wearing Rubies' (TB)	ESgI WCAu
'Webelos' (SDB)	MRav
'Wedding Vow' (TB)	EIri
'Welch's Reward' (MTB)	ESgI
'Welcome Discovery' (TB)	WCAu
'Welcome Return' (Sib)	CElw EBee GQue LRHS MMuc NLar SEND SWat WMoo
'Welfenfürstin' (Sib)	GBin SAko
'Welfenprinz' (Sib) ♀H7	SBch WAul
'Well Suited' (SDB)	EWoo WCAu
'Wench' (TB)	EWoo WCAu
'Westar' (SDB)	CKel EIri
'Westpointer' (TB)	CIri
'Westwell' (SDB)	WCAu
'What a Mixture' (TB) **new**	CIri
'What Again' (SDB)	XSen
'What's New' (TB) **new**	WCAu
'Whee' (SDB) **new**	WCAu
'Whispering Spirits' (TB)	WCAu
'White Caucasus' (Reticulata)	EPot LAma
'White City' (TB)	CKel EPfP ESgI EWoo GMaP LCro LRHS MBri MCot MRav MWhi NPer SCob SDeJ SPer SRms SWat WCAu WMnd
'White Excelsior' (Dut)	ECho
'White Gem' (SDB)	ESgI EWoo
'White Knight' (TB)	EBee ELan EPfP ESgI WMnd
I 'White Queen' (Sib)	ESgI SWat
'White Reprise' (TB)	ESgI XSen
I 'White Swan' (Sib)	EPri
'White Swirl' (Sib)	Widely available
'White Triangles' (Sib)	ELon EWoo
'White van Vliet' (Dut)	SDeJ
'White Wine' (MTB)	WCAu
'White-Wave' (TB)	XBlo
'Widow's Veil' (SDB)	ESgI
'Wild Irish Rose' (TB) **new**	WCAu
'Wild Jasmine' (TB)	WCAu
'Wild Missouri' (TB) **new**	EBee
'Wild Wings' (TB)	EWoo LRHS MCot SGbt WCAu
willmottiana	ECho
- 'Alba'	ECho
wilsonii ♀H7	CExl EBee GBin GKev SBrt
'Windjammer Seas' (TB)	SDys
'Winemaster' (TB)	EWoo SIri
'Winesap' (TB)	ESgI EWoo
'Winged Angel' (IB)	CIri
'Winning Edge' (TB)	WCAu
winogradowii ♀H7	CBro ECho EPot ERCP GKev LAma LLHF LRHS WAbe XEll
'Winter Olympics' (TB)	CAby CKel ELan EPfP LRHS MRav SPer WGwG
'Winter Pearl' (IB)	EWoo
'Wintry Sky' (TB)	WCAu
'Wise' (SDB)	WCAu
'Wish Upon a Star' (SDB)	WCAu
'Wishful Thinking' (TB)	SIri
'Wisteria Sachet' (IB)	WCAu
'Witch's Wand' (TB)	ESgI EWoo
'Wizard's Return' (SDB)	SIri
'Wonders Never Cease' (TB)	WCAu
'Wondrous' (TB)	ESgI

'Word of Warning' (La) new LLWG
'World Premier' (TB) WCAu
'Wrangler' (IB) EWoo SIri
xiphioides see *I. latifolia*
'Yankee Consul' (Sib) EPri
'Yaquina Blue' (TB) WCAu
'Yellow Flirt' (MTB) WCAu
'Yes' (TB) CJun ESgI
'Yippy Skippy' (SDB) WCAu
'Yosemite Nights' (TB) EWoo
'Yosemite Star' (TB) EWoo
'Youth Dew' (TB) EWoo
'Zakopane' (Sib) EBee EWes WAul
'Zantha' (TB) XSen
zenaidae GKev
'Zero' (SDB) CKel
'Zweites Hundert' (Sib) WFar

Isatis (*Brassicaceae*)

tinctoria CArn CBod CHab CHby ENfk GJos GPoy MHer MNHC SIde SPav SRms WHfH WJek

Ismene see *Hymenocallis*

Isodon (*Lamiaceae*)

calycinus SPlb
inflexus new CEvo
longitubus SBrt
- B&SWJ 11027 WCru
rubescens IMou WCot

Isolepis (*Cyperaceae*)

§ ***cernua*** CBen COtt CWat EShb LHop LRHS MSKA MWts NOak SCoo SHDw SPad WMAq

Isoloma see *Kohleria*

Isomeris see *Cleome*

Isoplexis see *Digitalis*

Isopogon (*Proteaceae*)

anemonifolius SPlb
anethifolius SPlb

Isopyrum (*Ranunculaceae*)

dicarpon see *Dichocarpum dicarpon*
nipponicum WCru WPGP
stoloniferum WCru
thalictroides EBee EPot GEdr LEdu LLHF SDys WCot

Isotoma (*Campanulaceae*)

sp. SWvt
§ ***axillaris*** CSpe NPer SCoo SPer SPoG WHea
- 'Fairy Carpet' CBod SRms
fluviatilis NLar

Itea (*Iteaceae*)

chinensis CExl
ilicifolia ♀H5 Widely available
* - 'Rubrifolia' ELan LRHS SLon SPoG
japonica 'Beppu' SSpi
virginica CAbP CBcs CMCN ELon ESwi MRav SLim SLon
§ - 'Henry's Garnet' ♀H5 CAbP CDoC CDul CLet CMCN CMac COtt CSBt ECrN ELan EPfP EWTr GBin IDee LAst LEdu LRHS MBri MGos NLar SCob SEle SHil SLim SPer SPoG SRGP SSpi SWvt WPGP
- Little Henry = 'Sprich'PBR CHGN CMac CSBt EBee ELan EPfP IVic LRHS LSRN NLar SCob SMDP
- 'Long Spire' NLar
- 'Merlot' MBlu NLar
- 'Sarah Eve' CMCN NLar SRGP
- 'Saturnalia' NLar
- Swarthmore form see *I. virginica* 'Henry's Garnet'
yunnanensis CExl MBlu NLar SSpi WSHC

Itoa (*Salicaceae*)

orientalis SVen

Ixeris (*Asteraceae*)

stolonifera XLum

Ixia (*Iridaceae*)

'Blue Bird' CCon ECho LAma NRog SDeJ
capillaris from Citrusdal ECho
'Castor' ECho NRog
curta ECho
dubia ECho
'Gemini' ECho
'Giant' CTca ECho GKev SDeJ
'Hogarth' ECho GKev LAma NRog
'Holland Glory' ECho NRog
latifolia var. ***latifolia*** ECho
lutea ECho
'Mabel' CWCL ECho GKev NRog WCot
maculata ECho
'Marquette' ECho GKev
mixed SDeJ
paniculata ECho
- 'Eos' GKev
'Panorama' ECho NRog
polystachya ECho
var. ***longistylis***
- var. ***lutea*** ECho
pumilio WCot
'Rose Emperor' ECho GKev LAma NRog SDeJ
scillaris new CTre
'Spotlight' ECho GKev NRog
thomasiae WCot
trifolia ECho
'Venus' CCon CTca CWCL ECho GKev LAma NRog SDeJ
versicolor ECho
viridiflora CDes ECho NRog WCot
- var. ***minor*** ECho WCot
'Vulcan' ECho NRog
'Yellow Emperor' CTca ECho GKev NRog SDeJ

Ixiolirion (*Ixioliriaceae*)

montanum ECho
pallasii see *I. tataricum*
§ ***tataricum*** EBee ECho LAma MCot SDeJ
- Ledebourii Group CAvo

J

Jaborosa (*Solanaceae*)

integrifolia CCon CExl EBee LEdu SBrt SVen WPGP XLum

Jacaranda (Bignoniaceae)

acutifolia misapplied	see *J. mimosifolia*
§ **mimosifolia** ♀H1c	CBcs EShb SPlb

Jacobinia see *Justicia*

Jamesbrittenia (Scrophulariaceae)

§ **microphylla**	CPBP
stellata	SPlb

Jamesia (Hydrangeaceae)

americana	CBcs CJun ESwi NLar SBrt WCru WSHC

Jasione (Campanulaceae)

§ **heldreichii**	NBir SRms
jankae	see *J. heldreichii*
§ **laevis**	ECho EPfP GAbr SRms WTcb
§ - 'Blaulicht'	CBod CMHG EAJP ECha EPfP GEdr LRHS NEgg NLar SPlb WCot WMoo
- Blue Light	see *J. laevis* 'Blaulicht'
montana	ECho MNHC SRms WPnn
perennis	see *J. laevis*

Jasminum ✿ (Oleaceae)

CC 4728	CExl
adenophyllum	MOWG
affine	see *J. officinale* f. *affine*
angulare ♀H2	CExl CHll CRHN MOWG
azoricum ♀H2	CBcs CDoC CHll CRHN CTsd EPfP EShb IDee MOWG SPre
beesianum	Widely available
bignoniaceum	WSHC
blinii	see *J. polyanthum*
dispermum	CRHN NLar
diversifolium	see *J. subhumile*
§ **floridum**	EWes
fruticans	CMac ELon LRHS SBrt SEND WCru XLum XSen
- RCB UA 22	WCot
giraldii Diels	see *J. floridum*
grandiflorum misapplied	see *J. officinale* f. *affine*
grandiflorum L. 'De Grasse' ♀H2	CRHN EShb MOWG
heterophyllum	see *J. subhumile*
humile	CExl MGil SEND WKif
- var. **glabrum**	see *J. humile* f. *wallichianum*
§ - 'Revolutum' ♀H5	CBcs CDul CMac COtt CRHN CSBt CWCL CWib EBee ECrN ELan EPfP EShb GCal LAst LHop LRHS MGos MRav NLar SEND SGbt SLon SPer SPoG SRms SWvt WHar WSHC
§ - f. **wallichianum** B&SWJ 2559	WCru
- - PAB 2534	LEdu
§ **laurifolium** f. **nitidum** ♀H2	MOWG
§ **mesnyi** ♀H3	CBcs CExl CHll CMac CRHN CSde CTri CWib EBak ELan EPfP EWTr LRHS MOWG SBch SEND SPer SVen WSHC
multiflorum	MOWG
multipartitum	CHll
- bushy	CSpe
nitidum	see *J. laurifolium* f. *nitidum*
§ **nudiflorum** ♀H5	Widely available
- 'Argenteum'	see *J. nudiflorum* 'Mystique'
- 'Aureum'	CKel ELan LRHS MAsh MBNS MRav NLar NSti SPer SPoG SRms
§ - 'Mystique' (v)	ELan LRHS MRav SLon SPoG
odoratissimum	MOWG
officinale	Widely available
- CC 1709	WMoo
§ - f. **affine**	CBcs CLet COtt CRHN CTri CWCL CWib ELan EPfP LRHS MAsh MRav SCoo SDix SLim SRms WHar WPat
§ - 'Argenteovariegatum' (v) ♀H5	CBcs CDul CKel CLet COtt CTsd CWGN CWib EHoe ELan EPfP LHop LRHS LSRN MAsh MBri MGos MHer MRav SEND SLim SPer SPoG SWvt WCFE WHar WPat WSHC
- 'Aureovariegatum'	see *J. officinale* 'Aureum'
§ - 'Aureum' (v)	CBcs CDoC CKel CMac CTsd CWCL CWSG CWib EBee ECtt ELan EPfP IBoy LRHS MAsh MBri MHer MJak NBir NPri SCoo SLim SLon SMad SPer SRms WPat
- 'Clotted Cream'	see *J. officinale* 'Devon Cream'
- 'Crûg's Collection'	WCru
§ - 'Devon Cream'PBR	Widely available
- Fiona Sunrise = 'Frojas'PBR ♀H5	Widely available
- 'Grandiflorum'	see *J. officinale* f. *affine*
- 'Inverleith' ♀H5	CDoC CKel CMac CWCL CWSG EBee ECtt ELan EPfP IArd LAst LBMP LBrs LHop LRHS MAsh MBNS MBri MGos MRav SCoo SHil SLim SMad SPad SPer SPoG WGrn WSHC
- 'Sunbeam' **new**	LRHS
- 'Variegatum'	see *J. officinale* 'Argenteovariegatum'
parkeri	CBcs CJun CMac CTri EBee ECho ELon EPfP GEdr GMaP LRHS MBNS NLar WPat XEll
- 'Bychan'	WAbe
§ **polyanthum** ♀H2	CArn CBcs CChe CExl CKel COtt CRHN CSBt CSde CTri EBak ELan EPfP IDee MBri MOWG SEND SLim SPer SPre SRms WHar
- dark-red-leaved	CExl EBee ELan WPGP
primulinum	see *J. mesnyi*
reevesii hort.	see *J. humile* 'Revolutum'
sambac ♀H2	CArn CDoC CHll CRHN ELan MOWG SPre
- 'Grand Duke of Tuscany' (d)	SPre
- 'Maid of Orleans' (d)	EShb SPre
sieboldianum	see *J. nudiflorum*
§ **simplicifolium** subsp. **suavissimum**	CHll CRHN
stenalobium	MOWG
× **stephanense**	Widely available
suavissimum	see *J. simplicifolium* subsp. *suavissimum*
§ **subhumile**	MOWG

Jatropha (Euphorbiaceae)

cinerea	SPlb
multifida	SPlb
podagrica ♀H1a	LToo

Jeffersonia (Berberidaceae)

diphylla	CArn CEvo CLAP EBee ECho EPPr EPot EPri GBin GKev LAma LEdu

	LRHS MNrw NBir NHar WAbe WCru WPGP WThu
dubia	CCon CLAP ECho EPot EWes LEdu LHop LLHF LRHS MNrw NBir NHar WAbe WCru WThu XEll
- 'Alba'	ECho WThu

jostaberry see *Ribes* × *culverwellii*

Jovellana (*Calceolariaceae*)

punctata	CBcs CDoC CExl CTsd EBee GCal IBlr SPlb
- var. ***coerulea***	IBlr
sinclairii	CExl CHll LLHF
violacea ♀H2	CAbb CBcs CDoC CExl CMac CPne CSde CTsd CWib EPfP GCal IBlr IMou IVic LRHS SEle SMad SVen WBod WPGP WSHC

Jovibarba ✿ (*Crassulaceae*)

§ ***allionii***	CBod CMea CTri CWil EDAr EPot LBMP MHer MSCN NMen WHal WHoo
- 'Oki'	ECho LRHS NMen SRms
allionii × ***hirta***	CTal CWil MSCN SDys SFgr
§ ***arenaria***	GAbr NMen XLum
- from Passo di Monte Croce Carnico, Italy	CWil
'Autumn Fires'	MSCN
* ***echiniformis***	XLum
'Emerald Spring'	SFgr
globiferum subsp. ***hirtum*** 'Blutrot' new	SFgr
- - 'Pascal' new	SFgr
§ ***heuffelii***	ECho LRHS NMen XLum
- 'Aiolos'	NHol
- 'Almkroon'	NHol NWad
- 'Anabokonak' new	NMen
- 'Angel Wings'	CWil NMen WHoo
- 'Aquarius'	CWil NMen
- 'Bandana' new	CWil
- 'Barbel' new	ESem
- 'Be Mine'	CWil NMen
- 'Beacon Hill'	CWil NMen
- 'Belcore'	CWil NMen XLum
- 'Benjamin'	CWil NMen
- 'Bermuda'	CWil
- 'Big Red'	NHol NWad
- 'Blaze'	CWil NMen
- 'Bolero'	CWil NMen
- 'Bora' new	NWad
- 'Brandaris'	SDys
- 'Brocade'	MSCN NHol NPri NWad
- 'Bronze Ingot'	CWil NMen WCot
§ - 'Cherry Glow'	CWil NMen
- 'Chocoleto'	NMen
I - 'Compacta'	CWil NMen
- 'Copper King'	CWil NMen
- 'Cover Girl'	CWil
- 'Deciso' new	CWil
- 'Elmo's Fire'	CWil NMen
- 'Eos Moment'	CWil NMen
- 'Fan Joy'	CWil NMen
- 'Fandango'	CWil MHom
- 'Gento'	NMen
- 'Geronimo'	CWil NHol NMen
- 'Giuseppi Spiny'	MHom NMen SPlb
- var. ***glabra***	WHoo
- - from Anaba Kanak, Bulgaria	CWil MHom NHol NWad
- - from Anthoborio, southern Caparthians	CWil
- - from Haila, Montenegro/ Kosovo	CWil NMen SFgr
- - from Jakupica, Macedonia	CWil NMen
- - from Kapaenianum	NMen
- - from Ljuboten, Balkans	CWil NMen
- - from Ošsljak, Albania	CWil NMen
- - from Pasina Glava, Macedonia	CWil
- - from Rhodope, Bulgaria	CWil MHom
- - from Treska Gorge, Macedonia	CWil NMen
§ - - 'Cameo'	CWil
- 'Gladiator'	CWil NMen
- 'Gold Rand'	NHol
- 'Grand Slam'	CWil NMen
- 'Green Land'	CWil NMen
- 'Greenstone'	CWil MHom NHol NMen
- 'Harmony'	CWil NHol
- 'Henry Correvon'	CWil NMen
- var. ***heuffelii***	NMen
- 'Hot Lips'	CWil
- 'Idylle'	CWil NMen
- 'Ikaros'	CWil NHol
- 'Inferno'	CWil MHom NMen
§ - 'Inge'	NMen
- 'Ithaca'	NHol NWad
- 'Iuno'	CWil NHol NWad
- 'Jade'	CWil NMen
I - 'Jovi King'	CWil NMen
- 'King Sunny'	CWil NMen
- var. ***kopaonikensis***	CWil MHom NMen
- 'Lorelei'	CWil
- 'Lucky Bell'	CWil NMen
- 'Mary Ann'	MHom NMen
- 'Miller's Violet'	CWil NMen
- 'Mink'	CWil NMen
- 'Minuta'	CWil NMen
- 'Movie Star'	CWil
- 'Mystique'	CWil NMen WHoo
- 'Nannette'	CWil NMen
- 'Orion'	CTal CWil NMen XLum
- 'Outline' new	CWil
- 'Passat'	NWad
- var. ***patens***	CWil NMen
- 'Pelister'	CWil
- 'Pink Skies'	CWil NMen
- 'Pink Star'	CWil NMen NWad
- 'Prisma'	CWil NMen
- 'Purple Haze'	XLum
- 'Purple Heide'	CWil NMen
- 'Red Rose'	CWil
- 'Serenade'	CWil NMen
- 'Silex'	CWil NMen
- 'Springael's Choice'	CWil NMen
- 'Sundancer'	CWil NMen
- 'Sungold'	NHol NWad
- 'Suntan'	CWil NWad
- 'Sylvan Memory'	CWil NMen
- 'Tan'	CWil NMen
- 'Tancredi'	CWil NMen
- 'Torrid Zone'	MBrN NMen
- 'Tuxedo'	CWil NMen
- 'Vesta'	CWil
- 'Violet'	CWil NMen SDys
- 'Wotan'	CWil
- 'Xanthoheuff'	CWil NMen
- 'Yodelheuff'	CWil NMen

§	***hirta***	CWil EDAr EUJe GAbr GKev NMen XLum
	- from Wintergraben, Austria	SPlb
	- 'Belansky Tatra'	CWil NMen
§	- subsp. ***borealis***	CWil
	- subsp. ***glabrescens***	EPot
	- - from High Tatra, Slovakia/Poland	XLum
	- - from Smeryouka, southern Carpathians	NMen
I	- 'Glauca'	SFgr
	- 'Hedgehog'	SFgr
	- var. ***neilreichii***	ECho LRHS MHom
	- 'Purpurea'	NPri XLum
	- 'Rax'	SFgr
	preissiana	NMen SFgr
§	***sobolifera***	EDAr GKev NMen SFgr SPlb WHal XLum
	- 'Bronze Globe'	SFgr
	- 'Green Globe'	CTal ECho LRHS NMen SDys
	- 'Miss Lorraine'	SFgr XLum

Jubaea (*Arecaceae*)

	sp.	ETod
§	***chilensis***	CBcs CPHo ETod LPal SBig SPlb WHor
	spectabilis	see *J. chilensis*

Juglans ✿ (*Juglandaceae*)

§	***ailanthifolia***	CBcs CMCN
	- B&SWJ 11026	WCru
	- var. ***cordiformis*** 'Brock' (F)	CAgr
	- - 'Campbell Cw3' (F)	CAgr
	- - 'Fodermaier' seedling	CAgr
	- - 'Rhodes' (F)	CAgr
	ailanthifolia* × *cinerea	see *J.* × *bixbyi*
§	× ***bixbyi***	CAgr
	cinerea (F)	CBcs
	- 'Beckwith' (F)	CAgr
	- 'Booth' seedling (F)	CAgr
	- 'Craxezy' (F)	CAgr
	- 'Kenworthy' seedling (F)	CAgr
	- 'Myjoy' (F)	CAgr
	hindsii	EBtc
	mandschurica B&SWJ 12550 from Korea	WCru
	mandshurica (F)	CBcs
	- BWJ 8097 from China	WCru
	- RWJ 9905 from Taiwan	WCru
	microcarpa	CMCN
	nigra (F) ♀H6	CBcs CCVT CDul CHab CLnd CMCN CMac COtt CSBt CTho CWib EBee ECrN ELan EPfP GTwe LAst LCro MAsh MBri MGos NOrn NWea SDea SEND SGol SPer WMat WMou
	- 'Bicentennial' (F)	CAgr
	- 'Emma Kay' (F)	CAgr
	- 'Laciniata' ♀H6	EPfP GBin MBlu WPat
	- 'Thomas' (F)	CAgr
	- 'Weschke' (F)	CAgr
	regia (F)	Widely available
	- 'Axel' (F)	CAgr WMat
	- 'Broadview' (F) ♀H6	Widely available
	- 'Buccaneer' (F) ♀H6	CAgr CArg CDul CLnd CTho EPom GTwe NOra SDea SKee WHar WMat
	- 'Chandler' (F)	CAgr
	- 'Corne du Périgord' (F)	CAgr
	- 'Excelsior of Taynton' (F)	CAgr MCoo WMat
	- 'Ferjean' (F)	CAgr
	- 'Fernette'PBR (F)	CAgr NOra WHar WMat
	- 'Fernor' (F)	CAgr WHar WMat
	- 'Franquette' (F)	CAgr GTwe MCoo NOra SPer WHar WMat
	- 'Hansen' (F)	CAgr
	- 'Hartley' (F)	CAgr
	- 'Laciniata' ♀H6	CMCN ERea WPat
	- 'Lara' (F)	CAgr GTwe NOra SBmr WMat
	- 'Mayette' (F)	CAgr
	- 'Meylannaise' (F)	CAgr
	- number 16 (F)	CAgr WHar WMat
	- 'Parisienne' (F)	CAgr SGol
	- 'Plovdivski' (F)	CAgr WHar WMat
	- 'Proslavski' (F)	CAgr CDul WHar WMat
	- 'Purpurea'	CMCN ERea MBlu
	- 'Rita' (F)	CAgr LBuc
	- 'Ronde de Montignac' (F)	CAgr
	- 'Soleze' (F)	CAgr
	- 'Sychrov' (F) **new**	WMat
	sieboldiana	see *J. ailanthifolia*
	sigillata **new**	LEdu

jujube see *Ziziphus jujuba*

Juncus (*Juncaceae*)

	articulatus	LLWG XLum
	bulbosus	CNat
	conglomeratus	EWay LLWG
	'Curly Gold Strike' (v)	MSKA
§	***decipiens*** 'Curly-wurly'	EPfP LRHS NWad SWat
	- 'Spiralis'	see *J. decipiens* 'Curly-wurly'
	effusus	CBen CWat EHon LRHS MSKA MWLS NPer SWat WMAq XLum
	- 'Carman's Japanese'	CKno NSti
	- 'Gold Strike' (v)	EPPr LLWG
§	- f. ***spiralis***	CBen CSpe CWat EHoe EHon ELan EPfP GMaP LBrs LRHS MAsh MBri MJak NBir NOak SLim SPlb SVic WMAq XLum
§	- - 'Unicorn'PBR	EBee LBMP
	ensifolius	CBen CWat EBee EHoe EWay EWes MMHG MSKA MWts NPer NSti
	filiformis 'Spiralis'	LPot WWEG
	inflexus	CBen CWat EHon MMuc MSKA SWat XLum
	- 'Afro'	EBee MMuc NBro NOak NWsh SPlb WWEG
	pallidus	EPPr GCal
	patens 'Carman's Gray'	CKno CWCL EPPr GCal GQue LRHS NNor NOak NWad NWsh WMoo WWEG
	- 'Elk Blue'	CKno
*	***pincei*** **new**	GEdr
	subnodulosus	LLWG
	'Swarm of Hedgehogs'	WWEG
	'Unicorn'	see *J. effusus* f. *spiralis* 'Unicorn'
	xiphioides	EHoe

Junellia (*Verbenaceae*)

	azorelloides	WAbe
§	***micrantha***	WAbe
	odonnellii	WAbe
§	***succulentifolia***	WAbe
	tridactylites **new**	WAbe

Juniperus ✿ (*Cupressaceae*)

	sp.	LPar

	chinensis	CMen
	- 'Aurea' ♀H6	CBcs CMac EFry
§	- 'Blaauw' ♀H6	CDoC CMac CMen EFry SGol SLim
	- 'Blue Alps' ♀H6	EFry LPar LRHS MBri MGos MMuc NEgg SCob SCoo SEND SGol SLim
	- 'Densa Spartan'	see *J. chinensis* 'Spartan'
	- 'Echiniformis'	CKen
	- 'Expansa Aureospicata' (v)	CDoC EFry EPfP SEND
§	- 'Expansa Variegata' (v)	CDoC CWib EFry EPfP SLim
	- 'Itoigawa'	CMen
§	- 'Kaizuka' ♀H6	EFry LPar SGol
	- 'Kaizuka Variegata'	see *J. chinensis* 'Variegated Kaizuka'
	- 'Kuriwao Gold'	see *J. × pfitzeriana* 'Kuriwao Gold'
	- 'Obelisk'	EFry
	- 'Oblonga'	EFry
§	- 'Parsonsii'	WCFE
	- 'Plumosa Aurea' ♀H6	EFry SLim
	- 'Plumosa Aureovariegata' (v)	CKen
	- 'Pyramidalis' ♀H6	CDoC CLet EFry EPfP MBri SCoo
	- 'San José'	CMen EFry
§	- var. ***sargentii***	CMen
	- 'Shimpaku'	CKen CMen
§	- 'Spartan'	EFry
	- 'Stricta'	CSBt EFry LBee NLar NOrn SGol SLim
	- 'Sulphur Spray'	see *J. × pfitzeriana* 'Sulphur Spray'
	- 'Torulosa'	see *J. chinensis* 'Kaizuka'
§	- 'Variegated Kaizuka' (v)	EFry SCoo SLim
	communis	CArn CDul CHab EFry GPoy NWea SIde
	- (f)	SIde
	- 'Arnold'	CDul NLar
	- 'Arnold Sentinel'	CKen
	- 'Barton'	NLar NWad
	- 'Barton Gem'	NWad
	- 'Brien'	CDoC CKen
	- 'Brynhyfryd Gold'	CKen
	- 'Compressa' ♀H7	CBcs CDoC CKen CLet CMac CSBt CTri CWib EFry EPfP EPot GEdr LAst LBee LRHS MAsh MBri MGos MJak NEgg NHol NWea SLim SPer SPoG WIce
§	- 'Constance Franklin' (v)	EFry
	- 'Corielagan'	CKen
	- 'Cracovia'	CKen
	- var. ***depressa***	GPoy SEND SGol
	- 'Depressa Aurea'	CKen CSBt EFry LBee
	- 'Depressed Star'	EFry SPoG WGor
	- 'Derrynane'	EFry
	- 'Effusa'	CKen
	- 'Gelb'	see *J. communis* 'Schneverdingen Goldmachangel'
	- 'Gold Cone'	CKen CLet EFry ELan EPfP EUJe LBee MAsh MBri MGos SLim SPoG WGor
	- 'Golden Showers'	see *J. communis* 'Schneverdingen Goldmachangel'
	- 'Goldschatz' ♀H7	CKen LAst LRHS SLim SPoG WGor
	- 'Green Carpet' ♀H7	CDoC CKen EFry ELan EPfP GKin LBuc LRHS MAsh MBri MGos NLar NPri SCoo SLim SPoG WCFE
	- 'Haverbeck'	CKen
	- 'Hibernica' ♀H7	CDul CLet CSBt EFry ELan EPfP LAst MGos MJak NPri NWea SLim SPer SPoG
	- 'Hibernica Aurea'	CMac
	- 'Hibernica Variegata'	see *J. communis* 'Constance Franklin'
	- 'Hornibrookii'	EFry NWea SRms
	- 'Kenwith Castle'	CKen
	- 'Meyer'	GKin
	- 'Pyramidalis'	SPlb
	- 'Rakete'	IVic
	- 'Repanda' ♀H7	CBcs CDoC CLet CMac CSBt CWib EFry EPfP LAst MAsh MBri MGos NLar NWea SCoo SGol SLim SPer SPoG
§	- 'Schneverdingen Goldmachangel'	IBoy MBri NLar SLim
	- 'Sentinel'	CDoC EFry WCFE WMou
	- 'Sieben Steinhauser'	CKen NLar
	- 'Silver Mist'	CKen
	- Suecica Group	EFry NWea
	- - 'Suecica Aurea'	EFry
	- 'Zeal'	CKen
	conferta	see *J. rigida* subsp. *conferta*
	- var. ***maritima***	see *J. taxifolia*
	davurica	EFry
	- 'Expansa'	see *J. chinensis* 'Parsonsii'
	- 'Expansa Albopicta'	see *J. chinensis* 'Expansa Variegata'
	- 'Expansa Variegata'	see *J. chinensis* 'Expansa Variegata'
	- 'Leningrad'	NLar
	foetidissima	CMen
	× ***gracilis*** 'Blaauw'	see *J. chinensis* 'Blaauw'
	'Grey Owl' ♀H7	EFry ELan EPfP MMuc NWea SEND SGol SLim
	horizontalis	CLet NWea
§	- 'Andorra Compact'	EPfP
I	- 'Andorra Variegata' (v)	SCoo
	- 'Bar Harbor'	CMac EFry
§	- 'Blue Chip'	EFry ELan EPfP LBee MGos MJak NBir NWea SCoo SPoG
	- 'Blue Moon'	see *J. horizontalis* 'Blue Chip'
	- 'Blue Rug'	see *J. horizontalis* 'Wiltonii'
	- 'Douglasii'	EFry
	- 'Emerald Spreader'	EFry ELan
	- 'Glauca'	EFry NWea
	- 'Golden Carpet' ♀H7	ELan EPfP LBuc LCro NLar
	- 'Golden Spreader'	CDoC
	- 'Grey Pearl'	CKen EFry
	- 'Hughes'	EFry LBee MBri MRav NWea
	- Icee Blue = 'Monber' ♀H7	CKen GKin LRHS MAsh MBri NLar SLim SPoG
	- 'Jade River'	EFry
	- 'Limeglow' ♀H7	CDoC CKen ELan EPfP MGos NLar NOrn SCoo SLim SPoG
	- 'Mother Lode'	CKen
	- 'Neumann'	CKen
	- 'Pancake'	NLar
	- 'Plumosa Compacta'	see *J. horizontalis* 'Andorra Compact'
	- 'Prince of Wales'	EFry MAsh NWea
	- 'Prostrata'	IBoy
	- 'Turquoise Spreader'	CSBt EFry MBri NWea SGol
	- 'Villa Marie'	CKen
§	- 'Wiltonii'	CDul EFry MGos NWea
	- 'Winter Blue'	LBee
	- 'Youngstown'	MBri SEND
	- 'Yukon Belle'	CKen
	× ***media***	see *J. × pfitzeriana*
§	× ***pfitzeriana***	CDul CMac SCob SGol
	- 'Arctic'	CDul NLar
	- 'Armstrongii'	EFry
	- 'Blaauw'	see *J. chinensis* 'Blaauw'
	- 'Blue and Gold' (v)	CKen EFry SPoG
	- 'Blue Cloud'	see *J. virginiana* 'Blue Cloud'

§	- 'Carbery Gold' ♀H7	CBcs CMac CSBt EFry GKin LBee LRHS MAsh MBri MGos NOrn SCoo SLim SPoG WGor
	- 'Gold Coast'	CDoC CKen CSBt EFry EPfP LBee MBri MGos SGol SLim WGor
	- Gold Sovereign = 'Blound'	LBee
	- 'Gold Star'	MBri
	- 'Hetzii'	EFry NLar NWea
	- 'King of Spring'	NLar SLim
§	- 'Kuriwao Gold'	CMac EFry GKin MBri MGos MRav SEND SGol
	- 'Mint Julep'	CSBt EFry EPfP MGos MJak SCob SCoo SGol SLim
	- 'Old Gold' ♀H7	EFry EPfP GKin LBee LCro MBri MGos MJak MMuc NEgg NPri NWea SCoo SEND SGol SLim SPlb WCFE WHar
	- 'Old Gold Carbery'	see *J.* × *pfitzeriana* 'Carbery Gold'
	- 'Pfitzeriana'	see *J.* × *pfitzeriana* 'Wilhelm Pfitzer'
	- 'Pfitzeriana Aurea'	CLet CMac EFry EPfP MGos NWea SCob SGol
	- 'Pfitzeriana Glauca'	EFry
§	- 'Sulphur Spray' ♀H7	CDul CWib EFry MAsh MMuc SEND SLim WCFE
§	- 'Wilhelm Pfitzer'	EPfP NWea
	phoenicea	XSen
§	***pingii*** 'Glassell'	CDoC NLar
	- 'Hulsdonk Yellow' PBR	LRHS MAsh NLar SPoG
§	- var. ***wilsonii***	CDoC CKen
	procera	WPGP
	procumbens 'Kishiogima'	LRHS NLar
	- 'Lighting Spot' **new**	NLar
	- 'Nana' ♀H7	CDoC CKen CLet CMac CSBt EFry EPfP LAst LBee LRHS MAsh MBri MGos MJak NEgg NHol NLar SCoo SLim SPoG WCFE
	recurva 'Castlewellan'	CDoC NLar WHor
	- var. ***coxii***	CDoC CDul CMac EFry NHol NLar NWea SMad WCFE
§	- 'Densa'	CDoC CKen
	- 'Nana'	see *J. recurva* 'Densa'
	rigida	CMen
§	- subsp. ***conferta***	CMac MBri SEND SGol
	- - 'All Gold' ♀H6	LRHS NLar SLim SPoG
*	- - 'Blue Ice'	CKen
	- - 'Blue Pacific'	CKen CLet EFry SGol SPoG
	- - 'Blue Tosho'	CDul NLar
	- - 'Emerald Sea'	EFry
	- - 'Silver Mist'	CKen
	sabina	CArn NWea
§	- 'Blaue Donau'	EFry
	- Blue Danube	see *J. sabina* 'Blaue Donau'
	- 'Knap Hill'	see *J.* × *pfitzeriana* 'Wilhelm Pfitzer'
	- 'Mountaineer'	see *J. scopulorum* 'Mountaineer'
	- 'Rockery Gem'	EFry
	- 'Skandia'	CKen
	- 'Tamariscifolia'	CBcs CLet CWib EFry GKin LBee LRHS MAsh MGos MJak NOrn NPri NWea SEND SGol SLim SPer SPoG WCFE
	- 'Variegata' (v)	EFry
	sargentii	see *J. chinensis* var. *sargentii*
	scopulorum 'Blue Arrow' ♀H7	Widely available
	- 'Blue Banff'	CKen
	- 'Blue Heaven'	EFry
	- 'Blue Pyramid'	EFry
	- 'Moonglow'	EFry
§	- 'Mountaineer'	EFry
	- 'Silver Star' (v)	EFry
	- 'Skyrocket'	CBcs CCVT CDul CMac CNWT CSBt CWib ECrN EFry EPfP GGal LAst MGos MJak MRav NWea SCob SEND SGol SPlb WCFE WHar WMou
	- 'Springbank'	EFry WCFE
	- 'Wichita Blue'	EFry EPfP IVic
	squamata 'Blue Carpet' ♀H7	Widely available
	- 'Blue Spider'	SLim
	- 'Blue Star' ♀H7	CDoC CJun CKen CLet CMac CSBt EFry ELan EPfP EPot LAst LBee LCro LRHS MBri MGos MJak NEgg NHol NLar NPri NWad NWea SGol SLim SPer SPoG WCFE
	- 'Blue Star Variegated'	see *J. squamata* 'Golden Flame'
	- 'Chinese Silver'	EFry
	- 'Dream Joy'	CKen NLar NWad
	- 'Filborna'	LBee
	- 'Floreant'	SLim
	- 'Glassell'	see *J. pingii* 'Glassell'
§	- 'Golden Flame' (v)	CKen
	- 'Holger' ♀H7	CDoC CDul CLet CMac EFry EPfP LAst LBee MAsh MBri MGos MJak NHol NLar SCoo SLim SPoG WGor
	- 'Meyeri'	EFry NWea SGol
	- 'Wilsonii'	see *J. pingii* var. *wilsonii*
§	***taxifolia***	CSBt
	virginiana	NWea
§	- 'Blue Cloud'	SLim
	- 'Burkii'	EFry
	- 'Frosty Morn'	CKen
	- 'Glauca'	EFry NWea
	- 'Golden Spring'	CKen
	- 'Helle'	see *J. chinensis* 'Spartan'
	- 'Hillspire'	EFry
	- Silver Spreader = 'Mona'	CKen EFry
	- 'Sulphur Spray'	see *J.* × *pfitzeriana* 'Sulphur Spray'

Justicia (*Acanthaceae*)

	americana	LLWG
	aurea	EShb
§	***brandegeeana*** ♀H1b	IDee MOWG
	- 'Lutea'	see *J. brandegeeana* 'Yellow Queen'
	- variegated (v)	EShb
§	- 'Yellow Queen'	EShb
	- yellow-flowered	EShb
§	***carnea***	CHll EShb MOWG WCot
	- 'Alba'	EShb
	- dark-leaved	CHll EShb
	- 'Radiant'	SMad
§	***floribunda***	MOWG
	guttata	see *J. brandegeeana*
	pauciflora	see *J. floribunda*
	'Penrhosiensis'	EShb
	pohliana	see *J. carnea*
	rizzinii ♀H1b	CBcs CHll LSou MHtn SRot WHil
	spicigera	EShb
	suberecta	see *Dicliptera sericea*

K

Kadsura (*Schisandraceae*)

coccinea B&SWJ 11793	WCru
- FMWJ 13489 **new**	WCru
heteroclita FMWJ 13385 **new**	WCru

- WWJ 11947	WCru
japonica	CBcs
- B&SWJ 1027	WCru
- B&SWJ 4463 from Korea	WCru
- B&SWJ 11109 from Japan	WCru
- from Japan	EPfP WSHC
- 'Fukurin' (v)	NLar
- 'Variegata' (v)	EBee EPfP LRHS WSHC
- white fruit	CBcs NLar

Kaempferia ✿ (*Zingiberaceae*)

pulchra 'Bronze Peacock'	MJak
rotunda	LAma LTro

Kageneckia (*Rosaceae*)

oblonga	SPlb

Kalanchoe (*Crassulaceae*)

beharensis ♀H1b	CDTJ CDoC ELan EShb EUJe WCot
- 'Fang' ♀H1b	CDTJ CDoC ELan EShb
- 'Rusty'	CDTJ CSpe
§ ***delagoensis***	EShb
fedtschenkoi	EShb
hildebrandtii new	EShb
laciniata	EShb
orgyalis	EShb
pinnata	EShb
pubescens	EShb
pumila ♀H1b	EShb SBch
serrata	EShb
sexangularis	EShb
'Tessa' ♀H1b	CDes WCot
thyrsiflora	EShb
- 'Bronze Sculpture'	CAbb EUJe
- 'Variegata' new	EShb
tomentosa ♀H1b	CDoC EShb LAll WCot
tubiflora	see *K. delagoensis*

Kalimeris (*Asteraceae*)

§ ***incisa***	MMuc MRav WBor
- 'Alba'	ECha MTis NLar WFar XLum
- 'Blue Star'	ECha ECtt MSpe MTis NLar WCAu WFar WPtf WSHC
- 'Charlotte'	EWes MSpe MTis NBre NDov SAko
- 'Madiva'	CSam EBee IMou LHop LPla NDov SAko
- 'Nana Blue'	EBee NDov
'Mon Jardin'	LPla WCot
§ ***mongolica***	CAby CDes CMac ECGP ECha LPla MMuc SAko SDix WFar WSHC
- 'Antonia'	LPla NDov WCot
§ ***pinnatifida***	LRHS
- 'Hortensis'	ECtt MNrw
§ ***yomena*** 'Shogun' (v)	CBod ECha ECtt EHoe ELan EPfP LEdu MNrw MPie MSpe NBir NLar NSti SPer WFar WWEG
- 'Variegata'	see *K. yomena* 'Shogun'

Kalmia ✿ (*Ericaceae*)

angustifolia ♀H4	SRms
- f. ***rubra*** ♀H6	CBcs CDoC CDul EBee ELan EPfP LRHS MAsh NLar NPri SPer
I - 'Rubra Nana'	CMac
latifolia	CBcs ELan EPfP LRHS NPri NWea SPer SWvt
- 'Bandeau'	GGGa
- 'Bridesmaid' new	NLar
- 'Bullseye'	LRHS NLar SAko SPoG
- 'Carousel'	CBcs NLar
- 'Clementine Churchill'	CMac
- 'Eskimo'	GGGa
- 'Freckles' ♀H6	MPkF SPoG
- 'Galaxy'	GGGa IVic LRHS NLar SAko
- 'Ginkona'	GGGa SAko
- 'Kaleidoscope'	GGGa IVic MGos NLar
- 'Little Linda' ♀H6	SAko
- 'Minuet'	CBcs GGGa IVic LRHS MLea NLar SLim SPoG SWvt
- 'Mitternacht'	GGGa
- 'Moyland'	GGGa
- f. ***myrtifolia***	LRHS MLea
- - 'Elf'	IVic LRHS MAsh MGos MPkF NLar SAko SLim
- 'Nani'	GGGa
- 'Nipmuck'	MPkF
- 'Olympic Fire' ♀H6	CBcs GBin GGGa IVic LRHS NLar SLim SWvt
- 'Olympic Wedding'	SPoG
- 'Ostbo Red'	CBcs CDoC CDul CMac GBin IVic LRHS MLea MMuc MPkF SAko SPoG SWvt
- 'Peppermint'	GGGa IVic NLar
- 'Pink Charm' ♀H6	IVic SAko
- 'Pinkobello'	GGGa
- 'Pinwheel'	LRHS MJak NLar SAko SLim SPoG
- 'Quinnipiac'	MJak
- 'Sarah'	LRHS MLea
- 'Snowdrift'	NLar
polifolia	CBcs LCro NHar SPer WThu
- f. ***leucantha***	NHar WThu

Kalmiopsis (*Ericaceae*)

leachiana 'Glendoick'	NLar

× *Kalmiothamnus* (*Ericaceae*)

'Haytor'	ITim
ornithomma 'Cosdon'	WAbe
'Sindelberg'	ITim WAbe

Kalopanax (*Araliaceae*)

pictus	see *K. septemlobus*
§ ***septemlobus***	CBcs CDul ELan EPfP EUJe GBin MMuc NLar SEND SPtp
- var. ***magnificus*** B&SWJ 10900	WCru
- f. ***maximowiczii***	EPfP IVic MBlu NLar

Keckiella (*Plantaginaceae*)

§ ***antirrhinoides***	SBrt
§ ***cordifolia***	CEvo

Keiskea (*Lamiaceae*)

japonica pink-flowered	SBrt

Kelleria (*Thymelaeaceae*)

dieffenbachii	WThu

Kelseya (*Rosaceae*)

uniflora	WAbe

Kennedia (*Papilionaceae*)

coccinea	SVen
macrophylla	CRHN
nigricans	MOWG
prostrata	SBrt SPlb
rubicunda	CRHN MOWG

Kentia (*Arecaceae*)

belmoreana	see *Howea belmoreana*
forsteriana	see *Howea forsteriana*

Kentranthus see *Centranthus*

Kerria (*Rosaceae*)

japonica misapplied single	see *K. japonica* 'Simplex'
japonica (L.) DC. (d)	see *K. japonica* 'Pleniflora'
- 'Albescens'	CBot WCot
- 'Golden Guinea' ♀H5	CExl CMac ECtt ELan EPfP GGal IFro LRHS MAsh MGos MNrw MRav SCob SCoo SHil SPer SRms SWvt WFar
§ - 'Picta' (v)	CDul CMac CWib EBee ELan MGos MRav MSwo SCob SGol SLim SLon SPer SPoG SRms WFar
§ - 'Pleniflora' (d) ♀H5	Widely available
§ - 'Simplex'	CDul CExl CMac GGal NWea
- 'Variegata'	see *K. japonica* 'Picta'

Kiggelaria (*Flacourtiaceae*)

africana	SVen

Kirengeshoma (*Hydrangeaceae*)

palmata	Widely available
- dwarf	WCot
- Koreana Group ♀H7	Widely available
- 'Margarita' **new**	EBee

Kitaibela (*Malvaceae*)

vitifolia	CExl CSpe ELan EPPr EWld EWoo MPie NBid SEND SGSe SPad SPav SPlb

Kitchingia see *Kalanchoe*

kiwi fruit see *Actinidia deliciosa*

Kleinia (*Asteraceae*)

articulata	see *Senecio articulatus*
grantii	CSpe WCot
repens	see *Senecio serpens*

Knautia (*Caprifoliaceae*)

§ ***arvensis***	CArn CElw CHab CWld EBee EPfP EWoo LCro LRHS MHer MNHC NLar NMir SGSe SPer SPhx SRms WHer WMoo WOut WSFF
- 'Rachael'	CElw
- white-flowered	SPhx WSHC
dipsacifolia	SHar
'Jardin d'en Face'	CBod EPfP LRHS
§ ***macedonica***	Widely available
- 'Crimson Cushion'	CSpe ECtt LSou
- dark-flowered **new**	IFro
- 'Mars Midget'	CBod CExl CHll COtt CSpe EBee ELan ELon EPfP GMaP GQue IBoy LAst LCro LRHS LSou MGos MSpe NLar NPri SBea SCob SPad SPhx SPoG SWvt WFar WHoo WSHC
- Melton pastels	CBod CExl COtt EBee ELan EPfP GJos IBoy LRHS LSRN MCot MGos NLar NPer SPhx SPoG SRkn SRot SWat SWvt WFar
- pink-flowered	CSam
- 'Red Knight'	CBod EPfP LHop LPal LRHS MBNS MCot SGSe SHil WCAu
- red-flowered	CWib
- short	ECtt
- tall, pale-flowered	SPhx
- 'Thunder and Lightning'^PBR (v)	CBct CBod CMea CMos CWGN EBee ECtt EPfP EWes IBoy IKil LBMP LBuc LRHS MAvo MHol MNrw MPie MRav NLar SPad SPer SPoG WCot WHil
sarajevensis	MAvo

Knightia (*Proteaceae*)

excelsa	CBcs

Kniphofia ✿ (*Asphodelaceae*)

'Ada'	ELon EWes SGSe
albescens	NLos SPlb XLum
'Alcazar'	CBcs CPrp ECtt ELon EPfP IBoy LOPS LPal LSRN MAvo MBri MHer SCob SGSe SPer SRkn SWvt WCAu WCFE WFar WMnd WWEG
'Ample Dwarf'	ECtt WCot
'Amsterdam'	MWat SHar
angustifolia	SPlb
'Apricot'	LRHS
'Apricot Souffle'	EPri SGSe WCot
'Atlanta'	LRHS SGSe
'Aurora'	XLum
'Barton Fever' ♀H6	WCot
baurii	CExl SPlb
'Bees' Jubilee'	MAvo MNrw NChi
'Bees' Lemon'	Widely available
§ 'Bees' Sunset' ♀H5	CAvo CDes CSam EAEE EBee ECha ECtt EPfP GCra LPla LRHS MAvo MNrw MWat SEND SGSe SMHy SWvt WAul WHil WWEG
'Bees' Yellow'	SBch
'Bitter Chocolate'	WCot
'Border Ballet'	LRHS NBir NGdn NLar SWat WFar XLum
brachystachya	ELon GCal SPlb
'Bressingham Comet'	CRos EAEE ECtt LCro LEdu LRHS MAvo NBir NCGa SHil
Bressingham Sunbeam = 'Bresun'	EAEE EBee ECtt LRHS NBir WWEG
'Bressingham Yellow'	ECtt
'Brimstone' Bloom ♀H5	CBod CElw CPrp EAEE ECtt EPfP GBin LEdu LHop LRHS NBir SEND SGSe SPtp SRkn SWvt WFar WGwG WMnd WWEG
bruceae	EPri SPlb SVen
'Buttercup' ♀H5	CAvo LOPS LSRN WSHC
'Butterfly'	EBee
'Candlelight'	CCse EBee ECtt EPri MAvo SAko SGSe WSHC
'Candlemass'	CTca
caulescens	Widely available
- 'Coral Breakers'	CBod CExl CPrp CTca ECtt ELon GAbr GCal LRHS MAvo MHol NEgg NLos SDix SKHP SMad SPer SPoG WCot
- 'John May'	CAby CBod CBot EBee ECtt ESwi LRHS MAvo SCob SMad SWvt WCot
- 'Oxford Blue' **new**	CDes
- short	ECha
- 'Tiny Girl'	ECtt
'Chichi'	MAvo WCot
'Christmas Cheer'	CDes EBee
citrina	CCon GCra GLog IBoy LAst MBrN NGBl WCot WHar WHil XLum
'C.M. Prichard' misapplied	see *K. rooperi*
'C.M. Prichard' Prichard	WCot
'Cobra'	ECtt GBin GMaP LRHS SAko WAul WCot WHil

	Name	Suppliers
	'Coral Flame' ♀H5	EBee LRHS
	'Coral Sceptre'	WCot
	'Creamsicle'PBR (Popsicle Series)	ECtt SCob WCot WHlf
	'Dingaan'	CAbb EBee ECtt MBel MNrw MTis NBir NLar WCot
	'Dorset Sentry'	CAbb CAby EBee ECtt ELon EPfP EWoo LRHS MBel MGos MNrw NBir NEgg NLar SGSe SKHP SMad SPhx WCot WFar WWEG
	drepanophylla	MHer
	'Drummore Apricot'	CMHG CPrp EAEE ECha ECtt ELan EPfP GBin GBuc IBoy LRHS LSRN MAvo NBir NEgg SEND SPtp WCot WFar WGwG
	'Early Buttercup'	CTca WFar
	'Elvira'PBR	CPne EBee ECtt LRHS
	Ember Glow = 'Tneg'PBR (Glow Series)	CPne EBee ECtt
	ensifolia	CTca ECtt NGdn SVen WMnd XLum
	'Erecta'	CPne CTal
	'Ernest Mitchell'	WCot
	Express hybrids	XLum
	'Fairyland'	NGBl
	'Fiery Fred' ♀H6	CBod CPrp EBee ECGP ECtt ELon EPfP GQue LRHS MAvo SBod SGSe SPtp WAul WCot
	Fire Glow = 'Tnfg'PBR (Glow Series)	CMos MAvo NCGa NLar
	'First Sunrise'PBR	ECtt LRHS MBri MJak
	'Flamenco'	ELon LRHS NGdn SCob
	'Flaming Torch'	EBee ECtt
	'Florence Bedecked'	WCot
	foliosa Hochst.	LEdu
	'Frances Victoria'	WCot
	galpinii misapplied	see *K. triangularis* subsp. *triangularis*
	'Gilt Bronze'	WCot
	'Gladness'	MAvo MTis NBir SGSe WCot WWEG
	'Gloire d'Orléans'	XLum
	'Goldelse'	EBee LRHS NBir
	'Goldfinch'	CCse CSam SGSe
	gracilis	LEdu
	'Grandiflora'	CMac MWhi WHar
	'Green and Cream'	MHCG
	'Green Goddess'	SGSe
	'Green Jade'	Widely available
	'Green Jewel' **new**	LRHS
	'H.E. Beale'	WCot
	'Hen and Chickens'	EBee ECtt ESwi MAvo SMad WCot
	hirsuta	CCon EBee LRHS NLos WSHC
	- JCA 3.461.900	SKHP
	- 'Fire Dance'	CSde EAJP LRHS LSun
	- 'Traffic Lights'	WHar
	'Ice Queen'	CAvo CCon EBee ECha ECtt ELon EPPr EPri EWoo GBin MAvo MHer MNrw MRav MSpe MTis NChi NLar SEND SGSe SGol SMad SRms SWvt WCAu WCot WWEG
	ichopensis	LEdu NLos SVen WPGP
	'Incandesce' ♀H5	WCot
	'Innocence' ♀H4	EPfP LRHS
	'Jabulani' **new**	CDes
	'Jane Henry'	CDes EBee LEdu
	'Jenny Bloom'	COtt CPrp CRos EAEE ECtt ELan ELon EPfP EWoo GBin GBuc GCal GMaP LAst LEdu LRHS MRav NLar NSti SPtp WAul WCot WFar WWEG
	'Jess's Delight'	WCot
	'John Benary'	CPrp CRos EAEE EBee ECtt GBin GLog GMaP IKil LLWG LRHS MBel MSpe NBir NEgg NGdn NLar SEND SPer SPtp WCot WGwG WKif
	'Jonathan' ♀H5	WCot
	laxiflora	EPri NLos WPGP
	'Lemon Popsicle' (Popsicle Series)	CMea CWGN LAst LRHS NPri SCob
	'Light of the World'	see *K. triangularis* subsp. *triangularis* 'Light of the World'
	'Limelight'	EBee
	linearifolia	CEvo CExl CPrp EBee GCra NLos SPlb WCot XLum
	'Little Elf'	XLum
	'Little Maid'	Widely available
	'Little Red Rooster'	EAEE
	littoralis	SGSe
	'Lord Roberts'	GCal MAvo MRav SGSe SMad WCot WPGP
	'Luna'	WCot
	macowanii	see *K. triangularis* subsp. *triangularis*
	'Maid of Orleans'	ELon
	'Mango Popsicle'PBR (Popsicle Series)	CAbb CBod CPne ECtt EWTr LRHS LSou MBel MBri NLar SCob WCot WHlf
	'Mermaiden'	CCon CMHG ECtt MNrw WCot
	'Minister Verschuur'	EBee ECtt GQue LRHS MBri
	'Modesta'	WSHC
	'Molten Lava'	CDes
	'Moonstone' ♀H5	CHVG CPrp EBee ECtt GBin LLHF LPla LSun MAvo MNrw MTis NLar NSti SEND WCot
	'Mount Etna'	WCot
	multiflora	CTca NLos
	- cream-flowered	NLos
	- 'November Glory'	WCot
	- yellow/orange-flowered	NLos
	'Nancy's Red'	Widely available
	nelsonii Mast.	see *K. triangularis* subsp. *triangularis*
	'New Sensation' **new**	WCot
§	'Nobilis' ♀H6	Widely available
	northiae ♀H4	CBot CExl CHid CTca EAla EBee ELan ELon EPri EUJe EWes GCal LEdu LRHS LSun MNrw NLos SEND SGSe SMad SPlb SWvt WCot WCru WPGP XLum
	'Old Court Seedling'	GGal SGSe
	'Orange Vanilla Popsicle' (Popsicle Series)	ECtt LRHS SCob SPad SPoG WHoo
§	'Painted Lady'	CSam CSde CTca CTri EBee ECtt GMaP LAst MAvo MHol MNrw NCGa NLar SMHy SWvt WCot
	'Papaya Popsicle'PBR (Popsicle Series)	CMea CWGN EBee ECtt LRHS LSou MBri NPri SBea SCob SPoG WHlf
	parviflora	XLum
	pauciflora	CTre WCot
	'Penny Rockets' ♀H6	LRHS
	'Percy's Pride'	Widely available
	'Pfitzeri'	SRms
	'Pineapple Popsicle'PBR (Popsicle Series)	CAbb CWGN ECtt MBri NLar SCob WHlf
	× ***praecox***	NLos SGSe
	'Primrose Upward' ♀H6	WCot
I	'Primulina' Bloom	EBee LRHS SAko
	'Prince Igor' misapplied	see *K.* 'Nobilis'
	'Prince Igor' Prichard	ECtt MLHP NBir SGSe
	pumila	LLHF

	Name	Suppliers
	'Red Rocket'PBR	EBee EWoo IBoy LRHS MBri MNrw WCot
	'Redhot Popsicle' (Popsicle Series) new	LRHS SPoG WCot
	'Rich Echoes' ♀H5	CAvo CMea CWGN EBee ECGP ECtt ELon ESwi GBin LEdu LLHF MHol MTis NLar WCot WRHF
	ritualis	CExl SKHP WWEG
§	***rooperi*** ♀H5	Widely available
I	- 'Torchlight'	CPne
	'Rosea Superba'	EBee
	'Royal Castle'	CExl GMaP LRHS NBir NGdn SCob SEND WFar WWEG XLum
	'Royal Standard' ♀H5	CBcs CBod CMac COtt CPrp CRos ECtt ELan ELon EPfP GAbr ILea LCro LOPS LRHS LSRN MBri NLar SCob SPer SPoG SPtp SWvt WFar WGwG WHil WMnd WWEG
	rufa Baker	LEdu MAvo WPGP
	'Safranvogel' ♀H4	EBee ECtt SGSe SMad WCot
	'Samuel's Sensation' misapplied	see *K.* 'Painted Lady'
	'Samuel's Sensation' Samuel ♀H5	CCon EBee ECtt LRHS LSun NLar SAko SGSe SRGP SWvt WCot WWEG
	sarmentosa	CExl NLos SGSe SPlb SVen WCot XLum
	'Saturn'	MAvo
	'Scorched Corn'	MAvo
	'Sherbet Lemon'	MNrw WCot
	'Shining Sceptre' misapplied	see *K.* 'Bees' Sunset'
	'Son of Notung'	IBlr
	'Springtime'	WCot
	'Star of Baden-Baden'	EBee NBir SEND SMad WCot WWEG
	Stark's early perpetual-flowering hybrids	XLum
	'Strawberries and Cream'	CBcs CMac CTsd CWCL EBee ECha ECtt ELon EWld GQue LAst SBod SGbt SWvt
	stricta	XLum
	'Sunningdale Yellow' ♀H6	CCse EAEE ECha ECtt GMaP MAvo MLHP SMHy SRms WWEG
	'Tawny King' ♀H5	Widely available
	'Tetbury Torch'PBR	CBod CExl CMos CPrp CWGN EAEE EBee ECtt GBin GQue LRHS MAvo MCot SGSe SPtp SWvt WAul WWEG
	thomsonii	CExl GCal NGdn
	- 'Kichocheo'	EBee GCal MAvo WCot
	- var. ***snowdenii*** misapplied	see *K. thomsonii* var. *thomsonii*
	- var. ***snowdenii*** ambig.	CCon CExl CPne WPGP XLum
§	- var. ***thomsonii***	SMHy
	- - 'Stern's Trip' ♀H4	CDes EBee
	'Timothy' ♀H5	Widely available
	'Toffee Nosed' ♀H5	Widely available
	'Torchbearer'	WCot
	'Torchlight' Wallace	SGSe
	triangularis	WFar XLum
§	- subsp. ***triangularis***	CBro EPfP GBuc LAst LRHS LSRN SCob SMad SPer SRms SVen SWat XLum
§	- - 'Light of the World'	CAby CBcs CPne CPrp CTca CWld EAEE ECtt EWTr GAbr GBin LAst LEdu LRHS MHer NBir NLar SCob SGSe SPer SPtp SWvt WCot WFar WGrn
	'Tuckii'	SRms
	typhoides	NBir NLos SPlb
	tysonii	SPlb XLum
	- subsp. ***tysonii***	NLos
	uvaria	CPrp EBee LCro LPal LRHS NBir NLos SCob SPer SRms SVic WCot WMnd XLum XSen
	'Vanilla'	EWoo LRHS LSRN NLar SEND SGSe WWEG
	'Vesta'	EBee LRHS
	'Victoria' Prichard	SGSe
	'Vincent Lepage'	EBee LHop NLar SAko
	'Wol's Red Seedling'	CAby CSam ECtt ELon EUJe EWoo GAbr GBin MCot MNrw NGdn SBch SEND SPoG WCot WGrn WHoo
	'Wrexham Buttercup' ♀H6	CSam EBee ECtt ELan EPfP GMaP GQue LRHS LSRN LSun MCot MHol MNrw MTis NPri SCob SEND SGSe WCot WHal WHoo WWEG
	'Yellow Bird' new	EBee
	'Yellow Cheer'	WCot
	'Yellow Hammer' Slieve Donard	CSam ECha ELon SEND WHil

Knowltonia (*Ranunculaceae*)

	Name	Suppliers
	filia	CExl

Koeleria (*Poaceae*)

	Name	Suppliers
	cristata misapplied	see *K. macrantha*
	glauca	CBod CWib ECha EHoe EPPr EPfP EShb GMaP LRHS MBNS MJak MWhi NBro NGdn NWsh SCob SLim SPlb SWvt WFar WWEG XSen
§	***macrantha***	XLum
	pyramidata	SMea XLum
	vallesiana	EHoe SMea

Koelreuteria (*Sapindaceae*)

	Name	Suppliers
	elegans subsp. ***formosana*** new	CMCN
	paniculata	Widely available
	- 'Beachmaster' new	NLar
	- 'Coral Sun'PBR ♀H5	CExl CMHG ELan EPfP EUJe LCro LRHS MBlu MBri MGos NLar NOrn SPoG WCot WMat WPat
	- 'Fastigiata'	CDul EBee EPfP MBlu MBri SCoo WHar WHor
	- 'Rosseels'	NLar
	- 'September'	EPfP MBlu

Kohleria (*Gesneriaceae*)

	Name	Suppliers
	'Ampallang'	WDib
	'An's Nagging Macaws'	WDib
	'Brazil Gem'	WDib
	'Cybele'	EABi WDib
	'Dark Velvet'	WDib
	eriantha ♀H1c	CDoC CTsd WDib
	'Flashdance' new	WDib
	'Hcy's Jardin de Monet'	WDib
	'Heartland's Blackberry Butterfly'	WDib
	hirsuta	WDib
	'Jester' ♀H1c	EABi WDib
	'Manchu'	WDib
	'Marquis de Sade'	EABi WDib
	'Queen Victoria' new	WDib
	'Red Ryder'	EABi
	'Roundelay'	WDib
	'Ruby Red'	WDib
	'Ryssiten'	EABi
	'Silver Feather'	WDib

§	'Sunrise'	WDib
	'Sunshine'	see *K.* 'Sunrise'
	'Texas Rainbow'	WDib
	warszewiczii ♀H1c	WDib

Kolkwitzia (*Caprifoliaceae*)

	amabilis	CExl CSBt CTri ECGP ELan EPfP GGal NEgg NWea SCob SGol SPlb SRms WCFE WHar WMoo WRHF WSHC
	- Dream Catcher = 'Maradco'	CMac EPfP MRav NEoE NLar SCob WPat
	- 'Pink Cloud' ♀H5	Widely available

Kosteletzkya (*Malvaceae*)

	virginica	MHol SBrt SPhx

kumquat see *Citrus japonica*

Kunzea (*Myrtaceae*)

	ambigua	EBee ECou IDee MOWG SPlb
	- pink-flowered	ECou
	- prostrate	ECou
	baxteri	CTre CTsd MOWG
	ericifolia	SPlb
§	***ericoides***	CTsd ECou
	- 'Auckland'	ECou
	parvifolia	SPlb
	pauciflora	SPlb

L

Lablab (*Papilionaceae*)

§	***purpureus***	SHDw
	- 'Ruby Moon'	CSpe

+ *Laburnocytisus* (*Papilionaceae*)

	'Adamii'	CDul CMac EBee ELan EPfP ESwi GBin IVic LAst LSRN MGos MPkF NLar NOrn SAko SPer

Laburnum ✿ (*Papilionaceae*)

	alpinum	NWea SPlb
	- 'Pendulum'	CCVT CDul CLnd ELan IDee LCro LSRN MAsh MGos MRav NOrn SGol SPer SPoG
§	***anagyroides***	CDul CWib MMuc NWea SEND SRms WBod
	- 'Erect' **new**	WMat
	'Famous Walk'	see *L.* × *watereri* 'Vossii'
	vulgare	see *L. anagyroides*
	× ***watereri***	IBoy
§	- 'Vossii' ♀H6	Widely available

Lachenalia (*Asparagaceae*)

	algoensis	ECho
§	***aloides***	CGrW CPne CTal ECho NRog SDeJ
	- var. ***aurea*** ♀H2	CTre ECho NRog SBch WCot
I	- var. ***luteola***	ECho
	- 'Nelsonii'	ECho SBch WCot
	- 'Pearsonii'	ECho NRog
	- var. ***quadricolor*** ♀H2	CDes CGrW CPrp CTsd ECho NRog WCot
	- var. ***vanzyliae*** ♀H2	NRog WCot
	anguinea	ECho
	attenuata	ECho
	bachmanii	NRog
	barkeriana	ECho
	bolusii	ECho
§	***bulbifera*** ♀H2	CDes CPne ECho GKev WCot
	- 'George' ♀H2	CTal ECho WCot
	capensis	ECho
	carnosa	ECho
	comptonii	ECho
	contaminata ♀H2	CGrW CPrp CTre ECho NRog WCot
§	***corymbosa*** ♀H2	CTal ECho NRog
	elegans	ECho
	- var. ***membranacea***	ECho
	- var. ***suaveolens***	ECho NRog
	ensifolia	CTal ECho LLHF NRog WCot
§	- subsp. ***ensifolia*** ♀H2	ECho NRya
	fistulosa	ECho
	framesii	ECho
	'Fransie' (African Beauty Series)	ECho
	gillettii	ECho
	glaucophylla	ECho
	hirta	ECho
	juncifolia	ECho NRog
	- var. ***juncifolia***	ECho
	kliprandensis	NRog
	lactosa	ECho
	latimerae	CPne ECho
	leipoldtii	ECho
	'Lemon Ripple' (v)	WCot
	liliiflora	CGrW CTal ECho NRog
	longibracteata	ECho
§	***longituba*** ♀H3	CPBP CTal ECho NRog WCot
	marginata	ECho
	mathewsii	ECho NRog
	mediana	ECho NRog
	montana	ECho
	multifolia	ECho
	mutabilis	ECho WCot
	'Namakwa' (African Beauty Series)	ECho NRog
	namaquensis	ECho NRog
	namibiensis	ECho
	nardoubergensis	ECho
	neilii	ECho
	nervosa	ECho
	obscura	ECho WCot
	orchioides var. ***glaucina***	CDes ECho NRog WCot
	orthopetala	CDes ECho NRog
	pallida	ECho NRog
§	***paucifolia***	ECho
	pendula	see *L. bulbifera*
	polyphylla	ECho
	pusilla	ECho WCot
	pustulata ♀H2	ECho NRog WCot
	- blue-flowered	CGrW ECho NRog
	- yellow-flowered	ECho NRog
	reflexa	ECho NRog
	'Robijn' (African Beauty Series)	ECho
	'Rolina' (African Beauty Series)	ECho
	'Romaud' (African Beauty Series)	CDes ECho NRog WCot
	'Romelia' (African Beauty Series)	ECho WCot
	'Ronina' (African Beauty Series)	CPrp ECho GKev NRog WCot
	'Rosabeth' (African Beauty Series)	ECho NRog WCot
	rosea	ECho NRog
	rubida	CDes CGrW ECho WCot

'Rupert' (African Beauty Series) ♀H2	ECho GKev NRog WCot
splendida	ECho
stayneri	CLak
thomasiae	ECho
trichophylla	ECho
tricolor	see *L. aloides*
unicolor	ECho NRog WCot
unifolia	ECho NRog
violacea	ECho
- var. ***glauca***	ECho
viridiflora ♀H2	ECho NRog WCot
xerophila	ECho
zebrina	ECho
zeyheri	ECho NRog WCot

Lactuca (*Asteraceae*)

alpina	see *Cicerbita alpina*
intricata	SIgm
perennis	EPPr EWld WHer
virosa	CArn

Lagarostrobos (*Podocarpaceae*)

§ ***franklinii***	CBcs CDoC IDee SAko WPGP
- 'Fota' (f)	WThu
- 'Picton Castle' (m)	WThu

Lagenaria (*Cucurbitaceae*)

siceraria 'Speckled Swan'	SVic

Lagerstroemia (*Lythraceae*)

indica ♀H1c	CBod EPfP SEND SPlb SSpi SVen WSHC
- B&SWJ 12660	WCru
- Dynamite = 'Whit II'	LRHS
- Petite Pinkie = 'Monkie'	IDee
- 'Red Imperator'	CBcs SEND
- Rhapsody in Pink = 'Whit VIII' **new**	LRHS
- 'Rosea'	CBcs LRHS SEND
subcostata CWJ 12352	WCru
'Tuskegee'	WPGP

Lagunaria (*Malvaceae*)

patersonii	CHII WPGP

Lagurus (*Poaceae*)

ovatus	SAdn

Lallemantia (*Lamiaceae*)

canescens	GEdr

Lamiastrum see *Lamium*

Lamium ✿ (*Lamiaceae*)

album	CArn CHab NMir
- 'Friday' (v)	NBir WHer WWEG
armenum	WAbe
flexuosum	EPPr
§ ***galeobdolon***	CTri CWib CWld EShb MHer SRms WHer WWtn
§ - 'Florentinum' (v)	CMac EBee ECha ELan MMuc MRav SPer
- 'Hermann's Pride'	CBod EBee EHoe ELan ELon EPfP GMaP LRHS NBir NDov NMir SPer SPoG SRms SWvt WAul WHoo WMoo XLum
- 'Kirkcudbright Dwarf'	EBee EPPr EWes GBin NBre XLum
§ - 'Silberteppich'	ECha MRav XLum
- 'Silver Angel'	XLum
- Silver Carpet	see *L. galeobdolon* 'Silberteppich'
- 'Variegatum'	see *L. galeobdolon* 'Florentinum'
garganicum subsp. ***garganicum***	CCse EWes LPla
- subsp. ***pictum***	see *L. garganicum* subsp. *striatum*
- subsp. ***reniforme***	see *L. garganicum* subsp. *striatum*
§ - subsp. ***striatum***	WAbe
(Lami Series) 'Lami Blush'	LRHS
- 'Lami Pink'	LRHS
- 'Lami Mega Purple' **new**	EBee
luteum	see *L. galeobdolon*
maculatum	GKev MCot MMuc NChi SRms WWtn
- 'Album'	ELan EPfP SHar SPer SRms WWtn
- 'Anne Greenaway' (v)	EWes
§ - 'Aureum'	ECtt EHoe ELan SWvt XLum
- 'Beacon Silver'	CMac COtt CWib EAJP EBee ECha ECtt ELan EPfP EShb LCro LPot LRHS MGos MHer MLHP MMuc MSCN MWhi NBir SCob SPer SPlb SPoG SRGP SRms SWvt WHar WWEG XLum
- 'Beedham's White'	NSti
- 'Brightstone Pearl'	EBee EWes EWld MAvo
- 'Cannon's Gold'	CBod ECtt EWes LPot SWvt WMoo WWEG
- 'Chequers' ambig.	EBee ELan SPer
- 'Dingle Candy'	MHCG NWad
- 'Elisabeth de Haas' (v)	EWes NBre
- 'Forncett Lustre'	EBee EWes
- 'Ghost'	ECtt EPPr LBuc
- 'Gold Leaf'	see *L. maculatum* 'Aureum'
- Golden Anniversary = 'Dellam'PBR (v)	ECtt ELan LAst LSRN MHer NBro SWvt
- 'Golden Nuggets'	see *L. maculatum* 'Aureum'
- 'Golden Wedding'	SRms
- 'Ickwell Beauty' (v)	EBee WHil WWEG
- 'Margery Fish'	SRms
- 'Moonglow'	EBee
- 'Orchid Frost'	CHid EBee ECtt EHoe ELon GQue LHop
- Pink Chablis = 'Checkin'PBR	CBod ELon LRHS NLar
- 'Pink Nancy'	SWvt
- 'Pink Pearls'	CSBt NLar SHar WMoo WWEG
- 'Pink Pewter'	EBee ECGP ECha ECtt EHoe ELan EPfP EShb EWoo GMaP IPot LRHS SCob SPer SPlb SPoG WWEG
- 'Purple Winter'	EPPr
- 'Red Nancy'	CBod CFis ELan ELon LRHS MBri SWvt XLum
§ - 'Roseum'	CWib EBee ELan MCot MRav NChi SPer WMoo XLum
- 'Shell Pink'	see *L. maculatum* 'Roseum'
- 'Silver Shield'	EWes
- 'Sterling Silver'	CSam
- 'White Nancy'	Widely available
- 'Wootton Pink'	MHCG MHer NBir NLar SWvt
orvala	Widely available
- 'Album'	CExl CLAP EBee ELan EPPr GBin IPot LEdu LHop LRHS MAvo NBir NLar SHar WHer
- pink-flowered	CSpe
- 'Silva'	CExl CLAP EPPr EPfP GBin IPot LEdu LRHS WCot WSHC
purpureum	GJos
sandrasicum	WAbe

Lampranthus (*Aizoaceae*)

aberdeenensis	see *Delosperma aberdeenense*

	apricot-flowered	LRHS
	aurantiacus	CBcs
	blandus	CBcs
	'Blousey Pink'	SVen
§	***brownii***	CBcs ECho ELan EPfP LRHS SPlb WPnn
	deltoides	see *Oscularia deltoides*
	edulis	see *Carpobrotus edulis*
	glaucus	SEND
	multiradiatus	SEND
	oscularis	see *Oscularia deltoides*
	'Pink'	CBod ELan EUJe SPlb WPnn
	purple-flowered	CBod EUJe SPlb
	roseus	CSma ECho LRHS
	'Salmon Pink'	SPlb WPnn
	'Shanklin'	SPlb SVen
	spectabilis	CBcs CTri GLet WPnn
	- orange-flowered	CAbb CBod EUJe
	- purple-flowered	SPlb
	- 'Tresco Apricot'	ECho
	- 'Tresco Brilliant'	CHVG ELon MSCN SEND WPnn
	- 'Tresco Fire'	CAbb CExl CSma ELon SPlb SVen
	- 'Tresco Orange'	WPnn
	- 'Tresco Purple'	CWCL ELan
	- 'Tresco Red'	ELon EUJe SEND WPnn
	- white-flowered	GKev SPlb SVen WPnn
	- yellow-flowered	SVen WPnn
	stipulaceus	SPlb

Lamprocapnos (*Papaveraceae*)

§	***spectabilis*** ♀H7	Widely available
	- 'Alba' ♀H7	Widely available
	- 'Gold Heart' PBR	CBcs CBod CWGN EBee ECha ECtt EHoe EPfP ESwi GKev GLet IBoy ITim LHop LRHS MBri MGos MHol MRav NLar NSti SCob SGol SPoG WCot WFar WHil
	- 'Valentine'	Widely available
	- 'White Heart'	GJos

Lamprothyrsus (*Poaceae*)

	hieronymi RCB RA K2-2	CDes MAvo WCot WPGP

Lanaria (*Lanariaceae*)

	lanata	CLak

Lancea (*Phrymaceae*)

	tibetica	GEdr

Lantana ✿ (*Verbenaceae*)

	'Calippo Tutti Frutti'	EShb EUJe LSou
	camara	CArn ELan EShb SPhx
	- (Lucky Series) Lucky Improved Flame **new**	LAst
	- - Lucky Red Flame = 'Balandimfla'	LAst
	- - Lucky Sunrise Rose = 'Balandrise' PBR	EPfP LAst
	- - Lucky White = 'Balucwite' PBR	EPfP
	- 'Mine d'Or'	EUJe
	'Chapel Hill Gold' **new**	CMan
	'Dallas Red' **new**	CMan
	'Miss Huff'	CMan EBee
§	***montevidensis***	CSam
	'Pink Caprice' **new**	CMan
	sellowiana	see *L. montevidensis*
	'Silver Mound' **new**	CMan
	'Spreading Sunset'	CMan MOWG
	'Sunny Side Up' **new**	CMan

Lapageria ✿ (*Philesiaceae*)

	rosea ♀H3	CBcs CExl CFil CPne CRHN CTsd SAdn SChF SWvt WPGP
	- var. ***albiflora*** ♀H3	CPne CRHN SChF
	- 'Beatrix Anderson' **new**	CRHN
	- 'Flesh Pink'	CExl CRHN
	- 'Pink Panther'	CRHN

Lapeirousia (*Iridaceae*)

	anceps	ECho
	corymbosa	ECho
	cruenta	see *Freesia laxa*
	divaricata	ECho
	fastigiata	ECho
	laxa	ee *Freesia laxa*

Lapiedra (*Amaryllidaceae*)

	martinezii	ECho

Lapsana (*Asteraceae*)

	communis 'Inky'	CNat

Lardizabala (*Lardizabalaceae*)

	biternata	see *L. funaria*
§	***funaria***	CFil

Larix ✿ (*Pinaceae*)

	decidua	CCVT CDul CMen ECrN ELan EPfP EWTr MGos MMuc NEgg NWea SEND SMad SPlb WHar WMou
	- 'Corley'	CKen
§	- var. ***decidua***	MJak
	- 'Globus'	SLim
	- 'Horstmann Recurved'	NLar
	- 'Krejci'	NLar
	- 'Little Bogle'	CKen MAsh MBlu NEgg NLar
	- 'Oberförster Karsten'	CKen NLar
	- 'Pendula'	CMen
	- 'Puli' ♀H7	LRHS MAsh MBlu NHol NLar SLim SPer WMat
	- 'Roman'	NLar
	- 'Schwarzenburg'	SLim
	× ***eurolepis***	see *L.* × *marschlinsii*
	europaea DC.	see *L. decidua* var. *decidua*
	gmelinii var. ***gmelinii***	CMen
	- 'Tharandt'	CKen SLim
§	***kaempferi***	CCVT CDul CLnd CMen ELan EPfP LBuc LPal NEgg NWea SCoo SEWo WMou
	- 'Bambino'	CKen
	- 'Bingman'	CKen
	- 'Blue Ball'	CKen NLar
	- 'Blue Dwarf' ♀H7	MAsh MBri
	- 'Blue Rabbit'	CKen NEgg
	- 'Cruwys Morchard'	CKen
	- 'Diana'	CKen CMen MAsh MGos NEgg NHol NLar NOrn SLim
	- 'Elizabeth Rehder'	CKen
	- 'Grant Haddow'	CKen
	- 'Grey Green Dwarf'	MAsh
	- 'Grey Pearl'	CKen LRHS MAsh
	- 'Hanna's Broom'	SLim
	- 'Hobbit'	CKen NEgg
	- 'Jakobsen'	NLar
*	- 'Jakobsen's Pyramid'	CMen MAsh NOrn WMat
	- 'Lobby Dosser'	CMen NEgg
I	- 'Nana' ♀H7	CKen CMen NEgg NHol SBod
I	- 'Nana Prostrata'	CKen
	- 'Paper Lanterns'	NLar

- 'Pendula' EPfP SPoG
- 'Stiff Weeper' ♀H7 LRHS MGos MPkF NEgg NLar NOrn SLim
- 'Varley' CKen
- 'Wehlen' CKen
- 'Wolterdingen' CKen NLar

laricina 'Arethusa Bog' CKen
- 'Bear Swamp' CKen SLim
- 'Bingman' CKen
- 'Hartwig Pine' CKen
- 'Newport Beauty' CKen
- 'Stubby' NLar SLim

leptolepis see *L. kaempferi*

§ × ***marschlinsii*** CCVT MMuc NWea
- 'Domino' CKen CMen SLim
- 'Gail' CKen
- 'Julie' CKen
- 'Snapewood Broom' SLim

Laser (*Apiaceae*)

trilobum SPhx
- PAB 3382 LEdu WPGP

Laserpitium (*Apiaceae*)

latifolium EBee

§ ***siler*** CArn CSpe IMou NDov SMHy SPhx SPlb WSHC

Lasiagrostis see *Stipa*

Lasiospermum (*Asteraceae*)

bipinnatum SPlb

Lastreopsis (*Dryopteridaceae*)

hispida ESwi

Latania (*Arecaceae*)

loddigesii LPal

Lathraea (*Orobanchaceae*)

clandestina CAvo

Lathyrus ✿ (*Papilionaceae*)

§ ***articulatus*** CSpe

§ ***aureus*** CHid CLAP CSpe EBee GBin GBuc GCal GJos IFro MCot MHer MNrw NBid NBir NChi SBrt SKHP WAul WHal WHea WHil
- 'Cally Variegated' (v) GCal

chloranthus SPav

cirrhosus EBee

clymenum articulatus see *L. articulatus*

cyaneus misapplied see *L. vernus*

davidii EWes LEdu SBrt WCot WSHC

'Erewhon' CHid WHlf

eucosmus EBee LLHF

fremontii hort. see *L. laxiflorus*

grandiflorus ♀H7 CTri EBee ECGP NChi SDix SMHy SWat WCot

heterophyllus EBee SGSe

incurvus SPhx

inermis see *L. laxiflorus*

japonicus EBee
- subsp. ***maritimus*** GJos SPhx WCot WHil

latifolius ♀H7 CArn CRHN CSde ECrN EPfP LAst MHer MHol MWhi NPer SRms SVic WBor WBrk WCot WHer XLum

§ - 'Albus' ♀H7 CFlo CTri ELan SGSe SPav SRms WKif XLum
- 'Blushing Bride' WCot
- Pink Pearl see *L. latifolius* 'Rosa Perle'
- 'Red Pearl' CBcs CFlo CKel EBee ELan EPfP GAbr LBuc LRHS LSRN MBel MBri MNHC NLar NPri SEND SPav SPer SPlb SPoG SWvt WCot

§ - 'Rosa Perle' ♀H7 CBcs CFlo CKel CLet CTri EBee ECha LCro LHop LRHS LSRN MBri MNHC MRav NBir NLar NPer SGSe SPer SPoG SWvt WMoo XLum
- Weisse Perle see *L. latifolius* 'White Pearl'
- 'White Pearl' misapplied see *L. latifolius* 'Albus'

§ - 'White Pearl' ♀H7 CBcs CKel CLet EBee ECha EPfP GAbr LBuc LCro LRHS LSRN MBel MBri MHer MRav NBir NLar NPer SPer SPoG SWvt XLum

§ ***laxiflorus*** CDes EBee MCot MMuc WHea WMoo WSHC

linifolius EBee NLar WHfH

montanus GPoy

nervosus CSpe MCot SRms

niger CFis CSpe CWCL EBee EWld GJos LEdu LHop LSou MCot MHer MMHG WWEG

nissolia WSFF

odoratus SVic
- 'Anniversary' MCot
- 'Beth Chatto' MCot
- 'Betty Maiden' MCot
- 'Blue Medley' MCot
- 'Burnished Bronze' MCot
- 'Charlie's Angel' ♀H2 LCro LOPS MCot
- 'Cupani' MNHC SPhx
- 'Dark Passion' MCot
- 'Dawn' MCot
- 'Ethel Grace' MCot
- 'Evening Glow' ♀H2 MCot

I - 'Fragrantissima' (mixed) CHid
- 'George Priestley' MCot
- 'Gwendoline' ♀H2 **new** LCro LOPS
- 'High Scent' ♀H2 **new** LCro LOPS
- 'Honey Pink' MCot
- 'Honeymoon' MCot
- 'Jilly' ♀H2 MCot
- 'Karen Louise' **new** LCro LOPS
- 'Linda C' **new** LCro LOPS
- 'Lord Nelson' SPhx
- 'Marion' MCot
- 'Marti Caine' MCot
- 'Matucana' CSpe LCro LOPS
- 'Midnight' LCro LOPS SPhx
- 'Milly' MCot
- 'Misty Mountain' MCot
- 'Mollie Rilstone' MCot
- 'Mrs Bernard Jones' ♀H2 MCot
- 'Mrs Collier' SPhx
- 'Painted Lady' LCro LOPS
- 'Promise' MCot
- 'Restormel' LCro LOPS MCot
- 'Richard and Judy' MCot
- 'Tutankhamun's Pea' WHfH
- 'Wedding Day' ♀H2 MCot
- 'White Frills' SPhx

palustris EBee LLWG SPlb

pisiformis EBee

pratensis CHab EBee NMir WSFF

roseus EBee GCal WHea WSHC

rotundifolius ♀H7 CHid GLog NSti SPhx WSHC
- 'Tillyperone' ♀H7 EBee SPhx WSHC

sativus CHid CSpe ELan MCot
- f. ***albus*** CSpe
splendens SBrt
subandinus SPlb
sylvestris EBee GJos WBrk
transsylvanicus EBee GBin SPhx
tuberosus CArn CHid CRHN EBee LEdu WCot WSHC
'Tubro' EBee
venetus EBee EWes GCal MNrw WSHC
§ ***vernus*** 🏆^{H5} Widely available
- 'Albiflorus' MNrw XEll
- 'Alboroseus' 🏆^{H5} CLAP CPla ELan EPfP EWTr GBuc GCal GCra IFro LHop MNrw NBir NChi NLar SPhx SPoG SWat SWvt WCAu WCot WHoo
- var. ***albus*** CLAP CMea MNrw WCot
- ***aurantiacus*** see *L. aureus*
- 'Caeruleus' CLAP WHoo
* - 'Cyaneus' SHar SWat WCot
- 'Dama Emily' SHar
- 'Dama Violetta' SHar
I - 'Filifolius' CSpe MCot
- 'Flaccidus' CAby CFis EBee MNrw SBrt WCot WKif
* - 'Gracilis' EBee LEdu NLar SHar WPGP
I - 'Gracilis Alboroseus' SHar
- 'Indigo Eyes' CDes
- 'Little Elf' SHar
- 'Madelaine' WCot
I - 'Pendulus' SHar
- purple-flowered LRHS MMuc SEND
- 'Rainbow' CLAP EPfP LRHS
- 'Rosenelfe' GBuc LEdu MHer SBea SHar SPhx SPoG WCot WHal WSHC
- f. ***roseus*** ECha LRHS MMuc MRav NBir SEND SRms WBrk WCot
- 'Spring Melody' EBee MRav SHar
- 'Subtle Hints' SHar WCot
- 'Winter Blush' SHar

Laurelia (*Atherospermataceae*)

§ ***sempervirens*** CBcs SAko WPGP
serrata see *L. sempervirens*

Laureliopsis (*Atherospermataceae*)

philippiana CBcs EBee IArd NLar WPGP

Laurentia see *Isotoma*

Laurus (*Lauraceae*)

§ ***azorica*** CBcs
canariensis see *L. azorica*
nobilis 🏆^{H4} Widely available
- f. ***angustifolia*** 🏆^{H4} CJun CMac CTsd IDee LRHS MBlu MHer MRav NLar SCob SEND SPoG
- 'Aurea' 🏆^{H4} CBcs CDul CLet CMac EBee ELan ELon EPfP LRHS MHer MMuc NLar SCob SEND SLim SLon SMad SPoG SWvt WMoo
- clipped pyramid LSRN
- 'Crispa' MRav
- variegated (v) CMac SRms

Lavandula ✿ (*Lamiaceae*)

sp. LPar
'After Midnight' see *L.* 'Avonview'
'Alba' see *L. angustifolia* 'Alba', *L.* × *intermedia* 'Alba'
'Alba' ambig. CWib NYoL SIde SPer
§ ***angustifolia*** Widely available
- 'Alba' misapplied see *L. angustifolia* 'Blue Mountain White'
§ - 'Alba' ELan EPfP EWoo GPoy GQue LBuc LSRN MHer MRav MSwo NYoL SCob SLon SPlb SVen WGwG WJek XSen
- 'Alba Nana' see *L. angustifolia* 'Nana Alba'
- 'Arctic Snow' CBcs EPfP LRHS LSRN MBri MHer MSwo NBes NGdn NPri NYoL SDow SFai SHil SPoG SPpl SRms WLav XSen
- Aromatico Blue = 'Lablusa'^{PBR} LRHS
- Aromatico Forte Blue = 'Laa20001' **new** LRHS
- Aromatico Silver = 'Lasila' LRHS
- 'Ashdown Forest' ELan ENfk GQue LRHS MHer MLHP MNHC NYoL SAdn SBch SCob SDow SFai SPer SRGP SRms WJek WLav XSen
- 'Babelle' XSen
- 'Backhouse Purple' SDow XSen
- 'Beechwood Blue' 🏆^{H5} NYoL SCob SDow WLav
- 'Belle Hélène' XSen
- 'Betty's Blue' SDow XSen
- Blue Cushion = 'Lavandula Schola'^{PBR} LOPS LSRN MAsh NYoL SFai SPoG SRms WLav
- Blue Ice = 'Dow3'^{PBR} EAEE LOPS MNHC NDov NLar NYoL SDow SFai SGol SLim SRms WLav XSen
- 'Blue Lance' CBod MHol
- 'Blue Mountain' XSen
§ - 'Blue Mountain White' LRHS SDow SHil WLav XSen
- 'Blue Rider' EAEE EWTr LRHS NGdn NYoL WGwG WLav
- Blue Scent = 'Syngablusc' LRHS
§ - 'Bowles's Early' NYoL WGwG XSen
- 'Bowles's Grey' see *L. angustifolia* 'Bowles's Early'
- 'Bowles's Variety' see *L. angustifolia* 'Bowles's Early'
- 'Cedar Blue' ELan ENfk MHer MHol NYoL SDow SHDw SRms WGwG WJek WLav XSen
- 'Coconut Ice' NYoL WLav XSen
- 'Compacta' SDow WLav XSen
- 'Dursley White' WLav
- 'Dwarf Blue' CBod ENfk EPfP LSRN MHed NYoL SPpl SRms WFar XSen
- 'Elizabeth' LCro LSRN NYoL SCob SDow SFai SPoG SRms WLav XSen
- Ellagance Series **new** XSen
- - 'Ellagance Ice' CBod CWSG LAst LRHS SRms
- - 'Ellagance Pink' **new** LCro LOPS
- - 'Ellagance Purple' LCro LOPS LRHS SHil SRms
- - 'Ellagance Sky' LBMP LBuc LCro LOPS LRHS SHil SRms
- 'Essence Purple' **new** CBod
- 'Folgate' 🏆^{H5} CBod ECtt ENfk EPfP EWTr MHer MNHC NGdn NYoL SDow SRms WHoo WJek WLav WMnd XSen
- Garden Beauty = 'Lowmar'^{PBR} (v) LBuc LRHS SPoG XSen
- Granny's Bouquet = 'Lavang38' LSRN NYoL XSen
- 'Havana' GBin LRHS
§ - 'Hidcote' 🏆^{H5} Widely available
- 'Hidcote Pink' CWCL CWib LSou MHer MNHC MRav NGdn NYoL SCob SDow SPer SPpl SRms SWat WMnd XSen

- 'Hidcote Superior' LBMP LSun NGdn

- 'Imperial Gem' ♀H5 Widely available

- 'Jean Davis' see *L. angustifolia* 'Rosea'

- 'Lady' LRHS NPer

- 'Lady Ann' CWCL SDow WLav XSen

- 'Lavenite Petite'PBR LBMP LLHF LRHS LSRN NLar NYoL SDow SFai SPoG SRms WLav XSen

- Little Lady = 'Batlad' ♀H5 CMea EBee ECtt LAst LBMP LOPS LRHS LSRN MAsh MBri MNHC MPie MSwo NBes NLar NYoL SFai SGol SPoG SRms SWvt WHoo WLav XSen

- Little Lottie = 'Clarmo' ♀H5 CWCL GQue LSRN MHer NYoL SDow SWvt WLav XSen

- 'Loddon Blue' EPfP GQue LOPS LRHS MAsh NYoL SDow SFai SHil SRms WLav XSen

§ - 'Loddon Pink' ELan EPfP GMaP LRHS MAsh MBri MMuc MNHC MRav NGdn NYoL SEND SFai SHil SRms WLav XSen

- 'Luberon' XSen

- 'Lullaby Blue' SDow XSen

- 'Lumières des Alpes' XSen

- 'Maillette' NGdn NYoL SDow SRms WLav XSen

- 'Matheronne' XSen

- 'Melissa' MHol XSen

- Melissa Lilac = 'Dow4'PBR CBcs CSBt EAEE ENfk EWTr LBMP LCro LOPS LRHS LSRN MBri MGos MHer MNHC NDov NLar NYoL SDow SFai SHil SPpl SRkn SRms WLav XSen

- 'Middachten' XSen

- 'Miss Dawnderry' SDow

- 'Miss Donnington' see *L. angustifolia* 'Bowles's Early'

- 'Miss Katherine'PBR ♀H5 ECtt ELan EPfP LBMP LRHS MAsh NLar NYoL SDow SPoG WLav XSen

- Miss Muffet = 'Scholmis' ♀H5 LLHF NYoL SBch SDow SRms WLav XSen

- 'Mont Ventoux' XSen

- 'Montagne de Lure' XSen

- 'Munstead' Widely available

§ - 'Nana Alba' ♀H5 CArn EBee ELan ENfk EPfP GMaP GPoy LRHS MAsh MHer NYoL SBch SDow SPer SRms SWvt WJek XSen

- 'Nana Atropurpurea' SDow XSen

- 'Nikita' XSen

- 'No 9' SDow XSen

- 'Pacific Blue' LRHS MBri SHil XSen

- 'Perle de Rosée' XSen

- 'Peter Pan' ECtt ELan GBuc LSRN MHer MNHC NGdn NYoL SDow WLav XSen

- Platinum Blonde = 'Momparler'PBR **new** LSou SFai SPoG WHlf

- 'Princess Blue' LRHS NYoL WLav XSen

§ - 'Rosea' Widely available

- 'Royal Blue' **new** SFai

- 'Royal Purple' CBcs EWes GQue LSou NGdn NYoL SDow SWvt WLav XSen

- 'Royal Velvet' SDow XSen

- 'Saint Jean' SDow XSen

- 'Siesta' XSen

- 'Silver Blue' XSen

- 'Silver Mist' CBod CMea EPfP NYoL SRms WHer

- 'Thumbelina Leigh'PBR EBee LBMP MAsh NYoL SDow SFai SRms XSen

- 'Twickel Purple' CBcs CWCL CWld EAEE EBee ELan ENfk EPfP LBMP LHop LRHS LSRN MHed MHol MNHC NYoL SBod SCob SDow SFai SPer SPpl SRms SWat SWvt WGwG WLav XSen

- 'Walberton's Silver Edge' see *L.* × *intermedia* Walberton's Silver Edge

aristibracteata MHer WLav

§ 'Avonview' MHer SDow WHoo WLav

'Ballerina' ♀H4 LRHS SDow

§ 'Bee Brilliant'PBR ENfk WLav

§ 'Bee Cool'PBR ENfk MHer NYoL WLav

§ 'Bee Happy' CWCL ENfk NBir NYoL WJek WLav

§ 'Bee Pretty' ENfk

'Bella Zealand' (Bella Series) LRHS

'Blue Star' EPfP LRHS NGdn SHil SRms

'Bouquet of Roses' LRHS SHil

buchii var. ***buchii*** SDow SVen WLav

'Bulls Cross' WLav

canariensis MHer SDow SVen WLav

× ***chaytoriae*** 'Gorgeous' SDow

- 'Joan Head' XSen

- 'Molton Silver' XSen

- 'Richard Gray' ♀H4 CBod LSRN MHed MHer MNHC NYoL SDow SIgm SLim SRms WLav WMnd XSen

§ - 'Sawyers' ♀H4 Widely available

- 'Silver Sands' EPfP LBMP LRHS LSou NYoL SFai SPoG

× ***christiana*** LRHS NLar NYoL SDow SFai SHDw SVen WJek WLav

'Coco Deep White on Rose' (Coco Series) LRHS

'Cornard Blue' see *L.* × *chaytoriae* 'Sawyers'

Crème Brûlée = 'Lavsts10' LRHS

dentata ELan ENfk GPoy MNHC SEND SRms WJek XSen

§ - var. ***candicans*** MHer MNHC NYoL SDow SRms WJek WLav XSen

- var. ***dentata*** NYoL

- - 'Dusky Maiden' LRHS SDow WLav

- - 'Ploughman's Blue' NYoL SVen WGwG

- - f. ***rosea*** SDow

- - 'Royal Crown' ♀H3 MHer WLav

- - Serenity = 'Lavden123'PBR LRHS

- 'Harmony' LRHS

- silver-leaved see *L. dentata* var. *candicans*

'Devonshire Compact' CSBt EAJP MHol SRms WJek

'Devonshire Compact White' LRHS

'Fathead' CBcs CBod EBee ECtt ELan EPfP LBMP LRHS LSRN MGos MHer MNHC NBir NGdn NLar NPri NYoL SCob SCoo SDow SFai SGol SLim SPoG WJek WLav

'Flaming Purple' SDow XSen

× ***ginginsii*** 'Goodwin Creek Grey' ♀H4 MHer NYoL SDow SGol SRms WGwG WLav XSen

'Hazel' EPfP LRHS

'Heavenly Blue' EPfP

'Helmsdale'PBR CSBt CWSG ELan EPfP GBin GMaP IKil LCro LRHS LSRN MAsh MHer MRav NGdn NLar NYoL SCob SCoo SFai SGol SLim SPer

heterophylla misapplied see *L.* × *heterophylla* Viv. Gaston Allard Group

§ × ***heterophylla*** Viv. Gaston Allard Group WLav

- - 'African Pride' NYoL SVen

'Hidcote Blue' see *L. angustifolia* 'Hidcote'

× ***intermedia*** 'Abrialii' SDow XSen

§ - 'Alba' ♀H5 CBot CMea MHed MHer MMuc MNHC NYoL SCob SEND SVen WKif XSen

	Name	Suppliers
	- 'Arabian Night'	see *L.* × *intermedia* 'Impress Purple', 'Sussex'
	- 'Arabian Night' ambig.	SRms
§	- Dutch Group	CSBt CWib ENfk EPfP LRHS MNHC MRav MSwo NYoL SBod SCoo SDow SFai SLim SPer SPoG SPpl SRms SWat XSen
	- 'Edelweiss'	CBod CSBt CWib ENfk EPfP LRHS MNHC MRav NEgg NGdn NYoL SCob SDow SFai SGol SPoG SPpl SRms SWvt WLav XSen
	- 'Enigma'	CBar
	- 'Fragrant Memories'	NYoL SDow SIde WLav XSen
	- 'Fred Boutin'	SGol
*	- 'Futura'	XSen
	- Goldburg = 'Burgoldeen' (v)	MBri SGol
	- 'Grappenhall' misapplied	see *L.* × *intermedia* 'Pale Pretender'
	- 'Grappenhall' ambig.	SPpl WCAu
	- 'Grey Hedge'	NYoL SPpl SRms WLav
	- 'Gros Bleu'	SDow SFai WLav XSen
	- 'Grosso'	Widely available
	- (Heavenly Series) 'Heavenly Angel' **new**	SDow
	- - 'Heavenly Night' **new**	LRHS SDow
	- - 'Heavenly Scent' **new**	LRHS SDow
	- 'Hidcote Giant' ♀H5	EPfP GCal LRHS MBri NPer NYoL SDow SHil WKif WLav XSen
§	- 'Impress Purple'	NYoL SDow WLav XSen
	- 'Jaubert'	XSen
	- 'Julien'	XSen
	- 'Lullingstone Castle'	ENfk NYoL SDow SRms WJek WLav
	- 'Nizza'	XSen
	- 'Old English' misapplied	see *L.* × *intermedia* 'Seal'
	- 'Old English'	CBod ENfk SDow SRms
	- Old English Group	MMuc MNHC NYoL SEND WHoo WJek WLav XSen
	- Olympia = 'Downoly'	SDow
	- 'Olympiad' **new**	SFai
§	- 'Pale Pretender'	CSBt GQue MHer MRav MSwo NYoL SDow SPer SRms WJek XSen
	- 'Provence'	LRHS SDow SFai SPpl XSen
	- Pure Platinum = 'Niko' **new**	SFai
§	- 'Seal'	CArn ENfk GMaP MNHC NYoL SCob SDow SRms WJek XSen
	- 'Sumian'	XSen
	- 'Super'	XSen
§	- 'Sussex' ♀H5	CBod CFis EPfP LRHS NYoL SDow WLav XSen
	- 'Twickel Purple'	CWib ECtt ELan EWes LSRN NLar NYoL SGol SWat WJek
§	- Walberton's Silver Edge = 'Walvera' (v)	CSBt EBee EPfP LBuc LRHS MBri MGos SCoo SDow SFai SPoG SRms XSen
	'Jamboree'	WLav
	Javelin Compact Blue = 'Jin Cobule'PBR **new**	LRHS
	'Jean Davis'	see *L. angustifolia* 'Rosea'
	lanata ♀H3	CArn ECha GPoy SRms WJek WLav
§	***latifolia***	CArn XSen
I	'Lavender Lace'	LSRN
	'Loddon Pink'	see *L. angustifolia* 'Loddon Pink'
	'Madrid Blue'	see *L.* 'Bee Happy'
	'Madrid Pink'	see *L.* 'Bee Pretty'
	'Madrid Purple'	see *L.* 'Bee Brilliant'
	'Madrid White'	see *L.* 'Bee Cool'
	'Marshwood'	CTri
	minutolii	SDow
	multifida	MHer WLav
	officinalis	see *L. angustifolia*
	Passionné = 'Lavsts 08'PBR ♀H4	CWSG WLav
	pedunculata	XSen
	- subsp. ***lusitanica***	EPfP LRHS SHil
	- - Lusi Pink = 'Wijs02' **new**	SFai
§	- subsp. ***pedunculata***	CAby CBar ECha ECrN ECtt EPfP LAst LCro LOPS LPot LRHS LSRN MAsh MGos MJak MMuc MSwo NGdn NYoL SCob SDow SEND SFai SGol SLim SPer SPoG SRms SWat WJek
	- - 'James Compton' ♀H3	CWib ECha LRHS MAsh NGdn NYoL
	- - 'Wine'	CBcs
	- subsp. ***sampaiana*** 'Purple Emperor'	EPfP LRHS MBri NYoL SHil WLav
	pedunculatus subsp. ***lusitanica*** 'Lusi Purple' **new**	SFai
	pinnata	ENfk EPfP LRHS MHer MHol MNHC SDow
	'Pretty Polly' ♀H4	CAbP CBcs ELan EPfP LRHS NYoL SDow SFai SRkn WLav
	'Pukehou'	EPfP LRHS SCoo SDow WLav
	'Regal Splendour'PBR	CSBt ECtt ELan EPfP LCro LRHS LSRN MAsh MBri MGos MHer MNHC NPri NYoL SCob SCoo SDow SFai SGol SHil SLim SPoG SRms WLav
	Rocky Road = 'Fair09'PBR	LCro LOPS NYoL SFai WLav
	'Rosea'	see *L. angustifolia* 'Rosea'
	rotundifolia	SDow
	'Russian Anna'	LSRN
	'Saint Brelade'	LRHS
	'Silver Edge'	see *L.* × *intermedia* Walberton's Silver Edge
	Silver Sands = 'Fair 14'PBR	EWoo
	'Somerset Mist'	WLav
	spica nom. rejic.	see *L. angustifolia*, *L. latifolia*
	- 'Hidcote Purple'	see *L. angustifolia* 'Hidcote'
	stoechas	Widely available
	- var. ***albiflora***	see *L. stoechas* subsp. *stoechas* f. *leucantha*
	- 'Anouk'PBR	EBee ELan EPfP LRHS SPoG
	- 'Antibes' (Provençal Series)	LRHS SRms
	- 'Avignon' (Provençal Series)	SRms
	- (Bella Series) Bella Lavender = 'Bellav'	LRHS SHil
	- - 'Bella Peach'	LRHS SHil
	- - Bella Rose = 'Belros'	LRHS SHil
	- - Bella Rouge = 'Belrou'	LRHS
	- blue-flowered	LRHS
	- 'Boysenberry Ruffles'PBR (Ruffles Series)	LRHS
	- Castilliano Violet	CBod
	- 'Coco Deep Pink' (Coco Series)	LRHS SHil
	- 'Coco Deep White on Blue' (Coco Series)	SHil
	- 'Dark Royalty'PBR	ELan
	- deep rose-flowered	LRHS
	- 'Lace'	LSRN WLav
	- Lavender Lace = 'Colace'	NYoL
	- (Little Bee Series) Little Bee Deep Purple = 'Florvendula Deep Purple'	LRHS

- - Little Bee Deep Rose = 'Florvendula Deep Rose'	LRHS
- - Little Bee Lilac = 'Florvendula Lilac'	LRHS
- subsp. ***luisieri*** 'Tickled Pink'PBR	CWCL
- 'Night of Passion'	LRHS SDow
- 'Papillon'	see *L. pedunculata* subsp. *pedunculata*
- subsp. ***pedunculata***	see *L. pedunculata* subsp. *pedunculata*
- 'Pink Angels' **new**	ELan
- 'Purley'	SRms
- Ruffles Series	ENfk
- 'Silver Anouk'PBR	CBod EPfP LRHS
§ - subsp. ***stoechas*** f. ***leucantha***	CWCL CWib LRHS MSwo SCob SDow SHil
- - - 'Snowman'	CBcs CSBt EPfP LCro LRHS MAsh MHer SCob SCoo SFai SLim SPoG SWvt
- - Lilac Wings = 'Prolil'PBR	EPfP LLHF LRHS MBri NLar SCoo SFai SHil WLav
- - 'Provençal'	LRHS MBri MGos SCob SCoo SHil
- - 'Purple Wings'	ELan EPfP LOPS LRHS MAsh MGos SFai SLim
- - f. ***rosea***	WHil
- - - 'Kew Red'	CBcs CTri CWib EAJP ECrN ENfk LCro LOPS LRHS MGos MHer MNHC NBFr NYoL SDow SFai SLim SRms SWvt WGwG WHar WJek WLav
- 'Sugarberry Ruffles'PBR (Ruffles Series)	ENfk
- 'Victory'	LRHS MBri MGos SHil SPoG
- 'With Love'PBR	SDow
Tiara = 'Fair 10'PBR	CSBt CWSG ENfk LCro LOPS LRHS LSRN MBri MGos NLar NPri NYoL SCoo SDow SFai SHil SLim SRms WLav
'Van Gogh'	SDow
vera misapplied	see *L.* × *intermedia* Dutch Group
vera DC.	see *L. angustifolia*
viridis	CLau CPla ELan EPfP LRHS MHer NPer SDow SRms WAbe WJek WLav
'Whero Iti'	SDow
'Willow Vale' ♀H3	EPfP LBMP LCro LRHS MAsh MHer NYoL SDow SFai SRms SWvt WJek
'Willowbridge Calico'PBR	NYoL

Lavatera (*Malvaceae*)

arborea	CArn SChr SEND WHer
- 'Rosea'	see *L.* × *clementii* 'Rosea'
- 'Variegata' (v)	ELan NPer SEND WCot WTou
bicolor	see *L. maritima*
cachemiriana	NPer
Chamallow = 'Inovera'PBR	LRHS LSRN SPoG
× ***clementii*** 'Barnsley'	Widely available
- 'Barnsley Baby'	EBee ELan LBMP LBuc LPfy LRHS MBri NGdn NLar NPer NPri SHar SHil SPer SRkn SWvt WBor
- 'Blushing Bride'	CDoC EPfP LRHS LSRN MBri MGos NLar SEND SPer SWvt
- 'Bredon Springs' ♀H5	CDoC CDul COtt CSBt CWSG ECha ELon EPfP LHop LRHS LSRN MAsh MGos MMuc MSwo NGdn SEND SGol SLim SPer SWvt WHar
- 'Burgundy Wine' ♀H5	CBcs COtt EBee ELan EPfP EUJe LBMP LRHS MAsh MBri MGos MJak MSwo NBir NEgg NGdn NLar NPer NPri SGbt SHil SLim SLon SPer SPoG SWvt WFar WHar
- 'Candy Floss' ♀H5	LRHS MAsh NBir NLar NPer SGol
- 'Eye Catcher'	COtt CSBt IVic LRHS MSwo NLar SPer WHar
- 'Kew Rose'	CDoC COtt LRHS MMuc MSwo NLar NPer SEND SLim SRms XLum
- 'Lavender Lady'	LHop NPer SEND
- 'Lisanne'	LRHS MSwo SGol
- 'Mary Hope' ♀H5	CDoC EPfP LRHS MAsh MBri MGos SEle SHil SWvt
- Memories = 'Stelav'	LRHS LSRN
- 'Pavlova'	CExl
§ - 'Pink Frills'	SWvt WCot WFar
- Red Rum = 'Rigrum'PBR ♀H5	CDoC CMac COtt CSBt EPfP LBuc LLHF LPfy LSRN MGos MHol NEgg NLar NPri SCob SEND SHar SLim SPoG SWvt WFar
§ - 'Rosea' ♀H5	CBcs CDul CLet CMac CNec CWSG EBee ECrN EPfP LAst LBMP LCro LRHS LSRN MGos NBir NEgg NHol NPri SBod SCob SGbt SGol SHil SLon SPer SPoG SWvt WHar
§ - 'Wembdon Variegated' (v)	NPer
'Frederique'	CMac CSBt LBuc LRHS NLar SWvt
'Grey Beauty'	LHop SMad
'Magenta Magic'	NLar SPoG
§ ***maritima*** ♀H3	CAbP CDoC CExl CLet CMac CNec CSde ELan EPfP LHop LRHS NPri SEND SPer SRkn SWvt WFar WKif WSHC
- 'Princesse de Lignes'	XLum
olbia	SDix SPlb SRms WFar
- 'Lilac Lady'	EBee ECha ECrN ELan LRHS MGos NLar SLim WFar WHar WKif
'Peppermint Ice'	see *L. thuringiaca* 'Ice Cool'
'Pink Frills'	see *L.* × *clementii* 'Pink Frills'
'Rosea'	see *L.* × *clementii* 'Rosea'
'Sweet Dreams'PBR	LSou NLar
thuringiaca	GCal NNor
- 'First Light'	GCal MPie SPhx
§ - 'Ice Cool'	SCob SWvt WKif
- 'Saalestrand' **new**	LCro
'Variegata'	see *L.* × *clementii* 'Wembdon Variegated'
'White Angel'PBR	GBin NLar
'White Satin'PBR	NHol

Ledebouria (*Asparagaceae*)

adlamii	see *L. cooperi*
concolor misapplied	see *L. socialis*
§ ***cooperi***	CTal EAJP ECho EPri EShb GKev LEdu LHop LRHS SBch WBor WPGP
'Gary Hammer' **new**	CEvo
maculata	see *Drimia indica*
§ ***socialis***	ECho GKev LEdu LToo MCot SBch WCot
violacea	see *L. socialis*

Ledum see *Rhododendron*

Leiophyllum (*Ericaceae*)

buxifolium ♀H5	EPfP NLar WThu
- subsp. ***hugeri***	GBin

Lembotropis see *Cytisus*

Lemna (Araceae)

gibba	NPer
minor	CWat MSKA NPer SWat
polyrrhiza	see *Spirodela polyrrhiza*
trisulca	CWat EHon EWay MSKA NPer SWat

lemon see *Citrus × limon*

lemon, rough see *Citrus × taitensis*

lemon balm see *Melissa officinalis*

lemon grass see *Cymbopogon citratus*

lemon verbena see *Aloysia citrodora*

lemonquat see *Citrus × japonica × C. × limon*

Leonotis (Lamiaceae)

leonitis	see *L. ocymifolia*
leonurus	CBcs CDTJ CHGN CHll ECre EShb EWes LRHS MSCN SLim SLon SMad SPlb XLum
nepetifolia	CHll
- var. ***nepetifolia*** 'Staircase'	SPav
§ ***ocymifolia***	CExl LSou
- var. ***raineriana***	CHll

Leontice (Berberidaceae)

albertii	see *Gymnospermium albertii*
leontopetalum new	EBee

Leontodon (Asteraceae)

autumnalis	CHab NMir
hispidus	CHab NMir
§ ***rigens***	CSpe CTal GEdr MHer MMuc NBid NBir SDix WMoo
- B&SWJ 12527	WCru
- 'Girandole'	see *L. rigens*

Leontopodium (Asteraceae)

alpinum	CTri CWib ECho EPfP EPot GAbr LRHS MAsh NPri SPlb SPoG SRms WTor XLum
- 'Everest'	EDAr
- 'Matterhorn'	GEdr
- 'Mignon'	ECho EWes GMaP WAbe
artemisiifolium new	GKev
coreanum	GKev
haplophylloides new	GKev
jacotianum	CPBP
kurilense new	SPlb
longifolium new	GKev
muscoides new	CPBP
nanum	CPBP
§ ***ochroleucum*** var. ***campestre***	NLar
palibinianum	see *L. ochroleucum* var. *campestre*
pusillum	EPot WAbe
souliei	SRot XLum

Leonurus (Lamiaceae)

artemisia	see *L. japonicus*
cardiaca	CArn CBod GPoy MHer MNHC SIde SRms WHfH XSen
- 'Crispa'	SMad
- 'Grobbebol'	EBee ESwi
§ ***japonicus***	SHar
macranthus	EFEx
- var. ***alba***	EFEx
sibiricus misapplied	see *L. japonicus*
sibiricus L.	GCal

Leopoldia (Asparagaceae)

comosa	see *Muscari comosum*
spreitzenhoferi	see *Muscari spreitzenhoferi*
tenuiflora	see *Muscari tenuiflorum*

Lepechinia (Lamiaceae)

bella	CSpe EBee SDys
chamaedryoides	CExl CSpe
fragans	SBrt
hastata	CCse CDes CFil CSpe SBrt SIgm WJek WOut
salviae	CCon MMuc

Lepidium (Brassicaceae)

campestre	CHab
latifolium	CArn ENfk LEdu

Lepidothamnus (Podocarpaceae)

§ ***laxifolius***	WThu

Lepidozamia (Zamiaceae)

peroffskyana	CBrP

Leptinella (Asteraceae)

'County Park'	ECou EDAr
dendyi	EWes GEdr MHer NSla WIce
dioica	GBin
hispida	see *Cotula hispida* (DC.) Harv.
§ ***minor***	WMoo
§ ***pectinata***	ITim
§ ***potentillina***	CTal CTri ECha ECho ECou EHoe GBin GEdr MBNS MSCN NLar NPri NWad SRms WMoo WPtf XLum
§ ***pyrethrifolia***	ECho EDAr GEdr
§ ***squalida***	ECha ECho GBin NLar NSti WMoo
§ - 'Platt's Black'	CBcs CTal EBee ECha ECho ECou EDAr EHoe EShb EWes GAbr GBin GCrg IBoy LEdu MSCN NLar NPri SBch SMad SWvt WFar WGwG WMoo WTcb WWFP XLum

Leptocodon (Campanulaceae)

gracilis	EWld
- HWJK 2155	WCru

Leptodactylon (Polemoniaceae)

§ ***californicum***	CPBP

Leptospermum ✿ (Myrtaceae)

citratum	see *L. petersonii*
'Copper Glow'	ECou
'Copper Sheen'	CBcs
'County Park Blush'	ECou
cunninghamii	see *L. myrtifolium*
'Electric Red' (Galaxy Series)	CAbb LRHS SAko SEle SLim
ericoides	see *Kunzea ericoides*
flavescens misapplied	see *L. glaucescens*
flavescens Sm.	see *L. polygalifolium*
§ ***glaucescens***	SPlb
§ ***grandiflorum***	ELan EPfP MMuc SSpi SVen WSHC
grandifolium	ECou LRHS
'Havering Hardy'	ECou
humifusum	see *L. rupestre*
juniperinum	SPlb

'Karo Pearl Star' CBcs
'Karo Silver Ice' CBcs
'Karo Spectrobay' CBcs
laevigatum SVen
- 'Yarrum' ECou
§ ***lanigerum*** CExl CMHG CTri CTsd ECou EPfP SPlb SVen
- 'Cunninghamii' see *L. myrtifolium*
liversidgei ECou SPlb
minutifolium ECou
§ ***myrtifolium*** CBcs CMac CTri CTsd ECou EWes
- 'Newnes Forest' ECou
nitidum SPlb
obovatum CTsd GGal
§ ***petersonii*** CArn MHer MOWG
phylicoides see *Kunzea ericoides*
'Pink Cascade' SAko SEle
'Pink Surprise' ECou MOWG
§ ***polygalifolium*** CBcs SPlb
prostratum see *L. rupestre*
pubescens see *L. lanigerum*
'Red Cascade' SWvt
rodwayanum see *L. grandiflorum*
rotundifolium ECou SPlb
§ ***rupestre*** CDoC CSde CTri ECou SPlb SVen WSHC
rupestre* × *scoparium ECou
scoparium CArn CTsd ECou GPoy MNHC SPlb SVen WHfH WJek
- 'Adrianne' EPfP LRHS MRav
- 'Appleblossom' 🏆H3 EPfP SAko SEle SGol SLim
- 'Autumn Glory' SLim
- 'Blossom' (d) CBcs CMac MOWG
- 'Burgundy Queen' (d) CBcs CMac CSBt EUJe
- 'Chapmanii' CMHG WPGP
- 'Coral Candy' CBcs
- 'County Park Pink' ECou
- 'Crimson Glory' (d) CSBt
- 'Elizabeth Jane' MMuc WFar
- 'Essex' ECou
- 'Fred's Red' MHer
- 'Gaiety Girl' (d) CSBt
- var. ***incanum*** 'Keatleyi' 🏆H3 MOWG
- 'Jubilee' (d) CMac
- 'Kerry' CAbP
- 'Lady Bird' ECou
- 'Leonard Wilson' (d) CTri
- 'Martini' CAbb CBcs CDoC CMac CSBt EPfP LRHS MMuc SEND
- (Nanum Group) 'Kea' CBcs MHer MRav
- - 'Kiwi' 🏆H3 CAbP CAbb CBcs CDoC CLet CSBt CSde ECou ELon EPfP EUJe LRHS MAsh MMuc SEND SEle SLim SLon WFar
- - 'Nanum' ITim
- - 'Pipit' ITim
- - 'Tui' CMac CSBt
- 'Nichollsii' 🏆H3 SVen WSHC
- 'Nichollsii Nanum' 🏆H3 WAbe WPat WThu
- 'Pink Cascade' CBcs CMac CTri CWib SLim
- 'Pink Damask' IVic SWvt
- 'Pink Frills' ECou
- var. ***prostratum*** misapplied see *L. rupestre*
- 'Red Damask' (d) 🏆H3 Widely available
- 'Red Falls' CExl ECou
* - 'Ruby Wedding' ELan EPfP LRHS LSRN MAsh SLon SPoG
- 'Snow Flurry' CBcs EPfP LRHS SGol SLim SVen
- 'Sunraysia' CTsd
- 'Wingletye' ECou
- 'Winter Cheer' (d) CDoC EPfP LRHS SGol
- 'Wiri Donna' CSde
- 'Wiri Joan' (d) CBcs
- 'Wiri Linda' CBcs CMac
- 'Zeehan' ECou
sericeum MOWG
'Silver Sheen' 🏆H3 CAbb CDoC CSde EBee ECou ECre ELan EPfP LHop LRHS MAsh NLar SAko SPer SPlb SPoG SVen WPGP WPat
'Snow Column' ECou
turbinatum 'Thunder Cloud' ECou
'Wellington Dwarf' ECou

Lespedeza (*Papilionaceae*)

bicolor CAgr EBee LRHS SEND SKHP WCFE WFar WSHC
buergeri LRHS MMHG NLar WSHC
capitata EBee SPhx
formosa new EBee
japonica SPlb
thunbergii 🏆H5 CBcs CBot CDoC CDul CHll CLet CSde CWib EBee ELan EPfP EPri IDee IVic LRHS MAsh MBlu MGil MOWG SLon SMad SPer SPoG SSta WCFE WPGP WSHC
- 'Avalanche' NLar
- 'Gibraltar' WPGP
- 'Summer Beauty' CBcs LRHS NLar
- subsp. ***thunbergii*** 'Albiflora' ELan LRHS WPGP
- - 'Edo-shibori' NLar WPGP
- - 'White Fountain' EPfP LRHS SChF SKHP SPoG WSHC
tiliifolia see *Desmodium elegans*

Lesquerella (*Brassicaceae*)

arctica WCFE
- var. ***purshii*** GKev
intermedia SIgm
kingii sherwoodii GEdr

Leucadendron (*Proteaceae*)

argenteum CTre SPlb
daphnoides SPlb
'Deacon Red' new MPkF
discolor SPlb
eucalyptifolium SPlb
gandogeri CTre
'Inca Gold' 🏆H1c CTre MOWG
laureolum CTre
'Safari Sunset' 🏆H1c CTre IDee MPkF
'Safari Sunshine' CTre
salicifolium SPlb
salignum CTre
sessile CTre
strobilinum CTre

Leucaena (*Mimosaceae*)

leucocephala SPlb

Leucanthemella (*Asteraceae*)

§ ***serotina*** 🏆H7 Widely available
- 'Herbststern' IMou NLar

Leucanthemopsis (*Asteraceae*)

§ ***alpina*** ECho NSla
hosmariensis see *Rhodanthemum hosmariense*

Leucanthemum ✿ (*Asteraceae*)

	Name	Suppliers
	'Angel'	ELon NLar WGrn
	atlanticum	see *Rhodanthemum atlanticum*
	catananche	see *Rhodanthemum catananche*
	graminifolium	EPfP
	hosmariense	see *Rhodanthemum hosmariense*
	mawii	see *Rhodanthemum gayanum*
	maximum misapplied	see *L.* × *superbum*
§	***maximum*** (Ramond) DC.	NBro NPer
	- ***uliginosum***	see *Leucanthemella serotina*
	nipponicum	see *Nipponanthemum nipponicum*
	'Osiris Neige'	ECtt MAvo
	paludosum 'Snowland' **new**	LRHS
	'Real Galaxy'	LBuc LRHS MTis
	'Sante'	LCro MHol
	'Sunshine Peach'	EBee ECho SRot
§	× ***superbum***	CMac GAbr IBoy MHer MLHP MMuc SDix SEND WBrk
	- 'Aglaia' (d)	Widely available
	- 'Alaska'	CAni CBod CExl COtt CTsd EAEE EBee ELan EPfP IBoy LAst LHop LRHS LSun MCot NLar SCob SPer SWvt WRHF WWEG XLum
	- 'Amelia'	EBee LRHS NBre NLar
	- 'Andernach'	CAni
	- 'Anita Allen' (d)	CAni EBee ECtt WCot WWEG
	- 'Anna Camilla'	CAni
	- 'Antwerp Star'	NBre NLar WBrk
	- 'Banana Cream'	CBod CWGN EAEE ECtt EShb EUJe LAst LRHS MAsh MHol NLar NPri SCob SPoG STPC WHoo WTor
	- 'Banwell'	CAni
	- 'Barbara Bush' (v/d)	SWvt
§	- 'Beauté Nivelloise'	CAni CElw CHVG CPrp CWCL CWld EBee ECtt EPfP GBin IPot LCro LOPS LRHS NLar SHil SPer SPoG SRms SWat WWEG
	- 'Becky'	CCse CElw CMac EBee ECha ELan ELon EWes GBin LLHF LPfy LRHS LSRN LSou NEoE NLar SAko SRGP WCAu WWEG
	- 'Bishopstone'	CAni EBee ECtt ELan LBMP LEdu LLHF MSpe NCGa WWEG
	- 'Bridal Bouquet'	EBee ECtt LRHS
	- 'Brightside'	EBee ELan ELon GQue LRHS MWat WFar WMoo
	- Broadway Lights = 'Leumayel'PBR	EBee EPfP EWoo GBin IBoy IPot LPot LRHS MAsh MBri MRav NBir SCob SHil SPoG WCAu WFar WGrn WHil
	- 'Christine Hagemann'	CAni CElw EBee ECtt EWes GBin ILea IPot MAvo MNrw MRav NLar SHar WBrk WCFE WCot WWEG
	- 'Cobham Gold' (d)	CWCL NBre
	- 'Coconut Ice'	WWEG
	- 'Colwall'	CAni WWEG
	- 'Crazy Daisy'	CAni CBod CChe CTri CWib EAJP ECtt LRHS NFav NLar SRot SWvt WFar
	- 'Devon Mist'	CAni
	- 'Droitwich Beauty'	CAni ECtt LLHF MAvo WCFE WHil WHoo WWEG
	- 'Duchess of Abercorn'	CAni
	- 'Dwarf Snow Lady'	LSun NBre NLar
	- 'Easton Lady'	CAni
	- 'Eclipse'	CAni MAvo WWEG
	- 'Edgebrook Giant'	CAni SAko WBrk WWEG
	- 'Edward VII'	CAni
	- 'Eisstern'	EBee LEdu MAvo SHar
	- 'Elworthy Sparkler'	CElw MAvo WBrk WWEG
	- 'Engelina'PBR	EBee NLar SPoG WTor
	- 'Esther Read' (d)	EBee ECtt ELan EPfP GBin GMaP LRHS LSRN MBri NBro NEgg NLar SPoG SRGP SRms SWat SWvt WBrk WCot WMnd WWEG
§	- 'Everest'	CAni SRms WWEG
	- 'Exhibition'	WWEG
	- 'Fiona Coghill' (d)	CAni CElw CHVG CWGN EAEE ECtt EPfP GBin GBuc IBoy IKil LRHS LSou MBri MNrw MSpe NBir NEgg NGdn NLar WCot WFar WHoo WWEG
	- 'Firnglanz'	CAni GBin MAvo WWEG
	- 'Flore Pleno' (d)	MMuc SPlb
	- Freak! = 'Leuz0001'PBR	CKno EBee GBin LRHS MBri SHar SPoG
	- 'Goldfinch'	CMos EBee ECtt IPot LRHS SPoG WHil
	- 'Goldrausch'PBR	Widely available
	- 'Gruppenstolz'	CAni SAko
	- 'H. Seibert'	CAni CPrp MArl MAvo WWEG
	- 'Harry'	CAni
	- 'Highland White Dream'PBR	EAEE IKil LRHS
	- 'Horace Read' (d)	CAni CElw ECtt NBir SBch SWvt WWEG
	- 'Jennifer Read'	CAni WCFE WWEG
§	- 'John Murray' (d)	CAni EWes NBir NWsh WCot WWEG
	- 'Lacrosse'	EBee LRHS MBri SCob SHil
	- 'Laspider'	EBee LRHS SRot
	- 'Little Miss Muffet'	CSBt CWGN EBee ECtt LAst LLHF LRHS LSou MBNS NCGa WWEG
	- 'Little Princess'	see *L.* × *superbum* 'Silberprinzesschen'
	- 'Majestic'	CAni
	- 'Manhattan'	CAni CCse EBee EWes GBin
	- 'Margaretchen'	CAni MAvo WWEG
	- 'Marion Bilsland'	CAni MAvo MSpe NChi WBrk
	- 'Marion Collyer'	CAni
	- 'Mayfield Giant'	CAni CTri
	- 'Mount Everest'	see *L.* × *superbum* 'Everest'
	- 'Octopus'	CAni WBrk
	- 'Old Court'	see *L.* × *superbum* 'Beauté Nivelloise'
	- 'Paladin'PBR	EBee ECtt GBin IPot NLar SHar SPoG
	- 'Phyllis Smith'	CAni CPrp EBee ECtt ELan LCro LSRN MAvo MCot MHer MPie MRav MSCN NCGa NGdn SCob SGSe SMad WBrk WCAu WCot WMoo WWEG
	- 'Polaris'	EBee NBre WMoo XLum
	- 'Rags and Tatters'	CAni EBee ECtt EWes WWEG
	- 'Real Dream' **new**	LRHS LSou
	- 'Real Galaxy'PBR **new**	LSou
	- 'Real Glory'	ECtt LAst LRHS
	- 'Real Neat'	ECtt LRHS LSou MTis SCob SHar
	- 'Schwabengruss'	CAni
	- 'Shaggy'	see *L.* × *superbum* 'Beauté Nivelloise'
	- 'Shapcott Gossamer' **new**	CPou MTis SCob WCot
	- 'Shapcott Ruffles' **new**	MTis WCot
	- 'Shapcott Summer Clouds' **new**	LSun MBel MHol MSCN MTis SPoG WCot WRHF

§ - 'Silberprinzesschen' CAni CSBt ELon EPfP GJos GMaP LPot LRHS LSqH SPlb SRms WHar WMoo WRHF WWEG XLum
- 'Silver Spoon' EPfP LRHS
- 'Snehurka' CAni LLHF LRHS LSou MAvo WCot WHoo WWEG
- 'Snow Lady' CChe EBee EPfP LRHS NPer SRms WFar
- 'Snowcap' CHid ECha EPfP LCro LRHS MBel MBri MRav SBea SPer SPoG SWvt WCAu
- 'Snowdrift' CAni LBMP NBre NLar WBrk WCot WFar WMoo WTcb WWEG
- 'Snowstorm' MAvo
§ - 'Sonnenschein' CHVG CPrp EBee ECha ECtt ELan EPfP GMaP LHop LRHS LSRN LSou MArl MBri MCot MHer MHol MRav MSpe NBir NChi NEgg NGdn NSti SBea SPer SRms SWat WCAu WWEG
- 'Starburst' (d) EBee ELan LRHS SRms
- 'Stina' EBee MAvo WWEG
- 'Summer Snowball' see *L.* × *superbum* 'John Murray'
- 'Sunny Side Up'PBR CBod CHVG CWCL EBee ECtt LCro LHop LRHS MBri NLar SCob SRot WAul WFar WWEG
- Sunshine see *L.* × *superbum* 'Sonnenschein'
- 'T.E. Killin' (d) ♀H4 CBod CPrp EAEE EBee ECha ECtt ELan EPfP EUJe GBin GBuc LCro LRHS LSou MRav MWat SPoG SPtp WFar WHoo WPtf WWEG
- 'Victorian Secret'PBR ECtt GBin IPot LBuc LRHS MAsh MNrw NLar SCob SMad SPoG WHil WMoo WWEG
- 'White Iceberg' (d) CAni
- White Mountain = 'Gfleuwhmtn'PBR LRHS NPri STPC
- 'White Tutu' MAvo
- 'Wirral Pride' CAni ELon EPfP WBrk WMnd WWEG
- 'Wirral Supreme' (d) ♀H5 Widely available
'Tizi-n-Test' see *Rhodanthemum catananche* 'Tizi-n-Test'
§ ***vulgare*** CArn CBod CHab CMac CWld ENfk EPfP EShb GJos LCro MHer MJak MNHC NMir SDix SEND SIde SPhx WFar WHer WJek WMoo WOut WSFF WShi XLum XSen
- 'Filigran' LRHS WFar
- 'Löffelstiel' **new** SAko
§ - 'Maikönigin' NLar SAko WHrl XLum
- May Queen see *L. vulgare* 'Maikönigin'
- 'Sunny' CBre

Leucocoryne (*Alliaceae*)

alliacea ECho
'Andes' ♀H3 ECho GKev NRog
coronata SPlb
'Dione' ECho GKev NRog SDeJ
'Double Fantasy' NRog
hybrids CGrW ECho
ixioides ECho
* ***- alba*** ECho NRog
- 'Blue Ocean' ECho GKev NRog SDeJ
pauciflora NRog
purpurea ♀H3 CGrW ECho NRog
'Spotlight' ECho GKev NRog
'Sunny Stripe' ECho
vittata NRog
'White Dream' ECho GKev NRog SDeJ

Leucogenes (*Asteraceae*)

grandiceps NSla WAbe
leontopodium NSla WAbe WIce
tarahaoa WAbe

Leucogenes × *Raoulia* see × *Leucoraoulia*

Leucojum ✿ (*Amaryllidaceae*)

aestivum CAby CBcs CTri EBee ECGP ECho EPfP LAma LHop MCot MSCN NChi NEgg NHol SBod SDeJ SEND SRms WBod WCot WFar WHea WRHF WShi
- 'Gravetye Giant' ♀H7 Widely available
- var. ***pulchellum*** CElw
autumnale see *Acis autumnalis*
roseum see *Acis rosea*
tingitanum see *Acis tingitana*
trichophyllum see *Acis trichophylla*
valentinum see *Acis valentina*
vernum ♀H5 Widely available
- var. ***vagneri*** CLAP ECha SDys

Leucophyllum (*Scrophulariaceae*)

frutescens EBee

Leucophysalis (*Solanaceae*)

sinense BWJ 8093 WCru

Leucophyta (*Asteraceae*)

brownii 'Silver Sand' LAst LSou

Leucopogon (*Ericaceae*)

§ ***colensoi*** WThu
ericoides GKev
§ ***fraseri*** NHar WThu

× *Leucoraoulia* (*Asteraceae*)

§ ***loganii*** WAbe

Leucosceptrum (*Lamiaceae*)

canum CExl
- GWJ 9424 WCru
japonicum B&SWJ 10804 WCru
- B&SWJ 10981 WCru
- 'Golden Angel' GEdr
- 'Silver Angel' (v) **new** GEdr
stellipilum var. ***formosanum*** IMou
- - B&SWJ 1926 WCru
- - RWJ 9907 SBrt WCru
- var. ***tosaense*** B&SWJ 8892 WCru
- 'Variegatum' (v) **new** GEdr

Leucospermum (*Proteaceae*)

conocarpodendron 'Mardi Gras Ribbons' EBee
cordifolium CTre
glabrum SPlb

Leucothoe (*Ericaceae*)

sp. LPar
axillaris 'Curly Red'PBR CBod CDoC CRos CWSG EBee ELan EPfP IVic LPar LRHS MGos MJak MPkF NLar SHil SLim SLon SPoG SWvt
- Twisting Red = 'Opstal20'PBR MBlu

Carinella = 'Zebekot'	CRos EBee LRHS MGos NLar SHil SPoG
davisiae	NLar
§ ***fontanesiana***	CMac GKev
- 'Makijaz'[PBR] (v)	CRos EPfP LRHS MGos SHil
- 'Rainbow' (v)	Widely available
- 'Rollissonii' ♀H6	MRav SRms
- Whitewater = 'Howw'[PBR] (v)	LRHS MGos MPkF NLar NPri SHil
keiskei 'Royal Ruby'	CRos LRHS LSou MGos MJak MPkF NEgg NLar NWad SGbt SGol SHil SLim SPoG WFar WMoo
Lovita = 'Zebonard'	MBri MRav NLar SCoo
Red Lips = 'Lipsbolwi'[PBR]	EPfP IVic LPar
Scarletta = 'Zeblid' ♀H6	Widely available
walteri	see *L. fontanesiana*

Leuzea (*Asteraceae*)

centaureoides	see *Stemmacantha centaureoides*

Levisticum (*Apiaceae*)

officinale	CAgr CArn CBod CHby CLau ENfk EPfP GAbr GPoy LEdu MHer MJak MMuc MNHC NPri SDix SEND SIde SPlb SRms SVic SWat WHer WHfH WJek

Lewisia ✿ (*Portulacaceae*)

'Archangel'	NRya
Ashwood Carousel hybrids	CPBP CTri ECho MAsh NHar NRya
Birch strain	CBcs ECho ELan
brachycalyx ♀H4	ECho EWes LLHF
brachycalyx* × *cotyledon	LLHF
Brynhyfryd hybrids pink-flowered **new**	GKev
- white-flowered **new**	GKev
- hybrids yellow-flowered **new**	GKev
cantelovii	CWCL MAsh
columbiana	CTal ECho ECou MAsh
- 'Alba'	NRya NSla
- 'Rosea'	MAsh
- subsp. ***rupicola***	ITim MAsh NSla
- subsp. ***wallowensis***	MAsh
congdonii	MAsh
cotyledon ♀H4	CWCL ECho GKev GMaP ITim LLHF LRHS MMuc NFav NSla SIgm WIce
- f. ***alba***	CWCL
- - 'Snowstorm'	LLHF
- 'Ashwood Ruby'	MAsh
- Ashwood strain	ECho EPfP EWes LRHS MAsh SRms WOld
- 'Brannan Bar'	MAsh
- var. ***cotyledon***	LLHF
- double-flowered (d)	GKev
- var. ***howellii***	LLHF
- hybrid	ECho EPot GKev LHop LRHS NRya SPoG
- 'John's Special'	MAsh
- magenta-flowered	CWCL ECho GKev
- orange-flowered	CWCL
§ - 'Regenbogen'	ECho MHol WRHF
- rose-pink-flowered	CWCL
- salmon-flowered	CWCL
- Sunset Group ♀H4	ECho EPfP GCrg LAst MHer NLar WHar
- 'White Splendour'	MAsh
'George Henley'	ECho EPot EWes LLHF MAsh NRya WAbe
glandulosa	NSla
leeana	MAsh
'Little Mango'	EDAr NSla
'Little Peach'	CPBP CSma ECho ECtt EDAr EPot GBin GKev MAsh NRya NSla
'Little Plum'	CMea CPBP CSma ECho ECtt EDAr GCrg LRHS MAsh NLar NRya NSla WHoo
longipetala	ECho
§ ***nevadensis***	CPne ECho EDAr EPot GCrg ITim LRHS NRya SIgm
- ***bernardina***	see *L. nevadensis*
- 'Rosea'	ECho NRya NSla
oppositifolia	LLHF MAsh
- 'Richeyi'	GKev
'Pinkie'	MAsh
pygmaea	CWCL ECho EWes ITim LRHS MAsh MHer NBir NRya NSla SPlb XLum
- carmine-flowered **new**	GKev
pygmaea* × *rediviva	LLHF
Rainbow mixture	see *L. cotyledon* 'Regenbogen'
'Rawreth'	ECho LLHF WAbe
rediviva	CPBP LLHF
- white-flowered	GKev
serrata	MAsh SIgm
'Trevosia'	MAsh
tweedyi ♀H4	CPBP EAEE ECho EPot LHop LRHS MAsh NRya SIgm WAbe WThu
- 'Alba'	LLHF MAsh WAbe
- 'Elliott's Variety'	MAsh
- 'Rosea'	EAEE ECho EPot LHop LRHS MAsh WAbe
- yellow-flowered **new**	GKev

Leycesteria (*Caprifoliaceae*)

crocothyrsos	CBcs CWib EBee ELan NLar
formosa	Widely available
- from Longstock	SLon
- brown-stemmed	IFoB
- 'Gold Leaf'	LPmr MGos MHer MNHC SPad WFar WPtf
- Golden Lanterns = 'Notbruce'[PBR] ♀H4	CBcs CDoC CLet CMac COtt CSBt EBee ELan EPfP LBMP LBuc LRHS LSRN LSou MAsh MBri MGos MMHG MMuc MSwo NEgg NLar SCoo SHil SLim SPer SPoG SWvt WMoo
- 'Golden Pheasant' (v)	EHoe
- 'Lydia'	LRHS
- 'Purple Rain'	EWes GBin LRHS MGos NLar SHil

Leymus (*Poaceae*)

from Falkland Islands	EPPr
§ ***arenarius***	Widely available
cinereus	WCot
hispidus	see *Elymus hispidus*

Lhotzkya see *Calytrix*

Liatris (*Asteraceae*)

aspera	SPhx
cylindracea	SPhx
elegans	EPfP SPlb
ligulistylis	EBee LEdu SBea SPhx
mucronata	NLar NQui
pycnostachya	CEvo EBee NDov NLar NQui SAko SRms

	scariosa	CEvo
	- 'Alba'	CBcs NDov SAko
§	***spicata***	Widely available
	- 'Alba'	CBod CMac COtt CSBt EAJP ECha ELan EPfP GKev LAst LEdu LSRN MNrw MSCN NGdn NLar SCob SPer SPlb XLum
	- ***callilepis***	see *L. spicata*
	- 'Floristan Violett'	CTri EBee EPfP GMaP LRHS MBel MHer MJak MWhi NDov NEgg NLar NQui SCob SCoo SPlb SPoG SWvt WFar WGwG WMnd WMoo WWEG WWtn XLum
	- 'Floristan Weiss'	CExl CTri EPPr EPfP ERCP GKev GMaP LRHS MBel MHer MRav MWhi NCGa NLar SDeJ SPoG SWvt WFar WGwG WHil WMnd WMoo WWEG WWtn
	- Goblin	see *L. spicata* 'Kobold'
§	- 'Kobold'	CLet CMac EBee ELan EPfP EWoo GKev IBoy LAst LCro LRHS MBri MHer MRav NBir NEgg NGdn NLar SGbt SHil SPad SPtp SRms SWvt WFar WGwG WHil WMoo WWEG XLum
	squarrosa	SPhx

Libanotis see *Seseli*

montana	see *Seseli libanotis*

Libertia ✿ (*Iridaceae*)

	'Amazing Grace'	CDes EBee GCal
	'Ballyrogan Blue'	CDes
*	***breunioides***	CExl WPGP
	caerulescens	CBod CExl CMac EAJP ECho EPfP EWTr LRHS NBir NCGa SMad SPer SPtp WMoo
	chilensis	see *L. formosa*
	elegans	CExl EBee
§	***formosa***	CBcs CBod CBro CElw CExl CHid CLet COtt CTri ECho ELan GCal GCra GGal GKev LRHS MMuc NChi NSti SCob SEND SPer SPtp SRms SWvt WHer
	- brown-stemmed	IFoB
	grandiflora ♀H3	Widely available
	'Highlander'	ELon LRHS MHol
	ixioides	CBcs ECha ECho ECou ILea LEdu MMuc SPtp WPGP
	- 'Goldfinger' (v)	Widely available
	- hybrid	SDix
	- 'Tricolor'	CSde ECha MRav WMoo
	ixioides* × *peregrinans	LPal
	'Nelson Dwarf'	GCal
	paniculata	CExl
	peregrinans	Widely available
	- 'Gold Leaf'	CBcs CJun CTri CTsd ELan EPfP EUJe GBuc LAst LHop LRHS SMad SWvt
	- 'Gold Stripe'	ELan SPad SWvt
*	***procera***	CBod CCon CSpe EBee EPfP IVic LEdu LRHS SMad SPtp WKif WPGP WSHC
	pulchella	CSde
	'Red Devil'	MHol
	sessiliflora	CExl NBir
	- RB 94073	SMad
	'Taupo Blaze'	CBcs CMac EBee LRHS MRav SLon
	'Taupo Sunset'PBR	CExl ELon EPfP EUJe LAst LPal LRHS MBNS MPkF SWvt WHil
	tricococca HCM 98.089	WPGP

Libocedrus (*Cupressaceae*)

chilensis	see *Austrocedrus chilensis*
decurrens	see *Calocedrus decurrens*

Libonia see *Justicia*

Licuala (*Arecaceae*)

dasyantha new	CBlu
mattanensis 'Mapu' new	CBlu

Ligularia (*Asteraceae*)

	amplexicaulis	GCal
	'Bottle Rocket'PBR new	CMos NLar
	'Britt Marie Crawford'PBR ♀H6	Widely available
	calthifolia	EBee
	clivorum	see *L. dentata*
§	***dentata***	ECtt GGal NBro NLar SBea SRms SWat WBod
	- 'Dark Beauty'	MWhi
	- dark-leaved	WWEG
	- 'Desdemona'	Widely available
	- 'Enkelrig'	EBee
	- 'Midnight Lady'	CBod EAJP EHoe ELan ESwi LAst MHol NLar SPad WWEG
	- 'Orange Princess'	NPer
	- 'Osiris Fantaisie' (v)	CAbP CExl CMos ECtt EWes GBee ILea LLHF MAvo MBel MHol MNrw MWts NLar NMyG NSti SMad SPoG WBor WCot WFar WPnP WWEG
	- 'Othello'	CBod COtt EBee ECtt EHon EPfP LRHS NBid NEgg NGdn NLar NWad SCob SWat SWvt WWEG
	- 'Sommergold'	ECha WFar
	- 'Twilight'	CBct ECtt MBNS
	dictyoneura	GKev
§	***fischeri***	ECha LEdu NBre SGSe
	- B&SWJ 2570	WCru
	- B&SWJ 4381	WCru
	- B&SWJ 4478	WCru
	- B&SWJ 5653	WCru
	- B&SWJ 8802	WCru
	- CC 7311 new	GKev
	- var. ***megalorhiza*** 'Cheju Charmer'	ELon WCru WWEG
	'Franz Marc'	GCal
	'Gold Torch'	CBct ECtt NLar
§	'Gregynog Gold' ♀H6	ECha ECtt ELan GMaP LRHS MRav MWhi NBro NLar WWEG
	× ***hessei***	GMaP LRHS MMuc SWat WWtn
	hodgsonii	CKno EPPr LEdu MRav
	- B&SWJ 10855	WCru
	intermedia B&SWJ 606a	WCru WSHC
	japonica	CLAP ECha GCra LEdu LRHS MWhi NLar WWtn
	- B&SWJ 2883	WCru
	- 'Rising Sun'	CExl NLar WCot WCru
	'Laternchen'PBR	ECtt GBin IBal MWts NLar SAko
	'Little Rocket'PBR	CBct CBod CExl ECtt EPfP LLWG MBNS MPie MWts NBro NGdn SCob WFar WHil
	'Osiris Café Noir'	CAbb EBee ECtt NLar SCob WFar WHil
	'Osiris Pistache' (v)	EBee ECtt
	× ***palmatiloba***	see *L.* × *yoshizoeana* 'Palmatiloba'
§	***przewalskii***	Widely available
	- SSSE 176	WCot
	- 'Dragon Wings' new	EWTr MHol NLar SCob WBor
	- 'Dragon's Breath'	ECtt MAsh MHol

	- 'Light Fingered'	NBre
	sibirica	CSam EShb MMuc NLar SEND WMoo WWEG
	- B&SWJ 4383	WCru
	- B&SWJ 5841	WCru
	- var. ***speciosa***	see *L. fischeri*
	smithii	see *Senecio smithii*
	speciosa	see *L. fischeri*
	stenocephala	EBee NBro NLar SCob SWat WWtn XLum
	'Sungold'	CMac CSam ECtt LRHS NGdn
	tangutica	see *Sinacalia tangutica*
	'The Rocket' ♀H5	Widely available
	tussilaginea	see *Farfugium japonicum*
	- 'Aureo-maculata'	see *Farfugium japonicum* 'Aureomaculatum'
	veitchiana	CBod CCon CSam GCal GKev SWat WWtn
	vorobievii	GCal NLar
	'Weihenstephan'	GCal LRHS
	wilsoniana	ECtt LLWG LRHS MMuc MRav SEND SWat WFar WWEG WWtn
§	× ***yoshizoeana*** 'Palmatiloba'	ELan ELon EWes GBee GCal LEdu LRHS MRav SPhx SWat WFar WWtn
	'Zepter'	CBct ECtt EShb EUJe GBuc GCal GQue LRHS MBNS MMuc MWhi NEgg NHol NLar NWad WCot WWEG WWtn

Ligusticum (*Apiaceae*)

	lucidum	CEvo CMCN EBee EPfP IVic LEdu SPhx WBor WFar WPGP
	- subsp. ***lucidum***	CSpe
	porteri	CArn
§	***scoticum***	CArn CBod CHid EBee EShb EWes GPoy LCro LEdu LHop LRHS MHer NChi SDix SGSe SRms WJek WOut WPtf
	- variegated (v) **new**	LEdu WCot

Ligustrum ✿ (*Oleaceae*)

	sp.	LPar
	B&L 12261 **new**	WPGP
	chenaultii	see *L. compactum*
§	***compactum***	ETod
§	***delavayanum***	EBee EBtc GKev STrG WPGP
	- B&L 12083	CExl
	ibota	EBtc NLar
	- Musli = 'Muster'[PBR] (v)	LRHS SHil WCot
	ionandrum	see *L. delavayanum*
	japonicum	ECrN LPar LRHS LSRN SEND SGol SPer
I	- 'Aureum'	LAst
	- 'Coriaceum'	see *L. japonicum* 'Rotundifolium'
*	- 'Coriaceum Aureum'	LRHS
	- Green Century = 'Melgreen'[PBR]	GBin LRHS WMat
	- 'Korea Dwarf'	NLar
	- 'Macrophyllum'	EPfP
§	- 'Rotundifolium'	CAbP CBcs CDoC CDul CExl EBee ELan EPfP IVic LRHS MRav NLar SMad SPer SPoG WCFE WCot WFar
§	- 'Silver Star' (v)	NLar SGol
§	- 'Texanum'	CDoC ECrN EPfP NLar WCFE
	- 'Texanum Argenteum'	see *L. japonicum* 'Silver Star'
	- 'Variegatum' (v)	SGol
	lucidum ♀H5	CCVT CDoC CDul CEvo CSBt CSde CTri ELan EWTr GCal LAst LPar MRav NLar SCob SEND SGol SPer SWvt
	- Guiz 296	CExl
	- 'Curly Wurly'	LRHS SPoG
	- 'Excelsum Superbum' (v) ♀H5	CCVT CJun CMac ECrN ELan EPfP LHop LPar LRHS LSRN SGol SPoG SSpi WCot
	- 'Golden Wax'	CJun MRav SSpi
	- 'Tricolor' (v) ♀H5	CDoC CJun ELan EPfP LRHS SPer SPoG SSpi SWvt
	ovalifolium	Widely available
§	- 'Argenteum' (v)	CBcs CCVT CDoC CDul CMac COtt CTri CWib ECrN EHoe ELan EShb MMuc MRav NEgg SEND SGol SLim SPer SPoG SWvt
	- 'Aureomarginatum'	see *L. ovalifolium* 'Aureum'
§	- 'Aureum' (v) ♀H5	Widely available
	- 'Lemon and Lime' (v)	CBod CDoC COtt EBee EHoe ELan EPfP LHop LRHS LSRN SCob SCoo SHil SWvt
	- 'Variegatum'	see *L. ovalifolium* 'Argenteum'
	quihoui	CBot CTri EBee ECre ELan EPfP GKin IDee LHop LRHS MBlu NLar SDix SEND SKHP SLon SMad SPer SPoG SSpi
	sempervirens	EPfP
	sinense	CMCN MRav
	- 'Multiflorum'	CWib WFar
	- 'Pendulum'	LRHS
	- 'Variegatum' (v)	CJun LHop MRav SPer
	- 'Wimbei'	WPat
	strongylophyllum	CExl
	texanum	see *L. japonicum* 'Texanum'
	tschonoskii	NLar
	undulatum 'Lemon Lime and Clippers'	EShb LRHS MBNS NLar NPri SCob SDix SLim WMoo
	'Vicaryi'	CJun ELan EPfP EWld LRHS MGos NEoE SCob SDix SGol SHil SMad SPer WFar
	vulgare	CArg CArn CBcs CBod CCVT CDul CHab CMac CTri ECrN EPfP LBuc MMuc MSwo NBes NWea SCob SEND SEWo SWvt WMat WMou WSFF
	- 'Aureovariegatum' (v)	CNat
	- 'Lodense'	EBtc

Lilium ✿ (*Liliaceae*)

	sp.	LRHS
	'4 You' (Ia-b) **new**	LRHS
	'Abbeville's Pride' (Ia/b)	CBod GKev SDeJ
	'Acapulco' (VII-/d)	CBod LAma NGdn SDeJ
	'Adonis' (Ic/d)	GEdr
	African Queen Group (VI-/a) ♀H6	ERCP GKev LAma SCoo SRms
	- 'African Queen' (VIb-c/a)	CBro LOPS MCri SDeJ
	'Altari' (VIIIa-b/b)	MCri SDeJ
	amabile var. ***luteum*** (IXc/d)	MCri
	'Ambergate'	SDeJ
	'Anastasia' (VIIIb-c/b-d)	EPfP GKev LAma SDeJ
	'Annemarie's Dream' (Ia/c)	GKev SDeJ
	'Apeldoorn' (Ia/b)	MCri NNor
	Apollo (Ia-b)	see *L.* 'Blizzard'
	'Arabian Knight' (IIc/d)	GKev LAma LRHS SDeJ
	'Arena' (VIIa/b)	SCoo
	Asiatic hybrids (I)	LRHS NGdn
	auratum (IXb/c)	CTsd ECho EFEx EPfP GBuc
	- 'Gold Band'	see *L. auratum* var. *platyphyllum*

	- 'Golden Ray' (IXb/c)	GBuc
§	- var. ***platyphyllum*** (IXb/c)	MCri NNor SDeJ
	- - B&SWJ 4824	WCru
	- - B&SWJ 5041	WCru
	- var. ***virginale*** (IXb/c)	MCri SDeJ
	'Barbara North' (Ic/d)	GEdr
	'Barbaresco' (VIIa-b/b)	SCoo
	'Barcelona' (Ia/b-c)	NNor
	'Belgrado'PBR (VIIa/b-c)	SDeJ
	'Belladonna'PBR (VIIIb-a/b)	SDeJ
	'Belle Epoque' (VIIb/b-c)	SDeJ
	'Bergamo' (VIIb/b)	SCoo SDeJ
	'Beverly Dreams' **new**	ERCP
	'Black Beauty' (VIIIb-c/d)	CTsd EPfP GBin GKev LAma LCro LOPS MCri NNor SDeJ
	'Black Bird' (Ia/b)	CBod MAsh
	'Black Dragon'	see *L. leucanthum* var. *centifolium* 'Black Dragon'
§	'Blizzard' (Ia/b)	NNor SDeJ
	'Bonbini' (VIIIa-b/b)	LRHS
	'Boogie Woogie' (VIIIa-b/b)	SDeJ
	'Bracelet' (VIIIa-b/b)	SDeJ
	Brasilia = 'Zora' (VIIa/b-c)	SDeJ
	Bright Pixie = 'Ceb Bright' (Ia/b)	CBod MAsh SDeJ
	'Bright Star' (VIb-c/c)	LAma MCri
	brownii (IXb-c/a)	ECho
	bulbiferum (IXa/b)	ECho GKev
	- var. ***croceum*** (IXa/b)	XEll
	Bullwood hybrids (IV)	GBuc
	'Butter Pixie'PBR (Ia/b)	CBod NNor SDeJ
§	***canadense*** (IXc/a)	GBuc GEdr GKev LAma WCru XEll
	- var. ***coccineum*** (IXc/a)	GBuc
	- var. ***flavum***	see *L. canadense*
	'Cancun' (Ia/b-c)	SDeJ
	candidum (IXb/a)	CAvo CBcs CBro CPne CTca CWCL EBee ECha ECho ELan EPot ERCP GKev LAma LSun MCri MHer NLar NRog SDeJ SRms
	'Capuchino' (Ia-b/c)	MBri
	'Casa Blanca' (VIIb/b-c) ♀H6	CAvo CBro EPfP GKev LAma LCro LOPS LSun MCri NBir NLar NNor SCoo SDeJ
	'Cecil' (VIIIa/b)	GKev SDeJ
	'Centerfold' (Ia-b/b)	NNor
	cernuum (IXc/d)	ECho GKev LAma MCri SDeJ
*	- 'Album'	ECho SDeJ
	'Chameleon' (II) **new**	LAma
	'Chill Out' (VIIa) **new**	LCro
§	'Chocolate Canary' (Ic/-)	SDeJ
	Citronella Group (Ic/d)	ECho SDeJ
	'Claude Shride' (IIc/d)	GKev LAma SDeJ
	'Cocktail Twins' (Ia/b)	GKev SDeJ
	'Coldplay' (VII a-b/b-c)	LBuc LRHS
	columbianum (IXc/d)	ECho
	- B&SWJ 9564	WCru
	'Con Amore' (VIIb/b)	SCoo
	'Conca d'Or'PBR (VIIIb/b)	LRHS SDeJ
	'Connecticut King' (Ia/b)	MCri
	'Corina' (Ia/b)	NNor
	'Côte d'Azur' (Ia/b-c)	NNor
	'Creation' (VIa/b)	SDeJ
	'Crimson Pixie' (Ia/b)	CBod CBro SDeJ
	'Crossover' (Ia-b) **new**	LRHS
	× ***dalhansonii*** (IIc/d)	CAby WCot
	- 'Guinea Gold' (II) **new**	LAma
§	- 'Marhan' (IIc/d)	ECho GBuc
	- 'Mrs R.O. Backhouse' (IIc/d)	ECho GEdr GKev SDeJ
	dauricum var. ***alpinum*** (IXa/b)	MCri
	davidii (IXc/d)	CExl EBee ECho GBuc LAma MCri SDeJ WBor WCru
	- var. ***unicolor*** (IXc/d)	GBuc
§	- var. ***willmottiae*** (IXc/d)	MCri WCru
	'Debby' (VIII a-b/b-c)	CSut
	'Delicate Joy' (Ia/b) **new**	LRHS
	'Diabora' (Ia/b)	GBuc
	'Dimension' (I a/b-c)	LAma LCro LOPS
	'Disco' (Ia)	SDeJ
	distichum (IXb-c/d) B&SWJ 4465	WCru
	- B&SWJ 794	WCru
	'Dizzy' (VIIa-b/b-c)	CBod CSut CTsd MCri NNor SDeJ
	'Dot to Dot' **new**	LRHS
	duchartrei (IXc/d)	CAby CExl ECho GKev LAma NSla WAbe WCru
	'Electric' (Ia/b-c)	MCri NNor
	'Electric Yellow'	see *L.* 'Yellow Electric'
	'Elodie'PBR (Ia/b)	CAvo CSut LAma
	'Elusive' (VIIIb/b-d)	SDeJ
	'Enchantment' (Ia/b)	SDeJ
	'Expression' (VII)	SDeJ
	'Eyeliner'PBR (VIII a/b)	LAma
	'Fangio' (VIIIa/b)	NNor
	fargesii (IXc/d)	CExl GKev
	'Fata Morgana' (Ia/b) ♀H6	CSut GKev LAma NNor SCoo SDeJ
	'Fire King' (Ib/d)	GKev SCoo SDeJ SRms
	'Fopapo'	SDeJ
	'Forever Susan' (Ia/b)	SDeJ
	formosanum (IXb/a)	CPne MCri
	- short, from high altitude RWJ 10005 (IX b/a)	WCru
	- var. ***formosanum*** B&SWJ 1589 (IXb/a)	WCru
	- var. ***pricei*** (IXb/a)	EAJP EBee ECho EDAr ELan EPot GBin LRHS MHer NSla SHil WIce
	- - 'Snow Queen' (Vb/a)	SDeJ
	'Friso' (VIIIb/b)	CBro EPfP GKev
	'Garden Party' (VIIb/b) ♀H6	GKev SDeJ
	'Gay Lights' (II)	WCot
	'Gironde' (Ia/b)	SDeJ
	'Glossy Wings' (VIIIa-b/b)	NNor
	'Gluhwein'PBR (VIII a/b-b)	LRHS
	Golden Splendor Group (VIb-c/a) ♀H6	GKev LAma MCri SCoo SDeJ
	'Golden Stone' (VIIIa-b/b)	GKev SDeJ
	'Gran Paradiso' (Ia/b)	MCri SRms
	'Grand Cru' (Ia/b)	MCri NNor SDeJ
	grayi (IXc/a)	GBuc
	Green Magic Group (VI-/a)	NNor
	'Hannah North' (Ic/d)	GEdr
	hansonii (IXb-c/d)	CWCL ECha ECho GBuc GKev LAma MCri SDeJ
	- B&SWJ 4309	WCru
	- B&SWJ 8506	WCru
	- B&SWJ 8528	WCru
	- B&SWJ 4756 from Aomori, Japan	WCru
	hansonii × ***martagon*** (II) **new**	ERCP
	henryi (IXc/d) ♀H6	CAvo CBro EBee ECho GKev LAma MCri NLar NNor SCob SDeJ WCru
	'Hit Parade' (VII)	SDeJ
	× ***hollandicum*** (Ia/b)	MCri
	'Honeymoon' (VIIIa-b/b)	SDeJ
	'Hot Spot' (VII) **new**	LRHS
	'Hotline' (VIIa) **new**	LCro
	'Ibarra' (Ia/b)	MCri

'Ice Pixie' (Ia/b) SDeJ
'Inuvik' (Ia/b) CBod MAsh
'Ivory Pixie' (Ia/b) CBod GKev SDeJ
japonicum (IXb/a) EFEx
'Jo's Choice' SDeJ
'Josephine' (VIIa/b) SDeJ
'Journey's End' (VIIb/c) LAma
'Joy' see *L.* 'Le Rêve'
'Karen North' (Ic/d) GEdr
'King Pete' (Ib/b-c) SDeJ
'Kingdom'PBR (VIIIa/b-c) SDeJ
'Lady Alice' (VI-/d) GKev SDeJ
'Lake Tulare' (IV c/c-d) GEdr
§ ***lancifolium*** (IXc/d) CArn CHid CPne EPot EWld GBin XLum
- B&SWJ 4352 WCru
- var. ***flaviflorum*** (IXc/d) CBro EBee GBuc IBoy MCri SDeJ
- 'Flore Pleno' (IXc/d) CSut EPPr GCal GKev LHop LRHS MHer NBir NNor SDeJ WCot WCru XLum
* - var. ***forrestii*** (IX) MCri
- var. ***fortunei*** (IXc/d) GCal SDix
- - B&SWJ 539 WCru
- pink-flowered SDeJ
- 'Splendens' (IXc/d) CBro EBee ECho EPfP GKev MCri NBid NNor SDeJ SPhx WCot
'Landini'PBR (Ia/b) CSut SDeJ
'Lankon' (VIIIc/a) ERCP
lankongense (IXc/d) CWCL ECho EPot GBin GBuc GGGa GKev LAma LRHS WCru
- BWJ 7554 WCru
- BWJ 7691 WCru
'Latvia' (Ia/b) MCri SDeJ
'Lazy Lady' see *L.* 'Chocolate Canary'
§ 'Le Rêve' (VIIa-b/b) NNor SDeJ
leichtlinii (IXc/d) CAby CAvo CBro EBee ECho EPot GBin GKev IMou LLHF MCri SDeJ WOld
- B&SWJ 4519 WCru
- 'Iwashimiza' (IXc/d) MCri
leucanthum (IXb-c/a) LAma
- var. ***centifolium*** (IXb-c/a) MCri WCru
- - BWJ 8130 WCru
§ - - 'Black Dragon' (IXb-c/a) MCri
lijiangense (IXc/d) GKev MCri
I 'Linda' (Ia/b) SDeJ
'Little John' (VIIa-b/b) SDeJ
'Little Kiss' (Ia/d) SDeJ
Lollypop = 'Holebibi' (Ia/b) CBod CSut GBuc NNor SCoo
longiflorum (IXb/a) CTsd EBee ECho MCri SCoo XLum
- B&SWJ 11376 WCru
- 'Rose' SDeJ
- 'Variegata' (V) **new** MAvo
§ - 'White American' (Vb/a) CBro ECho EWoo
- 'White Heaven'PBR (Vb/a) EPfP LCro LOPS
lophophorum (IXc/b) EPot GKev LAma
'Lovely Girl' (VII-/b) SDeJ
'Luxor' (Ia/b) CTsd NBir
mackliniae (IXc/a) ♀H5 CWCL ECho EWes GBuc GCal GCra GGGa GKev ITim NBir NHar WAbe WHal WPGP
- PAB 9668 **new** LEdu
- from Nagaland, India GGGa
- deep pink-flowered GGGa
'Manitoba Morning' (IIc/c) GKev LAma LRHS
'Mapira' (I) CHid
'Marco Polo' SCoo SDeJ
'Marhan' see *L.* × *dalhansonii* 'Marhan'
'Marie North' (Ic/d) GEdr
'Maroon King' (II) **new** GKev
martagon (IXc/d) ♀H7 CAvo CBro CCon CTca EBee ECha ECho ELan EPot ERCP GBuc GEdr GKev GPoy LAma LCro LRHS NBir NChi NLar SDeJ SRms WAbe WPnP WShi WWFP
- var. ***albiflorum*** (IXc/d) GBuc GKev
- var. ***album*** (IXc/d) CAvo CBro CWCL ECho ELan EPot GBin GKev LAma LCro NBir NChi SDeJ WShi
- var. ***cattaniae*** (IXc/d) GBuc GEdr MCri
- var. ***hirsutum*** (IXc/d) GEdr
* - var. ***rubrum*** CBro CWCL
'Maru' (VIIa/b) LBuc LRHS
medeoloides (IXc/d) ECho EFEx GBuc
- B&SWJ 4184 WCru
- B&SWJ 4363 WCru
'Mediterrannee' (VIIb/d) NNor
michiganense (IXc/d) GBuc
'Miss Feya' (VIII b/c) LAma SDeJ
'Miss France' (VIIb/b-c) SDeJ
I 'Miss Lily' (VIII b/c) SDeJ
'Miss Lucy'PBR (VIIa-b/b-c) CHid LAma SDeJ
Miss Rio see *L.* 'Rio'
'Mister Job' (VIIIa/c) GKev SDeJ
'Mona Lisa' (VIIb/b-c) GKev LAma LRHS MCri NGdn NLar NNor SDeJ
monadelphum (IXc/d) ECho LAma SDeJ
'Mont Blanc' (Ia/b-c) SDeJ
'Monte Negro' (Ia/b) MCri
'Montezuma'PBR (VIIa-b/b) SDeJ
'Montreux' (Ia/b-c) SDeJ
'Mount Duckling' (Ia-b/b) CBod
'Mountain Joy' (Ia) **new** LRHS
'Muscadet'PBR (VIIa-b/b) GKev LAma NGdn SDeJ
§ ***nanum*** (IXc/b) ECho LAma WAbe WHal
nepalense (IXc/a) CAby CBcs CBro CCon CExl CHid CTca CWCL ECho EPot ERCP GBin GBuc GEdr GKev LAma LRHS MCri SDeJ WAbe WCru XLum
- B&SWJ 2985 WCru
'Nerone' (Ia/b) CHid NNor
'Netty's Pride' (Ia/b-c) CAvo CBro CHid ERCP GBuc GKev MCri SDeJ WCot
'New Wave' (Ia/b) SDeJ
'New Yellow' LRHS
'Night Flyer' (Ib-c/b-c) SDeJ
nobilissimum (IXa-b/a) EFEx
'Nove Cento' (Ia/b) MCri SDeJ
'Olivia' (Ia) LAma
Olympic Group (VI-/a) MCri
'Orange County' (Ia/b) SDeJ
'Orange Electric' (Ia/b) GKev SDeJ
'Orange Marmalade' (IIb/c-d) GKev LAma LRHS SDeJ
'Orange Pixie' (Ia/b) CBod MAsh MCri NNor SCoo
'Orange Planet' (VIa/a) **new** GKev
'Orange Twinkle' (Ib-c/b) SDeJ
'Orange Twins' (Ia-b) **new** LRHS
'Orania'PBR (VIIIb/b) GKev SDeJ
oriental hybrids (VII) SDeJ
* Oriental Superb Group NGdn
§ ***oxypetalum*** (IXb-c/b) ECho
- var. ***insigne*** (IXb-c/b) ECho GBin GBuc WAbe WHal
pardalinum (IXc/d) ♀H6 CAvo CBro CWCL EBee ECho EPot ERCP GKev WBor WCru
- var. ***giganteum*** (IXc/d) EPfP MCri MNrw
- subsp. ***pardalinum*** (IXc/d) GBuc
§ - subsp. ***vollmeri*** (IXc/d) GBuc WCru

§ - subsp. ***wigginsii*** (IXc/d) WCru
× ***parkmanii*** 'Rosy Dimple' (VIIa/b) SDeJ
parvum (IXa-b/a) ECho GBuc
'Patricia's Pride' (Ia-b/b-c) MCri SDeJ
'Peach Butterflies' (Ic/d) SDeJ
'Peach Dwarf' (Ia/b-c) SDeJ
'Peach Pixie' (Ia/b) NBir SCoo
'Pearl Jennifer' (Ib-a/c) SDeJ
'Pearl Jessica' (Ib-c/b-c) SDeJ
'Pearl Loraine' (Ib-c/b-c) SDeJ
'Pearl Sonja' (Ib/b) SDeJ
'Pearl Stacey' (Ib-c/c) GKev SDeJ
'Peggy North' (Ic/d) GEdr
'Penthouse' (VIIa/b) LRHS
philippinense (IXa-b/a) EWoo GKev LAma WPGP
'Pimento' (VIIa/b) SDeJ
'Pink Blossom' (Ia) **new** LRHS
'Pink Expression' (VII) **new** LRHS
'Pink Flavour' (Ic/c) GKev SDeJ
'Pink Heart' LBuc LRHS
'Pink Morning' (IIc) **new** LRHS
Pink Perfection Group (VIb/a) 🏆H6 CBro ERCP GKev LAma MCri NNor SCoo SDeJ SPer
'Pink Pixie'[PBR] (Ia/b) CBod GKev NNor SDeJ
'Pink Planet' (VIa/a) **new** GKev
'Pink Tiger' (VIIIb/c) NNor
pitkinense (IX) GBuc GKev
poilanei misapplied see *L. primulinum*
poilanei Gagnep. see *L. primulinum* var. *poilanei*
'Precious Joy' (Ia) **new** LRHS
§ ***primulinum*** (IXc/a) GKev
- HWJ 681 WCru
- WWJ 11679 WCru
- var. ***ochraceum*** (IXc/a) LAma WCru
- aff. var. ***ochraceum*** KWJ 12064 WCru
§ - var. ***poilanei*** **new** EBee
'Proud Bride' (VIIa/b) CBod MAsh
§ ***pumilum*** (IXc/d) 🏆H6 EBee ECho EPot GKev LAma MCri SDeJ
'Purple Prince' (VIIIa-b/a-b) SDeJ
'Push Off' (Ia-b) **new** LRHS
pyrenaicum (IXc/d) CAby ECho GBuc GKev WShi XEll
'Red Carpet' (Ia/b) MCri NNor SDeJ
'Red County' (Ia/c-b) SDeJ
'Red Electric' (Ia/b) SDeJ
'Red Eyes' (VIIa) **new** LRHS
'Red Flavour' (Ic/b-c) GKev
'Red Hot' (VIIIc-d/b) SDeJ
'Red Twinkle' SDeJ
'Red Velvet' (Ic/d) CAvo SDeJ
regale (IXb/a) 🏆H6 CAvo CBro CCon CTca CTsd CWCL EBee ECha ELan EPfP EPot ERCP GKev LAma LCro MCri NLar NNor SCob SDeJ SPer WCot
- 'Album' (IXb/a) CAvo EBee ERCP GKev IMou LAma LCro LOPS LRHS MCri NLar NNor SCob SCoo SDeJ WCot
§ - 'Royal Gold' (IXb/a) MCri
'Reinesse' (Ia/b) SDeJ
§ 'Rio' (VIIb/b) SCoo
'Robert Swanson' (VIIIb-c/b) GKev LAma SDeJ
'Robina' (VIIIa-b/b-c) WCot
'Rose Arch Fox' **new** LAma
'Rosefire' (Ia/b) NNor
'Rosella's Dream' (Ia/b) GKev SDeJ
'Rosemary North' (Ic/d) CDes
'Rosselini' (VIIIa-b/b) SDeJ
rosthornii (IXc/d) CExl EBee GKev LAma WCru
'Royal Fantasy' (VIIIa-b/b) NNor
'Royal Gold' see *L. regale* 'Royal Gold'
rubellum (IXb/a) EFEx GEdr
'Russian Morning' (IIc) **new** LRHS
'Russian Red' **new** LAma
sachalinense (IXa/b) RBS 0235 EPPr
'Salinas' (VIIa/b) GKev SDeJ
'Salmon Tiger' SDeJ
'Salmon Twinkle' (Ib-c/c) SDeJ
'Sapporo'[PBR] (VII) **new** ILea
sargentiae (IXb-c/a) GCal WCot WCru
'Satisfaction' (VIIIa-b/-) SDeJ
'Scarlet Delight' (VIIb-c/c-d) GKev SDeJ
'Scheherazade' (VIIIc/d) LAma MCri SDeJ
'Set Point' (VIIb/b) SDeJ
'Silly Girl' (Ia/-) NNor
'Slate's Select' **new** LAma
'Smoky Mountain' (VIIIc/d) GKev SDeJ
'Souvenir'[PBR] (VIIa-b/b) NGdn
'Spark' (Ia-b/b) NNor
speciosum (IXb-c/d) B&SWJ 4847 WCru
- B&SWJ 4924 WCru
- var. ***album*** (IXb-c/d) ECho GKev LEdu MCri NBir SDeJ
- var. ***gloriosoides*** (IXb-c/d) GKev LAma
- var. ***rubrum*** (IXb-c/d) ECha ECho EPfP LAma LOPS MCri NBir SDeJ SPer SRms
§ - - 'Uchida' (IXb-c/d) CExl GKev MCri SDeJ
'Sphinx' (Ia/d) NNor WCot
'Spring Pink' (Ia/-) ERCP GKev SDeJ
'Stainless Steel' (Ia/b) SDeJ
'Star Gazer' (VIIa/c) CBod CBro GKev LAma LRHS NNor SCob SCoo SDeJ
'Starfighter' (VIIa-b/c) CSut SDeJ
'Sterling Star' (Ia/b) MCri NNor
Stones = 'Holebobo' (Ia/b) NNor
'Sulphur King' WCot
sulphureum (IXb-c/a) LAma
'Sunny Morning' (IIc/c) GKev LAma
superbum (IXc/d) EBee GBuc GKev LAma WCru WPGP
'Sutton Court' (II) GBuc
'Sweet Lord' (Ia/b) GKev SDeJ
'Sweet Surrender' (Ib-c/c-d) GKev MCri NNor SDeJ
'Tailor Made' (Ia/b) GKev SDeJ
taliense (IXc/d) ECho LAma WCru
'Tarragona'[PBR] (VIIIb/b) SDeJ
tenuifolium see *L. pumilum*
Tiger Babies Group (VIIIb-c/c-d) CAvo
'Tiger Edition' (VIIa-b) **new** CBod LCro LOPS
'Tigerwoods' (VIIa/c) LCro LOPS
tigrinum see *L. lancifolium*
'Tom Pouce' (VIIa/b) SDeJ
'Toronto' (Ia-b/b) SDeJ
'Toscane' (Ia/b-c) SDeJ
Triumphator = 'Zanlophator'[PBR] (VIIIb/a-b) GKev ILea MCri NNor SDeJ
tsingtauense (IXa/c) EBee GKev LAma MCri SDeJ
- B&SWJ 519 WCru
- B&SWJ 4263 WCru
- B&SWJ 4698 WCru

'Uchida Kanoka'	see *L. speciosum* var. *rubrum* 'Uchida'
'Urandi' (VIIIc/b)	SDeJ
'Val Di Sole'[PBR] (Ia/b)	SDeJ
'Venezuela'[PBR] (VIIa-b/b-c)	NLar SDeJ
'Venture' (Ia/b)	NNor
'Vermeer' (Ia-b/b-c)	ILea
'Visaversa' (VIIIa-b/b)	SDeJ
'Vivaldi' (Ia/b)	SDeJ
vollmeri	see *L. pardalinum* subsp. *vollmeri*
wallichianum (IXb/a)	ECho EPot GKev LAma SDeJ XLum
wardii (IXc/d)	CExl
'White American'	see *L. longiflorum* 'White American'
'White Paradise' (V)	SCoo
'White Planet' (VIa/a) **new**	GKev
'White Present' (Vb/a)	GKev SDeJ
'White Twinkle' (Ia-b/b)	SDeJ
wigginsii	see *L. pardalinum* subsp. *wigginsii*
willmottiae	see *L. davidii* var. *willmottiae*
'Wine Electric' (Ia/c)	SDeJ
xanthellum var. ***luteum*** (IXb-c/d)	CDes WCru
§ 'Yellow Electric' (Ia/b-c)	MCri SDeJ
'Yellow Eye'	SDeJ
'Yellow Planet' (VIb-a/a) **new**	GKev
'Yeti' (Ia/b)	SDeJ
'Zulu'	LRHS

lime see *Citrus × aurantiifolia*

lime, djeruk see *Citrus amblycarpa*

lime, Philippine see *Citrus × microcarpa*

limequat see *Citrus × floridana*

Limnanthes (*Limnanthaceae*)

douglasii ♀H7	EPfP MNHC
- subsp. ***rosea***	CSpe

Limonium (*Plumbaginaceae*)

bellidifolium	CMea EDAr
'Blauer Diamant'	EWoo
chilwellii	EBee LRHS MWat
cosyrense	CMea MHer
dregeanum	WThu
dumosum	see *Goniolimon tataricum* var. *angustifolium*
gmelinii	SPlb
* - subsp. ***hungaricum***	XLum
latifolium	see *L. platyphyllum*
§ ***platyphyllum***	CBod CBot CChe CCon COtt EPfP EWoo GMaP LAst LHop LRHS LSun MBel MHer MMuc MWat SCob SEND SMHy SPer SRms WHar WHoo XSen
- 'Robert Butler'	GCal GQue MRav
- 'Violetta'	CBod EBee ELan EPfP LAst LRHS MBel MPie SPer WAul WHoo
sinuatum	SVic
tataricum	see *Goniolimon tataricum*
vulgare	LRHS WHer XSen

Linaria (*Plantaginaceae*)

aeruginea	CPBP
- 'Lindeza Violet' **new**	CSpe
- 'Neon Lights'	CSpe EDAr NGdn SPoG
- subsp. ***nevadensis*** 'Gemstones'	SBch
alpina	CSpe GJos NRya NSla SRms
anticaria 'Antique Silver'	CExl LSou MRav
Blue Lace = 'Yalin'	LSou
cymbalaria	see *Cymbalaria muralis*
§ ***dalmatica***	EBee ECGP ELan EPPr MPie NBid SHar SIgm SPad SPhx WCot WHea WMoo
dalmatica × ***purpurea***	WCot
× ***dominii*** 'Carnforth'	SHar WWEG
- 'Yuppie Surprise'	CHid NBir
'Florence Lily Sophia Brown'	WCot
genistifolia	WCot
- W&B BGB-6 **new**	WCot
- subsp. ***dalmatica***	see *L. dalmatica*
hepaticifolia	see *Cymbalaria hepaticifolia*
* ***lobata alba***	ECho SPlb
maroccana 'Licilia Peach' **new**	CSpe
origanifolia	see *Chaenorhinum origanifolium*
pallida	see *Cymbalaria pallida*
'Peachy'	CSpe ECtt MAvo MCot MHol MPie MSCN MTis SBod SPad SPoG WCot WRHF
pilosa	see *Cymbalaria pilosa*
purpurea	CTri CWld EHoe ELan EPfP IFoB MHer MLHP MNHC NBro NPer NPol SEND SPhx SRms WCot WFar WMoo WSFF XLum
- 'Alba'	see *L. purpurea* 'Springside White'
- 'Brown's White Strain'	CAby CBre CSpe EBee EPPr IBoy LRHS SPad WCot
- 'Canon Went'	CAby CBre CSpe CTri CWib EBee EHoe ELan EPfP EWoo GJos LRHS MMuc MNHC NBir NBro NGBl NPol SGbt SHil SPer SPhx SRms SWvt WCAu WFar WKif WMoo
- 'Freefolk Piccolo'	SHar
- pink-flowered	CSpe
- 'Radcliffe Innocence'	see *L. purpurea* 'Springside White'
§ - 'Springside White'	GJos LRHS NBir NGdn SBch SPhx WFar XLum
repens	WCot WHer
× ***sepium***	WCot
'Tarte au Citron' **new**	WCot
triornithophora	CCon LBMP MHol SPlb WKif WMoo
- 'Pink Budgies'	EBee LSou
- purple-flowered	WMoo
- 'Rosea'	CSpe
vulgaris	CHab CWld EDAr EPfP MHer MLHP MNHC NMir SRms WHer WHfH WMoo
- f. ***peloria***	CPBP

Lindelofia (*Boraginaceae*)

anchusoides misapplied	see *L. longiflora*
anchusoides (Lindl.) Lehm.	EPPr NBid
§ ***longiflora***	EBee GCal GCra LPla WHea WSHC

Lindera (*Lauraceae*)

aggregata	CBcs WPGP
angustifolia FMWJ 13156	CEvo WCru
benzoin	CBcs EPfP LRHS MBlu NLar
erythrocarpa	EPfP
- B&SWJ 6271	WCru
- B&SWJ 8730	WCru

metcalfiana var. ***dictyophylla*** KWJ 12312	WCru
obtusiloba ♀H5	CAbP MBlu WPGP
- B&SWJ 8723	WCru
- B&SWJ 11054	WCru
- B&SWJ 12555 from Korea	WCru
praecox	EPfP
- B&SWJ 10802	WCru
- B&SWJ 10953 from north Japan	WCru
- B&SWJ 11125 from south Japan	WCru
reflexa	NLar
sericea B&SWJ 11123	WCru
- B&SWJ 11141	WCru
- var. ***lancea*** B&SWJ 11071	WCru
- - B&SWJ 11118	WCru
strychnifolia	EPfP
tonkinensis FMWJ 13123	WCru
triloba B&SWJ 5570	WCru
- B&SWJ 11121	WCru
- B&SWJ 11466	WCru
umbellata B&SWJ 10881	WCru
- var. ***membranacea*** B&SWJ 6227	WCru
- - B&SWJ 10837	WCru

Lindernia (*Linderniaceae*)

grandiflora	CBod ESwi LLWG WTor

Linnaea (*Caprifoliaceae*)

borealis	CExl EPot ITim NSla WAbe XEll
- subsp. ***americana***	NHar WAbe

Linum (*Linaceae*)

arboreum ♀H4	GKev LLHF NBir
bienne	WCot
boissieri	LLHF
campanulatum	WThu
capitatum	EPot
flavum	GKev XSen
- 'Compactum'	CMea EBee ECho LLHF SRms
'Gemmell's Hybrid' ♀H4	ECho EPot EWes GCrg ITim NBir WAbe WThu
grandiflorum 'Bright Eyes' **new**	CSpe
- 'Rubrum'	CSpe
hypericifolium	MNHC SPhx
monogynum	ECou LLHF
§ - var. ***diffusum***	ECou
- 'Nelson'	see *L. monogynum* var. *diffusum*
narbonense	CBod CCse EWld SIgm SPhx
- 'Heavenly Blue'	NCGa
§ ***perenne***	CArn CBod ECha ELan ENfk EPfP GMaP LSun MHer MMuc MNHC SCob SIde SPer SPoG WCAu WJek
- 'Album'	EBee ECha ELan EPfP
- subsp. ***alpinum*** 'Alice Blue'	CPBP WAbe
§ - 'Blau Saphir'	GQue MBel NHol
- Blue Sapphire	see *L. perenne* 'Blau Saphir'
- 'Himmelszelt'	LSun
- 'Nanum Sapphire'	see *L. perenne* 'Blau Saphir'
- 'White Diamond'	SPoG
sibiricum	see *L. perenne*
suffruticosum subsp. ***salsoloides***	SBrt
- - 'Nanum'	WThu

uninerve	WAbe
usitatissimum	MHer SIde
- 'Blue Dress'	SPhx

Lippia (*Verbenaceae*)

sp.	SWvt
canescens	see *Phyla nodiflora* var. *canescens*
chamaedrifolia	see *Verbena peruviana*
citriodora	see *Aloysia citrodora*
dulcis	CArn ENfk
nodiflora	see *Phyla nodiflora*
repens	see *Phyla nodiflora*

Liquidambar ✿ (*Hamamelidaceae*)

acalycina	CDul CJun EBee EBtc ELan EPfP NLar SBir SCoo SGol SLim SSta WMat WPGP WPat
- 'Burgundy Flush' ♀H6	CJun NLar SBir SSta
- 'Spinners'	LRHS SBir SPoG SSpi
formosana	CDul CMCN CMac IArd LAst MSnd SBir SGol SSta WPGP
- 'Afterglow'	CJun NLar
- 'Ellen'	CJun NLar
- Monticola Group	CJun NLar SLim SSta
orientalis	CDul CJun CLnd CMCN EBtc EPfP LLHF SBir SSta WPat
- 'M. Foster'	NLar
styraciflua	Widely available
- 'Andrew Hewson'	CAbP CJun CLnd EBee EPfP IVic LRHS MBlu NLar SBir SSta WPat
- 'Anja'	CJun MBlu SBir SSta WPat
- 'Anneke'	CJun SBir SSta
- 'Aurea'	see *L. styraciflua* 'Variegata' Overeynder
- 'Aurea Variegata'	see *L. styraciflua* 'Variegata' Overeynder
- 'Aurora'	CJun SBir
- 'Burgundy'	CJun CLnd LLHF MBlu SBir SSta WPat
I - 'Corky'	SSta
- 'Elstead Mill'	CAbP
- 'Emerald Sentinel'	SSta
- 'Festeri'	SBir SSta WPat
- 'Festival'	CJun EUJe MBlu SGol
- 'Frosty' (v)	CJun SBir SSta
- 'Globe'	see *L. styraciflua* 'Gum Ball'
- 'Gold Beacon'	MPkF NLar
- 'Golden Sun' PBR **new**	NLar
- 'Golden Treasure' (v)	CDul CJun CLnd CMCN LRHS MGos SBir SGol SReu SSta
- 'Goldmember'	CJun SSta
- 'Granary Sunset'	SBir SSta
§ - 'Gum Ball'	CJun CLnd CMCN EBee ELon EPfP EWes LLHF LRHS NLar SBir SCob SLim SMad SSta SWvt WPat
- Happidaze = 'Hapdell'	CJun NLar SBir WPat
- 'Jennifer Carol'	CJun NLar SBir SSta
- 'Kia'	CAbP CJun LLHF SBir WPat
- 'Kirsten'	CJun
- 'Lane Roberts' ♀H6	Widely available
- 'Lynn'	SBir SSta
- 'Manon' (v)	CJun SPoG
- 'Midwest Sunset'	CJun MBlu NLar SBir WPat
- 'Moonbeam' (v)	CJun SBir SCob SLim SSta WPat
- 'Moraine'	CJun ESwi
- 'Naree'	CJun NLar SSta WPat
- 'Nina'	SSta
- 'Nyewood'	SBir
- 'Oconee'	EPfP LLHF NLar SLim SSta WPat
- 'Paarl' (v)	CJun CLnd NLar SGol

- 'Palo Alto' 🏆H6	CJun LLHF LRHS MBlu SAko SBir SCoo SLim SSta WMat WPGP WPat
- 'Parasol'	CAbP CJun CLnd EBtc SBir SSta
- 'Pendula'	CJun CLnd MBlu SBir SSta WPat
- 'Penwood' 🏆H6	CJun NLar SBir SSta WPat
- 'Red Sunset'	SSta
- 'Rotundiloba'	CJun CMCN EPfP LEdu LLHF LRHS MBlu SSta WPGP WPat
- 'Savill Torch'	SBir SSta
- 'Schock's Gold'	CJun NLar SSta WPat
§ - 'Silver King' (v)	CJun CLnd CMCN CMac EBee MGos MPkF NLar SCoo SGol SHil SLim SPer SPoG SReu SSta WPat
- 'Simone'	SBir SGol SSta
- 'Slender Silhouette' 🏆H6	Widely available
- 'Stared'	CDul CJun CLnd EBee EBtc EPfP GQue LRHS MBlu MBri MGos NLar SBir SCoo SLim SSta WMat WMou WPGP WPat
- 'Thea'	CAbP CJun CLnd EBee EPfP LRHS MBlu SBir SSta WPat
- 'Variegata' misapplied	see *L. styraciflua* 'Silver King'
§ - 'Variegata' Overeynder (v)	CJun CLnd CMac EBee ELan LRHS SBir SLim SSta
- 'White Star' (v)	CJun
- 'Woorby Rose'	NLar SBir
- 'Worplesdon' 🏆H6	Widely available

Liriodendron (*Magnoliaceae*)

'Chapel Hill'	MBlu NLar WPat
chinense 🏆H6	CBcs CDul CMCN EBee EPfP MBlu MPhe SGol WPGP
chinense* × *tulipifera	NOrn WPGP
'Doc Deforce's Delight'	LRHS MBlu MBri NLar
tulipifera 🏆H6	Widely available
- 'Ardis'	NLar
- 'Aureomarginatum' (v) 🏆H6	Widely available
- 'Fastigiatum'	CDoC CDul CLnd CMCN CTho EBee ECrN ELan EPfP MAsh MBlu MBri MGos NLar SGol SPer WPat
- 'Glen Gold'	MBlu NLar
- 'Heltorf'	NLar
- 'Integrifolium'	NLar
- 'Purgatory'	MBlu
- 'Roodhaan'	ESwi NLar
- 'Rotundiloba'	MBlu
- 'Snow Bird' (v)	EBee WMat

Liriope ✿ (*Asparagaceae*)

'Big Blue'	see *L. muscari* 'Big Blue'
§ ***exiliflora***	CLAP WWEG
- 'Ariaka-janshige' (v)	LRHS WWEG
- Silvery Sunproof misapplied	see *L. spicata* 'Gin-ryu', *L. muscari* 'Variegata'
§ ***gigantea***	CLAP
graminifolia misapplied	see *L. muscari*
hyacinthifolia	see *Reineckea carnea*
'Majestic'	CBct CLAP MHer WHoo
minor	CMac
§ ***muscari*** 🏆H5	Widely available
- B&SWJ 561	WCru
- 'Alba'	see *L. muscari* 'Monroe White'
- Amethyst = 'Liptp'	CBod
§ - 'Big Blue'	Widely available
- 'Christmas Tree'	EBee EPPr WHoo WMoo WWEG
- 'Evergreen Giant'	see *L. gigantea*
- 'Gold-banded' (v)	CBct CLAP EPfP LHop LRHS SCob WHil WWEG
- 'Goldfinger'	CExl EBee SMad WWEG
- 'Ingwersen'	CBod CExl CKno EBee ECho ELon EPPr EPfP EWTr EWoo SCob WWEG XLum
- Isabella = 'Lirf'	EBee EPPr
- 'John Burch' (v)	CBct CExl CLAP ELon LAst NLar SMad WGrn WWEG
- 'Lilac Wonder'	EPPr LRHS SCob
- 'Majestic' misapplied	see *L. exiliflora*
- 'Moneymaker'	EPPr GBin GKev LAst LRHS SCob XEll
§ - 'Monroe White'	CBct CBro CExl CLAP CMac EBee ELan EPfP EShb EWoo LAst LCro LOPS LPfy MJak MRav NBid NLar SCob SPer SPoG SWvt WWEG
- 'Okina' (v)	CDes CDoC CKno EBee ELon GEdr LHop LLHF LRHS MNrw MSCN NGBl NLar NSti SMad SPer WCot
- 'Pee Dee Ingot'	EShb
- 'Purple Passion'	EBee SCob
- 'Royal Purple'	CBct CLAP EAJP EBee ECtt ELon EWoo LRHS NLar SCob SPer WGrn WMoo WWEG
- 'Silver Ribbon'	CBro CLAP EPfP LSRN MGos WWEG
- 'Superba'	WCot
§ - 'Variegata' (v)	CBod CCon CDes CExl CLAP EBee ECho ELan EWes LAst LBMP LEdu LPal LRHS MAvo MJak NBir SPer SPoG SWvt WWEG
- variegated, white-flowered (v)	ECho
- 'Webster Wideleaf'	EBee WCot WWEG
platyphylla	see *L. muscari*
Pure Blonde = 'Lirblonde'	CBct ESwi
spicata	CBod EBee ECho EPPr EWoo GCal LRHS WWEG XLum
- B&SWJ 8821	WCru
- 'Alba'	ECho MRav
§ - 'Gin-ryu' (v)	CBct CExl CLAP CMac EAEE ELan ELon EPPr EPfP EShb EWes LEdu LPal LPot MRav SCob SGol SMad SPer WWEG XLum
- 'Silver Dragon'	see *L. spicata* 'Gin-ryu'
- 'Small Green'	WWEG

Listera (*Orchidaceae*)

ovata	WHer

Lithocarpus ✿ (*Fagaceae*)

densiflorus	CMCN
- var. ***echinoides***	CMCN
edulis	CExl CFil SKHP
§ ***glaber***	CFil

Lithodora (*Boraginaceae*)

§ ***diffusa***	ECho SGol SRot
- 'Alba'	CSma CTri ECho SPer SPoG
- 'Cambridge Blue'	SPer
- 'Compacta'	SRot WAbe
§ - 'Grace Ward' 🏆H5	CBod CWCL ECtt EPfP MHol MMuc NWad
§ - 'Heavenly Blue' 🏆H5	Widely available
- 'Inverleith'	ECho
- 'Pete's Favourite'	ECtt NWad WAbe WRHF
- 'Picos'	CMea ECho EPot NLar NSla NWad SBrt SIgm WAbe WThu
- 'Star' PBR	CHid CMHG ELan ELon EPfP NLar SCoo SPer SPoG SRot SWvt WFar WHil WIce

- 'White Star' WIce
× *intermedia* see *Moltkia* × *intermedia*
§ ***oleifolia*** ♀H4 ECho LLHF LRHS NBir
rosmarinifolia WCFE
zahnii ECho LLHF LRHS SVen
- 'Azure-ness' CPBP MCot SBch SChF WAbe
- compact SIgm

Lithophragma (*Saxifragaceae*)

heterophyllum EBee
parviflorum EWes

Lithospermum (*Boraginaceae*)

diffusum see *Lithodora diffusa*
doerfleri see *Moltkia doerfleri*
'Grace Ward' see *Lithodora diffusa* 'Grace Ward'
'Heavenly Blue' see *Lithodora diffusa* 'Heavenly Blue'
officinale GPoy NMir WHfH
oleifolium see *Lithodora oleifolia*
purpureocaeruleum see *Buglossoides purpurocaerulea*

Litsea (*Lauraceae*)

cubeba FMWJ 13011 WCru
glauca see *Neolitsea sericea*
japonica CBcs SVen

Littonia (*Colchicaceae*)

modesta CPne CRHN ECho

Livistona (*Arecaceae*)

chinensis ♀H1c CPHo LPal SBig SChr
decora LPal LTro
jenkinsiana NLos

Loasa (*Loasaceae*)

acanthifolia **new** GCal
triphylla var. ***volcanica*** EWes WSHC

Lobelia ✿ (*Campanulaceae*)

'Bordervale' **new** WBor
bridgesii CDTJ CExl CFil EWes GCal LRHS WKif WMoo
§ ***cardinalis*** ♀H3 CArn CMac EHon ELon GMaP NGBl NLar NPer SPlb SRms SWat SWvt WBod WFar WHil WMAq
- 'Bee's Flame' CBod CCon CLet CNor CPrp CWGN EAEE ECtt GBuc IKil LRHS MRav MSpe NEgg NGdn SPtp SRkn WWtn
- 'Black Truffle' **new** EBee
§ - 'Elmfeuer' CMHG CWCL ECtt EHoe EWoo IBoy NLar NPri SPlb SPoG SWvt XLum
- subsp. ***graminea*** var. ***multiflora*** CCon
- 'Illumination' ELon
§ - 'Queen Victoria' ♀H3 Widely available
- 'Russian Princess' misapplied CWCL EPfP IBoy LRHS MHol MSCN NGdn SPoG SRkn SWvt WCAu WFar WHar WWEG
chinensis LLWG
'Cinnabar Deep Red' see *L.* × *speciosa* 'Fan Tiefrot'
'Cinnabar Rose' see *L.* × *speciosa* 'Fan Zinnoberrosa'
Compliment Blue see *L.* × *speciosa* 'Kompliment Blau'
Compliment Deep Red see *L.* × *speciosa* 'Kompliment Tiefrot'
Compliment Purple see *L.* × *speciosa* 'Kompliment Purpur'
Compliment Scarlet see *L.* × *speciosa* 'Kompliment Scharlach'
'Compton Pink' CBod EAEE EBee ECtt ELan EShb EWes LBuc MCot SCob
davidii PAB 8547 **new** LEdu
Elizabeth Strangman selection CSpe NDov
erinus Blue Star = 'Wesstar'PBR LSou
- 'Cambridge Blue' **new** LAst
- 'Crystal Palace' LAst NPri
- (Fountain Series) 'Fountain Blue' NPri
- - 'Fountain White' NPri
- Hot Tiger = 'Wesloti'PBR LAst
- 'Kathleen Mallard' (d) SWvt
- Purple Star = 'Wespurstar'PBR LSou
- 'Richardii' see *L. richardsonii* hort.
- Riviera Series NPri
- 'Sapphire' NPri
- 'String of Pearls' LAst
- Super Star = 'Weslosu'PBR (Star Series) LAst LSou
- (Waterfall Series) Waterfall Blue = 'Balobwablu'PBR **new** LBMP
- - Waterfall White Sparkle = 'Balobwaspar' LBMP
- 'White Lady' **new** LAst
excelsa MTPN SBrt
- B&SWJ 9513 WCru
Fan Deep Red see *L.* × *speciosa* 'Fan Tiefrot'
Fan Deep Rose see *L.* × *speciosa* 'Fan Orchidrosa'
Fan Salmon see *L.* × *speciosa* 'Fan Lachs'
'Flamingo' see *L.* × *speciosa* 'Pink Flamingo'
fulgens see *L. cardinalis*
- Saint Elmo's Fire see *L. cardinalis* 'Elmfeuer'
× ***gerardii*** see *L.* × *speciosa*
gibberoa CDTJ
'Gladys Lindley' LRHS
'Hadspen Purple' see *L.* × *speciosa* 'Hadspen Purple'
inflata CArn GPoy
laxiflora CFis CHII WBod
- B&SWJ 9064 WCru
- var. ***angustifolia*** CAby CDTJ CPrp CSam CTre EShb EWld GCal SMHy SRms
linnaeoides SPlb
'Lipstick' WWEG
§ ***montana*** EWld WCot
- B&SWJ 8220 WCru
pedunculata see *Pratia pedunculata*
'Periwinkle Blue' LAst
'Queen Victoria' see *L. cardinalis* 'Queen Victoria'
§ ***richardsonii*** hort. LAst
sessilifolia CExl LLWG
- B&SWJ 8875 WCru
siphilitica Widely available
- 'Alba' CLet CSam EBee EPfP GCal SBch SPoG SRms SWat SWvt WBor WHrl WMoo WShi
- f. ***albiflora*** **new** LEdu
- blue-flowered CSpe NCGa SGSe SWat SWvt
- 'Rosea' MNrw
§ **×** ***speciosa*** IKil SVic SWat WMoo XLum
- 'Butterfly Blue' CNor SGbt SPad
- 'Butterfly Rose' SRot
- 'Cherry Ripe' LLHF
- 'Dark Crusader' CCon EBee ECtt ELan EPfP LRHS SWat WMnd

- Fan Series	MRav
- - 'Fan Blau'	ELan EPfP LPot LRHS MCot MHol SCob SPer
- - 'Fan Burgundy'	EPfP EWoo LRHS MCot MHer MHol NGdn NLar SCob SPer WTor
§ - - 'Fan Lachs'	CBod CWCL EPfP LRHS MHer SPer WTor
§ - - 'Fan Orchidrosa' 🏆^{H5}	EPfP LRHS SGSe SRot
- - 'Fan Scharlach' 🏆^{H5}	EPfP LRHS NLar SPoG SRot SWvt WOut
§ - - 'Fan Tiefrot' 🏆^{H5}	LRHS SRms SWvt WBor WOut
§ - - 'Fan Zinnoberrosa' 🏆^{H5}	SRms SRot SWvt WMoo
- 'Grape Knee-high'	LLHF LSRN WWEG
§ - 'Hadspen Purple'^{PBR}	CAby CBod CMHG CMac CMos CSpe CWGN EBee ECtt ELan EPfP EWTr IPot LHop LOPS LRHS LSRN MBri MCot MRav NCGa NDov SGSe SHar SRms SWat SWvt
- 'Kimbridge Beet'	CMac SGSe
§ - (Kompliment Series) 'Kompliment Blau'	SWvt
§ - - 'Kompliment Purpur'	MMuc MNrw SWvt
§ - - 'Kompliment Scharlach' 🏆^{H5}	CAby CWat EPfP MNrw NPer SWvt
§ - - 'Kompliment Tiefrot'	EPfP MMuc MNrw SWvt
- 'Monet Moment'	EBee ECtt EWes SWvt
- 'Pauline'	ECtt
- 'Pink Elephant' 🏆^{H3}	ECtt GCra SHar WCFE WFar WWEG
§ - 'Pink Flamingo'	ELan MBri SHar SPer WMoo
- 'Red Velvet'	WOut
- 'Ruby Slippers'	EBee ELan EPfP LSRN WWEG
- 'Russian Princess' purple-flowered	CBod CCon CPrp EAEE ECtt EHoe ELan EWoo LAst LHop LSou MBel MBri MCot MHer MPie MSpe NCGa NDov NHol SPer SPtp WFar WMnd
- 'Sparkling Burgundy'	LRHS
- 'Sparkling Ruby'	EPfP IKil LBuc MCot SWvt
- 'Tania'	Widely available
§ - 'Vedrariensis'	CBod CMac CSam CSpe CWib EAJP ECtt ELan EPfP GBuc LCro MBel MCot MHer MMuc MNrw NGBl SEND SPer SRms SWvt WCFE WFar WHoo WMnd XLum
- 'Will Scarlet'	LRHS
spicata	SBrt
'Tania's Sister'	WCot WGrn WOut
treadwellii	see *Pratia angulata* 'Treadwellii'
tupa	Widely available
- JCA 12527	IBlr
- Archibald's form	CExl GCra WPGP
- dark orange-flowered	SGSe
urens	CFil
valida	SWvt
- 'Delft Blue'	EBee
- 'True Blue'	CWGN SWvt
vedrariensis	see *L.* × *speciosa* 'Vedrariensis'
villosa	SGSe
Waterfall Light Lavender = 'Balwalila'^{PBR} (Waterfall Series)	LBMP
wollastonii	SPlb

Lobostemon (*Boraginaceae*)

belliformis new	CTre

Lobularia (*Brassicaceae*)

maritima Easter Bonnet Series	NPri
- 'Snow Crystals'	NPri
Snow Princess = 'Inlbusnopr'^{PBR}	NPri

Loeselia (*Polemoniaceae*)

mexicana	CHII

loganberry see *Rubus* × *loganobaccus*

Lomandra (*Asparagaceae*)

filiformis Savanna Blue = 'Lmf500'	ESwi LSou
hystrix	SPlb
longifolia	ECou GCal LEdu SPlb
- 'Kulnura'	ECou
- Nyalla = 'Lm400'^{PBR}	LHop
- Tanika = 'Lm300'^{PBR}	ESwi

Lomaria see *Blechnum*

Lomatia (*Proteaceae*)

dentata	LRHS MGil MRav
ferruginea	CBcs CDoC CExl CSde CTsd EPfP GGal SKHP WCru WPGP
fraseri	EBee EPfP LRHS SPoG SSpi
hirsuta	MGil SKHP
longifolia	see *L. myricoides*
§ ***myricoides***	CBcs CBct CExl CTsd EBee ELan EPfP IDee LRHS NLar SAko SKHP SLon SPer SSpi
silaifolia	LRHS SPoG
tinctoria	CBcs CDoC CExl CTre EPfP LRHS NLar SSpi WBod

Lomatium (*Apiaceae*)

columbianum	SIgm
grayi	SPhx
utriculatum	SIgm

Lonicera ✿ (*Caprifoliaceae*)

sp.	CMen
KR 291	ELon
KR 10106 new	WPGP
§ ***acuminata***	CCon LRHS
- B&SWJ 3480	WCru
- B&SWJ 6743	CRHN WCru
- B&SWJ 6815	WCru
- var. ***acuminata***	WCot
aff. ***acuminata*** NJM 11.033	WPGP
albertii	CDul EBee EPfP MBNS NLar SEND
alpigena	GJos
alseuosmoides	CBcs CDul CRHN EBee EWTr GBin LEdu LRHS MMuc NLar SEND SKHP SLon SPoG WCru WPGP WSHC
× ***americana*** misapplied	see *L.* × *italica*
§ ***americana*** (Mill.) K. Koch	CBcs CFlo EPfP LEdu MBri MMuc MSwo MWhi NLar NWea SEND SKHP SLim SRms WBor WSHC
§ × ***brownii*** 'Dropmore Scarlet'	Widely available
- 'Fuchsioides' misapplied	see *L.* × *brownii* 'Dropmore Scarlet'
- 'Fuchsioides' K. Koch	WSHC
caerulea	EPom MNHC MRav SCob SPoG SRms SVic WHar
- var. ***altaica***	LEdu
- 'Atut'	NLar
- 'Balalaika'	CAgr
- 'Duet'	NLar

Plant	Suppliers
- var. ***edulis***	CAgr EPfP EWTr LBuc LEdu MCoo MNHC SDea WMat
- - 'Blue Moon'	CAgr
- 'Eisbar'	CAgr
- 'Kalinka'	CAgr
- var. ***kamtschatica***	CAgr EPom LCro LOPS NLar WPGP
- - 'Fialka'PBR	NLar
- - 'Morena'PBR	EPom GGGa
- - 'Nimfa'	GGGa
- 'Kirke'	GBin NLar
* - var. ***longifolia***	NLar
§ ***caprifolium***	CArn CDoC CFlo CRHN ECrN ELan EPfP LRHS NLar SPer WCot
- 'Anna Fletcher'	CRHN LSRN WCFE
- 'Cornish Cream'	SGol
- f. ***pauciflora***	see *L.* × *italica*
- 'Spring Bouquet'	LRHS
Caprilia Ever = 'Inov42'PBR **new**	CKel EBee MJak
'Celestial' **new**	LRHS
chaetocarpa	WSHC
'Clavey's Dwarf'	EPPr GKin LLHF
crassifolia	NLar SBrt WSHC
- 'Little Honey'	EPPr MBNS MMHG MPie MRav NLar WCot
deflexicalyx	EPfP NLar
demissa	EPfP
'Early Cream'	see *L. caprifolium*
'Elegant'	LBuc SCob
elisae	CAbP CBot CMac EBee EPfP EWTr IMou NLar SSta WCot WSHC
etrusca	CCon MRav XSen
- 'Donald Waterer'	CFlo CRHN EPfP LRHS LSRN NLar WFar
- 'Michael Rosse'	CBot ELan IArd MBNS NLar SKHP
- 'Superba' ♀H5	CFlo CRHN EBee ELan EPfP LRHS NLar SEND SLim SPer WSHC
'Fire Cracker'	NLar SLon
flexuosa	see *L. japonica* var. *repens*
fragrantissima	Widely available
giraldii misapplied	see *L. acuminata*
giraldii Rehder	CBot CRHN WSHC
glabrata	NLar SCoo SLim
- B&SWJ 2150	WCru
glaucescens	WPat
'Golden Trumpet'	CWGN EPfP LRHS LSRN
grata	see *L.* × *americana* (Mill.) K. Koch
× ***heckrottii***	CSBt NLar
§ - 'American Beauty'	CKel LCro
- 'Gold Flame' misapplied	see *L.* × *heckrottii* 'American Beauty'
- 'Gold Flame' ambig.	CFlo COtt GKin LSRN NLar SCob
- 'Gold Flame' hort. ♀H5	CDul CMac CWld EBee ELan EPfP LBuc LRHS MAsh MBri MJak MMuc MRav SEND SLim SPer SPoG SRms SWvt WFar WMoo WSHC
hemsleyana **new**	CBot
§ ***henryi***	CBcs CDoC CDul CKel CMac CRHN CWib EPfP EWTr GKin IBoy LAst LCro LHop LRHS LSRN MGos MJak MMuc MSwo MWhi SCob SEND SLim SPer SPlb WFar WMoo WSHC
- B&SWJ 8109	WCru
- 'Copper Beauty'PBR	Widely available
- var. ***subcoriacea***	see *L. henryi*
hildebrandiana ♀H2	CDoC CExl CFil CHll CRHN MOWG NLar SKHP
hispidula	SBrt
'Honey Baby'PBR	ELon EPfP LLHF LRHS NHol NWad
implexa	CMCN
insularis	see *L. morrowii*
involucrata	CExl CHll CMCN CMHG CWib EPPr LHop MBNS MBlu MMuc NChi SEND SPer WCFE
- var. ***ledebourii***	CBcs ELan EPfP LAst LLHF LRHS MGil MMHG MRav NLar SKHP
- - 'Vian'	NLar
- 'Orange Dwarf'	SKHP
§ × ***italica***	CRHN CSam CTri EBee ECrN LRHS MBNS MJak MSwo NPer SCoo SKHP SPer
§ - Harlequin = 'Sherlite'PBR (v)	CKel CMac EHoe EPfP LHop LRHS MJak SLim SPlb SRms SWvt
japonica	CMen IBoy WFar
§ - 'Aureoreticulata' (v) ♀H5	CDul CMac CWib ECrN EHoe ELan EPfP EShb LRHS MGos MJak MRav MWhi NPer SGol SPer SRms WFar
- 'Cream Cascade'	COtt EWoo LRHS MSwo NLar SCoo SGol
- 'Dart's Acumen'	CRHN
- 'Dart's World'	CDoC CKel COtt CWld MBri NLar
- 'Halliana'	Widely available
- 'Hall's Prolific' ♀H5	CDoC CDul CKel CSBt ECrN ELan EPfP EWTr LBMP LBuc LCro LPfy LRHS LSRN MAsh MBlu MBri MGos MRav MSwo SCob SGol SLim SPad SPoG SWvt WFar WHar
§ - 'Horwood Gem' (v)	ECtt NLar SCoo SLim
- 'Maskerade' (v)	LLHF NBro NLar
- 'Mint Crisp'PBR (v)	CDoC CDul CKel CMac COtt CSBt CWGN CWld ECrN ECtt ELan EPfP EShb LAst LRHS LSRN LSou MBlu MBri MGos MJak NLar SGol SLim SLon SPad SPer SPoG SWvt WHar
- 'Peter Adams'	see *L. japonica* 'Horwood Gem'
- 'Princess Kate'	ELan MBri NLar NPri
- 'Red World'	WPat
§ - var. ***repens*** ♀H5	CDul CKel CMac COtt CSBt CTri CWSG ECrN ECtt ELan EPfP LAst LPfy LRHS MBri MRav MSwo NLar SCoo SGol SLim SLon SPad SPer SRms WMoo
- 'Variegata'	see *L. japonica* 'Aureoreticulata'
korolkowii	CBot CFil EPPr MBNS NBir NLar SEND WCFE WSHC
- 'Blue Velvet'	CAgr GBin MCoo NLar
- var. ***zabelii*** misapplied	see *L. tatarica* 'Zabelii'
- var. ***zabelii*** (Rehder) Rehder	ELan
lanceolata BWJ 7935	WCru
'Lemon Beauty' (v)	Widely available
maackii	CBot CHll CMCN EPPr EPfP GJos MRav NLar WCFE
- f. ***podocarpa***	MMuc NLar
* ***macgregorii***	CMCN
macrantha B&SWJ 11687	WCru
- WWJ 11606	WCru
'Mandarin' ♀H5	CDoC CRHN ELan LCro LRHS MBlu MJak NLar SCoo SGol SLim SWvt WPat WSHC
maximowiczii var. ***sachalinensis***	NLar
§ ***morrowii***	CMCN
myrtillus	NLar
nitida	CArg CBar CBcs CCVT CDul CLet CMac CMen COtt CSBt

	CTri ECrN EPfP LAst MMuc NBes NWea SCob SEWo SGol SPer WHar WMat
- 'Baggesen's Gold' 𝕐H5	Widely available
- Edmée Gold = 'Briloni'	MAsh
- 'Ernest Wilson'	EPPr
- 'Fertilis'	SPer
- 'Lemon Queen'	CWib ELan MBri MMuc MSwo SEND
§ - 'Maigrün'	CBar CBcs CCVT CDul EAEE EPfP EShb LRHS MSwo NEoE SCob SHil SPer SWvt WFar
- Maygreen	see *L. nitida* 'Maigrün'
- 'Red Tips'	EHoe EShb GKin NLar SCob SCoo WMoo
- 'Silver Beauty' (v)	CDul CMac CWib ECrN EHoe LAst LHop MGos MSwo SCob SPer SPlb SRms SWvt WFar WMoo
- 'Tidy Tips'	EPPr SCob
- 'Twiggy' (v)	CDoC CSBt EAEE EDAr EHoe EUJe LBuc LHop LRHS MAsh NHol NLar NWad STPC WGrn
periclymenum	CArn CCVT CDul CTri CWld ECrN GJos GPoy MHer MLHP MRav NMir NWea SCob SPlb WPnn WSFF
- 'Belgica' misapplied	see *L.* × *italica*
- 'Belgica'	Widely available
- 'Belgica Select'	EWoo
- Chic et Choc = 'Inov205'	LRHS WCot
- 'Florida'	see *L. periclymenum* 'Serotina'
- 'Fragrant Cloud'	LBuc
- 'Graham Thomas' 𝕐H5	Widely available
- 'Harlequin'	see *L.* × *italica* Harlequin
- 'Heaven Scent'	CFlo LBuc LCro LSRN NLar WFar WPnn
- 'Honeybush'	CDoC CJun CWGN CWld LBMP MAsh MGos NHol NWad SLim WFar WMoo
- 'La Gasnérie'	SLim
- 'Munster'	WSHC
- 'Purple Queen'	CChe
- 'Red Gables'	CRHN ELon LSRN MBNS MBri MGos NLar SCoo SLim SWvt WCot WKif WPat
- 'Scentsation'PBR	CFlo CKel CMac CSBt CWCL CWGN ELan EPfP EUJe LAst LBMP LRHS MAsh MBri NCGa NLar SCoo SLon
- 'Serotina' 𝕐H5	Widely available
- 'Sweet Sue'	CCon CFlo CKel COtt CRHN ELan ELon EPfP EWTr GBin LRHS LSRN MAsh MBNS MBri MGos MSwo NEgg NLar SCoo SPoG SWvt WFar WMoo
pileata	Widely available
- 'Moss Green'	CBod EShb MMuc
- 'Silver Lining' (v)	WCFE
pilosa (Kunth) Willd. ex Kunth	CRHN
- F&M 207	CFil WPGP
- F&M 256	CFil WPGP
prolifera	NLar
× ***purpusii***	CHll CMac CRHN CTri CWib EBee ECrN LSRN MBNS MLHP SCob SPer SRms WCFE WFar WSHC
- 'Spring Romance'	CMac
- 'Winter Beauty' 𝕐H5	Widely available
ramosissima	NLar
reticulata 'Silver'	NLar
saccata	EPfP
sempervirens	CBot CRHN CSBt IDee MBNS MRav WHar WSHC
- 'Cedar Lane'	LRHS
- 'Dropmore Scarlet'	see *L.* × *brownii* 'Dropmore Scarlet'
- 'Leo'	CWGN
- f. ***sulphurea***	WSHC
- - 'John Clayton'	EPfP LRHS SKHP
setifera 'Daphnis'	CJun
similis var. ***delavayi*** 𝕐H5	CBot CFlo CKel COtt CRHN CSde CWGN ELan EPfP LBMP LRHS MAsh MBri MRav NEgg SDix SEND SRms SWvt WCot WCru WSHC
'Simonet'	CWCL NLar
splendida	WSHC
standishii	CTri WFar
- var. ***lancifolia*** 'Budapest'	CBot ELan ELon EPfP LEdu LLHF LRHS MAsh MBlu MRav NLar WFar WPat
subaequalis	CFil CRHN
- Og 93.329	CExl SKHP WPGP WSHC
Sweet Isabel = 'Genbel'PBR	EPfP LRHS
syringantha	CArn CBcs CDoC CRHN CWld ECrN ELan EPfP EWTr IDee LAst LEdu LHop LRHS MMuc MNrw MRav NEgg NEoE NLar SEND SEle SPer WCFE WFar WSHC
- 'Grandiflora'	CBot GQui
tatarica	CBot CHll CMCN CWib MRav
- 'Alba'	CJun EPPr EWTr
- 'Arnold Red'	CBcs ELan EPPr EPfP MBlu MHer NLar SEND
- 'Hack's Red'	CBot CMCN CWib EPPr EPfP EWTr LEdu LHop LRHS SCoo SKHP SPer SPoG SVen SWvt WBor WCot WGrn
- 'Rosea'	EPPr
§ - 'Zabelii'	MNrw
× ***tellmanniana*** 𝕐H5	Widely available
- 'Joan Sayers'	SCoo SLim WCFE
- 'Pharaoh's Trumpet'	LRHS SLon
thibetica	MBlu
tomentella B&SWJ 2654	WCru
tragophylla 𝕐H5	CBot CDoC CKel CSBt ELan EWTr IDee IMou LEdu LRHS LSRN MBNS MMuc MRav NLar SCoo SEND SLim SPer SWvt WPat WSHC
- 'Maurice Foster'	CRHN ELan NLar WSHC
turczaninowii **new**	LLHF
webbiana	ELan
xylosteum	CArn EBtc EPPr NLar SSta

Lophomyrtus ✿ (*Myrtaceae*)

§ ***bullata*** 𝕐H2	CDTJ SPer
- 'Matai Bay'	LRHS
× ***ralphii*** 'Black Pearl'	CMac EShb LRHS MBri MPkF SCoo SEle SHil SLim SPoG SRkn WFar
- 'Kathryn'	CBcs CDoC COtt CSde CTsd ELan LRHS MPkF NLar SPoG SRGP
- 'Krinkly'	SVen
- 'Little Star' (v)	CBcs COtt CSde LRHS SEle WPat
- Logan's form (v)	CBcs EBee LRHS MGil NLar
- 'Magic Dragon'PBR (v)	CDoC EBee LCro LRHS MBri SEle SHil SPoG
- 'Multicolor' (v)	CBcs EPfP LRHS MRav SLim SVen
- 'Pixie'	CBcs COtt CSde LRHS MAsh SEle SLim SPoG SVen WPat
- 'Purpurea'	MPkF
- 'Red Dragon'	CAbP CBcs CMac EHoe LRHS LSou MAsh SLim WFar WPat

- 'Wild Cherry' COtt EBee LRHS

Lophosoria (*Dicksoniaceae*)

quadripinnata CCon CDTJ NLos SBig WPGP

Lophospermum (*Plantaginaceae*)

§ ***erubescens*** ♀H2 CRHN SBch
- 'Bridal Bouquet' CPla
Lofos Summer Cream = 'Sunasashiro' LAst
Lofos Wine Red = 'Sunasaro' LAst
§ 'Magic Dragon' CPla SEND SLim WBor
§ 'Red Dragon' CPla SBch
'Wine Red' EShb LAst

loquat see *Eriobotrya japonica*

Loropetalum (*Hamamelidaceae*)

chinense CWib
- 'Ming Dynasty' CAbP MAsh SSta WFar
- 'Rose Blush' SSpi
- var. ***rubrum*** CExl CWib
- - 'Blush' CBcs SEle SGol
- - 'Burgundy' MPkF
- - 'Daybreak's Flame' CBcs EBee MGil MPkF SGol SSta WCot
- - 'Fire Dance' CAbP CBcs CBct CDoC CExl CLet CSde CTsd CWib ELon EPfP EShb EUJe LCro LPar LPfy LRHS MAsh MGos MPkF SEle SPad SPoG SRkn SSpi SWvt WFar WHlf WPat
- - 'Fire Glow' LRHS MGos SHil
- f. ***rubrum*** 'Pipa's Red' MPkF
- 'Snowdance' CAbP
- 'Tang Dynasty' CBct EBee ESwi WFar

Lotononis (*Papilionaceae*)

galpinii SBrt

Lotus (*Papilionaceae*)

berthelotii CDTJ ECtt EOHP LPot MCot
- deep red-flowered ♀H1c SWvt
berthelotii* × *maculatus ♀H1c MSCN
corniculatus CArn CHab CWld GJos MCoo MHer MMuc MNHC NMir SEND SIde SRms WSFF
formosissimus new EBee
germanicus SPhx
'Gold Flash' LAst
hirsutus ♀H4 CArn CBod CChe CExl CWib ECha EHoe ELan EPfP LBMP LHop LPot MAsh MCot MRav SEND SIgm SLon SPer SPhx SPlb SPoG SRms SWvt WIce XLum XSen
- 'Brimstone' (v) CWib LHop LRHS MRav SPer SPoG SWvt XSen
- Little Boy Blue = 'Lisbob'PBR CLet CSBt EPfP LBMP LRHS SSpi
- 'Lois' LRHS SPoG
jacobaeus LHop MCot
maculatus EOHP MOWG
mearnsii new SPlb
pedunculatus CHab MCoo NMir WSFF
pentaphyllus CArn XSen
tetragonolobus SPhx SVic WSFF

lovage see *Levisticum officinale*

Loxostigma (*Gesneriaceae*)

kurzii GWJ 9342 WCru

Luetkea (*Rosaceae*)

pectinata GEdr

Luffa (*Cucurbitaceae*)

aegyptiaca SVic

Luma ✿ (*Myrtaceae*)

§ ***apiculata*** ♀H4 Widely available
§ - 'Glanleam Gold' (v) Widely available
- 'Nana' LEdu WJek
- 'Penlee' SRms WJek
- 'Rainbow's Gold' (v) EShb
- 'Saint Hilary' (v) CLet EPfP LRHS SRms WJek
- 'Variegata' (v) CTri SLim WFar
§ ***chequen*** CBcs CBod CSde EShb IDee LEdu MHer NLar SRms WJek WPGP

Lunaria (*Brassicaceae*)

§ ***annua*** CWCL EWoo LSun MNHC SIde SWat WCot WSFF
- var. ***albiflora*** ♀H7 NBir SEND SWat WCot WTou
I - - 'Alba Variegata' (v) ♀H7 CSpe MNHC WBor WBrk
- 'Chedglow' CNat LEdu
- 'Corfu Blue' CDes CSpe EBee EWes SPtp WCot WWFP
- 'Cynthia' new CNat
- 'Munstead Purple' ♀H7 CSpe
- 'Nettleton' CNat
- purple-leaved CMea
- purple-spotted new WBor
- 'Ruth' CNat LEdu WCot
- 'Variegata' (v) CNat NBir SWat WCot
biennis see *L. annua*
rediviva ♀H7 CSpe EBee ECGP ECha EPPr GAbr GBin GCal GCra IBlr IFro LEdu LPla LRHS MAvo MMuc MNHC MWat NBid NChi NPer NSti SEND WCAu WCot WFar WHer WHil WPGP
- 'Partway White' CFis CMil WCot

Lunathyrium (*Woodsiaceae*)

petersenii ISha
pycnosorum ISha

Lupinus ✿ (*Papilionaceae*)

albifrons EBee
- var. ***collinus*** SIgm
arboreus ♀H4 Widely available
- blue and white-flowered SCob WFar
- 'Blue Boy' ELan LRHS LSRN SWvt
- blue-flowered CWCL CWld EShb LRHS MCot NLar SPer SPlb SPoG SWvt WBor WFar
- 'Chelsea Blue' EPfP LRHS
- cream-flowered SCob
- 'Snow Queen' CWCL LRHS MGos SPoG SWvt
- 'Sulphur Yellow' SWvt
- white-flowered CSpe CWld EWTr MCot SPlb
- yellow and blue-flowered IBoy NBir SRkn WFar
- yellow-flowered CLet CWld ELan MLHP SWvt WWEG
arcticus EBee
Band of Nobles Series COtt MLHP
'Beefeater' CWCL EBee EWTr GBin LBuc LLHF LRHS MBri SPoG
'Bishop's Tipple' EWes

'Blossom'[PBR]	CWCL CWGN EWTr GBin IPot LLHF LRHS LSRN MBri NPri SPoG
'Camelot Blue'	EPfP
'Cashmere Cream'	CWCL EBee IPot LRHS MBri
'Chameleon'	CWCL LBuc LRHS MBri
chamissonis	CHll CPla CSpe CWCL ELan EWes LHop LRHS NLar SIgm SPer WKif
'Chandelier' (Band of Nobles Series)	Widely available
'Desert Sun'	CWCL ILea LRHS MBri
Dwarf Gallery hybrids	IBoy WRHF
'Dwarf Lulu'	see *L.* 'Lulu'
excubitus subsp. ***austromontanus*** new	SIgm
Gallery Series	CSBt GAbr IBoy SCoo SPlb WFar
- 'Gallery Blue'	ECtt ELan EPfP EShb IBoy LCro LOPS LSRN NLar NPri SCoo SPer SPoG WFar
- 'Gallery Pink'	ELan EPfP EShb IBoy LRHS NLar NPri SCoo SPer SPoG WFar
- 'Gallery Red'	ECtt ELan EPfP EShb IBoy LRHS NLar NPri SCoo SPer SPoG WFar
- 'Gallery Rose'	IBoy LSRN SPoG WFar
- 'Gallery White'	ELan EPfP EShb IBoy LBMP LRHS NLar NPri SCoo SPer SPoG WFar
- 'Gallery Yellow'	ECtt ELan EPfP EShb IBoy LBMP LRHS LSun NLar NPri SPer SPoG WFar
'Gladiator'	CWCL EBee ECtt EWes GBin ILea IPot LLHF LRHS LSou MBri MNrw SPoG
'Heathcliffe Blue'	WOut
'Inspiration'	MBri
'Judy Harper'	ECtt GBin IPot LRHS MAsh
'Jupiter'	CWCL EBee ILea LRHS NLar
'King Canute'	CWCL
latifolius subsp. ***parishii***	EBee
'Le Gentilhomme' (Band of Nobles Series)	MCot
§ 'Lulu'	EPfP IBoy LRHS SGbt SPer SPoG SWvt WHar
'Manhattan Lights'[PBR]	CWCL CWGN EWes EWoo GBin ILea IPot LLHF LRHS MBri NLar NPri SPoG
'Masterpiece'[PBR]	CWCL EWTr EWoo GBin ILea IPot LCro LLHF LRHS LSou MBri MCot SPoG
Minarette Group	CTri LRHS MAsh MNrw SRms
montanus	CHid
'Morello Cherry'	CWCL GJos SHar
mutabilis	LPfy
'My Castle' (Band of Nobles Series)	CBcs COtt CSBt CTri ECtt ELan EPfP GMaP IBoy LCro LRHS LSRN MBri MGos MJak MWat NGBl NLar NPri SGbt SHil SPer SPoG SWvt WFar WHar WHil WMoo
'Neptune'	CWCL
'Noble Maiden' (Band of Nobles Series)	Widely available
nootkatensis	GLog WThu
'Pam Ayres'	ECtt ELan GBin IPot LRHS
perennis	MMuc
'Persian Slipper'[PBR]	CWCL CWGN ECtt EWes EWoo GBin ILea IPot LBuc LLHF LOPS LRHS LSRN MBri MCot NPri SPoG
'Polar Princess'	CWCL ECtt ELan EWTr EWes GBin IPot LRHS MBri NPri NSti SWat
polyphyllus var. ***burkei***	EBee
'Purple Emperor'	EBee LRHS
'Purple Swirl'	CWCL ECtt LRHS MBri
'Rachel de Thame'	CWCL LRHS
'Red Arrow'	CWCL
'Red Rum'[PBR]	CWCL CWGN EWTr EWoo GBin ILea LBuc LCro LRHS LSRN MBri MNrw NLar NPri SPoG
'Rote Flamme'	ELon EWes LBMP SCob
Russell hybrids	CSBt EPfP IBoy LAst MHer MMuc SPlb SRms SVic SWvt WFar
'Saffron'[PBR]	CWCL EWoo GBin LBuc LRHS LSRN MBri NPri SPoG
'Salmon Star'[PBR]	CWCL GBin LRHS MBri MNrw NLar SPoG
'Sand Pink'	EWes
sericatus	EBee
'Silver Fleece'	CHid MMuc
'Tequila Flame'	CWCL GBin ILea LBuc LLHF LRHS LSou MBri SPoG
'Terracotta'	CWCL GBin ILea IPot LRHS LSou
texensis	CSpe
'The Chatelaine' (Band of Nobles Series)	Widely available
'The Governor' (Band of Nobles Series)	Widely available
'The Page' (Band of Nobles Series)	CAby CBcs CBod COtt CWld EAJP ELan ELon EPfP EWoo IBoy LCro LOPS LRHS LSRN MBri MCot MNHC MWat NLar NPri SCob SPer SPoG SWvt WFar WHar WMoo
'Thundercloud'	CDes EBee
'Towering Inferno'	CWCL ECtt EWes GBin LBuc LRHS MBri NLar NPri SPoG
'Tutti Frutti'	GJos IBoy WHar
variicolor	SIgm SMHy
Woodfield hybrids	COtt GAbr LRHS

Luzula (*Juncaceae*)

alpinopilosa	EPPr GBin
× ***borreri***	EPPr
- 'Botany Bay' (v)	GBin
'Engel'	EPPr EWes
forsteri	IMou
luzuloides 'Schneehäschen'	GBin WSHC
maxima	see *L. sylvatica*
nivalis	GAbr
nivea	Widely available
pedemontana	SMea
pilosa	GCal
- 'Grünfink' new	EBee
- 'Igel'	CKno LEdu NBid NDov SCob SMad
purpureosplendens	LEdu NOak
§ ***sylvatica***	ELan EPPr EWoo LPal LRHS MMuc MRav NBro NLar NMir SCob SEND SPer WHer WShi WWEG XLum
- from Tatra Mountains, Slovakia	EPPr
- 'A. Rutherford'	see *L. sylvatica* 'Taggart's Cream'
- 'Aurea'	CBot CKno ECha ELon EPPr EWoo LRHS MJak MMuc MRav NBid NOak NSti NWsh SEND SGSe WCot WFar WGrn WMoo WPat WPtf
- 'Aureomarginata'	see *L. sylvatica* 'Marginata'
I - 'Auslese'	EPPr EPfP WMoo
- 'Bromel'	EPPr SGSe
- 'Hohe Tatra'	CBod CSpe EHoe EPPr EWes GMaP LEdu MBNS MWhi NGdn NOak SCob SPoG WWEG

§ - 'Marginata' (v)	CBod CKno EBee ECha EHoe ELon EPPr EWoo GMaP LRHS LSun MBNS MMuc MRav MWhi NBid NGdn NLar NSti NWad SCob SEND SGSe WCot WHoo WMoo WWEG XLum
- 'Mariusz'	EPPr
* - f. ***nova***	ELon EPPr
- 'Solar Flair'	MWhi
- 'Starmaker'	CBod
§ - 'Taggart's Cream' (v)	EHoe GCal LRHS NBid NHol NWad WMoo WWEG
- 'Tauernpass'	EPPr GCal
- 'Thierry's Cream' (v)	WCot
- 'Wäldler'	EPPr
ulophylla	ECou GCrg GEdr WAbe WThu

Luzuriaga (*Luzuriagaceae*)

polyphylla	CTal
- HCM 98202	WCru
radicans	ECou GEdr IMou WCru WSHC
- RH 0602	WCru

Lychnis (*Caryophyllaceae*)

alpina	CMac ECho EDAr ITim MHtn NGdn NPri WFar XLum
- 'Alba'	GKev
- compact	ITim
- 'Rosea'	NBir
- 'Snow Flurry'	EDAr
§ × ***arkwrightii***	ECha ELan LRHS
- 'Orange Zwerg'	ELon SGbt
- Scarlet O'Hara = 'Pmoore05' **new**	SLon SPoG
- 'Vesuvius'	CBcs CMac EAEE EBee ELon NBir SDix SPer SRms WGwG WMnd XLum
chalcedonica 🏆[H7]	Widely available
- var. ***albiflora***	EPfP MBel NBro WCAu WHrl WMoo
- - 'Snow White'	SGSe
- 'Carnea'	EBee LRHS MBNS NGdn SPhx
- 'Dusky Salmon'	WOut
- 'Flore Pleno' (d)	EShb GCal NChi WCot
- 'Morgenrot'	MBel
- 'Pinkie'	NFav NLar NWad SGSe
- 'Rauhreif'	NLar SPhx
- 'Rosea'	EPfP NBir WHrl WMoo
* - 'Salmonea'	EPPr NBir SRms
cognata	CTal GEdr IMou
- B&SWJ 4234	WCru
§ ***coronaria*** 🏆[H7]	Widely available
- MESE 356	MAvo SPhx
- 'Abbotswood Rose'	see *L.* × *walkeri* 'Abbotswood Rose'
- 'Alba' 🏆[H7]	Widely available
- 'Angel's Blush'	NBir NLar SPav SRkn
- Atrosanguinea Group	CBod CBre EPfP GMaP IBlr LRHS MBel MHol MRav MSpe NEgg NGdn NPri NSti NWad SPer WCAu
- 'Blood Red'	CSpe EBee LRHS
- 'Cerise'	MArl NBir
- Gardeners' World = 'Blych' (d)	CBod CDes CSpe EBee ECtt ELon EWes GBin IKil LOPS LRHS LSou LSun MBNS MBel MHol MPie NSti SPer WBrk WCot
- Oculata Group	CBod CSpe CTsd EBee ECGP ELan EPfP LEdu LPot SPav SPlb WFar WKif WMoo
coronata	CTsd
§ - var. ***sieboldii***	SBrt SPhx
dioica	see *Silene dioica*
flos-cuculi	CArn CBod CHab CSam CWat CWld ECho EHon GJos GKev LEdu LLWG LRHS MHer MMuc MNHC MWLS NLar NMir SEND SPhx SRms WFar WHer WMAq WMoo WOut WPnP WSFF XLum
- var. ***albiflora***	CBre CElw CSam CWld EWoo MSKA NBro NLar WHer WMnd WMoo
- var. ***congesta***	WAbe
- Jenny = 'Lychjen'[PBR] (d)	CChe EBee ECtt ELan GBin GQue LBMP LBrs LEdu LLWG LRHS LSun MBNS MBel MHol MNrw MPie NSti SCob SMad SPad SPoG SRkn WBor WCot WGrn WHer WMnd
- 'Little Robin'	LLWG
- 'Nana'	ECho MHer NGdn NLar WTor
- 'White Robin'	Widely available
flos-jovis 🏆[H5]	ECha EPfP GJos LRHS NBir SGSe SRms WMoo XLum
- 'Hort's Variety'	EBee LRHS NBir NSti
- 'Minor'	see *L. flos-jovis* 'Nana'
§ - 'Nana'	MSCN SBch WAbe
- 'Peggy'	EBee LRHS NBre NGdn NLar
× ***haageana***	SRms
- 'Lumina Bronze Leaf Red'	LRHS
'Hill Grounds'	CDes CElw EBee ECtt WCot WSHC
miqueliana	WMoo
'Molten Lava'	ELan EPfP LRHS SGSe WHar
sieboldii 'Matsu Moto'	SGSe
§ ***viscaria***	CArn CWld ECha GCra GJos WFar WMoo
- 'Alba'	ECha NBre NBro XLum
- ***alpina***	see *L. viscaria*
§ - subsp. ***atropurpurea***	CFis EAJP EWes LRHS LSou MPie SRms WHrl WPtf
- 'Feuer'	EBee EWes GJos NGBl NLar SPhx WMoo WTcb
- 'Firebird'	EWes
- 'Plena' (d)	NBir SRkn
- 'Schnee'	GJos NLar
- 'Snowbird'	CTsd
- 'Splendens'	LPot WFar XLum
- 'Splendens Plena' (d) 🏆[H5]	XLum
§ × ***walkeri*** 'Abbotswood Rose' 🏆[H7]	IBlr
wilfordii	SHar
§ ***yunnanensis***	EBee NBid SGSe SPhx XLum
- ***alba***	see *L. yunnanensis*

Lycianthes (*Solanaceae*)

biflora FMWJ 13059	WCru
§ ***rantonnetii*** 🏆[H1c]	CHll ELan EPfP EUJe MOWG SEND SPoG WBor
- 'Variegata' (v)	CHll MSCN WCot

Lycium (*Solanaceae*)

afrum	SVen
barbarum	CAgr CBcs EPom LCro LEdu LOPS LRHS MCoo MJak MMuc NLar SBmr SCob SDea SEND SPre SVic SWvt WHar
- 'Big Lifeberry'	CAgr LEdu MCoo
- 'Number 1 Lifeberry'	CAgr
- 'Sweet Lifeberry'	CAgr LEdu
chinense	IBoy NQui

Lycopodium (*Lycopodiaceae*)

clavatum	GPoy

Lycopsis see *Anchusa*

Lycopus (*Lamiaceae*)

americanus	CArn
europaeus	CArn CHab CLau EBee GPoy LLWG MMuc WGwG

Lycoris (*Amaryllidaceae*)

albiflora	NRog
aurea	CCon CTsd ECho ERCP GKev LAma NRog SDeJ
caldwellii	NRog
chinensis	NRog
haywardii	NRog
houdyshelii	NRog
longituba	NRog
radiata	CCon CTsd ECho GKev LAma SDeJ
rosea	NRog
sanguinea	NRog
sprengeri	NRog

Lygeum (*Poaceae*)

spartum	XSen

Lygodium (*Lygodiaceae*)

japonicum	ISha WFib

Lygos see *Retama*

Lymania (*Bromeliaceae*)

smithii **new**	LAir

Lyonia (*Ericaceae*)

mariana	NLar
ovalifolia	CPne
villosa	CPne

Lyonothamnus (*Rosaceae*)

floribundus subsp. ***aspleniifolius***	CExl EBee EUJe WPGP

Lysichiton (*Araceae*)

sp.	GGal
americanus	Widely available
camtschatcensis ♀H7	CBcs CBen CBod CFwr CLAP CTsd CWat ECha EHon EPfP EUJe GBin GBuc LLWG LRHS NPer SMad SPer SSpi SWat SWvt WPnP WShi XLum
× ***hortensis***	ECha

Lysiloma (*Mimosaceae*)

watsonii	SPlb

Lysimachia (*Primulaceae*)

albescens	CExl GEdr SPad XLum
§ ***atropurpurea***	CSpe EAJP EBee ELan EPfP EShb GEdr GJos LRHS SPer WMnd
- 'Beaujolais'	CExl GJos IBoy LCro LPot LRHS LSRN MHol MNHC SCob SPer SPoG
- 'Geronimo'	CSpe
barystachys ♀H7	CPrp CSam LPla MBel MRav SHar WCot WFar XLum
- 'Huntingbrook'	CDes MAvo WPGP WWtn
Candela = 'Innlyscand'	CMos CSpe ECtt GBin LRHS LSou MHol MMuc NPri SPoG WCot WHil WMoo WTor
candida	WCot
ciliata	CMHG CMac ECha EHoe ELan GMaP LRHS MNrw NBir NGdn NLar SWat WWtn
§ - 'Firecracker' ♀H7	Widely available
- 'Purpurea'	see *L. ciliata* 'Firecracker'
clethroides ♀H7	Widely available
- 'Geisha' (v)	EBee WCot
- 'Lady Jane'	CLet MAvo MNrw SRms
- 'Leigong Storm' **new**	WPGP
§ ***congestiflora***	NPer
- 'Golden Falls'	CTsd
- 'Midnight Sun'PBR	ECtt LAst
- 'Outback Sunset'PBR (v)	ECtt LAst
- 'Persian Carpet'	WCot
- 'Persian Chocolate'	WCot WFar
'Elisabeth'PBR **new**	EBee WBod
ephemerum ♀H6	Widely available
fortunei	EBee XEll XLum
lichiangensis	CExl EBee GKev IMou LRHS NBir WMoo
lyssii	see *L. congestiflora*
minoricensis	SWat XLum
nemorum	CWld IMou
- 'Lola Playle'PBR	WCot
- 'Pale Star'	CBre EBee
nummularia	CSBt CTri CWat EHon EPfP GPoy MMuc MWLS NBir SGol SWat WBrk WHfH
- 'Aurea' ♀H5	Widely available
paridiformis var. ***stenophylla***	CExl
- - DJHC 704	EBee
punctata misapplied	see *L. verticillaris*
punctata L.	CSBt ECha EHon EPfP GMaP MHer MMuc MRav NBro NMir NPer SCob SEND SPer SPlb SRms SWat WBrk WCAu WFar WMAq WMoo
§ - 'Alexander' (v)	Widely available
- 'Gaulthier Brousse'	MHCG WCot WWEG
- Golden Alexander = 'Walgoldalex'PBR (v)	CChe CExl CLet ELon LBMP LRHS MBNS MBel MMuc NHol NLar NPri SHil SPoG WMoo
- 'Golden Glory' (v)	WCot
- 'Hometown Hero'	EBee
- 'Ivy Maclean' (v)	SWvt WWEG
- 'Variegata'	see *L. punctata* 'Alexander'
- ***verticillata***	see *L. verticillaris*
'Purpurea'	see *L. atropurpurea*
pyramidalis	WWEG
Snow Candles = 'L9902'	EBee
thyrsiflora	CWat EBee EHon EWay NPer SWat WCot WMAq
§ ***verticillaris***	CTri WCot
vulgaris	CArn CHab LLWG MSKA WMoo
- subsp. ***davurica***	WCot
- - B&SWJ 8632	WCru

Lysionotus (*Gesneriaceae*)

gamosepalus B&SWJ 7241	WCru
kwangsiensis HWJ 625 **new**	WCru
'Lavender Lady'	EBee NCGa
pauciflorus	CDes WAbe
- B&SWJ 303	WCru
- B&SWJ 335	WCru
- HWJ 643 from Vietnam **new**	WCru
- HWJ 811 from Vietnam	WCru
- dwarf B&SWJ 189	WCru
serratus HWJK 2426	WCru

Lythrum (*Lythraceae*)

alatum	NDov
anceps	NBre NLar
'Rose Dream'	NWad
salicaria	CArn CBen CHab CKno CWat CWld EHon ENfk GAbr GJos MCot MHer MLHP MMuc MNHC MWLS MWts NBro SEND SPlb SRms SWat WBrk WHer WMoo WPnP WSFF WShi XLum
- 'Augenweide'	XLum
- 'Blush' ♀H7	Widely available
§ - 'Feuerkerze' ♀H7	CAby CBod CMea EBee ECtt ELan ELon EPfP GBin LAst LBMP LHop LRHS LSou MBel MBri MCot MRav MSpe MWts NBir NEgg NHol NSti SCob SPer WFar WHil WWEG WWtn
- Firecandle	see *L. salicaria* 'Feuerkerze'
- 'Happy'	ELon
- 'Lady Sackville'	EBee ECtt ELon EPPr EWTr GMaP IKil IPot MCot MTis NLar WSHC WWEG
- 'Little Robert'	ECtt IBoy LBMP
- 'Morden Pink'	CBod EBee MMuc NLar SEND SPhx
- 'Prichard's Variety'	EBee WPGP
- 'Red Beauty'	LSun
- 'Robert'	Widely available
- 'Robin'	CBod ECtt GJos LLHF LRHS MBri MHol SGbt SRot SWvt
- 'Rose'	ELan NBir SWvt
- 'Swirl'	ECtt EPfP IKil LLWG MTis NLar SHar WHoo
- 'The Beacon'	EBee NLar SGSe SPad SRms
- Ulverscroft form	WHil
- 'Zigeunerblut'	CElw CKno CMHG ELon EPPr GQue MRav NLar SWat WHil
virgatum	CMHG NDov SMHy SPhx WCFE WMoo WOut WSHC
- 'Dropmore Purple'	Widely available
- 'Helene'	IMou NDov
- 'Rose Queen'	ECtt MRav SMHy
- 'Rosy Gem'	COtt EBee EPfP GJos GMaP IBoy LAst LRHS NBro SGSe SRms SWvt WHar WWEG
- 'The Rocket'	CAby CBod CSam CTri EPPr EPfP EShb GBee GQue LAst LRHS MPie MRav NBro NDov SPer SWvt WFar WPnP

Lytocaryum (*Arecaceae*)

§ ***weddellianum*** ♀H1b	LPal

M

Maackia (*Papilionaceae*)

amurensis	CBcs CDul CHGN CMCN ELan EPfP IDee IVic LRHS NLar
hupehensis	MBlu NLar

mace, English see *Achillea ageratum*

Macfadyena (*Bignoniaceae*)

uncata	MOWG
§ ***unguis-cati*** ♀H2	CRHN

Machaerina (*Cyperaceae*)

rubiginosa 'Variegata' (v)	EWay LLWG

Machilus see *Persea*

Mackaya (*Acanthaceae*)

§ ***bella*** ♀H1b	CHII EShb

Macleaya (*Papaveraceae*)

cordata misapplied	see *M.* × *kewensis*
§ ***cordata*** (Willd.) R. Br. ♀H6	EBee LHop LRHS LSun MBri MHol NBir SEND SPer SPlb SRms WCot WMoo XLum
§ × ***kewensis***	EBee SCob
- 'Flamingo' ♀H6	CExl CMos EBee ECha ECtt GBuc GQue LRHS MBNS MPie SWvt WHoo WWtn
§ ***microcarpa***	MHol SWat WWEG
- 'Kelway's Coral Plume' ♀H6	CBcs CBod CExl CMac EBee ECtt ELan EPfP EWoo GMaP LCro LPal LRHS LSRN MAvo MLHP MRav NBid NBro NEgg NLar NPri SDix SPer SPoG SWvt WBor WCot WMnd WWtn
- 'Spetchley Ruby'	CExl EBee MRav SPhx WCot WWEG XLum

Maclura (*Moraceae*)

pomifera	CArn CBcs CMCN IDee IVic LEdu MBlu SPlb
- 'Naughty Boy'	NLar
- 'Pretty Woman'	NLar
tricuspidata B&SWJ 12755	WCru

Macrodiervilla see *Weigela*

Macropiper (*Piperaceae*)

§ ***excelsum***	ECou

Macrozamia (*Zamiaceae*)

communis	CBrP LPal
dyeri	see *M. riedlei*
lucida	CBrP
moorei	CBrP
§ ***riedlei***	CBrP

Maddenia (*Rosaceae*)

hypoleuca	NLar

Maesa (*Primulaceae*)

japonica	CExl CTsd
- CWJ 12371	WCru
montana	CExl

Magnolia ✿ (*Magnoliaceae*)

acuminata	CBcs CMCN
- 'Blue Opal'	CBcs CJun
* - 'Kinju'	CJun MBri NLar
- 'Koban Dori'	CBcs CJun
- 'Moegi Dori'	NLar
- 'Patriot'	CMCN SKHP
- 'Patriot' × (× ***brooklynensis*** 'Yellow Bird')	IDee MAsh
- 'Seiju'	CJun
§ - var. ***subcordata***	NLar
- - 'Miss Honeybee'	CBcs CJun
- - 'Mister Yellowjacket'	CJun
- - 'Pierce's Park' **new**	SAko

acuminata × 'Elizabeth'	ERea
'Advance'	CBcs CJun NLar
'Albatross'	CBcs ERea WPGP
'Alex'	CJun
'Alixeed'	CJun
'Amber'	CJun
'Ambrosia'	CJun
amoena	CBcs CTho
- 'Multiogeca'	CWib
'Angelica'	CJun
'Anilou'	CJun
'Ann'	CExl
'Anna'	CJun
'Anne Rosse'	SAko SKHP WPGP
'Anticipation'	CJun CMHG SAko WPGP
'Apollo'	CBcs CDoC CJun IVic LSRN SAko SKHP WPGP
'Apricot Brandy'	LRHS NLar
'Archangel'	CJun
ashei	see *M. macrophylla* subsp. *ashei*
'Asian Artistry'	CJun
'Athene' ♀H5	CBcs CDoC CJun CMHG IVic SAko WPGP
'Atlas'	CBcs CDoC CJun CTho ERea SAko WPGP
'Aurora'	CBcs CDoC CJun
'Banana Split'	CJun LMil LRHS MAsh NLar
'Betty'	CBcs CDoC CDul CMac ELon EPfP EShb IDee LRHS LSRN LSou MBlu MGos MMuc NLar NPla SKHP SLim SSta
'Big Dude'	CBcs CJun EPfP ERea LRHS LSRN SAko SCob
biondii	CLnd IDee IMou LSRN NLar
'Black Beauty'	CBcs CJun LRHS WHor
'Black Swan' **new**	WPGP
Black Tulip = 'Jurmag1' PBR	CBcs CDoC ELan EPfP ERea IVic LBuc LCro LRHS MAsh MBri MGos NLar SCoo SKHP SLon WHor WPGP
'Blackbird' **new**	LRHS
'Blushing Belle'	CJun SAko
'Brenda'	CJun
'Brixton Belle'	WPGP
× ***brooklynensis*** 'Evamaria'	CTho LRHS NLar
- 'Golden Joy'	CDoC CJun LRHS MPkF
- 'Hattie Carthan'	CBcs CJun
- 'Woodsman'	CBcs MBri NLar WMat
- 'Yellow Bird'	CBcs CDoC CDul CJun CMCN CMHG CTho EPfP ERea IArd LMil LPar LRHS LSRN MAsh MBlu MBri MGos NLar NOrn SCob SHil SKHP SPoG WMat
'Burgundy Star' **new**	ERea
'Butterbowl'	CJun
'Butterflies'	CBcs CDoC CDul CJun CTho CTsd ELan ELon EPfP GBin LRHS LSRN MBlu MBri MGos NLar SAko SGol SKHP SSta WFar WMat
'Caerhays Belle' ♀H5	CBcs CJun IVic NLar SAko SKHP WPGP
'Caerhays Surprise' ♀H5	CBcs CJun LRHS SKHP WPGP
campbellii	CMCN ELan EPfP LRHS SKHP
- Alba Group	CBcs WPGP
- - 'Chyverton'	WPGP
- - 'Sir Harold Hillier'	CJun WPGP
- - 'Strybing White'	WPGP
- 'Ambrose Congreve'	WPGP
- 'Betty Jessel'	CBcs CJun CMHG WPGP
- 'Darjeeling' ♀H4	CBcs CJun IVic LRHS SKHP WPGP
- 'John Gallagher'	SKHP
- 'Lamellan Pink'	CTho SAko
- 'Lamellan White'	CTho
- 'Lionel de Rothschild' **new**	WPGP
- subsp. ***mollicomata***	EPfP SAko
- - 'Lanarth'	CBcs CJun WPGP
- - 'Peter Borlase'	WPGP
- 'Queen Caroline'	WPGP
- (Raffillii Group) 'Charles Raffill' ♀H4	CBcs CDul CTho ELan EPfP IDee IMou LRHS MGos SAko WHor WPGP
- - 'Kew's Surprise'	CBcs CJun WPGP
- 'Sidbury'	CBcs MBri WHor
campbellii × ***sprengeri***	WPGP
'Candy Cane'	CJun ERea
'Carlos'	CBcs CJun
cathcartii B&SWJ 11802	WCru
- HWJ 874	WCru
cavaleriei var. ***platypetala***	CBcs CExl
Chameleon	see *M.* 'Chang Hua'
§ 'Chang Hua'	CJun
chapensis	CBcs SKHP
'Charles Coates'	CJun EPfP NLar SAko WPGP
chevalieri B&SWJ 11802	WCru
- DJHV 06037	WCru
- HWJ 621	WCru
China Town = 'Jing Ning'	CJun
'Columnar Pink'	NLar
compressa	CBcs
'Coral Lake'	CJun SKHP
cordata	see *M. acuminata* var. *subcordata*
'Cornish Chough' **new**	WPGP
crassifolia	see *M. fansipanensis*
'Crystal Chalice'	CJun
'Cup Cake'	CJun
'Curlew' **new**	WPGP
'Curly Locks'	CJun
cylindrica misapplied	see *M.* 'Pegasus'
cylindrica ambig.	CBcs CMCN LRHS
cylindrica E.H.Wilson	EPfP
- 'Bjuv'	CJun
'Daphne' ♀H6	CBcs CJun CMHG EPfP ERea IVic LMil LRHS LSRN MAsh MBri NLar SAko SCob SKHP SPoG WPGP
'Darrell Dean'	CJun ERea
'David Clulow' ♀H5	CBcs CJun ERea LRHS SAko SKHP WPGP
dawsoniana	CBcs CTho EPfP IDee IMou
- 'Barbara Cook'	CJun SAko
- 'Chyverton Red'	CBcs WPGP
- 'Clarke'	SAko
- 'Valley Splendour'	CJun
'Daybreak' ♀H6	CBcs CJun ERea LRHS MBlu MBri MRav SGol SSta WMat WPGP
dealbata	see *M. macrophylla* subsp. *dealbata*
'Deborah'	CJun
decidua	CBcs SKHP
delavayi	CBcs CBrP CDul CFil CMCN EBee EPfP EUJe LRHS SBig WPGP
'Delia Williams' **new**	WPGP
§ ***denudata*** ♀H6	CBcs CMCN CTho CWib EPfP LMil LRHS MBlu MGos SEWo
- 'Double Diamond'	CBcs CJun
- 'Forrest's Pink'	CBcs LRHS
- Fragrant Cloud = 'Dan Xin'	CBcs CJun CWib WHar
- 'Gere'	CBcs CJun
- 'Ghost Ship'	CJun

	- late-flowered	see *M. denudata* 'Sleeping Beauty'
§	- 'Sleeping Beauty'	ERea
	- Yellow River = 'Fei Huang'	CBcs CDoC CJun CWib LCro MJak WHor WMat
	doltsopa	CBcs CExl SKHP SSta WPGP
	- NJM 12.028 **new**	WPGP
	- NJM 12.047 **new**	WPGP
	- 'Silver Cloud'	CBcs CExl
	'Early Rose'	CJun GGGa
	'Eleanor May'	CJun
	'Elegance'	CJun
	'Elisa Odenwald'	CJun
	'Elizabeth' ♀H6	CBcs CDoC CJun CMCN CTho ELan EPfP ERea GGGa IArd LCro LMil LPar LRHS LSRN MAsh MBlu MBri MGos NLar SKHP SPoG SWvt WMat
§	***ernestii***	CExl NLar WPGP
	'Eskimo'	CJun SKHP SSpi
	'Eternal Flames'	NLar
	'F.J. Williams'	CBcs WPGP
	Fairy Blush = 'Micjur01'	EPfP LCro LRHS
§	***fansipanensis*** FMWJ 13163 **new**	WCru
	'Felicity'	CJun
	Felix Jury = 'Jurmag2'PBR ♀H4	CBcs ELan EPfP ERea LRHS SAko SPoG
	figo	CBcs CDoC CExl CFil EBee ELan EPfP EShb LRHS SKHP SSta WBod WPGP
	figo × laevifolia	SKHP
	'Fireglow'	CJun CTho
	'Flamingo'	CJun
	floribunda NJM 09.179	WPGP
	- WWJ 11874	WCru
	- WWJ 11996	WCru
	- WWJ 12003	WCru
	- WWJ 12011	WCru
	- 'Furry Uok' **new**	WPGP
	- aff. var. ***tonkinensis*** DJHV06 105	WCru
	fordiana	CExl
§	***foveolata***	CWib
	- B&SWJ 11749	WCru
	- WWJ 11929	WCru
	- WWJ 11955	WCru
	'Frank Gladney'	CJun CTho
	'Frank's Masterpiece'	CJun ERea IArd SAko SKHP
	fraseri	SKHP
	- var. ***pyramidata***	SKHP
	'Galaxy' ♀H6	CBcs CDoC CDul CJun CMHG CMac ELon EPfP ERea GGGa IArd IDee LMil LRHS MAsh MBri MGos MMuc NLar NOrn SAko SEWo SLim SPoG SSta WMat
	garrettii	CPne
	'Genie'PBR	CBcs CDoC LRHS NLar SCob WPGP
	'George Henry Kern' ♀H6	CBcs CBot CDoC CDul CLnd CTho EPfP IArd LRHS MBri MGos MJak MMuc NEgg NLar NPri SEND SHil
	'Gladys Carlson'	CJun
	globosa	CBcs CExl
	- from Yunnan, China **new**	GCal
	'Gold Crown'	CBcs CJun LRHS
	'Gold Cup'	LRHS
	'Gold Star' ♀H6	CBcs CDoC CDul CJun CMHG CTho EBee EPfP LMil LRHS MGos NLar SAko SKHP SPoG WMat WPGP
	'Golden Endeavour'	CBcs CJun
	'Golden Gala'	CJun
	'Golden Gift'	CJun LRHS MAsh SSpi WPGP
	'Golden Pond'	CJun
	'Golden Rain'	CJun
	'Golden Sun'	CBcs CJun IArd
	'Goldfinch'	CJun
I	× ***gotoburgensis*** Chollipo clone	WPGP
I	- clone 2	CJun
	grandiflora	CMCN CWib EBee EPfP ESwi ETod LCro LEdu LPar LSRN MGos MMuc MRav NEgg NLar NOrn SCob SEWo
	- 'Blanchard'	CBcs CJun EUJe LRHS NLar
	- 'Bracken's Brown Beauty'	CMCN
	- 'Charles Dickens'	CJun
	- 'Edith Bogue'	CBcs CJun EUJe LRHS NEgg NLar
	- 'Exmouth'	Widely available
	- 'Ferruginea'	CBcs CDoC CJun EPfP NLar SGol
	- 'Flore Pleno' (d)	SGol
	- 'François Treyve'	CDoC EPfP LRHS LSRN
	- 'Galissonnière'	CBcs CCVT EPfP ERea ETod LPal LRHS MGos SCob SEND SGol SKHP SSpi SWvt WPGP
I	- 'Galissonnière Nana'	LPal
	- 'Goliath'	CBcs CBot CDul ECrN ELan EPfP LRHS SEWo SKHP SPer SSpi WPGP
	- 'Harold Poole'	CJun
	- 'Kay Parris' ♀H5	CJun EPfP LMil LRHS SKHP SPoG SSpi
	- 'Little Gem'	CBcs CDoC CJun ELan EPfP EUJe LCro LOPS LRHS SGol SSpi
	- 'Mainstreet'	CJun LRHS
	- 'Monlia'	CJun
	- 'Nannetensis'	CJun LRHS MBri
	- 'Overton'	CJun
	- 'Russet'	CJun
	- 'Saint Mary'	CJun
	- 'Samuel Sommer'	CJun SSpi
	- 'Symmes Select'	CJun
	- 'Treyvei'	CJun
	- 'Victoria' ♀H5	CDoC CDul CJun CTho ELan ELon EPfP LMil LRHS LSRN MAsh MBlu MGos NLar SPer SPoG SReu SSpi SSta WPGP
	'Green Bee'	CBcs CJun LRHS
	'Hawk'	WPGP
	'Heaven Scent' ♀H5	Widely available
	'Helen Fogg'	CJun
	heptapeta	see *M. denudata*
	'Honey Flower'	CJun
	'Honey Liz'	CBcs LMil LRHS SKHP
	'Honey Tulip' **new**	CBcs
§	'Hong Yun'	CJun
	'Hot Flash'	CBcs CJun NLar
	'Hot Lips'	CJun
	hypoleuca	see *M. obovata* Thunb.
	'Ian's Red'	CBcs CJun EBee IVic LRHS MBri SCob WMat WPGP
§	***insignis***	CBcs CExl LEdu SKHP WPGP
	- B&SWJ 11810 **new**	WCru
	- NJM 12.040 **new**	WPGP
	- WWJ 11854 **new**	WCru
	insignis × yuyuanensis	WPGP
	'Iolanthe'	CBcs CDoC CJun CMCN CMHG CTho ELan EPfP ERea IVic MAsh MBri MGos NOrn WPGP
	'Iufer'	CJun
	'J.C. Williams'	CBcs CDoC CJun CTho IVic LRHS WPGP

	Name	Suppliers
	'Jack Fogg'	MPkF SKHP
	'Jane'	CDoC CJun CMac ELan EPfP LMil LRHS MAsh MGos MRav NOrn
	'Janet'	SKHP
	'Jersey Belle'	CBcs CJun
	'Joe McDaniel'	CBcs CJun ERea IArd NLar SAko SKHP
	'John Congreve'	WPGP
	'Joli Pompom'	CBcs CJun LRHS SAko
	'Judy Zuk'	CBcs ERea LMil LRHS NLar SAko SKHP
	× ***kewensis*** 'Wada's Memory'	see *M. salicifolia* 'Wada's Memory'
	'Kinikuuso' **new**	EBee
	kobus	CBcs CCVT CDul CLnd CMCN CTho EPfP ERea GKin IArd MBlu NLar NWea SCob SEWo WBod WMou
	- B&SWJ 12751	WCru
	- 'Esveld Select'	CJun LRHS
	- 'Janaki Ammal'	CJun SAko
§	- 'Norman Gould'	CDoC CJun CMCN EPfP MBri NPla
	- 'Octopus'	CJun
	- pink-flowered	CBcs CJun
	- 'White Elegance'	CJun
	laevifolia	CExl CHid CTho EBee EPfP IDee SChF SKHP WPGP WSHC
	- 'Cascade'	SKHP
	- 'Dali Velvet'	CExl
	- 'Gail's Favourite' ♀H4	EPfP LMil LRHS MAsh SKHP SSpi
	- 'Michelle' **new**	SAko
	- 'Mini Mouse'	LRHS SKHP SPoG
	- 'Velvet and Cream'	IVic
	- 'Willow Leaf'	SKHP
	'Laura Saylor'	CJun
	'Leda'	CJun ERea NLar SSta WPGP
	'Legacy'	CJun SKHP WPGP
	'Legend'	CJun EPfP
	'Lennarth Jonsson'	CJun
	liliiflora 'Darkest Purple'	CJun LPar
§	- 'Nigra' ♀H6	Widely available
	- 'Raven'	LMil LRHS SKHP WPGP
*	'Limelight'	CJun EPfP WMat WPGP
	× ***loebneri*** 'Ballerina'	CBcs CDoC NLar
	- 'Donna' ♀H6	CBcs CJun EPfP LMil LRHS LSRN MAsh SKHP
	- 'Encore'	CJun
	- 'Green Mist'	CJun LRHS SSpi
	- 'Leonard Messel' ♀H6	Widely available
	- 'Lesley Jane'	CJun
	- 'Mag's Pirouette' ♀H6	CBcs CJun EBee EMil EPfP LLHF LMil LRHS MBri SAko SKHP SLim SPoG SSpi
	- 'Merrill' ♀H6	CBcs CDul CJun CLnd CMCN CMHG CMac CTho CWib ELan EPfP ERea LMil LRHS MAsh MGos MRav NEgg NLar SEND SGol SHil SKHP SPer SReu SSpi SSta
	- 'Neil McEacharn'	CJun
	- 'Pink Cloud'	CJun
	- 'Powder Puff'	CBcs CJun
	- 'Raspberry Fun'	CJun IArd
	- 'Snowdrift'	CJun
	- 'Star Bright'	CJun
	- 'White Stardust'	CJun
	- 'Wildcat' ♀H6	CBcs CJun LRHS NLar SAko SKHP
	- 'Willow Wood'	CJun
	'Lois' ♀H6	CBcs CJun EPfP ERea GGGa LMil LRHS LSRN SAko SKHP SSpi WPGP
	'Lombardy Rose'	NLar

	Name	Suppliers
	'Longsleeper' **new**	LRHS
	lotungensis	NLar
	'Lotus'	CBcs CJun WPGP
	'Lucy Carlson'	CJun
	macclurei	CBcs
	macrophylla	CBcs CBrP CFil CMac EPfP IArd IDee LRHS MBlu MPkF NLar SKHP WPGP
§	- subsp. ***ashei***	CFil CMCN IDee SKHP WPGP
	- subsp. ***ashei*** × ***virginiana***	CJun WPGP
§	- subsp. ***dealbata***	CFil
	macrophylla × ***macrophylla*** subsp. ***ashei***	SKHP
	macrophylla × ***sieboldii***	CJun LPar
	'Malin'	CJun
	'Manchu Fan'	CBcs CDoC CJun EMil EPfP IArd IVic LRHS LSRN SKHP SSpi WPGP
§	'March Til Frost'	CBcs CJun EBee NLar SKHP WPGP
	'Margaret Helen'	CBcs CDoC CJun CMHG WPGP
	'Marj Gossler'	CJun
	'Marjorie Congreve'	WPGP
	'Mark Jury'	SKHP
	martinii	CBcs SKHP
	'Mary Bee'	SKHP
	'Mary Nell'	CJun
	'Maryland'	CJun EPfP GGGa SKHP
	maudiae	CBcs CExl EPfP NLar SKHP SSpi WPGP
	'Maxine Merrill'	CBcs CJun SAko
	'May to Frost'	see *M.* 'March Til Frost'
	'Mazeppa'	WPGP
	'Milky Way' ♀H5	CDoC CDul CJun CMHG CTho EPfP ERea LMil MGos SKHP WPGP
	'Mister Yellowjacket'	CJun
	'Moondance'	CJun
	'Morning Calm'	SKHP
	'Nimbus'	CJun SKHP SSpi WPGP
	nitida	CBcs CExl CFil
	obovata Diels	see *M. officinalis*
§	***obovata*** Thunb.	CBcs CJun CMCN CTho EPfP NLar NWea SBig SSpi WMou WPGP
	- B&SWJ 12626	WCru
	obovata × ***sargentiana*** var. ***robusta***	WPGP
§	***officinalis***	CBcs EPfP NLar
	- var. ***biloba***	CBcs MBlu NLar WPGP
	'Old Port'	CBcs
	'Olivia'	CJun LRHS WPGP
	'Paul Cook'	CBcs SAko
	'Peachy'	CBcs CJun LRHS MBri
§	'Pegasus' ♀H6	CBcs CJun LMil SKHP SSpi SSta
	'Peppermint Stick'	CBcs CTsd LRHS WMat
	'Peter Dummer'	LMil
	'Peter Smithers'	CJun
	'Petit Chicon'	CBcs WPGP
	'Phelan Bright'	CJun SAko WPGP
	'Phillip Tregunna'	CBcs CMHG CTho SKHP WPGP
	'Phil's Masterpiece'	CJun
	'Pickard's Garnet'	CBcs SAko
	'Pickard's Stardust'	EPfP
	'Pickard's Sundew'	see *M.* × *soulangeana* 'Sundew'
	'Piet van Veen'	CJun
	'Pink Delight'	CJun
	'Pink Goblet'	LRHS
	'Pink Surprise'	CJun
	'Pinkie'	CJun EMil LSRN
	'Porcelain Dove'	CBcs CJun LMil LRHS SKHP WPGP

	Plant	Suppliers
	'Princess Margaret'	CBcs CJun MBri
	'Pristine'	EPfP LMil LRHS
	× ***proctoriana***	CAbP CBcs CDoC EBee LMil LRHS SKHP WPGP
	- 'Robert's Dream'	CJun LRHS MAsh SSta
	- 'Slavin's No 44'	CJun
	'Purple Breeze' **new**	MBlu NLar SAko
	'Purple Globe'	CJun EBee SKHP WPGP
	'Purple Platter'	CBcs
	'Purple Sensation'	CBcs CJun WPGP
	'Randy'	CBcs
	'Raspberry Ice'	CDoC CMHG CMac CTho EPfP LMil LRHS MAsh SPoG SRms WFar
	'Raspberry Swirl'	SSta
	'Rebecca's Perfume'	LRHS WMat
	'Red as Red'	CBcs LRHS
	'Red Baron'	CJun
	'Red Lion'	CBcs CJun
	'Ricki'	CJun CLet LSRN MBlu
	'Roseanne'	CJun
	rostrata	CBcs CExl CFil EBee IArd IMou SKHP WPGP
	'Rouged Alabaster'	CBcs CDoC
	'Royal Crown'	CBcs EMil EPfP IArd LRHS MRav
	'Royal Flush' **new**	NEgg
	'Ruby'	CJun
	salicifolia	CBcs CMCN SSpi
	- var. ***concolor***	CJun
	- 'Garden House Upright' **new**	EBee
	- 'Jermyns'	CJun
	- 'Louisa Fete'	CJun
*	- 'Rosea'	CJun
	- upright	WPGP
	- 'Van Veen'	CJun
§	- 'Wada's Memory' ♀H6	CDoC CDul CExl CHid CJun CMCN CTho ELan EMil EPfP ERea LMil LRHS MAsh MBlu MBri MMuc SKHP SSpi SSta WFar WMat
	- 'Windsor Beauty'	CJun ERea SSta
	sapaensis FMWJ 13315 **new**	WCru
	- FMWJ 13330	WCru
	- HWJ 533 **new**	WCru
	- NJM 09.168	WPGP
	'Sarah Coe' **new**	WMat
	sargentiana	SSta
	- 'Broadleas'	CJun
	- var. ***robusta***	CBcs CLnd CMCN CTsd ELan EPfP NLar
	- - 'Blood Moon'	CJun WPGP
	- - 'Multipetal'	WPGP
	- - 'Trengwainton Glory'	ERea
	'Satisfaction'	CBcs CJun LCro NLar
	'Sayonara' ♀H5	CJun ERea LRHS SSpi
	'Schmetterling'	see *M.* × *soulangeana* 'Pickard's Schmetterling'
	'Sentinel'	WMat
	'Serene'	CBcs CJun CMHG EPfP LMil LRHS MBri SAko WPGP
	Shirazz = 'Vulden'	CBcs CDoC CJun EPfP NLar SCob SKHP WPGP
	sieboldii	CBcs CJun CLnd CMCN CMac CTho CWCL ELan EPfP EWTr GKin LRHS LSRN MBlu MBri MGos MRav NLar SHil SKHP SPer WHor WPGP
	- B&SWJ 4127	WCru
	- 'Colossus' ♀H6	CJun IArd IDee MBlu SAko SKHP WPGP
	- 'Genesis'	CJun
	- 'Genesis' × ***tripetala***	CJun
	- 'Genesis' × ***virginiana***	CJun
	- 'Michiko Renge' (d)	CJun
	- 'Min Pyong-gal'	CJun
	- 'Pride of Norway'	CJun
	- subsp. ***sieboldii*** B&SWJ 12553 from Korea	WCru
	- subsp. ***sinensis***	CBcs CDoC CJun CMCN CTho ELan EPfP LPar NLar WPGP
I	- - 'Grandiflora'	CJun WPGP
	'Sir Harold Hillier'	CBcs WPGP
	'Sleeping Beauty'	SKHP
	'Snow Goose'	CJun
	'Solar Flair'	CBcs CJun IArd LRHS MBri NLar SKHP
	× ***soulangeana***	Widely available
	- 'Alba Superba'	CBcs CBot CDoC CTri EPfP GBin LCro LMil LRHS MBlu MBri MRav NLar SLim WFar
	- 'Alexandrina'	CBcs EPfP MBlu NLar
	- 'André Leroy'	EPfP
	- 'Beugnon' **new**	IArd
	- 'Brozzonii' ♀H5	CBcs CDoC CMac EPfP GCra IArd LMil LRHS MMuc SSta
	- 'Burgundy'	CBcs
	- 'Cleopatra'	CBcs
	- 'Fukuju'	CJun
	- 'Lennei'	CBcs CDoC CMCN CMac CSBt CTho EPfP IArd LAst LPar LRHS MGos MRav NLar NOrn SHil SPer SRms WFar
	- 'Lennei Alba'	CDoC CMCN CMac ELan IArd MBlu MBri WFar WMat
	- 'Lennei Alba' × ***sprengeri*** var. ***diva*** **new**	LPar
	- 'Nigra'	see *M. liliiflora* 'Nigra'
	- 'Pickard's Opal'	CMCN
	- 'Pickard's Ruby'	CBcs
§	- 'Pickard's Schmetterling' ♀H5	CBcs EPfP LMil LRHS MAsh
	- 'Pickard's Snow Queen'	CJun
	- 'Pickard's Sundew'	see *M.* × *soulangeana* 'Sundew'
	- 'Picture'	CMac CTri
	- 'Purpliana' **new**	NPri
	- Red Lucky	see *M.* 'Hong Yun'
	- 'Rubra' misapplied	see *M.* × *soulangeana* 'Rustica Rubra'
§	- 'Rustica Rubra'	CBcs CDoC CDul CLnd CMCN CMac CTri ELan EPfP LMil LRHS LSRN MAsh MBri SGol SRms SSpi WFar
	- 'San José'	CJun LMil LRHS MAsh
	- 'Speciosa'	SSta
§	- 'Sundew'	CDoC EPfP ERea
	- 'Superba'	CMac LPar
	- 'Verbanica'	EPfP LMil LRHS MAsh
	'Spectrum' ♀H6	CBcs CDoC CJun EPfP ERea IArd IDee IMou LMil LRHS MBlu MGos NLar SAko SKHP SSpi SSta
	sprengeri	CTsd CWib
	- from Guizhou, China **new**	WPGP
	- var. ***diva***	CBcs CExl SKHP WPGP
	- - 'Burncoose' ♀H6	CBcs CDoC SAko
	- - 'Copeland Court' ♀H6	CJun WPGP
	- - 'Dark Diva'	CJun
	- - 'Diva'	GGal LRHS SAko WPGP
	- - 'Eric Savill' ♀H6	CBcs CJun ERea IVic SKHP WPGP

- - 'Lanhydrock'	CJun LRHS SKHP WPGP
- - 'Marwood Spring'	CMHG ERea SKHP WPGP
- - 'Westonbirt'	WPGP
- var. ***sprengeri***	SKHP
'Spring Rite'	CJun SKHP
'Star Wars' 🏆H5	CBcs CCVT CDoC CDul CExl CJun CTho ELan EPfP ERea GGGa LMil LRHS MAsh MBri MGos NOrn SAko SKHP SPoG SSpi SSta WMat WPGP
'Stellar Acclaim'	CBcs CJun LMil
stellata	Widely available
- 'Centennial' 🏆H6	CDoC CJun CTho NLar
- 'Chrysanthemumiflora'	CJun ERea SKHP
- 'Dawn'	CJun
- 'Jane Platt' 🏆H6	CBcs CJun ELan EPfP ERea LMil LRHS MGos SKHP SPoG SSta WPGP
- f. ***keiskei***	CBcs CJun MGos NHol SKHP
- 'Kikuzaki'	CJun
- 'King Rose'	CBcs CDoC CJun CTsd EPfP LAst LRHS MAsh SPer
- 'Massey'	CJun
- 'Norman Gould'	see *M. kobus* 'Norman Gould'
- 'Rosea'	CDul CJun CLet CMCN CTho ELan ELon EPfP LMil LPar MGos MRav MSwo NEgg NLar NOrn NPri SCob SKHP
- 'Rosea Massey'	CJun WFar
- 'Royal Star' 🏆H6	Widely available
- 'Scented Silver'	CJun LRHS MAsh SKHP SPoG
- 'Shi-banchi Rosea'	CJun
- 'Two Stones'	SKHP
- 'Water Lily'	CBcs CBot CJun CMCN CTho ELan ELon EPfP LAst LOPS LRHS LSRN MAsh MBlu MGos NEgg SHil SKHP SPer SSta SPoG WFar WHor WPGP
- 'Wisley Stardust'	LRHS
'Summer Solstice'	CBcs CJun SAko WPGP
'Sun Ray'	CJun
'Sunburst'	CBcs CJun SRms
'Sundance'	CBcs CJun IArd MBlu MBri NLar
'Sunrise'	CBcs MBri
'Sunsation'	CBcs CJun ERea MBri
'Sunspire'	CJun ERea NLar
'Suntown'	CJun
'Susan' 🏆H6	Widely available
'Susanna van Veen'	CBcs CDoC CJun WPGP
'Swedish Star'	CJun
'Sweet Merlot'	CBcs CJun LRHS
'Sweet Valentine'	CBcs CJun SAko WPGP
'Sweetheart' 🏆H5	CBcs CJun
'Sybille'	CMCN WPGP
× ***thompsoniana***	CBcs CMCN NLar
- 'Olmenhof'	IArd SAko
'Thousand Butterflies'	CJun
'Tina Durio'	CBcs SAko SKHP WMat
'Todd Gresham'	CJun
'Todd's Forty Niner'	CBcs CJun
'Touch of Pink'	CBcs
'Tranquility'	CBcs CJun SKHP
tripetala	CBcs CExl CLnd CMCN CTho ELan EPfP LRHS MBlu NLar SBig SKHP SSpi SSta WPGP
- 'Bloomfield'	CJun
- 'Petite'	SKHP
'Ultimate Yellow'	CJun NLar
× ***veitchii***	CBcs EPfP
- 'Columbus'	CJun LRHS SKHP WPGP
- 'Peter Veitch'	CTho
virginiana	CBcs CJun CMCN EPfP NLar SBig SKHP SSpi WPGP
- 'Aiken County'	SKHP
- var. ***australis*** 'Green Shadow'	SGol
- - 'Henry Hicks'	CJun SAko
- - 'Satellite'	CJun NLar
- 'Havener'	SKHP
- Moonglow = 'Jim Wilson'	CJun EPfP MBlu WPGP
- 'Pink Halo'	CJun
'Vulcan'	CBcs CDoC CJun ELan EPfP LRHS MBri NOrn SAko SCoo SPoG
× ***watsonii***	see *M.* × *wieseneri*
'White Mystery'	CJun
§ × ***wieseneri***	CBcs CJun CMCN CMHG EPfP ERea LCro LMil MBlu SKHP SPer WPGP
- 'Aashild Kalleberg'	CBcs CJun SKHP SSpi WPGP
- 'Lupo Osti'	SKHP
wilsonii 🏆H6	CBcs CDoC CDul CExl CJun CMCN CTho CTri EBee ELan EPfP GGGa IArd IDee ITim LCro LOPS LRHS MBlu MBri MGos MMuc NLar SBrt SEND SKHP WPGP WSHC
- 'Gwen Baker'	CJun
'Yaeko'	CBcs CJun
'Yellow Fever'	CBcs CJun CTho EBee WPGP
'Yellow Garland'	CJun
'Yellow Lantern' 🏆H6	CAbP CBcs CDoC CJun EBee ELan EPfP GGGa LMil LRHS LSRN MAsh MBlu SPoG SSta WPGP
'Yellow Sea'	CJun SKHP
Yuchelia No. 1	CBcs
yunnanensis	CBcs CDoC MPkF
yuyuanensis	CBcs
zenii	CBcs CMCN IArd
- 'Pink Parchment'	CJun

× *Mahoberberis* (*Berberidaceae*)

aquisargentii	CMac EBee EMil EPfP GCal IVic LRHS MMuc MRav NLar SCob SEND SKHP WFar
'Dart's Desire'	NLar
miethkeana	SRms

Mahonia ✿ (*Berberidaceae*)

§ ***aquifolium***	CAgr CBcs CDul EAEE ECrN LPfy MGos MMuc MRav NWea SCob SEND SGol SPer SPlb SWvt WHar
- 'Apollo' 🏆H5	CBcs CSBt CWib ELan ELon EPfP LAst LHop LRHS LSRN MAsh MBlu MGos MJak MRav NLar SCob SCoo SPer SPoG SWvt WFar
- 'Atropurpurea'	CMac CSBt CTsd ELan EPfP LRHS MRav NLar SPer
- 'Cosmo Crawl'	LRHS MBri MGos SHil
- 'Fascicularis'	see *M.* × *wagneri* 'Pinnacle'
- 'Green Ripple'	NLar
- 'Moseri'	WPat
- 'Orange Flame'	NLar
- 'Smaragd'	CDoC CMac ELan EPfP LRHS LSRN MBlu MGos MRav NLar SCob WHar
- 'Versicolor'	MBlu
'Arthur Menzies'	LRHS NLar
§ ***bealei***	CBcs CBod CDul CRos CSBt EBee ELan ELon EPfP LRHS MAsh MGos MRav MSwo NEgg NPer NPla SCob SCoo SGol SKHP SLim SWvt
Blackfoot = 'Bokrafoot'[PBR]	CRos ELan EPfP LLHF LRHS MAsh SLon

bodinieri	WPGP
chochoco	CExl CFil SKHP
conferta	CFil
confusa* × *gracilipes	SKHP
§ ***duclouxiana*** new	CFil
eurybracteata	CDoC CExl CFil CLAP EBee IArd LLHF LRHS SKHP WPGP
- subsp. ***ganpinensis*** 'Soft Caress'	CBcs CDoC CRos EBee ELan EPfP EUJe LCro LOPS LRHS MGos MPkF NLar SCob SCoo SMad SPoG SWvt WCot
- 'Minganpi' PBR new	LSRN
- 'Sweet Winter' new	LRHS
eutriphylla misapplied	see *M. trifolia*
fargesii	see *M. sheridaniana*
fortunei	CBcs CFil
- 'Winter Prince'	NLar WSHC
fremontii	SBrt
gracilipes	CExl CFil EPfP EWes GCal IDee IMou MBlu NLar SBrt SChF SKHP SLon SMad WCru WHar WPGP
gracilis	CFil
haematocarpa	SIgm
huiliensis	see *M. sheridaniana*
japonica ♀H5	Widely available
- 'Gold Dust'	CMac MBlu NLar
- 'Hiemalis'	see *M. japonica* 'Hivernant'
§ - 'Hivernant'	EAEE NWea
lanceolata	CFil EBee WPGP
leschenaultii B&SWJ 9535	WCru
× ***lindsayae***	CFil WPGP
- 'Cantab' ♀H4	CFil EBee NLar SChF WPGP
lomariifolia	see *M. oiwakensis* subsp. *lomariifolia*
longibracteata	GKin
mairei	see *M. duclouxiana*
× ***media*** new	LPar
- 'Buckland' ♀H4	CBcs CDul CMac EPfP NLar SCob SPer SRms WPat
- 'Charity'	Widely available
- 'Lionel Fortescue' ♀H4	CBcs CMac CRos CSBt EBee ELan EPfP GKin LAst LHop LRHS MAsh NEgg SCob SKHP SPer SSpi SWvt WHor
- 'Winter Sun' ♀H4	Widely available
moranensis	CExl CFil EBee
- T 292	WPGP
napaulensis	CFil
- 'Maharajah'	IArd IDee IMou NLar
nervosa	CBcs CMac EBee EPfP MBlu NLar SKHP WCru WPGP
- B&SWJ 9562	WCru
nevinii	SBrt
nitens	CBcs WPGP
- 'Cabaret' PBR ♀H4	CBcs CRos EBee EPfP LCro LLHF LOPS LRHS MAsh MBlu MBri MGos SCob SHil SPoG
* ***nitida***	SKHP
oiwakensis	NLar WPGP
- B&SWJ 371	WCru
- B&SWJ 3660	WCru
§ - subsp. ***lomariifolia*** ♀H4	CExl CFil EPfP EWes LRHS SKHP
- - var. ***tenuifoliola*** new	CFil
pallida	CEvo CExl CFil SKHP WPGP
- from Tamazunchale, Mexico	CFil
- from Zimapan, Mexico	CFil
'Pan's Peculiar'	WPGP
pinnata misapplied	see *M.* × *wagneri* 'Pinnacle'
pinnata (Lag.) Fedde 'Ken S. Howard'	NLar WPGP
repens	NLar
- 'Rotundifolia'	SPlb
× ***savilliana***	CFil NLar WPGP
- 'Commissioner'	CWib
§ ***sheridiana*** new	CFil
siamensis	CFil
Sioux = 'Bokrasio' PBR	CRos LLHF LRHS MAsh SPoG
§ ***trifolia***	CFil GCal SKHP
trifoliolata var. ***glauca***	CFil CJun SKHP
× ***wagneri*** new	SWvt
- 'Aldenhamensis'	NLar
- 'Fireflame'	GCal
- 'Hastings' Elegant'	NLar
§ - 'Pinnacle' ♀H5	ELan EPfP IDee LRHS MAsh MBlu NLar SPer SPoG SWvt
- 'Sunset'	GKin MBlu NLar
- 'Undulata'	LRHS MBlu SRms
- 'Vicaryi' new	NLar

Maianthemum (*Asparagaceae*)

amoenum B&SWJ 10390	WCru
atropurpureum	WCru
bicolor	CDes CTal LEdu SWat
bifolium	CAvo CBct CCon CHid CTal ECho GCra GLog GMaP LEdu MAvo MNrw NBro SGSe SRms WCru WWEG XLum
§ - subsp. ***kamtschaticum***	CAvo CLAP ECha EPPr LEdu MAvo NLar NRya WCot WPGP WWEG
- - B&SWJ 4360	GKev WCru
- - CD&R 2300	WCru
- - var. ***pumilum***	CDes EBee GCal LEdu WCru
canadense	EAJP EBee ECho EPot GBuc GCal GKev LEdu MNrw NBid WCru
- 'Mullerthal' new	EBee
chasmanthum	see *M. bifolium* subsp. *kamtschaticum*
comaltepecense B&SWJ 10215	WCru
dilatatum	see *M. bifolium* subsp. *kamtschaticum*
flexuosum	LEdu
- B&SWJ 9069	WCru
- B&SWJ 9079	WCru
- B&SWJ 9150	WCru
aff. ***flexuosum*** B&SWJ 9026	WCru
- B&SWJ 9055	WCru
formosanum B&SWJ 349	EPPr WCru
forrestii	WCru
fuscum	GEdr WCru
- PAB 7749	LEdu
- var. ***cordatum***	WCru
gigas B&SWJ 10470	WCru
henryi	ECho EHrv GEdr GKev LEdu WCru WPGP
- BWJ 7616	WCru
japonicum	CTal EHrv LEdu
- B&SWJ 1179	WCru
- B&SWJ 4714	WCru
- B&SWJ 7306	WCru
'Mullerthal' new	GKev
oleraceum	CBct CExl GEdr GKev LEdu LRHS
- B&SWJ 2148	WCru
- purple-flowered	GEdr
paniculatum	EBee LEdu
- B&SWJ 9137	WCru
- B&SWJ 9140	WCru
- purple-flowered B&SWJ 9139	WCru

pendent, B&SWJ 10305 from Guatemala WCru
purpureum GEdr GKev
- G-W&P 150 EPPr
racemosum ♀H7 Widely available
- subsp. **amplexicaule** CAvo GCal ILea
- - 'Emily Moody' CBct CDes CExl CPou EBee EPPr EPfP SChF SKHP WCot WPGP
- dwarf ECho
- 'Major' LRHS
- subsp. **racemosum** new GKev
aff. **salvinii** CTal
- B&SWJ 9000 WCru
- B&SWJ 9088 WCru
- B&SWJ 10402 WCru
scilloideum CTal
- B&SWJ 10407 WCru
* - var. **roseum** B&SWJ 10335 WCru
stellatum CBct CCon CSam CTal EBee ECha ECho EPPr EPfP GBin GBuc GCal GEdr ILea LEdu LHop LRHS MBel NChi NLar SPoG WCru WWEG
szechuanicum WCru
tatsienense CBct CExl EHrv GEdr LEdu WCru

Maihuenia (*Cactaceae*)

poeppigii CCac SPlb
- F&W 9670 WCot

Maihueniopsis (*Cactaceae*)

darwinii new SPlb
- LB 347 new CCac
§ **glomerata** TG 63 new CCac

Maireana (*Amaranthaceae*)

georgei SPlb

Mallotus (*Euphorbiaceae*)

japonicus WPGP

Malus ✿ (*Rosaceae*)

§ 'Adirondack' ♀H6 CLnd EBee EPfP MAsh MBri MMuc NOra NPri SCoo SLon SPoG WJas WMat
'Admiration' see *M.* 'Adirondack'
× **adstringens** 'Hopa' CAgr CDul CLnd
- 'Simcoe' EBee
'Aldenhamensis' see *M.* × *purpurea* 'Aldenhamensis'
'Allow Super' (D) new WMat
'Amberina' CLnd
baccata CDul CLnd CMCN CTho GTwe MMuc NWea SCoo SEND SPlb
- var. **mandshurica** CTho
aff. **baccata** NWea
(Ballerina Series) 'Ballerina Bolero' (D) new WMat
- 'Ballerina Polka' (D) new WMat
- 'Ballerina Samba' (D) new WMat
'Barbara' new WMat
§ **bhutanica** CDul CLnd
- 'Mandarin' SCoo
'Braeburn Mariri' (D) new WMat
'Bramley 20' (C) new WMat
brevipes CLnd LRHS SCoo
- 'Wedding Bouquet' ♀H6 EBee ERea LBuc LCro LSRN MAsh MBri NLar NOra SPer WMat WMou
'Butterball' ♀H6 CDoC CDul CLnd CNWT CSBt CTho CTsd ECrN EPfP ERea GQue LAst NOra NWea SBmr SCoo SLim SPer SVic WHar WJas WMat WMou
'Candymint Sargent' MBri
'Captain Tom' (C/D) new WMat
'Cheal's Scarlet' CHab
* 'Cheal's Weeping' CLnd CMac EWTr LAst NEgg WMou
Coccinella = 'Courtarou' LRHS SGol
'Comtesse de Paris' ♀H6 CDul CLnd EBee EPfP LRHS MAsh MBlu MBri NOra NOrn WMat
Coralburst = 'Coralcole' MAsh MBri NOra WMat
coronaria var. **dasycalyx** 'Charlottae' (d) CDul CLnd EWTr SPer
- 'Elk River' EPfP MAsh NOra SCoo WMat
'Cowichan' CLnd ECrN
'Crimson Brilliant' CLnd
'Crittenden' MAsh MRav
'Dartmouth' CDul CHab CLnd CSBt CTri
'Directeur Moerlands' CArg CCVT CDoC CSBt CWSG ECrN EPfP IArd LRHS MMuc NOra NOrn SCoo SEND SPer SWvt WHar WMat
domestica '1400 Ke' PBR (F) new SBdl
- 'Acklam Russet' (D) CHab GTwd
- 'Acme' (D) ECrN SDea
- 'Adams's Pearmain' (D) CHab CTho CTri ECrN ERea GTwd GTwe LRHS MAsh MCoo NOra SBdl SCob SDea SKee WHar WMat WWct
- 'Admiral' PBR (D) ECrN ERea EWTr
- 'Akane' (D) SDea
- 'Akerö' (D) GTwd
- 'Alderman' (C) GTwd
- 'Alfriston' (C) CAgr CHab GTwd SKee WMat
§ - 'Alkmene' (D) ♀H6 CAgr ECrN NOra SDea SKee
- 'All Doer' (C/D/Cider) CTho SBmr
- 'Allen's Everlasting' (D) SDea
- 'Allington Pippin' (D) CHab CSBt CTho CTri ECrN ERea GTwd IArd LRHS MGos NOra SDea SKee WHar WMat
- Ambassy = 'Dalil' PBR (D) EBee SBmr
- 'American Mother' see *M. domestica* 'Mother'
- 'Ananas Reinette' (D) CHab ECrN SKee
- 'Anna Boelens' (D) SDea
- 'Annie Elizabeth' (C) CAgr CDul CHab CTho CWib ECrN GTwd GTwe IArd LAst LRHS MCoo MGos NOra SBmr SDea SKee SVic WHar WJas WMat WWct
- 'Anniversary' (D) SDea
- 'Antonovka' (F) new SKee
- 'Api' (D) GQue LSRN NOra NWea SCob SKee WHar WMat
- 'Api Noir' (D) SKee
- 'Ard Cairn Russet' (D) ECrN IArd SDea SKee
- 'Aromatic Russet' (D) SKee
- 'Arthur Turner' (C) ♀H6 CCVT CHab CTri ECrN EPom ERea GTwd GTwe IArd LAst LBuc MWat NOra SBdl SBmr SDea SKee WHar WJas WMat
- 'Arthur W. Barnes' (C) SKee
- 'Ashmead's Kernel' (D) ♀H6 Widely available
- 'Ashton Bitter' (Cider) CHab CTho CTri GTwe
- 'Askham Pippin' (F) MCoo
- 'Autumn Harvest' (C/D) new GTwd
- 'Autumn Pearmain' (D) SDea WHar
- 'Baker's Delicious' (D) EBee ECrN ERea NOra SDea SKee WHar WMat
- 'Ball's Bittersweet' (Cider) CTho
- 'Ballyfatten' (C) IArd

- 'Ballyvaughan Seedling' (D)	IArd
- 'Balsam'	see *M. domestica* 'Green Balsam'
- 'Banns' (D)	ECrN ERea
- 'Bardsey' (D)	CAgr CArg CHab EPom NOra SKee WGwG WHar WMat
- 'Barnack Beauty' (D)	CHab CTho GTwd LEdu NOra SKee
- 'Barnack Orange' (D)	GTwd SKee
- 'Baron Ward' (C)	CHab
- 'Baron Wood' (C)	SKee
- 'Baumann's Reinette' (D)	SKee
- 'Baxter's Pearmain' (D)	ECrN ERea SDea SKee
- 'Beauty of Bath' (D)	CAgr CArg CCVT CDul CHab CLnd CTho CTri CWib ECrN ELan EPom GTwd GTwe LAst LBuc LRHS MRav NOra SBdl SBmr SDea SKee SPer WHar WJas WMat WWct
- 'Beauty of Hants' (C/D)	ECrN SKee
- 'Beauty of Kent' (C)	GTwd SDea SKee
- 'Beauty of Moray' (C)	GTwd SKee
- 'Bedwyn Beauty' (C)	CTho
- 'Beeley Pippin' (D)	SDea SKee
- 'Bell Apple' (Cider/C)	CTho
- 'Belle de Boskoop' (C/D) 🏆H6	CAgr CHab ECrN GTwe MCoo NOra SBdl SCob SDea SKee
- 'Belle de Pontoise' (D) **new**	SKee
- 'Belledge Pippin' (C/D)	GTwd SBdl
- 'Belvoir Seedling' (C/D)	SKee
- 'Bembridge Beauty' (F)	CHab SDea
- 'Ben's Red' (D)	CAgr CDoC CTho SKee WMat
- 'Bess Pool' (D)	CHab GTwd MCoo SBdl SDea SKee
- 'Bewley Down Pippin'	see *M. domestica* 'Crimson King' (Cider/C)
- 'Bickington Grey' (Cider)	CTho
- 'Billy Down Pippin' (F)	CTho
- 'Bismarck' (C)	SKee
- 'Black Dabinett' (Cider)	CTho WMat
- 'Black Tom Putt' (C/D)	CTho
- 'Blenheim Orange' (C/D) 🏆H6	Widely available
- 'Blood of the Boyne' (D)	IArd
- 'Bloody Ploughman' (D)	CHab CLnd ECrN GBin GQue GTwd GTwe MWat NOra NPri SBdl SKee SLon WHar WMat
- 'Blue Moon' (D) **new**	LRHS
- 'Blue Pearmain' (D)	SDea SKee
- 'Blue Sweet' (Cider)	CTho
- Bolero	see *M. domestica* 'Tuscan'
- 'Bonum' (D/C)	WMat
- 'Boston Russet'	see *M. domestica* 'Roxbury Russet'
- 'Bountiful' (C)	CAgr CDul CLnd CMac CSBt CTri CWib ECrN EPom EWTr GTwd GTwe IArd LRHS LSRN MAsh MBri MRav NOra SBdl SBmr SDea SKee WHar WMat WWct
- 'Bow Hill Pippin' (C)	GTwd
- 'Box Apple' (D)	CDoC
- 'Braddick's Nonpareil' (D)	SKee
- 'Bradley's Beauty' (C/D)	NWea
- 'Braeburn' (D)	CAgr CDul CLnd CSBt CSut CTri CTsd ECrN EPom ERea LAst LBuc LEdu LRHS MWat NOra SBdl SBmr SCob SDea SEND SEWo SFrt SKee SPer WHar WJas WMat
- 'Braeburn Hillwell' (D)	EPom NOra
- 'Braintree Seedling' (D)	ECrN SKee
- 'Bramley's Seedling' (C) 🏆H6	Widely available
- 'Bramley's Seedling' clone 20 (F)	CDoC CTsd ERea LSRN MAsh MBri MNHC MWat NLar NOra SBdl SCoo SDea SKee SLim SPer SPoG WHar WWct
- 'Bramshott Rectory' (D/C)	SKee
- 'Bread Fruit' (C/D)	CDoC CTho
- 'Breakwell's Seedling' (Cider)	CTho
- 'Brenchley Pippin' (D)	SBdl
- 'Bridgwater Pippin' (C)	CTho
- 'Bright Future' (D)	EPom LRHS MCoo NOra WMat WWct
- 'Brith Mawr' (C)	WGwG
- 'Broadholme Beauty' (C)	EPom MAsh NOra WHar WMat
- 'Brookes's' (D)	WHar
- 'Brown Crofton' (D)	IArd
- 'Brown Snout' (Cider)	CTho SFrt
- 'Brownlee's Russet' (D)	CAgr CHab CTho CTri GTwd GTwe MCoo NEgg NOra NWea SBmr SDea SKee WHar WMat
- 'Brown's Apple' (Cider)	CAgr CHab CTri ECrN GTwe NOra SBdl SFrt WMat
- 'Broxwood Foxwhelp' (Cider)	SFrt
- 'Burley Grove' **new**	SBdl
- 'Burn's Seedling' (D)	CTho
- 'Burr Knot' (C)	SKee
- 'Burrowhill Early' (Cider)	CTho WMat
- 'Bushey Grove' (C)	SDea SKee
- 'Buttery Do' (F)	CTho
- 'Calville Blanc d'Hiver' (D)	NOra SBdl SKee
- 'Cambusnethan Pippin' (D)	GTwd SKee
- 'Camelot' (Cider/C)	SBmr
§ - 'Captain Broad' (Cider/D)	CDoC CTho
- 'Captain Kidd' (D)	EPom NOra SKee WHar
- 'Caravel' (D) **new**	GTwd
- 'Carlisle Codlin' (C)	GTwd NOra NWea SDea WMat
- 'Caroline' (D)	ECrN ERea
- 'Carswell's Honeydew' (D)	SKee
- 'Catherine' (C)	ECrN
- 'Catshead' (C)	CAgr CHab CTri CTsd ECrN GTwd IArd NOra SDea SKee WHar WMat WWct
- 'Cellini' (C)	NOra SDea SKee
- 'Cevaal' (D)	WWct
- 'Chacewater Longstem' (F)	CDoC
- 'Charles Ross' (C/D) 🏆H6	Widely available
- 'Charlotte'^{PBR} (C)	ECrN SDea SKee
- 'Chaxhill Red' (Cider/D)	CTho
- 'Cheddar Cross' (D)	CAgr CCVT CTri ECrN
- 'Chelmsford Wonder' (C)	ECrN SKee
- 'Chisel Jersey' (Cider)	CAgr CTri NOra SFrt SKee
- 'Chivers Delight' (D)	CAgr CSBt ECrN EPom ERea GTwd GTwe LRHS MCoo NOra SBmr SDea SKee WHar WJas
- 'Chorister Boy' (D)	CTho
- 'Christmas Pearmain' (D)	CAgr CTho ECrN GTwe SBmr SDea SKee WMat
- 'Christmas Pippin' (D)	CArg CDoC EPom ERea GQue LBuc LCro LRHS MCoo MWat NOra SBdl WMat
- 'Cider Lady's Finger' (Cider)	SKee
- 'Cissy' (D)	WGwG

Cultivar	Suppliers
- 'Claygate Pearmain' (D) ♀H6	CAgr CHab CTho CTri ECrN GTwe LRHS MCoo NOra SDea SKee SVic WHar WMat
- 'Clopton Red' (D)	ECrN
- 'Clydeside' (C)	GTwd
- 'Cobra' (F)	CAgr CDoC LBuc LRHS MAsh MBri MCoo NOra SPoG WHar WJas WMat
- 'Cockle Pippin' (D)	CAgr CTho SDea SKee
- 'Cockpit' (C)	CHab GTwd NWea
- 'Coeur de Boeuf' (C/D)	SKee
- 'Coleman's Seedling' (Cider)	CTho
- 'Collogett Pippin' (C/Cider)	CDoC CTho CTsd
- 'Colonel Vaughan' (C/D)	SKee
- 'Cornish Aromatic' (D)	CAgr CDoC CTho CTri CTsd GTwe LRHS NOra SBdl SBmr SDea SKee WHar WMat
- 'Cornish Gilliflower' (D)	CAgr CDoC CHab CTho CTsd EBee ECrN LRHS MCoo NOra SBdl SBmr SDea SKee WHar WMat
- 'Cornish Honeypin' (D)	CTho
- 'Cornish Longstem' (D)	CAgr CDoC CTho
- 'Cornish Mother' (D)	CDoC CTho CTsd
- 'Cornish Pine' (D)	CDoC CTho SDea SKee
- 'Coronation' (D)	CHab SDea SKee
- 'Corse Hill' (D)	CTho
- 'Costard' (C)	CHab SBmr
- 'Cottenham Seedling' (C)	SKee
- 'Coul Blush' (D)	GTwd GTwe SKee WMat
- 'Court of Wick' (D)	CAgr CDul CHab CTho CTri ECrN GTwd NOra SKee SVic WHar WMat
- 'Court Pendu Plat' (D)	CAgr CArg CHab CTho GQue GTwd LEdu MAsh MWat NOra NWea SBdl SBmr SDea SKee WHar WJas WMat WWct
- 'Cow Apple' (C)	SBdl
- 'Cox Cymraeg' (D)	WGwG
- 'Cox's Orange Pippin' (D)	Widely available
- 'Cox's Pomona' (C)	GTwd SDea WHar
- 'Cox's Rouge de Flandres' (D)	SKee
- 'Cox's Selfing' (D)	CDoC CDul CMac CTri CWSG CWib EPfP GTwe LBuc MAsh MBri MGos MNHC NLar SDea SKee SPer SPoG WHar WJas WMat WWct
- 'Crawley Beauty' (C)	CAgr CHab GTwd GTwe SBmr SDea SKee WHar WMat
- 'Crawley Reinette' (D)	CHab SKee
- 'Crimson Beauty of Bath' (D)	CAgr
- 'Crimson Bramley' (C)	IArd LAst SKee
- 'Crimson Cox' (D)	SDea
- 'Crimson Gravenstein' (C/D) **new**	SBmr
§ - 'Crimson King' (Cider/C)	CAgr SFrt
- 'Crimson King' (D)	CAgr CHab CTri
- 'Crimson Peasgood' (C)	ECrN SKee
- 'Crimson Queening' (D)	WHar
- 'Crimson Victoria' (Cider)	CTho
- Crispin	see *M. domestica* 'Mutsu'
- 'Croen Mochyn' (D)	WGwG
§ - 'Crowngold' (D)	EPom SBdl
- 'Cutler Grieve' (D)	GTwd SDea
- Cybèle = 'Delrouval' (D)	LRHS
- 'Dabinett' (Cider)	CAgr CArg CHab CTho CTri GTwe LAst LBuc LRHS NOra SBdl SDea SFrt SKee WHar WMat WWct
- 'D'Arcy Spice' (D)	CAgr ECrN EPfP ERea GQue MCoo MWat NOra SBmr SDea SFrt SKee WHar WMat WWct
- 'Dawn' (D)	SKee
- 'Deacon's Blushing Beauty' (C/D)	SDea
- 'Deacon's Millennium' (D)	SDea
- 'Decio' (D)	SKee
- Delbarestivale = 'Delcorf' (red) (D) ♀H6	LRHS
- 'Devon Crimson Queen' (D)	CTho
- 'Devonshire Buckland' (C)	CTho
- 'Devonshire Crimson Queen' (D)	SDea
- 'Devonshire Quarrenden' (D)	CAgr CDoC CDul CHab CTho CTsd GTwd NOra SBdl SBmr SDea SKee SVic WHar WMat
- 'Diamond' (D)	WGwG
- 'Discovery' (D) ♀H6	Widely available
- 'Discovery NFT' (D) **new**	SBdl
- 'Doctor Harvey' (C)	ECrN ERea SKee
- 'Doctor Kidd's Orange Red'	see *M. domestica* 'Kidd's Orange Red'
- 'Doddin' (D) **new**	WWct
- 'Domino' (C)	MCoo
- 'Don's Delight' (C)	CTho WMat
- 'Downton Pippin' (D)	CHab SKee WHar
- 'Dredge's Fame' (D)	CTho
- 'Duchess of Bedford' (D) **new**	SKee
- 'Duchess of Oldenburg' (C)	GTwd NOra SKee
- 'Duchess's Favourite' (D)	SKee
- 'Duck's Bill' (D)	SKee
- 'Dufflin' (Cider)	CTho
- 'Duke of Cornwall' (C)	CDoC CTho
- 'Duke of Devonshire' (D)	CSBt CTho CTri GTwd SDea SKee
- 'Dumeller's Seedling'	see *M. domestica* 'Dummellor's Seedling'
§ - 'Dummellor's Seedling' (C) ♀H6	CHab CTri GTwd MCoo MGos NOra SBdl SDea SKee WHar
- 'Dunkerton Late Sweet' (Cider)	CCVT CHab CTho LBuc SBmr WMat
- 'Dunn's Seedling' (D)	SDea
§ - 'Dutch Mignonne' (D)	SKee
- 'Early Blenheim' (D/C)	CTho
- 'Early Julyan' (C)	GTwd SKee
- 'Early Victoria'	see *M. domestica* 'Emneth Early'
- Early Windsor	see *M. domestica* 'Alkmene'
- 'Early Worcester'	see *M. domestica* 'Tydeman's Early Worcester'
- 'East Lothian Pippin' (C)	GTwd SKee
- 'Ecklinville' (C)	SBdl SDea
- 'Eden' (F)	WMat
- 'Edith Hopwood' (D)	ECrN
- 'Edward VII' (C) ♀H6	CHab MAsh NOra SBdl SDea SKee WHar WMat WWct
- 'Egremont Russet' (D) ♀H6	Widely available
- 'Ellis' Bitter' (Cider)	CTho GTwe LBuc SKee SVic
- 'Ellison's Orange' (D) ♀H6	Widely available
- 'Elmore Pippin' (D)	SBdl
- 'Elstar' (D) ♀H6	CCVT CLnd CWib ECrN EPom GTwe LAst NOra SDea SKee WHar
- 'Elton Beauty' (D)	SDea
§ - 'Emneth Early' (C) ♀H6	CAgr CHab CLnd ECrN ERea GTwd GTwe NOra SDea SKee WJas WMat WWct
- 'Empire' (D)	NOra SKee

	Cultivar	Suppliers
	- 'Encore' (C)	SDea
	- 'English Codlin' (C)	CTho CTri ERea
	- 'Epicure'	see *M. domestica* 'Laxton's Epicure'
	- 'Ernie's Russet' (D)	SDea
	- 'Eros' (D)	ECrN
	- 'Essex Pippin' (D)	ECrN
	- 'Evening Gold' (C)	SDea
	- 'Eve's Delight' (D)	SDea
	- 'Excelsior' (C)	ECrN
	- 'Exeter Cross' (D)	CSBt ECrN SDea
	- 'Exquisite' (D)	SKee
	- 'Fair Maid of Devon' (Cider)	CAgr CDul CTho WMat
	- 'Fairfield' (D)	CTho
	- 'Fairie Queen' (D) **new**	SKee
	- 'Falstaff'^{PBR} (D) ♀H6	CAgr CDul CTri ECrN EPfP EPom GTwe LSRN MGos NOra SBmr SCob SCoo SDea SKee SPer WHar
	- 'Fameuse' (D)	NOra
	- 'Farmer's Glory' (D)	CAgr CTho WMat
	- 'Fearn's Pippin' (D)	SKee
	- 'Feuillemorte' (D)	SKee
	- 'Fiessers Erstling' (C) **new**	SBdl
	- 'Fiesta'^{PBR} (D) ♀H6	Widely available
	- 'Fillbarrel' (Cider)	CHab
	- 'Fillingham Pippin' (C)	CHab
	- 'Firedance' (D) **new**	LRHS
	- 'Firmgold' (D)	SDea
	- 'First and Last' (D)	NOra WMat
	- 'Flame' (D)	ECrN
	- 'Flamenco'	see *M. domestica* 'Obelisk'
§	- 'Flower of Kent' (C)	CHab EPom MAsh NOra NWea SBdl SDea SKee WMat
	- 'Flower of the Town' (D)	CHab SBdl SKee
	- 'Forfar'	see *M. domestica* 'Dutch Mignonne'
	- 'Forge' (D)	CAgr CHab SDea SKee
	- 'Fortune'	see *M. domestica* 'Laxton's Fortune'
	- 'Forty Shilling' (D)	GTwd
	- 'Foxwhelp' (Cider)	CHab MGos NWea SKee
	- 'Francis' (D)	ECrN SKee
	- 'Frederick' (Cider)	CTho WMat
	- 'French Crab' (C)	SDea
	- 'Freyberg' (D)	NOra SKee
	- 'Fuji' (D)	NOra SDea SKee
	- 'Gala' (D)	CSBt EBee EPom LAst NOra SCob SCoo SDea SKee WHar WMat
	- 'Galaxy'^{PBR} (D)	NOra
	- 'Galloway Pippin' (C)	GTwd GTwe NOra SKee WMat
	- 'Garden Fountain' (D) **new**	LRHS
	- 'Garden Sun Red' (D) **new**	SBmr
	- 'Gascoyne's Scarlet' (C/D)	GTwd SBdl SDea SKee WHar
	- 'Gavin' (D)	CAgr SDea SKee
	- 'Genesis II' (C/D)	SDea
	- 'Genet Moyle' (C/Cider)	CTri GTwd MCoo WHar WMat
	- 'George Carpenter' (D)	CTri SDea SKee
	- 'George Cave' (D)	CDul CTho ECrN EMil GTwe IArd MCoo NOra SBmr SDea SEND SFrt WHar WJas
	- 'George Neal' (C) ♀H6	CAgr SBmr SDea SKee
	- 'Gibbon's Russet' (D)	IArd
	- 'Gilliflower of Gloucester' (D)	CTho
	- 'Gladstone' (D)	CAgr CTho GTwd NOra SKee WHar WMat WWct
	- 'Glansevin' (D)	WGwG
§	- 'Glass Apple' (C/D)	CTho
	- 'Gloria Mundi' (C)	SDea
	- 'Gloster '69' (D)	CLnd SDea
	- 'Gloucester Royal' (D)	CTho SKee
	- 'Gloucester Underleaf' (D)	CTho
	- 'Golden Ball' (Cider)	CTho
	- 'Golden Bittersweet' (D)	CAgr CTho WMat
	- 'Golden Delicious' (D) ♀H6	CCVT CDul CMac CSBt CWib EBee ECrN ELan EPom LAst LBuc LRHS MJak MMuc NOra NPri SBmr SCob SDea SEND SEWo SKee SVic WHar WMat
	- 'Golden Gate' (D) **new**	LRHS
	- 'Golden Glow' (C)	SDea
	- 'Golden Harvey' (D)	CAgr
	- 'Golden Knob' (D)	CTho CTri GTwd SKee
	- 'Golden Noble' (C) ♀H6	CAgr CDul CTho CTri ECrN EMil ERea GTwd GTwe IArd MCoo NOra SBdl SBmr SDea SKee
	- 'Golden Nugget' (D)	CAgr
	- 'Golden Pippin' (C)	CAgr NOra SKee WHar WMat
	- 'Golden Reinette' (D)	SKee
	- 'Golden Russet' (D)	CAgr ECrN NOra SDea SKee WHar
	- 'Golden Spire' (C)	CHab MCoo NOra SDea SKee WHar
	- 'Gooseberry' (C)	SKee
	- 'Goring' (Cider)	CTho
	- 'Grandpa Ailes' (D)	CTho
	- 'Grandpa Buxton' (C)	CHab
	- 'Granny Smith' (D)	CBcs CDul CSut CWib ECrN LAst LSRN NOra SBdl SDea SKee SPer SVic WHar WMat
	- 'Gravenstein' (D)	CHab GTwd NOra SDea SKee
§	- 'Green Balsam' (D)	CHab CTri
	- 'Green Roland' (C/D)	ECrN ERea
	- 'Greenfinch' (D) **new**	LRHS
	- 'Greensleeves'^{PBR} (D) ♀H6	CAgr CDul CMac CTri CWib EBee ECrN EPfP EPom GTwd GTwe LAst MAsh MGos MMuc NOra SBdl SBmr SCob SDea SEND SKee SLim SPer WHar WJas WMat WWct
	- 'Greenup's Pippin' (D)	CHab GTwd
	- 'Grenadier' (C) ♀H6	CAgr CDoC CHab CLnd CTri ECrN EPom GTwd GTwe MGos MJak MMuc MWat NLar NOra NWea SBdl SBmr SCob SDea SEND SKee SLon SPer WHar WJas WMat
	- 'Guillevic' (Cider)	CHab NWea
	- 'Gwell Na Mil' (D)	WGwG
	- 'Halstow Natural' (Cider)	CAgr CTho
	- 'Hambledon Deux Ans' (C)	SDea SKee
	- 'Hangy Down' (Cider)	CTho WMat
	- 'Harling Hero' (D)	ECrN
§	- 'Harry Master's Jersey' (Cider)	CAgr CTho CTri MWat NOra SBdl SDea SKee WHar WMat WWct
	- 'Harvester' (D)	CTho
	- 'Harvey' (C)	SDea
	- 'Hawthornden' (C)	CHab GTwd GTwe SKee
	- 'Hector MacDonald' (C)	GTwd
	- 'Herefordshire Beefing' (C)	SKee
	- 'Herefordshire Redstreak' (Cider)	CAgr CArg CDul LAst LBuc NOra SBdl WHar WMat
	- 'Herefordshire Russet'^{PBR} (D)	CDoC EPom ERea LBuc LRHS MAsh MBri MCoo MWat NLar NOra SBdl SKee SPer WHar WJas WMat WWct
	- 'Herring's Pippin' (C/D)	CTri SDea
	- 'Hoary Morning' (C)	CTho ECrN SDea SKee
	- 'Hocking's Green' (C/D)	CAgr CTho CTsd
	- 'Holland Pippin' (C)	WHar
	- 'Hollow Core' (C)	CAgr CTho

	Cultivar	Suppliers
	- 'Holstein' (D)	CTho NOra SBdl SDea SKee WHar
	- 'Honey Pippin' (D)	ECrN
	- 'Hood's Supreme' (D)	GTwd
	- 'Horneburger Pfannkuchen' (C)	SKee
	- 'Horsford Prolific' (D)	ECrN
	- 'Horsham Russet' (D)	EWTr
	- 'Hounslow Wonder' (C)	MWat
	- 'Howgate Wonder' (C)	Widely available
	- 'Hubbard's Pearmain' (D)	ECrN
	- 'Hunter's Majestic' (D/C)	ECrN
	- 'Huntingdon Codlin' (D)	SKee
	- 'Hunt's Duke of Gloucester' (D)	CTho
	- 'Hutton Square' (D) **new**	GTwd
	- 'Idared' (D) ♀H6	CWib ECrN NOra SBdl SDea SVic WHar WMat
	- 'Improved Keswick' (C/D)	CDoC CTho
	- 'Improved Lambrook Pippin' (Cider)	CTho CTri
	- 'Improved Redstreak' (Cider)	CTho
	- 'Ingrid Marie' (D)	NWea SBdl SDea
	- 'Irish Peach' (D)	CAgr CHab CTri ECrN EMil ERea GTwe IArd MCoo NOra SBmr SDea SKee WHar WMat
	- 'Isaac Newton's Tree'	see *M. domestica* 'Flower of Kent'
	- 'Isle of Wight Pippin' (D)	SBmr SDea
	- 'Isle of Wight Russet' (D)	SDea
	- 'Jackson's'	see *M. domestica* 'Crimson King' (Cider/C)
	- 'James Grieve' (D) ♀H6	Widely available
	- 'Jerseymac' (D)	SDea
	- 'Jester' (D)	ECrN SDea SKee
	- 'Joaneting' (D)	CAgr CHab
	- 'John Broad'	see *M. domestica* 'Captain Broad'
	- 'John Standish' (D)	CAgr CTri ERea SDea SKee
	- 'John Toucher's'	see *M. domestica* 'Crimson King' (Cider/C)
	- 'Johnny Andrews' (Cider)	CAgr CTho
	- 'Johnny Voun' (D)	CTho
	- 'Jonagold' (D) ♀H6	CLnd CTri CWib ECrN ELan EPom GTwe IArd NLar NOra SDea SKee SPer WWct
	- 'Jonagold Crowngold'	see *M. domestica* 'Crowngold'
§	- 'Jonagored'PBR (D)	NOra SDea WHar WMat
	- 'Jonathan' (D)	NOra SDea SKee
	- 'Jordan's Weeping' (C)	SDea
	- 'Josephine' (D)	SDea
	- 'Jubilee'	see *M. domestica* 'Royal Jubilee'
	- 'Julie's Late Golden' (F)	CTri
	- 'Jumbo' (C/D)	MAsh MBri MCoo NOra SKee WHar WJas WMat
	- 'Jupiter'PBR (D) ♀H6	CAgr CSBt CTri CWib ECrN EWTr GTwe LSRN MJak MRav NOra SBdl SDea SKee SLon WHar WJas WMat
	- 'Kapai Red Jonathan' (D)	SDea
	- 'Karmijn de Sonnaville' (D)	NOra SDea SKee
§	- 'Katja' (D)	Widely available
	- Katy	see *M. domestica* 'Katja'
	- 'Kent' (D)	ECrN SDea SKee
	- 'Kerry Pippin' (D)	IArd
	- 'Keswick Codlin' (C)	CHab CTho ECrN ERea GQue GTwd GTwe MBri MCoo NEgg NLar NOra NWea SBdl SBmr SDea SKee WHar WJas WMat
§	- 'Kidd's Orange Red' (D) ♀H6	CAgr CDul CLnd CMac CTri ECrN EPfP EPom GTwe LBuc LRHS MWat NOra SBdl SBmr SDea SFrt SKee SLon WHar WMat WWct
	- 'Kilkenny Pearmain' (D)	IArd
	- 'Kill Boy' (F)	CTho
	- 'Killerton Sharp' (Cider)	CTho
	- 'Killerton Sweet' (Cider)	CTho
	- 'Kim' (C/D) **new**	GTwd
	- 'King Byerd' (C/D)	CDoC CTho
	- 'King Coffee' (D)	WHar
	- 'King Luscious' (D)	SDea
§	- 'King of the Pippins' (D) ♀H6	CHab CLnd CTho CTri ECrN GTwd GTwe MCoo NOra SDea SKee SVic WHar
	- 'King Russet' (D) ♀H6	SDea
	- 'King's Acre Pippin' (D)	NOra SDea WHar WMat
	- 'Kingston Bitter' (Cider)	CTho
	- 'Kingston Black' (Cider/C)	CAgr CArg CDul CHab CTho CTri GTwe LBuc MGos NOra SBdl SDea SFrt SKee WMat
	- 'Kirton Fair' (D)	CTho
	- 'Knobby Russet' (D)	SBdl SKee
	- 'Lady Henniker' (C)	CDul CHab CTho ECrN GTwd SDea WHar
	- 'Lady Hollendale' (D)	SKee
	- 'Lady Lambourne' (C/D)	CHab
	- 'Lady of the Lake' (D) **new**	GTwd
	- 'Lady of the Wemyss' (C)	GTwd SKee
	- 'Lady Sudeley' (D)	CDoC CHab CTho GTwd SDea SKee
	- 'Lady's Finger' (C/D)	CDoC
	- 'Lady's Finger of Lancaster' (C/D)	CHab
	- 'Lady's Finger of Offaly' (D)	IArd SDea
	- 'Lake's Kernel' (D)	CTho
	- 'Lambourne Pippin' (F)	CTho
	- 'Lane's Prince Albert' (C) ♀H6	CAgr CHab CLnd CSBt CTri ECrN EPfP GTwe IArd MGos MRav MWat NOra NWea SBmr SCoo SDea SKee SVic WHar WJas WMat
	- 'Langley Pippin' (D)	SDea
§	- 'Langworthy' (Cider)	CTho
	- 'Lass o' Gowrie' (C)	GTwd
	- 'Laxton's Early Crimson' (D)	SKee
§	- 'Laxton's Epicure' (D) ♀H6	CAgr CHab ECrN LAst SDea SKee WHar
	- 'Laxton's Favourite' (D)	SKee
§	- 'Laxton's Fortune' (D) ♀H6	CArg CDul CHab CMac CSBt CTri CWib ECrN GTwd GTwe IArd LAst NOra SBdl SDea SKee WHar WJas WMat WWct
	- 'Laxton's Pearmain' (D)	MCoo
	- 'Laxton's Royalty' (D)	SDea
§	- 'Laxton's Superb' (D)	Widely available
	- 'Laxton's Triumph' (D) **new**	SKee
	- 'Leathercoat Russet' (D)	CAgr CTri
	- 'Lemon Pippin' (C)	EBee ECrN ELan NOra SDea SKee WHar
	- 'Lemon Pippin of Gloucestershire' (D)	CTho
	- 'Lemon Queen' (D)	GTwd
	- 'Liberty' (D)	SDea
	- 'Liddel's Seedling' (C/D)	GTwd
	- 'Limberland' (C)	CTho
	- 'Limelight' (D)	EBee ERea GTwd MAsh MBri MCoo NLar NOra SBdl SCoo SKee WHar WMat
	- 'Lobo' (D)	GTwd

- 'Lodi' (C) SDea
- 'London Pearmain' (D) ECrN
- 'London Pippin' (C) CAgr CTho
- 'Longkeeper' (D) CAgr CDoC CTho
- 'Longstem' (Cider) CTho
- 'Lord Burghley' (D) SDea
- 'Lord Derby' (C) CAgr CDoC CDul CHab CMac CTho CWib ECrN EPom GTwe MRav NOra SBdl SBmr SDea SEND SKee SPer SVic WHar WMat WWct
- 'Lord Grosvenor' (C) WHar
- 'Lord Hindlip' (D) CHab NOra SDea WMat WWct
- 'Lord Lambourne' (D) ♀[H6] Widely available
- 'Lord of the Isles' (Cider) CAgr CDoC
- 'Lord Rosebery' (D) GTwd
- 'Lord Stradbroke' (C) ECrN
- 'Lord Suffield' (C) CTri ECrN
- 'Lough Tree of Wexford' (D) IArd
- 'Love Beauty' (D) GTwd
- 'Lucombe's Pine' (D) CAgr CTho ECrN SVic
- 'Lucombe's Seedling' (D) CTho
- 'Lynn's Pippin' (D) ECrN
- 'Mabbott's Pearmain' (D) SDea SKee
- 'Machen' (D) WGwG
- 'Maclean's Favourite' (D) ECrN
- 'Madresfield Court' (D) SDea WWct
- 'Maggie Sinclair' (D) GTwd
- 'Major' (Cider) CAgr SFrt WMat
- 'Maldon Wonder' (D) ECrN
- 'Malling Kent' (D) SDea SFrt
- 'Maltster' (D) MCoo
- 'Manaccan Primrose' (C/D) CDoC
- 'Manks Codlin' (C) GTwd
- 'Mannington's Pearmain' (D) NOra SKee WMat
- 'Margil' (D) SDea WHar
- 'Markham Pippin' (D) MCoo
- 'Maxton' (D) ECrN
- 'May Queen' (D) SDea
- 'Maypole'[PBR] (D) SDea
- 'McIntosh' (D) NOra SKee
- 'Médaille d'Or' (Cider) SFrt SKee WMat
- 'Melba' (D) GTwd
- 'Melon' (D) SDea
- 'Melrose' (D) ECrN
- 'Merchant Apple' (D) CTho CTri
- 'Mère de Ménage' (C) WHar
- 'Meridian'[PBR] (D) CAgr CDoC ECrN LSRN MCoo NOra SBmr SDea WMat
- 'Merton Beauty' (D) SBdl
- 'Merton Champion' **new** SBdl
- 'Merton Knave' (D) SDea
- 'Merton Pearmain' (D) **new** SBdl
- 'Merton Prolific' (D) **new** SBdl
- 'Merton Russet' (D) SBdl SCob SDea SKee
- 'Merton Worcester' (D) ECrN SDea SKee
- 'Michaelmas Red' (D) GTwe SKee
- 'Michelin' (Cider) CAgr CTri GTwe LBuc MGos NOra SBdl SDea SKee WHar WMat WWct
- 'Miller's Seedling' (D) NOra SBdl SKee
- 'Millicent Barnes' (D) SDea
- 'Mollie's Delicious' (D) SKee
- 'Monarch' (C) CAgr CTri ECrN EPom GTwd GTwe SDea SKee
- 'Montfort' (D) ECrN
- 'Morgan's Sweet' (C/Cider) CHab CTho CTri NOra SBdl SDea SKee WMat
- 'Moss's Seedling' (D) SDea

§ - 'Mother' (D) ♀[H6] CAgr CDul CTri ECrN GTwe SBmr SDea SKee

§ - 'Mutsu' (C/D) CTri ECrN MRav NOra SDea SKee SPer WMat

- 'Nancy Jackson' (C) CHab GTwd
- 'Nanny' (D) SKee
- 'Nant Gwrtheyrn' (D) WGwG
- 'Nettlestone Pippin' (D) SDea
- 'New Rock Pippin' (D) SKee
- 'Newton Wonder' (C) ♀[H6] CAgr CDoC CDul CHab CSBt CTho CTri CWib ECrN EPom ERea GTwe IArd LAst MCoo MGos NOra SBdl SBmr SDea SFrt SKee WHar WJas WMat WWct
- 'Newtown Pippin' (D) SDea
- 'Nine Square' (D) CTho
- 'Nittany Red' (D) SDea
- 'No Pip' (C) CTho
- 'Nolan Pippin' (D) ECrN SBdl
- 'Nonpareil' (D) WHar
- 'Norfolk Beauty' (C) ECrN ERea
- 'Norfolk Beefing' (C) CHab ECrN ERea EWTr NOra SDea SKee WMat
- 'Norfolk Royal' (D) ECrN ERea GTwe NOra SBmr SDea SKee
- 'Norfolk Royal Russet' (D) ECrN ERea GTwd NOra SBdl SFrt SKee WMat
- 'Norfolk Winter Coleman' (C) ERea SKee
- 'Northcott Superb' (D) CTho
- 'Northern Greening' (C) WHar

§ - 'Northwood' (Cider) CTho WMat

- 'Nottingham Pippin' (D) **new** SBdl
- 'Nutmeg Pippin' (D) ECrN SDea
- Nuvar Cheerfull Gold (D) SKee
- Nuvar Freckles (D) SKee
- Nuvar Golden Elf (D) SKee
- Nuvar Golden Hills (D) SKee
- 'Oaken Pin' (D) CTho

§ - 'Obelisk'[PBR] (D) MAsh NOra SDea SKee WMat

- 'Old Pearmain' (D) SDea WHar
- 'Old Somerset Russet' (D) CTho
- 'Onibury Pippin' (D) WHar
- 'Orleans Reinette' (D) CAgr CLnd CTho CTri CWib ECrN EWTr GTwe IArd LBuc LRHS MWat NOra SBmr SDea SFrt WHar WJas WMat WWct
- 'Oslin' (D) GTwd GTwe SKee WMat
- 'Otava'[PBR] (C/D) SKee
- 'Paignton Marigold' (Cider) CTho
- 'Palmer's Rosey' (D) SKee
- 'Paroquet' (D) **new** SKee
- 'Pascoe's Pippin' (C/D) CTho
- 'Payhembury' (C/Cider) CAgr CTho CTri
- 'Pear Apple' (D) CAgr CTho
- 'Pearl' (D) NOra SDea WMat
- 'Peasgood's Nonsuch' (C) ♀[H6] CAgr CHab ECrN ERea GTwd GTwe IArd LRHS LSRN MAsh NOra SBdl SBmr SDea SFrt SKee SLon WMat
- 'Pendragon' (D) CTho
- 'Penhallow Pippin' (D) CTho
- 'Peter Lock' (C/D) CAgr CTho
- 'Peter's Pippin' (D) SDea

Name	Suppliers
- 'Peter's Seedling' (D)	SDea
- 'Pethyre' (Cider)	CCVT
- 'Pig Aderyn' (C)	CHab WGwG
- 'Pig y Colomen' (C)	WGwG
- 'Pig's Nose Pippin' (D)	CTsd
- 'Pig's Nose Pippin' Type III (D)	CAgr CTho
- 'Pig's Snout' (Cider/C/D)	CTho
- 'Pine Golden Pippin' (D)	GTwd
- 'Pineapple Russet' (C/D)	CAgr ERea MAsh
- 'Pinova'PBR (D)	CAgr EPom MCoo SBmr WHar
- 'Pitmaston Pine Apple' (D)	CArg CHab CTho CTri ECrN ERea GTwd IArd LAst LRHS MCoo MWat NOra SBdl SBmr SCob SDea SFrt SKee SLon WHar WMat WWct
- 'Pixie' (D) 🏆H6	CWib EPom GTwe MWat NOra SBmr SCob SDea SKee SLon WHar WWct
- 'Plum Vite' (D)	CAgr CTho CTri
- 'Plymouth Cross' (D)	GTwd
- 'Plympton Pippin' (C)	CDoC CTho CTri
- Polka = 'Trajan'PBR (D)	NOra SDea SKee
- 'Polly' (C/D)	CDoC
- 'Polly Prosser' (D)	SKee
- 'Polly Whitehair' (C/D)	CTho SDea
- 'Poltimore Seedling' (D)	CTho
- 'Pomeroy of Somerset' (D)	CHab CTho CTri
- 'Ponsford' (C)	CAgr CTho WMat
- 'Port Allen Russet' (C/D)	GTwd
- 'Port Wine'	see *M. domestica* 'Harry Master's Jersey'
- 'Porter's Perfection' (Cider)	NOra
- 'Prince Charles' (D)	SBdl
- 'Princesse' (F)	CLnd ECrN SDea
- 'Profit' (F)	CTho
- 'Pumpkin Sunset' **new**	SBdl
- 'Quarry Apple' (C)	CTho
- 'Queen' (C)	CAgr CTho ECrN SKee WHar
- 'Queen Cox' (D)	CLnd CSut CTri CWib ECrN EPom ERea LSRN NOra SBmr SDea SKee SLon SWvt WHar WMat
- 'Queens' (D)	CTho
- 'Quench' (Cider/D)	CTho
- 'Rajka'PBR (D)	CDoC GQue NOra SKee WWct
- 'Red Alkmene'	see *M. domestica* 'Red Windsor'
- 'Red Belle de Boskoop' (D)	CAgr
- 'Red Bramley' (C)	CDul CWib ECrN
- 'Red Charles Ross' (C/D)	SDea
- 'Red Delicious' (D)	NOra SKee
- 'Red Devil' (D)	CAgr CLnd CMac CTri CWSG ECrN EPom GTwd GTwe LAst LRHS MAsh MBri MRav MWat NLar NOra NPri SBdl SCob SCoo SDea SEWo SKee SLim SLon WHar WJas WMat WWct
- 'Red Ellison' (D)	CTho CTri ECrN ERea GTwe SDea
- 'Red Elstar' (D)	IArd
- 'Red Falstaff'PBR (D)	Widely available
- 'Red Fiesta' (F) **new**	LAst
- 'Red Fuji' (D)	SDea
- 'Red James Grieve' (D)	LSRN
- 'Red Joaneting' (D)	WHar
- 'Red Jonagold'	see *M. domestica* 'Jonagored'
- 'Red Jonathan' (D)	SDea
- 'Red Miller's seedling' (D)	ECrN SDea
- 'Red Pixie' (D)	GQue LRHS MCoo WMat
- 'Red Rattler' (D)	CTho CTri
- 'Red Roller' (D)	CTho
- 'Red Ruby' (F)	CTho
- 'Red Sauce' (C)	SKee
- 'Red Victoria' (C)	GTwe
§ - 'Red Windsor' (D)	CArg CDoC CDul CLnd CMac EBee EPom ERea LBuc LRHS MBri MWat NLar NOra SBdl SCoo SKee SLim SPoG WHar WJas WMat
- 'Redcoat Grieve' (D)	SDea
- 'Redsleeves' (D)	CAgr CLnd ECrN GTwd GTwe IArd NOra SDea
- Regali = 'Delkistar'PBR (D)	LRHS
- 'Reine des Reinettes'	see *M. domestica* 'King of the Pippins'
- 'Reinette Descardre' (D)	SVic
- 'Reinette Rouge Etoilée' (D)	SDea
- 'Resi'PBR (C/D)	WWct
- 'Reverend Greeves' (C)	SDea
- 'Reverend McCormick' (D)	CTho
- 'Reverend W. Wilks' (C)	CAgr CDoC CHab CSBt CTri ECrN EWTr GTwd LAst LRHS MAsh MBri NOra SBdl SBmr SDea SFrt SKee WHar WJas WMat WWct
- 'Ribston Pippin' (D) 🏆H6	CDul CTho CTri CWib ECrN ERea GTwd GTwe LBuc LRHS MCoo MRav MWat NOra NWea SBdl SDea SFrt SKee SLon WHar WJas WMat WWct
- 'Rival' (D)	CAgr SDea
- 'Rivers' Nonsuch' (D)	CHab SKee
- 'Rock' (C)	GTwd
- 'Rome Beauty' (D)	SDea
- 'Rosemary Russet' (D) 🏆H6	CAgr CHab CTho EBee EMil ERea GTwd GTwe LRHS MCoo NOra SBdl SBmr SDea SFrt SKee SLon WHar WMat WWct
- 'Rosette' (D)	EPom LBuc LCro LRHS MAsh NOra SPoG WMat
- 'Ross Nonpareil' (D)	CAgr IArd NOra SDea WHar WMat
- 'Rosy Blenheim' (D)	ECrN
- 'Roundway Magnum Bonum' (C/D)	CAgr CTho SDea
§ - 'Roxbury Russet' (D)	SKee
- 'Royal Gala' (D) 🏆H6	CMac ECrN EPom LBuc LRHS MRav SBdl SBmr SCob SDea SLon
§ - 'Royal Jubilee' (C)	SKee
- 'Royal Russet' (C)	ECrN SDea
- 'Royal Somerset' (C/Cider)	CTho CTri WMat
- Rubinette = 'Rafzubin' (D)	ECrN NOra SDea SKee
- Rubinette Rosso = 'Rafzubex'PBR (D)	NOra WMat
- 'Rubinola'PBR (D)	SKee WWct
- 'Ruby' Thorrington (D)	ECrN
- 'Saint Cecilia' (D)	CHab SDea WGwG
§ - 'Saint Edmund's Pippin' (D) 🏆H6	CHab CTho ECrN ELan EPfP ERea GTwd GTwe MCoo NOra SBmr SDea SFrt SKee
- 'Saint Edmund's Russet'	see *M. domestica* 'Saint Edmund's Pippin'
- 'Saint Everard' (D)	SKee
- 'Saint Martin's' (D) **new**	SKee
- 'Saltcote Pippin' (D)	SKee WMat
- 'Sam Young' (D)	CAgr IArd
- 'Samba' (C/D) **new**	LCro LOPS

- 'Sandlands' (D)	SDea
- 'Sandlin Duchess' (D) **new**	NOra WMat
- 'Sandringham' (C)	ECrN
- 'Sanspareil' (D)	CAgr
- 'Santana'[PBR] (D)	MBri NOra WMat
- 'Saturn' (D)	CAgr CCVT CTri ERea NOra SBdl SBmr SDea SKee WHar WMat WWct
- 'Saw Pits' (D)	CAgr
- 'Scarlet Crofton' (D)	IArd
- 'Scarlet Nonpareil' (D)	SDea
- 'Scarlet Pearmain' (D) **new**	GTwd
- 'Scotch Bridget' (C)	CArg CHab GBin GQue GTwd LRHS NBid NOra SCoo SKee WHar WMat WWct
- 'Scotch Dumpling' (C)	GBin GKin GQue GTwd GTwe MCoo NOra SKee WHar WMat
- 'Scotia' (C/D) **new**	GTwd
- 'Scrumptious'[PBR] (D) ♀H6	Widely available
- 'Seaton House' (C)	GTwd
- 'Sercombe's Natural' (Cider)	CTho
- 'Severn Bank' (C)	CTho
- 'Sharleston Pippin' (D)	SBdl
- 'Sheep's Nose' (C)	CHab CTho IArd SBdl SDea SKee
- 'Shenandoah' (C)	SKee
- 'Sidney Strake' (C)	CAgr
- 'Sir Isaac Newton's'	see *M. domestica* 'Flower of Kent'
- 'Sir John Thornycroft' (D)	SDea
- 'Sisson's Worksop Newtown' (D)	MCoo SKee
- 'Slack Ma Girdle' (Cider)	CLnd CTho NOra SKee WMat
- 'Smart's Prince Arthur' (C)	CHab SDea
- 'Smoothie' (C/D) **new**	SBdl
- 'Snell's Glass Apple'	see *M. domestica* 'Glass Apple'
- 'Somerset Lasting' (C)	CTri
- 'Somerset Redstreak' (Cider)	CAgr CHab CTho CTri GTwe NOra SBdl WHar WMat
- 'Sops in Wine' (Cider/D)	CTho CTsd ECrN NOra SVic WMat
- 'Sour Bay' (Cider)	CAgr CTho
- 'Sour Natural'	see *M. domestica* 'Langworthy'
- 'Sowman's Seedling' (C) **new**	GTwd
- 'Spartan' (D)	Widely available
- 'Spencer' (D)	CTri ECrN GTwd
- 'Spotted Dick' (Cider)	CTho
- 'Stamford Pippin' (D)	SDea
- 'Stanway Seedling' (C)	ECrN
- 'Star of Devon' (D)	SDea
- 'Stark' (D)	SDea
- 'Starking' (D)	ECrN
- 'Stark's Earliest' (D)	SVic
- 'Steyne Seedling' (D)	SDea
- 'Stirling Castle' (C)	CAgr GBin GQue GTwd NOra SKee WMat
- 'Stobo Castle' (C)	GTwd SKee
- 'Stockbearer' (C)	CTho
- 'Stoke Edith Pippin' (D)	SBdl WHar
- 'Stoke Red' (Cider)	CTho NOra SFrt SKee WMat
- 'Strawberry Pippin' (D)	CTho
- 'Striped Beefing' (C)	ECrN ERea
- 'Sturmer Pippin' (D)	CSBt CTri ECrN GTwe MWat NOra SBdl SDea SKee WHar WWct
* - 'Sugar Apple' (F)	CTho
- 'Sugar Bush' (C/D)	CTho
- 'Sugar Loaf'	see *M. domestica* 'Sugar Apple'
- 'Summerred' (D)	ECrN
- 'Sunburn' (D)	ECrN
- 'Sunlight'[PBR] (F)	MWat
- 'Sunnydale' (D/C)	SDea
- 'Sunrise'[PBR] (D)	NOra SCob SKee WHar
- 'Sunset' (D) ♀H6	Widely available
- 'Suntan' (D) ♀H6	CDoC CWib ECrN EWTr LAst MWat NOra SDea SKee
- 'Superb'	see *M. domestica* 'Laxton's Superb'
- 'Sussex Mother' (C/D)	CHab SKee
- 'Sweet Alford' (Cider)	CTho SBdl WMat WWct
- 'Sweet Bay' (Cider)	CAgr CTho
- 'Sweet Cleave' (Cider)	CTho
- 'Sweet Coppin' (Cider)	CTho CTri WMat
- 'Sweet Lilibet'	see *M. domestica* 'Red Windsor'
- 'Sweet Society' (D)	MAsh MCoo NOra SKee WHar WJas WMat
- 'Sylvia' (D) **new**	GTwd
- 'Tale Sweet' (Cider)	CTho
- 'Tan Harvey' (Cider)	CTho
- 'Taunton Cross' (D)	CAgr WMat
- 'Taunton Fair Maid' (Cider)	CTho
- 'Taylor's' (Cider)	CAgr SDea
- 'Ten Commandments' (Cider/D)	SBdl SDea WWct
- Tentation = 'Delblush'[PBR] (D)	SBmr SDea
- 'Tewkesbury Baron' (D)	CTho
- 'The Rattler' (Cider)	CDoC
- 'Thomas Jeffrey' (D)	GTwd
- 'Thomas Rivers' (C)	SDea SKee
- 'Thorle Pippin' (D)	GTwd SKee
- 'Thurso' (D)	GTwd
- Tickled Pink = 'Baya Marisa' (C/D)	EPom ERea LCro LOPS LRHS MBri NOra SPer WMat
- 'Tidicombe Seedling' (D)	CTho WMat
- 'Tom Putt' (C)	CAgr CArg CCVT CDul CHab CLnd CTho CTri CWib ECrN GTwe LBuc NOra SBdl SDea SKee WHar WJas WMat WWct
- 'Tommy Knight' (D)	CAgr CDoC CTho
- 'Topaz'[PBR] (D)	SKee
- 'Totnes Apple' (D)	CTho
- 'Tower of Glamis' (C)	CHab GBin GQue GTwd GTwe SKee
- Town Farm Number 59 (Cider)	CTho
- 'Tregonna King' (C/D)	CDoC CTho CTsd
- 'Tremlett's Bitter' (Cider)	CAgr CHab CTho NOra SBdl SDea SVic WMat
- 'Trwyn Mochyn' (C)	WGwG
§ - 'Tuscan'[PBR] (D)	MCoo MGos SDea SKee
- 'Twinings Pippin' (D)	SKee
§ - 'Tydeman's Early Worcester' (D)	CAgr CDul CHab CLnd CWib ECrN GTwe SBdl SBmr SDea SKee WWct
- 'Tydeman's Late Orange' (D)	CHab CTri ECrN GTwe IArd LAst MCoo NOra NWea SBdl SBmr SDea SFrt SKee WHar WMat
- 'Uncle John's Cooker' (C)	IArd
- 'Underleaf' (D)	SKee
- 'Upton Pyne' (C/D)	CTho SDea
- 'Vallis Apple' (Cider)	CTho
- 'Veitch's Perfection' (C/D)	CTho WMat
- 'Vicar of Beighton' (D)	ECrN
- 'Vicary's Late Keeper' (C)	CTho
- 'Vickey's Delight' (D)	NWea SDea
- 'Vista-bella' (D)	ECrN SDea SKee
- 'Wadey's Seedling' (D)	SKee
- 'Wagener' (D)	ECrN SDea SKee
- Waltz = 'Telamon'[PBR] (D)	SDea
- 'Warden' (D)	GTwd
- 'Warner's King' (C) ♀H6	CTho CTri GTwd NOra SBdl SDea SKee WHar
- 'Warrior' (F)	CTho

- 'Wealthy' (D)	SDea SKee
- 'Weight' (C)	GTwd
- 'Wellington' (C)	see *M. domestica* 'Dummellor's Seedling'
- 'Wellington' (Cider)	CAgr CTho
- 'Welsh Russet' (D)	SDea
- 'West View Seedling' (D)	ECrN
- 'White Alphington' (Cider)	CTho
- 'White Close Pippin' (Cider)	CTho
- 'White Melrose' (C)	GBin GQue GTwd GTwe NOra SDea SKee WMat
- 'White Transparent' (C/D)	SDea SKee
- 'Wick White Styre' (Cider)	CTho
- 'William Crump' (D)	CDul CHab CTho ECrN NOra SDea WHar WMat WWct
- 'Willoughby' (D)	MCoo
- 'Windsor' (F) **new**	SBmr
- 'Winston' (D) ♀H6	CAgr CCVT CMac CSBt CSut CTri ECrN MCoo NWea SBmr SDea SKee SVic WHar WWct
- 'Winter Banana' (D)	CHab ECrN GQue LEdu LRHS MCoo NOra SDea SKee SVic WHar WMat
- 'Winter Gem' (D)	CAgr CArg CCVT CDul CLnd ECrN EPom ERea LAst LBuc NOra SBdl SBmr SCob SDea SKee WHar WJas WMat
- 'Winter Lawrence' (D)	CTho
- 'Winter Peach' (D/C)	CAgr CTho ECrN
- 'Winter Pearmain' (D)	WHar
- 'Winter Quarrenden' (D)	SDea
- 'Winter Queening' (D/C)	SDea
- 'Winter Stubbard' (C)	CTho
- 'Wintergreen' (C)	CDoC
- 'Woodbine'	see *M. domestica* 'Northwood'
- 'Woodford' (C)	ECrN
- 'Woolbrook Pippin' (D)	CAgr CTho WMat
- 'Woolbrook Russet' (C)	CTho ECrN
- 'Worcester Pearmain' (D) ♀H6	Widely available
- 'Wormsley Pippin' (D)	ECrN
- 'Wyatt's Seedling'	see *M. domestica* 'Langworthy'
- 'Wyken Pippin' (D)	ECrN SDea WWct
- 'Yarlington Mill' (Cider)	CAgr CHab CTho CTri NOra SBdl SDea SFrt SKee SVic WMat WWct
- 'Yellow Ingestrie' (D)	CHab ERea GTwd LRHS MCoo NOra WHar WMat WWct
- 'Yellow Styre' (Cider)	CTho
- 'Yorkshire Greening' (C)	CHab GTwd NOra SBdl WHar
- 'Zabergäu Renette' (D)	NOra
'Donald Wyman'	CLnd EPfP MAsh NLar SCoo WMat
§ 'Echtermeyer'	CTri SDea
'Elise Rathke'	CLnd
'Evelyn'	CLnd WMat
§ 'Evereste' ♀H6	Widely available
florentina	CTho EPfP SBrt
- 'Rosemoor'	CLnd EBee
- 'Skopje'	EPfP WMou
floribunda ♀H6	Widely available
fusca	CLnd
'Gardener's Gold'	CTho
× ***gloriosa*** 'Oekonomierat Echtermeyer'	see *M.* 'Echtermeyer'
'Golden Gem'	CLnd EPfP GQue MAsh NOra NOrn SEWo WMat
'Golden Hornet'	see *M.* × *zumi* 'Golden Hornet'
'Gorgeous'	CDul CLnd CMac CNWT COtt CTho EBee ECrN EPfP GTwe LBuc LHop LRHS LSRN MAsh MBri MRav MSwo NOra NWea SCoo SEWo SKee SLim SPer SPoG WJas WMat WMou WWct
'Harry Baker'	CCVT CDul CLnd CMac COtt ECrN EMil EPfP EPom ERea LAst LRHS LSRN MAsh MBlu MBri MRav NOra SCoo SLim SPer SPoG WHar WJas WMat WMou WWct
× ***hartwigii***	CLnd
'Hillieri'	see *M.* × *scheideckeri* 'Hillieri'
'Honeycrisp' PBR	LRHS NOra WHar WMat
'Hornsea Herring' (D/C) **new**	LEdu
hupehensis ♀H6	CDoC CDul CLnd CMCN CSBt CTho CTri EBee EPfP IMou LHop MBlu MGos MRav NOra NWea SDix SPer WMat WMou
'Hyde Hall Spire'	SCoo
'Indian Magic'	CLnd EBee LRHS MAsh MBri NLar NOra WMat
'Indian Summer'	CLnd
Jelly King = 'Mattfru' ♀H6	CLnd EBee ECrN EPom LRHS LSRN MAsh MBri NLar NOra NWea SPer SPoG WHCr WHar WMat WMou
'John Downie' (C)	Widely available
'Kaido'	see *M.* × *micromalus*
kansuensis	CLnd
'Kemp'	SDea
'Lady Northcliffe'	CDul CLnd
'Laura' ♀H6	CDul CMac COtt EPfP EPom ERea LRHS LSRN MAsh MBri NLar NOra SCoo SKee SLim SLon SPoG WHar WJas WMat
'Lisa'	CLnd
'Louisa'	CLnd EPfP LCro NOra NWea SCoo SGol WMat
× ***magdeburgensis***	CCVT CDul CLnd CSBt
'Mary Potter'	CLnd
§ × ***micromalus***	CLnd NLar
× ***moerlandsii***	CLnd
- 'Liset'	CDul CLnd CSBt CWib EBee ECrN LHop MRav NEgg NLar NOra SCoo WFar
§ - 'Profusion'	CBcs CDul COtt CTri EBee ECrN ELan LAst LCro LOPS MGos MJak MRav MSwo NOra NPri NWea SCob SEND SGol SPer SWvt WJas
'Mokum'	CLnd
'Molten Lava'	CLnd MAsh
'Montreal Beauty'	CLnd WJas
niedzwetzkyana	CLnd CTho
Nuvar Marble	EBee MBri NOra NOrn SKee WMat
orthocarpa	CLnd
Perpetu	see *M.* 'Evereste'
'Pink Mushroom'	EWTr
'Pink Perfection'	CDoC COtt ECrN NOra NPri NWea WMat
'Pond Red'	CLnd
'Prairifire'	CDul CLnd LRHS MAsh MBri NOra NPri SCoo SLim SLon SPoG WMat WMou
prattii	CLnd CTho EPfP
- 'Pourpre Noir'	CLnd
'Princeton Cardinal' ♀H6	CLnd CMac EPfP MAsh MBri SCoo SLim SPoG
'Professor Sprenger'	see *M.* × *zumi* 'Professor Sprenger'
'Profusion'	see *M.* × *moerlandsii* 'Profusion'
prunifolia	MBlu
- var. ***rinkii***	CLnd

§	× ***purpurea*** 'Aldenhamensis'	CLnd SDea WHar
	- 'Eleyi'	CNWT LAst NWea
	- 'Lemoinei'	CDul CLnd
	- 'Neville Copeman'	CCVT CDoC CDul CLnd EPom EWTr WJas
	- 'Pendula'	see *M.* 'Echtermeyer'
	'R.J. Fulcher'	CLnd CTho
	'Ralph Shay'	CLnd
	'Red Ace'	CDul
	'Red Barron'	CLnd
	'Red Glow'	CDul ECrN MAsh WJas
	'Red Jade'	see *M.* × *scheideckeri* 'Red Jade'
§	'Red Jonaprince'[PBR] **new**	WMat
	Red Obelisk = 'Dvp Obel'	CLnd LBuc LRHS MBri NOra SCoo WMat
	'Red Peacock'	CLnd
	'Red Prince'	see *M.* 'Red Jonaprince'
	'Robinson'	CLnd
§	× ***robusta***	CLnd GTwe LSRN NWea SLon
	- 'Dolgo'	CLnd CSBt EPom ERea LCro MBlu NLar NOra SCoo SEWo SKee SPer WHar WMat WMou
	- 'Red Sentinel' ♀H6	Widely available
	- 'Red Siberian'	SDea SPer
	- 'Yellow Siberian'	CLnd
	'Rosehip'	CLnd EBee LBuc MBri NOra NOrn WMat
	'Royal Beauty'	CDoC CDul CLnd CWib EPfP EWTr LAst LRHS MAsh MBri MGos MJak MSwo NOra NOrn NPri SCoo SLon SPer WHar WMat WMou
	'Royalty'	Widely available
	'Rudolph'	CCVT CDul CLnd CNWT EBee ECrN EWTr GKin LBuc LHop LSRN MAsh MGos NOra NOrn SCoo SEWo SLim SPer SPoG WJas WMat
	'Ruth Ann'	CLnd
	sargentii	CDul CTho EWTr LRHS NOra NWea
	- 'Candy Mint' **new**	LRHS WMat
	- 'Tina'	CLnd LRHS MAsh WMat
	'Satin Cloud'	CLnd
§	× ***scheideckeri*** 'Hillieri'	CDul CLnd MBlu
§	- 'Red Jade'	CDul CLnd CMac COtt CTri CWib EBee ECrN ELan EWTr LAst MGos MRav MSwo NOrn NWea SPer WHar WJas
	Siberian crab	see *M.* × *robusta*
	sieboldii	see *M. toringo*
	sieversii	CDul CLnd
	sikkimensis B&SWJ 2431	WCru
	'Silver Drift'	CLnd
	'Simon' **new**	WMat
	'Snowcloud'	CDul CLnd ECrN MAsh NOrn SLim
	'Snowdrift'	CLnd
	spectabilis	CLnd
	'Street Parade'	CLnd
	× ***sublobata***	CLnd
	Sugar Tyme = 'Sutyzam'	CLnd
	'Sun Rival' ♀H6	CCVT CDoC CDul CLnd CMac COtt CSBt EPfP LRHS MAsh MBlu MBri MRav NOra NOrn SBmr SCoo SEWo SLim SPoG WHar WJas WMat
	sylvestris	CArg CCVT CDul CHab CLnd ECrN EPfP LBuc MJak MMuc MRav NBes NLar NWea SEND SEWo SPer SPre WMou
	'Tinsley Quince' (D) **new**	WMat
§	***toringo***	COtt CTho ECrN EPfP LEdu MBri NOra WSHC
I	- var. ***arborescens***	CLnd CTho
	- 'Browers'	CNWT
	- 'Scarlett' ♀H6	CDul CLnd EPfP IArd LRHS LSRN MBri NLar NOra NWea SCoo SEWo SLim SPoG WHar WMat WMou
	- 'Wintergold'	MMuc
	- 'Wooster'	CLnd
	toringoides	see *M. bhutanica*
	transitoria ♀H6	CDoC CDul CLnd CMac CTho EBee ECrN ELan EPfP EWTr GKin LRHS MAsh MBlu MBri MRav NLar NOra NWea SCoo SLau SPer WMat WMou WPGP
	- 'Thornhayes Tansy'	CDul CTho EBee LRHS NOra SLim WMat
	trilobata	CDul CLnd CTho EBee ELan EPfP GKin LHop MBlu MGos MMuc SCoo SEND
	- 'Guardsman'	EPfP MBlu MBri NPri WMat
	tschonoskii	CDoC CDul CLnd CMCN CMac COtt CSBt CTri CWib ELan EPfP EWTr GTwe LAst MBlu MBri MGos MJak MMuc NOrn NPri NWea SEND SPer SWvt WJas WMou
	'Van Eseltine'	CAgr CLnd CMac CSBt CWib EBee ECrN EPfP MAsh SPer WHar WJas
	'Veitch's Scarlet'	CDul CHab CLnd CSBt LEdu
	Velvet Pillar = 'Velvetcole' **new**	SPer SPoG
	Weeping Candied Apple = 'Weepcanzam'	CLnd
	'White Angel'	CLnd
	'White Star'	CCVT CDoC CDul CLnd CSBt EBee ECrN NOra SLon WMat
	'Winter Gold'	CDul LAst SGol
	'Wisley Crab'	CLnd LAst SDea SLon WMou
	yunnanensis	EPfP
	- var. ***veitchii***	CTho
	× ***zumi*** var. ***calocarpa***	CLnd
§	- 'Golden Hornet'	Widely available
§	- 'Professor Sprenger'	CLnd CSam EPfP MBri NOra SCoo

Malva (*Malvaceae*)

	alcea	CAgr
	- var. ***fastigiata***	CMac ECGP LRHS NBro SPer SRms
	bicolor	see *Lavatera maritima*
	moschata	CAgr CBcs CBod EAJP EBee ECha ELan ENfk EPfP GAbr GJos GPoy MHer MMuc MNHC NLar NMir NWad SIde SPer SPlb SRms SWat WHar WHer WJek WMoo WOut
§	- f. ***alba*** ♀H5	CBcs CBod CSpe EAJP ECha ELan EPfP GAbr GJos GMaP IFro LEdu LHop LRHS MHer MNHC NBir NGBl NLar SPer SPhx SPoG SRms SWvt WBrk WGwG WHlf WKif WMnd WMoo
	- 'Appleblossom'	CBod ELon
	- 'Romney Marsh'	see *Althaea officinalis* 'Romney Marsh'
	- 'Rosea'	EPfP GMaP LAst LRHS NPer SPoG SWvt WHar
	- 'Snow White'	see *M. moschata* f. *alba*
	sylvestris	CArn CBod NBro SRms SWat WHfH WJek WMoo

- 'Blue Fountain' PBR	SAko WKif
- 'Brave Heart'	SPav SWvt WHlf
- Marina = 'Dema' PBR	NLar SAko
- var. ***mauritiana***	CBod MSpe NPer WMoo
- - 'Bibor Fehlo'	EBee WHlf
- - 'Mystic Merlin'	SPav
- - 'Primley Blue'	CAby CBod ECtt ELan EPfP GMaP ILea LRHS MCot MRav NPer WBor
- - 'Zebrina'	CBod EPfP MSpe NGBl NPer SAko SWvt WMoo
- 'Perry's Blue'	NPer
- 'Windsor Castle'	MPie

Malvaviscus (*Malvaceae*)

arboreus	CHll

mandarin see *Citrus reticulata* Mandarin Group

mandarin, Cleopatra see *Citrus reticulata*

Mandevilla (*Apocynaceae*)

× ***amabilis*** 'Alice du Pont' ♀H1c	CMan ELan EShb MOWG SPre
- 'Passion Pink' (Parfait Series) (d)	IDee
'Audrey' PBR (Vogue Series)	CSpe CWGN LSou
boliviensis ♀H1c	CMan CRHN MOWG
'Ginger' (Vogue Series)	CAbb CWGN EShb LHop LSou
§ ***laxa*** ♀H1c	CBot CHGN CHll CMan CRHN CSpe ELan LRHS MOWG SBrt SVen WHrl WSHC
Rio White = 'Fisrix Whit' PBR (Rio Series)	CMan
'Ruby' (Vogue Series)	CAbb CWGN IDee LSou
sanderi	EShb SPre
- 'Pink of Hint'	CMan
splendens ♀H1c	CBcs CHll CMan MOWG
suaveolens	see *M. laxa*
(Sundaville Series) Sundaville Cosmos Crimson King = 'Sunmandecrikin' PBR	CMan
- Sundaville Cosmos Pink = 'Sunmandecos' PBR	CMan
- Sundaville Cosmos White = 'Sunmandeho' PBR	CMan
- Sundaville Cream Pink = 'Sunparapibra' PBR	CMan
- Sundaville Dark Red = 'Sunparabeni' PBR	CMan EBee
- Sundaville Pretty Red = 'Sunmanderemi' PBR	CMan
- Sundaville Pretty Rose = 'Sunparaprero' PBR	CMan
- Sundaville Red = 'Sunmandecrim' PBR	CMan
- Sundaville Red Star = 'Sunparasuji' PBR	CMan

Mandragora (*Solanaceae*)

autumnalis	WSFF
§ ***officinarum***	GCal GPoy SBrt SMad

Manfreda see *Agave*

elongata	see *Agave gracillima*
maculosa	see *Agave maculosa*
sileri	see *Agave sileri*
undulata	see *Agave undulata*
variegata	see *Agave variegata*
virginica	see *Agave virginica*

× *Mangave* see *Agave*

'Macha Mocha'	see *Agave* 'Macha Mocha'

Mangifera (*Anacardiaceae*)

indica (F)	SPre

Manglietia see *Magnolia*

yunnanensis	see *Magnolia insignis*

mango see *Mangifera indica*

Manihot (*Euphorbiaceae*)

carthaginensis	SPlb
grahamii	WCot

Mantisalca (*Asteraceae*)

salmantica	WCot

Mantisia (*Zingiberaceae*)

saltatoria PAB 4208	LEdu WPGP

Maranta (*Marantaceae*)

leuconeura	XBlo
var. ***erythroneura*** ♀H1b	
- var. ***kerchoveana*** ♀H1b	XBlo

Marchantia (*Marchantiaceae*)

polymorpha	CArn

Mariscus see *Cyperus*

marjoram, pot see *Origanum onites*

marjoram, sweet see *Origanum majorana*

marjoram, wild, or oregano see *Origanum vulgare*

Marrubium (*Lamiaceae*)

§ ***bourgaei*** var. ***bourgaei*** 'All Hallows Green'	ECha ECtt LRHS MRav NEgg
candidissimum	see *M. incanum*
* ***cylleneum*** 'Velvetissimum'	WCot XSen
§ ***incanum***	WCot XSen
lutescens	XSen
supinum	NBFr WHea
vulgare	CArn CBod ENfk GPoy MHer MNHC SIde SRms WHfH WJek

Marsdenia (*Asclepiadaceae*)

formosana CWJ 12354	WCru
oreophila	CRHN ELan GCal LRHS SKHP WPGP WSHC

Marshallia (*Asteraceae*)

grandiflora	CDes EBee
trinerva	ELon

Marsilea (*Marsileaceae*)

mutica	EWay
quadrifolia	EWay
- variegated (v)	LLWG

Mascarena see *Hyophorbe*

Massonia (*Asparagaceae*)

depressa ♀H2	CTal GKev NRog
echinata	CAbP CDes LSou NRog WCot
pustulata ♀H2	EUJe NRog WCot

Mathiasella (*Apiaceae*)

bupleuroides CFis LSou
- 'Green Dream' CAbP CAby CAvo CBcs CBod CBre CMea CSpe EBee ECtt EWld EWoo GBin LCro LRHS MAvo MBel MNrw NCGa NSti SCob SDix SLon SPoG WCot

Matricaria (*Asteraceae*)

chamomilla see *M. recutita*
maritima see *Tripleurospermum maritimum*
parthenium see *Tanacetum parthenium*
§ **recutita** GPoy MNHC
- 'Bodegold' WHfH
tchihatchewii XSen
'White Star' EPfP

Matteuccia (*Onocleaceae*)

orientalis ♀H5 CDTJ CDes CKel CLAP CLet CTal CWCL ECha EFer EPfP ERod GCal GMaP IBal LEdu LPal LRHS MMuc NBid NLar NMyG SEND WMoo WPnP XLum
pensylvanica CLAP
struthiopteris ♀H4 Widely available
- 'Jumbo' CLAP ISha LRHS
- 'The King' WCot

Matthiola (*Brassicaceae*)

fruticulosa 'Alba' CAby CDes EPfP WBor WPGP
- subsp. **perennis** NSti WHal
incana CBod LRHS MArl SVic WKif
- **alba** CHid CWld EBee ECha ELan LRHS LSou MAvo NCGa SEND SPad SPav WCot
- purple-flowered CWld SEND
- 'Vintage' mixed **new** NPri
scapifera CPBP
white-flowered perennial CArn CSpe NPer

Maurandya (*Plantaginaceae*)

§ **barclayana** IDee WHea
erubescens see *Lophospermum erubescens*
'Magic Dragon' see *Lophospermum* 'Magic Dragon'
'Red Dragon' see *Lophospermum* 'Red Dragon'

Maytenus (*Celastraceae*)

boaria CBcs CMCN EPfP GGal IArd IDee LEdu MGos NLar SEND WPat WSHC
disticha (Hook.f.) Urb. LEdu
magellanica SAko WPGP

Mazus (*Phrymaceae*)

miquelii EBee
reptans CBod CCon CDes ECho ECtt GEdr MSCN MSKA NLar NPer NQui WRHF XLum
- B&SWJ CExl
- 'Albus' CBod CCon ECho ECtt LLWG NLar SPlb
- 'Blue' LLWG

Mecardonia (*Plantaginaceae*)

'Sundona Early Yellow' LAst MCot

Meconopsis ✿ (*Papaveraceae*)

§ **baileyi** ♀H4 CBcs CBod CSBt CTri EBee ELan EPfP Epot GBuc GCra GGGa GKev GKin IBoy ITim LCro LOPS LRHS MBel MBri MMuc NBir NEgg NSum SPoG WFar WMoo
* - var. **alba** CBod EBee ELan GAbr GBin GCra GGGa GKev IMou LRHS MBel NSum
- 'Hensol Violet' CBod CPne EBee GBuc GCra GEdr GGGa GKev NSum
- violet-flowered ITim
Ballyrogan form GEdr
× **beamishii** GKev
betonicifolia misapplied see *M. baileyi*
'Cally Purple' **new** GCal
cambrica CExl CMac CTri EBee EHrv ELan EPfP EWoo LEdu MMuc WBrk WCot WFar WHer
- 'Anne Greenaway' (d) WCot
- var. **aurantiaca** WCot
- double-flowered (d) WCot
- - orange (d) NBir WCot
§ - 'Frances Perry' GCal WCot
- 'Muriel Brown' (d) WCot
- 'Rubra' see *M. cambrica* 'Frances Perry'
chelidoniifolia CAby GCra LRHS NBid WCru
× **cookei** EBee GKev NSum
- 'Old Rose' GBin GBuc GEdr GGGa GMaP NHar NLar
'Evelyn' GEdr
Fertile Blue Group EBee ITim
- 'Blue Ice' see *M.* (Fertile Blue Group) 'Lingholm'
- 'Cally Lingholm' GCal
- 'Lingholm' Widely available
- 'Louise' GEdr
- 'Mop-head' ♀H5 GEdr GMaP
§ George Sherriff Group GCal GCra MArl NBir
- 'Ascreavie' GBuc GEdr GMaP
- 'Barney's Blue' GEdr GMaP
- 'Dalemain' ♀H5 GBuc GEdr GMaP
- 'Branklyn' ambig. CExl GEdr WPGP
- 'Huntfield' GBin GEdr GGGa GKev GMaP
- 'Jimmy Bayne' GBin GEdr GGGa GMaP
- 'Susan's Reward' ♀H5 GEdr GMaP
grandis misapplied see *M.* George Sherriff Group
grandis ambig. CPla NEgg
- GS 600 see *M.* George Sherriff Group
- Balruddery form GEdr
horridula GCra GGGa MMuc
(Infertile Blue Group) 'Bobby Masterton' ♀H5 GCra GEdr GKev GMaP
- 'Bryan Conway' GEdr
- 'Crarae' GEdr GGGa
- 'Crewdson Hybrid' GBuc GCal GEdr GMaP
- 'Cruickshank' GKev
- 'Dawyck' see *M.* (Infertile Blue Group) 'Slieve Donard'
- 'Maggie Sharp' GEdr
- 'Mrs Jebb' ♀H5 GBuc GCra GEdr GMaP
- 'P.C.Abildgaard' ♀H5 GEdr GMaP
§ - 'Slieve Donard' ♀H5 GBuc GCal GCra GEdr GGGa GKev GKin GMaP LRHS
integrifolia GBin
'Inverewe' ♀H5 GEdr
'Keillour' ♀H5 GEdr
'Marit' ♀H5 GEdr GKev
napaulensis misapplied EBee GAbr GCra GKev ITim LHop NLar
- pink-flowered LCro LOPS
napaulensis DC. from Solukhumbu, Nepal GCra

- blue	MMuc
nudicaulis	see *Papaver nudicaule*
paniculata	EBee GGGa WPGP
- from Bhutan	GCra
- from Ghunsa, Nepal	CSma
- ginger foliage	CHid
pseudointegrifolia	GGGa GKev
punicea	GGGa GKev
quintuplinervia ♀H5	CLAP GBin GCra GEdr GKev NHar NSla
- Farrer's form	GEdr
- 'Kaye's Compact'	GEdr
regia hybrids	GGGa
× ***sarsonsii***	GKev
× ***sheldonii*** misapplied (fertile)	see *M.* Fertile Blue Group
× ***sheldonii*** misapplied (sterile)	see *M.* Infertile Blue Group
× ***sheldonii*** ambig.	CBcs CWCL GAbr NBir NLar NPer
simplicifolia	GGGa
'Stewart Annand'	GEdr GMaP
'Strathspey' new	GEdr
superba	GGGa
villosa	GCra GGGa
wallichii misapplied	see *M. wallichii* Hook.
wallichii ambig.	GAbr
§ ***wallichii*** Hook.	GGGa
'Willie Duncan'	GEdr GMaP

Medicago (*Papilionaceae*)

arborea	SEND SPlb
lupulina	CHab
sativa	WHer WSFF

medlar see *Mespilus germanica*

Meehania (*Lamiaceae*)

cordata	CDes EBee
urticifolia	EPPr GCal GEdr WSHC
- B&SWJ 1210	WCru
- 'Japanblau'	IMou
- 'Wandering Minstrel' (v)	WCot

Megaskepasma (*Acanthaceae*)

erythrochlamys	SVen

Melaleuca (*Myrtaceae*)

acerosa	ECou
acuminata	ECou SPlb
alternifolia	CArn CBcs CTsd ECou EShb GPoy MHer MOWG SPlb SVen
armillaris	CDoC CTsd ECou IDee SEND SPlb
blaeriifolia	ECou
cuticularis	SPlb
decussata	ECou SPlb
§ ***diosmatifolia***	CBcs CExl
diosmifolia new	CTre
elliptica	MOWG
ericifolia	CTri CTsd SEND SPlb
erubescens	see *M. diosmatifolia*
fulgens	ECou MOWG SPlb
- apricot-flowered	MOWG
* - 'Hot Pink'	MOWG
- purple-flowered	MOWG
gibbosa	CExl EBee ELan IDee IVic LSou MOWG SEND SVen WSHC
hypericifolia	CDoC CExl MOWG SPlb SVen
incana	MOWG
lateritia	ECou MOWG
linariifolia	ECou SPlb
nesophila	SPlb
pentagona var. ***subulifolia***	ECou
pulchella	MOWG
pungens	SPlb
pustulata	ECou SVen
spathulata	ECou
squamea	CTsd SEND SPlb
* ***squarmania***	MOWG
squarrosa	CExl ECou IDee MOWG SPlb SVen
tamariscina	ECou
thymifolia	ECou MOWG SPlb
trichophylla	SPlb
wilsonii	ECou IDee

Melandrium (*Caryophyllaceae*)

rubrum	see *Silene dioica*

Melanoselinum (*Apiaceae*)

§ ***decipiens***	CArn CEvo CSpe IMou LEdu LRHS MHer SDix WCru WJek WPGP

Melanoseris (*Asteraceae*)

taliensis BWJ 7891	WCru

Melasphaerula (*Iridaceae*)

graminea	see *M. ramosa*
§ ***ramosa***	ECho NRog

Melastoma (*Melastomataceae*)

intermedium new	ECou

Melia (*Meliaceae*)

§ ***azedarach***	CArn CBcs EShb GPoy SBrt SPlb
- B&SWJ 7039	WCru
- var. ***japonica***	see *M. azedarach*

Melianthus (*Melianthaceae*)

comosus	CDTJ CEvo ELan EPri ESwi EWes NLar NLos SCoo SPlb
dregeanus subsp. ***insignis***	NLos
major ♀H3	Widely available
minor	CHid
pectinatus	NLos
villosus	CCon CEvo CHGN EBee EWes NLos SPad SPlb WPGP

Melica (*Poaceae*)

altissima 'Alba'	SPhx
- 'Atropurpurea'	CBod ECha EHoe EPPr LEdu LHop LLWP LRHS MNrw MWhi NBid SEND SPlb WHea WMoo WWEG
californica	EPPr
ciliata	EAJP EHoe EPPr EPfP MWhi NDov WPtf WWEG XLum
nutans	CWCL EAJP EBee EHoe EPPr EShb GMaP MAsh NOak NWsh SMHy WCot
persica	EPPr MAvo
transsilvanica 'Atropurpurea'	MMuc
- 'Red Spire'	CWib MWhi SGol SHDw SMea WMoo XLum
uniflora	IMou MLHP NOak NWsh
- f. ***albida***	CKno EAJP ECha EHoe GCal LLWP MLHP MRav NDov NOak SMHy WCot WSHC

- 'Variegata' (v)	CBre ECGP ECha EHoe EShb GCal LPla MAvo NOak WCot WMoo WWEG

Melicytus (*Violaceae*)

sp.	WSHC
alpinus	ECou WThu
angustifolius	ECou
crassifolius	ECou WSHC
dentatus	ECou
obovatus	ECou NLar
ramiflorus	CDul ECou

Melilotus (*Papilionaceae*)

officinalis	CArn CHab GPoy SIde WHer
- subsp. ***albus***	CArn

Melinis (*Poaceae*)

nerviglumis 'Savannah'	CWib

Meliosma (*Sabiaceae*)

dilleniifolia subsp. ***cuneifolia***	CBcs CExl EBee SBrt WPGP
- subsp. ***flexuosa***	CBcs
- subsp. ***tenuis***	CBcs CExl
pinnata var. ***oldhamii***	CExl
simplicifolia subsp. ***pungens***	CBcs CExl
veitchiorum	CBcs CExl NLar SAko WPGP

Melissa ✿ (*Lamiaceae*)

	officinalis	CBod CHab CLau CPbn CTri ENfk GJos GMaP GPoy LEdu LPot MBri MHer MMuc MNHC NBir SEND SIde SPlb SRms SVic WBor WHfH WJek XLum
	- 'All Gold'	CBre CLau CPbn ECha EHoe ELan ENfk NBid SPer SPoG SRms
§	- 'Aurea' (v)	CArn CBod CExl CLau ELan GCra GMaP GPoy MBri MHer MMuc MRav NBid NBir NBro SEND SIde SPer SPoG SRms WHea WJek WMnd WMoo XLum
*	- 'Compacta'	CPbn GPoy
	- 'Gold Leaf'	NBFr
	- 'Lemona' **new**	CAgr
	- 'Lime Balm'	CPbn
	- 'Quedlinburger Niederliegende'	CArn CPbn
	- 'Variegata' misapplied	see *M. officinalis* 'Aurea'

Melittis (*Lamiaceae*)

melissophyllum	CAby CLAP CSpe GAbr IMou LEdu LRHS LSou MAvo MHol MNrw MPie MPnt MRav MSCN SHar WCAu WCot WOut WRHF
- subsp. ***albida***	SCob WCot
- 'Apple Blossom'	CDes
- pink-flowered	CLAP LEdu WBor WCot
- 'Royal Velvet Distinction'[PBR]	CBod CMos EBee LBMP LOPS LRHS MHol MRav MSCN SCob SGSe SHar SHil SPad SPoG WCot WHil WPtf

Melliodendron (*Styracaceae*)

xylocarpum	CExl

Menispermum (*Menispermaceae*)

canadense	CTri GPoy
dauricum	NLar

Mentha ✿ (*Lamiaceae*)

	sp.	CHab
	from Jamaica	CArn
	angustifolia Corb.	see *M.* × *villosa*
	angustifolia Host	see *M. arvensis*
	angustifolia ambig.	CPbn
	aquatica	CArn CBen CBod CHab CPbn CWat EHon GPoy LEdu MHer MJak MNHC MWLS MWts NMir NPer NPol NYoL SIde SPlb SRms SVic SWat WHer WMAq WMoo WPnP WSFF XLum
§	- var. ***crispa***	CPbn NYoL
	- krause minze	see *M. aquatica* var. *crispa*
	- 'Mandeliensis'	CPbn
§	***arvensis***	CArn CPbn MHer NYoL SIde
	- 'Banana'	CBod CPbn ENfk LEdu MHer MNHC NYoL SIde SRms SVic WJek
	- var. ***piperascens***	CBod LEdu MHer SIde SRms WJek
§	- - 'Sayakaze'	CArn CLau
	- var. ***villosa***	CPbn
	asiatica	CLau CPbn MHer
	'Berries and Cream'	CBod ENfk LEdu SRms WJek
	'Betty's Slovakian'	CPbn
	Bowles's mint	see *M.* × *villosa* var. *alopecuroides* Bowles's mint
*	***brevifolia***	CPbn
	cervina	CArn CBen CPbn CWat EHon LEdu MHer MSKA MWts SIde SRms SWat WJek XLum
*	- ***alba***	CPbn ENfk LLWG MHer MSKA MWts NYoL SRms WJek WMAq
I	'Chocolate Peppermint'	ENfk GAbr LEdu LLWG NBir NLar NYoL
	citrata	see *M.* × *piperita* f. *citrata*
	'Clarissa's Millennium'	CPbn
	cordifolia	see *M.* × *villosa*
	corsica	see *M. requienii*
	crispa L. (1753)	see *M. spicata* var. *crispa*
	crispa L. (1763)	see *M. aquatica* var. *crispa*
	crispa ambig. × (× ***piperita***)	CArn CPbn MJak
	cucumber mint	CPbn
	'Dionysus'	CPbn
	× ***dumetorum***	CPbn NYoL
	- wine mint	CPbn
	'Eau de Cologne'	see *M.* × *piperita* f. *citrata*
	eucalyptus mint	CPbn MHer
	gattefossei	CArn
	× ***gentilis***	see *M.* × *gracilis*
§	× ***gracilis***	CArn CLau CPbn ENfk GAbr NLar NPri NYoL SIde SVic
	- 'Aurea'	see *M.* × *gracilis* 'Variegata'
§	- 'Variegata' (v)	CLau CPbn ECha GPoy LEdu MCot MHer MNHC NPri NYoL SPlb SRms WHer WJek XLum
	haplocalyx	CArn CLau NYoL
	'Herbert McHale'	LEdu
*	'Hillary's Sweet Lemon'	CLau CPbn ENfk MHer NYoL SIde
	'Julia's Sweet Citrus'	CPbn MHer
*	***lacerata***	NYoL SIde
	lavender mint	CBod CLau GPoy LEdu MHer MNHC NYoL SRms WJek
§	***longifolia***	CLau CPbn ENfk LEdu MMuc NYoL SEND SPlb SRms
	- Buddleia Mint Group	CArn CLau CPbn EBee ENfk GAbr LEdu MHer MRav NSti NYoL SIde WJek XLum
	- - variegated (v)	CBod LEdu WJek

	- dwarf	CPbn
	- 'Habek'	EOHP
	- subsp. ***schimperi***	LEdu NYoL SRms WJek
	- silver-leaved	CArn CLau CPbn GAbr LEdu MHer MNHC NYoL SEND SRms WJek
*	- 'Variegata' (v)	CPbn GAbr NYoL SRms
	Nile Valley mint	CArn CLau LEdu NYoL SHDw SIde SRms WJek
	× ***piperita***	CArn CHby CLau CPbn CWld ECha EHoe GJos GPoy LCro MBri MHer MJak MNHC NPri NYoL SPlb SVic
	- 'Black Mitcham'	CArn CPbn NYoL XLum
	- black peppermint	CAgr CBod CHby CPbn ENfk EPfP GAbr LEdu LLWG MMuc MNHC NBir NLar NYoL SEND SRms WJek
§	- f. ***citrata***	CArn CBod CHby CLau CPbn CTri ECha GJos GMaP GPoy LEdu LLWG MBri MHer MNHC MRav NBir NLar NPri NYoL SHDw SIde SPlb SRms SVic WJek
	- - from Portugal	CPbn
*	- - 'Basil'	CBod CLau CPbn GLog LEdu MHer MNHC MRav NYoL SHDw SIde SRms SVic WGwG WJek XLum
	- - 'Bergamot'	CPbn SRms XLum
	- - 'Chocolate'	CArn CBod CLau CPbn ENfk EPfP GJos LBMP LEdu MHer MNHC NPer NYoL SHDw SIde SPlb SRms SVic WJek XLum
	- - 'Grapefruit'	CBod CPbn GLog LSou MHer MNHC NWad NYoL SRms WJek
	- - 'Lemon'	CLau CPbn ENfk GAbr GPoy LEdu MBri MHer MNHC NPer NYoL SHDw SIde SRms WJek
	- - 'Lime'	CPbn ENfk GAbr GLog LEdu MHer NYoL SHDw SIde SPlb SRms SVic WJek
	- - 'Orange'	CPbn ENfk LEdu MHer MMuc MNHC NPer NYoL SRms WHil WJek
	- - 'Reverchonii'	CPbn
	- - 'Swiss Ricola'	MHer NYoL
	- 'Crispa'	NPol
	- 'Logee's' (v)	CPbn
	- 'Milly Mitcham'	CPbn
	- f. ***officinalis***	CLau CPbn SIde
	- var. ***ouweneellii*** Belgian mint	CPbn
	- 'Persephone'	CPbn
	- 'Reine Rouge'	CPbn
	- 'Strawberry' new	ENfk
	- 'Swiss'	CBod LEdu MNHC NLar WJek
I	- Swiss mint	CArn CPbn ENfk
*	- white-flowered	CArn CPbn
	'Polynesian Mint'	CPbn
	pulegium	CArn CBod CHby CLau CPbn CTri ENfk GPoy LEdu LLWG MHer MMuc MNHC NPri SIde SPlb SRms SVic WHer WHfH WJek WSFF
	- 'Upright'	CArn CPbn ENfk GPoy MHer SHDw SIde SRms WJek
§	***requienii***	CArn CBod CLau CPbn CTri ECho ENfk GAbr GCal GPoy ITim LEdu MBri MHer MNHC NBir NRya NWad NYoL SDix SIde SPlb SRms WGwG WHfH WJek WTou
	rotundifolia misapplied	see *M. suaveolens*
	rotundifolia (L.) Huds.	see *M.* × *villosa*
	rubra var. ***raripila***	see *M.* × *smithiana*
	'Russian' curled leaf	CPbn
	'Russian' plain leaf	CPbn NYoL
	'Sayakaze'	see *M. arvensis* var. *piperascens* 'Sayakaze'
§	× ***smithiana***	CArn CLau CPbn ENfk GPoy LEdu MHer MNHC MRav NBir NYoL SRms WJek
	- 'Capel Ulo' (v)	CLau
	'South of France'	CPbn
§	***spicata***	CAgr CArn CBod CLau CPbn CTri CTsd ENfk GJos GPoy LBMP LPot MBri MCot MHer MJak MMuc MNHC NPol NPri NYoL SEND SPlb SRms WHer WJek XLum
	- Algerian fruity	CPbn LEdu
	- 'Austrian'	CPbn
*	- 'Brundall'	CLau CPbn NYoL SIde
	- 'Canaries'	CPbn
*	- var. ***crispa***	CArn CLau CPbn ECha ENfk LEdu LHop LPot MHer MMuc MNHC NRya NYoL SIde SPlb SRms WJek
	- - 'Moroccan'	CArn CLau CPbn CPrp ENfk GAbr GJos GLog GPoy LEdu MHer MNHC NLar NPri NYoL SHDw SIde SRms SVic WJek
	- - 'Persian'	CPbn
	- 'Crispula'	GAbr XLum
	- 'Guernsey'	CPbn SHDw SIde SRms
	- 'Irish'	CPbn
	- 'Kentucky Colonel'	CPbn LEdu
	- 'Mexican'	CArn CPbn
	- 'Newbourne'	CLau CPbn SRms
	- 'Pharaoh'	CArn CPbn
	- 'Rhodos'	CPbn
	- 'Russian'	CArn LEdu MHer SIde
	- 'Small Dole' (v)	SHDw
	- 'Spanish'	LEdu NLar SRms
	- 'Spanish Furry'	CPbn MHer
	- 'Spanish Pointed'	CLau CPbn WJek
	- 'Tashkent'	CArn CHby CLau CPbn ENfk LEdu MHer MNHC NYoL SHDw SIde SRms WGwG WHer WJek
	- subsp. ***tomentosa***	CPbn
*	- 'Variegata' (v)	CPbn SHDw
	- 'Verte Blanche'	CPbn
I	'Strawberry Mint' new	LEdu
§	***suaveolens***	CAgr CArn CBod CHby CLau CPbn ENfk GJos GMaP GPoy LBMP MBri MHer MLHP MNHC NYoL SIde SPlb SRms SVic WJek WSFF
*	- 'Grapefruit'	LEdu
	- 'Jokka'	CPbn
*	- 'Mobillei'	CPbn
*	- 'Pineapple'	CBod ENfk GLog WJek
	- subsp. ***timija***	CLau CPbn LEdu MHer WJek
	- 'Variegata' (v)	CArn CLau CPbn CTri ECha EHoe GJos GMaP GPoy LEdu MBri MCot MHer MMuc MNHC MRav NChi NPri SIde SPlb SRms SVic WHer XLum
	'Sweet Pear'	MHer NYoL
	sylvestris L.	see *M. longifolia*
I	'Tangerine Mint' new	LEdu
*	***verona***	CPbn NYoL
	× ***verticillata***	WJek
§	× ***villosa***	CArn CPbn MMuc SEND SRms
§	- var. ***alopecuroides*** Bowles's mint	CBre CLau CPbn CPrp GPoy LEdu MHer MNHC NBir NLar NSti NYoL SRms SWat WHer WJek
	- 'Jack Green'	LEdu
	viridis	see *M. spicata*

Menyanthes (*Menyanthaceae*)

trifoliata CBen CWat EHon EWay GPoy LLWG MMuc MSKA MWts NPer WHal WMAq WSFF WWtn XLum

Menziesia (*Ericaceae*)

alba see *Daboecia cantabrica* f. *alba*
ciliicalyx lasiophylla see *Rhododendron multiflorum* var. *purpureum*

Mercurialis (*Euphorbiaceae*)

perennis GPoy WHer WHfH WSFF WShi

Merendera (*Colchicaceae*)

attica NRog
eichleri see *M. trigyna*
filifolia NRog
§ ***montana*** EPot GKev NRog
- 'Norman Barratt' WCot
pyrenaica see *M. montana*
raddeana see *M. trigyna*
sobolifera ECho NRog WCot
§ ***trigyna*** NRog

Mertensia (*Boraginaceae*)

ciliata CCse SWat
franciscana EBee GCal
lanceolata GKev
§ ***maritima*** CCon CSpe CWld ECho EWes EWld GBee GKev GPoy LEdu LRHS NBir NLar SPlb WHoo
- subsp. ***asiatica*** see *M. maritima*
pterocarpa see *M. sibirica*
- var. ***yezoensis*** new SBrt
pulmonarioides see *M. virginica*
§ ***sibirica*** CSpe MMuc SPlb
§ ***virginica*** ♀H4 CBro CCon CLAP CWCL EBee ECho ECtt EHrv ELan EPfP EPot GKev IFro LAma LEdu LHop LRHS MBel MNrw MPie MSCN NBir NLar SRms WFar
viridis SPlb

Merwilla (*Asparagaceae*)

§ ***plumbea*** CEvo GKev WCot

Merxmuellera (*Poaceae*)

cincta see *Danthonia cincta*

Mesembryanthemum (*Aizoaceae*)

'Basutoland' see *Delosperma nubigenum*
brownii see *Lampranthus brownii*
crystallinum new NPri

Mespilus ✿ (*Rosaceae*)

'Flanders Giant' (F) new WMat
germanica (F) CBcs CDul CHab CLnd CMCN CTri ECrN ELan EWTr IDee NLar NWea SLon WFar
- var. ***apyrena*** (F) ERea WMat
- 'Brabant Giant' new SAko
- 'Bredase Reus' (F) SKee
- 'Dutch' (F) SDea SKee
- 'Iranian' (F) SKee
- 'Large Russian' (F) CAgr
- 'Macrocarpa' (F) SKee
- 'Monstrous' (F) SDea
- 'Nottingham' (F) ♀H6 Widely available
- 'Royal' (F) CAgr ERea LCro LOPS MBri MCoo NOra SCoo SKee WHar WMat
- 'Westerveld' (F) CLnd SAko SBmr SKee

Metapanax (*Araliaceae*)

davidii CFil SLon
delavayi SBig

Metarungia (*Acanthaceae*)

galpinii WHil

Metasequoia ✿ (*Cupressaceae*)

glyptostroboides Widely available
- 'Chubby'PBR EPfP NLar
- 'Emerald Feathers' ♀H7 SLim
- 'Fastigiata' see *M. glyptostroboides* 'National'
- Gold Rush = 'Golden Oji' ♀H7 Widely available
- 'Golden Dawn' NLar
- 'Hamlet's Broom' SLim
- 'Little Creamy' NLar
- 'Little Giant' MBlu
- 'Matthaei Broom' MBlu SLim
- 'McCracken's White' (v) NLar SMad
- 'Miss Grace' MAsh NLar SLim
§ - 'National' MBlu
- 'Royal Air' NLar
- 'Schirrmann's Nordlicht' SLim
- 'Sheridan Spire' MBlu
- 'Waasland' MBlu
- 'White Spot' (v) MBlu SLim

Metrosideros (*Myrtaceae*)

§ ***excelsa*** CHll ECou ECre ESwi
- 'Aurea' ECou
- 'Maori Princess' MPkF
- 'Parnell' CBcs
kermadecensis ECou
- 'Twisty' (v) CBcs
- 'Variegata' (v) CBcs ECou
lucida see *M. umbellata*
robusta CBcs SPlb
- ***aureovariegata*** (v) EShb
× ***subtomentosa*** 'Mistral' ECou
tomentosa see *M. excelsa*
§ ***umbellata*** CBcs CDoC CTsd ECou
- Gold Nugget = 'Lownug' LSou SLim
- Moonlight = 'Lowmoo' LSou SLim
villosa 'Tahiti' CBcs

Meum (*Apiaceae*)

athamanticum CArn CSpe EBee GCal GPoy LEdu LRHS MAvo MRav SPhx

Michauxia (*Campanulaceae*)

campanuloides CSpe EBee
tchihatchewii CDTJ CSpe LEdu NGBl

Michelia see *Magnolia*

fulgens see *Magnolia foveolata*
wilsonii see *Magnolia ernestii*

Microbiota (*Cupressaceae*)

decussata ♀H5 CBcs CDoC CMac CSBt ECho EFry LBee LRHS MBri MGos NHol NWea
- 'Gold Spot' (v) CDoC
- 'Jakobsen' CDoC CKen
- 'Trompenburg' CKen

Microcachrys (*Podocarpaceae*)

tetragona	CDoC ECou EFry IArd WThu

Microcoelum see *Lytocaryum*

Microlepia (*Dennstaedtiaceae*)

strigosa	CLAP EBee ISha LRHS
- 'MacFaddeniae'	EBee ISha LRHS

Micromeria (*Lamiaceae*)

sp.	SRms
corsica	see *Acinos corsicus*
fruticosa	WJek
graeca	CArn
juliana	XLum
rupestris	see *M. thymifolia*
§ ***thymifolia***	SPlb

Microseris (*Asteraceae*)

ringens	see *Leontodon rigens*

Microsorum (*Polypodiaceae*)

diversifolium	see *Phymatosorus diversifolius*
musifolium new	NLos

Microtropis (*Celastraceae*)

petelotii HWJ 719	WCru

Mikania (*Asteraceae*)

araucana	LSou

Milium (*Poaceae*)

effusum 'Aureum' ♀H7	Widely available
- 'Yaffle' (v)	CBod CBre CKno EPPr EShb LEdu WCot WPnP WWEG

Millettia (*Papilionaceae*)

japonica 'Hime Fuji'	NLar
murasaki-natsu-fuji	see *M. reticulata*
§ ***reticulata***	CExl

Mimetes (*Proteaceae*)

chrysanthus	SPlb

Mimosa (*Mimosaceae*)

pudica ♀H1c	CDTJ SPlb

Mimulus (*Phrymaceae*)

sp.	SVic
'Andean Nymph'	see *M. naiandinus*
§ ***aurantiacus*** ♀H2	CMac CSpe CTri EBak ECtt EShb LHop LPot MGil NPer SPlb WBod
× ***bartonianus***	see *M.* × *harrisonii*
× ***burnetii***	ECho SRms
cardinalis ♀H1c	EBee ELan EPfP EWes EWld MNrw MSKA NBir WMoo
- gold-flowered	EBee
- 'Red Dragon'	CBod CFis
cardinalis × ***lewisii***	EWes
cupreus 'Whitecroft Scarlet' ♀H5	ECho GCrg SRms
'Eleanor'	ECtt
glutinosus	see *M. aurantiacus*
- ***atrosanguineus***	see *M. puniceus*
- ***luteus***	see *M. aurantiacus*
§ ***guttatus***	NMir NPer SRms WMoo WPnP
§ × ***harrisonii***	EWes LSou
'Highland Orange'	ECho EPfP MAsh NPri SPlb SPoG
'Highland Pink'	ECho EPfP MAsh MHol NPri SPlb SPoG
'Highland Red' ♀H5	ECho ECtt EPfP GAbr GMaP MAsh NPri SPlb SPoG SRms WIce
'Highland Yellow'	ECho ECtt GMaP NPri SPlb SPoG WIce
hose-in-hose (d)	NPer
langsdorffii	see *M. guttatus*
lewisii ♀H1c	CBod CHll EBee EWes MNrw SRms
'Lothian Fire'	CWat
luteus	CBen CWat EHon GAbr LLWG NPer WBrk WMAq XLum
- 'Variegatus' ambig. (v)	NPer
* 'Major Bees'	MJak
'Malibu Orange'	EPfP
'Maximus' mixed new	NPri
moschatus	EBee LLWG
§ ***naiandinus*** ♀H4	EWes GCrg SPlb
'Orange Glow'	LLWG WHal
orange hose-in-hose (d)	NBir
§ 'Orkney Gold' (d)	ECtt
'Popacatapetl'	CSpe
primuloides	ECho EWes GCrg LLWG SPlb
§ ***puniceus***	CTri LHop SHil SRkn
ringens	CBen CBod CWat EBee EHon MSKA NBir NPer SPlb SRms WMAq WMoo
'Threave Variegated' (v)	EBee
'Vortex'	LSou
'Vortex Hot Spot' new	LSou
'Vortex Orange Glow' new	LSou
'Wisley Red'	ECho SRms
yellow hose-in-hose	see *M.* 'Orkney Gold'

Mina see *Ipomoea*

mint, apple see *Mentha suaveolens*

mint, Bowles's see *M.* × *villosa* var. *alopecuroides*

mint, curly see *M. spicata* var. *crispa*

mint, eau-de-Cologne see *M.* × *piperita* f. *citrata*

mint, ginger see *M.* × *gracilis*

mint, horse or long-leaved see *M. longifolia*

mint (pennyroyal) see *M. pulegium*

mint (peppermint) see *M.* × *piperita*

mint, round-leaved see *M. suaveolens*

mint (spearmint) see *M. spicata*

Minuartia (*Caryophyllaceae*)

capillacea	ECho
laricifolia	MMuc XSen
parnassica	see *M. stellata*
§ ***stellata***	EPot
§ ***verna***	ECho EDAr
- subsp. ***caespitosa***	CTri ECho
- - 'Aurea'	see *Sagina subulata* var. *glabrata* 'Aurea'

Mirabilis (*Nyctaginaceae*)

	Name	Suppliers
	dichotoma	EShb
	jalapa	CArn CExl CSpe EPfP GKev LAma LEdu SRms
	- red-flowered	SGSe WHil
	longiflora	EShb SBrt
	multiflora	EBee SBrt
	nyctaginea new	SPhx

Miscanthus ✿ (*Poaceae*)

	Name	Suppliers
	sp.	LPar
	capensis	SPlb
	chejuensis B&SWJ 8803	WCru
	'Dronning Ingrid'	CKno EPPr GBin IMou MNrw XLum
	'Elfin'	CKno
	flavidus B&SWJ 6749	WCru
	floridulus misapplied	see *M.* × *giganteus*
	floridulus ambig.	CCon MMuc MNrw SCob SPlb XLum
	floridulus (Labill.) Warb. ex K. Schum. & Lauterb. HWJ 522	WCru
§	× ***giganteus***	CKno EHoe EHrv ELon EPPr EUJe GCal GKev GQue IBoy LPfy MAsh MNrw NLos NWsh SCob SDys SGSe SMad SVic WCot WPGP WWEG
	- 'Aksel Olsen' new	SAko
	- 'Gilt Edge' (v)	CKno EPPr
	- 'Gotemba' (v)	EPPr EWes NWsh
	nepalensis	CAby CElw CExl CHVG CKno CSam CSde CWCL EBee ECha ECre EHoe EUJe EWes EWoo GCal LEdu LRHS LSun MAvo MNrw NDov NLos NOak NWsh SDix SGSe SPlb WPGP
	- NJM 09.141	WPGP
	- 'Shikola'	WCru
	oligostachyus	CChe IMou SDys
§	- 'Afrika'	CDes CKno EPPr GBin IMou MAvo MNrw WPGP XLum
I	- 'Nanus Variegatus' (v)	CKno EHoe LEdu WCot WPGP WWEG
	'Purpurascens'	CBod CKno CWCL ECha EHoe EPPr IBoy LPla LPot LRHS LSRN MNrw NOak SAko SCob SGSe SGol SPer WMoo
	sacchariflorus misapplied	see *M.* × *giganteus*
	sacchariflorus ambig.	CBcs CDul CKno ECha ELan EPfP LRHS MBrN NGdn SPer WMoo XLum
	sacchariflorus (Maxim.) Hack.	LEdu MWhi WWEG
	sinensis	CTri LEdu NOak WFar WHar WMoo WWEG XSen
	- from Yakushima, Japan	LAst SGSe
	- 'Abundance'	CKno CRos EPfP LRHS MMuc
	- 'Adagio'	CBod CKno CPrp CSde EAEE EHoe ELon EPPr EShb EWoo GBin GQue ILea LRHS MWhi NWad NWsh SCob SHDw SMHy SMad SMea WCot XLum
	- 'Afrika'	see *M. oligostachyus* 'Afrika'
	- 'Aldebaran'	EBee IMou
	- 'Andante'	CKno
	- 'Arabesque'	EPPr WWEG XLum
	- 'Augustfeder'	EPPr SMea WWEG XLum
	- 'Autumn Light'	EPPr SMea XLum
	- 'Blütenwunder'	EPPr XLum
	- 'Bogenlampe'	GBin
	- 'China' ♀H6	CKno CPar EAEE EHoe ELon EPPr EShb EWes GBin LEdu LRHS MAsh MAvo MNrw SDys SHDw SRms SWat WMoo WPGP WWEG XLum
	- 'Cindy'	CKno
	- var. ***condensatus***	LEdu LSou SMHy
	- - NJM 11.021	WPGP
	- - 'Cabaret' (v)	CBod CKno EAEE EHoe ELon EPPr EUJe GMaP ILea LBMP LEdu LHop LRHS LSRN NOak NWsh SEND SGSe SHDw WCot WHal WMoo WPGP WWEG XLum
	- - 'Central Park'	see *M. sinensis* var. *condensatus* 'Cosmo Revert'
§	- - 'Cosmo Revert'	EPPr LEdu NWsh WPGP
	- - 'Cosmopolitan' (v) ♀H5	Widely available
	- - 'Emerald Giant'	see *M. sinensis* var. *condensatus* 'Cosmo Revert'
	- - 'Laigong'	LEdu
	- 'David'	ELon EPPr LEdu MAvo MBNS XLum
	- 'Dixieland' (v)	CKno ELan ELon EPPr EWes IFoB IMou LEdu NLar WWEG XLum
	- 'Dreadlocks'	EPPr MAvo
	- 'Dresdner Silbersprudel' new	SAko
	- 'Emmanuel Lepage'	CKno EPPr XLum
	- 'Etincelle'	CKno EWes ILea XLum
	- 'Federriese'	GBin
	- 'Ferner Osten' ♀H7	Widely available
	- 'Flamingo' ♀H6	Widely available
	- 'Flammenmeer'	SAko
	- 'Gearmella'	EPPr XLum
	- 'Gewitterwolke' ♀H6	EPPr EWes SMHy XLum
	- 'Ghana' ♀H6	CKno CSpe EBee ELon EPPr GBin GQue IMou MAvo MNrw SDys SMHy XLum
	- 'Giraffe'	CDTJ CKno EWes LEdu WPGP WWEG XLum
	- 'Gnome'	CKno EAEE EHoe EPPr EShb EUJe GQue IMou LRHS MAsh MWhi WWEG
	- 'Gold Bar'PBR (v)	CBod CChe CDul CElw CKno CLet COtt CWGN EAEE ECha EHoe ELon EPfP EUJe LRHS LSRN LSou MAsh MBNS NGdn NWad SBea SEle SGol SPer SPoG WMoo WWEG
	- 'Gold und Silber' ♀H6	XLum
	- 'Goldfeder' (v)	XLum
	- 'Goliath'	CKno EHoe ELan ELon EPPr GBin GQue LBMP LEdu MBNS WPGP WWEG XLum
	- 'Gracillimus'	Widely available
	- 'Graziella'	CBod CKno CLet CSam CWCL CWib EHoe EPPr EPfP LBMP LRHS MBri MWhi NGdn NLar NOak SHil SPer SRms WBor WPGP XLum XSen
	- 'Grosse Fontäne' ♀H6	CCon EHoe ELan EPPr LEdu LRHS LSRN MWhi NWsh SGSe SMHy SMad WCot WMoo WWEG XLum
	- 'Gutenberg Gold'	XLum
	- 'Haiku'	CKno EPPr LEdu XLum
	- 'Helga Reich'	EWes WWEG
	- 'Hercules'	EBee EPPr MAvo XLum
	- 'Hermann Müssel'	CKno EBee EPPr EWes GBin GQue IMou LEdu LPla LRHS NOak SMHy SMea WWEG XLum
§	- 'Hinjo' (v)	CDul EAEE ECha EHoe ELon EPPr GBin GBuc GQue LRHS LSou NGdn NWsh SPoG WCot WPGP WWEG

I - 'Jubilaris' (v)	EPPr EWes GBin WWEG
- 'Juli'	EPPr LRHS WWEG XLum
- 'Kaskade' ♀H6	CKno CPar CPrp EHoe EPPr LEdu LRHS MMuc NDov NLar WMoo WWEG XLum
- 'Kirk Alexander' (v)	EPPr
- 'Kleine Fontäne' ♀H6	Widely available
- 'Kleine Silberspinne' ♀H6	Widely available
- 'Korea'	EPPr
- 'Krater'	EBee EHoe EPPr ILea LPla LRHS MBrN SDys SGSe SMea SWat WWEG
- 'Kupferberg'	XLum
- 'Kupferzwerg' **new**	EPPr
- 'Largo'	XLum
§ - 'Little Kitten'	CKno LEdu SGSe SMad SMea WMoo WPGP WWEG
- Little Nicky	see *M. sinensis* 'Hinjo'
- 'Little Zebra'[PBR] (v)	EBee EPfP EUJe GMaP LHop LSRN NLar NLos NOak SAko SCob SEle SMad SRms
- 'Malepartus'	Widely available
- 'Memory'	EPPr
- 'Moonlight'	GBin
- 'Morning Light' (v) ♀H6	Widely available
- 'Nippon'	CPrp EAEE EHoe EPPr GBin IPot LEdu LRHS MWhi NGdn NPri NWsh SCob SDys SPer WPGP WWEG XLum
- 'Nishidake'	EPPr XLum
- 'November Sunset'	EPPr EWes XLum
- 'Overdam'	IFoB NGdn
- 'Poseidon'	EPPr MAvo NChi SDys SMad WWEG XLum
- 'Positano'	CKno WPGP XLum
- 'Professor Richard Hansen'	CKno EPPr NWsh SMHy XLum
- 'Pünktchen' (v)	EAEE ECha EHoe EPPr GBin LEdu LRHS MAsh NOak SCob SHDw SMHy SMad SRms WMoo WWEG XLum
- 'Purple Fall'	CPar CSpe IPot LRHS LSou MAvo MNrw STPC
- 'Red Chief'	EPPr EWes GQue IMou IPot MAvo NLar
- 'Red Meister'	CKno CRos EPfP LRHS MAsh
- 'Red Star'	SRms
- 'Red Tower' **new**	EWes
- 'Red Wine' **new**	MNrw
- 'Rigoletto' (v)	EPPr
- 'Roland'	CKno EHoe EPPr GBin SMad XLum
- 'Roterpfeil'	EPPr
- 'Rotfeder'	EPPr
- 'Rotfuchs'	EBee LLWP MAvo XLum
- 'Rotsilber'	CBod CKno CSpe CWib ECha EHoe EPPr GBin GMaP IArd LRHS MJak MMuc MWhi NOak WHoo WMoo WWEG XLum
- 'Samurai'	EPPr GMaP GQue MAvo MNrw XLum
- 'Sarabande' ♀H6	EHoe EPPr GQue NLar SMHy WMoo XLum
- 'Septemberrot' ♀H6	CKno EPPr LEdu MMuc SCob SEND
§ - 'Silberfeder' ♀H6	Widely available
- 'Silberpfeil' (v)	NWsh
- 'Silberspinne'	CCse EBee EPPr GBin ILea LEdu LRHS MWat SCob SMHy SMea SPlb XLum
- 'Silberturm'	EPPr LPla XLum
- Silver Feather	see *M. sinensis* 'Silberfeder'
- 'Silver Sceptre'	MAvo SMHy
- 'Silver Stripe'	EPPr EWoo MAvo
- 'Sioux'	EBee EHoe EPPr EShb GBin GQue LRHS MAvo MBNS SPer WWEG
- 'Sirene'	CCon EAEE EHoe EPPr GQue MBNS MMuc MWhi XLum
- 'Spätgrün'	EPPr XLum
- 'Starlight'	CKno
- 'Strictus' (v) ♀H6	Widely available
- 'Super Stripe' (v)	EPPr IMou
- 'Taiwan' **new**	EBee EPPr
- 'Tiger Cub' (v)	CWCL EPPr EWes SGSe WWEG
- 'Undine' ♀H6	CCon CKno CMea ECha EHoe ELan EPPr EPfP LEdu MBel MBrN MMuc NWsh WMoo XLum
- 'Variegatus' (v)	Widely available
- 'Verneigung'	GBin
- 'Vorläufer'	EPPr GBin
- 'Westacre Wine'	EWes
- 'Wetterfahne'	EPPr LEdu
§ - 'Yaku-jima'	CBod CSam ECha EPPr LHop MMuc MWhi SCob SMea WWEG
- 'Yakushima Dwarf'	Widely available
- 'Zebrinus' (v) ♀H6	Widely available
- 'Zwergelefant'	EBee MAvo SMHy WWEG XLum
tinctorius 'Nanus Variegatus' misapplied	see *M. oligostachyus* 'Nanus Variegatus'
transmorrisonensis	CKno EHoe ELan EPPr EUJe LEdu LPla LRHS MAvo NDov NLos NWsh WCot WWEG XLum
- B&SWJ 3697	WCru
yakushimensis	see *M. sinensis* 'Yaku-jima', *M. sinensis* 'Little Kitten'

Mitchella (*Rubiaceae*)

repens	CBcs EBee EPot GBin LAst LEdu MNrw WAbe WCru
undulata B&SWJ 10928	WCru
* - f. ***quelpartensis*** B&SWJ 4402	WCru

Mitella (*Saxifragaceae*)

acerina B&SWJ 11029	EWld WCru
breweri	CCon CHid CMac EBee ECha GCal MRav WBor WMoo WOut WPnP
caulescens	ECha NBro
diphylla	EPPr MHer
formosana B&SWJ 125	EPPr WCru
furusei var. ***subramosa*** B&SWJ 11097	WCru
× ***inami*** B&SWJ 11122	WCru
japonica B&SWJ 4971	WCru
kiusiana	CLAP
- B&SWJ 5888	WCru
makinoi	CLAP
- B&SWJ 4992	CExl WCru
ovalis	EBee
pauciflora B&SWJ 6361	WCru
pentandra	EBee
stylosa B&SWJ 5669	WCru
yoshinagae B&SWJ 4893	CExl CHid EBee EPPr WCru WMoo

Mitraria (*Gesneriaceae*)

coccinea	CBcs CExl CHll CMac CTsd CWib ECho ELan GKev IDee IRos LRHS LSou MBlu NLar SLim SLon SPer SPlb SSpi WBod
- Clark's form	EUJe LAst NLar

- 'Lago Puyehue' CAbb CBcs CDoC CExl EPfP LRHS SPlb SVen SWvt WSHC WThu
- 'Lake Caburgua' CSpe EBee ELon EWld GCal GGal IArd NLar WHor

Modiolastrum (*Malvaceae*)

lateritium CHll CRHN CSpe CTri EPri LHop LRHS MAvo MNHC NBir SPhx SRms WBod WBor WHal WHar WPGP WSHC XLum

Moehringia (*Caryophyllaceae*)

muscosa WCot

Moenchia (*Caryophyllaceae*)

mantica WCot

Molinia ✿ (*Poaceae*)

altissima see *M. caerulea* subsp. *arundinacea*
'Autumn Charm' CKno
caerulea CKno CWib EPPr LRHS MAsh MBlu NChi
§ - subsp. ***arundinacea*** CKno CSpe CWCL ECha EPPr WPtf WWEG XLum
- - 'Automne Bronze' **new** EPPr
- - 'Bergfreund' CKno CSam EBee EHoe EPPr GBin LHop MAvo NWsh SMHy
- - 'Black Arrow' NDov
- - 'Breeze' CKno
- - 'Cordoba' CKno EBee EPPr GBin GQue IPot MAvo NDov SMHy SPhx WWEG XLum
- - 'Fontäne' CSam EHoe EPPr GQue LPla MAsh MAvo NWsh SGSe SPhx
- - 'Granada' **new** EPPr
- - 'Karl Foerster' Widely available
- - 'Les Ponts de Cé' **new** EPPr
- - 'Liebreiz' EPPr
- - 'Skyracer' CChe CKno CPrp CSde EBee EHoe ELan ELon EPPr EUJe GBin GCal GLog GQue LRHS MAsh MAvo MNrw MWhi SMHy SMad SPhx WCot WGrn WMoo WWEG
- - 'Staefa' EHoe
- - 'Sunbeam' **new** EPPr
- - 'Tears of Joy' EPPr
- - 'Transparent' Widely available
- - 'Windsaule' CKno EPPr MAvo SPhx
- - 'Windspiel' CBod CKno CSam CWCL EAEE EBee ECha EHoe EPPr EWoo GBin GQue IKil LEdu LRHS MAvo MNrw MSpe MWhi NDov NWsh SDix SPer SPhx WCot WMoo WPGP WPtf XLum
- - 'Zuneigung' CKno CPrp CSam EPPr LPla LRHS MAvo SPhx
- subsp. ***caerulea*** 'Carmarthen' (v) EHoe EPPr LRHS WWEG
- - 'Claerwen' (v) ECha EPPr MAvo SPhx WMoo
- - 'Coneyhill Gold' (v) EPPr
- - 'Dark Defender' EPPr NDov SPhx
- - 'Dauerstrahl' CKno EBee EPPr GCal GQue LPla MAsh MAvo MNrw NDov WWEG
- - 'Edith Dudszus' CBod CKno EAEE ECha EHoe ELan ELon EPPr GBin GQue LHop LPla LRHS MBel MBrN NCGa NDov NGdn NHol SCob SMHy SPhx WCot WGrn WMoo WWEG
- - 'Heidebraut' CBod EAEE EBee EHoe EHrv EPPr EWoo GBin GMaP GQue IBoy LOPS LRHS MBel MBri MRav NBro NCGa NDov NWsh SCob SPhx WMoo WWEG XSen
- - 'Igel' **new** EBee
- - 'Moorflamme' CSam EPPr MAvo MSpe SPhx
- - 'Moorhexe' Widely available
- - 'Overdam' EPPr NDov
- - 'Poul Petersen' CKno EBee EPPr LCro NDov SPhx WWEG
- - 'Rotschopf' **new** EBee
- - 'Strahlenquelle' CBod CSam ELan EPPr GCal GQue LPla LRHS MAvo MSpe MWhi NBro NDov NHol NWsh WCAu WWEG
- - 'Variegata' (v) ♀H7 Widely available
- 'Heidezwerg' EBee EPPr GBin
- 'Showers of Gold' SPhx
litoralis see *M. caerulea* subsp. *arundinacea*

Molopospermum (*Apiaceae*)

peloponnesiacum CAby CSpe EBee GBin GCal IMou LEdu MSpe SBrt SDix SMHy SPhx WCru WPGP WPtf WSHC

Moltkia (*Boraginaceae*)

§ ***doerfleri*** EBee GCal LHop NBir NChi SBrt WSHC
§ × ***intermedia*** ♀H5 CMea ECho LRHS SBch SBrt SIgm WAbe WThu
petraea ECho LHop LLHF LRHS WAbe

Moluccella (*Lamiaceae*)

laevis LCro SPhx SVic
- 'Pixie Bells' CSpe

Monadenium (*Euphorbiaceae*)

capitatum **new** LToo
magnificum **new** LToo
schubei **new** LToo

Monanthes (*Crassulaceae*)

laxiflora **new** WCot
pallens **new** WCot

Monarda (*Lamiaceae*)

sp. ENfk
'Adam' GBuc GCal LSRN MRav MSpe NLar WSHC
'Amethyst' ECtt EWes
'Aquarius' EAEE EPPr EWoo GQue IKil LAst LRHS MSpe WFar XLum
austromontana see *M. citriodora* subsp. *austromontana*
§ 'Balance' EBee ECtt GCal MRav MSpe NBro NDov NGdn SHar WSHC WWEG XLum
'Beauty of Cobham' ♀H4 Widely available
§ 'Blaustrumpf' CElw EAJP ECtt EPfP EWTr EWes EWoo GBBs GQue LRHS NLar SPer WHea WSHC WWEG XLum
Blue Stocking see *M.* 'Blaustrumpf'
Bowman see *M.* 'Sagittarius'
bradburyana CEvo GJos MMuc MNrw NBFr NDov SAko SBrt SPhx
'Cambridge Scarlet' Widely available
'Capricorn' WWEG XLum
citriodora GPoy MNHC NSti SIde SRms SWat

§	- subsp. ***austromontana***	NBir
	- - 'Bee's Favourite'	IKil
	'Comanche'	EWes
	'Croftway Pink'	Widely available
	didyma	CArn CBod CNec ENfk EPfP LPot NBro SRms SVic SWat WJek
	- 'Alba'	NLar
	- 'Coral Reef'	EWes LRHS WWEG
	- 'Cranberry Lace'PBR	CBot CRos EBee ECtt GBin LRHS MBri MSCN NLar SBea SGol SPoG
	- 'Duddiscombe'	CSam
	- 'Pink Lace'PBR	CBot CRos ECtt IBoy LRHS LSou LSun MBri MNrw MSpe NHol NLar SCob SPoG WHil
	- 'Sugar Lace'PBR	LRHS NLar
	'Earl Grey'	EBee ECtt GAbr MSpe NDov SCoo
	'Elsie's Lavender'	EBee EPfP LPla LRHS MTis NDov NLar WWEG
	'Elworthy'	CElw WWFP
	'Fireball'PBR	CBcs CBct CBod CBot CRos CWCL EBee ECtt ELon EShb EUJe EWoo LLHF LOPS LRHS LSRN LSou MBel MHol NHol NLar SPad WBor WFar WHil WTor
§	'Fishes'	CExl CMac EAEE EBee ECtt EHrv ELan EPPr EWes EWoo IKil LAst LEdu LRHS LSou MMuc MRav MSpe NDov NGdn NLar SGbt SPoG SWvt WPtf WWEG
	fistulosa	CArn CHby CMac GJos GPoy MHer MMuc MNHC NBFr SRms WJek WMoo XLum
	- var. ***menthifolia*** 'Mohikaner' **new**	NDov
	'Gardenview Scarlet' ♀H4	CBot CElw CSam CWCL EAEE ECtt EWes GCra GQue IKil LCro LEdu LPfy LRHS MCot MMuc MNrw MPie MSpe MWat NDov NFav NHol NSti SPoG SWvt WHoo WWEG
	Gemini	see *M.* 'Twins'
	'Gewitterwolke'	CSam MSpe MTis NDov WWEG
	'Hartswood Wine'	EBee ECtt EWes LEdu SMad WWEG
	'Jacob Cline'	EAJP ECtt EPPr EWes GBin IPot LRHS MSpe MTis NBre NCGa NLar SGbt SHar SMHy SPhx WBor WWEG XLum
	'Kardinal'	GBin LPla LRHS MTis NDov WWEG XLum
	Libra	see *M.* 'Balance'
	'Loddon Crown'	CTsd CWld ECtt ELon GQue LRHS MSpe MTis NHol NLar SBea SHar SIde WFar WSHC WWEG
	'Mahogany'	CMos EAEE EBee ECtt ELan EWTr GBuc GMaP GQue IBoy IKil ILea IPot LPla LRHS MBri MCot MNrw MRav MSpe MTis NSti SCob SPer SPhx SPoG WWEG XLum
	'Marshall's Delight' ♀H4	CBod CWCL EAEE EBee ECtt EWes GQue LAst LRHS MNrw MRav MSpe NLar SWvt WHoo
	'Melissa'	EBee LSRN NBre NLar WSHC
	menthifolia	GCal SRms
	'Mohawk'	EAEE ECtt EHrv EPPr EPfP GQue LRHS MPie MRav MSpe MTis NDov NGdn SDix WPtf WWEG XLum
	'Mrs Perry'	EWes
	'Neon'	MSpe NDov SPhx
	'On Parade'	CElw CSam CWCL CWld EAEE ECtt LRHS MMHG MSpe MTis NDov NGdn
	'Othello'	NDov
	'Ou Charm'	EBee EWes GBin NLar SMad
	Panorama Series	SPlb WMoo
	- 'Panorama Red Shades'	CWib EPfP MNHC WCFE
	'Pawnee'	LPla WWEG
	Petite Delight = 'Acpetdel'	CBcs ELan EWTr LSou MPkF NLar SMad XLum
	'Petite Wonder'	EBee
	'Pink Supreme'PBR	CBct CRos ECtt ELon LRHS LSou MHol MSpe NCGa NLar SCoo WHil WTor
	'Pink Tourmaline'	NDov WWEG
	Pisces	see *M.* 'Fishes'
	'Poyntzfield Pink'	GPoy LEdu
	Prairie Night	see *M.* 'Prärienacht'
§	'Prärienacht'	Widely available
	punctata	GJos MMuc MNHC SGSe SWat
	'Purple Ann'	XLum
	'Purple Tower'	EWes
	'Raspberry Wine'	CBod EAEE EBee ECtt EPPr LEdu LRHS MAvo MHol MTis WPGP
	'Ruby Glow'	CSam CWCL EHrv LRHS LSRN MMHG SMad
§	'Sagittarius'	EAEE EBee GQue LRHS MBNS MMHG MSpe NGdn NSti WWEG
	'Saxon Purple'	NDov XLum
§	'Schneewittchen'	CBod EAJP EBee ECha ECtt EHrv ELan EPfP GBin LCro LRHS MHer MHol MRav MSpe MTis NHol NLar NPri NSti SCob SCoo SGbt SIde SPer SPoG SWvt WCAu WWEG XLum
	'Scorpion'	EBee ECtt EHrv ELan EPPr EPfP GBin LCro LEdu LOPS LRHS MRav NBir NEgg NGdn NLar NSti SWvt WCAu WSHC XLum
	'Shelley'	ECha
	'Sioux'	EHrv EWes
	'Snow Maiden'	see *M.* 'Schneewittchen'
	'Snow Queen'	CMos CWCL EBee ECtt LRHS MBel MPie MSpe
	Snow White	see *M.* 'Schneewittchen'
	'Squaw' ♀H4	Widely available
	'Talud' ♀H4	MNrw NDov
§	'Twins'	CBod CWCL GKev LSRN NLar SWvt WSHC WWEG
	'Vintage Wine'	CWCL MMuc NDov
	'Violacea'	NHol
	'Violet Queen' ♀H4	CBod CWCL EAEE EBee ECtt ELan EWes GQue LEdu LRHS MBel MCot MSpe NEoE SCoo WPtf WWEG
	'Violette'	EBee MSpe
	'Westacre Purple'	EBee EPPr EWes

Monardella (*Lamiaceae*)

	macrantha subsp. ***hallii***	CPBP
	nana subsp. ***arida***	CPBP
	odoratissima	MHer NBFr

Monochoria (*Pontederiaceae*)

§	***hastata***	LLWG MSKA

Monopsis (*Campanulaceae*)

	Midnight = 'Yagemon'	LAst

Monstera (*Araceae*)

	deliciosa (F) ♀H1b	MBri XBlo
	- 'Variegata' (v) ♀H1b	MBri

Montbretia see *Crocosmia, Tritonia*

Montia (*Portulacaceae*)

	perfoliata	see *Claytonia perfoliata*
	sibirica	see *Claytonia sibirica*

Moraea (*Iridaceae*)

	algoensis	WCot
	alticola	CPne EBee ECho GCal SPlb
§	***aristata***	NRog WCot
	atropunctata	NRog
§	***bellendenii***	NRog WCot
	bipartita	NRog WCot
	ciliata	NRog WCot
	citrina	ECho
§	***collina***	ECho GKev NRog
	elegans	ECho
	flaccida	ECho
§	***fugax***	WCot
	gawleri	WCot
	gigandra	NRog WCot
	glaucopsis	see *M. aristata*
	huttonii	CCon CSpe CTca CTre CTsd EPri GAbr MHer SBrt SGSe SMad WCot WSHC
	incurva	ECho
	iridioides	see *Dietes iridioides*
	longifolia Sweet	see *M. fugax*
	longifolia (Jacq.) Pers.	MHol
	loubseri	NRog WCot
	lugubris	NRog
	lurida	WCot
	macrocarpa	NRog
	neglecta	ECho
	ochroleuca	ECho GKev NRog
	pavonia var. ***lutea***	see *M. bellendenii*
	polystachya	CGrW ECho NRog
	robusta	EBee GCal
	setifolia	ECho
	sisyrinchium	ECho
	- purple-flowered	ECho
	spathacea	see *M. spathulata*
§	***spathulata***	CCon CExl CTca EBee ECho GCal GKev WCot
	thomsonii	NRog
	tricolor	ECho
	tricuspidata	NRog
	tripetala	NRog
	tulbaghensis	NRog
	vegeta	ECho NRog WCot
	- brown-flowered	CDes
	villosa	ECho NRog WCot

Morella (*Myricaceae*)

	californica	CAgr
	pensylvanica	CAgr CArn CDul IVic NLar

Moricandia (*Brassicaceae*)

	moricandioides	WCot

Morina (*Caprifoliaceae*)

*	***afghanica***	GAbr
	alba	GCra
	longifolia	Widely available
	persica	EWes

Morinda (*Rubiaceae*)

	umbellata WWJ 11688	WCru

Morisia (*Brassicaceae*)

	hypogaea	see *M. monanthos*
§	***monanthos***	CPla CTsd GCrg GEdr LRHS SRot
	- 'Fred Hemingway'	ECtt LRHS NSla WAbe WCot

Morus ✿ (*Moraceae*)

§	***alba***	CArn CBcs CCVT CDul CHab CLnd CMCN CTho CWib ECrN ELan EPfP ERea LBuc LHop LRHS MRav SDea SVic WFar
	- 'Black Tabor'	CAgr
	- 'Issai'	GKev LRHS MGos SHil
	- 'Macrophylla'	CMCN MBlu NLar
	- 'Pakistan' (F)	CAgr ERea
	- 'Paradise'	CAgr WMat
	- 'Pendula'	CAgr CDoC CDul CMCN CMac CTho CTri ECrN ELan IDee MBlu MBri NPri SCoo SPoG WMat
	- 'Platanifolia'	CLnd MBlu
	- 'San Martin'	ERea
	- var. ***tatarica***	CAgr LEdu NLar
	'Capsrum' (F)	CAgr WMat
	'Carmen' (F)	CAgr WMat
	'Illinois Everbearing' (F)	CAgr ERea WMat
	'Italian' (F)	CAgr WMat
	'Ivory' (F)	CAgr WMat
	kagayamae	see *M. alba*
	latifolia 'Spirata'	NLar
	nigra (F)	Widely available
§	- 'Chelsea' (F) ♀H6	CDul CTho CTri ECrN EPfP EPom ERea GQue GTwe IVic LCro LRHS MBri MGos MWat NOra NWea SCoo SEWo SKee SLim SPer SPoG WHar WMat
	- 'Izvor' (F) **new**	CAgr
	- 'Jerusalem' (F) ♀H6	CTho EPom LRHS MCoo NOra SKee WHar WMat
	- 'King James'	see *M. nigra* 'Chelsea'
	- 'Large Black' (F)	EPom
	- 'Repsime' (F)	CAgr
	- 'Sham Dudu' (F)	CAgr
	rubra	NLar
	- 'Nana'	NLar
	'Wellington' (F)	CCVT CLnd GTwe LCro LOPS LRHS LSRN NOra WMat

Mosla (*Lamiaceae*)

	dianthera	EWld GCal MAvo

Mucuna (*Papilionaceae*)

	pruriens **new**	MOWG

Muehlenbeckia (*Polygonaceae*)

	astonii	CDoC EAla EBee ECou LRHS WPGP
	axillaris misapplied	see *M. complexa*
§	***axillaris*** (Hook. f.) Endl.	CBcs CDoC CTri EAla ECou SBig XLum
	- 'Mount Cook' (f)	ECou
	- 'Ohau' (m)	ECou
§	***complexa***	Widely available
	- (f)	ECou
	- 'Nana'	see *M. axillaris* (Hook. f.) Endl.
	- small-leaved	EUJe
	- 'Spotlight'[PBR] (v)	EShb
	- var. ***trilobata***	CBcs ECou EShb ESwi EUJe SSta XLum

	- 'Ward' (m)	ECou
	ephedroides	ECou
*	- var. ***muricatula***	ECou
	platyclados	see *Homalocladium platycladum*

Muhlenbergia (*Poaceae*)

	capillaris	LPal SDix SHDw SMad WCot
	dubia	WPGP
	dumosa	CKno SMad WCot WPGP
	japonica 'Cream Delight' (v)	EHoe
	lindheimeri	CKno SDix SMea WCot
	mexicana	SRms
	rigens	CKno WPGP XLum

Mukdenia (*Saxifragaceae*)

	acanthifolia	LEdu WPGP
	rossii	CAby CCon CLAP CTal EHrv ELon EWTr GCal IFro LEdu LPla LRHS MBel MNrw NBid NLar NMyG SGSe SHil WCru WOld WPGP WSHC WThu XLum
	- from Japan	GCal
	- 'Crimson Fans'	see *M. rossii* 'Karasuba'
	- dwarf	CDes CLAP CTal GCal MNrw
§	- 'Karasuba'	CBod CLAP CMos CSpe CTal CWGN EBee ECtt ELon EPfP EWoo GEdr IDee LBMP LEdu LRHS LSou MAvo MHol MMHG MPnt NLar NMyG SCob SPoG SWvt WCot WHil

mulberry see *Morus*

Murraya (*Rutaceae*)

*	***elliptica***	MOWG
	exotica	see *M. paniculata*
	koenigii	EOHP GPoy SCit SPre SVen WJek WSFF
§	***paniculata***	EShb MOWG

Musa ✿ (*Musaceae*)

	from Yunnan, China	see *M. itinerans* 'Yunnan'
§	***acuminata*** 'Dwarf Cavendish' (AAA Group) (F) ♀H1b	CBct CDoC CTsd ELan LHop NLos NPla XBlo
	- 'Siam Ruby' (AA Group) (F)	NLos
	- 'Williams' (AAA Group) (F)	XBlo
	- 'Zebrina' ♀H1b	CDTJ LRHS NLos XBlo
	basjoo ♀H2	CAbb CAby CBcs CBct CDoC CHll CSBt ELan EPfP EUJe IDee LCro LEdu LPal LRHS LSRN LTro MGos MMuc NLos NPla SChr SEND SHil SLim SPer SPlb SPoG
I	- 'Rubra'	ESwi
	'Cavendish Super Dwarf'	NLos XBlo
	cavendishii	see *M. acuminata* 'Dwarf Cavendish'
§	***coccinea*** ♀H1b	XBlo
	ensete	see *Ensete ventricosum*
	hookeri	see *M. sikkimensis*
	itinerans var. ***xishuangbannaensis*** 'Mekong Giant'	EUJe
§	- 'Yunnan'	NLos
	lasiocarpa ♀H1c	CDTJ CDoC CHll ESwi EUJe LTro MGos MPkF NLos NPla SBig SPlb
	nana misapplied	see *M. acuminata* 'Dwarf Cavendish'
	ornata ♀H1b	XBlo
§	***sikkimensis*** ♀H1c	CDTJ ELan ESwi EUJe LPal LTro SBig SPlb XBlo
	- 'Red Tiger'	CDTJ NLos
	uranoscopus misapplied	see *M. coccinea*
	velutina ♀H1b	NLos SBig

Muscari ✿ (*Asparagaceae*)

	adilii	NRog
	'Aleyna'	ECho NRog
	ambrosiacum	see *M. muscarimi*
	anatolicum	ECho NRog WCot
	armeniacum ♀H5	CBro CTri EAJP ECho EPfP LCro LOPS LPot LRHS MBri MMuc NRog SCob SEND SPer SRms WCot WShi
	- PAB 6748	LEdu
	- 'Album' **new**	SCob
	- 'Argaei Album'	ECho EPot NRog SBch
	- 'Artist'	NRog
	- 'Atlantic'	ECho EPfP LRHS NRog
	- 'Blue Pearl'	ECho NRog WPnP
	- 'Blue Spike' (d)	CBro ECho EPfP LAma MBri NBir NEgg NRog SDeJ WGwG
	- 'Cantab'	ECho SDeJ XLum
	- 'Christmas Pearl' ♀H4	ECho GKev NRog WCot
	- 'Côte d'Azur'	GKev
	- 'Cupido'	CGrW GKev
	- 'Dark Eyes'	ECho EPfP SCob
	- 'Early Giant'	ECho SDeJ
	- 'Fantasy Creation'	ECho NRog SDeJ
	- 'Gül'	CDes WCot
	- 'Heavenly Blue'	ECho
	- 'Icicle' **new**	WHil
	- 'Lady Blu' **new**	LRHS WRHF
	- 'New Creation'	ECho
	- 'Peppermint'	CTca ECho EPfP ERCP LAma LRHS WBor
	- 'Saffier' ♀H5	ECho LAma NRog WCot WHil
	- 'Valerie Finnis'	CAby CAvo CBre CBro CTca ECho EPPr EPfP EPot ERCP EShb MBri NLar SCob SDeJ SPhx WBrk WCot WPnP
	aucheri ♀H5	ECho NRya
*	- var. ***bicolor***	WCot
	- 'Blue Magic'	CAvo ECho EPot ERCP GKev LAma NRog SDeJ
	- 'Ocean Magic'	CBro ECho GBin GKev LAma MBri NLar
§	- 'Tubergenianum'	ECho
	- 'White Magic'	CAvo CBro ECho ERCP LAma LRHS SCob SDeJ WBor WBrk
§	***azureum*** ♀H5	CAvo CBro CTca ECho ELan EPfP ERCP GKev GMaP LAma LPot NLar NRog SPhx WCot
	- 'Album'	ECho LAma MBel NRog SPhx WCot
	- 'Bling Bling'	ECho
	'Baby's Breath'	see *M.* 'Jenny Robinson'
	'Big Smile'	GKev NRog WCot
	'Blue Dream'	ECho
	'Blue Eyes'	ECho WCot
	'Blue Star'	ECho
	botryoides	CAvo ECho LAma NRog SCob WCot
	- 'Album'	CAvo CBro CTca CTri ECho EPfP GKev LAma LCro LOPS LRHS MBri NRog SCob SDeJ SRms WCot WShi
	bourgaei	ECho WCot
	caucasicum	ECho WCot
	chalusicum	see *M. pseudomuscari*
	commutatum	ECho

§	***comosum***	CBro ECho EPfP ERCP MCot NEgg NRog WCot
	- 'Monstrosum'	see *M. comosum* 'Plumosum'
	- 'Pinard'	ECho
§	- 'Plumosum'	ECho ELan EPfP GKev LAma MBri NRog SCob SDeJ WCot
	dionysicum	ECho
	- HOA 8965	ECho
	discolor	ECho NRog
	grandifolium JCA 689.450	WCot
	inconstrictum	ECho
	'Ivor's Pink'	WCot
§	'Jenny Robinson' ♀H5	ECho EHrv IFoB LRHS SDys SMad WCot
	latifolium ♀H5	CAby CBro CTca ECho EPfP ERCP LAma LCro LRHS MBri MWat NEgg NLar NRog SCob SDeJ SGSe WBor WCot
*	- 'Blue Angels'	NBir
	macbeathianum	WCot
§	***macrocarpum***	CBro CTal CTca ECha ECho EPot GKev LAma NRog
	- 'Golden Fragrance' PBR	CAvo CBro CExl CHid ECho EPot ERCP GKev IFoB LAma LCro MCot MNrw MPie NRog SDeJ WCot WHil
	moschatum	see *M. muscarimi*
	'Mount Hood'	CBro ECho ERCP MBel SCob SDeJ
§	***muscarimi***	CAvo CBro CTca ECho IFoB LAma NLar NRog SDeJ WCot
	- var. ***flavum***	see *M. macrocarpum*
§	***neglectum***	ECho LAma MMuc NLar NRog SEND WCot WShi
	pallens	ECho NRog
	paradoxum	see *Bellevalia paradoxa*
	parviflorum	ECho WCot
	'Pink Sunrise'	ECho EPfP EPot ERCP SCob
§	***pseudomuscari*** ♀H5	CDes ECho GKev WCot
	racemosum	see *M. neglectum*
	'Rosy Sunrise'	WCot
	'Sky Blue'	ECho WCot
§	***spreitzenhoferi***	NRog
	'Superstar'	ECho
§	***tenuiflorum***	ECho WCot
	aff. ***tenuiflorum*** JCA 0.691.251	WCot
	tubergenianum	see *M. aucheri* 'Tubergenianum'
	'Venus'	GKev WCot
	'White Beauty'	ECho
	'Winter Amethyst'	WCot

Muscarimia (*Asparagaceae*)

ambrosiacum	see *Muscari muscarimi*
macrocarpum	see *Muscari macrocarpum*

Musella see *Musa*

Mutisia (*Asteraceae*)

	acerosa	MGil
	decurrens	MGil
	linearifolia	MGil
	oligodon	MGil
	retusa	see *M. spinosa* var. *pulchella*
	spinosa	MGil
§	- var. ***pulchella***	GGal
	subulata	MGil

Myoporum (*Scrophulariaceae*)

	acuminatum	see *M. tenuifolium*
	debile	see *Eremophila debilis*
	laetum	CExl IDee SVen
§	***tenuifolium***	SPlb SVen

Myosotidium (*Boraginaceae*)

§	***hortensia***	CAby CBcs CBct CBod CExl CSpe ECre EPfP ETod EUJe EWTr EWes EWoo GBin GCal GKev IBoy IKil LEdu LRHS WCot WPGP WSHC
	- 'True Blue'	CHid
	- white-flowered	IKil
	nobile	see *M. hortensia*

Myosotis (*Boraginaceae*)

	from Eyre Mountains, New Zealand	EPot
	capitata	GEdr
	colensoi	ECou EPot
	decumbens new	GEdr
	'Malmesbury'	CNat
	My Oh My = 'Myomark' PBR	LSou
	palustris	see *M. scorpioides*
	pulvinaris	CPBP WAbe
	pygmaea SDR 7257	GKev
	'Rolled Gold' new	GEdr
§	***scorpioides***	CBen CBod CHab CWCL CWat EHon MMuc MNrw MSKA MWLS MWts NMir SCoo SPlb SRms SWat WBrk WMAq WMoo WPnP WRHF XLum
	- 'Alba'	MSKA MWts
	- 'Ice Pearl'	ECha
	- Maytime = 'Blaqua' (v)	LLWG NBir
	- 'Mermaid'	CBen CWat ECha EWay LLWG SDix SWat WPtf
	- 'Pinkie'	CWat LLWG SWat
	- 'Snowflakes'	CWat EWay SWat
	- variegated (v)	MSKA
	sylvatica	LCro MMuc NMir
	- 'Bluesylva' (Sylva Series)	LRHS SPhx
	- 'Rosylva' (Sylva Series)	CWCL
	- 'Ultramarine'	WMoo
	- 'Victoria Indigo-blue' (Victoria Series)	CWCL EPfP
	traversii	SBch

Myrica (*Myricaceae*)

gale	CAgr CSde GPoy IVic MGos NLar SWat WGwG

Myricaria (*Tamaricaceae*)

germanica	NLar

Myriophyllum (*Haloragaceae*)

propinquum	LLWG
spicatum	EHon MSKA MWts WMAq
verticillatum	CWat EWay MSKA SCoo

Myrrhis (*Apiaceae*)

odorata	CArn CBre CCon CHby CLau CMac CSpe ECha ENfk GPoy IFro LHop LOPS LRHS MHer MMuc MNHC NPri SCob SDix SIde SPad SPer SRms SWvt WJek WPGP WSFF WWFP
- 'Forncett Chevron'	LEdu

Myrsine (*Primulaceae*)

africana	CBcs CFil CWib EShb MHer
aquilonia	ECou
australis	SVen
divaricata	ECou SVen

Myrteola (*Myrtaceae*)

§	***nummularia***	GAbr ITim NHar WAbe WThu

Myrtus ✿ (*Myrtaceae*)

	apiculata misapplied	see *Luma apiculata*
	bullata	see *Lophomyrtus bullata*
	chequen	see *Luma chequen*
	communis ♀H4	Widely available
	- 'Flore Pleno' (d)	MHer
	- 'Jenny Reitenbach'	see *M. communis* subsp. *tarentina*
	- 'Merion'	WJek
	- 'Microphylla'	see *M. communis* subsp. *tarentina*
	- 'Nana'	see *M. communis* subsp. *tarentina*
	- 'Pyewood Park'	SRms WJek
§	- subsp. ***tarentina*** ♀H4	Widely available
	- - 'Compacta'	LRHS SCoo SLon
	- - 'Microphylla Variegata' (v)	CBcs EShb LRHS MHer MNHC SPer SRms WHar WJek
I	- - 'Variegata' (v)	CBod CLet EOHP EPfP
	- 'Tricolor'	see *M. communis* 'Variegata'
§	- 'Variegata' (v)	CArn CBot CLet CMCN CMac CSBt CTri CWib CWld ELan ELon ENfk EPfP EShb LEdu LHop LRHS MGil MHer MSwo NLar SLon SPer SPoG WCFE WJek WSHC
	'Glanleam Gold'	see *Luma apiculata* 'Glanleam Gold'
	lechleriana	see *Amomyrtus luma*
	luma	see *Luma apiculata*
	nummularia	see *Myrteola nummularia*
	ugni	see *Ugni molinae*

N

Nandina (*Berberidaceae*)

	sp.	LPar
	Blush Pink = 'Aka'PBR **new**	LRHS SCob SPoG
	domestica	Widely available
	- B&SWJ 4923	LPar WCru
	- B&SWJ 11113	LPar WCru
	- 'Filamentosa'	EBee EPfP NLar SCob SMad
	- 'Fire Power'	Widely available
	- Flirt = 'Murasaki'PBR	LRHS SCob SPoG
	- 'Gulf Stream'	LBuc MGos NLar WPat
	- 'Harbour Dwarf'	CDoC LRHS NLar WFar
	- var. ***leucocarpa***	CMCN NLar
	- 'Nana'	see *N. domestica* 'Pygmaea'
	- Plum Passion = 'Monum'	EPfP LCro LRHS MAsh SCob SPoG
§	- 'Pygmaea'	CMen SGol
	- 'Richmond' ♀H5	CBcs CBot CDul ELan EPfP LAst LRHS MAsh MGos NLar NPri SCob SHil SLim SPer SPoG SRkn SWvt WFar
	- 'Seika'PBR	CBot CDoC EBee ELan EMil EPfP EUJe LAst LPar LRHS LSou MGos MHtn SCob SMad SPoG WCot
	- Sienna Sunrise = 'Monfar' **new**	LCro LOPS
	- 'Sunset'	EBee LSRN NLar SCob
	- 'Wood's Dwarf'	CBcs MPkF NLar

Nannorrhops (*Arecaceae*)

	arabica	see *N. ritchieana*
§	***ritchieana***	LPal LTro SPlb
	- blue-leaved	LPal
	- green-leaved	LPal

Napaea (*Malvaceae*)

dioica	CEvo SPhx WCot

Narcissus ✿ (*Amaryllidaceae*)

'Abalone' (2)	CQua
'Abba' (4) ♀H6	CFen CQua
'Abbey Road' (5)	CQua
'Aberfoyle' (2) ♀H6	CQua
'Abstract' (11a)	CQua
'Accent' (2)	CQua
'Accomplice' (3)	IRhd
'Achduart' (3)	CQua
'Achentoul' (4)	CQua
'Achnasheen' (3)	CQua
'Acropolis' (4)	CQua SDeJ
'Actaea' (9) ♀H6	CBro CFen CQua CTca LCro LOPS MBri SCob SDeJ
'Acumen' (2)	CQua
'Admiration' (8)	CQua
'Adorable Lass' (6)	CQua
'Ad-Rem' (2)	CFen LAma
'Adversane' (3)	CQua
'Advocat' (3)	CQua
'Aflame' (3)	CFen
'African Sunset' (3)	IRhd
'After All' (3)	CFen
'Agnes Mace' (2)	IRhd
'Ahwahnee' (2)	CQua IRhd
'Ainley' (2)	CQua
'Aintree' (3)	CQua
'Aircastle' (3)	CQua
'Airtime' (2)	IRhd
'Akepa' (5)	CQua
'Albatross' (3)	CQua GCro WShi
'Albus Plenus Odoratus'	see *N. poeticus* 'Plenus' ambig.
'Alex Jones' (2)	CQua
'All Rounder' (3)	IRhd
'Alpine Winter' (1)	IRhd
'Alston' (2)	IRhd
'Alto' (2)	IRhd
'Altruist' (3)	CQua ERCP LRHS SDeJ
'Altun Ha' (2)	CQua IRhd MGib
'Amabilis' (3)	GCro
'Amadeus Mozart' (2) **new**	CQua
'Amazing Grace' (2)	CQua IRhd
'Amber Castle' (2)	CQua
'Ambergate' (2)	CQua LAma SDeJ
'Ambergris Caye' (1)	CQua
'American Dream' (1) **new**	CQua
'American Goldfinch' (7)	CQua
'American Heritage' (1)	CQua IRhd
'American Robin' (6)	CQua
'American Shores' (1)	IRhd
'Amstel' (4)	CQua
'Andalusia' (6)	CQua
'Andrew's Choice' (7) ♀H6	CQua
'Angel' (3)	CQua
'Angel Face' (3)	CQua IRhd
'Angel Wings'	see *N.* 'Celtic Wings'
'Angelito' (3) ♀H6	IRhd
'Angel's Breath' (5) ♀H6	CQua
'Angel's Whisper' (5)	CQua
'Angel's Wings' (2)	CQua
'Angels Wood' (2)	IRhd
'Angkor' (4)	CQua MGib
'An-gof' (7)	CQua

	'Animal Crackers' (2)	CQua
	'Ann Sonia' (4)	IRhd
	'Anna Panna' (3)	IRhd
	'Annequin' (3)	CQua
	'Apollo Gold' (10)	CQua ECho
	'Apotheose' (4)	CFen SDeJ
	'Applins' (2)	IRhd
	'Apricot' (1)	CBro GCro
	'Apricot Whirl' (11a)	CQua
	'April Dawn' (2) **new**	IRhd
	'April Love' (1)	CQua
	'April Snow' (2)	CBro CQua
	'Ara' (6)	CQua
	'Aranjuez' (2)	CFen CQua
	'Arctic Gem' (3)	CQua
	'Arctic Gold' (1) ♀H6	CQua LAma
	'Areley Kings' (2)	CQua
	'Argent' (4)	CQua GCro
	'Argosy' (1)	CQua
	'Arid Plains' (3)	IRhd
	'Ariel'PBR (8)	GKev
	'Ark Royal' (1)	CFen
	'Arkle' (1) ♀H6	CQua SDeJ
	'Arleston' (2)	CQua IRhd
	'Armada' (2)	CFen CQua
	'Armidale' (3)	CQua IRhd
	'Armoury' (4)	CQua
	'Arndilly' (2)	CQua
	'Arpege' (2)	CQua
	'Arran Isle' (2)	IRhd
	'Arthurian' (1)	IRhd
	'Articol' (11a)	CQua
	'Arwenack' (11a)	CQua
	'Asante' (1)	IRhd
	'Ashland' (2)	IRhd
	'Ashmore' (2)	CQua IRhd
	'Ashton Wold' (2)	CQua
	'Asila' (2)	IRhd
	'Assertion' (2)	IRhd
§	***assoanus*** (13)	ECho EPot GCal GKev LLHF NSla
	'Astropink' (11a)	CQua
§	***asturiensis*** (13)	GKev LLHF
	- giant	see *N. asturiensis* 'Wavertree'
§	- 'Wavertree' (1)	CQua LLHF
	'Atholl Palace' (4)	IRhd MGib
	'Atlas Gold'	see *N. romieuxii* 'Atlas Gold'
	'Atricilla' (11a)	IRhd
	'Auchranie' (2)	IRhd
	'Audubon' (2)	CQua SDeJ
	'Aunt Betty' (1)	CQua IRhd
	'Auntie Eileen' (2)	CQua
§	***aureus*** (13)	CQua
	'Auspicious' (2)	IRhd
	'Autumn Habit' (3)	IRhd
	'Avalanche' (8) ♀H4	CFen CQua IRhd LCro LOPS SDeJ
	'Avalanche of Gold' (8)	CQua
	'Avalon' (2)	CQua ERCP
	'Avon Mill' (1) **new**	MGib
	'Avril Amour' (1)	IRhd
	'Azocor' (1)	IRhd
	'Baby Boomer' (7)	LAma LRHS
	'Baby Moon' (7)	CFen CQua CTca EPfP EPot ERCP GKev LAma MBri SDeJ
	'Back Flash' (2)	CQua
	'Badanloch' (3)	CQua
	'Badbury Rings' (3) ♀H6	CQua IRhd
	'Bailey' (2)	IRhd
	'Bala' (4)	CQua
	'Balalaika' (2)	CQua
	'Baldock' (4)	CQua
	'Ballydorn' (9)	IRhd
	'Ballygarvey' (1)	CQua
	'Ballygowan' (3)	IRhd
	'Ballyrobert' (1)	CQua
	'Baltic Shore' (3)	IRhd
	'Balvenie' (2)	CQua
	'Bandesara' (3)	CQua IRhd
	'Bandit' (2)	CQua IRhd
	'Banker' (2)	CQua IRhd
	'Banstead Village' (2)	CQua
	'Bantam' (2) ♀H6	CBro CQua SDeJ
	'Barbara Hunt' (7)	CQua
	'Barbary Gold' (2)	CQua IRhd
	'Barn Dance' (3) **new**	CQua
	'Barnesgold' (1)	IRhd
	'Barnham' (1)	CQua
	'Barnsdale Wood' (2)	CQua
	'Barnum' (1) ♀H6	IRhd
	'Barrett Browning' (3)	SDeJ
	'Barrii' (3)	CQua
	'Bath's Flame' (3)	CAvo CQua GCro WShi
	'Bear Springs' (4)	IRhd
	'Bear's Gold' (4)	CQua
	'Beaulieu' (1)	CQua
	'Beautiful Dream' (3)	CQua
	'Beauvallon' (4)	SDeJ
	'Bebop' (7)	CBro
	'Bedruthan' (2)	CQua
	'Beersheba' (1)	CQua
	'Belbroughton' (2)	CQua
	'Belcanto' (11a)	CQua SDeJ
	'Belfast Lough' (1)	IRhd
	'Belisana' (2)	SDeJ
	'Bell Rock' (1) ♀H6	CQua
	'Bell Song' (7)	CBro CFen CQua GKev LSou SDeJ WShi
	'Bella Estrella' (11a)	ERCP
	'Bells of Joy' (5) **new**	IRhd
	'Belzone' (2)	CQua
	'Ben Aligin' (1)	IRhd
	'Ben Hee' (2)	CQua IRhd
	'Berceuse' (2)	CQua IRhd
	'Bere Ferrers' (4)	CQua
	'Bergerac' (11a)	CQua
	'Bernardino' (2)	CQua GCro
	'Beryl' (6)	CBro CQua WShi
	'Best Friend' (3)	CQua
	'Best Seller' (1)	SPer
	'Bethal' (3)	CQua
	'Bethan-Sîan' (2)	CQua
	'Betsy MacDonald' (6)	CQua
	'Biffo' (4)	CQua
	Biggar Bountiful (2)	GCro
	'Bikini Beach' (2)	IRhd
	'Bilbo' (6)	CBro CQua
	'Billy Graham' (2)	CQua
	'Binkie' (2)	CBro CQua SPer
	'Birchwood' (3)	CQua IRhd
	'Birma' (3)	LAma SDeJ
	'Birthday Girl' (2)	IRhd
	'Bishops Light' (2)	CQua
	'Bittern' (12)	CQua SDeJ
	'Blackstone' (2)	CQua
	'Blair Athol' (2)	CQua
	'Blakey' (2) **new**	CQua
	'Blarney' (3)	CQua
	'Blisland' (9)	CQua
	'Blossom' (4)	CQua
	'Blossom Lady' (4)	CQua
	'Blue Danube' (1)	CQua IRhd

	Name	Suppliers
	'Blushing Maiden' (4)	CQua
	'Bob Spotts' (2)	CQua
	'Bobbysoxer' (7)	CBro CQua
	'Bobolink' (2)	CQua
	'Boconnoc' (2)	CQua
	'Bodelva' (2)	CQua
	'Bodwannick' (2)	CQua
	'Bolton' (7)	GCro
	'Bombay' (2)	CFen
	'Bon Viveur' (11a)	IRhd
	'Bonython' (1)	GCro
	'Border Beauty' (2) 🏆^{H6}	CQua
	'Bosbigal' (11a)	CQua
	'Boscastle' (7)	CQua
	'Boscoppa' (11a)	CQua
	'Boslowick' (11a) 🏆^{H6}	CQua
	'Bosmeor' (2)	CQua
	'Bossa Nova' (3)	CQua
	'Bossiney' (11a)	CQua
	'Bosvale' (11a)	CQua IRhd
	'Bosvigo' (11a)	CQua
	'Boughton Park' (1) **new**	MGib
	'Boulder Bay' (2) 🏆^{H6}	IRhd
	'Bouzouki' (2)	IRhd
	'Bowles's Early Sulphur' (1)	CDes
	'Boyne Bridge' (1)	IRhd
	'Brackenhurst' (2)	SDeJ
	'Brahms' (2)	CFen
	'Brandaris' (11a)	CQua
	'Bravoure' (1) 🏆^{H6}	CFen CQua SDeJ
	'Brentswood' (8)	CQua
	'Brian's Favorite' (2)	CQua IRhd
	'Bridal Crown' (4) 🏆^{H6}	CFen EPfP LAma LCro LOPS LRHS
	'Brideshead' (2)	CFen
	'Bright Flame' (2)	CQua
	'Bright Spangles' (8)	IRhd
	'Bright Spot' (8)	CQua
	'Brilliancy' (3)	CQua GCro
	'Brindaleena' (2)	IRhd
	'Brindle Pink' (2)	IRhd
	'Broadland' (2)	CQua
	'Broadwalk Beauty' (2) **new**	MGib
	'Broadway Star' (11b)	LAma SDeJ
	'Broadway Village' (2)	CQua
	'Brodick' (3)	CQua IRhd
	'Bronzewing' (1)	IRhd
	'Brooke Ager' (2) 🏆^{H6}	IRhd
	'Broomhill' (2) 🏆^{H6}	CQua
	'Broughshane' (1)	CQua
	broussonetii (13)	CFil
	- from Morocco	WPGP
	'Brunswick' (2)	CFen GCro SDeJ
	'Bryanston' (2) 🏆^{H6}	CQua
	'Buckshead' (4)	CQua
	'Budock Water' (2)	CQua
	'Bugle Major' (2)	CQua
	bulbocodium (13) 🏆^{H4}	CBro CDes GKev LCro LEdu LOPS LRHS SRms
§	- subsp. ***bulbocodium*** (13)	CBro MGib
§	- - var. ***citrinus*** (13)	GBuc LRHS SSpi
	- - var. ***conspicuus*** (13)	CAby CBro CQua CTca ECho ERCP GKev LAma MPie SBod SDeJ WCot WShi XLum
*	- - var. ***filifolius*** (13)	CBro
	- - var. ***nivalis*** (13)	ECho EPot GKev
§	- - var. ***tenuifolius*** (13)	EPot
§	- Golden Bells Group (10)	CAvo CHid CQua CTri CWCL ECho EPfP EPot GKev LRHS MBri MPie NHol SCob SDeJ
	- 'Ice Warrior' (10)	SKHP
	- var. ***mesatlanticus***	see *N. romieuxii* subsp. *romieuxii* var. *mesatlanticus*
	- subsp. ***obesus*** (13)	ECho GKev WAbe WCot
§	- - 'Diamond Ring' (10)	CQua ECho EPot LAma MNrw
	- subsp. ***praecox*** (13)	ECho LRHS
	- - var. ***paucinervis*** (13)	ECho
	- subsp. ***tananicus***	see *N. cantabricus* subsp. *tananicus*
	- subsp. ***vulgaris***	see *N. bulbocodium* subsp. *bulbocodium*
	'Bunclody' (2)	CQua
	'Bunting' (7) 🏆^{H6}	CQua
	'Burning Bush' (3)	IRhd
	'Burning Ring' (3)	IRhd
	'Burravoe' (1)	CQua
	'Burt House' (2)	IRhd
	'Busselton' (3)	IRhd
	'Bute Park' (4)	CQua
	'Butter and Eggs' (4)	GCro
	'Butterscotch' (2)	CQua
	'Cabernet' (2)	IRhd
	'Cacatua' (11a)	IRhd
	'Cadgwith' (2)	CQua
	'Cairngorm' (2)	SDeJ
	'Cairntoul' (3)	CQua
	'Calamansack' (2)	CQua
	'Calgary' (4)	CQua
	'California Rose' (4)	CQua IRhd
	'Camaraderie' (2)	IRhd
	'Camelot' (2) 🏆^{H6}	CFen CQua SDeJ
	'Cameo Angel' (2)	CQua
	'Cameo Baron' (2)	CQua
	'Cameo Frills' (2)	CQua
	'Cameo Gem' (1)	CQua
	'Cameo King' (2)	CQua
	'Cameo Marie' (3)	CQua
	'Camilla Duchess of Cornwall' (2)	CFen CQua
	'Campernelli' (7)	CQua
	'Campernelli Plenus'	see *N.* 'Double Campernelle'
	'Campion' (9)	CQua IRhd MGib
	canaliculatus Gussone	see *N. tazetta* subsp. *lacticolor*
	'Canaliculatus' (8)	CBro CFen CQua CTri ECho EPfP ERCP GKev LAma LCro LOPS LPfy LRHS MBri SCob SDeJ SPer
	canariensis (13)	CQua
	'Canary' (7)	CQua
	'Canarybird' (8)	CQua
	'Canasta' (11a)	CQua
	'Candlepower' (1) **new**	CQua
	'Canisp' (2)	CQua
	'Cantabile' (9) 🏆^{H6}	CQua MGib
	cantabricus (13)	CPne CQua ECho
	- subsp. ***cantabricus*** (13)	CFil
	- - var. ***foliosus*** (13) 🏆^{H4}	CFil ECho GKev WAbe
	- - var. ***kesticus*** (13) **new**	MGib
	- subsp. ***monophyllus*** (13)	MGib
§	- subsp. ***tananicus*** (13)	ECho
	'Cantatrice' (1)	CQua
	'Canterbury' (5)	CQua
	'Canticle' (9)	IRhd
	'Capax Plenus'	see *N.* 'Eystettensis'

'Cape Cornwall' (2)	CQua MGib
'Cape Helles' (3)	IRhd
'Cape Point' (2)	CQua IRhd
'Capisco' (3)	CQua
'Carbineer' (2)	CQua SDeJ
'Cardiff' (2)	CFen CQua
'Cargreen' (9)	CQua
'Carib Gipsy' (2) ♀H6	CQua IRhd
'Caribbean Snow' (2)	CQua MGib
'Carlton' (2) ♀H6	CFen CQua EPfP GKev LAma LCro LOPS LPfy SCob SDeJ
'Carn Brea' (3) **new**	CQua
'Carnearny' (3)	CQua
'Carnkeeran' (2)	CQua
'Carnkief' (2)	CQua
'Carnyorth' (11a)	CQua
'Carole Lombard' (3)	CQua
'Carolina Dale' (2)	IRhd
'Carra' (8)	CQua
'Carwinion' (2)	CQua
'Casiah' (2)	CQua
'Cassandra' (9)	GCro
'Cassata' (11a)	LAma NBir SDeJ
'Cassopolis' (2)	CQua
'Castanets' (8)	CQua IRhd
'Casterbridge' (2)	CQua IRhd
'Castle Rings' (4)	CQua
'Castlerock' (2)	CFen
'Catalyst' (2)	IRhd
'Cataract' (1)	IRhd
'Catistock' (2)	CQua
'Causeway Gem' (6)	IRhd
'Causeway Ringer' (3)	IRhd
'Causeway Sunset' (2)	IRhd
'Causeway Sunshine' (1)	IRhd
'Causeway Torch' (2)	IRhd
'Causeway Winner' (2)	IRhd
'Cavalli King' (4)	CQua
'Cavalryman' (3)	IRhd
'Caye Chapel' (3)	CQua
'Cazique' (6)	CQua
'Cedar Hills' (3)	CQua
'Cedric Morris' (1)	CDes CHid CLAP CQua ECha EWoo GBuc
'Celestial Fire' (2)	CQua
'Celtic Gold' (2)	CQua
§ 'Celtic Wings' (5)	IRhd
'Centenary Gold' (2)	CQua
'Centrefold' (3)	CQua
'Cha-cha' (6)	CBro CQua
'Changing Colors' (11a)	SDeJ
'Chanson' (1) ♀H6	CQua IRhd MGib
'Chanterelle' (11a)	LAma SDeJ
'Charity May' (6)	CQua
'Charlbury' (2)	IRhd
'Charleston' (2)	CQua
'Charlie Connor' (1)	CQua MGib
Charlotte van Plemp (1) **new**	GCro
'Chasseur' (2)	IRhd
'Chaste' (1)	CQua IRhd
'Chat' (7)	CQua
'Chateau Impney' (2)	IRhd
'Cheer Leader' (3)	CQua
'Cheerfulness' (4) ♀H6	CAvo CFen CQua LAma LCro LOPS LPfy MBri NPer SDeJ
'Cheesewring' (3)	CQua
'Cheetah' (1)	IRhd
'Chelsea Girl' (2)	CQua IRhd
'Cheltenham' (2)	CQua
'Chérie' (7)	CQua
'Cherish' (2)	CQua
'Cherry Glow' (3)	IRhd
'Cherry Ice' (2)	CQua
'Cherrygardens' (2)	CQua IRhd
'Chesapeake Bay' (1)	CQua
'Chesterton' (9) ♀H6	CQua
'Chickadee' (6)	CQua
'Chicken Hill' (1)	CQua
'Chickerell' (3)	CQua
'Chief Inspector' (1)	CQua IRhd
'Chiffon' (2)	CFen
'Chiloquin' (1)	CQua
'China Doll' (2)	CQua MGib
'China Gold' (10)	CQua
'Chinchilla' (2)	CQua IRhd
'Chingah' (1)	IRhd
'Chinita' (8)	CQua
'Chipper' (5)	CQua
'Chippewa' (3)	IRhd
'Chit Chat' (7) ♀H4	CQua LLHF MGib SDeJ SPlb
'Chiva' (7)	CBro GKev LLHF
'Chobe River' (1)	CQua IRhd
'Chortle' (3)	IRhd
'Chukar' (4) ♀H6	IRhd
'Churchfield Bells' (5)	CQua
'Churston Ferrers' (4)	CQua
'Chy Noweth' (2)	CQua
'Cinder Hill' (2)	IRhd
'Cisticola' (3)	CQua IRhd
citrinus	see *N. bulbocodium* subsp. *bulbocodium* var. *citrinus*
'Citron' (3)	CQua
'Citronita' (3)	CQua
'Citrus Souffle' (4) **new**	IRhd
'Clare' (7)	CBro CQua MGib
'Classic Gold' (10) ♀H6	CQua
'Claverley' (2)	CQua MGib
'Clean Sweep' (3)	IRhd
'Cloth of Gold' (8)	CQua
'Cloud Nine' (2)	CBro
'Clouded Yellow' (2)	CQua IRhd MGib
'Clouds Hill' (4)	CQua
'Clouds Rest' (2)	IRhd
'Clovelly Ayr' (9)	CQua
'Codlins and Cream'	see *N.* 'Sulphur Phoenix'
'Coker's Frome' (9)	CQua
'Coldbrook' (2)	CQua
'Colin's Joy' (2)	CQua
'Coliseum' (2)	IRhd
'Colleen Bawn' (1)	CQua WShi
'Colley Gate' (3)	CQua
'Colliford' (2)	CQua
'Colorama' (11a)	CQua
'Colorful' (2)	IRhd
'Colville' (9)	CQua
'Comal' (1)	CQua
'Come to Good' (2)	CQua
'Compressus'	see *N.* × *intermedius* 'Compressus'
'Compton Court' (3)	IRhd
'Conestoga' (2)	CQua IRhd
'Congress' (11a)	CQua
'Conly' (3)	IRhd
'Conowingo' (11a)	CQua
'Conspicuus' ambig.	LAma
'Conspicuus' (3)	GCro WShi
'Content' (1)	CQua
'Contralto' (2)	IRhd
'Cool Autumn' (2)	CQua
'Cool Crystal' (3)	CQua

Name	Suppliers
'Cool Evening' (11a)	CQua IRhd
'Cool Shades' (2)	CQua
'Coolmaghery' (2)	IRhd
'Coombe Creek' (6)	CQua
'Copper Nob' (2)	IRhd
'Copperdale' (2) **new**	MGib
'Copperfield' (2)	CQua
'Cora Ann' (7)	CBro
'Corbiere' (1)	CQua IRhd MGib
'Corbridge' (2)	CQua
'Corby Candle' (2) **new**	CQua MGib
'Corky's Song' (2)	CQua
'Cornish Chuckles' (12) ♀H6	CBro CFen CQua
'Cornish Pride' (2)	CFen
'Cornish Sun' (2)	CQua
'Cornish Vanguard' (2) ♀H6	CFen CQua
'Cornsilk' (11a)	CQua
'Corofin' (3)	CQua
'Coromandel' (2)	IRhd
'Corozal' (3)	CQua
'Corroboree' (2)	IRhd
'Cosine' (11a)	IRhd
'Cosmic Dance' (2)	IRhd
'Cotinga' (6)	CQua SDeJ
'Countdown' (2)	CQua
'Court Martial' (2)	CFen
'Coverack Glory' (2)	CQua
'Crackington' (4) ♀H6	CQua IRhd
'Cragford' (8)	MBri SDeJ
'Craig Stiel' (2)	CQua
'Creag Dubh' (2)	CQua
'Creed' (6)	CQua
'Crenver' (3)	CQua GCro
'Crevenagh' (2)	IRhd
'Crewenna' (1)	CBro CQua
'Crill' (7)	CQua
'Crimson Chalice' (3)	CQua IRhd
'Cristobal' (1)	CQua
'Crock of Gold' (1)	CFen
'Croesus' (2)	CQua
'Crofty' (6)	CQua
'Croila' (2)	CQua
'Crown of Gold' (2)	IRhd
'Crowndale' (4)	CQua IRhd MGib
'Crugmeer' (11a)	CQua
'Cryptic' (1)	CQua IRhd
'Crystal Star' (2)	CQua
'Cudden Point' (2)	CQua
'Cul Beag' (3)	CQua
'Culmination' (2)	CQua
'Cultured Pearl' (2)	CQua IRhd
'Cum Laude' (11a)	ERCP SDeJ
'Curlew' (7) ♀H6	CQua GKev LCro LOPS SDeJ WShi
'Curly' (2)	SDeJ
'Cuscarne' (8) **new**	CQua
cyclamineus (13) ♀H6	CAvo CBro CExl CFil ECho ENun GKev LEdu LLHF LRHS SKHP SRms
'Cyclope' (1)	CQua
cypri (13)	CQua
'Cyros' (1)	CQua
'Dailmanach' (2)	CQua IRhd
'Dailmystic' (2)	IRhd
'Dainty Miss' (7)	CQua
'Daisy Schäffer' (2)	GCro
'Dallas' (3)	CFen CQua
'Dalmeny' (2)	CQua
'Dambuster' (4)	IRhd
'Damson' (2)	CQua GCro
'Dan du Plessis' (8)	CFen CQua
'Dancing Queen' (2)	IRhd
'Dardanelles' (2)	IRhd
'Darlow Dale' (2)	IRhd
'Dateline' (3)	CQua IRhd
'David Alexander' (1)	CQua
'David Mills' (2)	CQua
'Dawn Brooker' (2)	CQua
'Dawn Call' (2)	IRhd
'Dawn Cloud' (2) **new**	CQua
'Dawn Run' (2)	IRhd
'Dawn Sky' (2)	CQua
'Daydream' (2)	CQua
'Daymark' (8)	CQua
'Daymer Bay' (1)	CFen
'Dayton Lake' (2)	CQua
'De Lacey' (11a)	CQua
'Dean' (2) **new**	CQua
'Dear Love' (11a)	IRhd
'Debutante' (2)	CQua
'December Bride' (11a)	CQua
'Decision' (2)	IRhd
'Defence Corps' (1)	IRhd
'Del Rey' (1)	CQua
'Delia' (6)	IRhd
'Dell Chapel' (3)	CQua
'Delnashaugh' (4)	CQua ERCP LAma NHol SDeJ
'Delos' (3)	CQua
'Delta' (11a) **new**	CQua
'Delta Flight' (6)	IRhd
'Demand' (2)	CQua
'Demeanour' (3)	IRhd
'Demmo' (2)	CQua IRhd MGib
'Dena' (3)	IRhd
'Denali' (1)	CQua IRhd
'Derek Tangye' (2)	CQua
'Derringer' (7)	CAvo
'Descant' (1)	IRhd
'Desdemona' (2) ♀H6	CQua SDeJ
'Desert Bells' (7)	CQua
'Desert Orchid' (2)	CQua
'Dewy Dell' (3)	IRhd
'Diamond Ring'	see *N. bulbocodium* subsp. *obesus* 'Diamond Ring'
'Dick Wilden' (4)	SDeJ
'Dickcissel' (7) ♀H6	CQua ERCP GKev
'Dignitary' (2)	IRhd
'Dimity' (3)	CQua
'Dimple' (9)	CQua IRhd
'Dinkie' (3)	CBro
'Discreet' (2)	IRhd
'Dispatch Box' (1) ♀H6	IRhd
'Disquiet' (1)	CQua IRhd
'Diversity' (11a)	IRhd
'Doctor Hugh' (3) ♀H6	CQua IRhd
'Doctor Jazz' (2)	CQua IRhd
'Doctor Who' (4) **new**	CQua
'Dolcoath' (2) **new**	CQua
'Doombar' (1)	CQua
'Dorchester' (4)	CQua IRhd
'Dorneywood' (1)	IRhd
'Dorothy Yorke' (2)	GCro
§ 'Double Campernelle' (4)	CQua ECho IFro MBri SDeJ WShi
double pheasant eye	see *N. poeticus* 'Plenus' ambig.
double Roman	see *N.* 'Romanus'
'Double White' (4)	CQua
'Doubleday' (4)	IRhd
'Doublet' (4)	CQua
'Doubtful' (3)	CQua

	'Dove Song' (2)	IRhd
	'Dove Wings' (6)	CQua
	'Dover Boy' (11a) **new**	CQua
	'Dover Cliffs' (2)	CQua
	'Downfield' (4)	IRhd
	'Downing College' (2)	CQua
	'Downlands' (3)	CQua
	'Dragon Run' (2)	CQua
	'Drama Queen' (11a)	IRhd
	'Draycote Water' (3) **new**	MGib
	'Dream Catcher' (2)	IRhd
	Dream Torte (1) **new**	GCro
	'Dreamlight' (3)	CQua
	dubius (13)	ECho EPot
	'Duiker' (6)	IRhd
	'Duke of Windsor' (2)	CFen
	'Dunadry Inn' (4)	IRhd
	'Dunchurch' (2) **new**	MGib
	'Dunkeld' (2)	CQua GCro
	'Dunkery' (4)	CQua IRhd MGib
	'Dunley Hall' (3)	CQua IRhd
	'Dunskey' (3)	CQua
	'Dupli Kate' (4)	IRhd
	'Dusky Lad' (2)	IRhd
	'Dusky Maiden' (2)	IRhd
	'Dutch Delight' (2)	IRhd
	'Dutch Lemon Drops' (5) ♀H6	CMea CQua EPot
	'Dutch Master' (1) ♀H6	CFen CQua EPfP LAma LCro LOPS SCob SDeJ
	'Early Bird' (3) **new**	EPot
	'Early Bride' (2)	CFen CQua
	'Early Splendour' (8)	CQua
	'Earthlight' (3)	CQua
	'Eastbrook Beauty' (2) **new**	MGib
	'Eastbrook Moonlight' (2) **new**	MGib
	'Eastbrook Snowflake' (3) **new**	MGib
	'Easter Moon' (2)	CQua LCro
	'Eastern Dawn' (2)	CFen CQua SDeJ
	'Eastern Promise' (2)	CQua IRhd
	'Eaton Song' (12) ♀H6	CBro CQua
	'Ebony' (1)	CQua
	'Eddy Canzony' (2)	CFen CQua
	'Eden Gold' (2)	CFen
	'Edenderry' (1)	IRhd
	'Edgbaston' (2)	CQua
	'Edge Grove' (2)	CQua
	'Editor' (2)	IRhd
	'Edward Buxton' (3)	CFen CQua GCro
	'Egard' (11a)	CQua
	'Egmont King' (2)	CQua
	'Eira Hibbert' (3)	CQua
	'Eland' (7)	CQua
	'Elburton' (2)	CQua
	'Electrus' (11a)	IRhd
	'Elegance' (2)	CAvo CQua
	elegans (13)	ECho EPot
	'Elegant Queen' (2)	IRhd
	'Elf' (2)	CQua
	'Elfin Gold' (6)	CQua
	'Elizabeth Ann' (6)	CQua IRhd
	'Elka' (1) ♀H6	CAby CAvo CBro CDes CQua ERCP LLHF MGib MPie SBod WShi
	'Elmbridge' (1)	IRhd
	'Elphin' (4)	CQua
	'Elrond' (2)	CQua
	'Elven Lady' (2)	CQua
	'Elvira' (8)	CQua WShi
	'Emcys' (6)	LLHF
	'Emerald City' (3)	IRhd
	'Emerald Pink' (3)	CQua
	'Emily' (2)	CQua
	'Eminent' (3)	CQua
	'Emperor' (1)	CQua
	'Empress of Ireland' (1)	CQua IRhd
	'English Caye' (1)	CQua IRhd
	'Ensemble' (4)	CQua
	'Epona' (3)	CQua
	'Erin' (3)	CQua
	'Erlicheer' (4)	CQua SDeJ
	'Escapee' (2)	IRhd
	'Estrella' (3)	CQua
	'Estremadura' (2)	CQua
	'Ethereal Beauty' (2)	IRhd
	'Ethos' (1)	IRhd
§	***eugeniae*** (13)	CFil MGib WCot
	'Euryalus' (1)	CQua
	'Evangeline' (3)	GCro
	'Eve Robertson' (2)	CQua
	'Evelyn Roberts' (11a)	CQua
	'Evening' (2)	CQua
	'Evesham' (3)	CQua IRhd MGib
	'Exotic Beauty' (4)	CQua
	'Eyeglass' (3)	CQua IRhd
	'Eyelet' (3)	CQua IRhd
	'Eype' (4)	IRhd
	'Eyrie' (3)	CQua IRhd
§	'Eystettensis' (4)	CBro IBlr
	'Fair Prospect' (2)	CQua
	'Fairgreen' (3)	CFen
	'Fairlawns' (3)	CQua
	'Fairmile' (3)	CQua
	'Fairy Chimes' (5)	CQua
	'Fairy Footsteps' (3)	CQua
	'Fairy Island' (3)	CQua
	'Fairy Magic' (2)	IRhd
	'Fairy Tale' (3)	CQua
I	'Faith' (1)	SDeJ
	'Falaise' (4) **new**	CQua
	'Falconet' (8) ♀H6	CQua SDeJ
	'Falmouth Bay' (3)	CQua
	'Falstaff' (2)	CQua
	'Far Country' (2)	CQua
	'Farro' (1)	IRhd
I	'Fashion' (11b)	CQua
	'Fashion Model' (2)	IRhd
	'Fastidious' (2)	CQua
	'February Gold' (6) ♀H6	CAvo CBro CQua CTri EPfP EPot ERCP GKev LAma LCro LOPS LPfy LRHS MBri NBir SDeJ SRms WShi
	'February Silver' (1)	CBro CQua EPot ERCP LAma SDeJ
	'Feeling Lucky' (2)	CQua
	'Felindre' (9)	CFen EPot
	'Feline Queen' (1)	IRhd
	'Feock' (3)	CQua
	'Ferial Wendy' (2)	CFen
	fernandesii (13)	ECho GKev WAbe WCot WThu
	- var. ***cordubensis*** (13)	CFil CQua ECho LLHF MGib
	- var. ***fernandesii*** (13) **new**	MGib
	'Ferndown' (3)	CQua IRhd
	'Ferral' (4)	IRhd
	'Fertile Crescent' (7)	CQua
	'Ffitch's Ffolly' (2)	CQua
	'Fiery Maiden' (2)	CFen

'Filoli' (1)	CQua
'Filskit' (2)	CQua
'Finchcocks' (2)	CQua
'Fine Gold' (1)	CQua
'Fine Romance' (2)	CQua IRhd MGib
'Fine Trim' (2) **new**	IRhd
'Finedon Feast' (2) **new**	MGib
'Fineshade' (1) **new**	MGib
'Finland' (2)	CFen CQua
Fintry Beauty (2) **new**	GCro
'Fiona Linford' (3)	IRhd
'Fiona MacKillop' (2)	CQua IRhd
'Fire-Blade' (2)	CQua
'Firebrand' (3)	CQua GCro
'Firefighter' (3)	IRhd
'Firehills' (2)	CQua IRhd
'Firetail' (3)	CQua EPot WShi
'Fiery Maiden' (2) **new**	CQua
'First Born' (6)	CQua
'First Hope' (6)	CFen
'Flambards Village' (4)	CQua
'Fletching' (1)	CQua IRhd
'Flirt' (6)	CQua
'Flomay' (7)	CQua
'Flor d'Luna' (2) **new**	MGib
'Florida Manor' (3)	IRhd
'Flower Record' (2)	LAma
'Flusher' (2)	CQua
'Flycatcher' (7)	CQua
'Flying Colours' (4)	IRhd
'Flying High' (3)	CQua
'Foff's Way' (1)	CQua
'Folkestone Girl' (11a) **new**	CQua
'Forge Mill' (2)	CQua
'Forged Gold' (2)	IRhd
'Fortescue' (4)	IRhd
'Fortissimo' (2)	SDeJ SPer
'Fortune' (2)	CQua LAma MBri SDeJ
'Fossie' (4)	CQua
'Foundling' (6)	CQua
'Fowey' (3)	CFen
'Foxfire' (2)	CQua
'Foxhunter' (2)	CQua
'Fragrant Breeze' (2)	CQua SDeJ
'Fragrant Rose' (2)	CQua EPfP ERCP IRhd
'Frances Delight' (11a)	CQua
'Francolin' (1)	IRhd
'Frank' (9)	IRhd
'Frank Miles' (2)	CQua GCro
'Freedom Rings' (2)	CQua
'Freedom Stars' (11a) 🏆H6	IRhd
'Fresco' (11a)	IRhd
'Fresh Lime' (1)	CQua MGib
'Fresno' (3)	IRhd
'Frigid' (3)	CQua
'Front Royal' (2)	CQua
'Frosted Pink' (2)	IRhd
'Frostkist' (6)	CBro CQua
'Frozen Jade' (1)	CQua IRhd
'Fruit Cup' (7)	LCro LRHS SDeJ
'Fuco' (1)	CQua
'Full House' (4)	SDeJ
'Fulwell' (4)	CQua
'Furbelow' (4)	CQua
'Furnace Creek' (2)	IRhd
'Fynbos' (3)	IRhd
'Gabriella Rose' (4)	CQua
gaditanus (13)	CBro
gaditanus × ***rupicola*** subsp. ***watieri*** (13)	ECho
'Gambas' (1)	CQua
'Gamebird' (1)	CQua IRhd
'Ganilly' (2)	CFen
'Garden Club of America' (2) **new**	MGib
'Garden News' (3)	IRhd
'Garden Opera' (7) 🏆H6	CFen
'Garden Treasure' (2)	IRhd
'Gatecrasher' (1)	IRhd
'Gay Kybo' (4) 🏆H6	CQua
'Gay Song' (4)	CQua
'Gay Time' (4)	CFen SDeJ
gayi (13)	CQua WShi
'Geevor' (4)	CQua
'Gellymill' (2)	CQua
'Gemini Girl' (2)	CQua
'Gentle Giant' (2)	SDeJ
'Geometrics' (2)	IRhd
'George Leak' (2)	CFen CQua
'Georgia Moon' (2)	CFen
'Georgie Girl' (6)	IRhd
'Georgie May' (2) **new**	CQua
'Geranium' (8) 🏆H6	CBro CFen CQua EPfP ERCP LAma LCro LOPS SDeJ SPer WShi
'Gettysburg' (2)	CQua
'Gigantic Star' (2)	SDeJ
'Gillan' (11a)	CQua
'Gin and Lime' (1)	CQua
'Gipsy Moon' (2)	CQua MGib
'Gipsy Queen' (1)	CBro CQua EPot LLHF WShi
'Gironde' (11)	CQua
'Glacier' (1)	CQua
'Glapthorne' (2)	CQua
'Glasnevin' (2)	CQua IRhd
'Glasney' (3)	CQua
'Glen Cassley' (3)	CQua
'Glen Clova' (2)	CQua
'Glen Lake' (2)	IRhd
'Glendermott' (2)	CQua
'Glendurgan' (2) **new**	CQua
'Glenfarclas' (1) **new**	CQua
'Glenside' (2)	CQua
'Glissando' (2)	CQua IRhd
'Gloria Townsin' (4) **new**	CQua
'Gloriosus' (8)	CQua
'Glorious' (8) **new**	CQua
'Glory of Lisse' (9)	WShi
'Glover's Reef' (1)	CQua
'Glowing Phoenix' (4)	CQua GCro
'Glowing Red' (4)	CQua
'Goblet' (1)	SDeJ
'Goff's Caye' (2)	IRhd
'Golant' (2)	CQua
'Gold Bond' (2)	CQua IRhd
'Gold Cache' (11a)	CQua
'Gold Charm' (2)	CQua
'Gold Convention' (2) 🏆H6	CQua IRhd MGib
'Gold Ingot' (2) 🏆H6	IRhd
'Gold Medallion' (1)	CQua
'Gold Top' (2)	CQua
'Golden Amber' (2)	CQua
'Golden Anniversary' (2)	CFen CQua
'Golden Aura' (2) 🏆H6	CQua
'Golden Bear' (4)	CQua
'Golden Bells'	see *N. bulbocodium* Golden Bells Group
'Golden Cheer' (2)	CFen CQua

'Golden Cycle' (6)	CQua
'Golden Dawn' (8) 𝕐H4	CFen CQua EPfP
'Golden Ducat' (4)	CFen CQua LAma MBri NBir SDeJ
'Golden Echo' (7)	EPfP
'Golden Flute' (2)	IRhd
'Golden Gamble' (11a)	IRhd
'Golden Harvest' (1)	CQua LAma NPer
'Golden Incense' (7)	CQua
'Golden Jewel' (2) 𝕐H6	CQua
'Golden Joy' (2)	CQua MGib
'Golden Lady' (1)	CQua
'Golden Lion' (1)	CFen
'Golden Marvel' (1)	CQua
'Golden Mary' (3)	GCro
'Golden Orbit' (4)	CQua
'Golden Peak' (1)	IRhd
'Golden Perfection' (7)	CQua
'Golden Phoenix' (4)	CQua WShi
'Golden Rain' (4)	CQua
'Golden Rapture' (1)	CQua
'Golden Sheen' (2)	CQua
'Golden Splash' (11a)	IRhd
'Golden Spur' (1)	CQua LAma
'Golden Torch' (2)	CQua
'Golden Twins' (7)	CQua
'Golden Vale' (1)	CQua
'Goldfinger' (1) 𝕐H6	CQua IRhd MGib
'Goldhanger' (2)	CQua IRhd MGib
'Golitha Falls' (2)	CQua
'Good Fella' (2)	CQua
'Good Intentions' (2)	IRhd
'Good Measure' (2)	CQua
'Good Success' (11a)	CQua
'Goonbell' (2)	CQua
'Goose Green' (3)	GKev
'Gorran' (3)	CQua
'Gossmoor' (4)	CQua
'Graduation' (2)	IRhd
'Grafton Brook' (1) **new**	MGib
'Grafton Gold' (2) **new**	MGib
'Grand Monarque'	see *N. tazetta* subsp. *lacticolor* 'Grand Monarque'
'Grand Opening' (4)	IRhd
'Grand Primo' (8) **new**	LCro LOPS
'Grand Primo Citronière' (8)	CQua EPfP
'Grand Prospect' (2)	CQua
'Grand Soleil d'Or' (8)	CQua LAma LCro LOPS SDeJ
'Great Expectations' (2)	CQua
'Great Warley' (2)	GCro
'Greatwood' (1)	CQua
'Greek Surprise' (4)	IRhd
'Green Howard' (3)	CQua
'Green Island' (2)	CFen SDeJ
'Green Lawns' (9)	CQua
'Green Lodge' (9)	IRhd
'Green Pearl' (3)	XEll
'Greenhithe Village' (3) **new**	MGib
'Greenodd' (3)	CQua
'Greenpark' (9)	IRhd
'Grenoble' (2)	CQua
'Gresham' (4)	CQua
'Gribben Head' (4)	CQua
'Groundkeeper' (3)	IRhd
'Guiding Spirit' (4)	CQua
'Gulliver' (3)	CQua GCro
'Gunwalloe' (11a)	CQua
'Guy Wilson' (2)	CQua MGib
'Gwawr' (2)	CQua
'Gwendoline Rae' (3) **new**	CQua
'Gwenllian' (3)	CQua
'Gwennap' (1)	CQua
'Gwinear' (2)	CQua
'Habit' (1)	IRhd
'Hacienda' (1)	CQua
'Half Moon Caye' (2)	CQua
'Halley's Comet' (3)	CQua IRhd
'Halloon' (3)	CQua
'Halzephron' (2)	CQua
'Hambledon' (2) 𝕐H6	CQua
'Hampton Court' (2)	CQua IRhd
'Hanley Swan' (1)	IRhd
'Hannah Jesse' (7) **new**	CQua
'Happy Dreams' (2)	IRhd
'Happy Fellow' (2)	CQua
'Happy Valley' (2)	IRhd
'Harbour View' (2)	IRhd
'Harmony Bells' (5)	CQua
'Harp Music' (2)	IRhd
'Harpers Ferry' (1)	CQua
Hartland's Irving (1) **new**	GCro
'Hartlebury' (3)	CQua
'Harvard' (2) **new**	CQua
'Hawangi' (3)	IRhd
'Hawera' (5) 𝕐H6	CAvo CBro CFen CQua CTca CTri EPfP EPot ERCP GKev LAma LCro LEdu LOPS LPot LRHS MBri MPie SDeJ SPer WShi
'Heamoor' (4) 𝕐H6	CQua
hedraeanthus (13)	EPot
'Helford Dawn' (2)	CQua
'Helford Sunset' (2)	CQua
'Helios' (2)	CQua GCro
hellenicus	see *N. poeticus* var. *hellenicus*
henriquesii	see *N. jonquilla* var. *henriquesii*
'Henry Irving' (1)	CQua GCro
'Hero' (1)	CQua
'Heslington' (3)	CQua
'Hexameter' (9)	CQua
'Hexworthy' (3)	CQua
'Hibernian' (4)	IRhd
'Hicks Mill' (1)	CQua
'High Life' (2)	CFen
'High Society' (2) 𝕐H6	CQua LCro LOPS SDeJ
'Highfield Beauty' (8) 𝕐H6	CQua
'Highgrove' (1)	CQua
'Highlite' (2)	CQua
'Hilda's Pink' (2)	CQua
'Hill Head' (9)	IRhd
'Hillstar' (7) 𝕐H6	CQua SDeJ
'Hindenburg' (1) **new**	CQua
hispanicus (13)	CQua ECho
'Hocus Pocus' (3)	IRhd
'Holland's Glory' (4)	GCro
'Holly Berry' (2)	CFen
'Hollypark' (3)	IRhd
'Hollywood' (2)	CFen
'Holme Fen' (2)	CQua IRhd
'Home Fires' (2)	CFen CQua
'Homestead' (2) 𝕐H6	IRhd
'Honey Pink' (2)	CQua
'Honeybird' (1)	CQua
'Honeybourne' (2)	CQua MGib
'Honeyorange' (2)	IRhd
'Hoopoe' (8) 𝕐H6	CQua GKev
'Hope House' (2)	IRhd

	'Horace' (9)	CQua GCro
	'Horn of Plenty' (5)	CQua
	'Hornpipe' (1)	IRhd
	'Hors d'Oeuvre' (1)	CBro
	'Hospodar' (2)	CQua GCro
	'Hot Affair' (2)	IRhd
	'Hot Date' (3) **new**	IRhd
	'Hot Gossip' (2)	CFen CQua
	'Hot Lava' (2) **new**	IRhd
	'Hotspur' (2)	CQua
	Howick Beauty (2)	GCro
	Howick's Half Nelson (2)	GCro
	'Hugh Town' (8)	CQua
	'Hugus' (7)	CQua
	'Hullabaloo' (2)	IRhd
	humilis misapplied	see *N. pseudonarcissus* subsp. *pseudonarcissus* var. *humilis*
	'Hummingbird' (6)	EPot
	'Hunting Caye' (2)	CQua
	'Huntley Down' (1)	CQua
	'Hyperbole' (2)	IRhd
	'Ice Dancer' (2)	CQua IRhd
	'Ice Diamond' (4)	CQua
	'Ice Emerald' (3)	IRhd
	'Ice Follies' (2) ♀H6	CFen CQua EPfP GKev LAma LCro LOPS MBri NBir SCob SDeJ SPer
	'Ice King' (4)	NBir SDeJ
	'Ice Wings' (5) ♀H6	CAvo CBro CFen CQua EPot MGib SDeJ WShi
	'Idless' (1)	CQua
	'Idol' (7)	CQua ECho EPot
	'Immaculate' (2)	CQua
	'Impeccable' (2)	IRhd
	'Inara' (4)	CQua
	'Inca' (6)	CQua
	'Inchbonnie' (2)	CQua
	× ***incomparabilis*** (13)	MMuc
	'Independence Day' (4)	CQua
	'Indian Maid' (7) ♀H6	CQua IRhd
	'Indian Ruler' (2)	CFen
	'Indora' (4)	CQua
	'Inglescombe' (4)	WShi
	'Inner Glow' (2)	IRhd
	'Innisidgen' (8)	CQua
	'Innovator' (4)	CQua IRhd
	'Innuendo' (2)	IRhd
	'Inny River' (1)	IRhd
	'Insulinde' (4) **new**	CQua
	'Interim' (2)	CFen CQua SDeJ
	× ***intermedius*** (13)	CBro CQua MGib WAbe
§	- 'Compressus' (8)	CBro CQua WShi
	'Intrigue' (7) ♀H6	CQua
	'Invercassley' (3)	CQua
	'Inverpolly' (2)	CQua
	'Irene Copeland' (4)	CQua GCro
	'Irish Cream' (3) **new**	CQua
	'Irish Fire' (2)	CQua
	'Irish Light' (2)	CQua
	'Irish Linen' (3)	CQua
	'Irish Minstrel' (2) ♀H6	CFen CQua
	'Irish Rum' (2)	CQua
	'Irish Trip' (7)	IRhd
	'Irish Wedding' (2)	CQua
	'Isambard' (4)	CQua
	'Island Pride' (8)	CQua
	'Ita' (2)	IRhd
	'Itsy Bitsy Splitsy' (11a)	IRhd
	'Itzim' (6) ♀H6	CBro CQua SDeJ
	'Jabberwocky' (11a)	CQua
	'Jack Snipe' (6) ♀H6	CAby CAvo CBro CQua EPfP EPot ERCP GKev LAma LCro MBri NHol SCob SDeJ WShi XEll
	'Jack Wood' (11a)	CQua IRhd
	'Jackadee' (2)	IRhd
	'Jacob Maurer' (6)	CQua
	'Jake' (3)	IRhd
	'Jamage' (8)	CQua
	'Jamaica Inn' (4)	CQua
	'Jambo' (2)	CQua
	'Jamboree' (2)	CQua
	'Jammin' (3)	IRhd
	'Janelle' (3)	CQua
	'Janet's Gold' (2)	IRhd
	'Jantje' (11a)	CQua
	'Jauno' (1)	IRhd
	'Javelin' (2)	CQua
	'Jeanine' (2)	CQua
	'Jeanne Bicknell' (4)	CQua
	'Jeannie Tangye' (2)	CQua
	'Jenny' (6) ♀H6	CBro CQua EPot ERCP GKev LAma LCro LOPS LRHS MBri NBir SDeJ WShi
	'Jenny Out' (7) ♀H6	CFen
	'Jersey Lace' (2)	CQua
	'Jersey Roundabout' (4)	CQua
	'Jersey Star' (4)	CQua
	'Jersey Torch' (4)	CQua
	'Jetfire' (6) ♀H6	CQua EPfP EPot ERCP GKev LAma LCro LOPS LPfy LPot LRHS LSou MBri NHol SCob SDeJ SPer WShi
	'Jim Lad' (2)	ECho
	'Jimmy Noone' (1)	CQua
	'Jim's Gold' (2)	CQua
	'Jodi' (11b)	IRhd
	'Jodi's Sister' (11a)	IRhd
	'Johanna' (5)	CBro
	'John Daniel' (4)	CQua
	'John Evelyn' (2)	GCro
	'John Lanyon' (3)	CQua
	'John's Delight' (3)	CQua
	'Joke Fulmer' (2)	CFen
	'Jolly Good' (2)	IRhd
	jonquilla (13)	CBro CQua ECho EPot LAma WShi
	- 'Flore Pleno' (4)	ECho
§	- var. ***henriquesii*** (13)	CFil CQua ECho EPot GKev MGib
	- var. ***jonquilla*** (13)	MGib
	'Joppa' (7)	CQua
	'Joy Bishop'	see *N. romieuxii* 'Joy Bishop'
	'Joybell' (6)	CQua
	'Juanita' (2)	CFen NPer SDeJ
	'Jules Verne' (2)	CQua
	'Julia Jane'	see *N. romieuxii* 'Julia Jane'
	'Jumblie' (12) ♀H6	CBro EPfP EPot LAma LRHS MBri SDeJ
	'Jumbo Gold' (1)	CTri
	juncifolius Req. ex Lag.	see *N. assoanus*
	'June Allyson' (2)	CFen
	'June Lake' (2)	CQua IRhd
	'Kabani' (9)	CQua
	'Kaka Point' (2)	IRhd
	'Kamau' (9)	IRhd
	'Kamms' (1)	CQua
	'Kamura' (2)	CQua
	'Karamudli' (1)	CQua
	'Kate Davies' (2)	CQua
	'Katherine Jenkins' (7)	CQua
	'Kathy A' (5)	IRhd

'Kathy's Clown' (6)	CQua
'Katie Heath' (5)	EPfP ERCP MBri SDeJ
'Katrina Rea' (6)	CQua
'Kaydee' (6) ♀H6	CQua IFro IRhd SDeJ
'Kea' (6)	CQua
'Keats' (4)	CQua
'Kebaya' (2)	CQua
'Kedron' (7)	ERCP
'Kelly Bray' (1)	CQua
'Ken Sunshine Johnson' (2) **new**	CQua
'Kenellis' (10)	EPot
'Kernow' (2)	CQua
'Kholmes' (10) **new**	MGib
'Kidling' (7)	CQua EPot
'Killara' (8)	CQua
'Killearnan' (9)	CQua
'Killigrew' (2)	CQua
'Killivose' (3)	CQua
'Kiltonga' (2)	IRhd
'Kilworth' (2)	CQua
'Kimmeridge' (3)	CQua
'King Alfred' (1)	CQua EPfP LCro LOPS SDeJ SPer
'Kingham' (1) **new**	CQua
'Kinglet' (7)	CQua
'King's Grove' (1)	CQua
'Kings Pipe' (2)	CQua
'Kingscourt' (1)	CFen CQua
'Kingsleigh' (1)	IRhd
'Kingsmill Lake' (2)	CQua
'Kit Hill' (7)	CQua
'Kitten' (6)	CQua
'Kiwi Magic' (4)	CQua IRhd
'Kiwi Sunset' (4)	CQua IRhd
'Knight of Saint John' (2)	CFen
'Knightsbridge' (1)	CQua
'Knocklayde' (3)	CQua
'Knowing Look' (3)	IRhd
'Kokopelli' (7) ♀H6	CBro CQua EPfP MGib SDeJ
'Korora Bay' (1)	IRhd
'Kuantan' (3)	MGib
'La Belle' (7)	LLHF SDeJ
'La Riante' (3)	GCro
'Ladies' Choice' (7)	IRhd
'Lady Ann' (2)	IRhd
'Lady Be Good' (2)	CQua IRhd
'Lady Diana' (2)	CQua IRhd
'Lady Eve' (11a)	IRhd
'Lady Godiva' (3)	GCro
'Lady Hilaria' (2)	CQua
'Lady Margaret Boscawen' (2)	CQua GCro
'Lady Marina Cowdray' (1)	CFen
Lady Mary's Gwyther (2) **new**	GCro
'Lady Moore' (3)	GCro
'Lady Sainsbury' (2)	CFen
'Lady Serena' (9)	CQua
'Lady's Favorite' (7)	IRhd
'Lake Alabaster' (2) **new**	CQua
'Lake District' (2)	IRhd
'Lake Tahoe' (2)	IRhd
'Lalique' (3)	CQua
'Lamanva' (2)	CQua
'Lamlash' (2)	IRhd
'Lanarth' (7)	GCro
'Lancaster' (3)	CFen CQua
'Landewednack Lady' (4)	CQua
'Langarth' (11a)	CQua
'Lapwing' (5)	IRhd
'Larkhill' (2)	CQua
'Larkwhistle' (6)	SDeJ
'Las Vegas' (1)	EPfP SDeJ
'Latchley Meadows' (2)	CQua
'Laura Webb' (4) **new**	CQua
'Laurelbank' (2)	IRhd
'Lauren' (3)	IRhd
'Laurens Koster' (8)	CQua
'Lava Flow' (3)	IRhd
'Lavender Lass' (6)	CQua
'Lavender Mist' (2)	CQua MGib
'Lazy River' (1)	MGib
'Leading Light' (2)	CQua
'Lee Moor' (1)	CQua
'Leedsii' (3)	CQua
'Lemma' (3)	IRhd
'Lemon Beauty' (11b)	CQua SDeJ
'Lemon Brook' (2) **new**	CQua
'Lemon Cocktail' (1)	IRhd
'Lemon Cycla' (6) **new**	CQua
'Lemon Drizzle' (2)	CQua
'Lemon Drops' (5)	CQua EPot ERCP SDeJ SPhx
'Lemon Haze' (2)	CQua
'Lemon Silk' (6)	CBro CQua
'Lemon Snow' (2)	IRhd
'Lemonade' (3)	CQua
'Lennymore' (2)	CQua IRhd MGib
'Lewis George' (1)	CQua
'Lezant' (3)	CQua
'Libby' (2)	IRhd
'Liberty Bells' (5)	CQua LAma MBri
'Liebeslied' (3)	CQua
'Lieke' **new**	EPot ERCP LCro LOPS
'Life' (7)	CQua
'Lifeline' (1)	IRhd
'Lighthouse' (3)	CQua
'Lighthouse Reef' (1)	CQua IRhd MGib
'Lilac Charm' (6)	CQua IRhd MGib
'Lilac Hue' (6)	CBro
'Lilac Mist' (2)	CQua IRhd
'Lilliput' ambig.	CQua
'Lima's Green Goddess' (8)	IRhd
'Lima's Shooting Stars' (12)	IRhd
'Limbo' (2)	CQua
'Limequilla' (7)	CQua IRhd
'Limpopo' (3)	IRhd
'Lincolnshire Lady' (3) **new**	CQua
'Lindsay Joy' (2)	CQua
'Lisburn' (3)	IRhd
'Lisnamulligan' (3)	IRhd
'Little Alice' (4)	IRhd
'Little Beauty' (1)	CBro CMea CQua LAma
'Little Becky' (12) **new**	MGib
'Little Dancer' (1)	CBro CQua
'Little Dianne' (8) **new**	IRhd
'Little Dorr' (4)	IRhd
'Little Flik' (12)	CQua ECho
'Little Jewel' (3)	CQua
'Little Karoo' (3)	IRhd
'Little Meg' (7)	CQua
'Little Oliver' (7) **new**	EPfP
'Little Rosie' (2)	IRhd
'Little Rusky' (7)	CBro CQua
'Little Sentry' (7)	CBro CQua
'Little Soldier' (10)	CQua
'Little Spell' (1)	ECho
'Little Tyke' (2)	CQua

'Little Witch' (6)	CAvo CBro CQua GCro GKev LAma SBod SCob SDeJ SPhx WShi
'Littlefield' (7)	CQua
'Livelands' (1)	CQua
'Liverpool Festival' (2)	CQua MGib
'Living Colour' (2) **new**	CQua
'Lizard Beacon' (2)	CQua
'Lobularis'	see *N. lobularis* (Haw.) Schult. & Schult. f.
lobularis misapplied	see *N. nanus*
§ ***lobularis*** (Haw.) Schult. & Schult. f.	CAby CAvo CBro CQua CTca CTri ECho EPot ERCP GKev LCro MBri SCob SDeJ WBor
'Loch Alsh' (3)	CQua IRhd
'Loch Assynt' (3)	CQua
'Loch Brora' (2)	CQua
'Loch Coire' (3)	CQua
'Loch Fada' (2)	CQua
'Loch Fyne' (2)	GCro
'Loch Hope' (2)	CQua
'Loch Leven' (2)	CQua
'Loch Loyal' (2)	CQua
'Loch Lundie' (2)	CQua
'Loch Maberry' (2)	CQua
'Loch Naver' (2)	CQua
'Loch Owskeich' (2)	CFen CQua
'Logan Rock' (7)	CQua
'Longitude' (1)	IRhd
'Lord Grey' (1)	GCro
'Lordship' (1)	CQua
'Lorikeet' (1)	CQua
'Lostwithiel' (2)	CQua
'Lothario' (2)	LAma MBri
'Lough Gowna' (1)	IRhd
'Louise de Coligny' (2)	ERCP
'Loveday' (2)	CFen
'Lowin' (1)	CFen
'Lubaantun' (1)	CQua
'Lucie Nottingham' (4)	CQua
'Lucifer' (2)	CAvo CQua GCro WShi
'Lucky Chance' (11a)	IRhd
'Lundy Light' (2)	CQua
'Lutana' (2)	IRhd
'Lyme Bay' (1)	IRhd
'Lynher' (2)	CQua
'Lyrebird' (3)	CQua
'Lyric' (9)	CQua
'Lysander' (2)	CFen CQua
MacEwan (2) **new**	GCro
'Madam Speaker' (4)	CQua MGib
'Madame Plemp' (1)	GCro
'Madison' (4)	CQua
Maggie Maybe (2) **new**	GCro
'Magic Moment' (3)	CQua
'Magician' (2)	CQua
'Magna Carta' (2)	CQua IRhd
'Magnificence' (1)	CFen CQua GCro
'Maker's Mark' (1)	CQua
'Mallee' (11a) ♀H6	IRhd
'Malpas' (3)	CQua
'Malvern City' (1)	CFen CQua
'Mamma Mia' (4)	IRhd
'Manaccan' (1)	CQua MGib
'Mangaweka' (6)	CQua
'Manly' (4) ♀H6	CQua ERCP
'Mantle' (2)	CQua
'Margaret Herbert' (7)	CQua
'Maria Pia' (11a)	IRhd
'Marie Curie Diamond' (7) ♀H6	CFen CQua
'Marie-José' (11b)	IRhd
'Marieke' (1)	LAma SDeJ
'Marilyn Anne' (2)	CQua
'Marjorie Hine' (2)	CQua
'Marjorie Treveal' (4)	CQua
'Market Merry' (3) **new**	GCro
'Marlborough' (2)	CQua
'Marlborough Freya' (2)	CQua
'Marshfire' (2)	CQua
'Martha Washington' (8)	CQua
'Martinette' (8)	CAvo CFen CQua CTca SDeJ
'Martinsville' (8)	CQua
marvieri	see *N. rupicola* subsp. *marvieri*
'Mary Copeland' (4)	CQua GCro
'Mary Kate' (2)	CQua
'Mary Lou' (6)	IRhd
'Mary Moore' (2) **new**	CQua
'Mary Rosina' (4)	CQua
'Mary Veronica' (3)	CQua
'Marzo' (7)	IRhd
'Masked Light' (2)	CFen
'Matador' (8)	CFen CQua IRhd
'Mawla' (1)	CQua
'Max' (11a)	CQua
'Maximus Superbus' (1)	CQua
'Maya Dynasty' (2)	CQua
Maybole Elegance (2) **new**	GCro
'Mayor's Choice' (11a)	CQua
'Maywood' (11a)	CQua
'Mazzard' (4)	CQua
'Media Girl' (2)	IRhd
× ***medioluteus*** (13)	CBro CQua WShi
'Medway Gold' (7) **new**	CQua
'Melancholy' (1)	CQua
'Melbury' (2)	CQua
'Meldrum' (1)	CQua
'Melen' (2)	CFen
'Memento' (1)	CQua
'Menabilly' (4)	CQua
'Mên-an-Tol' (2)	CQua
'Menehay' (11a) ♀H6	CQua
'Mer d'Or' (1)	IRhd
'Merlin' (3) ♀H6	CFen CQua LAma SDeJ
'Merry Bells' (5)	CQua
'Merrymeet' (4)	CQua
'Mersing' (3)	CQua
'Merthan' (9)	CQua
'Midas Touch' (1)	CQua
'Midget'	see *N. nanus* 'Midget'
Midtown Aerolite (2)	GCro
Midtown Alfie (1)	GCro
Midtown Amber (2) **new**	GCro
Midtown Autocrat = 'Autocrat' (2)	GCro
Midtown Brigadier (2)	GCro
Midtown Laurie (1) **new**	GCro
Midtown Noble (1)	GCro
Midtown Ruckle (1) **new**	GCro
'Mike Pollock' (8)	CFen CQua
'Milan' (9)	CQua
'Mill Grove' (2) **new**	MGib
'Millennium Gold' (1) **new**	CQua
'Millennium Sunrise' (2)	CQua
'Millennium Sunset' (2)	CQua
'Milly's Magic' (2)	CQua

'Minard' (4) **new**	CQua
Minicycla Group (6)	ECho
minimus misapplied	see *N. asturiensis*
'Minnow' (8) ♀H4	CAvo CBro CFen CHid CQua ECho EPfP EPot ERCP GKev LAma LCro LOPS LPfy LPot LRHS MBri NBir SCob SDeJ SPer
'Minnowlet' (11a) **new**	CQua
minor (13) ♀H5	CBro CPne CQua ECha ECho EPot GCro GKev WShi
- 'Douglasbank' (1)	EPot LLHF
- 'Little Gem' (1) ♀H6	CBro CQua CTri LAma SDeJ SPhx
- var. ***pumilus*** 'Plenus'	see *N.* 'Rip van Winkle'
- Ulster form (13)	IBlr
'Mint Julep' (3) ♀H6	SDeJ
'Mirar' (2)	CQua
Misleeding (2) **new**	GCro
'Misquote' (1)	CQua
'Miss Diddles' (7) **new**	CQua
'Miss Klein' (7)	LLHF
'Miss Muffit' (1)	CQua
'Miss Primm' (2)	IRhd
'Mission Bells' (5) ♀H6	CQua IRhd
'Mission Impossible' (11a)	CQua
'Mist of Avalon' (4)	CQua
'Misty Glen' (2) ♀H6	CQua EPfP MGib SDeJ
'Mite' (6) ♀H6	CAvo CBro CQua ECho EPot LAma LLHF
'Mithrel' (11a)	CQua
'Mitimoto' (10)	ECho
'Mitylene' (2)	CQua GCro
'Mitzy' (6)	LLHF
'Modern Art' (2)	CQua SDeJ
'Modulation' (2)	MGib
'Mondragon' (11a)	CQua
'Mongleath' (2)	CQua
'Monks Wood' (1)	CQua
'Monksilver' (3)	CQua
'Monmouthshire' (2) **new**	CQua
'Montclair' (2)	CQua
'Montego' (3)	CQua
'Monterrico' (4)	CFen
'Montroig' (2)	IRhd
'Moon Dream' (1)	CQua
'Moon Ranger' (3)	CQua
'Moon Shadow' (3)	CQua IRhd
'Moon Valley' (2)	IRhd
'Moonstruck' (1)	CQua
'Morab' (1)	CQua
'Moralee' (4)	CQua IRhd
'Morval' (2)	CQua
moschatus (13) ♀H6	CBro CQua ECho EPot GCro MGib WShi
'Mother Duck' (6) **new**	LRHS
'Motmot'	CQua
'Mount Fuji' (2)	CQua
'Mount Hood' (1) ♀H6	EPfP GKev LAma NBir SDeJ SPer
'Mountain Poet' (9) **new**	CQua
'Mousehole' (3) **new**	CQua
'Movie Star' (2)	IRhd
'Mowser' (7)	CQua
'Mr Sweet' (2)	CQua
'Mrs Langtry' (2)	CQua GCro WShi
'Mrs R.O. Backhouse' (2)	CQua GCro WShi
'Mullion' (3)	CQua
'Mulroy Bay' (1)	CQua IRhd
'Murlough' (9)	CQua
'Muscadet' (2)	CFen CQua
'My Story' (4) ♀H6	SDeJ
'My Sunshine' (2)	CQua
'My Sweetheart' (3)	CQua
'My Word' (2)	CFen
'Mystic' (3)	CQua
'Nacre' (2)	IRhd
'Naivasha' (2)	IRhd
'Namraj' (2)	CQua
'Nancegollan' (7)	CBro CQua
'Nangiles' (4)	CQua
'Nanpee' (7)	CQua
'Nanpusker' (2)	CFen
'Nansidwell' (2)	CQua
'Nanstallon' (1)	CQua
§ ***nanus*** (13)	CQua CWCL ECho GBuc
§ - 'Midget' (1)	CBro CQua ECho EPot ERCP GKev LAma SKHP
'Nare Celebration' (2)	CFen
'Narrative' (2)	IRhd
'Navarre' Buckland (2)	CFil
'Nederburg' (1)	IRhd
'Nelly' ambig.	CQua
Nelsonii Group late-flowering clone (2)	GCro
'Nessa' (7)	CQua
'Nether Barr' (2)	CQua
nevadensis (13)	SKHP
'New Hope' (3)	CQua
'New Life' (3)	CQua
'New Penny' (3)	CQua IRhd
'New World' (2)	CQua
'New-Baby' (7)	CQua SDeJ
'Newcomer' (3)	CQua
'Nickelodeon' (8)	CQua
'Night Music' (4)	CQua IRhd
'Nightcap' (1)	CQua
'Nightflight' (1) **new**	MGib
'Niphetos' (2)	GCro
'Nirvana' (7)	CBro
'Niveth' (5)	CAvo CFen CQua GCro LCro LOPS
§ ***nobilis*** (13)	CQua EPot
- var. ***leonensis*** (13)	CFil
'Nonchalant' (3)	CQua IRhd
'Norma Jean' (2)	CQua
'North Rim' (2)	CQua
'Noss Mayo' (6)	CQua
'Notre Dame' (2) ♀H6	CQua IRhd
'Nuage' (2)	CFen
'Numen Rose' (2)	IRhd
Nylon Group (10)	CBro ECho EPot EPri
- yellow-flowered (10)	ECho
'Nynja' (2)	CQua
'Oadby' (1)	CQua
'Obdam' (4)	SDeJ
'Obsession' (2)	CQua
obvallaris (13) ♀H6	CAvo CBro CFen CQua CTca ECho EPfP EPot ERCP GBuc GKev LCro MBri SDeJ SPer SPhx WHer WShi
'Ocarino' (4)	CFen CQua
'Ocean Blue' (2)	IRhd
'Odd Job' (12)	CQua
× ***odorus*** (13)	CQua WShi
- 'Plenus' (4)	CQua ERCP
'Oh Wow' (3) **new**	IRhd
old pheasant's eye	see *N. poeticus* var. *recurvus*
'Olympic Medal' (1)	IRhd
'Ombersley' (1)	CQua MGib
'Oops' (2)	IRhd
'Orange Phoenix' (4)	CQua WShi
'Orange Supreme' (2)	CQua

'Orange Tint' (2)	CQua
'Orange Walk' (3)	CQua IRhd
'Orangery' (11a)	LAma SDeJ
'Orbital Pink' (3)	IRhd
'Orchard Place' (3)	CQua
'Oregon Pioneer' (2)	IRhd
'Orkney' (2)	CQua
'Ormeau' (2)	CQua
'Ornatus' (9)	CQua GCro
'Oryx' (7) ♀H6	CQua
'Osmington' (2)	CQua
'Ouma' (1)	CQua
'Outline' (2)	IRhd
'Ouzel' (6)	CQua
'Owyhee' (2)	CQua
'Oxford Gold' (10) ♀H6	CQua
'Oykel' (3)	CQua
'Oz' (12)	LLHF
pachybolbus (13)	CQua ECho
'Pacific Coast' (8) ♀H6	CQua LCro LLHF LOPS MGib SBod
'Pacific Mist' (11a)	CQua
'Pacific Rim' (2)	CQua IRhd
'Pacific Waves' (3)	CQua
'Painted Desert' (3)	CQua
'Palace Pink' (2)	IRhd
'Pale Sunlight' (2)	CQua
'Palheiro' (2) **new**	MGib
pallidiflorus (13)	ECha
'Palmares' (11a)	CQua SDeJ
'Pamela Hubble' (2)	CQua
'Pamela Joan' (2)	CQua
'Pampaluna' (11a)	CQua IRhd
'Panache' (1)	CQua
panizzianus (13)	CFil CQua
'Panorama Pink' (3)	IRhd
'Paper White'	see *N. papyraceus*
'Paper White Grandiflorus' (8)	CQua EPfP MBri SDeJ SPer
'Paper White Zeva'	LSun
'Papillon Blanc' (11b)	ERCP LRHS
'Papua' (4)	CFen CQua
§ ***papyraceus*** (13)	CFil CQua
- 'Ziva' (8)	CAvo LCro LOPS SDeJ
'Paradigm' (4)	IRhd
'Paramour' (4)	IRhd
'Parcpat' (7)	CBro CQua
'Parisienne' (11a)	SDeJ
'Park Springs' (3)	CQua
'Parkdene' (2)	CQua
'Partisan' (2)	IRhd
'Party Time' (2)	IRhd
'Passionale' (2) ♀H6	CQua EPfP LAma NBir
'Pastiche' (2)	CQua
'Pat Brown' (2)	CQua
'Pat Redman' (3) **new**	CQua
'Patabundy' (2)	CQua
'Pathos' (3)	IRhd
'Patois' (9)	CBro CQua IRhd
'Patrick Hacket' (1) ♀H6	CQua
'Pay Day' (1)	CQua
'Peach Prince' (4)	CQua
'Pearl Wedding' (3)	CQua
'Pearlshell' (11a)	CQua
'Peeping Jenny' (6) **new**	ERCP
'Peeping Tom' (6) ♀H6	CBro CQua ERCP GKev LAma SDeJ SRms
'Peggy's Gift' (3)	IRhd
'Pelynt' (3)	CQua
'Pemboa' (1)	CQua
'Pencrebar' (4)	CAvo CQua EPot EShb LAma NHol SBod SDeJ WShi
'Pend Oreille' (3)	CQua
'Pengarth' (2)	CQua
'Penjerrick' (9)	CQua
'Penkivel' (2) ♀H6	CQua
'Pennance Mill' (2)	CQua
'Pennine Way' (1)	CQua
'Penny Perowne' (7)	CQua
'Pennyfield' (2)	CQua
'Penpol' (7)	CBro CFen CQua
'Penril' (6)	CQua
'Penselwood' (2)	CQua
'Penstraze' (7)	CQua
'Pentewan' (2)	CQua GCro
'Pentille' (1)	CQua
'Pentire' (11a)	CQua
'Penvale' (7)	CQua
'Peppercorn' (6)	CQua
'Percuil' (6)	CQua
'Perdredda' (3)	CQua
perez-chiscanoi (13)	CFil SKHP
'Perimeter' (3)	CQua
'Peripheral Pink' (2)	CQua
'Perlax' (11a)	CQua
'Perpetuation' (7)	CQua
'Personable' (2)	CQua
'Petanca' (5)	IRhd
'Peter Chown' (11a)	CQua
'Petit Four' (4)	LAma SDeJ
'Petrel' (5)	CBro CQua EPot ERCP GKev SBod SDeJ WShi
'Phantom' (11a)	CQua
'Phil's Gift' (1)	CQua
'Phinda' (2)	IRhd
'Phoenician' (2)	CQua
'Picatou' (3)	IRhd
'Picket Post' (3)	IRhd
'Picoblanco' (2)	CBro CQua
'Pinafore' (2)	EPfP
Pineapple Plemp (1) **new**	GCro
'Pineapple Prince' (2) ♀H6	CQua
'Pink Angel' (7)	CQua
'Pink Champagne' (4)	CQua
'Pink Charm' (2)	CQua SDeJ
'Pink China' (2)	CQua
'Pink Formal' (11a)	CQua
'Pink Gilt' (2)	IRhd
'Pink Glacier' (11a)	CQua
'Pink Holly' (11a)	CQua
'Pink Ice' (2)	CQua
'Pink Pageant' (4)	CQua IRhd
'Pink Paradise' (4)	CQua IRhd
'Pink Parasol' (1)	SDeJ
'Pink Perry' (2)	IRhd
'Pink Silk' (1)	CQua SDeJ
'Pink Smiles' (2)	CFen LRHS
'Pink Surprise' (2)	CQua
'Pink Tango' (11a)	CQua
'Pinza' (2) ♀H6	CQua SDeJ
'Pipe Major' (2)	CQua
'Pipers Barn' (7)	CQua
'Piper's Gold' (1)	CQua
'Pipestone' (2)	CQua
'Pipit' (7)	CAvo CBro CFen CQua EPfP EPot ERCP GKev LAma LPot MBri NBir SDeJ WShi
'Piraeus' (4)	IRhd

	'Pismo Beach' (2)	CQua
	'Pitchroy' (2)	CQua
	'Pitt's Diamond' (3)	CQua
	'Pixie's Sister' (7) ♀H6	CQua LLHF
	'Pledge' (1)	CQua
	'Plymouth Hoe' (1)	CQua
§	***poeticus*** var. ***hellenicus*** (13)	CBro CQua GCro IRhd
	- old pheasant's eye	see *N. poeticus* var. *recurvus*
	- var. ***physaloides*** (13)	CFil CQua ECho
	- 'Plenus' misapplied	see *N. poeticus* 'Spalding Double White', *N.* 'Tamar Double White'
§	- 'Plenus' ambig. (4)	CAby CBro CQua ERCP GQui SDeJ WShi
§	- var. ***recurvus*** (13) ♀H6	CAvo CBro CFen CQua CTca ECho EPfP ERCP GKev LAma LCro MGib NBir SCob SDeJ SPer SPhx WShi
§	- 'Spalding Double White' (4)	CQua EPot
	- white-flowered (13)	SDeJ
	'Poetry in Motion' (9) **new**	IRhd
	'Poet's Way' (9)	CQua IRhd
	'Pol Crocan' (2)	CQua IRhd
	'Pol Dornie' (2)	CQua
	'Pol Voulin' (2)	CQua IRhd MGib
	'Polar Ice' (3)	CFen CQua LAma SDeJ
	'Polbathic' (2)	CQua
	'Polgoon' (2)	CFen
	'Polgooth' (2)	CQua
	'Polindra' (2)	GCro
	'Polly's Pearl' (8)	CQua
	'Polmenor' (2)	CQua
	'Polnesk' (7)	GCro
	'Polonaise' (2)	CQua
	'Polruan' (7)	CQua
	'Poltreen' (4)	CQua
	'Polwheveral' (2)	CQua
	'Polyphant' (2) **new**	CQua
	'Pomona' (3)	GCro
	'Pooka' (3)	CQua IRhd
	Poolewe Pintuck (2) **new**	GCro
	'Popeye' (4)	EPfP
	'Poppy's Choice' (4)	CQua
	'Pops Legacy' (1)	CQua
	'Port Noo' (3)	IRhd
	'Porthchapel' (7)	CQua
	'Portloe Bay' (3)	CQua
	'Portrait' (2)	CQua
	'Portrush' (3)	CQua
	'Post Horn' (6)	CFen
	'Potential' (1)	CQua
	'Powerstock' (2)	IRhd
	'Praecox' (9)	CBro MGib
	'Prairie Fire' (3)	CQua IRhd
	'Pratincole' (3)	IRhd
	'Preamble' (1)	CQua
I	'Precocious' (2) ♀H6	CQua SDeJ
	'Predator' (1)	IRhd MGib
	'Premiere' (2)	CQua IRhd
	'Presidential Pink' (2)	CQua
	'Pretty Baby' (3)	CQua
	'Pride of Cornwall' (8)	CQua
	'Primegold' (2)	CFen
	'Primrose Beauty' (4)	CFen CQua
	'Princeps' (1)	CQua GCro
	'Princess Alexandra' (6)	CFen
	'Princess Diana' (6)	CFen
	'Printal' (11a)	SDeJ
	'Priorsford' (2)	IRhd
	'Prism' (2)	CQua
	'Problem Child' (2)	IRhd
	'Probus' (1)	CQua
	'Professor Einstein' (2)	EPfP SDeJ
	'Prologue' (1)	CQua
	'Prototype' (6)	IRhd LRHS
	'Proud Fellow' (1)	IRhd
	'Proverbial Pink' (2)	IRhd
	pseudonarcissus (13)	CHab CQua CWld GCro MMuc WHer WShi
I	- 'Concolor' **new**	CAvo
	- subsp. ***eugeniae***	see *N. eugeniae*
	- subsp. ***nobilis***	see *N. nobilis*
	- subsp. ***pseudonarcissus*** double-flowered (4)	CQua
§	- - var. ***humilis*** (13)	ECho
	'Ptolemy' (1)	CFen
	'Pueblo' (7)	CQua SDeJ
	'Pukenui' (4)	CQua
	'Pulsar' (2)	IRhd
	pumilus ambig. (13)	CQua ECho LLHF SDeJ
	'Punchline' (7) ♀H6	CQua
	'Punter' (2)	CQua IRhd
	'Puppet' (5)	CQua EPfP
	'Purbeck' (3) ♀H6	CQua IRhd
	'Quail' (7) ♀H6	CFen CQua CTca EPfP GKev LAma LSou MBri SDeJ
	'Quasar' (2) ♀H6	CQua
	Queen Anne's double daffodil	see *N.* 'Eystettensis'
	'Queen Fiona' (1)	IRhd
	'Queen Juliana' (1)	CQua
	'Queen Mum' (1)	CQua
	'Queen of Spain' (5)	CQua
	'Queen of the North' (3)	GCro
	'Queen's Guard' (1)	IRhd
	'Queensland' (2)	CFen
	'Quick Step' (7)	CQua
	'Quiet Hero' (3)	IRhd
	'Quiet Magic' (2)	IRhd
	'Quiet Man' (1)	IRhd
	'Radiant Gem' (8)	CQua
	radiiflorus (13)	EPot
	- var. ***poetarum*** (13)	CBro CQua
	- var. ***radiiflorus*** (13)	GCro
	'Radjel' (4)	CQua
	'Rainbow' (2) ♀H6	CQua SPer
	'Raj' (2) **new**	CQua
	'Rame Head' (1)	CQua
	'Rameses' (2)	CQua MGib
	'Ransom' (4)	IRhd
	'Rapid Stride' (6)	IRhd
	'Rapture' (6) ♀H6	CAvo CBro CQua ERCP IRhd MBri MGib WShi
	'Rashee' (1)	CQua
	'Raspberry Ring' (2)	CQua
	'Rathowen Gold' (1)	CQua
	'Ravenhill' (3)	CQua
	'Rebekah' (4)	CQua
	'Recital' (2)	CQua
	'Red Devon' (2)	CFen LCro LOPS LRHS SDeJ
	'Red Era' (3)	CQua
	'Red Mantle' (2) **new**	CQua
	'Red Marvel' (3)	CFen
	'Red Reed' (1)	IRhd
	'Red Socks' (6)	CQua
	'Refrain' (2)	CQua
	'Regal Bliss' (2)	CQua
	'Reggae' (6) ♀H6	CBro CQua LRHS SDeJ

	Name	Suppliers
	'Rembrandt' (1)	CFen CQua
	'Rendezvous Caye' (2)	CQua
	'Renovator' (1)	CQua
	'Repertoire' (3)	IRhd
	'Replete' (4)	CQua
	requienii	see *N. assoanus*
	'Resistasol' (1)	IRhd
	'Resolute' (2)	GCro
	'Reverse Image' (11a)	CQua
	'Rheban Red' (2)	IRhd MGib
	'Ribald' (2)	IRhd
	'Ridgecrest' (3)	CQua IRhd
	rifanus	see *N. romieuxii* subsp. *romieuxii* var. *rifanus*
	'Rijnveld's Early Sensation' (1) ♀H6	CAvo CBro CFen CMea CQua ECha ERCP LCro SDeJ
	'Rikki' (7)	CBro CQua
	'Rima' (1)	CQua
	'Rimmon' (3)	CQua
	'Rimski' (2)	IRhd
	'Ring Fence' (3)	IRhd
	'Ring Flash' (2)	IRhd
	'Ringhaddy' (3)	IRhd
	'Ringing Bells' (5)	CQua
	'Ringleader' (2)	CQua
	'Rio Bravo' (2)	IRhd
	'Rio Gusto' (2)	IRhd
	'Rio Lobo' (2)	IRhd
	'Rio Rondo' (2)	IRhd
	'Rio Rouge' (2)	IRhd
§	'Rip van Winkle' (4)	CAby CBro CFen CQua CTca EPfP EPot ERCP GCro GKev LAma LRHS MBri NHol SBod SCob SDeJ WShi
	'Rippling Waters' (5)	CQua LAma
	'Rising Star' (7) ♀H6	IRhd
	'Rival' (6)	CQua
	'River Dance' (2)	IRhd
	'River Queen' (2)	CQua IRhd
	'Roberta' (1)	CFen
	'Roberta Watrous' (7)	IRhd
	'Rock Creek' (3)	IRhd
	'Rockall' (3)	CQua
	'Rocoza' (2)	IRhd
	'Roger' (6)	CQua
	'Rogue' (2)	CBro
	'Romance' (2) ♀H6	LAma
§	'Romanus' (4)	CQua
	romieuxii (13) ♀H4	CBro ECho EPri GCal ITim LRHS WCot
	- JCA 805	CFil EPot
	- SF 370	WCot
	- subsp. ***albidus*** (13)	ECho
	- - var. ***albidus*** (13) **new**	MGib
§	- - var. ***zaianicus*** (13)	ECho GKev MGib
	- - - SB&L 82 from Morocco **new**	WCot
§	- 'Atlas Gold' (10)	ECho EPot
§	- 'Joy Bishop' (10)	ECho EPot
§	- 'Julia Jane' (10)	CQua ECho EPot GKev
*	- subsp. ***pallidus*** SB&L 237	WCot
	- subsp. ***romieuxii*** (13)	GKev
§	- - var. ***mesatlanticus*** (13)	ECho
§	- - var. ***rifanus*** (13)	ECho MGib
	- - B 8929	WCot
	- - var. ***romieuxii*** **new**	MGib
§	- 'Treble Chance' (10)	EPot
	'Rongoiti Gem' (4) **new**	CQua
	'Rosannor Gold' (11a)	CQua
	'Roscarrick' (6)	CQua
	'Rose Noble' (2)	CFen
	'Rose of May' (4)	CQua WShi
	'Rose of Tralee' (2)	CQua
	'Rose Royale' (2)	CQua
	'Rose Umber' (2)	IRhd
	'Rose Villa' (2)	CQua
	'Rosemary Pearson' (2)	CQua
	'Rosemerryn' (2)	CQua
	'Rosemoor Gold' (7) ♀H6	CBro CFen CQua
	'Rosemullion' (4)	CQua
	'Rosevine' (3)	CQua
	'Round Oak' (1)	CQua
	'Rowell Fair' (2) **new**	MGib
	'Roxton' (4)	IRhd
	'Royal Armour' (1)	CFen
	'Royal Ballet' (2)	CQua
	'Royal China' (2) **new**	MGib
	'Royal Connection' (8)	CQua
	'Royal Marine' (2)	CQua IRhd
	'Royal Princess' (3)	CQua ERCP MGib
	'Royal Regiment' (2)	CQua
	'Rubh Mor' (2)	CQua
	'Ruby Red' (2)	CQua
	'Ruby Rose' (4)	IRhd
	'Ruby Wedding' (2)	IRhd
	'Rubythroat' (2)	CQua
	'Ruddy Duck' (2)	IRhd
	'Ruddy Rascal' (2)	IRhd
	'Rugulosus' (7)	CBro CQua
	'Runkerry' (4)	IRhd
	rupicola (13)	CBro CQua ECho LLHF NSla WCot
§	- subsp. ***marvieri*** (13)	MGib
§	- subsp. ***watieri*** (13)	CBro CQua ECho EPot LLHF MGib
	'Rustom Pasha' (2)	CQua GCro
	'Rytha' (2)	CQua
	'Saberwing' (5)	CQua
	'Sabine Hay' (3)	CQua EPot ERCP
	'Sabrosa' (7) ♀H4	CBro CQua LLHF LRHS MGib
	'Sacajawea' (2)	CFen
	'Sacré Coeur' (2)	IRhd
	'Saffron Strand' (3) **new**	IRhd
	'Sagana' (9)	CQua
	'Sailboat' (7) ♀H6	CBro CQua EPfP MBri SPer
	'Saint Agnes' (8)	CQua
	'Saint Budock' (1)	CQua
	'Saint Day' (5)	CQua
	'Saint Dilpe' (2)	CQua
	'Saint Keverne' (2) ♀H6	CFen CQua GCro SDeJ
	'Saint Keyne' (8)	CQua
	'Saint Olaf' (3)	GCro
	'Saint Patrick's Day' (2)	CFen CQua LAma SDeJ
	'Saint Peter' (4)	CFen CQua
	'Saint Petroc' (9)	CQua
	'Saint Piran' (7)	CQua
	'Salakee' (2)	CQua
	'Salcey Forest' (1)	CQua
	'Salome' (2) ♀H6	CQua GKev LAma LCro LOPS NBir NPer SCob SDeJ
	'Salute' (2)	CQua
	'Samantha' (4)	CQua
	'Samsara' (3)	IRhd
	'Sandra's Diamond' (3)	CQua
	'Sandycove' (2)	CQua IRhd
	'Sandymount' (2)	CQua
	'Santa Claus' (4)	CQua

Name	Suppliers
'Sarah' (2)	CFen
'Sarah Dear' (2)	CQua
'Sarah Markillie' (11a)	CQua
'Sarchedon' (9)	GCro
'Sargeant's Caye' (1)	CQua IRhd MGib
'Satchmo' (1)	CQua
'Satin Blanc' (7)	IRhd
'Satsuma' (1)	CQua
'Saturn' (3)	CQua
'Savoir Faire' (2)	IRhd
'Saxby' (11a)	CQua
scaberulus (13)	ECho
'Scarlet Chord' (2)	CQua
'Scarlet Elegance' (2)	CQua
'Scarlet Gem' (8)	SDeJ
'Scarlet Tanager' (2)	IRhd
'Scarlett O'Hara' (2)	CFen
'Scented Breeze' (2)	IRhd
'Scilly Spring' (8)	CAvo
'Scilly White' (8)	CFen CQua WShi
'Scorrier' (2)	CQua
'Scrumpy' (2)	CQua
'Sea Dream' (3)	CQua
'Sea Gift' (7)	CBro
'Sea Green' (9)	CQua
'Sea Legend' (2)	CQua
'Sea Moon' (2)	IRhd
'Sea Princess' (3)	SDeJ
'Sea Shanty' (2)	IRhd
'Seagull' (3)	CAvo CQua LAma WShi
'Sealing Wax' (2)	CFen CQua MGib
'Season's Greetings' (7)	IRhd
'Segovia' (3) 🏆H6	CBro CQua EPot GKev LAma MGib SDeJ
'Sempre Avanti' (2)	LAma SDeJ
'Seraglio' (3)	CQua
'Serena Beach' (4)	IRhd
'Serena Lodge' (4) 🏆H6	CQua IRhd
serotinus (13)	ECho EPot GKev
'Sextant' (6)	CQua
'Shangani' (2)	IRhd
'Sharnden' (1) **new**	MGib
'Sheelagh Rowan' (2)	CQua IRhd MGib
'Sheer Joy' (6)	CQua
'Shepherd's Hey' (7)	CQua SDeJ
'Sherborne' (4) 🏆H6	CQua
'Sherpa' (1)	CQua IRhd
'Sheskin' (2)	IRhd
'Shindig' (2)	IRhd
'Shining Light' (2)	CQua
'Shockwave' (2)	CQua
'Shrimp Boat' (11a)	IRhd
'Sidley' (3)	CQua IRhd
'Sidney Torch' (2)	CFen
'Signet Ring' (3)	IRhd
'Signorina' (2)	IRhd
'Silent Valley' (1)	IRhd
'Silk Cut' (2)	CQua
'Silkwood' (3)	IRhd
'Silver Bells' (5)	IRhd
'Silver Chimes' (8)	CAvo CBro CFen CQua CTca EPfP LAma LCro LOPS NBir SDeJ
'Silver Convention' (1)	CQua MGib
'Silver Crystal' (3)	IRhd
'Silver Kiwi' (2)	CQua
'Silver Moon' (2)	CFen
'Silver Plate' (11a)	CQua
'Silver Sabre' (2)	IRhd
'Silver Smiles' (7)	SPhx
'Silver Surf' (2)	CQua IRhd
'Silversmith' (2)	CQua
'Silverthorne' (3)	CQua
'Silverwood' (3)	CQua IRhd
'Singing Pub' (3)	IRhd
'Sinopel' (3)	LAma SDeJ
'Sir Samuel' (2)	CQua
'Sir Watkin' (2)	CQua GCro
'Sir Winston Churchill' (4) 🏆H6	CQua EPfP LAma LCro LOPS LPfy LRHS SCob SDeJ SPer
'Sirius' (2)	GCro
'Sissy' (6)	CQua
'Skerry' (2)	CQua
'Skilliwidden' (2) 🏆H6	CQua
'Skookum' (3)	CQua
'Skywalker' (2)	IRhd
'Slieveboy' (1)	CQua
'Slipstream' (6)	IRhd
'Small Fry' (1)	CQua
'Small Talk' (1) 🏆H6	CQua LLHF
'Smarple' (10) **new**	MGib
'Smokey Bear' (4)	CQua
'Smooth Sails' (3)	CQua
'Snipe' (6)	CAvo CQua GKev WShi
'Snook' (6) **new**	CQua
'Snoopie' (6)	CQua
'Snow Bunting' (7)	CBro
'Snow Frills' (2) **new**	CQua
'Snowcrest' (3)	CQua
'Snowshill' (2)	CQua
'Snowy Canyon' (4) **new**	IRhd
'Soft Focus' (2)	IRhd
'Solar Eclipse' (2) **new**	IRhd
'Solar System' (3)	IRhd
'Solar Tan' (3)	CQua
'Soleil d'Or' (8)	CQua
'Solera' (2)	IRhd
'Solferique' (2)	CQua
'Soloist' (2)	IRhd
'Solveig's Song' (12)	WAbe
'Sonata' (9)	CQua
'Songket' (2)	CQua
'Sophia' (2)	CQua
'Sophie's Choice' (4)	CAvo
'Soprano' (2)	CQua IRhd MGib
'Sorcerer' (3)	CQua
'South Street' (2)	CQua
'Southease' (2)	CQua
'Southern Gem' (2)	GCro
'Spaniards Inn' (4)	CQua
'Sparkling Tarts' (8)	CQua
'Sparnon' (11a)	CQua
'Spartan Gold' (2)	IRhd
'Special Envoy' (2)	CQua
'Speenogue' (1)	IRhd
'Spellbinder' (1)	CQua SDeJ
'Spencer Tracy' (2)	CFen CQua
'Sperrin Gold' (1)	IRhd
'Spin Doctor' (3)	IRhd
'Spindletop' (3) 🏆H6	IRhd
'Spirit of Rame' (3)	CQua
'Split Vote' (11a)	IRhd
'Spoirot' (10) 🏆H6	CAby CQua ECho ERCP GBuc LEdu MGib MNrw SDeJ
'Sportsman' (2)	CQua
'Spring Dawn' (2)	EPfP LCro SPer
'Spring Morn' (2)	CQua IRhd
'Spun Honey' (4)	CQua
'Stadium' (2)	CFen LAma
'Stainless' (2)	SPhx
'Standard Value' (1)	CFen

	Name	Suppliers
	'Stann Creek' (1)	CQua
	'Stanway' (3)	CQua MGib
	'Star Glow' (2)	CQua
	'Star Quality' (3)	IRhd
	'Starfire' (7)	CQua
	'State Express' (2)	CQua IRhd
	'Statue' (2)	CFen
	'Steenbok' (3)	IRhd
	'Stella' (2)	CQua GCro GKev WShi
	'Stellar Glow' (3)	IRhd
	'Stenalees' (6)	CQua
	'Step Child' (6)	CQua
	'Step Forward' (7)	CQua
	'Steren' (7)	CQua
	'Stilton' (9)	CQua
	'Stinger' (2)	CQua
	'Stint' (5) ♀H6	CQua SDeJ
	'Stocken' (7)	CBro CQua ECho EPri WAbe
	'Stoke Charity' (2)	CFen CQua
	'Stoke Doyle' (2)	CQua MGib
	'Stonham Gold' (2) **new**	CQua
	'Stormy Weather' (1)	CQua
	'Stratosphere' (7) ♀H6	CQua SDeJ
	'Strines' (2) ♀H6	CQua MGib
	'Suave' (3)	CQua
	'Subtle Shades' (2)	IRhd
	'Sugar and Spice' (3)	CQua
	'Sugar Bird' (2)	IRhd
	'Sugar Cups' (8)	CQua
	'Sugar Loaf' (4)	CQua
	'Sugar Rose' (6)	CQua
	'Sugarbush' (7)	WShi
	'Suisgill' (4)	CQua
	'Sukey' (6)	CQua
§	'Sulphur Phoenix' (4)	CQua GCro WShi
	'Summer Solstice' (3)	IRhd
	'Sumo Jewel' (6)	CQua
	'Sun Disc' (7) ♀H6	CBro CFen CQua CTri ECho GKev LAma LCro LOPS MBri MGib MPie SCob SDeJ WShi
	'Sunbeam Valley' (1) **new**	MGib
	'Sunday Chimes' (5)	CQua
	'Sundial' (7)	CBro LAma
	'Sunny Girlfriend' (11a)	SDeJ
	'Sunnyside Up' (11a) ♀H6	SDeJ
	'Sunrise' (3)	CQua
	'Sunstroke' (2)	CQua
	'Suntory' (3)	CQua
	'Suntrap' (2)	IRhd
	'Surfside' (6) ♀H6	CQua
	'Surprise Packet' (2)	IRhd
	'Surrey' (2)	CQua IRhd
	'Suzie Dee' (6)	IRhd
	'Suzie's Sister' (6)	IRhd
	'Suzy' (7) ♀H6	CBro CFen SDeJ
	'Swaledale' (2)	CQua
	'Swallow' (6)	CQua SDeJ
	'Swallow Wing' (6)	IRhd
	'Swan of Avon' (1)	CQua
	'Swanpool' (3)	CQua
	'Sweet Blanche' (7)	CQua
	'Sweet Lorraine' (2)	CQua
	'Sweet Memory' (2)	CQua
	'Sweet Sue' (3)	CQua
	'Sweetness' (7) ♀H6	CAvo CBro CFen CQua GCro LAma LCro LOPS WShi
	'Swift Arrow' (6) ♀H6	CQua
	'Swing Wing' (6)	CQua
	'Swoop' (6)	SDeJ
	'Sydling' (5)	CQua
	'Taffeta' (10)	EPri
	'Tahiti' (4) ♀H6	CFen CQua LAma LCro LOPS LRHS SCob SDeJ
	× ***taitii*** (13)	WShi
	'Talgarth' (2)	CQua
	'Talskiddy' (6)	CQua
§	'Tamar Double White' (4)	CBro CFil CQua
	'Tamar Fire' (4) ♀H6	CQua
	'Tamar Lad' (2)	CQua
	'Tamar Lass' (3)	CQua
	'Tamar Snow' (2)	CQua
	'Tamara' (2)	CFen CQua
	'Tangent' (2)	CQua
	'Tangerine Tango' (4)	IRhd
	'Tao' (3)	CQua
	'Tasgem' (4)	CQua
	'Taslass' (4)	CQua
	tazetta (13)	CQua ECho
	- subsp. ***aureus***	see *N. aureus*
§	- subsp. ***lacticolor*** (13)	CFil CQua ERCP SDeJ
§	- - 'Grand Monarque' (8)	CBro CQua
	- subsp. ***ochroleucus*** (13)	CQua
*	- var. ***odoratus***	CQua
	- subsp. ***tazetta*** **new**	CQua
	'Teal' (1)	CQua
	'Tehidy' (3)	CQua
§	'Telamonius Plenus' (4)	CBro CQua WShi
	'Temba' (1)	IRhd
	'Temple Cloud' (4)	IRhd
	'Tenedos' (2)	GCro
	tenuifolius	see *N. bulbocodium* subsp. *bulbocodium* var. *tenuifolius*
	Tequila Sunrise Group (12)	IRhd
	'Terminator' (2)	CQua IRhd
	'Terracotta' (2)	CQua IRhd
	'Terrapin' (3)	IRhd
	'Terwegen' (4)	CFen
	'Tête-à-tête' (12) ♀H6	CAvo CBro CFen CQua CTca CWCL EPfP EPot ERCP GAbr GKev LAma LCro LOPS LPfy LPot LRHS LSou MBri SCob SDeJ SPer
	'Thalia' (5)	CAvo CBro CQua CTca EPfP ERCP GKev IFro LAma LCro LOPS LPfy LPot LRHS MBri NBir NHol SCob SDeJ SPer SPhx WShi
	'The Alliance' (6) ♀H6	CBro CQua
	'The Caley' (2)	CQua
	'The Grange' (1)	CQua
	'The Mount' (2)	IRhd
	'Therapia' (3) **new**	GCro
	'Thistin' (1)	IRhd
	'Thomas Kinkade' (2)	CQua
	'Thoughtful' (5)	CBro CQua
	'Three Oaks' (1)	CQua
	'Three Trees' (1)	IRhd
	'Tibet' (2)	CFen CQua
	'Tickled Pink' (11a)	IRhd
	'Tideford' (2)	CQua
	'Tidy Tippet' (2)	IRhd
	'Tiercel' (1)	CQua
	'Tiffany Jade' (3)	CQua
	'Tiger Moth' (6)	CQua
	'Timolin' (3)	CQua
	'Tinderbox' (2)	IRhd
	'Tingdene' (2) **new**	MGib
	'Tinhay' (7)	CQua

'Tiritomba' (11a)	CQua
'Tittle-tattle' (7)	CFen CQua
'Toby' (2)	SDeJ
'Top Hit' (11a)	CQua
'Topolino' (1) ♀H6	CAvo CBro CFen CQua EPot GKev IFro LAma LCro LOPS LRHS SCob
'Topsy Turvy' (4)	CQua
'Toreador' (3)	CFen
'Toretta' (3)	IRhd
'Torianne' (2) ♀H6	CQua
Torosay Elegance (2) **new**	GCro
'Torr Head' (9)	IRhd
'Torridon' (2)	CQua
'Toto' (12) ♀H6	CBro CQua ECho ERCP MBri SDeJ SPhx
'Tracey' (6)	CQua IRhd LAma
'Transmitter' (4) **new**	CQua
'Treasure Hunt' (2)	IRhd
'Trebah' (2) ♀H6	CQua
'Treble Chance'	see *N. romieuxii* 'Treble Chance'
'Treble Two' (7)	CQua
'Trecara' (3)	CQua
'Tregarrick' (2)	CQua
'Treglisson' (2)	CFen
'Trelawney Gold' (2)	CFen CQua
'Trelissick' (7)	CQua
'Tremelling' (2)	CFen
'Tremough Dale' (11a)	CQua
'Trena' (6) ♀H6	CQua ERCP MGib
'Trendy Trail' (3)	IRhd
'Trentagh' (3)	IRhd
'Trenwith' (1)	CQua
'Trepolo' (11b)	ERCP
'Tresamble' (5)	CBro CQua EPfP GCro LAma MBri SDeJ
'Tresham Gold' (2) **new**	MGib
'Trevaunance' (6)	CQua
'Treverva' (6)	CQua
'Treviddo' (2)	CQua
'Trevithian' (7)	CBro CQua GCro LAma SDeJ
'Trewarvas' (2)	CQua
'Tricollet' (11a)	SDeJ
'Trident' (3)	CQua
'Trielfin' (5)	IRhd
'Trigonometry' (11a) ♀H6	CQua IRhd
'Tripartite' (11a) ♀H6	CQua IRhd MGib SDeJ
'Triple Crown' (3) ♀H6	CQua IRhd
'Tristram' (2)	CQua
'Tropic Isle' (4)	CQua
'Tropical Heat' (2)	IRhd
'Trousseau' (1)	CFen CQua
'Tru' (3)	CQua
'Truculent' (3)	CQua
'Trueblood' (3)	IRhd
'Trumpet Warrior' (1) ♀H6	CQua IRhd MGib
'Tryst' (2)	CQua
'Tudor Minstrel' (2)	CQua
'Tuesday's Child' (5) ♀H6	CQua
'Turncoat' (6)	CQua
'Tutankhamun' (2)	CQua
'Tweety Bird' (6)	EPfP
'Twicer' (2)	CQua IRhd
'Twilight Zone' (2)	IRhd
'Twink' (4)	CQua GCro
'Twinkling Yellow' (7) ♀H6 **new**	CBro
Tyndrum Flame (3)	GCro
'Tyrone Gold' (1) ♀H6	CQua IRhd
'Tyrree' (1)	IRhd
'Tywara' (1)	CQua
'Ulster Bank' (3)	CQua
'Ulster Bride' (4)	CQua
'Ultimus' (2)	CQua
'Uncle Duncan' (1)	CQua IRhd
'Unique' (4) ♀H6	CQua LAma SDeJ
'Unsurpassable' (1)	CFen CQua GCro LAma
'Upalong' (12)	CQua
'Upshot' (3)	CQua
'Urchin' (2)	IRhd
'Utiku' (6)	CQua
'Val d'Incles' (3)	CQua IRhd
'Valdrome' (11a)	CQua
'Valediction' (3)	CQua
'Valinor' (2)	CQua
'Van Sion'	see *N.* 'Telamonius Plenus'
'Vanellus' (11a) ♀H6	IRhd
'Vanilla Peach' (11a)	SDeJ
'Vantage' (2)	CQua
'Vaticaan' (1)	SDeJ
'Velocity' (6)	LRHS MGib
'Vendell' (3)	IRhd
'Verdant Sparks' (7)	IRhd
'Verdin' (7)	CQua
'Verdoy' (2)	IRhd
'Verger' (3)	LAma MBri SDeJ
'Vernal Prince' (3) ♀H6	CQua
'Verona' (3) ♀H6	CQua
'Verran Rose' (2)	IRhd
'Vers Libre' (9)	CQua
'Version' (2)	IRhd
'Victoria' (1)	CQua
'Video Kid' (2)	IRhd
'Viking' (1) ♀H6	CQua
'Village Green' (3)	IRhd
'Vineland' (6) **new**	CQua
'Violetta' (2)	CQua
'Virginia Waters' (3)	CQua MGib
'Viva Diva' (3)	IRhd
'Volare' (2)	CQua
'Volcanic Rim' (3)	IRhd
'Vulcan' (2)	CQua
'W.P. Milner' (1)	CAby CAvo CBro CQua EPfP EPot ERCP GKev LAma MBri SDeJ SPhx WShi
'Walden Pond' (3)	CQua
'Waldorf Astoria' (4)	CQua IRhd
'Walton' (7)	CQua
'Waltz' (11a)	CQua
'War Dance' (3)	IRhd
'Warbler' (6) ♀H6	CQua LAma SDeJ
'Warleggan' (2)	CFen
'Warm Day' (2)	IRhd
'Warm Welcome' (2)	IRhd
'Warmington' (3)	CQua
'Warmwell' (3)	IRhd
'Watamu' (3)	IRhd
'Waterperry' (7)	CBro LAma
'Watership Down' (2)	CQua IRhd
'Watersmeet' (4)	CQua
watieri	see *N. rupicola* subsp. *watieri*
'Wave' (4)	CQua
'Wavelength' (3)	IRhd
'Wavertree'	see *N. asturiensis* 'Wavertree'
'Waxwing' (5)	CQua MGib
'Wayward Lad' (3)	IRhd
'Wee Bee' (1)	CQua

'Welcome' (2)	CFen CQua
'Welland Vale' (1) new	MGib
'Welsh Rugby Union' (1)	CQua
'Welsh Warrior' (1)	CQua
'Wendron' (1)	CFen
'West Post' (3)	IRhd
'Westward' (4)	CQua
'Whang-hi' (6)	CQua
'Wheal Bush' (4)	CQua
'Wheal Coates' (7) ♀H6	CQua
'Wheal Jane' (2)	CQua
'Wheal Kitty' (7)	CQua
'Wheal Rose' (4)	CQua
'Wheatear' (6)	CQua IRhd
'Whetstone' (1)	CQua
'Whipcord' (7) ♀H6	CQua IRhd
'Whisky Galore' (2)	CQua
'Whisky Mac' (2)	CQua
'White Convention' (1)	IRhd
'White Empress' (1)	CQua
'White Giant' (1)	GKev
'White Lady' (3)	CAvo CQua GCro LAma WShi
'White Lion' (4) ♀H6	CFen CQua LAma LRHS SDeJ
'White Marvel' (4)	CQua
'White Medal' (4)	SDeJ
'White Nile' (2)	CQua GCro
'White Star' (1)	IRhd
'White Tea' (2)	CQua IRhd MGib
'White Tie' (3)	CQua
'Whitewell' (2)	GCro
'Wicklow Hills' (3)	CQua
'Widgeon' (2)	CQua
'Wild Honey' (2)	CQua
'Wild Rover' (1)	IRhd
'Will Scarlett' (2)	CQua GCro
willkommii (13)	CBro CQua ECho EPot GKev
'Wimbledon County Girl' (2) ♀H6	CQua
'Winholm Jenni' (3)	CQua
'Winifred van Graven' (3)	CFen CQua
'Winter Waltz' (6)	CQua
'Wisley' (6) ♀H6	ERCP LRHS
'Witch Doctor' (3)	CQua
'Witch Hunt' (4)	IRhd
Woodcroft Gold (2)	GCro
'Woodland Prince' (3)	CQua
'Woodland Star' (3)	CQua
'Woodley Vale' (2)	CQua
'Woolsthorpe' (2)	CQua
'World Class' (5)	CQua
'Xit' (3)	CAvo CBro CQua GKev
'Xunantunich' (2)	CQua IRhd
'Yellow Belles' (5)	IRhd
'Yellow Cheerfulness' (4) ♀H6	CQua EPfP LAma LCro LOPS MBri SCob SDeJ SPer
'Yellow River' (1) ♀H6	LAma
'Yellow Triumphator' (1)	CFen
'Yellow Xit' (3)	CQua
'York Minster' (1)	CQua
'Young American' (1)	CQua
'Young Blood' (2)	CQua IRhd
'Your Grace' (2)	CQua
'Yummy Mummy' (2)	IRhd
'Yum-Yum' (3)	IRhd
zaianicus	see *N. romieuxii* subsp. *albidus* var. *zaianicus*
'Zekiah' (1)	CQua
'Zion Canyon' (2)	CQua
'Zoë's Pink' (3)	CQua
'Zwynner' (2)	IRhd

Nardostachys (*Caprifoliaceae*)

grandiflora	GPoy

Nassauvia (*Asteraceae*)

darwinii new	WAbe
gaudichaudii	SPlb WAbe
lagascae new	WAbe

Nassella (*Poaceae*)

cernua	WPGP
formicarum (Delile) Barkworth	EBee
neesiana new	SPhx
poeppigiana	see *Stipa poeppigiana*
pulchra	WPGP
tenuissima	see *Stipa tenuissima*
trichotoma	CAby CKno EHoe SPer WHal WPGP
- 'Palomino'	LRHS

Nasturtium (*Brassicaceae*)

'Banana Split'	ELan
officinale	MSKA MWLS SVic SWat

Natal plum see *Carissa macrocarpa*

nectarine see *Prunus persica* var. *nectarina*

Nectaroscordum (*Alliaceae*)

§ ***siculum***	CAvo CBre CBro CSpe CTri EAJP ECho ELan ERCP GCra GKev LCro LLWP LRHS MBel NBir NChi NSti SCob SDeJ SPer WBor
§ - subsp. ***bulgaricum***	CAby CBro CTca CWCL EBee ECha EHrv EPfP EPot IBlr LRHS LSun MNrw SPhx WBrk WCot WPnP XLum
tripedale	CAvo CBro ECho EPot

Neillia (*Rosaceae*)

affinis	CDul CExl EBee EWTr GCal IDee LLHF LRHS MMuc NBid NLar SLon SPad SWvt WPat
longiracemosa	see *N. thibetica*
sinensis	NLar
§ ***thibetica***	Widely available
thyrsiflora PAB 3267	LEdu
- var. ***tunkinensis*** FMWJ 13094 new	CEvo
- - HWJ 505	WCru

Nelumbo (*Nelumbonaceae*)

'Beautiful Dancer'	LLWG
'Carolina Queen'	LLWG
'Emerald Daybreak' (d)	LLWG
'High Noon'	LLWG
lutea new	XBlo
nucifera	XBlo
- 'Alba Striata'	LLWG
- 'Chawan Basu'	LLWG
- 'Hindu'	LLWG
'Penelope'	LLWG
'Perry's Giant Sunburst'	LLWG
'Pink 'n' Yellow'	EWay
'Pink Pretty Princess Payton'	LLWG
'Russian Red'	LLWG
'The President'	LLWG
'Wa Ba Sabie'	LLWG

'Wann Shou Hing'	LLWG

Nematanthus (*Gesneriaceae*)

'Apres'	WDib
'Black Magic'	WDib
'Christmas Holly'	WDib
'Freckles'	WDib
§ ***gregarius*** ♀H1c	WDib
§ - 'Golden West' (v)	WDib
- 'Variegatus'	see *N. gregarius* 'Golden West'
'Lemon and Lime'	WDib
radicans	see *N. gregarius*
'Tropicana' ♀H1c	WDib

Nemesia (*Scrophulariaceae*)

§ Amelie = 'Fleurame'PBR	EPfP LBuc SPoG
Aromatica Scarlet (Aromatica Series) **new**	LBMP
Berries and Cream = 'Fleurbac'PBR	ECtt EPfP LAst LBuc LSou SPoG
Blue Lagoon = 'Pengoon'PBR (Maritana Series)	EBee LAst SCoo
'Blueberry Ripple'	LAst LBMP LSou WGor
§ Bluebird = 'Hubbird'PBR	CHII
Candy Girl = 'Pencand' (Maritana Series)	SCoo
§ ***denticulata*** ♀H3	CBar CPrp EWoo GBee LHop LRHS MHer NEgg SCoo WHlf
- 'Confetti'	see *N. denticulata*
(Elph Series) Elph Dark Blue **new**	WCot
- Elph Yellow **new**	LBMP
'Fleurie Blue'	EPfP LBuc SPoG
Framboise = 'Fleurfram'	EPfP LBuc SPoG
fruticans Benth.	ELon
Golden Eye = 'Yateye'PBR	EBee MPnt SLon
Honey Girl = 'Penhon' (Maritana Series)	SCoo
Ice Pink = 'Fleuripi'	EPfP
'Innocence' ♀H3	CPrp SCoo
(Karoo Series) Karoo Blue = 'Innkablue'PBR	SCoo
- Karoo Soft Blue = 'Innkarsofb'PBR	CWGN MCot
- Karoo Violet Ice = 'Innemkavic'PBR	MCot NPri
Lagoon White	see *N.* Pure Lagoon
Maritana Sky Lagoon = 'Pensky' (Maritana Series)	SCoo
'Mirabelle'	EPfP LBuc SPoG
Myrtille = 'Fleurmyr'	EPfP LBuc SPoG
Nesia Dark Blue = 'Dannemes6' (Nesia Series)	LAst WGor
Opal Innocence	see *N.* Amelie
Provençal Dusky Blue = 'Fleurpdblu'PBR	EPfP
Provençal Dusky Pink = 'Fleurpdpnk'PBR	EPfP
§ Pure Lagoon = 'Penpur'PBR	LAst
Raspberries and Cream = 'Fleurrac'	EPfP LBuc SPoG
'Sugar Almond'	CMac
Sugar Frosted = 'Lowgreg'	LRHS SPoG
'Sugar Plum'	LRHS SLon
'Sundrops' **new**	LAst NPri
(Sunsatia Series) Sunsatia Cherry on Ice	EPfP NPri SPoG
- Sunsatia Blackberry = 'Inuppink'PBR	SCoo
- Sunsatia Cranberry = 'Intraired'PBR	SCoo
- Sunsatia Kumquat = 'Intraikum'PBR	MCot
- Sunsatia Lemon = 'Intraigold'PBR	LAst SCoo
- Sunsatia Peach = 'Inupcream'	CWGN SCoo
- Sunsatia Raspberry **new**	LSou
(Sunsatia Plus Series) **new** Sunsatia Plus Papaya = 'Innemnewpa'	NPri
- Sunsatia Pomelo = 'Innemsunpo'PBR	EPfP NPri
'Sweet Lady'	LAst LBMP LSou NPri
Sweet Scented Blush (Maritana Series) **new**	LBMP
sylvatica	CSpe
'Utopia Lavender' (Utopia Series)	EBee
'Vanilla Lady'	ECtt LAst LBMP LSou NPri
Vanilla Mist = 'Grega'	LRHS LSou SLon
'Wisley Vanilla'	EPfP LBuc SPoG

Nemophila (*Boraginaceae*)

menziesii 'Penny Black'	CSpe SPer

Neodypsis (*Arecaceae*)

decaryi	see *Dypsis decaryi*

Neolepisorus (*Polypodiaceae*)

lancifolius	CExl

Neolitsea (*Lauraceae*)

glauca	see *N. sericea*
polycarpa B&SWJ 11705	WCru
- KWJ 12309	WCru
§ ***sericea***	CBcs LEdu SSpi WPGP WSHC

Neomarica (*Iridaceae*)

caerulea	WCot

Neopanax (*Araliaceae*)

§ ***arboreus***	CDoC CTsd EBee ECou LEdu SBig WPGP
§ ***laetus*** ♀H3	CDoC LEdu SBig

Neoregelia (*Bromeliaceae*)

'Albomarginata' **new**	NEve
'Alpha'	LAir
ampullacea	LAir NEve
- large form	LAir
'Black Beauty' **new**	NEve
carolinae	LAir NEve
- 'Blush' **new**	NEve
- 'Marachelle' **new**	NEve
- Meyendorffii Group	LAir
- - 'Meyendorffii'	XBlo
- f. ***tricolor*** (v) ♀H1a	NEve
'Cheers'	LAir
'Chiquita Linda'	LAir NLos
concentrica **new**	NEve
- 'Big Blue' **new**	NEve

concentrica × 'Pink Polka Dot'	LAir
cruenta	LAir
- 'Bronze'	LAir
- red-leaved	LAir
'Devin's Delight'	LAir
'Donger' (v) new	NEve
'Dr Oeser'	NLos
dungsiana	LAir
'Fancy Free' new	NEve
farinosa new	NEve
'Fireball'	LAir NLos
'Flandria'	LAir
fluminensis × ***macwilliamsii***	LAir
'Fool's Gold'	LAir
'Fruit Salad'	LAir NEve
'Greenball' new	NEve
'Hojo Rojo'	XBlo
'Hula Lady'	LAir
'Irazu'	LAir
'Irish Mist'	LAir
'Jalapeno'	LAir
'Kahala Dawn'	LAir
'Lili Marlene'	LAir
lilliputiana	LAir
'Luca'	LAir NEve
'Marconfos'	XBlo
marmorata ♀H1a	NEve
- 'Variegata' new	NEve
'Michi'	LAir
'Mo Peppa Please'	LAir NEve
'Not Domino'	LAir
pauciflora	LAir NEve
pauciflora × ***wilsoniana***	LAir
'Peggy Pollard'	LAir
'Perfection'	LAir
* ***punctatissima*** var. ***rubra***	LAir
- - × 'Hannibal Lector'	NLos
- var. ***rubra*** × ***tigrina***	LAir
'Rafa' × 'Betty Head'	LAir
'Red of Rio' new	NEve
'Red on Green'	NLos
rubrifolia	LAir
'Sara Lee'	LAir
'Sarah Head'	LAir NEve
'Scarlet Charlotte'	NLos
'Shamrock'	LAir
spectabilis ♀H1a new	NEve
'Spicy'	NLos
'The Auctioneer'	LAir
'Tom Tom'	LAir
'Yellow Devil'	LAir
'Zoë' PBR	LAir
'Zuleica'	LAir NLos

Neoshirakia (*Euphorbiaceae*)

japonica	MBlu WPGP
- B&SWJ 8744	WCru

Neottia (*Orchidaceae*)

ovata	NLAp

Neottianthe (*Orchidaceae*)

cucullata	EFEx

Nepenthes (*Nepenthaceae*)

alata	NLos
albomarginata	NLos
aristolochioides × ***spectabilis***	NLos
bongso	NLos
bongso × ***inermis***	NLos
boschiana × ***densiflora***	NLos
burbidgeae	NLos
× ***burkei***	NLos
chaniana × (***clipeata*** × ***eymae***)	NLos
chaniana × ***veitchii***	NLos
clipeata × ***eymae***	NLos
copleandii	NLos
densiflora	NLos
densiflora × ***spectabilis***	NLos
diatas	NLos
eymae	NLos
fusca	NLos
glabrata	NLos
gracillima	NLos
inermis	NLos
inermis × ***singalana***	NLos
inermis × ***ventricosa***	NLos
'Lady Pauline' ♀H1b	NLos
lowii	NLos
maxima	NLos
mikei	NLos
mira × ***spathulata***	NLos
mira × ***spectabilis***	NLos
muluensis × ***lowii***	NLos
ovata	NLos
pilosa	NLos
pilosa × ***veitchii***	NLos
platychila × ***veitchii***	NLos
rajah	NLos
ramispina	NLos
sanguinea	NLos
sibuyanensis × ***spectabilis***	NLos
sibuyanensis × ***ventricosa***	NLos
singalana	NLos
spectabilis	NLos
spectabilis × ***talangensis***	NLos
talangensis	NLos
tobaica	NLos
truncata	NLos
veitchii	NLos

Nepeta ✿ (*Lamiaceae*)

sp.	LAst
from China	EWes
'Blue Beauty'	see *N. sibirica* 'Souvenir d'André Chaudron'
'Blue Dragon'	CMea ECtt GBin GQue LRHS LSou MAsh MSpe MTis NCGa NDov NLar SPoG WHoo
bucharica	GBuc
* ***buddlejifolium***	NLar
* - 'Gold Splash'	NLar
camphorata	SRms
cataria	CArn CBod CLau CTri CWld ENfk GJos GPoy LAst MHer MNHC NBro NLar SIde SRms SVic WHfH WJek WMoo
§ - 'Citriodora'	CBod ENfk GPoy SIde SPhx SRms WJek XLum
'Chettle Blue'	MAvo
citriodora Dum.	see *N. cataria* 'Citriodora'

Plant	Suppliers
clarkei	EPPr GMaP MRav MTis SWat WMoo
'Dropmore'	EBee
'Early Bird' new	EBee
§ × ***faassenii*** ♀H7	Widely available
- 'Alba'	EBee ECtt ELan EPfP LRHS NLar NRya WJek WWEG
- 'Blauknirps'	NDov
- 'Blue Wonder'	EBee EPfP LRHS MTis STPC
- 'Kit Cat'	ECtt GBBs GBuc GCal IBoy LHop LPla LRHS LSRN MAsh MTis NCGa NDov SAko SBod WCAu WCFE WHoo WSHC
- 'Limelight'	IBoy
- 'Senior'	XLum
glechoma 'Variegata'	see *Glechoma hederacea* 'Variegata'
govaniana	Widely available
grandiflora	MPie MRav NBre SIde WHrl
- 'Blue Danube'	GBin LPla MTis WWEG XLum
- 'Blue Elf' new	NDov
- 'Bramdean' ♀H6	CBod CElw CMea COtt CSde EBee ECtt EPfP EWes GBin LBMP LHop LRHS MCot MHer MRav MTis SPhx SRms WCAu WCot WWEG XLum
- 'Dawn to Dusk'	Widely available
- 'Pool Bank'	EBee ECtt EWes LPla MAvo MTis SIde XLum
- 'Summer Magic' new	LRHS SCob SHar
- 'Wild Cat'	EPfP MAvo MTis SPhx
- 'Zinser's Giant' new	SAko
hederacea 'Variegata'	see *Glechoma hederacea* 'Variegata'
'Hill Grounds'	WCot
italica	SHar WOut
Junior Walker = 'Novanepjun'	CKno LHop
kubanica	CSpe EBee IMou LPla MRav SMHy SPhx WCot
'Lamendi'	NDov
latifolia 'Super Cat'	EBee ELan EPfP
§ 'Leeds Castle'	CBod EBee ECGP ECtt EPfP LRHS MAvo MHer NCGa NGdn NSti SHar SPer SWat WHal WHil
'Limelight'	NLar WHil
longipes hort.	see *N.* 'Leeds Castle'
macrantha	see *N. sibirica*
'Maurice'	LPla MTis NDov WWEG
melissifolia	SBch
mussinii misapplied	see *N.* × *faassenii*
mussinii Spreng.	see *N. racemosa*
nervosa	CSpe ECha ELan EPfP LAst NBro NLar NSti SBrt SHar SPer WHar WHea WJek WSHC
- 'Blue Carpet'	CSpe NEgg
- 'Blue Moon'	CBod CWld EBee EPfP EWes LRHS LSou MBNS MHol MPie NBid NQui SRms
- 'Forncett Select'	CSam MRav NBre
- 'Pink Cat'	CWld EPfP LRHS NLar WFar
- 'Schneehäschen' new	SAko
§ ***nuda***	ECha ECrN EWes MRav SBrt SHar SMHy WHil WWEG
- subsp. ***albiflora***	ECha
* - 'Grandiflora'	NBre WMoo
- 'Isis'	NDov
- 'Purple Cat'	EBee EPfP LHop LLHF NDov
- 'Romany Dusk'	LEdu WPGP
- 'Snow Cat'	SPhx
pannonica	see *N. nuda*
parnassica	ECtt EPPr EWTr GLog GQue MBel MCot MHol MMuc MTis WHil WHrl WMnd WMoo WPtf
phyllochlamys	CPBP SRms
'Pink Candy'	NWad SRms
'Porzellan'	LPla
§ ***prattii***	CBod MMuc MWat NLar
'Purple Haze'PBR	CMea ECtt NLar
§ ***racemosa*** ♀H7	CArn CHby CLau CMac CNec CPbn EPfP GJos LRHS MCot MLHP MNHC MSCN SCob SIde WMoo
- RCB AM 3	WCot
- ***alba***	EAJP NBFr XLum
- 'Amelia'	EBee LPla MHer MPie MSpe MWhi WTor
- 'Blue Wonder'	ELan
- 'Grog'	CBod CWld LPla LRHS MTis NLar WWEG
- 'Little Titch'	CBod EBee ECha ECtt EPfP GBuc LRHS LSRN MAsh MCot NGdn NLar SCob SWat WWEG
- 'Senior'	MAsh
- 'Snowflake'	CBcs CMea ECtt ELan ELon EPfP EShb EWTr GMaP LRHS MAvo MCot MTis NBir NDov SCob SPer SWvt WCAu
- 'Superba'	LPla NBre
- 'Toria'	IMou MAvo MTis NDov WWEG
- 'Walker's Low' ♀H7	Widely available
* 'Rae Crug'	EWes
reichenbachiana	see *N. racemosa*
§ ***sibirica***	ECha ELan EPfP LRHS MHer MMuc MSCN NBid NBro NLar SRkn WCot WFar WJek XLum
§ - 'Souvenir d'André Chaudron' ♀H6	CAby CBod CMHG CSam CWCL EBee EHrv ELan EPfP EWTr GBuc GCal GMaP IPot LAst LHop LRHS LSou MCot MRav MTis NLar SCob SPer SPoG WHea WWEG
'Six Hills Giant'	Widely available
'Six Hills Gold'	CAby EBee LBuc SCob SPoG WHil
spicata new	LRHS
stewartiana	LLHF MRav WHil WMoo WWEG
subsessilis	CBod CMHG ECtt EHrv ELan EPfP GLog GMaP IBoy IKil LAst LRHS MBel MCot MRav MSpe NBid NBir NGdn NLar NSti NWad SCob SPhx SRms WCru WMnd WWEG
- 'Blue Dreams'	ELon MGos MHol NLar SCob SHar SPhx XLum
- 'Candy Cat'	ELan EPfP IBoy LPot MTis NBre NLar
- 'Cool Cat'	EBee ELan EPfP LSRN NBre NLar
- 'Laufen'	IPot
- Nimbus = 'Yanim'	CBod MPnt NFav
- 'Pink Dreams'	CBod EAJP EBee ELan EPfP GBee GJos LRHS MHer NBFr SCob SHar XLum
- pink-flowered	ECha EPPr SPhx WWEG
- 'Sweet Dreams'	CBod EPfP GJos LAst LHop LRHS MRav MSpe MTis NCGa NLar NSti WMnd XLum
- 'Washfield'	LHop MSCN NLar SAko
transcaucasica	SDix
- 'Blue Infinity'	CNor MSCN WHrl WMoo WWEG

Name	Suppliers
tuberosa	CArn CBod CSpe EBee ECha SBrt WCot WMoo WTcb WWEG XSen
'Veluws Blauwtje'	NLar
'Veluwse Wakel'	IMou
yunnanensis	EBee EPPr IPot MPie SPhx WHil WOut WPGP

Nephrolepis (*Lomariopsidaceae*)

Name	Suppliers
cordifolia	NLos
exaltata 'Verona'	WCot
falcata	NLos
- f. ***furcans***	NLos

Nerine ✿ (*Amaryllidaceae*)

Name	Suppliers
'Ada Bryson'	ECho
'Afterglow'	CPne ECho LAma LRHS WCot
'Alresford'	ECho
alta	see *N. undulata* Alta Group
'Ancilla'	ECho
'Angelico'	ECho
angustifolia	CEvo GKev WAbe
appendiculata	GKev
'Atlanta'	ECho
'Audrey Clarke'	CPne
'Aurora'	ECho WCot
'Bach'	ECho
'Baghdad'	ECho WCot
'Belladonna'	CWCL WCot
'Bennett-Poë'	WCot
'Berlioz'	ECho WCot
'Beth Chatto'	ECho
'Blanchefleur'	CTal WCot
bowdenii ♀H5	Widely available
- 'Alba' misapplied	see *N. bowdenii* 'Pallida'
- 'Alba' ambig.	CCon CPrp CTca EBee ECho ELan EPot ERCP SCoo SMHy
- 'Alba'	CBod CBro CWCL ECha EPri GKev LAma LRHS MNrw SCob SDeJ
- 'Albivetta'	EBee ECho EPri GKev LAma MNrw
- 'Blanca Perla'	EBee GKev WCot
- 'Castlewellan'	IBlr
- 'Codora'	see *N.* 'Codora'
- 'E.B. Anderson'	WCot
- 'Ella K'	CBod ECho EPfP EPot EPri ERCP GKev LAma MNrw SPer
- 'Eric Smith'	WCot
- 'Gletsjer' **new**	GKev LAma WCot
- Irish clone	WCot
- 'Isabel'	CBro CPrp CTsd ECha ECho ELan EPot EPri ERCP EWes GKev LAma WBor WCot WHoo
- 'Kathleen Pollock'	WCot
- 'Linda Vista'	WCot
- 'Manina'	CCse
- 'Marjorie'	EMal
- 'Mark Fenwick'	CBro CDes WCot
- 'Marnie Rogerson'	CBro CPne SMHy WCot
§ - 'Mollie Cowie' (v)	CCse CPrp GCal IBlr WCot WCru
- 'Mount Stewart'	CPne IBlr WCot
- 'Nikita'	ECho EPri ERCP GKev LAma LRHS MNrw SCob SDeJ WCot
- 'Ostara'	CBod CPrp EBee ELan EPot EPri GKev LAma LRHS MNrw WCot
§ - 'Pallida'	LRHS
- 'Patricia'	EBee EPot EPri GKev LAma MNrw
- 'Pink Frostwork'	EPri WCot
- 'Pink Surprise'	CAvo CDes EPri WCot
§ - 'Quinton Wells'	CTca WCot
- 'Richard Blakeway-Phillips'	WCot
- 'Robert Smith' **new**	WCot
- 'Rowie'	CPrp EBee EPri LRHS
- 'Sheila Owen'	WCot
- 'Sofie'	EBee
- 'Stam 63'	LAma
- 'Stefanie'	CAby CTsd EBee ELan EPri GKev LAma SDeJ
- Ted Allen No 2	WCot
- 'Variegata'	see *N. bowdenii* 'Mollie Cowie'
- 'Vesta K'	EPri GKev LAma
- 'Wellsii'	see *N. bowdenii* 'Quinton Wells'
'Brahms'	ECho
'Canasta'	WCot
'Cardinal'	ECho
'Caryatid'	WCot
'Catherine'	CPne WCot
'Catkin'	CPne WCot
'Clent Charm'	WCot
§ 'Codora'	ECho EPfP SPer WCot
'Corlette'	WCot
corusca 'Major'	see *N. sarniensis* var. *corusca*
'Cranfield'	WCot
crispa	see *N. undulata* Crispa Group
'Cynthia Chance'	ECho WCot
'Daphne'	ECho
'Diana Oliver'	CPne WCot
'Doris Vos'	WCot
'Elspeth'	WCot
'Exbury Red'	WCot
filamentosa misapplied	see *N. filifolia* Baker
filamentosa ambig.	CBro ECho
filamentosa W.F. Barker	CTal
§ ***filifolia*** Baker	ECho GKev WAbe
'Firelight'	CPne
flexuosa	see *N. undulata* Flexuosa Group
'Fucine'	CDes
gaberonensis	WAbe
'Gaiety'	WCot
'George'	ECho
'Glacier'	LRHS MNrw
gracilis	ECho GKev WCot
'Grania'	ECho
'Hamlet'	CPne
'Hanley Castle'	ECho
'Harlequin'	WCot
'Helena'	ECho
'Hera'	CBro
'Hertha Berg'	WCot
* ***hirsuta***	ECho GKev WAbe WCot
'Hotspur'	ECho
humilis ♀H2	ECho GKev
- from Franschhoek, South Africa	CTal
- Breachiae Group	CTal SBch
- Peersii Group from Toorwaterpoort, South Africa	CTal
huttoniae	ECho
'Iman'	WCot
'Isobel'	LRHS XEll
'Janet'	ECho WCot
'Jenny Wren'	CDes ECho WCot
I 'Judith' Norris	ECho
'King Leopold'	ECho WCot
'King of the Belgians'	ECho LAma LRHS

'Kinn McIntosh'	CDes EPri WCot
'Koko'	ECho
'Kola'	CDes
'Koriba'	ECho
krigei	ECho GKev WCot XEll
'Kyle'	WCot
'Kyrie'	ECho
'La Reine'	ECho
'Lady Cynthia Colville'	WCot
'Lady Downe'	WCot
'Lady Eleanor Keane'	ECho WCot
'Lady Havelock-Allen'	WCot
'Lady Llewellyn'	ECho WCot
'Lady St Aldwyn'	WCot
'Lambourne'	WCot
laticoma	WCot
'Lavant'	ECho
'Lawlord'	CDes WCot
'Leila Hughes'	WCot
'Lucinda'	CDes WCot
'Lyndhurst Salmon'	ECho WCot
'Malvern'	WCot
'Maria'	WCot
'Mars'	CTal
masoniorum ♀H2	CEvo CTal ECho GKev SBch WAbe
'Miss E. Cator'	CPne CTal WCot
'Miss Florence Brown'	WCot
'Miss Frances Clarke'	WCot
'Monet'	ECho
'Mrs C. Goldsmith'	ECho
'Mrs Cooper'	WCot
'Mrs Dent Brocklehurst'	WCot
'Murilla'	ECho
'Mystic'	ECho
'Natasha'	ECho
'Nena'	WCot
'November Cheer'	ECho LAma
'Oberon'	WCot
'Ophelia'	WCot
'Orange Flame'	ECho
'Paragon'	ECho
peersii	WCot
'Pink Triumph'	CAbP CBcs CTsd EBee ECho EPot ERCP EShb GKev LAma LRHS SDeJ SPer WCot WHoo
platypetala **new**	CEvo
'Plymouth'	CTal ECho
pudica	CTal SBch
- pink-flowered	WCot
'Purple Prince'	CDes
pusilla	CLak
'Quivotina'	WCot
'Red Pimpernel'	ECho LAma
'Regina'	WCot
'Rembrandt'	ECho WCot
'Rose Princess'	WCot
'Rotherside' **new**	CTal
'Rushmere Star'	CDes CTal ECho SChr WCot
'Ruth'	WCot
'Salmonia'	ECho
sarniensis ♀H2	CBro CPne ECha ECho EPot EPri GKev SKHP WCot
- 'Anne Baring'	ECho
* - 'Borde Hill White'	WCot
§ - var. ***corusca***	LAma
- - 'Major'	ECho SChr WCot
- var. ***curvifolia*** f. ***fothergillii***	ECho WCot
- 'Mottistone'	WCot
- 'Pink Petticoat' **new**	CTal
- 'Salmon Star'	LRHS
- var. ***sarniensis***	GKev
- 'Shell Pink'	CTal
'Sidney Smee'	CTal
Smee 275	CDes
'Snowflake'	MAsh WCot
'Stephanie'	CPne CTca ECho EShb LAma MNrw WCot WHoo
'Susan Norris'	WCot
'Tweedledee'	WCot
undulata	CAby CEvo CPne CTal CTca ECha ECho EHrv EPri GCal GKev IBal LAma LRHS MPie SDeJ SPer WHil
§ - Alta Group	GKev WCot
§ - Crispa Group	CBod EPfP
§ - Flexuosa Group	ECho EWoo MRav
- - 'Alba' ♀H3	CBro CPne EBee ECha ECho EPri GKev LRHS MRav WAbe WCot
× ***versicolor*** 'Mansellii'	CBro CDes SKHP WCot
'Vestal'	EPot
'Vicky'	WCot
'Virgo'	ECho LAma
'White Swan'	ECho
'Winter Sun'	LRHS
'Wolsey'	CPne ECho
'Wombe'	ECho
'Zeal Giant' ♀H3	CAvo CBro CDes CPne ECho GCal WCot
'Zeal Grilse'	CDes CPne ECho WCot
'Zeal Purple Stripe'	WCot
'Zeal Salmon'	CDes
'Zeal Silver Stripe'	CDes
'Zennor'	ECho WCot

Nerium (*Apocynaceae*)

oleander L.	CAbb CArn CBcs CHll CTri EBak ELan EShb MHtn SEND SPer SPlb SPoG
- 'Album'	CTri
- 'Album Plenum' (d)	XSen
* - 'Atlas'	XSen
- 'Cavalaire' (d)	XSen
- 'Commandant Barthélemy' (d)	XSen
- 'Flavescens Plenum' (d)	EShb XSen
- 'Hardy Red'	XSen
- 'Italia'	XSen
- 'Jannoch'	XSen
- 'Louis Pouget' (d)	XSen
- 'Madame Allen' (d)	EShb
- 'Margaritha'	XSen
- 'Professeur Granel' (d)	EShb
- 'Provence' (d)	XSen
- 'Red Beauty'	XSen
- 'Soleil Levant'	XSen
- 'Splendens Giganteum' (d)	EShb
- 'Tito Poggi'	XSen
- 'Variegatum' (v) ♀H2	CHll ELan EShb
- 'Villa Romaine'	XSen

Neviusia (*Rosaceae*)

alabamensis	CJun NLar

Nicandra (*Solanaceae*)

sp.	SEle

physalodes	CHby ELan ENfk GBee NBir WBod WSFF
- 'Violacea'	CSpe GLog SRms SWvt

Nicotiana (*Solanaceae*)

alata	CBod CSpe EPfP LCro WSFF
glauca	CDTJ CHGN CHll CSpe SPlb WHil
'Hopleys'	CSpe
knightiana	CDTJ CSpe
langsdorffii ♀H2	CSpe SPav SPhx
- 'Cream Splash' (v)	CPla
- 'Hot Chocolate'	CSpe WHil
'Lime Green'	CSpe ELan
mutabilis	CSpe LEdu SDys SPhx
'Perfume Deep Purple' (Perfume Series)	CSpe
× ***sanderae*** Cuba Series **new**	LAst NPri
- 'Cuba Deep Lime' **new**	LAst NPri
solanifolia **new**	SPlb
suaveolens	SPhx
sylvestris ♀H2	CBod CDTJ CSpe ELan EPfP MMuc NPri SDys SEND SPav SPhx SPoG SWvt WTou
'Tinkerbell'	CSpe MMuc

Nidularium (*Bromeliaceae*)

correia-araujoi	NLos
innocentii	XBlo
serratum	LAir

Nierembergia (*Solanaceae*)

§ ***repens***	ECho NLar NPri WCot XLum
rivularis	see *N. repens*

Nigella (*Ranunculaceae*)

damascena 'Miss Jekyll' ♀H7	CWCL LCro MNHC SPhx
- 'Miss Jekyll Alba' ♀H7	CSpe
- 'Oxford Blue' **new**	LCro
- Persian Jewels Group	SVic
hispanica L.	SPhx
papillosa 'African Bride'	CSpe MNHC
- 'Midnight'	CSpe

Nigritella see *Gymnadenia*

Niphidium (*Polypodiaceae*)

crassifolium **new**	EShb

Nipponanthemum (*Asteraceae*)

§ ***nipponicum***	CBod EBee ECho GCal IVic LAst LRHS MMuc NLar NSti SAko SRms WHil XLum
- 'Homa-giku'	NWad

Noccaea see *Thlaspi*

Nolina (*Asparagaceae*)

bigelovii	WCot XSen
* ***brevifolia***	CFil
durangensis	CFil EAla
hibernica **new**	CFil
lindheimeriana	WCot
longifolia	EAla
microcarpa	WCot XSen
nelsonii	CFil EAla LPal NLos SPlb
- F&M 307	WPGP
parviflora	EAla
- NJM 05.010	WPGP
texana	WCot XSen

Nomocharis (*Liliaceae*)

aperta	CExl ECho EHrv EPot GBin GBuc GCra GGGa GKev LAma LRHS NHar WCru
- ACE 2271	EHrv
mairei	see *N. pardanthina*
meleagrina	GKev LAma LRHS WAbe
nana	see *Lilium nanum*
oxypetala	see *Lilium oxypetalum*
§ ***pardanthina***	GBuc WAbe
- CLD 1490	GBuc
- f. ***punctulata***	GBuc GGGa
saluenensis	GGGa WAbe

Nonea (*Boraginaceae*)

lutea	LSou NSti WHal

Nothochelone see *Penstemon*

Nothofagus ✿ (*Nothofagaceae*)

§ ***alpina***	GBin
antarctica	CBcs CDul CMCN CNWT CTho EBee ELan EPfP EWTr GKin IVic LPal MAsh MBlu MBri MGos NWea SAko SWvt WHar WMat
- 'Benmore'	NLar
betuloides	CMCN GBin IArd SAko SPlb
cunninghamii	CBcs IArd IDee SAko SPlb
dombeyi ♀H5	CBcs CDoC CDul CFil CMCN EPfP GBin IArd IDee IVic MBlu SAko SWvt WPGP
fusca	IArd IDee SAko WPGP
glauca	CBcs GBin IVic SAko
menziesii	IDee SAko WPGP
moorei	EBee WPGP
nervosa	see *N. alpina*
nitida	GBin
obliqua	CMCN GAbr IVic SPlb
procera Oerst.	see *N. alpina*
pumilio	GBin

Notholaena see *Cheilanthes*

Notholirion (*Liliaceae*)

bulbuliferum	EBee ECho GCra
campanulatum	EBee ECho
macrophyllum	EBee ECho
thomsonianum	CTal ECho

Nothoscordum (*Alliaceae*)

sp.	GCal
bivalve	ECho GKev IMou
gracile	CCon
montevidense	ECho WCot
neriniflorum	see *Allium neriniflorum*
ostenii	CDes ECho WCot
strictum	EBee ECho

Nuphar (*Nymphaeaceae*)

advenum	LLWG
japonica	LLWG
lutea	CBen CHab EHon LCro MSKA SWat
pumila	LLWG

Nuytsia (*Loranthaceae*)

floribunda	SPlb

Nylandtia (*Polygalaceae*)

	spinosa	SPlb

Nymphaea ✿ (*Nymphaeaceae*)

	sp.	MWLS
	alba (H)	CBen CHab CWat EHon GQue LCro MSKA MWts NBir SVic SWat WMAq WPnP
	'Alba Plenissima' (H)	EWay
	'Albatros' misapplied	see *N.* 'Hermine'
§	'Albatros' Latour-Marliac (H)	CWat LLWG MSKA NPer SWat WPnP
	'Albatross'	see *N.*'Albatros' Latour-Marliac, *N.*'Hermine'
*	'Albida'	WMAq XBlo
	'Almost Black' (H)	CBen EWay LLWG MSKA
	'Amabilis' (H)	CBen EWay SWat WMAq
	'American Star' (H)	SWat
	'Andreana' (H)	EWay LLWG MSKA
	'Anna Epple' (H)	LLWG
	'Arc-en-ciel' (H)	CBen EWay LLWG SWat WMAq
	'Atropurpurea' (H)	CBen EWay LLWG MSKA NPer SWat WMAq
	'Attraction' (H)	CBen EHon EWay MSKA MWts NPer SVic SWat WMAq XBlo XLum
	'Augustus McCray' (H)	LLWG
	'Aurora' (H)	CBen CWat GQue LCro MWts SVic SWat WMAq
	'Barbara Davies' (H)	EWay LLWG MSKA
	'Barbara Dobbins' (H)	CBen EWay LLWG MSKA
	'Bateau' (H)	CBen LLWG
	'Berit Strawn' (H)	EWay
	'Bernice Ikins' (H)	LLWG
	'Betsy Sakata' (H)	EWay
	'Black Princess' (H)	EWay LCro LLWG
	'Brakeleyi Rosea' (H)	MSKA WMAq
	'Burgundy Princess' (H)	CWat EWay LLWG MSKA NPer
	candida (H)	CBen MSKA MWts NPer WMAq
	'Candidissima' (H)	CBen MWts SWat
§	***capensis*** (T/D)	XBlo
	'Carolina Sunset' (H)	EWay LLWG
	'Caroliniana Nivea' (H)	CBen EHon
	'Caroliniana Perfecta' (H)	CBen MSKA SWat
	'Celebration' (H)	EWay LLWG
	'Charlene Strawn' (H)	EWay LLWG WMAq
	'Charles de Meurville' (H)	CBen LLWG MSKA NPer SVic WMAq WPnP
	'Château le Rouge' (H)	CBen LLWG
	'Clyde Ikins' (H)	EWay LLWG MSKA
	'Colonel A.J. Welch' (H)	CBen EHon MSKA NPer SWat WMAq
	'Colorado' (H)	CBen EWay LLWG MSKA NPer
	colorata	see *N. capensis*
	'Colossea' (H)	CBen CWat MSKA NPer WPnP
	'Comanche' (H)	CBen EWay MSKA NPer WMAq
	'Conqueror' (H)	CBen LLWG MSKA NPer SVic SWat
	'Dallas' (H)	LLWG
§	'Darwin' (H)	CWat MSKA NPer SLon SWat WMAq WPnP
	× ***daubenyana*** (T/D)	ECho EWay
	'David' (H)	EWay LLWG
	'Debbie June' (H)	LLWG
	'Denver' (H)	EWay LLWG MSKA
	'Ellisiana' (H)	CBen LLWG MSKA NPer SWat
	'Escarboucle' (H) ♀H7	CBen CWat EWay LLWG MSKA NPer SVic SWat WMAq WPnP XBlo
§	'Fabiola' (H)	EHon LLWG MSKA NPer WMAq
	'Fiesta' (H)	CBen MSKA
	'Fire Crest' (H)	CBen GQue LLWG NPer SVic SWat WMAq
	'Florida Sunset' (H)	EWay
	'Fritz Junge' (H)	CBen
	'Froebelii' (H)	CBen CWat EHon EWay MSKA NPer SWat WMAq
	'Fulva' (H)	LLWG
	'Galatée' (H)	CBen MSKA
	'Geisha Girl' (H)	MSKA
	'Georgia Peach' (H)	EWay LLWG MSKA
	'Gladstoniana' (H) ♀H7	CBen EHon MSKA NPer SWat WMAq
	'Gloire du Temple-sur-Lot' (H)	CBen EWay LLWG NPer SWat WMAq
	'Gloriosa' (H)	CBen LLWG NPer SWat
	'Gold Medal' (H)	CBen EWay LLWG MSKA
	'Gonnère' (H) ♀H7	CBen CWat EHon EWay MSKA MWts NPer SLon SWat WMAq WPnP
	'Graziella' (H)	CBen MSKA WMAq
	'Gypsy' (H)	EWay LLWG
	'Hal Miller' (H)	LLWG
	'Hassell' (H)	LLWG
	'Hazorea Dagan White' (H)	EWay LLWG
	'Helen Fowler' (H)	WMAq
	× ***helvola***	see *N.* 'Pygmaea Helvola'
§	'Hermine' (H)	CBen MSKA MWts NPer SWat WMAq
	'Hidden Violet' (H)	LLWG
§	'Highlight'	EWay LLWG
	'Hilite'	see *N.*'Highlight'
	'Hollandia' misapplied	see *N.* 'Darwin'
	'Hollandia' Koster (H)	SWat
	'Indiana' (H)	CBen MSKA NPer WMAq
	'Inner Light' (H)	CBen EWay LLWG MSKA
	'J.C.N. Forestier' (H)	CBen
	'James Brydon' (H) ♀H7	CBen CWat EHon EWay MSKA MWts NPer SLon SVic SWat WMAq WPnP
	'Jean de Lamarsalle' (H)	LLWG MSKA
	'Jerusalem Dawn' (H)	LLWG MSKA
	'Joey Tomocik' (H)	CBen CWat EWay LLWG MSKA WMAq WPnP
	'Lactea' (H)	CBen LLWG
	'Laura Strawn' (H)	EWay
	'Laydekeri Fulgens' (H)	CBen EWay LLWG MSKA SWat WMAq
	'Laydekeri Lilacea' (H)	CBen SWat WMAq
	'Laydekeri Purpurata' (H)	EWay SWat
	'Laydekeri Rosea' misapplied	see *N.* 'Laydekeri Rosea Prolifera'
§	'Laydekeri Rosea Prolifera' (H)	CBen EWay
	'Lemon Chiffon' (H)	CBen
	'Lemon Mist' (H)	LLWG
	'Lily Pons' (H)	CBen EWay LLWG
	'Liou' (H)	CBen LLWG MSKA
	'Little Sue' (H)	EWay LLWG MSKA
	'Livingstone' (H)	LLWG
	'Lucida' (H)	CBen MSKA SWat WMAq
	'Madame Bory Latour-Marliac' (H)	CBen
	'Madame Wilfon Gonnère' (H)	CBen CWat EHon EWay MSKA MWts NPer SVic SWat WMAq

	'Mangkala Ubol' (H)	CBen
	'Marliacea Albida' (H)	CBen CWat EHon EWay LCro LLWG MSKA NPer SWat WMAq WPnP XBlo XLum
	'Marliacea Carnea' (H)	CBen EHon LCro MSKA MWts NPer SWat WMAq
§	'Marliacea Chromatella' (H) ♀H7	CBen CWat EHon EWay GQue MSKA MWts SVic SWat WMAq XBlo XLum
	'Marliacea Rosea' (H)	CBen MSKA SWat WMAq XBlo XLum
	'Martha' (H)	EWay
	'Mary' (H)	EWay LLWG
	'Masaniello' (H)	CBen EHon MSKA SWat WMAq
	'Maurice Laydeker' (H)	CBen LLWG
	'Maxima'	see *N.* 'Odorata Maxima'
	'Mayla' (H)	CBen EWay LLWG MSKA NPer
§	'Météor' (H)	CBen EWay MSKA WMAq
	mexicana	LLWG
	'Millennium Pink'	MSKA
	'Moorei' (H)	CBen MSKA SWat WMAq
	'Mrs Richmond' misapplied	see *N.* 'Fabiola'
	'Mrs Richmond' Latour-Marliac (H)	CBen SWat XBlo
	'Munkala Ubon' (H)	LLWG
	'Murillo' (H)	EWay
	'Neptune' (H)	LLWG
	'Newchapel Beauty'	WMAq
	'Newton' (H)	CBen CWat EWay LLWG MSKA SWat WMAq
	'Nigel' (H)	EWay LLWG MSKA SWat
	'Norma Gedye' (H)	CBen CWat MSKA SWat WMAq
	'Odalisque' (H)	CBen
§	***odorata*** (H)	CBen EHon MSKA WMAq
§	***odorata*** var. ***minor*** (H)	CBen EWay MSKA SWat WMAq
	- 'Pumila'	see *N. odorata* var. *minor*
	odorata subsp. ***tuberosa*** (H)	CBen
	'Odorata Alba'	see *N. odorata*
	'Odorata Juliana' (H)	EWay
§	'Odorata Maxima' (H)	WMAq
	'Odorata Sulphurea' (H)	SWat
§	'Odorata Sulphurea Grandiflora' (H)	CBen SWat XBlo
§	'Odorata Turicensis' (H)	MSKA
	'Odorata William B. Shaw'	see *N.* 'W.B. Shaw'
	'Pam Bennett' (H)	CBen LLWG
	'Pamela' (T/D)	EWay
	'Panama Pacific' (T/D)	XBlo
	'Patio Joe'	EWay LLWG MSKA
	'Paul Hariot' (H)	CWat EWay LLWG MSKA NPer SWat WMAq WPnP
	'Peace Lily' (H)	EWay LLWG MSKA
	'Peach Glow' (H)	EWay LLWG MSKA
	'Peaches and Cream' (H)	EWay LLWG MSKA
	Pearl of the Pool (H)	SWat
	'Perry's Baby Red' (H)	CBen CWat EWay LLWG MSKA MWts NPer WMAq
	'Perry's Crinkled Pink' (H)	CBen
	'Perry's Double White' (H)	EWay NPer WPnP
	'Perry's Double Yellow' (H)	LLWG MSKA
	'Perry's Dwarf Red' (H)	LLWG MSKA
	'Perry's Fire Opal' (H)	EWay LLWG NPer
	'Perry's Orange Sunset' (H)	LLWG MSKA
	'Perry's Pink' (H)	SWat WMAq
	'Perry's Red Bicolor' (H)	LLWG
	'Perry's Red Glow' (H)	LLWG MSKA
	'Perry's Red Star' (H)	EWay MSKA
	'Perry's Red Wonder' (H)	CBen
	'Perry's Viviparous Pink' (H)	CBen
	'Perry's White Star' (H)	LLWG
	'Perry's Yellow Sensation'	see *N.* 'Yellow Sensation'
	'Peter Slocum' (H)	CBen EWay SWat
	'Phoebus' (H)	CBen SWat
	'Picciola' (H)	LLWG
	'Pink Domino' (H)	MSKA
	'Pink Grapefruit' (H)	LLWG XBlo
	'Pink Opal' (H)	CBen CWat EWay LLWG
	'Pink Peony' (H)	EWay MSKA
	'Pink Pumpkin' (H)	EWay LLWG MSKA
	'Pink Sensation' (H)	CBen EWay LLWG MSKA NPer SLon SWat WMAq
	'Pink Sparkle' (H)	EWay LLWG
	'Pink Starlet' (H)	EWay
	'Pink Sunrise' (H)	EWay MSKA
	'Pöstlingberg' (H)	LLWG MSKA
	'Princess Elizabeth' (H)	EHon LLWG
	'Pygmaea Alba'	see *N. tetragona*
§	'Pygmaea Helvola' (H) ♀H7	CBen CWat EWay LCro LOPS MSKA MWts NPer SLon SVic SWat WMAq WPnP
	'Pygmaea Rubis' (H)	SWat WMAq
	'Pygmaea Rubra' (H)	CBen CWat EWay LCro LLWG MSKA MWts NPer SVic WMAq WPnP
	'Radiant Red' (H)	LLWG
	'Ray Davies' (H)	CBen LLWG
	'Red Paradise' (H)	LLWG MSKA
	'Red Spider' (H)	CWat EWay LLWG MSKA NPer SVic
	'Reflected Flame' (H)	EWay LLWG
	'Rembrandt' misapplied	see *N.* 'Météor'
	'Rembrandt' Koster (H)	CBen
	'René Gérard' (H)	CBen EHon GQue MSKA MWts NPer SWat WMAq WPnP
	'Rosanna Supreme' (H)	LLWG SWat
	'Rose Arey' (H)	CBen EWay LCro LLWG MSKA NPer SVic SWat WMAq
	'Rose Magnolia' (H)	CWat SWat
	'Rosennymphe' (H)	CBen MSKA NPer SWat WMAq WPnP
	'Rosy Morn' (H)	CBen LLWG MSKA
	'Seignouretti' (H)	LLWG
	'Shady Lady' (H)	LLWG MSKA MWts
	'Sioux' (H)	CBen MSKA NPer SVic WMAq XBlo
	'Sirbangpra' (H)	LLWG
	'Sirius' (H)	CBen LLWG MSKA SWat
	'Snow Princess' (H)	EWay
	'Solfatare' (H)	EWay LLWG
	'Splendida' (H)	WMAq
	'Starbright' (H)	EWay LLWG
	'Starburst' (H)	LLWG MSKA
	'Steven Strawn' (H)	LLWG
	'Sultan' (H)	MSKA
	'Sunny Pink' (H)	CBen EWay LLWG MSKA
	'Sunrise'	see *N.* 'Odorata Sulphurea Grandiflora'
	'Tan-khwan' (H)	LLWG
§	***tetragona*** (H)	CWat EWay LCro NPer WMAq WPnP
	- 'Alba'	see *N. tetragona*

'Texas Dawn' (H) — CBen CWat EWay LLWG MSKA SLon WMAq
'Thomas O'Brian' (H) — LLWG
'Tuberosa Flavescens' — see *N.* 'Marliacea Chromatella'
'Tuberosa Richardsonii' (H) — CBen EHon MSKA NPer
'Turicensis' — see *N.* 'Odorata Turicensis'
'Venusta' (H) — EWay
'Vésuve' (H) — LLWG MSKA SWat
'Virginalis' (H) — CBen LLWG MSKA NPer SWat WMAq
'Virginia' (H) — LLWG
§ 'W.B. Shaw' (H) — CBen EHon MSKA NPer SWat WMAq
'Walter Pagels' (H) — EWay LLWG MWts WMAq
'Wanvisa' (H) — CBen LLWG
'Weymouth Red' (H) — CBen
'White Sultan' (H) — CWat LLWG MSKA
'William Doogue' (H) — MSKA
'William Falconer' (H) — CBen CWat MSKA NPer SWat
'Wow' (H) — MSKA
'Yellow Princess' (H) — EWay
'Yellow Queen' (H) — MSKA
§ 'Yellow Sensation' (H) — CBen
'Yul Ling' (H) — EWay LLWG
'Zeus' — MSKA
'Ziyu' (H) — EWay

Nymphoides (*Menyanthaceae*)

indica — LLWG XBlo
peltata — CBen CBod CHab CWat EHon EWay MSKA NPer SVic WMAq WPnP XLum

Nyssa ✿ (*Nyssaceae*)

aquatica — CBcs
leptophylla — NLar SBir WPGP
shweliensis FMWJ 13122 **new** — WCru
sinensis — CAbP CBcs CDul CLet CMCN CMac CTho ELan EPfP IDee LRHS MAsh MBlu MPkF NLar SBir SPer WPat
- 'Jim Russell' 𝕐H5 — ESwi NLar SAko SBir WPGP
- Nymans form — LRHS SBir
- 'Select' **new** — ESwi
sylvatica — Widely available
- 'Autumn Cascades' — EBee ELan EPfP LRHS MAsh MBlu NLar SAko SBir SSpi SSta
- var. ***biflora*** — SSta
- Bulk's form — SSta
- 'Dirr' — SSpi
- 'Haymen's Red' — see *N. sylvatica* Red Rage
- 'Isabel Grace' — EPfP LRHS MAsh SBir SSpi
- 'Jermyns Flame' — CAbP EPfP LRHS MAsh NLar SBir
- Jolly = 'Yiping' (v) — MPkF
- 'Lakeside Weeper' — EBee SBir
- 'Miss Scarlet' (f) — NLar SBir SSta
- 'Pendula' — SBir
§ - Red Rage = 'Haymanred' — EPfP LRHS MAsh MPkF NLar SBir
- 'Red Red Wine' — EPfP IVic NLar SBir WPGP
- 'Sheffield Park' — CAbP LRHS MAsh SBir SLim SPer
- 'Valley Scorcher' — NLar
- 'Wildfire' — LRHS MPkF SBir SGol
- 'Windsor' — EPfP LRHS MAsh NLar SBir
- 'Wisley Bonfire' (m) 𝕐H6 — CAbP CBct EBee ELan EPfP LRHS MAsh NLar SBir SChF SPoG SSpi SSta WPGP
ursina — CBcs

O

Oakesiella see *Uvularia*

Ochagavia (*Bromeliaceae*)

carnea — WCot
- RCB RA S-2 — LSou
elegans — WCot
§ ***litoralis*** — CPne SMad WCot
* ***rosea*** — SPlb

Ocimum (*Lamiaceae*)

'African Blue' — CBod CLau CSpe ENfk GPoy LSou MHer SPoG SRms
§ × ***africanum*** 𝕐H1c — ENfk MNHC SHDw SIde WJek
- 'Lime' — ENfk MNHC
- Pesto Perpetuo = 'Perpetuo' PBR (v) — ENfk SRms
- 'Siam Queen' — CLau MHer SRms WJek
- 'Spicy Globe' — CLau
§ ***americanum*** — WJek
- 'Meng Luk' — see *O. americanum*
basilicum — CLau GPoy NPri SIde SRms SWat WJek
- 'Anise' — see *O. basilicum* 'Horapha'
- 'Ararat' — CLau
- ***camphorata*** — see *O. kilimandscharicum*
- 'Cinnamon' — CLau ENfk MNHC SHDw SRms WJek
- 'Dark Opal' — ENfk MNHC SHDw SRms
- 'Gecofure' — CLau
- 'Genovese' — CLau MHer MNHC
- 'Genovese Special Select' — CLau
- 'Glycyrrhiza' — see *O. basilicum* 'Horapha'
- 'Green Ruffles' — CLau EPfP WJek
- 'Holy' — see *O. tenuiflorum*
§ - 'Horapha' — CLau ENfk MHer MNHC SIde WJek
* - 'Horapha Nanum' — ENfk SRms WJek
- 'Magic Michael' — CLau
- 'Magic Mountain' — SPoG
- 'Magic White' — SPoG
- 'Mexican' — CLau
- 'Mrs Burns' Lemon' 𝕐H1c — WJek
- 'Napoletano' — CBod CLau ENfk SIde SWat WJek
- 'New Guinea' — CLau
- 'Osmin' PBR — CLau
- 'Pistou' — CLau
- 'Purple Delight' — CLau
- var. ***purpurascens*** — SIde
- - 'Purple Ruffles' — ENfk EPfP MNHC SIde SWat WJek
- - 'Red Rubin' — MHer WJek
- var. ***purpurascens*** × ***kilimandscharicum*** — CSpe GPoy
- 'Queenette' — CLau
- 'Sweet Genovese' — SVic
- 'Thai' — see *O. basilicum* 'Horapha'
canum — see *O. americanum*
× ***citriodorum*** — see *O.* × *africanum*
gratissimum — CLau
§ ***kilimandscharicum*** — CLau GPoy
minimum — CLau ENfk MHer MNHC SIde SRms WJek
sanctum — see *O. tenuiflorum*

'Spice'	CLau ENfk
§ ***tenuiflorum***	CLau GPoy MNHC SHDw SIde SPre WJek

Odontonema (*Acanthaceae*)

tubaeforme	MOWG

Oemleria (*Rosaceae*)

cerasiformis	CBcs CHGN CJun CTri EBtc EPfP LEdu LRHS MMuc NLar WBod WCot WGwG WSHC

Oenanthe (*Apiaceae*)

fistulosa	LLWG MSKA
javanica	LEdu
- 'Flamingo' (v)	CBod CWat EBee ELan EWay GCal LEdu MSKA MWts NBro WMAq WSHC XLum
lachenalii	LLWG
pimpinelloides	CHab LLWG

Oenothera ✿ (*Onagraceae*)

sp.	MHol
§ ***acaulis***	CSpe EBee MNrw WCot WPGP
§ - 'Aurea'	XLum
- 'Lutea'	see *O. acaulis* 'Aurea'
'Apricot Delight'	CWld GJos SGbt SPad WMnd WMoo
§ ***biennis***	CFis ELan ENfk GAbr GPoy MHer MNHC NBro SIde SPhx SRms WBrk WHea WHer WJek WSFF
'Blood Orange'	GEdr
childsii	see *O. speciosa*
cinaeus	see *O. fruticosa* subsp. *glauca*
'Colin Porter'	WMoo
'Copper Canyon'	SGSe
'Crown Imperial'	CMac LEdu LSou MArl NHol SHar SLon
Crown of Gold = 'Lishal'	LLHF LRHS
§ ***elata*** subsp. ***hookeri***	EWes NBre
erythrosepala	see *O. glazioviana*
'Finlay's Fancy'	WCru
§ ***fruticosa***	NLar SPlb
- 'African Sun'PBR	SRot
- 'Camel' (v)	NEoE WCot WHrl WWEG XLum
- Fireworks	see *O. fruticosa* 'Fyrverkeri'
§ - 'Fyrverkeri'	CBcs CMea CPrp ECtt ELan GMaP LEdu LHop LRHS MRav NGdn SCob SPer SWvt WWEG XLum
§ - subsp. ***glauca***	CElw CEvo CFis EPfP MHer SRms WJek
- - 'Erica Robin' (v)	CChe ECtt EHoe GBin LRHS LSou MAvo MNrw MRav NEgg NGdn SMad SRot SWvt WCot WHoo WWEG
- - 'Longest Day'	MBrN
- - Solstice	see *O. fruticosa* subsp. *glauca* 'Sonnenwende'
§ - - 'Sonnenwende'	CBre CElw LRHS NEoE NLar WMoo WWEG XLum
- Highlight	see *O. fruticosa* 'Hoheslicht'
§ - 'Hoheslicht'	EBee
- 'Lady Brookeborough'	MRav
- 'Michelle Ploeger'	NBre
- 'Silberblatt' (v)	EBee
- 'Yellow River'	CElw EBee
- 'Youngii'	EPfP LEdu MMuc SEND WJek WWEG
'Give-me-Sunshine'	SLon WMoo
glabra Miller	see *O. biennis*
§ ***glazioviana***	MNHC NBir
'Gold Dream' **new**	LSou
hookeri	see *O. elata* subsp. *hookeri*
kunthiana	CBod ECha WMoo
- 'Glowing Magenta'	SPoG
lamarckiana	see *O. glazioviana*
Lemon Drop = 'Innoeno131'PBR	LRHS MPkF
'Lemon Sunset'	EHoe LSou WMoo
linearis	see *O. fruticosa*
§ ***macrocarpa*** ♀H5	Widely available
- subsp. ***fremontii*** 'Shimmer' **new**	SAko SMad
- - 'Silver Wings'	LHop SPhx
- subsp. ***incana***	CMea CSpe SPhx WHoo
- 'Yellow Queen'	GJos
missouriensis	see *O. macrocarpa*
oakesiana	GKev SPhx
odorata misapplied	see *O. stricta*
odorata Hook. & Arn.	see *O. biennis*
odorata Jacquin	XLum
- cream-flowered	CSpe
organensis	CDes EBee MNrw
§ ***perennis***	NEoE SRms WThu XLum
pumila	see *O. perennis*
rosea	XLum
§ ***speciosa***	MMuc SEND SPhx SRms WJek XLum
* - 'Alba'	EBee EWes
- var. ***childsii***	see *O. speciosa*
- 'Pink Petticoats'	ECha LSun NPer
- 'Rosea'	SPlb
- 'Siskiyou'	CBcs CBod EAEE ECtt EPfP EWoo LBMP LEdu LRHS MNrw SCob SCoo SMad SPer WGwG WPGP XLum
- Twilight = 'Turner01'PBR (v)	CAbb LHop LRHS LSou NHol SCob SHar
§ ***stricta***	CMea GCal MNrw
- 'Sulphurea'	CMHG CMea EAJP ECGP ELan GCal IFro LRHS NPer SPhx WCot
'Summer Sun'	CBod EAEE ECGP LRHS
'Sunny Delight' **new**	CBod
taraxacifolia	see *O. acaulis*
tetragona	see *O. fruticosa* subsp. *glauca*
- var. ***fraseri***	see *O. fruticosa* subsp. *glauca*
versicolor 'Sunset Boulevard'	CBod CSpe CTsd EAJP GCal GJos LRHS MMuc SHar WMoo XLum

Olea (*Oleaceae*)

sp.	ETod LPar
europaea (F)	Widely available
- 'Arbequina' (F)	ETod SBig
- 'Chelsea Physic Garden' (F)	CDoC
§ - 'Cipressino' (F)	ESwi ETod LPal MGos SBig
- 'El Greco' (F)	CBcs
- 'Fastigiata'	EBee LRHS NPri
- 'Frantoio' (F)	ETod SBig
- 'Hojiblanca' (F)	EBee SBig
- 'Leccino' (F)	ETod SBig
- 'Manzanillo' (F)	ETod
- 'Maurino' (F)	SBig
- 'Peace'	CDoy
- 'Pendolino' (F)	SBig
- 'Picual' (F)	ETod SBig
- 'Pyramidalis'	see *O. europaea* 'Cipressino'

Olearia ✿ (*Asteraceae*)

arborescens 'Moondance' (v)	CBod LRHS SAko SCob
argophylla	CExl ECou
avicenniifolia	CMac ECou IVic
bullata	ECou
canescens	CPne
× ***capillaris***	CBcs EBee ECou
chathamica	IVic
§ ***cheesemanii***	CDoC CExl GGal LRHS NLar NWad SVen
coriacea	ECou
'County Park'	ECou
erubescens × ***ilicifolia***	SVen
furfuracea	ECou MMuc
glandulosa	ECou
gunniana	see *O. phlogopappa*
× ***haastii***	Widely available
- 'McKenzie'	ECou
'Havering Blush'	ECou
hectorii	ECou
§ 'Henry Travers'	CBcs CExl EPfP GCal IVic SAko SVen
ilicifolia	CTsd EPfP IVic LRHS MAsh
insignis	see *Pachystegia insignis*
lacunosa	IDee WHor
lepidophylla	ECou NLar
- silver-leaved	ECou
lirata	ECou
macrodonta 🏆H4	Widely available
- 'Major'	GGal NLar SCob
- 'Minor'	CMac CSde ELan EPfP GCal GQui IVic SPlb
× ***mollis*** (Kirk) Cockayne	CMac CSde EBee GQui LRHS
- 'Zennorensis' 🏆H3	CBcs EPfP IVic
myrsinoides	CSde
nummularifolia	CBcs CDoC CTri CTsd EBee ECou ELan EPfP GKin IVic LRHS NLar SPer SVen SWvt
- var. ***cymbifolia***	ECou
odorata	CPne ECou NLar
× ***oleifolia*** 'Waikariensis'	CExl CMac ECou GKin IDee IVic LRHS MAsh MMuc SEND SLon WCFE
paniculata	CDoC CSde CTri CTsd EPfP IDee IVic LRHS MMuc SAko SEND SVen
§ ***phlogopappa***	CTri ECou SVen WSHC
- 'Comber's Blue'	CBcs ELan EPfP GGal GKin IVic LRHS MAsh MMuc SAko SCob SLim SPer WGrn
§ - 'Comber's Pink'	CBcs CBod CExl CHid ELan ELon EPfP GKin LBMP LRHS MMuc MSCN NPer SAko SCob SEle SLim SPer SPoG WGrn WKif WSHC
- 'Rosea'	see *O. phlogopappa* 'Comber's Pink'
I - var. ***subrepanda*** (DC.) J.H.Willis	GGal
ramulosa	CExl CSde
- 'Blue Stars'	CMac ECou LRHS SLon SRms WGrn
rani misapplied	see *O. cheesemanii*
rani Druce	CPne
× ***scilloniensis*** misapplied	see *O. stellulata* DC.
× ***scilloniensis*** ambig.	CBcs EWld LRHS MAsh SCob SPoG
× ***scilloniensis*** Dorrien-Smith 🏆H3	MMuc SEND
- 'Master Michael' 🏆H3	CTri ECou ELon EWld IVic LRHS MOWG NLar SPer SPoG WCFE WGrn WPGP WSHC
semidentata misapplied	see *O.* 'Henry Travers'
solandri	CBod CDoC CMac CSde ECou EHoe IDee LRHS MMuc NLar SDix SEND
- 'Aurea'	CBcs
'Starburst'	WCot
'Stardust'	LRHS SPlb SVen
stellulata misapplied	see *O. phlogopappa*
§ ***stellulata*** DC.	CExl CMac CSBt CWib EPfP GGal SDix SLim SPer
- 'Michael's Pride'	CBod CExl
traversii	CBcs CBod CDoC CSBt CSde CTsd EPfP LRHS NWea SAko SEND SLim WHer
- 'Tweedledum' (v)	CBod CSde CWib EHoe
- 'Variegata' (v)	CBcs SEND
virgata	ECou NLar
- var. ***laxiflora***	WHer
- var. ***lineata***	CSde ECou MMuc NLar SEND WHer WSHC
- - 'Dartonii'	CBcs CBod CTsd ECou GBin LRHS NLar SPlb SVen

Oligoneuron see *Solidago*

Oligostachyum (*Poaceae*)

lubricum	see *Semiarundinaria lubrica*
oedogonatum	WPGP

olive see *Olea europaea*

Olsynium (*Iridaceae*)

biflorum	GEdr
§ ***douglasii*** 🏆H5	CBro ECho LLHF NRya NSla
- 'Album'	EBee ECho ELon EPot GBin LLHF MNrw NHar NRya NSla
- var. ***inflatum***	EWes
§ ***junceum***	CSpe WPGP
trinerve B&SWJ 10459	WCru

Omphalodes ✿ (*Boraginaceae*)

'Blue Eyes'	EBee MHol MPie WCot
cappadocica 🏆H5	CMac EPfP EWld IFoB LEdu NBro NPer NSla SRms SWat WBrk
- 'Cherry Ingram' 🏆H5	Widely available
- 'Lilac Mist'	EBee GBuc MRav SRms SWvt
- 'Starry Eyes'	Widely available
§ ***linifolia*** 🏆H3	CSpe LCro MCot SPhx WBor
- ***alba***	see *O. linifolia*
nitida	CSpe EWld IMou LLHF MNrw NQui
verna	CBod CTri EBee ECha ECho ELan EPPr EPfP EWTr GAbr GEdr GJos GMaP LHop LLWP LRHS MCot MNrw NChi NLar SCob SPer SPlb SPoG SWat WBod WCAu WFar WPGP
- 'Alba'	CBre CMac EBee ECha ECho ELan EPPr EPfP GAbr GBuc GCra GEdr GMaP LHop LLWP MBel MCot MNrw NBid NChi NGdn NLar SBod SCob SPer SRms SWat SWvt WPnP
- 'Elfenauge'	EBee GMaP IMou NBir WCot

- ***grandiflora*** WCot

Oncostema see *Scilla*

onion see *Allium cepa*

Onixotis (*Colchicaceae*)

stricta CLak WCot

Onobrychis (*Papilionaceae*)

viciifolia CWld SPhx

Onoclea (*Onocleaceae*)

sensibilis ♀H6 Widely available
- copper-leaved CJun WPGP
- 'Rotstiel' EBee

Ononis (*Papilionaceae*)

cristata WAbe
spinosa IMou MHer

Onopordum (*Asteraceae*)

acanthium CAby CArn ECha ELan ENfk GAbr GMaP GPoy LEdu LRHS LSun MHer MWat NBid NChi NGBl SBea SHar SIde SPhx WFar WHea WOut
algeriense new EBee
arabicum see *O. nervosum*
bracteatum EBee
illyricum WCot
§ ***nervosum*** ♀H7 CSpe SEND

Onosma (*Boraginaceae*)

alborosea CCse ECha ECre ELan GCal GCra SEND WKif
nana CTal EPot WOld
rigida SBrt

Onychium (*Pteridaceae*)

contiguum WCot
japonicum CExl EBee EFer ISha LRHS MRav NLos SGSe WCot

Ophiopogon ✿ (*Asparagaceae*)

sp. LPar
BWJ 8244 from Vietnam WCru
from India GCal
'Black Dragon' see *O. planiscapus* 'Nigrescens'
bodinieri CBct ECho EShb EWes LEdu
- B&L 12505 CLAP EBee EPPr
caulescens B&SWJ 8230 WCru
- B&SWJ 11813 WCru
aff. ***caulescens*** B&SWJ 11287 WCru
- HWJ 590 WCru WPGP
chingii EPPr EWes GCal LEdu WCot
* - 'Crispum' EBee
clavatus KWJ 12267 WCru
formosanus B&SWJ 3659 WCru
'Gin-ryu' see *Liriope spicata* 'Gin-ryu'
graminifolius see *Liriope muscari*
'Hosoba Kokuryu' EShb GBin
intermedius CBct CSpe EPPr EShb WCot
- GWJ 9387 WCru
§ - 'Argenteomarginatus' (v) EWes
- 'Variegatus' see *O. intermedius* 'Argenteomarginatus'
aff. ***intermedius*** new CEvo
§ ***jaburan*** CMac EBee LEdu WMoo WPtf
- 'Variegatus' see *O. jaburan* 'Vittatus'
§ - 'Vittatus' (v) EHoe ELan EWes LEdu MPkF WCot
japonicus CMac CTsd ECho EPPr EShb GPoy LEdu LPal SCob SGol XLum XSen
- B&SWJ 1871 WCru
- 'Albus' CLAP ECho EPri
- 'Compactus' WPGP
- 'Gyoku-Ryu' EBee GCal
- 'Kigimafukiduma' CExl CMac MRav SGol
- 'Kyoto' EPPr ESwi NOak
- 'Minor' CKno ELon EPPr LPal NLar SCob WPGP WWEG XLum
- 'Nanus Variegatus' (v) EBee
- 'Nippon' ECho EHoe EPPr NGdn
- 'Silver Dragon' (v) EPPr MBri WCFE
* - 'Tama-ryu Number Two' ECho EPPr
* - 'Variegatus' (v) CDTJ CMac ECho LEdu
aff. ***latifolius*** KWJ 12031 WCru
parviflorus GWJ 9387 WCru
- HWJK 2093 WCru
planiscapus CExl CKno CMHG CSpe ECha ECho EPPr NBro SPad SPtp WMoo WWEG
* - 'Albovariegatus' (v) WFar
- 'Black Beard' CKno EAEE EUJe EWTr GBin LRHS MAsh MBri
- 'Black Needle' new EBee
- 'Black Smaragd' new EBee
- 'Green Dragon' LRHS
- f. ***leucanthus*** EPPr WCot
- 'Little Tabby' (v) CDes CDoC CFil CLAP CMil EBee ECho ESwi WCot WGrn WHal WWEG
§ - 'Nigrescens' ♀H5 Widely available
scaber B&SWJ 1842 ESwi WCru
- B&SWJ 3655 WCru
'Spring Gold' EShb
umbraticola EBee

Ophrys (*Orchidaceae*)

apifera NLAp
bombyliflora NLAp
fuciflora NLAp
heldreichii NLAp
insectifera NLAp
lutea NLAp
reinholdii NLAp
speculum NLAp
sphegodes NLAp
- subsp. ***helenae*** NLAp
tenthredinifera NLAp

Oplopanax (*Araliaceae*)

horridus CArn
- B&SWJ 9551 WCru
japonicus WCru

Opopanax (*Apiaceae*)

chironium CArn SDix SPhx
- PAB 845 LEdu WPGP

Opuntia (*Cactaceae*)

angustata see *O. phaeacantha*

	Plant	Suppliers
	arenaria SB 964 from El Paso County, Texas new	CCac
	atrispina DJF 1020 new	CCac
	aurea new	CCac
	- red-flowered, from St George, Utah new	CCac
	aureispina SB 1002 new	CCac
	basilaris new	CCac
	- SB 1819 from Yucca Valley, California new	CCac
	- SB 1976 from Silver Peak, Nevada new	CCac
	- from Tonopah, Nevada new	CCac
	- 'Berlin' new	CCac
	bentonii from Galveston, Texas new	CCac
	'Budapest' new	CCac
	camanchica	see *O. phaeacantha*
	chisosensis SB 992 from Brewster County, Texas new	CCac
	chlorotica	CCac
	- NNS 99-262	WCot
	- 'Kurt' new	CCac
	'Claude Arno' new	CCac
	× ***columbiana*** from Wishram, Washington State new	CCac
	- 'Smithwick' new	CCac
	compressa	see *O. humifusa*
	cylindrarticulata	see *Cumulopuntia boliviana* subsp. *dachylifera*
	cymochila	see *O. tortispina*
	echinocarpa	see *Cylindropuntia echinocarpa*
	elata new	SChr
§	***engelmannii***	CCac SChr
	- from Beeville, Texas new	CCac
	- from Carrizozo, New Mexico new	CCac
	- var. ***engelmannii*** DJF 1400 new	CCac
	- - 'Natural Bridge' new	CCac
*	- f. ***inerme*** new	CCac
*	- var. ***sandia*** HK 1809 new	CCac
	erinacea var. ***utahensis***	see *O. polyacantha* var. *erinacea*
§	***ficus-indica***	CCac SPlb WCot
	fragilis	CCac SChr SKHP XSen
	- from Black Canyon, Gunnison, Colorado new	CCac
	glomerata	see *Maihueniopsis glomerata*
§	***humifusa***	CCac CDTJ EAla SChr WCot XLum XSen
	- from Monmouth County, New Jersey new	CCac
	- 'Louisiana' new	CCac
	joconostle	see *O. ficus-indica*
	lindheimeri	see *O. engelmannii*
	linguiformis	see *O. engelmannii*
	mackensenii	see *O. macrorhiza*
	macrocentra new	CCac
	- SB 103 from Rincon, New Mexico new	CCac
	- SB 911 from Orogrande, New Mexico new	CCac

	Plant	Suppliers
	- SB 994 from Eddy County, New Mexico new	CCac
§	***macrorhiza***	CCac
	- DJF 720 from Kenton, Oklahoma new	CCac
	- DJF 1299 from Reagan County, Texas new	CCac
	- DJF 86512 from Huerfano County, Colorado new	CCac
	- 'Apricot' new	CCac
	- 'Viola' new	CCac
	megapotamica BKN 124 from La Cumbrecita, Argentina new	CCac
	monacantha new	SEND
	orbiculata from Seymour, Texas new	CCac
§	***phaeacantha***	CCac SChr
	- DJF 162 new	CCac
	- DJF 913 new	CCac
	- DJF 970.18 from Fremont County, Colorado new	CCac
	- DJF 1139 from Albuquerque, New Mexico new	CCac
	- SB 1070 from Larimer County new	CCac
	- from White Canyon, Wayne County, Utah new	CCac
*	- var. ***albispina*** MUG 177 from Mohave County, Arizona new	CCac
	- 'Judge' new	CCac
	- var. ***major*** DJF 1138 new	CCac
	- - DJF 1139 from Albuquerque, New Mexico new	CCac
	- - SB 1092 from Santa Fe, New Mexico new	CCac
	- - SB 1763 from Manzano Mountains, New Mexico new	CCac
	- 'Minor' new	CCac
	- 'Pueblitos' new	CCac
	- 'Salmonea' new	CCac
	- 'Sunrise' new	CCac
	phaeacantha × ***pottsii*** new	CCac
	pisciformis new	CCac
	pollardii	see *O. humifusa*
	polyacantha	CCac EAla SChr SPlb
	- SB 912 new	CCac
	- SB 928 from Wyoming new	CCac
	- SB 1765 from Manzano Mountains, New Mexico new	CCac
	- SB 1911 from Lybrook, New Mexico new	CCac
	- from Alberta, Canada new	CCac
	- from Bicknell, Utah new	CCac
	- from Blind Valley, Millard County, Utah new	CCac
	- from Chaffee County, Colorado new	CCac

*	- from Januskowetz, Canada **new**	CCac
	- from North Dakota **new**	CCac
	- from Trout Creek Pass, Colorado **new**	CCac
	- from Wyoming **new**	CCac
	- 'Carmin'	XSen
	- 'Crystal Tide' **new**	CCac
*	- ***eranthemum*** **new**	CCac
§	- var. ***erinacea***	CCac SChr WCot
	- - from St. George, Utah **new**	CCac
	- - from Torrey, Utah **new**	CCac
	- - from Yucca Valley, California **new**	CCac
§	- var. ***hystricina*** **new**	CCac
	- - DJF 1001 **new**	CCac
	- - DJF 1338 **new**	CCac
	- - DJF 1339 from Belen, New Mexico **new**	CCac
	- - SB 478 **new**	CCac
	- - SB 485 from Marble Canyon, Arizona **new**	CCac
	- - 'Cactusmannia' **new**	CCac
	- - 'Hagen Miniature' **new**	CCac
	- - 'Halblech' **new**	CCac
	- - 'Hamm' **new**	CCac
	- - 'Heather' **new**	CCac
	- - 'Heidelberg' **new**	CCac
	- - 'Thornless Judge' **new**	CCac
	- 'Linz' **new**	CCac
*	- 'Nigra' **new**	CCac
	- 'Oettingen' **new**	CCac
	- var. ***polyacantha*** **new**	CCac
	- - from Laguna Pueblo, New Mexico **new**	CCac
	- 'Rom' **new**	CCac
	- 'Wibke' **new**	CCac
	pottsii DJF 1394 from Hildago County, New Mexico **new**	CCac
	- DJF 1441 from Albuquerque, New Mexico **new**	CCac
	- DJF 1447 from Albuquerque, New Mexico **new**	CCac
	- 'Bochum' **new**	CCac
*	- var. ***montana*** DJF 667 **new**	CCac
	rhodantha	see *O. polyacantha* var. *hystricina*
*	***sandiana*** **new**	CCac
	- DJF 475A **new**	CCac
	sanguinocula DJF 801 **new**	CCac
	santarita	CCac
	spinosior	see *Cylindropuntia spinosior*
	stenopetala HK 1985 **new**	CCac
	stricta **new**	CCac
	'Super Rutila 2' **new**	CCac
	tardospina	see *O. engelmannii*
§	***tortispina*** DJF 1139.38 **new**	CCac
	- from Gaza County, Colorado **new**	CCac

orange, sour or Seville see *Citrus* × *aurantium* Sour Orange Group

orange, sweet see *Citrus* × *aurantium* Sweet Orange Group

Orbeopsis (*Asclepiadaceae*)

lutea **new**	LToo

Orbexilum (*Papilionaceae*)

pedunculatum var. ***psoralioides***	SBrt SPhx

Orchis (*Orchidaceae*)

	anthropophora	EFEx NLAp
	elata	see *Dactylorhiza elata*
	foliosa	see *Dactylorhiza foliosa*
	fuchsii	see *Dactylorhiza fuchsii*
	italica	NLAp
	laxiflora	see *Anacamptis laxiflora*
	maculata	see *Dactylorhiza maculata*
	maderensis	see *Dactylorhiza foliosa*
	majalis	see *Dactylorhiza majalis*
§	***mascula***	ECho NLAp WHer
	militaris	NLAp
	morio	see *Anacamptis morio*
	purpurea	NLAp

oregano see *Origanum vulgare*

Oreocharis (*Gesneriaceae*)

aurea B&SWJ 11718	WCru

Oreomyrrhis (*Apiaceae*)

argentea	CSpe EBee SPhx

Oreopanax (*Araliaceae*)

	capitatus **new**	CFil
	floribundus	see *O. incisus*
§	***incisus***	WCru
	xalapensis B&SWJ 10444	WCru

Oreopteris (*Thelypteridaceae*)

§	***limbosperma***	WCot

Origanum ✿ (*Lamiaceae*)

	sp.	MJak
	from Kalamata	SEND
	acutidens	XSen
	amanum ♀H3	CPBP ECho EPot EWes NBir NSla SBch WAbe
	- var. ***album***	ECho WAbe
	'Amethyst Falls' **new**	XSen
	× ***applii***	CLau
	'Barbara Tingey'	CTal ECho EWes ITim MNrw SIgm SRms WCFE
	'Bristol Cross'	CTal EBee ECtt EPot LEdu MHer WTor XSen
	'Buckland'	ECho ECtt EPot ITim WAbe WSHC
	caespitosum	see *O. vulgare* 'Nanum'
§	***calcaratum***	ECho LLHF SIgm
	'Carol's Delight'	MHer
	creticum	see *O. vulgare* subsp. *hirtum*
	dictamnus	ECho EPot GPoy LLHF MHer SIgm WAbe WJek WOld XEll XSen
	'Dingle Fairy'	CPBP CWCL ECho ECtt EPot EWes MHer NBir SBch SIde SRot SWvt WMoo XSen

	ehrenbergii	XSen
	'Emma Stanley'	CPBP WAbe
	'Frank Tingey'	ECho LLHF
	'French' new	SRms
	'Gold Splash'	EPfP SIde WMoo
	'Golden Narrow'	EBee LRHS
	heracleoticum L.	see *O. vulgare* subsp. *hirtum*
	'Hot and Spicy'	CPbn ENfk LBMP LEdu MHer SRms WJek XSen
	'Ingolstadt' (v)	SPhx
	'Jekka's Beauty'	WJek
	'Kent Beauty' ♀H4	CMea CSpe CWCL EBee ECho ECtt ELan EPfP EPot EShb GBuc IMou LBMP LRHS LSou MHer NBir SPhx SWvt WAbe WHea WHoo WJek WKif WSHC XSen
	'Kent Beauty Variegated' (v)	ECho
	laevigatum ♀H7	ECho ELan EPfP MAvo MHer NBro NPer SIde WCot WKif WMoo WSHC XSen
I	- 'Aromaticum'	IMou
	- dwarf	SIgm
	- 'Herrenhausen' ♀H7	Widely available
	- 'Hopleys'	CBod CPrp CTri EAJP EBee ECha EHrv ELan EPfP LEdu LHop LRHS MBri MCot MHer MHol MMuc MRav MWat NBir NLar NPri SEND SPer SPhx SRms WHea WHoo WSHC XSen
	- 'Purple Charm'	EDAr SRms
	majorana	CArn CHab CLau CPbn ENfk GPoy LBMP MHer MNHC SIde SRms SVic SWat WJek
I	- 'Aureum'	GKev
	- Pagoda Bells = 'Lizbell'PBR	CBod CWCL SIde
	'Marchants Seedling'	NDov SMHy SPhx
	microphyllum	CArn
	minutiflorum	ECho LLHF
	'Norton Gold'	CBre ECha ECtt MHer NPer SIde
	'Nymphenburg'	LSou XSen
	onites	CBod CHby CLau ENfk LBMP MHer MNHC SIde SPlb SRms WJek
	Overseas Farm hybrid	MHer
	'Rosenkuppel' ♀H7	CBod CMea EBee ECha ECtt ELan EPPr LHop LOPS MHer MLHP NDov NLar SBch SPer SPhx SPlb SWvt WCAu WJek WMoo WWEG XSen
	'Rotkugel'	WCFE WWEG
	rotundifolium ♀H4	CMea ECho ELan LEdu MHer NBir SBch WThu
	scabrum	SBch
	subsp. ***pulchrum*** 'Newleaze'	
	'Teddy' new	EBee
	tournefortii	see *O. calcaratum*
	vulgare	CArn CHab CPbn CTsd CWld GJos GMaP GPoy LBMP MHer MJak MMuc MNHC NBro NMir NPol NPri SEND SIde SPlb SRms SVic WHer WJek WSFF XLum
	- from Israel	CLau
	- 'Acorn Bank'	CArn CBod CLau CPrp ECtt ENfk EWes LEdu MNHC NLar SIde SPoG SRms WHer WJek
	- var. ***album***	CLau
	- 'Aureum' ♀H6	Widely available
	- 'Aureum Crispum'	CBod CLau CPrp ECha ENfk GPoy NBid SIde SRms SWat WJek
	- 'Compactum'	CArn CBod CLau CMea CPrp EBee ECha ENfk GCal GPoy LEdu MHer MNHC NBir NPri NSla SIde SPlb SRms SWat WAbe WJek XLum XSen
	- 'Country Cream' (v)	CBod CElw CLau CPbn CPrp EBee ECtt EHoe ENfk EPfP EWes LBMP LPot MHer MLHP MNHC NBir NGdn NPri SPer SPoG SRms SRot SWat WCFE WMnd WWEG
	- var. ***formosanum*** B&SWJ 3180	WCru
§	- 'Gold Tip' (v)	CBod CLau CMea ENfk MCot MHer MHol MNHC SIde SPlb SRms SWat WHer WJek WWEG
	- 'Golden Shine'	EHoe EWes SIde
§	- subsp. ***hirtum***	CArn CHby CPbn GPoy SPlb WJek XSen
	- - 'Greek'	CBod CLau ENfk LEdu MHer MNHC SRms
§	- 'Nanum'	LHop SRms WJek
	- 'Nyamba'	GPoy
	- 'Pink Mist'	MNrw
	- 'Polyphant' (v)	CBod CPbn LSou NBir SHar SRms WJek XSen
	- 'Thumble's Variety'	CBod CElw CMea CPrp EAEE EBee ECha ECtt EHoe EPfP GCal LHop LRHS MBri MHer MRav NPri SWat SWvt WCFE WMnd WMoo WWEG XLum XSen
	- 'Tomintoul'	GPoy
	- 'Variegatum'	see *O. vulgare* 'Gold Tip'
	- 'White Charm'	CPbn EBee NWad SIde
	'Z'Attar'	MHer WJek

Orixa (*Rutaceae*)

	japonica	CExl NLar WPGP
	- 'Variegata' (v)	LRHS NLar

Orlaya (*Apiaceae*)

	grandiflora	CBre CCon CSam CSpe LCro LEdu LRHS MCot SBch SPhx WCot WHal WTor

Ornithogalum (*Asparagaceae*)

	algeriense	ECho
	arabicum	CBro CCon ECho GKev LAma MBri SDeJ
	arcuatum	WCot
	arianum	ECho
	balansae	see *O. oligophyllum*
	caudatum	see *O. longibracteatum*
	chionophilum	ECho
	cuspidatum	ECho
	dubium ♀H2	ECho ELan
	- hybrids	CGrW GKev
	fimbriatum	ECho
	juncifolium	GKev
	lanceolatum	ECho GKev WCot
§	***longibracteatum***	ECho GKev SChr WHer
	magnum	CAvo CBro CWCL EBee ECho EPot ERCP GBin GBuc GKev MCot MNrw SDeJ WCot
	montanum	GKev
	'Mount Everest'	GKev

'Mount Fuji'	GKev
multifolium from Loeriesfontein, South Africa	ECho
'Namib Gold'	GKev SDeJ
nanum	see *O. sigmoideum*
narbonense	ECho GKev
nutans ♀H4	CAvo CBro CHid CWCL EBee ECho EPot GBin GBuc GCal GKev LAma LRHS MMuc MNrw NBir SBod SDeJ SEND SGSe
§ ***oligophyllum***	ECho EPot MNrw MPie
§ ***orthophyllum***	ECho
polyphyllum	GKev
ponticum	ECho WCot
- 'Sochi' new	EBee ECho GKev
pyramidale	EBee ECho GKev MNrw
- short	SMHy
pyrenaicum	CAvo CSpe ECha GKev SRms WCot WShi XEll
reverchonii	EBee ECho ERCP
saundersiae	ECho GKev
sibthorpii	see *O. sigmoideum*
§ ***sigmoideum***	EBee
sintenisii	EBee ECho
tenuifolium	see *O. orthophyllum*
thyrsoides ♀H2	ECho GBin GKev LAma LCro LOPS LRHS SDeJ
ulophyllum	ECho
umbellatum	CAvo CHab CTri EBee ECho GKev GPoy LAma LHop MBri MCot MMuc MNrw SDeJ SEND SRms WShi

Ornithoglossum (*Colchicaceae*)

viride	CLak

Orontium (*Araceae*)

aquaticum	CBen CWat EHon EWay LLWG MSKA MWts NPer SWat WMAq

Orostachys (*Crassulaceae*)

furusei	NPri WHal
iwarenge	LHop
§ ***spinosa***	ECho EDAr EWes GKev LRHS SPlb WAbe WCot

Orthophytum (*Bromeliaceae*)

gurkenii	WCot

Orthrosanthus (*Iridaceae*)

chimboracensis	CCon
- JCA 13743	CPou
laxus	CBod CCon CWCL EAJP ECre LLHF NBir SMad WHrl WMoo
multiflorus	CBro CSde CTre EBee EPri IKil
polystachyus	CAby CTsd EAla LPla SGSe WHea WSHC

Oryzopsis (*Poaceae*)

hymenoides 'Rimrock'	SPhx
lessoniana	see *Anemanthele lessoniana*
miliacea	CSpe EHoe EPPr SDix SEND SIgm SMHy WCot WHea WPGP WSHC WWtn
paradoxa	EPPr

Oscularia (*Aizoaceae*)

§ ***deltoides*** ♀H2	LAll MSCN SVen

Osmanthus (*Oleaceae*)

sp.	LPar
armatus	CAbP CBcs CMac EBee EPfP LRHS NLar SEND SGol
× ***burkwoodii*** ♀H5	Widely available
§ ***decorus***	CBcs CDoC CHll CMac CTri EBee ELan EPfP MGos MRav NLar NWea SBrt SGol SPer
- 'Angustifolius'	NLar
delavayi ♀H5	Widely available
- 'Frank Knight' new	LRHS MAsh
- 'George Gardner'	CMac
- 'Latifolius'	CExl CJun LRHS MAsh SLon SWvt
- 'Pearly Gates'	LRHS
forrestii	see *O. yunnanensis*
× ***fortunei***	CBot CDoC CExl EBee EPfP LLHF LRHS MMuc SEND SMad WPat
fragrans	CBcs LPar SLon SWvt
- f. ***aurantiacus***	SCob
§ ***heterophyllus***	CBcs CDul CMac EBee ECrN ELan EPfP LPar MGos MRav NLar SCob SGol SPer SRms SSta
§ - all gold	ELan EMil EPfP LRHS SPer SPoG
- 'Argenteomarginatus'	see *O. heterophyllus* 'Variegatus'
§ - 'Aureomarginatus' (v)	CBcs CMHG CTsd EHoe ELon GKin SCob SLon
- 'Aureus' misapplied	see *O. heterophyllus* all gold
- 'Aureus' Rehder	see *O. heterophyllus* 'Aureomarginatus'
§ - 'Goshiki' (v) ♀H5	Widely available
- 'Gulftide'	CDul EPfP LRHS MAsh MGos MJak NLar
- 'Kembu' (v)	NLar
- 'Myrtifolius'	CMac NLar
- 'Ōgon'	EPfP NLar
- 'Purple Shaft' ♀H5	CAbP ELan EPfP LRHS MAsh
- 'Purpureus'	CBcs CDoC CDul CMHG CMac CTsd CWib EBee ELon GBin MBri MGos MMuc MRav MSwo NLar SCob SCoo SEND SGol SLon SPer SSpi
- 'Rotundifolius'	CBcs CMac NLar
- Tricolor	see *O. heterophyllus* 'Goshiki'
§ - 'Variegatus' (v) ♀H5	Widely available
ilicifolius	see *O. heterophyllus*
rigidus	NLar
serrulatus	CBot LRHS NLar
suavis	NLar
§ ***yunnanensis*** ♀H5	CBot CDoC CMCN EBee EPfP MBlu MRav NLar WPGP WPat WSHC

× *Osmarea* see *Osmanthus*

Osmaronia see *Oemleria*

Osmorhiza (*Apiaceae*)

aristata B&SWJ 1607	WCru
chilensis new	WCru

Osmunda ✿ (*Osmundaceae*)

asiatica	EBee WCru
cinnamomea ♀H7	CAby CDoC CKel CLAP CWCL EBee EWes ISha LEdu LRHS MMuc NLar NMyG SGSe
claytoniana	CLAP CLet EBee EFer ISha LRHS NLar WPnP XLum
japonica	CHid CLAP EBee ISha

regalis ♀H6 — Widely available
- from southern USA — CLAP
- 'Cristata' ♀H6 — CLAP ELan EPfP LRHS NBid SWvt WFib
- 'Purpurascens' — Widely available
- var. ***spectabilis*** — CLAP ISha LRHS
- 'Undulata' — WFib

Osteospermum (*Asteraceae*)

'African Queen' — see *O.* 'Nairobi Purple'
(Astra Series) 'Astra Outback Purple' — LAst
- 'Astra Purple Spoon' — WBor
barberae misapplied — see *O. jucundum*
'Blue Streak' — CMac
'Buttermilk' — ELan
'Cannington John' — LSRN
'Cannington Roy' — CBcs CMac CSam CSma EBee ECtt ELan ELon EPfP EWoo GAbr GBee LRHS LSRN SPoG
caulescens misapplied — see *O.* 'White Pim'
ecklonis — CBcs CDTJ CHll CTri EPfP NBro NGdn WPnn
- var. ***prostratum*** — see *O.* 'White Pim'
Flowerpower Double Series (d) — LBuc SPoG
- Flowerpower Double Purple = 'Kleoe10181' (d) **new** — LAst
- Flowerpower Double White = 'Kleoe10179'PBR (d) **new** — LAst
'Giles Gilbey' (v) — MBNS
'Gold Sparkler' (v) — SEND
'Helen Dimond' — LRHS
'Hopleys' ♀H3 — MHer SEND
'Iced Gem' — LBuc LRHS
'In the Pink' — LCro LOPS SPoG WNPC
'Irish' — ECtt EPot LSou SIgm WIce
§ ***jucundum*** ♀H3 — CMea CTri CWCL ECha LRHS LSRN MLHP MMuc NBir NChi NFav NPer SEND SPlb SRms WBod WCFE WIce WThu
- 'Blackthorn Seedling' ♀H3 — CMea CWGN ECha IVic NFav NGdn
- var. ***compactum*** — CBod CChe CMac CPBP CPrp CTsd CWCL ELan ELon EPfP EWoo GLog GMaP LRHS LSRN MAvo MSpe NPer NPri SPer SPoG SWvt WAbe WBrk
- 'Elliott's Form' — WHoo
- 'Nanum' — EDAr
§ 'Lady Leitrim' ♀H3 — CBar CChe CSma CWCL CWGN EBee ECha ECtt ELan ELon EPfP GCra GKev GLog LHop LRHS LSRN MAvo MSpe NPer NPri SPad SPer SPoG SWvt WHil WHoo
Milk Symphony = 'Seiremi' (Symphony Series) — CWCL
'Mirach' (Springstar Series) — CWCL
§ 'Nairobi Purple' — CBcs CBod CChe CPrp EBee ECtt ELan MHol NPri SEND SPoG SWvt WBor WBrk WHil
Orange Symphony = 'Seimora'PBR (Symphony Series) — CBcs MAvo
'Pale Face' — see *O.* 'Lady Leitrim'
'Peggyi' — see *O.* 'Nairobi Purple'
'Pink Gem' **new** — EDAr
'Port Wine' — see *O.* 'Nairobi Purple'
'Silver Sparkler' (v) — CDTJ ELan MHer SVen
'Snow Pixie' — CBod CWGN EBee ECtt EDAr ELan ELon EWoo LCro LOPS SPoG SWvt
'Stardust'PBR — ECtt LBuc LRHS NPer SCoo SPoG
(Sunny Series) 'Sunny Amanda'PBR — SPoG
- 'Sunny Bianca'PBR — SPoG
- 'Sunny Felix'PBR — SPoG
- 'Sunny Mary'PBR — SPoG
I 'Superbum' — MHol
'Tauranga' — see *O.* 'Whirlygig'
(Tradewinds Series) Tradewinds Deep Purple = 'Oste Deeppur'PBR — SPoG
- Tradewinds Pearl 10 = 'Tra Whit' — SPoG
'Tresco Peggy' — see *O.* 'Nairobi Purple'
'Tresco Purple' — see *O.* 'Nairobi Purple'
Voltage Yellow = 'Balvoyelo' — WHea
'Weetwood' ♀H3 — CPrp EBee ECtt ELan EPot EWoo GLog LHop LRHS MHer MLHP SPoG SWvt WFar
§ 'Whirlygig' — ELan
§ 'White Pim' ♀H3 — CDTJ CHll NPer SDix SEND
'Wine Purple' — see *O.* 'Nairobi Purple'
'Wisley Pink' — NEgg
Zanzibar Pink Bicolour = 'Akzapib'PBR (Cape Daisy Series) — SPoG
Zanzibar White with Ring = 'Akzawhir'PBR (Cape Daisy Series) — SPoG
'Zaurak' (Springstar Series) — CWCL

Ostrowskia (*Campanulaceae*)

magnifica — EPot

Ostrya (*Betulaceae*)

carpinifolia — CBcs CCVT CDul CLnd CMCN CTho CWib EBee ELan EPfP LRHS MBlu MBri MMuc NLar NWea SEND SGol SWvt WMat
japonica — CDul CMCN
virginiana — CDul

Otatea (*Poaceae*)

aztecorum — ERod

Othonna (*Asteraceae*)

cheirifolia — CMea CSde EWes NBir SEND SIgm XLum XSen
coronopifolia — SVen

Othonnopsis see *Othonna*

Ourisia (*Plantaginaceae*)

× ***bitternensis*** 'Cliftonville Crimson' — WAbe
- 'Cliftonville Damask' — WAbe
- 'Cliftonville Ling' — WAbe
- 'Cliftonville Old Rose' — WAbe
- 'Cliftonville Pink' — WAbe
- 'Cliftonville Roset' — WAbe
caespitosa var. ***gracilis*** — MHol NPri
coccinea — CCon CTal EWes GAbr GKev MAvo NBir WAbe WHal
'Loch Ewe' — CCon CExl CTal GAbr GKev
macrocarpa — GEdr

	macrophylla	NWad
	microphylla	WAbe
	- f. ***alba***	WAbe
	- 'Hollowcliffe'	WAbe
	modesta	GBin
	polyantha 'Cliftonville Scarlet'	WAbe
	'Snowflake' ♀H5	EBee GAbr GEdr GKev IMou WAbe

Oxalis (*Oxalidaceae*)

	from Mount Stewart	WMoo
	acetosella	GPoy MHer MMHG MMuc NMir NQui WHer WShi
	- var. ***rosea***	IFro IMou
	- var. ***subpurpurascens***	WCot
	adenodes	NRog
	adenophylla ♀H4	CElw CExl CTri ECho ELan EPot GEdr GKev GMaP LAma LHop LRHS MJak NEgg NFav NHol NLar NPri SDeJ SPer SPoG SRms
	adenophylla* × *enneaphylla	see *O.* 'Matthew Forrest'
	'Anne Christie'	CPBP NSla
	anomala	ECho
	arenaria F&W 10584	WCot
§	***articulata***	GBuc NPer SEND XLum
	- 'Alba'	WCot XLum
	- f. ***crassipes*** 'Alba'	WCot
	- 'Festival'	ECho GKev
§	- subsp. ***rubra***	GKev SDeJ
	bowiei	EBee ECho EPot WCot
	- 'Amarantha'	ECho
	brasiliensis	ECho EPot
	compressa	NRog
	convexula	NRog
	'Cuckoo' **new**	NSla
	'Dark Eye'	EPot
	dentata 'Pot of Gold' **new**	GKev
	deppei	see *O. tetraphylla*
§	***depressa***	CTri ECho EPot EWes GBin GKev LLHF NBir NSla SDeJ SRms
	eckloniana	ECho
	- var. ***sonderi***	ECho NRog
	enneaphylla ♀H4	CElw ECho ELon GBin GEdr LHop LLHF LRHS NRya SBch
	- F&W 2715	CPBP
	- 'Alba'	CElw CMea CPBP ECho NRya NSla
	- subsp. ***ibari***	ECho EPPr GEdr GKev NRya NSla
	- 'Minutifolia'	NRya
*	- 'Minutifolia Rosea'	CPBP
	- 'Rosea'	CElw ECho EPot GKev LLHF NLar NRya NSla SBch
	- 'Sheffield Swan'	CPBP ECho GEdr LLHF NHar NSla
	- 'Ute'	EPot GEdr
	fabifolia **new**	ECho
	'Fanny'	ECho GKev
	flava	CDes ECho NRog
	floribunda misapplied	see *O. articulata*
	fourcadei	ECho NRog
	foveolata	NRog
	gracilis **new**	ECho
	griffithii 'Pink Charm'	GEdr
	- 'Snowflake'	GEdr
	'Gwen McBride'	CPBP GEdr
	hedysaroides misapplied	see *O. spiralis* subsp. *vulcanicola*
	'Hemswell Knight'	CPBP
	hirta	EPot SBch
	- 'Gothenburg'	EBee ECho EPri GKev NRog
	imbricata	ECho LLHF NRog
	inops	see *O. depressa*
	'Ione Hecker' ♀H4	CMea ECho EPot GCrg GEdr GKev ITim NHar NLar NRya WOld
	'Irish Mist' (v)	ECho
	'Jay' **new**	NSla
*	***karroica***	ECho WCot
§	***laciniata***	CPBP ECho
	- hybrid	GEdr NHar
	lactea double-flowered	see *O. magellanica* 'Nelson'
	lasiandra	EBee ECho
	'Linnet' **new**	NSla
	loricata	ECho
	magellanica	CTri ECho GAbr IMou SPlb WMoo
	- 'Flore Pleno'	see *O. magellanica* 'Nelson'
§	- 'Nelson' (d)	EBee ECho ELon GCal MMuc NBir NPer WMoo WPtf
	massoniana ♀H2	CDes CSpe ECho WAbe WCot
§	'Matthew Forrest'	CPBP WCot
§	***megalorrhiza***	SChr
	melanosticta	ECho EPot GEdr LLHF NRog SDeJ WCot WIce
	monophylla	ECho
	namaquana	CDes ECho
	'Nightingale' **new**	NSla
	obtusa	ECho EPot MPie
	- apricot-flowered	CDes WCot
	- lilac-pink-flowered from Namaqualand **new**	CDes
	oregana	CHid CMac ECho ELon EWld GBuc SPhx WCot WCru WPGP
	- 'Bob Haszeldine' **new**	GEdr
	- 'Klamath Ruby'	WSHC
	- f. ***smalliana***	EBee EWld GEdr IMou LHop WCot WCru
	palmifrons	ECho
	perdicaria	ECho EPot EWes LHop LRHS NRog WAbe
	- 'Citrino'	WAbe
	polyphylla	EBee ECho
§	***purpurea***	ECho
	- yellow-flowered	ECho
	regnellii	see *O. triangularis* subsp. *papilionacea*
	'Ridgeway Jewel'	CPBP
	'Ridgeway Sapphire'	CPBP
	rosea misapplied	see *O. articulata* subsp. *rubra*
	'Sandpiper' **new**	NSla
	semiloba	ECho GCal NCGa
	Slack Top hybrids	NSla
	'Slack's 53'	NSla
	'Snipe' **new**	NSla
	speciosa	see *O. purpurea*
§	***spiralis*** subsp. ***vulcanicola***	GCal LSou
	- - 'Sunset Velvet'	WCot
	squamata	LLHF
	squamoso-radicosa	see *O. laciniata*
*	***stipularis***	ECho LLHF
	succulenta Barnéoud	see *O. megalorrhiza*
	succulenta ambig.	CHll
	'Sunny'	ECho GKev
	'Sweet Sue'	CPBP
§	***tetraphylla***	CExl ECho GKev NPer
	- 'Alba'	ECho
	- 'Iron Cross'	CHid ECho GKev LAma MPie NBir NPri SDeJ SPlb
	'Tina'	CPBP
	triangularis	CExl ECho NBir NPer NPri
	- 'Birgit'	ECho GKev SDeJ
	- Burgundy Wine = 'JR Oxburwi' (Xalis Series)	CWGN NPer

- 'Cupido'	ECho
- 'Marmer' (v)	GKev
- 'Mijke'	ECho GKev
§ - subsp. ***papilionacea*** ♀H2	ECho GKev LAma
- - 'Atropurpurea'	CSpe LHop SDeJ
- subsp. ***triangularis***	CHid ECho EUJe GKev MBel
tuberosa	GPoy LEdu
- 'Polar Bere'	LEdu
- scarlet-flowered, white-eye	LEdu
'Ute'	CPBP NSla SIgm
valdiviensis	NWad
versicolor ♀H2	ECho EPot NBir NRog SDeJ WAbe WCot
virginea	NRog
I 'Waverley Hybrid'	GBin GCrg GKev
'Wren' **new**	NSla
zeekoevleyensis	CDes NRog

Oxycoccus see *Vaccinium*

Oxydendrum ✿ (*Ericaceae*)

arboreum	CAbP CBcs CBct CDoC CDul CMCN EBee EPfP IArd IDee IVic LRHS MAsh MBlu MBri MMuc NLar SAko SPer SSta WBor WHar WPGP

Oxypetalum (*Apocynaceae*)

caeruleum	see *Tweedia coerulea*

Oxyria (*Polygonaceae*)

digyna	CAgr GEdr

Oxytropis (*Papilionaceae*)

campestris	EBee
coerulea	CPBP
hailarensis var. ***chankaensis***	CPBP
lambertii	CPBP
podocarpa	SPlb
purpurea	SPlb
sajanensis	CPBP

Ozothamnus (*Asteraceae*)

§ ***coralloides***	ECou WAbe WCot WThu
§ 'County Park Silver'	EBee EWes GCrg GEdr GKev
§ ***hookeri***	CDoC EBee MBrN SVen WCFE WJek WPGP WPat
§ ***ledifolius***	CBcs EPfP LRHS SPer WSHC
§ ***rosmarinifolius***	CBcs CDoC CTsd ELan EPfP EWld GGal LRHS MAsh MSwo SPer SVen WPnn
- 'Kiandra'	ECou
- 'Silver Jubilee'	CBcs CDoC CSBt ECrN ELan EPfP GCal LRHS MMuc MRav MSwo SLon SPer SPlb SRkn
§ ***selago***	ECou WCot
- 'Major'	SPlb
§ - var. ***tumidus***	WThu
'Sussex Silver'	CBcs CDoC
'Threave Seedling'	CBcs CDoC EBee ELan IVic LRHS MAsh SPer

P

Pachyphragma (*Brassicaceae*)

§ ***macrophyllum***	EBee ECGP ECha EHrv ELon EWTr GCal IBlr IMou LEdu LPla MMuc MRav NLar NSti SDix WCot WCru WPGP WSHC

Pachyphytum (*Crassulaceae*)

bracteosum	EUJe
compactum **new**	CDoC
glutinicaule RE 477	CDoC
oviferum ♀H2	WCot

Pachypodium (*Apocynaceae*)

lamerei ♀H1a	EUJe LToo SPlb
lealii subsp. ***saundersii***	LToo

Pachysandra (*Buxaceae*)

axillaris	EBee EPPr GCal SKHP WCot
- BWJ 8032	WCru
- 'Crûg's Cover'	EWld WCru
procumbens	EHrv IMou LHop NLar SKHP WCot
- 'Angola' (v)	WCot
stylosa	MRav
terminalis	Widely available
- 'Green Carpet'	Widely available
- 'Green Sheen' ♀H5	ECha EPPr EPfP ESwi EWTr LPal LRHS
- 'Silver Edge' (v) **new**	EBee
- 'Variegata' (v) ♀H5	Widely available

Pachystegia (*Asteraceae*)

§ ***insignis***	CPne LRHS SBrt SLim

× *Pachyveria* (*Crassulaceae*)

'Mrs Coombes'	CDoC

Paederota (*Plantaginaceae*)

§ ***bonarota***	EPot WAbe
lutea	CDes GEdr WAbe

Paeonia ✿ (*Paeoniaceae*)

sp.	LPar
'Ace of Hearts' **new**	GBin
'Age of Gold' (S)	GBin XGra
'Age of Victoria'	GBin
albiflora	see *P. lactiflora*
'America'	CKel EBen GBin NCGa WCAu
'Anna Marie' (S)	GBin
anomala	CCon EBen GBin GKev MPhe NLar WCot
- var. ***intermedia***	GCal
'Ariadne' (S)	GBin
arietina	see *P. mascula* subsp. *arietina*
'Athena'	EBen GBin WCAu
'Avant Garde'	WCAu
'Baby Whisper'	GBin
'Bai Xue Ta' (S)	NTPC
banatica	see *P. officinalis* subsp. *banatica*
'Banquet' (S)	GBin
§ 'Bartzella' (d) ♀H5	CEvo CKel EBen ELan ELon GBin ILea LRHS NLar WCAu WCot WHil XGra
'Black Panther' (S)	WCAu
'Black Pirate' (S) ♀H5	CKel
'Blaze'	CKel EWTr EWoo GMaP ILea LRHS NCGa WCAu WCot
'Border Charm'	EBen GBin XGra
'Boreas' (S)	GBin XGra
'Bowl of Cream' (d) **new**	EBen
'Bravura'	GBin
'Bridal Icing'	GBin WCAu
'Bride's Dream'	GBin

'Brightness'	XGra
'Brocaded Gown' (S)	GBin
broteroi	SKHP WThu
'Buckeye Belle' (d)	CKel EBee EBen ELan EPfP EWoo GBin GMaP IBoy ILea LAst LCro LRHS LSRN NCGa SCob SHar SPer SPoG SWat WCAu WCot XGra
'Burma Joy'	WCAu XGra
'Burma Midnight'	EBen GBin WCAu
'Burma Ruby'	GBin WCAu
'Callie's Memory'	CKel EBen GBin ILea NCGa WCAu WHil
cambessedesii ♀^{H3}	CBro CTal EPot GKev LHop LRHS NBir NSla SSpi WAbe WCot WKif
cambessedesii* × *mlokosewitschii	LRHS
'Cameo Lullaby'	GBin
'Canary Brilliant' PBR	GBin WCAu XGra
'Cardinal's Robe'	GBin
'Carina'	EBen GBin
'Carol'	WCAu
caucasica	see *P. mascula* subsp. *mascula*
'Chalice'	EBen GBin
× ***chamaeleon***	GBin SKHP
'Cheddar Royal'	GBin
'Cherry Ruffles'	EBen GBin WCAu
'Cherry Twist'	GBin
'Chinese Dragon' (S)	WCAu
'Chocolate Soldier'	CKel GBin WCAu
'Christmas Velvet' (d) **new**	EBen
'Claire de Lune'	CKel EBen GBin ILea LRHS SHar WCAu WCot WTor
'Claudia'	GBin WCAu
'Color Magnet'	GBin WCAu XGra
'Command Performance'	GBin WCAu
'Companion of Serenity' (S)	GBin
'Convoy' (d)	WCAu
'Copper Kettle'	CEvo CKel EBen GBin ILea
'Cora Louise'	CEvo CKel EBen ELan GBin ILea WCAu XGra
'Coral Charm' ♀^{H7}	CKel EBen GBin GMaP IBoy ILea LCro LSRN MMHG NCGa NLar SCob SDeJ SKHP WCAu WCot WHil XGra
'Coral Fay'	GBin WCAu
'Coral Scout'	GBin
'Coral Sunset'	CKel CWCL EBen EWTr GBin IBoy ILea LCro NCGa NLar SCob SDeJ WCAu XGra
'Coral Supreme'	GBin WCot
corallina	see *P. mascula* subsp. *mascula*
coriacea var. ***atlantica***	CBro
'Court Jester'	EBen ELan ILea
'Cutie'	GBin WCAu
'Cytherea'	EBen GBin LRHS WCAu WCot XGra
'Dad' **new**	EBen
'Daedalus' (S)	GBin
'Dancing Butterflies'	see *P. lactiflora* 'Zi Yu Nu'
'Daredevil' (S)	GBin
daurica	see *P. mascula* subsp. *triternata*
- subsp. ***coriifolia*** RCB UA 12	WCot
'Dawn Glow'	GBin
decomposita	MPhe
decora	see *P. peregrina*
'Defender'	EBen
delavayi (S)	CBcs CKel CPne CTsd CWCL ELan EPfP GBin GCal GKev GMaP LCro LHop LRHS MAsh MGos MLHP MMuc NBir NEgg SDix SEND SKHP SPer SPoG SRms SSpi WBod WCot

- BWJ 7775	WCru
- from China (S)	MPhe
- var. ***angustiloba*** f. ***alba*** (S)	CExl
§ - - f. ***angustiloba*** (S)	GBin GKev SCob SSpi
§ - - f. ***trollioides*** (S)	CExl
§ - var. ***delavayi*** f. ***lutea*** (S)	CCVT CDul EPfP EUJe GBin GKev IBoy IFro LEdu LRHS MAsh MGos MLHP MNHC NBir NEgg SCob SLon SMad SPoG SRms WBod WHar WHoo
- - f. ***lutea*** × 'Right Royal' **new**	XGra
- - f. ***lutea*** × 'Tria' **new**	XGra
- var. ***lutea***	see *P. delavayi* var. *delavayi* f. *lutea*
- 'Mrs Colville' (S)	GBin GCal
- 'Mrs Sarson' (S)	ELan EWes SWat
- Potaninii Group	see *P. delavayi* var. *angustiloba* f. *angustiloba*
- 'Tapestry' (S)	CSpe
- Trollioides Group	see *P. delavayi* var. *angustiloba* f. *trollioides*
delavayi* × *suffruticosa	LSRN
'Diana Parks'	GBin ILea NCGa NLar WCAu XGra
'Don Richardson'	WCAu
Drizzling Rain Cloud	see *P. suffruticosa* 'Shiguregumo'
'Early Bird'	EBen GBin
'Early Daybreak'	GBin
'Early Glow'	EBen GBin WCAu XGra
'Early Scout'	EBee EBen ELon GBin LRHS SCob WCAu XGra
'Early Windflower'	WCAu
'Echt Klasse'	GBin
'Eden's Perfume'	CBod ELon EPfP GBin IKil MSCN
'Eliza Lundy' (d)	EBen GBin WCAu XGra
'Elizabeth Foster'	GBin
'Ellen Cowley'	EBen GBin
emodi	CDes CKel EBen GBin GKev LRHS SHar WCAu WCot
'Etched Salmon'	CKel EBen GBin NCGa
'Eventide'	WCAu
'Ezra Pound' (S)	GBin
'Fairy Princess'	EBen GBin XGra
'Feng Dan Bai' (S)	NTPC
'Firelight'	EBen GBin WCAu
'First Arrival'	CKel EBen GBin ILea WCAu
'First Dutch Yellow'	see *P.* 'Garden Treasure'
'Flame'	EBee EBen EPfP EWTr GMaP ILea MBel MNrw NCGa NLar NSti SDeJ WCot XGra
'Fragrant Pink Imp'	GBin
'Fuchsia Cuddles'	XGra
§ Gansu Group (S)	CEvo CKel GKev MPhe NTPC
- 'Bai Bi Fen Xia' (S)	MPhe
- 'Bai Bi Lan Xia' (S)	MPhe
- 'Bei Ji Xiong' (S) **new**	MPhe
- 'Bing Shan Xue Lian' (S)	MPhe
- 'Bing Xin Zi' (S)	MPhe NTPC
- 'Cheng Xin' (S)	MPhe
- 'Dan Feng Zhan Chi' (S)	NTPC
- 'Dan Feng Zhu' (S) **new**	MPhe
- 'Dian Jin Bai Yan Wei' (S) **new**	MPhe
- 'Er Long Nao Hai' (S) **new**	MPhe
- 'Fen Die' (S)	NTPC
- 'Fen Guan Yu Zhu' (S)	NTPC
- 'Fen He' (S)	MPhe

- 'Fen Jin Yu' (S) NTPC
- 'Fen Jin Yu Zhu' (S) MPhe
- 'Fen Lou Dan Xia' (S) **new** MPhe
- 'Fen Mian Tao Sai' (S) MPhe
- 'Feng Xian' (S) MPhe
- 'Gu Cheng Xiang Hui' (S) MPhe
- 'Guang Hui Li Cheng' (S) **new** MPhe
- 'Gui Fu Ren' (S) **new** MPhe
- 'Han Hai Bing Xin' (S) **new** MPhe
- 'He Hua Deng' (S) MPhe
- 'He Ping Lian' (S) MPhe
- 'Hei Bai Fen Ming' (S) **new** MPhe
- 'Hei Fa Nü Lang' (S) **new** MPhe
- 'Hei Feng Die' (S) MPhe NTPC
- 'Hei Tian E' (S) MPhe
- 'Hei Xuan Feng' (S) MPhe
- 'Hei Yuan Shuai' (S) MPhe
- 'Hei Zhen Zhu' (S) **new** MPhe
- 'Hong Hai Qing Long' (S) **new** MPhe
- 'Hong Lian' (S) MPhe NTPC
- 'Hong Xia Ying Xue' (S) MPhe
- 'Huang He' (S) MPhe
- 'Huang Lian' (S) **new** MPhe
- 'Hui He' (S) MPhe
- 'Jiao Rong' (S) MPhe
- 'Jin Bo Dan Yang' (S) **new** MPhe
- 'Jin Cheng Ming Yue' (S) MPhe
- 'Ju Hua Fen' (S) MPhe
- 'Lan Hai Yiu Bo' (S) MPhe
- 'Lan He' (S) MPhe
- 'Lan Mo Shuang Hui' (S) **new** MPhe
- 'Lan Tian Meng' (S) MPhe
- 'Lan Xian Nü' (S) **new** MPhe
- 'Lan Yu San Cai' (S) MPhe NTPC
- 'Lan Zhang Cai Wei' (S) WKif
- 'Lan Zhen Zhu' (S) **new** MPhe
- 'Li Xiang' (S) MPhe
- 'Lian Chun' (S) MPhe
- 'Long Dan Fan' (S) **new** MPhe
- 'Long Yuan Hong' (S) MPhe
- 'Long Yuan Xia Nu' (S) **new** MPhe
- 'Mei Gui Sa Jin' (S) MPhe
- 'Mo Guan Yu Zhu' (S) **new** MPhe
- 'Mo Hai Yin Bo' (S) MPhe
- 'Mo Hai Yin Zhou' (S) MPhe
- 'Nong Mo Zhong Cai' (S) WKif
- 'Pan Pan' (S) **new** MPhe
- 'Ri Yue Tong Hui' (S) MPhe
- 'San Hua Nu' (S) **new** MPhe
- 'Shen Guang Yu Lu' (S) **new** MPhe
- 'Shu Sheng Peng Mo' (S) MPhe
- 'Tao Hua Nu' (S) MPhe
- 'Tian Shan Ri Chu' (S) **new** MPhe
- 'Tie Mian Wu Si' (S) MPhe
- 'Tong Xin Tong De' (S) **new** MPhe
- 'Wu Kong Xiu Xing' (S) **new** MPhe
- 'Xiang Lu Zi Yan' (S) MPhe
- 'Xiao Xue' (S) **new** MPhe
- 'Xiong Mao' (S) MPhe NTPC
- 'Xue Hai Bing Xin' (S) MPhe NTPC
- 'Xue Hai Dan Xin' (S) NTPC
- 'Xue Li Cang Jin' (S) **new** MPhe
- 'Xue Lian' (S) GBin MPhe NTPC WKif
- 'Xue Yuan Yu Hui' (S) MPhe
- 'Yan Chun' (S) **new** MPhe
- 'Yan Wei Bai' (S) **new** MPhe
- 'Ye Guang Bei' (S) MPhe
- 'Yin Yang Shan' (S) **new** MPhe
- 'Yu Ban Xiu Qiu' (S) MPhe
- 'Yu Guan Lan Dai' (S) MPhe
- 'Yu Lou Cang Jiao' (S) **new** MPhe
- 'Yu Lu Lian Dan' (S) MPhe
- 'Yu Rong Dan Xin' (S) MPhe
- 'Yu Shi Zi' (S) **new** MPhe
- 'Yuan Yang Pu' (S) MPhe
- 'Zi Ban Bai' (S) NTPC
- 'Zi Die Ying Feng' (S) MPhe NTPC
- 'Zi Hai Yin Bo' (S) MPhe
- 'Zi Lou Xiang Jin' (S) **new** MPhe
- 'Zi Yan' (S) MPhe NTPC
- 'Zong Ban Bai' (S) MPhe NTPC
- 'Zui Fei' (S) **new** MPhe

Gansu Mudan Group see *P.* Gansu Group
'Garden Peace' EBen WCAu
§ 'Garden Treasure' EBen GBin SDeJ WCAu WHil XGra
'Gold Standard' GBin
'Golden Bowl' CKel GBin
'Golden Dream' see *P.* 'Bartzella'
'Golden Isles' CKel
'Golden Thunder' CKel
'Golden Wings' GBin
'Grace Root' GBin
'Green Halo' GBin
'Happy' GBin
'Hei Hua Kui' see *P. suffruticosa* 'Hei Hua Kui'
'Henry Bockstace' (d) GBin ILea NLar SHar WCAu XGra
'Hephestos' (S) GBin XGra
'Heritage' GBin
'Hillary' CKel GBin ILea WCAu
'Ho-gioku' GBin
'Hong Bao Shi' (S) NTPC
'Honor' EBen WCAu
'Horizon' GBin
'Huo Lian Jin Dan' (S) NTPC
'Icarus' (S) GBin XGra
'Ice Storm' (S) GBin
'Illini Belle' GBin
'Illini Warrior' EBen GBin
'In the Mood' GBin
'Iphigenia' (S) GBin XGra
'Isani Gidui' see *P. lactiflora* 'Isami-jishi'
japonica misapplied see *P. lactiflora*
japonica (Makino) Miyabe & Takeda B&SWJ 10985 WCru
'Jay Cee' GBin WCAu
jishanensis MPhe
'Joseph Rock' see *P. rockii*
'Joyce Ellen' GBin NLar
'Jubilation' GBin
'Julia Rose' CKel EBen GBin ILea NCGa WCAu WHil XGra
'Kathryn Ann' GBin
kavachensis GKev
'Kinkaku' see *P.* × *lemoinei* 'Souvenir de Maxime Cornu'
'Kinko' see *P.* × *lemoinei* 'Alice Harding'
'Kinshi' see *P.* × *lemoinei* 'Chromatella'
'Kintei' see *P.* × *lemoinei* 'L'Espérance'
'Koikagura' CKel
'Kokamon' CKel
'Kun Shan Ye Guang' NTPC
§ ***lactiflora*** GCal LPfy MBel MPhe
- from East Russia **new** GCal

	- 'Abalone Pearl'	GBin XGra
	- 'Adolphe Rousseau'	CBcs CKel ILea LCro LOPS LRHS WCAu
*	- 'Afterglow'	CKel
	- 'Agida'	GBin LRHS MRav
	- ***alba***	MBel WBor
	- 'Albert Crousse'	CBcs CKel GBin MRav NBir SWat WCAu
	- 'Albert Niva' **new**	WCAu
	- 'Alertie' (d) **new**	GBin
	- 'Alexander Fleming'	EBee MBNS MHol MNrw NBir SWat WCAu WFar
	- 'Alice Harding'	CKel GBin WCAu
	- 'Allan Rogers' **new**	WCAu
	- 'Amabilis' (d)	ILea XGra
	- 'Amalia Olson' (d)	GBin WCAu XGra
	- 'Amibilis'	ELon WCAu
	- 'Angel Cheeks'	CKel EBee GBin LCro LOPS NCGa NLar WCAu
	- 'Anna Pavlova'	CKel
	- 'Antwerpen'	LRHS
	- 'Arabian Prince'	CKel
	- 'Argentine'	CKel WCAu
	- 'Armistice' (d)	WCAu
	- 'Asa Gray'	CKel
	- 'Auguste Dessert'	CKel GBin WCAu WCFE
§	- 'Augustin d'Hour'	CKel ILea SHar
	- 'Aureole'	CKel MRav
	- 'Avalanche'	EPfP GBin ILea NLar
	- 'Avalon' (d)	WCAu XGra
	- 'Ballerina'	CKel MRav
	- 'Barbara'	CKel GBin WCAu
	- 'Baroness Schröder'	CKel GBin WCAu XGra
	- 'Barrington Belle'	EBee EPfP GBin LRHS MBel WCAu WHoo
	- 'Barrymore'	CKel
	- 'Bayadere' (d)	GBin
	- 'Beacon'	CKel
	- 'Beatrice Kelway'	CKel
	- 'Belle Center'	GBin WCAu
	- 'Bess Bockstoce' **new**	WCAu
	- 'Bessie'	GBin
	- 'Best Man'	EBee NGdn WCAu
	- 'Bethcar'	CKel
	- 'Better Times'	WCAu
	- 'Bev'	GBin
	- 'Big Ben'	CKel EWTr GBin LRHS NLar SHar
	- 'Black Beauty' **new**	GBin WHil
	- 'Blaze of Beauty'	CKel
	- 'Blitz Tort'	GBin XGra
	- 'Bluebird'	CKel IBoy
	- 'Blush Queen'	CKel GBin WCAu
	- 'Border Gem'	GBin LRHS MRav WCAu
	- 'Bouchela'	NLar NSti
	- 'Boule de Neige'	GBin LHop
	- 'Bouquet Perfect'	GBin WCAu
	- 'Bower of Roses'	CKel
	- 'Bowl of Beauty' ♀H7	Widely available
	- 'Bowl of Cream'	CKel EBen GBin ILea LRHS SWat SWvt WCAu XGra
	- 'Break o' Day'	WCAu
	- 'Bridal Gown'	GBin WCAu
	- 'Bridal Veil'	CKel
	- 'Bridesmaid'	CKel
	- 'Bright Knight'	WCAu
	- 'British Beauty'	CKel
	- 'Bunker Hill'	CKel ELon GBin IBoy ILea LRHS SPer SWvt WCAu
	- 'Bu-te'	GBin
	- 'Butter Bowl'	GBin WCAu
	- 'Candeur'	CKel
	- 'Candidissima'	GBin
	- 'Captivation'	CKel
	- 'Carnival'	CKel
	- 'Caroline Allain'	CKel
	- 'Carrara'	GBin
	- 'Cascade'	CKel
	- 'Catherine Fontijn'	CKel EBen GBin ILea WCAu
	- 'Celebrity'	CWCL MSCN SCob
	- 'Charles Burgess'	CKel ELon GBin ILea SCob WCAu
	- 'Charles' White'	CKel GBin ILea NCGa NLar SDeJ WCAu
	- 'Charm'	GBin WCAu
	- 'Cheddar Charm'	GBin WCAu
	- 'Cheddar Supreme'	GBin
	- 'Cherry Hill'	GBin
	- 'Chestine Gowdy'	CKel
	- 'Chief Wapello'	GBin
	- 'Chiffon Clouds'	WCAu
	- 'Chiffon Parfait'	GBin XGra
	- 'Chippewa'	EBen GBin
	- 'Circus Circus'	GBin XGra
	- 'Claire Dubois'	CKel GBin
	- 'Commando' (d)	EBee
	- 'Cora Stubbs'	GBin NCGa SPer WCAu
	- 'Corinne Wersan' **new**	GBin
	- 'Cornelia Shaylor'	CKel WCAu
	- 'Couronne' **new**	EBen
	- 'Couronne d'Or'	GBin
	- 'Cream Puff'	EBen WCAu
	- 'Crimson Glory'	CKel
	- 'Crinkles Linens'	GBin
	- 'Dairy Anne'	XGra
	- 'Daisy Coronet'	XGra
	- 'Dawn Crest'	CKel
	- 'Dawn Pink'	WCAu
	- 'Dayspring'	CKel
	- 'Daystar'	MRav
	- 'Dayton'	GBin WCAu
	- 'Decorative'	CKel
	- 'Delachei'	CKel GBin
	- 'Dinner Plate'	CKel GBin NCGa SHar SPer WCAu
	- 'Do Tell'	CKel CWCL EBee EBen ELon EPfP GBin MMHG NCGa SPer WCAu
	- 'Docteur H. Barnsby'	CKel
	- 'Doctor Alexander Fleming'	CKel GBin ILea LRHS SDeJ SRot SWat SWvt
	- 'Don Juan'	CKel
	- 'Doreen'	CKel EBee GBin SHar WCAu WTor
	- 'Doris Cooper'	WCAu
	- 'Dorothy Welsh'	CKel
	- 'Dragon'	CKel
	- 'Dream Catcher'	GBin
	- 'Drumline'	SDeJ
	- 'Duchesse de Nemours' ♀H7	Widely available
	- 'Edulis Superba'	CWld ELan GBin ILea LEdu LRHS LSRN MBNS MRav NPer SHar SPer WCAu
	- 'Elaine'	MRav
	- 'Electric Festival'	GBin
	- 'Elizabeth Queen of the Belgians' (d)	XGra
	- 'Elizabeth Stone'	CKel
	- 'Ella Christine Kelway'	CKel
	- 'Elsa Sass'	GBin ILea NCGa WCAu XGra
	- 'Embraceable Pink'	GBin
	- 'Emma Klehm' (d)	CKel EBen GBin LSRN WCAu XGra
	- 'Emperor of India'	CKel
	- 'Emperor's Buttons'	XGra

- 'Enchantment'	CKel
- 'English Princess'	CKel
- 'Ethereal'	CKel
- 'Evelyn Tibbets'	GBin
- 'Evening Glow'	CKel
- 'Evening World'	CKel
- 'Fairy's Petticoat'	CKel GBin WCAu
- 'Fancy Nancy'	GBin
- 'Fashion Show'	CKel
- 'Félix Crousse' ♀H7	CBcs CBod CKel COtt CTri ELan ELon GBin GMaP IBoy ILea LRHS LSRN MBNS MGos MRav NBir NLar NPri SDeJ SPer SWat WCAu
- 'Felix Supreme'	GBin XGra
- 'Fen Yu Nu'	EBen
- 'Festiva Maxima' ♀H7	CKel CSBt CTri CWld EBee ELan EPfP EWoo GBin ILea LCro LOPS LRHS LSun NBir NEgg NLar NPri SPer SPoG SRkn SRot SWat SWvt WCAu WFar
- 'Festiva Supreme'	GBin
- 'Fiesta Posey'	WCAu
- 'Fiona' (d)	WCAu
- 'Firebelle'	WCAu
- 'Florence Ellis'	WCAu
- 'Florence Nicholls'	CKel ELan GBin ILea WCAu XGra
- 'Foxtrot'	GBin XGra
- 'France'	CKel
- 'Fuchsia Dragonfly'	GBin
- 'Fuji-no-mine'	GBin
- 'Garden Lace'	GBin SDeJ WCAu XGra
- 'Gardenia'	CKel EBee GBin IBoy LRHS NLar SDeJ WCAu WCot XGra
- 'Gay Paree'	CKel CWCL GBin IBoy MRav NCGa NLar SCob SHar WCAu
- 'Gayborder June'	CKel
- 'Général Joffre'	MRav
- 'Général MacMahon'	see *P. lactiflora* 'Augustin d'Hour'
- 'General Wolfe'	CKel
- 'Georgiana Shaylor'	EBen
- 'Germaine Bigot'	CKel GBin MRav WCAu
- 'Gertrude Allen'	GBin
- 'Gilbert Barthelot'	CKel WCAu WHil
- 'Gladys McArthur'	GBin
- 'Gleam of Light'	CKel
- 'Globe of Light'	CKel EBen GBin
- 'Glory Hallelujah'	WCAu
- 'Go-Daigo'	GBin
- 'Golden Fleece'	WCAu
- 'Goldilocks'	WCAu
- 'Great Sport'	MRav
- 'Green Lotus'	GBin XGra
- 'Guidon'	WCAu
- 'Gypsy Girl'	CKel
- 'Hakodate'	CKel
- 'Hansina Brand' (d)	GBin
- 'Happy Days'	WCAu
- 'Heartbeat'	CKel
- 'Helen Hayes'	WCAu
- 'Henri Potin'	GBin
- 'Her Grace'	CKel
- 'Herbert Oliver'	CKel
- 'Hermione'	CKel GBin WCAu XGra
- 'Hit Parade'	WCAu
- 'Honey Gold'	CKel GBin SPoG WCAu XGra
- 'Hot Chocolate'	GBin WCAu XGra
- 'Huang Jin Lun'	EBen
- 'Hyperion'	CKel EBen
- 'Immaculée'	CKel CWCL EBee GBin IBoy ILea LCro LHop LRHS LSRN MMHG MRav NCGa SCob SPoG XGra
- 'Inspecteur Lavergne'	CKel EBee EPfP GBin IBoy ILea LRHS MGos NGdn SGol SPer WCAu WCot XGra
- 'Instituteur Doriat'	CKel GBin LRHS WCAu
§ - 'Isami-jishi'	GBin
- 'Ivory Inspirations'	XGra
- 'Jacorma'	CCon GBin LRHS
- 'Jacques Doriat'	CKel
- 'Jadwigha'	EBee
- 'James Kelway'	CKel EBen GBin
- 'Jan van Leeuwen'	CKel EBee EBen ELon EPfP GBin GMaP LCro LOPS LRHS NCGa SPer WCAu WCot XGra
- 'Jappensha-ikhu'	GBin
- 'Jean Ericksen' **new**	WCAu
- 'Jeanne d'Arc'	CKel
- 'John Howard Wigell'	WCAu
- 'Johnny'	GBin
- 'Joker' **new**	WCAu
- 'Joseph Christie' (d)	EBee
- 'Joy of Life'	CKel
- 'Judith Eileen'	GBin
- 'June Morning'	CKel
- 'June Rose'	WCAu
- 'Kakoden'	GBin
- 'Kansas'	CKel CWCL EBee EBen ELan EPfP GBin IBoy ILea LRHS MBri MHol NBir NGdn NLar SPoG WCAu WCot WFar
- 'Karen Gray'	EBen GBin WCAu
- 'Karl Rosenfield'	Widely available
- 'Kathleen Mavoureen'	CKel
- 'Kelway's Betty'	CKel
- 'Kelway's Brilliant'	CKel EBen
- 'Kelway's Circe'	CKel
- 'Kelway's Daystar'	CKel
- 'Kelway's Exquisite'	CKel
- 'Kelway's Glorious'	CKel EPfP GBin ILea LRHS MBNS MRav NLar WCAu
- 'Kelway's Lovely'	CKel GBin
- 'Kelway's Lovely Lady'	CKel
- 'Kelway's Majestic'	CKel MRav
- 'Kelway's Scented Rose'	CKel
- 'Kelway's Supreme'	CKel SWat
- 'King of England'	GBin
- 'Knighthood'	CKel
- 'Königswinter'	GBin
§ - 'Koningin Wilhelmina'	EBee EBen EPfP GBin MNrw
- 'Krekler's Red'	WCAu
- 'Krinkled White'	CKel EBee EBen ELon EPfP EWoo GBin GMaP ILea LRHS LSRN MRav NCGa NLar NSti SDeJ SHar SKHP SPoG WCAu XGra
- 'La Belle Hélène'	CKel
- 'La Lorraine'	CKel
- 'Lady Alexandra Duff' ♀H7	CKel ELon EPfP GBin ILea LRHS MRav NBir NGdn SWvt WCAu XGra
- 'Lady Ley'	CKel
- 'Lady Mayoress'	CKel
- 'Lady Orchid'	EBen EPfP WCAu
- 'Lancaster Imp'	GBin WCAu
- 'Langport Triumph'	CKel
- 'Largo'	WCAu
- 'Laura Dessert' ♀H7	CKel EWTr GBin IBoy ILea LCro LRHS NCGa NLar SPer WCAu XGra
- 'Laura Shaylor'	WCAu
- 'Lavender Lotus'	XGra

- 'Le Cygne' GBin
- 'L'Éclatante' CKel GBin LRHS
- 'Legion of Honor' CKel
- 'Lemon Ice' CKel
- 'Lemon Queen' GBin
- § 'L'Étincelante' EBen CKel GBin
- 'Liebchen' WCAu
- 'Lights Out' GBin
- 'Lilac Times' CKel WCAu
- 'Lillian Wild' GBin WCAu
- 'Little Medicineman' EBee GBin XGra
- 'Little Pink Lullaby' GBin
- 'Lois Kelsey' GBin WCAu
- 'Lollipop' (d) CEvo ELan GBin ILea
- 'Longfellow' CKel GBin
- 'Lord Kitchener' CKel EPfP GBin LRHS WCAu
- 'Lorna Doone' CKel
- 'Lotus Queen' GBin NLar WCAu
- 'Louis van Houtte' CKel ILea NEgg XGra
- 'Love's Touch' (d) GBin
- 'Lowell Thomas' WCAu
- 'Lucky' XGra
- 'Lyric' CKel
- 'Ma Petite Cherie' (d) GBin WCAu XGra
- 'Madame Calot' EBee LRHS WCAu XGra
- 'Madame Ducel' CKel
- 'Madame Emile Debatène' CKel EBee MBNS WCAu WFar XGra
- 'Madame Gaudichau' MAvo WCot
- 'Madelon' CKel
- 'Maestro' GBin
- 'Magenta Glow' XGra
- 'Magenta Moon' WCAu
- 'Magic Orb' CKel
- 'Mandarin's Coat' GBin
- 'Margaret Clark' WCAu
- 'Margaret Truman' CKel EBee WCAu
- 'Marie Lemoine' CKel ELan GBin ILea LRHS WCAu XGra
- 'Marietta Sisson' WCAu
- 'Martha Reed' **new** WCAu
- 'Mary Elizabeth' GBin XGra
- 'Masterpiece' CKel
- 'May Treat' WCAu
- 'Midnight Sun' GBin WCAu
- 'Minnie Shaylor' EBen WCAu
- 'Mischief' MRav WCAu
- 'Miss America' ♀H7 EBen EPfP GBin NCGa WCAu XGra
- 'Miss Eckhart' CKel GBin
- 'Missie's Blush' GBin
- 'Mister Ed' GBin WCAu
- 'Mistral' CKel
- 'Monsieur Jules Elie' ♀H7 CKel EBee EPfP EWoo GBin IBoy ILea LCro LRHS NGdn NLar SHar SPer WCAu WHoo
- 'Monsieur Martin Cahuzac' CKel GBin LRHS WCAu
- 'Moon of Nippon' ILea LRHS SHar WCAu
- 'Moon River' EBen EPfP GBin WCAu WHoo
- 'Moonstone' CKel GBin SCob
- 'Morning Kiss' EBee
- 'Mother's Choice' CKel EWoo GBin LSRN MAvo NGdn NLar SHar WCAu WCot
- 'Mr G.F. Hemerik' CKel GBin IBoy WCAu WCot XGra
- 'Mrs Edward Harding' CKel WCAu
- 'Mrs Franklin D. Roosevelt' EBen GBin WCAu XGra
- 'Mrs J.V. Edlund' GBin
- 'Mrs Livingston Farrand' GBin
- 'My Pal Rudy' GBin WCAu
- 'Myrtle Gentry' CKel GBin WCAu
- 'Nancy Nicholls' WCAu
- 'Nancy Nora' SPer WCAu
- 'Nellie Shaylor' (d) EBen GBin NCGa WCAu
- 'Neomy Demay' CKel GBin NCGa
- 'Neon' GBin ILea LRHS
- 'Nice Gal' EBen GBin WCAu
- 'Nick Shaylor' EBen GBin WCAu XGra
- 'Nippon Beauty' CKel EBee GBin ILea LRHS MBel NCGa NLar SCob SDeJ SKHP WCAu WCot
- 'Nippon Gold' WCAu
- 'Noemie Demay' LRHS
- 'Norma Volz' GBin WCAu XGra
- 'Nymphe' CKel EBee ILea MRav NLar SDeJ WCAu
- 'Orlando Roberts' GBin
- 'Ornament' CKel
- 'Orpen' CKel
- 'Paola' CKel
- 'Paul Bunyan' GBin
- 'Paul M. Wild' CKel NLar WCAu
- * 'Pecher' CBod CKel LRHS MWhi NLar NPer WHil
- 'Peter Brand' CKel EBee ELan GBin LSRN NLar SCob WTor
- 'Petite Elegance' (d) WCAu
- 'Petite Porcelain' GBin WCAu XGra
- 'Philippe Rivoire' CKel WCAu
- 'Philomèle' EBen WCAu
- 'Pico' WCAu
- 'Picotee' WCAu
- 'Pillow Cases' WCAu
- 'Pillow Talk' CKel EBee EBen GBin ILea LRHS NLar SPoG WCAu
- 'Pink Cameo' WCAu WFar
- 'Pink Dawn' CBod EBee EPfP SPer WCAu
- 'Pink Delight' GBin WCAu
- 'Pink Giant' GBin WCAu
- 'Pink Jitterburg' XGra
- 'Pink Parfait' GBin NCGa NLar SPer WCAu
- 'Pink Princess' GBin WCAu
- 'Pink Spinners' XGra
- 'Plainsman' GBin
- 'Pom Pom' (d) WCAu
- 'Port Royale' GBin
- 'President Franklin D. Roosevelt' LRHS SWat
- 'President Lincoln' WCAu
- 'Président Poincaré' CKel MRav SWat
- 'President Taft' see *P. lactiflora* 'Reine Hortense'
- 'President Wilson' GBin
- 'Primevère' CBod CKel GBin ILea LAst LRHS NBir NCGa NLar NSti SCob SPer WCAu WFar
- 'Princess Bride' GBin WCAu
- 'Princess Margaret' WCAu
- 'Purple Spider' **new** EBee MHol
- 'Queen of Sheba' WCAu
- 'Queen Victoria' GBin
- 'Queen Wilhelmina' see *P. lactiflora* 'Koningin Wilhelmina'
- 'Raoul Dessert' WCAu
- 'Raspberry Splash' GBin
- 'Raspberry Sundae' CKel ELan ELon GBin ILea LRHS MRav NLar SPer SPoG WCAu WCot WHil
- 'Ray Payton' GBin
- 'Red Dwarf' CKel
- 'Red Emperor' WCAu
- 'Red Sarah Bernhardt' CKel EPfP GBin SDeJ

	Name	Suppliers
	– 'Red Satin' **new**	WCAu
§	– 'Reine Hortense'	CKel EBen GBin LRHS MRav
	– 'Renato'	GBin LSun XGra
	– 'Riches and Fame'	LRHS
	– 'Roland'	WCAu
	– 'Ruth Cobb'	WCAu
	– 'Salmon Dream'	CKel GBin
	– 'Sante Fe'	CBod CKel EBee EPfP ILea MSCN NLar WCAu
	– 'Sarah Bernhardt' 🏆H7	Widely available
	– 'Schaffe'	GBin
	– 'Sea Shell'	EBen GBin GMaP ILea WCAu XGra
	– 'Sebastiaan Maas'	EBee
	– 'Serene Pastel'	GBin WCAu
	– 'Shawnee Chief'	GBin
	– 'Shimmering Velvet'	CKel
	– 'Shirley Temple' (d)	CBod CKel CLet EBee ELan EPfP GBin GBuc IBoy IKil ILea LCro LRHS MBNS MBri MGos MHol MJak MRav NBir NGdn NPri SDeJ SPoG WCAu WFar
	– 'Silver Flare'	see *P. lactiflora* 'L'Étincelante'
	– 'Silver Rose'	GBin
	– 'Sir Ernest Shackleton' (d)	MRav
	– 'Sixteen Candles'	GBin
	– 'Soft Salmon Joy'	GBin WCAu XGra
	– 'Solange'	CKel GBin IKil ILea LRHS NLar SPer WCAu
	– 'Sorbet'	CKel EBee ELon EPfP ILea LHop LRHS MHol NBir NLar NPer SMad WCAu WFar
	– 'Springfield' (d)	XGra
	– 'Starlight'	CKel EBee GBin LCro LOPS LRHS MMHG NCGa SHar WCAu WCot
	– 'Strephon'	CKel
	– 'Summer Carnival'	XGra
	– 'Super Gal'	WCAu
	– 'Susie Q' (d)	EBen XGra
	– 'Suzanne Krekler'	WCAu
	– 'Svarte Petter' **new**	NCGa
	– 'Sweet Melody'	GBin WCAu
	– 'Sweet Rewards'	GBin
	– 'Sweet Sixteen'	WCAu
	– 'Sword Dance'	CKel ELon GBin IBoy ILea LRHS SDeJ WCAu XGra
	– 'Taff'	EBee
	– 'Tamate-boko'	WCAu
	– 'The Fawn' **new**	GBin NCGa WCAu
	– 'The Mighty Mo'	GBin
	– 'The Nymph'	LRHS NBir
	– 'Theatrical' (d)	WCAu
	– 'Thérèse'	WCAu
	– 'Tie Gan Zi' (d) **new**	EBen
	– 'Tom Eckhardt'	CKel GBin SPer WCAu
	– 'Top Brass'	CKel GBin ILea MRav NLar WCAu
	– 'Topeka Garnet'	GBin WCAu XGra
	– 'Toro-no-maki'	WCAu
	– 'Translucient'	CKel
	– 'Twitterpated'	EBee ELon
	– 'Unique' **new**	EBen ELan ILea WCAu
	– 'Ursa Minor' **new**	WCAu
	– 'Victoire de la Marne'	CKel ILea
	– 'Victoria Blush' (d)	WCAu
	– 'Violet Dawson'	GBin
	– 'Vivid Rose'	EBen GBin WCAu
	– 'Vogue'	CKel EBee GBin LRHS MRav SWvt WCAu
	– 'W.F. Turner'	CKel
	– 'Walter Faxon'	GBin

	Name	Suppliers
	– 'Waltz'	GBin
	– 'West Elkton'	GBin
	– 'Westerner'	GBin WCAu
	– 'White Cap'	CKel GBin ILea NCGa NLar WCAu WHil
	– 'White Grace'	GBin WCAu
	– 'White Imp' **new**	WCAu
	– 'White Rose of Sharon'	CKel
	– 'White Sands'	GBin
	– 'White Sarah Bernhardt'	SPer
	– 'White Wings'	CBcs CKel CTri EBen ELan EPfP GBin GMaP ILea LRHS MBel NCGa NLar NSti SPer SWat SWvt WCAu WCot
	– 'Whitleyi Major' 🏆H7	WCot
	– 'Wilbur Wright'	CKel GBin
	– 'Wine Red'	GBin
	– 'Wladyslawa'	GBin LRHS NLar SHar WCot
§	– 'Zi Yu Nu'	LRHS LSRN WCAu
	– 'Zuzu'	GBin WCAu
	'Lafayette Escadrille' (S)	WCAu XGra
	× ***lagodechiana***	GKev LEdu
	'Late Windflower'	CKel GBin GCra WCAu
	'Lavon' **new**	WHil
	'Leda' (S)	GBin XGra
	'Legion of Honour'	GBin
	× ***lemoinei*** (S)	WHal
§	– 'Alice Harding' (S)	CKel GBin
§	– 'Chromatella' (S)	CKel
	– 'High Noon' (S) 🏆H5	CKel GBin LRHS MPhe SKHP SWat WCot
§	– 'L'Espérance' (S)	WCAu
	– 'Marchioness' (S)	CKel GBin
§	– 'Souvenir de Maxime Cornu' (S)	CKel SKHP
	'Lemon Chiffon' **new**	GBin
	'Lemon Dream' PBR	NCGa XGra
	'Lilith' (S)	GBin
	lithophila	see *P. tenuifolia* subsp. *lithophila*
	'Little Red Gem'	GBin
	lobata 'Fire King'	see *P. peregrina*
	'Lois Arleen'	WCAu
	'Lovebirds'	GBin WCAu
	'Lovely Rose'	GBin WCAu
	ludlowii (S)	Widely available
	'Ludovica' (d) **new**	EBen
	lutea	see *P. delavayi* var. *delavayi* f. *lutea*
	'Mackinac Grand' **new**	GBin WCAu
	macrophylla	MPhe
	'Magenta Gem'	GBin XGra
	'Magical Mystery Tour' **new**	CEvo
	'Mai Fleuri'	GBin WCAu
	mairei	CExl EBen GGGa MPhe
	'Many Happy Returns'	CKel EBen GBin
	mascula	CBro EBen GEdr GKev IMou LHop LLHF NBir
§	– subsp. ***arietina***	CSpe EBee MWat
	– 'Immaculata'	MHol
§	– subsp. ***mascula***	GKev
§	– subsp. ***russoi***	CEvo GKev WThu
	– – 'Picotee'	GBin
	– – 'Reverchoni'	CTal
§	– subsp. ***triternata***	CKel GKev WCot
	'May Apple'	WCAu XGra
	'Memorial Gem' **new**	EBen
	'Merry Mayshine'	GBin XGra
	'Mikuhino-akebono'	CKel SDeJ
	mlokosewitschii 🏆H7	Widely available
	– hybrids	EBee GKev

mollis	see *P. officinalis* subsp. *villosa*
'Montezuma'	EBen GBin XGra
'Moonrise'	CKel GBin WCAu
'Morning Lilac'	CEvo
'Murad of Hershey Bar' (S)	GBin XGra
'My Love'	EBen GBin WCAu XGra
'Nike' (d)	XGra
'Normie' (d)	WCAu
'Norwegian Blush' **new**	CEvo
'Nosegay'	WCAu
'Nova'	CKel GBin
obovata 🏆H5	CCon CKel MPhe WCot
- var. ***alba*** 🏆H5	CExl GBin GEdr GKev LLHF
- var. ***willmottiae***	CExl MPhe
officinalis	CArn CEvo GCra GKev MCot
- WM 9821 from Slovenia	MPhe
- 'Alba Plena' (d)	CKel CPou EBee GMaP LRHS MRav NEgg NLar SWvt WCAu WFar WHil
- 'Anemoniflora Rosea' 🏆H7	LRHS SWvt WCAu
§ - subsp. ***banatica***	EBen GKev MPhe WCAu
- 'China Rose'	GBin
- 'Lize van Veen'	GBin
- 'Mutabilis Plena' (d)	IBlr
- 'Rosea Plena' (d) 🏆H7	CKel EBee ECtt EPfP GMaP LAst LRHS NEgg SCob SWat SWvt WCAu WFar XGra
- 'Rubra Plena' (d) 🏆H7	Widely available
§ - subsp. ***villosa***	CKel EBen ELan LRHS
'Old Faithful'	XGra
'Old Rose Dandy'	GBin
'Oriental Gold'	CKel
ostii (S)	CExl CKel GKev MPhe SKHP
§ - 'Feng Dan Bai' (S)	CKel GBin MPhe
'Pageant'	GBin XGra
'Paladin'	GBin
papaveracea	see *P. suffruticosa*
'Paramount'	GBin
'Pastel Splendor'	CKel EBen ELan GBin ILea NCGa XGra
'Paula Fay'	CKel EBee EBen EPfP GBin GMaP ILea IMou MRav SDeJ WCAu XGra
Peony with the Purple Roots	see *P. suffruticosa* 'Shou An Hong'
§ ***peregrina***	CBro CKel EBen ECho EPot GEdr GKev MPhe NLar SKHP SSpi WCot
- 'Fire King'	CKel GBin ILea NLar
§ - 'Otto Froebel' 🏆H7	CKel EBen GBin GCra NLar WCAu WCot
- 'Sunshine'	see *P. peregrina* 'Otto Froebel'
'Picotee'	EBen WCAu
'Pink Angel' **new**	EBen
'Pink Hawaiian Coral'	CKel EBee GBin ILea MMHG NCGa NLar WTor XGra
'Pink Tea Cup'	XGra
'Postilion'	EBen GBin
potaninii	see *P. delavayi* var. *angustiloba* f. *angustiloba*
'Prairie Charm'	GBin XGra
'Prairie Moon'	CKel GBin NLar WCAu
'Prince Charming'	WCAu
qiui	MPhe
'Raspberry Charm'	XGra
'Red Charm'	CKel CWCL EBee EBen EPfP EWoo GBin IBoy ILea LRHS NCGa WCAu
'Red Glory'	GBin WCAu
'Red Magic'	EBee EPfP MAvo WFar

'Red Red Rose'	EBen GBin WCAu XGra
'Renown' (S)	CKel
'Requiem'	GBin WCAu
§ ***rockii*** (S)	CKel CSpe EWoo GBin LRHS MPhe WCot
- from Tianshui, Gansu	MPhe
- from Wenshian, Gansu	MPhe
- hybrid	see *P.* Gansu Group
- subsp. ***linyanshanii*** (S)	GKev MPhe
'Roman Gold'	CKel GBin
romanica	see *P. peregrina*
'Rooster Reveille' (d)	XGra
'Rose Garland'	GBin
'Rosedale'	WCAu XGra
'Roselette'	EBen GBin NCGa WCAu
'Roselette's Child'	GBin
'Roy Pehrson's Best Yellow'	GBin
'Rubyette'	XGra
'Ruffled Pink Petticoats' (S)	GBin
russoi	see *P. mascula* subsp. *russoi*
'Salmon Beauty' (d)	WCAu
'Salmon Chiffon'	GBin XGra
'Savage Splendour'	GBin
'Scarlet Heaven'	CEvo CKel EBen GBin ILea
'Scarlet O'Hara'	CBod EBen EWoo GBin SPer WCAu WCot XGra
'Sequestered Sunshine' **new**	CEvo
'Serenade'	WCAu
'Shimano-fuji'	CKel
'Shining Light'	GBin NCGa SCob
'Show Girl'	EBen GBin NCGa WCAu XGra
'Showanohokori'	CKel
'Silver Dawn'	GBin
sinensis	see *P. lactiflora*
'Singing in the Rain' **new**	ILea
'Smith Family Yellow' **new**	CEvo
× ***smouthii***	GEdr
'Sonoma Kaleidoscope'	GBin ILea
'Soshi'	GBin LRHS NLar SHar
'Spring Carnival' (S)	GBin
'Squirt'	EBen GBin
'Stardust'	WCAu
sterniana	CExl
§ ***suffruticosa*** (S)	CWib ELan GKev MGos SSpi
- 'Akashigata' (S)	CKel
- 'Alice Palmer' (S)	CKel
- 'Bai Yu' (S)	GBin
- Bird of Rimpo	see *P. suffruticosa* 'Rimpo'
- Black Dragon Brocade	see *P. suffruticosa* 'Kokuryū-nishiki'
- Black Flower Chief	see *P. suffruticosa* 'Hei Hua Kui'
- Blue Lotus = 'Lan Fu Rong' (S)	CBcs
- Brocade of the Naniwa	see *P. suffruticosa* 'Naniwa-nishiki'
- 'Burgundy Wine' (S)	GBin
- 'Cardinal Vaughan' (S)	CKel
- 'Chu Wu' (S)	NTPC
- Colourful Butterfly = 'Hua Hu Die'	CBcs
- 'Da Hu Hong' (S)	SPoG
- 'Dou Lu' (S)	NTPC
- 'Duchess of Kent' (S)	CKel
- 'Duchess of Marlborough' (S)	CKel
- Eternal Camellias	see *P. suffruticosa* 'Yachiyo-tsubaki'
- Flames in the Furnace = 'Dan Lu Yan'	CBcs
- Flight of Cranes	see *P. suffruticosa* 'Renkaku'
- Floral Rivalry	see *P. suffruticosa* 'Hana-kisoi'
- Fragrant Jade	see *P.* 'Xiang Yu'
- 'Gekkyu-den' **new**	LRHS

	- 'Godaishu' (S)	CKel GBin LRHS SKHP
	- 'Guardian of the Monastery' (S)	GBin XGra
	- 'Hai Huang' (S)	NTPC WKif
§	- 'Hakuo-jisi' (S/d)	CKel LRHS
§	- 'Hana-kisoi' (S)	CKel GBin
	- 'Haru-no-akebono' (S)	CKel
	- 'Hei Hai Sa Jin' (S)	NTPC
§	- 'Hei Hua Kui' (S)	NTPC
	- 'Hinode-sekai' (S/d)	GBin
§	- 'Huang Hua Kui' (S)	NTPC
	- Jewel in the Lotus	see *P. suffruticosa* 'Tama-fuyo'
	- Jewelled Screen	see *P. suffruticosa* 'Tama-sudare'
	- 'Jin Zhi'	NTPC
	- 'Jing Ge' (S)	NTPC WKif
	- 'Jitsugetsu-nishiki' (S)	CKel
	- 'Joseph Rock'	see *P. rockii*
	- Kamada Brocade	see *P. suffruticosa* 'Kamada-nishiki'
§	- 'Kamada-nishiki' (S)	CKel GBin
§	- 'Kaow' (S)	CKel
	- King of Flowers	see *P. suffruticosa* 'Kaow'
	- King of White Lions	see *P. suffruticosa* 'Hakuo-jisi'
	- 'Kinkaku'	see *P.* × *lemoinei* 'Souvenir de Maxime Cornu'
	- 'Kinshi'	see *P.* × *lemoinei* 'Alice Harding'
	- 'Kokucho' (S)	CKel
§	- 'Kokuryū-nishiki' (S)	CKel SKHP
	- 'Koshi-no-yuki' (S)	CKel
	- 'Lan Bao Shi' (S)	GBin NTPC
	- 'Ma Nao He Hua' (S)	NTPC
	- 'Mo Sa Jin' (S)	NTPC
	- 'Montrose' (S)	CKel
*	- 'Mrs Shirley Fry' (S)	CKel
	- 'Mrs William Kelway' (S)	CKel
	- 'Mulberry Purple'	CBcs
§	- 'Naniwa-nishiki' (S)	CKel
	- 'Nigata Akashigata' (S)	CKel
	- Pride of Taisho	see *P. suffruticosa* 'Taisho-no-hokori'
	- 'Princess Chiffon' (S)	GBin
	- 'Reine Elisabeth' (S)	CKel
§	- 'Renkaku' (S)	CKel SKHP
§	- 'Rimpo' (S)	CKel GBin SKHP XGra
	- 'Seidai' **new**	LRHS
§	- 'Shiguregumo' (S)	CKel
	- 'Shimadaigin' (S)	CKel
	- 'Shimane-chōjuraku' (S)	CKel GBin
	- 'Shimane-hakugan' (S)	CKel
	- 'Shimane-otone-mai' (S/d)	GBin
	- 'Shimane-seidai' (S)	CKel
	- 'Shimanishiki' (S)	CKel SKHP
	- 'Shin Shima Kagayaki' (S)	CKel
	- 'Shintoyen' (S)	CKel
§	- 'Shou An Hong' (S)	NTPC
	- 'Snow Face Peach'	CBcs
	- Snow Lotus = 'Xue Lian'	CBcs
	- Snowy Pagoda = 'Xue Ta'	CBcs CKel SPoG
	- 'Sumi-no-ichi' (S)	CKel
	- 'Superb' (S)	CKel
§	- 'Taisho-no-hokori' (S)	CKel
§	- 'Taiyo' (S)	CKel SKHP
§	- 'Tama-fuyo' (S)	CKel
§	- 'Tama-sudare' (S)	CKel GBin
	- The Sun	see *P. suffruticosa* 'Taiyo'
	- 'Toichi Ruby' (S)	GBin XGra
	- 'Wu Long Peng Sheng' (S)	CKel GBin
§	- 'Yachiyo-tsubaki' (S)	CKel SKHP
	- 'Yin Hong Qiao Dui' (S)	CKel NTPC
	- 'Yoshinogawa' (S)	CKel
	- 'Yu Ban Bai' (S)	MPhe NTPC
	- 'Yu Pan Sheng Yan' (S)	NTPC
	- 'Zhao Fen' (S)	NPer SPoG
	suffruticosa × 'Ezra Pound' (S) **new**	XGra
	'Summer Glow' (d) **new**	EBen
	'Sunny Girl'	EBen GBin WCAu
	'Sunshine'	see *P. peregrina* 'Otto Froebel'
	'Taiheko'	CKel
	'Tango'	WCAu
	'Ten' i'	CKel
	tenuifolia	CAby CEvo CJun EBee EPot GBin GCal GEdr ILea SKHP SMad WCAu WCot
	- RCB UA 11	WCot
§	- subsp. ***lithophila***	MPhe
	- 'Rosea'	GBin WCAu
	'Terpsichore' (S)	GBin XGra
	'Tria' (S)	GBin
	veitchii	CKel EBen EPot GCal GKev GMaP ILea NBid NLar SSpi WCot WPGP WWFP
	- from China	MPhe
	- 'Alba'	GKev LPla
	- dwarf	WAbe
	- pale-flowered	GCal
	- var. ***woodwardii***	CCon CExl ECho GAbr GBin GCra GKev NWad SSpi WCAu WCot WHoo WThu
	'Vesuvian'	CKel
	'Viking Full Moon'	GBin
	'Wakatipu Wonder' (d) **new**	EBen
	'Walter Mains'	WCAu
	'White Emperor'	GBin
	'White Innocence'	EBen
	White Phoenix	see *P. ostii* 'Feng Dan Bai'
	'White Towers'	EBee EPfP WFar
	'Whopper'	GBin XGra
	'Wine Angel'	GBin
	'Wings of the Morning' (S)	GBin
	wittmanniana	CKel GBin GCal WCAu WCot
	- PAB 3673	LEdu
§	'Xiang Yu' (S)	SPoG
	'Yankee Doodle Dandy' (d)	CEvo
§	'Yao Huang' (S)	CBcs GBin
	Yao's Yellow	see *P.* 'Yao Huang'
	'Yellow Crown'	CKel GBin NLar WHil
	'Yellow Dream'	GBin
	'Yellow Emperor'	CDes GBin
	Yellow Flower of Summer	see *P. suffruticosa* 'Huang Hua Kui'
	'Yellow Gem'	GBin
	'Yellow Heaven'	GBin
	'Yokohama'	GBin
I	'Zephyrus' (S)	GBin XGra

Paesia (*Dennstaedtiaceae*)

scaberula	CDes CFil CLAP NBir WFib

Paliurus (*Rhamnaceae*)

spina-christi	CArn CBcs

Panax (*Araliaceae*)

ginseng	GPoy
japonicus	WCru
- BWJ 7932	WCru
quinquefolius	CEvo SBrt

Pancratium (*Amaryllidaceae*)

illyricum	GKev XEll
maritimum	ECho GKev NRog SDeJ

Pandorea (*Bignoniaceae*)

	jasminoides ♀H1c	CDoC CHll CRHN CTri EBak ECou EShb MOWG
	- 'Alba'	CRHN SPer
§	- 'Charisma' (v)	CDoC CHll EPfP EShb LSou MOWG SEND SPer SPoG
	- 'Lady Di'	MOWG
	- 'Rosea Superba' ♀H1c	CBcs CRHN LHop SEND SPer
	- 'Variegata'	see *P. jasminoides* 'Charisma'
	lindleyana	see *Clytostoma calystegioides*
	pandorana	CHll CRHN SLim
	- 'Golden Showers'	CBcs CRHN MOWG MRav SEND

Panicum (*Poaceae*)

	amarum	CBod
	var. ***amarulum*** new	
	- 'Dewey Blue'	EPPr MAvo SMHy
	bulbosum	CKno EHoe EPPr
	clandestinum	EHoe EPPr EWes IMou LRHS MMuc MWhi SEND SMea
§	'Fibre Optics'	CSpe EBee
	miliaceum	LRHS
	- 'Purple Majesty'	CWib
	- 'Violaceum'	SPhx
	oligosanthes var. ***scribnerianum***	SPhx
	virgatum	CKno WMnd WWEG XLum
	- 'Blue Tower'	CKno ELon EPPr LRHS SGSe SMea XLum
	- 'Cardinal'	EPPr MNrw
	- 'Cloud Nine'	CKno EPPr LRHS MAvo NOak SGSe SMHy WHal WRHF WWEG
	- 'Dallas Blues'	CBod CKno EBee ECha EHoe EPPr EShb EWes LAst LHop LRHS MAvo MCot MWhi NOak NSti NWsh SCob SGSe SHDw SMHy SPer SPoG WMoo WPGP WWEG XLum
	- 'Emerald Chief'	LSun MWhi
	- 'Farbende Auslese'	WWEG
	- 'Hänse Herms'	CBod CKno EHoe ELon EPPr LRHS MWhi NLar SMea WFar WWEG
	- 'Heavy Metal'	Widely available
	- 'Heiliger Hain'	EPPr MAvo WCot WWEG
I	- 'Kupferhirse'	EPPr MAvo
	- 'Kurt Bluemel' new	SAko
	- 'Nican'	EPPr
	- 'Northwind'	CKno EBee EHoe EPPr LRHS MAvo SCob SHDw SMHy SMad WFar WWEG
	- 'Pathfinder'	SGSe
	- 'Prairie Sky'	CBod CKno CPrp EAEE EBee EHoe ELon EPPr EUJe EWoo GBin LEdu LHop LRHS MAsh MAvo MMuc NBro NLar NWsh SCob SGSe SGbt SMHy SMad SMea WMoo WPGP WWEG
	- 'Purple Haze'	CKno EHoe EPPr LRHS WWEG
	- 'Red Cloud'	CKno MAvo SMHy WWEG
	- 'Rehbraun'	CSde EBee EHoe EPPr EPfP LEdu LHop LOPS LRHS MJak NOak SGol WWEG XLum
	- 'Rotstrahlbusch'	CKno CWib EBee EHoe EPPr EWoo GMaP LSun MAvo MWhi NOak SPer WCot WMoo WWEG XLum XSen
	- 'Rubrum'	EHoe ELan EPPr MAvo WMoo
	- 'Shenandoah'	Widely available
	- 'Squaw'	CBod CKno CMac CPrp CWib EAEE EHoe EPPr EPfP EShb EWoo LRHS MAvo MJak MMuc NLar NOak NWsh SBea SEND SGSe SMad SPer WCot WFar WMoo WWEG XSen
	- 'Straight Cloud'	EPPr
	- 'Strictum'	EHoe EPPr EWes GQue LEdu LPla MAvo SCob SMHy SPer SPhx WMoo WWEG
I	- 'Strictum Compactum'	CBod
	- 'Warrior'	CBod CKno CPrp EAEE EAJP EHoe EHrv ELan ELon EPPr EPfP EWTr GBin LHop LRHS MAsh MAvo MCot MWhi NWsh SCob SDix SGSe SPer WFar WWEG
	- 'Wood's Variegated' (v)	WCot

Papaver ✿ (*Papaveraceae*)

	aculeatum	CTca
	alboroseum	LLHF LRHS
	'Alpha Centauri' (SPS)	SWat
	alpinum	CSpe LRHS MAsh NGdn SWat
	amurense	SWat
	atlanticum	NBro NGdn SPlb
	- 'Flore Pleno' (d)	CSpe IFro NBro NGdn
	'Aurora' (SPS)	SWat
	'Beyond Red' (SPS)	SWat
	bracteatum	see *P. orientale* var. *bracteatum*
	'Bright Star' (SPS)	CDes GBin SWat
	burseri	SRot
	'Cathay' (SPS)	SWat
	commutatum ♀H5	CSpe ELan SPhx SWat
	- 'Ladybird' ♀H5	CBot SPoG SVic
	corona-sancti-stephani	SWat
	'Danish Flag'	CBot NNor
	dubium	CSpe SPhx
	- subsp. ***lecoqii*** new	SPhx
	'Eccentric Silk' (SPS)	SWat
§	'Fire Ball' (d)	GCal NBid NBro SWat WRHF WWEG
	glaucum	LRHS SPhx
	'Heartbeat' PBR (SPS)	CSpe EBee EPfP IPot LRHS LSun MBel SWat WCot WFar WRHF
	heldreichii	see *P. pilosum* subsp. *spicatum*
	hybridum 'Flore Pleno' (d)	NSti SWat
	'Jacinth' (SPS)	GBin SWat
	lateritium	CHid CPou SRms
	- 'Nanum Flore Pleno'	see *P.* 'Fire Ball'
	'Lauffeuer'	CSam ELon SWat
	'Matador' PBR ♀H7	CWCL EBee LBrs LRHS NLar NNor WCot
	'Medallion' (SPS)	CDes EPri GBin LRHS MAvo SWat
§	***miyabeanum***	CSpe ECho ELan LRHS SRot
	- ***tatewakii***	see *P. miyabeanum*
	'Moondance'	LRHS
	nanum 'Flore Pleno'	see *P.* 'Fire Ball'
§	***nudicaule***	SVic
	- Champagne Bubbles Group	CBod NNor SWat
	- - 'Champagne Bubbles Scarlet' new	NPri
	- var. ***croceum*** 'Flamenco'	NNor
	- Garden Gnome Group	see *P. nudicaule* Gartenzwerg Group
§	- Gartenzwerg Group ♀H7	CSpe EPfP LRHS NGdn NPri SPlb SPoG SRot SWvt WHar WRHF
	- orange-flowered	LRHS
	- 'Pacino'	EAJP LRHS NLar
	- 'Party Fun' (mixed)	CSpe EAJP
	- 'Summer Breeze Orange' ♀H7	NPri
	- 'Summer Breeze Yellow'	NPri

	- Wonderland Series	NNor
	- - 'Wonderland Orange'	ELan NPri
	- - 'Wonderland Pink Shades'	NPri
	- - 'Wonderland White'	ELan NPri
	- - 'Wonderland Yellow'	ELan
	orientale	CBcs CTsd EPfP LPal NBFr SRms SVic SWat WBod WHar
	- 'Abu Hassan'	IPot SWat
	- 'Aglaja' ♀H7	CElw CWCL ECtt LRHS MHol MPie NEgg NGdn NPri SPad SWat WCot
	- 'Aladin'	SWat
	- 'Ali Baba'	GCra SWat
	- 'Alison'	SWat
	- 'Allegro'	CBod CMac CSBt EAJP EBee ELon EPfP EWoo GMaP IBoy LRHS MBNS MRav NGdn SBod SCob SPer SPlb SVic SWat SWvt WFar
	- 'Arwide'	SWat
	- 'Aslahan'	MRav SWat
	- 'Atrosanguineum'	SWat
	- 'Avebury Crimson'	SWat
	- 'Baby Kiss'PBR	ECtt SWat WFar
	- 'Ballkleid'	SWat
	- 'Beauty Queen'	ECha MRav NGdn SWat
	- 'Bergermeister Rot'	SWat
	- 'Big Jim'	SWat
	- 'Black and White' ♀H7	ELan EPfP MPkF MRav NEgg SWat
	- 'Blackberry Queen'	SWat
	- 'Blickfang'	SWat
	- 'Bolero'	CWCL EBee ECtt EPri NLar WCAu
	- 'Bonfire'	SCob
	- 'Bonfire Red'	SWat
§	- var. ***bracteatum***	NBir SWat
	- 'Brilliant'	COtt EPfP NGdn SWat WFar WMoo
	- 'Brooklyn' (New York Series)	EBee ECtt LRHS LSRN MAvo SWat
	- 'Burning Heart'	CWCL CWGN ECtt EPri IBoy IPot LRHS SWat WCAu
	- 'Carmen'PBR	CWCL ECtt WCot
*	- 'Carneum'	LRHS WWEG
	- 'Carnival'	EBee SWat
	- 'Catherina'	SWat
	- 'Cedar Hill'	ECtt EPri EWes GCal MHol MRav SWat
	- 'Cedric Morris' ♀H7	ECha ELan MRav SWat WCot WMnd
	- 'Central Park' (New York Series)	CBod ELon ILea LRHS SPoG SWat WCAu WFar WHoo
I	- 'Charming' pink-flowered	CAby CMac ECtt SPhx SWat
	- 'Charming' red-flowered	LRHS
	- 'China Boy'	SWat
	- 'Clochard'	CElw ECtt SWat WCot
	- 'Coral Reef'	EPfP IFro MHer MLHP SWat WHar WMoo WRHF
	- 'Corrina'	SWat
	- 'Curlilocks'	ECtt ELan IBoy LRHS MRav SRms SWat SWvt WCot WFar WWEG
	- 'Derwisch'	SWat
*	- 'Diana'	SWat
	- 'Double Pleasure'	ECtt SWat
	- double red shades (d)	EAJP NGdn
	- 'Doubloon' (d)	SWat WFar
	- 'Dwarf Allegro Vivace'	LRHS
	- 'Earl Grey'	SWat
	- 'Effendi' ♀H7	ECtt SWat WCot
	- 'Elam Pink'	SWat WCot
	- 'Erste Zuneigung'	SWat
	- 'Eskimo Pie'	SWat
	- 'Eyecatcher'	ELon SGol
	- 'Fancy Feathers'PBR	ECtt SWat WHil
	- 'Fatima'	SWat
	- 'Feuerriese'	SWat
	- 'Feuerzwerg'	SWat
	- 'Fiesta'	ELon SWat
	- 'Firefly'PBR	CWCL SWat
	- 'Flamenco'	EBee IBoy SWat WFar
	- 'Flamingo'	IBoy SWat
*	- 'Flore Pleno' (d)	NGdn
	- 'Forncett Summer'	EAJP ECtt LBrs LRHS MAvo MRav NLar SPer SWat WCot WWEG
	- 'Frosty' (v)	SHar
	- 'Fruit Punch'	MNHC
	- 'Garden Glory'	ECtt LSRN MArl SWat WCAu
	- 'Glowing Embers'	ECtt SWat
	- 'Glowing Rose'	SWat
	- Goliath Group	ELan MRav NBro SCob SDix SRms SWat WFar WMnd
	- - 'Beauty of Livermere'	Widely available
§	- - 'Beauty of Livermere' clonal	ECtt WCot
	- 'Graue Witwe'	EBee SWat
	- 'Guardsman'	see *P. orientale* (Goliath Group) 'Beauty of Livermere' clonal
	- 'Halima'	SWat
	- 'Harlem' (New York Series)	CBod CElw CWCL EBee ELon EPfP LAst LCro MAvo MSCN MWhi SPer SWat
	- 'Harvest Moon' (d)	ECtt NPer SWat WHal WWEG
	- 'Heidi'	SWat
	- 'Hoo House Red' **new**	WHoo
	- 'Hula Hula'	SWat
	- 'Indian Chief'	EPri LRHS MRav NPer SHil WFar
	- 'Inferno'PBR	ECtt
	- 'John III' ♀H7	SPhx SWat
	- 'John Metcalf'	ECtt MRav SWat
	- 'Juliane'	ECha SWat
	- 'Karine' ♀H7	CElw CSam ECha ELan EPPr EPfP IBoy LHop LRHS SDix SGol SWat
	- 'Khedive' (d) ♀H7	EBee SWat
	- 'King George'	SWat
	- 'King Kong'	ECtt MBel MHol NLar SPer SWat WCot WFar
	- 'Kleine Tänzerin'	CSam MRav SWat WFar
	- 'Kollebloem'	SWat
	- 'Lady Frederick Moore'	SWat
	- 'Lady Roscoe'	SWat
	- 'Ladybird'	EPfP LRHS
	- 'Laffeuer'	SPhx
	- 'Lambada'	SWat
	- 'Lauren's Lilac'	LSRN SWat
	- 'Leuchtfeuer' ♀H7	SWat
	- 'Lighthouse' ♀H7	EBee SWat WCAu
	- 'Lilac Girl'	SWat
	- 'Little Candyfloss'PBR	SWat
	- 'Little Patty Plum'PBR	NLar
	- 'Louvre' (Parisienne Series)	ECtt SPoG SWat WFar
	- 'Maiden's Blush'	ECtt SWat
	- 'Manhattan' (New York Series)	CElw CSam ECtt ELon EPfP EWes LCro LOPS LRHS MNrw MSCN NSti SGbt SPer SPoG SWat WFar WHoo
	- 'Marcus Perry'	ECtt EWes LRHS NGdn SGol SWat
	- 'Marlene'	CFis ILea IPot LRHS SWat
	- 'Mary Finnan'	CTca SWat
	- 'Master Richard'	SWat
	- 'May Queen' (d)	ECtt ELon EWes IBlr MRav NSti SWat WCot WFar WPnn
	- 'May Sadler'	SWat
	- 'Midnight'	SWat
	- 'Miss Piggy'PBR	EBee ECtt IKil LLHF SGbt SPer SWat WCot WFar WHil

- 'Mrs H.G. Stobart' SWat
- 'Mrs Marrow's Plum' see *P. orientale* 'Patty's Plum'
- 'Mrs Perry' CMea COtt CSBt ECtt ELan IFro LRHS NGdn NPer SGbt SPer SRms SWat WBrk WCot WFar WMnd
- 'Nanum Flore Pleno' see *P.* 'Fire Ball'
- 'Noema' SWat
- 'Orange Glow' SWat WMoo
- 'Orangeade Maison' SWat
- 'Oriana' SWat
- 'Oriental' SWat
- 'Pale Face' SWat
- 'Papillon'[PBR] CBcs LRHS MPie NPri WCot WHar
- 'Paradiso'[PBR] EPfP

§ - 'Patty's Plum' Widely available
- 'Perry's White' CBcs CBod COtt CSBt CWCL EBee ECtt ELan ELon EPfP EWoo GMaP IBoy LHop LRHS MRav SGol SHil SPer SPoG SRkn SWat SWvt WCAu WMnd
- 'Persepolis' SGol
- 'Peter Pan' ELon SWat
- 'Petticoat' ECtt SWat
- 'Picotée' ECtt ELan LRHS MRav NEgg NLar SPer SPoG SRot SWat SWvt WCAu WFar WMoo
- 'Pink Lassie' SWat
- 'Pink Panda' SWat
- 'Pink Pearl'[PBR] EBee SWat WCot
- 'Pink Ruffles'[PBR] ECtt LCro LRHS SGbt SPoG SWat WFar
- 'Pinnacle' EPri SWat WFar
- 'Pizzicato' CBod CWib EPfP NNor NPer SWat WFar WHar WMoo
- 'Place Pigalle' (Parisienne Series) ECtt EPfP SPoG SWat
- 'Plum Pudding' CHid
- 'Polka' SWat
- 'Prince of Orange' SWat SWvt
- Princess Victoria Louise see *P. orientale* 'Prinzessin Victoria Louise'
- 'Prinz Eugen' SWat WFar

§ - 'Prinzessin Victoria Louise' COtt EAJP ELan EPfP EUJe IBoy LAst LRHS MMuc NGdn NLar NNor SEND SWat WBrk WHar
- 'Prospero' SWat
- 'Queen Alexandra' NGdn
- 'Raspberry Queen' CCon CMac CMea ECtt ELan EPfP EPri GMaP IBoy IPot LAst MArl MBel MRav NChi SWat WHal WMnd
- 'Raspberry Ruffles' SWat
- 'Rembrandt' LPal MJak SWat
- 'Rosenpokal' SWat
- 'Roter Zwerg' ECha SWat
- 'Royal Chocolate Distinction' CElw CSpe CWCL EBee ECtt ELan ELon EPPr EPfP GBin LOPS LRHS LSRN NPri NSti SPoG SRot SWat WFar
- 'Royal Wedding' Widely available
- 'Ruffled Patty'[PBR] ECtt EPfP LCro MHol SGbt SWat WCot
- 'Ruffled Princess of Orange'[PBR] SWat

* - 'Saffron' SWat
- 'Salmon Glow' (d) SWat WFar WWEG
- 'Salome' SWat
- 'Scarlet King' CMac SWat
- scarlet-flowered MMuc SEND
- 'Scarlett O'Hara'[PBR] (d) ECtt EPfP LLHF MPkF SPoG SWat WFar
- 'Showgirl' SWat

* - 'Silberosa' IPot SWat
- 'Sindbad' SWat
- 'Snow Goose' CMea CSpe CWGN EBee ECtt ELon ESwi GAbr IPot LLHF LRHS LSun MBel MHol NLar NPri SPoG SWat WCAu WCot WHoo WKif
- 'Snow Queen' WCAu
- 'Spätzünder' SWat
- 'Springtime' LAst MRav SWat WCAu
- 'Staten Island' (New York Series) MAvo
- Stormtorch see *P. orientale* 'Sturmfackel'

§ - 'Sturmfackel' SWat
- 'Suleika' SWat
- 'Sultana' CSam EPri MArl SWat
- 'Sunset'[PBR] SWat
- 'The Promise' SWat
- 'Tiffany' CMac ECtt LSRN MAvo NEgg SPoG SWat
- 'Trinity' SWat
- 'Türkenlouis' CBod ECtt GCra GMaP IBoy ILea LAst LRHS MRav NGdn NLar SHil SPer SWat WBrk WCAu WFar
- 'Turkish Delight' EHrv EWoo GCra LRHS MRav NBir NPri SHil SPoG SWat SWvt WMnd WWEG
- 'Tutu' SWat
- 'Victoria Dreyfuss' SWat
- 'Viola' SWat
- 'Violetta' SWat
- 'Walking Fire' MNrw
- 'Water Babies' SWat
- 'Watermelon' CWCL ECtt EWoo SWat
- 'White Ruffles'[PBR] CBod CWCL ECtt IKil SGbt SPoG SWat
- 'Wisley Beacon' SWat
- 'Wunderkind' SWat

pilosum SGSe SWat

§ - subsp. ***spicatum*** CCon CSpe ECha GBin GCal LHop LPla NBir WCot WHer WMoo

'Rhapsody in Red' (SPS) SWat

rhoeas CHab GPoy LCro MNHC NNor SVic WJek
- Angels' Choir Group (d) NNor SWat
- 'Bridal White' SPhx
- Mother of Pearl Group CSpe SPhx SWat
- Shirley Group CWCL NNor

rupifragum ECha GAbr WCot WPnn
- 'Double Tangerine Gem' see *P. rupifragum* 'Flore Pleno'

§ - 'Flore Pleno' (d) CLet CSpe EAJP GBin LAst MMuc NCGa NChi SVic WBrk WMoo

'Serena' (SPS) SWat

'Shasta' (SPS) EBee GBin LRHS MBel SWat WFar

'Snow White' (SPS) CDes SWat

somniferum CLau ENfk GPoy SVic SWat
- 'Blackcurrant Fizz' (d) LCro SPhx
- 'Boudoir Babe' (d) CSpe
- 'Danish Flag' CBot
- 'Double Shiraz' (d) **new** LRHS
- (Laciniatum Group) 'Crimson Feathers' NNor
- 'Lauren's Grape' CSpe LCro SPhx
- Paeoniiflorum Group (d) SWat
- - 'Black Beauty' (d) CSpe SDeJ SVic SWat
- - 'Black Paeony' (d) CBot LCro LRHS SPhx
- - 'Schwarzer Drachen' **new** LRHS
- 'Pink Chiffon' (d) SWat
- 'Ragged Red' (d) CSpe

- subsp. ***setigerum***	NNor
- single white-flowered	CSpe
- 'White Cloud' (d)	CSpe SWat
'Tequila Sunrise' (SPS)	MAvo SWat
'The Falklands' (SPS)	SWat
triniifolium	CSpe GCal MMuc WCot
'Vesuvius' (SPS)	GBin SWat
'Viva' (SPS)	CDes SWat
'Water Melon'	EPri

papaya (pawpaw) see *Carica papaya*

Parabenzoin see *Lindera*

Paracaryum (*Boraginaceae*)

racemosum	CPBP SIgm

Parachampionella see *Strobilanthes*

Paradisea (*Asparagaceae*)

liliastrum misapplied	see *P. lusitanica*
liliastrum (L.) Bertol. ♀H5	CHid EBee ECho EPfP EPri GCal LRHS NBid NChi WHil WPtf
- 'Major'	EBee ECho GKev ITim
§ ***lusitanica***	CAvo CDes CMHG CSam CSpe CTca EBee ECho ECtt EPot EPri GBin GCal GKev IBlr IBoy LEdu MCot MHol MSCN SGSe WCot WPGP WRHF

Parahebe (*Plantaginaceae*)

'Angela'	MSCN
× ***bidwillii***	GJos MHer NHar SRms SRot
- 'Kea'	ECho SRot
§ ***catarractae***	CExl CTri CWib EBee ECho ECou EPfP GAbr GCra ITim MLHP NBir NBro SRms WKif
- 'Avalanche'PBR	GMaP LRHS SCob WNPC
- blue-flowered	CDoC SPer WBor
§ - 'Delight' ♀H4	CExl EWes GMaP GQue LHop LRHS MHer NPer SDix SRot
- subsp. ***diffusa***	NPer
- 'Miss Willmott'	SPer SPlb
- 'Porlock'	GKev SRot WHoo
- 'Porlock Purple'	see *P. catarractae* 'Delight'
- 'Rosea'	ECho MAsh SRms
- white-flowered	CBot CSpe MLHP SRms
densifolia	see *Chionohebe densifolia*
§ ***formosa***	SPlb SVen
'Greencourt'	see *P. catarractae* 'Delight'
§ ***hookeriana***	ECou
'Kenty Pink' **new**	LRHS MMuc
linifolia	CTri
- 'Blue Skies'	EPot
§ ***lyallii***	EBee ECho EPfP GMaP MCot MHer MMuc MRav MSwo NQui SPlb SRms WKif
- 'Julie-Anne' ♀H4	GCal LRHS
- 'Rosea'	CTri
- 'Snowcap'	CDoC LRHS MRav SPlb
'Mervyn'	CNor CTri
§ ***perfoliata***	CBot CExl CMac CSde EBee ECha ELan EPri GAbr GCal GGal GMaP LEdu LHop LRHS MAsh MCot MMuc MNrw MRav NChi SDix SEND SPer SRms XLum
'Snow Clouds'	CMea EBee EPfP EWoo GKev MMuc SBch SDix SRot

Parakmeria see *Magnolia*

Paramongaia (*Amaryllidaceae*)

weberbaueri	CPne

Paranomus (*Proteaceae*)

reflexus	SPlb

Paraquilegia (*Ranunculaceae*)

§ ***anemonoides***	CExl GKev WAbe
grandiflora	see *P. anemonoides*

Parasenecio (*Asteraceae*)

delphiniifolius B&SWJ 5789	WCru
- B&SWJ 10885	WCru
- B&SWJ 11189	WCru WSHC
- B&SWJ 11415	WCru
farfarifolius	WCru
- var. ***acerinus*** B&SWJ 11549	WCru
- - B&SWJ 11554	WCru
- var. ***bulbifer***	WCru
hastatus var. ***farfarifolius***	see *P. maximowiczianus*
kiusianus B&SWJ 11460	WCru
§ ***maximowiczianus*** B&SWJ 11468	WCru
mortonii GWJ 9419	WCru
- HWJK 2214	WCru
tebakoensis B&SWJ 11167	WCru
- B&SWJ 11536	WCru

Paraserianthes (*Mimosaceae*)

distachya	see *P. lophantha*
§ ***lophantha*** ♀H2	CExl EAla EBak SPlb

Parasyringa see *Ligustrum*

Parathelypteris (*Thelypteridaceae*)

§ ***novae-boracensis***	ISha NLos

× *Pardancanda* (*Iridaceae*)

norrisii	see *Iris* × *norrisii*

Pardanthopsis (*Iridaceae*)

dichotoma	see *Iris dichotoma*

Parietaria (*Urticaceae*)

judaica	CArn GPoy WHer WSFF

Paris ✿ (*Melanthiaceae*)

chinensis	WCru
- B&SWJ 265 from Taiwan	WCru
delavayi	WCru
fargesii	ECho GKev LAma WCru
- var. ***brevipetalata***	WCru
- var. ***petiolata***	WCru
forrestii	WCru
incompleta	CArn CLAP EPot GCal LEdu MAvo WCru
japonica	GKev LAma WCru
lancifolia B&SWJ 3044 from Taiwan	WCru
mairei	WCru
polyphylla	CBro CCon ECho GEdr GKev LAma LRHS MNrw NBid NLar NWad SDix SKHP WCru WPnP
- B&SWJ 2125	WCru
- HWJCM 475	WCru
- var. ***stenophylla***	CCon EBee GKev LAma WCru

- var. ***yunnanensis***	ECho GEdr
* - - ***alba***	GCal
quadrifolia	CLAP CSpe EBee ECho EPfP GCal GEdr GKev GPoy LEdu MAvo MNrw NLar NMyG SKHP SPhx SSpi WCru WHer WPGP WPnP WShi
- SDR 2828	GKev
tetraphylla	WCru
thibetica	CCon EBee ECho GKev LRHS NBid NWad SKHP WCru
- var. ***apetala***	WCru
- var. ***thibetica***	GEdr
verticillata	LAma WCru
- 'Ryokutei' (d)	WCru

Parnassia (*Celastraceae*)

SDR 5128	EBee
foliosa **new**	GEdr
grandifolia	CEvo
nubicola	GKev
palustris	WHer
- var. ***izuinsularis***	GEdr
- var. ***yakushimensis***	GEdr

Parochetus (*Papilionaceae*)

§ ***africanus*** ♀[H2]	CHid ECre
communis misapplied	see *P. africanus*
communis ambig.	CCon CDes CExl MSCN NPer
- from Himalaya	EBee GCra

Paronychia (*Caryophyllaceae*)

sp.	SIgm
§ ***capitata***	CTri SRms WHoo
kapela	SPlb XSen
- 'Binsted Gold' (v)	XLum XSen
§ - subsp. ***serpyllifolia***	GBin XLum
nivea	see *P. capitata*
serpyllifolia	see *P. kapela* subsp. *serpyllifolia*

Parrotia (*Hamamelidaceae*)

persica	Widely available
- 'Bella' **new**	CJun EBee MBlu
- 'Biltmore'	CJun NLar SSta
- 'Burgundy'	CJun EPfP NLar
- fastigiate **new**	CJun
- 'Felicie'	CJun EPfP IArd NLar
- 'Het Plantsoen'	NLar
- 'Jodrell Bank'	CJun MBlu NLar SBir
§ - 'Lamplighter' (v)	CJun
- 'Pendula'	CJun CMCN EPfP MBlu SSta
- 'Persian Carpet'	NLar
- 'Summer Bronze'	CJun LRHS LSRN MAsh SBir
- 'Vanessa' ♀[H6]	CBcs CDoC CJun CLnd CMCN CMac EBee EPfP EWes GBin GKin IArd LRHS MAsh MBlu MGos NLar SAko SBir SGol SPoG SSta WMou
- 'Variegata'	see *P. persica* 'Lamplighter'
subaequalis	CDul CJun IArd NLar WPGP

Parrotiopsis (*Hamamelidaceae*)

jacquemontiana	CBcs CJun GBin IVic MBlu NLar

parsley see *Petroselinum crispum*

Parthenium (*Asteraceae*)

integrifolium	CArn GPoy IMou SPhx WCot

Parthenocissus (*Vitaceae*)

sp.	LPar
§ ***henryana*** ♀[H5]	Widely available
himalayana	CBcs
- 'Purpurea'	see *P. himalayana* var. *rubrifolia*
§ - var. ***rubrifolia***	CBcs CMac CRHN CWCL ELan EUJe GBin LRHS MRav SLim SLon SPtp WCru
inserta misapplied	see *P. quinquefolia*
inserta ambig.	CMac CTsd NLar
laetevirens	NLar
§ ***quinquefolia***	Widely available
- var. ***engelmannii***	CBcs EShb LAst LBuc SCob WCFE
- 'Guy's Garnet'	WCru
- Red Wall = 'Troki' **new**	LRHS
- Star Showers = 'Monham' (v)	EBee EPfP NLar
- 'Yellow Wall'[PBR]	LRHS
semicordata B&SWJ 6551	WCru
striata	see *Cissus striata*
thomsonii	see *Cayratia thomsonii*
§ ***tricuspidata***	CCVT CDul EBee EHoe EPfP IBoy LAst MAsh MGos SCob SGol SPer
- 'Beverley Brook'	CRHN ELon LRHS LSRN MBri NLar SPer SRms
- 'Crûg Compact'	WCru
- 'Fenway Park'	CFlo CKel EBee ELan LRHS MRav NLar
- 'Green Spring'	CBcs IArd MGos NLar
- 'Lowii'	CMac EBee EPfP LRHS MBlu MGos MRav NLar SLon
- 'Purpurea'	CKel
§ - 'Veitchii' ♀[H5]	Widely available

Pasithea (*Hemerocallidaceae*)

caerulea	CAbP CMea EBee EPri ESwi LHop LSun MBel MHol MSCN NGBl SBrt SPad SPoG SRkn WCot WPGP

Paspalum (*Poaceae*)

glaucifolium	MNrw
quadrifarium RCB RA S-5	WCot

Passiflora ✿ (*Passifloraceae*)

actinia	CRHN SPlb
§ 'Amethyst' ♀[H3]	CBcs CFlo CKel CRHN CSBt LHop LSRN SPoG
amethystina misapplied	see *P.* 'Amethyst'
§ ***amethystina*** Mikan	ECre LRHS
antioquiensis misapplied	see *P.* × *exoniensis*
antioquiensis ambig.	CBcs CTsd MOWG
antioquiensis H. Karst. ♀[H2]	CHll CRHN
× ***belotii*** 'Perfume Passion'[PBR]	EShb
'Betty Myles Young'	CKel CRHN LRHS
§ ***caerulea*** ♀[H4]	Widely available
- 'Clear Sky'[PBR]	CFlo CKel EBee ELan EPfP EUJe LRHS NLar
- 'Constance Eliott' ♀[H4]	CAgr CBcs CDoC CFlo CKel CMac COtt CRHN CSBt CWib ELan EPfP LBMP LCro LRHS MAsh MBri MHer MOWG NLar SCob SGol SPer SWvt
- ***rubra***	CSBt
- 'White Lightning'	CFlo CKel CWSG ELan LRHS NPri SHil SLim SPoG SWvt
× ***caeruleoracemosa***	see *P.* × *violacea*
chinensis	see *P. caerulea*
citrina	MOWG
* ***classica*** × ***coccinea***	CBcs CDoC ELan

	× ***colvillii***	CHll
	'Debby'	LSRN
	Eden = 'Hil Pas Eden' ♀H3	CFlo CKel MBri SCoo SRkn
	edulis (F)	CBcs CLau SPre SVic
§	× ***exoniensis*** ♀H2	CDoC CHll CRHN CSBt ECre
	'Hill House'	CHll
	incarnata (F)	GPoy IFro SPlb
	'Incense' (F) ♀H2	SPlb
	'Justine Lyons'	CKel LRHS
	'Lambiekins'	CKel LRHS
	'Lilac Lady'	see *P.* × *violacea* 'Tresederi'
I	***matthewsii*** 'Alba'	CRHN
	'Mavis Mastics'	see *P.* × *violacea* 'Tresederi'
	mayana	see *P. caerulea*
	mollissima misapplied	see *P. tarminiana*
	mollissima ambig. (F)	CBcs MOWG SPlb
	mollissima (Kunth) L.H. Bailey (F) ♀H2	CRHN
	onychina	see *P. amethystina* Mikan
	'Party Animal'	CKel LRHS
	'Pink Passion' PBR	ELan EShb
	'Poppet'	CKel LRHS
	'Purple Haze'	CKel CWib LRHS WBor
	quadrangularis (F) ♀H1a	CHll
	quinquangularis	CBcs
	rubra	SLim
	'Silly Cow'	CKel LRHS
	'Smythiana'	CBot
	'Star of Bristol' ♀H2	CKel SLim
	'Star of Surbiton'	LRHS
§	***tarminiana*** (F)	CRHN CSBt
	- white-flowered	CRHN
	tetrandra	CExl
	× ***tresederi***	see *P.* × *violacea* 'Tresederi'
§	× ***violacea*** ♀H2	CBcs CRHN
	- 'Lilac Lady'	see *P.* × *violacea* 'Tresederi'
§	- 'Tresederi'	ELan WFar
	- 'Victoria'	CSBt EBee EUJe LSou
	'White Wedding'	CKel

passion fruit see *Passiflora*

passion fruit, banana see *Passiflora mollissima* (Kunth) L.H. Bailey

Pastinaca (*Apiaceae*)

sativa	CHab SVic

Patersonia (*Iridaceae*)

occidentalis	LRHS SPlb

Patrinia ✿ (*Caprifoliaceae*)

	gibbosa	CSam CSpe CTal ECtt MLHP MMHG MMuc NLar SGSe SPhx WMoo WPnP WWFP
	- B&SWJ 874	WCru
	heterophylla HEHEHE 298	ITim
	aff. ***punctiflora*** **new**	NDov
	rupestris B&SWJ 12654	WCru
	scabiosifolia	CElw CHll CKno CSpe ECha ECtt EWld GJos MHer NBir NLar SDix SGSe SPhx WFar WHoo WMoo WTcb
	- B&SWJ 8740	WCru
	- 'Nagoya'	MNrw
	triloba	CPla CSpe CTal ECho GCal GEdr LRHS LSou MMHG WFar WMoo
*	- 'Minor'	ECho ECtt
	- var. ***palmata***	EBee GKev LHop WMoo
	villosa	CExl EBee GJos IMou NGdn WHil

Paulownia (*Paulowniaceae*)

	catalpifolia	NLar SAko
	elongata	NLar
	fargesii misapplied	see *P. tomentosa* 'Lilacina'
	fortunei	IVic MBlu SAko SPlb
	- Fast Blue = 'Minfast' ♀H5	CExl CHGN ESwi LLHF LSRN SGol WHar
	kawakamii	EBee EPfP SChF WBod WPGP
	- RWJ 9909	WCru
	'Purple Spendour' **new**	SAko
	tomentosa ♀H5	Widely available
	- 'Coreana'	CHll WCru
§	- 'Lilacina'	CBcs
	undulate-leaved, from Taiwan **new**	CMCN

Pavonia (*Malvaceae*)

praemorsa	EBee

pawpaw (false banana) see *Asimina triloba*

pawpaw (papaya) see *Carica papaya*

peach see *Prunus persica*

pear see *Pyrus communis*

pear, Asian see *Pyrus pyrifolia*

pecan see *Carya illinoinensis*

Pedicularis (*Orobanchaceae*)

SDR 7872 **new**	GKev
SDR 7920 **new**	GKev
SDR 7926 **new**	GKev

Peganum (*Nitrariaceae*)

harmala	SBrt

Pelargonium ✿ (*Geraniaceae*)

	'A.M. Mayne' (Z/d)	WFib
	'Abba' (Z/d)	WFib
	abrotanifolium (Sc)	ENfk EWoo MHer SVen WFib WGwG
	- broad-leaved	WCot
	acetosum	EWoo GCal MHer SPhx
	'Ada Green' (R)	WFib
	'Adam's Quilt' (Z/C)	LAll
	'Ade's Elf' (Z/St)	NFir
	'Ainsdale Beauty' (Z)	WFib
	'Ainsdale Duke' (Z)	NFir
	album	LAst
	'Alcyone' (Dw/d)	LAll
	'Alde' (Min)	LAll NFir
	'Aldwyck' (R) ♀H1c	WFib
	'Alex Kitson' (Z)	WFib
	'Algenon' (Min/d)	WFib
I	'Alice' (Min)	WFib
	'Alice Greenfield' (Z)	NFir
	'Allesley Shadow' (Dw/d)	WFib
	alpinum	MHer
	'Alta Bell' (R)	ELan
	'Always' (Z/d)	LAll
	'Amari' (R)	WFib
	'Ambrose' (Min/d)	LAll WFib
	Amelit = 'Pacameli' PBR (I/d)	MCot SSea
	Ameta = 'Pacmeta' PBR (Z)	SSea
	'Amethyst' (R)	LAll SCoo WFib

	(Angeleyes Series) Angeleyes Blueberry (A) **new**	LSou
	- Angeleyes Bicolor = 'Pacbicolor'[PBR] (A)	LAst MCot
	- Angeleyes Burgundy = 'Pacburg'[PBR] (A)	LAst LBMP
	- Angeleyes Orange = 'Paccrio'[PBR] (A)	EWoo LAst WCot
	- Angeleyes Randy (A)	SSea
	- Angeleyes Viola = 'Pacviola'[PBR] (A)	LSou
	'Angelique' (Dw/d)	LAll WFib
	'Ann Hoystead' (R) ♀H1c	NFir WFib
	'Anna Lisa Pope' (R)	NFir
	'Annsbrook Aquarius' (St)	NFir
	'Annsbrook Beauty' (A/C)	NFir WFib
	'Annsbrook Jupitor' (Z/St)	NFir
	Anthony = 'Pacan'[PBR] (Z/d)	LAst
	Antik Scarlet = 'Tikscarl'[PBR] (Antik Series) (Z)	LAst
	'Antoine Crozy' (Z × I/d)	WFib
	'Apache' (Z/d)	WFib
	appendiculatum	CLak MHer
	'Apple Betty' (Sc)	EWoo WFib
	'Apple Blossom Rosebud' (Z/d) ♀H1c	CDoC ECtt EShb LAll MHer SSea WFib
	'Apricot' (Dw/v)	LAll
	'Apricot' (Z/St)	LAst
	'April Hamilton' (I)	CWCL LCro WFib
	'April Showers' (A)	WFib
	'Arctic Frost'	WFib
§	'Arctic Star' (Z/St) ♀H1c	CDoC CSpe NFir WBrk WFib
	'Ardens' ♀H1c	CSpe EUJe EWoo LAll LCro LSou MCot MHer NFir SBod SSea SWvt WCot WFib WWFP
	'Ardwick Cinnamon' (Sc)	CDoC ENfk EWoo LAll MHer NFir WFib
	(Aristo Series) Aristo Apricot = 'Regapri' (R)	LAst
	- Aristo Black Beauty = 'Regblabe' (R) **new**	LAst
	- Aristo Darling = 'Regdar'[PBR] (R)	LAst
	- Aristo Orchid = 'Regorch' (R) **new**	LAst
	- Aristo Petticoat = 'Regpet'[PBR] (R) **new**	LAst
	'Arnside Fringed Aztec' (R)	MHer WFib
	'Ashby' (U/Sc) ♀H1c	CWCL ENfk EWoo LAll MHer NFir SBch SSea
	'Ashfield Blaze' (Z/d)	LAll
	'Ashfield Jubilee' (Z/C)	LAll NFir
	'Ashfield Monarch' (Z/d) ♀H1c	NFir
	'Ashfield Serenade' (Z) ♀H1c	WFib
	'Askham Fringed Aztec' (R) ♀H1c	MHer WFib
	asperum Ehr. ex Willd.	see *P.* 'Graveolens'
	'Athabasca' (Min)	LAll
	'Atlantic Burgundy'	CWCL MCot
§	'Atomic Snowflake' (Sc/v)	ENfk LAll MCot MNHC WFib
	'Atrium' (U)	MHer WFib
	'Attar of Roses' (Sc) ♀H1c	CArn CDoC ECtt ENfk EWoo LAll LCro MCot MHer NFir NPri SBch SIde SSea WBrk WFib WGwG
	'Aurora' (Z/d)	LAll LAst
	australe	EWoo MCot MHer NFir SBch SVen WFib
	'Australian Bute' (R)	LAll
	'Australian Mystery' (R/Dec) ♀H1c	CSpe NFir WFib
	'Aztec' (R) ♀H1c	LAll NFir WFib
	'Baby Bird's Egg' (Min)	WFib
	'Baby Brocade' (Min/d)	LAll
	'Baby Harry' (Dw/v)	WFib
	Balcon Imperial	see *P.* 'Roi des Balcons Impérial'
	'Balcon Lilas'	see *P.* 'Roi des Balcons Lilas'
	'Balcon Rouge'	see *P.* 'Roi des Balcons Impérial'
	'Balcon Royale'	see *P.* 'Roi des Balcons Impérial'
	'Balcony Red' (I)	ECtt
	'Ballerina' (R)	see *P.* 'Carisbrooke'
I	'Ballerina' (Min)	WFib
	'Banstead Village' (Z)	LAll
§	'Barbe Bleu' (I/d) ♀H1c	LCro NFir WFib
	'Barking' (Min/Z)	NFir
	'Barnston Dale' (Dw/d)	NFir
	'Bath Beauty' (Dw)	CSpe
	'Beacon Hill' (Min)	LAll
	'Beatrice Cottington' (I/d)	WFib
	'Beauty of Eastbourne' misapplied	see *P.* 'Lachskönigin'
	'Belinda Adams' (Min/d) ♀H1c	LAll NFir
	Belladonna = 'Fisopa' (I/d)	SCoo
	'Bembridge' (Z/St/d)	WFib
	'Ben Franklin' (Z/d/v) ♀H1c	NFir
	'Ben Matt' (R)	WFib
	'Ben Nevis' (Dw/d)	NFir
	'Berkswell Carnival' (A)	ELan
	'Berkswell Jester' (A)	LAll
	'Berkswell Lace' (A)	MHer
	Bernardo = 'Guiber'[PBR] (I/d)	LAst
	'Beromünster' (Dec)	EWoo MHer NFir WFib
	'Bert Pearce' (R)	WFib
	'Beryl Gibbons' (Z/d)	LAll
	'Beryl Reid' (R)	WFib
	'Bette Shellard' (Z/d/v)	NFir
	'Betty' (Z/d)	LAll
	'Betty Catchpole' (Z)	EWoo
	betulinum	WFib
	'Biedermeier' (R)	LAll
	'Big Apple' (Sc)	EWoo
	'Bird Dancer' (Dw/St) ♀H1c	CSpe MHer MNHC NFir WBrk
	'Birdbush Eleanor' (Birdbush Series) (Z)	WFib
	'Birthday Girl' (R)	CWCL WFib
	'Bitter Lemon' (Sc)	ECtt
	'Black Butterfly'	see *P.* 'Brown's Butterfly'
	'Black Knight' (A)	NFir
	'Black Knight' Lea (Dw/d/C) ♀H1c	NFir
	'Black Knight' (R)	CSpe ECtt EWoo MHer
	'Black Pearl' (Z/d)	LAll
	'Black Prince' (R/Dec)	CSpe EWoo NFir WFib
	'Black Velvet' (R)	EWoo LAll MCot
	'Black Vesuvius'	see *P.* 'Red Black Vesuvius'
	'Blackcurrant Sundae'	LAll
	'Blackcurrant Yhu' (Dec)	NFir
	'Blackdown Delight' (Z)	NFir
	'Blackdown Romance' (Z)	NFir
	'Blackdown Sensation' (Dw/Z) ♀H1c	NFir
	Blanca = 'Penwei'[PBR] (Dark Line Series) (Z/d)	LAst
	Blanche Roche = 'Guitoblanc' (I/d)	LAll LAst LSou MCot MHer SCoo SSea
§	'Blandfordianum' (Sc)	EWoo MHer

'Blandfordianum Roseum' (Sc)	EWoo MHer
'Blazonry' (Z/v)	WFib
(Blizzard Series) Blizzard Blue = 'Fisrain'PBR (I)	SCoo
- Blizzard Dark Red = 'Fisblizdark' (I)	CWCL EWoo
- Blizzard Red = 'Fizzard' (I)	SCoo
- Blizzard White = 'Fisbliz'PBR	SCoo
'Blue Beard'	see *P.* 'Barbe Bleu'
Blue Sybil = 'Pacblusy'PBR (I/d)	LSou
'Bob Newing' (Min/St)	WFib
'Bobberstone' (Z/St)	LAll WFib
'Bold Appleblossom' (Z)	WFib
'Bold Carmine' (Z/d)	LAll NFir
'Bold Carousel' (Z/d)	WFib
'Bold Flame' (Z/d)	WFib
'Bold Limelight' (Z/d)	WFib
'Bold Minstrel' (Z/d)	WFib
'Bold Pixie' (Dw/d)	WFib
'Bold Princess' (Z/d)	WFib
'Bold Special' (Z)	WFib
'Bold Sunrise' (Z/d)	NFir
'Bold Sunset' (Z/d) ♀H1c	NFir WFib
'Bold White' (Z)	NFir
'Bolero' (U) ♀H1c	LAll NFir WFib
'Bon Bon' (Min/St)	WFib
'Bonito' (I/d)	LAll
'Bontrosai'PBR (Sc)	MCot
'Bornholm' (d) **new**	LAll
'Bosham' (R)	WFib
bowkeri	WFib
'Brackenwood' (Dw/d) ♀H1c	LAll NFir
'Bramford' (Dw)	LAll
Bravo = 'Fisbravo' (Z/d)	WFib
'Break o' Day' (R)	LAll
'Brenda' (Min/d)	WFib
'Brenda Hyatt' (Dw/d)	LAll WFib
'Brian West' (Min/St/C)	WFib
'Brian West Butterfly' (Z/St) ♀H1c	WFib
'Bridesmaid' (Dw/d)	NFir
'Brightstone' (Z/d)	ECtt WFib
'Brilliant' (Dec)	ENfk WFib
'Brilliantine' (Sc)	ENfk EWoo MHer WFib
'Brixworth Charmer' (Z/v)	LAll
'Brixworth Pearl' (Z)	WFib
'Broadway' (Min)	LAll
'Brook's Purple'	see *P.* 'Royal Purple'
'Brookside Flamenco' (Dw/d)	LAll WFib
'Brookside Primrose' (Min/C/d)	WFib
'Brookside Serenade' (Dw)	WFib
§ 'Brown's Butterfly' (R)	ECtt EWoo WFib
'Brunswick' (Sc)	EWoo MHer WFib
'Burnaby' (Min/d)	LAll
'Burns Country' (Dw)	NFir
'Bushfire' (R) ♀H1c	EWoo WFib
'Butley' (Min)	LAll
Butterfly = 'Fisam'PBR (I)	NFir SCoo
'Butterfly Lorele' (Z/d) **new**	LAll
caespitosum	MHer
'Cal'	see *P.* 'Salmon Irene'
Calais = 'Paclai'PBR	LAst
'California Brilliant' (U)	MHer
'Calignon' (Z/St)	WFib
'Caligula' (Min/d)	LAll
'Cameo' (Dw/d)	LAll
'Camisole' (Dw/d)	LAll
'Camphor Rose' (Sc) ♀H1c	NFir
'Can-can' (I/d)	WFib
Candy Flowers White = 'Camwh' (Candy Flower Series) (R) **new**	LAst
canescens	see *P.* 'Blandfordianum'
'Cape Town' (Dw/z/v)	WFib
capitatum	ENfk MNHC WFib
'Capri' (Sc)	WFib
'Captain Starlight' (A) ♀H1c	EWoo LAll MHer NFir WFib
'Carefree' (U) ♀H1c	NFir WFib
§ 'Carisbrooke' (R) ♀H1c	WFib
'Carmel' (Z)	WFib
carnosum	MHer
'Carol Gibbons' (Z/d) ♀H1c	LAll NFir
'Caroline Schmidt' (Z/d/v)	LAll LAst MCot NFir WBrk WFib
'Carolyn Dean' (St) ♀H1c	NFir
'Carolyn Hardy' (Z/d)	WFib
Cascade Lilac	see *P.* 'Roi des Balcons Lilas'
'Cathay' (Z/St) ♀H1c	NFir
'Cathy' (R)	NFir
caucalifolium subsp. ***caucalifolium***	MHer
- subsp. ***convolvulifolium***	WFib
'Cézanne' (R)	LAll MCot
'Charity' (Sc) ♀H1c	CDoC ENfk LAll MCot MHer NFir WFib
'Charlotte Bronte' (Dw/v)	WFib
'Chelsea Gem' (Z/d/v) ♀H1c	LAll WFib
'Chelsea Morning' (Z/d)	WFib
'Cherry' (Min)	WFib
'Cherry Baby' (Dec)	MHer NFir
'Cherry Orchard' (R)	WFib
'Chew Magna' (R)	WFib
'Chieko' (Min/d)	WFib
'Chinz' (R)	NFir
§ 'Chocolate Peppermint' (Sc)	ECtt ELan ENfk EWoo MCot MHer NFir SEND WFib
'Chocolate Tomentosum'	see *P.* 'Chocolate Peppermint'
'Chocolate Twist' (St/C)	LAll LAst
'Choun Cho' (I) **new**	LCro
'Chrissie' (R)	WFib
'Christopher Ley' (Z)	LAll
'Cindy' (Dw/d)	WFib
'Citriodorum' (Sc) ♀H1c	ELan MCot MHer WFib
'Citronella' (Sc)	WFib WGwG
'Clara Read' (Dw)	LAll
'Claret Rock Unique' (U)	EWoo WFib
'Clatterbridge' (Dw/d) ♀H1c	LAll NFir
'Clorinda' (U/Sc)	CDoC ENfk EWoo LAll MCot MHer MNHC NWad SBch SSea WFib
'Coddenham' (Dw/d)	WFib
'Cola Bottles'	NPer
§ 'Colonel Baden-Powell' (I/d)	WFib
'Colwell' (Min/d)	WFib
'Concolor Lace'	see *P.* 'Shottesham Pet'
'Contrast' (Z/C/v)	CWCL LAll SCoo SPoG WFib
'Cook's Peachblossom'	LAll WFib
'Copthorne' (U/Sc) ♀H1c	EWoo MCot MHer WFib
cordifolium	GCal WFib
- var. ***rubrocinctum***	MHer NFir
coriandrifolium	see *P. myrrhifolium* var. *coriandrifolium*
'Cornell' (I/d)	WFib

cortusifolium MHer
'Cotta Lilac Queen' (I/d) LAll
'Cottenham Beauty' (A) NFir
'Cottenham Delight' (A) NFir
'Cottenham Glamour' (A) ♀H1c MHer NFir
'Cottenham Jubilee' (A) MHer
'Cottenham Surprise' (A) ♀H1c NFir
'Cottenham Wonder' (A) ♀H1c NFir
'Cottontail' (Min) LAll
cotyledonis CSpe WFib
'Countess of Scarborough' see *P.* 'Lady Scarborough'
'Cover Girl' (Z/d) WFib
'Covina' (R) WFib
'Cramdon Red' (Dw) WFib
'Crampel's Master' (Z) LAll
'Cream 'n' Green' (R/v) NFir
'Creamery' (d) CDoC WFib
'Creamy Nutmeg' (Sc/v) ENfk EShb EWoo MHer NFir NWad SEND SSea
'Creeting St Mary' (Min) LAll
'Creeting St Peter' (Min) LAll
'Crimson Unique' (U) ♀H1c CSpe ENfk EWoo MCot MHer WFib
§ ***crispum*** (Sc) GPoy
- 'Cy's Sunburst' (Sc) **new** MHer
§ - 'Golden Well Sweep' (Sc/v) WFib
- 'Major' (Sc) WFib
- 'Peach Cream' (Sc/v) ENfk WFib
- 'Variegatum' (Sc/v) ♀H1c ENfk GBin GPoy LAll MHer NFir SBch SIde WCot WFib
crithmifolium MHer
'Crock O Day' (I/d) LAll
'Crocketta' (I/d/v) ♀H1c NFir
'Crocodile' (I/C/d) ♀H1c ECtt ELan MHer MNHC NFir NWad WFib
'Crystal Palace Gem' (Z/v) LAll WFib
cucullatum WFib
- 'Flore Pleno' (d) MHer WFib
- subsp. ***strigifolium*** EWoo
'Cupid' (Min/Dw/d) WFib
§ 'Czar' (Z/C) SCoo
'Dainty Maid' (Sc) ENfk NFir
'Dale Queen' (Z) WFib
'Dame Anna Neagle' (Dw/d) LAll
'Dark Gigette' (Min) NFir
'Dark Red Irene' (Z/d) LAll WFib
'Dark Secret' (R) CSpe WFib
'Dark Venus' (R) WFib
'Darmsden' (A) ♀H1c NFir
'David John' (Dw/d) LAll
'Davina' (Min/d) WFib
'Dawn Star' (Z/St) NFir
'Deacon Arlon' (Dw/d) LAll
'Deacon Avalon' (Dw/d) WFib
'Deacon Barbecue' (Z/d) LAll WFib
'Deacon Birthday' (Z/d) LAll
'Deacon Bonanza' (Z/d) LAll WFib
'Deacon Clarion' (Z/d) LAll WFib
'Deacon Constancy' (Z/d) LAll
'Deacon Coral Reef' (Z/d) LAll WFib
'Deacon Fireball' (Z/d) LAll WFib
'Deacon Gala' (Z/d) LAll WFib
'Deacon Golden Bonanza' (Z/C/d) WFib
'Deacon Golden Lilac Mist' (Z/C/d) WFib
'Deacon Jubilant' (Z/d) LAll
'Deacon Lilac Mist' (Z/d) WFib
'Deacon Mandarin' (Z/d) WFib
'Deacon Minuet' (Z/d) LAll NFir WFib
'Deacon Peacock' (Z/C/d) WFib
'Deacon Picotee' (Z/d) LAll WFib
'Deacon Regalia' (Z/d) LAll
'Deacon Romance' (Z/d) LAll
§ 'Deacon Summertime' (Z/d) LAll WFib
'Deacon Sunburst' (Z/d) LAll
'Deacon Suntan' (Z/d) LAll
'Deacon Trousseau' (Z/d) LAll
'Deborah Miliken' (Z/d) ♀H1c NFir WFib
'Decora Impérial' (I) LAll
'Decora Lavender' see *P.* 'Decora Lilas'
§ 'Decora Lilas' (I) ECtt
'Decora Mauve' see *P.* 'Decora Lilas'
'Decora Pink' see *P.* 'Decora Rouge'
'Decora Red' see *P.* 'Decora Rouge'
§ 'Decora Rose' (I) ECtt
§ 'Decora Rouge' (I) ECtt LAst
'Deerwood Darling' (Min/v/d) WFib
'Deerwood Lavender Lad' (Sc) ENfk EWoo MHer WFib
'Deerwood Lavender Lass' CDoC MCot MHer
'Deerwood Pink Puff' (St/d) WFib
'Delightful' (R) WFib
'Delli' (R) ♀H1c CWCL MHer NFir NPer WFib
'Denebola' (Min/d) LAll
'Dennis Hunt' (Z/C) NFir
denticulatum MHer
§ - 'Filicifolium' (Sc) ELan ENfk LAll MCot MHer NFir WFib
'Designer Bright Red' **new** LAst
'Designer Hot Pink'PBR **new** LAst
Designer Peppermint Twist = 'Baldespep' (Designer Series) (Z) LAst
'Diana Palmer' (Z/d) LAll
'Diane' (Min/d) LAll
'Dibbinsdale' (Z) ♀H1c LAll NFir
dichondrifolium (Sc) LAll NFir WFib
dichondrifolium* × *reniforme (Sc) NFir
'Didi' (Min) LAll
'Display' ambig. (Dw/v) WFib
'Distinction' (Z) LAll NFir SPoG WFib
'Dolly Varden' (Z/v) ♀H1c LAll NFir WFib
'Donatella Bluet Champagne' (U) **new** NFir
'Donatella Orange Surprise' (Dec) **new** NFir
'Don's Helen Bainbridge' (Z/C) NFir
'Don's Mona Noble' (Z/C) NFir
'Don's Richard A. Costain' (Z/C) NFir
'Don's Silver Wedding' **new** LAll
'Don's Southport' (Z/v) NFir
'Don's Swanland Girl' (Min) LAll
'Doris Hancock' (R) WFib
'Double Pink' (R/d) WFib
'Dovedale' (Dw/C) WFib
'Dovepoint' (Dw/2) NFir
'Downlands' (Z/d) WFib
'Dragon's Breath' (Z/St) LAll

'Dresden White' (Dw)	WFib
Dresdner Apricot = 'Pacbriap'PBR (I/d)	SSea
'Duchess of Devonshire' (U)	WFib
'Duke of Buckingham' (Z/d)	LAll
'Duke of Devonshire' (Z/d)	LAll
'Duke of Edinburgh'	see *P.* 'Hederinum Variegatum'
'Dunkery Beacon' (R)	WFib
§ 'Dwarf Miriam Baisey' (Min)	LAll
'Dwarf Miriam Read'	see *P.* 'Dwarf Miriam Baisey'
'E. Dabner' (Z/d)	WFib
'East Sussex' (Dw/C)	LAll
echinatum	EWoo MHer
- 'Album'	EWoo WFib
'Eclipse' (Dw/d)	LAll
'Eden Gem' (Min/d)	LAll WFib
'Edith Stern' (Dw/d)	LAll
'Edmond Lachenal' (Z/d)	WFib
'Eileen Nancy' (Z)	NFir
'Eileen Postle' (R) ♀H1c	WFib
Elbe Silver = 'Pensil' (I) ♀H1c	LAst NFir SCoo
'Electra' (Z/d)	LAll
'Elizabeth Read' (Dw)	LAll
'Ellen Gray' (v) **new**	LAll
'Elmsett' (Dw/C/d)	LAll NFir WFib
'Els' (1870)	LAll
'Els' (Dw/St)	WBrk
'Elsi' (I × Z/d/v)	LAll WFib
'Elsie Gillam' (St)	WFib
'Embassy' (Min)	WFib
Emilia = 'Pactina'PBR	LAst SSea
'Emma Hössle'	see *P.* 'Frau Emma Hössle'
'Emma Jane Read' (Dw/d)	WFib
'Encore' (Z/d/v)	LAll
endlicherianum	EPot MHer WCot
'Erwarton' (Min/d)	LAll NFir
'Escapade' (Min/d)	LAll
'Eskay Gold' (A)	WFib
'Eskay Jewel' (A)	WFib
'Eskay Ruby' (A)	MHer
'Eskay Sugar Candy' (A)	WFib
'Eskay Verglo' (A)	WFib
Evening Glow = 'Bergpalais'PBR	SSea
'Evka'PBR (I/v)	LAst SCoo SSea
exstipulatum	EWoo MHer SVen
'Fair Ellen' (Sc)	LAll MHer WFib
'Fairlee' (DwI)	WFib
'Fairy Lights' (Dw/St)	LAll NFir
'Fairy Orchid' (A)	WFib
'Fallen Angel' (Z/St)	LAll
'Fandango' (Z/St)	LAll NFir WFib
'Fanny Eden' (R)	EWoo WFib
'Fantasia' white-flowered (Dw/d) ♀H1c	WFib
'Fareham' (R) ♀H1c	WFib
'Faye Brawner' (Z/St)	LAll
'Feuerriese' (Z)	LAll
'Fiat Queen' (Z/d)	WFib
'Fieldings Unique' (U)	EWoo NFir
'Fifth Avenue' (R)	WFib
'Filicifolium'	see *P. denticulatum* 'Filicifolium'
'Fir Trees Audrey B' (St)	NFir
'Fir Trees Betty' (U)	NFir
'Fir Trees Catkins' (A)	NFir
'Fir Trees Echoes of Pink' (A)	EWoo
'Fir Trees Eileen' (St)	NFir
'Fir Trees Ele' (A/v)	NFir
'Fir Trees Fantail' (Min)	NFir
'Fir Trees Fiesta' (R)	NFir
'Fir Trees Flamingo' (Dw)	NFir
'Fir Trees Jack' (Z/Dw)	NFir
'Fir Trees Janet' (Dw)	NFir
'Fir Trees Jennifer' (R/Dec)	NFir
'Fir Trees John Grainger' (Z/v)	NFir
'Fir Trees Mark' (R/Dec/v)	NFir
'Fir Trees Muffin' (Sc) **new**	NFir
'Fir Trees Pink Pom-Pom' (Dw/St/C/d)	NFir
'Fir Trees Ruby Wedding' (C)	NFir
'Fir Trees Silver Wedding' (Z/C/d)	NFir
'Fir Trees Sparkler' (Min/C)	NFir
'Fir Trees Val' (Z)	NFir
'Firebrand' (Z/d)	LAll
'First Blush' (R)	WFib
'First Love' (Z) ♀H1c	NFir
'Flaming Katy' (Min) ♀H1c	NFir
'Flamingo'	COtt
'Fleurette' (Min/d)	LAll
'Fleurisse' (Z)	WFib
'Floria Moore' (Dec)	EWoo NFir SSea
(Flower Fairy Series) Flower Fairy Berry = 'Sweberry'PBR	LAst SSea
- Flower Fairy Rose = 'Swero'PBR (Z)	LAst LSou
- Flower Fairy Velvet = 'Swevel' (Z) **new**	SSea
- Flower Fairy White Splash = 'Swewhi'PBR (Z)	LAst LSou SSea
'Flowton' (Dw/d)	LAll
Foxy = 'Pacfox'PBR (Z)	LAst LSou
fragrans	ENfk LAll
Fragrans Group (Sc)	EWoo GPoy MCot MHer WFib WGwG
§ - 'Fragrans Variegatum' (Sc/v) ♀H1c	CDoC NFir WFib
- 'Snowy Nutmeg'	see *P.* (Fragrans Group) 'Fragrans Variegatum'
'Fraiche Beauté' (Z/d)	WFib
'Francis Gibbon' (Z/d)	WFib
'Francis Parmenter' (Min/I/v)	LAst
'Francis Parrett' (Min/d) ♀H1c	LAst WFib
'Frank Hazel' (Dw/Z)	NFir
'Frank Headley' (Z/v) ♀H1c	CDoC EShb LAll LAst MCot NPer SCoo SSea WFib WOld
§ 'Frau Emma Hössle' (Dw/d)	LAll WFib
'Freak of Nature' (Z/v)	LAll MHer NFir WFib
'Frensham' (Sc)	ENfk MHer WFib
'Freshwater' (St/C)	WFib
'Friary Wood' (Z/C/d)	NFir WFib
'Friesdorf' (Dw/Fr)	MCot MHer NFir WBrk WFib
'Fringed Aztec' (R) ♀H1c	CWCL MHer NFir WFib
'Frosty' misapplied	see *P.* 'Variegated Kleine Liebling'
'Frosty Petit Pierre'	see *P.* 'Variegated Kleine Liebling'
'Frou Frou'	LAll
frutetorum	MHer
fruticosum	EWoo WFib
'Fuji' (R)	NFir

	Name	Suppliers
	fulgidum	EWoo LAll MCot MHer WFib
	'Gabriel' (A)	EWoo
	'Galilee' (I/d)	LAll
	Galleria Sunrise = 'Sunrise' (R)	LAll
	'Galway Star' (Sc/v) 🏆H1c	MHer WFib
	'Ganther' (Dec)	WFib
	'Garland' (Dw/d)	LAll
	'Garnet Rosebud' (Min/d)	LAll NFir WFib
	'Gartendirektor Herman' (Dec) 🏆H1c	ELan EWoo NFir WFib
	'Gaudy' (Z)	WFib
	'Gemini' (Z/St/d) 🏆H1c	CWCL NFir WFib
	'Gemma' (R)	LAll NFir
	'Gemstone' (Sc) 🏆H1c	ENfk MHer
	'Genie' (Z/d)	LAll WFib
	'Gentle Georgia' (R)	WFib
	'Georgia' (R)	WFib
	'Georgia Peach' (R)	WFib
	'Georgina Blythe' (R) 🏆H1c	WFib
	'Gerald Wells' (Min)	LAll
	gibbosum	CDoC CSpe EWoo MHer WFib WHer
	'Ginger Frost' (Sc/v)	WFib
	'Ginger Rogers' (Z) 🏆H1c	NFir
	'Glacis'PBR (Quality Series) (Z/d)	LSou SSea
	'Gladys Evelyn' (Z/d)	WFib
	'Gladys Weller' (Z/d) 🏆H1c	NFir WFib
	glaucum	see *P. lanceolatum*
	'Gleam' (Z/d)	LAll
§	***glutinosum***	WFib
	'Goblin' (Min/d)	LAll
	Golden Angel	see *P.* 'Sarah Don'
	'Golden Brilliantissimum' (Z/v)	WFib
	'Golden Chalice' (Min/v)	WFib
	'Golden Clorinda' (U/Sc/C)	SEND
	'Golden Ears' (Dw/St/C) 🏆H1c	NFir NPer WFib
	'Golden Edinburgh' (I/v)	WFib
	'Golden Harry Hieover' (Z/C)	LAll
	'Golden Lilac Gem' (I/d)	WFib
	'Golden Princess' (Min/C)	WFib
	'Golden Square' (Dw/St)	WFib
	'Golden Staphs' (Z/St/C)	LAll MHer NFir
	'Golden Stardust' (Z/St)	LAll
	'Golden Tears' (MinI/C/d)	ECtt
	'Golden Wedding' (Z/d/v)	NFir
	'Golden Well Sweep'	see *P. crispum* 'Golden Well Sweep'
	'Goldstone Copper' (Min/d)	LAll
	'Good Vibrations' **new**	LAll
	'Gooseberry Leaf'	see *P. grossularioides*
	'Grace Thomas' (Sc) 🏆H1c	MHer WFib
	'Grace Wells' (Min)	WFib
	'Grand Slam' (R) 🏆H1c	NFir WFib
	'Grandad Mac' (Dw/St) 🏆H1c	NFir
	grandiflorum	EWoo MCot MHer WFib
	graveolens L'Hér.	see *P.* 'Graveolens'
	graveolens ambig.	SEND
	graveolens *sensu* J.J.A. van der Walt	SBch WFib
§	'Graveolens' (Sc)	ENfk GPoy LAll MHer SVen WBrk WFib
	'Graveolens Minor' (Sc)	EWoo
	'Great Blakenham' (Min)	LAll
	'Great Bricett' (Dw/d)	LAll
	'Great Glemham Lemon' (Sc)	EWoo
	'Green Eyes' (I/d)	MHer
	'Greetings' (Min/v)	LAll WFib
§	'Grenadier' (Z)	LAll
	'Grey Lady Plymouth' (Sc/v)	CDoC LCro MCot MHer WFib
	'Grey Sprite' (Min/v)	WFib
§	***grossularioides***	MHer
	'Gwen' (Min/v)	NFir
§	'Hannaford Star' (Z/St)	WFib
	'Happy Anniversary' (Dw/C)	NFir
	'Happy Appleblossom' (Z/v/d)	LAll NFir
	'Happy Thought' (Z/v) 🏆H1c	LAll MCot NFir SCoo WFib
	'Harbour Lights' (R)	WFib
	'Harewood Slam' (R)	WFib
	'Harlequin Pretty Girl' (I × Z/d)	LAll WFib
	'Harlequin Rosie O'Day' (I)	WFib
	'Harvard' (I/d)	WFib
	'Hazel' (R)	WFib
	'Hazel Cherry' (R)	WFib
	'Hazel Choice' (R)	NFir
	'Hazel Perfection' (R) 🏆H1c	NFir
	'Hazel Stardust' (R)	NFir
§	'Hederinum Variegatum' (I/v)	ECtt WFib
	'Helen Bainbridge' (Z/C)	LAll
	'Helen Christine' (Z/St)	NFir WFib
	'Hemley' (Sc)	LAll
	'Henry Weller' (A) 🏆H1c	NFir WFib
	'Hermione' (Z/d)	WFib
	'Highfields Always' (Z/d)	LAll
	'Highfields Appleblossom' (Z)	LAll
	'Highfields Attracta' (Z/d)	WFib
	'Highfields Ballerina' (Z/d)	LAll
	'Highfields Candy Floss' (Z/d)	LAll NFir
	'Highfields Charisma' (Z/d)	LAll
	'Highfields Choice' (Z) 🏆H1c	LAll
	'Highfields Contessa' (Z/d)	LAll
	'Highfields Dazzler' (Z)	LAll
	'Highfields Delight' (Z)	WFib
	'Highfields Fancy' (Z/d)	LAll NFir
	'Highfields Festival' (Z/d) 🏆H1c	LAll NFir WFib
	'Highfields Flair' (Z/d)	LAll
	'Highfields Melody' (Z/d)	WFib
	'Highfields Orange' (Z)	LAll
	'Highfields Pink' (Z)	LAll
	'Highfields Pride' (Z)	LAll WFib
	'Highfields Prima Donna' (Z/d)	LAll
	'Highfields Salmon' (Z/d)	LAll
	'Highfields Serenade' (Z)	LAll
	'Highfields Snowdrift' (Z)	NFir
	'Highfields Sugar Candy' (Z/d)	LAll
	'Highfields Supreme' (Z)	LAll
	'Highfields Symphony' (Z)	LAll WFib
	'Highfields Vogue' (Z)	LAll
	'Hilbre Island' (Z/C/d)	NFir
	'Hills of Snow' (Z/v)	LAll MHer WFib
	'Hindoo' (R × U) 🏆H1c	EWoo NFir WFib
	'Hintlesham' (Min)	LAll

hispidum	MHer
'Hitcham' (Min/d)	WFib
'Holbrook' (Dw/C/d)	NFir WFib
'Holt Beauty'	EWoo
'Honeywood Suzanne' (Min/Fr)	LAll
'Honneas' (Dw)	LAll
'Hope Valley' (Dw/C/d) 🏆H1c	NFir
Hot Spot Ria = 'Ria'PBR (Z) **new**	LAll
'House and Garden' (R)	NFir
'Hula' (R × U)	EWoo
'Ian Read' (Min/d)	LAll
'Ibiza' (Dw/C)	LAll
'Ice Cap' (Min) **new**	LAll
'Icecrystal'PBR (Sweetheart Series) (Z/d)	SSea
'Icing Sugar' (I/d)	WFib
ignescens	EWoo NFir
'Immaculatum' (Z)	WFib
'Imperial Butterfly' (A/Sc) 🏆H1c	ENfk NFir WFib
incrassatum	MHer
ionidiflorum	CSpe EShb MCot MHer MNHC
'Irene' (Z/d)	WFib
'Irene Toyon' (Z)	WFib
'Islington Peppermint' (Sc)	NFir WFib
'Ivalo' (Z/d)	WFib
'Ivory Snow' (Z/d/v)	NFir WFib
'Jacey' (Z/d)	LAll
'Jack of Hearts' (I × Z/d)	WFib
'Jack Wood' (Z/d)	NFir
§ 'Jackie' (I/d)	LAll WFib
'Jackie Davies' (R)	EWoo
'Jackie Gall'	see *P.* 'Jackie'
'Jackie Totlis' (Z/St)	WFib
'Jackpot Wild Rose' (Z/d)	WFib
'Jacqui Caws' (Dw)	LAll
'Janet Hofman' (Z/d)	WFib
'Janet James'	LAll
'Janet Kerrigan' (Min/d)	WFib
'Jayne' (Min/d)	LAll
'Jayne Eyre' (Min/d)	WFib
'Jean Bart' (I)	LAll
'Jeanie Hunt' (Z/C/d)	NFir
§ 'Jeanne d'Arc' (I/d)	WFib
'Jer'Rey' (A)	EWoo WFib
'Jessica'	LAll
'Jip's Bunjy'	NFir
'Jip's Desert Poppy' (Z/Min)	WFib
'Jip's Eleanor Renton' (Dw/d)	WFib
'Jip's Freda Burgess' (Z/C/d)	LAll NFir
'Jip's Megan' (Z/C/D)	NFir
'Jip's Pip' (Z/C/d)	NFir
'Jip's Proud Sentinel' (Dw/d)	WFib
'Jip's Rosy Glow' (Min/d) 🏆H1c	NFir
'Joan Fontaine' (Z)	WFib
'Joan Morf' (R) 🏆H1c	EWoo NFir WFib
'Joan of Arc'	see *P.* 'Jeanne d'Arc'
'John Squires' (Z/C/d) **new**	LAll
'John's Angela'	LAll
'John's Pride' (Dw)	NFir
'Joy' (R) 🏆H1c	CSpe NFir WFib
'Judith Thorp' (R)	LAll
'Julie Smith' (R)	WFib
'Just Bella' (d)	NFir
'Just Beth' (Z/C/d)	NFir
'Just Joss' (Dw/d)	NFir
'Just William' (Min/C/d)	WFib
'Kamahl' (R)	WFib
'Karen' (Dw/C)	LAst LSou
'Karl Hagele' (Z/d)	WFib
'Karmin Ball'	WFib
'Karrooense'	see *P. quercifolium*
'Katie' (R)	EWoo
'Keepsake' (Min/d)	LAll WFib
'Keith Vernon' (Z)	NFir
'Kenny's Double' (Z/d)	ECtt WFib
'Kerensa' (Min/d)	WFib
'Kesgrave' (Min/d)	WFib
'Kewense' (Z)	EShb
'Kimono' (R) 🏆H1c	NFir
'King Edmund' (R) 🏆H1c	NFir
'King of Denmark' (Z/d)	LAll WFib
'King Solomon' (R)	WFib
§ 'Kleine Liebling' (Min)	WFib
'Kyoto' (R)	NFir
'Kyra' (Min/d)	LAll
'La France' (I/d) 🏆H1c	LAll LCro MCot WFib
'La Paloma' (R)	WFib
Laced Red Mini Cascade = 'Achspen' (I) 🏆H1c	NFir
§ 'Lachskönigin' (I/d)	WFib
'Lady Alice of Valencia'	see *P.* 'Grenadier'
'Lady Ilchester' (Z/d)	WFib
'Lady Love Song' (R)	NFir WFib
'Lady Mary' (Sc)	EWoo MHer
'Lady Mavis Pilkington' (Z/d)	WFib
'Lady Plymouth' (Sc/v) 🏆H1c	CDoC ELan ENfk EPfP EWoo GLog LAll MCot MHer NFir NWad SEND WFib WGwG
§ 'Lady Scarborough' (Sc)	ENfk EWoo MHer WFib
laevigatum	MHer
'Lancastrian' (Z/d)	MHer WFib
§ ***lanceolatum***	MHer
'Lara Ballerina' 🏆H1c	NFir SBch
'Lara Beacon'	EWoo
'Lara Candy Dancer' (Sc) 🏆H1c	WFib
'Lara Jester' (Sc)	ENfk EWoo WFib
'Lara Rajah' (R)	EWoo
'Lara Starshine' (Sc) 🏆H1c	ENfk EWoo MHer NFir WFib
'Lara Waltz' (R/d)	WFib
'Laurel Hayward' (R)	WFib
'Lauren Alexandra' (Z/d)	WFib
'Lavender Grand Slam' (R) 🏆H1c	LAll NFir
'Lavender Lindy' (Sc)	CDoC EWoo WCot
'Lavender Mini Cascade'	see *P.* Lilac Mini Cascade
'Lavender Sensation' (R)	WFib
'Lawrenceanum'	LCro WFib
'L'Élégante' (I/v) 🏆H1c	EWoo LAll MCot MHer WFib
'Lemon Crisp'	see *P. crispum*
'Lemon Fancy' (Sc) 🏆H1c	CDoC LAll MHer NFir NWad WFib
'Lemon Kiss' (Sc)	CSpe EWoo
'Leslie William Burrows'	EWoo
'Letitia' (A)	ENfk
Lila Compakt-Cascade	see *P.* 'Decora Lilas'
Lilac Cascade	see *P.* 'Roi des Balcons Lilas'
'Lilac Gem' (Min/I/d)	ENfk MCot
§ Lilac Mini Cascade = 'Lilamica'PBR (I) 🏆H1c	LAst NFir
'Lilian Pottinger' (Sc) 🏆H1c	ENfk EWoo MHer NFir SSea

	'Lilian Woodberry' (Z)	WFib
	Lilly = 'Paclill'[PBR]	LAst
	'Limoneum' (Sc)	ENfk MHer
	'Lincolnshire Lady' (R) **new**	ECtt
	'Lipstick' (St)	WFib
	'Lisa Jo' (St/v/Dw/d)	WFib
	'Little Alice' (Dw/d) ♀H1c	LAll NFir WFib
	'Little Fi-fine' (Dw/C)	NFir
	'Little Gem' (Sc)	ENfk MHer WFib
	'Little Jim' (Min/d)	NFir
	'Little Jip' (Z/d/v) ♀H1c	LAll NFir WFib
	'Little Spikey' (St/Min/d)	WFib
	longifolium	WBod
	'Lord Baden-Powell'	see *P.* 'Colonel Baden-Powell'
	'Lord Bute' (R) ♀H1c	CDoC CSpe ECtt EWoo LAst LCro MCot MHer NFir NPer SVen WBod WFib WGwG
	'Lord de Ramsey'	see *P.* 'Tip Top Duet'
	'Lord Roberts' (Z)	WFib
	Lorena = 'Pacdala'[PBR] (Dark Line Series) (Z/d)	LAst
	'Lotusland' (Dw/St/C) ♀H1c	NFir WFib
I	'Louise' (R) ♀H1c	NFir
	'Love Song' (R/v)	NFir WFib
	'Lucy Gunnett' (Z/d/v) ♀H1c	NFir
	'Lyewood Bonanza' (R)	CWCL WFib
	'Mabel Grey' (Sc) ♀H1c	CDoC CSpe ENfk EWoo LAll MHer MNHC NFir NPer WFib
§	'Madame Auguste Nonin' (U/Sc)	ENfk LAll MHer NFir WFib
	'Madame Butterfly' (Z/d/v)	NFir
	'Madame Crousse' (I/d) ♀H1c	EWoo WFib
	'Madame Layal' (A) ♀H1c	MHer NFir WFib
	'Madame Margot'	see *P.* 'Hederinum Variegatum'
	'Madame Salleron' (Min/v)	LAll LSou
	'Madge Taylor' (R)	NFir
	'Magda' (Z/d)	LAll
	magenteum	MHer NFir
	'Magic Lantern' (Z/C)	NFir
	'Magnum' (R)	WFib
	'Mandarin' (R)	LAll
	'Mangles' Variegated' (Z/v)	WFib
	'Manx Maid' (A)	NFir
	'Maple Leaf' (Sc)	EWoo
	'Maréchal MacMahon' (Z/C)	ENfk
	'Margaret Soley' (R) ♀H1c	WFib
	'Margaret Thorp'	LAll
	'Margaret Waite' (R)	WFib
	'Margery Stimpson' (Min/d)	WFib
	'Marie Rudlin' (R)	LAll
	'Marie Thomas' (Sc)	SBch
	Marimba = 'Fisrimba'[PBR]	SCoo
	'Marion Saunders' (Dec)	WFib
	'Mariquita' (R)	WFib
	'Mark' (Dw/d)	WFib
	'Marmalade' (Min/d)	LAll
	'Marquis of Bute' (R/v)	NFir
	'Martha Parmer' (Min)	LAll
	'Martin Parrett' (Min/d)	WFib
	'Mary Harrison' (Z/d)	WFib
	'Maureen' (Min)	LAll
I	'Maureen' Hoddinott (Z/d)	MHer
	'Mauve Beauty' (I/d)	WFib
	(Maverick Series) 'Maverick Appleblossom' (Z)	LAst
	- 'Maverick Orange' (Z)	LAst
	- 'Maverick Red' (Z)	LAst
	- 'Maverick Violet' (Z)	LAst
	- 'Maverick White' (Z)	LAst
	'Maxime Kovalevski' (Z)	WFib
	'Maxine' (Z/C)	NFir
	'Maxine Colley' (Z/d/v)	LAll
	'May Day' (R)	WFib
	'May Magic' (R)	NFir WFib
	'Meadowside Dark and Dainty' (St)	NFir WFib
	'Meadowside Fancy' (Z/d/C)	LAll
	'Meadowside Harvest' (Z/St/C)	NFir
	'Meadowside Julie Colley' (Dw)	NFir
	'Meadowside Mahogany' (Z/C)	LAll
	'Meadowside Midnight' (St/C)	WFib
	'Meadowside Orange' (Z/d)	LAll
	'Medley' (Min/d)	WFib
	'Megan Hannah' (Dw/c/d)	NFir
	'Melanie Day' (St) ♀H1c	NFir
	Melocherry = 'Pacmel'[PBR] (Tempo Series) (Z/d)	SSea
	Melosilver = 'Penber' (Tempo Series) (Z/d/v)	LAll
	'Memento' (Min/d)	LAll WFib
	'Mendip' (R)	WFib
	'Mendip Barbie' (R) ♀H1c	NFir
	'Mendip Blanche' (R) ♀H1c	NFir
	'Mendip Lorraine' (R)	NFir
	'Mendip Louise' (R) ♀H1c	NFir
	'Mendip Sarah' (R)	NFir
	'Meon Maid' (R)	WFib
	'Mere Casino' (Z)	WFib
	'Mexican Beauty' (I)	WFib
	'Mexicana'	see *P.* 'Rouletta'
	'Mexicanerin'	see *P.* 'Rouletta'
	'Michael' (A) ♀H1c	MHer NFir
	'Michelle West' (Min)	WFib
	'Milden' (Dw/Z/C) ♀H1c	NFir
	Millennium Dawn (Dw)	LAll
	'Millfield Gem' (I/d)	WFib
	'Millfield Rose' (I/d)	EWoo LAll
	'Mini-Czech' (Min/St)	ECtt LAll WBrk
	'Minnie' (Z/d/St)	WBrk
	'Minstrel Boy' (R)	EWoo WFib
	'Minx' (Min/d)	WFib
	'Miriam Basey'	see *P.* 'Dwarf Miriam Baisey'
	'Miss Burdett Coutts' (Z/v)	MHer WFib
	'Miss McKinsey' (Z/St/d)	LAll NFir
	'Miss Muffett' (Min/d)	WFib
§	'Miss Stapleton'	EWoo LCro MHer WFib
	'Misterioso' (R)	EWoo WFib
	'Misty Morning' (R)	EWoo WFib
	'Mixed Blessings' (Min/C) **new**	LAll
	'Modesty' (Z/d)	WFib
	'Mohawk' (R)	LAll WFib
	'Mole'	see *P.* 'The Mole'
	'Molly' (A)	ENfk
	'Monkwood Rose' (A)	NFir
	'Monsieur Ninon' misapplied	see *P.* 'Madame Auguste Nonin'
§	'Monsieur Ninon' (U)	WFib
	'Mont Blanc' (Z/v)	LAll WFib
	'Montague Garabaldi Smith' (R)	WFib
	'Moon Maiden' (A)	EWoo WFib

Name	Suppliers
'Moonlight'	LAst
Moonlight Violino (Moonlight Series) (Z)	LAst
'Moor' (Min/d)	LAll
Morning Sun = 'Pacmorsu'PBR (Green Leaf Series) (Z)	LAll LAst
'Morval' (Dw/C/d) ♀H1c	LAll WFib
'Morwenna' (R)	LAll MHer NFir WCot WFib
'Mosaic Gay Baby' (I/v/d)	WFib
'Mosaic Red' (Z)	LAll
'Mr Henry Cox' (Z/v) ♀H1c	LAll MHer NFir WFib
'Mr Wren' (Z)	ELan LAll LAst WFib
'Mrs Cannell' (Z)	WFib
'Mrs Farren' (Z/v)	MCot
'Mrs G.H. Smith' (A) ♀H1c	NFir WFib
'Mrs Kingsbury' (U)	WFib
'Mrs Martin' (I/d)	WFib
'Mrs McKenzie' (Z/St)	WFib
'Mrs Parker' (Z/d/v)	LAll NFir WFib
'Mrs Pat' (Dw/St/C) ♀H1c	NFir
'Mrs Pollock' (Z/v)	ELan LAll LAst MCot NEgg SCoo WBrk WFib
'Mrs Quilter' (Z/C) ♀H1c	ECtt LAll WBrk WFib
'Mrs Salter Bevis' (Z/Ca/d)	LAll
'Mrs W.A.R. Clifton' (I/d)	WFib
mutans	WFib
§ 'Mutzel' (I/v)	LAll NFir
'My Chance' (Dec)	NFir WFib
§ ***myrrhifolium*** var. ***coriandrifolium***	MHer NFir WFib
'Mystery' (U) ♀H1c	LCro NFir WFib
'Narina' (I)	SCoo
'Needham Market' (A)	ENfk
'Neil Jameson' (Z/v)	LAll
'Nellie Nuttall' (Z)	WFib
Neona = 'Pacneon'PBR (Z)	SSea
'Nervous Mabel' (Sc) ♀H1c	MHer WFib
'Nettlestead' (Dw) **new**	LAll
'New Gypsy' (R)	CWCL
'New Life' (Z)	NFir
'New York' (Z) **new**	NFir
'Newbridge' (St/Min/d)	LAll
'Nicola Buck' (R) ♀H1c	NFir
'Nicor Star' (Min)	WFib
'Night' (I)	EWoo
'Noel' (Z/Ca/d)	LAll
'Noele Gordon' (Z/d)	LAll WFib
oblongatum	CDes
'Occold Embers' (Dw/C)	LAll
'Occold Profusion' (Dw/d)	NFir
'Occold Shield' (Dw/C/d) ♀H1c	LAll MHer NEgg NFir WBrk WFib
'Occold Tangerine' (Z)	WFib
'Occold Volcano' (Dw/C/d)	WFib
'Octavia Hill' (Z)	LAst
odoratissimum (Sc) ♀H1c	ENfk EWoo GPoy LAll MHer NFir SSea WFib
'Odyssey' (Min)	WFib
'Old Spice' (Sc/v)	ENfk MCot NFir WFib
'Oldbury Duet' (A/v) ♀H1c	LAst MHer NFir
'Olivia' (R)	WFib
'Opera House' (R)	WFib
'Orange Fizz' (Sc) ♀H1c	EWoo MHer NFir
'Orange Imp' (Dw/d)	LAll
'Orange Parfait' (R)	WFib
'Orange Splash' (Z)	LAll
'Orangeade' (Dw/d)	LAll WFib
'Orangesonne' (Z/d)	LAll
'Orchid Clorinda' (Sc)	WFib
'Orion' (Min/d)	WFib
'Orsett' (Sc) ♀H1c	GLog LAll
'Otto's Red' (R)	NFir
'Our Flynn' (Z/St)	WFib
'Our Gynette' (Dec)	EWoo LAll
PAC cultivars	see under selling name
'Pagoda' (Z/St/d)	LAll MHer WFib
'Paisley Red' (Z/d)	NFir WFib
'Pam Tutcher' (St)	NFir
'Pamela Vaughan' (Z/St)	WFib
'Pampered Lady' (A)	NFir
panduriforme	WFib
papilionaceum	ELan EWoo MCot MHer NFir WFib
'Parisienne' (R)	EWoo WFib
'Party Dress' (Z/d)	WFib
'Pat Hannam' (St)	WFib
'Paton's Unique' (U/Sc) ♀H1c	CDoC ELan ENfk EWoo LAll MCot MHer NFir SVen WCot WFib
'Patricia Andrea' (T) ♀H1c	LAll NFir NPer WFib
'Paul Crampel' (Z)	EWoo MCot MHer WFib
'Paul West' (Min/d)	LAll SBch
'Peace' (Min/C)	WFib
'Peach Princess' (R)	NFir
'Pegasus' (Min)	LAll
'Peggy Franklin' (Min) **new**	LAll
'Peggy Sue' (R)	LAll
PELFI cultivars	see under selling name
peltatum	WFib
'Penny' (Z/d)	WFib
'Penny Dixon' (R)	NFir
'Penny Lane' (Z)	WFib
'Pensby' (Dw)	NFir
'Penve'PBR (Quality Series) (Z/d)	SSea
'Peppermint Lace' (Sc)	EWoo
'Percy Hunt' (R)	NFir
'Perfect' (Z)	WFib
'Pershore Princess'	WBrk
'Peter Beard' (Dw/d)	LAll
'Peter Godwin' (R)	WFib
'Peter's Choice' (R)	WFib
'Petit Pierre'	see *P.* 'Kleine Liebling'
'Petite Blanche' (Dw/d)	LAll
'Phyllis Richardson' (R/d)	LAll
'Phyllis Variegated' (U/v)	ECtt ENfk EWoo LAll MHer NFir WCot
'Pink Aurore' (U)	WFib
'Pink Bonanza' (R)	NFir WFib
'Pink Capitatum'	see *P.* 'Pink Capricorn'
§ 'Pink Capricorn' (Sc)	CDoC ENfk EWoo LAll LCro NPri WFib
'Pink Champagne' (Sc)	MHer
'Pink Dolly Varden' (Z/v)	WFib
'Pink Fondant' (Min/d)	WFib
'Pink Gay Baby'	see *P.* 'Sugar Baby'
'Pink Happy Thought' (Z/v)	LAll WFib
'Pink Hindoo' (Dec)	EWoo
'Pink Ice' (Min/d)	NFir
'Pink Mini Cascade'	see *P.* 'Rosa Mini-cascade'
'Pink Needles' (Min/St)	WFib
'Pink Pet' (U)	ECtt NFir
'Pink Rambler' (Z/d)	WFib
'Pink Rosebud' (Z/d)	WFib
'Pippa' (Min/Dw)	NFir
'Playboy Blush' (Dw) **new**	LAll
'Playmate' (Min/St)	WFib
'Plum Rambler' (Z/d)	ECtt EShb WBrk WFib
'Polka' (U) ♀H1c	EWoo NFir WFib
Polka (Z/d) **new**	LAll
'Pompeii' (R)	NFir WFib

'Porchfield' (Min/St)	WBrk
(Precision Series) Precision Bicolour (I) **new**	LBMP
- Precision Bright Lilac	NPri
- Precision Bright Red	LBMP NPri
- Precision Burgundy Red **new**	LBMP NPri
- Precision Dark Red	NPri
- Precision Light Pink = 'Klep02060'PBR (I)	NPri
- Precision Rose Lilac	NPri
'Preston Park' (Z/C)	WFib
'Pretty Polly' (Sc)	WFib
'Prim' (Dw/St/d)	WFib
'Prince of Orange' (Sc) ♀H1c	ENfk EWoo GPoy MCot MHer NFir SIde WFib
'Princeanum' (Sc) ♀H1c	WFib
'Princess Abigail' (Dw/d)	NFir
'Princess Alexandra' (Z/d/v)	LAll
'Princess Josephine' (R)	WFib
'Princess of Balcon'	see *P.* 'Roi des Balcons Lilas'
'Princess of Wales' (R)	LAll WFib
'Princess Virginia' (R/v)	WFib
'Priory Salmon' (St/d)	EShb
'Priory Star' (St/Min/d)	WFib
pseudoglutinosum	WFib
'Pulsar Salmon' (Pulsar Series) (Z) **new**	LRHS
'Pungent Peppermint' (Sc)	MNHC
'Purple Heart' (Dw/St/C) ♀H1c	NFir
'Purple Rogue' (R)	WFib
Purple Sybil = 'Pacpursyb'PBR	LAst SSea
'Purple Unique' (U/Sc)	ENfk EWoo MCot MHer NFir SVen WFib
'Pygmalion' (Z/d/v)	WFib
'Quantock' (R)	WFib
'Quantock Angelique' (A)	NFir
'Quantock Candy' (A) ♀H1c	EWoo NFir
'Quantock Clare' (A)	NFir
'Quantock Classic' (A)	NFir
'Quantock Darren' (A)	NFir
'Quantock Double Dymond' (A)	NFir
'Quantock Kendy' (A) ♀H1c	NFir
'Quantock Kirsty' (A) ♀H1c	EWoo NFir
'Quantock Louise' (A)	NFir
'Quantock Marjorie' (A) ♀H1c	NFir
'Quantock Matty' (A) ♀H1c	NFir
'Quantock Mr Nunn' (A)	NFir
'Quantock Perfection' (A)	NFir
'Quantock Sally' (A/d)	NFir
'Quantock Star' (A)	NFir
'Quantock Ultimate' (A) ♀H1c	NFir
'Queen Esther' (Z/d/St)	LAll
'Queen of Denmark' (Z/d)	LAll WFib
'Queen of Hearts' (I × Z/d)	WFib
'Queen of the Lemons'	EWoo
quercifolium (Sc)	ECtt GPoy WFib
radens (Sc)	ENfk WFib
'Rads Star' (Z/St)	NFir
'Radula' (Sc) ♀H1c	LAll MHer WFib
'Radula Roseum' (Sc)	EWoo WFib
'Ragamuffin' (Dw/d)	LAll
'Rager's Star' (Dw)	LAll
(Rainbow Series) Rainbow Neon = 'Genraineon' (I)	LAst SSea
- Rainbow White = 'Genrawhite' (I)	SSea
'Raspberry Ripple' (A)	NFir
'Raspberry Sundae' (R)	LAll
'Ray Bidwell' (Min)	NFir WFib
'Red Admiral' (Min/d/v)	LAll
§ 'Red Black Vesuvius' (Min/C)	WFib
'Red Cactus' (St)	NFir
'Red Cascade' (I) ♀H1c	LAll LAst WFib
'Red Ice' (Min/d)	LAll NFir
'Red Pandora' (Z) ♀H1c	LAll NFir WFib
'Red Pimpernella'	LAll
'Red Rambler' (Z/d)	LAll WBrk WFib
'Red Robin' (R)	ENfk WCot
'Red Silver Cascade'	see *P.* 'Mutzel'
'Red Spider' (Dw/Ca)	WFib
'Red Startel' (Z/St/d)	WFib
'Red Susan Pearce' (R)	WFib
'Red Witch' (Dw/St/d)	LAll MHer WBrk WFib
§ Red-Mini-Cascade = 'Rotemica' (I)	LAll
'Redondo' (Dw/d)	EWoo LAll
'Reflections' (Z/d)	WFib
'Reg 'Q'' (Z/C)	NFir
'Regalia Lavendel' (R)	LAst
'Regalia Lilac' (R)	LAst
'Regalia Red' (R)	LAst
'Regina' (Z/d)	LAll WFib
'Rembrandt' (R)	LAll WFib
'Renate Parsley' ♀H1c	CDes CDoC LCro MHer NFir WFib
reniforme	GPoy MHer WFib
'Reverend David Harley' (Z)	NFir
'Richard Collins' (St) **new**	LAll
'Richard Gibbs' (Sc)	ENfk MHer
'Richard Key' (Z/d/C)	WFib
Ricky = 'Pacric'PBR	LAst
'Rietje van der Lee' (A)	ENfk WFib
'Rigel' (Min/d)	LAll NFir
'Rimey' (St)	NFir
'Rimfire' (R) ♀H1c	CWCL EWoo LAll LCro MHer NFir NWad WFib
'Rio Grande' (I/d)	LAll MHer NFir WFib
'Rober's Lemon Rose' (Sc)	ENfk MHer SEND WBrk
'Rober's Salmon Coral' (Dw/d)	LAll
'Robert Fish' (Z/C)	SCoo
'Robert McElwain' (Z/d)	WFib
'Robin' (Sc)	LAll
'Robin's Unique' (U)	WFib
'Robyn Hannah' (St/d)	MHer NFir
rodneyanum	CDes
'Rogue' (R)	WFib
§ 'Roi des Balcons Impérial' (I)	SSea
§ 'Roi des Balcons Lilas' (I)	LAll SSea
'Roller's Echo' (A)	WFib
'Roller's Pathfinder' (I/d/v)	LAll
'Roller's Pioneer' (I/v)	ENfk EWoo LAll
'Roller's Satinique' (U)	MHer
'Rollison's Unique' (U)	MHer WFib
'Romeo' (R)	EWoo LAll
'Rookley' (St/d)	NFir
'Rosa della Sera' (St)	LAll
§ 'Rosa Mini-cascade' (Mini Cascade Series) (I) ♀H1c	NFir
'Rose Bengal' (A)	ENfk
'Rose of Amsterdam' (Min/d)	WFib

'Rose Paton's Unique' (U/Sc)	LAll
'Rose Silver Cascade' (I)	LAll MCot MHer
'Rosebud Supreme' (Z/d)	WFib
'Roseto' (Dec) **new**	NFir
'Rosina Read' (Dw/d)	LAll
'Rosita' (Dw/d)	LAll
'Rosmaroy' (R)	WFib
'Rosy Dawn' (Min/d)	LAll WFib
'Rote Mini-cascade'	see *P.* Red-Mini-Cascade
§ 'Rouletta' (I/d)	LAst WFib
'Royal Ascot' (R)	EWoo NFir
Royal Candy Cane = 'Klep01028' (Royal Series) (I) **new**	SSea
Royal Lavender = 'Klepp07196' PBR (Royal Series) (I) **new**	SSea
Royal Magenta = 'Klepp10206' (Royal Series) (I) **new**	SSea
'Royal Norfolk' (Min/d) ♀H1c	LAll NFir
'Royal Oak' (Sc) ♀H1c	CDoC ENfk LAll MCot MHer MNHC NWad SBch SVen WFib
§ 'Royal Purple' (Z/d)	WFib
Royal Red = 'Kleroder' PBR (Royal Series) (I) **new**	SSea
'Royal Surprise' (R) ♀H1c	EWoo NFir
'Ruben' (d)	LSou
'Ruben' (Z/d)	LAst
'Ruby' (Min/d)	WFib
'Ruffled Velvet' (R)	EWoo
'Rushmere' (Dw/d)	WFib
'Rushmoor Golden Rosebud' (Z)	WFib
'Rushmoor Mrs Eve Scott' (Z/d)	WFib
Sailing = 'Klesail'	SSea
'Saint Elmo's Fire' (St/Min/d)	MHer WFib
Saint Malo = 'Guisaint' (I)	NFir
'Salmon Beauty' (Dw/d)	WFib
§ 'Salmon Irene' (Z/d)	WFib
Salmon Princess = 'Pacsalpri' PBR	LAst LSou
'Salmon Queen'	see *P.* 'Lachskönigin'
Salmon Queen = 'Pacsalque' PBR (Z) **new**	SSea
'Salmon Slam' (R)	LAll
'Samantha' (R)	WFib
'Samantha Stamp' (Dw/C/d)	WFib
Samelia = 'Pensam' PBR (Dark Line Series) (Z/d)	LAst SSea
'Sancho Panza' (Dec)	CSpe WFib
'Sandra Lorraine' (I/d)	WFib
Sangria Nova = 'Gendana' PBR (Z)	SSea
'Sanguineum'	CSpe
'Santa Maria' (Z/d)	LAll
§ 'Sarah Don' (A/v)	ECtt LAst WFib
'Sarah Hunt' (Min/d) ♀H1c	NFir
'Sassa' PBR (Quality Series) (Z/d)	LAst SSea
'Satsuki' (R) ♀H1c	NFir
'Scarlet Gem' (Z/St)	WBrk WFib
'Scarlet Pet' (U) ♀H1c	ENfk NFir
'Scarlet Rambler' (Z/d)	EShb WFib
'Scarlet Unique' (U)	EWoo MCot SSea WFib
schizopetalum	MHer WFib
'Schottii' ♀H1c	CDoC EWoo LCro MHer NFir WFib
'Scottow Star' (Z/C)	WFib
'Seaview Silver' (Min/St)	WFib
'Seaview Sparkler' (Z/St)	WFib
'Seeley's Pansy' (A)	EWoo MHer
'Sefton' (R) ♀H1c	WFib
'Shan Hoy' (Dw)	NFir
'Shanks' (Z) ♀H1c	NFir
'Shannon'	EWoo SBch WFib
'Shaun Jacobs' (Min/d)	LAll
'Shimmer' (Z/d)	LAll
Shocking Orange = 'Pacshorg' PBR (Quality Series)	LAst
'Shogan' (R)	NFir
§ 'Shottesham Pet' (Sc)	CDoC ECtt ENfk EWoo MHer NWad
sidoides ♀H1c	CDes CSpe CTre EWoo GPoy LAll LCro LHop MCot MHer NFir SBch SChr SDix SMHy SPhx SVen WBod WFib WHer
- black-flowered	CTca SBrt
Sidonia = 'Pensid' PBR (Dark Line Series) (Z/d)	LAst
'Sienna' (R)	NFir
'Sil Claudio' PBR (Z)	LAst
'Sil Falko' PBR (I)	LAst LSou
'Sil Frauke' PBR (Z)	LAst
'Sil Friesia' PBR (Z)	LAst
'Sil Hero' PBR (Z)	LAst
'Sil Lara' PBR (Z)	LAst
'Sil Lenja' PBR (Z)	LAst
'Sil Linus' PBR (Z)	LSou
'Sil Liske' PBR (Z)	LAst
'Sil Magnus' PBR (Z)	LAst
'Sil Malaika' PBR (I)	LSou
'Sil Okka'	LAst
'Sil Pia' PBR (I)	LSou
'Sil Quirin' PBR (I)	LAst
'Sil Raiko' PBR	LAst
'Sil Sören'	LAst
'Sil Teske' PBR (I)	LAst
'Sil Tomke' PBR (I)	LAst LSou
'Silky'	LAll
'Silver Anne' (R/v)	NFir
'Silver Blazon' (Z/Dw/C/v)	WFib
'Silver Delight' (v/d)	WFib
'Silver Kewense' (Dw/v)	WFib
'Silver Snow' (Min/St/d)	WFib
'Silver Wings' (Z/v)	LAll NFir
'Simplicity' (Z)	LAll
'Skelly's Pride' (Z)	LAll WFib
'Skies of Italy' (Z/C/d)	WFib
'Sneezy' (Min)	NFir
'Snow Cap' (MinI) ♀H1c	NFir
'Snowbaby' (Min/d)	WFib
'Snowdrift' (I/d)	LAll WFib
'Snowflake' (Min)	see *P.* 'Atomic Snowflake'
'Snowstorm' (Z)	WFib
'Sofie'	see *P.* 'Decora Rose'
'Solferino' (A)	ENfk
Solidor (I/d) ♀H1c	NFir
Solo = 'Guillio' (Z/I)	LAll
'Something Else' (Z/St/d)	LAll
'Something Special' (Z/d) ♀H1c	LAll NFir WFib
Sophie Casade	see *P.* 'Decora Rose'
'Sophie Dumaresque' (Z/v) ♀H1c	NFir WFib

Name	Suppliers
'Sophie Emma' (Z)	NFir
'South American Bronze' (R) ♀H1c	WFib
'South American Delight' (R)	LAll
'Southern Peach' (Min/d)	LAll
'Souvenir de Prue'	EWoo
'Spanish Angel' (A) ♀H1c	CWCL MHer NFir WFib
'Sparkler' (Z)	LAll
'Spellbound' (R)	WFib
'Spital Dam' (Dw/d)	LAll NFir
'Spitfire' (Z/Ca/d/v)	LAll WFib
§ 'Splendide' ♀H1c	CSpe MHer NFir SWvt WFib
'Spot-on-bonanza' (R) ♀H1c	NFir WFib
'Springfield Black' (R)	LAll MCot
'Springtime' (Z/d)	WFib
'Stadt Bern' (Z/C)	LAll NFir
× ***stapletoniae***	see *P.* 'Miss Stapleton'
'Star Flecks' (St) ♀H1c	LAll NFir
'Startel Salmon' (Z/St)	MHer
'Stella Bird Dancer' (Min/St)	LAll
'Stella Vernante'	LAll
'Stellar Arctic Star'	see *P.* 'Arctic Star'
'Stellar Hannaford Star'	see *P.* 'Hannaford Star'
'Stenbury' (Dw/d) **new**	LAll
'Stolen Kisses' (Min/D)	LAll
'Strawberries and Cream' (Z/St)	NFir
'Strawberry Fayre' (Dw/St)	WFib
'Stringer's Souvenir' (Dw/d/v)	LAll
§ 'Sugar Baby' (DwI)	LAll MHer WFib
'Summer Cloud' (Z/d)	WFib
'Summertime' (Z/d)	see *P.* 'Deacon Summertime'
'Sun Rocket' (Dw/d)	WFib
'Sundridge Moonlight' (Z/C)	NFir WFib
'Sundridge Surprise' (Z)	WFib
Sunflair Rose = 'Genrose' (Sunflair Series) (I/d) **new**	LAll
'Sunraysia' (Z/St)	WFib
'Sunset Snow' (R)	LAll WFib
'Sunspot' (Min/C)	NFir
'Sunspot Petit Pierre' (Min/v)	WFib
'Sunstar' (Min/d)	WFib
'Supernova' (Z/St/d)	WFib
'Supreme Burgundy' **new**	NPri
'Supreme Lilac'	NPri
'Supreme Orange' **new**	NPri
'Supreme Red'	NPri
'Supreme White'	NPri
'Surcouf' (I)	WFib
(Survivor Series) Survivor Blue (Z) **new**	LBMP
- Survivor Dark Red (Z) **new**	LBMP
- Survivor Scarlet (Z) **new**	LBMP
- Survivor White (Z) **new**	LBMP
'Susan Payne' (Dw/d)	LAll MHer
'Susan Pearce' (R)	LAll
'Susie 'Q'' (Z/C)	LAll
'Sussex Gem' (Min/d)	LAll WFib
'Sussex Lace'	see *P.* 'White Mesh'
'Swainham Mellow Yellow' (Z)	LAll
'Swanland Lace' (I/d/v)	WFib
'Swedish Angel' (A)	WFib
'Sweet Mimosa' (Sc) ♀H1c	CDoC ELan ENfk EWoo LAll LAst LPot MCot MHer NFir SBch WFib WGwG
'Sweet Sixteen' (R)	WFib
'Sweet Sue' (Min)	LAll
'Swiss Star' (Z/St) **new**	LAll
'Sybil Holmes' (I/d)	WFib
'Tamie' (Dw/d)	LAll NFir
'Tammy' (Dw/d)	LAll
'Tangerine' (Min/Ca/d)	LAll
tetragonum	EWoo MHer WFib
'The Boar' (Fr) ♀H1c	EShb EWoo MCot WFib
'The Culm' (A)	WFib
'The Czar'	see *P.* 'Czar'
'The Joker' (I/d)	WFib
'The Kenn-Lad' (A)	EWoo
'The Marchioness of Bute' (R)	LAll MHer NFir WFib
§ 'The Mole' (A)	WFib
'The Tamar' (A)	EWoo MHer
'The Yar' (Z/St)	WFib
'Thomas Earle' (Z)	CDoC WFib
'Tilly' (Min)	NFir
'Timothy Clifford' (Min/d)	LAll
'Tinker West' (Z/St/Dw)	WFib
§ 'Tip Top Duet' (A) ♀H1c	EWoo MHer NFir WFib
'Tirley Garth' (A)	WFib
tomentosum (Sc) ♀H1c	CDoC CSpe ENfk EWoo GLog GPoy LAll LCro MCot MHer MNHC NFir NWad WFib WHea
- 'Chocolate'	see *P.* 'Chocolate Peppermint'
Tommy = 'Pactommy' (I)	LAst SSea
'Topscore' (Z/d)	WFib
'Tornado' (R) ♀H1c	LCro NFir WFib
'Torrento' (Sc)	MHer WFib
'Tortoiseshell' (R)	WFib
'Toscana Okka' (Toscana Series) (I)	LAst LSou
'Tracy' (Min/d)	LAll NFir
transvaalense	NFir
Trend Dark Red = 'Gentreak'PBR (Z) **new**	LAll
tricolor misapplied	see *P.* 'Splendide'
tricolor Curt.	NFir
tricuspidatum	EWoo WCot
trifidum	CDoC EWoo WFib
'Triomphe de Nancy' (Z/d)	WFib
triste	EWoo MCot MHer NFir WCot WFib
'Trudie' (Dw/Fr)	LAll MHer WFib
'Turkish Coffee' (R)	WFib
'Turkish Delight' (Dw/C)	NFir WFib
'Turtle's Surprise' (Z/d/v)	WBrk
'Turtle's White' (R)	LAll
'Tweenaway' (Dw)	NFir
'Two Dees' (Dw/d)	LAll
'Tyabb Princess' (R)	EWoo
'Uncle Ernie' (Z/C) **new**	LAll
'Unique Aurore' (U)	MHer
'Unique Mons Ninon'	see *P.* 'Monsieur Ninon'
'Urchin' (Min/St)	NFir WFib
'Ursula Key' (Z/c)	WFib
'Ursula's Choice' (A)	WFib
'Val Merrick' (Dw/St)	WFib
'Valentine' (Z/C)	WFib
'Vancouver Centennial' (Dw/St/C) ♀H1c	LAll MCot MHer NEgg NFir SCoo SSea WFib
'Vandersea' (Sc)	EWoo MCot
'Variegated Attar of Roses' (Sc/v)	NWad
'Variegated Clorinda' (Sc/v)	WFib
'Variegated Fragrans'	see *P.* (Fragrans Group) 'Fragrans Variegatum'

§	'Variegated Kleine Liebling' (Min/v)	WFib
	'Variegated Petit Pierre' (Min/v)	MHer WFib
	'Vectis Blaze' (I)	EWoo
	'Vectis Cascade' (I)	EWoo
	'Vectis Finery' (St/d) ♀H1c	NFir
	'Vectis Glitter' (Z/St) ♀H1c	LAll NFir WBrk WFib
	'Vectis Imp' (Min/Z) new	LAll
	'Vectis Pink' (Dw/St)	WFib
	'Vectis Purple' (Z/d)	WFib
	'Vectis Sparkler' (Dw/St)	NFir
	'Vectis Spider' (Dw/St)	LAll
	'Vectis Starbright' (Dw/St)	LAll WFib
	'Vectis Volcano' (Z/St)	WFib
	'Velvet Duet' (A) ♀H1c	NFir
	'Venus' (Min/d)	LAll
	'Verona Contreras' (A)	NFir
	'Vic Claws' (Dw/St)	NFir
	'Vicki' (R)	EWoo
	'Vicki Town' (R)	WFib
	'Vicky Claire' (R)	EWoo NFir WFib
	Vicky = 'Pacvicky'PBR (I)	LAst SSea
	Victor = 'Pacvi' (Quality Series) (Z/d)	LSou
	'Vienna' (Z) new	NFir
	'Village Hill Oak' (Sc)	LAll
	Ville de Dresden = 'Pendresd'PBR (I)	EWoo LAst
	'Vina' (Dw/C/d)	WFib
	violareum misapplied	see *P.* 'Splendide'
	'Viscossisimum' (Sc)	MHer
	viscosum	see *P. glutinosum*
	'Vivat Regina' (Z/d)	WFib
	'Voodoo' (U) ♀H1c	CSpe ECtt EWoo MCot MHer NFir WCot WFib
	'Wantirna' (Z/v) ♀H1c	LAll NFir
	'Warrenorth Coral' (Z/C/d)	WFib
	'Washbrook' (Min/d) ♀H1c	NFir
	'Waveney' (Min)	LAll
	'Wedding Royale' (Dw/d)	LAll WFib
	'Welling' (Sc)	ENfk MHer NFir
	'Wendy Jane' (Dw/d)	WFib
	'Wendy Read' (Dw/d)	LAll WFib
	'Westdale Appleblossom' (Z/C/d)	LAll WFib
	'Westside' (Z/d)	MHer WFib
	'Westwood' (Z/St)	WFib
	'Whisper' (R)	EWoo WFib
	'White Bird's Egg' (Z)	WFib
	'White Boar' (Fr)	EShb EWoo NFir WFib
	'White Bonanza' (R)	WFib
	'White Butterfly' (Z/C)	LAll
	'White Chiffon' (R)	LAll
	'White Eggshell' (Min)	WFib
	'White Feather' (Z/St)	MHer
	'White Glory' (R) ♀H1c	NFir
§	'White Mesh' (I/v)	NFir
	'White Unique' (U)	SBch WFib
	Wico = 'Guimongol'PBR (I/d)	LAst
	'Wild Spice' (Sc)	LAll
	'Wilhelm Kolle' (Z)	WFib
	'Wilhelm Langath' (Z/v)	EShb SCoo WBrk
	'Willa' (Dec)	WFib
	'Win Ellison' (St) new	CDoC
	'Winford Festival'	LAll
	'Winnie Read' (Dw/d)	LAll
	'Wolverton' (Z)	WFib
	'Wootton's Unique' (U)	CSpe EWoo
	'Wychwood' (A/Sc)	EWoo
	'Yale' (I/d) ♀H1c	WFib
	'Yan le Grounch' (Z/C)	WFib
	'Yhu' (R)	NFir WFib
	'York Florist' (Z/d/v)	LAll
	'Yvonne' (Z)	WFib
	'Zama' (R)	NFir
	'Zena' (Dw)	LAll
	'Zinc' (Z/d)	WFib
	'Zofia Pope' (R)	NFir
	zonale	WFib
	'Zulu King' (R)	WFib
	'Zulu Warrior' (R)	WFib

Peliosanthes (*Asparagaceae*)

	arisanensis B&SWJ 3639	WCru
	caesia B&SWJ 5183	WCru
	teta subsp. ***humilis*** RWJ 10044	WCru

Pellaea (*Pteridaceae*)

	atropurpurea	NLos
	falcata	EShb ISha NLos
	ovata	SPlb
	paradoxa 'Glowstar' new	ISha
	rotundifolia ♀H1b	CLAP ISha LPal LRHS WBor
	viridis	WPGP

Peltandra (*Araceae*)

	undulata	see *P. virginica* (L.) Schott
§	***virginica*** (L.) Schott	EWay NPer SWat
	- 'Snow Splash' (v)	EWay

Peltaria (*Brassicaceae*)

	alliacea	CSpe LEdu WCot
*	***dumulosa***	EBee WCot

Peltiphyllum see *Darmera*

Peltoboykinia (*Saxifragaceae*)

§	***tellimoides***	CLAP EBee GCal GKev LPla NBir WMoo WPnP
	watanabei	CDes CLAP CSpe EBee ESwi GEdr IMou LEdu MMHG MSCN NLar SPad WCru WMoo WPGP WPnP

Pennantia (*Pennantiaceae*)

	baylisiana	ECou
	corymbosa	ECou

Pennellianthus see *Penstemon*

Pennisetum ✿ (*Poaceae*)

	× ***advena*** 'Fireworks'PBR (v)	EBee EPfP EUJe LPar LRHS MAsh SCob SLon SWvt WCot
§	- 'Rubrum' ♀H2	CBcs CExl CKno EShb EUJe LPal MAsh NWsh SCoo SHDw SMad SPoG SRot SWvt WCot
§	***alopecuroides***	CBcs CWCL EAEE ECha EHoe EPfP LRHS LSou MJak NGdn SCob SLim SPer SPlb SWat SWvt WBod WHar WWEG XLum XSen
	- B&SWJ 11434	WCru
	- Autumn Wizard	see *P. alopecuroides* 'Herbstzauber'
	- 'Black Beauty'	CSpe MAvo SMHy WWEG
	- 'Cassian's Choice'	CKno EHoe ELon EWes NCGa SHar WWEG
	- 'Caudatum'	CKno
	- 'Dark Desire' new	CKno

	- 'Gelbstiel'	CKno EPPr LRHS
	- 'Hameln'	Widely available
§	- 'Herbstzauber'	CCon CKno EHoe LHop MAvo NLar XLum
	- 'Little Bunny'	CKno CSde CWib EBee EHoe ELan ELon EPfP EShb GCal IVic LPal LRHS LSRN MBri NGdn SCob SMea SWvt WWEG XSen
	- 'Little Honey' (v)	CKno NLar XLum
	- 'Magic'	CBod ELon EPPr MAvo WWEG
	- 'Moudry'	CExl CKno CSde EBee EHoe ELon EPfP LHop LPal LRHS MAvo NLar NSti SHDw XLum
	- 'National Arboretum'	EBee EPPr
	- 'Reborn'	MAvo
	- 'Red Head'	CAbP CKno CMea EBee ELon EPfP EUJe EWes LRHS LSou MAvo NSti WCot
	- f. ***viridescens***	CKno ELan EPPr EShb LEdu LRHS SCob SMad SPhx WPtf WWEG XLum
	- 'Weserbergland'	CKno EBee EHoe ELon EPPr WWEG
	- 'Woodside'	CKno CPrp EHoe LEdu SMad XLum
	caffrum **new**	WCot
	clandestinum	EShb
	compressum	see *P. alopecuroides*
	'Fairy Tails'	CKno EPPr EPfP LRHS MAsh NDov SMHy SPoG
	flaccidum	EPPr
	glaucum 'Purple Baron'	MAsh
	- 'Purple Majesty'	CSpe SWvt
	incomptum	EHoe XLum
	- purple-flowered	CCon
	longistylum misapplied	see *P. villosum*
	macrourum	CBod CKno CSam CSde CSpe ECha EHoe ELon EUJe LEdu LHop LRHS MAvo MNrw MSpe MWhi NDov NWsh SEND SMHy SMad SPtp WPGP
	- 'Short Stuff'	CKno
	massaicum 'Red Bunny Tails'	CChe ELon EUJe LRHS
	- 'Red Buttons'	see *P. thunbergii* 'Red Buttons'
	orientale 🏆H5	CAby CKno CPrp CSde CSpe ECha EHoe EPfP EWoo LHop LPal LRHS LSun MNrw MRav NBir NWsh SEND SGSe SPer SPtp SRkn SWvt WBod WCot WHoo WKif WWEG XLum
	- 'Karley Rose'[PBR]	CKno CPar EHoe EWes EWoo IBoy IPot LEdu LHop LRHS MAvo MWhi NDov NOak NWsh SCob SMad SWvt WWEG
I	- 'Robustum'	EBee EPPr MAvo WPGP
	- 'Shogun'	CKno CSam EPPr LRHS SMHy WCot
	- 'Tall Tails'	CBod EHoe EPPr EWes EWoo LRHS MWhi NDov SMea WWEG XLum
	'Paul's Giant'	CKno XLum
	purpureum 'Vertigo' **new**	CBod
	rueppellii	see *P. setaceum*
§	***setaceum*** 🏆H6	CWib EPfP LCro NWsh SHDw SWvt WCot
	- 'Rubrum'	see *P.* × *advena* 'Rubrum'
	- 'Sky Rocket'[PBR]	LRHS MBri
	- 'Summer Samba'	EBee LRHS MBri
	thunbergii	CAby CBod GKev LRHS
§	- 'Red Buttons'	CKno EBee EHoe ELon EPfP EShb LEdu LRHS MAsh MAvo NOak SHDw SMHy SMea SPhx WHea WHoo
§	***villosum*** 🏆H3	CAby CBod CExl CKno CMac CSpe EAJP ECha EHoe ELan EPPr EPfP EShb LEdu LHop LOPS LRHS LSRN MWhi SEND SGSe SMad SMea SPhx WWEG XLum XSen
	- 'Nemira' **new**	EBee

pennyroyal see *Mentha pulegium*

Penstemon ✿ (*Plantaginaceae*)

	sp.	SVic
	NJM 09.028	WPGP
	'Abbotsmerry'	CWCL ECtt EPfP LLHF MBNS MCot NLar SLon
	albertinus	see *P. humilis*
§	'Alice Hindley' 🏆H4	Widely available
	alpinus	EDAr
	ambiguus	SBrt
	'Amy Gray'	WAvo
§	'Andenken an Friedrich Hahn' 🏆H5	Widely available
	antirrhinoides	see *Keckiella antirrhinoides*
	'Apple Blossom' misapplied	see *P.* 'Thorn'
	'Apple Blossom' 🏆H3	Widely available
	aridus	GEdr
	arizonicus	see *P. whippleanus*
	arkansanus	CEvo
	'Ashton'	WAvo
	attenuatus subsp. ***militaris***	SPlb
	'Audrey Cooper'	CChe CMac MBNS
	'Axe Valley Penny Mitchell'	ECtt
	'Axe Valley Suzie'	CAby
	azureus	GKev
	'Barbara Barker'	see *P.* 'Beech Park'
§	***barbatus***	CFis CTal SPer SRms WTcb
	- subsp. ***coccineus***	CAby CCon EAJP GBin MBNS XLum
	- 'Iron Maiden'	LRHS SGSe
	- 'Jingle Bells'	IFro NBFr
	- orange-flowered	SPlb
	- 'Peter Catt'	CMea
	- Pinacolada Series	LRHS
	- - 'Pinacolada Blue'	LRHS
	- - 'Pinacolada Dark Rose'	LRHS
	- - 'Pinacolada Rosy Red'	LRHS
	- - 'Pinacolada White'	LRHS
	- var. ***praecox***	MBNS MHol SRot
	- - f. ***nanus*** 'Rondo'	EAJP LRHS
	'Beckford'	CWCL EWTr LLHF MBNS
§	'Beech Park' 🏆H3	ELan EPfP EWes LRHS
	'Bisham Seedling'	see *P.* 'White Bedder'
	'Blackbird'	Widely available
	'Blue Riding Hood'[PBR] (Riding Hood Series) **new**	LCro LRHS SPoG
	'Blue Spring' misapplied	see *P. heterophyllus* 'Blue Spring'
	'Blueberry Fudge' (Ice Cream Series)	LRHS LSou LSun MAvo WCot
	'Blueberry Taffy'[PBR]	ECtt NCGa
	'Bodnant'	LAst LLHF MBNS WAvo WBod WHoo WHrl
	bradburii	see *P. grandiflorus*
	'Bredon'	MBNS WAvo
	brevisepalus **new**	CEvo
	'Bubblegum' (Ice Cream Series)	CAby LRHS LSun WCot
	'Burford Purple'	see *P.* 'Burgundy'

	Name	Suppliers
	'Burford Seedling'	see *P.* 'Burgundy'
	'Burford White'	see *P.* 'White Bedder'
§	'Burgundy'	CCon CMac CWCL ECtt GMaP LLWP LRHS MHol NBir NPer SPoG SRms WAvo XLum
	calycosus	CEvo
§	***campanulatus***	EPot EWes LRHS SRms
	- PC&H 148	SDys
	- ***pulchellus***	see *P. campanulatus*
	- 'Roseus' misapplied	see *P. kunthii*
	'Candy Pink'	see *P.* 'Old Candy Pink'
	cardwellii	EWes
	cardwellii* × *davidsonii	WAbe
	'Castle Forbes'	GMaP MBNS SRms
	'Cathedral Rose'	ELan EPfP LRHS
	'Catherine de la Mare'	see *P. heterophyllus* 'Catherine de la Mare'
	'Centra'	MBNS XLum
	centranthifolius	EBee SIgm
	'Charles Rudd'	COtt CWCL ECtt ELan ELon EPfP LSRN MBNS NLar SBod SEND SRms SWvt WHrl
§	'Cherry' 🏆H3	ECtt GBee MBNS SHar WHea WWEG
	'Cherry Ripe' misapplied	see *P.* 'Cherry'
§	'Chester Scarlet' 🏆H3	ECtt MBNS SDix WCFE WKif XLum
	'Choirboy'	EWes
	clutei	LLHF
	cobaea	GLog SBrt
	comarrhenus	SBrt
	'Comberton'	MBNS WAvo
	confertus	CTri EBee ECho EPot SBrt XLum
	- RCB/MO A-7	WCot
	'Connie's Pink' 🏆H4	MBNS SRms WAvo WWEG
	cordifolius	see *Keckiella cordifolia*
	'Cottage Garden Red'	see *P.* 'Windsor Red'
§	'Countess of Dalkeith'	ECtt ELan GBin LLWP MCot MRav SHar SRms SWvt WAvo WCFE WCot
	crandallii subsp. ***atratus***	SBrt
	cristatus	see *P. eriantherus*
*	***cyananthus*** var. ***utahensis***	WCot
	aff. ***cyananthus***	SBrt
	cyaneus	GKev
	'Dark Towers'[PBR]	CAbb CMos CSpe ECtt IPot LRHS MSCN SLon SPad SPoG WHil WHlf
	davidsonii	ECho EWes GCrg GEdr NSla SIgm WAbe WOld
	- var. ***davidsonii***	WAbe
	- var. ***menziesii*** 'Microphyllus'	EPot GCrg GEdr LLHF NHar NSla NWad WAbe
	- var. ***praeteritus***	GEdr
	- 'Silverwells'	GEdr
	'Dazzler'	SWvt
	'Delfts Blue Riding Hood'[PBR] (Riding Hood Series)	CSpe EBee LCro
	'Devonshire Cream'	CWCL MBNS
	diffusus	see *P. serrulatus*
	digitalis	CEvo MBNS NFav
§	- 'Husker Red'	Widely available
	- 'Mystica'	EBee LRHS
	- 'Purpureus'	see *P. digitalis* 'Husker Red'
	- 'Ruby Tuesday'	EWes WPGP
	- white-flowered	EBee
	discolor pale lavender-flowered	NBir
§	'Drinkstone Red'	EHrv MBNS SDix SDys
	'Drinkwater Red'	see *P.* 'Drinkstone Red'
	(Elgar Series) 'Elgar Crown of India'	MHol WCot
	- 'Elgar Enigma'	EBee LLHF MHol WCot
	- 'Elgar Firefly'	MHol WCot
	- 'Elgar Light of Life'	MHol WCot
	- 'Elgar Nimrod'	EBee MHol WCot
	'Ellenbank Amethyst'	SDys
	'Ellwood Red Phoenix'	MBNS
	'Elmley'	MBNS WAvo
§	***eriantherus***	LLHF SPlb
	Etna = 'Yatna'	CRos ECtt EPfP LAll LRHS MBNS SRms
	euglaucus	EBee GKev LLHF MMuc
	- NNS 07-397	GKev
§	'Evelyn' 🏆H4	CLet CMea CTri ECha ELan EPfP IBoy LRHS LSRN MBNS MCot MHer MRav SPer SPoG SRGP SRms SWvt WAvo WBod WKif WSHC WWEG XLum
	'Fanny's Blush'	SWvt
	'Firebird'	see *P.* 'Schoenholzeri'
	'Flame'	MBNS SLon WAvo WWEG
	'Flamingo'	CWCL ELon EPfP EWes GBBs GBin LAst LRHS MBNS NLar SGbt SHil SRms SWvt WHoo WMnd WWEG
	fruticiformis var. ***incertus*** new	EBee
§	***fruticosus*** var. ***scouleri*** 🏆H5	MAsh MMuc SEND
	- - 'Albus' 🏆H5	CSpe WAbe
	- - 'Amethyst'	SRms WAbe
	- var. ***serratus*** 'Holly'	SIgm
	Fujiyama = 'Yayama'[PBR]	CSam CWGN ECtt EPfP LAll LHop LRHS SLon SPad SRms SWvt
	'Garden Red'	see *P.* 'Windsor Red'
	'Garnet'	see *P.* 'Andenken an Friedrich Hahn'
	gentianoides B&SWJ 10271	WCru
	'Geoff Hamilton'	CWCL ECtt LSRN MBNS NLar SLon SPoG WAvo
	'George Elrick'	LLHF WHoo
§	'George Home' 🏆H3	EWes MBNS SRms
	'George Moon'	SPad
	'Gilchrist'	ECtt SLon
	glaber	CMHG CMea GBee LHop LLWP LSRN SPlb WKif WSHC
	- 'Roundway Snowflake'	SHar SPhx
	globosus	SBrt
	'Gloire des Quatre Rues'	XLum
	gormanii	GEdr
§	***grandiflorus***	CCon EBee EPfP SBrt
	- 'Prairie Snow'	EBee
	- 'War Axe'	EDAr
	hallii	EPot EWes SBrt
	hartwegii 'Albus'	LHop SHar SIgm SRms
	- 'Picotee Red'	CWCL LRHS
§	***heterophyllus***	LRHS MNrw MSCN NBir NGBl SRkn SRms WHea
	- 'Blue Eye'	MBrN
	- 'Blue Gem'	CElw CTri
§	- 'Blue Spring'	CSpe EPfP LRHS MRav SPoG WBod
§	- 'Catherine de la Mare' 🏆H4	CBod EBee ELan EWoo GBin LHop LRHS LSRN MWat NBir SBch SCob SHar SPer SWvt WHrl WKif XLum
	- 'Electric Blue'	CBod CKno LAst LRHS SLon
	- 'Heavenly Blue'	Widely available
	- 'Jeanette'	CMea WTor
	- 'Margarita BOP' new	EBee

	- 'Roundway White'	WCot
	- 'True Blue'	see *P. heterophyllus*
	- 'Züriblau'	CCon EBee SGSe SPlb
§	'Hewell Pink Bedder' ♀H4	CBod EPfP EWoo GBin GBuc LPot LRHS MBNS MRav NCGa SHil SPtp SRms SWvt WHil WMnd
	'Hewitt's Pink'	SLon
	hidalgensis	WCot
	'Hidcote Pink' ♀H3	Widely available
	'Hidcote Purple'	SHar WHoo XLum
	'Hidcote White'	LPot MHer SWvt
	'Hillview Pink'	SLon XLum
§	***hirsutus***	EBee SGSe XLum
	- var. ***pygmaeus***	CMea ECho EDAr MHer NRya SBrt SPlb WHoo WIce
*	- - f. ***albus***	EBee ECho WHoo
	'Hopleys Variegated' (v)	LRHS SWvt
	'Hot Pink Riding Hood'[PBR] (Riding Hood Series) new	EBee LCro LRHS SPoG
§	***humilis***	SBrt
	'James Bowden'	MBNS
	'John Booth'	MBNS
	'John Nash' misapplied	see *P.* 'Alice Hindley'
	'John Nash'	SRms
	'John Spedan Lewis'	SLon
	'Joy'	MBNS
	'Juicy Grape' (Ice Cream Series)	LAll LSun WCot WHil
	'June'	see *P.* 'Pennington Gem'
	'Kate Gilchrist'	SLon
	Kilimanjaro = 'Yajaro'	EPfP LRHS SLon SRms WFar
	'King George V'	Widely available
	'Knight's Purple'	ECtt
	'Knightwick'	WWEG
§	***kunthii***	MAsh
§	***laetus*** subsp. ***roezlii***	ECho EPot GCrg SBrt
	'Lane Fox'	WCot
	'Lavender Riding Hood' (Riding Hood Series)	LRHS
§	'Le Phare'	XLum
	'Lilac and Burgundy'	MBNS SHar SRms SWvt WWEG
	'Lilac Frost'	LLHF MMuc SRGP WMoo
	'Lilliput'	GBin SLon SPoG WHil
	linarioides 'Marilyn Ross'	ECtt
	'Lord Home'	see *P.* 'George Home'
	'Lucinda Gilchrist'	SLon
	lyallii	CCon ELan GKev SRms WCot
	'Lynette'	MBNS SBch
	'Macpenny's Pink'	CMac MBNS WAvo
	'Madame Golding'	MBNS XLum
	'Marble Riding Hood'[PBR] (Riding Hood Series) new	LRHS
	'Margery Fish' ♀H3	CFis ECtt EWes WWEG
	'Martley'	WWEG
	'Maurice Gibbs' ♀H3	CBcs ECtt EPfP EWes LHop LSRN MBNS MBel SBod SRms WHlf WMnd
	'Melting Candy' (Ice Cream Series)	LRHS LSun MAvo WCot
	mensarum	CFis CMea NCGa
	× ***mexicanus*** 'Sunburst Amethyst'	MNHC NFav SPhx SRms XLum
	- 'Sunburst Ruby'	CPla NFav SLon
	'Midnight'	ECtt ELan EWTr GBin LPot MBNS MRav MSwo SEND SHar SWvt WCFE WWEG XLum
	'Modesty'	MBNS SRms
	'Mother of Pearl'	CBcs CCon EHrv ELan EPfP EShb GBin GMaP LHop LRHS LSRN MBNS MCot MSwo MWat SHar SRms SWvt WWEG
	'Mrs Miller'	MBNS
	'Mrs Morse'	see *P.* 'Chester Scarlet'
	'Mrs Oliver'	EWes
	multiflorus	EBee
	murrayanus new	CEvo
§	'Myddelton Gem'	MWat SRms
	'Myddelton Red'	see *P.* 'Myddelton Gem'
	newberryi ♀H5	WIce
	- f. ***humilior***	EPot
§	- subsp. ***sonomensis***	GCrg NSla SRms WAbe
	'Newbury Gem'	MBNS SHar SWvt
	'Oaklea Red'	GBin
§	'Old Candy Pink'	SWvt
	'Osprey' ♀H3	CMac CMea CWCL ECtt ELan EPfP GBin LAst LRHS MBNS NBir SRms SWvt WMnd WWEG
	ovatus	CBod CCon CMac CSpe EBee ELan SPhx SRms
	'Overbury'	ECtt SRms WAvo
	'Papal Purple'	LLWP MAsh MBNS MHer NBir SHar SPhx SRms XLum
	parvulus	SBrt
	'Patio Bells Pink'	MLHP
	'Patio Wine'	MBel WAvo
	'Peace'	GBin MBNS
§	'Pennington Gem' ♀H3	ELan LCro LOPS MHer NBir SGSe SHar SRms SWvt WBod
	'Pensham Amelia Jane'	CAby CBot CNec COtt CWGN EBee ECtt ELon EPfP LAll LHop LLWP LRHS LSRN LSou MAsh MBNS MHol NLar NPri SHil SLon SPer SRms SWvt WCot WGor WHil
	'Pensham Arctic Fox'	CSpe ECtt LRHS SLon
	'Pensham Arctic Sunset'	SLon WHrl
	'Pensham Avonbelle'	MBNS SRms
	'Pensham Bilberry Ice'	LSun MBNS SWvt WMnd
	'Pensham Blackberry Ice'	CLet ECtt LAll LSou MBNS SLon SRms
	'Pensham Blueberry Ice'	ECtt LSou MBNS SWvt
	'Pensham Capricorn Moon'	ECtt
	'Pensham Charlotte Louise'	ECtt ELon LAll LRHS SRms
	'Pensham Czar'	CAby CBot CNec COtt ECtt ELon EPfP LAll LRHS LSou LSun MAsh MBNS MBri MCot MGos NCGa NPri SGbt SHil SLon SPer SPoG SRkn SRms SWvt WBor WHil WHrl
	'Pensham Dorothy Wilson'	LRHS
	'Pensham Eleanor Young'	COtt ECtt EPfP LAll LRHS LSou MBNS SLon SPoG SPtp SWvt
	'Pensham Freshwater Pearl'	SRms WHoo
	'Pensham Great Expectations'	ECtt
	'Pensham Jessica Mai'	ECtt LRHS LSou SPer SRms SWvt WHil
	'Pensham Just Jayne'	ECtt ELon EPfP LAll LRHS LSRN MBNS SLon SRms SWvt WHoo WMnd XLum
	'Pensham Kay Burton'	EPfP WMnd
	'Pensham Laura'	CAby CBod CNec CSam CWGN ECtt EPfP LAll LCro LOPS LRHS LSRN MAsh MBNS MBel MHol NLar NPri SHil SLon SPad SPer SWvt WHoo
	'Pensham Loganberry Ice'	LSou MBNS SLon
	'Pensham Marjorie Lewis'	WMnd
	'Pensham Miss Wilson'	SRms

	Name	Suppliers
	'Pensham Plum Jerkum'	CAby CBot CWGN ECrN ECtt ELon EPfP LAll LCro LHop LOPS LRHS LSou MBNS MBri MCot MHer MPie NLar NPri SCob SHil SLon SPad SPer SWvt WHoo WMnd
	'Pensham Princess'	ECtt WGor
	'Pensham Raspberry Ice'	CLet MBNS SLon WMnd
	'Pensham Son of Raven'	WAvo
	'Pensham Tayberry Ice'	ECtt MBNS SLon WMnd
	'Pensham Victoria Plum'	CElw EShb SHar WHoo
	'Pensham Wedding Bells'	SRms
	'Pensham Wedding Day'	CBod CSpe CWCL EBee ELan EPfP LAll LRHS LSRN LSou MBNS MBri MCot NPri SCob SLon SPer SPoG SPtp WHoo WMnd
	'Pensham Westminster Belle'	ECtt WHil
	'Pershore Anniversary'	WAvo
	'Pershore Carnival'	SRms WAvo WHrl
	'Pershore Fanfare'	WAvo WHrl
	'Pershore Festival'	WAvo
	'Pershore Pink Necklace'	CWCL ECtt SRms SWvt WAvo WWEG
	'Phare'	see *P.* 'Le Phare'
	(Phoenix Series) Phoenix Appleblossom 09 = 'Peni Ablos09'	CRos LRHS SHil
	- Phoenix Lavender = 'Peni Laver'	CRos LRHS SHil
	- Phoenix Magenta 09 = 'Peni Mag09'	CRos LRHS SHil
	- Phoenix Pink 09 = 'Peni Pina09' PBR	CRos LRHS
	- Phoenix Red = 'Pheni Reeda' PBR	CRos LRHS SHil
	- Phoenix Rose = 'Penharros' PBR	LRHS SHil
	- Phoenix Violet 09 = 'Peni Vio09' PBR	CRos EPfP LRHS SHil
	'Phyllis'	see *P.* 'Evelyn'
	pinifolius ♀H4	CCon CMea CTri EBee ECho ELon EPot EUJe EWTr GCrg GKev ITim LHop LRHS MBel MMuc NHar WThu XLum
	- 'Mersea Yellow'	CCon CMea ECho ELan EPfP EPot GCrg GKev ITim LHop LRHS MHer MMuc NHar NLar SLon SPlb XLum
	- 'Wisley Flame' ♀H4	ECho EPfP EPot EWes GCrg GKev MBNS MHer MSCN SCob SIgm
	'Pink Bedder'	see *P.* 'Hewell Pink Bedder', 'Sutton's Pink Bedder'
	'Pink Endurance'	MBNS WHal
	'Port Wine' ♀H3	CMea CTri ELon EPfP GMaP LHop LPot LRHS LSRN MCot MWat NBir SPoG SWvt WAvo WKif WMnd WWEG
	'Prairie Twilight' PBR new	WHlf
	'Precious Gem'	WHlf
	'Pretty Petticoat'	IPot LRHS
	'Priory Purple'	WHrl
	procerus var. ***brachyanthus***	GKev
§	- var. ***formosus***	WAbe
§	- 'Roy Davidson' ♀H5	ECho EPot NHar WAbe
	- var. ***tolmiei***	EPot GCal GEdr MPie WAbe
	pubescens	see *P. hirsutus*
	pulchellus Greene	see *P. procerus* var. *formosus*
	pulchellus Lindl.	see *P. campanulatus*
	'Purple and White'	see *P.* 'Countess of Dalkeith'
	'Purple Bedder'	CMac COtt EBee ELan EPfP GBin LRHS LSRN MBri MWat NBir SHil SPoG SPtp SRkn SRms SWvt XLum
	'Purple Passion'	CElw EBee EHrv ELan EPfP EWes EWoo LRHS SCob
	'Purple Riding Hood' (Riding Hood Series)	EBee LCro LRHS SPoG
	'Purple Sea'	MHol
	'Purpureus Albus'	see *P.* 'Countess of Dalkeith'
§	***putus***	SGSe
	'Raspberry Ripple' (Ice Cream Series)	LSou LSun
	'Raven' ♀H3	Widely available
	'Razzle Dazzle'	SPlb WCot
	'Red Knight'	GCra MBNS
	'Red Riding Hood' PBR (Riding Hood Series)	EPfP LCro LRHS
	'Red Rocks'	GBin WCot
	'Red Sea'	MHol
	'Rich Purple'	MBNS SPlb XLum
	'Rich Ruby' ♀H3	CAby CFis CWCL EHrv ELan EPfP EWes LLWP LRHS NBir SHar SPlb SPtp SWvt WCAu WWEG
	richardsonii var. ***richardsonii***	SBrt
	roezlii Regel	see *P. laetus* subsp. *roezlii*
	roezlii ambig.	MAsh SBrt
	'Ron Sidwell'	WAvo
	'Rosy Blush'	MBNS SPlb
	'Roy Davidson'	see *P. procerus* 'Roy Davidson'
	'Royal White'	see *P.* 'White Bedder'
	'Rubicundus' ♀H4	CWCL ELan EPfP GBBs GBin LRHS LSRN MBNS SLon SWvt WBor WHil
	'Ruby' misapplied	see *P.* 'Schoenholzeri'
	'Ruby Candle'	ECtt LRHS
	rupicola ♀H5	EPot LHop
	- 'Albus'	WThu
	- 'Conwy Lilac'	SRms WAbe
	- 'Conwy Rose'	GCrg WAbe WThu
	'Russian River'	EBee ECtt EPfP LRHS SPlb SWvt XLum
	rydbergii	SPlb
	'Samsong'	WCFE
§	'Schoenholzeri' ♀H4	Widely available
	scouleri	see *P. fruticosus* var. *scouleri*
	sepalulus new	SBrt
§	***serrulatus***	EWes GKev XLum
	'Sherbourne Blue'	LPot WAvo WCot
	'Sissinghurst Pink'	see *P.* 'Evelyn'
	'Six Hills'	CMea EPot SDys WAbe WOld
	'Skyline'	EPfP
	smallii	CAby CFis EDAr EPPr EPfP EWes LRHS LSRN MHer SPhx WPGP
	'Snow Storm'	see *P.* 'White Bedder'
	'Snowflake'	see *P.* 'White Bedder'
	sonomensis	see *P. newberryi* subsp. *sonomensis*
	'Sour Grapes' misapplied	see *P.* 'Stapleford Gem'
	'Sour Grapes' ambig.	CAby CBcs EHoe EHrv EWoo IBoy LAll LPot MBel MHtn MJak NGdn SCob SHil WBod WCAu WWEG
§	'Sour Grapes' M. Fish ♀H4	CMac CWCL CWld EBee ECha ELan EPfP EShb GBin GMaP IBoy LAst LCro LEdu LOPS LRHS LSRN MHer MSwo NLar SEND SHar SPer SPoG SPtp WCot WHea WHil WKif WMnd
	'Southgate Gem'	GBee GKev MBNS MHCG MWat SRms SWvt WAvo
	'Souvenir d'Adrian Regnier'	MBNS MHCG

	'Souvenir d'André Torres' misapplied	see *P.* 'Chester Scarlet'
	speciosus	SBrt
	'Spitfire'	WCFE
§	'Stapleford Gem' ♀H3	CBod CFis CMac CWCL ELan EWTr GBuc LBMP LRHS MBel MBri MRav NPri SHar SRms SWvt WHar WHoo WMnd WWEG
	aff. 'Stapleford Gem'	SLon
	'Storm'	WHlf
	'Strawberries and Cream' (Ice Cream Series)	CBod CWCL EBee ELon LAll LSun NLar SCob SRkn WCot WHil
	'Strawberry Taffy'[PBR] (Taffy Series) **new**	LBMP
	strictus	CCon EBee EPPr MBNS NFav SBrt
§	'Sutton's Pink Bedder'	MBNS
	'Sweet Cherry' (Ice Cream Series)	ECtt LSou LSun WCot WHil
	'Sweet Joanne'[PBR]	WHlf
	tall, pink-flowered	see *P.* 'Welsh Dawn'
	'Ted's Purple'	WCFE
	teucrioides	CPBP EPot
	'The Juggler'	ECtt MBNS SWvt
§	'Thorn'	COtt ECtt LRHS MJak MWat NBir SPhx SRms SWvt WAvo WWEG
	'Threave Pink'	ECtt LLWP MRav SHar SWvt WAvo
	'Thundercloud'	ECtt WAvo
	'Torquay Gem'	LLHF MBNS
	'True Sour Grapes'	see *P.* 'Sour Grapes' M. Fish
	'Tubular Bells Purple' **new**	CWCL
	uintahensis	SBrt
	utahensis	GBee
	'Vanilla' (Ice Cream Series)	LSun
	'Vanilla Plum' (Ice Cream Series)	LRHS LSou LSun MBri WHil
	venustus purple-flowered **new**	SBrt
	versicolor	SBrt
	Vesuvius = 'Yasius'	CBod CRos ECtt EPfP LRHS SLon SRms WCAu WFar
	virens	EBee
	virgatus	EBee
	- 'Blue Buckle'	IPot LRHS MHol SPlb
	- subsp. ***putus***	see *P. putus*
	'Watermelon Taffy' (Taffy Series)	ECtt
§	'Welsh Dawn'	MBNS
§	***whippleanus***	EDAr LRHS MMuc SPlb
§	'White Bedder' ♀H3	Widely available
	'Whitethroat' Sidwell	MBNS
I	'Whitethroat' purple-flowered	WCot
	wilcoxii	SBrt
	'Willy's Purple'	ECtt
§	'Windsor Red'	CTri ECtt EPfP LRHS MBNS SLon SRms SWvt WAvo WCot
	'Woodpecker'	ECtt IPot MAvo MBNS SRms WAvo

Pentaglottis (*Boraginaceae*)

§	***sempervirens***	EPfP SRms WSFF

Pentapanax see *Aralia*

Pentapterygium see *Agapetes*

Pentas (*Rubiaceae*)

lanceolata	EShb
- Balloon Lilac = 'Peba 458' **new**	EShb

Penthorum (*Saxifragaceae*)

sedoides	LLWG

pepino see *Solanum muricatum*

peppermint see *Mentha* × *piperita*

Perezia (*Asteraceae*)

recurvata	ITim

Pericallis (*Asteraceae*)

	aurita	CRHN
	× ***hybrida*** Senetti Series	MGos NPer NPri SPoG
	- - Senetti Blue Bicolor = 'Sunseneribuba'[PBR]	MGos SPoG
	- - Senetti Blue = 'Sunsenebu'[PBR]	SPoG
	- - Senetti Magenta Bicolor	MGos SPoG
	- - Senetti Magenta = 'Sunsenere'[PBR]	SPoG
§	***lanata*** (L'Hér.) B. Nord.	CHll EShb
	- Kew form	CSpe

Perilla (*Lamiaceae*)

§	***frutescens*** var. ***crispa***	CSpe SHDw
	- green-leaved	CLau
	- var. ***japonica***	GPoy
	- var. ***nankinensis***	see *P. frutescens* var. *crispa*
	- var. ***purpurascens***	CLau WJek

Periploca (*Apocynaceae*)

graeca	CBcs CMac EBee SLon
purpurea B&SWJ 7235	WCru
sepium	CExl

Pernettya see *Gaultheria*

Perovskia (*Lamiaceae*)

abrotanoides	XLum
atriplicifolia	CArn CBot CDul CMea ELan MGil MHer MNHC NSti WHea WKif WMnd XSen
- 'Blue Shadow'	EWTr LRHS NLar
'Blue Haze'	GCal SMHy
'Blue Spire' ♀H5	Widely available
'Filigran'	CWld EBee ELan GBin GBuc GCal LRHS LSou MNHC SMad SPad SPoG WFar WGrn WGwG WPat XSen
'Hybrida'	GCal LRHS
Lacey Blue = 'Lisslitt'[PBR]	ECrN EPfP LRHS MAsh MBri NLar SCob SWvt WHlf
'Little Spire'[PBR]	Widely available
'Longin'	LRHS

Persea (*Lauraceae*)

indica B&SWJ 12535	WCru
japonica B&SWJ 8410	WCru
- B&SWJ 12789	WCru
thunbergii	CBcs CFil
- B&SWJ 12747	WCru

Persicaria (*Polygonaceae*)

	sp.	CHab
	B&SWJ 11268 from Sumatra	WCru
§	***affinis***	CBcs CSBt EAEE EHrv GAbr LSun MSCN MWhi NBro SCob SWat WFar WMoo WTcb
	- 'Darjeeling Red' ♀H5	Widely available

	Name	Suppliers
	- 'Dimity'	see *P. affinis* 'Superba'
	- 'Donald Lowndes' ♀H5	Widely available
	- 'Kabouter'	GBin IPot NLar SAko WBor
§	- 'Superba' ♀H5	Widely available
	alata	see *P. nepalensis*
	alpina	CBot CDes CSpe EBee ECha EHoe EHrv EPPr GBin GCal GMaP IPot LEdu LRHS MAvo MHol MRav NDov SDix SMad WCot WHil WMoo WWEG WWtn
	amphibia	LLWG MSKA SWat XLum
§	***amplexicaulis***	CBre CKno CPrp ELan EWes GMaP MBel MCot MHer MWhi WBor WFar WMoo WRHF WWtn XLum
	- 'Alba'	Widely available
	- 'Anouk'	EBee
	- 'Atrosanguinea'	CKno CMac CTri ECha ELan LRHS MMuc MRav MSpe NBir NLar SEND SPer SRms SWat SWvt WCAu WFar WOld WWEG XLum
	- 'Betty Brandt'	GBin
	- 'Blackfield' PBR	CBcs CBct CKno CMos CSpe EBee ECha ECtt ELon EPPr EWes GBin GMaP GQue IBoy IKil IPot LRHS MAvo MBNS MBel MHol MNrw MSpe NDov NLar SCob STPC WCot
	- 'Blush Clent'	WHoo
	- 'Clent Charm'	MHCG NChi WOut
	- 'Cottesbrooke Gold'	ECtt MAvo
	- 'Dikke Floskes'	MAvo WCot
	- 'Early Pink Lady'	WMoo
	- 'Eastfield' (v)	WCot
	- 'Fascination'	WCot
	- 'Fat Domino' PBR	CKno EBee GBin GQue IKil IPot MNrw NDov NLar SAko SCob WCAu
	- 'Firedance'	CAby CKno EHoe ELon EPPr GQue IPot NDov SMHy SPhx SWat WCAu WCot WFar
	- 'Firetail'	Widely available
	- 'Golden Arrow' (v)	CBct LRHS MHtn SPoG WHil WMoo
	- 'High Society'	GBin WCAu
	- 'Inverleith'	CBct CBre CKno EBee ECGP ECha ECtt EPPr GBin GBuc GMaP GQue LRHS MAvo MBel MHer MMuc MSpe NBir SAko SCob WCAu WCot WMoo WOut WPGP WPnP
I	- 'Jo and Guido's Form'	CHVG ELon NLar WCAu WFar
	- 'JS Caliente' PBR	CHVG CKno CMea ECGP ECtt ELon GBin GQue LRHS LSun MSCN NBir SCob WCot WPnP
	- 'JS Delgado'	CKno CMos EBee MNrw
	- 'Lisan'	GBin
	- Orange Field = 'Orangofield' PBR	CBct CKno EBee ECtt ELon EPPr EWoo GBin GQue IKil LAst LHop LRHS MBel MHol MJak MNrw MSpe NDov NLar SAko SCob WBor WCAu
	- var. ***pendula***	EBee GBin GQue NBir WFar WMoo
	- - HWJK 2255	WCru
	- 'Pink Elephant'	see *P.* 'Pink Elephant'
	- 'Pink Knot'	LRHS
	- 'Pink Lady'	ECGP MPie
	- 'Rosea'	Widely available
	- 'Rowden Gem'	IPot WMoo WOut
	- 'Rubie's Pink'	ECha
	- 'Sangre'	GBin
	- 'September Spires'	NDov
	- 'Seven Oaks Village'	GBin SCob
	- 'Summer Dance'	CKno EBee ECtt EPPr GQue LPla
	- Taurus = 'Blotau'	CElw CHVG CKno CSam ECha ECtt EPPr GBin GBuc GQue IPot LRHS MBri NCGa NLar NSti SCob SMHy WCAu WFar WHil WHoo WPGP WWEG
	- 'White Eastfield'	SPhx
§	***bistorta***	CArn GPoy LAst LOPS LPfy LSun MHer MMuc MWhi NBir NLar SEND SRms SWat WFar WOut
	- subsp. ***carnea***	EBee ECha EHoe ELon EPPr GBin LPla LRHS MBNS MMuc NBir NBro NDov WCot WMoo WTcb WWtn
	- 'Hohe Tatra'	EBee EPPr GMaP LRHS NDov WCot WFar
	- 'JS Calor' PBR	EBee GBin GQue
	- 'Superba' ♀H7	Widely available
	campanulata	CBod CElw ECha ECtt EHoe GAbr GMaP IFro LPot MAvo MMuc MRav MSpe MWhi NBro NEgg SEND SPer WFar WMoo WOut WTcb WWtn
	- Alba Group	CElw CFis GBin MPie NBro WMoo
	- var. ***lichiangense***	GBin
	- 'Madame Jigard'	GBin
	- 'Rosenrot'	CBre GBin ILea NBir SAko SWat WOld
	- 'Southcombe White'	GBin
§	***capitata***	CHVG LLWG XLum
	- 'Pink Bubbles'	EHoe LAst NBir SWvt
	chinensis B&SWJ 11268	WCru
	dshawachischwilii	LPla
	emodi	GKev
*	***hydropiper*** var. ***rubra***	WJek
	'Indian Summer'	GCal
	'Johanniswolke'	GBin IPot
*	***kahil***	GBin WCot
*	***macrophylla***	EBee
	- CC 5790	GKev
	microcephala	EWes MHer
	- 'Dragon's Eye' PBR	EBee WNPC
	- 'Red Dragon' PBR	Widely available
	milletii	CAby EBee GBuc LRHS MSpe NDov WCru
§	***mollis***	WPGP
	nakaii	EBee
	neofiliformis	EShb WTcb
§	***nepalensis***	CExl EPPr EShb IMou MTPN
	'October Pink'	CSam SMHy
§	***odorata***	CArn CLau ENfk GPoy MHer MNHC SHDw SRms WJek
	orientalis	CSpe
§	'Pink Elephant'	CKno CMos CSam EPPr GBin GQue MAvo MNrw MWhi NDov NLar SCob STPC WWEG
	pinnate-leaved **new**	GKev
	polystachya	see *P. wallichii*
	'Purple Fantasy'	CBod CBot EBee IKil LHop MAvo MHol MSpe SCob SMad WHil WMoo WNPC
	'Red Baron'	EPPr
§	***runcinata***	EBee MMuc NBir WMoo WWtn
	scoparia	see *Polygonum scoparium*
	sphaerostachya Meisn.	see *P. macrophylla*
	tenuicaulis	CBre EHrv GBin SBch WCru WMoo WWtn
§	***tinctoria***	WSFF
§	***vacciniifolia*** ♀H5	Widely available
§	***virginiana***	EPPr GCal LEdu LSun SDix WMoo WWtn
	- 'Alba'	EPPr

- var. ***filiformis***	CSam CSpe ELan LBMP LPla MPie SBrt SPoG SRkn SWvt WAul WCot WHil
- - 'Ballet'	MAvo WCot
- - 'Batwings'	ESwi LRHS SGSe SPtp
- - 'Compton's Red'	CSam ECha ECtt EShb EUJe GCal LHop NLos SBrt WAul WCot
- - 'Lance Corporal'	CMac EHoe EPPr EShb EUJe GBin LPot MAvo NLar SPhx
- - 'Moorland Moss'	WMoo
- Variegated Group (v)	ECha EShb EUJe MBNS WCot WMoo
- - 'Painter's Palette' (v)	CBod CMac CNor ECha ECtt EHoe ELan EPPr EShb EUJe GBuc LRHS MHol MRav NBid NSti SDix SGSe SMad SPer SWvt WAul WCot WCru WMoo XLum
§ ***wallichii***	CSpe MMuc SDix SEND SWat WCot WMoo WWtn XLum
§ ***weyrichii***	EPPr GCal NBir NBro NLar WFar WMoo WWtn XLum

persimmon see *Diospyros virginiana*

persimmon, Japanese see *Diospyros kaki*

Petalostemon see *Dalea*

Petamenes see *Gladiolus*

Petasites (*Asteraceae*)

albus	GPoy MHer NLar NSti
fragrans	LLWG SWat WHer XLum
§ ***frigidus*** var. ***palmatus***	NLar
- - JLS 86317CLOR	SMad
- - 'Golden Palms'	CHid EHrv EUJe LPla WBor
hybridus	EBee MSKA SWat
- 'Variegatus' (v)	XLum
japonicus	CAgr CBcs GPoy
- var. ***giganteus***	CHid ECha EPfP EUJe LEdu MBel SGSe SWat WCru
§ - - 'Nishiki-buki' (v)	CMac EBee ECha EPPr EUJe EWld GQue LEdu MHer MSKA NBir NSti SGSe SMad WBor WFar WWEG XLum
- - 'Variegatus'	see *P. japonicus* var. *giganteus* 'Nishiki-buki'
- f. ***purpureus***	EPPr SGSe
palmatus	see *P. frigidus* var. *palmatus*
paradoxus	CDes EWld LEdu LPot MBel WCot WFar WPGP

Petrocallis (*Brassicaceae*)

lagascae	see *P. pyrenaica*
§ ***pyrenaica***	GEdr WAbe
- white-flowered	WAbe

Petrocoptis (*Caryophyllaceae*)

pyrenaica	SRms

Petrocosmea (*Gesneriaceae*)

barbata **new**	WDib
begoniifolia	WAbe WDib
§ ***cryptica***	CTal WDib WThu
- 'Yumebutai' **new**	WDib
'Fluffer Nutter' **new**	WDib
forrestii	CTal WAbe WDib
grandiflora	WAbe WDib
- 'Crème de Crûg'	CDes WCru
'Ht-2' **new**	WDib
iodioides	WDib
kerrii	WCot WDib
'Keystone's Angora' **new**	WDib
'Keystone's Bantam' **new**	WDib
'Keystone's Barnswallow' **new**	WDib
'Keystone's Belmont' **new**	WDib
martini	CTal
mengliangensis **new**	WDib
minor	CPBP WAbe WDib
parryorum **new**	WDib
'Rosemary Platz' **new**	WDib
rosettifolia misapplied	see *P. cryptica*
sericea	WAbe

Petromarula (*Campanulaceae*)

pinnata	EBee

Petrophytum (*Rosaceae*)

caespitosum	WAbe
cinerascens	GEdr
§ ***hendersonii***	WAbe

Petrorhagia (*Caryophyllaceae*)

'Pink Starlets'	EPfP LHop
saxifraga ♀H4	CSpe ECho EPPr NLar SRms WBor WMoo XLum

Petroselinum (*Apiaceae*)

§ ***crispum***	ENfk GPoy LPot MJak MNHC NPri SIde SPoG SRms WJek
- 'Bravour' ♀H4	CLau MHer
- 'Champion Moss Curled'	SVic
- 'Darki'	CLau
- French	CLau ENfk MHer MNHC NPri SPoG SRms WJek
- 'Italian'	see *P. crispum* var. *neapolitanum* plain-leaved
- 'Moss Curled' ♀H4	SRms
§ - var. ***neapolitanum*** plain-leaved	CLau ENfk SIde SPoG SRms SVic
§ - var. ***tuberosum***	MHer MNHC SIde SRms SVic
hortense	see *P. crispum*
tuberosum	see *P. crispum* var. *tuberosum*

Petteria (*Papilionaceae*)

ramentacea	EBtc

Petunia (*Solanaceae*)

'Baby Duck Yellow'	NPri
'Back to Black'	LAst
Belinda (Tumbelina Series) (d) **new**	LAst NPri
Black Satin = 'Dueswebsa'PBR (Sweetunia Series) **new**	LBMP
Black Velvet = 'Balpevac'PBR	LAst NPri
Black Velvet Improved **new**	LBMP
Blueberry Ice (Sweetunia Series) **new**	LBMP
Candyfloss = 'Kercan'PBR (Tumbelina Series) (d)	LSou NPri
Caramello (Sweetunia Series) **new**	LBMP
(Cascadias Series) Cascadias Bicolor Pastel = 'Dancasbipas'	NPri
- Cascadias Rim Magenta **new**	LBMP NPri

- Cascadias Rim Violet	LAst NPri
Cherry Ripple = 'Kerripcherry'PBR (Tumbelina Series) (d)	LSou
Conchita Evening Glow = 'Conglow'PBR (Conchita Series)	NPri
'Corona Amethyst' (Corona Series)	NPri
Daddy Series	CWCL
(Easy Wave Series) Easy Wave Blue = 'Pas320593'	NPri
- Easy Wave Burgundy Star = 'Pas760702'	NPri
- Easy Wave Coral Reef = 'Pas481972'	NPri
- Easy Wave Neon Rose = 'Pas760700'	NPri
- Easy Wave Pink = 'Pas3189'	NPri
- Easy Wave Plum Vein = 'Pas739163'	NPri
- Easy Wave Red	NPri
- Easy Wave White = 'Pas760712'	NPri
exserta **new**	CSpe EBee
Famous Lilac Picotee = 'Kleph08152' (Famous Series) **new**	LBMP
(Fanfare Series) 'Fanfare Appleblossom'	LBMP
- 'Fanfare Blue'	NPri
- 'Fanfare Crème de Cassis'	LBMP NPri
- 'Fanfare Hot Rose'	NPri
- 'Fanfare Red'	LBMP
- 'Fanfare Royal Purple' **new**	LBMP
- 'Fanfare White'	LBMP
- 'Fanfare Yellow'	LBMP NPri
Grape Ice = 'Dueswegrice'PBR (Sweetunia Series) **new**	LBMP
Hot Rod Red = 'Dueswehotre'PBR (Sweetunia Series) **new**	LBMP
Inga (Tumbelina Series) (d)	LSou
Joanna (Tumbelina Series)	LAst LSou
(Littletunia Series) Littletunia Bicolour Illusion	LAst
- Littletunia Blue Vein	NPri
Margarita = 'Kermar' (Tumbelina Series)	LAst
Melissa = 'Kermelis'PBR (Tumbelina Series) (d)	LAst LSou
(Mini Me Series) 'Mini Me Double Purple Picotee' **new**	LAst
- 'Mini Me Soft Pink' **new**	LAst
multiflora Frenzy Series **new**	LAst
- - Frenzy Grand Rapids mixed **new**	LAst
- - Frenzy Morn mixed **new**	LAst
- - 'Frenzy Light Blue' **new**	NPri
- - 'Frenzy Plum Bicolour'	NPri
- - 'Frenzy Star' **new**	NPri
- - 'Frenzy Yellow'	LAst
patagonica	ECho WAbe
'Pink Star' (Designer Series)	LAst
'Potunia Papaya' (Potunia Series)	LAst
Priscilla = 'Kerpril'PBR (Tumbelina Series) (d)	LAst LSou NPri
'Purple Flash' (Designer Series)	LBMP NPri
'Rosy Wave'PBR	NPri
Soft Pink Morning (Sweetunia Series) **new**	LBMP
'Stardust' (Designer Series)	LAst
Supercascade Series	CWCL
(Supertunia Series) Supertunia Bordeaux = 'Lanbor'PBR	NPri
- Supertunia Pretty Much Picasso = 'Bhtun31501'PBR	NPri
- Supertunia Royal Velvet = 'Kakegawa S28'PBR	NPri
(Surfinia Series) Surfinia Blue Picotee	LSou
- Surfinia Blue = 'Sunblu'	LAst LBMP LSou NPri
- Surfinia Blue Vein = 'Sunsolos'PBR	LAst
- Surfinia Burgundy = 'Keiburtel'PBR	LAst
- Surfinia Double Blue Star = 'Sunsurfelevi'PBR (d)	LAst
- Surfinia Double Red = 'Keidoreral'PBR (d)	LAst
- Surfinia Giant Purple = 'Sunlapur'PBR	LBMP
- Surfinia Hot Pink 06 = 'Sunrovein'PBR	LAst LBMP
- Surfinia Hot Pink = 'Marrose'	LSou
- Surfinia Hot Red = 'Sunhore'PBR	LBMP NPri
- Surfinia Impulz Yellow = 'Sunpatiki'PBR	LAst NPri
- Surfinia Lime = 'Keiyeul'PBR	LAst
- Surfinia Pink Ice = 'Hakice'PBR (v)	LAst NPri
- Surfinia Purple = 'Shihi Brilliant'	LAst LSou NPri
- Surfinia Red = 'Keirekul'PBR	LAst
- Surfinia Rose Vein = 'Sunrove'PBR	LAst
- Surfinia Sky Blue = 'Keilavbu'PBR	LAst NPri
- Surfinia Sweet Pink = 'Sunsurfmomo'PBR	LSou
- Surfinia Vanilla = 'Sunvanilla'PBR	LSou
- Surfinia Variegated Mini Purple (v)	LAst
- Surfinia White = 'Kesupite'	LAst
(Surprise Series) Surprise Lime **new**	LBMP
- Surprise Marine = 'Duesurmar'PBR **new**	LBMP
- Surprise White = 'Duesurimwi'PBR **new**	LBMP
Susanna (Tumbelina Series)	LAst
Sweet Sunshine Burgundy = 'Kleph09191' (Sweet Sunshine Burgundy) **new**	LBMP

Victoria = 'Kervic'PBR (Tumbelina Series)	LSou

Peucedanum (*Apiaceae*)

* ***aromaticum***	IMou
officinale	CBod GBin LRHS SPlb SPtp
ostruthium	GPoy LEdu WPtf
- 'Daphnis' (v)	CSpe EBee LEdu LPla MAvo MNrw MSCN NChi NEoE NLar WCFE WCot WHrl WSHC WWFP XLum
verticillare	CArn CSam CSpe EBee GAbr IMou LRHS MBel SDix SKHP SPhx WSHC WWEG

Peumus (*Monimiaceae*)

boldus	IDee

Phacelia (*Boraginaceae*)

bolanderi	EBee
californica	EBee
sericea	EBee

Phaedranassa (*Amaryllidaceae*)

BKBlount 2623	WCot
carmiolii	WCot
dubia	NRog WCot
glauciflora	NRog
tunguraguae	NRog
viridiflora	ECho NRog WCot

Phaedranthus see *Distictis*

Phaenocoma (*Asteraceae*)

prolifera	SPlb

Phaenosperma (*Poaceae*)

globosa	CSam CSpe EBee ECha EHoe EPPr EShb GQue NLos NWsh WCot WPGP XLum

Phaiophleps see *Olsynium*

nigricans	see *Sisyrinchium striatum*

Phalaris (*Poaceae*)

arundinacea	LPot MBNS MSKA MWLS SCob SPlb SVic SWat
- cream-flowered	WWEG
- 'Elegantissima'	see *P. arundinacea* var. *picta* 'Picta'
- var. ***picta***	CBen CDul CTri CWib MJak MSKA NBir NPer SPoG XLum XSen
- - 'Arctic Sun' (v)	CKno EBee ELon EPPr GBin LLWG LRHS SPoG STPC WWEG
- - 'Aureovariegata' (v)	CBcs MRav NPer SWat WMoo XLum
- - 'Feesey' (v) ♀H7	Widely available
- - 'Luteopicta' (v)	EPPr MMuc WWEG XLum
§ - - 'Picta' (v)	ELan EPfP LRHS MMuc SEND SPer SWat WMoo
- - 'Streamlined' (v)	EPPr LLWG NWsh
- - 'Tricolor' (v)	EHoe

Phanerophlebia (*Dryopteridaceae*)

caryotidea	see *Cyrtomium caryotideum*
falcata	see *Cyrtomium falcatum*
fortunei	see *Cyrtomium fortunei*

Pharbitis see *Ipomoea*

Phedimus see *Sedum*

Phegopteris (*Thelypteridaceae*)

§ ***connectilis***	EFer NHar
decursive-pinnata	CDes CLAP EBee LPal LRHS SEND WFib WPnP
hexagonoptera	NLos

Phellodendron (*Rutaceae*)

amurense	CBcs CDul CLnd CMCN EBee ELan EPfP GBin IVic LRHS MBlu MBri SAko SEND WBor WPGP
- B&SWJ 11000	WCru
japonicum B&SWJ 11175	WCru
sachalinense	LEdu

Phenakospermum (*Strelitziaceae*)

guianense	XBlo

Pherosphaera (*Podocarpaceae*)

fitzgeraldii	CKen WThu

Philadelphus ✿ (*Hydrangeaceae*)

SDR 2823	CExl
SDR 4862	GKev
SDR 4945	GKev
SDR 4946	CExl GKev
SDR 5111	GKev
affinis new	CFil
'Atlas' (v)	NLar
'Avalanche'	CExl MMuc NLar SPer SRms
'Beauclerk' ♀H6	CBod CDoC CDul CLet COtt CTri EBee EPfP EWTr GGal GQui IVic LRHS MBri MGos MMuc MRav NLar NWea SCob SKHP SLim SMad SPer SRms SWvt WHar WPat
'Belle Etoile' ♀H6	Widely available
'Bialy Karzel'	NLar
'Bicolore'	NLar WAvo WHar
'Boule d'Argent' (d)	WHar
'Bouquet Blanc'	MRav NLar SRms WCFE WPat
brachybotrys	MRav
'Buckley's Quill' (d)	CWld EBee EPfP EWes LRHS MRav SGol SWvt WGrn
'Burfordensis'	CBot CWSG LAst MMuc MRav SEND
calcicola	CFil
caucasicus	CFil
coronarius	CBcs CBod CDul EPfP LBuc MLHP MRav NWea
- 'Aureus' ♀H6	Widely available
- 'Bowles's Variety'	see *P. coronarius* 'Variegatus'
§ - 'Variegatus' (v) ♀H6	Widely available
coulteri	WPGP
'Coupe d'Argent'	MRav
'Dainty Lady'	LBuc LRHS SLon
'Dame Blanche' (d)	EPfP EWTr LSou MRav NLar WBor
delavayi	CFil EPfP GBin GGal LEdu NLar SDix SKHP SPer WPGP
- var. ***calvescens***	MRav
- aff. var. ***calvescens*** BWJ 8005	WCru
- f. ***melanocalyx***	EPfP GCra MRav SChF WPGP
- - B&L 12168	CFil EBee WPGP
- - 'Nyman's Variety' ♀H6	CBot CExl CFil SKHP WKif WPGP
'Enchantement' (d)	MRav SDix
'Erectus'	CSBt CWib EBee ELon EPfP EWTr LRHS MRav NLar SKHP SLim SPer SPoG WAvo WPat
'Etoile Rose'	WAvo WMoo

'Falconeri'	MRav
'Frosty Morn' (d)	CBcs CBod EPfP EWTr LRHS MBlu MMuc MRav NBro NLar SEND SPer SPoG
incanus B&SWJ 8616	WCru
§ 'Innocence' (v) ♀H6	CBot CExl CMac CTsd EHoe ELan EPfP LAst LRHS MAsh MGos MMuc MRav MSwo NEoE SEND SGol SKHP SLim SPad SPer SPoG SRms WFar WPat WSHC
'Innocence Variegatus'	see *P.* 'Innocence'
§ ***insignis***	MRav
karwinskianus	CFil
- F&M 152	WPGP
'Lemoinei'	CBcs CBod CDul CTri MGos NWea SCob SGol WGrn WHar
'Lemon Hill'	NLar
lewisii	CExl
- L 1896	CExl
- 'Snow Velvet'	EPfP LLHF LRHS
'Limestone'	MRav
maculatus	CFil WPat
- 'Mexican Jewel'	CExl CFil EBee ELon NLar SKHP SMad SPad WKif WPGP WPat WSHC
- 'Scented Storm'	CMHG WPGP
- 'Sweet Clare' ♀H5	LCro LRHS SHil
maculatus* × *mexicanus	CFil
madrensis	LHop MRav
- F&M 326	CFil WPGP
'Manteau d'Hermine' (d) ♀H6	Widely available
'Marjorie'	NLar
mexicanus	CFil GCal
- B&SWJ 10253	WCru
- 'Rose Syringa'	CExl CFil SKHP WPGP WPat
mexicanus* × *palmeri	WPGP
microphyllus	CBot CDul CMCN CTri EBee ELan ELon EPfP EWTr LAst LRHS MAsh MGos MRav SKHP SLon SPer SPoG SSpi WFar WKif WPGP WPat WSHC
- var. ***occidentalis***	NLar
'Miniature Snowflake' (d)	MAsh SPoG WPat
'Minnesota Snowflake' (d)	CBcs EPfP EWes LRHS LSRN MMuc MRav NLar SGol WFar
'Mont Blanc'	CBcs GKin MRav NLar
'Mrs E.L. Robinson' (d)	CMac CWld ELon EPfP LAst LLHF LRHS MAsh MBri MGos NEgg NLar SHil WAvo WBor WCFE
myrtoides B&SWJ 10436	WCru
'Natchez' (d)	CBod CMac EAEE ELon EWTr LEdu LLHF NLar SMad WHar
'Oeil de Pourpre'	MRav
palmeri	CFil WPGP WPat
'Patricia' new	WAvo
pekinensis	CExl NLar
'Perryhill'	MRav
'Polar Star'	ELon GBin NLar WKif
purpurascens	CBot CExl CJun EBee EPfP EWes GBin GLog GQui LLHF MGos MMHG MRav NLar SChF SKHP WPGP WPat
- BWJ 7540	WCru
'Purpureomaculatus'	ELon LLHF MRav WPGP WPat
sargentianus	CFil
satsumi	NLar
- B&SWJ 10811	WCru
- B&SWJ 11004	WCru
schrenkii	CFil NLar
- B&SWJ 8465	EBee ESwi WCru
sericanthus	NLar
§ 'Silberregen' ♀H6	CBod CDul CMac CSam CWld EBee ELon EPfP EWTr LRHS MAsh MGos MMuc MRav NEoE NLar SGol SPoG SRms SWvt WBod WGrn WPat
Silver Showers	see *P.* 'Silberregen'
'Snowbelle' (d)	CDoC EPfP LBMP LRHS MBri NBro NLar SKHP SWvt WBor
'Snowflake'	COtt WMoo
'Snowgoose'	LRHS
'Souvenir de Billiard'	see *P. insignis*
'Starbright' PBR	EPfP LRHS MAsh SCob SPoG
subcanus	CExl
- L 524	CExl CFil
'Sybille' ♀H6	CBot CDul CMac CWld ECrN EPfP LHop LRHS MAsh MRav MSwo SDix SKHP SRms SSpi WKif WPat WSHC
tomentosus	CExl
- AC 3678	MSnd
- B&SWJ 2707	WCru
- GWJ 9215	WCru
'Velléda'	WAvo
'Virginal' (d)	Widely available
'Voie Lactée'	EWTr MRav NLar
White Rock = 'Pekphil' ♀H6	CBot CMac EBee EPfP IVic LLHF LRHS LSRN MRav NLar SKHP SLim SPer
'Yellow Hill'	CMac EPfP LRHS NLar SKHP

Philesia (*Philesiaceae*)

buxifolia	see *P. magellanica*
§ ***magellanica***	CExl CFil CRHN GGGa IBlr ITim MGil SSpi WAbe WCru WSHC
- 'Rosea'	CRHN CWib EPfP IBlr SSpi

Phillyrea (*Oleaceae*)

angustifolia	CBcs CDul CFil CMCN EBee ELan EPfP EUJe IVic LRHS MGos MMuc MRav NLar SBig SEND SPer SSpi WPGP WPat WSHC XSen
- f. ***rosmarinifolia***	CDul CExl ELan
- - 'French Fries'	EBee EPfP WPGP
decora	see *Osmanthus decorus*
§ ***latifolia***	CBcs CDul CFil CTsd EBee ELan EPfP EShb EUJe LRHS NLar SEND SSpi WPGP XSen
media	see *P. latifolia*

Philodendron (*Araceae*)

'Angra dos Reis'	see *P. cordatum*
§ ***angustisectum*** ♀H1b	XBlo
bipinnatifidum ♀H1c	SEND XBlo
corcovadense	XBlo
§ ***cordatum***	XBlo
elegans	see *P. angustisectum*
erubescens 'Red Emerald'	XBlo
* ***radiatum*** var. ***pseudoradiatum*** 'Simmonds'	XBlo
* ***rubrum***	XBlo
scandens 'Green Emerald'	XBlo
- 'Mica'	XBlo
tripartitum	XBlo
xanadu	LPal XBlo

Philotheca (*Rutaceae*)

§ ***myoporoides***	LRHS

Phlebodium (*Polypodiaceae*)

§ ***aureum*** ♀H1b	CSpe WCot
– var. ***areolatum*** new	EShb
– 'Blue Star'	ISha
– 'Mandaianum'	ISha NLos
pseudoaureum	ISha WCot

Phleum (*Poaceae*)

phleoides	EHoe LRHS MMHG
pratense	EHoe MAvo NMir WSFF

Phlomis (*Lamiaceae*)

NJM 10.020	WPGP
alpina	SPlb
* ***anatolica***	LRHS NLar SKHP
– 'Lloyd's Variety'	see *P. grandiflora* 'Lloyd's Silver'
angustifolia	LRHS XSen
anisodonta white-flowered	XSen
armeniaca	XSen
atropurpurea BWJ 7922	WCru
bourgaei	XSen
bovei subsp. ***maroccana***	SEND WHal XLum XSen
breviflora HWJCM 250	WCru
capitata	XSen
cashmeriana	CCon ECha EHoe EWld GCal GJos LAst LRHS LSou MHol SKHP SPhx WCFE WWEG
chrysophylla ♀H4	CAbP ECha ELan EPfP LRHS MAsh MRav NLar SDix SKHP SPer WCFE XSen
crinita	XSen
× ***cytherea***	XSen
'Edward Bowles'	CBot CDul ECha EPfP LRHS LSRN MRav NLar SEND SIgm SKHP SWvt XSen
* 'Elliot's Variety'	CExl
fruticosa ♀H4	Widely available
grandiflora	SEND XSen
– NJM 10.014	WPGP
§ – 'Lloyd's Silver' ♀H5	CAbP CSam ELan LRHS MAsh NLar SPer
herba-venti	XSen
italica	Widely available
– 'Pink Glory'	CMac
lanata	CAbP CSde ELan EPfP LAst LRHS SBrt SCob SPer WCFE WSHC XSen
– 'Pygmy'	XSen
'Le Sud'	WCot XSen
leucophracta	SVen
longifolia	EBee EPfP LRHS MNrw NLar SBrt SEND SKHP SPer WGrn WPGP XSen
– var. ***bailanica*** ♀H4	CBot CSam EPfP LRHS SKHP XLum
– var. ***longifolia***	SKHP
lunariifolia	XSen
lychnitis	SIgm XSen
lycia	LRHS XSen
– NJM 10.015	WPGP
– NJM 10.016	WPGP
macrophylla	SPhx
× ***margaritae***	XSen
monocephala	XSen
nissolei	XSen
purpurea	CAbP CExl ELan EPfP LRHS MAsh NBir SEND WCot WGrn XSen
I – 'Alba'	CBot EBee EPfP EWTr GMaP LRHS SKHP XSen
– subsp. ***caballeroi***	XSen
§ ***russeliana*** ♀H7	Widely available
– 'Dappled Shade' (v)	WCot
samia Boiss.	see *P. russeliana*
samia L.	CBod CKno CMac EWoo LHop LRHS MMHG MMuc NBir NGdn NLar SAko SEND SKHP WOut WPtf XSen
sieheana	XSen
taurica	EPfP LSun SPhx
× ***termessi***	XSen
tuberosa	CArn CBcs CBod CCon CKno CPou EHoe EPfP EWTr LEdu LRHS LSRN MMuc NGdn NLar SDix SGSe SPhx WCAu WCFE WPtf XLum XSen
– 'Amazone' ♀H5	CBod CKno CMos ECha EHrv EPfP GBin GMaP LCro MBel MRav NBid NDov NSti SCob SMad WFar WMnd WSHC
– 'Bronze Flamingo'	CKno EPfP GJos LAst LRHS MBel MNrw MPnt MRav NLar SKHP SPoG WMnd WWEG
viscosa misapplied	see *P. russeliana*

Phlox ✿ (*Polemoniaceae*)

Adessa White (Adessa Series) new	EBee
adsurgens ♀H5	WAbe
– 'Alba'	WAbe
– 'Red Buttes'	ECho
– 'Wagon Wheel'	ECho ECtt EPot EWes GBuc GCrg LHop LRHS NHar SPlb SRms SRot WAbe WIce
'Amazone'	CBod
amplifolia	MSpe XLum
– 'Winnetou'	SAko
× ***arendsii*** 'Andrew'	WCot
– 'Anja'	SAko
– 'Autumn's Pink Explosion'	WCot
– 'Babyface'	ELon NGdn
– 'Casablanca'	EBee NDov
– 'Dylan'	WCot
– 'Eyecatcher'	NBro
– 'Gary'	WCot
– 'Hesperis'	CSam EBee ECha ELon GBin GQue LRHS MAvo MSpe MTis NDov NLar SPhx WCAu WHil
– 'Luc's Lilac' ♀H7	ECtt EPPr GBin LLHF MCot MSpe NBro NEgg NGdn NSti SGbt SPhx WAul WCot
§ – 'Miss Jill' (Spring Pearl Series)	EBee ELan EPfP IPot LCro LOPS WCot
§ – 'Miss Karen' (Spring Pearl Series)	EBee ELan NBro
§ – 'Miss Margie' (Spring Pearl Series)	LEdu
§ – 'Miss Mary' (Spring Pearl Series) ♀H7	ECtt ELan EPfP MSpe NLar
§ – 'Miss Wilma' (Spring Pearl Series)	EBee ELan EPfP
– 'Paul'	MNrw WCot
– 'Ping Pong'	SGbt
– 'Pink Attraction'	MNrw NBro
– 'Purple Star'	EPfP
– 'Utopia' ♀H7	CSam EBee ELon IMou IPot LPla NDov NLar SPhx WCot
austromontana	CTal EPot NWad
bifida	ECho
– 'Alba'	ECho LLHF
– blue-flowered	ECho
– 'Colvin's White'	ECho

- 'Frohnleiten'	NHar
- 'Minima Colvin'	ECho
- 'Ralph Haywood'	CPBP CWCL ECtt EPot
- 'Starbrite'	NLar
- 'Thefi'	MNrw WIce
borealis	see *P. sibirica* subsp. *borealis*
caespitosa	CMea CPBP ECho EWes
- subsp. ***pulvinata***	see *P. pulvinata*
- 'Zigeunerblut'	CMea CPBP CTal ECho EPot GCrg ITim NWad WAbe WHal
canadensis	see *P. divaricata*
carolina 'Bill Baker' ♀H5	CSam ECha ECtt ELon EPPr EPfP GMaP LSRN MNrw NBir NCGa NGdn NSti SGSe SIgm WCAu WCFE WKif WPtf WSHC XLum
- 'Magnificence'	EBee EWes LHop NLar SMad SPhx SPlb WCot WSHC
- 'Miss Lingard' ♀H5	CBod CSam EAEE EAJP ECtt ELon LRHS LSou MCot MMuc MRav NBir NGdn NLar NSti WCot WWEG
'Charles Ricardo'	CSam
'Chattahoochee'	see *P. divaricata* subsp. *laphamii* 'Chattahoochee'
'Daniel's Cushion'	see *P. subulata* 'McDaniel's Cushion'
diffusa	EPot
§ ***divaricata*** ♀H4	SPlb
- 'Blue Dreams'	CCon ECtt MNrw WFar
- 'Blue Perfume'	CAby EBee ECtt LCro NBro NGdn
- 'Charles'	XLum
- 'Clouds of Perfume'	CAby CBod CWCL EAEE EAJP ECtt EPfP EWTr GBuc GEdr GMaP LCro LOPS LRHS LSRN LSou MAsh MSCN MSpe NDov NEgg NLar SAko SGbt SPoG SWvt WAul WFar WGwG WWEG
- 'Dirigo Ice'	ECho LHop LRHS SAko
- 'Eco Texas Purple'	MSCN NCGa WSHC
- 'Fuller's White'	CWCL
- subsp. ***laphamii***	EBee EWes
§ - - 'Chattahoochee' ♀H4	CBcs CBod CWCL EAEE EAJP ECho ECtt EHrv ELan EPfP EWes GBin GBuc LBMP LHop LOPS LPot LRHS MAsh MCot MNrw NLar SPoG SRkn SRot SWvt WAbe WCAu WCFE WHoo
- 'May Breeze'	EAJP ECho ECtt EHrv GCra GMaP LHop LRHS MNrw MSCN SHar WSHC
- 'Plum Perfect'	ECtt
- 'White Perfume'	CMos CWCL EBee EWes LRHS LSou NBro NLar SHar WFar WTor WWEG XLum
douglasii	SRms
- 'Alba'	GJos
- 'Apollo'	CPBP CTri ECho ECtt EPot
- 'Boothman's Variety' ♀H5	ECho ECtt ELan GCrg ITim MLHP SRms
- 'Crackerjack' ♀H5	CTri ECho ECtt EDAr ELan ELon EPot EUJe GAbr GCrg GJos GKev GMaP ITim LRHS MAsh MHer MHol MLHP MWat NBir NEgg NHol NPri NSla SPoG WIce
- 'Eva'	ECho ECtt EDAr ELon GCrg GMaP ITim LHop LRHS LSRN MAsh MHol MSCN NBir NLar NPri NSla NWad SBch
- 'Georg Arends'	ECtt GJos
- 'Ice Mountain'	CMea CTal ECho ECtt ELan EPot NEgg NHol NSla NWad SPoG SRot
- 'Iceberg' ♀H5	ECho GJos
- 'J.A. Hibberson'	EPot GCrg NWad
- 'Lilac Cloud'	CTal ECho ECtt EDAr GJos NEoE NPri NRya
- Lilac Queen	see *P. douglasii* 'Lilakönigin'
- 'Lilac Wonder'	CPBP
§ - 'Lilakönigin'	CTri
- 'Napoleon'	ECho ECtt ITim NWad
- 'Ochsenblut'	CSma ECho EPot GEdr LLHF LRHS MHer MLHP NHar NLar NWad SIgm
- 'Red Admiral' ♀H5	ECho ECtt ELan EPfP EWes GCrg GMaP NPri NWad WCFE
- 'Rose Cushion'	ECho EDAr EWes GCrg
- 'Rose Queen'	ECho
- 'Rosea'	ECho EDAr ELan MMuc
- 'Silver Rose'	ECho ECtt WRHF
- 'Sprite'	SRms
- 'Tycoon'	see *P. subulata* 'Tamaongalei'
- 'Violet Queen'	ECho EPot EWes
- 'Waterloo'	CMea ECho ECtt EPot GCrg LRHS
I - 'White Admiral'	CTri ECho ECtt ELan LHop LSRN MHol NPri
drummondii 'Classic Cassis'	SPoG
- 'Grammy Pink and White'	NPri
I - 'Phlox of Sheep'	CWCL
'Fancy Feelings' (Feelings Series)	NBro NLar
'Flare'	see *P. paniculata* 'Neon Flare'
glaberrima 'Morris Berd'	CDes EBee MAvo WSHC
hendersonii	CPBP WAbe
idahoensis	SPhx
'Jeff's Pink'	MSCN
'Junior Surprise'	GBin
'Kelly's Eye' ♀H5	ECho ECtt EPot GCrg LRHS NBir NHar SPoG
kelseyi 'Lemhi Purple'	CPBP ECho WAbe
- 'Rosette'	ECho NWad
Light Pink Flame = 'Bareleven'PBR	ECtt EPfP SPoG
Lilac Flame = 'Barten'PBR	EPfP SPoG WHil
longifolia subsp. ***brevifolia***	WAbe
maculata 'Alba'	SAko WAul WCAu
- 'Alpha' ♀H6	CSam CWCL EBee ECha ECtt EPfP EWoo GBuc GCra GMaP ILea LRHS LSou MSpe MWhi NCGa NLar SGbt SKHP SPer SWvt WFar WSHC XLum
- Avalanche	see *P. maculata* 'Schneelawine'
- 'Delta'	EBee EPPr GBuc LRHS NLar SAko SGbt SPer SRkn SWvt WFar
- 'Natascha'	Widely available
- 'Omega' ♀H6	CExl CMac EAEE EBee ECtt EWTr EWoo GAbr GBuc ILea LEdu LSou MCot MMuc MNrw MSpe NGdn NLar SGbt SKHP SPer SWvt WCAu WFar WWEG
- 'Princess Sturdza' ♀H6	SDix
- 'Reine du Jour'	CSam ELon IVic LPla NDov SPhx
- 'Rosalinde'	ECtt ELon GAbr GBin GBuc LRHS LSou MCot MMuc MRav NLar SAko SWvt WSHC WWEG XLum
§ - 'Schneelawine'	LRHS SPlb
'Matineus'	SPhx
'Millstream'	see *P.* × *procumbens* 'Millstream'
'Millstream Blue'	EPfP
'Millstream Jupiter'	ECho
'Minnie Pearl'	EWes NDov SKHP WCot
'Mystic Green'	LAst

nivalis 'Jill Alexander'	SBch
– 'Nivea'	GJos
ovata L. **new**	CEvo
paniculata	CEvo GCra NBid NDov SDix WCot
– 'A.E.Amos'	ELon
– 'Aida'	EBee
– var. ***alba***	SDix WCAu WCot
– 'Alba Grandiflora' ♀H7	GMaP MAvo MNrw WCot WHrl
– 'Alexandra'[PBR]	MSCN NLar
– 'All in One'	EBee ECtt MAvo
– 'Amethyst' misapplied	see *P. paniculata* 'Lilac Time'
– 'Amethyst' Foerster	CCon CWld GQue LRHS MRav MSpe NBir NCGa NLar SWat
– 'Anne'	CSam
– 'Auslese D. Bach'	CSam
– 'Balmoral'	CMac EBee ECtt GCra MLHP NEgg NSti SWat SWvt WWEG
– 'Barnwell'	SWat
– 'Becky Towe'[PBR] (v) ♀H7	ECtt LLHF LRHS MHer MHol MNrw MSpe NEgg NHol WCot
– 'Betty Margarite'	NDov
– 'Blue Boy'	EBee ECtt ELan ELon EPfP GMaP LAst LRHS NBir NBro NEgg NLar SKHP SRms SWvt WFar WMnd
– 'Blue Evening'	LCro LOPS MCot
– 'Blue Ice'	NBro
– 'Blue Paradise'	Widely available
– 'Blushing Bride'	SRms
– 'Border Gem'	CAby CBcs CMac ECtt ELon EShb LAst LRHS MCot MRav MSpe MTis NChi NLar SDix SWat SWvt WBrk WCAu WHrl
– 'Branklyn'	GCra
– 'Brigadier'	CTri EBee ECtt ELan ELon GMaP LRHS MCot MSpe NEgg NGdn SPer SRms WFar
– 'Bright Eyes'	Widely available
– 'Burgi'	SDix
– 'Candy Floss'	ELon
– 'Candy Twist' **new**	MSCN
– 'Cardinal'	MTis NDov
– 'Caroline van den Berg'	SRms
– 'Cecil Hanbury'	NLar WSHC
– 'Charlotte'	MSpe
– 'Cherry Red'	WMoo
– 'Chintz'	MRav SRms
– 'Cinderella'	ECtt MTis
– Compact Lilac	see *P. paniculata* Sweet Summer Favourite
– 'Cool Water'	LAst
– Coral Flame = 'Barsixtytwo'[PBR] (Flame Series)	CBod CMac CMea LBMP LSou NLar SRkn
– 'Cosmopolitan'[PBR]	MAsh MBri MNrw NLar WFar
– Count Zeppelin	see *P. paniculata* 'Graf Zeppelin'
– 'Danielle' ♀H7	CSBt MSCN SGol SHar
– 'Darwin's Choice'	see *P. paniculata* 'Norah Leigh'
– 'David' ♀H7	Widely available
– 'David's Lavender' ♀H7	ELon LRHS
– 'Delilah'[PBR]	CWGN ECtt
– 'Discovery'	EHrv EShb EWes MCot MRav MSpe NEgg SHar SWat WFar
– 'Doghouse Pink'	SDix
– 'Dresden China'	SHar SWat WCAu
– 'Duchess of York'	MAvo SDix
§ – 'Düsterlohe'	CSBt CSam EBee ECtt ELon GBin GBuc GQue IPot MRav MTis NBir NDov NLar SAko SGol SPer SWat WCAu WCot WHoo XLum
– 'Early Light Pink'	IPot
– 'Eclaireur' misapplied	see *P. paniculata* 'Düsterlohe'
– 'Eclaireur' Lemoine	MAvo SWat
– 'Eden's Flash'	CElw ECtt MPie MSpe
– 'Eden's Glory'	MAvo
– 'Eden's Smile'	ECtt MSpe
– 'Elisabeth' (v)	EPfP LSRN NWad
– 'Elizabeth Arden'	ECtt MAvo MSpe MTis NLar SWat
– 'Elizabeth Campbell'	GCal LRHS
– 'Empty Feelings' (Feelings Series)	NBro
– 'Ending Blue'	MAvo
– 'Etoile de Paris'	see *P. paniculata* 'Toits de Paris' Symons-Jeune
– 'Europa'	EBee ECtt ELan MCot NBir NGdn NLar SPer WCAu
– 'Eva Cullum' ♀H7	CSam EBee ECtt EHrv ELan ELon EPfP GCra GMaP LOPS LRHS MArl MCot MSpe NCGa NLar SAko SPer SWat WCAu WCot
– 'Eva Foerster' ♀H7	XLum
– 'Eventide'	CMac CSam ECtt EPfP GQue LRHS MArl MCot MNrw MRav MSpe MWat SBod SPer SWat WFar WHrl WPtf
– 'Ferris Wheel'	EBee ECtt
– 'Flamingo' ♀H7	EBee ECtt LRHS MSpe NLar SWvt XLum
– 'Fondant Fancy'[PBR]	NLar SPoG WFar
– 'Franz Schubert' ♀H7	CSam ECtt ELan EPfP EWoo GBin GCra LCro LRHS MAvo MBel MCot MLHP MSpe NBir NChi NGdn NLar NSti SPer SWat SWvt WCot WFar WKif
§ – 'Frau Alfred von Mauthner'	GKev
– 'Frosted Elegance' (v)	EBee WWEG
– 'Fujiyama'	see *P. paniculata* 'Mount Fuji'
– 'Giltmine' (v)	EBee
– 'Goldmine'[PBR] (v)	CAby ECtt LRHS MHol MNrw SPoG WCot
§ – 'Graf Zeppelin'	ECtt MSpe MTis NHol SRms XLum
– 'Grenadine Dream'[PBR] ♀H7	CWGN EBee ELon LAst LRHS MNrw SPoG WCot
– 'Grey Lady' ♀H7	MNrw
– 'Harlequin' (v)	CMac CWGN ECha ECtt ELon GMaP LRHS MHol NBro NEgg NLar NSti SGSe SPer SPoG WCot
– 'Ice Cream'	ELon WHlf
– 'Irene Mast'	CSam
– 'Iris'	MNrw SRms WCot
– 'Jade'	CAby EBee ECtt ELon EWoo GBin GQue LRHS MCot MHol MNrw NLar NSti WCot WPtf XLum
– 'Jeff's Blue'	EBee ELon LAst MAsh WCot
– 'Judy'	GBin LSRN MAvo NBro
§ – 'Juliglut'	SWat WCot
– July Glow	see *P. paniculata* 'Juliglut'
– 'Junior Bouquet'	MHol NLar
– 'Junior Dream'	NLar SPad
– 'Katarina'	CElw ECtt
– 'Katherine'	IPot LRHS MSpe NLar
– 'Katja'[PBR] **new**	ELon MAsh
– 'Kirchenfürst'	CElw IPot LCro LRHS MSpe MTis NBir SAko SHil XLum
– 'Kirmesländler'	ECtt EWTr GBin IPot LCro LOPS LPla MTis NLar SAko SWat
– 'Lads Pink'	SDix
– 'Lady Clare'	SRms
– 'Landhochzeit'	EBee

	Name	Suppliers
	- 'Laura'	CBod CLet ECtt ELon EPfP GBin IPot LHop LRHS MTis NBro SGSe SGol SRkn SRms SWvt WBor WMnd WSHC XLum
§	- 'Lavendelwolke'	CSam GCal LRHS MSpe MTis NBir NLar SWat WCot
	- Lavender Cloud	see *P. paniculata* 'Lavendelwolke'
	- 'Le Mahdi' ♀H7	NLar SRms SWat
	- 'Lichtspel'	LPla NDov SPhx
§	- 'Lilac Time'	CElw EBee ECtt ELon EPfP GKev LRHS LSRN MMuc MTis NLar SHil SPer SWat SWvt
	- 'Little Boy'	CElw ECtt ELon MNrw NLar SGbt WHil
	- 'Little Laura'	CElw ECtt EWTr LSRN MSpe NLar NWad SPoG WCot WHoo
	- 'Little Princess'	ELon NLar WMnd
	- 'Little Sara'	NDov
	- 'Lizzy' PBR	NLar
	- 'Logan Black'	EBee GCal SHar
	- 'Long Border Mauve' **new**	SDix
	- Magical Favorite	see *P. paniculata* Sweet Summer Favourite
	- 'Manoir d'Hézèques'	WCot
	- 'Mary Christine' (v)	CDes NBid
	- 'Maude Stella Dagley'	MSpe
	- 'Mia Ruys'	MArl MLHP
	- 'Midnight Feelings' (Feelings Series)	NBro
	- 'Mike's Favourite' **new**	EBee
	- 'Milly van Hoboken'	WKif
	- 'Miss Elie' ♀H7	SGSe
	- 'Miss Holland'	NGdn SGbt XLum
	- 'Miss Jill'	see *P.* × *arendsii* 'Miss Jill'
	- 'Miss Karen'	see *P.* × *arendsii* 'Miss Karen'
	- 'Miss Kelly'	EHrv EShb MSpe NLar WHoo
	- 'Miss Margie'	see *P.* × *arendsii* 'Miss Margie'
	- 'Miss Mary'	see *P.* × *arendsii* 'Miss Mary'
	- 'Miss Pepper' ♀H7	CLet CWCL ECtt ELon EWoo LRHS MMuc MSpe NGdn NLar SEND SGol WBor WHil
	- 'Miss Universe'	SGSe
	- 'Miss Wilma'	see *P.* × *arendsii* 'Miss Wilma'
	- 'Monica Lynden-Bell' ♀H7	CAby CWGN ELon EWoo GBin GMaP LBMP LRHS MBel MHol MMuc MNrw MPie MRav MSpe NBid NChi NLar NSti SGbt SKHP SPoG WAul WCot WHoo WKif WPtf WSHC
	- 'Monte Cristallo'	MSpe
	- 'Mother of Pearl' ♀H7	GQue IPot LRHS MWat NEgg SPer
§	- 'Mount Fuji'	Widely available
	- 'Mount Fujiyama'	see *P. paniculata* 'Mount Fuji'
	- 'Mrs A.E. Jeans'	SRms
	- 'Mystique Black'	EBee ECtt WPtf
	- 'Natural Feelings' PBR (Feelings Series)	NBro NLar
§	- 'Neon Flare' (Neon Series)	CWGN ECtt
	- 'Newbird'	ECtt EPfP IBoy LRHS MSpe SRms
	- 'Nicky'	see *P. paniculata* 'Düsterlohe'
	- 'Nirvana'	CSam
§	- 'Norah Leigh' (v) ♀H7	Widely available
	- 'Orange Perfection'	see *P. paniculata* 'Prince of Orange'
	- 'Othello'	CSam ECGP ECtt ELon MSpe NGdn NSti WHoo WMnd
	- 'Otley Choice'	CSam EBee ECtt LRHS MRav NCGa NSti SDix SWat WHrl
	- 'Otley Purple'	MHer
	- 'P.D. Williams'	WCot
	- 'Pallas Athene'	IPot
	- 'Pastorale'	WCot
	- (Peacock Series) Peacock Cherry Red ♀H7	LRHS WCFE
	- - Peacock Lilac ♀H7	EPfP LRHS
	- - Peacock Neon Purple ♀H7	LRHS WMoo
	- - Peacock Purple Bicolor	LRHS
	- - Peacock White ♀H7	LRHS
	- 'Peppermint Twist'	CWCL CWGN EBee ELon LRHS LSou LSun MAsh MBri MHol MMuc MNrw NEgg NLar SPad SWvt WCot WFar WHil
	- 'Picasso'	EBee ECtt MSpe
	- 'Pina Colada' PBR	CWGN ECtt LSun MAsh NLar SPoG WFar WHil
	- Pink Eye Flame = 'Barthirtyfive' PBR ♀H7	EPfP LBMP LSou MBri SCob SKHP SPoG SRkn WHil
	- 'Pink Lady' PBR	EBee ELon LAst WFar
	- 'Pink Posie' (v)	WCot
	- Pink Red Eye Flame = 'Barthirtyfour' PBR	EPfP LSou SPoG
	- 'Pinky Hill'	CSBt EBee
	- 'Pleasant Feelings' PBR (Feelings Series)	NBro
	- 'Popeye'	LPla WCot
	- 'Prime Minister'	ELon
§	- 'Prince of Orange' ♀H7	CBcs CSam EBee ECtt ELon EPfP IBoy LAst LRHS LSRN MAvo MCot MJak MRav MSpe NEgg NLar NWad SGbt SGol SHil SPer SWvt WBor WCAu WCot WMnd XLum
	- 'Prospero' ♀H7	CSam CSpe MRav NBid SWat
	- Purple Eye Flame = 'Barthirtythree' PBR ♀H7	LLHF LRHS LSou MBri SKHP SRkn SWvt WFar WHil
	- 'Purple Kiss' PBR	CWGN ECtt LSou MHol WFar WHil
	- 'Rainbow'	ELon NLar
	- 'Red Caribbean'	ECtt LSou
	- 'Red Feelings' (Feelings Series)	NBro
	- 'Red Flame'	CWGN CWld EBee ECtt EPfP GBin LRHS LSou MHol MNrw NLar SKHP SRkn WFar
	- 'Red Riding Hood'	ECtt ELon EPfP IBoy ILea LAst LRHS MBri MSCN SRkn
I	- 'Reddish Hesperis'	MAvo
	- 'Rembrandt'	CExl ELon EPfP EWoo LCro LOPS XLum
	- 'Rijnstroom'	CBcs ECha ECtt ELon MArl NLar SCob WBrk WCAu WHil
	- 'Robert Poore'	ECtt ELon
	- 'Rosa Goliath'	CSam
	- 'Rosa Pastell' ♀H7	CAby CSpe ECGP ECtt EHrv ELon EWoo GBin GQue IPot LPla LRHS MAvo MHol MPie MTis NDov NLar SPer SPoG WAul WCot
	- 'Rosanne'	IPot
	- 'Rowie'	NBid
	- 'Rubymine' (v)	LLHF
	- 'Sandringham'	EHrv LRHS MArl MRav NBir SPer SWvt
§	- 'Schneerausch'	LPla SPhx
	- 'Septemberglut'	EBee EPfP LRHS NLar SHil
	- 'Shockwave' (v)	WCot
	- 'Skylight'	LSRN NBro SDix
	- Snowdrift	see *P. paniculata* 'Schneerausch'
	- 'Speed Limit 45'	WCot
	- 'Spitfire'	see *P. paniculata* 'Frau Alfred von Mauthner'
	- 'Starburst'	NBro
	- 'Starfire' ♀H7	Widely available
	- 'Steeple Bumpstead'	WCot

I - 'Stellata'	EBee LRHS
- 'Sternhimmel'	LPla MSpe MTis
- 'Strawberry Daiquiri'[PBR]	WFar WHil
- (Sweet Summer Series) Sweet Summer Candy = 'Ditosdre'[PBR]	MAsh
- - Sweet Summer Dream = 'Ditomdre'[PBR]	IKil
- - Sweet Summer Fantasy = 'Ditopur'[PBR] **new**	IKil
§ - - Sweet Summer Favourite = 'Ditomfav'[PBR] 🏆H7	WCAu
- - Sweet Summer Festival = 'Ditoros'[PBR]	MAsh
- - Sweet Summer Purple White	see *P. paniculata* Sweet Summer Temptation
- - Sweet Summer Queen = 'Ditoran'	IKil MAsh
- - Sweet Summer Surprise = 'Ditomsur'[PBR]	ECtt WCAu
§ - - Sweet Summer Temptation = 'Ditostem'[PBR]	MAsh
- - Sweet Summer Wine = 'Ditowine' **new**	IKil
- 'Swizzle'	CWGN ECtt LSun MBri WBor WFar
- 'Tenor'	CCon CMac CTri CWCL ECtt ELon EPfP GBuc IBoy LAst LRHS MCot MJak MSpe NLar SCob SWvt WCAu WSHC
- 'Tequila Sunrise'[PBR]	MBri MNrw
- 'The King' 🏆H7	EBee ECtt MAvo NBro NLar SWat WSHC
- 'Tiara'[PBR] (d)	EBee ECtt ELon LRHS MBri MPie SWvt WCot
§ - 'Toits de Paris' Symons-Jeune	WSHC
- 'Twister'	EBee ELon MAsh MNrw MSCN NPri WFar
- 'Uspekh' 🏆H7	CAby CSam EBee ECtt EPPr EWes LEdu LRHS MCot MRav MSpe MWhi NBro NCGa NLar NSti SDix SPer WCAu WFar WHrl
- 'Valentina'[PBR] **new**	IPot
- 'Van Gogh'	CCse
- 'Velvet Flame' 🏆H7	EPfP LSou MBel MBri SKHP WCot
- 'Vintage Wine'	MNrw
- 'Violetta Gloriosa'	ELon LPla
- 'Visions' 🏆H7	WHil
- 'Volcano Betty'	GBin
- 'Watermelon Punch'	ECtt NLar WFar
- 'Wendy House'	EBee ECtt LEdu LLHF MNrw NHol WRHF
- 'Wenn Schon Denn Schon'	EBee
- 'White Admiral' 🏆H7	CBcs CElw EBee ECtt EHrv ELan ELon EPfP EWoo GCra GKev GMaP IBoy LRHS MHer MSpe MWat NEgg SCob SPer SPhx SRms SWat SWvt WCAu WMnd WSHC WWEG XLum
- White Flame = 'Bartwentynine'[PBR] 🏆H7	CMea CWGN ECtt EPfP GBin IPot LBMP LCro LOPS LRHS LSou MBri NLar SCob SKHP SWvt WCot
- 'Wilhelm Kesselring'	EBee ECtt ELon LRHS MTis WBor
- 'Windsor'	EBee ECtt ELon EPfP EWTr MSpe NDov NEgg NHol SRms SWvt
- 'Younique White'	MAsh
(Paparazzi Series) 'Paparazzi Angelina'	WHlf
- Paparazzi Lindsay = 'Ppphl07101'	WHlf
- 'Paparazzi Miley'	WHlf
'Peppermint Candy'	WFar
'Petticoat'	CMea CPBP CSma ECtt SIgm WIce
Pink Flame = 'Bartwelve'[PBR]	EPfP GBin LLHF LRHS LSou MBri NLar NPri SRkn
'Pride of Rochester'	ECho ECtt GJos LHop LRHS
§ × ***procumbens*** 'Millstream' 🏆H5	ECtt
- 'Variegata' (v)	EBee ECha ECho ECtt GCrg NPri SRot
§ ***pulvinata***	WAbe
'Purple Elite'	WHlf
Purple Flame = 'Barfourteen'[PBR]	CBod EBee EPfP GBin LBMP LRHS LSou NPri SCob SRkn WFar
× ***rugelii***	EWld
'Sandra'	NLar
'Scented Pillow'	SGSe
'Sherbet Cocktail'[PBR]	CWGN EBee NHol NLar WPtf
§ ***sibirica*** subsp. ***borealis***	EDAr
'Special Purple Star' (Adessa Series) **new**	EBee
stolonifera	MNrw
I - 'Alba'	EBee EPfP
- 'Ariane'	ECha ECtt LSou MCot
- 'Blue Ridge' 🏆H5	CExl EBee ECha ECtt EPfP LRHS LSRN MHol MRav SRms
- 'Fran's Purple'	ECtt EWld MNrw NBro WCFE WTor
- 'Home Fires'	EBee ECho ECtt EPfP LEdu LRHS MNrw NBro SPlb XLum
- 'Montrose Tricolor' (v)	NBro
- 'Purpurea'	EBee EPfP LEdu LSou SGSe WPGP
subulata 'Alexander's Surprise'	CMea ECho ECtt EDAr EPfP EPot GCrg LBee LRHS MAsh NBir NPri SIgm
- 'Amazing Grace'	CTal CTri CWCL ECho EDAr EPfP EWes GEdr GJos IPot LAst LHop LRHS MSCN NPri NSla NWad SPoG WHoo WIce
- 'Apple Blossom'	ECho NHol SPoG SRms
- 'Atropurpurea'	ECho EDAr EPfP LRHS SPoG XLum
- 'Bavaria'	CMea CPBP ECho ECtt EPfP GJos IPot LLHF LRHS MBel NLar NPri WIce
- Beauty of Ronsdorf	see *P. subulata* 'Ronsdorfer Schöne'
- 'Blue Eyes'	see *P. subulata* 'Oakington Blue Eyes'
- 'Bonita'	ECho ECtt GCrg GJos LRHS MAsh WHoo WIce XLum
- 'Bressingham Blue Eyes'	see *P. subulata* 'Oakington Blue Eyes'
- 'Candy Stripe'	see *P. subulata* 'Tamaongalei'
- 'Cavaldes White'	ECtt
- 'Coral Eye'	ECtt
- 'Drumm'	see *P. subulata* 'Tamaongalei'
- 'Emerald Cushion'	CBod CTri ECho ECtt EDAr ELon EPfP LAst NHol NLar NPri SGbt WCFE
- 'Emerald Cushion Blue'	CExl CTri EAJP ECho ECtt EPfP LAst LRHS MAsh MHCG MSCN NBir NPri SBch SPlb SPoG WAbe
- 'Fort Hill'	ECtt
- 'G.F. Wilson'	see *P. subulata* 'Lilacina'
- 'Holly'	ITim NHol NWad

- 'Jupiter' ECho
- 'Kimono' see *P. subulata* 'Tamaongalei'
§ - 'Lilacina' CMea ECha ECho MAsh WIce
§ - 'Maischnee' CPBP CTal CTri ECho ECtt MAsh SPlb
- 'Marjorie' CTal ECho ECtt GEdr GJos LBee MHer NBir SPoG
- May Snow see *P. subulata* 'Maischnee'
§ - 'McDaniel's Cushion' ♀H5 Widely available
- 'Mikado' see *P. subulata* 'Tamaongalei'
- 'Millstream Daphne' ECho ECtt NLar WTor
- 'Moonlight' ECho GJos SIgm
- 'Nettleton Variation' (v) ECho ECtt EDAr ELon EPot EWes GCrg LHop LRHS MMuc NPri NRya SPoG WHoo WIce
§ - 'Oakington Blue Eyes' CTri SRms
- 'Purple Beauty' CMea CTal ECho ECtt GJos LAst LHop LLHF LRHS MMuc NHar NPri NWad SBch SEND SPoG WCFE WSHC XLum
- 'Red Wings' ♀H5 ECho ECtt EPfP LRHS SRms
§ - 'Ronsdorfer Schöne' EPfP LBee LLHF NBir
- 'Samson' ECho GJos LRHS LSRN WOld
- 'Scarlet Flame' CBod CMea ECho ECtt EDAr EPfP GJos MAsh NHol NPri SBch WHil WHoo WIce
- 'Snow Queen' see *P. subulata* 'Maischnee'
- 'Snowflake' GCrg MSCN NPri
§ - 'Tamaongalei' CBod CMea CTri ECho ECtt EDAr ELon EWes GCrg GJos GKev GMaP LAst LBMP LRHS MHol MMuc NPri NWad SBch SEND SHar SIgm WCFE WHoo WIce
- 'Temiskaming' CTri ECho ECtt EDAr EWes GCrg LHop LRHS MBel MLHP SRms WSHC
- 'White Delight' CMea ECho ECtt EPfP GJos LAst LBee LRHS SPoG
- 'Winifred' NEgg

Sweet Summer Sensation = 'Ditosse'PBR (Sweet Summer Series) **new** IKil
'Swirly Burly' GQue NLar
'Tiny Bugles' CPBP CTal
Violet Flame = 'Barsixtyone'PBR CBod CMea EPfP LRHS MHol NLar SPer SPoG WCot WRHF
White Eye Flame = 'Barsixty'PBR CBod CMea CWGN EPfP IPot LBMP LRHS NLar SCob
'White Kimono' ECho LRHS
'Zwergenteppich' EPfP LLHF LRHS WTor

Phoenix (*Arecaceae*)

canariensis ♀H1c CBcs CExl CWib EAla EPfP EUJe IVic LPal MBri MMuc SEND SPlb SPoG STrG
dactylifera (F) LTro SBig
loureiroi var. ***pedunculata*** from Kashmir **new** LTro
reclinata XBlo
roebelenii ♀H1b CDTJ CDoC LPal MBri SBig
- 'Multistem' XBlo
theophrasti CPHo LPal LTro

Phormium ✿ (*Hemerocallidaceae*)

sp. LPar
§ 'Alison Blackman'PBR CBcs CDoC COtt EPfP GBin IVic LPal LRHS LSRN MAsh MBri MGos MJak NLar SCob SCoo SEND SHil SPoG SRkn SWvt
'Amazing Red' LPal SAko SCob
'Apricot Queen' (v) CAbb CBcs CDoC CSBt CWib EPfP LCro LPal LRHS LSRN MGos NLar SCob SEND SHil SPer SPoG
Back in Black = 'Seilack'PBR CLet EUJe LRHS MWhi NPri SCob SHil WFar
'Black Adder'PBR CBcs CBod CBot EBee EPfP EUJe IBoy ILea LBuc LPal LRHS LSRN MAsh MJak SCob SEND SPer SPoG
'Black Rage' CBcs EPfP LRHS NLos
Black Velvet = 'Seivel'PBR IBoy LRHS MHtn MSwo NPla SHil
'Bronze Baby' CBcs CDoC CMea CNec CSBt EHoe ELan ELon EPfP LCro LRHS LSRN MGos MSwo NLar SCob SLim SPer SPoG SWvt
'Buckland Ruby' EBee
'Chocolate Fingers' CBcs
'Chocomint'PBR EBee
colensoi see *P. cookianum*
§ ***cookianum*** GGal SCob
- subsp. ***hookeri*** 'Cream Delight' (v) ♀H4 CAbb CBcs CDoC CLet COtt CSBt CWib EPfP EUJe LPal LRHS LSRN MAsh MGos MSwo NFav SCob SCoo SGol SHil SPer SWvt WGrn
- - 'Tricolor' (v) ♀H4 CBcs CDTJ CDoC CDul CLet COtt CSBt CWib ELan ELon EPfP EUJe GBuc LCro LOPS LRHS MGos MMuc NPla SAko SCob SEND SGol SHil SLim SPer SPoG SRms SWvt WGrn
'Crimson Devil' CBcs LRHS MBri MGos NPri SHil SLim
Dark Avocado = 'Westado'PBR EBee MAsh SLim
'Dark Delight' CBcs CDoC LTro
'Duet' (v) ♀H3 CBcs CWib EBee EPfP MMuc SEND SWvt
'Dusky Chief' CDoC CSBt EPfP LPal NLar
'Emerald Isle' CDoC
'Evening Glow' (v) CBcs CDoC COtt CSBt ELan ELon EPfP EUJe LCro LPal LRHS LSRN LTro MBri MGos NLar NPri SCob SEND SPoG SWvt WGrn
'Firebird' ELon EUJe LRHS LSRN MBri SHil SWvt
'Flamingo' (v) CBcs CDTJ CDoC CNec CSBt ELan ELon EPfP LRHS LSou MBri MGos MHol NLar SBod SCob SLim SPer SPoG
'Glowing Embers' CBcs ELon
'Gold Ray' (v) CBcs CBod CDoC EBee EPfP EUJe LRHS MBri MJak MWhi NLos NPri SCob SCoo SHil SWvt WHil
'Gold Sword' (v) CDoC CSBt EPfP LRHS NEgg SCob
'Golden Alison' see *P.* 'Alison Blackman'
'Green Sword' CBcs
'Jack Spratt' (v) ECou EHoe SWvt
'Jessie' **new** NLos
'Jester' (v) CBcs CBod CDoC CLet COtt CSBt EBee ELan ELon EPfP EUJe LPal LRHS LSRN MAsh MBri MGos MJak MSwo NEgg NLos NPla SCob SCoo SHil SLim SPer SPoG SRkn WGrn
'Limelight' SWvt
§ 'Maori Chief' (v) CSBt EPfP LRHS SWvt WFar
§ 'Maori Maiden' (v) CBcs CDoC CDul COtt CTri ELon EPfP LRHS MGos MSwo SWvt
§ 'Maori Queen' (v) CBcs CBod CChe CDTJ CDoC COtt CSBt ELon EPfP ILea LCro LPal LRHS MBri MGos MSwo SCob SCoo SEND SHil SPer SPoG SWvt

§ 'Maori Sunrise' (v) CBcs CDoC ELon IArd LCro LOPS LPal LRHS LSRN MGos SCob SCoo SLim SPer SWvt
'Margaret Jones'PBR CBcs LSRN SLim
'Merlot'PBR NPri
'Moonraker'PBR CBcs MHol
'Pink Panther' (v) CAbb CBcs CBod CDoC CWib ELan ELon EPfP LRHS LSRN MBri MGos NLar NPla NPri SCob SHil SPoG
'Pink Stripe' (v) CBcs CChe CDoC CNec CSBt LPal LRHS MAsh MBri MGos MJak NPri SCob SHil SPoG SWvt
'Platt's Black' CBcs CDoC COtt EPfP EUJe IBoy LCro LRHS LSRN MBri MGos MJak MSwo NBir NLar NPla SCob SHil SLim SPer SPoG SRkn SWvt WFar WGrn
'Rainbow Chief' see *P.* 'Maori Chief'
'Rainbow Glossy' **new** NLos
'Rainbow Maiden' see *P.* 'Maori Maiden'
'Rainbow Queen' see *P.* 'Maori Queen'
'Rainbow Sunrise' see *P.* 'Maori Sunrise'
'Red Fingers' CBcs
'Red Sensation' ELon
I 'Rubrum' EUJe SEND
'Sundowner' (v) ♀H3 CBcs CDoC CDul CLet COtt CSBt CTsd EBee ELan EPfP LCro LPal LRHS MAsh MBri MGos MJak MMuc NBir NEgg NLar SCob SCoo SEND SHil SLim SPer SPoG SWvt WGrn
'Sunset' (v) CBcs CSBt EUJe SWvt
'Surfer' (v) CBcs WGrn
'Surfer Bronze' CBcs CSBt
'Surfer Green' NLos
'Sussex Velvet' SLim
tenax Widely available
- 'All Black' LRHS MBri MGos SCoo SHil
- 'Bronze' CTsd EAla SWvt
- 'Co-ordination' CBcs
- dwarf CSpe
- 'Glenorchy Green' EAEE
- In The Red = 'Seied'PBR MHol
- 'Joker' (v) CBcs CDoC CMea ELon LPal NLar NLos
* - ***lineatum*** SEND
- Purpureum Group ♀H4 CBar CDoC CDul CLet CSBt CWib EBee ELan ELon EPfP LPal LRHS MJak MMuc MSwo NLar SCob SEND SGol SHil SLim SLon SPer SPlb WFar
- 'Tiny Tiger' EPfP
- 'Tom Thumb' CBcs
- 'Variegatum' (v) ♀H5 CDTJ CDul CLet EBee EPfP EUJe LPal LPar MGos MJak MMuc NPri SCob SEND SPer SRms
- 'Veneer'PBR **new** NLos
- 'Yellow Queen' LPal WFar
variegated (v) **new** SCob
'Wings of Gold' EBee
'Yellow Wave' (v) ♀H4 Widely available

Photinia ✿ (*Rosaceae*)

arbutifolia see *Heteromeles salicifolia*
beauverdiana var. ***notabilis*** CJun EPfP NLar
Corallina = 'Bourfrits'PBR EBee NLar
davidiana CMac CTri ELan EPfP IDee MGil MRav NLar SCob SRms SVen
- 'Palette' (v) CBcs CDul CMac CWib EBee EHoe ELan ELon EPfP LHop LRHS MAsh MGos MMuc MSwo NEgg SCob SGol SPer SPoG SRms SWvt WFar WMat WMoo
- var. ***undulata*** 'Fructu Luteo' CAbP GGal MMuc MRav SEND
- - 'Prostrata' CMac CTri MRav NLar
I × ***fraseri*** 'Atropurpurea Nana' EPfP MGos
- 'Birmingham' CMac EWes
- 'Canivily' ♀H5 IVic LRHS MBri MGos MPkF SGol SHil
- Cracklin' Red = 'Parred' ELon MPkF WMoo
- 'Goldstar' MPkF
* - 'Ilexifolium' ESwi
- 'Little Red Robin' Widely available
- 'Louise' (v) **new** EBee LBuc
- Magical Volcano = 'Kolmavoca' **new** LCro NLar SGol
- Pink Marble = 'Cassini' (v) ♀H5 CBcs CNec EBee ELan ELon EPfP EUJe LBuc LCro LPar LPfy LRHS MAsh MBri MGos MJak MPkF NPri SCob SEND SGol SHil SLim SLon SPer SPoG SRms
- 'Red Robin' ♀H5 Widely available
- 'Red Select' NPri WPat
- 'Robusta' CMac EPfP LRHS SWvt
- 'Scarlet Blaze' **new** LRHS
§ ***glabra*** 'Parfait' (v) CAbP CMac EBee LRHS MAsh SLon
- 'Pink Lady' see *P. glabra* 'Parfait'
- 'Rubens' EPfP LRHS MAsh MRav
- 'Variegata' see *P. glabra* 'Parfait'
integrifolia HWJ 946 WCru
lasiogyna CMCN
lucida WCru
microphylla B&SWJ 11837 WCru
- HWJ 564 WCru
niitakayamensis MSnd
- CWJ 12435 WCru
'Redstart' CAbP CMac EBee ELan EPfP LRHS MMuc NLar SLon SPer SWvt WFar WMoo
§ ***serratifolia*** CAbP CBcs CBot CDul CMCN ELan EPfP NLar SBrt SEND SPer WFar WPGP
- Curly Fantasy = 'Kolcurl'PBR IVic LRHS MRav NLar
- 'Jenny' LRHS NLar WFar
serrulata see *P. serratifolia*
§ Super Hedge = 'Branpara'PBR EShb LRHS LSou MSwo WFar
'Super Red' CSBt NLar
villosa CAbP CTho EPfP MBri MSnd SPoG WPat
- B&SWJ 8665 WCru
- var. ***coreana*** B&SWJ 8789 WCru
- var. ***laevis*** CExl EBee EPfP MBri WPGP
- - B&SWJ 8877 WCru
- f. ***maximowicziana*** MBri NLar
* - var. ***zollingeri*** B&SWJ 8903 WCru

Phragmites (*Poaceae*)

sp. CHab
from Sichuan, China EPPr
§ ***australis*** CBen CHab CWat MMuc MSKA MWLS NMir SVic SWat WMAq WPnP XLum

- subsp. ***australis*** var. ***striatopictus*** EPPr
- - 'Variegatus' (v) CBen CKno CWat EBee EPPr EShb LLWG MMuc MPie MWhi NBir NWsh SEND SMad WWEG WWtn XLum
- subsp. ***humilis*** CHab
- subsp. ***pseudodonax*** EPPr
communis see *P. australis*
karka 'Candy Stripe' (v) CBen EPPr MSKA

Phuopsis (*Rubiaceae*)

§ ***stylosa*** Widely available
- 'Purpurea' ECGP MNrw MRav NChi NDov

Phycella (*Amaryllidaceae*)

cyrtanthoides WCot

Phygelius (*Scrophulariaceae*)

aequalis CTca MRav WMoo
- ***albus*** see *P. aequalis* 'Yellow Trumpet'
- 'Aureus' see *P. aequalis* 'Yellow Trumpet'
- 'Cream Trumpet' see *P. aequalis* 'Yellow Trumpet'
- 'Indian Chief' see *P.* × *rectus* 'African Queen'
- 'Sani Pass' CPrp ELon GMaP MHer SCob SPlb
- 'Trewidden Pink' 🏆[H5] CLet CWib EBee ELan ELon GBin LHop MSCN SGSe SWvt WMnd WMoo XLum
§ - 'Yellow Trumpet' 🏆[H5] CEvo CSBt CTca CWib ELan ELon EPfP GMaP IBoy LSRN MAsh MLHP MMuc SEND SGbt SLim SWvt WMnd WMoo XLum
Candy Drops Cream = 'Kerphycrem'[PBR] (Candy Drops Series) NGBl SCob
capensis CHll CWib ELan GCra GGal MHer SRms WMnd WOut WRHF
'Golden Gate' see *P. aequalis* 'Yellow Trumpet'
Logan form GBin
'Midas Touch' ELon NLar SPad
New Sensation = 'Blaphy'[PBR] EPfP MRav SCob SWvt
'Passionate'[PBR] NLar
§ × ***rectus*** 'African Queen' 🏆[H5] EBee ELan EPfP LPot MLHP MMuc MRav MSwo NBir NGdn SEND SPlb SWvt WKif WMnd XLum
- 'Bridgetown Beauty' GCal
- Candy Drops Deep Rose = 'Kerphyros'[PBR] NGBl
- 'Devil's Tears' 🏆[H5] CBcs CPrp ELan GKev LPot LRHS MMuc NEgg SCob SEND SGSe SLim SWvt WHar WHil WMoo
- 'Ivory Twist' ELon LHop
- 'Jodie Southon' ELon LSou SDys WCot
- 'Moonraker' CAby CBcs CHll CPrp CTri ELan ELon EPfP GBin LRHS MAsh MHer MRav NGdn NLar SCob SEND SGSe SPer SPlb SRms WHil WKif XLum
- 'Raspberry Swirl' ELon
- 'Salmon Leap' 🏆[H5] CBcs CTri ELan EPfP GBin GBuc LRHS LSRN MBNS MGos MMuc MRav NEgg NFav SCob SEND SLim SPlb SWvt WMnd
- Somerford Funfair Series IBoy
- - Somerford Funfair Apricot = 'Yapapr' SWvt
- - Somerford Funfair Coral = 'Yapcor'[PBR] EBee EPfP LBMP LPot LRHS MAsh MBri NLar SBod SCob SLim SRkn SWvt WFar
- - Somerford Funfair Cream = 'Yapcre'[PBR] EPfP LRHS NLar SGSe SLim SWvt WFar
- - Somerford Funfair Orange = 'Yapor'[PBR] EPfP LRHS MAsh MBri NLar SGSe SLim SPoG SWvt WFar
- - Somerford Funfair Wine = 'Yapwin' CAby CBot CChe CDul ELan EPfP EShb LPot LRHS MAsh MBNS MBri NPri SCob SGSe SLim SPoG SWvt
- - Somerford Funfair Yellow = 'Yapyel'[PBR] EPfP LRHS MAsh MBri SLim SPoG SWvt
§ - 'Winchester Fanfare' CLet CSBt ELan GBin LRHS MGos MRav SCob SEND SLim SPer SWvt WKif
- 'Winton Fanfare' see *P.* × *rectus* 'Winchester Fanfare'
'Rory'[PBR] SRms
Snow Queen = 'Crosnoque'[PBR] (Croftway Series) SCob

Phyla (*Verbenaceae*)

lanceolata LLWG
§ ***nodiflora*** ECha MHer SRms WJek XSen
- 'Alba' MMuc SEND
§ - var. ***canescens*** XLum

Phylica (*Rhamnaceae*)

pubescens new CTre

× *Phylliopsis* (*Ericaceae*)

'Coppelia' 🏆[H5] ITim NHar
'Crinoline' NHar WAbe
hillieri 'Askival' WThu
- 'Pinocchio' GEdr GKev NHar WAbe WThu
- 'Sugar Plum' GEdr LRHS NHar NLar SWvt WAbe WThu
'Hobgoblin' ITim WAbe
'Mermaid' ITim NHar WAbe WThu
'Sprite' CWSG ITim
'Swanhilde' WAbe WThu
'Titania' WAbe

Phyllitis see *Asplenium*

scolopendrium see *Asplenium scolopendrium*

Phyllocladus (*Podocarpaceae*)

trichomanoides var. ***alpinus*** CDoC CDul ECou EUJe NWad WThu

Phyllodoce (*Ericaceae*)

aleutica ECho NHar NLar SRms WThu
§ - subsp. ***glanduliflora*** 'Flora Slack' WThu
- - white-flowered see *P. aleutica* subsp. *glanduliflora* 'Flora Slack'
caerulea 🏆[H5] ECho
- ***japonica*** see *P. nipponica*
- 'Murray Lyon' NHar WAbe WThu
- 'W.M. Buchanan's Peach Seedling' NHar
empetriformis ECho SRms WThu
§ ***nipponica*** NHar WThu
'Peach' NLar WThu
tsugifolia new NLar

Phyllostachys ✿ (*Poaceae*)

sp. ETod
angusta ERod MWht SBig
arcana WJun
- 'Luteosulcata' CEnt CFil ERod MMuc MWht WJun
§ ***atrovaginata*** ERod SGol WJun

	aurea ♀H5	Widely available
	- 'Albovariegata' (v)	ENBC EPfP ERod LRHS MWht WJun
	- 'Flavescens Inversa'	ERod LPal MMuc MWht WJun
	- 'Holochrysa'	CDTJ CFil CJun ERod LPal MMuc MWht NLar WJun
	- 'Koi'	CDTJ CEnt ERod MWht SBig SGol WJun WPGP
	aureocaulis	see *P. aureosulcata* f. *aureocaulis*, *P. vivax* f. *aureocaulis*
	aureosulcata	CWib ERod LPar MWht WJun WMoo
	- f. ***alata***	see *P. aureosulcata* f. *pekinensis*
§	- f. ***aureocaulis***	Widely available
	- 'Harbin'	ERod
	- 'Harbin Inversa'	ERod
	- 'Lama Tempel'	CDTJ CFil CJun
§	- f. ***pekinensis***	SBig
	- f. ***spectabilis*** ♀H5	Widely available
	bambusoides	CDTJ ERod SBig SDix WJun
	- 'Allgold'	see *P. bambusoides* 'Holochrysa'
	- 'Castillonii' ♀H5	CBcs CEnt ENBC ERod EUJe EWes LEdu LPal MMuc MWht NLar SBig SDix SEND WJun WPGP
	- 'Castillonii Inversa'	ENBC ERod EWes LEdu MWht WJun WPGP
	- 'Castillonii Inversa Variegata' (v)	WJun
	- 'Castillonii Variegata' (v)	ERod
§	- 'Holochrysa' ♀H5	CDTJ CEnt ERod LPal MAvo MMuc MWht SEND WJun WPGP
	- 'Kawadana' (v)	ERod WJun
	- f. ***lacrima-deae***	CDTJ
	- 'Marliacea'	ERod SBig WJun
	- 'Sulphurea'	see *P. bambusoides* 'Holochrysa'
	- 'Tanakae'	CDTJ SBig
	- 'Violascens'	SBig
	bissetii ♀H5	Widely available
	congesta misapplied	see *P. atrovaginata*
	decora	ERod MMuc MWht SEND WJun
	dulcis	CEnt EPfP ERod LPal MWht SBig WJun
§	***edulis***	CAgr ELon ERod SBig SPlb WJun
	- 'Bicolor'	WJun
§	- 'Heterocycla'	XBlo
	- f. ***pubescens***	see *P. edulis*
	fimbriligula	WJun
	flexuosa	CBcs CEnt LPal MWht SGol WJun
	glauca	EPfP ERod LCro MWht SBig
	- f. ***yunzhu***	ERod MWht WJun
	heteroclada	CEnt WJun
	- 'Solid Stem' misapplied	see *P. purpurata* 'Straight Stem'
	heterocycla	see *P. edulis* 'Heterocycla'
	- var. ***pubescens***	see *P. edulis*
	humilis	CEnt ENBC ERod EUJe LPal MMuc MWhi MWht SBig SEND WJun
	incarnata	WJun
	iridescens ♀H5	ERod ETod MWht SBig WJun
	lithophila	ERod
	makinoi	ERod
	mannii	ERod MWht
	nidularia	ERod SBig WJun
	nigra ♀H5	Widely available
	- 'Boryana'	CCVT CEnt EPfP ERod EUJe MGos MMuc MWht SBig SEND SWvt WJun WMoo
	- 'Hale'	MWht
	- f. ***henonis*** ♀H5	ENBC ERod MMuc MWht NLar SBig SEND SGol WJun WPGP
	- 'Megurochiku'	ERod MWht WJun
	- f. ***nigra***	CFil
	- f. ***punctata***	ENBC ERod MAvo MMuc MWht SEND WJun WMoo
	- 'Tosaensis'	ERod
	nuda	ERod MWht WJun
	- f. ***localis***	ERod MWht
	parvifolia	CEnt ERod MWht WJun
	platyglossa	ERod
	praecox	WJun
	- f. ***viridisulcata***	ERod WJun
	prominens	ERod
	propinqua	ERod LPal MWht WJun
§	***purpurata*** 'Straight Stem'	MWht
	rubicunda	WJun
	rubromarginata	CEnt ERod MMuc MWht WJun
	'Shanghai 3'	ERod
	stimulosa	ERod MWht WJun
	sulphurea 'Houzeau'	ERod MMuc SEND
§	- f. ***sulphurea***	ERod WJun
	- 'Sulphurea'	see *P. sulphurea* f. *sulphurea*
§	- f. ***viridis***	ERod SBig
	violascens	CEnt ERod EUJe MWht SBig WJun
	viridiglaucescens	CDTJ ERod ETod MBrN MMuc MWht SBig SEND WJun
	viridis	see *P. sulphurea* f. *viridis*
	vivax	ENBC EPfP ERod EUJe MMuc MWht NLar SBig WJun
§	- f. ***aureocaulis*** ♀H5	CAbb CAgr CBcs CCVT CDoC CEnt CWSG EAla ENBC EPfP ERod ETod EUJe IBoy LCro LEdu LPal LRHS LSRN MGos MMuc MWhi MWht NLar SBig SCob SEND SGol WJun WPGP
	- - 'Huangwenzhu'	CDTJ ENBC ERod EUJe MWht WJun
	- 'Katrin'	LEdu
*	- 'Sulphurea'	XBlo

× *Phyllothamnus* (*Ericaceae*)

	erectus	WThu

Phymatosorus (*Polypodiaceae*)

§	***diversifolius***	SGSe WPGP

Phymosia (*Malvaceae*)

§	***umbellata***	MOWG WPGP

Phyodina see *Callisia*

Physalis (*Solanaceae*)

	alkekengi ♀H7	CTri EPfP NBir NLar SWvt
	- var. ***franchetii***	CBcs CBod CMac CSBt EBee ECha ELan EPfP LAst LBMP LCro LRHS MBel MHer MNrw NBir NBro NEgg NPri SMad SPer SPoG SRms WFar WMnd WOld WTcb
	- - dwarf	LRHS NLar
	- - 'Gigantea'	CWld ECGP LSun NLar SPlb WFar XLum
	- - 'Gnome'	see *P. alkekengi* var. *franchetii* 'Zwerg'
	- - 'Variegata' (v)	EWes LEdu SEND WPGP
§	- - 'Zwerg'	EBee LRHS LSun
	- 'Halloween King'	EBee LRHS NLar NPri
	- 'Halloween Queen'	LRHS NLar WHil
	campanula B&SWJ 10409	WCru
	edulis	see *P. peruviana*
§	***peruviana*** (F)	SHDw SPlb SVic

Physaria (*Brassicaceae*)

	alpina	GKev SPlb
	saximontana new	GKev

Physocarpus (*Rosaceae*)

	'Burning Embers'	SRms
	'Korona'	WMoo
	Little Devil	see *P. opulifolius* 'Donna May'
	'Midnight'	WMoo
	opulifolius	CDul
	- Amber Jubilee = 'Jefam' new	LRHS
	- 'Angel Gold'	CNec EBee ELan EMil LRHS MAsh NPri
	- 'Chameleon' new	EMil LBuc SPoG
	- Coppertina	see *P. opulifolius* Diable D'Or
	- 'Dart's Gold' 🏆H7	Widely available
§	- Diable D'Or = 'Mindia'PBR	CBar COtt EPfP LCro LPfy LRHS LSRN MAsh MBlu MBri MGos MPkF NEgg NLar NPla SGbt SGol SHil WCot WMoo
	- 'Diabolo'PBR 🏆H7	Widely available
§	- 'Donna May'PBR	EPfP LRHS SCob SLon
§	- Lady in Red = 'Tuilad'PBR 🏆H7	Widely available
§	- 'Luteus'	CWib MGos MRav WMoo
	- 'Nugget'	LRHS MBri MGos
	- 'Red Baron'	LHop
	- Ruby Spice	see *P. opulifolius* Lady in Red
	- Summer Wine = 'Seward'PBR	EPfP EWes LHop LRHS MAsh
	- 'Tilden Park'	SGol
	ribesifolius 'Aureus'	see *P. opulifolius* 'Luteus'

Physoplexis (*Campanulaceae*)

§	***comosa*** 🏆H5	CPBP EPot WAbe

Physostegia (*Lamiaceae*)

	angustifolia	GQui NBre
I	'Aquatica'	LLWG
§	***virginiana***	CBod CSBt CTri GMaP LHop MBel SPoG SRms SWat WCFE WOld
	- 'Alba'	CBod CNec CSBt CTri EAJP EBee EHrv ELon GAbr GJos GMaP LEdu LSun NChi SBod SDix SPlb WCAu WHrl XLum
§	- 'Crown of Snow'	CCon EBee EPfP MHer MRav MWhi SBea SPoG SWvt WHar WMoo WWEG
	- 'Crystal Peek White' new	EBee
	- 'Grandiflora'	CCon
	- 'Miss Manners'	CMac ECGP ECtt LRHS MBri MPie NBre NCGa NGdn NLar SBod
	- 'Olympic Gold' (v)	NWad
	- 'Pink Manners'	STPC
	- 'Red Beauty'	WTcb
	- 'Rose Crown'	SPer
	- 'Rose Queen'	CTri NBre NChi NPri WTcb
	- 'Rosea'	CNec EPfP GJos IFoB MMuc MNHC MWhi NGdn SHar SPad SPoG SWvt WHrl WWEG
	- Schneekrone	see *P. virginiana* 'Crown of Snow'
	- 'Snow Queen'	see *P. virginiana* 'Summer Snow'
§	- var. ***speciosa*** 'Bouquet Rose'	CBod CMac COtt CPrp EBee ECGP ECha EHrv EPfP LEdu LRHS MRav NBir NLar SGbt SPer SWvt WCAu WHar WMoo WRHF WWEG XLum
	- - Rose Bouquet	see *P. virginiana* var. *speciosa* 'Bouquet Rose'
	- - 'Variegata' (v)	CBod CMac CSBt EBee ECtt EHoe EHrv ELan ELon EPfP LHop MHer MRav NBir NGdn NHol SBea SPer SRms SWat WCAu WCot WMnd WWEG XLum
§	- 'Summer Snow' 🏆H7	CBcs COtt ECha ELan EPfP EWoo LHop LRHS NGBl NLar SPer SRms SWat WCAu WCot WMnd
	- 'Summer Spire'	EHrv
	- 'Vivid' 🏆H7	CBod CMac ECha ELan ELon EPfP LAst LRHS MBri MHer MNrw MPie MRav NCGa NEgg NGBl NHol NLar SDix SPer SPlb SRms WCAu WCot WGwG WHil WMnd WWEG WWtn XLum

Phyteuma (*Campanulaceae*)

	balbisii	see *P. cordatum*
	charmelii	GEdr WHoo
	comosum	see *Physoplexis comosa*
§	***cordatum***	GJos
	halleri	see *P. ovatum*
	hemisphaericum	ECho GEdr GJos NSla
	humile	WThu
	nigrum	ECho GEdr LLHF NBid WBor WCot
	orbiculare	GEdr GJos
§	***ovatum***	SPlb
	scheuchzeri	CDes CWld EBee ECho EPfP EWld GBin GEdr SBea SGSe SMad SPad SRms WCot WIce WTcb XLum
	spicatum	CDes GEdr GJos NBro
	- subsp. ***coeruleum***	GJos

Phytolacca (*Phytolaccaceae*)

	acinosa	EWld GPoy SBrt SWat WHil
	- HWJ 647	WCru
§	***americana***	CAby CArn CLet EBee ELan EPfP ESwi EUJe GPoy MBNS MHer MNHC MPie NLar NLos SRms SWat WHea WMnd
	- B&SWJ 8817A	WCru
	- 'Silberstein' (v)	EBee ESwi MBNS MHol NLar NLos
	- 'Variegata' (v)	CLet
	bogotensis	WCru
	clavigera	see *P. polyandra*
	decandra	see *P. americana*
	dioica	CArn CExl SPlb
	esculenta	LEdu SEND
	icosandra B&SWJ 8988	WCru
	- Purpurascens Group B&SWJ 11251	GCal SRms WCru
	japonica B&SWJ 3005	NBid WCru
	- B&SWJ 3522	WCru
	'Laka Boom'	EUJe
	octandra B&SWJ 9514	WCru
	- B&SWJ 10151	WCru
§	***polyandra***	NBid NBro SRms
	rivinoides B&SWJ 10264	WCru
	rugosa B&SWJ 10263	WCru

Picea (*Pinaceae*)

	sp.	LPar
§	***abies***	CCVT CDul CLnd CMac CSBt CTho CTri CWib EFry EPfP LBuc MJak MMuc NEgg NWea SCoo SEND SPoG WHar WMou
	- 'Acrocona' 🏆H7	LRHS MBri NLar
	- 'Archer'	CKen
	- 'Aurea'	ELan
	- 'Barus' new	NLar
	- 'Capitata'	CKen

	- 'Clanbrassiliana' ♀H7	CKen ELan LRHS NWad WGor
	- Columnaris Group	NEgg
I	- 'Congesta'	CKen
	- 'Crippsii'	CKen
I	- 'Cruenta'	CKen SLim
	- 'Cupressina'	CKen
	- 'Diffusa'	CKen NLar
	- 'Dumpy'	CKen NHol
	- 'Emsland' **new**	NLar
	- 'Excelsa'	see *P. abies*
	- 'Fahndrich'	CKen CMen
	- 'Formanek'	CMen
	- 'Four Winds'	CKen
	- 'Frohburg'	CKen LRHS NEgg
	- 'Gold Drift'	NLar
	- 'Gregoryana'	CKen
	- 'Heartland Gem'	CKen
	- 'Horace Wilson'	CKen CMen NLar
	- 'Humilis'	CKen
	- 'Hystrix'	CMen NLar NWad
	- 'Inversa' ♀H7	CKen MBlu SLim
	- 'J.W. Daisy's White'	see *P. glauca* var. *albertiana* 'J.W. Daisy's White'
	- 'Jana'	CKen NLar
	- 'Jermyns Broom No. 1' **new**	CKen
	- 'Kral'	CKen
	- 'Little Gem' ♀H7	CDoC CKen CMen ELan EUJe GEdr MAsh MGos NHol NLar NWad NWea SCoo SLim WGor
	- 'Marcel'	CKen
	- 'Mini Kalous'	CKen
	- 'Nana Compacta'	CKen CMen MAsh WGor
	- 'Nidiformis' ♀H7	CDoC CKen CMac CMen CSBt CTri EUJe LPot LRHS MGos NWea SGol SRms
	- 'Norrköping'	CKen
	- 'Ohlendorffii'	CKen
	- 'Pachyphylla'	CKen
	- 'Pseudomaxwellii'	LRHS
	- 'Pumila'	WCFE
	- 'Pusch'	CKen CMen NLar SLim
	- 'Pygmaea'	CKen NLar NWad
	- 'Reflexa'	NEgg
	- 'Remontii'	MBri NWea WGor
	- 'Rydal' ♀H7	CBcs CDoC CDul CKen LRHS MAsh MBri NEgg NLar NWea
	- 'Saint Mary's Broom'	NEgg
	- 'Spring Fire'	CKen
	- 'Tompa'	NLar
	- 'Typner'	CKen
	- 'Vermont Gold'	CKen NLar
	- 'Walter Bron'	NLar
	- Will's Dwarf	see *P. abies* 'Wills Zwerg'
§	- 'Wills Zwerg'	SGol
§	***alcoquiana***	NWea SLim
	var. ***alcoquiana***	
	- var. ***reflexa***	MPkF
	bicolor	see *P. alcoquiana* var. *alcoquiana*
I	- 'Prostrata'	NEgg
	breweriana ♀H6	CDoC CDul CMac CTho EPfP GKin IDee LEdu LRHS MBlu MGos MJak MMuc NEgg NLar NWea SLim SSta WCFE WMou
	- 'Kohout's Dwarf'	CKen
	chihuahuana	SLim
	engelmannii	CDul NWea
	- 'Bush's Lace' **new**	NLar
	- 'Compact'	SLim
	- subsp. ***engelmannii***	CKen
	- 'Jasper'	CKen NLar
	- 'Lace'	SLim
	glauca	NWea
	- var. ***albertiana*** Alberta Blue = 'Haal'PBR	CKen EUJe LRHS
	- - 'Alberta Globe' ♀H7	CDoC CSBt EFry GEdr GKin LRHS MAsh MBri MGos NEgg NHol NWad SCoo SPoG
	- - 'Conica' ♀H7	CBcs CDoC CMac CMea CSBt EFry EPfP EUJe LCro LOPS LRHS MAsh MBri MGos MJak MMuc NEgg NHol NOrn NWad NWea SBod SEND SGol SPer SPoG SRms WCFE
	- - 'Gnome'	CKen
§	- - 'J.W. Daisy's White' ♀H7	CBcs CDoC CKen EFry ELan EPfP EUJe GKin LRHS MAsh MGos MJak NHol NLar NWad NWea SCoo SLim SPer SPoG
	- - 'Laurin' ♀H7	CKen NWad SLim WGor
	- - 'Lilliput'	CKen EFry NLar NWad NWea SPoG WGor
	- - 'Piccolo'	CBcs CKen NEgg NLar SLim
	- - 'Sander's Blue'	CKen EPfP GKin LRHS MBri NLar SPoG
	- - 'Tiny'	CKen NWad
	- 'Arneson's Blue Variegated' (v)	CKen MAsh MBri SLim
	- 'Biesenthaler Frühling'	CKen SLim
	- 'Blue Planet'	CKen IVic NLar
	- 'Coerulea'	NEgg
	- 'Cy's Wonder'	CKen
	- 'Dendroforma Gold'	CKen
	- 'Echiniformis' ♀H7	CKen GKin NLar
	- 'Goldilocks'	CKen
	- 'Jalako Gold' **new**	NLar
I	- 'Julian Potts Monstrosa'	NLar
§	- 'Nana'	CKen
	- 'Pendula'	CKen SLim
	- 'Pixie'	CKen
	- 'Pixie Dust'	CKen NLar
	- 'Rainbow's End' (v)	CKen NLar SPoG
	- 'Sleeping Giant'	NLar
	- 'Spring Surprise'	CKen
	glehnii 'Sasanosei'	CKen
	- 'Shimezusei'	CKen
	jezoensis	CKen CMen NLar NWea
	- 'Aurea'	SLim
	- subsp. ***hondoensis***	CMen
	- 'Marianbad'	CKen
	- 'Yatsabusa'	CKen CMen
	koraiensis	CDul NLar NWea
	kosteri 'Glauca'	see *P. pungens* 'Koster'
	koyamae 'Bedgebury Blue'	SLim
	- 'Bedgebury Cascade'	NLar SLim
	likiangensis	CDul CMCN CTho EBtc EPfP
	- var. ***balfouriana***	see *P. likiangensis* var. *rubescens*
§	- var. ***rubescens***	NLar SLim WHor
	mariana	EPfP NWea
	- 'Austria Broom'	CKen
	- 'Bill Archer'	NWad
	- 'Blue Teardrop'	CKen
	- 'Doumetii'	NLar
	- 'Fastigiata'	CKen
	- 'Nana' ♀H7	CDoC CKen CMac CMen EFry EPfP GEdr MAsh MGos MMuc NHol NWad NWea SCoo SEND SLim SPoG
I	- 'Pygmaea'	CKen NWad
	meyeri	CTho

morrisonicola	CKen
omorika 🏆H7	CBcs CCVT CDul CJun CMCN CMac CTho EPfP MMuc NWea SEND SEWo WCFE WHar
- 'de Ruyter'	IVic NEgg
- 'Frohnleiten'	CKen
- 'Frondenberg'	CKen
- 'Halone'	CKen
- 'Karel'	CKen
- 'Minimax'	CKen
- 'Nana' 🏆H7	LRHS NEgg SLim WCFE
- 'Pendula' 🏆H7	CDoC MBlu SLim SSta
- 'Pendula Bruns'	MBlu NLar SLim SMad
- 'Peve Tijn'	NLar
- 'Pimoko'	CKen NEgg NLar SLim
- 'Pimpf'	IVic
- 'Pygmy'	CKen
- 'Schneverdingen'	CKen
- 'Tijn'	CKen SLim
- 'Treblitsch'	CKen NLar SLim
- 'Tremonia'	NLar
orientalis 🏆H7	CDul IDee NWea WThu
- 'Aurea' (v) 🏆H7	CMac EFry ELan MGos MJak
- 'Aureospicata'	CDoC CTho MAsh MBlu NEgg SLim
- 'Bergman's Gem'	CKen
- 'Golden Start'	NEgg NLar SLim
- 'Juwel'	CKen NLar
- 'Kenwith'	CKen
- 'Mount Vernon'	CKen NLar
- Nana Group	GKin
- 'Professor Langner'	CKen NLar
- 'Shadow's Broom'	CMen NEgg
- 'Skylands' 🏆H7	CKen ELan MAsh MBri MGos NEgg NLar SLim
- 'Tom Thumb'	CKen NLar
- 'Wittboldt'	CKen MBri
pungens	CCVT LPar
- 'Blaukissen'	CKen
- 'Blue Diamond'	MJak SPoG
- 'Blue Pearl'	CKen NLar
- 'Donna's Rainbow' **new**	NLar
- 'Edith' 🏆H7	CKen LAst NEgg NLar NOrn SLim WMat
- 'Erich Frahm'	CCVT MAsh MBri NLar SPoG WMat
- 'Fat Albert' 🏆H7	CCVT NEgg NWea SLim SPoG
- 'Frieda'	NLar SLim
- Glauca Group	CCVT CDul CMac LPar MMuc NWea SCoo SPoG WMou
- - 'Glauca Pendula'	EUJe
- - 'Glauca Procumbens'	CKen NWea
§ - - 'Glauca Prostrata'	CMac EFry SLim
I - - 'Globosa' 🏆H7	CBcs CCVT CKen CSBt EFry EPfP LPar LRHS MAsh MBri NEgg NHol NPri NWea SBod SCoo SLim SPoG WCFE
- - 'Hoopsii' 🏆H7	CDoC CDul EFry EPfP GKin IVic LAst LPar LRHS MAsh MBri MGos MJak NEgg NLar NOrn NWea SEWo SLim SPoG SWvt WMat
- - 'Hoto'	EFry
- - 'Iseli Fastigiate'	CCVT GKin MAsh NEgg NLar SCoo SLim SPoG
§ - - 'Koster'	EFry EPfP LAst MAsh NWea SPoG WMou
- - 'Moerheimii'	EFry
- - 'Oldenburg'	NEgg NLar NWea SLim
- - 'Thomsen'	EFry
- 'Glauca Globosa'	see *P. pungens* 'Globosa'
- 'Globe'	CKen CMen
- 'Gloria'	CKen NLar SLim
- 'Hunnewelliana'	EPfP
- 'Iseli Foxtail'	LAst
- 'Lucky Strike'	CKen NLar
- 'Maigold' (v)	CKen IVic SLim
- 'Montgomery'	CKen
- 'Mrs Cesarini'	CKen NLar SLim
- 'Nimetz'	CKen
- 'Prostrata'	see *P. pungens* 'Glauca Prostrata'
- 'Saint Mary's Broom'	CKen
- 'Schovenhorst'	EFry
- 'Snowkiss'	NEgg
- 'The Blues'	CKen NLar
- 'Thuem'	EFry EPfP NEgg
- 'Waldbrunn'	CKen NLar SLim
- 'Wendy'	CKen
- 'Yvette'	NLar
purpurea	LRHS
retroflexa	NWea
schrenkiana	CMCN
sitchensis	CDul MAsh NWea
- 'Christine Berkau'	NLar
- 'Harwood Silver' **new**	SLim
- 'Nana'	NLar
- 'Papoose' **new**	SLim
- 'Pévé Wiesje'	NLar
- 'Silberzwerg'	CKen NLar SLim
- 'Strypemonde'	CKen NEgg
- 'Tenas'	CKen NLar SPoG
smithiana	CDul CTho EPfP NLar
- 'Sunray'	SLim
wilsonii	CKen NLar

Picrasma (*Simaroubaceae*)

ailanthoides	see *P. quassioides*
§ ***quassioides***	CMCN EBee EPfP WPGP

Picris (*Asteraceae*)

echioides	see *Helminthotheca echioides*

Picrorhiza (*Plantaginaceae*)

kurrooa	GPoy LEdu

Pieris (*Ericaceae*)

sp.	LPar
'Balls of Fire'	CMac
'Bert Chandler'	CMac GKin
'Firecrest' 🏆H5	GKev NLar
'Flaming Silver' (v) 🏆H5	Widely available
'Forest Flame' 🏆H5	Widely available
formosa B&SWJ 2257	WCru
- var. ***forrestii***	CWib
- - 'Charles Michael'	CExl
- - 'Jermyns'	CMac MRav
- - 'Wakehurst' 🏆H5	CAbP CDul CExl CMac COtt CTri EPfP GKin LMil LRHS MAsh MGos MMuc MRav SCob SPer SSpi WHor
Havila = 'Mouwsvila' (v)	CMac MAsh NWad
japonica	CMac GGal
- 'Astrid'	IVic
- 'Bisbee Dwarf'	WThu
- 'Bonfire' 🏆H5	CRos ELan IVic LRHS LSou MBri MGos MMuc NLar SCob SHil SLim SPoG WHar
- 'Carnaval' (v) 🏆H5	CMac COtt CSBt CWib ELan ELon EShb GEdr IBoy IVic LBuc LRHS LSRN LSou MAsh MBri MGos MRav NLar NPri SAko SCob SCoo SHil SLim SPer SPoG SWvt WFar
- 'Cavatine' 🏆H5	CMHG IVic
§ - 'Christmas Cheer'	CMac LRHS LSRN WMoo

- 'Compacta'	WAbe
- 'Cupido'	IVic MAsh MGos MMuc NLar SLim WBod WFar
- 'Debutante' ♀H5	CBcs COtt CWib ELan GBin GKin IVic LRHS MAsh MBri MGos NLar SAko SCob SCoo SSpi SWvt WFar WHar
- 'Don'	see *P. japonica* 'Pygmaea'
- 'Dorothy Wyckoff'	MAsh SSta
- 'Flaming Star'	COtt SWvt
- 'Flamingo'	CMac
I - 'Katsura'PBR	Widely available
- 'Little Heath' (v)	Widely available
- 'Little Heath Green'	CDoC CMac ELon GKin IBoy MAsh MGos MMuc NEgg SCob SPer SPoG SWvt WFar WMoo
- 'Minor'	GKev NWad WFar WThu
- 'Mountain Fire' ♀H5	Widely available
- 'Passion'PBR	CDoC COtt IVic LRHS MPkF NLar SAko SCob SPer
- 'Pink Delight' ♀H5	CAbP CNec LRHS LSRN MRav SRms
- 'Prelude' ♀H5	CSBt LRHS MAsh NLar WAbe WHar
- 'Purity' ♀H5	CBcs CDoC CMHG CMac CNec MAsh MGos NEgg NLar SLim SPer SWvt WFar WHar
§ - 'Pygmaea'	NWad WThu
- 'Ralto'PBR	MBri MRav NLar
- Ralto Rose = 'Opstal10' **new**	MPkF
- Red Mill = 'Zebris'	IVic LSou SLim SPer SSpi
- 'Rondo'	IVic
- 'Rosalinda'	MAsh
- 'Sarabande' ♀H5	GKin IVic LRHS MMuc MPkF SCob SHil
- 'Scarlett O'Hara'	CSBt NLar
- Taiwanensis Group	GKin NLar SRms WFar
- 'Temple Bells'	CSBt
- 'Valley Rose'	CSBt ELan GKin IVic LLHF MGos NLar SSpi
- 'Valley Valentine' ♀H5	CBcs CDoC CLet CMac CSBt CWib EPfP EUJe GEdr IVic LCro LMil LRHS LSRN MAsh MBri MGos MJak MMuc MPkF SAko SCob SCoo SHil SLim SPer SPoG SWvt
- 'Variegata' misapplied	see *P. japonica* 'White Rim'
- 'Variegata' ambig.	SCob
- 'Variegata' (Carrière) Bean (v)	EPfP LRHS MRav WHar
- 'Wada's Pink'	see *P. japonica* 'Christmas Cheer'
- 'White Pearl'	CMac EPfP IVic MAsh
§ - 'White Rim' (v)	CDul CMac SPlb
- 'William Buchanan'	NWad WThu
- var. ***yakushimensis***	NLar
nana	WThu
'Tilford'	CMac

Pilea (*Urticaceae*)

libanensis **new**	EShb
§ ***microphylla***	EShb
muscosa	see *P. microphylla*

Pileostegia (*Hydrangeaceae*)

viburnoides	CBcs CBot CMac CRHN EBee ELan EPfP EUJe GCal GGal IDee LHop LPfy LRHS MGos MMuc MRav NLar SEND SLon SPer SPoG SSpi SSta WCot WPGP WPat WSHC
- B&SWJ 3565	WCru
- B&SWJ 7132	WCru
- B&SWJ 3570 from Taiwan	WCru

Pilosella (*Asteraceae*)

§ ***aurantiaca***	CArn ELan IRos LEdu LPot LRHS MHer MNHC NBid SIde SPhx SRms WCot WHer WMoo WOut WSFF
§ - subsp. ***carpathicola***	MMuc
§ ***officinarum***	NRya
tardans	CFis

Pilularia (*Marsileaceae*)

globulifera	MSKA

Pimelea (*Thymelaeaceae*)

coarctata	see *P. prostrata*
drupacea	ECou IArd IDee SAko
ferruginea	ECou SVen WThu
- 'Magenta Mist'	MOWG
oreophila	WThu
§ ***prostrata***	CTri EPot
tomentosa	LRHS

Pimpinella (*Apiaceae*)

anisum	SVic
major	LEdu
- 'Rosea'	Widely available
minima rosea	NDov
saxifraga	CHab WSFF
tripartita PAB 6112	LEdu WPGP

pineapple see *Ananas comosus*

pineapple guava see *Acca sellowiana*

Pinellia (*Araceae*)

cordata	CAby CDes ECho GKev LEdu WCot WCru
pedatisecta	CCon CDes GKev MRav WCot
pinnatisecta	see *P. tripartita*
ternata	EBee ECho EWld GEdr NLar WCot
- B&SWJ 3532	WCru
§ ***tripartita***	CExl ECho GKev LTro WCot
- B&SWJ 1102	WCru
- 'Dragon Tails' (v)	SKHP
- 'Purple Face'	WCru

Pinguicula (*Lentibulariaceae*)

ehlersiae	EFEx SPlb
esseriana ♀H1c	EFEx
grandiflora ♀H4	ECho EECP EFEx EWld NLos NRya
longifolia subsp. ***longifolia***	EFEx
moranensis var. ***caudata***	EFEx
- ***moreana***	EFEx
- ***superba***	EFEx
vulgaris	EFEx WHer

pinkcurrant see *Ribes rubrum* (P)

Pinus ✿ (*Pinaceae*)

sp.	LPar
albicaulis 'Flinck'	CKen
- 'Nana'	see *P. albicaulis* 'Noble's Dwarf'
- 'No 3'	CKen
§ - 'Noble's Dwarf'	CKen
aristata ambig.	LRHS
aristata Engelm.	CDul CMen WHor
- 'Bashful'	CKen NLar
- 'Cecilia'	CKen
- 'Jeff'	NLar

	- 'Kohout's Mini'	CKen
	- 'Sherwood Compact'	CKen MAsh
	- 'Silver Love'	NLar
	- 'So Tight'	CKen
	armandii	CDoC CDul CMCN EPfP LRHS WPGP
	- 'Gold Tip'	CKen
	austriaca	see *P. nigra* subsp. *nigra*
	ayacahuite	CKen
	- var. ***veitchii***	EBee WPGP
	balfouriana dwarf	CKen
	banksiana	CDul NWea
	- 'Chippewa'	CKen
I	- 'Compacta'	CKen
	- 'H.J. Welch'	CKen
	- 'Neponset'	CKen
	- 'Schneverdingen'	CKen NEgg NLar
	bhutanica	WPGP
	bungeana	CDul EPfP MBlu
	- 'Diamant'	CKen NLar
	- 'June's Broom'	CKen
	canariensis	IDee
	cembra	CAgr CDul EPfP MJak MMuc NWea
	- 'Aurea'	see *P. cembra* 'Aureovariegata'
§	- 'Aureovariegata' (v)	NLar SLim
	- 'Barnhourie'	CKen
	- 'Blue Mound'	CKen
	- 'Compacta Glauca'	NLar
I	- 'David'	NLar
	- 'Inverleith'	CKen
	- 'Jermyns'	CKen
	- 'King's Dwarf'	CKen
	- 'Ortler'	CKen
	- 'Stricta'	CKen
	- witches' broom	CKen
	cembroides NJM 09.022A	WPGP
	contorta	CBcs CDoC CDul NWea SPlb
	- 'Asher'	CKen
	- 'Chief Joseph' ♀H7	CKen MAsh NLar SLim
	- var. ***latifolia***	CDul
	- 'Spaan's Dwarf'	CKen MBri SLim
	- 'Taylor's Sunburst'	CKen NLar
	coulteri	EPfP SKHP
	densiflora	CDul CMCN EUJe
	- 'Alice Verkade' ♀H7	CMen EUJe LPar LRHS MAsh MBri NEgg NLar
	- 'Golden Ghost'	NLar
	- 'Jim Cross'	CKen
	- 'Low Glow'	CKen NEgg SBod SLim SPoG
	- 'Oculus-draconis' (v)	NLar SLim
	- 'Pendula'	CKen MBlu NEgg SLim
I	- 'Pygmaea'	WHor
	- 'Umbraculifera'	CMen GKin SSta
	- 'Vibrant'	NLar
	× ***densithunbergii*** 'Jane Kluis' ♀H7	CMen LAst LRHS NLar SLim SPoG
	edulis	CMCN
	- 'Juno'	CKen
	elliottii var. ***densa***	CKen
	fenzeliana	CKen
	flexilis 'Blackfoot'	NLar
	- 'Cheyenne'	NLar
	- 'Extra Blue'	NLar
	- 'Firmament'	NLar SLim WMat
	- 'Glenmore Dwarf'	CKen
	- 'Nana'	CKen
I	- 'Pygmaea'	NLar
	- 'Red Elk'	NLar
	- 'Ririe'	CKen MAsh
	- 'Tarryall'	CKen
	- 'Vanderwolf's Pyramid'	NLar
	- WB No 1	CKen
	- WB No 2	CKen
	greggii	CDul EBtc
	griffithii McClell.	see *P. wallichiana*
	halepensis	SEND
§	***heldreichii***	CDul EPfP GKin NWea SLim WMat
	- 'Aureospicata'	NLar
	- 'Compact Gem' ♀H7	CDoC CKen EUJe MBri NEgg SLim
	- 'Dolce Dorme'	CKen
	- 'Green Pyramid' **new**	NLar
	- 'Groen'	CKen
	- var. ***leucodermis***	see *P. heldreichii*
	- 'Malink'	CKen IVic SAko SLim
	- 'Ottocek'	CKen
	- 'Pygmy'	CKen
	- 'Satellit' ♀H7	CKen EUJe LRHS NEgg NLar SLim
	- 'Schmidtii'	see *P. heldreichii* 'Smidtii'
§	- 'Smidtii' ♀H7	CDoC CKen CMen EUJe LRHS MBri NEgg NLar SAko SLim SPoG
	- 'Zwerg Schneverdingen'	CKen SLim
	× ***holfordiana***	WPGP
	jeffreyi	CMCN CTho NWea
	- 'Joppi'	CKen SLim
	koraiensis	GKin LEdu SLim
	- 'Bergman'	CKen
	- 'Blue Ball'	CKen
	- 'Dragon Eye'	CKen SLim
	- 'Jack Corbit'	CKen
	- 'Shibamichi' (v)	CKen
	- 'Silveray'	NLar
	- 'Silvergrey'	CKen
	- 'Spring Grove'	CKen
	- 'Winton'	CKen NLar
	leucodermis	see *P. heldreichii*
	monophylla 'Miney'	NLar
	- 'Wrinkle'	NLar
	montezumae 'Sheffield Park'	SLim
	monticola 'Ondulata'	NLar
	- 'Pendula'	CKen
	- 'Pygmy'	see *P. monticola* 'Raraflora'
§	- 'Raraflora'	CKen
	- 'Windsor Dwarf'	CKen
	mugo	CArn CBcs CDul CMac EFry EPfP LPar MAsh MGos MJak MNHC NWea SCob WBor
	- 'Allgäu'	CKen
	- 'Benjamin'	CKen LRHS SAko
	- 'Bisley Green'	NLar
	- 'Bonita' **new**	LRHS
	- 'Brownie'	CKen
	- 'Carsten' ♀H7	CDoC CKen ELan EPfP LRHS MAsh MBri NEgg SAko SCoo SLim SPoG
	- 'Chameleon'	NLar
	- 'Corley's Mat'	CKen LAst MGos
	- 'Devon Gem'	NEgg
	- 'Dezember Gold'	IVic NLar SLim
	- 'Flanders Belle'	SLim
	- 'Gnom'	CDul EFry ELan GKin LRHS MAsh MGos NEgg NLar SBod SCoo
	- 'Gold Star'	CMen LRHS SLim
	- 'Golden Glow'	CKen NLar SCoo SLim SPoG
	- 'Hana'	NLar
	- 'Hesse'	SCoo
	- 'Hoersholm'	CKen
	- 'Hulk'	CKen
	- 'Humpy' ♀H7	CKen CMen MAsh MBri NEgg SCoo SLim
	- 'Ironsides'	CKen

	- 'Jacobsen'	CKen NLar SLim
	- 'Janovsky'	CKen
	- 'Kissen' ♀H7	CKen EPfP MBri NHol SLim
	- 'Kleiner Wimbachi'	NLar
	- 'Kobold'	NEgg
	- 'Krauskopf'	CKen
	- 'Laarheide'	SPoG
	- 'Laurin'	CKen
	- 'March'	CKen
	- 'Mini Mops'	CKen
	- 'Minikin'	CKen
	- 'Mops' ♀H7	CDul CMac CMen EFry EPfP LAst LRHS MAsh MBlu MGos NEgg NWea SBod SCob SCoo SLim SPoG SSta
	- 'Mops Midget'	CMen MAsh NEgg SBod
	- var. ***mughus***	see *P. mugo* subsp. *mugo*
§	- subsp. ***mugo***	NWea SCob SGol
	- 'Mumpitz'	CKen LRHS
	- 'Northern Lights'	CKen
	- 'Ophir' ♀H7	CBcs CKen CMen EFry ELan EPfP LAst LRHS MAsh MGos NEgg SCob SCoo SLim SPoG SSta
	- 'Pal Maleter' (v)	SCoo SLim SPoG
	- 'Paul's Dwarf'	CKen
	- 'Picobello'	LRHS MAsh NHol NLar SLim
	- 'Piggelmee'	CKen IVic NLar
	- 'Pincushion'	LRHS NLar
	- Pumilio Group	CDoC EAEE EFry EPfP GQue LAst LRHS MGos MMuc NLar NWea SEND WMoo
	- var. ***rostrata***	see *P. mugo* subsp. *uncinata*
	- subsp. ***rotundata*** 'Ježek'	CKen NLar
	- 'Rushmore'	CKen
	- 'Ruze' **new**	LRHS NLar
	- 'Sherwood Compact'	NLar SLim
	- 'Spaan'	CKen
	- 'Sunshine' (v)	CKen
	- 'Suzi'	CKen
	- 'Suzy Hexe'	NWad
	- 'Trompenburg'	NEgg
	- 'Tuffet'	CKen LRHS NHol SLim
	- 'Uelzen'	CKen NLar
§	- subsp. ***uncinata***	CDul LPal NWea
	- - 'Adam' **new**	NLar
	- - 'Etschtal'	CKen
	- - 'Grüne Welle'	CKen SLim
	- - 'Kaktus' **new**	NLar
	- - 'Kostelnicek'	CKen
	- - 'Leuco-like'	CKen
	- - 'Offenpass'	CKen
	- - 'Paradekissen'	CKen
	- - 'Süsse Perle'	CKen
	- 'Varella'	CKen IArd LPal NLar SCoo SLim
	- 'White Tip'	CKen
	- 'Winter Gold'	EFry ELan EPfP EUJe LAst LPal LRHS MGos MJak NHol SSta
	- 'Winter Sun'	MAsh NLar
	- 'Winzig'	CKen
	- 'Yellow Tip' (v)	NHol
	- 'Zundert'	CKen SPoG
	- 'Zwergkugel'	CKen
	muricata	CDoC EBtc NWea
	nigra	CBcs CDul CLnd CMac CTri EUJe LPal MGos MRav SGol WMou
	- var. ***austriaca***	see *P. nigra* subsp. *nigra*
	- 'Bambino'	CKen
	- 'Black Prince' ♀H7	CKen GQue NEgg SLim WMat
	- 'Bobo'	CKen
	- var. ***calabrica***	see *P. nigra* subsp. *laricio*
	- 'Cebennensis Nana'	CKen
	- var. ***corsicana***	see *P. nigra* subsp. *laricio*
	- 'Frank'	CKen NLar SLim
	- 'Green Tower'	NLar
	- 'Hornibrookiana'	CKen
	- 'Komet'	IVic NLar SLim
§	- subsp. ***laricio***	CCVT CDoC CDul CMac ECrN IVic MMuc NWea SEND
	- - 'Aurea'	MBlu
	- - 'Bobby McGregor'	CKen
	- - 'Globosa Viridis'	NEgg
	- - 'Goldfingers'	NLar
	- - 'Pygmaea'	CKen NEgg
	- - 'Wurstle'	CKen
	- subsp. ***maritima***	see *P. nigra* subsp. *laricio*
	- 'Moseri'	CKen LRHS MAsh NEgg NLar
§	- subsp. ***nigra***	CCVT CDoC CJun CLnd CTho LBuc LRHS MMuc NWea SCob SEND SEWo SGol
	- - 'Birte'	CKen
	- - 'Bright Eyes'	NEgg SLim
	- - 'Schovenhorst'	CKen
	- - 'Skyborn'	CKen
	- - 'Strypemonde'	CKen NEgg
	- - 'Yaffle Hill'	CKen
	- 'Obelisk'	CKen NLar
	- 'Oregon Green'	CKen
	- 'Pierrick Bregéon' PBR	LRHS
	- 'Richard'	CKen SLim
	- 'Spielberg'	SAko
	oocarpa	EBtc
	palustris	CDoC CDul IVic SKHP SSpi
	parviflora	CDul NEgg SPlb
	- 'Aaba-jo'	CKen
	- 'Adcock's Dwarf' ♀H7	CDoC CKen NEgg SBod SLim
	- 'Al Fordham'	CKen
	- 'Aoi'	CKen CMen NLar
	- 'Ara-kawa'	CKen CMen
	- 'Atco-goyo'	CKen
	- Azuma-goyo Group	CKen CMen LRHS
I	- 'Baasch's Form'	CKen NLar
	- 'Bergman'	MAsh
	- 'Blue Angel'	LRHS MBlu
	- 'Blue Giant'	CDul IArd MBlu SAko
	- 'Blue Lou'	NLar
	- 'Bonnie Bergman' ♀H7	CDoC CKen EPfP LRHS NHol NLar
	- 'Catherine Elizabeth' **new**	CKen
	- 'Chikusa Goten'	IArd SAko
	- 'Dai-ho'	CKen
	- 'Daisetsusan'	CKen
	- 'Dendo'	NLar
	- 'Dougal'	CKen
	- 'Floppy Joe'	NLar
	- 'Fukai' (v)	CKen NHol NLar WBor
	- 'Fukiju'	CKen
	- Fukushima-goyo Group	CKen CMen
	- 'Fuku-zu-mi'	CKen IVic
	- 'Fu-shiro'	CKen
	- 'Gimborn's Ideal'	IVic
	- 'Gin-sho-chuba'	CKen
	- Glauca Group	LRHS MAsh MBlu NEgg SGol SKHP
I	- 'Glauca Nana'	CKen
	- 'Green Wave'	CKen
	- 'Gyok-ke-sen'	CKen
	- 'Gyo-ko-haku'	CKen
	- 'Gyokuei'	CKen
	- 'Gyokusen Sämling'	CKen NLar
	- 'Gyo-ku-sui'	CKen CMen

- 'H2'	CKen
- 'Hagaromo Seedling'	CKen CMen
- 'Hakko'	CKen
- 'Hatchichi'	CKen
- 'Hobbit'	NWad
- 'Ibo-can'	CKen CMen
- 'Ichi-no-se'	CKen
- 'Iri-fune'	CKen
- Ishizuchi-goyo Group	CKen NLar
- 'Jade Tiers' **new**	LRHS
- 'Jim's Mini Curls'	CKen
- 'Ka-ho'	CKen
- 'Kanrico'	CKen
- 'Kanzan'	CKen
- 'Kiyomatsu'	CKen
- 'Kobe'	CKen
- 'Kokonoe'	CKen CMen
- 'Kokuho'	CKen
- 'Kusu-dama'	CKen
- 'Lorraine' **new**	CKen
- 'Masami'	CKen
- 'Meiko'	CKen CMen
- 'Michinoku'	CKen
- 'Momo-yama'	CKen
- 'Myo-jo'	CKen
- Nasu-goyo Group	CKen
- 'Negishi' ♀H7	CDoC CKen CMen LRHS MAsh NEgg SLim
- 'Ogon-goyo'	CKen
- 'Ogon-janome'	CKen MAsh NEgg SLim
- 'Ossorio Dwarf'	CKen
- var. ***pentaphylla***	IVic
- 'Regenhold'	CKen
- 'Richard Lee'	CKen MAsh
- 'Ryo-ku-ho'	CKen
- 'Ryu-ju'	CKen IArd NLar
- 'Sa-dai-jin'	CKen
- 'San-bo'	CKen
§ - 'Saphir'	CKen IArd SAko
- 'Schoon's Bonsai'	LRHS NHol NLar
- 'Setsugekka'	CKen
- 'Shika-shima'	CKen
- Shikoku-goyo Group **new**	LRHS
- 'Shimada'	CKen
- 'Shin Sen'	LRHS NLar
- 'Shin Sho' **new**	LRHS
- Shiobara-goyo Group	CKen
- 'Shirobana'	NLar
- 'Shizukagoten'	CKen SLim
- 'Shu-re'	CKen NLar
- 'Sieryoden'	CKen
- 'Smout'	CKen
- 'Tani-mano-uki'	CKen
- 'Tempelhof'	NOrn
- 'Tenysu-kazu'	CKen LRHS MAsh NLar
- 'Tokyo Dwarf'	CKen
- 'Tribune'	NLar
- 'Tsai's Cushion'	NLar
- 'Walker's Dwarf'	CKen
- 'Watnong'	CKen
- 'Zelkova'	CMen
- 'Zui-sho'	CKen
patula ♀H4	CBcs CDoC CHII EPfP EUJe IDee IVic NWea SBig SCoo SPlb SPoG WMat WPGP
peuce	CDul EPfP NWea
- 'Arnold Dwarf'	CKen NLar
- 'Cesarini'	CKen
- 'Daniel'	CKen
- 'Thessaloniki Broom'	CKen
pinaster	CBcs CDoC CDul CLnd EPfP GQue IVic MMuc SBod SEND
pinea ♀H5	CAgr CArn CCVT CDoC CDul CLnd CTho EPfP ETod EUJe IDee IVic LPal LPar MGos MMuc SCoo SEND SEWo SGol SLim SPlb WPGP
- 'Queensway'	CKen
ponderosa	CDul CLnd EPfP LRHS NWea
- var. ***scopulorum***	NWea
pseudostrobus	WPGP
pumila 'Buchanan'	CKen
- 'Draijer's Dwarf'	SLim
- 'Dwarf Blue'	NHol NLar
- 'Glauca' ♀H7	CDoC CKen MAsh NLar
- 'Globe'	EUJe MAsh NLar SLim
- 'Jeddeloh'	CKen
- 'Knightshayes'	CKen
- 'Pinocchio'	CKen
- 'Säntis'	CKen
- 'Saphir'	see *P. parviflora* 'Saphir'
pungens **new**	CDul
radiata	CBcs CCVT CDoC CDul CLet CLnd CMac CNWT CSde CTho CTri ECrN ELan EPfP EUJe MMuc NWea SBod SCoo WMat
- Aurea Group	CDoC ELan LRHS MAsh MBri NEgg SBod SCoo SLim SPoG WMat
- 'Bodnant'	CKen
- 'Isca'	CKen
- 'Marshwood' (v)	CKen SLim
resinosa 'Don Smith'	CKen
- 'Joel's Broom'	CKen
- 'Quinobequin'	CKen
roxburghii	EBtc
× ***schwerinii***	CDoC CKen
- 'Wiethorst' ♀H7	CKen LRHS SLim WHar WMat
sibirica 'Blue Smoke'	CKen
- 'Mariko'	CKen
strobiformis 'Coronado'	CKen
- 'Loma Linda'	CKen SLim
strobus	CBcs CCVT CDul CLnd CMen EPfP LPar LRHS MGos MMuc NWea SEND
§ - 'Alba'	SLim
- 'Amelia's Dwarf'	CKen NLar
- 'Angel Falls'	CKen
- 'Anna Fiele'	CKen MBri NEgg NLar
- 'Bergman's Mini'	CKen SLim
- 'Bergman's Pendula Broom'	CKen
I - 'Bergman's Sport of Prostrata'	CKen
- 'Beth'	CKen
- 'Bloomer's Dark Globe'	CKen
- 'Blue Shag' ♀H7	EUJe NLar SCoo SLim
- 'Brevifolia'	CKen
- 'Cesarini'	CKen
- 'Densa'	CKen
- 'E.R.'	NLar
- 'Ed's Broom'	CKen
- 'Elkins Dwarf'	CKen NEgg
- 'Fastigiata'	CDul CKen SAko
- 'Golden Candles'	NLar
- 'Golden Showers'	NLar
- 'Green Curls'	CKen
- 'Green Twist'	NLar
- 'Greg'	CKen
- 'Hershey'	CKen
- 'Hillside Gem'	CKen

	- 'Horsford'	CKen NLar SLim
	- 'Horsford Sister'	CKen
	- 'Jamaican Curls' **new**	CKen
	- 'Julian Pott'	CKen NLar
	- 'Julian's Dwarf'	CKen
	- 'Krügers Lilliput'	LRHS NLar SLim
	- 'Louie'	CKen MAsh NLar
	- 'Mary Butler'	CKen NLar
	- 'Merrimack'	CKen
	- 'Minima' ♀H7	CDoC CDul CKen EUJe LRHS MBlu NEgg NWea SLim SPoG
	- 'Minuta'	CKen LRHS
§	- Nana Group	NEgg SEWo
	- 'Nana'	see *P. strobus* Nana Group
	- 'Nana Compacta'	LRHS NEgg
	- 'Niagara Falls' **new**	CKen
	- 'Nivea'	see *P. strobus* 'Alba'
	- 'Northway Broom'	CKen
	- 'Pacific Sunrise'	NLar
	- 'Paul Waxman' **new**	NLar
	- 'Pendula'	CKen IDee LRHS MBlu
I	- 'Pendula Broom'	CKen
	- 'Prostrata'	SLim
	- 'Pygmaea' **new**	LRHS
	- 'Radiata'	CTri
I	- 'Radiata Aurea'	NEgg
	- 'Reinshaus'	CKen
	- 'Sayville'	CKen
	- 'Sea Urchin'	CKen LRHS MAsh NLar SLim
	- 'Secrest'	LRHS NLar
	- 'Stowe Pillar'	NLar SLim
	- 'Tiny Kurls'	CKen MAsh
	- 'Torulosa'	MBlu
	- 'Uncatena'	CKen
	- 'Verkade's Broom'	CKen NEgg
	- 'White Mountain'	EUJe MBlu NLar SLim
	sylvestris	Widely available
	- 'Abergeldie'	CKen
	- 'Alderly Edge'	CMen
	- 'Andorra'	CKen
	- 'Argentea Compacta' **new**	LRHS
	- Aurea Group	CDul CKen CMac CMen EFry ELan EUJe MAsh MBlu MJak NEgg NWea SCoo SLim SSta WMat
	- 'Avondene'	CKen
	- 'Bergfield'	CMen
	- 'Beuvronensis' ♀H7	CMen MGos NEgg SLim
	- 'Buchanan's Gold'	CKen
	- 'Burghfield'	CMen
	- 'Chantry Blue'	CMen EFry MAsh MBri MGos NEgg NLar SCoo SLim SPoG WMat
	- 'Clumber Blue'	CKen
	- 'Dereham'	CKen NLar
	- 'Doone Valley'	CKen NEgg
	- 'Edwin Hillier'	CMen NEgg SLim WMat WPGP
	- Fastigiata Group	CDoC CDul CKen CMac CMen GQue LPar LRHS SCoo SLim WCFE
	- 'Frensham' ♀H7	CKen LRHS MAsh MBri MGos
	- 'Gold Coin' ♀H7	CDul CKen EPfP MAsh NEgg NLar SPoG WGor
	- 'Gold Medal'	CKen SLim
	- 'Grand Rapids'	CKen
	- 'Gwydyr Castle'	CKen
	- 'Hillside Creeper'	CKen SLim
	- 'Humble Pie'	CKen
	- 'Jeremy'	CKen NEgg
	- 'John Boy'	CMen
	- 'Kelpie'	SLim
	- 'Kenwith'	CKen
	- 'Lakeside Dwarf'	CMen
	- 'Lodge Hill'	CMen MAsh NEgg SLim
	- 'Longmoor'	CKen
	- 'Martham'	CKen CMen
	- 'Mitsch Weeping'	CKen
	- 'Nana' misapplied	see *P. sylvestris* 'Watereri'
	- 'Nana Compacta'	CMen
§	- 'Nisbet's Gem'	CKen CMen NLar SLim
	- 'Padworth'	CMen
	- 'Perkeo'	NLar
	- 'Piskowitz'	CKen
	- 'Pixie'	CKen
I	- 'Prostrata'	NEgg SLim
	- 'Repens'	CKen
	- 'Saint George'	CKen
	- 'Sandringham'	NLar
	- 'Saxatilis'	CKen CMen
	- subsp. ***scotica***	GQue NWea
	- 'Scott's Dwarf'	see *P. sylvestris* 'Nisbet's Gem'
	- 'Sentinel'	CKen
	- 'Skjak I'	CKen
	- 'Skjak II'	CKen SLim
	- 'Spaan's Slow Column'	CKen SLim
	- 'Tage'	CKen
	- 'Tanya'	CKen
	- 'Tilhead'	CKen
	- 'Treasure'	CKen MBri
	- 'Trefrew Quarry'	CKen
	- 'Troll Guld'	NLar
	- 'Umbraculifera' **new**	NEgg
	- 'Vargguld'	CKen
§	- 'Watereri'	CNWT EFry LAst LPar LRHS MJak NLar SCob SCoo
	- 'Westonbirt'	CKen CMen MAsh
	- 'Wintergold'	LPar NEgg SPer
	- 'Wittichenau' **new**	CKen
	taeda	EPfP WPGP
	taiwanensis	CDul EPfP
	thunbergii	CDul CLnd CMCN CMen ELan GQue IDee MMuc SBod
	- 'Akame'	CKen CMen
	- 'Akame Yatsabusa'	CMen
	- 'Aocha-matsu' (v)	CKen CMen
	- 'Arakawa-sho'	CKen CMen
	- 'Banshosho'	CKen CMen
	- 'Beni-kujaku'	CKen CMen
	- 'Compacta'	CKen CMen
	- var. ***corticosa*** 'Fuji'	CMen
	- - 'Iihara'	CMen
	- 'Dainagon'	CKen CMen
	- 'Eechee-nee'	CKen
	- 'Hayabusa'	CMen
	- 'Iwai'	CMen
	- 'Janome' (v)	CMen
	- 'Katsuga'	CMen
	- 'Kotobuki'	CKen CMen
	- 'Koyosho'	CMen
	- 'Kujaku'	CKen CMen
	- 'Kyokko'	CKen CMen
	- 'Kyushu'	CKen CMen
	- 'Mikawa'	CMen MBlu
	- 'Miyajuna'	CKen CMen
	- 'Nishiki-ne'	CKen CMen
	- 'Nishiki-tsusaka'	CMen
	- 'Ogi-matsu'	CKen
	- 'Ōgon'	CMen NLar SLim
	- 'Porky'	CKen CMen
§	- 'Sayonara' ♀H7	CMen MAsh NEgg NLar
	- 'Senryu'	CKen CMen
	- 'Shinsho'	CKen CMen
	- 'Shio-guro'	CKen CMen

- 'Suchiro' NEgg
- 'Suchiro Yatabusa' CKen CMen
- 'Sunsho' CKen CMen
- 'Taihei' CKen CMen
I - 'Thunderhead' ♈H7 CDoC CKen CMen NLar SLim
- 'W.B.' CKen
- 'Yatsubusa' see *P. thunbergii* 'Sayonara'
- 'Ye-i-kan' CKen
- 'Yoshimura' CMen
- 'Yumaki' CKen CMen

uncinata see *P. mugo* subsp. *uncinata*
virginiana 'Wate's Golden' CKen NLar
§ ***wallichiana*** ♈H6 Widely available
- 'Densa Hill' SLim
- 'Frosty' CKen
- 'Nana' ♈H6 CKen NLar SCoo SLim
- 'Umbraculifera' MAsh
- var. ***wallichiana*** EUJe
- 'Zebrina' (v) MBlu NHol NLar SMad

yunnanensis LRHS

Piper (*Piperaceae*)

auritum GPoy LEdu
excelsum see *Macropiper excelsum*
heydei B&SWJ 10445 WCru

Piptanthus (*Papilionaceae*)

forrestii see *P. nepalensis*
laburnifolius see *P. nepalensis*
§ ***nepalensis*** CBcs CDul CSpe EAla EBee ELan EPfP LAst LHop LRHS MGil MGos MPie MSCN NBid NLar SBrt SPer SRms WCot WPat
aff. ***nepalensis*** SWvt
tomentosus CFil

Pistacia (*Anacardiaceae*)

atlantica XSen
chinensis CBcs EBee EBtc EPfP WPGP
lentiscus CArn CBcs EBee EUJe LRHS SEND SVen XSen
terebinthus XSen
- NJM 11.004 WPGP

Pistia (*Araceae*)

stratiotes MSKA NPer SCoo

Pitavia (*Rutaceae*)

punctata IArd SAko

Pitcairnia (*Bromeliaceae*)

bergii CHII
heterophylla WCot
recurvata WCot
ringens WCot

Pittosporum ✿ (*Pittosporaceae*)

sp. ETod LPar
anomalum CDoC CTsd ECou ELon MOWG SEle
- (f) ECou
- (m) ECou
- 'Falcon' ECou

'Arundel Green' (f) ♈H4 CDoC ELon EPfP ETod LRHS LSRN MAsh MBri SCob SHil SLim SWvt
bicolor CPne GQui WPGP
buchananii SVen
colensoi ECou
- 'Cobb' (f) ECou
- 'Wanaka' (m) ECou

'Collaig Silver' EPfP LRHS MAsh SAko SLim
crassifolium CBcs CSde CTsd ECou
- 'Havering Dwarf' (f) ECou
- 'Napier' (f) ECou
- 'Variegatum' (v) CBcs WPat

'Crinkles' (f) ECou SVen
daphniphylloides EBee ELan SAko WPGP
- B&SWJ 6789 WCru
- CWJ 12404 WCru
- RWJ 9913 WCru

'Dark Delight' (m) ECou
'Essex' (f/v) ECou
eugenioides CSam CSde SEND
- 'Platinum' (v) ELan
- 'Variegatum' (v) ♈H4 CBcs CDoC CDul CLet CMac CSde EHoe ELan EPfP EUJe GQui IArd LAst LHop LRHS MBri MGos NLar SAko SCob SEND SHil SKHP SLim SVen

'Garnettii' (v) ♈H4 Widely available
glabratum B&SWJ 11685 WCru
heterophyllum ECou ECrN ELan EPfP EWes LRHS MMHG SEND
- variegated (v) EBtc ECou LRHS WSHC

'Holbrook' (v) CSam
'Humpty Dumpty' ECou
illicioides var. ***angustifolium*** B&SWJ 6771 WCru
- - RWJ 9846 WCru
- var. ***illicioides*** B&SWJ 6712 WCru
- - PAB 9004 LEdu WPGP

× ***intermedium*** CWib SWvt
- 'Craxten' (f) ECou

michiei ECou
- (f) ECou
- (m) ECou
- 'Jack' (m) ECou
- 'Jill' (f) ECou

'Nanum Variegatum' see *P. tobira* 'Variegatum'
obcordatum ECou
oblongilimbum DJHV 06137 WCru
'Oliver Twist' ETod LRHS LSRN SCob SCoo
omeiense EWes SKHP
- VdL 80626 WPGP

pimeleoides var. ***reflexum*** (m) ECou
ralphii CMCN CTsd ECou
- 'Green Globe' SKHP
- 'Variegatum' (v) LRHS SKHP WPGP

ralphii × ***tenuifolium*** ECou
'Saundersii' (v) SCoo
'Tadina Gold' ETod
tenuifolium Widely available
- 'Abbotsbury Gold' (f/v) Widely available
- 'Atropurpureum' CBcs ELan ETod
- 'Brockhill Compact' LRHS SAko SLim
- 'Cornish Mist' CTsd
- 'County Park' EUJe
- 'County Park Dwarf' ECou

§ - 'Eila Keightley' (v) CMHG
- 'Elizabeth' (m/v) CAbP CBcs CDoC CMac CNec ECou EHoe EPfP EShb ETod EUJe IArd LRHS LSRN LSou MAsh MBri MGos MRav SCob SCoo SEND SHil SLim SPoG
- 'French Lace' CBcs CSde ELan SEND WFar

- 'Gold Star'	CBcs CChe CDoC COtt EAEE EHoe ELan EPfP LAst LBMP LPar LRHS MAsh MBri MGos SBod SCob SCoo SLim SPer SPoG SWvt WMoo WRHF
- 'Golden King'	CDoC CMHG CMac CSBt EPfP LRHS MAsh MBri MGos SHil SLim SPoG SRms
- 'Golf Ball' PBR	CBcs CDoC EPfP EUJe LCro LPfy LRHS LSRN MBri MGos SCob SHil
- 'Green Elf'	ECou
- 'Green Thumb'	CMac ELan
- 'Irene Paterson' (m/v) ♀H4	Widely available
- 'John Flanagan'	see *P. tenuifolium* 'Margaret Turnbull'
- 'Limelight' (v)	CSBt EBtc EPfP LHop LRHS LSRN MGos SLim SPoG
- 'Loxhill Gold'	IArd LRHS SGol SHil
- 'Malahide' (v) **new**	MGos
§ - 'Margaret Turnbull' (v)	CBcs ECou ELan EPfP EWes GKin LHop LRHS MGos SGol SHil
- 'Marjory Channon' (v)	ELan EPfP LRHS
- 'Moonlight' (v)	CBcs EHoe LRHS MRav SCob
- 'Mountain Green'	CMac
- 'Pompom'	EBee IVic LRHS
- 'Purpureum' (m)	CMac CSBt CSam CTri EPfP EUJe EWoo LAst LRHS LSRN MAsh MMuc NEgg SCob SEND SHil SLim SPer SPoG SRms WFar WSHC
- 'Silver Magic' (v)	CBcs COtt EPfP LRHS SCob SEle SRkn
- 'Silver Princess' (f)	ECou
- 'Silver Queen' (f/v) ♀H4	Widely available
- 'Silver Sheen' (m)	CBcs CJun CLet CMac COtt ECou LRHS
- 'Stevens Island'	CBcs CDoC CJun
- 'Stirling Gold' (f/v)	ECou EWes
- 'Sunburst'	see *P. tenuifolium* 'Eila Keightley'
- 'Tandara Gold' (v)	CBcs CDoC CLet COtt CSBt ECou EHoe ELan ELon EPfP ETod EUJe LBMP LRHS MAsh MBri MGos SCob SCoo SLim SPoG WCot
- 'Tiki' (m)	CBcs
- 'Tom Thumb' ♀H4	Widely available
- 'Tresederi' (f/m)	CTsd
- 'Variegatum' (m/v)	CBcs CDoC CLet CSBt EAEE ECou ELon ETod LCro LRHS LSRN MGos MSwo SCob SGbt SHil SLim SPer SWvt WHar
- 'Victoria' (v)	CBcs LRHS LSRN MGos SHil SLim
- 'Warnham Gold' (m) ♀H3	CBcs CDoC CMac CSde CWib EBee ECou ELan EPfP GKin IVic LRHS MAsh MGos SHil SLim SPoG SSpi SVen WCot
- 'Wendle Channon' (m/v)	CBcs CMHG CMac COtt CSBt EHoe EPfP ETod LBMP LRHS MAsh SGol SLim WSHC
- 'Wrinkled Blue'	CBcs CDoC EPfP ETod LRHS MAsh MRav SPoG
tobira ♀H3	Widely available
- B&SWJ 12758	WCru
* - 'Nanum'	CBcs CDoC CLet CMac EAEE ELan EPfP ETod EUJe LCro LHop LPal LPar LRHS MGos MOWG SCob SLim SPer SPoG
- 'Tall 'n' Tough'	WPGP
§ - 'Variegatum' (v) ♀H4	CBcs CDoC CLet CMac CSde CWib ELan EPfP EUJe IVic LHop LRHS LSRN MGos NLar SCob SEND SKHP SLim SLon SPer SPoG WSHC
'Trim's Hedger'	CBod CTho
truncatum	CExl ELan EPfP SKHP
viridiflorum	EShb

Pityrogramma (*Pteridaceae*)

trifoliata	WCot

Plagianthus (*Malvaceae*)

betulinus	see *P. regius*
lyallii	see *Hoheria lyallii*
§ ***regius***	CBcs

Plagiorhegma see *Jeffersonia*

Plantago (*Plantaginaceae*)

asiatica 'Variegata' (v)	NBro
coronopus	CAgr
holosteum	GKev
lanceolata	CAgr CArn CHab WHfH WSFF
major	CArn GPoy WSFF
- 'Atropurpurea'	see *P. major* 'Rubrifolia'
- 'Bowles's Variety'	see *P. major* 'Rosularis'
- 'Brenda'	CNat
- 'Everywhere I Glow'	CNat
- 'Rosenstolz'	CFis
§ - 'Rosularis'	CBre CFis CSpe EBee LEdu NBro NChi SPav SRms WHer
§ - 'Rubrifolia'	CBod CHid CSpe EShb LLWG MHer MMuc NBid NBro NChi SHar WMoo WPGP WSFF XLum
media	CHab MHer
nivalis	GEdr
rosea	see *P. major* 'Rosularis'
triandra 'Wanaka'	IMou

Platanthera (*Orchidaceae*)

bifolia	NLAp
chlorantha	NLAp
hologlottis	EFEx
metabifolia	EFEx

Platanus ✿ (*Platanaceae*)

sp.	LPar
× ***acerifolia***	see *P.* × *hispanica*
§ × ***hispanica*** ♀H6	CBcs CCVT CDul CLnd CMCN EBee ECrN ELan EPfP LAst LPar MGos MMuc NWea SCob SEND SEWo SGol SPer WMat WMou
- 'Bloodgood'	CTho
- 'Pyramidalis'	ECrN
orientalis	CCVT CDul CLnd CMCN CTho EPfP SCob WPGP
- PAB 346	LEdu
- 'Cuneata'	ECrN
§ - f. ***digitata*** ♀H6	CCVT CDul CLnd CMCN CTho EBee EPfP ERod
- var. ***insularis***	WPGP
- 'Laciniata'	see *P. orientalis* f. *digitata*
- 'Minaret'	CDul
- 'Mirkovec'	EPfP IArd

Platycarya (*Juglandaceae*)

strobilacea	CBcs CMCN LEdu

Platycerium (*Polypodiaceae*)

alcicorne misapplied	see *P. bifurcatum*
§ ***bifurcatum*** ♀H1b	EAla XBlo
- 'Netherlands'	NLos

	ellisii new	NLos
	grande hort.	see *P. superbum*
	hilii new	NLos
	'Lemoinei'	NLos
§	***superbum*** ♀H1b	IDee NLos

Platycladus (*Cupressaceae*)

§	***orientalis*** 'Aurea Nana' ♀H6	CKen CLet CMac CSBt CWib EFry ELan EPfP LBee LRHS MGos MJak NWad NWea SGol SLim SPoG WCFE
	- 'Autumn Glow'	CKen
	- 'Beverleyensis'	NLar
	- 'Conspicua'	CKen CSBt CWib EFry
	- 'Elegantissima'	EFry LRHS
	- 'Franky Boy' ♀H6	CDoC NLar SLim SPoG
	- 'Golden Pygmy'	CKen
	- 'Juniperoides'	EFry
	- 'Kenwith'	CKen
	- 'Magnifica'	EFry
	- 'Meldensis'	CDoC CTri EFry
	- 'Minima'	EFry
	- 'Minima Glauca'	CKen
I	- 'Pyramidalis Aurea'	LBee
	- 'Rosedalis'	CKen CSBt EFry EPfP LBee
	- 'Sanderi'	WCFE
	- 'Southport'	LBee
	- 'Summer Cream'	CKen EFry

Platycodon ✿ (*Campanulaceae*)

	grandiflorus ♀H5	CLau CTri CTsd ECha ECho EPfP EWld LHop MHer SRms WHar WHoo
	- 'Albus'	ECho EPfP SPer SWvt WHar WHoo
	- Apoyama Group ♀H5	WHoo WThu
	- - 'Fairy Snow'	WHoo
	- (Astra Series) 'Astra Blue'	EPfP LHop LRHS SPoG SRot
	- - 'Astra Pink'	LRHS SPoG
	- - 'Astra White'	SPoG
	- 'Blue Pearl'	WHoo
	- 'Florist Blue'	SGSe
	- 'Florist Rose'	SGSe
	- 'Florist Snow'	SGSe
	- 'Fuji Blue'	ELon WHoo XLum
	- 'Fuji Pink'	ECho ELan LHop MRav SWvt WHoo XLum
	- 'Fuji White'	ELan ELon WHoo XLum
	- 'Hakone'	MRav WHoo
	- 'Hakone Blue'	EPfP NBre SGSe
	- 'Hakone Double Blue' (d)	ELan SRms
	- 'Hakone White'	EPfP MRav SGSe
	- 'Mariesii' ♀H5	CAby CBod CSBt EAEE ELon EPfP IBoy LPla MMuc MNHC MRav NBir NEgg SEND SPer SPlb SRms SWvt WAul WHoo
	- Mother of Pearl	see *P. grandiflorus* 'Perlmutterschale'
§	- 'Perlmutterschale'	EBee MRav
	- 'Pink Star'	EBee
	- ***pumilus***	WHoo
	- 'Sentimental Blue'	CWib XLum
	- 'Shell Pink'	see *P. grandiflorus* 'Perlmutterschale'
	- 'Willy'	XLum
	- 'Zwerg'	NBre

Platycrater (*Hydrangeaceae*)

	arguta	EBee WCru WPGP
	- B&SWJ 6266	WCru

Plecostachys (*Asteraceae*)

§	***serpyllifolia***	LAst

Plectranthus (*Lamiaceae*)

	sp.	LAst
	from Puerto Rico	CArn
	ambiguus	EOHP
	- 'Manguzuku' ♀H1c	EOHP
	- 'Nico'	EOHP
	- 'Umigoye'	EOHP
	amboinicus	EOHP LAll MNHC WJek
*	- 'Variegatus' (v)	EOHP
	- 'Well Sweep Wedgewood' (v)	EOHP
	argentatus ♀H1c	CBcs CDoC CSpe CTsd EOHP EUJe EWld GCal IDee MCot MPie SDix SRkn WHea WKif
	- 'Hill House' (v)	CHll CPne EOHP EShb MPie
	- 'Silver Shield'	EShb
	australis misapplied	see *P. verticillatus*
	barbatus	EOHP
	- 'Vicki'	CPne
	behrii	see *P. fruticosus*
	Blue Angel = 'Edelblau' (Cape Angels Series)	EOHP
	caninus	SPoG
	ciliatus	EOHP EShb EUJe SRkn
	- 'Easy Gold' (v) ♀H1c	EOHP
	- 'Richard'	CPne
	- 'Sasha' (v)	CDoC CHll ECtt EOHP EShb EWld
	'Cloud Nine'	EOHP
	coleoides 'Marginatus'	see *P. forsteri* 'Marginatus'
	- 'Variegatus'	see *P. madagascariensis* 'Variegated Mintleaf'
	Cuban oregano	EOHP
	ecklonii	EOHP
	- 'Medley Wood'	EOHP
	ernstii	EOHP
	excisus	CDes EBee IMou SBrt WPGP
	forskohlii	EOHP
§	***forsteri*** 'Marginatus'	EOHP WHea
	'Frills'	EOHP
§	***fruticosus***	EOHP EUJe
	- 'Behr's Pride'	EOHP
	- 'James' ♀H1c	EOHP EUJe
	hadiensis var. ***tomentosus***	EOHP
	- - 'Carnegie'	EOHP
	- - green-leaved	EOHP
	- - 'Penge' (v)	EOHP
	- var. ***woodii***	EOHP
	madagascariensis	EOHP
	- gold-leaved	EOHP
	- 'Lothlorien' (v)	EOHP
§	- 'Variegated Mintleaf' (v) ♀H1c	EOHP MNHC SRms
	'Marble Ruffles'	EOHP
	menthol-scented, large-leaved	EOHP
	menthol-scented, small-leaved	EOHP
	Mona Lavender = 'Plepalila'PBR ♀H1c	EOHP
	montanus	EOHP
	mutabilis	EOHP
	neochilus	CSpe
§	***oertendahlii*** ♀H1c	EBak EOHP
	- silver-leaved	EOHP
	ornatus	NPla
	- 'Pee Off'	EOHP

- variegated (v)	EOHP
prostratus	EOHP
pseudomarrubioides	EOHP
purpuratus small-leaved	EOHP
rotundifolius	LEdu
saccatus	EOHP
subsp. ***longitubus***	
- subsp. ***pondoensis***	EOHP
sinensis	LRHS
spicatus	EOHP
strigosus	EOHP
Swedish ivy	see *P. verticillatus, P. oertendahlii*
§ ***thyrsoideus***	EOHP
venteri	EOHP
§ ***verticillatus***	EOHP EWld
- 'Barberton'	EOHP
- 'Pink Surprise'	EOHP
Vick's plant	EOHP
zatarhendii	EOHP
zuluensis	CArn CDoC CPne EOHP EUJe EWld SDix SRkn WBor
- dark-leaved	EOHP
- 'Sky'	EOHP

Pleioblastus (*Poaceae*)

akebono	see *P. argenteostriatus* 'Akebono'
§ ***argenteostriatus*** 'Akebono'	ERod
§ - 'Okinadake' (v)	MWht
§ - f. ***pumilus***	EHoe ERod MMuc MWht NLar SPlb
auricomus	see *P. viridistriatus*
- 'Vagans'	see *Sasaella ramosa*
chino var. ***argenteostriatus***	see *P. argenteostriatus* 'Okinadake'
- f. ***elegantissimus***	CCon CEnt EPfP ERod EShb MMuc SBig SEND WJun WMoo
- var. ***hisauchii***	ERod MWht WJun
fortunei	see *P. variegatus* 'Fortunei'
'Gauntlettii'	see *P. argenteostriatus* f. *pumilus*
glaber 'Albostriatus'	see *Sasaella masamuneana* 'Albostriata'
§ ***hindsii***	ERod
§ ***humilis***	ENBC MWhi
- var. ***pumilus***	see *P. argenteostriatus* f. *pumilus*
linearis	ERod LRHS MWht SBig WJun WMoo
§ ***pygmaeus***	CDul CTri CTsd EHoe ELan ENBC GKev MBrN MJak MWhi NBro SCob SGol SRms WMoo
§ - 'Distichus'	CEnt ENBC EPPr MJak WMoo
§ - 'Mirrezuzume'	CExl
* - var. ***pygmaeus*** 'Mini'	MMuc SEND WCot
§ ***simonii***	LRHS MMuc MWht SEND XBlo
- 'Variegatus' (v)	LRHS SPer
§ ***variegatus*** (v) ♀H4	CBcs CDoC CDul CEnt EHoe ELan ELon ENBC EPfP LEdu LPot LRHS MBrN MJak MWht SCob SDix SLim SPlb SWvt WJun WMoo XBlo
§ - 'Fortunei' (v)	CTsd MMuc NLar SEND SGol
- 'Tsuboii' (v)	CAbb CDTJ ERod MBrN SGol WJun WMoo
§ ***viridistriatus*** ♀H5	CBcs CDoC CDul CEnt CExl CWib ECha EHoe ELon EPfP ERod GMaP LEdu LHop LRHS MJak MMuc MRav MWht NLar NWsh SCob SDix SEND SGol SPer SRms WJun WMoo XBlo
- f. ***variegatus*** (v)	CTsd SWvt WMoo

Pleione (*Orchidaceae*)

sp.	NDav
Alishan gx 'Merlin'	LYaf
- 'Mother's Day'	GEdr LYaf
- 'Mount Fuji'	LYaf
Anstice Harris gx	LYaf
Asama gx 'Red Grouse'	GEdr LYaf
Askia gx	GEdr
aurita	GEdr GKev LYaf
× ***barbarae***	IFoB LYaf
Barcena gx	LYaf
Berapi gx	WBla
- 'Purple Sandpiper'	LEdu LYaf
Brigadoon gx 'Stonechat'	LEdu
Britannia gx 'Doreen'	EPot LEdu LYaf
§ ***bulbocodioides***	CExl CFil EPot GEdr LYaf
- 'New Forest'	GEdr
§ - 'Yunnan'	GEdr IFoB
Burnsall gx	GEdr
Captain Hook gx	LYaf
Caroli gx 'Cape Robin'	LYaf
chunii	EFEx GEdr LAma LYaf
Confirmation gx	LYaf
Eastfield gx 'Purple Emperor'	LYaf
Eiger gx	LYaf
El Pico gx 'Pheasant'	LYaf
Erebus gx 'Redpoll'	GEdr
formosana ♀H3	CCon CFil CPne ECho EFEx EPot GKev LAma LCro LEdu LOPS LRHS MHer WBla WFar WPGP
- Alba Group	ECho GKev WFar
- - 'Claire'	IFoB LEdu LYaf WBla
- - 'Snow Bunting'	LEdu LYaf
- 'Cairngorm'	GKev IFoB
- 'Greenhill'	LYaf
- 'Hanka'	GKev
- 'Hayata' **new**	GKev
- Hyb 8001	IFoB
- 'Iris'	IFoB
- 'Litomysi'	GKev
- 'Pitlochry'	LYaf
- 'Polar Sun'	WBla
- (Pricei Group) 'Oriental Grace'	IFoB LYaf
- - 'Oriental Splendour'	LYaf
- 'Snow Cap'	ECho
- 'Snow White'	CExl CFil LEdu LYaf WPGP
forrestii	ECho EFEx EPot GKev LAma WBla
Fuego gx	GKev IFoB
Gerry Mundey gx	GEdr
- 'Tinney's Firs'	LYaf
Glacier Peak gx	LYaf
§ ***grandiflora***	GKev
Harlequin gx 'Norman'	LYaf
Hekla gx	IFoB WBla
- 'Locking Stumps'	GEdr
- 'Partridge'	GEdr
- 'Partridge' × **Zeus Weinstein gx**	GEdr
hookeriana	GKev WBla
humilis	GKev LYaf
- orange-red-flowered **new**	GKev
- purple-flowered **new**	GKev
Irazu gx	IFoB
- 'Cheryl'	GEdr
Jake Butterfield gx **new**	LYaf
Jorullo gx 'Long-tailed Tit'	GEdr LYaf
Keith Rattray gx 'Kelty'	LYaf

Kenya gx 'Bald Eagle' LYaf
Krakatoa gx 'Wheatear' LYaf
Lascar gx 'Dipper' LYaf
- 'Purple Finch' LYaf
Lhasa gx 'Blushes' LYaf
limprichtii ♀H3 ECho EFEx EPot GKev IFoB LEdu LYaf
Liz Shan gx 'Pretty Girl' **new** LYaf
Lyn Butterfield gx LYaf
maculata EFEx GKev
Mageik gx 'Black Kite' LYaf
Mandalay gx 'Purple Rain' LYaf
- 'Strawberry Fields' LYaf
Marion Johnson gx 'Bubs' **new** LYaf
Mauna Loa gx LYaf
- 'Glossy Starling' LYaf
Mawenzi gx LYaf
Michael Butterfield gx LYaf
Novarupta gx 'Raven' LYaf
Orinoco gx 'Gemini' GEdr
Orizaba gx GEdr
- 'Fish Eagle' LYaf
Pelee gx 'Cape Weaver' **new** LYaf
pinkepankii see *P. grandiflora*
Piton gx EPot LYaf
§ ***pleionoides*** GKev LYaf
pogonioides misapplied see *P. pleionoides*
pogonioides (Rolfe) Rolfe see *P. bulbocodioides*
praecox GKev
Quizapu gx 'Peregrine' LYaf
Rakata gx IFoB
- 'Locking Stumps' EPot GEdr
- 'Redwing' LYaf
- 'Shot Silk' GEdr LYaf
Red Colobus gx **new** LYaf
'Rossini' ECho GKev WBla
Salek gx 'Eagle Owl' LYaf
Santa Maria gx 'Nightjar' LYaf
Santorini gx LYaf
- 'Yellow Wagtail' LYaf
saxicola GKev LYaf
scopulorum EFEx LYaf
Shantung gx CCon EPot LAma
- 'Double Cream' **new** LYaf
- 'Ducat' LYaf
- 'Gerry Mundey' LYaf
- 'Muriel Harberd' ♀H3 GEdr
- 'Ridgeway' LYaf
Shasta gx LYaf
Sinope gx **new** LYaf
Sirena gx LYaf
Sorea gx GEdr
Soufrière gx GEdr
speciosa Ames & Schltr. see *P. pleionoides*
Stromboli gx WBla
- 'Fireball' CExl CFil EPot LEdu
Taal gx 'Red-tailed Hawk' LYaf
× ***taliensis*** LYaf
Tibesti gx LYaf
Toff gx LYaf
Tolima gx 'Moorhen' LEdu LYaf
Tongariro gx CPBP ECho EPot GEdr GKev LCro LEdu LOPS WBla
Ueli Wackernagel gx GEdr
- 'Pearl' LYaf
'Verdi' ECho GKev WBla
Versailles gx EPot
- 'Bucklebury' GEdr LEdu
- 'Muriel Turner' GEdr
Vesuvius gx EPot GKev
- 'Leopard' GKev LYaf
- 'Phoenix' EPot GKev LYaf
- 'Tawny Owl' GEdr
'Vivaldi' ECho GKev WBla
Volcanello gx WBla
- 'Honey Buzzard' GEdr LYaf
- 'Song Thrush' LYaf
Whakari gx LYaf
Wharfedale gx 'Pine Warbler' LYaf
yunnanensis misapplied see *P. bulbocodioides* 'Yunnan'
yunnanensis ambig. GEdr GKev LAma
Zeus Weinstein gx IFoB LYaf WCot
- 'Desert Sands' GEdr

Pleomele see *Dracaena*

Pleurospermum (*Apiaceae*)

sp. CSpe
SDR 7941 **new** GKev
SDR 7985 **new** GKev
from Nepal WCot
benthamii B&SWJ 2988 WCru
camtschaticum B&SWJ 12627 WCru
yunnanense BWJ 7952A WCru

plum see *Prunus domestica*

Plumbago (*Plumbaginaceae*)

§ ***auriculata*** ♀H2 CBcs CDoC CSBt CTri CWCL EBak ELan EPfP EPri EShb EUJe IDee MHtn MOWG MRav SEND SPer SPoG SRms
- f. ***alba*** ♀H2 CBcs CDoC CRHN EPfP EShb IDee MOWG SEND
- 'Crystal Waters' CSam EShb
- dark blue-flowered CRHN CSpe
- (Escapade Series) 'Escapade Blue' CWGN EShb SPre
- - 'Escapade White' **new** EShb
capensis see *P. auriculata*
larpentiae see *Ceratostigma plumbaginoides*

Plumeria (*Apocynaceae*)

sp. WSFF
rubra ♀H1b XBlo
- 'Golden Glow' XBlo
- 'Velvet Red' XBlo

Pneumatopteris (*Thelypteridaceae*)

pennigera NLos

Poa (*Poaceae*)

alpina SMea XLum
chaixii EHoe EPPr
cita IMou
colensoi EHoe
glauca EShb
× ***jemtlandica*** EHoe EPPr
labillardierei CKno CWCL EBee ECha EHoe EPPr IMou LRHS MAvo MBel MMuc NWsh SEND XLum
pratensis CHab

Podalyria (*Papilionaceae*)

calyptrata SPlb
sericea SPlb

Podanthus (*Asteraceae*)

ovatifolius	SVen

Podocarpus ✿ (*Podocarpaceae*)

acutifolius	CBcs CDoC ECou
- (f)	ECou
- (m)	ECou
alpinus R. Br. ex Hook. f.	CDul
andinus	see *Prumnopitys andina*
'Autumn Shades' (m)	NLar
'Blaze' (f)	CBcs CDoC LEdu SLim
chilinus	see *P. salignus*
'Chocolate Box' (f)	ECou MAsh NLar SLim
'County Park Fire'[PBR] (f) 𝕐H6	CBcs CDoC ECou EFry EPfP ESwi MAsh MBri MGos NHol NLar SCoo SLim SWvt WGor
'County Park Treasure'	ECou
cunninghamii 'Roro' (m)	CBcs CDoC ECou
cunninghamii* × *nivalis (f)	ECou
dacrydioides	see *Dacrycarpus dacrydioides*
elongatus 'Blue Chip'	CBcs
'Flame'	CDoC EFry MAsh NLar SLim
'Guardsman'	ECou LRHS
'Havering' (f)	CDoC ECou
henkelii	CBcs
'Jill' (f)	ECou
latifolius	ECou
lawrencei	CBcs EFry
- (f)	ECou
- 'Blue Gem' (f)	CDoC ECou MAsh MGos MMuc SCoo SLim
- 'Kosciuszko'	ECou
- 'Pine Lake'	ECou
- 'Purple King' new	NLar
- 'Red Tip'	CDoC MBri NLar
'Lucky Lad'	ECou
macrophyllus	CDoC
- 'Aureus'	CBcs
'Maori Prince' (m)	CDoC NLar
matudae	CFil
nivalis	CBcs CDul CMac ECou SRms WThu
- 'Arthur' (m)	ECou
- 'Bronze'	CDoC GCal
- 'Christmas Lights' (f)	ECou
- 'Hikurangi'	CDoC
- 'Kilworth Cream' (v) 𝕐H6	CBcs CDoC ECou ESwi LRHS NHol SLim SWvt WGor
- 'Little Lady' (f)	ECou
- 'Moffat' (f)	CDoC ECou
- 'Otari' (m)	CDoC ECou MAsh NLar
- 'Ruapehu' (m)	CDoC
nubigenus	CBcs CMCN
'Red Embers' (f)	CDoC ECou ESwi SCoo SLim
§ ***salignus*** 𝕐H5	CBcs CDoC CDul CExl CTsd EPfP EUJe GGal IDee SLim WSHC WThu
- (f)	ECou
- (m)	ECou
'Soldier Boy'	ECou
spicatus	see *Prumnopitys taxifolia*
'Spring Sunshine' (f)	ECou
totara	CBcs CBrP ECou LEdu
- 'Aureus'	CBcs CDoC ECou LRHS
- 'Pendulus'	CDoC ECou
'Young Rusty' (f)	CBcs CDoC LRHS

Podophyllum (*Berberidaceae*)

aurantiocaule	CExl GGGa
- subsp. ***aurantiocaule*** new	GEdr
§ ***delavayi***	CBct CCon CExl ECho GEdr GKev SKHP WCru
difforme	CBct CLAP ECho GKev LEdu SKHP
emodi	see *Sinopodophyllum hexandrum* var. *emodi*
- var. ***chinense***	see *Sinopodophyllum hexandrum* var. *chinense*
hexandrum	see *Sinopodophyllum hexandrum*
- var. ***chinense***	see *Sinopodophyllum hexandrum* var. *chinense*
'Kaleidoscope' (v)	CBct CLAP EBee ECtt ELan ESwi EUJe GEdr MBel MHol NLar SKHP SPoG WCot
peltatum	CAby CArn CBct CBro CHid CLAP CWCL EBee ECho EHrv EPfP EWld GBBs GBin GKev GPoy LAma LEdu NHar NLar NMyG NSti SMad SPhx WBor WCot WCru WPGP WPnP
pleianthum	CBct CLAP ECho GCal GEdr WCru
- B&SWJ 282 from Taiwan	WCru
- short	WCru
* ***tsayuensis***	GEdr
veitchii	see *P. delavayi*
versipelle	GKev LEdu SKHP WCru
- 'Spotty Dotty'[PBR] (v)	CBct CExl CLAP ECtt ELan EPot ESwi EUJe EWTr GEdr IBoy IKil LEdu LRHS MAvo MHol MMHG MNrw NLar NSti SHeu SKHP SMad SPoG WCot

Podranea (*Bignoniaceae*)

§ ***ricasoliana*** 𝕐H1c	EShb MOWG SPoG WBor

Pogonatherum (*Poaceae*)

* ***distichum***	XBlo

Pogonia (*Orchidaceae*)

sp.	NDav

Pogostemon (*Lamiaceae*)

from An Veleniki Herb Farm, Pennsylvania	CArn
§ ***cablin***	EOHP GPoy
patchouly	see *P. cablin*

Polanisia (*Capparaceae*)

dodecandra new	CSpe

Polemonium ✿ (*Polemoniaceae*)

ambervicsii	see *P. pauciflorum* subsp. *hinckleyi*
'Apricot Beauty'	see *P. carneum* 'Apricot Delight'
archibaldiae 𝕐H5	NBir SRms WSHC
'Blue Pearl'	CBod COtt EBee ELan GJos LRHS MAsh MHol MNrw NBro NGdn NLar WPtf
§ ***boreale***	NPol SWvt WMoo
- 'Heavenly Habit'	GJos LRHS NGdn
brandegeei misapplied	see *P. pauciflorum*
§ ***brandegeei*** Greene	GBin WTcb
- subsp. ***mellitum***	see *P. brandegeei* Greene
§ ***caeruleum***	Widely available
- CC 7325 new	CEvo
- subsp. ***amygdalinum***	see *P. occidentale*
- 'Bambino Blue'	CBod EWoo SWvt WHar
- Brise d'Anjou = 'Blanjou'[PBR] (v)	CMac CMea COtt CWCL ECtt ELan EPfP EShb EWes IBoy LRHS MAsh MBri NBir NGdn NPol SCob SMad SPer SWvt WWtn

	- subsp. ***caeruleum*** f. ***albiflorum***	CBre CSBt CWCL CWld EBee ECha EHrv ELan EPfP EWTr EWoo GAbr LRHS MBNS MBel MHer MRav NBro NGBl SGbt SPer SPoG SRms WMoo
I	- f. ***dissectum***	NPol
	- 'Filigree Clouds'	NGdn NLar
	- 'Filigree Skies'	NGdn NLar
	- var. ***grandiflorum***	see *P. caeruleum* subsp. *himalayanum*
§	- subsp. ***himalayanum***	CSpe GAbr WMoo
	- - CC 7325 **new**	EWld GKev
	- 'Humile'	see *P.* 'Northern Lights'
	- 'Idylle'	NPol
	- 'Larch Cottage' (v)	NPol
	- 'Pam' (v)	NPol
	- 'Sky Blue'	MBel WWtn
	- 'Snow and Sapphires' (v)	CWGN EBee ECtt MPnt NLar NPer NPol SWvt
	- 'Southern Skies'	NPol
	- subsp. ***vulgare***	NPol
	- white-flowered	GJos IBoy MMuc
	carneum	CTri EBee ECha LRHS MCot NLar NPol WMoo
§	- 'Apricot Delight'	GJos MNHC MNrw NGdn NLar NPol SGbt SPad SPer WPtf WWEG WWtn
	cashmerianum	see *P. caeruleum* subsp. *himalayanum*
	chartaceum	LLHF
	'Churchills'	CBre EBee NPol WSHC
	'Dawn Flight'	NPol
	'Eastbury Purple'	CElw NPol
	'Elworthy Amethyst'	CElw EBee NPol
	eximium	ECho LLHF
	flavum	see *P. foliosissimum* var. *flavum*
	foliosissimum misapplied	see *P. archibaldiae*
	foliosissimum A. Gray	NPol
	- var. ***albiflorum***	see *P. foliosissimum* var. *alpinum*
§	- var. ***alpinum***	NPol
	- 'Bressingham'	NPol
	- 'Cottage Cream'	CDes LEdu NPol WCot
§	- var. ***flavum***	NPol
	- var. ***foliosissimum***	NPol
	- 'Scottish Garden'	NPol
	- 'White Spirit'	NPol
	'Glebe Cottage Lilac'	EBee GCra NBir NPol
	'Glebe Cottage Violet'	NPol
	'Hannah Billcliffe'	CDes CElw ECtt EWes MBrN MTis NPol
	'Heaven Scent'PBR	EBee ECtt MBri NDov NLar WGrn
	'Heavenly Blue'	IBoy
§	'Hopleys'	GCal LHop MBNS MNrw
	× ***jacobaea***	EPPr EWes WCot
	'Katie Daley'	see *P.* 'Hopleys'
	'Lambrook Mauve'	Widely available
	liniflorum	GKev
	'Mary Mottram'	NPol
	mellitum	see *P. brandegeei* Greene
	'North Tyne'	NChi NPol
§	'Northern Lights'	Widely available
	'Norwell Mauve'	MAvo MNrw NPol
§	***occidentale***	NPol
§	***pauciflorum***	ECtt ELan EWld GJos GKev IFro NBir WHea WMoo
§	- subsp. ***hinckleyi***	GKev NPol NQui
§	- subsp. ***pauciflorum***	NPol
	- silver-leaved	see *P. pauciflorum* subsp. *pauciflorum*
	- 'Sulphur Trumpets'	SWvt
	- subsp. ***typicum***	see *P. pauciflorum* subsp. *pauciflorum*
	'Pink Beauty'	EBee ECtt ELan EPfP GBuc NGdn NPol WWtn
	pulchellum Salisb.	see *P. reptans*
	pulchellum Turcz.	see *P. caeruleum*
	pulcherrimum misapplied	see *P. boreale*
	- 'Tricolor'	see *P. boreale*
	pulcherrimum Hook.	ECho NBro
	- subsp. ***pulcherrimum***	LLHF
§	***reptans***	CArn GPoy MHer NBro NPol SRms WMoo WOut
	- 'Album'	see *P. reptans* 'Virginia White'
	- 'Blue Ice'	NPol
	- 'Firmament'	EBee MAvo
*	- 'Sky Blue'	NBro WRHF
	- 'Stairway to Heaven'PBR (v)	Widely available
	- 'Touch of Class'PBR (v)	MAsh MAvo MHol NLar SPoG
§	- 'Virginia White'	CBre CElw EWes MAvo MTis NChi NPol SBch
	- 'White Pearl'	MHol
	'Ribby'	NPol
	× ***richardsonii*** misapplied	see *P.* 'Northern Lights'
	× ***richardsonii*** Graham	see *P. boreale*
	'Sapphire'	CBre LRHS
	'Sonia's Bluebell'	CDes CElw CWCL ECGP ECtt EPPr EWes EWld MAvo MNrw MPie MTis NDov NLar NPol NSti SBch WWFP
	'Sunnyside Storm'	NPol
	'Theddingworth'	CDes NPol WFar
	viscosum	GKev LLHF NPol SPlb
	- f. ***leucanthum***	NPol
	yezoense	NBre NPol
	- var. ***hidakanum***	NPol NWad
	- - Bressingham Purple = 'Polbress'	Widely available
	- - 'Halfway to Paradise' **new**	CMos
	- - 'Purple Rain'	Widely available

Polianthes (*Agavaceae*)

	elongata	WCot
§	***geminiflora***	WCot
	rosei	see *Agave gracillima*
	tuberosa ♀H1c	CBcs ECho GKev LCro LOPS SPer XLum
	- 'The Pearl' (d)	ECho GKev LAma SDeJ WCot XLum

Poliomintha (*Lamiaceae*)

bustamanta	NBir SPhx

Poliothyrsis (*Salicaceae*)

sinensis	CBcs EPfP IArd IDee NLar WPGP

Pollia (*Commelinaceae*)

japonica	CCon ESwi EWes SBrt WCot

Polygala (*Polygalaceae*)

	'Africana'PBR **new**	CTre
	calcarea 'Lillet' ♀H5	ECho EPot EWes GEdr LHop LLHF LRHS SIgm WAbe WThu
	chamaebuxus ♀H5	GKev LLHF MAsh MGos NLar NSla SRms WThu
I	- ***alba***	LBee NLar WAbe
§	- var. ***grandiflora*** ♀H5	CBcs CCon ECho EPfP GAbr GEdr IVic LBee LHop MAsh MGos NSla SPlb SPoG WAbe WIce

	– 'Purpurea'	see *P. chamaebuxus* var. *grandiflora*
	– 'Rhodoptera'	see *P. chamaebuxus* var. *grandiflora*
§	× ***dalmaisiana*** 🏆H2	CAbb CDoC CRHN CSde CSpe CTsd CWGN EBee ECre ELan EPri LRHS SEND WAbe WCFE
	'Dolomite'	GEdr
	myrtifolia 🏆H2	CTre ELan GFai IDee LRHS MGos SAdn SPlb
	– Bibi Pink = 'Polylap'	SAdn
	– 'Grandiflora'	see *P.* × *dalmaisiana*
	virgata	CBcs

Polygonatum ✿ (*Asparagaceae*)

	Og 94047	CDes LEdu
	SBQE 310	CDes LEdu
	acuminatifolium 'Ogon'	EBee
	altelobatum B&SWJ 286	WCru
	– B&SWJ 1886	GKev WCru
	arisanense B&SWJ 271	WCru
	– B&SWJ 3839	WCru
§	***biflorum***	Widely available
	– dwarf	LRHS
	canaliculatum	see *P. biflorum*
	cathcartii B&SWJ 2429	WCru
	– yellow-flowered B&SWJ 2412 **new**	WCru
	cirrhifolium	CBro CCon CCse EBee ECho EPot GEdr GKev LEdu LRHS MAvo MNrw NWad SKHP WCru WPGP
	– ARGS 320	EPPr
	– from China **new**	WCru
	– red-flowered	NLar
	commutatum	see *P. biflorum*
	'Corsley'	CPou
	cryptanthum	GKev WCru
	curvistylum	CAby CAvo CBct CCon CLAP CTal EHrv EPPr EWld GEdr GKev IFoB ILea IMou MAvo NLar NRya SPhx WCru WSHC
	– pink-flowered	SBch
	cyrtonema misapplied	see *Disporopsis pernyi*
	cyrtonema Hua	WCru
	– B&SWJ 271	LEdu MAvo
*	***desoulavyi*** var. ***yezoense*** B&SWJ 764	WCru
	falcatum misapplied	see *P. humile*
	falcatum A. Gray	EBee NRya
	– B&SWJ 1077	EHrv WCru
	– B&SWJ 5054	WCru
	– 'Shikoku Silver'	SMHy WCru
	– 'Variegatum'	see *P. odoratum* var. *pluriflorum* 'Variegatum'
	'Falcon'	see *P. humile*
	filipes	EHrv EPPr WCru
	fuscum	WCru
	geminiflorum	CBct CLAP WCru WFar
	– McB 2448	GEdr
	giganteum	see *P. biflorum*
	glaberrimum	CBct
§	***graminifolium***	CAby CBct CLAP CPBP CTal ECho EPPr WCru WThu
	– G-W&P 803	ECho
§	***hirtum***	CAby CBct CLAP CPrp ECho EPPr IFoB LEdu LRHS NMyG WCru
	– BM 7012	ECho
	– 'Robustum'	ECho WCru
	hookeri	CAby CBct CExl CSpe CTal ECho EHrv EPPr EPot EWld GBin GEdr GKev ITim LEdu LRHS NBid NCGa NLar NMyG NRya NSla NWad SGSe SPhx WAbe WCru WFar WWEG
§	***humile***	CBct CBot CDes CLAP CTal EAJP EBee ECho EHrv ELan EPPr EPfP EWTr GCal GEdr IBal LEdu LHop MAvo MHer NGdn NLar NMyG SCob SGSe SWvt WBor WCru WPGP XLum
I	– 'Variegatum' (v)	CMac
§	× ***hybridum*** 🏆H7	Widely available
	– 'Bere'	LEdu WPGP
	– 'Betberg'	CAvo CBct CCon CDes CLAP ECha EHrv ELon EPPr IFoB IMou LEdu NBir WCot
	– 'Flore Pleno' (d)	CBct WHer
	– 'Nanum'	CBct CHid MRav WCot
	– 'Purple Katie'	NMyG
§	– 'Striatum' (v)	Widely available
	– 'Variegatum'	see *P.* × *hybridum* 'Striatum'
	– 'Wakehurst'	EHrv
	– 'Weihenstephan'	GCal IPot
	– 'Welsh Gold' (v)	CAvo
	inflatum	ECho GEdr WCru
	– B&SWJ 922	WCru
	involucratum	ECho WCru
	– B&SWJ 4285	WCru
	japonicum	see *P. odoratum*
	kansuense	ECho
	kingianum	GKev
	– yellow-flowered	CDes
	– – B&SWJ 6545	WCru
	– – B&SWJ 6562	WCru
	'Langthorn's Variegated' (v)	ELan
	lasianthum	ECho GKev SMHy WCru
	– B&SWJ 671	NMyG WCru
	latifolium	see *P. hirtum*
	maximowiczii	EBee EPPr WCru WPGP
	mengtzense f. ***mengtzense*** white-flowered HWJ 861	WCru
	– f. ***tonkinense*** B&SWJ 8246	WCru
	– – HWJ 551	WCru
	– – HWJ 567	WCru
	– – HWJ 573	WCru
	– – HWJ 588	WCru
	'Multifide'	EBee GKev
	multiflorum misapplied	see *P.* × *hybridum*
	multiflorum L.	Widely available
	– CC 4572	WCot
	– 'Flore Pleno' (d)	WFar
	– var. ***ramosum*** **new**	LEdu
	– ***giganteum*** hort.	see *P. biflorum*
	– 'Ramosissima'	SMHy WCru
*	***nanum*** 'Variegatum' (v)	CBcs ECho
	nodosum	WCru
§	***odoratum***	CAvo CBct CBro CTal CTsd EBee ECho EHrv EPfP GMaP LCro NBid NLar NMyG NRya SCob WCru WWEG
	– RBG 93-101	EBee
	– 'Angel's Wings'	MAvo
	– 'Byakko' (v)	GEdr
§	– dwarf	CTal ECho LEdu
	– 'Flatmate'	WCru
	– 'Flore Pleno' (d)	CDes CLAP ECho EHrv GKev LEdu MHer NMyG WCot WHoo
	– 'Grace Barker'	see *P.* × *hybridum* 'Striatum'
	– 'Koryu'	GEdr

- var. ***odoratum*** **new**	GKev
§ - var. ***pluriflorum*** 'Variegatum' (v)	Widely available
- 'Red Stem'	CTal ECho EHrv GKev WCru
- 'Silver Wings' (v)	CBct CLAP CPrp ECha EHrv IPot NBir NLar
- 'Spiral Staircase' **new**	GKev
- var. ***thunbergii***	WCru
- - 'Variegatum' (v) **new**	CWld
- 'Ussuriland'	EBee EPPr GCal MAvo
- 'Ussuriland Roundleaf'	GCal MAvo
officinale	see *P. odoratum*
oppositifolium B&SWJ 2537	WCru
§ ***orientale***	CBct CLAP ECho GKev
pluriflorum	see *P. graminifolium*
polyanthemum	see *P. orientale*
prattii	CTal ECho ILea WCru
- CLD 325	LEdu
pubescens	CBct ECho EHrv LEdu WCru WThu
pumilum	see *P. odoratum* dwarf
punctatum misapplied.	see *P. mengtzense*
punctatum ambig.	CBct GEdr LEdu NBid WPGP
punctatum Royle ex Kunth B&SWJ 2395	CBct WCru
racemosum	IMou
roseum	CLAP EPPr GKev LLHF MAvo SGSe WCru
sewerzowii	EPPr
sibiricum	CBct GEdr WCru WFar
- DJHC 600	CDes EBee LEdu WPGP
singalilense **new**	GKev WCru
stenanthum	ECho
- B&SWJ 5727	LEdu WCru
- B&SWJ 11425 **new**	WCru
stenophyllum	CAvo EBee IMou WCru
stewartianum	CLAP EBee EPPr ILea NRya
tessellatum PAB 8336	LEdu
aff. ***tessellatum*** B&SWJ 9752	WCru
verticillatum	CBct CBro CHid CTal EBee ECha EPPr EPfP GEdr IFoB LEdu LRHS MNrw MRav SKHP SMad WCru WFar WPGP WWtn
- B&SWJ 2147	WCru
- CLD 1308	EPPr
- PAB 2455	LEdu
- 'Giant One'	IMou
- 'Himalayan Giant'	CHid ECho EPPr MAvo SGSe WPnP
- 'Krynica'	LEdu WPGP
* - 'Roseum'	CAvo SGSe
- 'Rubrum'	CAby CBct CDes CLAP EBee EHrv EPPr GEdr GKev ILea LEdu LHop LRHS MAvo NBid NChi NLar WCot WCru WHoo WWEG
- 'Serbian Dwarf'	CBct CHid CTal ECho GEdr IPot LEdu WPGP
aff. ***verticillatum***	CSpe IFoB
aff. ***wardii*** B&SWJ 6599	WCru
yunnanense **new**	CBct LEdu
zanlanscianense	CBct CDes EBee ECho EHrv EWld WCru

Polygonum (*Polygonaceae*)

affine	see *Persicaria affinis*
amplexicaule	see *Persicaria amplexicaulis*
aubertii	see *Fallopia baldschuanica*
baldschuanicum	see *Fallopia baldschuanica*
bistorta	see *Persicaria bistorta*
capitatum	see *Persicaria capitata*
compactum	see *Fallopia japonica* var. *compacta*
equisetiforme misapplied	see *P. scoparium*
filiforme	see *Persicaria virginiana*
forrestii	GKev
- SDR 7940 **new**	GKev
molle	see *Persicaria mollis*
multiflorum	see *Fallopia multiflora*
odoratum	see *Persicaria odorata*
polystachyum	see *Persicaria wallichii*
runciforme	see *Persicaria runcinata*
§ ***scoparium***	EHoe EPPr ESwi EWes SDys SVen WOld WTor XLum
tinctorium	see *Persicaria tinctoria*
vacciniifolium	see *Persicaria vacciniifolia*
weyrichii	see *Persicaria weyrichii*

Polylepis (*Rosaceae*)

australis	CPne CSpe ESwi IDee IMou LEdu SAko SMad WCot WHil
- tall	WPGP

Polymnia (*Asteraceae*)

uvedalia	see *Smallanthus uvedalius*

Polypodium ✿ (*Polypodiaceae*)

sp.	MLHP
appalachianum **new**	SKHP
aureum	see *Phlebodium aureum*
- 'Glaucum'	CSpe WCot
australe	see *P. cambricum*
calirhiza 'Sarah Lyman'	CDes SKHP
§ ***cambricum***	EFer SGSe WCot WFib
- 'Barrowii'	CLAP WAbe WFib WGwG
I - 'Cambricum' 🏆[H7]	CLAP GCal WAbe
- 'Conwy'	WFib
- 'Cristatum'	CLAP WFib
- (Cristatum Group) 'Grandiceps Forster'	CLAP
- - 'Grandiceps Fox' 🏆[H7]	MRav WFib
- 'Hornet'	WFib
- 'Macrostachyon'	CLAP GBin NBid WFib
- 'Oakleyae'	EWld SMHy WCot
- 'Omnilacerum Oxford'	CLAP
- 'Prestonii'	WCot WFib
- Pulcherrimum Group	CLAP SDys
- - 'Pulcherrimum Addison'	CDes EBee LEdu WCot WFib WPGP
- - 'Pulchritudine'	CLAP GBin LLWG WCot
- 'Richard Kayse' 🏆[H7]	CDes CLAP EWes SMHy WAbe WCot WFib WPGP
- Semilacerum Group	EFer
- - 'Carew Lane'	WFib
- - 'Falcatum O'Kelly'	WCot
- - 'Robustum'	WFib
- 'Whilharris' 🏆[H7]	CLAP SMHy
I × ***coughlinii*** bifid	WFib
glycyrrhiza	CLAP GPoy SKHP WFib
- bifid	see *P.* × *coughlinii* bifid
- 'Longicaudatum' 🏆[H7]	CLAP EFer EShb NMyG WCot WFib
- 'Malahatense' (sterile)	CDes EBee WCot WPGP
interjectum	CLAP EFer EShb MRav
- 'Cornubiense' 🏆[H7]	CHVG CLAP ECGP EWld GBin NBid NBir SMHy
- 'Glomeratum Mullins'	WFib
macaronesicum **new**	WCot
× ***mantoniae***	WFib
- 'Bifidograndiceps'	GBin NBid WFib
scouleri	CFil CLAP EFer ISha LRHS MRav NBro WCot WPGP

	vulgare	Widely available
	- 'Bifidocristatum'	see *P. vulgare* 'Bifidomultifidum'
	- 'Bifidomulticeps'	WCot
§	- 'Bifidomultifidum'	CDoC CLAP CWCL ELon EPfP GCal GEdr ISha LLWP MGos MRav NLar SGSe WCot WMoo
*	- 'Congestum Cristatum'	SRms
	- 'Cornubiense Grandiceps'	GCal SRms
*	- 'Cornubiense Multifidum'	EBee WCot
	- 'Elegantissimum'	NBid WFib
	- 'Parsley'	WCot
	- 'Trichomanoides Backhouse'	CDes CLAP GCal WAbe WFib
	'Whitley Giant'	CAby CDoC EBee ECtt ESwi GBin GEdr ISha ITim LLWG LSun MMuc MPie NMyG SEND WCot

Polypompholyx see *Utricularia*

Polyspora (*Theaceae*)

§	***axillaris***	CHII EBee
	- CWJ 12363	WCru
	longicarpa DJHV 06041	WCru
	- WWJ 11604	WCru
	speciosa B&SWJ 11708 from Vietnam **new**	WCru
	- B&SWJ 11750	WCru
	- WWJ 11934	WCru

Polystichum ✿ (*Dryopteridaceae*)

	acrostichoides	CDTJ CLAP EBee ERod LEdu LRHS MBri MMuc NLar WPGP XLum
	aculeatum ♀H7	CLAP CLet ECha EFer ELan EPfP ERod EShb GMaP LAst LCro LEdu LHop LRHS MBri MCot MGos MMuc NBid NEgg NLar SCob SEND SRms SWvt WFib WMoo XLum
	- 'Cristatum Wollaston'	WCot
I	- Densum Group	EFer
	- 'Portia'	WFib
	bissectum	CExl
	braunii	CBcs CLet CMac CWCL EPfP GBin GMaP IKil LRHS NBid NLar WFib WPnP XLum
	caryotideum	see *Cyrtomium caryotideum*
	× ***dycei*** ♀H6	CDes ISha LRHS MWhi NLos
	falcatum	see *Cyrtomium falcatum*
	fortunei	see *Cyrtomium fortunei*
	imbricans	CLAP
	interjectum	MRav
	makinoi	CLAP EPPr GBin ISha LLWG LRHS NBid NEgg SPlb WFib WMoo
	mayebarae	EBee ISha
	munitum ♀H7	Widely available
	aff. ***munitum***	LPal
	neolobatum	WFib
	- BWJ 8182	WCru
	nepalense **new**	NLos
	polyblepharum ♀H7	Widely available
	- 'Jade'	CMac EBee LRHS
	prescottianum	GCra
	proliferum misapplied	see *P. setiferum* Acutilobum Group
	proliferum (R. Br.) C. Presl	CLAP SBig WFib WPGP
*	**- *plumosum***	LAst LPal SPad SWvt
	richardii	SBig
	rigens	CLAP EFer ISha LPal LRHS LSou NLar SGSe SRms SRot WFib
	setiferum ♀H7	Widely available
§	- Acutilobum Group	CLAP CWSG ECha GMaP LLWG LPal LRHS NLos SCob SDix SPer SRms WMoo WPGP XLum
	- Congestum Group	CKel NBro NCGa NEgg NHol NLar SMad SPer SRms WFib WPat
	- - 'Congestum'	CLAP CLet CWCL ELan EPPr EPfP ERod IKil ISha LBMP LHop LRHS MRav NBir NEgg NGdn NHol SPad SPoG SPtp WMoo XLum
	- - 'Congestum Cristatum'	LAst
	- 'Cristatopinnulum'	NHar WPGP
	- Cristatum Group	CLAP SRms
	- (Decompositum Group) 'Proliferum'	CWCL EBee
	- Divisilobum Group ♀H7	CLAP EFer ELan MCot MGos MLHP SPer SRms WAbe WFar WFib WHoo WPGP
	- - 'Caernarfon'	CFil CLAP
	- - 'Dahlem'	CDoC CLAP CLet EBee ECha ECtt EFer ELan ELon EPfP GBin GEdr GMaP LRHS LSRN NBid NEgg SPer SPoG WFib WMoo WPtf XLum
	- - 'Divisilobum Densum' ♀H7	CLAP EPfP MRav NBir
	- - 'Divisilobum Grandiceps' **new**	CFil
	- - 'Divisilobum Iveryanum' ♀H7	CFil CLAP EFer SRms WFib
	- - 'Divisilobum Laxum'	CLAP EBee
§	- - 'Divisilobum Wollaston'	CDTJ CFil CKel CLAP CLet CTal CWCL ECtt ELon GEdr IBal ISha LLWG LRHS MBel MRav NBid NLar SHil WCot WMoo
	- - 'Herrenhausen'	Widely available
	- - 'Madame Patti'	CFil
	- - 'Mrs Goffey'	CFil WFib
	- Foliosum Group	CLAP EFer
	- 'Gracile'	MRav NBir
	- 'Grandiceps'	CLAP EFer
	- 'Hamlet'	WFib
	- 'Helena'	WFib
	- 'Hirondelle'	SRms
	- 'Leinthall Starkes' **new**	EBee
	- Lineare Group	WFib
	- Multilobum Group	CLAP SRms WFib
	- 'Othello'	CFil WFib
	- Perserratum Group	NBid WFib
	- 'Plumo-Densum'	see *P. setiferum* Plumosomultilobum Group
	- 'Plumosodensum'	see *P. setiferum* Plumosomultilobum Group
	- Plumosodivisilobum Group	CLAP ECha LPal NBid NBro SGSe SMHy WAbe WFib
	- - 'Baldwinii'	CLAP WFib
	- - 'Bland'	WFib
§	- Plumosomultilobum Group	CLAP CWCL EAJP EBee EPfP GBin GEdr ISha LCro MCot MGos NBir NCGa NLar NMyG WCot WFib WHoo WMoo WPat
I	- - 'Plumosomultilobum Densum'	CAby CHVG ECtt LRHS LSun MBel SBod SCob WCot XLum
	- Plumosum Group	CLAP CMac CSpe CTal EFer ELon LLWG MJak SRot
	- - dwarf	CSBt
*	**- *plumosum grande*** 'Moly'	SRms
	- Proliferum Group	see *P. setiferum* Acutilobum Group

- 'Proliferum Wollaston' see *P. setiferum* (Divisilobum Group) 'Divisilobum Wollaston'
- 'Pulcherrimum Bevis' ♀H6 CAby CDoC CFil CHid CLAP CSpe EBee ELon ESwi EUJe GBin IKil ISha ITim LPal MAvo MCot MMuc MPie NGdn NMyG SDix SEND SGSe SWvt WCot WFib WPGP WPat
- (Pulcherrimum Group) 'Pulcherrimum' ISha
- (Ramosum Group) 'Ramo-cristatum' **new** EBee
- (Rotundatum Group) 'Cristatum' CLAP ISha
- - 'Phillips' **new** EBee
- 'Smith's Cruciate' CLAP MRav MWhi WFib
- 'Wakeleyanum' EFer SRms
tsussimense ♀H6 Widely available
vestitum SBig

Polyxena (*Asparagaceae*)

* ***brevifolia*** ECho
corymbosa see *Lachenalia corymbosa*
ensifolia var. ***ensifolia*** see *Lachenalia ensifolia* subsp. *ensifolia*
longituba see *Lachenalia longituba*
odorata see *Lachenalia ensifolia* subsp. *ensifolia*
paucifolia see *Lachenalia paucifolia*

Pomaderris (*Rhamnaceae*)

apetala CExl
elliptica CExl

pomegranate see *Punica granatum*

Poncirus see *Citrus*

Ponerorchis (*Orchidaceae*)

graminifolia GKev LAma WCot
- purple-on-white-flowered ECho GKev
- red point ECho GKev
- white-flowered GKev

Pontederia (*Pontederiaceae*)

cordata ♀H5 CBen CWat EHon EPfP EWay MSKA MWts NPer SCoo SPlb SWat WMAq XLum
- f. ***albiflora*** CWat EHon EPfP EWay MWts XLum
- 'Blue Spires' MSKA
§ - var. ***lancifolia*** CBen EWay LLWG MNrw MSKA MWts NPer SWat
- pink-flowered LLWG
dilatata see *Monochoria hastata*
lanceolata see *P. cordata* var. *lancifolia*

Populus ✿ (*Salicaceae*)

× ***acuminata*** WMou
alba CBcs CCVT CDul CLnd CMac CSBt CTho CTri CWib ECrN LBuc NOrn NWea SCob SEWo SGol SPer WMou
- 'Bolleana' see *P. alba* 'Pyramidalis'
- 'Nivea' SEND
§ - 'Pyramidalis' SRms WMou
§ - 'Raket' CCVT CLnd CTho ECrN ELan NWea SPer
- 'Richardii' CLet EBtc EGFP WCot WMou
- Rocket see *P. alba* 'Raket'
§ 'Balsam Spire' (f) CDul CTho NWea WMou
§ ***balsamifera*** CCVT CSBt CTri ECrN MGos SPer WCot
- 'Vita Sackville West' MBlu
× ***canadensis*** EWld
§ - 'Aurea' ♀H6 CDul CTho CWib ECrN SPer WMat WMou
- 'Columbia' WMou
- 'Eugenei' (m) WMou
- 'Robusta' (m) CCVT CDul CLnd CTri NWea WMou
- 'Serotina' (m) WMou
× ***canescens*** CLnd
- 'Tower' WMat
deltoides 'Fuego' SGol
- 'Purple Tower' PBR ELan EPfP MBlu MMHG MMuc SMad SPoG WCot
× ***generosa*** 'Beaupré' WMou
× ***jackii*** 'Aurora' (f/v) CBcs CCVT CDul CLnd CMac CSBt CTsd LBuc LPot MGos MMuc NPri NWea SGol SPer WHar WMou
lasiocarpa CBcs CExl CLnd CMCN EPfP IArd IDee MBlu SGol WMou WPGP WPat
nigra CHab CMac CTho CTri CTsd NOrn NWea SCob WSFF
- (f) ECrN MMuc SEND
- (m) MMuc SEND
- subsp. ***betulifolia*** CCVT CDul CHab CLnd NWea WMou
- - (f) EBtc WMou
- - (m) EBtc WMou
§ - 'Italica' (m) ♀H6 CCVT CDul CLnd CMac CTho CTri CWib ECrN ELan LBuc MGos NWea SEND SEWo SPer WMou
- 'Pyramidalis' see *P. nigra* 'Italica'
purdomii EBee WPGP
'Serotina Aurea' see *P.* × *canadensis* 'Aurea'
simonii 'Fastigiata' WMou
szechuanica WMou
§ - var. ***tibetica*** WMou
tacamahaca see *P. balsamifera*
'Tacatricho 32' see *P.* 'Balsam Spire'
tremula CCVT CDul CHab CLnd CMac CTho CTri CWib ECrN ELan GQue LBuc MJak MMuc NWea SCob SEND SEWo SPer WHar WMou WSFF
§ - 'Erecta' ♀H7 CDul CTho MBlu MMuc SEND WMat
- 'Erecta' × ***tremuloides*** **new** NOrn
- 'Fastigiata' see *P. tremula* 'Erecta'
- 'Pendula' (m) CTho ECrN
trichocarpa CDul SPer
- 'Fritzi Pauley' (f) CDul CTho WMou
violascens see *P. szechuanica* var. *tibetica*
× ***wilsocarpa*** 'Beloni' WPGP WPat
wilsonii WPGP
yunnanensis WMou

Porophyllum (*Asteraceae*)

ruderale CLau WJek

Portulaca (*Portulacaceae*)

grandiflora SVic
- Happy Hour mixed (d) **new** LAst
- Happy Trails mixed (d) **new** LAst
oleracea CArn ENfk MHer SVic WJek
- var. ***aurea*** MNHC WJek

Potamogeton (*Potamogetonaceae*)

crispus	CWat EHon MSKA MWts WDra WMAq WSFF
malainus	LLWG
natans	LLWG MSKA WDra WSFF XLum

Potentilla ✿ (*Rosaceae*)

	sp.	NBes
	alba	CTri ECha ECho ELan GCal LPot MLHP MRav NChi NSti NWad SPer WSHC
	alchemilloides	CMac
	ambigua	see *P. cuneata*
	ancistrifolia var. ***dickinsii***	GEdr
	andicola	EBee
	anserina	CAgr MHer NMir WHer XLum
	- 'Golden Treasure' (v)	EBee WHer
	anserinoides	WMoo
	arbuscula misapplied	see *P. fruticosa* 'Elizabeth'
	- 'Beesii'	see *P. fruticosa* 'Beesii'
	'Arc-en-ciel'	Widely available
	argentea	SPlb WFar XLum
	arguta	EBee
	argyrophylla	see *P. atrosanguinea* var. *argyrophylla*
	atrosanguinea	Widely available
	- CC 6871	GKev
	- CC 7167	GKev
	- CC 7327 **new**	GKev
§	- var. ***argyrophylla***	CCon CSam CWCL EBee ECha ELan EPfP GCal ITim MMuc MRav NBir NBro NChi NLar SEND SRms WMoo XLum
	- - 'Golden Starlit'	EDAr IBoy
§	- - 'Scarlet Starlit'	CAby EDAr EPfP IBoy LRHS NCGa
	- 'Fireball' (d)	EPfP GJos
	- var. ***leucochroa***	see *P. atrosanguinea* var. *argyrophylla*
*	- 'Sundermannii'	LLHF SBrt
	aurea	ECho ECtt EPfP GBin
	- 'Aurantiaca'	NLar
§	- 'Goldklumpen'	ECtt MRav NEoE
	- 'Plena' (d)	NRya
	'Blazeaway'	CBod ECtt LRHS MArl MAvo MBNS NEoE NGdn WCot
	calabra	ECha EWes SPhx WHer
	caulescens **new**	SBrt
§	***cinerea***	CTri ECho LLHF
	clusiana	CPBP
§	***crantzii***	CMea SRms
	- 'Nana'	see *P. crantzii* 'Pygmaea'
§	- 'Pygmaea'	ECho ECtt NBir
§	***cuneata*** ♀H5	ECho GAbr GKev MMuc SEND
	davurica 'Abbotswood'	see *P. fruticosa* 'Abbotswood'
	delavayi	MNrw
	dombeyi	IMou
	'Emilie' (d)	CSpe CWCL ECtt GAbr GBuc GCal IKil MBNS MBel MCot MNrw NEoE NLar SWvt WBor WCot
§	***erecta***	GPoy MNHC WHfH
	eriocarpa	CPBP ECho EPot GCrg NSla WAbe WIce
	- var. ***tsarongensis***	WAbe
	'Esta Ann'	CAby CBod CMac ECtt GBuc LHop MArl MAvo MBNS MCot MNrw NCGa NLar SRGP
	'Etna'	CWCL ECtt ELan GBuc LRHS MAvo MLHP MNrw NBir NLar WHrl WMoo WPtf
	'Everest'	see *P. fruticosa* 'Mount Everest'
	'Fireflame'	NLar WMoo
	fissa	MNrw NBir NLar SPhx
	'Flambeau' (d)	CWCL ECtt EShb GBuc GKin IPot LAst LPla LRHS MArl MAvo MRav MSpe NCGa NEoE NGdn NLar NSti WMoo
	'Flamenco'	CSam CTri ECtt LRHS MArl MAvo MBNS MBri MLHP MNrw MRav NBir SHar WFar WMoo
	fragariiformis	see *P. megalantha*
	fruticosa	LBuc NWea
§	- 'Abbotswood' ♀H7	Widely available
	- 'Abbotswood Silver' (v)	WMoo
	- 'Annette'	CMac MBrN NEoE NLar WRHF
	- 'Apple Blossom'	CWib
	- var. ***arbuscula*** hort.	see *P. fruticosa* 'Elizabeth'
	- 'Argentea Nana'	see *P. fruticosa* 'Beesii'
	- 'Baby Bethan'PBR (d)	LLHF
§	- 'Beesii'	EPfP LRHS MAsh SIgm
	- 'Bo-Peep'	LRHS
	- 'Chelsea Star' ♀H7	CDoC CMac LRHS LSRN MAsh MGos SHil
	- 'Chilo' (v)	WMoo
	- 'Clotted Cream'	SGbt
	- var. ***dahurica*** 'Hersii'	see *P. fruticosa* 'Snowflake'
	- Danny Boy = 'Lissdan'	LRHS SLon SPoG
	- 'Daphne'	NWad
	- 'Dart's Cream'	MBri
	- 'Dart's Golddigger'	CTri NWad
	- 'Daydawn'	CBcs CBod CDul CMac CTri CWSG ELan EPfP LHop LRHS MAsh MLHP MMuc MRav MSwo NBir NEgg NLar NWad SGol SLim SPer SWvt WHar WMoo
	- 'Farreri'	see *P. fruticosa* 'Gold Drop'
	- 'Floppy Disc'	ELan
	- 'Glenroy Pinkie'	MRav
§	- 'Gold Drop'	CMac NHol
	- 'Golden Dwarf'	WMoo
	- 'Goldfinger'	CBod CChe CMac CSBt EBee ELan EPfP IBoy LHop LRHS MAsh MGos MJak MMuc MRav MSwo NEgg SCob SCoo SEND SLim SPer SPlb SPoG WHar WMoo
	- Goldkugel	see *P. fruticosa* 'Gold Drop'
	- 'Goldstar'	COtt CWSG IArd LRHS MBri NPri SCob SEND SLim SLon SRms WFar
	- 'Goldteppich'	LBuc
	- 'Grace Darling'	ECrN ELan EPfP EWes NBir NEgg SRGP SWvt WHar WMoo WRHF
	- 'Groneland' ♀H7	ELan EPfP LRHS MAsh SCoo SPoG
	- 'Haytor's Orange'	CWib
	- 'Hopleys Orange' ♀H7	CDoC CSBt CWSG ELon EMil EPfP EWes LHop LRHS MBri NHol NPri SCob SEND SGbt SGol SHil SRms WFar WMoo
	- 'Hurstbourne'	NEoE
	- 'Jackman's Variety' ♀H7	CDoC CLet CWib EPfP IBoy LRHS MAsh SCob SRms
	- 'Katherine Dykes'	CDul CTri CWib EPfP GKin LAst LBMP LRHS LSRN MAsh MGos NEgg NWea SCob SCoo SGbt SLim SPer SRms WFar WHar WMoo
	- 'King Cup' ♀H7	EPfP LRHS MAsh
§	- 'Klondike'	CBcs CSBt NWea
	- 'Kobold'	CDul LRHS MBri NLar
	- 'Lemon and Lime'	see *P. fruticosa* 'Limelight'

§	- 'Limelight' ♀H7	CDoC CSBt ELan EPfP GKin LHop LRHS MAsh MBri MRav MSwo NEoE NWad SHil SPer SRms WHar
	- 'Lovely Pink'	see *P. fruticosa* 'Pink Beauty'
§	- 'Maanelys'	CSBt ELan NWea SPer WMoo
	- 'Macpenny's Cream'	CMac
§	- 'Manchu'	CMac MRav SCob SPer WCFE WPat
	- Mango Tango = 'Uman'PBR	CSBt EBee EMil EPfP LHop LRHS LSRN MBri NLar SPoG STPC WFar
§	- Marian Red Robin = 'Marrob'PBR ♀H7	CDoC CLet COtt CSBt CWib ELan EPfP GKin IBoy LAst LCro LRHS MAsh MBri MRav MSwo NPri NWea SCoo SLim SLon SPer SPoG SWvt
	- 'McKay's White'	NLar
	- 'Medicine Wheel Mountain' ♀H7	CDoC ELan EWes IArd LRHS MAsh MBri MGos MPkF MRav NLar NWad SCob SCoo SGol SHil SLim SPer SPoG
	- Moonlight	see *P. fruticosa* 'Maanelys'
§	- 'Mount Everest'	CTri MMuc NWea SEND SLon
	- 'Nana Argentea'	see *P. fruticosa* 'Beesii'
	- 'New Dawn'	COtt GKin MBri
	- 'Orangeade'	EPfP LRHS MAsh MBri NLar SCoo SPoG
*	- 'Peachy Proud'	NEoE
§	- 'Pink Beauty'PBR ♀H7	Widely available
	- Pink Paradise = 'Kupinpa'PBR	NCGa
	- 'Pink Pearl'	WMoo
	- 'Pink Queen'	NLar
	- 'Pink Whisper'	COtt NEoE
	- 'Pretty Polly'	ELan EPfP LAst LRHS MSwo NHol NLar NWad WFar WMoo
	- 'Primrose Beauty' ♀H7	Widely available
§	- Princess = 'Blink'	CBcs CDul EBee ELan EPfP LRHS MAsh MJak MRav SCob SCoo SGol SLim SRms WFar WMoo
	- 'Red Ace'	Widely available
	- 'Red Lady'PBR	CDoC EPfP LAst LRHS MBri NHol SCob SHil SPoG STPC WMoo
	- Red Robin	see *P. fruticosa* Marian Red Robin
	- 'Red Surprise'	WFar
	- 'Royal Flush'	NWad
	- 'Setting Sun'	LBuc
	- 'Snowbird'	NEoE SLim WFar
§	- 'Snowflake'	CBcs WMoo
	- 'Sommerflor' ♀H7	CDoC EPfP LRHS MAsh
	- 'Sophie's Blush'	MRav NWea
§	- (Sulphurascens Group) 'Elizabeth'	CBcs CDul COtt CWib ECrN ELan EPfP LAst LBMP LRHS LSRN MGos MJak MMuc MSwo NHol NWea SCob SGol SLim SPer SRms SWvt WCFE WFar WHar WMoo
	- - 'Longacre Variety'	CMac CTri IArd MSwo NLar NWea
	- 'Summer Dawn'	LBuc
	- 'Summer Sorbet'	LRHS
	- 'Sunset'	CBcs CMac CWib ELan GKin LSRN MJak NBir NWea SCob SCoo SLim SPer SRms WFar WMoo
	- 'Tangerine'	Widely available
	- 'Tilford Cream'	COtt CSBt CTri ECrN ELan EPfP GKin IBoy LRHS LSRN MJak MNHC MRav MSwo NBir NEgg NHol SCob SGbt SGol SLim SPer SRms WCFE WFar WHar WMoo
	- 'Tom Conway'	CMac NLar
	- var. ***veitchii***	CSBt

	- 'Vilmoriniana'	CTri ELan EMil EPfP GCal LRHS MAsh MLHP MRav NLar NWea SPer SPoG SWvt WPat
	- 'Whirligig'	CMac
	- 'White Lady'	MPkF SPer
	- 'Wickwar Beauty'	CWib
	- 'William Purdom'	WHar
	- 'Yellow Bird' ♀H7	LRHS MAsh
	'Gibson's Scarlet' ♀H7	Widely available
§	***glandulosa*** subsp. ***nevadensis***	CTri ECho EWld MAsh SRms
	'Gloire de Nancy' (d)	EBee GBuc IKil MRav NBir NChi NLar
	'Gold Clogs'	see *P. aurea* 'Goldklumpen'
	'Herzblut'	NLar
	hippiana **new**	EBee
	× ***hopwoodiana***	CMea CSpe CWCL EAJP EBee ECha ECtt ELan EPPr GCal GJos GMaP IKil ILea LAst LHop MCot MNrw MRav NBir NCGa NChi NDov NLar SCob SPer WCAu WMoo WPtf
	× ***hybrida*** 'Jean Jabber'	EBee GLog MAvo MRav NEoE NLar SRGP WHea
	'Jack Elliot'	NEoE
	kurdica	XLum
	'Lemon Drops'	LAst
	'Light My Fire'	EBee ECtt LLHF MBNS MSCN
§	'Majland'	EBee NDov
	'Mandshurica'	see *P. fruticosa* 'Manchu'
	'Maynard's'	see *P.* 'Majland'
§	***megalantha***	CBcs CBro CLet EAJP ECtt EDAr ELan EPfP EPri GCal GCra LAst LEdu LHop LRHS MBNS MLHP MNrw MRav NBir NBro SGbt SPer SRms SRot WHea WMoo XLum
	- 'Gold Sovereign'	EBee EPfP LRHS MBri NEoE NLar
	'Melton Fire'	EAJP EPfP GJos GKin GQue LBMP MNHC MNrw NBir WMoo WPnP
	micrantha 'Purple Haze' **new**	LEdu
	- 'Purple Heart'	WPGP
	'Monarch's Velvet'	see *P. thurberi* 'Monarch's Velvet'
	'Monsieur Rouillard' (d)	CElw CMac CSam CSpe ECtt GCra IPot LRHS MArl MCot MNrw MRav NGdn NLar WHoo WHrl WMnd
	'Mont d'Or'	EBee MRav NLar
	nepalensis	EHoe LRHS MLHP NBro NChi XLum
	- 'Helen Jane'	GBuc GJos GQue IBoy LEdu MHer NBir NHol NLar NWad SBea SPad WFar WMoo WPtf WOut
	- 'Master Floris'	WFar WHal
§	- 'Miss Willmott'	Widely available
	- 'Ron McBeath'	CCon CKno CLet COtt CWCL ECtt ELan EPfP GBin GCra ITim LAst MAvo MRav NHol NLar NSti SGol SPer SPoG SRGP SRkn SWvt WGwG WHoo WMoo WPtf
	- 'Roxana'	CCon ELan MRav NBro NLar SRGP WMoo
	- 'Shogran'	GJos GQue LRHS NHol NLar WPtf
§	***neumanniana***	MAsh NBir
	- 'Goldrausch'	IMou MRav
§	- 'Nana'	ECho ECtt EPot GCrg MHer NRya NWad SPlb SRms WHoo WIce WMoo XLum
	nevadensis	see *P. glandulosa* subsp. *nevadensis*
	nitida	EPot MAsh SRms WAbe

- 'Alba' ECho EPot
- 'Rubra' CMea CPBP ECho EDAr GEdr NBir NHar NSla SRms WAbe
nivalis ECho
ovina var. ***ovina*** LLHF
- - NNS 08-374 GKev
palustris CWat EBee EWay LLWG MWts NLar NMir WMoo XLum
parvifolia 'Klondike' see *P. fruticosa* 'Klondike'
pedata LLWP NChi XLum
peduncularis CC 5717 GKev
'Pink Panther' see *P. fruticosa* Princess
aff. ***polyphylla*** CHP&W 314 GKev
porphyrantha EPot GEdr LLHF
recta NPri WTou XLum
- 'Alba' GMaP NEgg WPtf
- 'Citrina' see *P. recta* var. *sulphurea*
- 'Macrantha' see *P. recta* 'Warrenii'
§ - var. ***sulphurea*** CAby CMea EAJP ELon EPau EWoo GAbr LAst LSun MCot MLHP MMuc MNrw NBir NLar NSti NWad SBch SPhx SRkn WBrk WCAu WHal WHea WHoo WHrl WMnd WMoo WPtf XLum
§ - 'Warrenii' CSBt EPfP GMaP LAst LRHS MRav NBir NEgg SHar SPer SRms WHal WHrl WMoo XLum
'Roxanne' (d) LRHS MHer
rupestris CMea ECha LSun MHer NLar NSti WCAu WFar WHal WHea WMoo WOut WPtf
× ***russelliana*** new LRHS
'Scarlet Starlet' see *P. atrosanguinea* var. *argyrophylla* 'Scarlet Starlit'
speciosa EWes WMoo
sterilis CHid WHer WSFF
* ***sundermanii*** WHrl
tabernaemontani see *P. neumanniana*
thurberi CMea LRHS MCot MNrw NLar SPhx WHrl WMoo XLum
§ - 'Monarch's Velvet' Widely available
tommasiniana see *P. cinerea*
× ***tonguei*** 𝕐H5 Widely available
tormentilla see *P. erecta*
tridentata see *Sibbaldiopsis tridentata*
'Twinkling Star' EBee WPtf
verna misapplied see *P. neumanniana*
- 'Pygmaea' see *P. neumanniana* 'Nana'
'Versicolor Plena' (d) NLar
villosa see *P. crantzii*
'Volcan' CAby CWCL ECtt EWes GBuc GQue IKil IPot NChi SMHy WCAu WHal
'White Queen' GLog MRav SHar
'William Rollisson' 𝕐H6 Widely available
willmottiae see *P. nepalensis* 'Miss Willmott'
'Yellow Queen' CMac CTri EBee GKin GMaP LPot LRHS MNrw MRav NLar SBod SPer WCAu

Poterium see *Sanguisorba*

sanguisorba see *Sanguisorba minor*

Prangos (*Apiaceae*)

ferulacea WCot

Pratia (*Campanulaceae*)

§ ***angulata*** 'Treadwellii' ECha ECho ECtt GEdr SPlb WHal
montana see *Lobelia montana*
§ ***pedunculata*** CBar CTri ECha ECho ECou ECtt EDAr ELan EPfP EWTr GAbr LLWG LSun SIgm SPlb SRms SRot WMoo WPtf
I - 'Alba' CBod ECho EWes
- 'County Park' CExl CMea CSpe CTri ECha ECho ECou ECtt EDAr ELan ELon EWTr GAbr LLWG LRHS MSCN NDov SBod SPlb SPoG SRms SRot WIce WMoo XLum
- 'White Stars' ECho LLWG

Preslia see *Mentha*

Primula ✿ (*Primulaceae*)

sp. SVic
(Si) MAsh
acaulis see *P. vulgaris*
'Adrian Jones' (Au) IPen ITim
agleniana (Cy) IPen
'Alan Robb' (Pr/Prim/d) ECtt NGdn
albenensis (Au) EPot IPen
'Alexina' (*allionii* hybrid) (Au) GKev MFie NHar
algida (Al) ECho GKev
§ ***allionii*** (Au) GKev IPen NSum WAbe
- HNG 12 IPen ITim
- 'Agnes' (Au) IPen ITim MFie
- 'Aire Waves' see *P.* × *loiseleurii* 'Aire Waves'
- 'Alan Burrow' (Au) IPen
- var. ***alba*** (Au) IPen MFie
- 'Allen Moonbeam' (Au) ITim
- 'Allen Queen' (Au) IPen
- 'Andrew' (Au) IPen WAbe
- 'Anna Griffith' (Au) CPBP CTal IPen ITim MFie WAbe WHil
- 'Anne' (Au) EPot IPen ITim
- 'Aphrodite' (Au) IPen NHar
- 'Apple Blossom' (Au) CLet
- 'Archer' (Au) IPen ITim NWad
- 'Ares' (Au) NHar
- 'Aries Violet' (Au) IPen NHar
- 'Austen' (Au) EPot MFie
- 'Avalanche' (Au) IPen WAbe
- 'Beryl' (Au) IPen
- 'Biddy' (Au) IPen
- 'Bill Martin' (Au) EPot IPen ITim NWad
- 'Blood Flake' (Au) IPen ITim
- 'Broadwell No 4' (Au) CPBP
- 'Cherry' (Au) WAbe
- 'Chivalry' (Au) CPBP
- 'Circe's Flute' (Au) NHar
- 'Cissie' (Au) CPBP IPen
- 'Claude Flight' (Au) IPen MFie
- 'Crowsley Variety' (Au) ITim
- 'Crusader' (Au) CTal WAbe
- 'Crystal' (Au) CPBP MFie
- 'Daniel Burrow' (Au) IPen
- 'David Burrow' (Au) IPen
- 'David Philbey' (Au) CPBP IPen
§ - 'Edinburgh' (Au) IPen NWad
- 'Edrom' (Au) IPen NWad
- 'Ekli Weib' (Au) IPen
- 'Elizabeth Baker' (Au) IPen ITim MFie
- 'Elizabeth Burrow' (Au) IPen WAbe
- 'Elizabeth Earle' (Au) IPen ITim
- 'Elliott's Large' see *P. allionii* 'Edinburgh'
- 'Elliott's Variety' see *P. allionii* 'Edinburgh'
- 'Emily Jane' (Au) IPen
- 'Eureka' (Au) CPBP EPot ITim LLHF WAbe
- 'Eveline Burrow' (Au) CPBP WAbe

	- 'Fanfare' (Au)	IPen MAsh NHar
	- 'Flute' (Au)	IPen
	- 'Frank Barker' (Au)	IPen
	- 'Gabriele' (Au)	MFie
	- 'Gavin Brown' (Au)	IPen ITim
	- 'Gilderdale Glow' (Au)	CPBP IPen MFie
	- 'Giuseppi's Form'	see *P. allionii* 'Mrs Dyas'
	- 'Grace Burrow' (Au)	IPen
	- 'Grandiflora' (Au)	ITim
	- 'Hannah' (Au)	EPot IPen
	- 'Hartside 6' (Au)	IPen ITim NHar
	- 'Hartside 12' (Au)	IPen
	- 'Hazey' (Au)	ITim
	- 'Hemswell' (Au)	ITim
	- 'Herald' (Au)	ITim
	- 'Hocker Edge' (Au)	ITim MFie NWad
	- 'Horwood' (Au)	ITim
	- 'Huntsman' (Au)	MFie
	- 'Hythe Dorothy' (Au)	IPen
	- 'Imp' (Au)	IPen
	- Ingwersen's form (Au)	MFie
	- 'Io 2' (Au)	NHar
	- 'Ion's Amethyst' (Au)	NHar
	- 'Isobel' (Au)	IPen LLHF
	- 'Jacqueline' (Au)	IPen
	- 'James' (Au)	IPen WAbe
	- 'Jan' (Au)	IPen
	- 'Jenny' (Au)	IPen
	- 'Joe Elliott' (Au)	IPen ITim
	- 'Joseph Collins' (Au)	IPen
	- 'Julia' (Au)	IPen
	- 'Kate Evans' (Au)	IPen
§	- 'Kath Dryden' (Au)	IPen LLHF
§	- 'Ken's Seedling' (Au)	IPen MFie
	- KRW	see *P. allionii* 'Ken's Seedling'
	- 'Laura Louise' (Au)	IPen
	- 'Lepus' (Au)	IPen WAbe
	- 'Lindisfarne' (Au)	IPen
	- 'Lindum Prima' (Au)	IPen
	- 'Lindum Whisper' (Au)	LLHF
	- 'Lismore 81/19/2' (Au)	MFie
	- 'Lismore 87/3/2' (Au)	MFie
	- 'Little O' (Au)	NWad
	- 'Louise' (Au)	IPen
	- 'Lucy' (Au)	IPen NHar
	- 'Malcolm' (Au)	IPen ITim WAbe
	- 'Margaret Earle' (Au)	IPen
	- 'Marion' (Au)	IPen XBar
	- 'Marjorie Wooster' (Au)	CPBP IPen MFie XBar
	- 'Martin' (Au)	IPen ITim
	- 'Mary Anne' (Au)	WAbe
	- 'Mary Berry' (Au)	IPen MFie NWad
	- 'Maurice Dryden' (Au)	IPen WAbe
	- 'Megan' (Au)	IPen
	- 'Molly' (Au)	IPen
§	- 'Mrs Dyas' (Au)	IPen MFie NWad WAbe
	- 'Neon' (Au)	IPen
	- 'Neptune's Wave' (Au)	NHar
	- 'New Dawn' (Au)	ITim MFie NHar
	- 'Pale Venus' (Au)	IPen NHar
	- 'Peace' (Au)	MFie
	- 'Peggy Wilson' (Au)	EPot EWld IPen NWad WThu
	- 'Pennine Pink' (Au)	CPBP IPen
	- 'Perkie' (Au)	IPen
	- 'Phoebe's Moon' (Au)	IPen NHar
	- 'Pinkie' (Au)	IPen WAbe
	- 'Praecox' (Au)	IPen
	- 'Quip' (Au)	IPen
	- RAH form	MFie
	- 'Raymond Wooster' (Au)	IPen NWad

	- 'Roger Bevan' (Au)	IPen
	- 'Saint Dalmas' (Au)	IPen
	- 'Scimitar' (Au)	IPen MFie
	- 'Serendipity' (Au)	IPen
	- 'Snowflake' (Au)	IPen WAbe
	- 'Stanton House' (Au)	MFie
	- 'Stephen' (Au)	IPen MFie
	- 'Tranquillity' (Au)	CPBP CTal ITim NHar
	- 'Travellers' (Au)	IPen
	- 'Viscountess Byng' (Au)	IPen ITim WAbe
	- white-flowered, thrum-eyed (Au)	IPen
	- 'William Earle' (Au)	CPBP CTal IPen ITim WAbe XBar
	allionii* × *auricula misapplied 'Old Red Dusty Miller' (Au)	ECho NWad XBar
	allionii* × *auricula misapplied 'Blairside Yellow' (Au)	ECho IPen NSum WThu
	allionii* × *clusiana (Au)	ECho
	allionii* × *hirsuta (Au)	NWad
	allionii × 'Lismore Jewel' (Au)	ITim
	allionii × 'Lismore Treasure' (Au)	ITim
	allionii* × *pedemontana	see *P.* × *sendtneri*
	allionii* × *pubescens (Au)	ECho
	allionii* × *pubescens 'Harlow Car' (Au)	ITim
	allionii × 'Snow Ruffles' (Au)	IPen ITim
	allionii × 'White Linda Pope' (Au)	IPen MFie NHar NWad
	alpicola (Si) ♀H7	CAby CLAP CPne CTsd CWCL GAbr GKev IPen NBid NBro NCGa NGdn NSum NWad SEND WAbe WCot XBar
	- var. ***alba*** (Si)	CPla CSta GAbr GBuc GKev IPen NBid SEND
§	- var. ***alpicola*** (Si)	CLAP EBee GBin GBuc GCra GKev IPen MMuc
	- hybrids (Si)	CBod WMoo
	- 'Kevock Sky' (Si)	CWCL GKev
	- 'La Luna' (Si)	CSta MMuc
	- var. ***luna***	see *P. alpicola* var. *alpicola*
	- mixed (Si)	ECho GKev
	- var. ***violacea*** (Si)	CCon CLAP CPla CSta EBee GAbr GBin GCra GKev IPen MMuc MNrw NBid NCGa WHil
	- - wine red-flowered (Si)	CWCL GKev
	'Altaica'	see *P. elatior* subsp. *meyeri*
	altaica grandiflora	see *P. elatior* subsp. *meyeri*
	'Amethyst' (Pr/Poly)	ECtt
	amethystina subsp. ***brevifolia*** (Am)	GKev
	amoena	see *P. elatior* subsp. *meyeri*
	'Amy Smith'	GAbr
	angustifolia (Pa)	LLHF
	anisodora	see *P. wilsonii* var. *anisodora*
	'Annemijne'	GEdr WCot
	apoclita (Mu)	GKev LLHF
	× ***arctotis***	see *P.* × *pubescens*
	'Arduaine' (Pe)	LLHF
	aurantiaca (Pf)	CCon CPla CWCL EBee GBin GKev IPen
	aureata (Pe)	GKev IPen
	auricula ambig. (Au)	CBod NSla
	auricula L. (Au) ♀H5	EDAr GKev IPen LRHS MFie NBro SPer SPlb SPoG WAbe WRHF

- subsp. ***bauhinii*** (Au) GKev
I ***auricula*** misapplied (Au) ECha
- A74 (Au) SEND
- K85 (Au/S) SPop
- '1-2-3' (Au) EBee
- 'A.C. Hadfield' (Au) MFie
- '2nd Vic' (Au/S) SPop
- 'Abdor' (Au/St) SPop
- 'Abrigde' (Au/d) WAln
- 'Abundance' (Au/A) EWoo NDro SPop WCre
- 'Achates' (Au/A) IPen WAln
- 'Admiral' (Au/A) WAln
- 'Adrian' (Au/A) EWoo GAgs IPen MFie NBro NDro SPop WCre WHil XBar
- 'Adrian's Cross' (Au/A) EWoo
- 'Adrienne' (Au/A) SPop
- 'Adrienne Ruan' (Au/A) NDro WAln
- 'After Glow' (Au/St) SPop
- 'Aga Khan' (Au/A) WAln
- 'Agamemnon' (Au/A) EWoo IPen LLHF MFie NDro SPop WAln
- 'Airy Fairy' (Au/S) SPop
- 'Alamo' (Au/A) MFie SPop WCre
- 'Alan Ball' (Au) WAln
- 'Alan Ravenscroft' (Au/A) MFie SPop WHil
- 'Albert Bailey' (Au/d) EWoo GAbr GAgs IPen ITim MFie NDro SPop WCre WHil
- 'Albury' (Au/d) IPen WCre
- 'Alchemist' (Au/S) IPen SPop WAln WCre
- 'Alexandra Georgina' (Au/A) MFie WAln
- 'Alf' (Au/A) IPen MFie NDro SPop WHil
- 'Alfred Charles' (Au/A) SPop WAln
- 'Alfred Niblett' (Au/S) GAgs IPen
- 'Alice' (Au/d) IPen
- 'Alice Haysom' (Au/S) CWCL ELan EWoo GAbr GAgs IPen ITim MAsh NDro SPop WCre WHil XBar
- 'Alicia' (Au/A) EWoo GAbr GAgs MFie NDro SPop WCre XBar
- 'Alison' (Au/S) GAgs
- 'Alison Jane' (Au/A) GAgs IPen MFie SPop WCre WHil XBar
- 'Alison Telford' (Au/A) WHil
- 'Allard' (Au/A) WAln
- 'Allegro' (Au/A) WAln
- 'Allensford' (Au/A) WCre
- 'Alloway' (Au/d) WAln
- 'Almand' (Au/d) WAln
- 'Almondbury' (Au/S) NDro SPop
- alpine mixed (Au/A) EPfP SRms
- 'Amazon' (Au/St) SPop
- 'Amber Light' (Au/S) SPop WAln
- 'Amethyst' (Au/S) GAgs WAln
- 'Amicable' (Au/A) EWoo GAgs IPen MFie NDro NSum SPop WCre WHil
- 'Amore' (Au/St) SPop WAln
- 'Ancient Order' (Au/A) IPen WAln
- 'Ancient Society' (Au/A) EWoo GAgs IPen MFie NWad SPop WHil
- 'Andrea Julie' (Au/A) GAgs IPen NDro SPop WCre WHil
- 'Andrew Hunter' (Au/A) IPen MFie NDro NSum SPop WCre
- 'Andy Cole' (Au/A) EWoo IPen NDro SPop WAln WCre
- 'Angel Eyes' (Au/St) GAbr IPen NDro SPop WHil
- 'Angel Islington' (Au/S) NDro
- 'Angela Gould' (Au) EWoo MFie SPop WHil
- 'Angela Grace' (Au/d) new XBar
- 'Angela Short' (Au/St) IPen SPop WAln
- 'Angostura' (Au/d) EWoo IPen SPop WCre WHil
- 'Ann Brookes' (Au/d) WAln
- 'Ann Taylor' (Au/A) GAgs IPen WAln
- 'Anne Hyatt' (Au/d) GAbr NDro SPop
- 'Anne Swithinbank' (Au/d) IPen WAln
- 'Annie Tustin' (Au/S) SPop
- 'Ansells' (Au/S) WAln
- 'Antoc' (Au/S) EWoo SPop
- 'Anwar Sadat' (Au/A) EWoo GAbr GAgs MFie NDro WCre WHil
- 'Apple Blossom' (Au/B) NDro WHil
- 'Applecross' (Au/A) GAgs IPen NDro SPop WCre WHil
- 'Apricot Truffle' (Au/d) SPop
- 'April Moon' (Au/S) GAbr MFie NDro SPop WCre WHil
- 'April Tiger' (Au/St) EWoo WAln
- 'Aquarius' (Au/d) SPop
- 'Arab Prince' (Au/A) WAln
- 'Arab Queen' (Au/A) WAln
- 'Arabian Night' (Au/A) WAln
- 'Arapaho' (Au/A) SPop WAln
- 'Arctic Fox' (Au) MFie WAln WHil
- 'Argentine' (Au/S) XBar
- 'Argus' (Au/A) EWoo GAbr GAgs IPen LSun MFie NSum NWad SPop WCre WHil XBar
- 'Arlene' (Au/A) WAln
- 'Art Deco' (Au/B) new WAln
- 'Arthur Delbridge' (Au/A) MFie NDro SPop WHil
- 'Arundel Cross' (Au) IPen
- 'Arundell' (Au/S/St) CWCL EBee GAbr GAgs IPen ITim MFie NDro NSum SPop WCre WHil XBar
- 'Arwen' (Au/A) IPen MFie SPop
- 'Ascot Gavotte' (Au/S) WAln
- 'Ashcliffe Gem' (Au/A) GAgs IPen NDro WAln
- 'Astolat' (Au/S) EBee EWoo GAbr GAgs GKev IPen NDro SBch SPop WCre WHil XBar
- 'Athene' (Au/S) IPen ITim NDro SPop WAln
- 'Atlantic' (Au/S) NDro NEgg
- 'Aubergine' (Au/B) NDro SPop
- 'Audacity' (Au/d) IPen MFie NDro WAln
- 'Audrey' (Au/S) SPop
- 'Aurora' (Au/A) EDAr MFie NSum WAln WCre
- 'Austin' (Au/A) IPen SPop WAln
- 'Autumn Fire' (Au/A) EWoo GAbr GAgs SPop WCre
- 'Autumn Glow' (Au/d) SPop
- 'Aviemore' (Au/A) WCre
- 'Avon Angel' (Au/d) SPop
- 'Avon Bunny' (Au/d) new SPop
- 'Avon Carrier' (Au/d) SPop
- 'Avon Citronella' (Au) EWoo SPop
- 'Avon Eclipse' (Au/d) SPop
- 'Avon Elegance' (Au/d) SPop
- 'Avon Khaki' (Au/d) SPop
- 'Avon Tan' (d) GAbr GAgs WCre
- 'Avon Toro' (Au/d) SPop
- 'Avon Twist' (Au/d) EWoo SPop
- 'Avril' (Au/A) IPen NDro SPop WAln WHil
- 'Avril Hunter' (Au/A) GAgs IPen ITim MFie MHer NDro NSum WCre WHil XBar
- 'Awesome' (Au/St) SPop
- 'Aztec' (Au/d) WAln
- 'Baby Blue' (AU) WHil
- 'Bacchante' (Au/d) SPop WAln
- 'Bacchus' (Au/A) MFie NDro SPop WHil
- 'Baggage' (Au) EWoo GAbr GAgs IPen MAsh NDro SPop WCre WHil
- 'Bailey Boy' (Au/B) NDro
- 'Balbithan' (Au/B) EWoo GAgs
- 'Ballynahinch' (Au) ITim
- 'Baltic Amber' (Au) EWoo GAbr GAgs MFie SPop WAln WBla WCre WHil

- 'Bank Error' (Au/S) IPen NDro SPop WAln
- 'Barbara Mason' (Au) WAln
- 'Barbara Weinz' (Au/S) WAln
- 'Barbarella' (Au/S) IPen MFie NDro SPop WCre
- Barnhaven Border hybrids (Au/B) XBar
- Barnhaven doubles (Au/d) GAbr NSum XBar
- 'Barnhaven Gold' (Au) IPen
- 'Barr Beacon' (Au/A) IPen ITim NDro
- 'Basilio' (Au/S) NDro WAln
- 'Basuto' (Au/A) EWoo GAbr GAgs IPen ITim MFie NDro SPop WCre WHil
- 'Beatrice' (Au/A) CTri EWoo GAbr GAgs IPen MFie NDro SPop WCre WHil WIce XBar
- 'Beauty of Bath' (Au/S) WAln
- 'Beckminster' (Au/A) WAln
- 'Bedford Lad' (Au/A) WCre
- 'Beechen Green' (Au/S) EWoo IPen ITim MAsh NDro SPop WCre
- 'Behold' (Au) WAln WCre
- 'Belgravia Gold' (Au/B) NDro WCre
- 'Bella' (Au/d) WAln
- 'Bellamy Pride' (Au/B) GAbr IPen MAsh NDro SPop WCre
- 'Belle Zana' (Au/S) EWoo GAgs IPen MFie NDro SPop WCre WHil
- 'Ben Lawers' (Au/S) SPop
- 'Ben Wyves' (Au/S) IPen SPop WBla WCre
- 'Bendigo' (Au/S) EWoo MFie SPop WAln WCre
- 'Bengal Rose' (Au/S) SPop
- 'Benno' (Au/St) EWoo
- 'Benny Green' (Au/S) IPen MFie SPop WCre
- 'Beppi' (Au) WHil
- 'Bessie' (Au/d) XBar
- 'Best Wishes' (Au/F) WAln
- 'Bethan McSparron' (Au/B) NDro
- 'Betty Stewart' (Au/A) WAln
- 'Bewitched' (Au/A) MFie NDro WAln
- 'Bilbao' (Au/A) WAln
- 'Bilbo Baggins' (Au/A) MAsh NDro SPop WAln
- 'Bill Bailey' (Au/d) EWoo GAbr GAgs NDro WCre
- 'Bilton' (Au/S) SPop WCre
- 'Bingley Folk' (Au/B) NDro SPop
- 'Bisto' (Au/S) SPop WAln
- 'Bitterne Beauty' (Au/d) IPen SPop
- 'Bitterne Bounty' (Au/d) SPop
- 'Bitterne Buttercup' (Au/d) SPop
- 'Bitterne Primrose' (Au/d) SPop
- 'Bittersweet' (Au/St) SPop
- 'Bizarre' (Au) GAgs WCre
- 'Black Adder' (Au/S) IPen SPop WAln
- 'Black Diamond' (Au/d) MFie SPop WHil
- 'Black Ice' (Au/S) WAln
- 'Black Jack'PBR (Au/d) EBee ECtt GBin LBMP LCro LOPS MHol NLar WTor
- 'Blackfield' (Au/S) SPop
- 'Blackhill' (Au/S) ITim MFie SPop
- 'Blackpool Rock' (Au/St) CWCL MFie SPop WAln WCre XBar
- 'Blairside Yellow' (Au/B) ECho LLHF NSla WAbe
- 'Blakeney' (Au/d) MFie NDro
- 'Blossom' (Au/A) GAbr MFie SPop
- 'Blossom Dearie' (Au/St) SPop
- 'Blue Bonnet' (Au/A/d) EWoo GAbr GAgs ITim MFie NDro WAln WCre
- 'Blue Boy' (Au/S) WAln WHil
- 'Blue Chip' (Au/S) EWoo GAgs IPen MFie NDro SPop WCre WHil
- 'Blue Cliff' (Au/S) IPen SPop WAln
- 'Blue Denim' (Au/S) IPen
- 'Blue Fire' (Au/S) MFie SPop
- 'Blue Frills' (Au) NDro WAln
- 'Blue Heaven' (Au/A) EWoo IPen NDro SPop WCre
- 'Blue Jean' (Au/S) GAbr GAgs IPen MFie SPop WCre
- 'Blue Lace' (Au) WAln
- 'Blue Merle' (Au/B) NDro
- 'Blue Night' (Au/B) GAgs ITim
- 'Blue Nile' (Au/S) SPop WCre
- 'Blue Ridge' (Au/A) WAln
- 'Blue Skies' (Au/St) SPop
- 'Blue Steel' (Au/S) WAln
- 'Blue Veil' (Au/S) SPop
- 'Blue Velvet' (Au/B) EWoo GAbr IPen LLHF MFie NBro NDro SBch SPop WCre WHil
- 'Blue Wave' (Au/d) MFie SPop
- 'Blue Yodeler' (Au/A) GAgs MFie NDro NSum SPop WBla WCre WHil
- 'Blue Yonder' (Au/S) WAln
- 'Blush Baby' (Au/St) EBee EWTr EWoo GAbr GAgs NDro NWad SPop WBla WCre WHil XBar
- 'Blusher' (Au/St) WAln
- 'Blyth Spirit' (Au/A) NDro SPop WAln WCre
- 'Bob Dingley' (Au/A) IPen SPop
- 'Bob Lancashire' (Au/S) GAbr GAgs IPen ITim MFie NDro SPop WBla WHil XBar
- 'Bokay' (Au/d) WAln
- 'Bold Tartan' (Au/St) IPen SPop WAln
- 'Bolero' (Au/A) SPop WAln
- 'Bollin Tiger' (Au/St) WAln
- 'Bonafide' (Au/d) SPop WAln WCre
- 'Bonanza' (Au/S) SPop WAln
- 'Bookham Firefly' (Au/A) GAbr GAgs IPen MFie SPop WCre WHil
- 'Border Bandit' (Au/B) GAbr GAgs MFie SPop WAln
- 'Border Beauty' (Au/St) NDro
- 'Border Blue' (Au/B) WAln
- 'Border Patrol' (Au/B) WAln
- 'Border Tawny' (Au/B) NDro
- 'Boromir' (Au/A) EWoo MFie SPop WAln
- 'Bournebrook' (Au/A) WAln
- 'Bowen's Blue' (Au/B) EWoo SPop
- 'Bradford City' (Au/A) CFis CWCL EBee GAgs LCro LOPS NDro SPop WHil XBar
- 'Bradmore Bluebell' (Au) GAbr NDro
- 'Bramley Rose' (Au/B) SPop
- 'Bran' (Au/B) NDro
- 'Brandaris' (Au/A) WAln
- 'Branno' (Au/S) WAln
- 'Branston' (Au/d) **new** XBar
- 'Brass Dog' (Au/S) WAln
- 'Brasso' (Au) IPen MAsh MFie NDro SPop WAln
- 'Brazen Hussy' (Au/d) MFie WAln
- 'Brazil' (Au/S) CTal EBee GAbr GAgs IPen MFie NDro SPop WCre WHil
- 'Brazos River' (Au/A) EWoo IPen MFie SPop WAln WHil
- 'Breckland Joy' (Au/A) WAln
- 'Brenda's Choice' (Au/A) EWoo GAgs IPen MFie NDro SPop WBla WCre
- 'Brentford Bees' (Au/St) WAln
- 'Bright Eyes' (Au/A) IPen MFie WCre
- 'Bright Ginger' (Au/S) EWoo SPop WAln WCre
- 'Brimstone and Treacle' (Au/d) SPop WAln
- 'Broad Gold' (Au/A) MFie SPop WBla WCre
- 'Broadwell Gold' (Au/B) GAbr NDro NSum SPop WCre
- 'Brocade' (Au/St) WCre
- 'Brompton' (Au/S) SPop

- 'Brookfield' (Au/S) GAbr GAgs IPen MFie NDro SPop WBla WCre WHil
- 'Broughton' (Au/S) SPop
- 'Brown Ben' (Au) EWoo IPen MFie WCre WHil
- 'Brown Bess' (Au/A) GAbr GAgs IPen MFie WCot WCre WHil
- 'Brown Sugar' (Au/d) **new** SPop
- 'Brown Tan Double' (Au/d) EWoo GAgs
- 'Brownie' (Au/B) EWoo GAbr GAgs NBir NDro NSum SPop WCre WHil XBar
- 'Brownie Point' (Au/B) NDro
- 'Bucks Green' (Au/S) NDro SPop
- 'Bunty' (Au/A) MFie
- 'Buoyance' (Au/A) WAln
- 'Burnished Gold' (Au/d) WAln
- 'Bush Baby' (Au/B) NDro NSum
- 'Buttercup' (Au/d) SPop
- 'Buttermere' (Au/d) WAln WCre
- 'Butternut' (Au/S) WAln
- 'Butterwick' (Au/A) EWoo GAbr GAgs IPen MFie NDro NEgg SPop WBla WCre XBar
- 'C.G. Haysom' (Au/S) GAbr GAgs NDro SPop WCre WHil
- 'C.W. Needham' (Au/A) GAbr IPen ITim MFie NDro SPop WCre XBar
- 'Cadiz Bay' (Au/d) WAln
- 'Café au Lait' (Au/A) XBar
- 'Callisto' (Au/d) SPop
- 'Calypso' (Au/d) NDro SPop WAln
- 'Cambodunum' (Au/A) IPen MFie NDro NSum SPop WCre WHil
- 'Camelot' (Au/d) ELan EWoo GAgs MFie NBro NDro SPop WCre WHil
- 'Cameo' (Au/A) GAgs
- 'Cameo Beauty' (Au/d) EWoo NDro SPop
- 'Camilla' (Au/A) WAln
- 'Candida' (Au/d) GAgs IPen SPop WBla
- 'Candy Stripe' (Au/St) GAgs SPop
- 'Cappela' (Au/d) WAln
- 'Caramel' (Au/A) GAbr GAgs IPen WAln
- 'Cardinal Red' (Au/d) NDro SPop
- 'Cardington' (Au/A) WAln
- 'Carioca' (Au/A) WAln
- 'Carl Andrew' (Au/S) WAln
- 'Carmel' (Au/d) EWoo MAsh SPop WAln WBla WCre
- 'Carnival' (Au/A) WAln
- 'Carole' (Au/A) MFie SPop WBla WHil
- 'Carreras' (Au) MFie
- 'Carsa Wakes' (Au/d) SPop WAln
- 'Carzon' (Au/A) NDro
- 'Catherine Wheel' (Au/St) SPop WAln
- 'Catta Ha' (Au/d) NDro
- 'Celtic One' (Au/St) NDro SPop
- 'Ceri Nicolle' (Au/B) NDro
- 'Chadwick End' (Au/S) WAln
- 'Chaffinch' (Au/S) EWoo GAbr GAgs IPen NDro SPop
- 'Chamois' (Au/B) EWoo GAbr IPen MFie NDro WCre WHil
- 'Chanel' (Au/S) EWoo SPop WAln WCre
- 'Chantilly Cream' (Au/d) WAln
- 'Charles Bronson' (Au/d) GAbr GAgs MFie NDro WAln
- 'Charles Rennie' (Au/B) EWoo MFie NDro SPop WAln WHil
- 'Charlie's Aunt' (Au/A) WAln
- 'Charlotte Brookes' (Au/d) SPop WAln
- 'Checkmate' (Au) EWoo GAgs MFie SPop WAln
- 'Cheeky' (Au/d) SPop
- 'Chelsea Bridge' (Au/A) EWoo GAgs IPen MFie NDro SPop WBla WCre WHil
- 'Cheops' (Au/A) GAgs IPen MFie NDro NEgg WCre XBar
- 'Cherry' (Au/S) GAbr GAgs IPen SPop WCre
- 'Cherry Picker' (Au/A) GAgs MFie NDro SPop WCre
- 'Cheyenne' (Au/S) EWoo GAbr GAgs MFie NDro SPop WCre
- 'Chiffon' (Au/S) CPBP EWoo IPen NDro NSum SPop WCre
- 'Chiquita' (Au/d) EWoo SPop WCre
- 'Chirichua' (Au/S) WAln
- 'Chloë' (Au/S) IPen MFie SPop
- 'Chloris' (Au/S) MFie SPop
- 'Choir Boy' (Au/A) WAln
- 'Chorister' (Au/S) CPBP EBee GAbr GAgs IPen ITim MFie NDro NSum SPop WCre WHil
- 'Chyne' (Au) EWoo
- 'Cicero' (Au/A) MFie SPop WAln
- 'Cinders' (Au/St) SPop
- 'Cindy' (Au/A) NDro
- 'Cinnamon' (Au/d) EWoo GAgs ITim MFie NDro SPop WCre WHil
- 'Cinnamon' (Au/S) GAbr
- 'Ciribiribin' (Au/A) WAln
- 'Citron-Ella' (Au/d) MFie SPop
- 'Clara' (Au/d) SPop
- 'Clare' (Au/S) IPen MFie NDro SPop WCre
- 'Clarish' (Au) ITim
- 'Classic' (Au/A) WAln
- 'Clatter-Ha' (Au/d) NSum SPop WCre WHil
- 'Claud Wilson' (Au/St) SPop WAln WCre
- 'Claudia Taylor' (Au) EWoo SPop
- 'Cleft Stick' (Au) IPen
- 'Clipper' (Au/S) SPop WAln
- 'Cloth of Gold' (Au/A) NDro WCre
- 'Clotted Cream' (Au/B) NDro
- 'Cloud Nine' (Au/S) WCre
- 'Clouded Yellow' (Au/S) SPop WBla WHil
- 'Cloudy Bay' (Au) NDro WCot
- 'Cloverdale' (Au/d) WAln
- 'Clunie' (Au/S) IPen MFie NDro WCre XBar
- 'Clunie II' (Au/S) GAgs IPen
- 'Cobden Meadows' (Au/A) WAln WCre
- 'Cockle' (Au/S) SPop
- 'Cocoa' (Au/d) **new** XBar
- 'Coffee' (Au/S) IPen MFie NDro SPop WHil
- 'Colbury' (Au/S) NDro SPop WCre XBar
- 'Colonel Champney' (Au/S) EWoo NDro SPop
- 'Comet' (Au/S) IPen NDro NSum
- 'Confederate' (Au/S) WAln
- 'Connaught Court' (Au/A) EWoo IPen LLHF NDro WCre
- 'Conquistador' (Au/A) IPen NDro WAln
- 'Conservative' (Au/S) EWoo GAbr IPen
- 'Consett' (Au/S) EWoo GAgs IPen MFie SPop WHil
- 'Cooks Hill' (Au/d) WAln
- 'Cooper's Gold' (Au/B) NDro
- 'Coop's Green' (Au/S) EWoo
- 'Copper King' (Au/B) WAln
- 'Coppi' (Au/A) EWoo IPen NDro SPop
- 'Coral' (Au/S) GAgs SPop
- 'Corn Dolly' (Au/S) SPop
- 'Cornish Cream' (Au/B) IPen NDro
- 'Cornmeal' (Au/S) GAgs MFie NDro SPop WAln WHil
- 'Corntime' (Au/S) IPen SPop WAln WCre
- 'Corona' (Au/S) WAln
- 'Corporal Jones' (Au/S) SPop WCre
- 'Corporal Kate' (Au/St) WAln
- 'Corrie Files' (Au/d) MFie SPop WAln
- 'Cortez Silver' (Au/S) SPop WAln

- 'Cortina' (Au/S) CPBP ECho EWoo GAbr GAgs IPen ITim MFie NDro SPop WHil
- 'Country Maid' (Au/A) WAln
- 'County Park Red' (Au/B) NDro
- 'Coventry Street' (Au/S) MAsh MFie NDro NSum SPop WCre
- 'Crackley Tagetes' (Au/d) ECho
- 'Crackling Rosie' (A/d) new WAln
- 'Craig Vaughan' (Au/A) MFie NDro NSum SPop XBar
- 'Cranborne' (Au/A) SPop WAln
- 'Crecy' (Au/A) MFie SPop WAln WHil
- 'Cressida' (Au/d) SPop
- 'Crimple' (Au/S) NDro SPop WAln WHil
- 'Crimson Black' (Au/B) SPop
- 'Crimson Glow' (Au/d) EWoo GAgs LCro LOPS MAsh MFie NDro NSum SPop WBla WHil
- 'Crinoline' (Au/S) NDro SPop
- 'Cuckoo Fair' (Au/S) EWoo GAbr GAgs IPen NDro SPop WCre
- 'Cuddles' (Au/A) EWoo MFie WAln WCre
- 'Curly Wurlie' (Au) GAbr
- 'Curry Blend' (Au/B) GAbr IPen NDro SPop WHil
- 'Custard Cream' (Au) WHil
- 'Cutie Pie' (Au/St) IPen SPop WCre
- 'Cuttlefish' (Au/St) SPop
- 'Cyrn Las' (Au/St) new SPop
- 'Daftie Green' (Au/S) EWoo GAbr GAgs IPen NDro WCre
- 'Dakota' (Au/S) EWoo MFie SPop
- 'Dales Red' (Au/B) EWoo GAgs IPen MAsh MFie NDro NSum SPop WHil
- 'Damerham' (Au/A) new SPop
- 'Dan Tiger' (Au/St) EWoo MFie SPop WAln WHil
- 'Daniel' (Au/A) EWoo NDro SPop WAln
- 'Daniel T. Taylor' (Au/A) NDro WAln
- 'Daphnis' (Au/S) SPop WAln
- 'Darent Tiger' (Au/St) XBar
- 'Dark Eyes' (Au/d) EWoo GAbr GAgs MFie NDro NSum SPop WHil
- 'Dark Lady' (Au/A) WAln
- 'Dark Red' (Au/S) IPen
- 'Darth Vader' (Au/d) XBar
- 'David Beckham' (Au/d) SPop WAln
- 'Day by Day' (Au/St) SPop
- 'Decaff' (Au/St) WAln
- 'Deckchair' (Au/St) MFie NDro SPop
- 'Dedham' (Au/d) WAln
- 'Del Boy' (Au/A) SPop WAln
- 'Delicious' (Au/St) SPop
- 'Delilah' (Au/d) GAbr GAgs ITim MAsh MFie NDro NSum SPop WHil
- 'Denise' (Au/S) WAln
- 'Denna Snuffer' (Au/d) GAbr MFie
- 'Derrill' (Au/B) NDro SPop
- 'Devon Cream' (Au/d) ECho IPen MFie NDro SPop WCre
- 'Diamond' (Au/d) WAln
- 'Diane' (Au/A) IPen MFie
- 'Dick Rogers' (Au/B) NDro
- 'Dido' (Au/B) new XBar
- 'Digby' (Au/d) NDro WAln
- 'Digit' (Au/d) NDro WAln
- 'Dilemma' (Au/A) SPop
- 'Dill' (Au/A) IPen MFie NSum SPop WAln WHil
- 'Dilly Dilly' (Au/A) GAbr MFie NDro SPop
- 'Divint Dunch' (Au/A) IPen LLHF MFie NDro SPop WCre WHil
- 'Doctor Duthie' (Au/S) SPop WAln
- 'Doctor Lennon's White' (Au/B) GAbr IPen MFie MHer NDro SPop WCre WHil
- 'Doctor Woolhead' (Au/S) SPop
- 'Dolly' (Au/B) new NDro
- 'Dolly Viney' (Au/d) GAbr WAln
- 'Don Carlos' (Au/d) new XBar
- 'Donhead' (Au/A) MFie NDro SPop WCre WHil
- 'Donn' (Au/d) SPop WAln WCre
- 'Donna Clancy' (Au/S) MFie SPop WCre
- 'Dorado' (Au/d) SPop WAln
- 'Doreen Stephens' (Au/A) GAgs
- 'Doris Jean' (Au/A) MFie NDro
- 'Dorothy' (Au/S) WAln
- 'Doublet' (Au/d) ECho GAbr GAgs IPen MFie NDro NSum SPop WCre WHil
- 'Doubloon' (Au/d) ECho XBar
- 'Doublure' (Au/d) EWoo GAbr GAgs NDro SPop WCre WHil
- 'Douglas Bader' (Au/A) GAgs MFie NDro SPop WCre WHil
- 'Douglas Black' (Au/S) EWoo GAbr GAgs IPen MFie NDro SPop WCre WHil
- 'Douglas Green' (Au/S) EWoo GAgs IPen NDro WCre
- 'Douglas Red' (Au/A) IPen
- 'Douglas White' (Au/S) MFie SPop
- 'Dovedale' (Au/S) NDro SPop WAln
- 'Dowager' (Au/A) MFie
- Downtown Doubles (Au/d) SPop
- 'Doyen' (Au/d) EWoo IPen ITim MFie NDro WAln WCre WHil
- 'Dragon's Hoard' (Au/A) new WAln
- 'Drax' (Au/A) SPop WAln
- 'Dream' (Au/St) SPop
- 'Dubarii' (Au/A) MFie WAln
- 'Duchess of Malfi' (Au/S) SPop WAln
- 'Duchess of York' (Au) LLHF
- 'Duke of Edinburgh' (Au/B) NDro WAln
- 'Dusky Girl' (Au/A) NDro WAln
- 'Dusky Maiden' (Au/A) EWoo GAbr GAgs MFie NDro NSum SPop WCre WHil
- 'Dusky Yellow' (Au/B) ECho NDro
- 'Dusty Miller' (Au/B) EBee ECho LRHS NBir
- 'Eastern Promise' (Au/A) EWoo GAgs MFie NDro NSum SPop WBla WHil
- 'Eaton Dawn' (Au/S) MFie SPop
- 'Ed Spivey' (Au/A) NDro WBla WCre
- 'Eddy Gordon' (Au/A) IPen WAln
- 'Eden Alexander' (Au/B) MFie NDro
- 'Eden Blue Star' (Au/B) EWoo GAbr GAgs NDro SPop
- 'Eden Carmine' (Au/B) MFie MHer NDro SPop
- 'Eden Cynthia' (Au/B) IPen MFie
- 'Eden David' (Au/B) MFie NDro SPop WHil
- 'Eden Ensign' (Au/B) SPop
- 'Eden Fanfare' (Au/B) NDro
- 'Eden Goldfinch' (Au/B) GAbr GAgs IPen MAsh SPop
- 'Eden Grace' (Au/B) new SPop
- 'Eden Greenfinch' (Au/B) EWoo GAbr GAgs MFie NDro SPop WCre
- 'Eden Moonlight' (Au/B) MFie SPop WAln WCre WHil
- 'Eden Sunrise' (Au/B) NDro
- 'Edinburgh' (Au/A) WAln
- 'Edith Allen' (Au/A) WAln
- 'Edith Major' (Au/d) MFie SPop WHil
- 'Edith Mather' (Au/S) WAln
- 'Edward Sweeney' (Au/S) WAln
- 'Eggborough' (Au/A) SPop
- 'Eglinton' (Au) NDro WCre
- 'Eileen K' (Au/S) NDro
- 'El Zoco' (Au/S) SPop
- 'Elara' (Au/d) SPop
- 'Elegance' (Au/S) SPop
- 'Elf Star' (Au/A) SPop WAln

- 'Eli Jenkins' (Au) WAln
- 'Elizabeth Ann' (Au/A) GAbr NDro SPop
- 'Ellen Thompson' (Au/A) EWoo GAbr IPen MFie NDro SPop WCre WHil XBar
- 'Elsie' (Au/A) WCre
- 'Elsie May' (Au/A) EWoo IPen ITim MFie NDro SPop WCre WHil
- 'Elsinore' (Au/S) IPen SPop WCre
- 'Emberglow' (Au/d) WAln
- 'Embley' (Au/S) NDro SPop WCre
- 'Emery Down' (Au/S) NDro SPop WBla WCre
- 'Emily' (Au/d) IPen
- 'Emma Louise' (Au) IPen
- 'Emmett Smith' (Au/A) NBro NDro WAln
- 'Ems Blue' (Au/B) **new** WAln
- 'Ems Choice' (Au/B) **new** WAln
- 'Enigma' (Au/S) SPop WAln
- 'Enlightened' (Au/A) MFie NDro
- 'Envy' (Au/S) MFie WAln
- 'Erica' (Au/A) GAbr IPen MFie NDro NSum SPop WCre WHil
- 'Erjon' (Au/S) MFie SPop
- 'Error' (Au/S) MFie WAln
- 'Eschman Starflower' (Au/S) WHil
- 'Esso' (Au/S) WAln
- 'Ethel' (Au) NDro
- 'Ethel Wild' (Au/d) SPop
- 'Ethel Wilkes' (Au/d) MFie WAln
- 'Etna' (Au/S) WAln
- 'Ettrick' (Au/S) WAln
- 'Europa' (Au/d) SPop
- 'Eve Guest' (Au/A) EWoo NDro SPop WAln
- 'Eventide' (Au/S) GAgs SPop
- 'Everest Blue' (Au/S) EWoo GAbr GAgs SPop WCre XBar
- 'Everest Flush' (Au/S) WAln
- 'Excalibur' (Au/d) EWoo GAbr GAgs NDro NSum SPop WCre
- 'Exhibition Blau' (Exhibition Series) (Au/B) WHil
- 'Eye Candy' (Au/St) SPop
- 'Eyeopener' (Au/A) IPen MFie NDro SPop WHil
- 'Fabuloso' (Au/St) EWoo NDro SPop WBla WCre
- 'Fairy' (Au/A) WAln
- 'Fairy Light' (Au/S) SPop WAln
- 'Fairy Moon' (Au/S) IPen WAln
- 'Fairy Queen' (Au/S) WAln
- 'Falcon' (Au/S) SPop WAln
- 'Faliraki Fanciful' (Au) EWoo
- 'Faloonside' (Au) IPen
- 'Falstaff' (Au/d) WAln
- 'Fanciful' (Au/S) EWoo MFie NDro WHil XBar
- 'Fancy Free' (Au) SPop
- 'Fancy Pants' (Au/S) SPop
- 'Fandancer' (Au/A) WAln
- 'Fandango' WCre
- 'Fanfare' (Au/S) EWoo MFie NDro SPop WBla WHil
- 'Fanny Meerbeck' (Au/S) GAbr GAgs IPen MFie NDro SPop WBla WHil
- 'Fantasia' (Au/d) SPop WAln
- 'Faro' (Au/S) NDro SPop WCre
- 'Favourite' (Au/S) EWoo GAbr GAgs IPen ITim MAsh MFie NDro SPop WBla WCre WHil XBar
- 'Fearless' (Au/S) WAln
- 'Fen Tiger' (Au/St) SPop WAln
- 'Fenby' (Au/S) EWoo SPop
- 'Fennay' (Au/S) EWoo NSum WAln
- 'Ferrybridge' (Au/A) IPen NDro WAln
- 'Fiddler's Green' (Au/d) CPBP EWoo GAbr GAgs IPen NDro SPop WCot WCre XBar
- 'Figaro' (Au/S) EWoo MFie NDro SPop WCre
- 'Figurine' (Au/d) WAln
- 'Finchfield' (Au/A) GAbr IPen MFie NDro WAln WCre
- 'Finley' (Au/B) NDro
- 'Firecracker' (Au) IPen WAln
- 'Firenze' (Au/A) MFie SPop
- 'Firsby' (Au/d) EWoo MFie NDro SPop WAln WBla WHil
- 'First Green' (Au/St) **new** SPop
- 'First Lady' (Au/A) IPen SPop WAln WBla WCre
- 'First Light' (Au/B) NDro SPop
- 'Fishtoft' (Au/d) MFie SPop
- 'Fitzroy' (Au/d) EWoo SPop
- 'Fleecy' (Au/S) SPop
- 'Fleet Street' (Au/S) GAbr GAgs MFie NDro SPop WHil
- 'Fleminghouse' (Au/S) GAbr SPop WCre
- 'Florence Brown' (Au/S) IPen ITim
- 'Fluffy Duckling' (Au/S) SPop
- 'For You' (Au/St) SPop
- 'Foreign Affairs' (Au/S) SPop
- 'Forest Beech' (Au/d) SPop
- 'Forest Bordeaux' (Au/d) SPop
- 'Forest Bracken' (Au/d) SPop
- 'Forest Burgundy' (Au/d) GAgs SPop
- 'Forest Burnt Gold' (Au/d) SPop
- 'Forest Cappuccino' (Au/d) EWoo SPop
- 'Forest Duet' (Au/d) EWoo SPop
- 'Forest Fire' (Au/d) EWoo GAbr MFie SPop
- 'Forest Glade' (Au/d) SPop
- 'Forest Gorse' (Au/d) SPop WCre
- 'Forest Lemon' (Au/d) EWoo MFie SPop WCre
- 'Forest Lime' (Au/d) SPop
- 'Forest Pines' (Au/S) SPop WAln
- 'Forest Shade' (Au/d) SPop
- 'Forest Sunburst' (Au/d) SPop
- 'Forest Sunlight' (Au/d) SPop
- 'Forest Sunshine' (Au/d) **new** SPop
- 'Forest Twilight' (Au/d) EWoo MFie SPop WCre
- 'Foxfire' (Au/A) WAln
- 'Fradley' (Au/A) IPen MFie NDro WAln WCre WHil
- 'Françoise' (Au/d) XBar
- 'Frank Bailey' (Au/d) EWoo MFie SPop WAln
- 'Frank Crosland' (Au/A) MFie NDro NSum WCre WHil
- 'Frank Faulkner' (Au/A) WAln
- 'Frank Jenning' (Au/A) NDro WAln
- 'Frank Taylor' (Au/S) EWoo
- 'Fred Booley' (Au/d) EWoo GAbr GAgs IPen LLHF MFie NDro NSum SPop WHil XBar
- 'Fred Livesley' (Au/A) WAln
- 'Freestyle' (Au/B) **new** WAln
- 'Fresco' (Au/A) SPop WAln
- 'Freya' (Au/S) SPop
- 'Friskney' (Au/d) EWoo SPop WAln
- 'Frittenden Yellow' (Au/B) GAbr SPop
- 'Frosty' (Au/S) EWoo NDro SPop WBla WCre
- 'Fuller's Red' (Au/S) ITim NDro SPop WCre WHil
- 'Funny Valentine' (Au/d) EWoo IPen MFie NDro SPop WBla WCre WHil
- 'Fuzzy' (Au/St) WAln
- 'G.L. Taylor' (Au/A) IPen NDro
- 'Gaia' (Au/d) EWoo SPop WCre WHil
- 'Gail Atkinson' (Au/A) SPop WAln WBla
- 'Galatea' (Au/S) WAln
- 'Galator' (Au/A) WAln
- 'Galen' (Au/A) GAbr SPop WCre
- 'Ganymede' (Au/d) SPop WAln

- 'Gary Pallister' (Au/A) SPop WAln WBla WCre
- 'Gateshead' (Au/S) WCre
- 'Gavin Ward' (Au/S) WAln
- 'Gay Crusader' (Au/A) GAbr IPen MFie NDro SPop WCre WHil
- 'Gazza' (Au/A) WAln
- 'Gee Cross' (Au/A) GAgs IPen MFie WCre
- 'Geldersome Green' (Au/S) NDro SPop
- 'Gemini' (Au/S) NDro
- 'General Champney' (Au) WCre
- 'Generosity' (Au/A) GAgs MFie NDro WCre WHil
- 'Geoffrey Bick' (Au/A) SPop
- 'Geordie' (Au/A) WAln
- 'George Edge' (Au/B) NDro
- 'George Harrison' (Au/B) GAgs SPop
- 'George Jennings' (Au/A) MFie NDro SPop
- 'George Swinford's Leathercoat' (Au/B) GAbr NDro
- 'Geronimo' (Au/S) GAbr IPen MAsh MFie NDro SPop WBla WCre
- 'Gimli' (Au/A) WAln
- 'Girl Guide' (Au/S) WHil
- 'Gizabroon' (Au/S) CFis CWCL EWoo GAbr GAgs LCro LOPS MFie NDro NEgg NLar SPop WBla WCre WHil XBar
- 'Glasnost' (Au/S) WAln
- 'Glazebrook' (Au/S) SPop
- 'Gleam' (Au/S) CTal CWCL EBee ECho EDAr GAgs GKev IPen LLHF MFie NDro NPri NSum SPop WBla WCre WHil XBar
- 'Glencoe' (Au/S) EWoo GAgs NDro SPop
- 'Gleneagles' (Au/S) EWoo GAgs IPen SPop WAln WBla WCre
- 'Glenelg' (Au/S) EWoo GAbr ITim MFie NDro NSum SPop WBla WCre WHil
- 'Glenluce' (Au/S) EWoo GAgs SPop
- 'Gloire de Dijon' (Au/S) XBar
- 'Gnome' (Au/B) GAbr GAgs IPen NDro
- 'Goeblii' (Au/B) MFie NDro SPop WHil
- 'Gold Seal' (Au/d) SPop
- 'Gold Seam' (Au/A) EWoo MFie WAln WHil
- 'Golden Boy' (Au/A) MFie NDro NSum SPop WAln
- 'Golden Chartreuse' (Au/d) EWoo GAbr NDro SPop
- 'Golden Fleece' (Au/S) EWoo GAbr MAsh MFie NDro SPop WCre
- 'Golden Girl' (Au/A) WAln
- 'Golden Glory' (Au/A) WAln
- 'Golden Harvest' (Au/A) SPop
- 'Golden Hind' (Au/d) EWoo GAbr GAgs MFie NBro NDro SPop
- 'Golden Splendour' (Au/d) EWoo GAgs IPen ITim MFie NDro NSum SPop WBla WCre WHil
- 'Golden Wedding' (Au/A) GAgs IPen MFie SPop WAln WCre WHil
- 'Goldie' (Au/S) NDro
- 'Gollum' (Au/A) MFie NDro SPop WAln WBla
- 'Good Report' (Au/A) GAgs MAsh MFie NDro NSum SPop WBla WHil
- 'Goody Goody' (Au/St) SPop
- 'Googie' (Au/d) SPop
- 'Gordon Files' (Au/S) WAln
- 'Gorey' (Au/A) IPen MFie WCre WHil
- 'Gorgeous George' (Au/St) SPop
- 'Grabley' (Au/S) EWoo SPop WCre
- 'Grace' (Au/S) WAln
- 'Grace Ellen' (Au/S) WAln
- 'Grand Slam' (Au/D) MFie
- 'Grandad's Favourite' (Au/B) EWoo NDro SPop
- 'Green Abundance' (Au/B) EWoo
- 'Green Café' (Au/S) SPop
- 'Green Finger' (Au/S) EWoo MFie SPop WHil
- 'Green Frill' (Au) GAgs NDro
- 'Green Goddess' (Au/St) EWoo WAln
- 'Green Heart' (Au/S) EWoo SPop
- 'Green Isle' (Au/S) EWoo GAbr IPen MFie NDro SPop WCre XBar
- 'Green Jacket' (Au/S) IPen SPop WCre
- 'Green Lane' (Au/S) XBar
- 'Green Meadows' (Au/S) GAgs SPop WAln
- 'Green Mouse' (Au/S) WAln
- 'Green Mustard' (Au/S) SPop
- 'Green Parrot' (Au/S) EWoo GAbr NDro SPop WCre WHil
- 'Green Shank' (Au/S) EWoo GAgs IPen NDro SPop WHil XBar
- 'Green Woodpecker' (Au/S) IPen
- 'Greenfield's Fancy' (Au) EBee
- 'Greenfinch' (Au/S) EWoo
- 'Greenfinger' (Au/S) WAln
- 'Greenheart' (Au/S) SPop
- 'Greenpeace' (Au/S) EWoo GAbr GAgs SPop WAln WBla WCre
- 'Greswolde' (Au/d) EWoo MFie SPop WAln
- 'Greta' (Au/S) CWCL ECho EWoo GAbr GAgs IPen MFie NDro SPop WCre WHil
- 'Gretna Green' (Au/S) EWoo SPop
- 'Grey Bonnet' (Au/S) SPop WAln
- 'Grey Cloud' (Au/B) NDro WHil
- 'Grey Dawn' (Au/S) WAln
- 'Grey Edge' (Au) ECho
- 'Grey Friar' (Au/S) SPop WAln
- 'Grey Hawk' (Au/S) IPen SPop WAln
- 'Grey Lady' (Au/S) WAln
- 'Grey Ladywood' (Au/d) **new** SPop
- 'Grey Lag' (Au/S) SPop WHil XBar
- 'Grey Monarch' (Au/S) GAbr IPen MFie SPop WAln WCre WHil
- 'Grey Owl' (Au/S) SPop WAln
- 'Grey Ridge' (Au/S) WAln
- 'Grey Shrike' (Au/S) SPop WAln
- 'Grizedale' (Au/S) SPop
- 'Groupie' (Au/St) SPop
- 'Grüner Veltliner' (Au/S) SPop WCre
- 'Guinea' (Au/S) CTal EWoo GAbr IPen ITim MFie SPop WCre
- 'Gwai Loh' (Au) NDro
- 'Gwen' (Au/A) MFie NDro SPop WAln WCre XBar
- 'Gwen Baker' (Au/d) IPen MFie NDro SPop WAln WCre
- 'Gwenda' (Au/A) SPop WAln WHil
- 'Gypsy Rose Lee' (Au/A) MFie
- 'H Old Gold' (Au/S) NDro
- 'Habanera' (Au/A) MFie NDro NSum SPop WCre
- 'Haffner' (Au/S) IPen SPop
- 'Hallmark' (Au/A) EWoo MFie NDro WAln
- 'Handsome Lass' (Au/St) EWoo GAgs IPen MFie NDro SPop WAln WCre
- 'Hannah' (Au/A) WAln
- 'Harlequin' (Au/B) NDro
- 'Harmony' (Au/B) EWoo MFie NBro NDro XBar
- 'Harry Hotspur' (Au/A) IPen MFie NDro NSum SPop WCre WHil
- 'Harry 'O'' (Au/S) MFie NDro SPop WCre
- 'Harthorpeburn' (Au/B) NDro
- 'Harvest Glow' (Au/S) IPen NDro SPop WHil
- 'Harvest Gold' (Au/S) NDro WCre

- 'Havana' (Au/d) SPop WAln
- 'Hawkwood' (Au/S) GAbr GAgs IPen MFie NDro NEgg WBla WCre WHil XBar
- 'Hazel' (Au/B) MFie NDro WCre
- 'Hazel' (Au/A) IPen ITim MFie NDro SPop WHil
- 'Headdress' (Au/S) EWoo GAbr GAgs IPen MFie SPop
- 'Heady' (Au/A) CWCL EWoo GAgs MFie NDro WCre WHil XBar
- 'Heart of Gold' (Au/A) MFie SPop WAln
- 'Hearts of Oak' (Au/A) WAln
- 'Heaven Scent' (Au) WHil
- 'Hebers' (Au) NDro SPop WAln
- 'Helen' (Au/S) GAbr IPen MFie NDro SPop WCre WHil
- 'Helen Barter' (Au/S) NDro NSum SPop WCre WHil
- 'Helen Ruane' (Au/d) EBee EWoo GAgs GKev SPop WCre
- 'Helena' (Au/S) IPen MFie SPop WAln WCre WHil
- 'Helena Brown' (Au/S) SPop WAln
- 'Helena Dean' (Au/d) SPop WAln
- 'Helluinn' (Au/d) SPop
- 'Henry's Bane' (Au/St) SPop
- 'Her Nibs' (Au/St) MAsh SPop WCre
- 'Hermia' (Au/A) MFie SPop WHil
- 'Hetty Woolf' (Au/S) GAbr GAgs ITim NDro SPop WCre
- 'Hew Dalrymple' (Au/S) NDro SPop WAln
- 'High Hopes' (Au) WAln
- 'Highland Park' (Au/A) NDro SPop
- 'Hillhook' (Au/A) WAln
- 'Hillview Hermes' (Au/S) WHil
- Hillview selection (Au) WHil
- 'Hinton Admiral' (Au/S) EWoo GAbr GAgs IPen NDro SPop WCre WHil XBar
- 'Hinton Fields' (Au/S) CPBP EBee EShb EWTr GAbr GAgs IPen LCro MFie NDro NEgg NPri SPop WBla WCre WHil
- 'Hobby Horse' (Au) EWoo GAgs ITim
- 'Holyrood' (Au/S) EWoo GAbr IPen ITim NDro SPop WAln XBar
- 'Honey' (Au/d) GAbr NBro NDro NEgg NSum SPop
- 'Honeydawn' (Au/B) NDro
- 'Hopleys Coffee' (Au/d) EWoo GAbr NDro SPop WAln WCre
- 'Hopton Gem' (Au/B) NDro
- 'Hot Chocolate' (Au/d) new SPop
- 'Howard Telford' (Au/A) MFie SPop
- 'Hughie' (Au/A) WAln
- 'Humphrey' (Au/S) WAln
- 'Hurstwood Midnight' (Au) MFie WAln XBar
- 'Iago' (Au/S) NDro SPop WAln
- 'Ian Greville' (Au/A) IPen MFie NDro SPop WBla
- 'Ibis' (Au/S) WAln WCre
- 'Ice Cap' (Au/d) SPop
- 'Ice Maiden' (Au/A) EWoo GAbr IPen MFie NDro SPop WBla WCre WHil
- 'Icon' (Au/St) SPop
- 'Ida' (Au/A) IPen
- 'Idmiston' (Au/S) EWoo GAbr GAgs IPen NDro SPop WCre WHil XBar
- 'Ilona' (Au/d) SPop
- 'Imari Stripe' (Au/St) WHil
- 'Immaculate' (Au/A) MFie SPop WBla WCre WHil
- 'Impassioned' (Au/A) MFie SPop WBla WCre XBar
- 'Impeccable' (Au/A) IPen MFie
- 'Imperturbable' (Au/A) IPen MFie NDro SPop
- 'Indian Love Call' (Au/A) GAbr GAgs IPen ITim MFie NDro SPop WBla WCre WHil
- 'Innsworth' (Au/A) SPop WAln
- 'Iris Scott' (Au/A) ITim NDro
- 'Isabel' (Au/S) WAln
- 'Isabella' (Au/A) NDro WAln
- 'Jac' (Au/S) SPop
- 'Jack Dean' (Au/A) EWoo MFie SPop WCre WHil XBar
- 'Jack Horner' (Au) WAln
- 'Jack Redfern' (Au/A) NDro
- 'Jaffa' (Au/A) EWoo NDro NSum WAln WCre
- 'James Arnot' (Au/S) GAbr IPen NDro SPop WAln WCre XBar
- 'James Watham' (Au/S) WAln
- 'Jane' (Au/S) WAln
- 'Jane Myers' (Au/d) WAln WHil
- 'Janet' (Au) ECho
- 'Janet Watts' (Au) GAgs WCre
- 'Janie Hill' (Au/A) MFie SPop WBla WCre
- 'Jealous Lover' (Au/St) SPop
- 'Jean Fielder' (Au/A) NDro SPop WAln
- 'Jean Jacques' (Au/A) WAln

I - 'Jean Jacques' (Au/d) new XBar

- 'Jean Walker' (Au/B) SPop
- 'Jeanne' (Au/A) EWoo MFie
- 'Jeannie Telford' (Au/A) MFie NDro SPop WCre
- 'Jeff Scruton' (Au/A) SPop WAln
- 'Jenny' (Au/A) EWoo IPen MFie NDro NRya SPop WCre
- 'Jersey Bounce' (Au/A) EWoo GAbr ITim NDro WAln WCre
- 'Jesmond' (Au/S) WAln
- 'Jessie' (Au/d) EWoo
- 'Jilting Jessie' (Au/St) GAgs IPen NDro SPop
- 'Joan Butler' (Au) WAln
- 'Joan Curtis' (Au/d) SPop
- 'Joan Elliott' (Au/A) GAbr
- 'Joanne' (Au/A) EWoo GAbr GAgs MFie NDro SPop WCre
- 'Joe Perks' (Au/A) EWoo GAgs IPen ITim MFie NBro NDro SPop WCre WHil XBar
- 'Joel' (Au/S) EWoo GAgs IPen ITim MFie NDro SPop WBla WCre
- 'Johann Bach' (Au/B) EWoo SPop
- 'John Stewart' (Au/A) MFie SPop
- 'John Wayne' (Au/A) EWoo GAbr MFie NDro WBla WCre WHil
- 'John Woolf' (Au/S) NDro
- 'Jonathon' (Au/A) EWoo NDro WAln
- 'Jorvik' (Au/S) MFie SPop WCre
- 'Joy' (Au/A) IPen LLHF MFie NDro NSum NWad SPop WCre WHil
- 'Joyce' (Au/A) EWoo GAbr GAgs IPen MFie NDro NSum SPop WHil
- 'Judith Borman' (Au/d) NDro
- 'Julia' (Au/S) SPop WAln
- 'Julia Jane' (Au/B) NDro WCre
- 'Julie Nuttall' (Au/B) EWoo GAgs NDro NWad SPop WHil
- 'June' (Au/A) NDro SPop
- 'Jungfrau' (Au/d) MFie NDro SPop WAln
- 'Jupiter' (Au/S) SPop WAln
- 'Jupp' (Au) EBee EWTr GAgs LCro LOPS
- 'Jura' (Au/A) WAln
- 'Just Steven' (Au/A) SPop WAln
- 'Justin Case' (Au/B) new WAln
- 'K S' (Au/S) NDro
- 'Karen Cordrey' (Au/S) EBee ECho EWoo GAbr GAgs IPen ITim MFie NDro NSum SPop WBla WHil
- 'Karen McDonald' (Au/A) MFie NDro SPop
- 'Kate Haywood' (Au/B) NDro WCre WHil
- 'Kath Dryden' see *P. allionii* 'Kath Dryden'

- 'Kelso' (Au/A) MFie
- 'Ken Chilton' (Au/A) EWoo GAgs MFie NDro SPop WCre WHil
- 'Kenco' (Au/d) SPop
- 'Kentucky Blues' (Au/d) IPen MFie SPop WAln
- 'Kercup' (Au/A) EWoo MFie SPop WCre
- 'Kerry' (Au/A) EBee GAgs WAln
- 'Kersey' (Au/S) SPop
- 'Kevin' (Au/A) SPop WAln
- 'Kevin Keegan' (Au/A) MFie NDro NSum SPop WHil
- 'Key West' (Au/A) NDro SPop WAln
- 'Khachaturian' (Au/A) MFie NDro WAln
- 'Kilby' (Au/A) GAgs SPop WBla
- 'Kim' (Au/A) IPen MFie NDro SPop WCre WHil
- 'Kimberworth Boy' (Au/A) NDro
- 'Kincraig' (Au/S) SPop WAln
- 'King George' (Au/d) MFie WAln WHil
- 'King Kong' (Au) WAln
- 'Kingcup' (Au/A) GAbr GAgs MFie SPop WCre
- 'Kingfisher' (Au/A) EWoo GAbr GAgs IPen ITim MFie NDro SPop WHil
- 'Kingpin' (Au/St) NDro
- 'Kintail' (Au/A) MFie
- 'Kiowa' (Au/S) SPop WCre
- 'Kirklands' (Au/d) EWoo ITim MFie NDro SPop WCre WHil
- 'Knights' (Au/S) SPop
- 'Kohinoor' (Au) MFie WHil
- 'Königin der Nacht' (Au/St) EWoo MFie NDro SPop WCre WHil
- 'Lady Daresbury' (Au/A) MFie NDro SPop WCre WHil
- 'Lady Day' (Au/d) SPop WAln
- 'Lady Diana' (Au/S) EWoo IPen NDro
- 'Lady Emma Monson' (Au/S) EWoo SPop
- 'Lady Joyful' (Au/S) WCre
- 'Lady of the Vale' (Au/A) NDro WAln
- 'Lady Penelope' (Au/S) WAln
- 'Lady Zoë' (Au/S) EWoo LLHF MAsh MFie NDro SPop WCre
- 'Laguna' (Au/d) **new** SPop
- 'Lambert's Gold' (Au) GAbr SPop
- 'Lambrook Gold' (Au/B) NDro
- 'Lamplugh' (Au/d) IPen NSum SPop WHil
- 'Lancelot' (Au/d) EWoo SPop
- 'Landy' (Au/A) MFie NDro SPop WCre
- 'Langley Park' (Au/A) IPen MFie NDro SPop WCre WHil
- 'Laphroaigh' (Au/S) WAln
- 'Laptop' (Au/St) SPop WBla WCre
- 'Lara' (Au/A) MFie WCre
- 'Laredo' (Au/A) EWoo WAln
- 'Larry' (Au/A) EWoo GAgs LLHF MFie NDro SPop WCre XBar
- 'Late Romantic' (Au) ECtt GAbr GAgs GBin MHol NLar WIce WTor
- 'Lavender and Old Lace' (Au/d) SPop
- 'Lavender Lady' (Au/B) IPen NDro NEgg
- 'Lavender Ridge' (Au/B) WAln
- 'Lavenham' (Au/S) SPop WAln
- 'Laverock' (Au/S) NBir NBro NEgg WCre WHil
- 'Laverock Fancy' (Au/S) EWoo GAbr GAgs IPen NDro
- 'Lazy River' (Au/A) EWoo NDro WAln
- 'Leather Jacket' (Au) GAbr WCre WHil
- 'Leathercoat' (Au) EWoo SPop
- 'Lechistan' (Au/S) GAgs IPen MAsh MFie NDro SPop WCre WHil
- 'Lee' (Au/A) IPen MFie NDro WAln WCre
- 'Lee Clark' (Au/A) MFie WAln
- 'Lee Paul' (Au/A) EWoo GAbr GAgs IPen MFie NDro SPop WAln WBla WCre WHil
- 'Lee Sharpe' (Au/A) EWoo IPen MFie NDro SPop WAln
- 'Legolas' (Au/A) SPop WAln
- 'Lemmy Getatem' (Au/d) IPen WHil
- 'Lemon Drizzle' (Au/S) WAln
- 'Lemon Drop' (Au/S) EWoo IPen ITim MFie NBro NDro SPop WCre
- 'Lemon Ice' (Au/S) IPen WAln
- 'Lemon Ridge' (Au/B) **new** WAln
- 'Lemon Sherbet' (Au/B) EWoo GAbr GAgs IPen NDro SPop WHil
- 'Lemon Zest' (Au/d) WAln
- 'Lemonade' (Au) GAgs
- 'Leona' (Au/d) **new** SPop
- 'Lepton Jubilee' (Au/S) EWoo GAbr NDro WAln
- 'Leroy Brown' (Au/A) WAln
- 'Lester' (Au/d) MFie SPop WAln WHil
- 'Leverton' (Au/d) EWoo SPop
- 'Lewis Telford' (Au/A) SPop
- 'Lich' (Au/S) NDro
- 'Lichfield' (Au/A/d) EWoo IPen SPop WCre
- 'Light Fantastic' (Au/S) SPop
- 'Light Hearted' (Au/A) MFie NDro
- 'Light Music' (Au/d) WAln
- 'Likely Lad' (Au/St) EWoo SPop
- 'Lila' (Au/S) NDro SPop WAln WCre
- 'Lilac Domino' (Au/S) GAbr GAgs IPen MFie NDro NEgg SPop WCre WHil
- 'Lilac Ladywood' (Au/d) MFie SPop
- 'Lillian Hill' (Au/A) EWoo MFie WAln
- 'Lillibet' (Au/A) NDro
- 'Lima' (Au/d) IPen SPop WAln
- 'Limaki' (Au/d) SPop
- 'Lime Ridge' (Au) WAln
- 'Limelight' (Au/A) EWoo IPen NDro SPop
- 'Limelight' (Au/S) IPen SPop
- 'Lincoln Biscuit' (Au/d) SPop
- 'Lincoln Bullion' (Au/d) EWoo MAsh NDro SPop WBla WCre XBar
- 'Lincoln Charm' (Au/d) GAbr SPop
- 'Lincoln Chestnut' (Au/d) EWoo NDro SPop WBla WCre XBar
- 'Lincoln Consort' (Au/d) SPop
- 'Lincoln Elf' (Au/d) SPop
- 'Lincoln Gem' (Au/d) SPop
- 'Lincoln Glow' (Au/d) SPop
- 'Lincoln Halo' (Au/d) SPop
- 'Lincoln Imperial' (Au/d) GAgs NDro SPop
- 'Lincoln Major' (Au/d) SPop
- 'Lincoln Pride' (Au/d) SPop
- 'Lincoln Storm' (Au/d) **new** SPop
- 'Lincoln Whisper' (Au/d) NDro
- 'Linda' (Au/A) SPop WAln
- 'Lindley' (Au/S) GAgs NDro SPop
- 'Lindsey Moreno' (Au/S) WAln
- 'Ling' (Au/A) GAbr MFie NDro SPop WCre
- 'Linnet' (Au/B) NDro
- 'Lintz' (Au/B) MFie NDro SPop WCre WHil
- 'Linze 2' (Au/S) NDro
- 'Lisa' (Au/A) EWoo GAbr GAgs IPen MFie SPop WCre WHil
- 'Lisa Clara' (Au/S) EWoo GAbr GAgs IPen MAsh MFie NDro SPop WCre
- 'Lisa's Smile' (Au/S) EWoo MFie NDro SPop WHil
- 'Little Bo Peep' (Au) WAln
- 'Little Rosetta' (Au/d) GAbr GAgs MFie NDro NSum WCre WHil
- 'Lizzie Files' (Au/A) SPop WAln
- 'Lockyer's Gem' (Au/B/St) IPen NDro NEgg

- 'Lolita' (Au/St) EWoo GAgs SPop WHil
- 'Lord Saye and Sele' (Au/St) CWCL EWoo GAbr GAgs IPen ITim MAsh MFie NCGa NDro NEgg NSum NWad SPop WBla WCre WHil XBar
- 'Lothlorien' (Au/A) WAln
- 'Louis' (Au/d) XBar
- 'Louisa Woolhead' (Au/d) EWoo SPop
- 'Louise Jordan' (Au/A) NDro
- 'Love Nest' (Au/S) SPop
- 'Lovebird' (Au/S) EWoo GAbr MFie NDro SPop WCre WHil XBar
- 'Lucia' (Au/B) **new** XBar
- 'Lucky Sport' (Au/B) **new** WAln
- 'Lucky Strike' (Au) WAln
- 'Lucy Locket' (Au/B) EWTr GAbr IPen LCro LOPS NDro NEgg NSum WCre WHil
- 'Ludlow' (Au/S) GAbr SPop WCre
- 'Lune Tiger' (Au/St) SPop
- 'Lupy Minstrel' (Au/S) IPen MFie NDro SPop WAln WCre
- 'Lusty Lad' (Au/St) SPop
- 'Lyn' (Au/A) WCre
- 'Lynn' (Au/A) WAln
- 'Lynn Cooper' (Au) EWoo SPop
- 'MacWatt's Blue' (Au/B) GAbr IPen NDro SPop WCre WHil
- 'Macy the Cat' (Au) WHil
- 'Madelaine Palmer' (Au/d) SPop
- 'Maggie' (Au/S) EWoo GAbr NDro SPop WCre
- 'Magnolia' (Au/B) WCre WHil
- 'Maizie' (Au/S) WCre
- 'Mandarin' (Au/A) GAbr GAgs MFie NDro NSum SPop WBla WCre WHil XBar
- 'Mandy' (Au/S) MFie
- 'Manka' (Au/S) SPop
- 'Mardi Gras' (Au/d) WAln
- 'Margaret' (Au/S) EWoo GAbr
- 'Margaret Faulkner' (Au/A) GAbr MFie WBla WCre
- 'Margaret Irene' (Au/A) IPen SPop WCre
- 'Margaret Martin' (Au/S) IPen MFie NDro SPop WCre
- 'Margaret Merril' (Au) GAbr
- 'Margot Fonteyn' (Au/A) EWoo GAbr IPen MFie SPop WAln WBla WHil
- 'Mariandl' (Au/A) **new** EBee
- 'Marie Crousse' (Au/d) CFis CMea GMaP IPen ITim MFie NDro NPri SPop WCot WCre WHil
- 'Marie Pierre' (Au/d) XBar
- 'Marion Howard Spring' (Au/A) MFie WCre
- 'Marion Tiger' (Au/St) SPop WAln
- 'Mark' (Au/A) GAgs IPen MFie NBro SPop WCre
- 'Marmion' (Au/S) EWoo GAbr GAgs IPen ITim MFie NDro SPop WBla WCre WHil XBar
- 'Martha Livesley' (Au/A) WAln
- 'Martha's Choice' (Au/A) WAln
- 'Martin Fish' (Au) WCre
- 'Martin Luther King' (Au/S) EWoo NDro SPop WCre WHil XBar
- 'Mary' (Au/d) GAbr NDro SPop WAln
- 'Mary Poppins' (Au/S) MFie NDro
- 'Mary Taylor' (Au/S) WAln
- 'Mary Zach' (Au/S) EWoo MFie SPop WAln WHil
- 'Matthew Yates' (Au/d) EBee GAbr GAgs IPen ITim MFie NDro NPri SPop WCot WCre WHil WWFP
- 'Maureen Millward' (Au/A) IPen MFie SPop
- 'May' (Au/A) EWoo NDro WCre
- 'May Be' (Au/B) **new** WAln
- 'May Booley' (Au/d) SPop
- 'Mazetta Stripe' (Au/S/St) GAbr GAgs MFie NBro NDro SPop WBla WCre WHil
- 'Meadow Sweet' (Au/S) WAln
- 'Meadowlark' (Au/A) EWoo ITim MFie SPop WHil
- 'Megan' (Au/d) SPop WAln
- 'Mehta' (Au/A) IPen MFie NDro SPop WAln
- 'Mellifluous' (Au) GAgs MFie WCre WHil
- 'Melody' (Au/S) IPen NDro SPop
- 'Menin' (Au/d) SPop
- 'Mere Green' (Au/S) EWoo WAln
- 'Mere Peppermint' (Au) EWoo WAln
- 'Merlin' (Au/S) IPen MFie NSum
- 'Merlin Stripe' (Au/St) CWCL EBee IPen NDro SPop WCre WHil XBar
- 'Mermaid' (Au/d) GAbr IPen
- 'Merridale' (Au/A) GAbr MFie SPop WCre WHil
- 'Mersey Tiger' (Au/S) EWoo GAbr GAgs ITim MFie NDro NSum SPop WHil
- 'Metis' (Au/d) SPop
- 'Mexicano' (Au/A) WAln
- 'Michael' (Au/S) MFie SPop WAln WHil
- 'Michael Wattam' (Au/S) NDro SPop WAln
- 'Mick' (Au/A) MFie WCre WHil
- 'Midland Marvel' (Au/St) SPop
- 'Midnight' (Au/A) WAln
- 'Mikado' (Au/S) IPen MFie NSum SPop WBla WCre WHil XBar
- 'Milkmaid' (Au/A) MFie WMAq
- 'Millicent' (Au/A) MFie WCre WHil
- 'Millie Redfern' (Au/d) SPop
- 'Minley' (Au/S) CPBP EWoo GAbr GAgs MFie NBir NDro NEgg SPop WCre WIce
- 'Minotaur' (Au/A) SPop
- 'Minstead' (Au/S) SPop
- 'Minstrel' (Au/S) MFie NDro SPop WCre
- 'Minty' (Au/St) SPop
- 'Mipsie Miranda' (Au/d) SPop
- 'Mirabella Bay' (Au/A) WAln
- 'Miranda' (Au/d) SPop
- 'Miriam' (Au/A) EWoo SPop WAln
- 'Mish Mish' (Au/d) GAbr NDro WHil
- 'Miss Bluey' (Au/d) EWoo NDro SPop WAln XBar
- 'Miss Jones' (Au/St) SPop
- 'Miss Muffet' (Au/S) WAln
- 'Miss Newman' (Au/A) NSum SPop
- 'Miss Pinky' (Au) EWoo NDro SPop WCre
- 'Mist' (Au/S) WAln
- 'Mojave' (Au/S) EWoo GAbr GAgs IPen MFie NDro NEgg NSum SPop WCre WHil XBar
- 'Mollie Langford' (Au/A) MFie NDro SPop WCre WHil
- 'Mondeo' (Au/A) WAln
- 'Monet' (Au/S) WAln
- 'Moneymoon' (Au/S) EWoo GAbr IPen NDro SPop WCre WHil
- 'Monica' (Au/A) MFie
- 'Monk' (Au/S) EWoo MFie SPop WAln WCre WHil
- 'Monmouth Star' (Au/St) SPop WHil
- 'Moon Fairy' (Au/S) NDro SPop WAln WCre
- 'Moondance' (Au/d) WAln
- 'Moonglow' (Au/S) EWoo GAbr
- 'Moonlight' (Au/S) WAln
- 'Moonrise' (Au/S) EWoo MFie NDro
- 'Moonriver' (Au/A) EWoo SPop WCre WHil
- 'Moonshadow' (Au/d) WAln
- 'Moonshine' (Au/d) SPop WAln
- 'Moonstone' (Au/d) SPop WAln
- 'Morello' (Au/d) **new** XBar
- 'Morning Glory' (Au/B) **new** WAln
- 'Morven' (Au) GAbr

- 'Moscow' (Au/S) SPop
- 'Moselle' (Au/S) GAgs MFie NDro SPop WAln
- 'Mossy Vale' (Au/S) SPop
- 'Mr A' (Au/S) EWoo GAgs NDro WHil
- 'Mr Bojangles' (Au/d) MFie SPop WAln
- 'Mr Greenfingers' (Au) WCre
- 'Mrs Cairn's Blue' (Au/B) NDro
- 'Mrs J.H. Watson' (Au) WCre
- 'Mrs L. Hearn' (Au/A) EWoo GAbr IPen ITim MFie NDro SPop WCre WHil
- 'Mrs R. Bolton' (Au/A) WCre WHil
- 'Mrs Robinson' (Au/St) NDro SPop
- 'Mrs Wilson' (Au) GAbr
- 'Muriel James' (Au/A) SPop
- 'Murray Lakes' (Au/A) EWoo NDro SPop WAln
- 'Mustard Sauce' (Au/B) NDro
- 'My Buddy' (Au/St) SPop WCre
- 'My Delight' (Au/d) SPop
- 'My Fair Lady' (Au/A) MFie NDro SPop
- 'My Friend' (Au/B) NDro SPop
- 'Myfanwy' (Au/B) **new** WAln
- 'Myoleboots' (Au/B) SPop
- 'Myrtle Park' (Au/A) WAln
- 'Mystery' (Au) GAbr
- 'Nancy Dalgetty' (Au/B) NDro SPop
- 'Nantenan' (Au/S) GAbr MFie NDro SPop WBla WCre
- 'Neat and Tidy' (Au/S) CTal EWoo GAbr GAgs MFie NDro NPri SPop WBla WCre
- 'Nefertiti' (Au/A) EWoo IPen MFie SPop WCre WHil
- 'Nessun Dorma' (Au/A) EWoo NDro WAln
- 'Neville Telford' (Au/S) GAbr GAgs IPen MFie NDro SPop WCre WHil
- 'Newbottle' (Au/S) SPop WAln WHil
- 'Newsboy' (Au/A) WAln
- 'Newton Harcourt' (Au/A) SPop WHil
- 'Nicholas Loakes' (Au/S) WAln
- 'Nick Drake' (Au/d) SPop
- 'Nickity' (Au/A) EWoo GAbr GAgs IPen ITim MFie NDro NSum SPop WAln WCre WHil XBar
- 'Nicola Jane' (Au/A) EWoo GAgs SPop WAln
- 'Nigel' (Au/d) GAbr MFie NDro
- 'Night and Day' (Au/St) SPop WAln WCre
- 'Night Dance' (Au/S) WCre
- 'Nightwink' (Au/S) WAln
- 'Nil Amber' (Au) GAbr SPop
- 'Nina' (Au/A) NDro SPop WAln
- 'Nita' (Au/d) SPop WAln
- 'No 21' (Au/S) NDro SPop
- 'No Deal' (Au/S) WCre
- 'Nocturne' (Au/S) EWoo IPen NBro NDro NSum SPop WBla WCre
- 'Noelle' (Au/S) EBee EWoo IPen
- 'Nona' (Au/d) EWoo MFie NDro NSum SPop
- 'Nonchalance' (Au/A) MFie NDro SPop WHil
- 'Norma' (Au/A) EWoo MFie NDro SPop
- 'Northern Lights' (Au/S) GAbr WAln
- 'Nureyev' (Au/A) EWoo SPop
- 'Nymph' (Au/d) EWoo GAbr GAgs MFie NDro SPop WBla WCre WHil
- 'Oakie' (Au/S) SPop WAln
- 'Oban' (Au/S) MFie NDro SPop WBla XBar
- 'Odette' (Au) IPen MFie SPop WHil
- 'O'er the Moon' (Au/S) WAln
- 'Oikos' (Au/B) NDro SPop
- 'Ol' Blue Eyes' (Au/St) SPop WAln
- 'Old Black Isle Dusty Miller' (Au/B) NDro WHil
- 'Old Buffer' (Au/St) SPop
- 'Old Clove Red' (Au/B) EWoo GAbr GAgs IPen MFie NDro NSum WCre WHil
- 'Old Cottage Blue' (Au/B) GAbr NDro
- 'Old England' (Au/S) EWoo GAbr MFie NDro SPop WBla WCre
- 'Old Gold' (Au/S) GAbr IPen NDro SPop WAln WBla WCre
- 'Old Gold Double' (Au/d) EWoo
- 'Old Irish Blue' (Au/B) IPen NDro NEgg WCre
- 'Old Irish Green' (Au/B) EWoo GAbr GAgs NDro NSum
- 'Old Irish Scented' (Au/B) CTal EWoo GAbr IPen MFie NBro NDro WHil
- 'Old Irish Yellow' (Au/B) NDro NEgg
- 'Old Mustard' (Au/B) NDov NDro SBch SMHy WCre
- 'Old Pink Dusty Miller' (Au/B) GAbr IPen

§ - 'Old Purple Dusty Miller' (Au/B) GAbr
- 'Old Red' (Au) GAgs
- 'Old Red Dusty Miller' (Au/B) GAbr LLHF NSum SPop WHil
- 'Old Red Elvet' (Au/S) GAbr GAgs SPop WCre
- 'Old Smokey' (Au/A) EWoo MFie NDro SPop WHil XBar
- 'Old Suffolk Bronze' (Au/B) GAbr GAgs ITim NDro WCre WHil
- 'Old Tall Purple Dusty Miller' (Au/B) WCre
- 'Old Timer' (Au/S) SPop
- 'Old Yellow Dusty Miller' (Au/B) CTal EWes EWoo GAbr IPen NBro NDro NRya NWad WCre WHil
- 'Old-Fashioned' (Au/B) NDro
- 'Oldfield' (Au/d) **new** SPop
- 'Olivia' (Au/d) SPop
- 'Olton' (Au/A) IPen MFie WCre XBar
- 'Onyx' (Au/B) **new** WAln
- 'Ophir' (Au) WBla
- 'Optimist' (Au/St) EWoo IPen NDro SPop
- 'Opus One' (Au/A) EWoo WAln
- 'Orb' (Au/S) IPen MFie NDro SPop WBla WCre WHil
- 'Ordvic' (Au/S) NDro WAln
- 'Orlando' (Au/S) MFie NDro SPop WAln
- 'Orwell Tiger' (Au/St) EWoo GAgs IPen MFie NDro SPop WCre
- 'Osbaston Bullseye' (Au/St) SPop
- 'Osborne Green' (Au/B) GAbr GAgs GBin SPop WCre WHil
- 'Osorno' (Au/d) SPop
- 'Ossett Sapphire' (Au/A) NDro SPop
- 'Otto Dix' (Au/A) SPop WAln
- 'Overdale' (Au/A) NDro SPop WAln
- 'Oyster' (Au/B) **new** WAln
- 'Paddlin' Madeleine' (Au/A) EWoo GAgs NDro WAln
- 'Pageboy' (Au/A) WAln
- 'Paleface' (Au/A) EWoo GAgs IPen MFie NDro NSum SPop WBla WCre
- 'Pam Tiger' (Au/St) WAln
- 'Panache' (Au/S) WAln
- 'Pang Tiger' (Au/St) EWoo WAln
- 'Papageno' (Au/St) WAln
- 'Paphos' (Au/d) IPen SPop
- 'Paradise Yellow' (Au/B) EWoo GAbr MFie NDro NEgg SPop WCre
- 'Paragon' (Au/A) IPen ITim MFie WAln WCre WHil
- 'Parakeet' (Au/S) WAln
- 'Paris' (Au/S) WAln
- 'Party Animal' (Au/St) SPop
- 'Party Time' (Au/S) IPen SPop WBla WCre

- 'Pass Me By' (Au) IPen
- 'Passchendaele' (Au/d) SPop WCre
- 'Passing Cloud' (Au/d) WAln
- 'Pastiche' (Au/A) MFie WCre
- 'Pastures New' (Au) WAln
- 'Pat' (Au/S) SPop
- 'Pat Barnard' (Au) IPen
- 'Pat Mooney' (Au/d) NDro
- 'Patience' (Au/S) ITim NDro SPop WHil
- 'Patricia Barras' (Au/S) EWoo WAln
- 'Pauline' (Au/A) EWoo MFie SPop
- 'Pavarotti' (Au/A) NDro SPop
- 'Peewit' (Au/S) WAln
- 'Pegasus' (Au/d) EWoo NDro SPop
- 'Peggy' (Au/A) GAbr WHil
- 'People's Choice' (Au/d) SPop
- 'Pequod' (Au/A) MFie NDro SPop WBla
- 'Perdito' (Au/S) WAln
- 'Perito Moreno' (Au/d) SPop
- 'Perseus' (Au/S) WAln
- 'Phantom' (Au/d) EWoo SPop WAln
- 'Pharaoh' (Au/A) CWCL EWoo GAbr GAgs MFie NDro SPop WBla WCre XBar
- 'Phoenix' (Au/A) WAln
- 'Phyllis Douglas' (Au/A) EWoo GAgs IPen MFie NDro NEgg SPop WCre WHil
- 'Piccadilly' (Au/S) MAsh MFie SPop
- 'Pierot' (Au/A) GAgs IPen MFie NDro NSum SPop WCre WHil XBar
- 'Piers Telford' (Au/A) CPBP CTal EBee EWoo GAbr GAgs IPen LCro MFie NDro NEgg NSum SBch SPop WCre WHil XBar
- 'Piglet' (Au/d) GAgs NDro SPop WBla WHil
- 'Pikey' (Au/S) SPop
- 'Pimlico' (Au/S) SPop
- 'Pimroagh' (Au/A) EWoo SPop
- 'Pink Floyd' (Au/A) SPop
- 'Pink Fondant' (Au/d) GAbr NDro
- 'Pink Hint' (Au/B) NDro SPop
- 'Pink Lady' (Au/A) GAbr GAgs MFie NBro NSum SPop WHil
- 'Pink Lilac' (Au/A/S) NDro
- 'Pink Triumph' (Au) NDro WHil
- 'Pinkerton' (Au/d) EWoo SPop WAln
- 'Pinkie' (Au/A) WHil
- 'Pinkie Dawn' (Au/B) IPen NDro WCre
- 'Pinky' (Au/d) WCre
- 'Pinstripe' (Au) EWoo GAbr GAgs IPen NDro NSum SPop WCre WHil
- 'Pioneer Stripe' (Au/S) GAbr GAgs IPen SPop WCre
- 'Pippin' (Au/A) CPBP GAbr GAgs IPen MFie NBro NDro SPop WCre WHil XBar
- 'Pixie' (Au/A) EWoo GAgs IPen MFie SPop WCre WHil
- 'Playboy' (Au/A) NDro SPop WAln
- 'Plum Pudding' (Au/d) SPop WAln
- 'Poacher's Starlight' (Au/d) **new** NDro
- 'Polar Sight' (Au/B) **new** WAln
- 'Polestar' (Au/A) MFie NDro SPop WCre WHil
- 'Polly' (Au/B) EBee GAgs GKev NDro WCre
- 'Pollyanna' (Au/B) **new** WAln
- 'Pop's Blue' (Au/S/d) NEgg SPop
- 'Portree' (Au/S) GAbr SPop
- 'Post Master' (Au/S) WAln
- 'Pot o' Gold' (Au/S) CPBP EBee ECho EWoo GAgs IPen MFie NDro NEgg SPop WBla WCre WHil XBar
- 'Powder and Paint' (Au/A) WAln
- 'Powder Puff' (Au/B) EWoo NDro SPop
- 'Prague' (Au/S) EWoo GAbr IPen MFie NBir NDro SPop WCre
- 'Pretender' (Au/A) MFie SPop
- 'Pretty Prop' (Au/St) SPop
- 'Pretty Purple' (Au/d) SPop WAln
- 'Pride of Poland' (Au/S) EWoo SPop WCre
- 'Prince Bishops' (Au/S) SPop WAln
- 'Prince Charming' (Au/S) EWoo GAgs IPen ITim MFie SPop WCre
- 'Prince Igor' (Au/A) SPop
- 'Prince John' (Au/A) MFie NBro NDro SPop WBla WCre WHil
- 'Pristine' (Au/B) **new** WAln
- 'Proctor's Yellow' (Au/B) NDro
- 'Prometheus' (Au/d) EWoo GAbr GAgs LLHF MFie NDro NSum SPop WHil
- 'Prosperine' (Au/S) SPop WAln WCre
- 'Psyche' (Au/S) SPop WAln
- 'Ptarmigan' (Au) WAln
- 'Pumpkin' (Au) GAbr
- 'Puppy Love' (Au/St) SPop
- 'Purbeck' (Au/B) SPop
- 'Purple Dusty Miller' see *P. auricula* 'Old Purple Dusty Miller'
- 'Purple Emperor' (Au/A) MFie
- 'Purple Frills' (Au) MFie
- 'Purple Glow' (Au/d) WAln
- 'Purple Haze' (Au) SPop
- 'Purple Knight' (Au/S) WAln
- 'Purple Lace' (Au/d) SPop
- 'Purple Lovely' (Au) MFie SPop
- 'Purple Orient' (Au/d) SPop
- 'Purple Patch' (Au/d) SPop
- 'Purple Promise' (Au) GAbr ITim SPop
- 'Purple Prose' (Au/St) EWoo MFie SPop WHil
- 'Purple Rose' (Au/d) WAln
- 'Purple Royale' (Au/B) NDro
- 'Purple Sage' (Au/S) EWoo ITim MFie NDro SPop WCre WHil
- 'Purple Star' (Au/d) SPop
- 'Purple Velvet' (Au/S) CWCL EWoo IPen NDro SPop
- 'Quatro' (Au/d) EWoo GAgs SPop
- 'Queen Alexandra' (Au/B) EWoo GAbr NDro WHil
- 'Queen Bee' (Au/S) GAbr MFie SPop WBla
- 'Queen's Bower' (Au/S) SPop WCre
- 'Queenswood' (Au/S) EWoo WCre
- 'Quintessence' (Au/A) EWoo MFie WCre WHil
- 'R.L. Bowes' (Au/A) NDro
- 'Rab C. Nesbitt' (Au/A) SPop WAln
- 'Rabley Heath' (Au/A) EWoo GAbr GAgs MFie NDro SPop WCre WHil
- 'Rachel' (Au/A) EWoo WAln WCre
- 'Rachel de Thame' (Au/S) WAln
- 'Rachel Labouchere' (Au/S) WAln
- 'Radiance' (Au/A) SPop
- 'Radiant' (Au/A) IPen
- 'Rag Doll' (Au/S) NDro WAln
- 'Ragnald the Magnificent' (Au/S) WAln
- 'Rajah' (Au/S) ECho EWoo GAbr GAgs IPen ITim MAsh MFie NDro NEgg SPop WBla WCre WHil
- 'Raleigh Stripe' (Au/St) EWoo GAbr GAgs IPen ITim WAln WBla WCre
- 'Rameses' (Au/A) IPen MFie NDro WCre
- 'Rebecca Baker' (Au/d) SPop WHil
- 'Red Admiral' (Au) EWoo SPop WAln
- 'Red Arrows' (Au) SPop WAln
- 'Red Baron' (Au/S) WAln WCre

- 'Red Beret' (Au/S) SPop
- 'Red Bordeaux' (Au/S) GAgs NDro
- 'Red Carpet' (Au/S) SPop
- 'Red Diamond' (Au/d) WAln
- 'Red Embers' (Au/S) SPop WAln WCre
- 'Red Ensign' (Au/B) NDro
- 'Red Gauntlet' (Au/S) EWoo GAbr GAgs GKev IPen MFie NDro SPop WCre
- 'Red King' (Au/S) WAln
- 'Red Mark' (Au/A) MFie SPop WHil XBar
- 'Red Rum' (Au/S) GAbr MFie SPop WAln WCre
- 'Red Sonata' (Au/S) SPop
- 'Red Spin' (Au/S) SPop
- 'Red Vulcan' (Au) WCre
- 'Red Wire' (Au/St) EWoo NDro NSum SPop WCre
- 'Redcar' (Au/A) GAbr MFie NDro WCre
- 'Reddown Apricot' (Au/B) NDro
- 'Reddown Bat' (Au/d) SPop
- 'Reddown First Swallow' (Au/B) NDro
- 'Reddown Rainman' (Au/B) NDro
- 'Reddown Tickled Pink' (Au/B) NDro
- 'Redstart' (Au/S) EBee EWoo GAgs GKev IPen ITim WCre WHil
- 'Regency' (Au/A) NDro WAln
- 'Regency Dandy' (Au/St) SPop
- 'Regency Denja' (Au) IPen
- 'Regency Emperor' (Au/St) EWoo IPen SPop WCre WHil
- 'Regency Paperchase' (Au/St) SPop
- 'Regency Peppermint Tea' (Au/St) SPop
- 'Regency Saint Clements' (Au/St) SPop WAln WCre
- 'Remus' (Au/S) CPBP ECho ELan EWoo GAbr GAgs IPen LLHF MFie NDro NEgg SPop WCre WHil XBar
- 'Rene' (Au/A) EWoo GAbr IPen MFie SPop WCre WHil XBar
- 'Renown' (Au/A) IPen NDro WAln WCre
- 'Requiem' (Au/d) WAln
- 'Resi' (Au) GAgs WHil
- 'Respectable' (Au/A) WAln
- 'Reverie' (Au/d) SPop WAln
- 'Reynardine' (Au/d) SPop WAln
- 'Rhinegold' (Au/d) **new** XBar
- 'Riatty' (Au/d) GAbr GAgs MFie NDro SPop
- 'Richard Shaw' (Au/A) IPen NDro SPop
- 'Ring of Bells' (Au/S) EWoo SPop WAln WCre
- 'Ring of Fire' (Au/A) **new** WAln
- 'Risdene' (Au) IPen SPop WAln WCre
- 'Rivendell' (Au/A) WAln
- 'Robbo' (Au/B) EWoo NDro
- 'Robert Green' (Au/S) EWoo SPop WAln
- 'Robert Lee' (Au/A) WAln
- 'Roberto' (Au/S) SPop WAln
- 'Robin Hood Stripe' (Au/St) EWoo NDro SPop WBla WCre
- 'Robinette' (Au/d) EWoo GAbr IPen SPop
- 'Rock Sand' (Au/S) EWoo GAbr GAgs MFie NDro SPop WBla WCre WHil
- 'Rockbourne' (Au/A) SPop
- 'Rodeo' (Au/A) EWoo GAbr IPen SPop
- 'Rolts' (Au/S) ECho EWoo GAbr GAgs IPen NBro NDro SPop WBla WCre WHil XBar
- 'Rondy' (Au/S) ITim MFie SPop WAln WHil
- 'Ronnie Johnson' (Au) WAln
- 'Ronny Simpson' (Au) WCre
- 'Rosalie' (Au) SPop
- 'Rosalie Edwards' (Au/S) EWoo MFie SPop WCre
- 'Rose Conjou' (Au/d) EWoo GAbr GAgs IPen MFie NDro SPop WCre WHil XBar
- 'Rose Kaye' (Au/A) GAbr IPen WCre
- 'Rosebud' (Au/S) GAbr GAgs
- 'Rosemarket Rackler' (Au/B) NDro
- 'Rosemary' (Au/S) EWoo MFie SPop WCre WHil
- 'Rosewood' (Au) SPop WAln WCre
- 'Rosie' (Au/S) NDro
- 'Rothesay Robin' (Au/A) WAln
- 'Rowena' (Au/A) IPen MFie NSum SPop WCre WHil
- 'Roxborough' (Au/A) EWoo GAgs IPen
- 'Roxburgh' (Au/A) MFie NDro SPop WCre
- 'Roy Keane' (Au/A) IPen MFie SPop WAln WBla WCre
- 'Royal Mail' (Au/S) MFie NDro SPop WAln WBla
- 'Royal Marine' (Au/S) MFie SPop WAln
- 'Royal Scot' (Au/S) SPop
- 'Royal Velvet' (Au/S) GAbr GAgs IPen NDro WHil
- 'Ruby Hyde' (Au/B) EWoo GAbr NDro WCre
- 'Ruddy Duck' (Au/S) SPop WAln WCre
- 'Rumbled' (Au/St) MAsh
- 'Runwell' (Au/B) NDro
- 'Rustig' (Au/B) **new** WAln
- 'Rusty Dusty' (Au) GAbr GAgs
- 'Ryecroft' (Au/A) WAln
- 'Sabrina' (Au/A) WAln
- 'Saginaw' (Au/A) EWoo WAln
- 'Sailor Boy' (Au/S) GAgs MFie NDro SPop WAln
- 'Saint Boswells' (Au/S) GAbr SPop
- 'Saint Elmo' (Au/A) GAbr GAgs MFie SPop WCre
- 'Saint Quentin' (Au/S) WAln
- 'Salad' (Au/S) EWoo GAbr GAgs
- 'Sale Green' (Au/S) EWoo MFie SPop
- 'Sally' (Au/A) MFie
- 'Sam Brown' (Au/S) WAln
- 'Sam Gamgee' (Au/A) WAln WCre
- 'Sam Hunter' (Au/A) NDro SPop
- 'Samantha' (Au/A) EWoo MFie WAln WBla WCre
- 'Samantha' (Au/d) EWoo MFie SPop WAln
- 'San Gabriel' (Au/A) WAln
- 'Sanctuary Wood' (Au/d) SPop
- 'Sandhills' (Au/A) MAsh MFie SPop WCre WHil
- 'Sandmartin' (Au/S) MFie
- 'Sandpiper' (Au/d) SPop WAln
- 'Sandra' (Au/A) ELan GAbr GAgs IPen MFie NDro SPop WBla WCre WHil
- 'Sandra's Lass' (Au/A) EWoo SPop
- 'Sandwood Bay' (Au/A) EWoo GAbr MFie NEgg SPop WCre WHil
- 'Sappho' (Au/S) IPen SPop WAln
- 'Sarah Gisby' (Au/d) MAsh MFie NDro SPop WBla WCre
- 'Sarah Grey' (Au/d) WAln
- 'Sarah Humphries' (Au/d) WAln
- 'Sarah Lodge' (Au/d) GAbr GAgs IPen NDro SPop WCre WHil
- 'Sarah Suzanne' (Au/B) NDro
- 'Saruman' (Au/A) WAln
- 'Sasha Files' (Au/A) IPen WAln
- 'Satchmo' (Au/S) SPop
- 'Satin Doll' (Au/d) MFie SPop
- 'Satsuma' (Au/d) SPop WAln
- 'Scaraben' (Au) GAbr
- 'Schaumburg' (Au/B) NDro
- 'Schicchi' (Au/d) **new** XBar
- 'Scipio' (Au/S) SPop WAln
- 'Scorcher' (Au/S) EWoo GAbr IPen LLHF MFie NDro NSum SPop WBla

- 'Sea Lavender' (Au/d) WAln
- 'Sea Mist' (Au/d) WAln
- 'Searchlight' (Au) WCre
- 'Second Victory' (Au) NDro WCre WHil XBar
- 'Seen-a-Ghost' (Au/S) SPop
- 'Serendipity' (Au/B) **new** WAln
- 'Serenity' (Au/S) MFie SPop WBla WCre WHil
- 'Sergeant Wilson' (Au) SPop WAln
- 'Serre' (Au/d) SPop
- 'Shaheen' (Au/S) IPen
- 'Shalford' (Au/d) GAbr MFie SPop WCot WCre WHil
- 'Sharmans Cross' (Au/S) MFie SPop WAln
- 'Sharon Louise' (Au/S) IPen SPop WCre
- 'Shaun' (Au/d) ECtt GAbr GAgs MHol NLar NPri WCre WIce
- 'Sheila' (Au/S) GAbr IPen NDro SPop WCre WHil
- 'Shere' (Au/S) EWoo MFie NDro SPop WCre
- 'Shergold' (Au/A) IPen MFie WCre WHil
- 'Sherwood' (Au/S) EWoo GAbr IPen NDro SPop WCre WHil
- 'Shining Hour' (Au/St) SPop
- 'Shirley' (Au/S) SPop WAln
- 'Shotley' (Au/A) MFie SPop
- 'Show Bandit' (Au/St) SPop
- 'Showtime' (Au/S) NDro SPop WCre
- 'Sibsey' (Au/d) EWoo GAgs NDro NSum SPop
- 'Sidney' (Au/A) WAln
- 'Silmaril' (Au) SPop WAln
- 'Silver City' (Au/S) WAln
- 'Silver Rose' (Au) WCre
- 'Silver Surfer' (Au/St) WAln
- 'Silverway' (Au/S) EWoo SPop WAln WCre WHil
- 'Simply Red' (Au) EWoo IPen MAsh MFie NDro SPop WAln WBla XBar
- 'Sir John' (Au/A) MFie NDro WCre WHil
- 'Sir John Hall' (Au) MFie
- 'Sir Robert' (Au/d) SPop WAln
- 'Sir Titus Salt' (Au/S) WAln
- 'Sirbol' (Au/A) EWoo GAgs IPen MFie MHer NDro SPop WBla WCre WHil
- 'Sirius' (Au/A) EWoo GAbr GAgs IPen MFie MHer NDro NSum NWad SPop WBla WCre WHil
- 'Skerne Tiger' (Au/St) **new** SPop
- 'Skylark' (Au/A) GAbr GAgs IPen NDro SPop WBla WCre WHil XBar
- 'Skyliner' (Au/A) NDro
- 'Slack Top Red' (Au) NSla
- 'Sleeping Beauty' (Au/d) SPop
- 'Slim Whitman' (Au/A) MFie NDro SPop WAln WBla WHil
- 'Slioch' (Au/S) EWoo GAbr GAgs IPen NSum SPop WCre WHil
- 'Slip Anchor' (Au/A) WAln
- 'Smart Tar' (Au/S) WAln
- 'Smoothy' (Au/St) SPop
- 'Snips' (Au/St) **new** SPop
- 'Snooty Fox' (Au/A) GAbr IPen MFie SPop WCre
- 'Snooty Fox II' (Au/A) MFie WBla
- 'Snow Maiden' (Au/d) SPop WAln
- 'Snowstorm' (Au/S) IPen SPop
- 'Snowy Owl' (Au/S) GAbr IPen MFie NDro SPop WCre
- 'Snowy Ridge' (Au/B) **new** WAln
- 'Solario' (Au/F) WAln
- 'Solero' (Au/St) IPen SPop
- 'Soliloquy' (Au) NDro
- 'Somersby' (Au/d) IPen
- 'Soncy Face' (Au/A) MFie SPop WBla WCre WHil
- 'Song of India' (Au/A) SPop
- 'Sonia Nicolle' (Au/B) NDro
- 'Sonny Boy' (Au/A) SPop WAln
- 'Sooty' (Au/d) IPen SPop
- 'Sophie' (Au/d) MFie SPop WAln
- 'Sophie' (Au/A) NDro
- 'South Barrow' (Au/d) GAbr GAgs SPop WCre WHil
- 'Southease Jane' (Au) WAln
- 'Southport' (Au) EWoo GAbr
- 'Sparky' (Au/A) MFie NDro WAln
- 'Spartan' (Au) SPop WAln
- 'Spitfire' (Au/S) MFie
- 'Spokey' (Au) IPen
- 'Spring Meadows' (Au/S) EWoo GAbr MAsh MFie NDro NEgg SPop WCre WHil
- 'Springtime' (Au/A) SPop
- 'Stant's Blue' (Au/S) IPen MFie NDro SPop WCre
- 'Star Spangle' (Au/St) NDro WCre
- 'Star Wars' (Au/S) EWoo GAbr GAgs MFie SPop WAln WCre WHil XBar
- 'Star Wars II' (Au) MAsh
- 'Stardust' (Au/S) WCre
- 'Starlight' (Au/S) SPop
- 'Starling' (Au/B) EWoo GAbr IPen NDro SPop
- 'Starry' (Au/S) NDro
- 'Starsand' (Au/S) WAln WCre
- 'Stella' (Au/S) SPop
- 'Stella Coop' (Au/d) NDro WAln
- 'Stella North' (Au/A) WAln
- 'Stella South' (Au/A) IPen SPop WCre
- 'Stetson' (Au/A) WAln
- 'Stoke Poges' (Au/A) NDro
- 'Stoney Cross' (Au/S) SPop WAln
- 'Stonnal' (Au/A) MFie SPop WHil
- 'Stormin' Norman' (Au/A) EWoo MFie NDro SPop WHil
- 'Stormy Cloud' (Au/B) **new** WAln
- 'Stormy Weather' (Au/St) SPop WCre
- 'Strawberry Fields' (Au/S) SPop WCre
- 'Stripe Tease' (Au/St) SPop
- 'Striped Ace' (Au/St) NDro SPop WCre WHil
- 'Stripey' (Au/d) IPen
- 'Stromboli' (Au/d) EWoo GAbr GAgs MFie NDro SPop WBla WCot WCre
- 'Stuart West' (Au/A) WCre
- 'Stubb's Tartan' (Au/S) MFie WAln
- 'Subliminal' (Au/A) NDro
- 'Sue' (Au/A) MFie SPop WCre
- 'Sue Ritchie' (Au/d) EWoo SPop
- 'Suede Shoes' (Au/S) SPop
- 'Sugar Plum Fairy' (Au/S) EWoo GAbr GAgs NDro NSum SPop WCre WHil
- 'Sultan' (Au/A) WAln
- 'Summer Sky' (Au/A) SPop WCre
- 'Summer Wine' (Au/A) EWoo MFie SPop
- 'Sumo' (Au/A) EWoo GAbr GAgs MFie NDro SPop WBla WCre WHil
- 'Sunflower' (Au/A/S) EWoo GAbr GAgs ITim MAsh MFie NDro SPop WCre WHil
- 'Sunlight' (Au/A) WAln
- 'Sunlit Tiger' (Au/S) EWoo WAln
- 'Sunray' (Au/St) SPop
- 'Sunrise Beauty' (Au/S) **new** SPop
- 'Sunsplash' (Au) WBla WCre
- 'Sunspot' (Au/A) EWoo IPen WAln
- 'Sunstar' (Au/S) NDro NSum WCre
- 'Super Para' (Au/S) EWoo GAbr GAgs GKev IPen MFie NDro SPop WBla WCre WHil
- 'Superb' (Au/S) MFie SPop WAln
- 'Surething' (Au/A) WAln
- 'Susan' (Au/A) GAbr GAgs MFie NDro SPop WCre

- 'Susannah' (Au/d) EWoo GAgs GMaP IPen MFie NDro NSum SPop WCre WHil
- 'Sweet Chestnut' (Au/S) WAln
- 'Sweet Georgia Brown' (Au/A) MFie WAln
- 'Sweet Pastures' (Au/S) GAbr GAgs IPen MFie SPop WCre
- 'Swiss Royal Velvet' (Au/B) NDro
- 'Sword' (Au/d) CPBP EWoo GAbr GAgs IPen MFie NDro NSum NWad SPop WCre XBar
- 'Symphony' (Au/A) GAgs ITim MFie NDro SPop WBla WCre WHil XBar
- 'T.A. Hadfield' (Au/A) EWoo GAgs MFie NDro SPop WBla WCre WHil
- 'Tachete' (Au/d) **new** XBar
- 'Taffeta' (Au/S) EBee GAbr GAgs LCro LOPS NDro NSum SPop WCre WHil
- 'Tall Purple Dusty Miller' (Au/B) SPop
- 'Tally-ho' (Au/A) SPop WAln
- 'Tamar Gold' (Au/d) SPop WAln WCre
- 'Tamar Mist' (Au) WAln WHil
- 'Tamino' (Au/S) IPen SPop WAln
- 'Tango' (Au/d) WAln
- 'Tarantella' (Au/A) GAbr MFie NDro SPop WCre
- 'Tawny Owl' (Au/B) GAbr NBro
- 'Tay Tiger' (Au/St) EWoo GAbr GAgs MFie NDro SPop WCre WHil XBar
- 'Taylor's Grey' (Au/S) SPop
- 'Teawell Pride' (Au/d) EWoo SPop WCre WHil
- 'Ted Gibbs' (Au/A) EWoo MFie NDro SPop WBla WCre WHil
- 'Ted Roberts' (Au/A) EWoo ITim MFie NDro SPop WBla WCre WHil
- 'Teem' (Au/S) GAbr IPen NDro SPop WCre XBar
- 'Telesto' (Au/d) SPop
- 'Telford's Surprise' (Au/A) WAln
- 'Temeraire' (Au/A) MFie SPop WHil
- 'Tenby Grey' (Au/S) SPop WCre
- 'Tender Trap' (Au/A) IPen WAln
- 'Terpo' (Au/A) EWoo MFie WAln WBla WCre WHil
- 'Tess' (Au/A) XBar
- 'The Argylls' (Au/St) SPop
- 'The Baron' (Au/S) GAbr GAgs GKev IPen MFie SPop WBla WCre WHil XBar
- 'The Bishop' (Au/S) GAgs IPen MFie SPop WAln WCre WHil
- 'The Bride' (Au/S) MFie SPop WCre
- 'The Cardinal' (Au/d) EWoo WAln
- 'The Czar' (Au/A) MFie NDro SPop WCre
- 'The Egyptian' (Au/A) IPen MFie NDro SPop WBla WCre WHil
- 'The Few' (Au/St) SPop
- 'The Hobbit' (Au/A) WAln
- 'The Lady Galadriel' (Au/A) NDro
- 'The Maverick' (Au/S) MFie SPop
- 'The President' (Au/d) WAln
- 'The Raven' (Au/S) EWoo GAbr GAgs ITim MFie SPop WAln WBla WCre WHil
- 'The Sneep' (Au/A) EWoo GAgs IPen ITim MFie NDro SPop WBla
- 'The Snods' (Au/S) EWoo IPen MFie NDro SPop WBla WCre
- 'The Wrekin' (Au/S) SPop

I - 'Theodora' (Au/S) XBar
- 'Thetis' (Au/A) EWoo MFie SPop WCre
- 'Thisbe' (Au/A) NDro
- 'Thou Swell' (Au/St) **new** SPop
- 'Three Way Stripe' (St) EWoo GAbr GAgs WBla WCre WHil
- 'Thutmoses' (Au/A) WAln
- 'Tiger Tim' (Au/St) EWoo SPop WAln
- 'Tim' (Au) GAbr IPen ITim NDro SPop
- 'Timpany Blues' **new** ITim
- 'Tim's Fancy' (Au/S) NDro WCre
- 'Tinker' (Au/S) WAln
- 'Tinkerbell' (Au/S) EWoo IPen MFie SPop WCre
- 'Tiptoe' (Au/St) SPop WCre
- 'Titania' (Au) SPop
- 'Toddington Green' (Au/S) WAln
- 'Toffee Crisp' (Au/A) EWoo GAbr GAgs IPen NDro SPop WBla XBar
- 'Toffee Nosed' (Au/St) SPop
- 'Tom Farmer' (Au) SPop WCre
- 'Tomboy' (Au/S) EWoo IPen MFie NDro SPop WBla WCre
- 'Tony Bray' (Au/A) SPop
- 'Toolyn' (Au/S) EWoo GAgs NDro WAln
- 'Top Cat' (Au/d) WAln
- 'Top Style' (Au/d) SPop WAln
- 'Tosca' (Au/S) CWCL GAbr GAgs IPen MAsh NSum SPop WBla WCre WHil XBar
- 'Trafalgar Square' (Au/S) EWoo GAbr GAgs MFie NDro SPop WBla WCre
- 'Tregor Stripe' (Au/St) XBar
- 'Trident' (Au/d) WAln
- 'Trish' (Au) GAbr
- 'Trojan' (Au/S) GKev IPen WCre
- 'Trouble' (Au/d) EWoo GAbr IPen MFie NDro WCre WHil
- 'Troy Aykman' (Au/A) MFie NDro SPop WAln WHil
- 'Trudy' (Au/S) EWoo GAbr GAgs IPen ITim NDro SPop WCre WHil
- 'True Briton' (Au/S) IPen MFie NDro SPop WBla WCre
- 'Trumpet Blue' (Au/S) MFie SPop WAln WHil
- 'Tudor Rose' (Au/S) NDov WAln
- 'Tumbledown' (Au/A) EWoo IPen MFie NDro SPop
- 'Tummel' (Au/A) EWoo GAbr GAgs NDro SPop WBla WCre WHil
- 'Tupelo Honey' (Au/d) WAln
- 'Turnberry' (Au/S) SPop
- 'Turnbull' (Au/A) IPen
- 'Tut Tut' (Au/A) SPop
- 'Tweedy' (Au/St) SPop
- 'Twiggy' (Au/S) GAbr NDro NSum SPop
- 'Two Steeples' (Au/A) SPop
- 'Typhoon' (Au/A) EWoo IPen MFie SPop WHil
- 'Uncle Arthur' (Au/A) MFie WAln WHil
- 'Unforgettable' (Au/A) MFie
- 'Upper Crust' (Au/St) SPop WBla WCre
- 'Upton Belle' (Au/S) IPen MFie NDro SPop WAln WCre
- 'Ursula' (Au/d) WAln
- 'Ushba' (Au/d) SPop
- 'V2 Green' (Au/S) WCre
- 'Valerie' (Au/A) IPen MFie SPop WCre
- 'Valerie Clare' (Au) MFie SPop WAln WHil
- 'Vee Too' (Au/A) GAbr MFie NDro SPop WCre WHil
- 'Vega' (Au/A) EWoo SPop WAln
- 'Velvet Moon' (Au/A) EWoo MFie SPop WAln
- 'Velvet Truffles' (Au/d) **new** SPop
- 'Venetian' (Au/A) EWoo GAgs MFie NDro SPop WAln WBla WHil
- 'Venus' (Au/A) WAln
- 'Vera' (Au/A) SPop WAln
- 'Vera Eden' (Au) WAln
- 'Vera Hill' (Au/A) WAln
- 'Verdi' (Au/A) EWoo SPop WAln
- 'Vesuvius' (Au/d) EWoo IPen NDro SPop WCre
- 'Victoria' (Au/S) SPop WAln

- 'Victoria de Wemyss' (Au/A)	IPen MFie NDro WBla WCre WHil XBar
- 'Victoria Jane' (Au/A)	WAln
- 'Victoria Park' (Au/A)	WAln
- 'Violet Surprise' (Au/St)	NDro
- 'Vulcan' (Au/A)	MFie NBro WCre XBar
- 'W. Muller' (Au)	NBro
- 'Walhampton' (Au/S)	SPop
- 'Walmar' (Au/B) **new**	WAln
- 'Walter Lomas' (Au/S)	WAln
- 'Walton' (Au/A)	CPBP EWoo GAbr GAgs IPen MFie NDro SPop WCre WHil XBar
- 'Walton Heath' (Au/d)	EWoo GAbr GAgs IPen MFie NDro SPop WBla WCot WCre WHil
- 'Waltz Time' (Au/A)	MFie
- 'Wanda's Moonlight' (Au/d)	SPop WAln WCre
- 'Warpaint' (Au/St)	NDro NSum
- 'Warwick' (Au/S)	MFie SPop
- 'Watchett' (Au/S)	SPop
- 'Wayward' (Au/S)	WAln WCre
- 'Wedding Day' (Au/S)	EWoo GAgs ITim MFie SPop WBla WCre
- 'Wentworth' (Au/A)	IPen WAln
- 'Wheal' (Au)	EWoo SPop
- 'Whistlejacket' (Au/S)	MFie NDro SPop WBla
- 'White Ensign' (Au/S)	EWoo GAbr GAgs IPen ITim MFie NDro SPop WCre WHil
- 'White Pyne' (Au/B)	NDro
- 'White Satin' (Au/S)	SPop WAln WCre
- 'White Water' (Au/A)	EWoo MFie NDro SPop WCre WHil
- 'White Wings' (Au/S)	GAgs IPen ITim MFie NDro NSum SPop WCre
- 'Whitecap' (Au/S)	WAln
- 'Whoopee' (Au/A)	EWoo WAln
- 'Whorton's Claret' (Au/S)	WAln
- 'Wichita Falls' (Au/A)	NDro WAln
- 'Wide Awake' (Au/A)	EWoo MFie SPop
- 'Wild and Grey' (Au/S)	NDro
- 'Wilf Booth' (Au/A)	MFie SPop WBla
- 'William Gunn' (Au/d)	MFie SPop WAln WBla WCre
- 'Willow Tree' (Au/S)	WAln
- 'Wincha' (Au/S)	ITim MFie NDro NEgg SPop WBla WCre XBar
- 'Windways Mystery' (Au/B)	GAbr GAgs NDro
- 'Windways Pisces' (Au/d)	WAln
- 'Windy Goldtop' (Au/A)	WAln
- 'Winifrid' (Au/A)	EWoo GAbr MFie NDro SPop WCre
- 'Witchcraft' (Au)	IPen SPop
- 'Woodlands Lilac' (Au/B)	NDro WHil
- 'Woodmill' (Au/A)	EWoo GAgs IPen MFie NDro NSum SPop WBla WCre WHil XBar
- 'Wookey Hole' (Au/A)	MFie NDro SPop
- 'Wor Jackie' (Au/S)	SPop
- 'Wycliffe Harmony' (Au/B)	NDro
- 'Wycliffe Midnight' (Au/B)	GAbr NDro WAln WHil
- 'Wye Hen' (Au/St)	SPop WAln
- 'Wye Lemon' (Au/S)	EWoo SPop
- 'X2' (Au)	GAgs WBla WHil
- 'Xavier' (Au)	EBee
- 'Yacoubi' (Au/A)	SPop
- 'Yellow Ace' (Au)	GAbr
- 'Yellow Border' (Au/B)	WCre
- 'Yellow Hammer' (Au/S)	WAln
- 'Yellow Isle' (Au/S)	WAln
- 'Yellow Muff' (Au/S)	WAln
- 'Yellow Ribbon'	WAln
- 'Yes Indeed' (Au/St)	SPop
- 'Yitzhak Rabin' (Au/A)	IPen SPop WHil
- 'Yorkshire Grey' (Au/S)	GAbr IPen NDro SPop WAln WCre
- 'Ypres' (Au/d) **new**	SPop
- 'Zambia' (Au/d)	EWoo GAbr IPen NDro WCre
- 'Ziggy' (Au/St)	SPop
- 'Zimmer' (Au/St)	EWoo SPop WCre
- 'Zircon' (Au/S)	SPop WAln
- 'Zodiac' (Au/S)	WAln
- 'Zoe' (Au/A)	SPop WAln
- 'Zoe Ann' (Au/S)	WAln
- 'Zorro' (Au/St)	WAln
auriculata (Or)	GKev SVic
- subsp. ***olgae*** (Or)	GKev
'Barbara Midwinter' (Pr)	CDes CJun EBee GAbr GEdr LLHF NHar SHar WCot
Barnhaven Blues Group (Pr/Prim)	NCGa NSum XBar
Barnhaven doubles (Pr/Prim/d)	XBar
Barnhaven Gold-laced Group	see *P.* Gold-laced Group Barnhaven
Barnhaven hybrids	NSum
'Beamish Foam' (Pr/Poly)	GAbr
'Beatrice Wooster' (Au)	GAbr IPen LRHS MFie
'Beeches' Pink'	GAbr GEdr NHar NSum NWad
beesiana (Pf) ♀H6	Widely available
(Belarina Series) Belarina Amethyst Ice = 'Kerbelpicotee' (Pr/Prim/d) **new**	MHol WHil
- Belarina Butter Yellow = 'Kerbelbut'PBR (Pr/Prim/d)	CExl CWCL ELon EPfP LLHF MFie NLar SPer SRot WHil
- Belarina Cobalt Blue = 'Kerbelcob'PBR (Pr/Prim/d)	CAby CExl CWCL ELon LLHF MFie NLar SPer SRot WHil
- Belarina Cream = 'Kerbelcrem'PBR (Pr/Prim/d)	CAby CExl CWCL ELon LLHF MFie SPer SRot WBor WHil WTor
- Belarina Pink Ice = 'Kerbelpice'PBR (Pr/Prim/d)	CWCL ELon MFie NLar SPer WBor WHil
- Belarina Rosette Nectarine = 'Kerbelnec'PBR (Pr/Prim/d)	CExl CWCL ECtt ELon MFie MHol SPer WHil WTor
- Belarina Valentine = 'Kerbelred' (Pr/Prim/d) **new**	CWCL LLHF MHol WBor WHil WTor
bellidifolia (Mu)	GKev IPen NGdn WHil
beluensis	see *P.* × *pubescens* 'Freedom'
× ***berninae*** (Au)	WCre
§ - 'Windrush' (Au)	WAbe
'Betty Green' (Pr/Prim)	GAbr
'Bewerley White'	see *P.* × *pubescens* 'Bewerley White'
bhutanica	see *P. whitei* 'Sherriff's Variety'
bileckii	see *P.* × *forsteri* 'Bileckii'
'Blindsee' (Au)	CTal EPot MFie NHar
blinii (Y)	EHrv GKev LLHF
'Blue Julianas' (Pr)	NCGa NSum XBar
'Blue Riband' (Pr/Prim)	LLHF NWad SIgm
'Blue Sapphire' (Pr/Prim/d)	CBod CDes GAbr GBin NCGa WHil
'Blutenkissen' (Pr/Prim)	GAbr
'Bon Accord Purple' (Pr/Poly/d)	WRHF XBar
boothii subsp. ***repens*** (Pe)	MNrw
'Boothman's Ruby'	see *P.* × *pubescens* 'Boothman's Variety'

'Bouquet' (Pr/Prim/d) XBar
bracteata (Bu) GKev WAbe
§ - subsp. ***dubernardiana*** (Bu) GKev WAbe
bracteata × ***bracteata*** subsp. ***dubernardiana*** (Bu) EPot
§ ***bracteosa*** (Pe) GKev
brevicula (Cy) SDR 4452 GKev
'Brittany Blue' (Pr/Prim/d) XBar
'Broadwell Chameleon' ITim
'Broadwell Milkmaid' 🏆H5 CPBP IPen MFie WAbe
'Broadwell No 1' (Au) **new** EPot
'Broadwell Oliver' (Au) IPen
'Broadwell Pink' (Au) IPen
'Broadwell Ruby' (Au) ITim WAbe
'Broadwell Snowstorm' CPBP
'Broadwell Violet' CPBP IPen
'Broxbourne' 🏆H5 ITim MFie
'Buckland Wine' (Pr/Prim) CElw CFis GAbr GEdr
× ***bulleesiana*** (Pf) CAby CBod CBot CSta CWCL EPfP GBin GBuc GKev LRHS MCot MFie MWts NBro NChi NEgg NGdn NHol NLar NSum SAko SWat WFar WHar WMoo WPnP
- Moerheim hybrids (Pf) GAbr
bulleyana (Pf) 🏆H7 Widely available
- ACE 2484 SWat
- hybrids (Pf) **new** GKev
'Burgundy Ice' (Pr/Prim/d) XBar
burmanica (Pf) CPla GAbr GBuc GKev IPen MMuc SWat WMoo
- SDR 5801 GKev
'Butter's Bronze' (Pr/Prim) WOut
'Butterscotch' (Pr/Prim) NCGa NSum XBar
'Caerulea Plena' (Pr/Prim) NBid
calderiana subsp. ***calderiana*** (Pe) GKev
- subsp. ***strumosa*** (Pe) GKev
Candelabra hybrids (Pf) CBre CBro CHVG ECho GAbr IPen ITim LSou MLHP NBir NGdn SGSe SWat WOut
'Candy Parade' (Pr) **new** WHil
Candy Pinks Group (Pr/Prim) NCGa NSum XBar
capitata (Ca) CMac ECho EPfP EPot EWld GKev IBoy IPen LRHS MBel MCot MLHP SCob SPer WCot
- CC 3843 GKev
- CC 6536B GKev
- subsp. ***mooreana*** (Ca) CAby CCon CExl CHid CLAP CLet CSta CTsd ECho EDAr EPfP GKev IPen NGdn NSum SPlb SRot WAbe XBar XLum
- 'Norverna Blue' (Ca) LRHS MHol
- 'Noverna Deep Blue' (Ca) SHil WCot
- 'Salvana' **new** EBee
'Captain Blood' (Pr/Prim/d) IPot
Carnation Victorians Group (Pr/Poly) XBar
carniolica (Au) GKev WCot
cernua (Mu) GKev IPen LLHF NSum XBar
'Charlotte' (Pr/Prim) IPen
Chartreuse Group (Pr/Poly) XBar
'Cheshire Life' CMea
§ ***chionantha*** (Cy) 🏆H6 CLAP CSta CWCL ECho GBin GBuc GCra GEdr GKev MMuc NBir NCGa NGdn NLar NSum SPer WAbe
- SDR 4426 GKev
- subsp. ***chionantha*** (Cy) GBuc GKev IPen MHol
§ - subsp. ***sinoplantaginea*** (Cy) NLar
§ - subsp. ***sinopurpurea*** (Cy) CLAP CSta EBee EPfP GBin GBuc GKev IPen NBir NCGa NSum WAbe
- - SDR 4418 GKev
chungensis (Pf) CAby CBod CLAP CMea CSta EBee EPfP GBin GCra GKev GLog IPen MHol NGdn NHol NLar NMyG NSum SWvt WAbe WHil WMAq WMoo XBar
§ ***chungensis*** × ***pulverulenta*** (Pf) CHid GKev NLar SAko
× ***chunglenta*** see *P. chungensis* × *pulverulenta*
'Cisca' GEdr WCot
'Clarence Elliott' (Au) 🏆H5 CPBP EPot IPen MFie MPnt NHar NWad WAbe WThu
'Clarissa White' (Pr/Poly) **new** XBar
clarkei (Or) GEdr WAbe
clusiana (Au) WAbe
cockburniana (Pf) 🏆H6 GAbr GKev GQui IPen NCGa SWat WAbe XBar
- SDR 1967 EBee
- SDR 5952 **new** GKev
- hybrids (Pf) SWat
- 'Kevock Sunshine' (Pf) EBee GKev IPen
concholoba (Mu) GKev WHil
'Corporal Baxter' (Pr/Prim/d) ECtt EPfP EWTr LLHF XBar
cortusoides (Co) CLAP EPfP GCra IPen NPri
'Cottage Cream' SVic
Cowichan Amethyst Group (Pr/Poly) CWCL NCGa XBar
Cowichan Blue Group (Pr/Poly) CDes NCGa NSum XBar
Cowichan Garnet Group (Pr/Poly) CDes NCGa NSum XBar
Cowichan strain (Pr/Poly) CElw
Cowichan Venetian Group (Pr/Poly) CHVG NCGa NSum XBar
Cowichan Yellow Group (Pr/Poly) NCGa NSum XBar
'Coy' (Au) WAbe
'Craddock White' (Pr/Prim) CFis GAbr GEdr
'Craven Gem' (Pr/Poly) GBuc
Crescendo Series (Pr/Poly) GAbr MMuc WHil
'Crimson Velvet' (Au) GAbr IPen WThu XBar
crispa see *P. glomerata*
cuneifolia subsp. ***heterodonta*** (Cu) GKev
darialica (Al) GKev LLHF
'Dark Rosaleen' (Pr/Poly) CElw CExl CHVG CWGN ECtt EHoe GAbr GBuc GEdr LBMP LLHF MBNS MFie MHol MMuc MNrw MPie NCGa NDov NLar NWad SAko SEND WCot XBar
'David Valentine' (Pr) CFis GAbr GBuc GEdr WCot XBar
davidii (Da) GKev
'Dawn Ansell' (Pr/Prim/d) CWCL ECtt EPfP GAbr GBuc GMaP MBNS MHol MNrw MRav NBir NCGa NSum SPer WCAu WHer WHil
Daybreak Group (Pr/Poly) CWCL NCGa XBar
deflexa (Mu) IPen
denticulata (De) 🏆H5 Widely available
- CC 4629 GKev
- var. ***alba*** (De) CBcs CTri EBee ECha ECho EPfP GAbr GBin GCra GMaP LRHS LSun MBel MFie MMuc NGdn NLar NPri

	SCob SGbt SPer SPoG WBor WFar WGwG WMoo WWtn
- blue-flowered (De)	CWCL ECho EPfP GAbr LLWG NLar NPri WBor
- 'Bressingham Beauty' (De)	EBee LRHS
- 'Glenroy Crimson' (De)	CLAP EBee LLHF
- hybrids	CBod SCob WFar XBar
- lilac-flowered (De)	ECho EHon LRHS NHol SCob WTor
- 'Prichard's Ruby' (De)	CBod
- purple-flowered (De)	ECho WMoo
- red-flowered (De)	ECho EPfP MFie NBir SCob WMoo
- 'Robinson's Red' (De)	GBuc
- 'Ronsdorf' (De)	NLar
- 'Rubin' (De)	CBod CWCL CWat EBee ECho EHon GAbr GBin GMaP LLWG LRHS MBrN MLHP NChi NLar SPer SPoG SRms XLum
- 'Rubinball' (De)	MSCN NHol
× ***deschmannii***	see *P.* × *vochinensis*
'Desert Sunset' (Pr/Poly)	NCGa XBar
'Devon Cream' (Pr/Prim)	GBuc
'Don Keefe'[PBR]	CBod CMHG EBee ECtt ELon GAbr GBin LLHF MBNS MBel MFie MHol MMuc MNrw MPie NGdn NHar NLar NWad SCob WCot WMoo
'Dorothy' (Pr/Poly)	MRav
'Double Lilac'	see *P. vulgaris* 'Lilacina Plena'
dubernardiana	see *P. bracteata* subsp. *dubernardiana*
'Duchess of York' (Pr/Poly)	GAbr GEdr LLHF LLWP NLar WCot
'Duckyls Red' (Pr/Prim)	CDes WHal
'Dusky Lady'	CLAP
'Early Bird' (*allionii* hybrid) (Au)	EPot IPen ITim MFie XBar
'Easter Bonnet' (Pr/Prim)	LRHS MMuc NBid SEND XBar
edgeworthii	see *P. nana*
§ ***elatior*** (Pr) ♀H5	CArn CBod CMac CPla ECho EWoo GKev GMaP MBel MHer MHol MNHC MNrw NChi NEgg NLar NPri SPer SPoG SWvt WBod WBrk WCot
- hose-in-hose (Pr/d)	NBid
- hybrids (Pr)	EPfP SPlb
- 'Magnifica' (Pr) **new**	GKev
§ - subsp. ***meyeri*** (Pr)	LLHF
- subsp. ***pallasii*** (Pr)	GKev
- subsp. ***pseudoelatior*** (Pr)	WAbe
'Elizabeth Browning'	GAbr WCot
'Elizabeth Killelay'[PBR] (Pr/Poly/d)	CBct CBod CExl CMea CWCL CWGN ECtt ELan GBin GBuc IBoy MMuc MNrw MPie NBir NEgg NGdn NHar NLar NSti NSum NWad SPer SPoG WBor WCot
'Ellen Page' (Au)	MFie
'Elpino' **new**	CBod
erratica (De)	GKev
'Ethel Barker' (Au)	IPen MFie NWad
'Eugénie' (Pr/Prim/d)	ECtt MRav NCGa WHil
euprepes	see *P. melanantha*
faberi (Am) **new**	GKev
'Fairy Rose' (Au)	IPen ITim NWad
farinosa (Al)	IPen NGdn WAbe
fasciculata (Ar)	GKev
- CLD 345	GEdr WAbe
- SDR 3092	GKev
'Feuerkönig' (Au)	NDro
'Fire Opal'	LRHS
Firefly Group (Pr/Poly)	NCGa WCot
§ ***firmipes*** (Si)	GKev IPen LPot WHil
§ ***flaccida*** (Mu)	ECho GEdr GKev IPen NHar NSum WAbe
- Cox 14026 **new**	GKev
Flamingo Group (Pr/Poly)	XBar
florindae (Si) ♀H7	Widely available
- bronze-flowered (Si)	GQui NBir
- 'Dave's Red' (Si)	LEdu
- hybrids (Si)	CMac EHrv EShb GAbr GMaP MLHP NCGa WFar WHar WHil WWtn XBar
- Keillour hybrids (Si)	CBod CLAP IBoy NGdn NLar SWvt
- 'Muadh' (Si)	MMuc SEND
- orange-flowered (Si)	CSam IPen LLWG MNrw WMoo
- peach-flowered (Si)	CSpe
- 'Ray's Ruby' (Si)	CLAP GBuc GEdr MNrw NBir WCot WMoo
- red and copper hybrids (Si)	CAby SWvt WHoo
- red-flowered (Si)	CSpe GBin IPen LLWG MMuc NBid NLar NSum WFar
- terracotta-flowered (Si)	NGdn
Footlight Parade Group (Pr/Prim)	XBar
forbesii (Mo) CC 4084	CExl
forrestii (Bu)	GKev IPen WAbe
- SDR 3304	GKev
- SDR 4304	CExl
- SDR 7839 **new**	GKev
§ × ***forsteri*** (Au)	NLar
§ - 'Bileckii' (Au)	ECho GMaP LLHF NBir NHar NSla
- 'Dianne' (Au)	ECho EDAr GAbr GCrg GKev LLHF NBro NRya WAbe WThu
- 'Dianne' hybrids (Au)	NHar
'Francisca' (Pr/Poly)	Widely available
'Fred Salter'	NRya
frondosa (Al) ♀H5	ECho GCra GKev IPen MFie MHol MLHP MPnt WAbe
Fuchsia Victorians Group (Pr/Poly)	CWCL NCGa XBar
'Gareth' (Pr/Poly)	GEdr
'Garnet' (*allionii* hybrid) (Au)	MFie XBar
'Garryarde Crimson'	GEdr LLHF
'Garryarde Guinevere'	see *P.* 'Guinevere'
gemmifera (Ar)	ECho LLHF
geraniifolia (Co)	CLAP GCra GKev
§ 'Gigha' (Pr/Prim)	CLAP GAbr GBin GKev MNrw XBar
'Gilded Ginger'	NCGa XBar
'Ginger Spice' (Au)	NDro WHil
glaucescens (Au)	GKev
§ ***glomerata*** (Ca)	GKev IPen
'Glowing Embers' (Pf)	GKev LLHF NBir
glutinosa All.	see *P. allionii*
Gold-laced Group (Pr/Poly)	CBod CBre CPla CWCL ECtt ELon EPfP IPen LCro LRHS LSRN MAsh MAvo MCot MMuc MNHC NEgg NGdn NLar NSla NSum NWad SEND SGSe SPer SPlb SPoG WHil WHoo WIce
§ - Barnhaven (Pr/Poly)	GBuc MFie NBir XBar
- Beeches strain (Pr/Poly)	CWCL IPen XBar
- red-flowered (Pr/Poly)	IPen XEll
'Gold-laced Jack in the Green' Barnhaven	XBar
gracilipes (Pe)	CLAP LLHF
- early-flowering (Pe)	GCra
- late-flowering (Pe)	CLAP GCra
- 'Major'	see *P. bracteosa*
- 'Minor'	see *P. petiolaris* Wall.
graminifolia	see *P. chionantha*

Grand Canyon Group (Pr/Poly) CWCL NCGa XBar
grandis (Sr) GAbr GKev IPen
'Green Lace' (Pr/Poly) ECtt
'Groenekan's Glorie' (Pr/Prim) CFis GAbr GBuc GEdr NBir NSum
§ 'Guinevere' (Pr/Poly) ♀^{H6} Widely available
'Hall Barn Blue' (Pr/Prim) CSam CSpe ECho GEdr GMaP MHCG MMuc NHar NMyG SEND WCot
§ ***halleri*** (Al) EPot IPen MFie XBar
- 'Longiflora' see *P. halleri*
handeliana EBee GKev
Harbinger Group (Pr/Prim) CWCL WHil XBar
Harbour Lights mixture (Pr/Poly) CWCL NCGa XBar
Harlow Car hybrids (Pf) EPfP GQui LRHS NCGa NLar NSla NWad WHil WMoo
Harvest Yellows Group (Pr/Poly) CWCL XBar
'Hazel's White' GKev
helodoxa see *P. prolifera*
'Hemswell Blush' (Au) GKev ITim LLHF MFie NHar WCre
'Hemswell Ember' (Au) CPBP
'Heritage Cream' (Pr/Prim) EBee
heucherifolia (Co) IPen WHil
- SDR 3224 GKev
hidakana (R) GEdr
'High Point' (Au) MFie
hirsuta (Au) IPen MMuc SEND
- 'Lismore Snow' (Au) NHar NWad
- red-flowered (Au) EBee MMuc
hirsuta × minima see *P. × forsteri*
hoffmanniana NHar NSum
hose-in-hose (Pr/Poly/d) MNrw
hose-in-hose, Barnhaven (Pr/Poly) XBar
'Hyacinthia' (Au) IPen MFie
ianthina see *P. prolifera*
'Ilana' IPen
incana (Al) GKev
Indian Reds Group (Pr/Poly) CWCL NCGa XBar
'Ingram's Blue' (Pr/Poly) CDes EPfP MHol
Inshriach hybrids (Pf) CAby CMHG IBoy
integrifolia (Au) GKev
§ 'Inverewe' (Pf) ♀^{H5} CCon GBin GBuc GCra GKev GQui NBir
involucrata see *P. munroi*
ioessa (Si) EWes GCra GKev IPen
- hybrids (Si) WAbe
'Iris Mainwaring' (Pr/Prim) CFis ECtt GAbr GCra GEdr LLHF MCot
irregularis (Pe) WAbe
'Jackie Richards' (Au) CTal GKev MFie
Jack-in-the-Green Group (Pr/Poly) CLAP CWCL MNrw WBor WMoo
- Barnhaven (Pr/Poly) XBar
- red-flowered (Pr/Poly) MMuc WHil
- white-flowered (Pr/Poly) IFro
'Janet Aldrich' CPBP
japonica (Pf) CMHG CSam ECha GQui IPen LRHS MSCN NBro NGdn SWat WAbe WMoo
- 'Alba' (Pf) CAby CHVG CSta CTri ECho EHon EPfP EShb EWoo GBuc GEdr IPen LRHS MBel MFie NGdn NWad SPer WAbe WFar
- 'Apple Blossom' (Pf) Widely available
* - 'Atropurpurea' (Pf) IPen
- 'Carminata' (Pf) IPen
* - 'Carminea' (Pf) GEdr GKev IPen MFie MSCN NBro NCGa NGdn NMyG NWad WFar WHil WWtn
- 'Cherry Red' (Pf) IPen
- 'Cleo' (Pf) IPen
- 'Fuji' (Pf) GKev NBro
- 'Holly' (Pf) IPen
- hybrids (Pf) CMac GCra MRav SPer WFar
- 'Jim Saunders' (Pf) SLon
- 'Miller's Crimson' (Pf) ♀^{H6} Widely available
- 'Oriental Sunrise' (Pf) CMil EHrv GBuc GKev IPen LLHF NCGa WHil XBar
- pale pink-flowered (Pf) ITim NSum
- 'Peninsula Pink' (Pf) IPen
- 'Pinkie' (Pf) IPen
- 'Postford White' (Pf) ♀^{H6} Widely available
- 'Purpurascens' (Pf) IPen
- Redfield strain (Pf) IPen NPri
- red-flowered (Pf) IPen WAbe
- 'Splendens' (Pf) IPen
I - 'Striatum' (Pf) EBee GKev
- 'Valley Red' (Pf) GKev IPen ITim NMyG
'Jay-Jay' (Pr) **new** GAbr
jesoana (Co) GKev LLHF
- B&SWJ 618 WCru
'Jewel' (Pr) **new** GAbr
'Joan Hughes' (*allionii* hybrid) (Au) WAbe
'Joanna' ECou GBuc MPnt
'Johanna' (Pu) GAbr GCrg GEdr GKev NGdn NHar NSum WAbe WCot
'John Fielding' (Pr) CBro CElw EBee
'Jo-Jo' (Au) CTal EPot MFie WAbe XBar
'Jubilee' (Pr/Prim/d) **new** LCro
juliae (Pr) ECho EDAr GCrg LRHS NBid NHar NSum SPlb WAbe
I - 'Millicent' (Pr) WCot
- white-flowered (Pr) NSum
'Juliana's Fireflies' (Pr/Poly) CWCL XBar
'Ken Dearman' (Pr/Prim/d) CBod ECtt MRav NBir NCGa
kewensis (Sp) ♀^{H2} GKev XBar
kialensis (Y) WAbe
'Kinlough Beauty' (Pr/Poly) CFis ECtt GBuc GMaP LLHF XBar
§ ***kisoana*** (Co) CExl CLAP GEdr GKev IPen LLHF WCru XBar
- var. ***alba*** (Co) GEdr NHar
- 'Lyo-beni' (Co) GEdr NHar
- 'Noushoku' **new** GEdr
- var. ***shikokiana*** see *P. kisoana*
'Koblenz' (Au) NHar
komarovii (Pr) LEdu
'Kusum Krishna' CBod GAbr GBin GEdr MBNS MHol MPie NHar NSti NWad WCot WHil
'Lady Greer' (Pr/Poly) ♀^{H5} CBod CDes CMac CSam CTal EBee ECtt EPfP GAbr GBuc GEdr GKev GMaP LHop LLWP MCot MHer NChi NGdn NHar NLar NSum WHer XBar
'Lambrook Mauve' (Pr/Poly) CElw CFis GAbr
latisecta (Co) IPen
§ ***laurentiana*** (Al) GKev
'Lea Gardens' (*allionii* hybrid) (Au) IPen MFie NWad
'Lee Myers' (*allionii* hybrid) (Au) IPen MFie XBar

	Name	Suppliers
	'Lemon and Lime'	CMea
	leucophylla	see *P. elatior*
	'Lilac Domino' (Au)	IPen
	lilacina	IPen
	'Lilian Foster' **new**	WCot
	'Lilian Harvey' (Pr/Prim/d)	CElw
	limbata (Cy)	GKev LLHF
	'Lindum Angelic' (Au) **new**	NHar
	'Lindum Aria' (Au) **new**	NHar
	'Lindum Buttermilk'	IPen
	'Lindum Celebration' (Au)	NHar
	'Lindum Crepes Suzette'	IPen ITim MFie NHar
	'Lindum Finale' (Au)	IPen ITim
	'Lindum First Kiss'	IPen ITim
	'Lindum Frosty Moon'	IPen ITim
	'Lindum Gecko' (Au) **new**	NHar
	'Lindum Lace'	IPen
	'Lindum Lancelot' (Au)	NHar
	'Lindum Lavender Mist' **new**	MFie
	'Lindum Lyric' (Au) **new**	NHar
	'Lindum Malcolm's Mate'	CPBP IPen
	'Lindum Moonlight'	IPen LLHF MFie
	'Lindum Morning Flight' (Au) **new**	NHar
	'Lindum Pixie'	IPen
	'Lindum Rapture' (Au)	IPen
	'Lindum Rhapsody'	LLHF
	'Lindum Serenade' (Au)	IPen
	'Lindum Smoke'	IPen NHar
	'Lindum Snowball' (Au)	NHar
	'Lindum Snowdrift' (Au)	IPen
	'Lindum Storm Cloud' (Au) **new**	NHar
	'Lindum Wedgwood' (Au)	EPot IPen ITim MFie NHar
	'Lingwood Beauty' (Pr/Prim)	CAby CElw CFis CSam GAbr WAbe
	'Lipstick'	CHid
	'Lismore Bay' (Au)	GKev
	'Lismore Peardrop' (Au) **new**	EPot
	'Lismore Pink Ice' (Au)	WThu
	'Lismore Sunshine'	NHar WThu
	'Lismore Treasure' (Au)	CPBP MFie
	'Lismore Yellow' (Au)	CPBP NHar WAbe XBar
	Lissadel hybrids (Pf)	NLar
	'Little Egypt' (Pr/Poly)	CWCL NCGa XBar
	littoniana	see *P. vialii*
	'Lizzie Green' (Pr/Prim)	NLar
	'Loisach'	NHar
	× ***loiseleurii*** 'Aire Mist' (Au) 🏆H5	EPot IPen ITim NHar NRya NSla NSum NWad WAbe WThu XBar
§	- 'Aire Waves' (Au)	CWCL ITim NHar NWad WAbe
	- 'Pink Aire Mist' (Au)	ITim
	- 'White Waves' (Au)	IPen
	longiflora	see *P. halleri*
	luteola (Or)	ECho GKev LLHF NGdn NSum
	'Ma7' (Au) **new**	EPot
	macrocalyx	see *P. veris*
	macrophylla (Cy)	GAbr
	'MacWatt's Claret' (Pr/Poly)	ECho GAbr GBuc LLWP SBch
	'MacWatt's Cream' (Pr/Poly)	CFis EBee GAbr GCra GEdr LLHF LRHS NHar NLar WCot WHil
	magellanica (Al)	WAbe
	mairei (Al) **new**	GKev
	'Maisie Michael'	CDes GEdr LLHF WAbe
	marginata (Au) 🏆H5	CPne CTal ECho EWoo IPen LHop LRHS MFie MMuc NSla NSum SBch SEND WAbe WBla
	- 'Adrian Evans' (Au)	GEdr GKev SBch
	- 'Alba' (Au)	LRHS MFie NBro NRya NWad WThu XBar
	- 'Ardfearn' (Au)	GEdr
	- 'Arthur Branch' (Au)	MFie
	- 'Baldock's Purple' (Au)	IPen
	- 'Barbara Clough' (Au)	GEdr IPen MFie NRya NWad XBar
	- 'Beamish' (Au) 🏆H5	GEdr NBro NRya NSla NWad
	- 'Beatrice Lascaris' (Au)	CTal GEdr MFie NRya WAbe
	- 'Caerulea' (Au)	ITim MFie NWad
	- 'Clear's Variety' (Au)	IPen ITim LLHF
	- 'Doctor Jenkins' (Au)	IPen NLar NRya NWad
	- 'Dolomites' (Au)	NWad
	- 'Drake's Form' (Au)	ECho IPen NLar NRya XBar
	- dwarf (Au)	ECho GEdr LRHS MFie NRya
	- 'Earl L. Bolton'	see *P. marginata* 'El Bolton'
§	- 'El Bolton' (Au)	IPen NRya NWad
	- 'Elizabeth Fry' (Au)	IPen MFie
	- 'Grandiflora' (Au)	IPen NWad
	- 'Highland Twilight' (Au)	IPen NSla
	- 'Holden Variety' (Au)	IPen ITim MFie NRya NWad
	- 'Holly Leaf' (Au)	GEdr
	- 'Ivy Agee' (Au)	IPen NRya
	- 'Janet' (Au)	ECho GEdr LLHF NWad WBla
	- 'Jenkins Variety' (Au)	ECho
	- 'Johannes Holler' (Au)	ITim NRya
	- 'Kesselring's Variety' (Au)	CMea ECho IPen ITim LLHF MFie NWad WAbe
	- 'Laciniata' (Au)	ECho IPen LRHS
	- 'Lemon Sorbet' (Au)	IPen
	- lilac-flowered (Au)	IPen
	- 'Linda Pope' (Au) 🏆H5	ECho EPot GEdr IPen NBir NHar NSum WAbe WThu XBar
	- maritime form (Au)	IPen
	- 'Millard's Variety' (Au)	IPen NWad
	- 'Miss Fell' (Au)	IPen
	- 'Mrs Carter Walmsley' (Au)	NRya
	- 'Nancy Lucy' (Au)	WAbe
	- 'Napoleon' (Au)	GEdr IPen ITim MFie MSCN NWad
	- 'Peggy Fell' (Au)	NWad
	- 'Prichard's Variety' (Au) 🏆H5	ECho GEdr IPen ITim LLHF MFie MSCN NLar NRya WAbe
	- 'Rosea' (Au)	IPen
	- 'Rubra' (Au)	ITim
	- 'Sheila Denby' (Au)	IPen
	- violet-flowered (Au)	ECho
	- 'Waithman's Variety' (Au)	IPen NRya
	- wild-collected (Au)	MFie
	'Maria Talbot' (*allionii* hybrid) (Au)	CTal IPen
	'Marianne Davey' (Pr/Prim/d)	WKif
	'Marie Crousse' (Pr/Prim/d)	NLar
	Marine Blues Group (Pr/Poly)	CWCL NSum XBar
	'Maris Tabbard' (Au)	EPot IPen MFie XBar
	'Mars' (*allionii* hybrid) (Au)	IPen MFie NWad XBar
	'Marven' (Au)	EPot IPen
	'Mary Anne'	GAbr
	'Mascara Blue' (Pr)	SVic
	Mauve Victorians Group (Pr/Poly)	NCGa XBar
	maximowiczii (Cy)	ECho EDAr GBin GEdr IPen LLHF NGdn NHar NLar NSum
	- Red-flowered Group	GBuc GKev IPen
	megaseifolia (Pr)	GBuc GKev IPen
§	***melanantha*** (Cy)	GKev
	- 'Nightglow' (Cy) **new**	GKev
	- 'Stardust' (Cy) **new**	GKev
	'Melenoc'h' (Pr/Prim/d)	XBar

Plant	Suppliers
§ × ***meridiana*** 'Miniera' (Au)	IPen MFie
Midnight Group	CHVG CWCL XBar
'Miel' (Pr/Prim/d)	XBar
'Mike Smith'	IPen
'Miniera'	see *P.* × *meridiana* 'Miniera'
minima (Au)	NBro WAbe
- var. ***alba*** (Au)	NHar
minima × ***wulfeniana***	see *P.* × *vochinensis*
'Miss Doris' (Pr/Prim/d)	XBar
'Miss Indigo' (Pr/Prim/d)	CTsd CWCL ECtt EPfP GAbr GBin GMaP MBNS MFie MHol MRav NSum SPer WCAu WMoo
mistassinica var. ***macropoda***	see *P. laurentiana*
miyabeana (Pf)	GKev IPen
modesta (Al)	XBar
- var. ***faurieae*** (Al)	GKev IPen
- - f. ***leucantha*** (Al)	GKev
- var. ***samanimontana*** (Al)	GKev
'Moerheimii'	GEdr
monticola	GKev
'Moorland Apricot'	WMoo
moupinensis (Pe) ♀H4	CExl LLHF
'Mrs Eagland'	GAbr
'Mrs Frank Neave' (Pr/Prim)	GAbr GEdr IPen
'Mrs Marjorie Banks' (Pr)	GKev
'Mrs McGillivray' (Pr/Prim)	GAbr
§ ***munroi*** (Ar)	GKev IPen NHar WAbe XBar
- white-flowered (Ar)	WAbe
§ - subsp. ***yargongensis*** (Ar)	EBee GEdr GKev IPen XBar
- - SDR 3096	GKev
- - SDR 6121	GKev
muscarioides (Mu)	GKev IPen
Muted Victorians Group (Pr/Poly)	NCGa NSum XBar
'Myline'	WThu
§ ***nana*** (Pe)	IPen
nepalensis	see *P. tanneri* subsp. *nepalensis*
'Netta Dennis' (Pe)	LLHF NHar
New Pinks Group (Pr/Poly)	NCGa NSum XBar
'Nightingale'	ITim
nivalis Pallas	see *P. chionantha*
nivalis ambig.	NSum
nutans Delavay ex Franch.	see *P. flaccida*
obconica (Ob) ♀H1c	GKev
- SDR 7606	GKev
'Oberau'	IPen
'Old Port' (Pr/Poly)	CAby CSam EBee GEdr GKev NSum
Old Rose Victorians Group (Pr/Poly)	NCGa NSum XBar
optata (Cy)	GKev
orbicularis (Cy)	ECho GEdr GKev LLHF NLar
Osiered Amber Group (Pr/Prim)	NCGa NSum XBar
'Page'	IPen MFie
palinuri (Au)	IPen
palmata (Co)	GEdr GKev NHar
'Paris '90' (Pr/Poly)	CWCL NCGa NSum XBar
parryi (Pa)	CSta EBee GKev LLHF
pedemontana 'Alba' (Au)	MFie WThu
'Perle von Bottrop' (Pr/Prim)	ECtt GAbr GEdr NHar WCot
petelotii (Ch)	WAbe
'Peter Klein' (Or)	GBuc GKev LLHF WAbe
petiolaris misapplied	see *P.* 'Redpoll'
§ ***petiolaris*** Wall. (Pe)	GCra NHar NSum
- Sherriff's form	see *P.* 'Redpoll'
'Petticoat'	ECtt WCot

Plant	Suppliers
'Pink Aire' (Au)	MFie NPri XBar
'Pink Cabbage' (Poly)	CDes
'Pink Fairy' (Au)	IPen ITim
'Pink Grapefruit' (Pr/Prim/d)	XBar
'Pink Ice' (*allionii* hybrid) (Au)	MFie NHar NWad XBar
poissonii (Pf)	CSta CTri CTsd CWCL EBee ELan EPfP GBin GKev GQui IPen LRHS NGdn NLar NSum WAbe WShi
- SDR 4617	GKev
- SDR 5959	GKev
polyanthus (Pr/Poly)	CWCL
polyneura (Co)	CWCL ECho GEdr GKev IPen MHol MSnd NGdn WCot
'Port Wine' (Pr)	GAbr GCra GEdr
'Powdery Pink'	LRHS
Primlet Series (Pr/Prim)	SVic
§ ***prolifera*** (Pf) ♀H4	CMHG CSta EPfP GBuc GCra GKev GMaP GQui IPen LHop LRHS MMuc MSCN NGdn SWat WAbe WMoo XBar
§ × ***pubescens*** (Au) ♀H5	IPen LRHS MHer NGdn
- 'A.E. Matthews' (Au)	NWad
- 'Apple Blossom' (Au)	IPen MFie
§ - 'Bewerley White' (Au)	EBee ECho EPfP IPen NDro NPri
- 'Blue Wave' (Au)	IPen MFie SPop
§ - 'Boothman's Variety' (Au)	CBod CTri ECho EPfP EWoo ITim MFie NHar NSla WHoo
- 'Carmen'	see *P.* × *pubescens* 'Boothman's Variety'
- 'Chamois' (Au)	MFie
- 'Christine' (Au)	CMea GKev IPen MHer NBir NSum WCot
- 'Cream Viscosa' (Au)	SPlb
- 'Faldonside' (Au)	IPen MFie NSla NSum WThu
§ - 'Freedom' (Au)	CTal CTri ECho EWoo IPen MFie NBir NHar NLar NSla XBar
- 'George Harrison' (Au)	MFie
- 'Harlow Car' (Au)	CMea GQui IPen MFie MPnt NSum NWad
- 'Hazel's White' (Au)	ITim
- 'Joan Danger' (Au)	IPen NDro
- 'Joan Gibbs' (Au)	IPen ITim MFie XBar
- 'Kath Dryden' (Au)	ITim
- 'Lilac Fairy' (Au)	EPot IPen ITim NWad WThu
- 'Moonlight' (Au)	NDro
- 'Mrs G.F. Wilson' (Au)	ECho
- 'Mrs J.H. Wilson' (Au)	CTal ECho GCrg MFie NRya XBar
- 'Pat Barwick' (Au)	IPen MFie NDro NRya NWad
- 'Rufus' (Au) ♀H5	EWes GAbr GEdr NDro WThu XBar
- 'S.E. Matthews' (Au)	GAgs
- 'Sid Skelton' (Au)	IPen NRya
- 'Slack Top Violet' (Au)	NSla
- 'Snowcap' (Au)	CPBP IPen ITim XBar
- 'Sonya' (Au)	IPen
- 'The General' (Au)	CTri GEdr IPen MFie
§ - 'Wedgwood' (Au)	GAbr IPen MFie NSum XBar
- 'Winnifred' (Au)	WHil
- yellow-flowered (Au)	IPen
pulchella (Pu)	GKev
pulverulenta (Pf) ♀H6	Widely available
- 'Bartley' (Pf)	WWtn
- Bartley hybrids (Pf) ♀H6	CWCL EBee EWTr GKev MMuc NSum SEND WMoo XBar
- 'Bartley Pink' (Pf)	CPla GBuc
'Purple' (Primlet Series) (Pr/Prim)	LRHS
'Quaker's Bonnet'	see *P. vulgaris* 'Lilacina Plena'
'Rachel Kinnen' (Au)	GAbr IPen MFie XBar

	Plant	Suppliers
	'Ramona' (Pr/Poly)	CWCL NCGa XBar
	'Raspberry Ripple' (Pr/Prim/d)	XBar
	'Ravenglass Vermilion'	see *P.* 'Inverewe'
	'Red' (Primlet Series) (Pr/Prim)	LRHS
	'Red Ruffles' (Pr/Poly/d)	CBod ECtt
§	'Redpoll' (Pe)	GBuc LLHF NHar
	reidii (So)	GEdr GKev
	- CC 7341 **new**	GKev
	- var. ***williamsii*** (So)	GEdr GKev IPen
*	- - ***alba*** (So)	GEdr
	reticulata (Si)	GKev
	'Reverie' (Pr/Poly)	XBar
	'Rheniana' (Au)	IPen MFie NRya
	'Rick Lupp'	IPen
	'Romeo' (Pr/Prim)	CLAP LLHF NWad WCot
	'Rose' (Primlet Series) (Pr/Prim)	LRHS
	rosea (Or) ♀H5	CAby CBod CElw CWCL EBee ECho EPfP GKev GLog IPen MFie MMuc NBid NBir NRya SEND WPnP
	- CC 5260	GKev
	- 'Gigas' (Or)	CLet EDAr NPri NRya WBor WMAq
	- 'Grandiflora' (Or)	CBod CMac ECho EPfP GCrg GKev LHop LRHS NCGa NLar NPri SPoG SRms SWat XLum
	'Rosemary Cottage'	CDes GAbr WCot
	'Rowallane Rose' (Pf)	IPen
I	'Rowena'	GAbr GCra LLHF WCot
	'Roy Cope' (Pr/Prim/d)	NBir
	'Roydon Ruby'	GEdr
	rubra	see *P. firmipes*
	'Ruby Tuesday' (Au)	NDro
	rusbyi (Pa)	GKev WHil
	- subsp. ***ellisiae*** (Pa)	IPen
	'Sapphire'	XBar
	'Saracen'	IPen MFie
	saxatilis ambig. (Co)	MFie
§	'Schneekissen' (Pr/Prim)	CSam CWCL GAbr GBuc GCra LLHF MHer NBro NChi SCob WTor
	scotica (Al)	GAbr GKev GPoy NSla WAbe
	secundiflora (Pf)	CCon CLAP CSta ECho ELan EPot EWTr GAbr GBin GBuc GCra GKev LLWG MMuc NBir NSum SBrt SPer SPlb SWat WAbe WMoo WWFP XBar
	- SDR 4401	GKev
	- SDR 4435	GKev
§	× ***sendtneri*** (Au)	MFie
	× ***serrata***	see *P.* × *vochinensis*
	serratifolia (Pf)	GKev
	- SDR 5165	GKev
	'Shizuko Hara'	IPen
	sibthorpii	see *P. vulgaris* subsp. *sibthorpii*
	sieboldii (Co) ♀H5	CCon ECho EWld GKev IPen MAsh MLHP MNrw NSla SBch SRms WAbe WBla WHea
	- 'Aaimayama' (Co)	CSta WHil
	- 'Aiaigasa' (Co)	WFar
	- 'Akinoysool' (Co)	WFar
	- 'Andromeda' (Co)	EBee WHil
	- 'Aoba-no-fue' (Co)	CAby CSta WHil
	- 'Asahi' (Co)	WFar
	- 'Asahigata' (Co)	CSta WHil
	- 'Ayanami' (Co)	WFar
	- 'Ayasegawa' (Co)	CSta WHil
	- 'Beeches Star' (Co)	EBee
	- 'Benjamin' (Co)	CSta WHil
	- 'Bide-a-Wee Blue' (Co)	NBid
	- 'Bide-a-Wee Lace' (Co)	NBid
	- 'Bijyonomai' (Co)	WFar
I	- 'Blue Lagoon' (Co)	EBee EPfP LLHF LRHS NLar WFar WHil
	- 'Blue Shades' (Co)	IPen
	- blue-flowered (Co)	CLAP CSta CWCL WHil
	- 'Blush' (Co)	CLAP CSta WHil WWEG
	- 'Boykavitch' (Co)	WHil
	- 'Bureikou' (Co)	WFar
	- 'Carefree' (Co)	CLAP CSta ECtt IPen LLHF NBro NLar WBla WHil
	- 'Carmine Pink' (Co) **new**	WHil
	- 'Cherubim' (Co)	CLAP CSta EBee GCra LRHS WBla WHil
	- 'Clouds Over Blighty' (Co)	EBee
	- 'Daikoshi' (Co)	CSta WHil
	- 'Daiminnisiki' (Co)	NHar
	- 'Dancing Ladies' (Co)	CLAP ECtt IPen NBro NCGa NHar WBla WFar WHil XBar
	- 'Dart Rapids' (Co)	CDes CSta WHil WSHC
	- 'Duane's Choice' (Co)	CAby CCon CLAP CSta WHil
	- 'Edasango' (Co)	WFar
	- 'Edomurasaki' (Co)	CSta WFar WHil
	- 'Essie' (Co)	CSta
	- 'Frilly Blue' (Co)	CSta EBee LRHS WWEG
	- 'Fujijishi' (Co)	WFar
	- 'Galactic' (Co)	CSta
	- 'Galaxy' (Co)	NBro
	- 'Geisha Girl' (Co)	CLAP CSpe CSta EBee LRHS MRav NLar WAbe WBla WFar WHil WWEG
	- 'Ginhukurin' (Co)	CSta WFar WHil
	- 'Gunmia Niizatia' (Co)	CSta
	- 'Hakutsuri' (Co)	WFar
	- 'Hatagarasi' (Co)	WFar
	- 'Hatusugato' (Co)	NHar WFar
	- 'Heart's Desire' (Co)	EBee
	- 'Higurasi' (Co)	WFar
	- 'Hinokoromo' (Co)	WFar
	- 'Inikina White' (Co)	WFar
	- 'Inokima Minoura' (Co)	WFar
	- 'Jessica' (Co)	CSta WHil
	- 'Kansenden' (Co)	WFar
	- 'Karagoromo' (Co)	WFar
	- 'Kashima' (Co)	CAby CSta WHil
	- 'Kotonosirabe' (Co)	WFar
	- 'Lacewing' (Co)	WHil
	- f. ***lactiflora*** (Co)	CLAP CSta IPen LRHS NBro SRot WHil
	- 'Lilac Sunbonnet' (Co)	CLAP EPfP LLHF NHar WFar
	- 'Managuruma' (Co)	WFar
	- 'Manakoora' (Co)	CAby CLAP EBee ECtt EHrv IPen NBro NCGa NSum WFar XBar
	- 'Mangetu' (Co)	WFar
	- 'Martin Nest Blue' (Co)	CSta WHil
	- 'Martin Nest Pale Pink' (Co)	CSta
	- 'Masasino' (Co)	WFar
	- 'Matsu-no-yuki' (Co)	CSta WBla WHil
	- 'Mikado' (Co)	CCon CLAP CSta EBee ECtt IPen LRHS WHil WWEG
	- 'Musashino' (Co)	CSta WHil
	- 'Noboruko' (Co)	CSta WHil
	- 'Okinanotomo' (Co)	WFar
	- 'Oshibori' (Co)	CSta WHil
	- 'Our White' (Co)	WHil
	- 'Pago-Pago' (Co)	CDes CLAP CSta ECtt EHrv IPen NBro WBla WFar WHil XBar
	- 'Pink Laced' (Co)	WFar
	- pink-flowered (Co)	CCon CWCL GKev NBir

- 'Saiun' (Co)	CSta WHil
- 'Sangoguko' new	MNrw
- 'Sekidaiko' (Co)	CSta
- 'Senyuu' (Co)	WFar WHil
- 'Seraphim' (Co)	CLAP EBee LRHS MMHG NLar WFar WHil WWEG
- 'Seto-no-ume' (Co)	CSta WHil
- 'Shiokemuri' (Co)	CSta WHil
- 'Shishifunjin' (Co)	CSta WHil
- 'Sinipukurn' (Co)	WFar
- 'Sinseiu' (Co)	WFar
- 'Siritonbo' (Co)	WFar
- 'Snowdrop' (Co)	CBcs ECtt LHop LSou MBel MHol MNrw MPie NCGa NMyG WBla WCot WFar WMoo
- 'Snowflake' (Co)	CBod CLAP CSta EBee EPfP GKev LRHS NLar WAbe WBla WFar
- 'Sorcha's Pink' (Co)	CSta WHil
- 'Sousiarai' (Co)	CSta
- 'Spring Blush' (Co)	CSta WHil
- 'Spring Song' (Co)	CSta WHil
- 'Sumizomegenji' (Co)	CSta WHil
- 'Sweetie' (Co)	WFar
- 'Syosin' (Co)	CSta
- 'Tagonoura' (Co)	CSta WHil
- 'Tah-ni' (Co)	NBro NSum WHil
- 'Taoyami' (Co)	CSta WHil
- 'Tatutanoyuube' (Co)	CSta
- 'Tokimeki' (Co)	WFar
- 'Toyonoharu' (Co)	WBla WFar
- 'Tukasamesi' (Co)	CSta
- 'Turunokegoromo' (Co)	CSta WHil
- 'Winter Dreams' (Co)	CAby CLAP CWCL ECtt EHrv NBid NBro NCGa NHar NSum WFar XBar
- 'Yuuhibeni' (Co)	CSta
sikkimensis (Si) ♀H6	CSta EBee ECho EPot EWTr GKev IPen LRHS MMuc MSnd NGdn NSum SPoG XBar
- CC 5730	GKev
- CC 5986	GKev
- CC 6783 new	GKev
- SDR 3099	GKev
- SDR 4919	GKev
- SDR 5933	GKev
- SDR 7426	GKev
- var. ***pseudosikkimensis*** (Si)	GKev IPen
- - SDR 4528	GKev
- var. ***pudibunda*** (Si)	EBee GKev
- 'Ruby Shades' (Si)	GEdr
- 'Tilman Number 2' (Si)	GBuc
aff. ***sikkimensis*** (Si)	IPen NGdn
'Silver Lace Charlotte'	WIce
Silver-laced Group (Pr/Poly)	EPfP MMuc NLar SEND SPoG SWvt WIce
- black-flowered (Pr/Poly)	XEll
sinoplantaginea	see *P. chionantha* subsp. *sinoplantaginea*
sinopurpurea	see *P. chionantha* subsp. *sinopurpurea*
'Sir Bedivere' (Pr/Prim)	EBee GAbr GBuc NHar WCot
'Siska' (Pr/Poly)	GAbr
smithiana	see *P. prolifera*
'Snow Carpet'	see *P.* 'Schneekissen'
'Snow White' (Pr/Poly)	GBin GEdr MRav
Snowcushion	see *P.* 'Schneekissen'
'Snowruffles'	ITim
sonchifolia (Pe)	CCon CLAP GKev
- subsp. ***emeiensis***	GKev
- subsp. ***sonchifolia***	GKev
sorachiana	see *P. yuparensis*
'Sorbet' (Pr/Poly)	XBar
spectabilis (Au)	CDes GBin GKev
specuicola (Al)	GKev
Spice Shades Group (Pr/Poly)	CHid NCGa XBar
× ***steinii***	see *P.* × *forsteri*
stenocalyx (Pu)	GKev
stenodonta (Pf)	GKev
'Stradbrook Charm' (Au)	CPBP CWCL EPot MFie WThu
'Stradbrook Dainty' (Au)	MFie
'Stradbrook Dream' (Au)	ITim MFie XBar
'Stradbrook Lilac Lustre' (Au)	MFie
'Stradbrook Lucy' (Au)	GEdr IPen ITim NWad
'Stradbrook Mauve Magic' (Au)	MFie
stricta (Al)	GKev
Striped Victorians Group (Pr/Poly)	NCGa NSum XBar
'Strong Beer' (d)	EBee ECtt GEdr MHol MMuc MNrw MPie NMyG NSti NSum NWad SAko WBrk WCot WKif
stuartii (Cy)	GKev
'Sue Jervis' (Pr/Prim/d)	EWTr MRav NBir SPer WCAu
suffrutescens (Su)	WAbe
'Sundae' (Pr/Prim/d)	XBar
'Sunrise' (Primlet Series) (Pr/Prim)	LRHS
'Sunshine Susie' (Pr/Prim/d)	XBar
szechuanica (Cy)	IPen LLHF
takedana (Bu)	GEdr
'Tango' (Pr/Prim)	NCGa NDro XBar
tangutica (Cy)	GKev IPen
tanneri (Pe)	GKev
§ - subsp. ***nepalensis*** (Pe)	GKev
'Tantallon' (Pe)	LLHF NHar
Tartan Reds Group (Pr/Prim)	CWCL XBar
'Tawny Port' (Pr/Poly)	CElw CFis
'Theodora' (Pr)	CTal GAbr GEdr
'Tie Dye' (Pr/Prim)	CBod ELan EPot LLHF MHol MMuc MNrw MPie NLar NWad SAko WCot WWFP
'Tinney's Moonlight' (Pe)	NHar
'Tipperary Purple' (Pr/Prim)	ECtt GAbr
'Tomato Red' (Pr/Prim)	CDes CFis EBee LHop LLHF WCot
'Tony' (Au) ♀H5	CPBP EPot IPen MFie XBar
'Top Affair' (Au/d)	IPen WAln
'Tortoiseshell' (Pr/d)	CHid ECtt
Traditional Yellows Group (Pr) new	XBar
'Tregor Rose' (Pr/Prim/d)	XBar
* ***urumiensis***	GEdr
'Val Horncastle' (Pr/Prim/d)	ECtt EPfP GAbr GMaP MFie
Valentine Victorians Group (Pr/Poly)	XBar
× ***venusta*** (Au)	GKev
'Vera Maud' (Pr)	NCGa NSum XBar
§ ***veris*** (Pr) ♀H5	Widely available
- PAB 3777	LEdu
- subsp. ***columnae*** (Pr)	EDAr GKev
I - 'Coronation Cowslips' (Pr)	GBuc XBar
- 'Katy McSparron' (Pr/d)	CBod CExl EBee ECtt GEdr MAvo MHol MNrw MPie NLar NSti SAko SPer SPoG WCot
- 'Lady Agatha' (Pr)	XBar

- subsp. ***macrocalyx*** (Pr)	WCot
- orange-flowered (Pr)	WMoo
- red-flowered (Pr)	NBid NGdn SPer WMoo
- 'Sunset Shades' (Pr)	EAJP ECGP EPfP GBuc NGdn NLar SWvt XEll
vernalis	see *P. vulgaris*
verticillata (Sp)	GKev IPen
§ ***vialii*** (So) 𝕐H5	Widely available
'Vicky'	IPen
Violet Victorians Group (Pr/Poly)	NCGa XBar
virginis (Am) new	GKev
§ × ***vochinensis*** (Au)	NHar
§ ***vulgaris*** (Pr/Prim) 𝕐H7	Widely available
- var. ***alba*** (Pr/Prim)	NSla WBrk
- 'Alba Plena' (Pr/Prim/d)	GAbr GCal NSum
- 'Avoca' new	GEdr NHar WCot
- 'Avondale' (Kennedy Irish Series) (Pr/Prim) new	CAby LLHF MHol NHar WCot
- Barnhaven Gold	XBar
- 'Carrigdale' new	GEdr NHar WCot
- 'Claddagh' new	GEdr NHar WCot
- Cornish pink (Pr/Prim) new	GKev
- Drumcliffe = 'K74'PBR	CSpe EBee ECtt EHoe GAbr GEdr LLHF MBel MHol MMuc MNrw MPie NCGa NDov NHar NLar NSti WCot
- 'Dunbeg' (Kennedy Irish Series) (Pr/Prim) new	CAby LLHF NHar WCot
- 'Glengarriff' (Kennedy Irish Series) (Pr/Prim) new	GEdr NHar WCot
- 'Golden Gem' (Pr/Prim/d) new	WCot
- green-flowered	see *P. vulgaris* 'Viridis'
- hybrids (Pr/Prim)	LSun WFar
- Innisfree = 'K72'PBR	CAby CMea EBee ECtt GAbr GEdr LLHF MBel MMuc MNrw MPie NCGa NHar NLar NMyG NSti NWad SEND SPad WCot
§ - 'Lilacina Plena' (Pr/Prim/d)	CWCL EBee GAbr GCal IFro LLHF MRav NCGa NSum SIgm WHer
- 'Moneygall' (Kennedy Irish Series) (Pr/Poly) (d) new	NHar
- var. ***pulchella*** (Pr/Prim)	CDes
§ - subsp. ***sibthorpii*** (Pr/Prim) 𝕐H5	CCon CMHG CSam EBee ECho ELon EPfP GBuc IPen LLWP LRHS MCot MFie MHer MNrw MRav NBro NCGa NChi NWad SKHP SPtp SRms WHil
- - TCM 12-370 new	CEvo
- - pale-flowered (Pr/Prim)	GBuc
- 'Taigetos' (Pr/Prim)	CBro CExl CHid
- 'Tara' new	GEdr NHar
§ - 'Viridis' (Pr/Prim/d)	CCon MNrw
- subsp. ***vulgaris*** (Pr/Prim/d) 𝕐H5	WMAq
waltonii (Si)	CLAP CSta CWCL EPfP GBin GKev IPen MNrw NLar NSum
- hybrids (Si)	ELon GEdr
'Wanda' (Pr/Prim) 𝕐H7	CBcs CTri ECho GAbr GCra GKev LBMP LRHS MBel MCot MHer MMuc NBid SRms WBrk WCFE WCot
Wanda Group (Pr/Prim)	CHVG ECho LBMP NBro SVic
- 'Wanda Hose-in-hose' (Pr/Prim/d)	GCra LLWP NBir WHer WHil
- 'Wanda Jack-in-the-Green' (Pr/Prim)	CLAP WCot
wardii	see *P. munroi*
warshenewskiana (Or)	CLAP EWes GBuc GCrg GJos GKev NHar NRya WAbe WGwG
watsonii (Mu)	GKev NHar SWat
- ACE 1402	IPen
- maroon-flowered (Mu) new	GKev
'Waxenstein' (Au) new	EPot
'Wedgwood'	see *P.* × *pubescens* 'Wedgwood'
'Wharfedale Bluebell' (Au)	IPen NBir NHar WThu
'Wharfedale Buttercup' (Au)	IPen ITim NHar NWad
'Wharfedale Butterfly' (Au)	NWad
'Wharfedale Crusader' (Au)	IPen
'Wharfedale Gem' (*allionii* hybrid) (Au)	EPot MFie NSla NWad XBar
'Wharfedale Ling' (*allionii* hybrid) (Au)	CTal MFie NHar NPri NWad XBar
'Wharfedale Sunshine' (Au)	CPBP IPen
'Wharfedale Superb' (*allionii* hybrid) (Au)	MFie XBar
'Wharfedale Village' (Au)	IPen MPnt NHar WThu
'White Linda Pope' (Au)	NSla NWad WThu
'White Petticoat' (d)	NDov
'White Wanda' (Pr/Prim)	GAbr XBar
'White Waves' (*allionii* hybrid) (Au)	ITim
§ ***whitei*** 'Sherriff's Variety' (Pe)	CLAP
'William Genders' (Pr/Poly)	GAbr GEdr
wilsonii (Pf)	CBod CSta CTri CWCL EWld GAbr LLWG NGdn SGSe SWat WWtn XBar
§ - var. ***anisodora*** (Pf)	CLAP GBin GKev GLog IPen NGdn NWad XBar
- var. ***wilsonii*** (Pf)	GKev
'Windrush'	see *P.* × *berninae* 'Windrush'
'Winter White'	see *P.* 'Gigha'
'Wisley Crimson'	see *P.* 'Wisley Red'
§ 'Wisley Red' (Pr/Prim)	CElw
'Woodland Walk' (Pr/Prim)	EPfP
woodwardii (Cy)	GKev
wulfeniana (Au)	EBee EPot
yargongensis	see *P. munroi* subsp. *yargongensis*
'Yellow' (Primlet Series) (Pr/Prim)	LRHS
§ ***yuparensis*** (Al)	EBee GBuc GKev IPen
- white-flowered (Al)	GKev
zambalensis (Ar)	GKev IPen
- SDR 1611	GKev
'Zebra Blue' new	NPri
'Zenobia'	WCre

Prinsepia (*Rosaceae*)

sinensis	MBlu NLar SLon WSHC

Pritchardia (*Arecaceae*)

affinis	XBlo
hillebrandii	LPal
pacifica	XBlo

Pritzelago (*Brassicaceae*)

alpina	GCrg NSla

Prosartes (*Liliaceae*)

§ ***hookeri***	CLAP EBee ECho LLHF MNrw SGSe WCru
§ - var. ***oregana***	EBee EPPr IBlr IFoB WCru
§ ***lanuginosa***	EBee EPPr LEdu LRHS WCru WPGP

§ ***maculata*** CAby CDes CLAP CTal IFoB LEdu MNrw NLar WCru
§ ***smithii*** EBee ECho EPfP EPot GKev GLog LEdu MNrw NBir NLar SGSe WCot WCru WPGP WSHC
- 'Rick' (v) CTal

Prospero (*Asparagaceae*)

obtusifolium subsp. ***intermedium*** new WCot

Prostanthera (*Lamiaceae*)

aspalathoides CSde CTsd MOWG
'Badja Peak' CTsd EBee EUJe EWes LRHS MAsh MOWG SLim
baxteri MOWG
- 'Silver Ghost' SLim
cryptandroides new CBcs
cuneata ♀H4 Widely available
- 'Alpine Gold' (v) CMHG LRHS MAsh
- 'Blushing Bride' CMac EUJe LBuc
- Kew form WPGP
denticulata new CTsd
* ***digitiformis*** CTsd
incana new CTsd
incisa CTsd
lasianthos CBcs CHll CTsd LRHS MOWG SLim SPlb SVen
- 'Kallista Pink' CTsd MOWG
- var. ***subcoriacea*** CExl
latifolia CTsd
magnifica MOWG
melissifolia CTsd ECre
§ - var. ***parvifolia*** CBcs CTsd
'Mint Delight' SLim
'Mint Royale' EUJe LEdu LRHS SLim
'Mint-Ice' LRHS SLim
nivea ECou
ovalifolia ♀H3 CPne ECou MOWG
I - 'Variegata' (v) CBcs CExl CHGN CMac CTsd LRHS LSou MOWG MSCN WGrn
phylicifolia CPne CTsd MOWG
'Poorinda Ballerina' CTsd EBee LRHS MAsh SLim SPer SPoG SRkn WWFP
'Poorinda Petite' CDoC CTsd LRHS
rhombea new CTsd
rotundifolia ♀H3 CAbb CBod CSde CTri CTsd EBee ECho MGil MNHC MOWG MSCN SPer SVen WCFE WGrn
- 'Chelsea Girl' see *P. rotundifolia* 'Rosea'
§ - 'Rosea' ♀H3 CDoC CLet CTsd ECou EPfP LHop LRHS MOWG SEND
rugosa new CTsd
sericea LRHS
sieberi misapplied see *P. melissifolia* var. *parvifolia*
sieberi Benth. CTre CTsd MOWG
I - 'Variegata' (v) new CTsd
spinosa CTsd MOWG
'Starlight' (v) new CTsd
walteri CTsd LRHS MOWG

Protea (*Proteaceae*)

aurea SPlb
- subsp. ***aurea*** CTre
burchellii SPlb
'Clark's Red' new MPkF
coronata CTre SPlb
cynaroides CBlu CTre IDee SBig SPlb
effusa SPlb
eximia CTre SPlb
grandiceps SPlb
lacticolor SPlb
laurifolia SPlb
lepidocarpodendron new CTre
longifolia new CTre
nana SPlb
neriifolia CTre SPlb
obtusifolia SPlb
'Pink Crown' new MPkF
repens CTre SPlb
scolymocephala SPlb
subvestita CTre SPlb
susannae CTre SPlb

Prumnopitys (*Podocarpaceae*)

§ ***andina*** CBcs CDoC SLim
elegans see *P. andina*
§ ***taxifolia*** CDoC ECou

Prunella (*Lamiaceae*)

§ ***grandiflora*** CHby CPrp ECha SRms SWat WOut
- 'Alba' CBre EBee ECha EPfP GMaP NLar SPer SRms WCAu WOut
- 'Blue Loveliness' GBee SWvt
- 'Carminea' EBee MRav SPer
- 'Freelander' MNHC
- light blue-flowered WBor
- 'Loveliness' CMac CPrp ECha GMaP MRav NBro NGdn NSti SPer SPlb SRGP WCAu WFar
- 'Pagoda' CSpe NLar
- 'Pink Loveliness' CPrp SRms WFar
- 'Rosea' WFar WOut
- 'Rubra' NLar WOut
- violet-flowered EPfP
- 'White Loveliness' CMac CPrp
hyssopifolia XSen
incisa see *P. vulgaris*
laciniata EBee
- dark purple-flowered new SBrt
Summer Daze = 'Binsumdaz'PBR EBee ECtt LSou NSti SPoG STPC
§ ***vulgaris*** CArn CHab CWld ENfk GPoy MHer MNHC NMir SRms WHer WHfH WJek WMoo WOut
- 'Blue Pearl' new CBod
- f. ***leucantha*** WHer
- 'Rose Pearl' CBod LRHS LSRN
× ***webbiana*** see *P. grandiflora*
- 'Gruss aus Isernhagen' EBee

Prunus ✿ (*Rosaceae*)

sp. LPar
'Accolade' (d) ♀H6 Widely available
§ 'Amanogawa' ♀H6 Widely available
amygdalus see *P. dulcis*
andersonii SBrt
angustifolia new LPar
Aprium Series (F) ERea
armeniaca 'Alfred' (F) CDul ERea GTwe SDea SKee SPer WHar
- 'Bergeron' (F) new LRHS WMat
- 'Blenheim' (F) ERea
- 'Bredase' (F) CWib ERea SDea
- 'De Nancy' see *P. armeniaca* 'Gros Pêche'
- 'Delicot' (F) SFrt
- 'Early Moorpark' (F) CAgr CWib EPfP GTwe MAsh MBri NOra SBmr SDea SEND SLon WHar WMat
- 'Farmingdale' (F) SDea

	- Flavorcot = 'Bayoto'[PBR] (F)	CAgr EPfP EPom ERea GTwe MCoo NOra SBmr SFrt SKee SPer WHar WMat
	- 'Garden Aprigold' (F)	EPom MGos SBmr SPoG WMat
	- 'Goldcot' (F)	CAgr CDul CTho ERea MAsh MBri MCoo NOra SDea SKee SPoG WHar WMat
	- 'Golden Glow' (F)	CAgr CTho EPfP EPom ERea LAst LRHS MAsh MBri MCoo NOra SKee WHar WMat
	- 'Goldrich' (F)	CAgr
§	- 'Gros Pêche' (F)	SVic WHar
	- 'Hargrand' (F)	CAgr SVic
	- 'Harogem' (F)	CAgr
	- 'Hemskirke' (F)	ERea SKee
	- 'Hongaarse' (F)	SDea
	- 'Isabella' (F)	ERea
	- 'Moniqui' (F)	ERea
	- 'Moorpark' (F) ϒH4	CDul CHab CSBt CTri CWib ELan EWTr GTwe LAst LBuc MMuc MRav NPri SDea SKee SPer
	- 'New Large Early' (F)	ERea MMuc SDea SEND
	- Orange Summer = 'Zaitorde'[PBR] (F) **new**	EPom
	- 'Petit Muscat' (F)	EPom ERea SFrt SKee
	- 'Tomcot' (F)	CAgr CTho CTri EPfP EPom ERea GTwe LBuc LEdu LRHS LSRN MAsh MBri MCoo NOra SBmr SFrt SKee SPoG WHar WMat
	- 'Tross Orange' (F)	CWib SDea
	- 'Vigama' (F) **new**	LRHS MCoo WMat
	'Asano'	CLnd
	avium	Widely available
	- 'Amber Heart' (F)	NOra SBdl SKee WMat
	- 'Archduke' (F)	SKee
	- 'August Heart' (F)	SKee
	- 'Bigarreau de Schrecken' (F)	SKee
	- 'Bigarreau Gaucher' (F)	NOra SBdl SKee WHar WMat
§	- 'Bigarreau Napoléon' (F)	CArg ELan EPom GTwe LSRN NOra SBdl SBmr SKee SVic WMat
	- 'Bing' (F) **new**	SBmr
	- 'Birchenhayes'	see *P. avium* 'Early Birchenhayes'
	- 'Black Eagle' (F)	SKee
	- 'Black Elton' (F)	SKee
	- 'Black Heart' (F)	CWib ELan MMuc SEND
	- 'Black Tartarian' (F)	SKee
	- 'Bottlers'	see *P. avium* 'Preserving'
	- 'Bradbourne Black' (F)	SKee WHar
	- 'Bullion' (F)	CTho
	- 'Burcombe' (F)	CTho
	- Celeste = 'Sumpaca'[PBR] (D)	CAgr CMac CTri EMil ERea GTwe LRHS MBri MCoo NLar NOra SBdl SDea SLim SPoG WHar WMat
	- 'Cherokee'	see *P. avium* 'Lapins'
	- 'Colney' (F) ϒH5	ERea GTwe NOra SBmr SKee WHar WJas WMat
	- 'Coroon' (F)	SKee
	- 'Danelia' (D) **new**	WMat
	- 'Dun' (F)	CHab CTho WMat
§	- 'Early Birchenhayes' (F)	CTho
	- 'Early Rivers' (F)	CDul CLnd CSBt CWib GTwe IArd LSRN NOra SBmr SDea SKee SVic WHar WMat WWct
	- 'Elton Heart' (F)	SKee
	- 'Emperor Francis' (F)	SKee
	- 'Fastigiata'	WHar
	- 'Fice' (F)	CTho
	- 'Florence' (F)	SKee
	- 'Früheste der Mark' (D)	SKee
	- 'Giorgia' (D) **new**	WMat
	- 'Goodnestone Black' (D)	SKee
	- 'Governor Wood' (F)	SKee
	- 'Grandiflora'	see *P. avium* 'Plena'
	- 'Greenstem Black' (F)	CTho
	- 'Hannaford' (D/C)	CHab CTho
	- 'Hertford' (F) ϒH5	NOra SBmr SKee WHar WMat
	- 'Inga' (F)	SKee
	- 'Karina' (D)	SFrt WMat
	- 'Kassins Frühe Herz' (F)	SKee
	- 'Kentish Red' (F)	SKee
	- 'Knight's Early Black' (D) **new**	WMat
	- 'Kordia' (D)	EPom GTwe NOra SFrt SKee WHar WMat
	- 'Kozerska' (F) **new**	WMat
§	- 'Lapins' (F)	CAgr CDul CLnd CTho CTri ECrN EPfP EPom GTwe LEdu MAsh MBri MRav NOra SBdl SBmr SDea SKee WHar WJas WMat WWct
	- 'Mansfield Black' (F) **new**	SKee
	- 'May Duke'	see *P.* × *gondouinii* 'May Duke'
	- 'Merchant' (F) ϒH5	NOra SBdl SBmr SFrt SKee WMat WWct
	- 'Mermat' (F)	SKee
	- 'Merpet' (F)	SKee
	- 'Merton Bigarreau' (F)	CArg GTwe NOra SBdl SBmr WHar WMat
	- 'Merton Crane' (F)	SKee
	- 'Merton Favourite' (F)	SKee
	- 'Merton Glory' (F)	CAgr CSBt EPfP GTwe IArd MAsh NOra SBdl SBmr SEND SEWo SKee SLim WHar WMat WWct
	- 'Merton Late' (F)	SKee
	- 'Merton Marvel' (F)	SKee
	- 'Merton Premier' (F)	ELan SKee SVic
	- 'Merton Reward'	see *P.* × *gondouinii* 'Merton Reward'
	- 'Mizia' (D) **new**	WMat
	- 'Nabella' (F)	IArd MAsh WJas
	- 'Napoléon'	see *P. avium* 'Bigarreau Napoléon'
	- 'Noble' (F)	SKee
	- 'Noir de Guben' (F)	SKee WHar WMat
	- 'Noir de Meched' (D)	SKee
	- 'Octavia' (D) **new**	WMat
	- 'Old Black Heart' (F)	SKee
	- 'Penny'[PBR] (F)	CAgr EPom GTwe NOra SBdl SFrt SKee WHar WMat WWct
	- 'Petit Noir' (F)	GTwe NOra WMat
§	- 'Plena' (d) ϒH6	Widely available
§	- 'Preserving' (F)	CTho
	- 'Regina' (F)	CSut NLar NOra SBdl SBmr SFrt SKee WHar WMat
	- 'Ronald's Heart' (F)	SKee
	- 'Roundel Heart' (F)	NOra SKee WHar WMat
	- 'Sasha' (F)	SFrt
	- 'Schneiders Späte Knorpel' (D)	SFrt
	- 'Skeena'[PBR] (F) **new**	LRHS MCoo NOra WMat
	- 'Small Black' (F)	CHab CTho
	- 'Stella' (F) ϒH5	Widely available
	- 'Stella Compact' (F)	CWib ECrN EWTr LAst LSRN SDea WHar
	- 'Strawberry Heart' (F)	SKee
	- 'Summer Sun' (D) ϒH5	CAgr CDul CLnd CSut CTho CTri EPfP EPom ERea GTwe LBuc LRHS MAsh MBri MCoo MGos NLar NOra SBdl SCoo SDea SFrt SKee SLim SPoG WHar WMat WWct

	Name	Suppliers
	- 'Summit' (F)	CLnd SBmr SKee WMat
	- 'Sunburst' (D)	Widely available
	- 'Sweetheart' (F)	CAgr CDul CLnd EPom GTwe LRHS LSRN MAsh MBri NOra SBdl SKee SLim SPoG SVic WHar WMat
	- 'Sylvia' (F)	CAgr NOra WHar WMat
	- 'Turkish Black' (F)	SKee
	- 'Van' (F)	CAgr CSBt IArd NOra SBdl WHar WMat
	- 'Vanda' PBR (F) **new**	WMat
	- 'Vega' (F)	CAgr ERea GTwe NOra SBmr SFrt SKee WHar WJas WMat
	- 'Waterloo' (F)	SKee
	- 'White Heart' (F)	CHab CWib ECrN SKee
§	'Beni-tamanishiki' 🏆H6	WMat
	'Beni-yutaka' 🏆H6	CCVT CTsd LAst MAsh MBri MRav MSwo NOrn SCob SCoo SLim WHar WMat
	'Bilski' **new**	WMat
	'Blaze'	see *P. cerasifera* 'Nigra'
	× ***blireana*** (d) 🏆H6	CDul CLnd CTri ECrN EPfP MBri MGos MRav MSwo NLar NWea SCoo SEND SPer SPoG WHar
	Blushing Bride	see *P.* 'Shōgetsu'
	campanulata 'Felix Jury'	EBee WMat
	Candy Floss	see *P.* 'Matsumae-beni-murasaki'
	cerasifera (F)	CAgr CDul CHab CTri ECrN EPfP EPom LBuc LPar NWea SDea SKee SPer SVic
	- 'Golden Sphere' (F)	CAgr CArg CLnd CTho CTri EPom NOra SBdl SDea SKee SPer WHar WMat
	- 'Gypsy' (F)	CAgr CDul CLnd CTho LRHS NOra SKee SPer WHar WMat
	- 'Hessei' (v)	EBee LRHS MBri MGos MHtn MMHG MRav NOrn
	- 'Kentish Red' (F)	MMuc SEND
§	- Myrobalan Group (F)	ECrN MRav SDea SPre SVic WMat
§	- 'Nigra' 🏆H6	Widely available
	- 'Pendula'	ECrN SWvt
§	- 'Pissardii'	CWib ECrN EPfP LCro LSRN NOrn NWea SCob SCoo SLon SWvt WJas WMou
*	- 'Princess'	NOrn
	- 'Ruby' (F)	CAgr EPom ERea MBri
	cerasus 'Maynard'	LSRN
	- 'Meteor Korai' **new**	LCro LOPS LRHS MCoo WMat
	- 'Montmorency' (F)	NOra SKee
	- 'Morello' (C) 🏆H6	Widely available
	- 'Nabella' (F)	SKee
	- 'Rhexii' (d)	CDul ECrN MAsh MBri
	- 'Semperflorens'	CLnd
	'Cheal's Weeping' **new**	SBmr
	Chocolate Ice	see *P.* 'Matsumae-fuki'
§	× ***cistena*** 🏆H6	CBcs CDul CLet EBee ELan EPfP LRHS MAsh MBri MGos MMuc MSwo NBes SCoo SGol SHil SPoG SWvt WCFE
	- 'Crimson Dwarf'	see *P.* × *cistena*
	'Collingwood Ingram' 🏆H6	EBee EBtc EPfP LRHS MBlu MBri NOrn SLim WMat
	'Cot 'n' Candy' **new**	SBmr
	'Daikoku'	LRHS WMat
	davidiana	SPlb
	'Delma' PBR (F)	WHar WMat
	domestica (D/C)	SPre
	- 'Allgroves Superb' (D)	ERea
	- 'Angelina Burdett' (D)	CHab SBdl SDea SKee
	- 'Anna Späth' (C/D)	SKee
	- 'Ariel' (C/D)	SDea SKee
	- 'Avalon' (D)	CAgr CCVT CLnd GTwe IArd LBuc NOra SBdl SBmr SDea SFrt SKee WHar WMat
	- 'Beauty' (D)	CSut
	- 'Belgian Greengage' (F)	CHab SKee
	- 'Belgian Purple' (C)	SKee
	- 'Belle de Louvain' (C)	CDul CHab CLnd CTho CTri GTwe NOra SBdl SDea SKee WHar WMat WWct
	- 'Black Diamond'	see *P. salicina* 'Black Diamond'
	- 'Blaisdon Red' (C)	CTho GTwe WHar WMat
	- 'Blue Imperatrice' (C/D)	SKee
	- 'Blue Tit' (C/D) 🏆H5	CAgr CTho EPom ERea GTwe LSRN MAsh MMuc NOra SBmr SDea SEND SKee WHar WMat WWct
	- 'Bohemian' (C)	SKee
	- 'Bonne de Bry' (D)	SKee
	- 'Brandy Gage' (C/D)	SKee
	- 'Bryanston Gage' (D)	CTho SKee WMat
	- 'Burbank's Giant'	see *P. domestica* 'Giant Prune'
	- 'Cambridge Gage' (D) 🏆H5	Widely available
	- 'Chrislin' (F)	CTho
	- 'Coe's Golden Drop' (D)	CAgr CArg CHab CLnd ECrN ERea GTwe IArd LAst LRHS MBri MGos MRav NOra SBdl SDea SFrt SKee SPer WHar WMat WWct
	- 'Conwy Castle' (F) **new**	WMat
	- 'Count Althann's Gage' (D)	CHab ERea GTwe SDea SKee WWct
	- 'Crimson Drop' (D)	SKee
	- 'Cropper'	see *P. domestica* 'Laxton's Cropper'
	- 'Curlew' (C)	SDea
	- 'Czar' (C) 🏆H6	Widely available
	- 'Delicious'	see *P. domestica* 'Laxton's Delicious'
	- 'Denbigh' (C)	CHab WGwG
	- 'Denniston's Superb'	see *P. domestica* 'Imperial Gage'
	- 'Diamond' (C)	SKee
	- 'Dittisham Black' (C)	CTho
	- 'Dittisham Ploughman' (C)	CTho SKee WMat
	- 'Dunster Plum' (F)	CTho CTri CWib WMat
	- 'Early Laxton' (C/D) 🏆H5	CHab LAst MMuc SDea SEND SKee
	- 'Early Prolific'	see *P. domestica* 'Early Rivers'
§	- 'Early Rivers' (C)	CAgr CDul CHab CSBt CTho CTri ELan EPom ERea EWTr GTwd GTwe LRHS LSRN NOra NWea SBdl SCoo SDea SKee SPer WHar WMat WWct
	- 'Early Transparent Gage' (C/D)	CAgr CMac CSBt CTho ECrN ERea GTwe IArd LAst LBuc LRHS MBri MCoo NOra SBdl SCoo SDea SFrt SKee WHar WMat
	- 'Early Victoria' (C/D)	SDea
	- 'Edda' (D)	NOra WHar WMat
	- 'Edwards' (C/D) 🏆H5	CTri CWib EMil SDea SKee
	- 'Excalibur' (D)	CAgr EPom GTwd GTwe IArd LBuc LSRN NOra SBmr SDea SKee WHar WMat
	- 'Finger Plum' (F) **new**	WMat
§	- German Prune Group (C)	LRHS MCoo NOra SKee WMat
§	- 'Giant Prune' (C)	CDul ECrN GTwe MMuc SBdl SDea SEND SKee WHar
I	- 'Godshill Big Sloe' (F)	SDea
	- 'Godshill Blue' (C)	SDea
	- 'Godshill Minigage' (F)	SDea
	- 'Gold Dust' (F)	SPoG WMat

Plant	Suppliers
- 'Golden Transparent' (D)	LAst MCoo SKee
- 'Goldfinch' (D)	MCoo MMuc SEND SKee
- 'Gordon Castle'	GQue GTwd NLar SKee WHar WMat
- Green Gage Group	see *P. domestica* Reine-Claude Group
- - 'Lindsey Gage' (F)	SKee
- 'Grey Plum' (F)	CTho
- 'Grove's Late Victoria' (D)	WWct
- 'Guinevere' (C)	CAgr EPom LRHS MBri MCoo NOra SBdl SFrt WHar WMat
- 'Guthrie's Late Green' (D)	SKee
- 'Haganta'PBR (F)	CAgr ERea NOra SFrt WHar WMat
- 'Herman' (D)	CAgr CMac EPom GTwe LRHS MAsh MBri MCoo NOra SBmr SDea SFrt SKee WHar WMat
- 'Heron' (C)	GTwe NOra SKee WHar WMat WWct
- 'Impérial Épineuse' (D)	SKee
§ - 'Imperial Gage' (D) ♀H5	CAgr CArg CLnd CMac CSBt CTho CTri EPom EWTr GQue GTwe LEdu LRHS MAsh MMuc NOra SBdl SDea SEND SKee WHar WMat
- 'Italian Prune' (F)	CLnd
- 'Jefferson' (D) ♀H5	CAgr CHab CLnd GTwe IArd NOra SBdl SDea SKee SVic WHar WMat
* - 'Jubilaeum' (D)	CAgr CMac EPom GTwe LBuc LRHS NOra SBdl SBmr SCoo SEWo SKee WHar
- 'Kea' (C)	CTho SKee WMat
- 'Kirke's' (D)	CHab CTho ERea GTwe LAst NOra SDea SKee WHar WMat
- 'Landkey Yellow' (F)	CTho WMat
- 'Langley Gage' (D)	CAgr ERea SDea
- 'Late Muscatelle' (D)	SKee
- 'Late Transparent Gage' (D)	SKee
§ - 'Laxton's Cropper' (C)	CHab GTwe LAst SKee WHar
§ - 'Laxton's Delicious' (D)	CHab
- 'Laxton's Early Gage' (D/C)	SKee
- 'Laxton's Gage' (D)	SDea SKee
- 'Laxton's Jubilee' (C/D)	CSBt NLar WMat
- 'Mallard' (D) ♀H6	NOra SKee WHar WMat
- 'Manaccan' (C)	CTho WMat
- 'Manns No. 1' (C/D) **new**	WMat
- 'Marjorie's Seedling' (C) ♀H5	Widely available
- 'Meritare' (F) **new**	NOra WMat
- 'Merton Gage' (D)	SKee
- 'Merton Gem' (D)	SKee
- 'Monarch' (C)	SKee
- Old English gage	CLnd ECrN EPom ERea LAst SBdl
- 'Opal' (D) ♀H6	Widely available
- 'Oullins Gage' (C/D) ♀H5	Widely available
- 'Pershore' (C) ♀H6	CAgr CHab CWib ERea GTwe LRHS MBri NOra SDea SKee WHar WMat WWct
- 'Pershore Emblem' (F) **new**	WWct
- 'Pond's Seedling' (C)	CSBt SDea SKee
- 'Pozegaca' (D)	SKee
- 'President' (C)	CHab MMuc SDea SEND SKee
- 'Primate' (D/C)	SKee
- 'Priory Plum' (D)	SDea
- 'Purple Pershore' (C)	CAgr CHab CTri CWib GTwe IArd LAst NEgg NOra SDea SKee WHar WMat WWct
- 'Queen's Crown' (C/D) **new**	WMat
- 'Quetsche d'Alsace'	see *P. domestica* German Prune Group
- 'Reeves' (C) ♀H5	IArd NOra SKee WHar
- 'Reine-Claude Dorée'	see *P. domestica* Reine-Claude Group
§ - Reine-Claude Group (D)	CSBt ELan GTwe MMuc SDea SEND SKee SLim SPer WMat
- - 'Ingall's Grimoldby Green Gage' (D)	SKee
- - 'Old Green Gage'	see *P. domestica* (Reine-Claude Group) 'Reine-Claude Vraie'
- - 'Reine-Claude de Bavais' (D)	CArg CLnd CTri GTwe NOra SDea SKee WHar WMat
- - 'Reine-Claude de Moissac' (D)	SKee
- - 'Reine-Claude de Vars' (D)	SVic
- - 'Reine-Claude Violette' (D)	SKee
§ - - 'Reine-Claude Vraie' (C/D)	CAgr CMac CSBt CWib EPfP EPom LBuc LRHS LSRN MAsh NOra NPri WJas WMat
§ - - 'Willingham Gage' (C/D)	ERea GTwe LRHS LSRN NOra SKee WHar WMat
- 'Royale de Vilvoorde' (D)	SKee
- 'Sanctus Hubertus' (D) ♀H5	CTri SDea WHar WWct
- 'Seneca' (D)	EPom NOra SBmr WHar WMat
- 'Severn Cross' (D)	SKee
- 'Stanley' (C/D)	SVic
- 'Stella'	CCVT ELan LAst LOPS LSRN NEgg NPri SLim WHar
- 'Stella's Star'	LBuc LRHS MCoo NOra WMat
- 'Stint' (C/D)	SKee
- 'Swan' (C)	ERea GTwe NOra SKee WHar WMat WWct
- 'Syston White'	MGos
- 'Thames Cross' (D)	CLnd NOra SKee
- 'Transparent Gage' (D)	SKee
- 'Utility' (D)	SKee
- 'Valor' (D) ♀H5	NOra WHar
- 'Verity' (C/D)	SKee WMat
- 'Victoria' (D) ♀H5	Widely available
- 'Violetta'PBR (D)	CAgr GTwe WHar
- 'Warwickshire Drooper' (C)	CAgr CHab CTho CWib ERea GTwe IArd LAst MAsh NOra SDea SKee SLon SPer WHar WMat WWct
- 'Washington' (D)	SDea SKee
- 'White Magnum Bonum' (C)	SDea
- 'Willingham'	see *P. domestica* (Reine-Claude Group) 'Willingham Gage'
§ ***dulcis***	CDul CHab CLnd CTri CWib ELan EPfP EPom LAst LRHS MGos MMuc NWea SCoo SDea SEND SWvt
- 'Ai' (F)	CAgr
- 'Ardéchoise' (F)	CAgr
- 'Ferraduel' (F)	CAgr
- 'Ferragnés' (F)	CAgr
* - 'Phoebe' (F)	CAgr
Easter Bonnet = 'Comet'PBR	CTri LRHS
'Flavor King' (Pluot Series) (D) **new**	WMat
'Flavour Supreme' (F)	EPom
Fragrant Cloud	see *P.* 'Shizuka'
Frilly Frock = 'Fpmspl' (v)	EBee LRHS LSRN MBri NLar SPoG WMat
'Fugenzō'	CSBt EBee WMat
glandulosa 'Alba Plena' (d)	CDul CMac CSBt LBMP MAsh SGol SPlb SRms SWvt WCFE
- 'Rosea Plena'	see *P. glandulosa* 'Sinensis'
§ - 'Sinensis' (d)	CDul CExl CSBt SRms

	Name	Suppliers
§	× ***gondouinii*** 'May Duke' (F)	SKee WHar
§	- 'Merton Reward' (F)	SKee
	grayana B&SWJ 10903	WCru
	'Gyoikō'	CLnd EBee WMat
	'Hally Jolivette'	ELan GKin MAsh MBlu NOrn WMat
§	'Hanagasa' ♀H6	LRHS MBri NLar NWea WMat WMou
	'Hillieri Spire'	see *P.* 'Spire'
	'Hilling's Weeping'	EBee LCro LOPS SLon
	himalaica	LRHS WMat
	'Hokusai' ♀H6	CDul EPfP NLar SGol WMat
	Hollywood	see *P.* 'Trailblazer'
	'Horinji'	LRHS MBri SCoo WMat
	'Howard No. 3' **new**	WMat
	'Ichiyo' (d) ♀H6	CDul CLnd EBee ECrN EPfP LAst LRHS MBri SCoo WMat
	× ***incam*** 'Okamé' ♀H6	Widely available
	- 'Shosar' ♀H6	CWib ECrN MAsh SCoo SPer
	incisa	CTri NEgg
	- 'Beniomi'	MRav
	- 'February Pink'	CJun SGol
	- 'Fujimae' ♀H6	LAst NLar
	- 'Kojo-no-mai' ♀H6	Widely available
	- 'Mikinori'	CJun CMac CSBt EBee EPfP MAsh MBlu MJak MMuc NLar SCoo SEND WMat
	- 'Oshidori' (d) ♀H6	CMac CSBt EBee ELon EPfP LRHS MBri MMHG MRav SRms WMat
	- 'Paean'	EBee NLar
	- 'Pendula' ♀H6	LCro LOPS SCoo WMat
	- 'Praecox'	CHGN CSBt CTho EPfP LRHS SCoo WMat
§	- f. ***yamadei*** ♀H6	CJun LBMP MAsh NLar NOrn
	insititia (F)	NWea
	- 'Abergwyngregin' (C)	NOra WMat
	- 'Aylesbury Prune' (C) **new**	WMat
	- 'Black Bullace' (F)	ERea
	- 'Blue Violet Damson' (F)	CAgr ERea GTwe MCoo NLar NOra SKee WHar WMat
§	- 'Bradley's King Damson' (C)	GQue MCoo NLar NOra SBdl SKee WHar WMat
	- bullace (C)	ERea LEdu SDea
	- 'Countess' (C)	CTri
	- 'Dittisham Damson' (C)	CTho WMat
	- 'Farleigh Damson' (C) ♀H6	CAgr CArg CHab CLnd CWib ECrN EPfP EPom ERea EWTr GTwd GTwe IArd LAst LBuc LEdu MJak MMuc NLar NOra NWea SBdl SDea SKee SPer SVic WHar WJas WMat WWct
	- 'Godshill Damson' (C)	SDea
	- 'King of Damsons'	see *P. insititia* 'Bradley's King Damson'
	- 'Langley Bullace' (C)	CAgr CDul ERea GTwe LEdu NOra SKee WHar WMat
	- 'Lisna' (C)	CTri WMat
	- 'Merryweather Damson' (C)	Widely available
	- 'Mirabelle Countess' (C) **new**	WMat
	- 'Mirabelle de Nancy' (C)	CAgr CDul CLnd CTho EPom ERea GTwe LAst NOra SBdl SBmr SDea SEWo SFrt SKee WHar WMat
	- 'Mirabelle de Nancy' red (C)	SDea
	- 'Mirabelle Ruby' (C)	CArg ERea LRHS NOra SBdl SFrt WMat
§	- 'Prune Damson' (C) ♀H6	Widely available

	Name	Suppliers
	- 'Shepherd's Bullace' (C)	CTho ERea SKee
	- 'Shropshire Damson'	see *P. insititia* 'Prune Damson'
	- 'Small Bullace' (C)	SKee
	- 'Westmorland Prune' (C)	CHab
	- 'Yellow Apricot' (C)	ERea SKee
	'Jō-nioi'	CDul CLnd CTho MBri
§	'Kanzan' ♀H6	Widely available
§	'Kiku-shidare-zakura'	Widely available
	'Kobuku-zakura'	EBee WMat
	Korean hill cherry	see *P. verecunda*
	'Kursar'	CDoC CDul CLnd COtt CSBt CTho CTri EBee EPfP GKin LRHS LSRN MAsh MBri NOrn NWea SCoo SEWo SLim SLon SPer SWvt WMat
	laurocerasus	CBcs CCVT CDul CMac CWSG EBee ECrN ELan EPfP EShb GKin IBoy LAst LPar MGos MMuc MRav NPri NWea SCob SEND SGol SPer WMat WMoo WMou
	- 'Angustifolia'	IBoy
	- 'Aureovariegata'	see *P. laurocerasus* 'Taff's Golden Gleam'
	- 'Camelliifolia'	CMac CTri MBlu
	- 'Castlewellan' (v)	CDoC CDul CTri EBee ELan ELon EPfP EShb IBoy LHop LRHS MGos MRav MSwo NLar NWad SCob SDix SPer SPoG SSta WHar WMoo WRHF
	- 'Caucasica'	ECrN NBes NLar SCob SGol
	- 'Cherry Brandy'	SCob SGol
	- Etna = 'Anbri' PBR ♀H5	CMac EAEE LBuc LRHS LSou MAsh MBri SCob SWvt
	- Genolia = 'Mariblon' PBR	MBri SGol
	- 'Green Marble' (v)	CTri EHoe
	- 'Greentorch' PBR	LRHS
	- 'Herbergii'	NBes
	- 'Ivory' PBR **new**	WMoo
§	- 'Latifolia'	EUJe LRHS
	- 'Magnoliifolia'	see *P. laurocerasus* 'Latifolia'
	- 'Marbled White'	see *P. laurocerasus* 'Castlewellan'
	- 'Miky'	CJun
	- 'Mount Vernon'	CTri MBlu SCob
	- 'Novita'	CBod CWSG ECrN EPfP NLar NPri
	- 'Otto Luyken' ♀H5	CBcs CCVT CDul CLet CMac CTri EBee EHoe ELan EPfP LAst LBuc LHop LRHS MAsh MGos MJak MSwo NBes NBir NEgg NLar NWea SCob SGol SPer SPlb WFar WHar
	- 'Reynvaanii'	CJun MBri
	- 'Rotundifolia' ♀H5	Widely available
§	- 'Taff's Golden Gleam' (v)	CJun
	- 'Van Nes'	CJun MAsh
	- 'Variegata' misapplied	see *P. laurocerasus* 'Castlewellan'
	- 'Variegata' ambig. (v)	CWib SRms
	- 'Whitespot'	MMuc SEND
	- 'Zabeliana'	CDul CMac CTri MJak MSwo NEgg NWea SCob SPer SRms WHar
	litigiosa	EBee EMil WMat
	'Little Pink Perfection'	MBri NBes NOrn SCoo SPoG WMat
	lusitanica ♀H5	Widely available
	- subsp. ***azorica***	CDoC CExl EBee LRHS WPGP
	- 'Myrtifolia' ♀H5	CBar CLet CTri EAEE EPfP EShb LAst LRHS MBri MRav NLar SCob SGol SHil SLon SWvt WCFE WMat WMoo
	- 'Variegata' (v)	CBar CMac CTri CWib ELan ELon LBMP LHop MGos MMuc MRav MSwo SCob SDix SGol SPer SPoG SSta SWvt WFar WHar WMoo
	maackii	CLnd MMuc NOrn WMou

- 'Amber Beauty'	CBcs CDul EBee EPfP GBin GKin LRHS LSRN MRav SEND SGol SLon WMat
mahaleb	CNWT
'Mahogany Lustre'	MGos
maritima	LEdu
§ 'Matsumae-beni-murasaki'	NLar NOra WHar WMat
'Matsumae-beni-tamanishiki'	see *P.* 'Beni-tamanishiki'
§ 'Matsumae-fuki' ♀H6	COtt EBee LSRN MBri NLar NOrn NWea SLim WHar WMat
'Matsumae-hanagasa'	see *P.* 'Hanagasa'
maximowiczii B&SWJ 10967	WCru
'Mount Fuji'	see *P.* 'Shirotae'
mume	CMCN CMen
- 'Alba' **new**	LPar
- 'Beni-chidori' ♀H5	CBcs CDul CLnd CMac CWib EBee ELan EPfP IVic LCro LOPS LRHS MAsh MBlu MBri NLar NOrn SAko SCob SCoo SPoG WJas WMat
§ - 'Omoi-no-mama' (d)	CMen SAko
- 'Omoi-no-wac'	see *P. mume* 'Omoi-no-mama'
myrobalana	see *P. cerasifera* Myrobalan Group
nigra **new**	WMat
nipponica var. ***kurilensis*** 'Brillant'	CBcs CSBt GBin LBMP LRHS MAsh MBri MMHG NHol NLar NOrn SPoG
- - 'Ruby'	LSRN MBri NEgg
'Oku-miyako' misapplied	see *P.* 'Shōgetsu'
padus	CArg CCVT CDul CHab CLnd CMac CSBt CTri ECrN LBuc MGos MJak MMuc MSwo NLar NWea SCob SEND SEWo WMou
- 'Albertii'	CCVT MBri WMat
- 'Colorata' ♀H6	CArg CDul CMac CTho EBee ECrN ELan LHop MGos MRav NLar NPri SGol SPer SWvt
- 'Grandiflora'	see *P. padus* 'Watereri'
- 'Le Thoureil' **new**	MMHG
- 'Purple Queen'	ECrN SCob SGol
§ - 'Watereri' ♀H6	CArg CCVT CDul CMCN CMac CTho CWib ECrN ELan EPfP GBin LAst LHop NOrn NWea SEWo SGol SPer SPoG WMat WMou
'Pandora' ♀H6	Widely available
§ ***pendula*** f. ***ascendens*** 'Rosea' ♀H6	CLnd MRav WFar WMat
- 'Pendula Plena Rosea' (d)	WFar WMat
§ - 'Pendula Rosea'	CDoC CDul CLnd CTri CWib EPfP MAsh SCob SPer WJas
§ - 'Pendula Rubra' ♀H6	CCVT CDoC CLnd CMac CSBt CWib EBee ELan EPfP LAst LHop LRHS MBri MSwo NOrn SCoo SLim SPer SPoG WMat WMou
§ - 'Stellata' ♀H6	MBri NLar WMat
persica	CPne SPre
- 'Amber' (F) **new**	SBmr
- 'Amsden June' (F)	CLnd CWib EBtc ERea GTwe LEdu NOra NRog SDea SKee WHar WMat
- 'Avalon Pride' (F)	CAgr CSut EPfP EPom ERea LBuc MCoo NRog SBmr SFrt SKee
- 'Barrington' (F)	ERea
- 'Bellegarde' (F)	ERea NOra NRog SDea SKee WMat
- 'Black' (F)	ERea
- 'Bonanza' (F)	EPom ERea LSRN
- 'Carman' (F) **new**	WMat
- 'Champion' (F)	CLnd NRog SDea
- 'Crimson Bonfire' (F)	EPom SBmr
- 'Crimson Cascade' (F) **new**	ELan
- 'Darling' (F)	SVic
- 'Diamond' (F)	EPom SBmr
- 'Dixi Red' (F)	CAgr ERea SBmr
- 'Doctor Hogg' (F)	ERea SDea
- 'Duke of York' (F) ♀H4	CTri ERea GTwe SBmr SDea SKee
- 'Dymond' (F)	ERea
- 'Early Alexander' (F)	ERea
- 'Foliis Rubris' (F)	CDul LRHS
- 'Francis' (F)	SKee
- 'Frost' (F)	ERea NRog WMat
- 'Garden Lady' (F)	EPom GTwe NOra SLim WHar WMat
- 'Gorgeous' (F) **new**	SKee WMat
- 'Grosse Mignonne' (F) **new**	SKee
- 'Hale's Early' (F)	GTwe MMuc MRav NOra NRog SKee SLim SPer WHar WMat
- 'Harken' (F)	ERea
- 'Hylands' (F)	SDea
- 'Jalousia' (F)	EPom NRog
- 'Johnny Brack' (F)	ERea NRog
- 'Kestrel' (F)	ERea SKee
- 'Madison' (F)	ERea
- 'Mesembrine' PBR (F)	EPom
- 'Natalia' (F)	SDea
- var. ***nectarina*** Crimson Gold (F)	SDea
- - 'Earliglo' (F) **new**	LRHS NOra WMat
- - 'Early Blaze' (F)	LEdu
- - 'Early Gem' (F)	ERea SDea
- - 'Early Rivers' (F) ♀H4	ERea GTwe LAst LSRN SDea WMat
- - 'Elruge' (F)	ERea SDea
- - 'Fantasia' (F)	EPfP SBmr SDea
- - 'Fire Gold' (F)	ERea SDea
- - 'Flavortop' (F)	EPfP ERea
- - 'Garden Beauty' (F/d)	SPoG WMat
- - 'Honey Kist' PBR (F)	EPom SBmr
- - 'Humboldt' (F)	CAgr CDul ERea GTwe LAst SDea SPoG WHar WMat
- - 'John Rivers' (F)	SDea SPer
- - 'Lord Napier' (F) ♀H4	CAgr CDoC CDul CSBt CTri CWib EPfP EPom ERea LAst LBuc LRHS MAsh MGos MJak MWat NOra SBmr SDea SEND SKee SLim SPer SPoG SVic WHar WMat
- - 'Madame Blanchet' (F)	SDea
- - 'Nectared' (F)	CWib
- - 'Nectarella' (F)	EPom ERea LSRN NOra SLim WHar WMat
- - 'Pineapple' (F)	CAgr CTri ERea GTwe SBmr SDea SKee WHar WMat
- - Rubis = 'Necta Zee' PBR	EPom SBmr
- - 'Ruby Gold' (F)	SDea
- - 'Sauzee Bel'	EPom
- - 'Sauzee King' (F)	EPom
- - 'Snow Baby'	EPom
- - 'Snow Queen' (F) **new**	SBmr
- - 'Terrace Ruby' (F)	MGos SPoG WMat
- 'Oriane' PBR (F)	NRog
- 'Pallas' (F)	ERea
- 'Peregrine' (F) ♀H4	Widely available
- 'Purpurea'	GKin
- 'Raritan Rose' (F)	ERea
- 'Red Top' (F)	EPfP SBmr
- 'Redhaven' (F)	CAgr CWib ERea NRog SDea SKee SVic WHar WMat
- 'Redwing' (F)	CAgr SBmr
- 'Reliance' (F)	SDea
- 'Robin Redbreast' (F)	CAgr SDea

Name	Suppliers
- 'Rochester' (F) 𝕐H4	CAgr CDul CSBt CTri CWib EPom ERea GTwe LAst LRHS LSRN MBri MGos MMuc NOra NRog SBmr SDea SEND SKee SLim SPer SPoG WHar WMat
- 'Royal George' (F)	NRog
- 'Rubira' (F)	NRog
- 'Sanguine de Savoie' (F)	EPom LRHS NOra NRog WMat
- 'Sanguinole' (F)	CSut SKee
- 'Saturne' (F)	EPom ERea MAsh NOra NRog SKee WHar WMat
- 'Springtime' (F)	SDea
- 'Terrace Amber' (F)	SPoG WMat
- 'Terrace Diamond' (F)	SPoG WMat
- 'Terrace Garnet' (F)	MGos WMat
- 'Terrace Pearl'	MGos
- 'Wassenberger' (F)	SDea
× ***persicoides*** 'Ingrid' (F)	CAgr CDul EBtc ECrN ERea LBuc LRHS MBri MCoo MGos NOra SCoo WHar WMat
- 'Pollardii'	NWea WJas
- 'Robijn' (F)	CAgr EPom LBuc LEdu SFrt SKee SVic
- 'Spring Glow'	CCVT CDoC CDul CLnd EMil EPfP LAst LRHS MBri MSwo NWea SCoo SLim SLon WJas WMat
'Petite Noir'	CLnd LRHS
Pink Parasol	see *P.* 'Hanagasa'
'Pink Perfection' 𝕐H6	CBcs CDul CLnd CSBt CWib ECrN ELan ELon EPfP LAst LRHS MBri MGos MSwo NLar NOrn SBmr SCob SPer WHar WJas WMat WMou
'Pink Shell'	CLnd EPfP MAsh MBri WMat
pissardii	see *P. cerasifera* 'Pissardii'
'Pissardii Nigra'	see *P. cerasifera* 'Nigra'
pumila var. ***depressa***	MRav SAko
'Purple Candy' **new**	SBmr
'Royal Burgundy' (d) 𝕐H6	Widely available
rufa	CDul CJun CLnd CTho EBee EBtc GKin LRHS SKHP SLon WMat WPat
salicina 'Abundance' (F)	ERea
- 'Beauty'	ERea
§ - 'Black Diamond' (F)	SDea
- 'Howard Miracle' (F)	ERea
- 'Lizzie' (F)	EPom SBmr
- 'Mariposa' (F)	ERea
- 'Methley' (D)	CAgr ERea LRHS NOra SFrt SPoG WHar WMat
- 'Ozark Premier' (F)	ERea
- 'Santa Rosa' (F)	ERea
- 'Satsuma' (F)	ERea
- 'Sierra' (F)	ERea
sargentii	Widely available
- 'Charles Sargent' 𝕐H6	CMCN GBin MBlu
- 'Columnaris'	GBin WMat
- 'Rancho'	CLnd MAsh SCoo SLim SPer SPoG WMat
× ***schmittii***	CCVT ECrN MMuc SPer WJas WMat
'Sekiyama'	see *P.* 'Kanzan'
serotina	NLar
§ ***serrula***	Widely available
- 'Branklyn' 𝕐H6	EBee MGos NLar SCob
- 'Dorothy Clive' 𝕐H6	LSRN
- 'Princesse Sturdza'	MBlu
- var. ***tibetica***	see *P. serrula*
serrula × ***serrulata***	CBcs CTho WPGP
serrulata 'Erecta'	see *P.* 'Amanogawa'
- 'Grandiflora'	see *P.* 'Ukon'
- 'Longipes'	see *P.* 'Shōgetsu'
- 'Miyako' misapplied	see *P.* 'Shōgetsu'
- var. ***pubescens***	see *P. verecunda*
- 'Rosea'	see *P.* 'Kiku-shidare-zakura'
'Shidare-zakura'	see *P.* 'Kiku-shidare-zakura'
'Shimizu-zakura'	see *P.* 'Shōgetsu'
'Shiro' (D)	ERea SFrt
'Shirofugen' 𝕐H6	Widely available
§ 'Shirotae' 𝕐H6	Widely available
§ 'Shizuka' 𝕐H6	COtt CWib ECrN ELon LAst LRHS MBri MSwo NLar NOrn NWea SCob SCoo SLim SPer SPoG WHar WMat WMou
§ 'Shōgetsu' 𝕐H6	CBcs CDul CLnd CMac CSBt CTho EBee ELan EPfP LAst LRHS MAsh MBri MMuc NEgg NLar NOrn SCob SEWo SLim SPer SPoG WHar WMat WMou
× ***sieboldii*** 'Caespitosa'	see *P.* 'Takasago'
'Snow Goose'	CDoC CMac EBee ELan EPfP LAst LHop LRHS MBlu MMuc NEgg NLar SCoo SGol WMat
'Snow Showers'	CCVT CDoC CMac COtt ELan LCro LRHS LSRN MAsh MBri MGos MMuc NOrn NWea SEND SLim SPer SPoG WMat
spinosa	Widely available
- 'Plena' (d)	CTho MBlu
- 'Purpurea'	CDul CTho EGFP MBlu WMou
§ 'Spire' 𝕐H6	Widely available
Spring Snow	see *P.* 'Beni-tamanishiki'
'Stefania' **new**	WMat
× ***subhirtella*** var. ***ascendens***	see *P. pendula* f. *ascendens*
- 'Autumnalis'	Widely available
- 'Autumnalis Rosea'	Widely available
- 'Falling Stars'	SLon
- 'Fukubana'	CLnd CMac EBee EPfP MAsh MBri NLar WMat
- 'Pendula' misapplied	see *P. pendula* 'Pendula Rosea'
- 'Pendula Rosea'	see *P. pendula* 'Pendula Rosea'
- 'Pendula Rubra'	see *P. pendula* 'Pendula Rubra'
- 'Rosea'	see *P. pendula* f. *ascendens* 'Rosea'
- 'Stellata'	see *P. pendula* 'Stellata'
'Sunset Boulevard' 𝕐H6	CLnd LSRN MBri MGos WMat
'Tai-haku' 𝕐H6	Widely available
§ 'Takasago'	EBee MBri
'Taoyame' 𝕐H6	CLnd
tenella	ECha WCot
- 'Fire Hill'	CJun CSBt CWib ELan EPfP LRHS LSRN MGos NLar SKHP SPer WCot WJas
'The Bride' 𝕐H6	CDul CJun EBee EPfP LCro LOPS LRHS MAsh MBri SCoo SEWo WMat
tibetica	see *P. serrula*
'Tiltstone Hellfire'	EBee GBin MBri WMat
tomentosa	SBrt SEND
§ 'Trailblazer' (C/D)	CDul CLnd CMac CSBt ECrN EMil IVic LAst MRav MSwo SCob SLon WMou
triloba	CBcs CWib ECha MBlu MGos NWea
- 'Multiplex' (d)	SRms WJas
§ 'Ukon' 𝕐H6	CBcs CDoC CDul CLnd CMCN CMac CTho CTri EBee ECrN EPfP LCro LOPS LRHS MAsh MBri MGos MRav NLar NWea SGol SLim SPer WFar WHar WMat
'Umineko'	CCVT CDul CLnd CWib ECrN LRHS MGos MMuc SEND SEWo SPer WHar

§	***verecunda***	CLnd NWea WJas
	- 'Autumn Glory' ♀H6	CTho
	'Victoria Willis' **new**	WMat
	virginiana 'Schubert'	CDul ECrN NWea WMou
	'White Cloud'	CDul
	'Woodfield Cluster'	IArd
	yamadae	see *P. incisa* f. *yamadei*
	× ***yedoensis***	CCVT CDoC CDul EBee MBri MRav SLon SPer WHar WMat WMou
	- 'Ivensii'	CBcs CDul CSBt CWib LHop NWea SCoo SPer
	- 'Pendula'	see *P.* × *yedoensis* 'Shidare-Yoshino'
	- 'Perpendens'	see *P.* × *yedoensis* 'Shidare-Yoshino'
§	- 'Shidare-Yoshino'	CCVT CDoC CDul CLnd COtt CSBt EBee ECrN LRHS MAsh MBri MGos MRav MSwo NLar NOrn NWea SLim SLon WMat
§	- 'Somei-Yoshino' ♀H6	CCVT CLnd CMCN CTho CTri EPfP MBri NWea SLim WHar WJas
	'Yoshino'	see *P.* × *yedoensis* 'Somei-Yoshino'
	'Yoshino Pendula'	see *P.* × *yedoensis* 'Shidare-Yoshino'

Psammisia (*Ericaceae*)

	ulbrichiana	WPat

Pseuderanthemum (*Acanthaceae*)

	carruthersii var. ***atropurpureum*** 'Rubrum'	LSou

Pseudocydonia (*Rosaceae*)

§	***sinensis***	CAgr CBcs CEvo CMen SSta WHil

Pseudofumaria see *Corydalis*

	alba	see *Corydalis ochroleuca*

Pseudogynoxys (*Asteraceae*)

§	***chenopodioides***	CRHN CSpe SVen

Pseudolarix (*Pinaceae*)

	amabilis ♀H6	CDul CMen CTho EPfP GBin MBlu MBri MPkF NWea SCoo SLim SMad
	kaempferi (Lamb.) Gordon	see *Larix kaempferi*

Pseudomuscari see *Muscari*

Pseudopanax (*Araliaceae*)

	(Adiantifolius Group) 'Adiantifolius'	CBcs CDoC EBee ECou ESwi SVen
	- 'Cyril Watson' ♀H3	CBcs CDoC ELan LRHS SBig SVen WCot
	arboreus	see *Neopanax arboreus*
	'Bronze Eagle' **new**	LRHS
	chathamicus	CDoC ECou
	County Park hybrids	ECou
	crassifolius	CAbb CBcs CBrP CDTJ ECou ELon ESwi EUJe GBin IDee LRHS NLos SBig SMad SPoG WCot
	'Dark Star' **new**	LRHS
	discolor	ECou LEdu
	ferox	CAbb CBcs CBrP CDTJ CTsd ECou ESwi EUJe GBin IDee LRHS NLos SBig SLim SPoG SVen
	'Forest Gem'	CDoC
	'Gecko Gold' (v) **new**	LRHS
	laetus	see *Neopanax laetus*
	lessonii	CBcs CBrP ECou
	- 'Black Ruby'	ECou
	- 'Gold Splash' (v) ♀H3	CBcs CDoC EPfP IVic LRHS SBig SEND SLim SVen
	- 'Goldfinger'	LRHS
	- 'Rangitira'	CBcs CDoC LRHS SBig SLim
	'Linearifolius'	LEdu
	linearis	ECou
	'Purpureus' ♀H3	CDoC EBee ESwi SEND SVen
	'Sabre'	CBcs CDoC EBee ECou EUJe LRHS SLim
	'Trident' ♀H3	CDoC ECou LRHS SBig SLim SVen

Pseudosasa (*Poaceae*)

	amabilis misapplied	see *Arundinaria gigantea*
§	***japonica*** ♀H5	CAbb CBcs CBod CDoC CEnt CTsd CWib EAla ENBC EPfP LCro LOPS LPal LPar LRHS MMuc MWht NLar SCob SEND SEWo SPer SPoG WCFE WJun WMoo
§	- 'Akebonosuji' (v)	CEnt MWht WJun WPGP
I	- var. ***pleioblastoides***	MWht
	- 'Tsutsumiana'	ELon ERod EUJe MWht NLar SBig WJun
	- 'Variegata'	see *P. japonica* 'Akebonosuji'
	usawai	WJun
	viridula	ERod MWht

Pseudotsuga (*Pinaceae*)

§	***menziesii***	CBcs CDul CLnd EPfP MBlu MMuc NWea SEND
	- 'Bhiela Lhota'	CKen
	- 'Blue Wonder'	CKen
	- 'Densa'	CKen
	- 'Fastigiata'	CKen
	- 'Fletcheri'	CKen
	- 'Foxy Fir' **new**	NLar
	- var. ***glauca***	CDul CTho
	- 'Glauca Pendula'	CDul CKen MBlu
I	- 'Gotelli's Pendula'	CKen
	- 'Graceful Grace'	CKen
	- 'Hillside Pride'	NLar
	- 'Idaho Gem'	CKen NLar
	- 'Julie'	CKen
	- 'Knaphill'	LRHS
	- 'Little Jamie'	CKen
	- 'Lohbrunner'	CKen
	- 'McKenzie'	CKen
	- 'Nana'	CKen
	- 'Serpentine'	MBlu
	- 'Stairii'	CKen
	- 'Uwes Golden'	SLim
	- 'Vladstein' **new**	NLar
	taxifolia	see *P. menziesii*

Pseudowintera (*Winteraceae*)

§	***colorata***	CBcs CDoC CExl CMac CPla CTsd CWib GAbr GGal GKin IDee IVic MPkF MRav NLar WPat WSHC
	- 'Marjorie Congreve'	CBcs GKin IArd IDee IVic LRHS WPat
	- 'Moulin Rouge'	CBcs CDoC LRHS
	- 'Red Glow'	CBcs
	- 'Red Leopard'	CBcs CDoC CMil LBMP LRHS NLar SEle

Psidium (*Myrtaceae*)

	cattleyanum	see *P. littorale* var. *longipes*
	guajava (F)	SPlb XBlo
	littorale (F)	CPne
§	- var. ***longipes*** (F)	EShb XBlo

Psilotum (*Psilotaceae*)

	nudum	ECou

Psoralea (*Papilionaceae*)

aphylla	SVen
* ***fleta***	SPlb
glabra	SPlb
glandulosa	SBrt SPlb WSHC
* ***macrothyrsa***	EBee
oligophylla	SPlb
onobrychis	SPhx
pinnata	CExl

Psychotria (*Rubiaceae*)

capensis	CExl

Ptelea (*Rutaceae*)

trifoliata	CArn CBcs CDul CLnd CWib ELan EPfP MBlu NWea SChF SPer SRms WPGP
- 'Aurea' ♀H5	CAbP CBcs CBot CDul CExl CJun CTho ELan EPfP GBin LHop LRHS MBlu MBri MMuc NLar SMad SPer SSpi WBor WPGP
- 'Fastigiata'	EPfP

Pteracanthus see *Strobilanthes*

Pteridium (*Dennstaedtiaceae*)

aquilinum	XLum

Pteridophyllum (*Papaveraceae*)

racemosum	CTal EFEx WCru

Pteris (*Pteridaceae*)

cretica ♀H1c	CTsd
- var. ***albolineata*** ♀H1c	CHVG LPal LRHS WCot XBlo
- 'Mayi' (v)	LRHS
- 'Ouvradii'	SPlb
- 'Parkeri'	LPal LRHS
- 'Rowei'	LPal LRHS XBlo
- 'Wimsettii'	LRHS
* ***staminea***	XBlo
tremula	EShb
wallichiana	CFil EBee WPGP

Pterocarya ✿ (*Juglandaceae*)

fraxinifolia	CBcs CCVT CDul CMCN CTho ECrN EPfP GQui IArd IDee MBlu MMuc MRav SAko SEND
macroptera var. ***insignis***	CExl CFil WPGP
× ***rehderiana***	CTho MBlu
rhoifolia	CDul SAko
stenoptera	CBcs CDTJ CDul CMCN CTho NLar
- 'Fern Leaf' ♀H6	CExl CFil CHid EBee LRHS MBlu WMou WPGP

Pterocephalus (*Caprifoliaceae*)

parnassi	see *P. perennis*
§ ***perennis***	CMea ECho MHer NBir NRya SRms WAbe WHoo
pinardii	WAbe
spathulatus	WAbe

Pterodiscus (*Pedaliaceae*)

aurantiacus	LToo
luridus	LToo
ngamicus	LToo

Pterostylis (*Orchidaceae*)

curta ♀H2	CTal ECho

Pterostyrax (*Styracaceae*)

corymbosa	CBcs CJun CMCN MBlu NLar SSpi
hispida ♀H5	CAbP CBcs CDoC CDul CHGN CJun CMCN CTsd CWib EPfP EWTr GBin IDee IVic LRHS MBlu MRav NLar SAko SChF WFar WGrn WHar WHor
psilophyllus	WPGP

Ptilostemon (*Asteraceae*)

chamaepeuce from Cyprus **new**	SBrt
§ ***diacantha***	EPfP IFoB LRHS WCot
niveus	WCot

Ptilotrichum see *Alyssum*

Ptilotus (*Amaranthaceae*)

exaltatus	SPlb
- 'Benjo'PBR **new**	EBee

Pueraria (*Papilionaceae*)

montana var. ***lobata***	CArn

Pulicaria (*Asteraceae*)

§ ***dysenterica***	CHab LLWG MWLS NMir WHer WSFF

Pulmonaria (*Boraginaceae*)

angustifolia ♀H7	EPfP GKev GMaP MNrw SHeu SRms
- 'Azurea'	CElw CHVG CTca ELan EPPr EPfP EWoo GAbr GMaP MCot MMuc MRav NBro NLar SEND SRms
- 'Blaues Meer'	EBee ECtt GAbr LBMP LRHS MNrw SGbt SHeu
- 'Munstead Blue'	CElw CLAP GBuc MCot MRav NRya SRms
'Apple Frost'	LRHS SGol SHeu WCAu WWEG
'Barfield Regalia'	NSti WWEG
'Benediction'	CDes EBee MAvo MNrw NSti WCot
'Beth Chatto'	CElw
'Beth's Pink'	GAbr
'Blake's Silver'	CAby CBre CMea EBee ECtt LPla MAvo MBel MHol MNrw NEgg NSti SPer SPoG WBrk WCot WGrn WHoo WPGP
'Blauer Hügel'	NSti
'Blauhimmel'	GCra
'Blue Buttons'	CCon ECtt WWEG
'Blue Crown'	CElw EWes
'Blue Ensign' ♀H6	Widely available
'Blue Moon'	see *P. officinalis* 'Blue Mist'
'Blue Pearl'	LRHS
'Blueberry Muffin'	CSpe
'Bubble Gum'PBR	CWCL LRHS MBri SHeu SPoG
'Caborn Raspberry' **new**	LLWP
Cally hybrid	CLAP GCal
'Cedric Morris'	CElw
'Chintz'	MAvo
'Cleeton Red'	MNrw
'Coral Springs'	GBuc NLar
'Cotton Cool'	CBod CLAP CTal CTca EAEE EBee ECha ECtt EShb EWoo GBin GBuc LRHS MAvo MBNS MBel MCot MRav MSpe NEgg NHol NSti NWad SGbt SHeu WMoo WSHC WWtn
'Crawshay Chance'	CElw SMHy
'Dark Vader'	ECtt GBin LRHS MNrw SHeu SPoG

	Name	Suppliers
	'Darkling Thrush'	CDes
	'Diana Clare' 🏆H6	Widely available
	'Elworthy Rubies'	CDes CElw
	'Excalibur'	ECtt NLar SHeu WRHF
	'Fiona'	WWEG
	'Glacier'	CTca EPfP MNrw WCot WWEG
	'Hazel Kaye's Red'	LLWP
	'High Contrast'	ECtt LRHS SHeu
	'Highdown'	see *P.* 'Lewis Palmer'
	'Ice Ballet' (Classic Series)	CLAP EBee ECtt EPfP SCob SHeu WCAu
§	'Lewis Palmer' 🏆H7	CBro CSam CTca CWCL GCal GMaP LRHS MNrw NBir SRGP SRms WHea WHoo WWEG
	'Little Star'	CElw EBee ECha ECtt GBuc LRHS MAvo SHeu SRGP WFar WWEG
	longifolia	CBod EAEE ECha EHoe ELan EPfP GAbr GBin NBir NLar NSti
§	- 'Ankum'	CElw CLAP NBir WCot WSHC WWEG
	- 'Bertram Anderson'	CLet CTca EBee ECtt GMaP IBoy LRHS NBir NLar SCob SHeu SPer SRGP SRms SWvt WMnd WWEG
	- subsp. ***cevennensis***	CLAP LRHS NLar NSti SHeu WFar WWEG
	- 'Coen Jansen'	see *P. longifolia* 'Ankum'
	- 'Dordogne'	CLAP NBir NLar
	- 'Howard Eggins'	WWEG
	'Mado'	ECha WWEG
	'Majesté'	CBot CLAP CWib ECha EHrv ELan EPfP EWes GBuc GMaP IFro LRHS MBri MRav NBir NLar NSti SCob SHeu SPer SPoG WCot WMnd WWEG
	'Margery Fish'	CLAP CSam EPfP LRHS SHeu WMnd
	'Mary Mottram'	CElw ECtt NBir NSti SHeu WCot WMnd
	'Mawson's Blue' 🏆H6	CLAP EWes NBir NChi SWvt WMoo WSHC
	'Merlin'	CLAP SKHP
	'Milky Way'	ECtt SHeu
	mollis	GCal IMou LRHS MNrw NSti WCAu
	- 'Royal Blue'	MRav
	'Monksilver'	CElw
	'Moonshine' PBR	ECtt LRHS SHeu
	'Moonstone'	CElw
	'Mournful Purple'	ELon
	'Mrs Kittle'	CCon CSam CWCL GQue IMou LRHS MRav NBir NGdn NHol NSti SHeu WMnd WWEG
	'Netta Statham'	NSti
	'Nürnberg'	CElw WWEG
	officinalis	CHby IFoB MLHP NChi SIde WBrk
§	- 'Blue Mist'	CLAP ELan GMaP NBir WCot WMnd WMoo
	- 'Bowles's Blue'	see *P. officinalis* 'Blue Mist'
	- Cambridge Blue Group	EPfP MRav NBir NGdn WCot WWtn
	- 'White Wings'	CLAP EBee NLar
	'Oliver Wyatt's White'	CLAP SRGP
	Opal = 'Ocupol'	Widely available
	'Pierre's Pure Pink'	LRHS SHeu SPoG
	'Pink Haze' PBR	EBee ECtt ITim LOPS LRHS MHol MPie NLar SCob SWvt
	'Raspberry Splash' PBR	CLAP CWCL ECtt EShb GBin GKev LBMP LRHS MMuc NLar SCob SEND SGol SHeu SIde SPoG SWvt
*	'Rowlatt Choules'	MNrw
	'Roy Davidson'	CLAP CSam CTca ECtt EPfP LCro LHop LRHS NBir NHol NSti SRms SWvt WCAu WGwG WWEG
	rubra	CBcs CElw CWCL ECha ELan EPPr GAbr LCro LLWP LOPS MJak MLHP MMuc MNrw NBid NSti SEND SHeu SRms WCAu WHea
	- var. ***alba***	see *P. rubra* var. *albocorollata*
§	- var. ***albocorollata***	CBre CElw EBtc GAbr GBin NBid WWEG
	- 'Barfield Pink'	ELan GCal IFro NBir NLar SHeu
	- 'Bowles's Red'	CBod CNec EHrv GMaP IFoB LRHS MNrw MRav NBir NGdn NLar SPer WCAu WFar WGwG WHoo WMnd WWtn
	- 'David Ward' (v)	CCon CPla CWCL ECha ECtt EHrv ELan GCra GMaP MRav MSCN NBir NSti SHeu SPer SPoG WCFE WCot WMnd WSHC WWEG
	- 'Rachel Vernie' (v)	CLAP MAvo WWEG
	- 'Redstart'	CBod CSBt CSam CTca ECtt EWoo GKev LEdu LHop LLWP LRHS MNrw MRav NBir NGdn NLar SGol SHeu SRms SWvt WFar WMnd WMoo WWEG
§	***saccharata***	ECha ELan GMaP IFro MMuc SRms
	- 'Alba'	CElw IFro MMuc SEND SRms
	- Argentea Group 🏆H7	CTri ELan EPfP GMaP MMuc MRav NGdn SEND WBrk WWEG
	- 'Dora Bielefeld'	CBod CLAP COtt CTal ECha EHrv EPPr EPfP EWTr GBuc GMaP LLWP LRHS MNrw MRav NBir NChi NEgg NGdn NHol SHeu SPer SRGP SWvt
	- 'Frühlingshimmel'	CElw MRav NSti
	- 'Glebe Cottage Blue'	CElw
	- 'Leopard'	CLAP CLet CMea CSam CTca CWCL ECha ECtt GBin GBuc GMaP LRHS MBel MNrw NBir NGdn NSti SBod SHeu SWvt WCAu WCot WGwG WHoo WWEG
	- 'Mrs Moon'	CNec COtt CTri CWib ECtt ELon EPfP GMaP IKil NLar SGol SHeu SPer SWvt WCAu WMnd WWEG
	- 'Old Rectory Silver'	NBir
	- 'Picta'	see *P. saccharata*
	- 'Reginald Kaye'	ECha EWes MAvo
	- 'Silverado' PBR	ECtt MBri SHeu SWvt
	- 'Stanhoe'	EWes
	'Saint Ann's'	LRHS NSti
	'Samurai'	CWCL GBin LRHS MAvo MBel MBri NSti SHeu WFar
	'Silver Bouquet' PBR	CElw ECtt GBin LSou SHeu
	'Silver Lance'	SHeu
	'Silver Sabre'	IBlr
	'Silver Shimmers' PBR	SHeu
	'Sissinghurst White' 🏆H7	Widely available
	'Smoky Blue'	CLAP ECtt MRav SCob SHeu SWat WWEG
	'Spilled Milk'	SHeu
	'Spotted Dick' **new**	SMHy
	'Stillingfleet Meg'	CLAP EAEE ECtt EPfP LRHS MBNS NGdn NSti NWad SHeu SRGP WCot WGwG WWFP WWtn
	'Trevi Fountain'	CBod CHid CLAP CWCL EBee ECha ECtt EShb GBin GJos LRHS NPri NSti SHar SHeu SIde SPoG WCAu WCot WFar
	'Vera May' 🏆H7	MNrw
	'Victorian Brooch' PBR	CBod CLAP CSam CWCL ECtt GBin IBoy LRHS LSou MHol MNrw NPri SHeu SIde SPad SPoG WWEG
	'Weetwood Blue'	CBre CLAP CTca EBee MNrw
	'Wendy Perry'	LRHS

Pulsatilla (Ranunculaceae)

	alba	CBro
	albana	CBro ECho LHop LLHF LRHS
	- 'Lutea'	EBee EWTr LLHF
	alpina	ECho NGdn SPlb SRms
§	- subsp. ***apiifolia*** ♀H5	EBee IFro NRya
	- subsp. ***sulphurea*** misapplied	see *P. alpina* subsp. *apiifolia*
	ambigua	CPBP GKev LLHF NRya
	'Blue Select' (Pr/Prim)	IBoy
	campanella	GEdr LLHF
	caucasica	CBro ECho LRHS
	cernua	LHop
	georgica	GEdr
	halleri ♀H5	EBee ECho GKev
	- subsp. ***slavica*** ♀H5	LLHF
	- subsp. ***taurica***	GEdr
	lutea	see *P. alpina* subsp. *apiifolia*
	montana	SPlb
	occidentalis	EBee GEdr
§	***patens***	EDAr LLHF NGdn WIce
	- subsp. ***flavescens***	EBee
	pratensis	GPoy SRms
	- subsp. ***nigricans***	EBee GEdr LHop SBrt
	regeliana new	LLHF
	rubra	NGdn SPad SRot
*	***serotina***	EBee GKev
	turczaninovii	LLHF LPla
*	***turkestanica***	GEdr
§	***vernalis*** ♀H5	GEdr NLar NSla WAbe XEll
	violacea	CBcs GKev
§	***vulgaris*** ♀H5	Widely available
	- 'Alba'	Widely available
	- 'Barton's Pink'	CBro ECho EPot LHop LLHF LRHS SRot
	- 'Blaue Glocke'	CAby CBod GEdr LRHS MBel NPri SHar SWvt WHil XSen
	- 'Eva Constance'	CBro ECho LHop LLHF LRHS
	- 'Gotlandica'	LLHF
	- subsp. ***grandis***	GEdr LRHS NSla
	- - 'Budapest Seedling'	GEdr
	- - 'Carminea' new	GBuc
	- - 'Papageno'	CBod CSpe EAEE ECho GCrg MAvo MBel MHol NCGa NHol NLar NSla WIce WRHF
	- Heiler hybrids	CBod EAEE LLHF MRav NCGa NDov NEgg NGdn NSla SVic
	- 'Perlen Glocke'	EBee EDAr GEdr LRHS LSun MHer NLar
	- pink-flowered	CMea LLHF NSla WFar
	- Red Clock	see *P. vulgaris* 'Röde Klokke'
	- red-flowered	CTsd EBee GBuc IBoy SCob SGbt WFar
§	- 'Röde Klokke'	CAby CBod EAJP ECtt EPfP EPot EWoo GEdr LRHS MBel MCot MNrw MWat NPri NWad SHar SHil SWvt WCot WHil XLum XSen
	- Rote Glocke	see *P. vulgaris* 'Röde Klokke'
	- var. ***rubra***	CMea CNec ECho ELan EPPr EPfP GMaP LRHS MBri MHer MNHC NBir NLar SPer SPoG SRms SRot WHoo WIce WTor
	- violet blue-flowered	EPfP LRHS MWat SHil
§	- 'Weisse Schwan'	EBee EPfP GEdr GMaP SRot
	- 'White Bells'	GEdr NHol
	- White Swan	see *P. vulgaris* 'Weisse Schwan'

Pultenaea (Papilionaceae)

daphnoides	SVen
juniperina	SPlb SVen

pummelo see *Citrus maxima*

Punica (Lythraceae)

	granatum	CArn CBcs CBod CMen CTsd ELan EPfP IDee LPal MOWG SCob SEND SPre SVic SWvt WJek
	- 'Chico' (d)	CBcs SEND
	- 'Legrelleae' (F/d)	SEND WPat
	- 'Maxima Rubra' (d)	EShb XSen
	- var. ***nana*** ♀H3	CMen EAJP EBee EBtc EOHP EPfP EShb LEdu LRHS MHer SRms SVen SVic WPat
	- f. ***plena*** (d)	CBcs EBee LRHS MRav WCFE WPat
	- - 'Flore Pleno Luteo' (d)	LRHS
	- 'Provence' (F)	EPom XSen
*	- 'Striata'	MOWG
	- 'Wonderful' (F)	CAgr

Puschkinia (Asparagaceae)

scilloides	ECho NBir
- 'Aragat's Gem'	ECho
- var. ***libanotica*** ♀H5	CAby ECho EPfP EPot ERCP GKev LAma LCro LEdu LOPS LRHS MPie SDeJ SEND SPer WRHF WShi
- - 'Alba'	ECho EPot GKev LAma SDeJ SPer

Putoria (Rubiaceae)

calabrica	WHil

Puya (Bromeliaceae)

RH 1809	WCot
RH 2910A	WCot
RH 2961C	WCot
RH 3425B	WCot
alpestris	CFil EShb SBig SPlb WCot
assurgens	LTro WCot
berteroana	CAbb CBcs CDTJ EAla EShb EUJe SPlb SVen WCot
boliviensis	WCot
castellanosii	LTro NLos WCot
chilensis	CAbb CBcs CDTJ CDoC LRHS NLos SPlb SVen WCot
coerulea	CCon CDTJ CTsd MGil NLos SPlb
- var. ***monteroana***	WCot
dyckioides	LTro WCot
- red-bracted	WCot
ferruginea	EUJe LTro NLos SPlb WCot
gilmartiniae F&W 8697	WCot
harmsii	LTro NLos WCot
laxa	EAla EUJe WCot
mirabilis	CDTJ EAla ESwi GBin LAir NLos
raimondii	WCot
venusta	CDTJ EAla NLos SPlb SVen WCot
yakespala	WCot

Pycnanthemum (Lamiaceae)

curvipes new	CEvo
incanum	SPhx
montanum	GBin
muticum	LEdu LPla SBrt WPGP
pilosum	CArn CLau MHer MNHC SPhx XLum
tenuifolium	NLar SBrt SPhx
virginianum	EBee SPhx

Pycnostachys (Lamiaceae)

urticifolia	EOHP EWes SDys

Pygmea see *Chionohebe*

Pyracantha (*Rosaceae*)

	sp.	LPar
	Alexander Pendula = 'Renolex'	LHop MRav MSwo SRms
	angustifolia	LPar WCFE
	'Apache' **new**	LPar
§	***atalantioides***	SPlb WCFE
	'Brilliant'	SCoo
	coccinea 'Lalandei'	CMac
	- 'Red Column'	Widely available
	- 'Red Cushion'	MJak MRav SCob SRms
	crenulata	WCFE
	Dart's Red = 'Interrada'	COtt CSBt WHar
	'Fiery Cascade'	LRHS SHil SPoG
	gibbsii	see *P. atalantioides*
	'Golden Charmer'	CMac COtt EPfP IBoy LAst LRHS MBri MGos MSwo NEgg NLar NWea SCob SCoo SGol SPer SPoG SRms SWvt WFar
	'Golden Glow'	SLim
	'Golden Sun'	see *P.* 'Soleil d'Or'
	'Harlequin' (v)	SCob SGol WFar
	'Knap Hill Lemon'	MBlu
	koidzumii 'Victory'	ECrN NLar
	'Mohave'	CMac CTri ECrN ELan ELon IBoy LRHS MAsh NWea SCob SCoo SGol SLim SRms SWvt
	'Mohave Silver' (v)	CMac CWSG ELan EShb LBMP LRHS MAsh NHol
	'Navaho'	SEWo
	'Orange Charmer'	CDul CMac CTri ELan LHop LRHS MBri MGos NHol NLar NWea SCob SPer SPlb WFar WHar WMoo
	'Orange Glow' ♀H6	Widely available
	'Red Charmer'	NHol
*	'Red Pillar'	EUJe NWea
	rogersiana	CDul NWea
	- 'Flava' ♀H6	CDul CLet CSBt EPfP LRHS MAsh NEgg NWea SPoG SWvt
	'Rosedale'	LRHS WHar
	Saphyr Jaune = 'Cadaune' PBR	CBcs CCVT CDoC CSBt CWSG EBee ECrN EPfP LCro LRHS MGos MRav NHol NPri SCob SCoo SGol SPer WHar
	Saphyr Orange = 'Cadange' PBR ♀H6	CBcs CCVT CDoC CMac CSBt CWSG EBee ECrN EPfP LCro LRHS MBri MGos MRav NEgg NPri SCob SCoo SGol SPer WHar
	Saphyr Rouge = 'Cadrou' PBR ♀H6	CBcs CCVT CChe CDoC CLet CMac CSBt CWSG EBee ECrN ELan EPfP LCro LRHS MBri MGos MMuc MRav NPri SCob SCoo SEND SGol SPer SWvt WFar WHar
	'Shawnee'	CMac CWib MSwo
§	'Soleil d'Or'	Widely available
	'Sparkler' (v)	CMac EHoe SCob SMad
	'Teton' ♀H6	CMac COtt ELan EPfP LAst LRHS MAsh MBri MGos MJak MSwo NWea SCob SGol SHil SRms WFar
	'Watereri'	NWea
	'Yellow Sun'	see *P.* 'Soleil d'Or'

Pyrethropsis see *Rhodanthemum*

Pyrethrum see *Tanacetum*

+ *Pyrocydonia* (*Rosaceae*)

'Danielii' (F)	IDee SAko

Pyrola (*Ericaceae*)

rotundifolia	LEdu WHer

Pyrostegia (*Bignoniaceae*)

venusta	MOWG

Pyrrocoma (*Asteraceae*)

clementis	EBee

Pyrrosia (*Polypodiaceae*)

caudifrons	WCot
hastata	CMen WCot
linearifolia 'Urakoryu Jishi'	CMen
lingua	CMen WPGP
polydactyla	CMen
sheareri	ISha

Pyrus ✿ (*Rosaceae*)

	amygdaliformis	CMCN
	- W&B B-10 **new**	WCot
	calleryana 'Bradford'	CLnd
	- 'Chanticleer'	Widely available
	- 'Chanticleer' variegated (v)	CDul MAsh
	- 'Redspire'	CCVT
	caucasica **new**	WMat
	communis (F)	CArn CCVT CDul CTri ECrN LBuc NWea SPer SPlb WMou
	- 'Abbé Fétel' (D)	SKee
	- 'Ayrshire Lass' (D) **new**	GTwd
	- 'Bambinella' (D)	SKee
	- 'Barland' (Perry)	CHab
	- 'Barnet' (Perry)	CHab
	- 'Baronne de Mello' (D)	CTho NOra SKee WMat
	- 'Beech Hill' (F)	CDul ECrN SGol SPer
	- 'Belle Julie' (D)	SKee
	- 'Bellissime d'Hiver' (C)	SKee
	- Benita = 'Rafzas' **new**	LCro LOPS LRHS MBri MCoo WMat
	- 'Bergamotte d'Automne' (D)	SKee
	- 'Bergamotte Esperen' (D)	SKee
	- 'Beth' (D) ♀H6	Widely available
	- 'Beurré Bedford' (D)	SKee
	- 'Beurré Clairgeau' (C)	SKee
	- 'Beurré d'Amanlis' (D)	SKee
	- 'Beurré d'Anjou' (F)	SKee
	- 'Beurré de Beugny' (D)	SKee
	- 'Beurré de Naghin' (C/D)	SKee
	- 'Beurré Diel' (D)	SKee
	- 'Beurré Dumont' (D)	CAgr
	- 'Beurré Giffard' (D)	CAgr
	- 'Beurré Gris d'Hiver' (D)	SKee
	- 'Beurré Hardy' (D) ♀H6	Widely available
§	- 'Beurré Précoce Morettini' (D)	SDea
	- 'Beurré Six' (D)	SKee
	- 'Beurré Sterckmans' (F) **new**	SKee
	- 'Beurré Superfin' (D) ♀H6	GTwe SKee WHar
	- 'Bishop's Thumb' (D)	SDea SKee
	- 'Black Worcester' (C)	CDul CHab GTwe MAsh NOra SDea SKee WHar WJas WMat WWct
	- 'Blakeney Red' (Perry)	CHab NOra SDea WHar WMat
	- 'Blickling' (D)	SKee
	- 'Bon Chrétien d'Hiver' (D)	SKee

- 'Brandy' (Perry) CAgr CHab CTho NOra SDea SFrt SKee SVic WHar WMat
- 'Bristol Cross' (D) CAgr CHab SKee
- 'Butt' (Perry) CHab
- 'Calebasse Bosc' (D) NOra SKee
- 'Cannock' (F) WMat
- 'Catillac' (C) ♀H6 CAgr CHab ECrN GTwe NOra SKee WHar WMat
- 'Chalk' see *P. communis* 'Crawford'
- 'Chaumontel' (D) SKee
- 'Clapp's Favourite' (D) CHab CTho ECrN ELan NOra SKee SVic WMat
- 'Comte de Lamy' (D) SKee
- 'Concorde'^{PBR} (D) ♀H6 Widely available
- 'Conference' (D) ♀H6 Widely available
- 'Craig's Favourite' (D) GTwd

§ - 'Crawford' (D) GTwd
- 'Dana's Hovey' (F) **new** SKee
- 'Deacon's Pear' (D) SDea
- Delbardélice = 'Delété' (F) LRHS
- 'Devoe' (D) SDea
- 'Docteur Jules Guyot' (D) CAgr SDea SKee
- 'Doyenné Boussoch' (D) SKee
- 'Doyenné d'Été' (D) ERea MCoo
- 'Doyenné du Comice' (D) ♀H6 Widely available
- 'Duchesse d'Angoulême' (D) SKee
- 'Durondeau' (D) ERea GTwe NOra SBdl SDea SKee WMat
- 'Emile d'Heyst' (D) GQue GTwe MCoo SBdl SKee WHar WMat
- 'Fair Maid' (D) GTwd
- 'Fertility' (D) CLnd SFrt
- 'Fertility Improved' see *P. communis* 'Improved Fertility'
- 'Fondante d'Automne' (D) CAgr CTho NOra SBdl SKee WHar WMat
- 'Forelle' (D) ERea SKee
- 'Garden Gem' (F) **new** SBmr WMat
- 'Garden Pearl' (F) **new** SBmr
- 'Gin' (Perry) CHab WMat
- 'Glou Morceau' (D) CAgr CArg ECrN ERea GTwe LRHS MCoo MWat NOra SBdl SDea SFrt SKee WHar WMat
- 'Gorham' (D) ♀H6 CAgr CDul CTho GTwe NOra SKee WHar WMat
- 'Green Horse' (Perry) CHab WMat
- 'Green Pear of Yair' (D) GTwd
- 'Hacon's Incomparable' (D) SKee
- 'Harley Gum' (F) WHar
- 'Harrow Delight' (D) SDea
- 'Harvest Queen' (D/C) CAgr SDea
- 'Hellen's Early' (Perry) CHab ERea SKee WHar WMat
- 'Hendre Huffcap' (Perry) CAgr CHab CTho NOra SFrt WHar WMat
- 'Hessle' (D) CAgr CHab GTwd NWea SDea SKee
- Humbug = 'Pysanka' (F) EPom GQue LBuc LRHS MBri NOra WHar WMat

§ - 'Improved Fertility' (D) CAgr ERea SBmr SDea SKee
- Invincible = 'Delwinor' (D/C) CAgr CArg CDoC CDul CTho EPom LBuc LRHS MAsh MBri MCoo MNHC NLar NOra SBdl SLim WHar WMat
- 'Jargonelle' (D) CAgr CDul CHab CTho GTwe SBdl SDea SKee WHar WMat
- 'Joséphine de Malines' (D) ♀H6 CAgr ERea GTwe IArd NOra SBdl SDea SKee WHar
- 'Judge Amphlett' (Perry) CTho NOra WHar WMat
- 'Kieffer' (C) CAgr
- 'Laird Lang' (D) **new** GTwd
- 'Laxton's Early Market' (C/D) SKee
- 'Laxton's Foremost' (D) CAgr SKee
- 'Le Lectier' (D) SKee
- 'Légipont' (F) CAgr
- 'Louise Bonne of Jersey' (D) ♀H6 CAgr CMac CTri ECrN EPom ERea GTwe IArd LAst LRHS MGos NOra SBdl SBmr SDea SKee WHar WMat WWct
- 'Maggie' (D) **new** GTwd
- 'Marguérite Marillat' (D) SDea
- 'Marie-Louise' (D) SKee WHar
- 'Merrylegs' (Perry) CHab
- 'Merton Pride' (D) CAgr CLnd CTho GTwe IArd LRHS MCoo MWat NOra SBdl SDea SKee WHar WMat
- 'Moonglow' CAgr ERea LRHS NOra SDea SKee WMat
- 'Moorcroft' (Perry) SKee
- 'Morettini' see *P. communis* 'Beurré Précoce Morettini'
- 'Nec Plus Meuris' (F) **new** SKee
- 'Nouveau Poiteau' (C/D) CAgr
- 'Nuvar Celebration' (F) SKee WMat
- 'Nye Russet Bartlett' (F) CAgr
- 'Old Home' (Perry) **new** WMat
- 'Oldfield' (Perry) CHab
- 'Olivier de Serres' (D) SKee
- 'Onward' (D) ♀H6 CAgr CArg CDul CHab CLnd CTho CTri CWib ECrN EPom ERea GTwe IArd LRHS MAsh MBri NLar NOra NWea SBdl SDea SKee WHar WMat WWct
- 'Ovid' (D) CAgr

§ - 'Packham's Triumph' (D) CAgr CDoC CTri CWib ECrN GTwe LAst NOra SBmr SDea SKee WHar WMat
- 'Parsonage' (Perry) CHab
- 'Passe Crassane' (D) SKee
- 'Pear Apple' (D) CHab SDea
- 'Penrhyn' (D) WGwG WMat
- 'Pero Nobile' (D) SKee
- 'Petit Muscat' SKee

I - 'Petite Poire' (F) EPom
- 'Pitmaston Duchess' (C/D) ♀H6 ECrN ERea GTwe MCoo SDea SKee WHar WMat WWct
- 'Précoce de Trévoux' (D) SKee WHar
- 'Président Barabé' (F) SKee
- 'Red Comice' (D/C) GTwe SKee
- 'Red Pear' (Perry) CHab WMat
- 'Red Sensation Bartlett' (D/C) EPom GTwe LBuc NOra SKee WMat
- 'Robin' (C/D) ERea SDea SKee WMat
- 'Roosevelt' (D) SKee
- 'Santa Claus' (D) SDea SKee
- 'Seckel' (D) NOra SKee
- 'Shipova' (F) CAgr MAsh NOra WHar WMat
- 'Sierra' (D) CAgr
- 'Snowdon Queen' (D) CHab WGwG
- 'Souvenir du Congrès' (D) CAgr
- 'Starkrimson' (D) SKee
- 'Summer Bergamot' (F) **new** GTwd
- Super Comice Delbard = 'Delbias' (F) **new** LRHS

- 'Taynton Squash' (Perry)	LRHS NOra WMat
- 'Terrace Pearl' (D)	SPoG WMat
- 'Tettenhall Dick' (C/D)	WHar
- 'Thorn' (Perry)	CAgr CHab SKee WHar WMat
- 'Triomphe de Vienne' (D)	SKee
- 'Triumph'	see *P. communis* 'Packham's Triumph'
- 'Uvedale's St Germain' (C)	SKee
- 'Verdi' (F)	EPom
- 'Vicar of Winkfield' (C)	ECrN SDea SKee
- 'Williams' Bon Chrétien' (D/C) ♀H6	Widely available
- 'Williams' Red' (D/C)	GTwe LHop NPri SKee
- 'Williams' Rouge Delbard' (F)	EPom
- 'Winnal's Longdon' (Perry)	WHar WMat
- 'Winter Nelis' (D)	CAgr CHab CTri CWib ECrN GTwe LAst NOra SDea SKee WHar WMat WWct
- 'Woodhall' (F) new	WMat
cordata	CDul CTho
elaeagnifolia	MAsh
- var. ***kotschyana***	CDul SLim
- 'Silver Sails'	CLnd CMac EBee EMil MBri SCoo SSpi WMat
fauriei	CTho
× ***michauxii***	SVen
nivalis	CDul CLnd CTho EBee ECrN EPfP LBuc LEdu NOrn NWea SPer
- 'Catalia'	MAsh WMat
pashia	CMCN EBee LEdu NLar WMat
pyraster	CDul CHab WCot
pyrifolia '20th Century'	see *P. pyrifolia* 'Nijisseiki'
- 'Chojuro' (F)	LEdu
- 'Hosui' (F)	CAgr LEdu SVic
- 'Kosui' (F)	SVic
- 'Kumoi' (F)	CAgr EPom ERea LRHS MAsh MCoo SDea WHar WMat
§ - 'Nijisseiki' (F)	CDul SVic
- 'Shinko' (F)	CAgr LEdu
- 'Shinseiki' (F)	CAgr CLnd ERea MAsh SDea SKee WHar WMat
- 'Shinsui' (F)	SDea SKee
* ***salicifolia*** var. ***orientalis***	CTho
- 'Pendula' ♀H6	Widely available
ussuriensis	CTho

Q

Qiongzhuea see *Chimonobambusa*

Quercus ✿ (*Fagaceae*)

acerifolia	EPfP
acherdophylla	SBir WPGP
§ ***acuta***	CMCN
acutifolia	SBir
acutifolia × ***mexicana***	SBir
acutissima	CBcs CDul CMCN EPfP NLar SBir SGol
- PAB 7957 new	LEdu
- 'Gobbler'	EBee ESwi
aegilops	see *Q. ithaburensis* subsp. *macrolepis*
affinis ♀H5	CMCN EPfP SBir
agrifolia	CDul CMCN EBtc
alba	CDul CMCN WPGP
* ***alentejana*** new	CMCN
aliena	CDul CMCN
- PAB 8972	LEdu
alnifolia	CDul WPat
arkansana	CDul SBir WPat
× ***atlantica***	SBir
austrina	CMCN SBir
× ***beadlei***	see *Q.* × *saulii*
× ***benderi***	SBir
berberidifolia	CMCN SBir
bicolor	CDul CMCN EPfP MBlu WPGP
× ***bimundorum***	SBir
§ - 'Crimschmidt'	CDul CLnd EBee EPfP ESwi LRHS MBlu MBri SAko SBir SGol
borealis	see *Q. rubra*
breweri	see *Q. garryana* var. *breweri*
buckleyi	CMCN LRHS SBir
× ***bushii***	CMCN EPfP MBlu MBri SBir WPat
- 'Seattle Trident'	EPfP LRHS MBlu MBri SAko
canariensis ♀H5	CDul CMCN CTho EPfP SGol WPGP WPat
candicans	SBir
× ***capesii***	SBir WPat
castanea	WPGP
castaneifolia	CDul CMCN
- 'Green Spire' ♀H6	CLnd CMCN EBee EPfP MBlu MBri
cerris	CArg CBcs CCVT CDoC CDul CLnd CMCN EBee ECrN EPfP MGos MMuc NWea SCob SEND SGol SPer
- 'Afyon Lace'	MBlu SBir WPat
§ - 'Argenteovariegata' (v)	CMCN EBee ELan EPfP MAsh MBlu MBri SBir WPat
- 'Athena'	MBlu
- 'Curly Head'PBR	SMad
- 'Variegata'	see *Q. cerris* 'Argenteovariegata'
- 'Wodan'	MBlu
chenii	CDul SBir
chrysolepis	CBcs CMCN EPfP
coccifera	CLet CMCN EPfP SGol SVen WCot WPGP
coccinea	CBcs CDul CLnd CMCN CTho CTri ECrN EPfP MBlu MMuc MWht NEgg NWea SBir SEWo SPer SPoG WPat
- 'Campanile' new	SAko
- 'Splendens' ♀H6	CDoC CDul CHll CJun CMCN CTri ELan EPfP IArd MAsh MBlu MBri NLar SGol SMad SPer WPat
conspersa	SBir
crassifolia	WPGP WPat
crassipes	SBir
Crimson Spire	see *Q.* × *bimundorum* 'Crimschmidt'
crispipilis	SBir
dalechampii	CMCN SBir
dentata	CDul CMCN
- 'Carl Ferris Miller'	CBcs CDul CMCN EBee EPfP ESwi LLHF LRHS MBlu MBri SAko SBig SBir SCob WHor WPGP WPat
- 'Pinnatifida'	CDul CMCN EPfP IDee LLHF MBlu MPkF NLar SAko WCot WPat
- 'Sir Harold Hillier'	MBlu MBri SAko WHor
- subsp. ***yunnanensis***	SBir
dolicholepis	CMCN SBir
'Doring's Zweizack'	SBir
douglasii	CDul CMCN SSpi

	Name	Suppliers
	dumosa	CMCN
	- G 315	WPGP
	× ***dysophylla***	CFil WPGP
	ellipsoidalis	CDul CMCN NLar SBir SGol
	- 'Hemelrijk' 🏆H6	CMCN EPfP LRHS MBlu MBri SBir WPGP WPat
	emoryi	SBir
	engleriana PAB 8183 new	LEdu
	× ***exacta***	SBir
	fabrei	CMCN SBir
	faginea	CDul CMCN WPGP
	- subsp. ***broteroi***	CMCN
	falcata	CMCN EBtc SBir
	- var. ***pagodifolia***	see *Q. pagoda*
	× ***fernaldii***	CMCN EPfP MBlu
	frainetto	CDul CMCN CTho EBee EPfP NWea SGol SPer WMou
	- 'Hungarian Crown' 🏆H6	CMCN EPfP MBlu SBir
	- 'Tortworth'	SMad
	- 'Trump'	CDul CMCN MBri
	fruticosa	see *Q. lusitanica*
	fusiformis	SBir
	gambelii	CBcs CMCN EBtc MPkF
	garryana	CBcs CMCN EPfP WPGP
§	- var. ***breweri***	CMCN
	- var. ***fruticosa***	see *Q. garryana* var. *breweri*
	georgiana	CDul CMCN EPfP SBir
	germana	CFil
	gilva	CMCN SBir
	glabra	see *Lithocarpus glaber*
	glabrescens	WPGP
	glandulifera	see *Q. serrata* Thunb.
	glauca	CDul CMCN EPfP NLar
	graciliformis	WPat
	gravesii	CMCN EPfP SBir
	greggii	WPGP
	grisea	CMCN
	× ***hastingsii***	CMCN SBir
	× ***hawkinsiae***	SBir
	× ***haynaldiana***	SBir
	hemisphaerica	CMCN EPfP SBir
	× ***heterophylla***	CMCN EPfP SBir
	× ***hickelii***	CMCN EPfP SBir
	hirtifolia	WPGP
	× ***hispanica***	EUJe
	- 'Ambrozyana'	CDul CMCN NLar
	- 'Bloemendaal'	MBri
	- 'Diversifolia'	CDul CMCN EPfP IArd MBlu NLar WPat
	- 'Fulhamensis'	CDul CMCN IArd MBlu MMuc SBir SEND SGol WMou
§	- 'Lucombeana' 🏆H6	CDul CHGN CMCN CSBt CTho EBee ELan EPfP MBlu MMuc SBir SPer
	- 'Suberosa'	CTho
	- 'Waasland Select'	IArd MBri NLar SGol WMou
	- 'Wageningen'	CDul CMCN LRHS MBri SBir
	hypoleucoides	CMCN EPfP
	ilex	Widely available
	- 'Fordii'	SBir
	ilicifolia	CMCN EPfP SBir WPGP WPat
	imbricaria	CBcs CDul CMCN EPfP SBir WPat
	incana Roxb.	see *Q. leucotrichophora*
	ithaburensis	CDul
§	- subsp. ***macrolepis***	CMCN LEdu SBir
	- - 'Hemelrijk Silver'	EPfP MBlu SBir WPGP WPat
	× ***jackiana***	SBir
	kelloggii	CBcs CDul CMCN EPfP WPGP
	× ***kewensis*** 🏆H6	CMCN SBir WMou
	laevigata	see *Q. acuta*
	laevis	CMCN EPfP SBir
	'Langtry'	SBir
§	***laurifolia***	CDul CMCN EPfP SBir
	laurina	SBir WPGP
§	***leucotrichophora***	CMCN LEdu SBir WPGP
	liaotungensis	see *Q. wutaishanica*
	× ***libanerris***	SBir
	- 'Rotterdam'	CMCN SBir
	libani	CDul CMCN EPfP
	lobata	CMCN LEdu
	× ***lucombeana***	see *Q.* × *hispanica* 'Lucombeana'
	- 'William Lucombe'	see *Q.* × *hispanica* 'Lucombeana'
	× ***ludoviciana***	EPfP SBir WPat
§	***lusitanica*** Lam.	SBir
	lyrata	CMCN SGol
	- 'Arnold'	MBlu
	macranthera	CDul CMCN EPfP
	macrocarpa	CDul CMCN EPfP WPat
	macrolepis	see *Q. ithaburensis* subsp. *macrolepis*
	marilandica	CDul CMCN EPfP MBlu MBri SBir WPat
	'Mauri'	CDul IArd LRHS MBlu MBri SBir
	mexicana	CMCN IArd SAko SBir WPGP
§	***michauxii***	CBcs CDul CMCN EPfP MBlu
	mohriana	SBir
	mongolica	CBcs CDul MBlu SBig
	- subsp. ***crispula***	CMCN
	muhlenbergii	CDul CMCN MBlu MPkF SBir
	- 'Dallas'	EPfP
	myrsinifolia new	CBcs NLar
	myrtifolia	SBir
	nigra	CDul CMCN EGFP EPfP SBir
	- 'Beethoven'	MBlu SBir
I	- 'Nyewoodii'	SBir
	nuttallii	see *Q. texana*
	obtusa	see *Q. laurifolia*
	oglethorpensis	SBir WPat
	pacifica G 301	WPGP
	- G 305	WPGP
	- G 313	WPGP
§	***pagoda***	CDul CMCN EGFP SBir WPat
	palustris 🏆H6	CArg CCVT CDoC CDul CLnd CMCN CTho EBee ELan EPfP MAsh MBlu MMuc NEgg NLar NWea SBir SCob SEWo SGol SPer WMou
	- 'Flaming Suzy'	MBlu
	- 'Green Dwarf'	CMCN MBlu NLar SEWo SLim WPat
	- Green Pillar = 'Pringreen'	MBlu MBri MGos NLar SGol WMat
	- 'Isabel'	EPfP ESwi LRHS MBri WHor WMat WPat
	- 'Pendula'	CMCN
	- 'Silhouette'	CJun SBir
	- 'Swamp Pygmy'	CMCN EBee EPfP ESwi EUJe LRHS MBlu SCob
	- 'Windischleuba'	MBlu
	pannosa	SBir
	parvula var. ***parvula***	SBir
§	× ***pauciloba***	CMCN
	pedunculata	see *Q. robur*
	pedunculiflora	see *Q. robur* subsp. *pedunculiflora*
§	***petraea***	CArg CDoC CDul CHab CLnd CTri ECrN EPfP MBlu NWea SCob SGol WMou
	- 'Acutiloba'	SBir
	- 'Laciniata'	see *Q. petraea* 'Laciniata Crispa'
§	- 'Laciniata Crispa'	CDul CMCN EPfP MBlu
	- Mespilifolia Group	CDul

§ - 'Purpurea'	CMCN EPfP MBlu NLar
- 'Rubicunda'	see *Q. petraea* 'Purpurea'
§ ***phellos***	CDul CMCN EBee EBtc EPfP MBlu MBri NLar SBir
- Hightower = 'Qpsta' **new**	SGol
aff. ***phellos*** **new**	ECrN
phillyreoides	CBcs CDul CLet CMCN EPfP WPat
polymorpha	CDul CMCN EGFP MPkF SBir
Pondaim Group	CMCN WMou WPat
pontica	CMCN EPfP LLHF MBlu WPat
prinoides	CMCN
prinus misapplied	see *Q. michauxii*
§ ***prinus*** L.	CMCN WPGP
pubescens	CDul CMCN MMuc SEND
pumila Michx.	see *Q. prinus* L.
pumila Walt.	see *Q. phellos*
pungens	CMCN
pyrenaica	CDul CMCN CTho EBtc MMuc SBir SEND
- 'Pendula' ♀H6	CMCN EPfP
rhysophylla	CMCN EPfP IArd MBlu SBir WPGP
- 'Maya' ♀H5	CDul CJun EBee ELan EPfP EUJe IArd LLHF LRHS MBri MRav NLar SBir SGol WHor WMat WPGP WPat
× ***riparia***	SBir
§ ***robur***	Widely available
- 'Argenteomarginata' (v)	CMCN MBlu WPat
- 'Atropurpurea'	MPkF NWea
- 'Blue Gnome'	MBlu
- 'Compacta'	MBlu WPat
- 'Concordia'	CMCN EBtc ELan EPfP MBlu NLar SAko SKHP
- 'Dissecta'	CMCN
- 'Facrist'	CDul SBir
- Fastigiata Group	CDoC CDul CLnd COtt CTho EBee EPfP IArd IVic LCro LHop MGos NWea SBir SCob SGol SLim SPer
- - 'Koster' ♀H6	CDul CMCN CMac CNWT CTri EPfP MBlu MRav NWea SCob SPoG WMat
- - 'Zeeland'	SBir
- 'Filicifolia' misapplied	see *Q. robur* 'Pectinata'
- 'Filicifolia'	WPat
- var. ***haas***	CDul
- 'Irtha'	EPfP MBlu
- 'Menhir'	CMCN LLHF MAsh MBlu WCot WPat
§ - 'Pectinata'	EPfP MBlu WPat
§ - subsp. ***pedunculiflora***	CMCN
- 'Pendula'	CMCN MBlu WPat
- 'Purpurascens'	CDul CMCN
- 'Purpurea'	MBlu
- 'Raba'	CMCN
- 'Rita's Gold'	WPat
§ - 'Salfast'	CDul MBlu
- 'Salicifolia Fastigiata'	see *Q. robur* 'Salfast'
- 'Strypemonde'	CMCN
- 'Timuki'	IArd MBlu WPat
- 'Totem' **new**	WHor
- 'Tromp Dwarf' **new**	MBlu
- Variegata Group (v)	WPat
- - 'Fürst Schwarzenburg' (v)	MBlu
robur × ***macrocarpa*** × ***virginiana***	SBir
× ***rosacea*** 'Westcolumn'	WPat
rotundifolia	CAgr CMCN EBee EPfP WPGP
§ ***rubra***	Widely available
- 'Aurea'	CJun CMCN EBee EPfP MBlu MBri WHor
- 'Bolte's Gold'	CJun LRHS MBlu MBri WHor WMat
- 'Cyrille'	SBir
- 'Magic Fire' ♀H6	CMCN EPfP MBlu SBir
- 'Red Queen'	EPfP MBlu
* - 'Sunshine'	CDul CMCN MBlu MBri WCot WPat
× ***rudkinii***	EPfP
rugosa	CFil
× ***runcinata***	SBir WPat
salicina	WPGP
× ***sargentii*** 'Thomas'	CDul EPfP MBlu MBri
sartorii	SBir
§ × ***saulii***	CMCN SBir
× ***schochiana***	EPfP MBlu MBri SBir WPat
× ***schuettei***	SBir
semecarpifolia	CMCN MBlu WPat
§ ***serrata*** Thunb.	CDul CMCN EPfP LEdu MBri SBir WPGP
- 'Herkenrode'	MBlu
sessiliflora	see *Q. petraea*
shumardii	CDul CMCN EPfP MBlu NLar SBir SGol
- 'Del Rio'	MBlu
sinuata subsp. ***breviloba***	SBir
stellata	CDul CMCN EPfP SBir
× ***sternbergii***	SBir
suber	CAgr CBcs CDul CFil CMCN CTho EBee ELan EPfP EUJe IArd LEdu MGos MMuc SEND SPer WPGP
- 'Sopron'	CDul EPfP MBlu
§ ***texana***	CMCN EPfP SBir
- 'New Madrid'	CDul EBee EPfP ESwi LLHF LRHS MBlu MBri SAko SBir SPer WCot WHor WMat WPat
tomentella	SBir
trojana	CDul CMCN SBir
tuberculata	WPGP
turbinella	CMCN
× ***turneri***	CDoC CDul CLet CMCN CTho EPfP MBri
- 'Pseudoturneri' ♀H6	CBcs CDul EBee ELan MBlu SGol WMou
undulata Torr.	see *Q.* × *pauciloba*
vacciniifolia	CMCN
variabilis	CMCN EPfP MPkF SGol WPat
velutina	CBcs CDul CJun CMCN CTho EPfP IVic NLar SBir WPat
- 'Albertsii'	CJun MBlu
- 'Habiflax'	SBig
- 'Oakridge Walker'	MBlu
- 'Rubrifolia'	CJun CMCN EPfP
'Vilmoriana'	CMCN IArd
virginiana	CBcs CDul CMCN SBir
× ***warburgii***	EPfP
× ***warei*** 'Chimney Fire'	EPfP MBlu MBri
- Kindred Spirit	see *Q.* × *warei* 'Nadler'
§ - 'Long'	EBee EPfP IArd MBlu MBri MPkF NLar WMat
§ - 'Nadler'	MBri SGol
- Regal Prince	see *Q.* × *warei* 'Long'
- 'Riverbank Lodge' **new**	SBir
- 'Windcandle'	LRHS MBlu MBri SBir
wislizeni	CBcs CDul CMCN NLar SBir
§ ***wutaishanica***	SBir

Quillaja (*Quillajaceae*)

saponaria	CArn CLet IDee SPlb

quince see *Cydonia oblonga*

Quisqualis (*Combretaceae*)

indica	MOWG

R

Racosperma see *Acacia*

Radermachera (*Bignoniaceae*)

sinica ♀H1b	EShb

× *Ramberlea* (*Gesneriaceae*)

'Inchgarth'	WAbe

Ramonda (*Gesneriaceae*)

§ ***myconi*** ♀H5	CLAP ECho EPot EWes LLHF NSla SRms WAbe
- var. ***alba***	CLAP ECho GKev WThu
- 'Jim's Shadow'	WAbe
- 'Rosea'	LLHF
nathaliae ♀H5	CPBP ECho SIgm WAbe WThu
- 'Alba'	CLAP NSla WAbe XEll
pyrenaica	see *R. myconi*
serbica	WThu

Ranunculus (*Ranunculaceae*)

abnormis	WAbe
aconitifolius	CCon EBee ECho EHrv GCra GMaP NLar SHar SWat WFar WHal WMnd WMoo WSHC
- 'Flore Pleno' (d) ♀H7	Widely available
acris	CHab NBir NMir NPer WSFF
- subsp. ***acris*** 'Stevenii'	EPPr LPla SDix WHal
- 'Citrinus'	CElw LLWG LSun MHol WCot WFar WHal WHrl WMoo WPtf
- 'Flore Pleno' (d) ♀H7	Widely available
- 'Hedgehog'	ECho EPPr MMHG
- 'Sulphureus'	CBre WHal
alpestris	ECho GEdr LLHF NSla
amplexicaulis	GMaP NHar NSla
aquatilis	CWat EHon MSKA MWts SWat WHer WMAq WSFF
× ***arendsii*** 'Moonlight'	CElw MMHG
asiaticus	ERCP WAbe
- 'Aviv Red' **new**	LCro LOPS
- 'Aviv Rose' **new**	LCro LOPS
- 'Aviv White' **new**	LCro LOPS
- 'Bloomingdale Pink Shades' (Bloomingdale Series)	SDeJ
§ ***bulbosus*** 'F.M. Burton'	GBuc NRya WCot
- ***farreri***	see *R. bulbosus* 'F.M. Burton'
- 'Speciosus Plenus'	see *R. constantinopolitanus* 'Plenus'
calandrinioides ♀H4	ECho EWes IFoB NBir SBrt WAbe WThu
§ ***constantinopolitanus*** 'Plenus' (d)	EWld GCal MNrw MRav NBid NBro NLar WCot WMoo
cortusifolius	ECre SBrt SWat
crenatus	ECho GEdr
ficaria	see *Ficaria verna*
- anemone-centred	see *Ficaria verna* 'Collarette'
- var. ***aurantiacus***	see *Ficaria verna* Aurantiaca Group
- 'Bowles's Double'	see *Ficaria verna* 'Double Bronze', 'Picton's Double'
- subsp. ***bulbilifer***	see *Ficaria verna* subsp. *verna*
- 'Cupreus'	see *Ficaria verna* Aurantiaca Group
- double, cream-flowered	see *Ficaria verna* 'Double Mud'
- double, yellow-flowered	see *Ficaria verna* Flore Pleno Group
- 'E.A. Bowles'	see *Ficaria verna* 'Collarette'
- 'Holly'	see *Ficaria verna* 'Holly Green'
- subsp. ***major***	see *Ficaria verna* subsp. *chrysocephala*
- 'Wisley Double'	see *Ficaria verna* 'Double Bronze'
flammula	CBen CBod CHab CWat EHon EWay MSKA MWts SWat
- 'Golden Tower' **new**	EBee
- subsp. ***minimus***	EWay
gouanii	NRya
'Gowrie'	GEdr
gramineus ♀H5	CCon CEvo EBee ECho GBin LRHS NRya SRms WCot XEll
- 'Pardal'	WCot
hederaceus	LLWG
illyricus	NRya WHal
kochii	CTal ECho GEdr MNrw NRya WCot
lanuginosus	EPPr
lingua	SPlb WSFF
- 'Grandiflorus'	CBen EHon MSKA NPer SWat WHal WMAq WPnP
millefoliatus	CPBP ECho GBuc WAbe
montanus double-flowered (d)	SHar WCot
- 'Molten Gold' ♀H5	EBee ECho GEdr GMaP MMHG MRav
nivicola	WCot
parnassiifolius	GAbr GEdr LLHF MNrw WAbe WCot
'Pauline Violet'	IFro
platanifolius	EBee LPla LRHS SBrt SMHy
'Purple Heart' (d)	EPfP LCro LOPS
repens 'Buttered Popcorn' (v)	EBee
- 'Cat's Eyes' (v)	EBee
- 'Gloria Spale'	CBre
- var. ***pleniflorus*** (d)	CBre LLWG SRot
- 'Snowdrift' (v)	EBee
- 'Timothy Clark' (d)	CBre
sartorianus silver-leaved **new**	GEdr
seguieri	ECho LHop LLHF LRHS WAbe
speciosus 'Flore Pleno'	see *R. constantinopolitanus* 'Plenus'

Ranzania (*Berberidaceae*)

japonica	GEdr GKev WCru

Raoulia (*Asteraceae*)

australis misapplied	see *R. hookeri*
australis ambig.	GAbr GMaP SMad WTor
australis Hook.f. ex Raoul	EPot GKev ITim LEdu MAsh
§ - Lutescens Group	ECha ECho
haastii	ECou
§ ***hookeri***	CMea CTal ECha ECho EPot EWes MAsh SIgm SPlb SRms WAbe
× ***loganii***	see × *Leucoraoulia loganii*
lutescens	see *R. australis* Lutescens Group
petriensis	WAbe
× ***petrimia*** 'Margaret Pringle'	WAbe
tenuicaulis	ECha EPot SPlb

raspberry see *Rubus idaeus*

Ratibida (*Asteraceae*)

columnifera	ELan EPfP LRHS
- f. ***pulcherrima***	CSpe ELan EPfP LRHS SGSe XLum
- - 'Red Midget'	CBod CSpe EBee LHop LRHS

pinnata	CSam CSpe EPfP LSRN NBir SPhx SPlb WCot WTcb XLum

Ravenala (*Strelitziaceae*)

madagascariensis	SPlb XBlo

Ravenea (*Arecaceae*)

rivularis	XBlo

Rechsteineria see *Sinningia*

redcurrant see *Ribes rubrum* (R)

Reevesia (*Sterculiaceae*)

pubescens	CBcs

Regelia (*Myrtaceae*)

velutina	SPlb

Rehderodendron (*Styracaceae*)

indochinense B&SWJ 12115 new	WCru
- WWJ 11869 new	WCru
kwangtungense WWJ 11940 new	WCru
kweichowense WWJ 12019	WCru
macrocarpum	CBcs CFil WPGP
- B&SWJ 11841 new	WCru
- KWJ 12310 new	WCru
- WWJ 11952 new	WCru

Rehmannia (*Plantaginaceae*)

angulata misapplied	see *R. elata*
§ ***elata*** ♀H2	CCon CMos CSam CSpe CWCL ELan EPfP IDee LAst LBMP LHop LLWP LRHS LSun MMuc MNHC SDys SGSe SRms WFar XLum
glutinosa ♀H2	CSpe
piasezkii	WPGP

Reineckea (*Asparagaceae*)

§ ***carnea***	CCon CExl CHid CHll ECha ECho ELan EPPr GBin GCal GEdr GKev IMou LEdu MMuc MPie NSti SDys SEND SGSe SPlb WCot WCru WPGP XLum
- B&SWJ 4808	ELon WCru
- SDR 330	EPPr GKev
- 'Baoxing Booty'	IMou WCru
- 'Variegata' (v)	EShb WCot
aff. ***carnea*** from Sichuan	WCot
incurva 'Crûg's Linearleaf'	WCru
yunnanensis	see *R.carnea*

Reinwardtia (*Linaceae*)

§ ***indica***	CExl CHll
trigyna	see *R. indica*

Remusatia (*Araceae*)

hookeriana	GBin LRHS
- B&SWJ 2529	WCru
pumila	LRHS
vivipara	LRHS

Reseda (*Resedaceae*)

alba	MHer
lutea	CWld SIde SRms
luteola	CBod CHab CHby GPoy MHer MNHC WHer WHfH WSFF

Restio (*Restionaceae*)

festuciformis	CTre
paniculatus	CDTJ CTre
similis	CTre
subverticillatus	CTre
tetraphyllus	CTre EBee ESwi SPlb SPoG

Retama (*Papilionaceae*)

§ ***monosperma***	SBrt

Reynoutria see *Fallopia*

Rhamnus (*Rhamnaceae*)

alaternus	XSen
§ - 'Argenteovariegata' (v) ♀H5	Widely available
- 'Variegata'	see *R. alaternus* 'Argenteovariegata'
cathartica	CCVT CDul CHab CLnd CTri ECrN EShb LBuc NLar NWea SEWo WMou WSFF
davurica B&SWJ 12609	WCru
frangula	see *Frangula alnus*
imeretina	EBee WCot WPGP WPat
ludovici-salvatoris	SBrt
lycioides subsp. ***oleoides***	XSen
pallasii	NLar
taquetii	NLar

Rhaphidophora (*Araceae*)

decursiva	XBlo

× *Rhaphiobotrya* (*Rosaceae*)

§ 'Coppertone'	LPal SEND WPGP

Rhaphiolepis (*Rosaceae*)

× ***delacourii***	CWib ECrN ELan EPfP LAst SEND SRms
- 'Coates' Crimson'	CBcs CTsd EBee ELan EPfP IVic LHop LRHS MAsh MGil WPat WSHC
- Enchantress = 'Moness'	CTsd ELan EPfP LRHS MAsh MRav SLon
- 'Pink Cloud'	EPfP LRHS
- 'Spring Song'	SLon
indica	SEND
- B&SWJ 8405	WCru
- 'Coppertone'	see × *Rhaphiobotrya* 'Coppertone'
- Springtime = 'Monme'	CBcs EPfP IVic LCro LOPS LRHS
integerrima new	CMCN
umbellata	CBcs CTri CWib EBee ELan EPfP LAst LHop LRHS MAsh MGil MRav SEND SEle SHil SLon SVen WPGP WPat WSHC
- f. ***ovata*** B&SWJ 4706	WCru

Rhaphithamnus (*Verbenaceae*)

cyanocarpus	see *R. spinosus*
§ ***spinosus***	CBcs EBee EPfP LEdu LRHS MGil

Rhapidophyllum (*Arecaceae*)

hystrix	CBrP LPal

Rhapis ✿ (*Arecaceae*)

§ ***excelsa*** ♀H1b	LPal WCot XBlo
humilis	LPal
multifida	LPal

Rhazya (*Apocynaceae*)

orientalis	see *Amsonia orientalis*

Rheum ✿ (*Polygonaceae*)

	Chen Yi	WCot
	GWJ 9329 from Sikkim	WCru
§	'Ace of Hearts' ♀H6	Widely available
	'Ace of Spades'	see *R.* 'Ace of Hearts'
	acuminatum	CSpe
	- HWJCM 252	WCru
	- HWJK 2354	WCru
	- PAB 2487	LEdu WPGP
	alexandrae	CBct CCon ESwi EWes GBin GCal GEdr GKev LEdu MMHG MMuc MNrw NLar SPlb WFar
	- SDR 1830	GKev
	- SDR 2924	EBee
	- SDR 6031	GKev
	altaicum PAB 1055	LEdu
§	***australe***	CAgr CArn CCon EBee GCal LRHS NBro NLar WBor WCot WFar
	- 'Pink Marble' (v)	WCot
	'Cally Dwarf'	GCal
	'Cally Giant'	EBee EWes GCal
	× ***cultorum***	see *R.* × *hybridum*
	delavayi	GCal NLar
	- BWJ 7592	WCru
	emodi	see *R. australe*
	'Great Bere' **new**	LEdu
*	***henryi***	EBee
§	× ***hybridum***	SEND
	- 'Brandy Carr Scarlet'	MRav
	- 'Canada Red'	GTwe
	- 'Cawood Delight'	GTwe
	- 'Champagne'	CAgr EPfP EPom GTwe LBuc LCro LEdu LOPS LRHS NPri SBmr SCob SKee SPer WMat
	- 'Fenton's Special'	CTri GTwe LEdu MCoo MRav
	- 'Fulton's Strawberry Surprise' ♀H4	GTwe
	- 'Glaskin's Perpetual'	CAgr CLet CWib EPfP LBuc LRHS NPri SBmr WHar
	- 'Goliath'	MCoo
	- 'Grandad's Favorite' ♀H4	LRHS
	- 'Hawke's Champagne' ♀H4	GTwe WCot
	- 'Holsteiner Blut'	NLar SCob SPoG
	- 'Livingstone'PBR	EPom LCro LOPS LRHS
	- 'Mac Red' ♀H4	GTwe
	- 'Pink Champagne'	EPfP GQue
	- 'Prince Albert'	GTwe
	- 'Raspberry Red' ♀H4	CSut EPfP EPom LBuc LCro LRHS NPri
	- 'Red Champagne'	ELan EPfP LBuc SCob
	- 'Red Prolific'	GTwe
	- 'Reed's Early Superb' ♀H4	GTwe
	- 'Stein's Champagne' ♀H4	GTwe
	- 'Stockbridge Arrow'	CArg CMac CSut CTri EMil GTwe SFrt
	- 'Stockbridge Guardsman'	GTwe
	- 'Strawberry'	GTwe LCro LOPS NBir
	- 'Sutton's Cherry Red'	GTwe
	- 'The Sutton'	CWib EPfP GTwe
	- 'Thompson's Terrifically Tasty' **new**	SBmr
	- 'Timperley Early' ♀H4	Widely available
	- 'Timperley Early 1' **new**	MJak
	- 'Timperley Early 2' **new**	MJak
	- 'Timperley Early 30' **new**	MJak
	- 'Tingley Cherry'	GTwe
	- 'Victoria'	Widely available
	- 'Victoria 1' **new**	MJak
	- 'Victoria 2'	LAst MJak
	- 'Victoria 9' **new**	MJak
	- 'Zwolle Seedling'	GTwe
	kialense	CBct EBee LEdu NBid NSti WPGP WWEG
	nobile	EPot GEdr GKev
	officinale	CBct CCon GCal SIde SWat
	palmatum	CArn CBcs CLet EBee ECha ELan EPfP GCra LCro LRHS MGos MRav NGdn SCob SDix SHar SWat
	- 'Atropurpureum'	see *R. palmatum* 'Atrosanguineum'
	- 'Atropurpureum Dissectum'	IBoy
§	- 'Atrosanguineum'	CBct CBod CCon CMac ECha ELan EPfP EShb EUJe EWoo GCal IFro LRHS MBel MGos MMuc MRav NBid NBro NEgg NWad SEND SPer SPlb SPoG SPtp SWat WCru WFar WMnd
	- 'Bowles's Crimson' ♀H7	CBct MGos MRav NBid WCot
	- 'Ferguson's Red' **new**	WCot
	- 'Hadspen Crimson' ♀H7	CAby CBct ECtt MNrw WCot
	- 'Red Herald'	CBct WCot WWEG
	- 'Rubrum'	CBct LRHS NBir
	- 'Savill'	MRav WWEG
	- var. ***tanguticum***	Widely available
	rhaponticum	NLar
	ribes	WCot WCru
	spiciforme	CFil WPGP
	tanguticum	COtt
	tataricum	EBee LEdu WPGP

Rhexia (*Melastomataceae*)

	virginica **new**	SBrt

Rhinanthus (*Orobanchaceae*)

	minor	CHab CWld LCro

Rhodanthemum (*Asteraceae*)

	'African Eyes'	ECho ELan EPfP EWoo LRHS MBrN MBri MGos MHol NPri SPoG SRot SVen
	Agadir	see *R.* Moondance
§	***atlanticum***	ECho EWes
	'Casablanca' (Atlas Daisy Series)	LRHS WHil
§	***catananche***	CPBP ECho EPot EWes MBNS SRot WAbe
§	- 'Tizi-n-Test'	ECho
	- 'Tizi-n-Tichka'	ECho EPot EWes LHop LRHS
§	***gayanum***	EWes
	- 'Flamingo'	see *R. gayanum*
	- 'Pretty in Pink'	LAst
§	***hosmariense*** ♀H4	ECha ECho ELan EPfP EPot GCrg GMaP LHop LRHS MCot MHol SCoo SEND SPer SRms SRot WAbe WHoo WIce
	'Marrakech' (Atlas Daisy Series) **new**	WBod WHil
§	Moondance = 'Usrhod0701'	EPfP LRHS
	Tangier (Atlas Daisy Series)	EPfP LRHS

Rhodiola (*Crassulaceae*)

	SSSE 10	NWad
	crassipes	see *R. wallichiana*
	cretinii HWJK 2283	WCru
§	***fastigiata***	CSpe GCal WCot WThu
	- BWJ 7544	SKHP WCru
§	***heterodonta***	ELan MRav WCot
	himalensis misapplied	see *R.* 'Keston'

	himalensis (D. Don) Fu	CTri GKev
	integrifolia subsp. ***integrifolia***	EDAr
§	***ishidae***	CTri
§	'Keston'	CTri
§	***kirilovii***	LRHS
	- var. ***rubra***	EPfP LRHS
§	***pachyclados***	CTal ECho ECtt EUJe GBin GCrg GJos GKev GMaP LRHS MHer MMuc NBir NPri NRya NWad SEND SPlb SRot SWvt XLum
	aff. ***purpureoviridis***	WFar
	rhodantha	NLar
§	***rosea***	Widely available
	semenovii	NLar
	sinuata HWJK 2318	WCru
	- HWJK 2326	WCru
§	***trollii***	ECho EPot LHop LRHS SPlb
§	***wallichiana***	MLHP NBid
	- GWJ 9263	WCru
	- HWJK 2352	WCru
§	***yunnanensis*** BWJ 7941	WCru

Rhodochiton (*Plantaginaceae*)

§	***atrosanguineus*** ♀H2	CBcs CSpe CWCL ELan EPfP GBee LBuc MPie NPri SLon SPer WFar WHea
	volubilis	see *R. atrosanguineus*

Rhodocoma (*Restionaceae*)

capensis	CAbb CBod CCon CTre CTsd NLos
gigantea	CCon CTre LRHS SPlb

Rhododendron ✿ (*Ericaceae*)

	sp.	GKin LPar MGos SEWo
	'A.J. Ivens'	see *R.* 'Arthur J. Ivens'
	aberconwayi	LMil WBod
	- 'His Lordship'	GGGa LMil MSnd
	acrophilum (V)	GGGa
	'Addy Wery' (EA)	CDoC GKin SPer
	adenogynum	GGGa LMil MSnd
	adenopodum	GGGa MSnd
	adenosum	GGGa
	'Admiral Piet Hein'	SReu SSta
	'Adonis' (EA/d) ♀H5	CBcs CMac LMil SLdr
	'Advance' (EA)	SLdr
	aeruginosum	see *R. campanulatum* subsp. *aeruginosum*
	aganniphum	MSnd
	- var. ***flavorufum***	MSnd
	- 'Rusty'	MSnd
	'Aksel Olsen'	CTri GEdr
	'Aladdin' (*auriculatum* hybrid)	GGGa SSta
	'Aladdin' (EA)	SLdr
	Aladdin Group	LPar SReu
	Albatross Group	SReu
	- 'Albatross'	SSta
	- 'Albatross Townhill Pink'	LMil
	'Albert Schweitzer' ♀H5	CDoC CDul COtt CWri LMil MGos NLar SLdr SLim
	albertsenianum	MSnd
	albrechtii (A)	CBcs CPne GGGa IVic LMil SLdr
	- Whitney form (A)	LMil WMoo
	'Alexander' (EA) ♀H4	IVic LMil LSRN SAko SLdr
	'Alice' (hybrid) ♀H5	CMac LMil SLdr
	Alison Johnstone Group	CBcs SLdr SReu
	- 'Alison Johnstone'	GGGa WThu
	'All Gold'	GGGa
	Alpine Gem Group	GQui
	- 'Alpine Gem'	IVic
	'Altaclerense'	LMil
§	***alutaceum*** var. ***alutaceum*** Globigerum Group	GGGa
§	- var. ***iodes***	MSnd
§	- var. ***russotinctum***	MSnd
	- - R 158	SLdr
§	- - Triplonaevium Group	GGGa
	amagianum (A)	LMil
	'Amaretto' **new**	IVic SAko
	ambiguum	LMil MSnd
	- 'Golden Summit'	GGGa
	- 'Jane Banks'	LMil
	'Ambrosia' (EA)	CSBt
	'America'	SCob
	'Amethyst' (EA)	GGal
	'Amity'	CWri LMil MMuc MSnd SLdr WGwG
	Amor Group	SLdr
	'Anah Kruschke'	LCro MAsh SPoG
	'Analin'	see *R.* 'Anuschka'
	'Anatta Gold' (V)	GGGa
	'Anchorite' (EA)	SLdr
	Angelo Group	CWri LMil SReu
	- 'Angelo'	LMil SLdr SSta
	'Ann Lindsay'	SLdr WMoo
	'Anna Baldsiefen'	GKin SLim SPoG
	'Anna Rose Whitney'	CBcs CTri CWri EPfP LPar LRHS MAsh MBri MJak SLim
	'Annabella' (K)	SReu SSta
	annae	GGGa LMil
	'Anne Frank' (EA)	CWSG WBod
	'Anne Teese'	GGGa
	'Annegret Hansmann'	GGGa
	'Anneke' (A)	CDoC LMil MGos MMuc MPkF NHol NLar SReu SSta WMoo
	anthopogon	LMil
	- 'Betty Graham'	GGGa
	- subsp. ***hypenanthum*** 'Annapurna'	GGGa ITim WAbe
	anthosphaerum	GGGa
	'Antilope' (Vs) ♀H6	CBcs CWri LMil MLea MMuc SReu SSta
	(Antonio Group) 'Antonio'	LMil
§	'Anuschka'	LMil MAsh MBri
	anwheiense	GGGa
	aperantum	GGGa
	apodectum	see *R. dichroanthum* subsp. *apodectum*
	'Apotrophia'	SLdr
	'Apple Blossom' ambig.	CMac GKin
	'Appleblossom' (EA)	see *R.* 'Ho-o'
	'Apricot Blaze' (A)	SReu SSta
	'Apricot Fantasy'	LMil
	'Apricot Surprise'	CTri MAsh MBri
	'April Chimes'	WThu
	'April Gem'	SAko
	'April Rose'	SAko
	'April Showers' (A)	LMil
	'Aprilmorgen' **new**	SAko
	'Aquamarin'	IVic
	'Arabesk' (EA)	CDoC GKin LMil MAsh MGos
	arborescens (A) ♀H6	CTsd GGGa LMil MSnd
	arboreum	GGGa IDee LMil MSnd NLar SLdr SReu
	- B&SWJ 2244	WCru
	- subsp. ***arboreum***	MSnd
	- subsp. ***cinnamomeum*** ♀H4	GGGa LMil MSnd SLdr
	- - var. ***album***	GGGa MSnd SReu

	- - 'Everest Reunion'	LMil
	- - var. ***roseum***	GGGa
	- - - 'Tony Schilling'	GKin IDee LMil LRHS SReu SSta
	- subsp. ***delavayi***	GGGa LMil MSnd SLdr
	- 'Heligan'	SReu
§	- subsp. ***zeylanicum***	GGGa
	- - 'Rubaiyat'	LMil
	'Arctic Fox' (EA)	GGGa
	'Arctic Regent' (K)	GQui
	'Arctic Tern' ♀H5	CDoC CSBt CTri GQui LMil MGos MLea SPer WBod WThu
	'Ardeur' (EA)	MGos
§	***argipeplum***	GGGa MSnd
	(Argosy Group) 'Argosy'	LMil SReu
	argyrophyllum	MSnd SLdr
	- subsp. ***argyrophyllum***	GGGa SLdr
§	- subsp. ***hypoglaucum***	GGGa MSnd
	- subsp. ***nankingense***	GGGa
	- - 'Chinese Silver' ♀H6	GGGa IDee LMil MSnd SLdr SReu
	'Arima' (K)	GGGa
	arizelum	GCal GGGa LMil MSnd
	- subsp. ***arizelum*** Rubicosum Group	GGGa LMil
	'Arkona'	IVic SAko
	armitii (V)	GGGa
	'Arneson Gem' (A) ♀H6	CBcs CDoC GGGa LMil MBri MGos MMuc NLar SLdr
	'Arneson Ruby' (K)	GGGa
§	(Aronense Group) 'Fumiko' (EA)	CDoC CSBt CTsd LCro LMil MGos MLea SHil SLdr WFar
§	- 'Hanako' (EA)	MLea
§	- 'Kazuko' (EA)	CDoC LCro LPfy MGos SHil
§	- 'Satschiko' (EA) ♀H5	CBcs CDoC CSBt CTsd CWSG GGGa LPfy LRHS MGos MJak MMuc NPri SHil
	'Arpège' (Vs)	LMil NLar SLdr SReu
	'Arthur Bedford'	CSBt SReu
§	'Arthur J. Ivens'	SLdr
	'Arthur Osborn'	SSpi
	'Arthur Stevens'	MSnd SLdr
	'Asa-gasumi' (Kurume) (EA)	SLdr
	asterochnoum	GGGa MSnd
	'Astrid'	IVic LSRN SAko
	atlanticum (A)	GGGa LMil
	- 'Seaboard' (A)	LMil
	augustinii	CBcs CWri GGGa GGal LMil MLea MSnd NLar SLdr SSpi SSta WBod
	- 'Carolles' **new**	LRHS
§	- subsp. ***chasmanthum***	GGGa
	- compact EGM 293	LMil
	- Electra Group	LMil SLdr
§	- - 'Electra' ♀H3	GGGa
	- Exbury form	GGGa LMil SReu
§	- subsp. ***hardyi***	GGGa
*	- 'Trewithen'	GGGa LMil
I	- 'Werrington'	CExl SLdr SReu
	aureum	GGGa WThu
	auriculatum	GGGa LMil MSnd SLdr SSta
	- Reuthe's form	SReu
	auriculatum* × *hemsleyanum	GGGa
	auritum	SLdr
	'Aurora' (K)	SLdr
	austrinum (A)	LMil NLar
	- yellow-flowered (A)	LMil
	Autumn Magic	see *R.* 'Herbstzauber'
	(Avalanche Group) 'Avalanche'	LMil
	Avocet Group	LMil
	'Award'	LMil

	Azrie Group	SLdr
§	'Azuma-kagami' (Kurume) (EA)	LMil LSRN MPkF SLdr
	'Azurika'	IVic
	'Azurro'	LMil SLdr
	'Babuschka'	LMil
	'Baden-Baden' ♀H5	CMac CTri GEdr GKin LMil MAsh NEgg SLdr WBod
	baileyi	MSnd
*	'Baker's Lavender' (EA)	SLdr
	balangense	GGGa
	balfourianum	GGGa
	'Balzac' (K)	GKin LMil MAsh NEgg
	'Bandoola'	SReu
	'Barbara Coats' (EA)	SLdr
	'Barbara Reuthe'	SSta
	'Barbarella'	IVic
	barbatum	GGGa LMil MSnd
	'Barbecue' (K)	LMil
	'Bariton'	GGGa
	'Barmstedt'	CWri MAsh WMoo
	'Barnaby Sunset'	GGGa IDee LMil LRHS MAsh MBri
	'Bashful' ♀H5	CBcs CSBt MJak
§	***basilicum***	GGGa LMil
	- AC 616	MSnd
	'Bastion'	LMil
	× ***bathyphyllum***	GGGa
	bauhiniiflorum	see *R. triflorum* var. *bauhiniiflorum*
	beanianum	GGGa
	- APA 60	GGGa
	- KC 0122	GGGa
	- compact	see *R. piercei*
	'Beatrice Keir'	LMil MSnd SReu SSta
	'Beattie' (EA)	SLdr
	(Beau Brummell Group) 'Beau Brummell'	LMil
	'Beaulieu Manor'	GQui
	'Beauty of Littleworth'	CBcs
	beesianum	GGGa
	- AC 1528	MSnd
	'Beethoven' (Vuykiana) (EA)	SLdr
	Belami = 'Hachbela'	IDee LMil NLar SAko
	'Belkanto'	GKin MJak MMuc
	'Bellini'	LMil LRHS NLar
	'Ben Cruachan' (K)	GGGa
	'Ben Lawers' (K)	GGGa
	'Ben Lomond' (K)	GGGa
	'Ben Morrison' (EA)	LMil
	'Ben Vorlich' (K)	GGGa
	'Ben Vrackie' (K)	GGGa
	'Bengal'	GEdr LRHS LSRN MAsh MGos NLar SCob SLdr SLim
	'Bengal Beauty' (EA)	SLdr
	'Bengal Fire' (EA)	CMac SLdr
	benhallii 'Honshu Blue'	GGGa
	- 'Plum Drops'	GGGa
	- 'Slieve Donard'	CMac
	- 'Ylva'	GGGa
	'Beni-giri' (Kurume) (EA)	CMac MGos
	'Bergensiana'	SReu SSta
	'Bergie Larson' ♀H4	CBcs IVic LMil MLea MMuc SLdr
	'Berg's 10'	MLea
	'Berg's Yellow'	CWri MMuc
	'Bernard Shaw'	SSta
	'Bernstein'	LMil MAsh MJak
	'Berryrose' (K) ♀H6	CBcs CDoC CMac CSBt CTri EPfP GKin LMil LRHS MAsh MBri MGos MJak MSnd NLar SLdr SPer SReu SSta WFar

	'Beryl Taylor'	GGGa
	'Betty Anne Voss' (EA)	LCro LMil LSRN MAsh MBri SCoo SLdr
	'Betty Wormald'	CMac CWri MLea SLdr SPer
	bhutanense	GGGa
	Bibiani Group	LMil
	'Bijou de Ledeberg' (Indian) (EA/v)	CMac
	'Billy Budd'	SLdr
	'Birthday Girl'	CBcs LMil LSRN MAsh MLea
	(Biskra Group) 'Biskra'	GGGa LMil
	'Blaauw's Pink' (Kurume) (EA) ♀H4	CDoC CMac CSBt EPfP GKin GQui LCro LMil MBri MMuc MPkF SGol SLdr SPer SPlb SPoG SReu WBod
	'Black Knight' (EA)	SLdr
	'Black Magic'	CDoC GKin LMil
	'Black Sport'	MLea
	'Black Widow'	SSta
	'Blattgold' (v)	LMil
	Blaue Donau	see *R.* 'Blue Danube'
	'Blaue Jungs'	GGGa
	'Blewbury' ♀H5	LMil SReu
	'Blue Boy'	LMil
	'Blue Chip'	SLdr
§	'Blue Danube' (EA) ♀H3	CBcs CDoC CMac CSBt CTri CWSG EPfP GGGa GKin IVic LCro LMil LRHS MAsh MBri MGos MJak NEgg NLar NPri SGol SHil SLdr SLim SPer SPoG SReu SSta
	Blue Diamond Group	CBcs ECho EPfP GEdr SReu
	- 'Blue Diamond'	CMac CSBt ECho LRHS LSRN MAsh MJak SLdr WGwG
	'Blue Jay'	MMuc
	'Blue Monday' (EA)	SLdr WBod
	'Blue Peter' ♀H5	CBcs CSBt CWri LMil LRHS MAsh MLea MMuc NHol NLar SPer SReu SSta WMoo
	'Blue Pool'	LMil
	Blue Ribbon Group	SLdr
	'Blue Silver'	GGGa IVic LMil MAsh MBri
	'Blue Steel'	see *R. fastigiatum* 'Blue Steel'
	Blue Tit Group	CBcs CDoC CDul EPfP GGGa LRHS MAsh MGos NLar SCob SLdr SLim SPer SReu SSta
	Bluebird Group	CMac CSBt SLdr
	'Blueshine Girl'	SLdr
	'Blurettia'	CWri MMuc
	'Blutopia'	LMil
	Bohlken's Juditha	GGGa LMil
	Bohlken's Kronjewel	GGGa
	Bohlken's Laura	GGGa LMil
	Bohlken's Lupinenberg	GGGa LMil
	Bohlken's Lupinenberg Laguna **new**	LMil
	Bohlken's Snow Fire	GGGa LMil
	(Bonito Group) 'Bonito'	LMil
	boothii	GGGa
	- HECC 10077	GGGa
	Bo-peep Group	CBcs
	- 'Bo-peep'	GQui LMil SLdr
	'Boskoop Ostara'	LMil
	'Boule de Neige'	MAsh MGos NLar SPer
	'Bouquet de Flore' (G) ♀H6	LMil
	Bow Bells Group	CDoC MLea
	- 'Bow Bells' ♀H4	ECho EPfP GEdr LMil LRHS MAsh MBri MGos NHol NLar SLdr WBod
	'Bowjingles'	GGGa
	brachyanthum subsp. ***hypolepidotum***	GGGa
	brachycarpum 'Roseum Dwarf'	GGGa
	'Brambling'	GGGa
	'Brazier' (EA)	SLdr
	'Bremen'	LMil
	'Briane' (EA)	GGGa
	Bric-à-brac Group	CBcs
	- 'Bric-à-brac'	SLdr
	'Bright Forecast' (K)	CWri IVic MLea
	'Brigitte'	CWri IVic LSRN MAsh
	'Brilliant' (EA)	MGos SHil
	'Brilliant Blue' (EA)	MAsh
	'Britannia'	COtt CSBt CWri MJak NHol SReu SSta
	(Brocade Group) 'Brocade'	SLdr
	'Bronze Fire' (A)	NHol SLdr SReu SSta
	'Brown Eyes'	GKin MMuc
	'Bruce Brechtbill'	CWri GGGa GKin MAsh MBri MMuc
	'Bruce Hancock' (Ad)	SLdr
§	'Bruns Gloria'	LMil
	'Bruns Schneewitchen'	LMil SReu SSta
	'Buccaneer' (Glenn Dale) (EA)	SLdr
	'Bud Flanagan'	MMuc
	bullatum	see *R. edgeworthii*
	'Bungo-nishiki' (Wada) (EA/d)	CMac WThu
	bureavii ♀H5	GGGa IDee LMil MSnd SReu SSta
	bureavii × ***yakushimanum***	SReu
	bureavioides	LMil MSnd
	'Burletta'	IVic
	burmanicum	CBcs CPne GGGa GGal
	Bustard Group	LMil
	'Busuki'	GGGa LMil
	'Butter Brickle'	LMil MLea SLdr
	'Buttermint'	SLdr
	'Caerhays Lavender' (EA)	CBcs
	calendulaceum (A)	GGGa LMil
	- red-flowered (A)	LMil
	- yellow-flowered (A)	LMil
	Calfort Group	SLdr
	- 'Calfort'	GGGa
	callimorphum	GGGa
	- var. ***myiagrum***	MSnd
	calophytum ♀H5	CPne GGGa LMil LRHS MSnd SLdr
	calostrotum	WAbe
	- subsp. ***calostrotum*** KR 9983	MSnd
	- 'Gigha' ♀H4	GGGa IDee LMil MAsh WAbe
§	- subsp. ***keleticum*** ♀H4	GCal GEdr GGGa ITim MGos NLar NSla
	- - R 58	GGGa LMil
§	- - Radicans Group	GEdr GGGa IVic MLea NSla WAbe WThu
	- - - USDAPI 59182/R11188	MLea
	- - - mound form	ITim
	- subsp. ***riparium***	ITim
§	- - Nitens Group	GGGa MMuc WAbe WThu
	caloxanthum	see *R. campylocarpum* subsp. *caloxanthum*
	'Calsap'	GGGa LMil
	Calstocker Group	LMil
	camelliiflorum	GGGa
	campanulatum	GGGa IDee LMil MSnd SReu WAbe
	- HWJCM 195	WCru
	- HWJCM 409 **new**	WCru
§	- subsp. ***aeruginosum***	GGGa LMil MSnd
	'Campfire' J.B. Gable (EA)	SLdr

	campylocarpum	GGGa LMil MSnd
§	- subsp. ***caloxanthum***	GGGa
§	- - Telopeum Group	MSnd
	campylogynum	GGGa LMil WAbe
	- SBEC 0519	GGGa
	- 'Album'	see *R.* 'Leucanthum'
	- black-flowered	IVic
	- Charopoeum Group	WThu
	- - 'Patricia'	ECho GEdr NLar NSla
	- (Cremastum Group) 'Bodnant Red'	GGGa WThu
	- Myrtilloides Group ♀H4	ECho GGGa GQui LMil MSnd WAbe WThu
	- plum-flowered	WAbe
	- salmon-pink-flowered	ECho WAbe
	camtschaticum	GGGa LMil WThu
	- red-flowered	GGGa
	canadense (A)	GGGa
	- f. ***albiflorum*** (A)	GGGa LMil
	- dark-flowered (A)	LMil
	'Candy Striped Pink'	IVic SAko
§	***canescens*** (A)	LMil
	'Cannon's Double' (K/d) ♀H6	CBcs CDoC CWri GKin LMil MBri MGos MLea MMuc NLar SLdr SPer WMoo
	'Canzonetta' (EA/d) ♀H5	EPfP GGGa LMil LRHS MAsh MBri SAko SLdr
	'Capriccio'	LMil
	'Captain Jack'	GGGa
	'Caractacus'	SCob
	'Carat' (A)	NLar
	cardiobasis	see *R. orbiculare* subsp. *cardiobasis*
	(Carita Group) 'Carita Charm'	LMil
	- 'Golden Dream'	LMil
	(Carmen Group) 'Carmen' ♀H5	ECho ELon GEdr GGGa GKev GKin IDee LMil MAsh MLea MMuc SLdr
	carneum	GGGa
	'Carolina Spring' (v)	LMil
	'Caroline Allbrook'	CWri GGGa MAsh MLea NLar SLdr
	'Caruso'	IVic SPoG
	'Cary Ann'	CTri LRHS MAsh MBri SReu
	'Casablanca' (EA)	SLdr
	'Cassata'	LMil
	'Cassley' (Vs)	LMil
	catacosmum	GGGa
	catawbiense	GKev SLdr
	'Catawbiense Album'	CTri MAsh
	'Catawbiense Boursault'	SLdr
	'Catawbiense Grandiflorum'	MAsh MGos
	'Catharine van Tol'	LMil
	caucasicum	GGGa
	'Caucasicum Pictum'	LMil SLdr
	'Cayenne' (EA)	SLdr
	'Cecile' (K) ♀H6	CBcs CDoC CMac CTri CWri GBin GKin LMil LSRN MBri MMuc SLdr SPer SReu
	'Celestial' (EA)	CMac
	'Centennial Gold'PBR	COtt
	cephalanthum	GGGa LMil
	- subsp. ***cephalanthum*** SBEC 0751	WThu
	- - Crebreflorum Group	GGGa LMil WAbe WThu
	- - Nmaiense Group	GGGa
	- subsp. ***platyphyllum***	GGGa
	- - AC 1926	MSnd
	cerasinum	LMil MSnd
	- 'Cherry Brandy'	GGGa MSnd
	- 'Coals of Fire'	GGGa MSnd
	'Cetewayo'	CWri GGGa
	chaetomallum	see *R. haematodes* subsp. *chaetomallum*
	chamaethomsonii	GGGa
	- var. ***chamaethomsonii***	MSnd
	- - Rock form	GGGa
	championae	GGGa
	'Chanel' (Vs)	GGGa SReu SSta
	changii	GGGa
	'Chanticleer' (Glenn Dale) (EA)	SLdr
	chapaense	see *R. maddenii* subsp. *crassum*
	'Chariots of Fire' (EA)	LMil
	charitopes	GCal LMil
	- F 25570	GGGa LMil
	- subsp. ***charitopes***	MSnd
§	- subsp. ***tsangpoense***	GGGa GQui
*	'Charlotte de Rothschild' (A)	SLdr
	'Charlotte Megan' (A)	LMil
	Charmaine Group	WBod
	'Charme La'	GGGa
	chasmanthum	see *R. augustinii* subsp. *chasmanthum*
	'Cheer'	CWri MAsh MMuc NEgg SLim
	'Chelsea Seventy'	MSnd SLdr
	'Chenille' (K/d)	SLdr
	'Cherokee' (EA)	SLdr
	'Cherries and Cream'	LMil
	'Cherry Cheesecake'	MGos NLar
	'Cherry Drops' (EA)	EPfP LRHS MAsh
	Cherry Kiss = 'Hachcher'PBR	GGGa LMil SAko
	'Chetco' (A)	LMil
	'Chevalier Félix de Sauvage'	LMil SReu
	'Chikor'	CBcs ECho GBin GGGa GKin MAsh MBri MGos MMuc NLar WThu
	'Chinchilla' (EA)	GQui
	'Chink'	MSnd WBod
	'Chionoides'	SLdr
	'Chipmunk' (EA/d)	GGGa LRHS MAsh MBri
	'Chippewa' (Indian) (EA)	CTri IVic LMil
	'Chocolate Ice' (K/d)	SLdr
	(Choremia Group) 'Choremia' ♀H3	LMil
	christi (V)	GGGa
	'Christina' (Vuykiana) (EA/d)	MMuc SLdr
	'Christmas Cheer' (*caucasicum* hybrid) ♀H5	CBcs CDoC CSBt CWri GBin GGGa GGal GKin LMil LPar MAsh MGos MLea NLar SCob SLdr SReu
	'Christmas Cheer' (EA/d)	see *R.* 'Ima-shojo'
	chrysodoron	MSnd
	ciliatum	CBcs GGGa SLdr
	ciliicalyx	CBcs
	Cilpinense Group	CBcs GGGa SPer
	- 'Cilpinense' ♀H3	CMac CSBt CWri ECho EPfP LMil LRHS MAsh MMuc NPri SLdr WBod
	cinnabarinum	LMil MSnd SLdr
	- SDR 3914 **new**	GKev
	- subsp. ***cinnabarinum*** BL&M 234	LMil
	- - Blandfordiiflorum Group	GGGa MSnd SLdr
	- - 'Nepal'	LMil
	- - Roylei Group	GGGa LMil
	- - - 'Vin Rosé'	LMil
	- Cinzan Group	LMil
§	- (Conroy Group) 'Conroy'	LMil
§	- subsp. ***tamaense*** KW 21003	MSnd

§	- subsp. ***xanthocodon***	GGGa LMil MSnd
§	- - Concatenans Group	GGGa LMil MSnd SLdr
	- - - KW 5874	LMil
	- - Purpurellum Group	GGGa MSnd
	'Cinzia' (K)	GGGa
	circinnatum	GGGa
	citriniflorum	LMil
	- R 108	LMil
	- var. ***citriniflorum***	LMil MSnd
	- var. ***horaeum***	GGGa MSnd
	'Claudine'	IVic
	clementinae	GGGa MSnd
	- F 25705	LMil
	- subsp. ***aureodorsale***	GKev
	'Cliff Garland'	GQui LMil WBod
	'Coccineum Speciosum' (G) 🏆H6	CDoC CMac CSBt GKin LMil SReu SSta
	coeloneurum	GGGa LMil
	- EGM 334	LMil
	- NN 0926	MSnd
	collettianum	GGGa
	'Colonel Coen'	CWri GBin GKin LMil MMuc
	Colonel Rogers Group	SLdr SReu
	'Colyer' (EA)	SLdr
	Comely Group	SLdr
	comisteum C 6541	GGGa
	concatenans	see *R. cinnabarinum* subsp. *xanthocodon* Concatenans Group
	concinnoides	GGGa
	concinnum	GGGa
	- Pseudoyanthinum Group 🏆H5	GGGa GQui MSnd
	'Connie' (Kaempferi) (EA)	SReu SSta
	'Conroy'	see *R. cinnabarinum* 'Conroy'
	'Contina'	LMil
	'Conversation Piece' (EA)	SLdr
	'Cool Haven'	IDee LMil NLar
	'Coral Sea' (EA)	SReu
	'Coral Seas' (V)	GGGa
	'Corany' (A)	LMil MGos NLar SLdr
	coriaceum	GGGa LMil MSnd
	'Corneille' (G/d)	CSBt LMil MPkF SReu
	'Coronation Day'	LMil
	coryanum 'Chelsea Chimes'	MSnd
	'Cosmopolitan'	CDul COtt LMil MGos MMuc SPoG WMoo
	'Cotton Candy'	LMil
	'Countess of Haddington'	CBcs IDee LMil SLdr
	Cowslip Group	CTri LMil MAsh MGos MLea
	- 'Cowslip' 🏆H4	CDoC LRHS
	coxianum	GGGa
	'Crane' 🏆H5	EPfP GGGa GQui IVic LMil LRHS MAsh MBri SLdr
	crassum	see *R. maddenii* subsp. *crassum*
	'Cream Crest'	GKin GQui LMil MGos NLar SLim WMoo
	'Creamy Chiffon'	CWri MLea WGwG
	crenulatum	GGGa
	'Crete'	LMil
	crinigerum	CPne GGGa LMil
	- var. ***crinigerum***	MSnd
	- var. ***euadenium***	MSnd
	'Crinoline' (EA)	SLdr
	Crossbill Group	CBcs SLdr
	'Crosswater Belle'	IDee LMil NLar
	'Crosswater Red' (A)	LMil
	'Csárdás'	GGGa IVic
	cubittii	see *R. veitchianum* Cubittii Group
	cucullatum	see *R. roxieanum* var. *cucullatum*
	cumberlandense (A)	GGGa LMil
	- 'Sunlight'	LMil
	cuneatum	MSnd
	'Cunningham's Blush'	SGol
	'Cunningham's White'	CBcs CDul CTri CWri ELan EPfP GBin GGGa GGal LCro LMil LRHS MAsh MGos MMuc NHol NLar NPri SCob SLdr SLim SPer SPoG SReu SSta
	'Cupcake'	GGGa
	'Curlew' 🏆H4	CBcs CMac GEdr GKin LMil MAsh MBri MMuc MSnd NHol SLdr SReu SSpi
	cyanocarpum	GGGa MSnd
	'Cynthia' 🏆H5	CBcs CMac CSBt CWri GGGa LMil LSRN MBri MMuc MSnd NEgg SLdr SPer SReu SSta WMoo
	'Dagmar'	IVic SAko
	dalhousiae	GGGa
	- LS&T 6694	MSnd
§	- var. ***rhabdotum***	GGGa
	(Damozel Group) 'Damozel'	LMil
	'Danuta'	IVic SAko
	'Dartmoor Pixie'	WThu
	'Dartmoor Shepherd's Delight' **new**	SReu
	dasycladum	see *R. selense* subsp. *dasycladum*
	dauricum	WBod
	- 'Album'	see *R. dauricum* 'Hokkaido'
§	- 'Hokkaido'	GGGa
	- 'Mid-winter' 🏆H6	GGGa LMil
	davidii	GGGa LMil NEgg
	davidsonianum 🏆H3	GGGa GGal LMil MSnd
	- Bodnant form	LMil
	- 'Caerhays Blotched'	GGGa
	- 'Ruth Lyons'	LMil
	'Daviesii' (G) 🏆H6	CBcs CDoC CDul CSBt CTri CWri ELan EPfP GKin GQui LCro LMil LRHS MAsh MBri MLea MMuc MSnd NLar NPri SLdr SPer SPoG SReu SSpi SSta WHor WMoo
	'Daybreak' (EA/d)	see *R.* 'Kirin'
	'Daybreak' (K)	GQui
	'Dear Barbara'	LMil LSRN
	'Dear Grandad' (EA)	CTri LMil LSRN MBri
	'Dear Grandma' (EA)	LMil LSRN
	'Dearest' (EA)	LMil LRHS MAsh MBri NPri
	'Debutante'	SReu SSta
	decorum 🏆H4	CPne GGGa LMil MSnd SLdr
	- SDR 5805	GKev
	- subsp. ***cordatum*** C&H 7132	GGGa
	- 'Cox's Uranium Green'	SReu
§	- subsp. ***diaprepes***	GCal MSnd
	- late-flowering	LMil
	- pink-flowered	GGGa
	decorum × ***yakushimanum***	SReu
§	***degronianum*** subsp. ***degronianum***	LMil MSnd
	- subsp. ***heptamerum*** 'Ho Emma'	IDee LMil LRHS
	- - 'Oki Island'	LMil
	- 'Rae's Delight'	LMil
	dekatanum	GGGa
	deleiense	see *R. tephropeplum*
	'Delicatissimum' (O) 🏆H5	CBcs CDoC CWri GGGa GKin GQui LRHS MBri MPkF MSnd WGwG

	'Delta'	COtt MGos MMuc NLar SCob SLdr SLim
	dendrocharis	LMil
	- Cox 5016	GGGa WAbe
	- Glendoick Gem ='Gle002'	GGGa
	'Denise'	IVic SAko
*	'Denny's Rose' (A)	LMil SReu SSta
	'Denny's Scarlet'	NHol SReu SSta
	'Denny's White' (A)	LMil NHol SReu SSta
	denudatum	LMil MSnd
	- EGM 294	LMil
	- NN 0908	MSnd
	Diamant Group lilac-flowered (EA)	ECho LMil MLea
	- pink-flowered (EA)	ECho MLea
§	- purple-flowered (EA)	ECho MLea
§	- red-flowered (EA)	ECho MLea SLdr WBod
	- rosy red-flowered (EA)	ECho
	- white-flowered (EA)	ECho
	'Diamant Purpur'	see *R.* Diamant Group purple-flowered
	'Diamant Rot'	see *R.* Diamant Group red-flowered
I	'Diana'	SLdr
	'Diana van Herzeele'	SCob
	diaprepes	see *R. decorum* subsp. *diaprepes*
	dichroanthum	GGGa LMil
§	- subsp. ***apodectum***	GGGa LMil MSnd
	- subsp. ***dichroanthum***	MSnd
	- - AC 1079	MSnd
§	- subsp. ***scyphocalyx***	GGGa LMil MSnd
	- subsp. ***septentrionale***	GGGa
	didymum	see *R. sanguineum* subsp. *didymum*
	'Diorama' (Vs)	SReu SSta
	discolor	see *R. fortunei* subsp. *discolor*
	diversipilosum 'Milky Way'	GGGa
	'Doc'	CBcs CMac SLdr SReu SSta
	'Doctor Arnold W. Endtz'	SReu
	'Doctor H.C. Dresselhuys'	MMuc
	'Doctor M. Oosthoek' (M)	CSBt GKin SReu
	'Doctor Reiger'	MGos NLar
	'Doctor Stocker'	MSnd
	'Dominik'	GGGa
	'Dopey' ♀H4	CBcs CDul CWri EPfP GGGa LMil LRHS MAsh MBri MGos MJak MLea MSnd NHol NLar SCob SLim SReu SSta
	'Dora Amateis' ♀H6	CBcs CDoC ECho GGGa IDee IVic LMil LRHS MAsh MBri MGos MMuc NLar SAko SLdr SLim SReu WThu
	Dormouse Group	CBcs ECho LMil MAsh NLar SReu SSta
	'Dorothy Amateis'	GKev
	'Dorothy Hayden' (EA)	SLdr
	'Dörte Reich'	GGGa
	'Dotella'	GGGa
	'Double Beauty' (Vuykiana) (EA/d)	SReu SSta
	'Double Damask' (K/d)	SLdr
	'Double Dots' (d)	LMil
	double yellow-flowered (A/d)	SLdr
	'Douglas McEwan'	SLdr
	Dragonfly Group	SReu SSta
	'Dreamland' ♀H5	CBcs CDoC CWri EPfP LCro LMil LRHS MAsh MBri MGos MLea MMuc MSnd NLar SCob SLdr SLim SPoG SReu SSta
	dryophyllum misapplied	see *R. phaeochrysum* var. *levistratum*
	'Dufthecke'	see *R.* White Dufthecke
	'Düsselfeuer'	IVic
	'Dusty Miller'	LRHS MAsh MBri MJak MSnd SLdr
	'Earl of Donoughmore'	SReu SSta
	'Easter Parade' (EA)	SLdr
	eastmanii (A)	GGGa
	ebianense NN 904	GGGa
	'Ebony Pearl'	CBcs SLdr
	eclecteum	GCal GGGa LMil MSnd
§	***edgeworthii*** ♀H3	CBcs GCal GGGa WAbe
	'Edith Bosley'	CDoC MGos NLar SLdr SPer
	'Edna Bee' (EA)	LMil SLdr
	'Egret' ♀H4	CDoC ECho GEdr GGGa LMil MBri MLea MSnd NSla SLdr WBod
	'Eider'	GGGa MAsh
	'Eileen'	LMil
	'El Camino'	MMuc SLdr
	Eldorado Group	GQui
	(Eleanore Group) 'Eleanore'	SLdr
	'Electra'	see *R. augustinii* 'Electra'
	elegantulum	LMil MSnd
	(Elisabeth Hobbie Group) 'Elisabeth Hobbie' ♀H5	CDoC IDee LMil MGos NLar SLdr
	'Eliska'	IVic
	'Elizabeth'	CDul CTri CTsd CWri GBin LRHS LSRN MSnd NHol WBod
	'Elizabeth' (EA)	CMac CSBt EPfP SLdr
	Elizabeth Group	CBcs LMil MAsh SLdr SPer SReu
§	- 'Creeping Jenny'	ECho GGGa GGal MSnd SLdr WBod
	'Elizabeth Jenny'	see *R.* 'Creeping Jenny'
	'Elizabeth Lockhart'	ECho GQui WBod
	'Elizabeth Red Foliage'	CTri GGGa LMil LRHS MAsh MBri SPer
	'Else Frye'	GGGa
	'Elsie Lee' (EA/d) ♀H5	CSBt CTrh LMil MAsh MMuc SLdr SReu
	'Emasculum'	SLdr
	'Emma Williams'	CBcs
	'Endsleigh Pink'	CBcs CWri LMil
	'English Roseum'	LMil
	eriocarpum 'Gumpō' (EA)	CMac SLdr
	eriogynum	see *R. facetum*
	'Ernest Inman'	LMil
	erosum	MSnd
	'Eruption'	IVic SAko
	'Esmeralda'	CMac
	'Esther May' (A)	SReu SSta
	'Etna' (EA)	SLdr
	'Etta Burrows'	CWri GGGa
	'Euan Cox'	GGGa
	euchaites	see *R. neriiflorum* subsp. *neriiflorum* Euchaites Group
	'Eucharis' (Glenn Dale) (EA) **new**	SCob
	euchroum	MSnd
	eudoxum	MSnd
	'Eunice Ann' (A) **new**	SReu SSta
	'Europa'	SReu SSta
	'Eurydice'	LMil
	eurysiphon	MSnd
	'Evelyn Hyde' (EA)	SLdr
	'Evening Fragrance' (A)	LMil
	'Everbloom' (EA)	SLdr
	Everred ='851C'PBR	GGGa MBri
	exasperatum	GGGa
	- KW 6855	LMil
	Exburiense Group	MMuc

	Name	Suppliers
	'Exbury Calstocker'	LMil
	'Exbury White' (K)	GQui
	excellens	CPne GGGa IDee LMil
	eximium	see *R. falconeri* subsp. *eximium*
	'Explorer' (EA)	MJak
	'Exquisitum' (O) ♀H5	CBcs CDoC CWri GGGa GKin LMil MBri MMuc
	exquisitum	see *R. oreotrephes* Exquisitum Group
	'Extraordinaire'	GGGa LMil SReu SSta
	faberi	GGGa
	Fabia Group	CWri
	- 'Fabia' ♀H3	CBcs CMac GGGa GGal GKin LMil MAsh SLdr
§	- 'Fabia Tangerine'	CMac MLea
	'Fabia Waterer'	LMil
§	***facetum***	GGGa LMil
	'Faggetter's Favourite' ♀H5	LMil SReu SSta
	Fairy Light Group	LMil SLdr
	faithae CGG 14142	GGGa
	falconeri ♀H3	GGGa LMil MSnd NEgg SLdr
§	- subsp. ***eximium***	GGGa GKev LMil MSnd
	'Falling Snow'	IVic SAko
	'Fanal' (K)	NLar SLdr
	'Fanny'	see *R.* 'Pucella'
	'Fantastica' ♀H6	CDoC CWri ELan EPfP GGGa IDee LMil LRHS MAsh MBri MGos MLea MMuc NLar NPri SLim SPoG
	fargesii	see *R. oreodoxa* var. *fargesii*
	farinosum NN 0904	MSnd
	'Fashion' (EA)	SLdr
	fastigiatum	LMil MSnd NSla SLdr
	- SBEC 804/4869	GGGa WThu
§	- 'Blue Steel' ♀H6	CBcs CTri ECho GKin IVic LMil LRHS MAsh MBri SLdr SPlb SReu WAbe
	- 'Indigo Steel'	GGGa
	'Fastuosum Flore Pleno' (d) ♀H6	CBcs CMac CSBt CWri GGGa LMil MLea SLdr SPer SReu SSta
	'Fatima'	LMil
	faucium	GGGa
	'Favorite' ambig. (EA)	SLdr
	'Fawley' (K)	SLdr
	'Fedora' (Kaempferi) (EA)	CBcs CTsd
	Feenkissen = 'Hachkissen'PBR (EA)	IVic SAko
	ferrugineum	GGGa LMil
	'Feuerwerk' (K)	IVic MMuc NLar
	fictolacteum	see *R. rex* subsp. *fictolacteum*
	Fine Feathers Group	WBod
	'Fire Rim'	LRHS MAsh
	'Fireball' (K) ♀H6	CBcs CDoC CDul CTri CWri EPfP GBin GGGa GKin LMil LRHS MAsh MBri MGos MLea MMuc NLar SLdr SPer SPoG WMoo
	'Fireball' (hybrid)	MJak
	'Firecracker' (A)	LRHS MAsh MBri
	'Fireglow' (EA)	GKin LMil
	'Firelight' (hybrid)	CDoC GKin LMil MGos NLar
§	'Firestorm' **new**	LRHS NPri
	'Flaming Gold'	LRHS LSRN MAsh MBri
	'Flanagan's Daughter'	LMil MAsh
	'Flautando'	IVic LMil
	Flava Group	see *R.* Volker Group
	flavidum	GGGa MMuc
	fletcherianum 'Yellow Bunting'	GGGa
	floccigerum	LMil MSnd
	- AC 1863	MSnd
	- bicoloured	GGGa
	floribundum	GGGa LMil SLdr
	'Florida' (EA/d) ♀H4	CMac LMil MGos NLar SLdr SReu
	'Flower Arranger' (EA)	LMil MAsh MBri SCoo
	formosanum	GGGa
	formosum	CBcs GGGa
§	- var. ***formosum*** Iteaphyllum Group	GGGa GGal
	- - 'Khasia'	GGGa
	- var. ***inaequale***	GGGa
	forrestii	GCal
	- subsp. ***forrestii***	LMil
	- - Repens Group	GKev LMil
	- - - 'Seinghku'	GGGa WThu
	- Tumescens Group	GGGa WThu
	Fortune Group	SLdr
	fortunei ♀H6	GGGa IDee LMil SLdr
§	- subsp. ***discolor*** ♀H5	LMil MSnd
	- - (Houlstonii Group) 'John R. Elcock'	IDee LMil
	- - 'Hummeltanz'	IVic SAko
	- - var. ***kwangfuense*** AC 5208	LMil
	- 'Mrs Butler'	see *R.* 'Sir Charles Butler'
	fragariiflorum	GGGa
	'Fragrantissimum' ♀H2	CBcs CDoC CMac CSBt CTsd CWri ECre GGGa GGal IDee LMil MRav NLar SKHP SLdr WBod
	'Frans van der Bom' (M)	MBri
	'Fraseri' (M)	LMil
	'Fred Peste' ♀H4	CDoC GKin LMil MAsh MBri MGos MLea MMuc MSnd SLdr SLim
	(Fred Wynniatt Group) 'Fred Wynniatt'	LMil MSnd
	'Fred Wynniatt Stanway'	see *R.* 'Stanway'
	'Freya' (R/d)	LMil LSRN
	'Fridoline' (EA)	IVic SAko
	'Frigate' (EA)	SLdr
	'Frilly Lemon' (Ad)	EPfP SLdr
	'Frosted Orange' (EA)	LMil MAsh
	'Frühlingsbeginn'	IVic
	'Frühlingsglühen'	IVic
	'Fulbrook'	IDee LMil
	fulgens	GGGa LMil MSnd
	fulvum ♀H4	GCal GGGa GKin IDee LMil MSnd NLar SReu SSta
	- KR 7614	LMil
	- subsp. ***fulvoides***	MSnd
	'Furnivall's Daughter' ♀H5	CDul CMac COtt CSBt CWri GBin GGGa LMil MBri MMuc MSnd NHol SLdr SReu SSta WMoo
	'Gabrielle Hill' (EA)	MAsh SLdr
	'Gaiety' (Glenn Dale) (EA)	LMil SLdr
	galactinum	GGGa IDee LMil LRHS MSnd NLar
	'Galathea' (EA)	MMuc
	'Gandy Dancer'	CWri SLdr
	'Garden State Glow' (EA/d)	SLdr
	'Gartendirektor Glocker'	CWri ECho GGGa IVic MAsh MGos MSnd SLim
	'Gartendirektor Rieger' ♀H5	CWri GGGa IVic LMil NLar SReu
	'Gauche' (A)	GQui
	'Gaugin'	GQui
	'Geisha' (EA)	SGol
	'Geisha Lilac'	see *R.* 'Hanako'
	'Geisha Orange'	see *R.* 'Satschiko'
	'Geisha Pink'	see *R.* 'Momoko'
	'Geisha Purple'	see *R.* 'Fumiko'
	'Geisha Red'	see *R.* 'Kazuko'
	'Gena Mae' (A/d)	GGGa SLdr
	'General Practitioner'	SLdr

	'General Wavell' (EA)	CMac GGal SLdr
	'Gene's Favourite'	SReu SSta
	genestierianum	GGGa MSnd
	'Genoveva'	SAko
	'Geoffroy Millais'	LMil
	'Georg Arends' (A)	EPfP LMil LRHS MAsh MGos SLdr
	'George Hyde' (EA)	EPfP LRHS LSRN MAsh MBri SCoo
	'George Johnstone'	SLdr
	'George Reynolds' (K)	MLea
	'George's Delight'	MSnd
§	× ***geraldii***	SLdr
	'Germania'	CBcs CDoC COtt IDee LMil LPar LRHS MAsh MBri NLar NPri SCob SPoG SReu SSta
	Gertrud Schäle Group	CDoC CTri MGos
	'Gibraltar' (K) ♀H6	CBcs CDoC CDul CMac CSBt CTri CWri EPfP GGGa GKin LMil MAsh MBri MGos MJak NHol NLar SLdr SLim SPer SReu SSta WMoo
	Gibraltar Group	WFar
	'Gilbert Mullie' (EA)	LMil MGos NLar SLim SReu SSta
	'Gillian Bramley' **new**	SLdr
	'Gill's Crimson'	SReu
	'Ginger' (K)	CSBt GKin LMil
	'Ginny Gee' ♀H5	CBcs CDoC CSBt CWri ECho EPfP GEdr GGGa GKin IVic LMil LRHS MAsh MBri MGos MLea MSnd NEgg NLar NSla NWad SReu SSta WBod
§	'Girard's Hot Shot' (EA)	LMil LPar LRHS MPkF SReu SSta
§	'Girard's Variegated Hot Shot' (EA/v) ♀H4	CDoC GGGa LMil LPar MAsh NEgg SHil SLdr
	'Gislinde' (A) **new**	SAko
	'Glacier' (EA)	SLdr
	'Glamour' **new**	LMil
	glanduliferum	GGGa SLdr
	- EGM 347	LMil
	glaucophyllum	GGGa LMil MSnd
	- Borde Hill form	LMil
	- 'Deer Dell'	LMil
	- var. ***glaucophyllum***	MSnd
§	- subsp. ***tubiforme***	GGGa
	Glendoick Butterscotch = 'Gle003'	GGGa
	Glendoick Crimson = 'Gle004' (EA)	GGGa
	Glendoick Dream = 'Gle005' (EA)	GGGa
	Glendoick Ermine = 'Gle006' (EA)	GGGa
	Glendoick Frolic = 'Gle007'	GGGa
	Glendoick Garnet = 'Gle008' (EA)	GGGa
	Glendoick Glacier = 'Gle009' (EA)	GGGa
	Glendoick Goblin = 'Gle010' (EA)	GGGa
	Glendoick Gold = 'Gle011'	GGGa
	Glendoick Ice Cream = 'Gle013'	GGGa
	Glendoick Mystique = 'Gle014'	GGGa
	Glendoick Petticoats = 'Gle015'	GGGa
	Glendoick Rosebud = 'Gle022' (EA)	GGGa
	Glendoick Ruby = 'Gle016'	GGGa
	'Glendoick Silver'	GGGa
	Glendoick Snowflakes = 'Gle001' (EA)	GGGa
§	'Glendoick Tanager'	GGGa
	Glendoick Vanilla = 'Gle017'	GGGa
	Glendoick Velvet = 'Gle018'	GGGa
	'Glenna'	GGGa
	'Gletschernacht'	IVic SAko
	glischrum	GGGa
	- subsp. ***glischroides***	GGGa LMil
§	- subsp. ***rude***	GGGa MSnd
	globigerum	see *R. alutaceum* var. *alutaceum* Globigerum Group
	'Glockenspiel' (K/d)	SLdr
	'Gloria'	see *R.* 'Bruns Gloria'
	'Glory of Littleworth' (Ad)	LMil
	'Glowing Embers' (K)	CDoC CMac CTri CWri GKin LMil LRHS MAsh MBri MGos MLea NHol NLar SLim SPer SReu SSta
	'Goblin'	MSnd SLdr
	'Gog' (K)	CSBt
§	'Goldbukett'	GGGa MBri SAko
	Golden Bouquet	see *R.* 'Goldbukett'
	'Golden Coach'	CWri MLea MSnd SLdr
	'Golden Eagle' (K) ♀H6	CBcs CDoC GKin LMil MGos MJak MLea MSnd NLar SLdr SReu SSta WMoo
	Golden Everest = 'Hachgold'PBR	GGGa SAko
	'Golden Flare' (A)	CBcs CDoC CSBt CWri GBin GKin MBri MMuc NEgg SLdr
	'Golden Fleece'	LMil
	'Golden Gate'	CDoC CSBt MMuc
	'Golden Horn' (K)	GQui
	(Golden Horn Group) 'Golden Horn'	SLdr
	'Golden Lights' (A)	CWri GKin LMil MBri NEgg NLar
	'Golden Princess'	LMil
	'Golden Ruby'	CBcs SPer
	'Golden Splendour'	LMil
	'Golden Sunset' (K) ♀H6	CMac EPfP LMil MAsh MBri MLea SReu SSta WFar
	'Golden Torch' ♀H4	CBcs CDoC CDul COtt CWri EPfP LMil LRHS MAsh MBri MGos MJak MLea MSnd NLar NPri SLdr SLim SPer SPoG SReu
	'Golden Wedding'	CSBt CWri LMil LRHS LSRN MAsh MBri MJak MSnd SLdr
	'Golden Wit'	MAsh MMuc NEgg
	'Golden Wonder' **new**	MHtn
	'Goldflimmer' (v)	CDoC EPfP GGGa GKin LPar LRHS MAsh MBri MGos MJak MMuc NLar NPri SCob SLim SPoG
	(Goldfort Group) 'Goldfort'	SReu
	'Goldika'	LMil
	'Goldinetta'	GGGa IDee LMil LRHS SAko
	'Goldkollier'	IVic
	'Goldkrone' ♀H5	CWri ELon EPfP GGGa LCro LMil MAsh MHtn MLea SPoG SReu SSta
	'Goldpracht' (K)	IVic
	Goldschatz = 'Goldprinz'	CBcs IVic SPoG
	'Goldsworth Orange'	CWri LMil SLdr
	'Goldsworth Yellow'	CSBt
	'Goldtopas' (K)	CTri GGGa GKin LMil LRHS MBri
	'Gomer Waterer' ♀H6	CBcs CDoC CDul CMac COtt CSBt CWri ECho EPfP GGGa LMil LPar LRHS MAsh MBri MGos MJak MMuc NLar SCob SLdr SPer SPoG SReu SSta
	'Goosander'	MMuc
	'Gorbella'	CDoC MGos SReu
	Gowenianum Group (Ad)	LMil SPer

'Grace Seabrook' 🏆^{H5}	CDul CSBt CTri CWri GGGa MBri MLea MMuc SLdr SPer SReu
'Graf Lennart'	GGGa
Graffito = 'Hachgraf'	GGGa IDee IVic LMil LRHS NLar
'Graham Thomas'	LMil
'Grand Slam'	MSnd
grande	GGGa LMil MSnd SLdr
- KR 9483	WPGP
- pink-flowered	MSnd
gratum	see *R. basilicum*
'Graziella'	GGGa LCro LRHS MBri MGos SPoG SSta
'Greensleeves'	LMil MAsh
'Greenway' (Kurume) (EA)	CBcs SLdr
griersonianum	GGGa LMil
griffithianum	MSnd
- B&SWJ 2425	WCru
- KR 10075	MSnd
'Gristede' 🏆^{H5}	CDoC ECho IDee LMil LRHS MGos NLar SReu SSta
groenlandicum	MLea NLar SPer WSHC
- 'Compactum'	NLar
- 'Helma'	IVic NLar
- 'Lenie'	NLar
(Grosclaude Group) 'Grosclaude'	LMil
'Grouse' × ***keiskei*** var. ***ozawae*** 'Yaku Fairy'	ECho
'Grumpy'	CBcs CSBt CWri ELan EPfP GBin LMil LRHS MAsh MBri SCob SReu
'Gumpo Pink' (Satsuki) (EA)	SLdr
'Gumpo White' (EA)	LCro LRHS MAsh MBri SPoG WBod
'Gundula'	LMil
'Gunter Dinger'	IVic
'Gwenda' (EA)	CTri SLdr
'Gwendoline' (A)	SReu SSta
habrotrichum	GGGa LMil
'Hachmann's Brasilia'	SSta
'Hachmann's Charmant'	EPfP GGGa LRHS SAko SPoG
'Hachmann's Constanze'	LMil
'Hachmann's Eskimo'	LMil SLdr
'Hachmann's Feuerschein'	SAko
'Hachmann's Junifeuer'	SAko SReu SSta
Hachmann's Kabarett = 'Hachkaba'	LMil MGos NLar SPoG
'Hachmann's Mamamia' **new**	SAko
'Hachmann's Marlis' 🏆^{H6}	LMil MBri SPoG SReu
§ 'Hachmann's Metallica'	GGGa LCro LMil LRHS MBri SPoG
Hachmann's Picobello = 'Hachpico'^{PBR}	EPfP GGGa LRHS SAko SPoG
'Hachmann's Pinguin'	SAko
§ 'Hachmann's Polaris' 🏆^{H7}	CDoC COtt LMil MGos MJak NLar SReu
'Hachmann's Porzellan' 🏆^{H6}	LMil
§ 'Hachmann's Rokoko' (EA)	LMil SReu SSta
'Hachmann's Sunny Boy'	LRHS MBri
§ 'Hachmann's Tanaga'	GGGa
haematodes	GGGa LMil SLdr
§ - subsp. ***chaetomallum***	GGGa LMil MSnd
- subsp. ***haematodes***	LMil
'Halfdan Lem' 🏆^{H4}	CBcs CDoC GGGa GKin LMil MAsh MBri MGos MMuc SLim SPer SReu SSta
'Hallelujah'	IVic
'Halopeanum'	GGGa
'Halton'	LMil
'Hamlet' (M)	LMil
'Hammondii'	LMil
'Hampshire Belle'	LMil SReu SSta
hanceanum 'Canton Consul'	GGGa
- Nanum Group 🏆^{H5}	CBcs GGGa
'Hanger's Flame' (A)	LMil
Hans Hachmann = 'Hachhans'	GGGa LMil LRHS
'Hansel'	CDoC CWri MAsh MMuc SLdr
'Hardijzer Beauty' (Ad)	SLdr
'Hardy Gardenia' (EA/d)	LMil SReu SSta
hardyi	see *R. augustinii* subsp. *hardyi*
'Harkwood Red' (EA)	SLdr
'Harry Tagg'	SLdr
Harry White's hybrid (A)	SReu SSta
'Harvest Moon' (K)	CDoC LMil MBri MGos NLar SLdr SSta
'Hatsu-giri' (EA)	CMac LMil SLdr SReu SSta
(Hawk Group) 'Crest' 🏆^{H3}	CWri GGGa LMil SSta
'Heather Macleod' (EA)	SLdr
heatherae	GGGa LMil
'Heidi'^{PBR} (EA)	SLdr
'Helen Close' (Glenn Dale) (EA)	SLdr
'Helena Evelyn' (A)	LMil
'Helene Schiffner'	LMil SReu
heliolepis	GGGa LMil
- var. ***fumidum***	see *R. heliolepis* var. *heliolepis*
§ - var. ***heliolepis***	GGGa GKev
hemidartum	see *R. pocophorum* var. *hemidartum*
hemsleyanum	LMil MSnd SLdr
'Herbert' (EA)	CDoC CMac MGos NLar SLim
§ 'Herbstzauber'	LMil MAsh
'Heureuse Surprise' (G)	SLdr
§ 'Hexe de Saffelaere' (EA) **new**	MGos NLar
'High Summer'	LMil LRHS NLar
'Hilda Margaret'	SReu
'Hilda Niblett' (EA)	MBri
'Himmelberg'	GGGa
'Hinamayo'	see *R.* (Obtusum Group) 'Hinomayo'
'Hino-crimson' (Kurume) (EA) 🏆^{H4}	CBcs CDoC CMac CSBt CTri GKin LMil LRHS MAsh MBri MGos NHol NLar SAko SGol SLdr SPer SPoG SReu SSta
'Hinode-giri' (EA)	CMac CSBt CTsd SLdr SReu
hippophaeoides	GKev LMil MSnd SLdr
- SDR 4216 **new**	GKev
- 'Bei-ma-shan'	see *R. hippophaeoides* 'Haba Shan'
§ - 'Haba Shan' 🏆^{H6}	GGGa LMil WThu
hirsutum	LMil MSnd
- f. ***albiflorum***	MSnd
- 'Flore Pleno' (d)	ECho
hirtipes	GGGa MSnd
hodgsonii	LMil MSnd SLdr
- B&SWJ 2195A	WCru
* 'Hogi-kasane' (A)	NLar
'Holden'	MGos
'Homebush' (K/d) 🏆^{H6}	CBcs CDoC CMac CTri CWri EPfP GBin LCro LMil MAsh MBri MGos MJak MPkF NLar SLdr SPer SPoG SReu SSta WMoo
'Honey Butter'	LMil NLar SLim
'Honeysuckle' (K)	NHol SReu SSta
§ 'Ho-o' (Kurume) (EA)	SLdr
'Ho-oden' (EA) **new**	MPkF
hookeri	LMil
- Tigh-na-Rudha form	GGGa

'Hoppy'	CBcs CWri LMil MAsh MBri MGos MLea MMuc MSnd NLar SLdr SLim SPoG
'Horizon Monarch' ♀H4	CBcs CDoC CWri GGGa GKin IVic LMil LRHS MBri MGos MLea NLar SLdr SLim SPer SReu SSta WMoo
horlickianum	GGGa
'Hortulanus H. Witte' (M)	CSBt LRHS MPkF SReu SSta
'Hot Shot'	see *R.* 'Girard's Hot Shot'
'Hot Shot Variegated'	see *R.* 'Girard's Variegated Hot Shot' (EA/v)
'Hotei'	CBcs CSBt ECho EPfP GKin LMil LRHS MAsh MBri MLea NEgg NHol SLdr SReu SSta
(Hotspur Group) 'Hotspur' (K)	CWri GBin SLdr SPer
- 'Hotspur Red' (K) ♀H6	CDoC GKin LMil MAsh MBri NEgg WMoo
huanum	GGGa LMil
- EGM 316	LMil
'Hugh Koster'	SLdr
aff. ***huidongense***	LMil
'Hullaballoo'	IDee LMil LRHS
Humming Bird Group	CMHG GEdr LMil SLdr SReu SSta WBod
hunnewellianum	MSnd
'Hussar'	CWri LMil
'Hyde and Seek'	GQui
'Hydon Dawn' ♀H5	CBcs CWri LMil MLea MMuc MSnd SLdr SReu SSta
'Hydon Hunter' ♀H5	CBcs MSnd SReu SSta
'Hydon Velvet'	CBcs LMil SAko SLdr SReu WMoo
hylaeum	MSnd
Hyperion Group	SReu
hyperythrum	GGGa LMil MSnd
hypoglaucum	see *R. argyrophyllum* subsp. *hypoglaucum*
'Ice Cube'	MLea MMuc NLar SLdr
'Iceberg'	see *R.* 'Lodauric Iceberg'
(Idealist Group) 'Idealist'	LMil
'Ightham Yellow'	SLdr SReu
§ 'Ilam Melford Lemon' (A)	LMil
§ 'Ilam Ming' (A)	LMil
'Ilam Violet'	LMil
'Imago' (K/d)	LMil
§ 'Ima-shojo' (Kurume) (EA/d)	CMac LRHS LSRN SLdr
impeditum	CBcs CSBt CWib ECho ELan GBin GEdr GKev GQui MGos MJak MLea MMuc MSnd SCob SLdr SPer SReu SSta
- 'Blue Steel'	see *R. fastigiatum* 'Blue Steel'
- 'Indigo'	GKin SLdr SReu WAbe
- 'Pygmaeum'	NHar WAbe WThu
imperator	see *R. uniflorum* var. *imperator*
(Impi Group) 'Impi'	LMil
indicum (EA)	CTsd
§ - 'Macranthum' (EA)	SLdr
'Ingrid Mehlquist'	GGGa
Inkarho Lilac Dufthecke = 'Rhodunter 149'PBR	LMil
insigne ♀H6	GGGa LMil MSnd
- Reuthe's form	SReu
insigne × yakushimanum	SReu
Intrifast Group	GGGa
iodes	see *R. alutaceum* var. *iodes*
'Irene Koster' (O) ♀H5	CDoC CSBt CWri GGGa GKin LMil LRHS MBri MGos MPkF NLar SLim SPer
'Irohayama' (Kurume) (EA) ♀H3	CBcs CMac EPfP GQui LMil LRHS MAsh NPri
irroratum	LMil SLdr
- subsp. ***irroratum***	MSnd
- 'Polka Dot'	GGGa LMil
- subsp. ***yiliangense*** EGM 339	LMil
'Isabel'	LRHS NPri
'Isabel' (EA)	MAsh MBri
'Isola Bella'	GGGa
'Issho-no-haru' (EA)	WBod
iteaphyllum	see *R. formosum* var. *formosum* Iteaphyllum Group
'Ivette' (Kaempferi) (EA)	CMac
Iviza Group	LMil
'Izumi-no-mai' (EA)	SLdr
'J.C. Williams'	CBcs
'J.M. de Montague'	see *R.* 'The Honourable Jean Marie de Montague'
'Jack A. Sand' (K)	GGGa
'Jackwill' **new**	SAko
(Jalisco Group) 'Jalisco Elect'	CWri
- 'Jubilant'	LMil
'James Burchett' ♀H6	LMil SReu
'James Gable' (EA)	MAsh SLdr
Janet Group	LMil
'Janet Rhea' (EA)	SLdr
japonicum (A. Gray) J.V. Suringar	see *R. molle* subsp. *japonicum*
- var. ***pentamerum***	see *R. degronianum* subsp. *degronianum*
jasminiflorum (V)	GGGa
'Jason'	LMil
javanicum (V)	GGGa
'Jean Marie Montague'	see *R.* 'The Honourable Jean Marie de Montague'
'Jeff Hill' (EA)	SLdr
'Jenny'	see *R.* 'Creeping Jenny'
'Jessica Rose' (A)	LMil
'Jim Russell' (*ciliicalyx* hybrid)	GGGa
'Jingle Bells'	GGGa
'Joan Paton' (A)	SLdr
'Joanna'	CBcs
'Jock'	SLdr
Jock Group	CBcs CMHG
'Jock Brydon' (O)	GGGa LMil
'Johann Sebastian Bach' (EA)	SLdr
'Johann Strauss' (EA)	WBod
'Johanna' (EA) ♀H5	CDoC CTri EPfP LMil LRHS MAsh MBri MGos NHol NPri SLdr SPer WBod
'John Cairns' (Kaempferi) (EA)	CMac SLdr
'John Walter'	SCob
johnstoneanum	CBcs GGGa SLdr
- KW 7732	SLdr
- 'Double Diamond' (d)	IDee LMil
'Jolie Madame' (Vs) ♀H6	CWri EPfP GKin LMil LRHS MAsh MBri MGos MLea MMuc NLar NPri SLdr SPer
'Joseph Haydn' (EA)	WBod
'Joseph Hill' (EA)	NLar
'Jubilee'	SLdr
'Juliette' (EA)	IVic
'June Fire' (A)	GGGa SReu SSta
'Juniduft' (A)	GGGa
kaempferi (EA)	LMil SLdr
§ - 'Mikado' (EA)	LMil SLdr SReu
- orange-flowered (EA)	CMac

	Name	Suppliers
	'Kali'	GGGa
	'Kalinka'	LMil MAsh MBri MGos MMuc NLar SPoG
	'Karen Triplett'	LMil
	'Karin'	MJak
	'Karl Naue'	SReu
	'Kasane-kagaribi' (EA)	SLdr
	'Kate Waterer' ♀H5	SReu
	'Kathleen' van Nes (EA)	SLdr
	'Katisha' (EA)	SLdr
	'Katy Watson'	SReu SSta
	'Keija' (EA)	SLdr
	keiskei compact	ITim
	- Cordifolium Group	WAbe
	- var. ***ozawae*** 'Yaku Fairy' ♀H5	LMil WAbe WThu
	keleticum	see *R. calostrotum* subsp. *keleticum*
	'Kelsay's Double'	MLea
	'Ken Janeck'	GGGa
§	***kendrickii***	GGGa
	'Kermesinum' (EA)	CTri MAsh MGos NWad SHil SLdr SLim SReu
I	'Kermesinum Rosé' (EA) ♀H5	CDoC CSBt LMil MGos NLar SLdr SLim SReu
	kesangiae	GGGa LMil
	- KR 9444	GKev
	- var. ***album***	GGGa
	Kewense Group	CWri
	keysii	CPne GGGa LMil
	(Kilimanjaro Group) 'Kilimanjaro'	LMil SReu
	'Kimbeth'	GGGa
	'King George' Loder	see *R.* 'Loderi King George'
	kingianum	see *R. arboreum* subsp. *zeylanicum*
	'Kings Ride'	LMil
§	'Kirin' (Kurume) (EA/d)	LMil LPar MPkF NLar SLdr
	'Kirsten Begeer'	IVic
	kiusianum (EA)	LMil SReu
I	- 'Album' (EA)	LMil SReu WAbe
	- 'Hillier's Pink' (EA)	LMil
	- var. ***kiusianum*** (EA) **new**	SLdr
	'Kleine Geisha' **new**	SAko
	'Kleiner Prinz' (EA)	SAko
	'Klondyke' (K) ♀H6	CBcs CDoC CSBt CTri EPfP GGGa GKin LCro LMil LRHS MAsh MGos NLar NPri SLdr SPer SPoG SReu
	'Kluis Sensation' ♀H5	CMac CSBt SLdr SReu SSta
	'Kluis Triumph'	SReu
	'Knap Hill Apricot' (K)	LMil
	'Knap Hill Red' (K)	CDoC LMil
	'Kobold' (EA)	SLdr
	'Koichiro Wada'	see *R. yakushimanum* 'Koichiro Wada'
	'Kokardia'	LMil NLar SAko
	'Kokette'	IVic SAko
	kongboense	GGGa WAbe
	'Königstein' (EA)	IVic LMil MGos SHil SReu SSta
§	'Koningin Emma' (M)	GKin LMil NLar SLdr
	'Konsonanz'	IVic
	'Koromo-shikibu' (EA)	GGGa MPkF
	'Koromo-shikibu White' (EA)	GGGa
	'Koster's Brilliant Red' (M)	CSBt LCro MBri SReu SSta
	'Kranenfee' (A)	GGGa
§	'Kure-no-yuki' (Kurume) (EA/d)	LMil
	kyawii	CPne GGGa
	'Lackblatt'	see *R.* (Volker Group) 'Flavum Lackblatt'
	(Lactcombei Group) 'Robert Keir'	SLdr
	lacteum	GGGa LMil
	'Lady Alice Fitzwilliam' ♀H3	CBcs CDoC CMHG CMac ECre GGGa GKin IDee LMil
	'Lady Annette de Trafford'	IDee
	'Lady Chamberlain Salmon Trout'	see *R.* 'Salmon Trout'
§	(Lady Chamberlain Group) 'Salmon Trout'	LMil LSRN
	'Lady Clementine Mitford' ♀H5	CSBt CWri LMil MLea MMuc SLdr SPer SReu
	'Lady Eleanor Cathcart'	SLdr
	'Lady Elphinstone' (EA)	SLdr
	'Lady Louise' (EA)	SLdr
	'Lady Robin' (EA)	SLdr
	'Lady Romsey'	LMil
	laetum (V)	GGGa
	Lamellen Group	LMil
	lanatoides	GGGa
	lanatum	GGGa LMil SLdr
	'Langworth'	CWri LMil MLea MMuc SLdr SReu
	lanigerum	LMil SReu
	'Lanzette'	IVic
	lapponicum Parviflorum Group	GGGa
	'Lapwing' (K)	NLar
	'Laramie'	GGGa
*	***laterifolium***	GGGa
	Laura Aberconway Group	SLdr
	'Lavender Brilliant' (EA)	SLdr
	'Lavender Girl' ♀H5	CMac LMil SLdr SReu SSta
	'Lavendula'	SAko
	'Le Progrès'	LMil
	'Lea Rainbow'	MLea
	'Ledifolium'	see *R.* × *mucronatum*
	'Ledifolium Album'	see *R.* × *mucronatum*
	'Lee's Dark Purple'	COtt CWri LMil
	'Lee's Scarlet'	LMil
	'Lemon Dream'	LMil LRHS MAsh MBri MGos NLar NPri SLim
*	'Lemon Drop' (A)	GGGa
	'Lemon Meringue'	LMil
	'Lemonora' (M)	CBcs GKin
	'Lem's 45'	CBcs CWri SLdr SPer
	'Lem's Cameo' ♀H3	GGGa LMil LRHS NLar SReu SSta
	'Lem's Monarch' ♀H4	CBcs CDoC CDul COtt CWri GGGa LMil MBri MLea MMuc SLdr SReu SSta
	'Lem's Tangerine'	LMil
	'Lemur' (EA)	ECho GGGa LMil MLea MMuc NLar WThu
	'Leni'	LRHS MAsh MBri
	'Leo' (EA)	SLdr
	'Leonardslee Giles'	SLdr
	'Leonardslee Primrose'	SLdr
	'Leonore'	LMil
	lepidostylum	CMac CWri GGGa ITim LMil
	lepidotum	GGGa
	- var. ***album***	GGGa
	- yellow-flowered McB 110	WThu
§	***leptocarpum***	GGGa
§	'Leucanthum'	GGGa WThu
	leucaspis	GGal SLdr
	'Leuchtpolster'	IVic
	'Lewis Monarch'	GQui
	'Libretto'	LMil
	'Lila Pedigo'	CWri MMuc SLdr SPer
	'Lilac Time' (EA)	SLdr
	'Lilactina'	SLdr

	Name	Suppliers
	'Lily Marleen' (EA)	CTri
	'Linda' ♀H5	CBcs CWri EPfP GGGa LMil LSRN MAsh MBri MJak MLea MMuc SCob
	'Linda Stuart' (EA)	GGGa
	lindleyi	GGGa
	- 'Geordie Sherriff'	GGGa
	'Linearifolium'	see *R. stenopetalum* 'Linearifolium'
	'Linnet' (K/d)	SLdr
	'Lionel's First'	LMil
	Lionel's Triumph Group	LMil
	'Little Beauty' (EA)	SLdr
	'Little Ben'	ECho ITim
	'Loch Arkaig'	GGGa
	'Loch Awe'	GGGa LMil
	'Loch Earn'	GGGa
	'Loch Faskally'	GGGa
	'Loch Laggan'	GGGa
	'Loch Leven'	GGGa
	'Loch Linnhe'	GGGa SReu SSta
	'Loch Lomond'	GGGa
	'Loch Morar'	GGGa
	lochiae (V)	GGGa
	'Lochinch Spinbur'	GQui
	Lodauric Group	SReu
§	- 'Lodauric Iceberg'	LMil SReu
	'Lodbrit'	SReu
	Loderi Group	SLdr
	- 'Loderi Fairy Queen'	SLdr
	- 'Loderi Game Chick'	LMil SLdr
	- 'Loderi Georgette'	SLdr
	- 'Loderi Helen'	LMil SLdr
§	- 'Loderi King George' ♀H4	CBcs CWri GGGa GKin IVic LMil MLea SLdr SPer SReu SSta WGwG
	- 'Loderi Patience'	SLdr
	- 'Loderi Pink Coral'	LMil SLdr
	- 'Loderi Pink Diamond' ♀H4	CWri LMil SLdr
	- 'Loderi Pink Topaz'	SLdr
	- 'Loderi Pretty Polly'	SLdr
	- 'Loderi Princess Marina'	SLdr
	- 'Loderi Sir Edmund'	LMil SLdr
	- 'Loderi Sir Joseph Hooker'	SLdr
	- 'Loderi Titan'	SLdr SReu SSta
	- 'Loderi Venus' ♀H4	CBcs LMil SLdr SReu SSta
	- 'Loderi White Diamond'	SLdr
	'Loder's White' ♀H3	CBcs LMil SReu SSta
	longesquamatum	GGGa MSnd
	longipes	GGGa LMil MSnd SLdr
	- EGM 336	LMil
	- var. ***chienianum***	LMil MSnd
	'Looking Glass'	MMuc
	'Lord Roberts' ♀H6	CBcs CDoC CMac CSBt CTri CWri EPfP GBin GGGa LCro LMil MAsh MGos MJak MLea MMuc NHol NLar SLdr SLim SPer SReu SSta WMoo
	'Loreley'	SAko
	'Lori Eichelser'	WBod
	'Louis Pasteur'	SCob SReu
	'Louisa' (EA)	MAsh NLar
	'Louise Dowdle' (Glenn Dale) (EA)	SLdr
	'Lovely William'	CMac LMil SLdr
	lowndesii	WAbe
	'Lucy Lou'	GGGa
	ludlowii	GGGa WAbe
	'Luisella'	IVic
	'Lullaby' (EA)	SLdr
	luteiflorum	GGGa
	- KW 7833	MSnd
	lutescens	CBcs CTsd LMil MSnd SLdr SReu WAbe WThu
	- 'Bagshot Sands' ♀H3	GGGa LMil SLdr
	- 'Exbury'	CExl
	luteum (A)	Widely available
	- 'Golden Comet' (A)	GGGa
	lyi	GGGa
*	'Mac Ovata'	CMac
	macabeanum ♀H3	CBcs CDoC GBin GGGa GKev GKin LMil MLea MSnd NEgg SLdr SPer SReu SSpi SSta
	- NAPE 052	GGGa
	- Reuthe's form	SReu
	macabeanum* × *wardii	GGGa
	'Macarena'	IVic LMil SAko
	macgregoriae (V)	GGGa
	macranthum	see *R. indicum* 'Macranthum'
	macrosmithii	see *R. argipeplum*
	'Macrostemon' (EA)	WBod
	maculiferum	GGGa
	'Madame Ad. van Hecke' (EA)	CTri GKin IVic LMil LPfy MAsh MBri MGos SHil SLim
	'Madame Albert van Hecke' (EA) **new**	SLdr
	'Madame de Bruin'	SLdr
	'Madame Galle'	CDoC MGos NLar
	'Madame Masson' ♀H6	CDoC CDul COtt CTri CWri ELan LMil LRHS MAsh MBri MGos MLea MMuc NLar NPri SLdr SPer SReu SSta
	maddenii	CDoC IDee LMil SAko
§	- subsp. ***crassum***	CBcs CExl CPne GGGa IVic MSnd SKHP
§	- subsp. ***maddenii*** Polyandrum Group	CBcs GGGa GGal GQui SAko
	'Madleen' **new**	SAko
	'Maggie'	IVic
	'Magic Flute' (EA)	LRHS MAsh MBri
I	'Magic Flute' (V)	LMil SCoo
	magniflorum	GGGa
	- NN 0959	MSnd
	'Maharani'	GGGa
	'Maifeier' **new**	LMil
	'Mai-ogi' (EA)	IVic SAko
	'Maischnee' (EA)	GGGa
	'Maja' (G)	SReu SSta
	Major Group	LMil
§	***makinoi*** ♀H5	GGGa LMil SReu SSpi SSta
	- 'Fuju-kaku-no-matsu'	MGos
	'Makiyak'	LMil SAko
	mallotum	CPne GGGa IDee LMil MSnd
	'Mandarin Lights' (A)	NLar
	'Manderley'	LMil
	maoerense	GGGa
	'Maraschino' (EA)	GGGa IVic SAko
	'Marchioness of Lansdowne'	CWri SLdr
	'Mardi Gras'	CDoC MGos NEgg NLar SLdr
	'Margaret Blain'	SReu
	Margaret Dunn Group	CWri
	'Maria Elena' (EA/d)	CDoC LMil LRHS MGos NLar
	'Maricee'	MBri
	'Marie Curie'	LMil
	'Marie Fortie'	LMil MGos NLar
	'Marie Hoffman'	LMil
	'Marilee' (EA)	CDoC EPfP IVic LRHS MAsh NLar SLdr
	'Marinja' (EA)	LMil
	'Marinus Koster'	SReu SSta
	'Marion Street'	LMil

'Markeeta's Prize' ♀H4	CDoC CWri EPfP GGGa LMil LRHS MAsh MBri MGos MLea MMuc NLar NPri SLim SReu
'Marlies' (A)	NLar
'Marmot' (EA)	ECho MLea MMuc NLar
'Marsalla'	NLar SAko
'Martha Isaacson' (Ad)	CWri LMil MLea SLdr SReu
'Martha Wright'	EPfP GGGa LRHS MAsh MBri NPri
martinianum	GGGa
'Maruschka' (EA) ♀H5	GGGa IVic LCro LMil LRHS MAsh SAko SPoG
'Mary Forte'	SCob
'Mary Helen' (Glenn Dale) (EA)	CDoC CWSG LMil LRHS MAsh MBri MGos NLar SCoo SLdr SLim SPoG SReu
'Mary Poppins' (A)	CDoC GKin LMil LSRN MBri MGos MMuc NLar SCoo SLdr SLim WMoo
Matador Group	SReu
- 'Matador'	GGGa LMil SLdr
'Mathie' (A)	SReu SSta
maximum	GGGa
§ 'Maxwellii' (EA)	CMac SLdr
May Day Group	CBcs CWri MGos WBod
- 'May Day' ♀H3	CDul CMac MAsh MMuc SLdr
'Mayor Johnstone'	CTri EPfP MAsh NPri
'Mazurka' (K)	IVic
meddianum var. ***atrokermesinum*** F 2649	LMil
Medusa Group	SLdr
megacalyx	GGGa
'Megan' (EA)	LSRN MAsh SLdr WGwG
megaphyllum	see *R. basilicum*
megeratum	GGGa
- 'Bodnant'	GGGa ITim WAbe WThu
mekongense	GCal
- var. ***mekongense*** Rubroluteum Group	see *R. viridescens* Rubroluteum Group
- - Viridescens Group	see *R. viridescens*
'Melford Lemon'	see *R.* 'Ilam Melford Lemon'
'Melidioso'	LMil
'Melina' (EA/d)	LMil MBri
'Melville'	SSta
'Mendosina'	IVic
mengtszense	MSnd
menziesii	IVic
'Merganser' ♀H4	GGGa LMil MLea WThu
'Merlin' (Glenn Dale) (EA)	LMil
Metallica	see *R.* 'Hachmann's Metallica'
metternichii var. ***pentamerum***	see *R. degronianum* subsp. *degronianum*
'Mi Amor'	GGGa
'Michael Hall'	LMil
'Michael Hill' (EA)	MAsh
'Michael's Pride'	CBcs GQui
'Michiko' (EA)	IVic SAko
microgynum	GGGa MSnd
- Gymnocarpum Group	MSnd
microleucum	see *R. orthocladum* var. *microleucum*
micromeres	see *R. leptocarpum*
'Midnight Beauty'	EPfP SAko
'Midnight Mystique'	GGGa SReu SSta
'Midsummer'	IVic MMuc SLdr
'Midsummer Mermaid' (A)	CDoC LMil MAsh
'Mikado' (EA)	see *R. kaempferi* 'Mikado'
'Millennium Gold'PBR	LMil LRHS NLar
'Milton' (R)	LMil
'Mimi' (Kaempferi) (EA)	CMac
'Ming'	see *R.* 'Ilam Ming'
miniatum CER 9927	GGGa
minus	CBcs
- var. ***minus*** (Carolinianum Group) 'Epoch'	LMil
'Moerheim' ♀H5	CBcs CWri ECho LRHS MAsh MMuc NPri SLim
§ 'Moerheim's Pink'	LMil SLdr
(Mohamet Group) 'Mohamet'	LMil
'Moidart' (Vs)	LMil NLar
'Moira Salmon' (EA)	SLdr
§ ***molle*** subsp. ***japonicum*** (A)	LMil LPar NEgg
- subsp. ***molle*** (A)	LMil
Mollis, orange-flowered (M)	GKin SRms
Mollis, pink-flowered (M)	GKin SRms
Mollis, red-flowered (M)	GKin
Mollis, salmon-flowered (M)	GQui
Mollis, yellow-flowered (M)	GKin GQui SRms
'Molly Ann'	ECho LSRN NLar
'Molten Gold' (v)	GGGa LMil LRHS MAsh MBri MJak
§ 'Momoko' (EA)	CDul LRHS WFar
monanthum	GGGa
monosematum	see *R. pachytrichum* var. *monosematum*
'Monsieur Marcel Ménard' ♀H6	CBcs CDoC CDul COtt GGGa LMil LRHS MAsh MGos NLar NPri SCob SLdr SReu SSta
montroseanum	GGGa LMil MSnd SLdr
'Moon Maiden' (EA)	GGal GQui
Moonstone Group	MLea
'Moonstone Pink'	SLdr
'Moonstone Yellow'	MSnd SLdr
§ 'Morgenrot'	MMuc SAko
morii	GGGa
'Morning Cloud'	EPfP LRHS MAsh MGos NHol NLar SLim SReu SSta
Morning Red	see *R.* 'Morgenrot'
'Moser's Maroon'	CBcs CWri GGGa MGos MMuc NLar SLdr
'Mother of Pearl'	SLdr
'Mother's Day' (Kurume) (EA) ♀H4	CDoC CDul CMac CSBt CTri EPfP GKin GQui LCro LMil LRHS LSRN MAsh MBri MGos MJak NEgg NHol NPri SCob SLdr SLim SPer SPoG SReu SSta WBod WFar
'Mount Everest'	LMil SReu SSta
'Mount Rainier' (A)	LRHS
'Mount Saint Helens' (A)	CDoC LMil MGos NLar SLdr SLim SPer
'Mount Seven Star'	see *R. nakaharae* 'Mount Seven Star'
moupinense	GGGa MSnd
- 'Fulmar'	GGGa
'Mrs A.T. de la Mare' ♀H6	LMil SReu SSta
'Mrs Betty Robertson'	CMac GBin SLdr
'Mrs Charles E. Pearson' ♀H6	CSBt LMil SLdr SReu SSta
'Mrs Davies Evans'	SReu SSta
'Mrs Emil Hager' (EA)	SLdr
'Mrs Furnivall' ♀H6	CWri GGGa MLea SReu
'Mrs G.W. Leak'	CSBt CWri GGGa LMil SReu
'Mrs J.C. Williams' ♀H6	LMil
'Mrs J.G. Millais'	LMil
'Mrs James Horlick'	CWri
'Mrs Lionel de Rothschild'	CBcs CWri SReu
'Mrs Marks'	LMil
'Mrs P.D. Williams'	SReu
'Mrs T.H. Lowinsky' ♀H6	CBcs CDoC CDul CMac GGGa GKin LMil MAsh MGos MLea MMuc NLar SLdr SLim SPer SReu
§ × ***mucronatum*** (EA)	MSnd SLdr

	Name	Suppliers
	'Mucronatum'	see *R.* × *mucronatum*
	mucronulatum	MSnd
	- B&SWJ 786	WCru
	- B&SWJ 8657	WCru
	- var. ***chejuense***	see *R. mucronulatum* var. *taquetii*
	- 'Cornell Pink' Υ^{H5}	GGGa
§	- var. ***taquetii***	GGGa
	'Mulroy Cream'	LMil
	multiflorum	CPne
§	- var. ***purpureum***	GGGa
	'Mum' **new**	LMil
	'Muneira' (EA)	IVic
	'Muriel'	SLdr
	'Nabucco' (A)	EPfP GGGa MMuc SLdr WMoo
	nakaharae (EA) Υ^{H5}	MSnd SLdr SReu WAbe
	- 'Mariko' (EA)	WAbe WThu
§	- 'Mount Seven Star' (EA) Υ^{H5}	ECho GGGa LMil NWad SLdr WAbe WPat WThu
§	- orange-flowered (EA)	ECho LMil LRHS MAsh SLdr SReu
	- pink-flowered (EA)	ECho MPkF SLdr SReu
	- red-flowered (EA)	ECho
	'Nakahari Orange'	see *R. nakaharae* orange-flowered
	nakotiltum	MSnd
	'Nancy Evans' Υ^{H4}	CDoC CSBt EPfP GGGa GGal GKin LMil LRHS LSRN MAsh MGos MLea NLar NPri SLdr SLim SReu SSpi SSta
	'Nancy of Robinhill' (EA)	SReu
	'Nancy Waterer' (G) Υ^{H6}	SReu
	'Nanki Poo' (EA)	SLdr
	'Naomi' (EA)	GQui SLdr
	(Naomi Group) 'Exbury Naomi'	LMil
	- 'Naomi Hope'	LMil
	- 'Naomi Nautilus'	LMil
	- 'Naomi Pink Beauty'	LMil
	- 'Naomi Stella Maris'	LMil
	'Narcissiflorum' (G/d) Υ^{H6}	GKin LMil LRHS MPkF NLar SReu
	'Naselle'	SReu
	'Ne Plus Ultra' (V)	GGGa
	Negligé = 'Hachneg'^{PBR} (EA) **new**	LMil MBri
	neriiflorum	GGGa GKev LMil MSnd
	- CN&W 906	LMil
	- subsp. ***neriiflorum*** AC 1356	MSnd
§	- - Euchaites Group	LPar
§	- - Phoenicodum Group Farrer 877	MSnd
	'Newcomb's Sweetheart'	LMil
	'Niagara' (Glenn Dale) (EA) Υ^{H5}	CMac LMil SLdr
	'Nichola' (EA)	LSRN
	'Nico' (EA)	CMac LRHS MAsh MBri WBod
	'Nicoletta'	LMil
	'Night Sky' Υ^{H5}	CDoC EPfP GGGa LMil LRHS MAsh MBri MGos MSnd NLar SLdr
	'Nightingale'	SReu
	nigroglandulosum	GGGa
	'Ninotschka'	IVic
	nipponicum	GGGa
	'Nishiki' (EA)	CMac
	nitens	see *R. calostrotum* subsp. *riparium* Nitens Group
	nitidulum var. ***omeiense***	GGGa WThu
	nivale subsp. ***boreale*** Ramosissimum Group	GGGa
§	- subsp. ***nivale***	GKev ITim
	niveum Υ^{H4}	CBcs CPne GGGa LMil MSnd SReu
	- B&SWJ 2611	WCru
	- B&SWJ 2659	WCru
	- B&SWJ 2675	WCru
	nobleanum	see *R.* Nobleanum Group
§	Nobleanum Group	CBcs GGGa LMil MSnd SLdr SSta
	- 'Nobleanum Coccineum'	LMil SLdr SReu
	- 'Nobleanum Venustum'	CWri LMil SReu SSta
	Nobleanum Album Group	GGGa LMil SReu SSta
	(Norderney Group) 'Oudijk's Sensation'	CBcs CWri GQui MAsh MMuc SLdr
	'Nordlicht' (EA)	SLdr
	'Noriko' (EA)	SLdr
	'Norma' (R/d)	SReu
	'Northern Hi-Lights' (A)	CDoC GKin LMil LRHS MBri MGos MPkF NLar SLim SPer
	'Nova Zembla'	CBcs CDoC CTri EPfP GGGa LMil LRHS MAsh MGos MMuc NEgg SCob SLim SPer SReu SSta WMoo
	'Nuccio's Blue Moon' (EA)	LMil SLdr
	nudiflorum	see *R. periclymenoides*
	nudipes	MSnd
	nuttallii	GGGa LMil
	nymphaeoides CGG 14027	GGGa
	'Oban'	GEdr ITim NSla WAbe
	Obtusum Group (EA)	SLdr
	- 'Amoenum' (EA/d)	CBcs CDoC CMac CSBt CTsd LMil SLdr SPer
	- 'Amoenum Coccineum' (EA/d)	SLdr SReu SSta
§	- 'Hinomayo' (EA) Υ^{H5}	CMac CTri EPfP GKin GQui LMil MPkF SLdr SPer SReu
	occidentale (A)	CDul GGal GKin LMil
	- SIN 1830	GGGa
	ochraceum Υ^{H5}	GGGa LMil
	'Odee Wright'	CTri CWri LRHS MAsh
	'Odoratum' (Ad)	MLea
	'Oh! Kitty'	MLea SLdr
	'Oi-no-mezame' (Kurume) (EA)	SLdr
	'Old Gold' (K)	SLdr
	'Old Port'	CWri LMil
	oldhamii (EA)	CBcs
	'Olga' Υ^{H5}	LMil SReu SSta
	'Olga Niblett' (EA)	SReu SSta
	oligocarpum	GGGa
	'Opossum' (EA)	GGGa
	'Orange Beauty' (Kaempferi) (EA)	CBcs CDoC GGGa MAsh SGol SLdr SReu
	'Orange King' (EA) Υ^{H5}	LMil MGos SLdr SPoG
	orbiculare Υ^{H5}	GGGa LMil MSnd SLdr
§	- subsp. ***cardiobasis***	GGGa MSnd
	'Orchid Lights'	MAsh MBri
	'Oregon' (EA)	SLdr
	Oregonia Group	LMil
	oreodoxa	LMil
§	- var. ***fargesii*** Υ^{H6}	GGGa LMil MSnd
	- - AC 4052	MSnd
	- var. ***oreodoxa***	GGGa LMil
	oreotrephes Υ^{H4}	IDee LMil MSnd
	- 'Bluecalyptus'	GGGa
§	- Exquisitum Group	SLdr
	- 'Pentland'	GGGa LMil
	'Orion' ambig.	NLar
§	***orthocladum*** var. ***microleucum***	GGGa WThu
	'Osaraku Seedling' (EA)	CDoC EPfP LRHS
	'Osmar' Υ^{H5}	GGGa
	'Ostara'	CBcs
	'Osterschnee'	IVic
	'Oudijk's Favorite'	SLdr
	'Oxydol' (K)	IVic SLdr

§	***pachypodum***	GGGa
	pachysanthum ♀H6	GGGa GKin LMil MSnd SReu SSpi
	- 'Crosswater'	LMil MAsh
	pachysanthum* × *yakushimanum	SReu
	pachytrichum	GGGa
§	- var. ***monosematum***	MSnd
	'Palestrina' (Vuykiana) (EA) ♀H4	CBcs CDul CMac CSBt EPfP GBin GGal GKin MAsh MJak MMuc SGol SLdr SPer SReu SSta
	'Palma'	see *R. parmulatum* 'Palma'
	paludosum	see *R. nivale* subsp. *nivale*
	'Pancake'	CMac
	'Panda' (EA) ♀H5	CSBt CTri ECho EPfP GGGa LMil LRHS MAsh MBri MLea SSta
	'Paprika Spiced'	MLea
	'Parfait' (EA)	LMil
	'Parkfeuer' (A)	GGGa IVic MBri
	parmulatum	LMil
	- KW 5876	LMil
	- 'Ocelot'	GGGa SLdr
§	- 'Palma'	WBod
	parryae AM (*roseatum*)	GGGa
	'Patty Bee' ♀H5	CBcs CSBt CTri CWri ECho EPfP GBin GEdr GGGa GKev LMil LRHS MAsh MBri MGos MLea NLar NPri NSla SLdr SLim SReu SSpi SSta
	'Peach Blossom'	see *R.* 'Saotome'
	'Pearce's American Beauty'	LMil
	'Pearl Betteridge' **new**	LMil
	'Peep-bo' (EA)	SLdr
	'Peeping Tom'	NHol SReu SSta
	'Peggy'	LMil
	pemakoense	GGGa SLdr WThu
	'Pemakofairy'	WThu
	pendulum	GGGa
	Penelope Group	SReu
	'Penheale Blue' ♀H5	CTsd GKin LMil
	'Penjerrick'	GGGa
	'Penny Tomlin'	SReu SSta
	pentaphyllum (A)	GGGa
	'Peppermint Candy'	LMil
	'Peppina'	GGGa LMil MBri
	'Percy Wiseman' ♀H5	CBcs CDoC CDul COtt CSBt CWri EPfP GBin GGGa GKin LMil LRHS MAsh MBri MGos MJak MLea MMuc MSnd NEgg NLar SCob SLdr SLim SPer SPoG SReu SSta
§	***periclymenoides*** (A)	GGGa GKev LMil
	'Persil' (K) ♀H6	CBcs CMac CSBt CTri CWri EPfP GGGa GKin LMil LRHS MAsh MBri MJak MMuc NEgg NHol NLar SCoo SLdr SPer SReu SSta WFar WMoo
	'Peter Chapell'	GGGa
	'Peter Gable' (EA)	SLdr
	'Peter Koster' (hybrid)	GKin SLdr
	Petticoat = 'Hachpett' (EA) **new**	LMil
	petrocharis	GGGa
	'Pfauenauge'	GGGa
	phaeochrysum	MSnd
§	- var. ***levistratum***	MSnd
	- var. ***phaeochrysum***	GKev
	- - C 12529	GGGa
	- - SDR 4237	GKev
	'Phalarope'	GEdr MMuc SReu
	phoenicodum	see *R. neriiflorum* subsp. *neriiflorum* Phoenicodum Group
	'Phyllis Korn'	CWri IVic LMil SAko
§	***piercei***	GGGa LMil MSnd
	'Pine Marten' (EA)	GGGa
	pingianum	GGGa
	'Pink Bride'	SLdr
	'Pink Cameo'	CWri
	'Pink Cherub' ♀H6	LMil MAsh MLea
I	'Pink Delight' (K)	GKin MMuc
	'Pink Delight' (V)	SLdr
	'Pink Drift'	CSBt ECho GEdr LMil NSla SLdr SPer WThu
	'Pink Gin'	LMil
	'Pink Pancake' (EA) ♀H4	CDoC EPfP GKin LMil LRHS MAsh MBri MPkF NPri SLdr
	'Pink Pearl' (EA)	see *R.* 'Azuma-kagami'
	'Pink Pearl' (hybrid) ♀H4	CBcs CDul CMac CSBt CTri CWri EPfP GGGa LCro LMil MAsh MBri MMuc SLdr SPer SPoG SReu SSta
	'Pink Pebble' ♀H5	CBcs CExl ELon MAsh MLea
	'Pink Perfection'	CMac SLdr
	'Pink Polar Bear'	GKin LMil
	'Pink Ruffles' (K)	WBod
	'Pintail'	GGGa LMil LRHS MAsh
	'Pipit'	GGGa
	'Pippa' (EA)	CMac
	'PJM Elite'	SAko
	'PJM Regal'	IVic
	'PJM Victor' **new**	SAko
	platypodum CGG 14005	GGGa
	'Pleasant White' (EA)	LMil LRHS MGos NLar
	'Plover'	GGGa
	pocophorum	MSnd
§	- var. ***hemidartum***	MSnd
	- var. ***pocophorum***	GGGa
	'Point Defiance'	CWri MLea MSnd SPer
	'Polar Bear' (EA)	SLdr
	Polar Bear Group	CWri LMil MLea
	- 'Polar Bear'	CHll CSBt GGGa GKin IVic LMil SLdr SReu
	'Polaris'	see *R.* 'Hachmann's Polaris'
	'Polaris' (EA)	NLar
	'Polarnacht'	CBcs CDoC GGGa GKin IVic LMil SAko SLdr
	poluninii	GGGa
	- KR 8231	LMil
	polyandrum	see *R. maddenii* subsp. *maddenii* Polyandrum Group
§	***polycladum*** Scintillans Group	GGGa
	polylepis	MSnd
	- AC 3810	MSnd
	'Polyroy'	GGGa
	'Pomegranate Splash'	GGGa
	ponticum	CDul CMac CTri CWri NHol WFar
	- 'Filigran'	IVic
	- 'Roseum'	SGol
§	- 'Variegatum' (v)	CBcs CMac EPfP MAsh MBri MGos MLea NPri SCob SLdr SPer SPoG SRms SSta
	populare KC 0126	GGGa
	'Praecox' ♀H4	CBcs CDoC CSBt ECho EPfP GGGa GKev GKin LMil LRHS MAsh MBri MGos MJak MMuc NLar NPri SLdr SLim SPoG SReu WBod
	Praecox Group **new**	MJak
	praestans	CPne GGGa GKin LMil MSnd
	prattii	GGGa
	preptum	GGGa
	'President Roosevelt' (v)	CBcs CSBt EPfP GKin MAsh MJak NPri SPoG SReu SSta
	'Pride of Leonardslee'	SLdr

'Pridenjoy'	LMil
primuliflorum ♀H5	MSnd WAbe
- 'Doker-La'	GGGa LMil WAbe
'Prince Camille de Rohan'	LMil
'Princess Alice'	CBcs IDee SLdr
'Princess Anne' ♀H5	CBcs CMHG ECho ELon IDee LMil LRHS MAsh MGos MLea NLar SLdr SLim SPer SPoG SReu SSta WBod
'Princess Margaret of Windsor' (K)	GQui LMil
principis	GGGa LMil
- 'Lost Horizon'	LMil
prinophyllum (A)	GGGa GKin LMil
'Prins Bernhard' (EA)	MAsh SLdr
'Prinses Juliana' (Vuykiana) (EA)	SLdr SReu
'Professor Hugo de Vries'	SLdr
pronum	GGGa
- R.B. Cooke form	GGGa
- Towercourt form	GGGa
proteoides	GGGa
protistum	GCal GGGa
pruniflorum	GGGa
prunifolium (A)	GGGa LMil
przewalskii	GGGa MSnd
pseudochrysanthum ♀H5	GGGa LMil MSnd SReu
- dwarf	GGGa
pseudociliipes	CPne GGGa
Psyche Group	see *R.* Wega Group
'Psyche' (EA)	SLdr
'Ptarmigan' ♀H5	ECho GEdr GGGa LMil MSnd SLdr WPat WThu
pubicostatum AC 2051	MSnd
§ 'Pucella' (G)	CWri
pudorosum	GGGa
'Pulchrum Maxwellii'	see *R.* 'Maxwellii'
pumilum	GGGa WAbe WThu
'Pumuckl'	IVic SAko
'Purple Cushion' (EA)	EPfP LRHS MAsh NPri
'Purple Diamond'	see *R.* Diamant Group purple-flowered
'Purple Gem'	CDoC MGos MMuc
'Purple Passion' PBR	CDoC LMil MGos NLar SLdr SPer
'Purple Queen' (EA/d)	MAsh
'Purple Splendor' (Gable) (EA)	CMac SGol SLdr
'Purple Splendour'	CBcs CSBt CWri LMil MGos MLea MMuc NEgg NLar SPer SReu SSta WMoo
'Purple Triumph' (Vuykiana) (EA) ♀H5	LMil SLdr
'Purpureum Grandiflorum'	LMil
'Purpurtraum' (EA) ♀H5	LMil SAko
'Pyari'	GGGa
qiaojiaense NN 0903	GGGa MSnd
'Quail'	GGGa SLdr
'Queen Alice'	MGos NLar
'Queen Anne's'	GGGa
Queen Emma	see *R.* 'Koningin Emma'
'Queen Mary'	SReu SSta
'Queen Souriya'	SReu
'Quentin Metsys' (R)	SLdr SReu
quinquefolium (A)	GGGa LMil SLdr
Rabatz = 'Hachraba'	GGGa IVic LMil LRHS MBri NLar SAko SPoG
racemosum ♀H4	LMil MSnd
- BWJ 7811 **new**	WCru
- SDR 3336	GKev
- SDR 4218 **new**	GKev
- 'Rock Rose' ♀H5	EPfP IDee LMil
'Racine' (G)	SReu
'Racoon' (EA)	GGGa
radicans	see *R. calostrotum* subsp. *keleticum* Radicans Group
'Radistrotum'	SAko
'Raimunde' (K)	IVic SAko
'Ramapo' ♀H6	CDoC ECho GGGa LMil LRHS MAsh MBri MGos MMuc NLar SLdr SLim SPer SReu
'Raoul Millais'	LMil
'Raphael de Smet' (G/d)	SReu
'Raphaela' **new**	SAko
'Rasputin'	COtt LMil
'Razorbill' ♀H4	CDoC GGGa GKin LMil LRHS MGos NLar SLim
recurvoides	GGGa LMil MSnd SLdr SReu
- Keillour form	GGGa
'Red and Gold'	GGGa LRHS NPri
'Red Dawn'	LRHS MLea
'Red Delicious'	LMil SLdr
'Red Diamond'	see *R.* Diamant Group red-flowered
'Red Fountain' (EA)	ECho SLdr
'Red Jack'	COtt LMil MGos SCob SPer SPoG SReu SSta
'Red Panda' (EA)	GGGa
'Red Pimpernel' (EA)	SLdr
'Red Sunset' (A)	SLdr
'Red Wood'	GGGa
'Redwing' (EA)	see *R.* 'Hexe de Saffelaere', *R* 'Redwings'
'Redwing' ambig. (EA)	CDoC MAsh
§ 'Redwings' (EA)	SLdr
'Rennie' (A)	GKin MMuc
'Renoir' ♀H5	CSBt LMil SReu
reticulatum (A)	LMil MSnd SReu
'Reuthe's Purple'	SReu WAbe WThu
'Rêve d'Amour' (Vs)	SReu SSta
'Rex' (EA)	MAsh
rex ♀H4	GGGa GKev GKin LMil SLdr
- EGM 295	LMil
§ - subsp. ***fictolacteum*** ♀H4	GGGa GKin LMil MSnd SLdr
- - Miniforme Group	MSnd
- subsp. ***rex*** ♀H4	MSnd
- - NN 0904	MSnd
rex × yakushimanum	SReu
rhabdotum	see *R. dalhousiae* var. *rhabdotum*
'Rhododendronpark Graal-Müriz'	SReu SSta
'Ria Hardijzer' (Ad)	LMil
rigidum	GGGa MSnd
- 'Album'	LMil
'Ring of Fire'	CWri IVic LMil MLea
'Ripe Corn'	MSnd
'Ripples' (EA)	CTrh
ririei	GGGa
'Robert Croux'	SLdr
'Robert Seleger'	EPfP GGGa GKin LMil MAsh MBri SReu
'Robert Whelan' (A)	SReu SSta
'Robin Hill Frosty' (EA)	SLdr
'Robin Hill Gillie' (EA)	SLdr
'Robinette'	CBcs CWri MAsh SLdr
'Rocket'	CDoC CTri LMil MAsh MGos MLea MMuc SLdr SLim SPoG
'Roehr's Peggy Ann' (EA)	LMil
'Rokoko'	see *R.* 'Hachmann's Rokoko'
'Ronny' **new**	SAko
'Rosa' (EA)	MGos
Rosalind Group	CMac
- 'Rosalind'	WFar

'Rosalinda' (EA)	SLdr
'Rosata' (Vs) ♀H5	GGGa GKin SReu SSta
'Rose Bud'	CSBt CTri WBod
'Rose Elf'	WThu
'Rose Glow' (A)	SReu SSta
'Rose Gown'	SReu
'Rose Greely' (Gable) (EA) ♀H5	CDoC MGos NLar SLdr SLim SPer SReu
'Rose Haze' (Vs)	SReu SSta
'Rosebud' (EA/d)	CBcs CMac SLdr SReu SSta
roseum	see *R. canescens*
'Roseum Elegans'	CDoC LMil MAsh MGos SCob SLim
'Rosevallon'	MSnd
Rosinetta = 'Hachrosi' (EA)	GGGa LMil
'Rosy Dream'	CWri MAsh MMuc
'Rosy Fire' (A)	LMil SReu
'Rosy Lea'	MLea
'Rosy Lights' (A)	LMil MPkF
'Rotglocke'	IVic
rothschildii	GGGa LMil MSnd SLdr
'Rotkäppchen'	IVic SAko
rousei (V)	GGGa
roxieanum	GGGa LMil MSnd SLdr
- AC 1753	MSnd
§ - var. ***cucullatum***	GGGa GKev
- - SDR 2600 new	GKev
- var. ***oreonastes*** ♀H5	GGGa IVic LMil MSnd
- - Nymans form	SReu
- var. ***parvum***	GGGa
'Royal Command' (K)	CBcs CTri CWri GKin LMil MBri
'Royal Ruby' (K)	CWri MMuc
'Royal Windsor'	LMil
'Roza Stevenson'	SLdr
'Rubicon'	CWri GGGa MAsh SLdr
rubiginosum ♀H4	GGGa LMil MSnd
- SDR 5160 new	GKev
- pink-flowered	LMil
rubroluteum	see *R. viridescens* Rubroluteum Group
'Ruby Glow' (EA)	GGal
'Ruby Hart'	GGGa LSRN MMuc
Ruby Wedding	see *R.* 'Firestorm'
rude	see *R. glischrum* subsp. *rude*
rufum	GGGa
rugosum Sinclair 240 (V)	GGGa
rushforthii	GGGa
russatum ♀H5	CBcs GGGa LMil MSnd SLdr SSpi WAbe
- blue-black-flowered	GKin LMil
* - 'Collingwood Ingram'	GGGa
- 'Purple Pillow'	MMuc
Russautinii Group	SLdr
Russellianum Group	GGal
russotinctum	see *R. alutaceum* var. *russotinctum*
'Ryde Heron' (EA)	SLdr
'Sabina' (EA)	SLdr
'Sacko'	CDoC CWri GGGa LMil MGos NLar SLim
'Saffrano'	COtt
'Saffron Queen'	CBcs CTsd SLdr
'Saint Breward'	GQui MLea
'Saint Merryn' ♀H5	CBcs CWri GEdr SLdr
'Saint Minver'	SLdr
'Saint Tudy'	SLdr
'Saint Valentine' (V)	GGGa
'Sakata Red' (EA)	WBod
'Salmon Sander' (EA)	SLdr
'Salmon's Leap' (EA/v)	CMac ELan LMil LRHS MAsh MBri SReu SSta
saluenense	LMil SLdr WThu
'Sammetglut'	CWri
'Samuel Taylor Coleridge' (M)	GKin
sanguineum	LMil MSnd
§ - subsp. ***didymum***	GGGa MSnd SLdr
- subsp. ***sanguineum*** var. ***haemaleum***	GGGa LMil MSnd
- - var. ***sanguineum*** F 25521	LMil
'Santa Maria' (EA) ♀H5	LMil LSRN NLar SReu SSta
santapaui (V)	GGGa
§ 'Saotome' (EA)	SLdr
'Sapphire'	WThu
'Sappho'	CBcs CMac CWri ECho GGGa GKin LMil LRHS MLea NEgg NLar SLdr SPer SReu SSta WGwG
sargentianum	GGGa NHar WAbe WThu
- 'Whitebait'	ITim
'Sarled' ♀H5	GGGa ITim LMil NHar WAbe WThu
'Saskia' (K)	IVic SAko
'Satan' (K) ♀H6	CDoC LMil LRHS MGos NLar SReu SSta
Satsuki (EA)	ITim SLdr
'Saturnus' (M)	GKin
§ ***scabrifolium*** var. ***spiciferum***	MSnd SLdr WAbe
'Scarlet Wonder' ♀H5	CBcs CDoC CDul CMHG CSBt CWri EPfP GEdr GGGa GKin LMil LRHS MAsh MBri MGos MJak MMuc NPri SLdr SReu WBod
schistocalyx F 17637	MSnd
schlippenbachii (A)	CBcs CPne GGGa GKev IDee LMil MSnd SLdr
'Schneekrone' ♀H6	GGGa
Schneeperle = 'Hachschnee' (EA) ♀H5	IVic LMil LRHS MGos SAko SHil
'Schneespiegel'	GGGa
scintillans	see *R. polycladum* Scintillans Group
'Scintillation' ♀H6	CBcs CWri GGGa LMil MAsh MBri MGos MLea MMuc NLar SLdr
scopulorum	GGGa SLdr
'Scotian Bells'	GGGa
scottianum	see *R. pachypodum*
'Scottish Marmalade'	GGGa
'Scout' (EA)	MAsh SLdr
scyphocalyx	see *R. dichroanthum* subsp. *scyphocalyx*
searsiae	MSnd
'Seaview Sunset'	GGGa MGos NLar
'Second Honeymoon'	CWri MLea MMuc
seinghkuense	GGGa LMil
- CCH&H 8106	LMil
§ ***selense*** subsp. ***dasycladum***	MSnd
- subsp. ***jucundum***	GGGa
semnoides	GGGa LMil
'Sennocke'	LMil
'September Song' ♀H4	CWri GGGa LMil MAsh MLea NHol
'Septembercharm'	LMil LRHS
serotinum	GGGa LMil
serpyllifolium (A)	CBcs CTsd
'Sesterianum'	CMHG
Seta Group	SReu
- 'Seta'	CAbP SLdr WThu
'Shamrock' ♀H5	CDoC ELon EPfP GEdr GKev LRHS MAsh MBri MGos MLea NEgg NLar NSla SLim SPoG WThu
'Sheila' (EA)	CSBt LRHS MAsh NPri
'Shelley' (EA)	LMil LSRN

shepherdii	see *R. kendrickii*
sherriffii	GGGa MSnd
'Shiko' (EA)	MAsh
'Shiko Lavender' (A)	SPoG
Shilsonii Group	LMil
'Shin-sekai' (Kurume) (EA/d)	SLdr
'Shrimp Girl'	GKin MSnd
sichotense	GGGa
sidereum	GCal GGGa
siderophyllum	GGGa MSnd
sikangense	GGGa MSnd
- var. ***exquisitum***	GGGa GKev
'Silbervelours'	IVic
§ 'Silberwolke' ♀H6	IVic LMil MAsh
'Silkeborg Silence'	GGGa
Silver Cloud	see *R.* 'Silberwolke'
'Silver Edge'	see *R. ponticum* 'Variegatum'
'Silver Glow' (EA)	CMac
'Silver Jubilee' ♀H4	LMil LRHS
'Silver Moon' (Glenn Dale) (EA)	SLdr
'Silver Queen' (EA)	LPar MPkF
'Silver Sixpence'	CBcs EPfP LSRN MBri MJak MLea MMuc SLdr
'Silver Skies'	LMil
'Silver Slipper' (K) ♀H6	CBcs GKin LMil MLea NHol SReu SSta WFar
'Silver Sword' (EA/v)	EPfP MGos
'Silverwood' (A)	LMil
'Silvester' (Kurume) (EA)	CTri LMil LRHS MAsh MPkF SLdr SReu WBod
'Simona'	LMil SAko
simsii (EA)	CMac LMil SLdr
sinofalconeri	GGGa IDee LMil MSnd
- KR 7342	LMil
- SEH 229	LMil
sinogrande ♀H3	CBcs CPne ELon GBin GCal GGGa GKev GKin IDee LMil NEgg SPer
- APA 106	GGGa
- KR 4027	LMil
§ 'Sir Charles Butler'	LMil
'Sir Charles Lemon' ♀H3	CDoC CWri GGGa LMil MAsh SPer
'Sir Robert' (EA)	MAsh MBri
'Sleepy'	CBcs CSBt MAsh MLea MSnd NHol SLdr
smirnowii	GGGa IDee LMil LRHS MSnd
smithii	see *R. argipeplum*
'Sneezy' ♀H5	CBcs COtt CSBt CWri EPfP GGGa LMil LRHS MAsh MJak MMuc MSnd SLdr SLim SSta
'Snipe'	CTri ECho GBin GEdr LMil LRHS MAsh MBri MGos MMuc NLar SLdr SLim SReu WBod WThu
'Snow Crown' (*lindleyi* hybrid)	MAsh MGos
'Snow Hill' (EA) ♀H5	LMil
'Snow Lady'	CBcs CTsd EPfP GEdr GKin GQui LRHS MAsh MMuc SLdr SReu
'Snow Pearl'	EPfP MAsh MBri
Snow Queen Group	LMil SReu
- 'Snow Queen'	LMil
'Snowbird' (A)	GGal SLdr
'Snowbird' (EA)	CDul
'Snowflake' (EA/d)	see *R.* 'Kure-no-yuki'
'Snowwhite' (EA)	MGos
'Soho' (EA)	GQui
'Soir de Paris' (Vs) ♀H6	CSBt GGGa GKin IVic LMil NHol SReu SSta WFar WGwG
'Soldier Sam'	SReu

(Solent Group) 'Drury Lane' (K)	GQui LMil
'Solidarity'	MLea SLdr SReu SSta
'Solway' (Vs)	LMil
'Sommerduft' (A)	IVic
'Son de Paris' (A)	GQui
'Sonata'	CWri GBin GGGa GGal SReu
'Sonatine'	LMil
'Songbird'	GEdr LMil MSnd SLdr WBod
sororium (V)	LMil
- KR 3085	LMil
souliei	LMil SSpi
- deep pink-flowered	GGGa
'Souvenir de D.A. Koster'	SLdr
'Souvenir de Doctor S. Endtz'	SReu
'Souvenir of Anthony Waterer'	SReu SSta
'Souvenir of W.C. Slocock'	MMuc
'Spätlese'	IVic
'Spek's Orange' (M)	GKin
sperabile	GGGa
- var. ***weihsiense***	MSnd
sphaeranthum	see *R. trichostomum*
sphaeroblastum	GGGa MSnd
- var. ***wumengense***	GGGa
- - KR 1481	MSnd
spiciferum	see *R. scabrifolium* var. *spiciferum*
'Spinner's Glory'	MAsh
spinuliferum	CBcs GGGa
- NN 10945	MSnd
'Spitfire'	NHol SReu SSta
'Spring Beauty' (EA)	SReu
'Spring Morning'	CPne SReu
'Spring Pearl'	see *R.* 'Moerheim's Pink'
'Spring Rose'	SLdr
'Spring Sunshine'	LMil LRHS
'Squirrel' (EA) ♀H5	ECho GGGa GKin LMil MAsh MLea SLdr SLim SReu WBod
'Staccato'	IVic
'Stadt Essen'	LMil SLdr
'Stadt Westerstede'	LMil
stamineum	GGGa
§ 'Stanway'	LMil
'Starbright Champagne'	MAsh MBri
'Statuette'	IVic SAko
§ ***stenopetalum*** 'Linearifolium' (EA)	CMac LMil SLdr WAbe WBod
stenophyllum	see *R. makinoi*
stewartianum	CPne GGGa
'Stewartstonian' (EA)	CMac MMuc SReu
'Stoat' (EA)	GQui NLar
'Stopham Girl' (A)	LMil
'Stopham Lad' (A)	LMil
'Strategist'	SLdr
'Strawberry Cream'	EPfP GGGa LRHS MAsh MBri
'Strawberry Ice' (K) ♀H6	CBcs CDoC CDul CSBt CWri ELan EPfP GBin GGGa GKin LMil MAsh MBri MMHG SLdr SReu WMoo
'Strawberry Sundae'	MLea MMuc NEgg SLdr
strigillosum	GGGa MSnd
- Reuthe's form	SReu
subansiriense	GGGa
suberosum	see *R. yunnanense* Suberosum Group
'Suga-no-ito' (Kurume) (EA)	SLdr
sulfureum JN 11062	MSnd
'Summer Blaze' (A)	SLdr
'Summer Dawn'	LMil
'Summer Flame'	SReu

	Name	Suppliers
	'Summer Fragrance' (A) ♀H6	LMil SReu SSta
	'Summer Snow'	IVic SAko
	'Summer Sorbet'	LMil
	'Sun Chariot' (K)	CBcs
	Sunkist Group	SLdr
	'Sunset Pink' (K)	CDul ELan SLdr
	'Sunspray'	SReu SSta
	'Sunte Nectarine' (K) ♀H6	GKin GQui NLar
	suoilenhensis NVD 18	GGGa
	'Surprise' ambig. (EA)	CDoC CTri SLdr
	'Surrey Heath'	CBcs CDoC CWri EPfP LMil MAsh MGos MJak MMuc MSnd NLar SLdr SLim SPer
	'Susan' (EA)	MSnd SSta
	'Susan' J.C.Williams	LMil SReu
	'Susannah Hill' (EA)	CBcs SLdr
	sutchuenense	GGGa LMil MSnd
	- var. ***geraldii***	see *R.* × *geraldii*
	'Swamp Beauty'	CWri MAsh MLea MMuc SLdr WGwG
	'Swansong' (EA)	CMac
	'Sweet Simplicity'	CWri
	'Swift' ♀H4	ECho GBin GGGa GQui LMil LRHS MAsh MBri MMuc SLdr
	'Sylphides' (K)	CMac
	'T.S. Black' (EA)	SLdr
	taggianum	GGGa
	'Talavera'	LMil SSpi
	taliense	LMil
	- SBEC 0350	GGGa
	- 'Honigduft'	IDee LMil LRHS NLar
	Tally Ho Group	LMil
	tamaense	see *R. cinnabarinum* subsp. *tamaense*
	Tanaga	see *R.* 'Hachmann's Tanaga'
	Tanager	see *R.* 'Glendoick Tanager'
	'Tanager' (K) **new**	SLdr
	'Tangerine'	see *R.* 'Fabia Tangerine'
	tapetiforme	GGGa
	'Taurus' ♀H5	CDoC CWri GGal GKin IVic LMil LRHS MAsh MLea MMuc MSnd NLar SAko SLdr SReu WMoo
	taxifolium (v)	GGGa
	'Teal'	ECho
	'Ted Millais'	LMil
	'Teddy Bear'	CWri LMil MLea SReu SSta
	telopeum	see *R. campylocarpum* subsp. *caloxanthum* Telopeum Group
	Temple Belle Group	ECho GEdr WBod
	'Teniers' (R)	SReu
§	***tephropeplum***	CPne GGGa MSnd WAbe
	- Deleiense Group	see *R. tephropeplum*
I	'Tequila Sunrise' USA	LMil
	'Terra-cotta'	LMil
	'Terra-cotta Beauty' (EA)	NWad WThu
	(Tessa Group) 'Tessa'	CBcs
	thayerianum	GGGa MSnd
§	'The Honourable Jean Marie de Montague' ♀H4	CWri GGGa GKin LMil MAsh MGos MLea MMuc MSnd NLar SPer SReu SSta
	'Thomas David' (A)	LMil
	thomsonii	GCal GGGa GKin LMil MSnd SReu
	- AC 113	MSnd
	- B&SWJ 2638	WCru
	- TDA 073	MSnd
	- subsp. ***lopsangianum***	GGGa
	'Thor'	GGGa SReu
	'Thunderstorm'	SReu

	Name	Suppliers
	'Tibet'	GQui LMil
	'Tidbit' ♀H3	CMac GGGa LMil MLea NLar SLdr
	'Tinkerbird'	CDoC GGGa LRHS MAsh MBri MGos NLar NPri
	'Tinner's Blush'	CBcs
	titapuriense	GGGa
	'Titian Beauty'	CBcs CDoC CSBt CWri ELan EPfP GGGa LMil LRHS MAsh MGos MMuc NEgg NLar SAko SLim SPer SPoG WMoo
	'Titness Park'	LMil
	'Tit-Willow' (EA)	LRHS MAsh MBri SCoo
	'Tom Hyde' (EA)	LSRN
	tomentosum	WThu
	'Torchlight' (EA) ♀H5	LMil LRHS MGos NLar
	'Toreador' (EA)	SLdr
	'Torridon' (Vs)	LMil
	Tortoiseshell Group	SCob
	- 'Champagne' ♀H3	CBcs CSBt LMil LRHS MAsh MGos NPri SPer SReu
	- 'Tortoiseshell Orange' ♀H3	CBcs CDoC CDul CSBt CWri LMil MBri NLar SCob SLim SPer SReu SSta
	- 'Tortoiseshell Wonder' ♀H3	CWri EPfP LMil LRHS MAsh
	'Toucan' (K)	CSBt LMil
	'Tower Dainty' (A)	GGGa
	'Tower Daring' (A)	GGGa
	'Tower Dragon' (A)	LMil
	traillianum	LMil MSnd
	'Tree Creeper'	GGGa GKin LMil SLdr
	'Tregedna Red'	SReu
	'Trewithen Orange'	SLdr
	trichanthum	GGGa
	- 'Honey Wood'	LMil SLdr
	trichocladum	CPne GKev
§	***trichostomum***	GGGa WAbe
	- Ledoides Group	LMil
	triflorum	GGGa LMil
§	- var. ***bauhiniiflorum***	CBcs GGGa SLdr
	- var. ***triflorum*** Mahogani Group	GGGa MSnd
	- - AC 3386	MSnd
	trilectorum	GGGa
	triplonaevium	see *R. alutaceum* var. *russotinctum* Triplonaevium Group
	'Tromba'	LMil SAko
	tsangpoense	see *R. charitopes* subsp. *tsangpoense*
	tsariense	GGGa LMil MSnd
	- var. ***trimoense***	GGGa LMil
	- - KW 8288	LMil
	- 'Yum Yum'	GGGa
	tubiforme	see *R. glaucophyllum* subsp. *tubiforme*
	'Tuffet' (EA)	LMil SLdr
	'Tunis' (K)	LRHS MAsh NPri
	'Turaço'	GGGa SLdr
	'Turnstone'	GGGa
	ungernii	GGGa MSnd
§	***uniflorum*** var. ***imperator***	GGGa
	'Unique' (*campylocarpum* hybrid)	MAsh MSnd SLdr SReu
	'Unique' (G)	CBcs EPfP GGGa GGal MMuc SPer
	'Unique Marmalade'	LMil MLea SLdr
	'Ursine'	IVic
	uvariifolium var. ***griseum***	LMil MSnd
	- 'Reginald Childs'	LMil
	'Valencia'	IVic
	valentinianum	CBcs GGGa MSnd SLdr WAbe
	- F 24347	MSnd
	- var. ***oblongilobatum***	GGGa

'Van'	CDoC LMil MGos NLar SLim
'Van Houttei Flore Pleno' (G/d)	SReu
'Van Nes Sensation'	LMil
Vanessa Group	GGal LMil
- 'Vanessa Pastel' ♀^{H3}	CMac GGGa LMil SReu SSta
Varna Group	WBod
vaseyi (A) ♀^{H5}	CBcs GGGa LMil
- 'White Find'	GGGa
- white-flowered (A)	LMil
'Vayo' (EA)	SLdr
§ ***veitchianum*** Cubittii Group	CBcs GGGa
- KNE Cox 9001	GGGa
venator	GGGa MSnd
'Venetia' (K)	SReu SSta
'Venetian Chimes'	CSBt MJak MSnd
vernicosum	GGGa MSnd
- AC 1901	MSnd
- AC 4102	MSnd
'Vida Brown' (Kurume) (EA/d)	CMac MMuc SLdr SReu WThu
'Vinecourt Dream' (M)	GKin MMuc NLar SLdr
'Vinecourt Duke' (A/d)	CWri GKin MMuc MPkF NEgg NLar
'Vinecourt Troubador' (K/d)	SPer
'Vineland Dream' (K/d)	CWri GKin
'Vintage Rosé' ♀^{H5}	LMil MMuc SSta
'Violetta' (Glenn Dale) (EA)	SLdr
'Violette Funken'	LMil
'Virginia Richards'	LPar SCob SLdr
Virginia Richards Group	CWri LPar LRHS MAsh
§ ***viridescens***	MSnd
- 'Doshong La'	GGGa LMil
§ - Rubroluteum Group	SLdr
viscidifolium	GGGa
viscosum (A) ♀^{H6}	CBcs CDoC GGGa GQui LMil MBri MGos MMHG MMuc MSnd NLar SPer SReu
- 'Grey Leaf' (Vs)	LMil
- f. ***rhodanthum*** (A)	LMil
- 'Roseum' (Vs)	LMil
'Viscount Powerscourt'	SLdr
'Viscy' ♀^{H5}	CDul CWri GKin LMil LRHS MMuc MSnd NLar SLdr
§ Volker Group	CDul CWri EPfP IDee LMil LRHS MAsh MBri
§ - 'Flavum Lackblatt'	MSnd SLdr
'Vollblut'	SReu SSta
'Vulcan' ♀^{H4}	GGGa LMil MLea SCob
'Vuyk's Rosyred' (Vuykiana) (EA) ♀^{H4}	CBcs CDoC CDul CMac CTri GKin LMil MAsh NHol NWad SGol SLdr SPer SPoG SReu WBod WFar
'Vuyk's Scarlet' (Vuykiana) (EA) ♀^{H4}	CBcs CDoC CMac CSBt CTri CTsd GKin LRHS MAsh MBri MMuc NHol NPri NWad SGol SLdr SPer SPlb SReu SSta
'W B I' **new**	SReu
'W.E. Gumbleton' (M)	SReu
'W.F.H.' ♀^{H3}	CWri IDee LMil MSnd SLdr
'Wagtail'	GGGa
Walküre = 'Hachwalk'	LMil
wallichii	GGGa LMil MSnd
- Heftii Group	GGGa
'Wallowa Red' (A)	MLea MMuc MPkF
'Wally Miller'	MAsh
walongense	GGGa
'Wanna Bee'	LMil
wardii	GGGa LMil MSnd
- L&S 5679	GGGa MSnd
- var. ***puralbum***	GGGa
- var. ***wardii*** AC 3425	MSnd
- - AC 3469	MSnd
'Ward's Ruby' (EA)	CTrh SLdr
wasonii	LMil MSnd
- f. ***rhododactylum***	MSnd
- yellow-flowered	GGGa
'Water Baby' (A)	LMil
'Water Girl' (A)	GGGa LMil
'Waterfall'	SLdr
watsonii	MSnd
'Wee Bee' ♀^{H5}	CBcs CDoC ECho EPfP GEdr GKin LMil LRHS MAsh MGos MLea MMuc NLar SAko SLim SReu SSta WBod
§ Wega Group	SLdr
'Weinlese' **new**	SAko
'Wendy'	MAsh
'Western Lights' (A)	MBri
'Westminster' (O)	LMil
'Weston's Pink Diamond' (d)	LMil
'What a Dane'	GGGa
'Whidbey Island'	LMil
'Whisperingrose'	LMil
'White Brocade'	SReu SSta
§ White Dufthecke = 'Rhodunter 48'PBR	LMil
'White Frills' (EA)	SLdr
'White Gold'	GGGa
'White Grandeur' (EA)	CTrh
'White Jade' (EA)	SLdr
'White Lady' (EA)	SLdr
'White Lights' (A) ♀^{H7}	CTri MBri SAko
'White Moon' (EA) **new**	MPkF
'White Pearl' (EA)	LSRN
'White Perfume' (A)	SReu SSta
'White Prince' (EA/d) **new**	MPkF
'White Rosebud' (EA)	SReu SSta
'White Swan' (hybrid)	SReu
'White Swan' (K)	GKin
'Whitethroat' (K/d) ♀^{H6}	CWri EPfP GQui LMil LRHS MBri MMHG MMuc SLdr SReu SSta
'Whitney's Dwarf Red'	WMoo
'Wigeon'	LMil
wightii	GGGa MSnd
'Wilgen's Ruby'	CDoC CSBt MGos SLdr SLim
'Wilgen's Surprise' **new**	SCob
'Willbrit'	CBcs CWri MAsh MMuc SLdr
williamsianum ♀^{H4}	CBcs CMac ECho GBin GGGa LMil MLea MSnd SLdr SReu WBod
- 'Andrea'	IVic
- Caerhays form	CExl
'Willy' (Kaempferi) (EA)	LMil SLdr
wiltonii ♀^{H5}	GGGa LMil
'Windsor Hawk'	CWri
'Windsor Lad'	SReu
'Windsor Sunbeam' (K)	CWri
'Wine and Roses'PBR	GGGa LCro MBri
Winsome Group	CMac CWri GGGa MAsh SPer WBod
- 'Winsome' (hybrid) ♀^{H3}	CBcs GGal GKin MBri MGos NLar NPri SLdr SSta
'Winston Churchill' (M)	SReu SSta
'Winter Spice'	GGGa
'Winterpurpur'	IVic
'Witchery'	GGGa
'Wombat' (EA) ♀^{H5}	CDoC CTri EPfP GGGa LMil LRHS MAsh MBri MGos MMuc NLar NPri SLdr SReu
wongii	GGGa GQui MSnd SLdr
'Woodcock'	SLdr

'Wren' ♀H5	ECho GBin GEdr GGGa IVic LMil MAsh MLea SLdr SReu WThu
'Wryneck' (K)	SLdr
xanthocodon	see *R. cinnabarinum* subsp. *xanthocodon*
xanthostephanum	GGGa
'XXL'	SReu SSta
'Yaku Angel'	IVic LMil SAko
'Yaku Incense'	LMil MAsh MLea MMuc MSnd
'Yaku Prince'	MAsh MLea MMuc SLdr
'Yaku Princess'	CBcs
yakushimanum ♀H5	CBcs CMHG CWri ECho GKin LMil MAsh MBri MLea MMuc NHol SLdr SPer SReu SSta
- Exbury form	CMac SReu
- FCC form	see *R. yakushimanum* 'Koichiro Wada'
§ - 'Koichiro Wada' ♀H6	CExl CMac ELan GGGa IDee IVic LMil LRHS NLar SAko SLdr SReu
- 'Pink Parasol' **new**	SAko
- 'Schneekissen'	SAko
'Yellow Hammer' ♀H4	CBcs CDul CMac ELan GGGa GKin NLar SLdr
Yellow Hammer Group	CWri MSnd SPer SReu SSta
'Yellow Petticoats'	SReu SSta
yuefengense	GGGa
yunnanense	GGGa GGal GKev LMil MSnd SLdr
- SDR 4217	GKev
- SDR 4957	GKev
- SDR 4960	GKev
- 'Openwood' ♀H3	LMil
- pink-flowered	GGGa
- 'Red Throat'	SLdr
- red-blotched	LMil
§ - Suberosum Group	SLdr
- white-flowered	GGGa
zaleucum	CBcs GGGa LMil
- Flaviflorum Group	GGGa
- var. ***zaleucum***	MSnd
zeylanicum	see *R. arboreum* subsp. *zeylanicum*
ziyuanense AC 4211	MSnd

Rhodohypoxis ✿ (*Hypoxidaceae*)

sp.	WBla
'1000 Cranes'	CTal IBal LEdu
'Alice' **new**	CTal
'Andromeda'	CTal EWes IBal
'Ann Brazier'	NWad
'Annelies'	CTal
baurii ♀H4	CAvo CPne ECho IBal NBir NSla SPoG WAbe WBla WIce XLum
- 'Abigail'	EWes
- 'Alba'	CTal ECho EWes IBal NSla
- 'Albrighton'	CTri ECho EWes GEdr NBir NHol NWad WAbe WPat
- 'Apple Blossom'	CTal CTca ECho EWes GKev IBal LBee LEdu NHol NWad WAbe WBla WFar
- 'Badger'	NWad WAbe
- var. ***baurii***	ECho EWes GKev LRHS WBla
- var. ***baurii*** × ***baurii*** var. ***platypetala***	ECho
- 'Bridal Bouquet' (d)	CTal EWes GEdr IBal NHol WAbe WBla
- 'Caro' **new**	EWes
- 'Charlotte' **new**	EWes
- 'Coconut Ice'	CTal EWes IBal LEdu WBla
- var. ***confecta***	CElw CTal CTre ECho EWes GKev IBal NHol WFar WTor
- 'Daphne Mary'	EWes
- 'David Scott'	EWes
- 'Dawn'	CTal ECho EPot EWes GEdr GKev IBal LRHS SDys WAbe WBla
- 'Douglas'	CTal ECho EPfP EPot EWes GEdr GKev IBal LEdu NBir NHol WBla WPGP
- 'Dulcie'	CTal ECho EWes GEdr GKev IBal WAbe WBla
- 'Emily Peel'	CTal ECho EPot EWes GKev IBal WAbe WBla
- 'Eva-Kate'	CTal ECho EWes GKev IBal WAbe WBla WPat
- 'Fred Broome'	CTal CTca ECho EWes GEdr GKev IBal LEdu LRHS NHol NWad WBla WFar WPat
- 'Goliath'	EWes
- 'Harlequin'	CAby CTal ECho EWes GEdr GKev IBal NHol NWad WBla
§ - 'Helen'	CTal ECho EWes GEdr GKev IBal LEdu NHol WAbe WBla WPGP
- 'Jacqueline Potterton'	CTal
- 'Jeanette' **new**	EWes
- 'Kitty'	CTal EWes IBal WBla
- 'Lily Jean' (d)	CAby CTal CTri ECho EPfP EPot EWes GBin GEdr GKev IBal LRHS NWad WBla WCot XEll
- 'Luna'	EWes
- 'Margaret Rose'	CTal CTca ECho EWes GKev IBal NHol WBla
- 'Mars'	CTal EWes IBal LEdu LRHS NBir NHol WBla WPGP
- 'Monique'	EWes
- 'Pearl'	CTal ECho LRHS
- 'Perle'	ECho EWes GEdr IBal LRHS NHol NWad WBla
- 'Pictus' (v)	CTal ECho EWes GKev IBal LEdu LRHS NHol NWad WBla WPat
- pink hybrids **new**	LRHS
- 'Pink Pearl'	CTal EWes IBal NHol WAbe
- pink-flowered	ECho
- var. ***platypetala***	CTal CWCL ECho EPfP EPot EWes GEdr GKev IBal NHol NWad WAbe XEll XLum
- - Burtt 6981	EWes
- var. ***platypetala*** × ***milloides***	IBal LLHF NHol NWad WAbe
- 'Rebecca'	ECho EWes
- 'Red King'	EWes IBal
- red-flowered	ECho LRHS SPlb
- 'Ruth'	ECho EWes GEdr GKev IBal NHol SDeJ WAbe WBla
- 'Susan Garnett-Botfield'	CTal ECho EWes GEdr IBal LRHS WAbe WBla
- 'Tetra Pink'	ECho EWes GEdr IBal LRHS NHol NWad WBla
- 'Tetra Red'	CTal ECho EWes GEdr GKev IBal LRHS NHol NWad SDeJ WAbe WBla WFar
- 'The Bride'	EWes GEdr WBla
- white-flowered	CTca ECho EPot LRHS
'Betsy Carmine'	CTal GEdr IBal NWad WAbe WBla
'Blush'	ECho IBal
'Bright Eyes' (d)	EWes
'Burgundy'	LRHS
'Butterfly Wings'	CTal NWad
'Candy Stripe'	CTal ECho EWes GEdr LRHS NWad
'Carina'	CTal ECho EWes
'Carmine' **new**	WBla
'Caroline' **new**	EWes
'Cathy'	CTal EWes IBal

'Cayasan'	ECho WAbe
'Confusion'	EWes LEdu NHol NWad WAbe WBla
'Dainty Dee' (d)	EWes
deflexa	CMen CTal CTre ECho EPot EWes GKev IBal ITim LEdu LRHS NHol NSla NWad WBla WFar WPGP
- 'Janette' **new**	CTal
'Donald Mann'	CTal ECho EWes GEdr IBal LLHF NHol WAbe
'Dusky'	CTal ECho EPot EWes GEdr GKev IBal WBla
'E.A. Bowles'	CTal ECho EWes IBal NSla WBla WFar
'Ellicks'	CTal IBal
'Flashing Rubies'	CTal IBal
'Forge Robies'	EWes
'Garnett'	ECho EWes IBal WAbe WFar
'Gemma'	EWes
'Goya' (d)	ECho IBal WPat
'Great Scot'	ECho EWes GEdr GKev IBal LRHS WBla
'Heather'	CTal
'Hebron Farm Biscuit'	see *Hypoxis parvula* var. *albiflora* 'Hebron Farm Biscuit'
'Hebron Farm Cerise'	see × *Rhodoxis* 'Hebron Farm Cerise'
'Hebron Farm Pink'	see × *Rhodoxis hybrida* 'Hebron Farm Pink'
'Hinky Pinky'	GEdr
'Holden Rose' (d)	CTal ECho IBal NHol NWad WBla
'Hope'	CTal IBal
hybrids	ELan
'Indy' **new**	IBal
'Jap Double' (d)	CTal WBla
'Jupiter'	GEdr NWad
'Kiwi Joy' (d)	CMen CTal EPot EWes GEdr GKev IBal LLHF NHol NWad SDeJ WAbe WBla
'Knockdolian' **new**	WBla
'Knockdolian Red'	GEdr NHol NWad
'Lily Fan'	CTal
'Lisette' **new**	EWes
'Louise'	CTal IBal
'Midori'	CTal ECho EWes GEdr IBal LRHS NWad SDys
milloides	CAby CMen CPla CPne CTal CTca CTre CWCL ECho EPot EWes GCrg GEdr GKev IBal ITim LBee LEdu LRHS NHol NWad WFar WPGP XEll
- 'Claret'	CAby CElw CMen CSam CTal ECho ELon EWes GBin GEdr GKev IBal ITim LLHF LRHS NHol SDys WBla WFar WPat WTor
- 'Crimson' **new**	WBla
- 'Damask'	CTal ECho EPot EWes GKev IBal LRHS SDys WBla
- 'Donaldson'	CTal GKev WBla
- 'Drakensberg Snow'	EWes
- giant	CMen ECho GKev
- pink-flowered	CMen
- 'Susan' **new**	EWes
'Monty'	ECho EWes GEdr IBal LRHS NWad WAbe WBla
'Mystery'	EWes NHol WBla
'Naomi'	ECho EWes
'New Look'	CTal ECho EWes GEdr GKev IBal LLHF NWad WBla
'Ori Zuru'	ECho GEdr
'Origami'	CTal IBal LEdu WBla
'Pat Lacey'	CTal EWes IBal WBla
'Paula' **new**	IBal
'Pearl White'	ECho IBal
'Pink Ice'	CTal GEdr IBal NBir NWad WBla
'Pink Star'	LRHS WBla
'Pinkeen'	CTal ECho EWes IBal LLHF LRHS WAbe WBla
'Pinkie'	CTal IBal SDys
'Pintado'	CAby CTal ECho EWes GEdr IBal LEdu NWad SDys WBla
'Pretty in Pink'	CTal
'Raspberry Ice'	CTal ECho IBal NHol NWad WBla
'Roman'	CTal WBla
'Rosie Lee'	CTal EWes
'Shell Pink'	CTal EWes IBal NHol NWad WBla
Slack Top hybrids	NSla
'Snow'	EWes
'Snow White'	EWes NHol NLar WBla
'Starlett'	CTal EWes IBal LRHS NHol
'Starry Eyes' (d)	CTal ECho EWes IBal WBla
'Stella'	CTal ECho EPot EWes GEdr GKev IBal NHol NWad SDys WBla
'Sunburst'	GEdr NWad
'Telios'	IBal
'Tetra Rose'	GEdr WBla
'Tetra White'	see *R. baurii* 'Helen'
thodiana	CTal CTre ECho EWes GEdr GKev IBal NHol NWad WAbe WBla WFar
'Twinkle Star Mixed'	ECho LRHS
'Two Tone'	EWes
'Venetia'	CMea CTal ECho GKev IBal NHol NWad WBla
'Westacre Picotee'	EWes
'White Prince'	CTal
'White Wings'	CTal WBla
'Wild Cherry Blossom'	CTal ECho EWes IBal

Rhodohypoxis × *Hypoxis* see × *Rhodoxis*

R. baurii × ***H. parvula***	see × *Rhodoxis hybrida*

Rhodoleia (*Hamamelidaceae*)

championii WWJ 11858	WCru
aff. ***henryi*** B&SWJ 11782	WCru
parvipetala	WCru

Rhodophiala (*Amaryllidaceae*)

§ ***advena***	NRog
araucana	NRog
§ ***bifida***	NRog WCot
- pink-flowered	NRog
chilensis	NRog
elwesii	GKev
montana	WCot
phycelloides	NRog
pratensis	CPne WCot
rhodolirion	SPlb

Rhodora see *Rhododendron*

Rhodothamnus (*Ericaceae*)

chamaecistus	WAbe
sessilifolius	WThu

Rhodotypos (*Rosaceae*)

kerrioides	see *R. scandens*
§ ***scandens***	CExl CLet CTri CWib ELan EPfP GKin IDee LEdu LHop LRHS MGil MMHG MMuc MNrw NHol NLar NQui SAko SEND SLon SPoG SSpi WCru WHar WPat WSHC

× *Rhodoxis* ✿ (*Hypoxidaceae*)

'Anne Crock'	ECho EWes IBal
'Aurora'	CTal ECho EWes
'Betsy'	CTal EWes
'Bloodstone'	CTal ECho EWes IBal NHol NWad
'Fanny' new	EWes
'Hebron Farm Biscuit'	see *Hypoxis parvula* var. *albiflora* 'Hebron Farm Biscuit'
§ 'Hebron Farm Cerise'	CMen CTal ECho EWes GEdr GKev IBal LEdu LRHS SDys WBla
'Hebron Farm Rose'	LLHF
§ ***hybrida***	ECho EWes IBal WAbe WBla XLum
- 'Aya San'	CTal ECho EWes GKev IBal LRHS
§ - 'Hebron Farm Pink'	CBro CElw CMen ECho EWes GEdr GKev IBal LRHS NHol WAbe WBla
- 'Hebron Farm Red Eye'	CMen CTal ECho EWes GKev IBal
- 'Hebron Farm Red Eye' seedling new	CMen
- 'Pink Stars'	CTal ECho IBal
- 'Ruby Giant'	CTal ECho EWes GEdr
- 'White Stars'	ECho EWes
- (*Hypoxis parvula* × *Rhodohypoxis baurii* var. *platyphylla*) new	WBla
'Irene'	ECho
'Jenny' new	EWes
large red-flowered	CMen
'Little Pink Pet'	CTal EWes IBal
'Nippon'	CTal LRHS
'Otterlo Ruby' new	EWes
'Pink Tips'	CTal IBal
'Red Flyer' new	EWes
'Ria'	ECho EWes
'Sandra'	EWes
'Sandy'	CTal ECho EWes
'Sonja'	ECho
'Sue'	EWes

Rhoeo see *Tradescantia*

Rhopalostylis (*Arecaceae*)

sapida	CBrP
- 'Chatham Island'	CBlu
- 'East Cape'	SBig

rhubarb see *Rheum* × *hybridum*

Rhus (*Anacardiaceae*)

ambigua	ESwi
- B&SWJ 3656	WCru
- large-leaved B&SWJ 10884	WCru
aromatica	CAgr CArn CDul EBtc LRHS NLar
chinensis	CMCN IDee
copallinum	EBtc WOld
coriaria	CArn NLar
cotinus	see *Cotinus coggygria*
glabra	CArn CBcs CDoC EBtc SPer
- 'Laciniata' ambig.	SPoG
hirta	see *R. typhina*
incisa	SPlb
potaninii	EPfP LRHS NLar
× ***pulvinata*** (Autumn Lace Group) 'Red Autumn Lace' ♀H5	LRHS MBlu MBri MRav SPer
punjabensis	EGFP
§ ***radicans***	CArn GPoy WHer
succedanea	CDTJ
- NJM 10.154	WPGP
toxicodendron	see *R. radicans*
typhina	CBcs CDoC CDul CLnd EBee ELan EPfP GKin LCro LRHS MAsh MGos MMuc MRav NEgg NHol NLar NWea SCob SEND SGol SLim SPer SPoG SSta WFar
§ - 'Dissecta' ♀H6	CBcs CDoC CDul CLet CLnd CMac ELan EPfP LAst MBri MGos MJak MMuc MRav NEgg NLar NPri SCob SEND SGol SLim SPer WFar
- 'Laciniata' hort.	see *R. typhina* 'Dissecta'
- Radiance = 'Sinrus' ♀H6	LRHS MBlu SPoG
- Tiger Eyes = 'Bailtiger'PBR ♀H6	EBee ELan EPfP GKin LBuc LRHS MAsh MBri MGos NPri SCob SCoo SGol SHil SMad SPoG SWvt
§ ***verniciflua***	NLar SSpi
virens new	CFil

Rhynchelytrum see *Melinis*

Rhynchospora (*Cyperaceae*)

colorata	LLWG NPer
latifolia	CKno SDix SHDw

Ribes ✿ (*Grossulariaceae*)

alpinum	CExl ELan EPfP MRav MWht NWea SPer SRms
- 'Aureum'	CAbP EHoe NEgg
americanum 'Variegatum' (v)	EHoe WPat
aureum misapplied	see *R. odoratum*
aureum ambig.	IFro
aureum Pursh. subsp. ***gracillimum***	SBrt
§ × ***beatonii***	CBot CDoC CDul CExl CSBt CSde CWld EBee ECrN ELon EShb EWTr LEdu LRHS MAsh MMuc NLar SBrt SDix SGol SLim SLon SMad SPoG WCot WFar WHar WHor
'Ben Hope'PBR (B)	CAgr EPom MCoo SCoo SWvt WHar
'Black Velvet' (D)	CAgr MCoo
bracteosum	NLar
californicum	LHop SBrt
cereum	SBrt
§ × ***culverwellii*** (F)	CAgr CWib EPom GTwe LBuc LCro LEdu LOPS LSRN NLar SDea SPoG SVic WHar WMat
divaricatum	CAgr LEdu
gayanum	LEdu NLar
glaciale	WPGP
- PAB 3004 new	LEdu
× ***gordonianum***	see *R.* × *beatonii*
griffithii GWJ 9331	WCru
- PAB 4871	LEdu
jostaberry	see *R.* × *culverwellii*
laurifolium	CBcs CDoC CDul CExl CHGN CMHG CPla CTri EBee ELan EWTr EWes LAst LBMP LRHS MRav NLar SChF SCob SEND SPer WBod WCFE WFar WKif WRHF WSHC
- (f)	CMac EPfP SBrt SRms
- (m)	EPfP SBrt
- 'Mrs Amy Doncaster'	CMac LEdu WCot WPGP WPat
- Rosemoor form	CDoC ELan EPfP SKHP SPoG
lobbii	LRHS NLar
longeracemosum	GGGa
menziesii	CHll EWes GBin NQui WCot
× ***nidigrolaria*** new	SBdl

nigrum PAB 3755	LEdu
- 'Baldwin' (B)	CTri EPfP MAsh NLar SBdl SDea SKee SLim SPer SPoG WHar WMat
- 'Barchatnaja' (B)	CAgr
- 'Ben Alder' (B)	CAgr CWib LRHS SBdl SCoo SDea
- 'Ben Connan'PBR (B) ♀H6	Widely available
- 'Ben Gairn'PBR (B)	CAgr CSBt MCoo MMuc WHar
- 'Ben Lomond'PBR (B)	CAgr CMac CSBt CTri CWib EPfP GTwe LBuc LEdu LRHS LSRN MAsh MGos MJak MRav NEgg NLar NPri NWea SBdl SBmr SDea SEND SKee SPer SRms SVic WHar WMat
- 'Ben More' (B)	CAgr CWib MBri
- 'Ben Nevis' (B)	CAgr CTri CWib SDea SKee SPer
- 'Ben Sarek' (B)	Widely available
- 'Ben Tirran' (B)	CAgr CDoC CSBt CWib ERea LBuc LRHS LSRN MAsh MBri MGos NLar NPri SBdl SCoo SPoG SRms SWvt WHar WMat
- 'Big Ben'PBR (B) ♀H6	CArg EPom ERea LBuc LCro LOPS LRHS LSRN NLar SBmr SPer SPoG WMat
- 'Black Reward' (B)	CAgr
- 'Boskoop Giant' (B)	CAgr ELan NEgg SLim SPer WHar
- 'Byelorussian Sweet' (B)	CAgr
- 'Ebony' (B)	CArg CMac CSut EMil EPom ERea LEdu LRHS NPri SLon SVic
- 'Hystawneznaya' (B)	CAgr
- 'Jet' (B)	CAgr NEgg
- 'Karaka Black' (B)	ERea
- 'Kosmicheskaya' (B)	CAgr
- 'Loch Ness' (B)	ERea WHar
- 'Pilot Alexander Mamkin' (B)	CAgr
- 'Ruben'PBR (B) **new**	ERea
- 'Seabrook's' (B)	CAgr
- 'Titania' (B)	LRHS MBri NLar SPoG WMat
- 'Wellington XXX' (B)	CAgr EMil LBuc LEdu NWea SBmr SPer
§ ***odoratum***	Widely available
- 'Crandall'	CAgr LEdu
orientale PAB 7066 **new**	LEdu
praecox	CBcs MMuc SEND
roezlii	CBot
rubrum 'Blanka' (W)	CAgr CArg CMac CSut ERea SFrt
- 'Cascade' (R)	CAgr
- 'Cherry' (R)	CAgr
- 'Gloire de Sablons' (P)	EPom GTwe
- 'Jonkheer van Tets' (R) ♀H6	CAgr CSBt CWib EMil EPfP EPom GQue GTwe IArd LRHS LSRN MAsh MBri MCoo MMuc NLar NWea SBdl SBmr SDea SEND SKee SLim SPer SRms WHar WMat
- 'Junifer' (R)	CAgr EPom ERea GTwe LRHS SFrt SKee
- 'Laxton's Number One' (R)	CAgr CTri EPfP GTwe LCro LEdu LOPS LRHS LSRN MBri NLar NWea SBdl SBmr SDea SLim SPer SPoG SRms WHar WMat
- 'Lisette' (R)	CSut
- 'Red Lake' (R) ♀H6	CAgr CTri CWib ECrN ELan EPfP ERea GTwe LBuc LEdu MGos MJak NEgg NLar NPri SDea SKee SPer SPoG WMat
- 'Redstart' (R)	CAgr CSBt CTri CWib GTwe LBuc MAsh MBri NLar SBmr SKee SPoG WHar WMat
- 'Rolan' (R)	CAgr
- 'Rondom' (R)	CAgr SDea SVic
- 'Rosetta' (R)	CAgr SBdl
- 'Rovada' (R)	CAgr CArg CMac CSBt CSut CWib EPom ERea GTwe LBuc LEdu LRHS LSRN MAsh MBri NPri SBdl SBmr SFrt SKee SVic WHar WMat
- 'Roxby Red' (R)	LEdu MCoo
- 'Stanza' (R) ♀H6	CAgr GTwe MMuc SDea SEND
- 'Transparent' (W)	GTwe
§ - 'Versailles Blanche' (W/C)	CAgr CSBt CTri CWib EPfP EPom ERea GQue GTwe LBuc LCro LOPS LRHS LSRN MBri MGos MJak MMuc NPri SBmr SDea SKee SLim SPer SPoG WHar WMat
- 'Weisse Langtraubige' (W)	CAgr
- 'White Grape' (W) ♀H6	LEdu
- 'White Pearl' (W)	ELan SDea SVic
- White Versailles	see *R. rubrum* 'Versailles Blanche'
sanguineum	CDul CNec NBes NEgg WMoo
- 'Albescens'	CBot EPfP
- 'Brocklebankii'	CExl CMac EBee LRHS MGos MRav NLar SChF SCob SPer SPoG SRms WCFE WSHC
- 'Carneum'	LRHS
- double-flowered	see *R. sanguineum* 'Plenum'
- 'Elkington's White'	CDoC CRos EPfP ESwi EWTr LBuc LCro LHop LRHS LSRN MBri MGos NLar NSti SCoo SHil SLon WBor
- 'Flore Pleno'	see *R. sanguineum* 'Plenum'
- 'Icecrystal'	ESwi
- 'King Edward VII'	Widely available
- 'Koja' ♀H6	CBot CRos ELon EPfP GBin LEdu LRHS LSRN MGos MMuc NLar SCoo SHil SPoG WPat
- 'Lombartsii'	EPfP LRHS MRav
§ - 'Plenum' (d)	EPfP
- 'Poky's Pink'	EWTr LLHF LRHS MRav SPoG
- 'Pulborough Scarlet' ♀H6	Widely available
- 'Red Bross'	CDoC EPfP LRHS SWvt
- 'Red Pimpernel'	EPfP LRHS LSRN MAsh MBNS MGos SWvt WFar
- 'Somerset White' **new**	LRHS
- 'Taff's Kim' (v)	WCot
- 'Tydeman's White'	CDoC CExl CSBt ELan MGos NLar NWea WSHC
- var. ***variegata***	CMac
- White Icicle = 'Ubric' ♀H6	Widely available
speciosum ♀H4	Widely available
uva-crispa 'Achilles' (D)	GTwe
- 'Admiral Beattie' (F)	GTwe
- 'Annelii' (F)	CAgr
- 'Aston Red'	see *R. uva-crispa* 'Warrington'
- 'Blucher' (D)	GTwe
- 'Bright Venus' (D)	GTwe
- 'Broom Girl' (D)	GTwe
- 'Captivator' (C)	CSBt EPom GTwe LBuc LRHS MAsh MCoo MNHC NBes NLar SBdl SDea SKee SPoG WHar WMat
- 'Careless' (C/D) ♀H6	CMac CSBt EMil EPom GTwe LSRN MAsh MGos MJak NLar SBdl SDea SKee SPer WHar WMat
- 'Cook's Eagle' (C)	GTwe
- 'Criterion' (D)	GTwe
- 'Crown Bob' (C/D)	GTwe
- 'Dan's Mistake' (D)	GTwe
- 'Early Sulphur' (D)	ELan GTwe SDea
- 'Firbob' (D)	GTwe
- 'Forester' (D)	GTwe
- 'Freedom' (C)	GTwe
- 'Glenton Green' (D)	GTwe
- 'Golden Drop' (D)	GTwe
- 'Green Gem' (C/D)	GTwe

– 'Green Ocean' (D)	GTwe
– 'Greenfinch' (C) ♀H6	CAgr
– 'Gunner' (C/D)	GTwe
– 'Heart of Oak' (F)	GTwe
– 'Hedgehog' (D)	GTwe
– 'Hero of the Nile' (D)	GTwe
– 'High Sheriff' (D)	GTwe
– 'Hinnonmäki' (F)	CAgr ECrN LBuc NPri SDea SPer
– 'Hinnonmäki Grön' (F)	CSBt EMil EPfP LRHS LSRN MAsh MRav NPri SBdl SBmr SFrt WHar
– 'Hinnonmäki Gul' (D)	CAgr CSBt CSut EMil EPfP EPom ERea GTwe LBuc LEdu LRHS MAsh MGos NLar SBdl SBmr SDea SKee SPer SPoG SVic WHar WMat
– 'Hinnonmäki Röd' (C/D)	CAgr CMac EMil EPfP EPom ERea GTwe LBuc LCro LOPS LRHS LSRN MAsh MBri MCoo MNHC MRav NLar SBdl SBmr SDea SFrt SKee SPer SPoG SVic WHar WMat
– 'Howard's Lancer' (C/D)	GTwe SDea
– 'Invicta' (C/D) ♀H6	Widely available
– 'Ironmonger' (D)	GTwe
– 'Jubilee' (C/D)	LBuc
– 'Jubilee Careless' (C/D)	EPom
– 'Keepsake' (C/D)	GTwe SDea
– 'King of Trumps' (F)	GTwe
– 'Lancashire Lad' (C/D)	GTwe
– 'Langley Gage' (D)	GTwe MCoo
– 'Laxton's Amber' (D)	GTwe
– 'Leveller' (D) ♀H6	CTri ECrN GTwe LAst MCoo MGos SDea SPer WHar
– 'London' (C/D)	GTwe
– 'Martlet' (F)	GTwe MCoo SLim
– 'May Duke' (C/D)	SDea
– 'Pax'PBR (D)	CAgr CSut EPfP GTwe SBmr SDea SFrt SLim
– 'Peru' (D)	GTwe
– 'Pitmaston Green Gage' (D)	GTwe
– 'Plunder' (C)	GTwe
– 'Queen of Trumps' (D)	GTwe
– 'Red Champagne' (D)	GTwe
– 'Rokula'PBR (C/D)	ELan LRHS MBri MCoo WMat
– 'Scotch Red Rough' (D)	GTwe
– 'Snow' (F)	EPfP
– 'Snowdrop' (D)	GTwe
– 'Spinefree' (C)	GTwe
– 'Surprise' (D)	GTwe
– 'Victoria' (C/D)	GTwe
§ – 'Warrington' (F)	GTwe
– 'Whinham's Industry' (C/D) ♀H6	CSBt CTri ELan GTwe LAst LBuc LHop LRHS LSRN MGos MMuc NEgg SDea SEND SPer WHar
– 'White Lion' (C/D)	GTwe
– 'White Transparent' (C)	GTwe
– 'Whitesmith' (C/D)	CTri GTwe LSRN MCoo SDea
– 'Xenia' (D)	CArg EPfP EPom ERea GQue LCro LEdu LRHS NLar SPoG WMat
– 'Yellow Champagne' (D)	GTwe
valdivianum	WCot
– 'Kathleen'	EPfP LRHS
viburnifolium	NLar SBrt SEND
'Worcesterberry' (C)	CHab SDea SPer

Ricinus (*Euphorbiaceae*)

communis	CDTJ SPlb
– 'Carmencita' ♀H1c	NGBl SDys
– 'Carmencita Pink'	CDTJ
– 'Carmencita Red'	CDTJ NPri
– 'Dominican Republic'	CDTJ
– 'Gibsonii'	CDTJ
– 'Impala'	CDTJ
– 'New Zealand Black'	CDTJ CSpe SDys
– 'Zanzibariensis' ♀H1c	CDTJ

Rigidella see *Tigridia*

Riocreuxia (*Apocynaceae*)

torulosa	SPlb

Robinia (*Papilionaceae*)

× ***ambigua***	EBee SKHP
§ ***hispida***	CDul CWib ELan EPfP MBlu NLar NOrn SPer
– var. ***kelseyi***	CDul EBee EWes
– 'Macrophylla'	NLar
§ – var. ***rosea***	LSRN
– 'Rosea' misapplied	see *R. hispida*, *R. hispida* var. rosea
– 'Rosea' ambig.	CBcs EBee
× ***margaretta*** Casque Rouge	see *R.* × *margaretta* 'Pink Cascade'
§ – 'Pink Cascade'	CLnd CMac CTri EBee ECrN ELan EPfP LAst MAsh MGos MMuc SCoo SEND SGol SLim SPer WMat
neomexicana	SIgm
pseudoacacia	CAgr CCVT CDul CLnd CNWT ELan LBuc MCoo MMuc SCob SEND SGol SPlb
– 'Bessoniana'	CDul EBee ELan EPfP
– 'Frisia'	Widely available
– 'Inermis' hort.	see *R. pseudoacacia* 'Umbraculifera'
§ – 'Lace Lady'PBR	CSBt CWSG ECrN ELan EPfP EUJe LBuc LRHS MAsh MBri MGos NOrn SCoo SLim SPoG WMat
– 'Rozynskiana'	CDul
– 'Tortuosa'	EBee EBtc SPer
– 'Twisty Baby'	see *R. pseudoacacia* 'Lace Lady'
§ – 'Umbraculifera'	CDul CLnd ECrN LSRN MGos SCob SCoo
× ***slavinii*** 'Hillieri' ♀H5	CDul CLnd EBee ECrN ELan EPfP EUJe EWTr LSRN MAsh MBlu MBri NOrn SLon SPer SPoG

Rochea see *Crassula*

Rodgersia (*Saxifragaceae*)

CLD 1432	CExl
aesculifolia ♀H7	Widely available
– SSSE 306 **new**	SMHy
– green bud	IBlr
– var. ***henrici***	CLAP GBin GCal GLog IBoy LRHS MRav NBro NMyG SGbt SPer SWat WHoo WMoo
– – KW 21015 **new**	WCru
– – 'Cherry Blush'	GBin MSCN SPad
– – hybrid	CHid CLet ITim IVic NLar WWEG XLum
– pink-flowered	SSpi
– 'Red Dawn'	IBlr
– 'Red Leaf'	EWoo GCal IFoB WPnP
'Badenweiter'	ECha
'Blickfang' ♀H7	IBlr LRHS
'Bloody Mary'	ECtt GBin IMou LLWG SCob SKHP WFar
'Borodin'	EBee
'Bronze Peacock' **new**	ECtt MHol
Cally strain	GCal
'Dark Pokers'	EBee ECtt GBin NLar SPoG
'Die Anmutige'	IMou
'Die Schöne'	CLAP EBee NLar
'Die Stolze'	GBin IMou LEdu LLWG MBrN WFar

'Elfenbeinturm' IBlr
'Fascination' IBlr
'Herkules' EBee ECha ECtt EHoe ELon GBin GMaP IFoB LEdu LHop LRHS LSou MBNS MMuc NLar NQui SKHP SSpi WPnP WWEG
'Irish Bronze' 🏆H7 EAEE ECtt ELan EPfP GBin GQue ILea IVic LBMP LEdu LRHS LSRN MWhi MWts SMad WMoo WPnP
'Koriata' IBlr
'Kupfermond' CDes EBee IBlr NBir SMHy
'La Blanche' EBee ECtt ELon LEdu LRHS MHol NGdn NLar WCot WPnP WWEG
'Maigrün' IBlr
nepalensis CLAP EBee LEdu LRHS WPGP
- EMAK 713 IBlr
- HWJK 2140 WCru
'Parasol' CBro CMac IBlr NBir NHol SKHP SSpi WPGP WWtn
pinnata Widely available
- B&SWJ 7741A CBcs WCru
- L 1670 CExl ELan IBlr SSpi WPGP
- 'Alba' GCal IBlr LRHS
- 'Buckland Beauty' 🏆H7 CDes EBee IBlr LRHS SMHy SSpi WMoo WPGP
- 'Cally Coral' EBee GCal
- 'Cally Salmon' EWes GBin GCal IBlr IMou WPGP
- 'Candy Clouds' **new** EBee
- 'Chocolate Wing' Widely available
- 'Crûg Cardinal' GCal LRHS WCru
- 'Elegans' CCon EBee EHoe ELan EPfP GKev GMaP IBlr LAst LBMP LEdu LPal LRHS MHol MRav NEgg NHol NWad SGSe SPer SPoG SWvt WCFE
- 'Fireworks'PBR CCon CHid CLAP COtt EBee ECtt ELan EPfP GBin IMou NLar SPer SRkn WHil
- hybrids LRHS
- 'Jade Dragon Mountain' CDes GCal IBlr SKHP WPGP
- 'Maurice Mason' CExl CLAP EBee ECtt GKev IBlr NLar SDix SMHy WWEG
- 'Mont Blanc' IBlr
- Mount Stewart form IBlr
- 'Panache' IBlr
- 'Perthshire Bronze' IBlr
- pink-flowered WCru
- 'Rosea' IBlr
- 'Snow Clouds' EBee LSun
- 'Superba' 🏆H7 Widely available
- white-flowered GAbr SWat WCru
pinnata* × *sambucifolia IBlr
podophylla Widely available
- B&SWJ 10818 WCru
- B&SWJ 10823 WCru
- 'Braunlaub' CLAP GBuc GQue LLWG NBro WMoo WWEG
- 'Bronceblad' IBlr
- 'Crûg's Colossus' WCru
- Donard selection IBlr
- 'Rotlaub' 🏆H7 CAby CLAP EBee IBlr IMou IPot IVic WBor WMoo
- 'Smaragd' CLAP EShb GCal IBlr LRHS MRav NBir NLar
purdomii hort. CMac GCal LRHS WCot WPGP
'Reinecke Fuchs' IBlr
'Rosenzipfel' IBlr
sambucifolia CBcs CLAP CMac GBee GBin GCal ILea LEdu LRHS MLHP MMuc NBir NEgg NLar NSti SEND SPer SWat WFar WMoo WPnP WWEG XLum
- B&SWJ 7899 WCru
- dwarf, pink-flowered IBlr
- dwarf, white-flowered IBlr
- large, red-stemmed NBir
- 'Mountain Select' EBee GCal
'Stoke Gabriel' **new** CDes
tabularis see *Astilboides tabularis*

Roemeria (*Papaveraceae*)

hybrida CSpe

Rohdea (*Asparagaceae*)

japonica CMac WCot WFar WPGP
- B&SWJ 4853 WCru
- B&SWJ 5091 WCru
- 'Godaishu' (v) WCot
- 'Gunjaku' (v) WCot
- 'Lance Leaf' LEdu WPGP
- long-leaved WCot
- 'Miyakonojo' (v) WCot
- 'Talbot Manor' (v) CBct CDes WCot
- 'Tama-jishi' (v) WCot
- 'Tuneshige Rokujo' (v) WCot
tonkinensis HWJ 562 WCru
watanabei IMou
- B&SWJ 1911 WCru

Romanzoffia (*Boraginaceae*)

californica EBee
§ ***sitchensis*** CTri
suksdorfii Greene see *R. sitchensis*
tracyi CDes GEdr NRya
unalaschcensis EBee SRms

Romneya (*Papaveraceae*)

coulteri 🏆H7 Widely available
§ - var. ***trichocalyx*** CCon
§ - 'White Cloud' 🏆H5 CExl EBee MRav SChF SMad WPGP
× ***hybrida*** see *R. coulteri* 'White Cloud'
trichocalyx see *R. coulteri* var. *trichocalyx*

Romulea (*Iridaceae*)

atrandra NRog
§ ***autumnalis*** ECho
bulbocodium CBro ECho
- var. ***clusiana*** ECho
- var. ***crocea*** ECho EPot
- late-flowering CDes
- var. ***leichtliniana*** CDes ECho
camerooniana GKev
engleri CDes
hirta ECho
leipoldtii ECho
linaresii ECho
- subsp. ***graeca*** ECho
longituba see *R. macowanii*
§ ***macowanii*** ECho
montana ECho
monticola CDes
namaquensis ECho
nivalis ECho
ramiflora CExl ECho
rosea ECho
- var. ***speciosa*** see *R. autumnalis*
tabularis CDes ECho
tempskyana ECho EPot

Rondeletia (*Rubiaceae*)

amoena MOWG

Rorippa (*Brassicaceae*)

amphibia	LLWG MSKA
nasturtium-aquaticum	MWts WMAq

Rosa ✿ (*Rosaceae*)

sp.	SCob
FMWJ 13349 **new**	CEvo
NJM 11.048 from Guizhou, China	WPGP
NJM 11.077 from Guizhou, China	WPGP
NJM 11.079 from Guizhou, China	WPGP
A Shropshire Lad = 'Ausled'PBR (S) ♀H6	CNec CRos EPfP LBuc LPfy LRHS LSRN MBri NEgg NLar SCob SPer SSea SWCr
A Whiter Shade of Pale = 'Peafanfare'PBR (HT) ♀H6	CDoC CKel ECnt ESty LRHS MJak MRav SPer SSea SWCr
Abbeyfield Rose = 'Cocbrose' (HT)	MRav SPer
Abigaile = 'Tanelaigib' (F)	LSRN
Abracadabra = 'Korhocsel' (HT)	ESty
Abraham Darby = 'Auscot' (S)	CDoC CKel COtt CTri EBee ELan EPfP EShb EWTr IBoy LRHS LSRN MAsh MBri MJak MRav NEgg NLar SCob SEND SLon SPer SWCr
Absent Friends = 'Dicemblem'PBR (F)	ESty IBoy SRGP SWCr WBor
Absolutely Fabulous = 'Wekvossutono'PBR (F) ♀H6	CDoC COtt CSBt CWSG ECnt EPfP ESty LBrs LBuc LRHS LSRN LShp MAsh MBri MJak MRav NPri SCoo SPer SPoG SWCr
abyssinica	LEdu
'Adam' (ClT)	LSRN
'Adam Messerich' (Bb)	SLon
Adam's Rose = 'Wekromico' (F)	LSRN
'Adélaïde d'Orléans' (Ra) ♀H6	CRHN LBuc LRHS MBri MMuc MRav NLar SEND SPer
African Sunset = 'Jacpik'	MBri
Agatha Christie = 'Kormeita'PBR (ClF)	LRHS LSRN MAsh
'Aglaia' (Ra)	CPou
'Agnes' (Ru)	CDoC ELon EPfP EWTr IArd LRHS MCot MRav NLar SPer SRGP
'Aimée Vibert' (N)	MRav NLar SEND SPer SRGP
'Alain Blanchard' (G)	CPou EWTr
Alan Titchmarsh = 'Ausjive'PBR (S)	COtt CSBt LCro LOPS LRHS LSRN MBri SCoo SPer
§ × ***alba*** 'Alba Maxima' (A) ♀H7	EWTr GBin MRav NLar SEND SPer WFar WHer
§ - 'Alba Semiplena' (A) ♀H7	EPfP LRHS NLar SPer SWCr WHer
- Celestial	see *R.* 'Céleste'
- 'Maxima'	see *R.* × *alba* 'Alba Maxima'
Alba Meidiland = 'Meiflopan'PBR (S/GC)	EAEE
'Albéric Barbier' (Ra) ♀H5	CDoC CRHN CSBt CTri ECnt ELan EPfP EWTr LCro LRHS MBri MMuc MRav MSwo MWat NLar NWea SCob SEND SMad SPer SPoG SSea SWCr WHer
'Albertine' (Ra) ♀H6	Widely available
'Alchymist' (S/Cl)	CPou CRHN EPfP ESty LRHS MBri MRav NLar SPer WBor
Alec's Red = 'Cored' (HT)	CBcs CTri CWSG IBoy LSRN MJak MRav SPer SPoG SRGP SWCr
Alexander = 'Harlex' (HT) ♀H6	IBoy LSRN MRav SPer SSea SWCr
Alexander's Issie = 'Dicland'PBR (F)	IDic
'Alexandre Girault' (Ra) ♀H6	CRHN LBuc LRHS MBri SPer SWCr WHer
'Alfred de Dalmas' misapplied	see *R.* 'Mousseline'
Alfred Sisley = 'Delstrijor'PBR (S)	ESty LRHS MRav NLar SPoG
'Alfresco'PBR (ClHT)	MSwo
§ 'Alibaba'PBR (Cl) ♀H6	CDoC COtt ECnt ESty LRHS LSRN MAsh MRav SPer SPoG SWCr
'Alida Lovett' (Ra)	LRHS
Alison = 'Coclibee'PBR (F)	LSRN
Alissar, Princess of Phoenicia = 'Harsidon'PBR	CPou ESty NLar
§ 'Alister Stella Gray' (N) ♀H5	EBee ESty MBri MCot MMuc NEgg NLar SLon SPer SSea
All American Magic = 'Meiroylear'PBR (HT)	ESty
All Yours = 'Wekwestypla' (HT) **new**	LBrs
'Allgold' (F)	SCob
Alnwick Castle	see *R.* The Alnwick Rose
'Aloha' (ClHT) ♀H7	CBcs CDoC CKel CTri EBee ELon EPfP ESty LCro LRHS MCot MJak MRav NLar SCob SEND SPer SPoG SSea SWCr
alpina	see *R. pendulina*
'Alpine Sunset' (HT)	CTri ELon ESty LBuc MRav SCob SPer SPoG SWCr
altaica misapplied	see *R. spinosissima* 'Grandiflora'
altaica Willd.	see *R. spinosissima*
Altissimo = 'Delmur' (Cl)	CKel EWTr GGal LRHS SPer SSea SWCr
Always You = 'Webalways' (HT) **new**	ESty
Amanda = 'Beesian' (F)	ESty LSRN
'Amazing Grace' (HT)	LBuc
Amber Queen = 'Harroony' (F) ♀H6	CDoC CKel COtt CSBt CTri EAEE ELan IArd IBoy LBuc MAsh MRav MWat SPer SSea SWCr
Amber Sun	see *R.* County of Staffordshire
Amber Sweet Dream = 'Fryritz' (Patio)	CDoC CKel ECnt MRav MWat
amblyotis RBS 0262	GBin NLar
'Amélia'	see *R.* 'Celsiana'
Amelia = 'Poulen011'PBR (Renaissance Series) (S)	ECnt LSRN
'American Pillar' (Ra)	CDoC CKel COtt CRHN CSBt CTri CWSG EBee ECnt ELan EPfP IBoy LAst LRHS MAsh MBri MMuc MRav MSwo NLar SCob SPer SSea SWCr WBor
Anabell = 'Korbell' (F)	LSRN
§ 'Anemone' (Cl)	CPou
anemonoides	see *R.* 'Anemone'
Angela = 'Grifgela'	LSRN
Angela Rippon = 'Ocaru' (Min)	CSBt SPer
'Angela's Choice' (F)	LSRN
Anisley Dickson = 'Dickimono' (F)	SPer
Ann = 'Ausfete'PBR (S)	LSRN
Ann Henderson = 'Fryhoncho' (F)	LSRN
Anna Ford = 'Harpiccolo' (Min/Patio) ♀H5	SPer
Anna Livia = 'Kormetter' (F)	EBee

	Name	Suppliers
	Anne Boleyn = 'Ausecret'[PBR] (S)	EPfP IBoy LBuc LRHS MBri NEgg SCoo
	Anne Harkness = 'Harkaramel' (F)	SPer
	Antique = 'Antike' (F)	CPou
	Antique '89 = 'Kordalen'[PBR] (ClF)	LBrs LRHS MAsh
	Aphrodite = 'Tan00847'[PBR] (S) ♀H6	ESty MRav SWCr
	apothecary's rose	see *R. gallica* var. *officinalis*
	'Apple Blossom' (Ra)	SHar
	Apple Blossom = 'Noamel' (GC)	EShb
	'Apricot Silk' (HT)	CTri SPer
	Apricot Sunblaze = 'Savamark' (Min)	CSBt
	'Archiduc Joseph' misapplied	see *R.* 'Général Schablikine'
	'Arthur Bell' (F) ♀H7	CSBt CTri ELon EPfP ESty IArd IBoy LAst LBrs LRHS LSRN MAsh MBri MJak MRav MSwo MWat NEgg NPri SCob SPer SPoG SRGP SSea SWCr WBor
	arvensis	CCVT CHab LBuc MMuc NWea SCob
	'Astra Desmond' (Ra)	MNrw
	Audrey Wilcox = 'Frywilrey' (HT)	ESty
	Austrian copper rose	see *R. foetida* 'Bicolor'
	Austrian yellow	see *R. foetida*
	'Autumn' (HT)	LSRN
	'Autumn Delight' (HM)	NLar
	Autumn Fire	see *R.* 'Herbstfeuer'
	'Autumnalis'	see *R.* 'Princesse de Nassau'
	Avon = 'Poulmulti'[PBR] (GC)	CDoC ELan EPfP MRav SPer
	Awakening = 'Probuzení' (ClHT)	EBee MSwo NLar SWCr
	'Ayrshire Splendens'	see *R.* 'Splendens'
	Baby Gold Star (Min)	see *R.* 'Estrellita de Oro'
	Baby Masquerade = 'Tanba' (Min)	MRav SPer
	Babyface = 'Rawril'[PBR] (Min)	ESty
	'Ballerina' (HM/Poly) ♀H6	CDoC CDul CKel CSBt CTri EBee ECnt ELan EPfP ESty EWTr IBoy LCro LEdu LRHS LSRN MAsh MJak MRav MSwo MWat NEgg NLar SCob SMad SPer SSea SWCr WBor WKif
	'Baltimore Belle' (Ra)	CPou NLar
	banksiae (Ra)	CPou SRms
	- ***alba***	see *R. banksiae* var. *banksiae*
§	- var. ***banksiae*** (Ra/d)	CBot CDul CHll CKel CPou CRHN CSBt CTri CWld ELan EPfP GQui LCro LOPS LRHS SCob SEND SLon SPer XSen
	- 'Lutea' (Ra/d) ♀H5	Widely available
	- 'Lutescens' (Ra)	CBot WPGP
	- var. ***normalis*** (Ra)	CSBt CSam EPfP SKHP SLon WCot WHer WOut WPGP
I	- 'Rosea'	CBot LCro LOPS NLar SPer
	'Bantry Bay' (ClHT)	CSBt EBee ELan LAst LSRN SCob SLon SPer SSea SWCr
	Barbara Austin = 'Austop'[PBR] (S)	SCob
	Barbara Windsor = 'Ganleon'[PBR] (F)	SWCr
	Barkarole = 'Tanelorak'[PBR] (HT)	CSBt ESty
	'Baron Girod de l'Ain' (HP)	EBee ELon LAst LRHS LSRN MAsh MMuc MRav NEgg NLar SPer SWCr
	'Baroness Rothschild' ambig.	see *R.* Climbing Baronne Edmond de Rothschild
	Baroque Floorshow = 'Harbaroque'[PBR] (S)	CDoC CKel MRav
	Barry Stephens = 'Horcabellero' (HT)	LSRN
	Beatrix Potter = 'Beafolly' (S)	ESty
	Beautiful Britain = 'Dicfire' (F)	SCob
	'Belinda' (HM)	LSRN
§	Bella = 'Pouljill'[PBR] (Renaissance Series) (S)	CPou
	'Belle Amour' (A × D)	CPou
	'Belle de Crécy' (G)	CPou CTri LRHS MBri MNrw NLar SKHP SMad SPer
	'Belle des Jardins' misapplied	see *R.* × *centifolia* 'Unique Panachée'
	Belle Epoque = 'Adasilthe'[PBR] (HT)	SCob
	Belle Epoque = 'Fryyaboo'[PBR] (HT)	ESty SCob SMad
	Belle Happiness = 'Meileodevin' (Cl) **new**	ESty
	'Belle Isis' (G)	SPer
	'Belle Poitevine' (Ru)	CPou EBee
	Belmonte = 'Harpearl'[PBR] (F)	ESty
§	'Belvedere' (Ra) ♀H6	CPou EBee IBoy NLar SPer
	Benita = 'Dicquarrel' (HT)	IDic
	Benjamin Britten = 'Ausencart'[PBR] (S)	CSBt EPfP ESty IBoy LBuc LOPS LRHS MBri NEgg SCob
	Berkshire = 'Korpinka'[PBR] (GC) ♀H6	LRHS SCob SSea SWCr
	Beryl Joyce = 'Tan96145'[PBR] (HT)	CKel ESty LSRN MRav
	Best of Friends = 'Pouldunk'[PBR] (HT)	LSRN
	Best Wishes = 'Chessnut'[PBR] (ClHT/v)	LSRN SRGP
	'Betty Sherriff' (Cl)	CDoC
	'Betty's Smile' (HT)	LSRN
	'Bewitched' (HT)	LSRN
§	Bewitched = 'Poulbella'[PBR] (Castle Series) (F)	MBri SWCr
	Bianco = 'Cocblanco' (Patio/Min)	MRav MWat SPoG
	Bienvenue = 'Delrochipar' (Cl) **new**	ESty
	Big Purple = 'Stebigpu' (HT)	ECnt ESty
	Billet Doux = 'Delrosar' (S)	ESty
	Birthday Boy = 'Tan97607'[PBR] (HT)	CDoC ESty LSRN MRav SCob SWCr
	Birthday Girl = 'Meilasso'[PBR] (F)	CDoC CKel CSBt ESty LBrs LSRN MAsh MJak MRav MWat SCoo SRGP SVic SWCr
	Birthday Wishes (Patio)	see *R.* Shrimp Hit (Patio)
	Birthday Wishes = 'Guesdelay' (HT)	CTri LBrs LRHS LSRN MBri SSea
	Black Baccara = 'Meidebenne'[PBR] (HT)	ESty
	'Black Jack' (Ce)	see *R.* 'Tour de Malakoff'
	'Blairii Number Two' (ClBb)	CSam EBee EPfP MRav NEgg NLar SEND SPer
	'Blanche Double de Coubert' (Ru) ♀H7	CBcs CDoC CDul CKel CSBt CTri ECnt ELan EPfP EWTr GBin LBuc LCro LSRN MSwo NEgg NLar SCob SEND SPer SWCr

Name	Suppliers
'Blanche Moreau' (CeMo)	SKHP SPer
'Blanchefleur' (Ce × G)	CPou
'Blesma Soul' (HT)	CSBt
'Blessings' (HT)	CBcs CSBt CTri LBuc LSRN MAsh MBri MGos MJak MRav SCob SPer SWCr
'Bleu Magenta' (Ra) 🏆H7	CRHN ELan GBin IArd MCot NLar SEND SMad SWCr WKif
Bloom of Ruth = 'Harmedley'[PBR] (HT)	CSBt ECnt
'Bloomfield Abundance' (Poly)	CPou MMuc NLar SPer
'Blossomtime' (Cl)	SMad SPer
Blue for You = 'Pejamblu'[PBR] (F) 🏆H6	CDoC ECnt ELan EPfP ESty LBuc LPfy LRHS SCob SCoo SMad SPoG SSea SWCr
Blue Moon = 'Tannacht' (HT)	CTri ELan EPfP IBoy MGos MJak MRav SCob SPer SPoG SRGP
Blue Peter = 'Ruiblun' (Min)	ESty IBoy MBri
'Blush Boursault' (Bs)	MMuc
'Blush Noisette'	see *R.* 'Noisette Carnée'
'Blush Rambler' (Ra)	CSBt EPfP EWTr LBuc MMuc SMad SPer
Blushing Bride = 'Harfling' (F)	MBri
'Blushing Lucy' (Ra) 🏆H6	CPou EWTr MTPN SPer
Blythe Spirit = 'Auschool'[PBR] (S)	LRHS MBri NEgg SCob
'Bobbie James' (Ra) 🏆H6	CTri EBee EPfP LBuc LRHS MBri MRav MSwo NEgg NLar SCob SPer SPoG SSea SWCr WFar
'Bobby Charlton' (HT)	LSRN
Bobby Dazzler = 'Smi133-02' (F)	ESty
Bonica = 'Meidomonac' (GC) 🏆H6	Widely available
§ Bonita = 'Poulen009'[PBR] (Renaissance Series) (S)	ECnt
Boogie-Woogie = 'Poulyc006'[PBR] (Courtyard Series) (ClHT)	ECnt LRHS MAsh MBri SWCr
Born Again	see *R.* Renaissance
Boscobel = 'Auscousin' (S)	CRos EPfP ESty LBuc LRHS SCob
'Boule de Neige' (Bb)	CBcs CTri ECnt ELan EPfP IBoy LCro LRHS LSRN MBri MRav NLar SPer SWCr
'Bouquet d'Or' (N)	EBee NLar
Bowled Over = 'Tandolgnil'[PBR] (F) 🏆H6	ESty SWCr
§ ***bracteata*** (S)	CRHN ECre EWes SSea
Brave Heart = 'Horbondsmile' (F)	COtt MRav SPoG
Breath of Life = 'Harquanne'[PBR] (ClHT)	ELan EPfP LBuc MRav SPer SWCr
Breathtaking = 'Hargalore'[PBR] (HT)	ESty
'Brian's Star' (F)	LSRN
Bride and Groom = 'Smi10-98' (HT)	CDoC CKel ESty LSRN MRav SCoo
Bride = 'Fryyearn'[PBR] (HT)	LSRN MRav
Bridge of Sighs (Cl) = 'Harglowing'[PBR]	ECnt ESty LBuc LRHS LShp MAsh MBri SPoG SSea SWCr
Bright and Breezy = 'Dicjive' (F)	ECnt IDic
Bright as a Button = 'Chewsumsigns'[PBR] (S)	CKel COtt CSBt ESty GBin LShp NLar SLon SPer
Bright Fire = 'Peaxi'[PBR] (ClHT)	CKel MSwo SPer SSea
Bright Future = 'Kirora'[PBR] (Cl)	ESty
Bright Ideas = 'Horcoffdrop' (Cl)	LRHS LShp NPri
Brilliant Sweet Dream = 'Frysassy' (Patio)	ECnt LBrs LRHS
Britannia = 'Frycalm'[PBR] (HT) 🏆H6	ECnt
Broadlands = 'Tanmirsch'[PBR] (GC)	NLar SLon
Brother Cadfael = 'Ausglobe'[PBR] (S)	CNec CRos LAst LRHS MAsh MBri NEgg NLar SCob SCoo SPer SSea
Brown Velvet = 'Maccultra' (F)	ESty SPer
Brownie = 'Simstripe' (Cl)	ESty
§ ***brunonii*** (Ra)	CExl CPne CPou EWes
- CC 7290 **new**	EWld
- PAB 3083	LEdu
§ - 'La Mortola' (Ra)	NLar SPer
Brush-strokes = 'Guescolour' (F)	CDoC ESty
'Buff Beauty' (HM) 🏆H6	CKel CSBt CTri CWSG EBee ECnt ELan EPfP EWTr IBoy LCro LOPS LSRN MBri MCot MRav MSwo MWat NEgg NLar SCob SEND SMad SPer SSea SWCr WCFE WFar
§ Burgundy Ice = 'Prose'[PBR] (F)	CKel CSBt CWSG EAEE ECnt EPfP ESty LBuc LCro LRHS LShp MAsh MMuc MRav SCob SCoo SMad SPad SPoG SSea SWCr
'Burgundy Iceberg'	see *R.* Burgundy Ice
burnet, double pink	see *R. spinosissima* double, pink-flowered
burnet, double white	see *R. spinosissima* double, white-flowered
Buttercup = 'Ausband'[PBR] (S)	CRos EPfP LBuc LRHS
Buxom Beauty = 'Korbilant'[PBR] (HT) 🏆H6	EPfP ESty LBrs LRHS LSRN MBri SCoo SPoG SSea
'C.F. Meyer'	see *R.* 'Conrad Ferdinand Meyer'
californica 'Plena'	see *R. nutkana* 'Plena'
'Camayeux' (G)	CPou ECnt NLar SPer
Cambridgeshire = 'Korhaugen'[PBR] (GC)	CTri NLar SPer SSea SWCr
Camelot = 'Tan05372'[PBR] (Cl)	ESty
Camille Pisarro = 'Destricol' (F)	ESty
'Canary Bird'	see *R. xanthina* 'Canary Bird'
Candy Land = 'Wekrosopela'[PBR] (Cl) **new**	ECnt ESty
canina (S)	CArg CArn CCVT CDul CHab CLnd CTri ECrN EPfP EPom LBuc LCro LOPS MJak MMuc MRav NBes NLar NWea SCob SEWo SPer WHar WMat WMou WOut
'Cantabrigiensis' (S) 🏆H6	EWTr LRHS NLar SLon SPer
'Capitaine John Ingram' (CeMo)	NLar SEND SLon
'Captain Scarlet' (ClMin)	ESty
'Cardinal de Richelieu' (G)	CBcs CPou CSam CTri EPfP GCra IBoy LCro LRHS LSRN LShp MBri MCot MRav MSwo MWat NEgg NLar SCob SEND SMad SPer SPoG
Carefree Days = 'Meirivouri' (Patio) 🏆H6	EPfP IBoy LRHS SPoG SSea
Cariad = 'Auspanier'[PBR] (HM)	LBuc LRHS

	Name	Suppliers
	Caring for You ambig.	LSRN
	Caritas = 'Meikolyma'[PBR] **new**	EBee
	'Carol' (F)	see *R.* 'Carol Amling'
§	'Carol Amling' (F)	LSRN
	Carol Ann = 'Peapost' (F) **new**	LSRN
	'Caroline Testout'	see *R.* 'Madame Caroline Testout'
	Caroline Victoria = 'Harprior'[PBR] (HT)	COtt LSRN
	Carolyn Knight = 'Austurner' **new**	CRos LCro LOPS LRHS
	Carris = 'Harmanna'[PBR] (HT)	MAsh
§	Casino = 'Macca' (ClHT)	CTri ELon MRav SPer
	'Castle Apricot'	see *R.* Lazy Days
	'Castle Cream'	see *R.* Perfect Day
	'Castle Fuchsia Pink'	see *R.* Bewitched = 'Poulbella'
	'Castle Peach'	see *R.* Imagination = 'Pouldron'
	'Castle Shrimp Pink'	see *R.* Fascination = 'Poulmax'
	'Castle Yellow'	see *R.* Summer Gold
§	'Cécile Brünner' (Poly) ♀[H6]	CKel CTri ELan LRHS LSRN MCot MMuc MWat NLar SPer SSea
	Cecily Gibson = 'Evebright' (F)	ESty
	Celebration Time	see *R.* Cinco de Mayo
§	'Céleste' (A) ♀[H7]	CTri EWTr NLar SEND SPer
	'Célina' (CeMo)	LSRN
	'Céline Forestier' (N)	CPou EWTr NLar SEND
§	'Celsiana' (D) ♀[H7]	CPou CSam EWTr LSRN NLar SPer
	Centenary = 'Koreledas'[PBR] (F)	MAsh SCoo
§	× ***centifolia*** (Ce)	CArn LRHS SMad SPer
§	- 'Cristata' (Ce) ♀[H7]	ELon LEdu LRHS MAsh MMuc NLar SPer WBor
§	- 'De Meaux' (Ce)	NLar SPer
§	- 'Muscosa' (CeMo)	LEdu
§	- 'Unique' (Ce)	EWTr NLar
§	- 'Unique Panachée' (Ce)	CPou
	'Centifolia Variegata'	see *R.* × *centifolia* 'Unique Panachée'
	'Cerise Bouquet' (S) ♀[H7]	GGal NLar SPer WKif
§	Champagne Moment = 'Korvanaber'[PBR] (F) ♀[H6]	CBcs CDoC COtt CSBt ECnt ELan EPfP ESty LBrs LRHS LSRN MBri MGos MJak MRav NPri SMad SPer SPoG SRGP SSea SWCr
	'Champneys Pink Cluster' (China hybrid)	LRHS SCob
	Chandos Beauty = 'Harmisty'[PBR] (HT) ♀[H6]	CDoC CKel COtt ECnt EPfP ESty LRHS LSRN MAsh MBri MRav SSea SWCr
	'Chanelle' (F)	SDix SPer
	Chapeau de Napoléon	see *R.* × *centifolia* 'Cristata'
	Charles Austin = 'Ausles' (S)	CDoC MRav
	Charles Darwin = 'Auspeet'[PBR] (S)	EPfP LBuc LRHS MAsh MBri NEgg SCob SCoo SPer
	Charles de Gaulle	see *R.* Katherine Mansfield
	'Charles de Mills' (G) ♀[H7]	CDoC CKel CSam CTri EBee ECnt ELan EPfP GCra LCro LRHS LSRN LShp MBri MCot MRav MSwo MWat NLar SKHP SPer SWCr WHer
	Charles Rennie Mackintosh = 'Ausren' (S)	CSBt LBuc MAsh MBri NEgg
	Charlie's Rose = 'Tanellepa' (HT) ♀[H6]	ELan ESty LSRN
	Charlotte = 'Auspoly'[PBR] (S) ♀[H6]	CRos EBee ECnt ELan EPfP ESty LBuc LCro LOPS LRHS LSRN MBri MJak NEgg SCob SCoo SEND SPer SSea SWCr

	Name	Suppliers
	Charlotte Vieli = 'Diclooker' (F)	IDic
	Chartered = 'Diclingo' (F)	IDic
	Chartreuse de Parme = 'Delviola' (S)	CDoC CPou ESty MRav NLar
	'Château de Clos-Vougeot' (HT)	IArd
	Chatsworth = 'Tanotax'[PBR] (Patio/F) ♀[H6]	MRav SPer
	Checkmate = 'Diclanky' (Cl)	IDic
	Checkmate = 'Tuckmate' (Patio) **new**	SMad
§	Cheek to Cheek = 'Poulslas'[PBR] (Courtyard Series) (ClMin)	LRHS MAsh SWCr
	Cheerful Charlie = 'Cocquimmer'[PBR] (F)	LSRN MRav
	Cherie	see *R.* Songs of Praise
	Cherry Brandy '85 = 'Tanryrandy'[PBR] (HT)	CSBt
	Cheshire = 'Korkonopi'[PBR] (County Rose Series) (S)	LRHS
	'Chevy Chase' (Ra)	MCot
	Chianti = 'Auswine' (S)	NLar
	Chicago Peace = 'Johnago' (HT)	SCob
	Child of Achievement	see *R.* Bella
	Chilterns = 'Kortemma'[PBR] (GC)	SWCr
	'Chinatown' (F/S) ♀[H7]	CTri IBoy MAsh MBri MRav SCob SPer
	chinensis misapplied	see *R.* × *odorata*
	- 'Mutabilis'	see *R.* × *odorata* 'Mutabilis'
	- 'Old Blush'	see *R.* × *odorata* 'Pallida'
	chinensis Jacq. var. ***spontanea***	WPGP
	Chloe = 'Poulen003'[PBR] (Renaissance Series) (S)	CPou EBee ECnt LSRN SLon SWCr
	Chris = 'Kirsan'[PBR] (ClHT)	ESty LBrs LSRN SWCr
	Christopher = 'Cocopher' (HT)	LSRN
	Christopher Columbus = 'Meinronsse' (HT)	IArd
	Christopher Marlowe = 'Ausjump'[PBR] (S)	MBri SCoo
	Cider Cup = 'Dicladida' (Min/Patio)	IBoy IDic
§	Cinco de Mayo = 'Wekcobeju'[PBR] (F)	CDoC CKel ECnt LBrs MAsh MRav
	'Cinderella' (Min)	CSBt EWTr NLar
	Cinderella = 'Korfobalt' (ClS)	CDoC CPou EBee SWCr
	City Lights = 'Poulgan'[PBR] (Patio)	CSBt
	City Livery = 'Harhero 2000' (F)	EPfP MAsh
	City of Carlsbad	see *R.* Hanky Panky
	'City of Leeds' (F)	SPer
	City of London = 'Harukfore' (F)	CSBt SPer
	City of York = 'Direktör Benschop' (Cl/HT)	MCot
	Clair Matin = 'Meimont' (ClS)	CPou
	Claire Austin = 'Ausprior'[PBR] (S)	CRos EPfP ESty LBuc LCro LOPS LRHS LSRN MAsh MBri NLar SCob SCoo SWCr
	'Claire Jacquier' (N)	MMuc SPer SWCr

	Name	Suppliers
	Claire Marshall = 'Harunite'[PBR] (F)	ESty
	Claire Rose = 'Auslight'[PBR] (S)	EBee LSRN
	'Clarence House' (Cl)	ELan LRHS MBri NPri
	Claret = 'Frykristal'[PBR] (HT) 🏆H6	ECnt ESty LRHS MAsh MBri MRav SPoG SWCr
	Claude Monet = 'Jacdesa' (HT)	ESty
	'Clementina Carbonieri' (T)	CPou EBee NLar
	Cleo = 'Beebop' (HT)	LSRN
	Cleopatra = 'Korverpea'[PBR] (HT)	MAsh SWCr
	'Cliff Richard' (F)	ESty LSRN
	'Climbing Alec's Red' (ClHT)	ELon SPer
	'Climbing Allgold' (ClF)	SLon
	'Climbing Arthur Bell' (ClF)	COtt CSBt CTri ESty IBoy LAst MSwo SCob SPer SPoG SSea SWCr
	'Climbing Ballerina' (Ra)	CSBt
§	Climbing Baronne Edmond de Rothschild = 'Meigrisosar' (ClHT)	CSBt
	'Climbing Blue Moon' (ClHT)	ELan SWCr
	'Climbing Cécile Brünner' (ClPoly) 🏆H6	CSBt CTri EBee ECnt EPfP LSRN MBri MRav NLar SCob SEND SPer SPoG SSea SWCr
§	'Climbing Columbia' (ClHT)	EBee EShb SPer
	'Climbing Crimson Glory' (ClHT)	CPou LBuc MBri
§	'Climbing Devoniensis' (ClT)	CPou
	'Climbing Ena Harkness' (ClHT)	CRos CTri MRav SEND SPer SPoG SWCr
	'Climbing Étoile de Hollande' (ClHT) 🏆H6	CKel CSBt CTri CWSG EPfP IBoy LBuc LCro MBri MJak MRav SEND SMad SPer SSea SWCr
	Climbing Fragrant Cloud = 'Colfragrasar' (ClHT)	CBcs ELan
	'Climbing Home Sweet Home' (ClHT)	LSRN
	'Climbing Iceberg' (ClF) 🏆H7	COtt CRos CSBt CTri EBee ELan EPfP ESty EUJe EWTr IArd LCro LEdu LPfy LSRN MBri MCot MJak MMuc MRav MSwo NEgg NLar NPri SCob SPer SPoG SSea SWCr
	'Climbing Jazz'	see *R.* That's Jazz
§	'Climbing Lady Hillingdon' (ClT) 🏆H4	CKel EPfP EShb LAst LBrs LBuc LRHS MBri MRav NEgg NLar SPer WBor
	'Climbing Lady Sylvia' (ClHT)	CKel CSBt EPfP LRHS LSRN SPer
	'Climbing Little White Pet'	see *R.* 'Félicité Perpétue'
	'Climbing Madame Caroline Testout' (ClHT)	CPou CTri EBee EPfP MRav SPer
	'Climbing Masquerade' (ClF)	CPou CTri MRav NEgg SCob SPer SSea SWCr
	'Climbing Mrs Herbert Stevens' (ClHT)	EPfP LRHS MRav SEND SPer
	'Climbing Mrs Sam McGredy' (ClHT)	CSBt NLar
	'Climbing Ophelia' (ClHT)	SPer
§	'Climbing Paul Lédé' (ClT)	EBee LRHS
	'Climbing Peace' (ClHT)	SPer
§	'Climbing Pompon de Paris' (ClMinCh)	CTri LRHS MNrw MRav SEND SPer
	'Climbing Ruby Wedding' (ClHT)	LSRN

	Name	Suppliers
	'Climbing Shot Silk' (ClHT) 🏆H6	CSam SPer
§	'Climbing Souvenir de la Malmaison' (ClBb)	CPou SPer
	'Climbing White Cloud'	see *R.* White Cloud = 'Korstacha'
	Coco = 'Korferse' (F)	LSRN
	'Coconut Ice' (HT)	SCob
	Colchester Beauty = 'Cansend' (F)	ECnt
§	'Colonel Fabvier' (Ch)	NLar
	colonial white	see *R.* 'Sombreuil'
	'Columbia' (HT)	CPou
	'Columbian'	see *R.* 'Climbing Columbia'
	'Commandant Beaurepaire' (Bb)	CPou SMad
	common moss	see *R.* × *centifolia* 'Muscosa'
	'Compassion' (ClHT) 🏆H6	Widely available
*	'Compassionate' (F)	MRav
	'Complicata' (G)	CPou CSam CTri EPfP EWTr LRHS MBri MCot MRav NLar SCob SEND SKHP SPer SSea SWCr
	'Comte de Chambord' misapplied	see *R.* 'Madame Boll'
	Comte de Champagne = 'Ausufo'[PBR] (S)	LBuc LRHS MBri SCoo
	'Comtesse Cécile de Chabrillant' (HP)	CPou EBee
	'Comtesse de Lacépède' misapplied	see *R.* 'Du Maître d'Ecole'
	'Conditorum' (G)	LEdu SMad
	Congratulations = 'Korlift' (HT)	CSBt ECnt IArd IBoy LSRN MGos MRav SCob SPer SVic SWCr
§	'Conrad Ferdinand Meyer' (Ru)	SPer
	Conservation = 'Cocdimple' (Min/Patio)	MJak
	'Constance Spry' (ClS) 🏆H6	CTri EBee EPfP LCro LOPS LRHS MBri MMuc MRav MSwo NEgg NLar SCob SEND SPer
§	'Cooperi' (Ra)	CAbP CRHN CSam CWib EBee EWTr LRHS SPer SSea WPGP
	Cooper's Burmese	see *R.* 'Cooperi'
	Coral Palace	see *R.* Imagination = 'Pouldron'
	Cordelia = 'Ausbottle'[PBR] (S)	MBri
	'Cornelia' (HM) 🏆H6	CBcs CTri EBee EPfP EWTr IArd LRHS LSRN MBri MCot MRav MWat NLar SCob SPer SRGP SWCr
	Coronation Street = 'Wekswetrup' (F)	LSRN
	Corvedale = 'Ausnetting'[PBR] (S)	CAbP
	cottage maid	see *R.* × *centifolia* 'Unique Panachée'
	Cottage Rose = 'Ausglisten'[PBR] (S)	LSRN MBri MRav
	Countess Celeste	see *R.* Imagination = 'Pouldron'
§	County of Staffordshire = 'Korsoalgu'[PBR] (GC/S)	LRHS
	County of Yorkshire = 'Korstarnow'[PBR] (GC) 🏆H6	ELan ESty LRHS
	Courage = 'Poulduf'[PBR] (HT)	ECnt
	Courvoisier = 'Macsee' (F)	CSBt
	Crazy for You = 'Wekroalt'[PBR] (F) 🏆H6	ESty LRHS LSRN MBri SWCr
	Cream Abundance = 'Harflax'[PBR] (Abundance Series) (F)	SSea SWCr

Crème de la Crème = 'Gancre'[PBR] (ClHT) — CKel CRos CSBt ECnt ELon ESty LRHS MAsh MRav SPer SPoG SRGP SSea SWCr
'Crépuscule' (N) — EWTr NLar
crested moss — see *R.* × *centifolia* 'Cristata'
Crimson Cascade = 'Fryclimbdown'[PBR] (ClHT) ♀H6 — ESty LRHS MAsh MBri MRav MSwo NPri SMad SPer SPoG SSea SWCr
crimson damask — see *R. gallica* var. *officinalis*
'Crimson Descant' (ClHT) — ECnt
'Crimson Shower' (Ra) — CKel CRos CTri ELan EWTr LBuc LRHS MAsh MBNS MBri MMuc MRav MSwo NEgg NLar SEND SPer WHer
Crimson Sweet Dream = 'Frynogo' (Patio) **new** — ECnt ESty
'Cristata' — see *R.* × *centifolia* 'Cristata'
Crocus Rose = 'Ausquest'[PBR] (S) ♀H6 — CKel EPfP LAst LCro LRHS MBri MRav MWat NEgg NLar SCob SPer SWCr
Crown Princess Margareta = 'Auswinter'[PBR] (S) — CRos ECnt ELan EPfP EShb ESty LBuc LRHS MBri NEgg NLar SCob SCoo SPer SWCr
cuisse de nymphe — see *R.* 'Great Maiden's Blush'
'Cupid' (ClHT) — SPer
I 'Cutie' (Patio) — ESty
Dacapo = 'Poulcy012'[PBR] (Courtyard Series) (ClPatio) — ECnt
'Dainty Bess' (HT) — EBee EWTr SSea
'Dale Farm' (F/Patio) — ESty
× ***damascena*** var. ***bifera*** — see *R.* × *damascena* var. *semperflorens*
§ - 'Professeur Émile Perrot' — LEdu WFar
§ - var. ***semperflorens*** (D) ♀H7 — CPou EWTr NLar SSea SWCr
- 'Trigintipetala' misapplied — see *R.* × *damascena* 'Professeur Émile Perrot'
§ - 'Versicolor' (D) — SPer SSea
Dancing Queen = 'Fryfeston' (ClHT) ♀H6 — CDoC ECnt ESty LRHS LSRN LShp MAsh MBri MRav NPri SPoG SWCr
Daniel = 'Webwhite' (HT) **new** — ESty
Danny Boy = 'Dicxcon'[PBR] (Patio) — IDic LSRN
'Danse du Feu' (ClF) — CBcs CKel CSBt CTri EBee ELan EUJe IBoy LAst LRHS MAsh MBri MRav SCob SPer SWCr
'Daphne' ambig. — LSRN
Darcey Bussell = 'Ausdecorum'[PBR] (S) ♀H6 — COtt CRos CSBt ECnt ELan EPfP ESty LBuc LCro LOPS LRHS LSRN MAsh MBri SCob SPer SWCr
'Darling Jenny' (HT) — LSRN
David Whitfield = 'Gana'[PBR] (F) — LSRN
David's Star = 'Hordadstar' (HT) **new** — LSRN
Dawn Chorus = 'Dicquasar'[PBR] (HT) ♀H6 — CSBt CWSG EPfP ESty IBoy MAsh MJak MRav SCob SPer SPoG SSea SWCr
'Daybreak' (HM) — CTri NLar
'De Meaux' — see *R.* × *centifolia* 'De Meaux'
'De Meaux, White' — see *R.* 'White de Meaux'
§ 'De Resht' (DPo) ♀H7 — CDoC CKel CPou CTri ECnt EPfP LRHS MBri MCot MRav NLar SPer SWCr
'Dear Daughter' (F) — ESty
'Dearest' (F) — CBcs SCob SPer SWCr
'Debbie Thomas' (HT) — LSRN
Deb's Delight = 'Legsweet'[PBR] (F) — LSRN
'Debutante' (Ra) ♀H7 — LRHS
'Deep Secret' (HT) — CBcs CKel CSBt CTri CWSG ECnt ELan ELon EPfP ESty LBrs LRHS MAsh MBri MCot MJak MRav SCob SPer SRGP SSea SWCr
'Deidre Hall' (HT) — LSRN
Della Balfour = 'Harblend'[PBR] (ClHT) — CDoC
Dentelle de Malines = 'Lenfiro' (S) — CAbP
Desert Island = 'Dicfizz'[PBR] (F) — ELon
'Designer Sunset' (Patio) — LBrs MBri
§ 'Desprez à Fleur Jaune' (N) — EBee IArd LBuc LRHS MRav NEgg SEND SPer SWCr
'Devon Maid' (ClHT) — EBee
'Devoniensis' (ClT) — see *R.* 'Climbing Devoniensis'
Diamond Anniversary = 'Morsixty' (Min) — LBuc LSRN
'Diamond Celebration' (HT) — LSRN
Diamond Days Forever = 'Fryjess'[PBR] (F) — LSRN
Diamond Days = 'Hartribe' (HT) — ESty
'Diamond Jubilee' (HT) — CDoC CSBt SWCr
Diamond = 'Korgazell'[PBR] (Patio) ♀H6 — EPfP ESty LRHS LSRN
'Diamond Wishes' — see *R.* Misty Hit
Diana = 'Tananaid'[PBR] (HT) — LSRN
Dick's Delight = 'Dicwhistle' (GC) — CDoC LSRN
Dioressence = 'Deldiore' (F) — ESty
Dizzy Heights = 'Fryblissful'[PBR] (ClHT) ♀H6 — MRav SPer
Dolly = 'Poulvision' (F) — LSRN
'Don Charlton' (HT) — NEgg
'Don Juan' (ClHT) — SWCr
Donna = 'Pekcoupamaple' (HT) — LSRN
'Doreen' (HT) — LSRN
'Doris Tysterman' (HT) — CTri LBuc SPer
Dorothy = 'Cocrocket'[PBR] (F) — LSRN MRav
'Dorothy Perkins' (Ra) — CRHN CTri LBuc LRHS MBri MRav MWat NPer SCob SPer SRGP WBod WHer
'Dortmund' (S) ♀H7 — NLar SPer SWCr
Double Delight = 'Andeli' (HT) — ESty IBoy LSRN SPer SSea SWCr
Douglas = 'Cocfresco' (F) — LSRN
'Dream Catcher' (F) **new** — ESty
Dream Lover = 'Peayetti'[PBR] (Patio) — ESty SWCr
'Dreaming Spires' (Cl) — MSwo SPer
§ 'Du Maître d'Ecole' (G) — LRHS WHer
Dublin Bay = 'Macdub' (ClF) ♀H6 — CDoC CKel CSBt CSam CTri CWSG EBee ECnt ELan ELon EPfP IArd IBoy LAst LPfy LRHS LSRN MAsh MBri MCot MRav MSwo MWat NLar NPri SPer SPoG SSea SWCr WBor
'Duc de Guiche' (G) ♀H7 — EWTr MMuc NLar SEND SLon WHer
Duchess of Cornwall = 'Tan97157' (HT) ♀H6 — CDoC CKel CSBt ESty MRav SCob SWCr
'Duchess of Portland' — see *R.* 'Portlandica'
Duchess of York — see *R.* Sunseeker
'Duchesse de Buccleugh' (G) — MRav

	Name	Suppliers
§	'Duchesse de Montebello' (G) ♀H7	CPou CSam EWTr GBin LRHS NLar SLon SPer
	Duke of Edinburgh (Patio)	see *R.* The Gold Award Rose
	'Duke of Wellington' (HP)	CPou
	'Duke of Windsor' (HT)	SPer
	'Dunwich Rose' (SpH)	EPfP LRHS NLar SCob SKHP SPer WCot
	'Dupontii' (S) ♀H6	LRHS NLar SKHP SPer
	'Dusky Maiden' (F)	EBee SWCr
	'Dutch Gold' (HT)	SPer
	'E.H. Morse'	see *R.* 'Ernest H. Morse'
	'Easlea's Golden Rambler' (Ra) ♀H6	EBee ESty LRHS MRav NEgg NLar SLon
	East Park = 'Harjope'PBR (HT)	ECnt ESty
	'Easter Morning' (Min)	SPer
§	Easy Does It = 'Harpageant'PBR (F) ♀H6	CDoC CKel EBee ECnt ESty MAsh MRav SWCr
	Easy Going = 'Harflow'PBR (F) ♀H6	IArd MAsh SWCr
§	Ebb Tide = 'Weksmopur'PBR (F)	ECnt ESty
	'Éclair' (HP)	WBor
	'Eddie's Crimson' (*moyesii* hybrid)	LSRN
	'Eddie's Jewel' (*moyesii* hybrid)	LSRN
	Eden Rose '88 = 'Meiviolin' (ClHT)	CPou SPer SWCr
	Edward's Rose = 'Smi73/7/97' (F)	ESty LSRN MRav
	eglanteria	see *R. rubiginosa*
	Eglantyne = 'Ausmak'PBR (S)	CDoC CKel CSBt ELan ELon EPfP LAst LCro LOPS LRHS MAsh MBri MRav SCob SPer SPoG SSea SWCr
	'Eleanor' (Patio)	LSRN
	Eleanor = 'Poulberin'PBR (S)	CPou EBee ECnt LSRN SLon
§	***elegantula*** 'Persetosa' (S)	LRHS NLar SKHP SPer
§	Elina = 'Dicjana' (HT) ♀H6	ECnt MJak MRav SPer SPoG SWCr
	'Elizabeth Harkness' (HT)	SPer
	Elizabeth of Glamis = 'Macel' (F)	CTri SPer
	Elizabeth Stuart = 'Maselstu' (Generosa Series) (S)	LSRN
	Elle = 'Meibderos'PBR (HT)	ESty LSRN
	Ellen = 'Auscup' (S)	LSRN
	'Ellen Willmott' (HT)	EBee MCot SPer
	'Elmshorn' (S)	CBcs
	Emilia Maria	see *R.* La Rose de Molinard
	Emily = 'Ausburton' (S)	LSRN
	'Emily Gray' (Ra)	CPou EBee LRHS LSRN MAsh MRav SCob SPer
	Emily Victoria = 'Boshipeacon' (F)	LSRN
	'Empereur du Maroc' (HP)	EBee IBoy
	'Ena Harkness' (HT)	CTri ELan LBuc LRHS MAsh SRGP
	Enchantress = 'Tan97281'PBR (HT)	ESty
§	'Enfant de France' (HP)	LSRN
§	England's Rose = 'Ausrace' (S)	LRHS
	English Garden = 'Ausbuff' (S)	CTri EPfP LRHS LSRN SPer
	'English Miss' (F)	CDoC CKel CPou EBee ECnt ELon ESty EWTr IBoy LRHS MAsh MBri MJak MRav SPer SPoG SWCr
	'English Princess' (F)	LBuc
	English Sonnet	see *R.* Samaritan

	Name	Suppliers
	'Erfurt' (HM)	EBee SPer
§	'Ernest H. Morse' (HT)	CSBt CTri IBoy MRav SPer
	Especially for You = 'Fryworthy'PBR (HT) ♀H6	CKel CSBt ESty LSRN SCob SCoo SSea SWCr
	Essex = 'Poulnoz'PBR (GC)	CKel MRav SCob SPer SPoG
§	'Estrellita de Oro' (Min)	SPer
	'Etain' (Ra)	ECnt
§	'Étendard' (ClHT)	CDoC EBee LPfy MMuc NLar SPer SPoG SWCr
	Eternally Yours = 'Macspeego'PBR (HT)	ESty
	Eternity = 'Moai150097' (F) **new**	LBrs
	Eternity = 'Ricity' (Min)	MBri
	Eternity = 'Twoetern' (HT)	MAsh
	'Ethel' (Ra)	CPou EBee LSRN
	'Étoile de Hollande' (HT)	COtt EBee ELan EUJe GBin LBuc LRHS MAsh MBNS MBri MCot NEgg NLar SCob SLon
	'Eugénie Guinoisseau' (Mo)	CPou
	Evelyn = 'Aussaucer'PBR (S)	CDoC CKel CSBt EBee EPfP ESty LRHS LSRN MBri MRav NEgg NLar SLon SPer SSea
§	Evelyn Fison = 'Macev' (F)	CSBt CTri ELan IBoy LSRN MBri SPer
	'Evelyn May' (HT)	LRHS LShp NPri
	'Excelsa' (Ra)	CDoC CSBt CSam CTri EPfP IArd IBoy MAsh MBri MRav NWea SCob SPoG WBor
	Eyes for You = 'Pejbigeye' (F) ♀H6	CKel CSBt ESty GBin LRHS SLon SPer SWCr
	'F.E. Lester'	see *R.* 'Francis E. Lester'
§	'F.J. Grootendorst' (Ru)	IBoy NEgg SPer
	Fab at 50 = 'Woraunt' (F)	LSRN
	Fabulous at 50 = 'Rawfabsal' (F)	LSRN
	Fabulous at 70 **new**	LSRN
	Fabulous at 80 = 'Rawcox' (F) **new**	LSRN
	'Fabvier'	see *R.* 'Colonel Fabvier'
	'Fairy Rose'	see *R.* 'The Fairy'
	Faithful Friend = 'Beachallenge' (S)	LSRN
	Falstaff = 'Ausverse'PBR (S)	CRos CSBt EPfP IBoy LAst LCro LOPS LRHS LSRN MBNS MBri MJak MMuc MRav MSwo NEgg SCob SPer SPoG SSea SWCr
	'Fantin-Latour' (*centifolia* hybrid) ♀H7	CDoC CTri ECnt ELan EWTr GCra IBoy LEdu LRHS MBri MCot MMuc MRav MWat NEgg NLar SEND SMad SPer
	farreri f. ***persetosa***	see *R. elegantula* 'Persetosa'
	Fascination = 'Jacoyel' (Castle Series) (HT)	SCoo
§	Fascination = 'Poulmax'PBR (F) ♀H6	ELon IBoy MAsh MBri MRav SPer SWCr
	Father's Favourite = 'Gandoug'PBR (F)	LSRN
	fedtschenkoana misapplied	SPer
	Fée des Neiges	see *R.* Iceberg
	'Felicia' (HM) ♀H6	CKel CSBt CSam CTri ECnt ELan EPfP GGal LCro LRHS MBri MCot MMuc MRav MSwo MWat NLar SEND SKHP SPer SSea SWCr WKif
	'Félicité Parmentier' (A × D) ♀H7	EPfP LRHS MBri MRav MWat NLar SPer SWCr
§	'Félicité Perpétue' (Ra) ♀H7	CBcs CDoC CTri ELan EPfP EWTr IBoy LPot LRHS MBri MMuc MRav

	MSwo NEgg NLar SEND SMad SPer SSea SWCr
'Fellemberg' (ClCh)	EBee
Fellowship = 'Harwelcome'PBR (F) ♀H6	MRav SCob SCoo SSea SWCr
'Ferdinand Pichard' (Bb) ♀H7	CKel CPou CRos CSBt CSam CTri EBee ECnt ELon EPfP ESty LCro LOPS LRHS MBri MCot MRav NEgg NLar SEND SKHP SMad SPer SPoG SSea SWCr WFar WKif
Ferdy = 'Keitoli'PBR (GC)	SPer
ferruginea	see *R. glauca* Pourr.
Festival = 'Kordialo'PBR (Patio)	COtt IBoy MRav SPer
Festive Jewel = 'Beacost' (S)	LRHS MBri NPri
Fighting Temeraire = 'Austrava'PBR (S)	CRos EBee EPfP LBuc LCro LOPS LRHS SSea
§ ***filipes*** 'Kiftsgate' (Ra) ♀H6	Widely available
§ 'Fimbriata' (Ru)	CPou LEdu NLar SPer
Fiona = 'Meibeluxen' (S/GC)	LSRN MSwo
Firestar	see *R.* Easy Does It
First Great Western = 'Oracharpam'PBR (HT)	ESty
'Fisher and Holmes' (HP)	EBee
Flashdance = 'Poulyc004' (ClMin)	ECnt
'Florence Mary Morse' (S)	SDix
Flower Carpet Amber = 'Noa97400a'PBR (GC) ♀H6	CDoC CSBt ELan IBoy LBuc LRHS MAsh NPri SCoo SPoG SWCr
'Flower Carpet Coral'PBR (GC) ♀H6	CSBt LBuc LRHS MAsh MBri NPri SCoo SWCr
Flower Carpet Gold = 'Noalesa'PBR (GC)	CDoC COtt ECnt IBoy LBuc LRHS MAsh MBri NPri SPoG
Flower Carpet Pink	see *R.* Pink Flower Carpet
Flower Carpet Red Velvet = 'Noare'PBR (GC/S) ♀H6	CDoC ELan EPfP IBoy LBrs LCro LOPS LRHS MAsh MBri NPri SCoo SPer SSea
Flower Carpet Ruby (GC)	COtt LBuc LRHS MAsh MBri NPri SCoo SPoG
Flower Carpet Scarlet = 'Noa83100b'PBR (GC) ♀H6	LBuc LRHS MAsh MBri
Flower Carpet Sunset = 'Deseo' (S)	LBrs LRHS MAsh MBri NPri SCoo
§ Flower Carpet Sunshine = 'Noason'PBR (GC) ♀H6	EBee LCro LOPS LRHS MAsh NPri SCoo SPer
Flower Carpet White = 'Noaschnee'PBR (GC) ♀H6	CDoC COtt CTri ECnt IBoy LCro LOPS LRHS MAsh MBri NPri SCoo SPer SPoG SSea SWCr
Flower Power = 'Frycassia'PBR (Patio) ♀H6	CKel COtt CSBt ECnt ELon ESty IBoy LRHS MAsh MBri MRav SPoG SWCr
Flower Power Gold = 'Fryneon' (Patio)	ECnt ESty LRHS MBri SPoG SWCr
§ ***foetida*** (S)	CBcs SPer
§ - 'Bicolor' (S)	NLar SPer
Fond Memories = 'Kirfelix'PBR (Patio)	ESty LSRN MBri SWCr
For You With Love = 'Fryjangle' (Patio)	LSRN
For Your Eyes Only = 'Cheweyesup' **new**	ECnt ESty
Forget Me Not = 'Coccharm'PBR (HT)	ESty
forrestiana (S)	LRHS
Fragrant Cloud = 'Tanellis' (HT)	CBcs COtt CTri CWSG ELan EPfP IBoy LRHS MAsh MBri MGos MRav SPer SPoG SWCr
'Fragrant Delight' (F) ♀H6	CKel CSBt ELan ELon MBri MJak MRav SCob SPer SPoG SSea
Fragrant Dream = 'Dicodour' (HT)	ESty IBoy MRav SSea
Fragrant Memories = 'Korpastato'PBR (HT)	CSBt SCoo SKHP
'Francesca' (HM)	EBee EWTr LRHS LSRN SPer
Francine Austin = 'Ausram' (S/GC)	LRHS MBri NEgg SPer
§ 'Francis E. Lester' (HM/Ra) ♀H6	CRHN CSam EBee ELan EPfP EWTr LCro LRHS MBri MCot MMuc NLar SEND SPer SRGP SSea SWCr WBor
× ***francofurtana*** misapplied	see *R.* 'Impératrice Joséphine'
- 'Empress Josephine'	see *R.* 'Impératrice Joséphine'
'François Juranville' (Ra) ♀H6	CHll CPou CRHN EPfP GGal IBoy LRHS LShp MBri MMuc MRav NLar SEND SLon SPer WFar WHer WKif
Freddie Mercury = 'Batmercury' (HT)	ESty LSRN NEgg
Free Spirit = 'Fryjeru'PBR (F) ♀H6	ECnt
Freedom = 'Dicjem' (HT) ♀H6	CDoC CKel CTri ECnt MJak MRav SCob SPer SVic
'Frensham' (F)	CBcs SSea
Friend for Life = 'Cocnanne'PBR (F) ♀H6	CDoC LSRN MRav
Friends Forever = 'Korapriber' (F) ♀H6	EPfP LBrs MAsh SWCr
'Fritz Nobis' (S) ♀H7	CPou NLar SPer
Frothy = 'Macfrothy'PBR (Patio)	ECnt ESty
'Fru Dagmar Hastrup' (Ru) ♀H7	CBcs CDoC CDul CKel CSBt CTri ECnt ELan EPfP EWTr IBoy LBuc LRHS MSwo NEgg NLar NWea SCob SEND SMad SPer SWCr
'Frühlingsgold' (SpH) ♀H7	CBcs ELan EWTr LRHS NLar NWea SPer
'Frühlingsmorgen' (SpH) ♀H7	EWTr SLon SMad SPer
Frytropic (HT) **new**	ESty
§ ***gallica*** var. ***officinalis*** (G) ♀H7	CTri EPfP GPoy LEdu LRHS MBri MHer MNHC MRav NLar SKHP SPer SRms SSea SWCr
§ - 'Versicolor' (G) ♀H7	CArn CDoC CKel CSBt CTri ECnt ELan EPfP GCra GPoy IBoy LEdu LRHS LSRN LShp MBri MCot MHer MNHC MRav NLar NSti SMad SPer SSea SWCr WBor WKif
Galway Bay = 'Macba' (ClHT)	CPou IBoy LBrs LBuc LRHS MAsh MBri NPri SPer SWCr
Garden of Roses	see *R.* Joie de Vivre
'Gardeners Glory'PBR (ClHT) ♀H6	ECnt ESty LRHS MRav SMad
'Gardenia' (Ra)	EBee EWTr LRHS MMuc MSwo NLar SPer WBod
'Garnette Carol'	see *R.* 'Carol Amling'
'Garnette Pink'	see *R.* 'Carol Amling'
'Gaujard'	see *R.* Rose Gaujard
'Gelbe Dagmar Hastrup'	see *R.* Yellow Dagmar Hastrup
§ 'Général Schablikine' (T)	EWTr NLar
Genesis = 'Fryjuicy'PBR (Patio)	ECnt MRav SWCr
gentiliana misapplied	see *R.* 'Polyantha Grandiflora'
Gentle Hermione = 'Ausrumba'PBR (S)	CRos ELan EPfP IBoy LBuc LRHS MBri NLar SCob SPer

Gentle Touch = 'Diclulu' (Min/Patio)	CKel COtt CSBt LAst MRav SMad SPer SPoG
Geoff Hamilton = 'Ausham'PBR (S)	CDoC EPfP IBoy LBuc LRHS LSRN MBNS MBri NEgg SCob SCoo SPer SSea
'Geoffrey Smith' (Cl)	LSRN
George Best = 'Dichimanher'PBR (Patio) ♀H6	ESty IDic LSRN
'Geranium' (*moyesii* hybrid) ♀H7	CBcs CDul CTri EBee ELan EPfP IArd IBoy LRHS MBri MRav NLar SCob SEND SPer SWCr WKif
Gerbe d'Or	see *R.* Casino
Gertrude Jekyll = 'Ausbord'PBR (S) ♀H6	Widely available
'Ghislaine de Féligonde' (Ra/S) ♀H6	CKel CPou CSam EPfP ESty LBuc LCro LRHS MBri MCot NLar SEND SPer SWCr
Ghita	see *R.* Millie
Giardina = 'Tan97286' (Cl)	ESty SWCr
gigantea	WPGP
gigantea × ***longicuspis***	WPGP
Giggles = 'Frynoodle'PBR (Patio)	ECnt
Ginger Syllabub = 'Harjolina'PBR (ClHT)	CKel CPou ECnt ELon ESty MRav SPer SPoG SRGP
Gipsy Boy	see *R.* 'Zigeunerknabe'
Glad Tidings = 'Tantide' (F)	IBoy MRav SPer SWCr
Glamis Castle = 'Auslevel'PBR (S)	CBcs CTri EBee EPfP IBoy LCro LOPS LRHS MBri NEgg SCob SCoo SPer SWCr
glauca ambig.	GCra MHer MSwo MWat SCob WBod
§ ***glauca*** Pourr. (S) ♀H7	CDul CMea CSBt CTri EBee ECnt ELan EPfP GGal LAst LCro LEdu LHop LRHS MLHP MMuc MRav NEgg NLar NWea SEND SGol SKHP SMad SPer SPoG SSea SWCr WCot WMoo
'Glenfiddich' (F)	CSBt CTri MRav MWat SPer
'Glenn Dale' (Cl)	CPou
Glenshane = 'Dicvood' (GC/S)	MRav
Global Beauty = 'Tan 94448' (HT)	ECnt ELon MRav SWCr
'Gloire de Dijon' (ClT)	CKel CSBt CTri EBee ECnt ELan EPfP IBoy LCro LRHS LSRN MBri MCot MRav MWat NEgg NLar SCob SPer SRGP SSea
'Gloire de France' (G) ♀H7	MRav WHer
'Gloire des Mousseuses' (CeMo)	CPou LRHS
'Gloire Lyonnaise' (HP)	EBee MMuc SLon
'Gloria Mundi' (Poly)	NEgg
Gloriana = 'Chewpope'PBR (ClMin)	CDoC CKel ECnt ESty EUJe MAsh MBri MRav MWat SCoo SKHP SPer SPoG SSea SWCr
'Glory of Seale' (S)	SSea
Glowing Amber = 'Manglow' (Min)	ESty
Gold Charm = 'Chewalbygold' (Cl)	ECnt ESty LBrs MAsh MBri
'Golden Anniversary' (HT)	LBuc
'Golden Anniversary' (Patio)	IBoy SPer SSea
'Golden Autumn' (HT)	LSRN
Golden Beauty = 'Clebeau' (Min) **new**	CKel
Golden Beauty = 'Korberbeni'PBR (F) ♀H6	CPou ESty MAsh MBri SWCr
Golden Beryl = 'Manberyl' (Min)	LSRN
Golden Celebration = 'Ausgold'PBR (S) ♀H6	CKel CRos CSBt CTri CWSG EBee ECnt EPfP ESty IBoy LAst LCro LOPS LRHS LSRN MAsh MBri MMuc MRav MSwo NLar SCob SLon SPer SPoG SSea SWCr
'Golden Dawn' (HT)	MAsh
Golden Eureka = 'Meikanaro' (F) **new**	ESty
Golden Gate = 'Korgolgat'PBR (ClHT) ♀H6	ECnt EPfP LRHS SSea
Golden Gate = 'Korrogilo'PBR (HT)	EBee
Golden Jewel = 'Tanledolg'PBR (F/Patio)	ESty
Golden Jubilee = 'Cocagold' (HT)	MRav
Golden Memories = 'Korholesea'PBR (F) ♀H6	CBcs CSBt MAsh MBri MGos MJak MRav NPri SCoo SPer SWCr
Golden Moment = 'Smi-99-2-04' (HT)	ESty MRav
Golden Parfum de Provence = 'Meifazedal' (HT)	ESty
'Golden Rambler'	see *R.* 'Alister Stella Gray'
'Golden Showers' (Cl)	CBcs CKel COtt CSBt CTri CWSG EBee ELan EPfP EUJe GGal IBoy LAst LCro LRHS LSRN MAsh MBri MJak MMuc MRav MWat NEgg NLar NPri SPer SPoG SSea SWCr WBor
Golden Smiles = 'Frykeyno'PBR (F) ♀H6	CDoC ECnt ESty MAsh SWCr
Golden Trust = 'Hardish'PBR (Patio)	MWat
Golden Wedding = 'Arokris'PBR (F)	CDoC CSBt CTri CWSG EBee ECnt ELan EPfP ESty IArd IBoy LBrs LCro LPfy LRHS LSRN MAsh MBri MGos MJak MRav MWat NEgg NPri SCob SPer SPoG SSea SVic SWCr
Golden Wedding Anniversary (F)	COtt LSRN
'Golden Wedding Celebration' (F)	ESty LSRN
'Golden Wings' (S)	CPou CTri ELan EPfP EWTr IBoy LRHS MRav MSwo MWat NLar SKHP SPer
'Goldfinch' (Ra)	ELan EPfP EWTr LRHS MBri MRav MWat NEgg NLar SEND SPer SPoG WBor WFar
Goldstar = 'Candide' (HT)	ECnt
Good as Gold = 'Chewsunbeam'PBR (ClMin)	CSBt ECnt ESty SPer SWCr
Good Life = 'Cococircus'PBR (HT)	SCoo SPer
Gordon Snell = 'Dicwriter' (F)	IDic
'Grace Abounding' (F)	LSRN
Grace = 'Auskeppy'PBR (S) ♀H6	CDoC CRos CSBt EBee EPfP EShb ESty LBuc LRHS LSRN MBri NEgg NLar SCob SPer SSea SWCr
'Graciously Pink' (Min)	MAsh MBri SPoG
Graham Thomas = 'Ausmas' (S) ♀H6	Widely available

Name	Suppliers
Grande Amore = 'Korcoluma'[PBR] (HT) 🏆[H6]	CSBt LBrs LSRN MAsh
'Grandma' (F)	LSRN
'Grandpa Dickson' (HT)	CBcs IBoy MAsh MBri SPer
Granny's Favourite (Patio/F)	LSRN
Great Expectations = 'Jacdal' (F)	SPoG
Great Expectations = 'Lanican' (HT)	CBcs
Great Expectations = 'Mackalves'[PBR] (F)	EPfP IArd MRav SCoo SPer
§ 'Great Maiden's Blush' (A) 🏆[H7]	MRav NLar
Greenall's Glory = 'Kirmac' (F/Patio)	CKel MRav
Greetings = 'Jacdreco'[PBR] (F)	MBri
'Grootendorst'	see *R.* 'F.J. Grootendorst'
Grouse = 'Korimro' (S/GC)	MMuc NLar SEND SLon SPer
'Gruss an Aachen' (Poly) 🏆[H6]	EPfP MJak NLar SPer
'Gruss an Teplitz' (China hybrid)	NLar SPer
'Guinée' (ClHT)	CDoC CKel CSBt CTri ELan EPfP EWTr LAst LRHS MRav MSwo NLar SPer SRGP SSea WCot
Guy Savoy = 'Delstrimen'[PBR] (F)	CDoC ESty LRHS MRav SLon
Guy's Gold = 'Harmatch'[PBR] (HT)	LBrs MAsh
Gwent = 'Poulurt'[PBR] (GC)	CSBt ELan LSRN SCob SEND SPer SSea
Gypsy Boy	see *R.* 'Zigeunerknabe'
Händel = 'Macha' (ClHT)	CBcs CDoC CKel COtt CSBt CTri CWSG ELan EPfP IBoy LBrs LBuc MAsh MBri MRav NEgg NLar NPri SPer SPlb SPoG SSea SWCr
§ Hanky Panky = 'Wektorcent'[PBR] (F)	CDoC ESty MBri MRav SCoo
Hannah Gordon = 'Korweiso' (F)	LBrs MAsh SPer SWCr
'Hansa' (Ru)	EMil LBuc SPer SWCr
Happy 70th Birthday = 'Rawday' (F) **new**	LSRN
Happy Anniversary ambig.	SSea
Happy Anniversary = 'Bedfranc'[PBR] (F)	LSRN MBri MWat SWCr
Happy Anniversary = 'Delpre' (F)	CTri LBrs LRHS MAsh MRav SPoG
'Happy Birthday' (Min/Patio)	ESty IBoy LCro LSRN SSea SWCr
Happy Child = 'Auscomp'[PBR] (S)	LRHS
Happy Days = 'Harquad'[PBR] (S)	CDoC
'Happy Golden Wedding' (F) **new**	CKel
Happy Retirement = 'Tantoras'[PBR] (F) 🏆[H6]	COtt ESty LBrs LBuc LSRN MAsh MBri MRav MWat NPri SCoo SPoG SSea SWCr
Happy Ruby Wedding = 'Frynoble'[PBR] (HT) **new**	CDoC LBrs MAsh
Happy Times = 'Bedone'[PBR] (Patio/Min)	LBrs
§ × ***harisonii*** 'Williams' Double Yellow' (SpH)	EWTr
Harlow Carr ambig.	CKel LRHS SCob
Harlow Carr = 'Aushouse'[PBR] (S)	CDoC CRos EPfP IBoy LBuc MRav SCob SCoo SPer
Harlow Carr = 'Kirlyl' (F)	MBri
'Harry Edland' (F)	SMad SWCr
'Harry Wheatcroft' (HT)	IBoy LBrs
Harvest Fayre = 'Dicnorth'[PBR] (F)	SPer
Havana Hit = 'Poulpah032'[PBR] (Patio)	EPfP LBrs MBri
'Havering Rambler' (Ra)	ELon
'Hazel Le Rougetel' (Ru)	WFar
'Headleyensis' (S)	SLon SPer
'Heart of Gold' (Ra)	COtt
Heart of Gold = 'Coctarlotte'[PBR] (HT) 🏆[H6]	ECnt ESty MRav
Heathcliff = 'Ausnipper' (S)	CRos CSBt EPfP ESty LBuc LRHS
'Helen Knight' (*ecae* hybrid) (S)	ESty MBri
Helen Robinson = 'Harlevel'[PBR] (HT) **new**	ESty
helenae	CTri GBin NLar SPer WPGP
Helen's Trust = 'Taytrust' (HT)	LSRN
§ 'Henri Martin' (CeMo) 🏆[H7]	CTri IBoy LEdu LRHS MAsh NEgg NLar SKHP SLon SPer
Henri Matisse = 'Delstrobla' (HT)	ESty LRHS MRav SPoG
§ 'Herbstfeuer' (RH)	CPou NLar
'Here's Sam' (HT) **new**	LSRN
Heritage = 'Ausblush' (S)	CKel CTri ELan EPfP MBri MJak MRav NEgg NLar SCob SPer SPoG SSea
'Hermosa' (Ch)	LRHS
Hertfordshire = 'Kortenay'[PBR] (GC) 🏆[H6]	ELan LRHS MMuc MRav SCob SEND SPer
§ 'Hidcote Yellow' (Cl)	LRHS SPer
High Flier = 'Fryfandango'[PBR] (ClHT)	MBri
High Hopes = 'Haryup'[PBR] (ClHT)	CWSG EPfP EUJe IBoy LBuc MAsh MBri SPer SSea
'Highdownensis' (*moyesii* hybrid) (S)	ELan
Hole-in-one = 'Horeagle' (F)	LSRN
holy rose	see *R.* × *richardii*
Hommage à Barbara = 'Delchifrou'[PBR] (HT)	EBee ESty MRav WKif
Honey Bunch = 'Cocglen'[PBR] (F)	CKel ELon MRav SPer SRGP
Honey Dijon = 'Weksproulses'[PBR] (F)	CSBt ESty
Honeybun = 'Tan98264'[PBR] (Patio)	ESty
'Honorine de Brabant' (Bb) 🏆[H6]	CPou LEdu LRHS MCot NLar SPer
Hope and Glory = 'Tan01360'[PBR] (HT)	ESty
Hot Chocolate = 'Wekpaltlez' (F) 🏆[H6]	CDoC CKel CSBt EBee ECnt ELan ELon EPfP ESty IBoy LAst LBrs LBuc LRHS LShp MAsh MBri MJak MRav MWat SCoo SMad SPad SPer SPoG SRGP SSea SWCr WBor
House Beautiful = 'Harbingo' (Patio)	MRav
'Hugh Dickson' (HP)	CPou LSRN NLar
hugonis	see *R. xanthina* f. *hugonis*
- 'Plenissima'	see *R. xanthina* f. *hugonis*

	Name	Suppliers
	Humanity = 'Harcross'[PBR] (F)	MRav
	Hyde Hall = 'Ausbosky'[PBR] (S)	CRos LBuc LRHS SCob SCoo
	Ice Cream = 'Korzuri'[PBR] (HT) ♀H6	CDoC CSBt CWSG EBee ECnt ESty IBoy LBrs MRav SCob SPer SPoG SWCr
§	Iceberg = 'Korbin' (F) ♀H6	Widely available
	'Illusion' (ClF)	SWCr
§	Imagination = 'Pouldron'[PBR] (F)	MAsh
	Impératrice Farah = 'Delivour'	ESty
§	'Impératrice Joséphine' (Gn) ♀H7	IBoy LRHS NLar
	In Memory Of	LSRN
	In Memory of my Dog = 'Rawbark' **new**	LSRN
	Indian Summer = 'Harwigwam' (ClMin)	MBri MJak
	Indian Summer = 'Peaperfume'[PBR] (HT) ♀H6	CKel CSBt CWSG LBuc MAsh MRav SPoG SWCr
	'Indigo' (DPo)	CPou
	Ingrid Bergman = 'Poulman'[PBR] (HT) ♀H6	CTri ECnt EPfP IBoy LBrs LRHS LSRN MBri MGos MRav MWat NPri SPer SPoG SWCr
	'Inspiration' (Cl/HT)	COtt LShp MAsh
	'Ipsilanté' (G)	WBor
	'Irène Watts' (Ch)	CPou LSRN NLar SKHP SWCr
	'Irene's Delight' (HT)	ESty LSRN
	Iris = 'Coczero' (HT)	LSRN
	Iris = 'Ferecha' (HT)	LSRN
	Irish Eyes = 'Dicwitness'[PBR] (F) ♀H6	CBcs ESty IArd IBoy IDic LBrs MAsh MBri MJak MRav SCoo SPer SPoG SWCr
	Irish Wonder	see *R.* Evelyn Fison
	Isabella = 'Poulisab'[PBR] (Renaissance Series) (S)	CPou CTri ECnt SLon SWCr
	Isis (HT)	see *R.* Silver Anniversary = 'Poulari'
	Isn't She Lovely = 'Diciluvit'[PBR] (HT) ♀H6	ESty IDic LSRN SWCr
	'Ispahan' (D) ♀H7	EPfP GCra LRHS MBri MCot NEgg NLar SLon SPer WFar
	Ivor's Rose = 'Beadonald' (S)	LRHS LShp MBri NPri
	Ivory Castle = 'Guesoverlay' (HT)	SWCr
	Ivory Romantica = 'Meisabeyla'[PBR] (HT)	ESty
	'Ivory Silk' (Min) **new**	LSRN
	Jack's Wish = 'Kirsil' (HT)	LSRN
§	× ***jacksonii*** 'Max Graf' (GC/Ru)	LRHS NLar
	- Red Max Graf	see *R.* Rote Max Graf
§	- White Max Graf = 'Korgram' (GC/Ru)	EAEE
	'Jacky's Favorite' (F)	LSRN
	Jacobite rose	see *R.* × *alba* 'Alba Maxima'
	Jacqueline du Pré = 'Harwanna' (S) ♀H6	CDoC CKel ECnt EPfP ESty LSRN MCot MRav MWat NLar SEND SLon SPer SSea SWCr
	'Jacques Cartier' misapplied	see *R.* 'Marchesa Boccella'
	Jam and Jerusalem = 'Frymojo'[PBR] (F)	CDoC CKel ECnt LBrs MRav
	James Galway = 'Auscrystal'[PBR] (S)	CSBt EPfP ESty IBoy LBuc LRHS MBri NEgg SCob SCoo SSea
	Janet = 'Auspishus'[PBR] (S)	LSRN MBri SSea
§	'Japonica' (CeMo)	EBee
§	Jardins de Bagatelle = 'Meimafris' (HT)	LSRN
	Jasmina = 'Korcentex'[PBR] (ClHT)	CPou EBee EPfP ESty MAsh
	'Jaune Desprez'	see *R.* 'Desprez à Fleur Jaune'
	Jayne Austin = 'Ausbreak'[PBR] (S)	CSBt LRHS SPer
	Jazz (ClF)	see *R.* That's Jazz
	'Jazz' (F)	LSRN
	Jean = 'Cocupland'[PBR] (Patio)	LSRN
	'Jenny Duval' misapplied	see *R.* 'Président de Sèze'
	Jenny's Rose = 'Cansit' (F)	EBee ECnt LSRN
	Jill's Rose = 'Ganjil'[PBR] (F)	LSRN
	Jilly Jewel = 'Benmfig' (Min)	LSRN
	'John Gwilliam'	MAvo MHCG
§	Joie de Vivre = 'Korfloci 01'[PBR] (Patio/S) ♀H6	CDoC COtt CPou CSBt CWSG EBee ELan EPfP ESty GBin IBoy LBrs LCro LRHS MAsh MBri MRav MWat NLar NPri SCoo SPer SPoG SWCr
	'Josephine Bruce' (HT)	CBcs LSRN
	'Joseph's Coat' (ClS)	CKel IArd LAst SWCr
	Joy Vieli = 'Dickaramel' (F)	IDic
	'Jubilee Celebration' (F)	EPfP LRHS
	Jubilee Celebration = 'Aushunter'[PBR] (S)	CRos CSBt LBuc LCro LOPS LRHS MBri NLar SPer
	Jude the Obscure = 'Ausjo'[PBR] (S)	CNec CSBt EPfP ESty LAst LBuc LRHS MBri NEgg SCob SWCr
	'Julia's Rose' (HT)	LSRN SPer
	Julio Iglesias = 'Meistemon'[PBR] (F)	ESty LSRN
	'Juno' (Ch)	CPou
	Just for You = 'Moryou' (Min)	LSRN
	'Just Jenny' (Min)	LSRN
	'Just Joey' (HT) ♀H6	CBcs CKel COtt CSBt CTri CWSG ECnt ELan ELon EPfP IArd IBoy LPfy LSRN MBri MJak MRav MWat NEgg SCob SPer SPoG SRGP SSea SWCr
	'Just Steve'	LSRN
	Kaffe Fasset = 'Tan07291' (F) **new**	CDoC
	'Katharina Zeimet' (Poly)	CKel CTri
§	Katherine Mansfield = 'Meilanein' (HT)	CSBt
	'Kathleen' (HM)	LSRN
	'Kathleen Harrop' (Bb)	CKel EBee LRHS MMuc MSwo NLar SEND SPer SRGP SWCr
	Kathleen Jane = 'Horcoed' (S/F)	LSRN
	Kathleen's Rose = 'Kirkitt' (F)	LSRN
	'Katie' (ClF)	LSRN
	'Kazanlik' misapplied	see *R.* × *damascena* 'Professeur Émile Perrot'
	Keep Smiling = 'Fryflorida' (HT) ♀H6	CDoC MAsh MBri MRav
	'Keith Maughan' (Cl)	LRHS NPri
§	Kent = 'Poulcov'[PBR] (Towne & Country Series) (S/GC) ♀H6	CKel CSBt EAEE ECnt ELan EPfP ESty IBoy LCro LPfy LSRN MMuc MRav MSwo NLar SCob SEND SPer SPoG SSea SWCr
	Kew Gardens = 'Ausfence'[PBR] (S) ♀H6	CDoC CKel EPfP GGal LBuc LRHS SCob SSea
	'Kew Rambler' (Ra)	CRHN CSam NLar SLon SPer
	'Kiftsgate'	see *R. filipes* 'Kiftsgate'

'Kim' (Patio) LSRN
Kind Regards = 'Peatiger' (F) LSRN
King's Macc = 'Frydisco'PBR (HT) ♀H6 SWCr
'King's Ransom' (HT) CSBt SPer SPoG
Kisses of Fire = 'Chewmultiseek' (Cl) **new** ECnt ESty
Knirps = 'Korverlandus'PBR (GC) LRHS
§ 'Königin von Dänemark' (A) ♀H7 CDoC EPfP IBoy LCro LRHS LSRN MAsh MBri MRav MWat NEgg NLar SKHP SPer SSea SWCr
Korona = 'Kornita' (F) SPer
'Korresia' (F) ♀H7 CDoC CSBt CTri ECnt EPfP ESty IBoy MAsh MBri MJak MRav SCob SPer SPoG SWCr
L.D. Braithwaite = 'Auscrim'PBR (S) CBcs CTri ELan EPfP IBoy LRHS MAsh MBNS MBri MJak MRav NLar SCob SPer SSea
'La Mortola' see *R. brunonii* 'La Mortola'
La Parisienne = 'Delpartricol' (F) ESty
'La Perle' (Ra) CRHN
'La Reine Victoria' see *R.* 'Reine Victoria'
§ La Rose de Molinard = 'Delgrarose'PBR (S) ♀H6 CPou ESty MRav NLar
La Rose de Petit Prince = 'Delgramau' (F) CDoC ESty MRav
'La Rubanée' see *R.* × *centifolia* 'Unique Panachée'
La Sévillana = 'Meigekanu' (F/GC) MSwo SPer WCot
'La Ville de Bruxelles' (D) ♀H7 CSam GBin LRHS NLar SLon SPer
'Lady Anne' (F) **new** LSRN
Lady Emma Hamilton = 'Ausbrother'PBR (S) ♀H6 CNec CRos EPfP ESty IBoy LBuc LRHS MAsh MBri SCob SCoo SPer SWCr
'Lady Gay' (Ra) WBor
'Lady Hillingdon' (ClT) see *R.* 'Climbing Lady Hillingdon'
'Lady Hillingdon' (T) MAsh MWat
'Lady Iliffe' (HT) SWCr
Lady Marmalade = 'Hartiger' (F) CDoC CKel CSBt ECnt ESty LBrs LCro LRHS MRav MWat NPri SCoo SPoG SWCr
Lady Mitchell = 'Haryearn' (HT) ECnt
Lady of Megginch = 'Ausvolume'PBR (S) EPfP LRHS MBri
Lady of Shalott = 'Ausnyson'PBR (S) ♀H6 COtt CRos LBuc LCro LOPS LRHS MAsh MBri SCob SSea
Lady Penelope = 'Chewdor'PBR (ClHT) CSBt
§ 'Lady Penzance' (RH) CBcs SPer
Lady Rose = 'Korlady' (HT) MAsh MBri
Lady Salisbury = 'Auscezed'PBR (S) CRos EPfP LBuc LCro LOPS LRHS SCob SCoo
'Lady Sylvia' (HT) LSRN NEgg SPer
laevigata (Ra) MMuc
- 'Anemonoides' see *R.* 'Anemone'
Laguna = 'Koradigel'PBR (Cl) EPfP MAsh
Laguna = 'Kormulen' (HT) LRHS
L'Aimant = 'Harzola'PBR (F) ♀H5 CSBt ESty MRav SWCr
'Lamarque' (N) CPou EWTr
Lancashire = 'Korstesgli'PBR (GC) ♀H6 CDoC ECnt ELan ESty LRHS LSRN MRav MSwo SSea SWCr
Lancelot = 'Tan03542'PBR (Cl) ESty
§ 'Lanei' (CeMo) EBee
Laura Ford = 'Chewarvel'PBR (ClMin) ♀H5 CDoC CKel COtt CTri IBoy MAsh MBri MGos MRav MWat SPer SPoG SSea
'Laura Louisa' (Cl) EWTr
'Laure Davoust' (Ra) CPou EBee MMuc NLar
Lavender Ice = 'Tan04249'PBR (F) ESty SWCr
'Lavender Lassie' (HM) CPou CSam NLar SPer SSea
Lavender Symphonie = 'Meiptima' (Patio) ESty
Lavinia see *R.* Lawinia
§ Lawinia = 'Tanklewi' (ClHT) ♀H6 CSBt LRHS MAsh SPer
'Lawrence Johnston' see *R.* 'Hidcote Yellow'
§ Lazy Days = 'Poulkalm'PBR (F) ECnt MAsh MBri
'Le Rêve' (Cl) EWTr
Le Rouge et le Noir = 'Delcart' (HT) ESty
'Le Vésuve' (Ch) CPou
Leah Tutu = 'Hornavel' (S) ESty LRHS LShp MBri NPri
Leaping Salmon = 'Peamight'PBR (ClHT) ♀H6 CSBt EBee ESty LSRN MRav SPer SRGP SWCr
'Leda' (D) EWTr SPer
'Lemon Pillar' see *R.* 'Paul's Lemon Pillar'
Léonardo de Vinci = 'Meideauri'PBR (F) CSBt
Leonidas = 'Meicofum'PBR (HT) ESty
'Léontine Gervais' (Ra) CRHN LRHS MBri
'Leo's Eye' (Ra) CPou EPfP
Leslie's Dream = 'Dicjoon' (HT) IDic
Let's Celebrate = 'Fryraffles' (F) CDoC ECnt ESty LBrs LRHS MAsh MRav
'Leverkusen' (ClF) ♀H7 CKel EBee EWTr LRHS MRav NLar SEND SPer SWCr
Lichfield Angel = 'Ausrelate'PBR (S) ♀H6 EPfP LBuc LRHS MAsh MBri NLar SCob SCoo
Lichtkönigin Lucia = 'Korlillub' (S) SSea
Life Begins at 40! = 'Horhohoho' (F) LSRN
Light Fantastic = 'Dicgottago' (F) ♀H6 IDic SWCr
'Lilac Dream' (F) SWCr
Liliana = 'Poulsyng'PBR (S) CPou ECnt LSRN SLon SWCr
Lilli Marlene = 'Korlima' (F) CSBt IBoy SPer
Lincoln Cathedral = 'Glanlin'PBR (HT) MJak SPer
Lincolnshire Poacher = 'Glareabit' (HT) NEgg
'Lincolnshire Yellow Belly' (F) ESty
Lion's Fairy Tale see *R.* Champagne Moments
Lisa = 'Kirdisco' (F) LSRN
Little Amy = 'Battamy' (Min) LSRN
Little Jackie = 'Savor' (Min) LSRN
Little Miss Sunshine = 'Dicgungho' (F) ECnt IDic
Little Rambler = 'Chewramb'PBR (MinRa) ♀H6 CDoC CSBt CWSG EBee ECnt ELan ESty MBri MGos MMuc MRav SCoo SPer SSea SWCr
'Little White Pet' see *R.* 'White Pet'
Lochinvar = 'Ausbilda'PBR (S) LRHS

Name	Suppliers
'Lolabelle'	CPou EBee
'Long John Silver' (Cl)	ELan SSea
longicuspis misapplied	see *R. mulliganii*
longicuspis Bertol. (Ra)	EBee EWTr
§ - var. ***sinowilsonii*** (Ra)	GCal
Look Good... Feel Better = 'Poulcas034'[PBR] (Castle Series) (Poly)	EPfP LBMP
Lord Byron = 'Meitosier' (ClHT)	ESty
'Lord Penzance' (RH)	EWTr NLar SPer
Lorna = 'Cocringer' (F)	LSRN
'L'Ouche' misapplied	see *R.* 'Louise Odier'
'Louis XIV' (Ch)	MCot
§ 'Louise Odier' (Bb)	CKel CTri EAEE EBee ECnt EPfP IArd LRHS LSRN MBri MRav MWat NLar SPer SRGP SWCr
Love & Peace = 'Baipeace'[PBR] (HT) ♀[H6]	ESty LBrs SWCr
Love Knot = 'Chewglorious'[PBR] (ClMin) ♀[H6]	CDoC CSBt ECnt EPfP ESty LBrs LRHS MAsh MMuc MRav SCoo SSea SWCr
§ Lovely Bride = 'Meiratcan'[PBR] (Patio)	EPfP LBrs LRHS MAsh MBri SCoo SPoG
Lovely Fairy = 'Spevu'[PBR] (Poly/GC)	WMoo
Lovely Lady = 'Dicjubell'[PBR] (HT) ♀[H6]	CKel CSBt ECnt ESty LSRN MRav SSea SWCr
Lovely Meidiland	see *R.* Lovely Bride
Lovely Pink = 'Meinoplius' (F) **new**	ESty
'Lovers' Meeting' (HT)	MJak MRav SPer SWCr
Loving Memory = 'Korgund81' (HT)	CKel COtt CSBt ECnt ESty IArd LSRN MAsh MGos MRav SPer SPoG SSea SVic SWCr
Lucky! = 'Frylucy' (F) ♀[H6]	CDoC COtt CSBt CWSG EPfP ESty LBuc LRHS LSRN LShp MAsh MRav NPri SCoo SPer SPoG SWCr
Lucy = 'Kirlis' (F)	LSRN
Ludlow Castle	see *R.* England's Rose
Luscious Lucy = 'Tucklucy' (Patio)	LSRN
'Lykkefund' (Ra)	CKel
Macartney rose	see *R. bracteata*, *R.* The McCartney Rose
Macmillan Nurse = 'Beamac' (S)	ESty LRHS LShp MBri MCot NPri
macrophylla (S) B&SWJ 2603	WCru
- CC 6259	GKev
- GWJ 9306 **new**	WCru
'Madame Alfred Carrière' (N) ♀[H5]	Widely available
'Madame Alice Garnier' (Ra)	CPou CRHN EBee SPer
'Madame Antoine Mari' (T)	CPou
§ 'Madame Boll' (DPo)	CKel COtt ESty EWTr LCro MSwo NLar
'Madame Butterfly' (HT)	LRHS
§ 'Madame Caroline Testout' (HT)	CTri LRHS SPoG SRGP
'Madame de la Roche-Lambert' (DPMo)	CPou
'Madame de Sancy de Parabère' (Bs)	IArd
'Madame Driout' (ClT)	CPou
'Madame Ernest Calvat' (Bb)	CPou
§ 'Madame Grégoire Staechelin' (ClHT) ♀[H6]	CDoC CTri ECnt ELan EPfP EWTr IBoy LBrs LCro LRHS LSRN MAsh MBri MRav MSwo NEgg NLar SCob SPer SPlb SPoG WKif
'Madame Hardy' (D) ♀[H7]	CDoC CPou CSBt EAEE ECnt EPfP EWTr LRHS LSRN MBri MRav MSwo MWat NEgg NLar SCob SPer SSea SWCr WFar
'Madame Isaac Pereire' (ClBb)	CDoC CSBt CTri ECnt EPfP IBoy MBri MCot MRav MSwo NLar SCob SMad SPer SPoG SSea SWCr WBor WFar
'Madame Knorr' misapplied	see *R.* 'Madame Boll'
'Madame Knorr' (DPo) ♀[H7]	CPou ECnt ELon EPfP LRHS MCot SPer SSea SWCr
'Madame Laurette Messimy' (Ch)	CPou EWTr
'Madame Lauriol de Barny' (Bb)	MRav NLar SLon
'Madame Legras de Saint Germain' (A × N)	CPou EWTr LRHS NLar SPer
'Madame Louis Lévêque' (DPMo)	CPou EWTr
'Madame Pierre Oger' (Bb)	CTri ECnt SKHP SPer
'Madame Plantier' (A × N)	CPou EWTr LRHS NLar SCob SEND SPer WFar
'Madame Rouge' (HT)	MAsh
'Madame Scipion Cochet' (HP)	CPou
'Madge' (HM)	SDix
Magic Carpet = 'Jaclover'[PBR] (S/GC) ♀[H6]	CDoC CKel ELan IBoy MGos MRav MSwo SPer SWCr
Maid Marion = 'Austobias'[PBR] (HM)	EPfP LBuc LRHS MAsh
Maid of Honour = 'Jacwhink' (F)	IDic
'Maid of Kent'[PBR] (Cl)	LBuc LSRN MAsh NLar SCob SCoo SPer SWCr
'Maiden's Blush' (A)	CArn CSam CTri ELan LEdu LRHS MBri MMuc SPer WHer
'Maiden's Blush, Great'	see *R.* 'Great Maiden's Blush'
'Maigold' (ClPiH) ♀[H7]	CBcs CTri ELan ELon EPfP LRHS MAsh MBri MCot MRav MSwo MWat NLar SCob SEND SMad SPer SWCr
Maltese rose	see *R.* 'Cécile Brünner'
Malvern Hills = 'Auscanary'[PBR] (Ra)	CRos CSBt EBee EPfP ESty LBuc LRHS MAsh MBri MMuc NLar SCob SWCr
Mamma Mia = 'Poulcy013' (Courtyard Series) (Ra)	CDoC
Mamma Mia! = 'Fryjolly'[PBR] (HT) ♀[H6]	COtt EBee ECnt ESty LBrs LRHS MAsh MBri MRav SPoG SWCr
Mamy Blue = 'Delblue' (HT)	ESty
'Mandarin' (F)	CKel SSea
Mandarin = 'Korcelin'[PBR] (Min)	ESty IBoy MRav
'Mannington Mauve Rambler' (Ra)	ESty
Many Happy Returns = 'Harwanted'[PBR] (F) ♀[H6]	CBcs CKel CSBt ECnt ELan EPfP IBoy LBrs LRHS LSRN MAsh MBri MGos MJak MRav MWat NPri SCob SPer SPoG SSea SVic SWCr
§ 'Marchesa Boccella' (DPo) ♀[H7]	CPou CSam CTri EBee EPfP LRHS MBri MCot NLar SEND SPer SSea SWCr WBor WHer
'Maréchal Davoust' (CeMo)	LEdu
'Maréchal Niel' (N)	EShb SPer SSea
'Margaret' (HT)	LSRN
Margaret Merril = 'Harkuly' (F)	CBcs CDoC CKel CSBt CTri CWSG EBee ECnt ELan EPfP ESty IArd

	Name	Suppliers
		IBoy LAst LBrs LCro LRHS LSRN MAsh MBri MJak MRav MWat SCob SPer SPoG SRGP SSea SWCr
	'Marguerite Hilling' (S)	CTri MSwo NLar SPer
	'Marie Louise' (D)	EBee
	'Marie Pavič' (Poly)	CPou
	Marigold Sweet Dream = 'Fryprospa' (Patio)	ECnt
	Marjorie Fair = 'Harhero' (Poly/S) 🏆H6	CDoC ELan EPfP ESty MRav
	Marry Me = 'Dicwonder'[PBR] (Patio) 🏆H6	ESty IDic SWCr
	'Martha' (Bb)	LSRN
I	'Mary' (Poly)	LSRN
	Mary Rose = 'Ausmary' (S)	CKel CSBt CTri ELan ELon EPfP IBoy LRHS LSRN MAsh MBri MJak MRav NLar SCob SLon SPer SPoG SSea SWCr WKif
	'Masquerade' (F)	CDoC CTri ELan EPfP MRav SPer SWCr
	Matawhero Magic	see *R.* Simply the Best
	Maurice Utrillo = 'Delstavo' (HT)	ESty
	'Max Graf'	see *R.* × *jacksonii* 'Max Graf'
	'Maxima'	see *R.* × *alba* 'Alba Maxima'
	Maxima Romantica = 'Meikerira' (HT)	ESty
	'May Queen' (Ra)	CPou EBee LRHS MMuc MRav NLar SEND SPer SWCr
	Mayor of Casterbridge = 'Ausbrid'[PBR] (S)	LRHS
	'McCartney Rose'	see *R.* The McCartney Rose
	'Meg' (ClHT)	CKel EBee EPfP EWTr LRHS LSRN MCot MMuc NLar SPer SRGP
	Melody Maker = 'Dicqueen'[PBR] (F)	IBoy
	Memory Lane = 'Peavoodoo'[PBR] (F)	LSRN
	'Mermaid' (Cl) 🏆H5	CBcs CDul CSBt CTri EPfP LHop LRHS MBri NLar SCob SEND SPer SSea SWCr
§	'Mevrouw Nathalie Nypels' (Poly)	CTri LRHS MMuc MRav NLar SPer
	Middlesborough Football Club = 'Horflame' (HT)	LSRN
§	Millie = 'Poulren013'[PBR] (Renaissance Series) (S) 🏆H6	COtt ECnt ESty LCro LPfy LRHS LSRN MBri SPoG SWCr
	Millie Rose = 'Wekblunez'[PBR] (HT)	SWCr
	Millionaire = 'Peazara' (F)	LSRN
	Mind Games = 'Dickylie' (F)	ECnt IDic
	'Minnehaha' (Ra)	SSea
	Mischief = 'Macmi' (HT)	LSRN SPer
	Miss Alice = 'Ausjake'[PBR] (S)	LSRN MBri
§	'Mister Lincoln' (HT)	MJak SPer
§	Misty Hit = 'Poulhi011'[PBR] (PatioHit Series) (Patio)	ECnt LSRN MBri SWCr
	Mitsouko = 'Delnat' (HT)	ESty
	Molineux = 'Ausmol'[PBR] (S) 🏆H6	CRos EPfP LRHS MAsh MBri SCob SPer SWCr
	Moment in Time = 'Korcastrav'[PBR] (F) 🏆H6	CBcs CDoC COtt EBee ECnt EPfP LShp MAsh MRav MWat NPri SCoo SPer SPoG SWCr
	Monica Bellucci = 'Meimonkeur' (HT)	ESty
	Moody Blue = 'Fryniche' (HT)	CDoC ECnt ESty IBoy LRHS LShp MAsh MRav MWat NPri SWCr
	'Moonlight' (HM)	CKel CTri ELan LRHS MRav MSwo SPer SWCr
	Moonshine = 'Tan97123'[PBR] (HT)	ECnt
	'Morletii' (Bs)	EWTr MMuc SEND
	'Morning Jewel' (ClF) 🏆H7	SPer SWCr
	Morning Mist = 'Ausfire' (S)	LBuc LRHS SSea
§	'Morsdag' (Poly/F)	ELan LSRN SCob SVic
	Mortimer Sackler = 'Ausorts'[PBR] (S) 🏆H6	ELon EPfP LAst LBuc LRHS MBri MMuc SCob SCoo SPer SSea SWCr
	moschata (Ra)	SSea
	- 'Autumnalis'	see *R.* 'Princesse de Nassau'
	- var. ***nepalensis***	see *R. brunonii*
	Mother's Day	see *R.* 'Morsdag'
I	'Mother's Day'	MJak SRGP
	Mother's Joy = 'Horsiltrop' (F)	LSRN
	Mountain Snow = 'Aussnow' (Ra)	LRHS MBri
	Mountbatten = 'Harmantelle' (F) 🏆H6	CKel ELan LBuc MRav SPer SPoG SWCr
§	'Mousseline' (DPoMo)	CPou EWTr MCot SPer
	'Mousseuse du Japon'	see *R.* 'Japonica'
	moyesii (S)	CTri ELan EWTr EWld GCra GKev LAst MWat NEgg NWea SKHP SPer
	'Mr Lincoln'	see *R.* 'Mister Lincoln'
	'Mrs Anthony Waterer' (Ru)	EBee SPer
	'Mrs Arthur Curtiss James' (ClHT)	MMuc
	Mrs Doreen Pike = 'Ausdor'[PBR] (Ru)	LRHS
	'Mrs Honey Dyson' (Ra)	CPou EWTr
	'Mrs John Laing' (HP)	LRHS NLar SLon SPer SWCr
	'Mrs Oakley Fisher' (HT)	MCot SDix SMad SPer SWCr WCot
	'Mrs Sam McGredy' (HT)	CPou LRHS NEgg
§	***mulliganii*** (Ra)	EPfP GKin MMuc SPer
	multibracteata (S)	CBcs
§	***multiflora*** 'Grevillei' (Ra)	MMuc SPer
	- 'Platyphylla'	see *R. multiflora* 'Grevillei'
	- wild-collected	GCal
	Mum in a Million	see *R.* Millie
	Mummy	see *R.* Newly Wed
	mundi	see *R. gallica* 'Versicolor'
	Munstead Wood = 'Ausbernard'[PBR] (S) 🏆H6	CNec COtt CRos EPfP EShb ESty LBuc LCro LOPS LRHS LSRN MBri SCob SPer
	'Mutabilis'	see *R.* × *odorata* 'Mutabilis'
	My Dad = 'Boselftay'[PBR] (F)	LSRN SWCr
	'My Darling Husband' (F)	LSRN
	'My Darling Wife' (F)	LSRN
	My Girl = 'Tan00798'[PBR] (HT)	ECnt
	'My Joy' (HT)	LSRN
	My Mum = 'Webmorrow'[PBR] (F)	ESty LSRN MBri SCob SWCr
	My Valentine = 'Mormyval' (Min) 🏆H6	LSRN MAsh MBri SPoG
	Myriam = 'Cocgrand' (HT)	LSRN
	Mystery Girl = 'Dicdothis'[PBR] (HT)	EBee ECnt
	Nancy = 'Poulninga' (Renaissance Series) (S)	CPou LSRN
	'Naomi' (HT)	CPou
	'Narrow Water' (Ra) 🏆H6	CPou EWTr SWCr
	Natalie = 'Poulren014' (Renaissance Series) (S)	LSRN
	Natasha Richardson = 'Harpacte' (F)	CKel MRav
	'Nathalie Nypels'	see *R.* 'Mevrouw Nathalie Nypels'

'National Trust' (HT)	CBcs CTri IArd IBoy MJak MWat SPer WBod
'Nevada' (S)	CSBt CTri ECnt ELan EPfP IArd IBoy LEdu LRHS MRav NLar SPer
Never Forgotten = 'Gregart' (HT)	LSRN
New Arrival	see *R.* 'Red Patio'
New Beginnings = 'Korprofko'[PBR] (F)	LSRN MAsh SWCr
§ 'New Dawn' (Cl) 🏆H7	Widely available
'New Home'	LSRN
§ Newly Wed = 'Dicwhynot'[PBR] (Patio) 🏆H6	LSRN SSea SWCr
Newsflash = 'Kendutch' (F)	ESty SWCr
Nice Day = 'Chewsea'[PBR] (ClMin)	CDoC CTri ELon EPfP ESty IBoy MAsh MRav SPer SPoG SSea
'Nicola' (F)	LSRN
Night Light = 'Poullight'[PBR] (Courtyard Series) (Cl)	ECnt
Night Owl = 'Wekpurosot' (Cl)	CDoC ESty MRav
Nina = 'Mehnina'[PBR] (S)	LSRN
Nina = 'Poulren018'[PBR] (Renaissance Series) (S)	ECnt
nitida	NWea SEND SPer
'Noaley'[PBR] (Min)	LRHS
Noble Antony = 'Ausway'[PBR] (S)	EBee EPfP LRHS MBri MWat SCob SSea
§ 'Noisette Carnée' (N) 🏆H7	CPou CTri EPfP EWTr GCra LEdu LRHS MBNS MBri MCot MRav NLar SPer SSea SWCr
Norfolk = 'Poulfolk'[PBR] (GC)	CKel CTri ESty MSwo SCob SPer
Nostalgia = 'Savarita' (Min)	COtt LRHS
Nostalgie = 'Taneiglat'[PBR] (HT) 🏆H6	CSBt ECnt ESty MBri MRav SPoG SSea SWCr
'Nozomi' (ClMin/GC)	CAbP CKel CTri ELan EPfP ESty MRav NLar SPer
'Nuits de Young' (CeMo) 🏆H7	EPfP LRHS MBri NLar SEND SKHP WHer
Nurse Tracey Davies = 'Frykookie'[PBR] (F) 🏆H6	SWCr
§ ***nutkana*** 'Plena' (S/D) 🏆H7	MCot NLar SKHP WHer
'Nymphenburg' (HM)	SPer
Octavia Hill = 'Harzeal'[PBR] (F)	MBri MRav NLar SPer SWCr
§ × ***odorata***	CPou
§ - 'Mutabilis' (Ch) 🏆H5	CDoC CKel CPou CRHN CTri ECre ELan EPfP EWTr GBin GGal LCro LRHS MCot MRav NLar SEND SKHP SPer SSea WBod WCFE WCot XSen
§ - 'Ochroleuca' (Ch)	CPou EBee
§ - 'Pallida' (Ch)	CPou EPfP LRHS MCot MRav MWat NLar SPer SSea
§ - Sanguinea Group (Ch)	SEND XSen
- - 'Bengal Crimson' (Ch) 🏆H5	CPou ECre EPfP EWTr LRHS LSRN SDix SKHP SLon WCot WKif
- - 'Bob's Beauty' (Ch)	WCot
§ - 'Viridiflora' (Ch)	CPou EBee LEdu LRHS SLon SMad SPer SSea WCot WHer
Odyssey = 'Franski'[PBR] (F)	ESty
Oh Wow! = 'Wekspitrib' (Cl)	ECnt ESty
officinalis	see *R. gallica* var. *officinalis*
'Oklahoma' (HT)	LAst
old blush China	see *R.* × *odorata* 'Pallida'
old cabbage	see *R.* × *centifolia*
Old John = 'Dicwillynilly' (F)	IDic LSRN
old pink moss rose	see *R.* × *centifolia* 'Muscosa'
Old Port = 'Mackati'[PBR] (F)	ESty IArd
old red moss	see *R.* 'Henri Martin', *R.* 'Lanei'
old velvet moss	see *R.* 'William Lobb'
'Old Velvet Rose'	see *R.* 'Tuscany'
old yellow Scotch (SpH)	see *R.* × *harisonii* 'Williams' Double Yellow'
Olivia = 'Wekquahofa' (HT)	LSRN
'Olympic Flame' (F)	EPfP MAsh MBri
Olympic Spirit = 'Peaprince' (F)	MAsh
'Omar Khayyám' (D)	NLar
omeiensis	see *R. sericea* subsp. *omeiensis*
Open Arms = 'Chewpixcel'[PBR] (ClMin) 🏆H6	ESty LBuc MAsh SPer SSea SWCr
'Ophelia' (HT)	LRHS
'Orange Sensation' (F)	CTri
§ Orange Sunblaze = 'Meijikatar'[PBR] (Min)	CSBt
'Orangeade' (F)	SCob
Oranges and Lemons = 'Macoranlem'[PBR] (S/F)	CSBt ESty IBoy LBrs SSea SWCr
Othello = 'Auslo'[PBR] (S)	LAst SPer
'Our Beth' (S)	LRHS LSRN MBri NPri
'Our Dream' (Patio)	LBrs MAsh MBri
Our George = 'Kirrush' (Patio)	LSRN
Our Hilda = 'Lancoro' (F)	LSRN
Our Jubilee = 'Coccages' (HT)	ESty SVic
Our Molly = 'Dicreason' (GC/S)	IDic LSRN SPer
Oxfordshire = 'Korfullwind'[PBR] (GC) 🏆H6	LRHS MRav SCob SSea
Painted Moon = 'Dicpaint' (HT)	ESty
Panache = 'Poultop'[PBR] (Patio/Min)	ECnt IBoy SWCr
'Papa Gontier' (T)	CPou
Papa Meilland = 'Meisar' (HT)	CSBt CTri SPer SSea
Paper Anniversary (Patio)	LBuc LSRN
Papi Delbard = 'Delaby' (ClHT)	ESty EWTr LSRN MRav
§ 'Para Ti' (Min)	SPer
I 'Parade' (Cl) 🏆H6	CKel NLar SWCr
'Parkdirektor Riggers' (F)	CSam EBee EWTr GBin MBri MMuc SCob SPer
Parks's yellow China	see *R.* × *odorata* 'Ochroleuca'
Parson's pink China	see *R.* × *odorata* 'Pallida'
Partridge = 'Korweirim' (GC)	SPer
Pas de Deux = 'Poulhult'[PBR] (Courtyard Series) (ClF)	MAsh
Pascali = 'Lenip' (HT)	CBcs CTri ELon IBoy MJak SCob SPer
Pat Austin = 'Ausmum'[PBR] (S)	CDoC CRos CSBt CTri EPfP IBoy LBrs LRHS LSRN MAsh MBNS MBri MRav MWat NEgg NLar SCob SEND SPer SWCr
Paul Gauguin = 'Delstrichoc' (HT)	ESty
'Paul Lédé' (ClT)	see *R.* 'Climbing Paul Lédé'
Paul McCartney (HT)	see *R.* The McCartney Rose
'Paul Neyron' (HP)	EWTr SPer
'Paul Noël' (Ra)	CRos LBuc
Paul Shirville = 'Harqueterwife'[PBR] (HT)	CKel SPer SWCr

	Name	Suppliers
	'Paul Transon' (Ra) ♀^{H6}	CPou CRHN EBee LRHS MBri MMuc NEgg NLar SEND SPer SRGP WHer
	'Paula's Rose' (Patio) **new**	LSRN
	'Paul's Himalayan Musk' (Ra) ♀^{H6}	Widely available
§	'Paul's Lemon Pillar' (ClHT)	CKel EPfP LRHS NLar SMad SPer SSea
	'Paul's Scarlet Climber' (Cl/Ra)	COtt ELan IBoy LBuc LRHS MAsh MJak MRav MSwo MWat SEND SPer SRGP
	'Paul's Single White Perpetual' (Ra)	CTri EWTr MMuc NLar
	'Pax' (HM)	CPou EBee WKif
	Peace = 'Madame A. Meilland' (HT) ♀^{H6}	CBcs CSBt CTri EBee ECnt ELan EPfP ESty IBoy LCro LRHS LSRN MAsh MBri MRav MWat NEgg NPri SCob SPer SPoG SRGP SSea SWCr
	Peacekeeper = 'Harbella'^{PBR} (F)	CSBt
	'Peach Grootendorst' (Ru)	CPou
	Peachy = 'Macrelea' (HT)	MAsh MBri SPoG
	Pearl = 'Korterschi'^{PBR} (F) ♀^{H6}	MAsh MRav SWCr
	Pearl Anniversary = 'Whitston'^{PBR} (Min/Patio)	CDoC CKel COtt CSBt ESty LBuc LSRN MRav SSea SWCr
	Pearl Drift = 'Leggab' (S)	EBee MCot MSwo SPer SWCr
	Peaudouce	see *R.* Elina
§	***pendulina***	WOut
	- 'Nana'	NWad
	'Penelope' (HM) ♀^{H5}	CDoC CSBt CTri EBee ECnt ELan EPfP IBoy LRHS LSRN MBri MCot MRav NLar SCob SEND SMad SPer SRGP SSea SWCr
	Penny Lane = 'Hardwell'^{PBR} (ClHT) ♀^{H6}	CDoC COtt CSBt EBee ECnt EPfP EUJe IBoy LAst LBuc LRHS MAsh MBri MRav NLar SCoo SPer SPoG SSea SWCr
	Penny Lane = 'Talpen' (Min)	MSwo
	× ***penzanceana***	see *R.* 'Lady Penzance'
	Peppermint Splash	see *R.* Rachel Louise Moran
	Perdita = 'Ausperd' (S)	LRHS
	Perennial Blue = 'Mehr9601' (Ra) ♀^{H6}	CDoC ESty MRav SCob SSea SWCr
	Perennial Blush = 'Mehbarbie'^{PBR} (Ra) ♀^{H6}	CDoC CKel ESty MRav SSea SWCr
§	Perfect Day = 'Poulcrem' (F)	ECnt
	Perfect Harmony = 'Tangustedv' (HT)	ESty
	Perfect Pet = 'Smi122-2-04' (F) **new**	ESty
§	'Perle d'Or' (Poly) ♀^{H6}	LRHS NLar SDix SLon SMad SPer
	Perle Noire = 'Delurt' (HT)	ESty
	Perpetually Yours = 'Harfable'^{PBR} (Cl)	LAst LBuc MRav SCoo
	Peter Pan = 'Chewpan'^{PBR} (Min) ♀^{H6}	LBrs SWCr
	Peter Pan = 'Sunpete' (Patio)	MAsh
	'Petite de Hollande' (Ce)	NLar SPer
	'Petite Lisette' (Ce × D)	NLar
	Pheasant = 'Kordapt' (GC)	SPer
	Phillipa = 'Poulheart'^{PBR} (S)	LSRN
	Phoebe (Ru)	see *R.* 'Fimbriata'
	'Phyllis Bide' (Ra) ♀^{H6}	CKel EBee EPfP EWTr IArd LCro LOPS LRHS MBri MCot MSwo NLar SEND SPer SRGP SSea SWCr
	Piccadilly = 'Macar' (HT)	CSBt CTri IBoy SPer SWCr
	Piccolo = 'Tanolokip' (F/Patio)	MRav SWCr
	'Picture' (HT)	SPer
	Pierre Cardin = 'Meilolipo'^{PBR} (HT) **new**	ESty
	Pigalle '84 = 'Meicloux' (F)	SWCr
	'Pilgrim'	see *R.* The Pilgrim
	'Pilgrim' (HT) **new**	MAsh
	pimpinellifolia	see *R. spinosissima*
	- 'Altaica'	see *R. spinosissima* 'Grandiflora'
	- double yellow-flowered	see *R.* × *harisonii* 'Williams' Double Yellow'
	Pink Abundance = 'Harfrothy'^{PBR} (Abundance Series) (F)	MBri
	Pink Bells = 'Poulbells' (GC)	SPer
	'Pink Bouquet' (Ra)	CRHN
	'Pink Favorite' (HT)	SCob SPer
	Pink Fizz = 'Poulycool' (ClPatio)	ECnt
§	Pink Flower Carpet = 'Noatraum'^{PBR} (GC) ♀^{H6}	CDoC COtt CSBt CTri ECnt ELan IBoy LCro LOPS LRHS MBri NPri SCoo SEND SPer SPoG SWCr
	'Pink Garnette'	see *R.* 'Carol Amling'
	'Pink Grootendorst' (Ru)	EPfP LRHS NEgg NLar SPer
§	Pink Hit = 'Poultipe'^{PBR} (Min/Patio)	ECnt LRHS LSRN MAsh MBri SWCr
	Pink Knock Out = 'Radcon' (S)	MAsh
	'Pink Leda' (D)	EBee
	Pink Martini = 'Tan04608' **new**	ESty
	pink moss	see *R.* × *centifolia* 'Muscosa'
	Pink Paradise = 'Delfluoro' (HT)	ESty
	'Pink Parfait' (F)	SPer
	Pink Perfection = 'Korpauvio'^{PBR} (HT)	ECnt LRHS MAsh SSea SWCr
	'Pink Perpétué' (Cl)	CBcs CDoC CNec COtt CSBt CTri CWSG ECnt ELan EPfP IBoy LAst LBuc LRHS MAsh MRav SPer SPoG SSea SWCr
	'Pink Showers' (ClHT)	MSwo
	Pirouette = 'Poulyc003'^{PBR} (ClS)	ECnt MAsh
	'Plaisanterie' (HM)	LRHS
	Pleine de Grâce = 'Lengra' (S)	GGal LEdu
	Poetry in Motion = 'Harelan'^{PBR} (HT)	LBrs MBri
	Polar Star = 'Tanlarpost' (HT)	CSBt ECnt MRav SPer SWCr
	'Polly' (HT)	LSRN
§	'Polyantha Grandiflora' (Ra)	SVic
	'Pompon de Paris' (ClMinCh)	see *R.* 'Climbing Pompon de Paris'
	'Pompon de Paris' (MinCh)	SCob WAbe
	Port Sunlight = 'Auslofty'^{PBR} (HM) ♀^{H6}	ESty IBoy LRHS MBri
	Portland rose	see *R.* 'Portlandica'
§	'Portlandica' (Po)	CTri LRHS SPer
	Portmeirion = 'Ausguard'^{PBR} (S)	SCoo
	Pour Toi	see *R.* 'Para Ti'
	'Precious Amber' (F)	MAsh
	'Precious Memories' (Min)	LSRN
	Precious Memories = 'Dichello'^{PBR} (F)	ESty

	Name	Suppliers
	'Precious Platinum' (HT)	MJak SPer
	Precious Time = 'Oramarpa'[PBR] (HT) **new**	ESty
§	'Président de Sèze' (G) ♀H7	CPou EWTr NLar SPer
	Pretty in Pink = 'Dicumpteen'[PBR] (GC) ♀H6	ECnt
	Pretty Jessica = 'Ausjess' (S)	LRHS LSRN MRav SPer
	Pretty Polly = 'Meitonje' (Min) ♀H6	CKel EPfP ESty IBoy LRHS MAsh MBri MRav MWat SPer SPoG SSea SWCr
	'Prima Ballerina' (HT)	CTri EPfP LRHS MAsh MBri SPer
	primula	NLar SPer
	primula* × *rugosa	MJak
	'Prince Charles' (Bb)	WKif
	Prince Jardinier = 'Meitroni'[PBR] (HT) ♀H6	ESty SWCr
	Princess Alexandra = 'Pouldra'[PBR] (Renaissance Series) (S) ♀H6	CTri ECnt NLar SWCr
	Princess Alexandra of Kent = 'Ausmerchant'[PBR] (S)	EPfP EShb ESty LRHS MBri SPer
	Princess Anne = 'Auskitchen'[PBR] (S) ♀H6	ECnt EPfP LBuc LCro LOPS LRHS MBri SCob
	Princess = 'Korspobux'[PBR] (HT)	ECnt
	'Princess of Wales' (HP)	EPfP
	Princess of Wales = 'Hardinkum'[PBR] (F) ♀H6	EPfP MJak MRav SPer SWCr
§	'Princesse de Nassau' (Ra)	SKHP
	'Princesse Louise' (Ra)	LRHS
	'Princesse Marie' misapplied	see *R.* 'Belvedere'
	'Prolifera de Redouté' misapplied	see *R.* 'Duchesse de Montebello'
	Proper Job = 'Tan02733'[PBR] (HT)	CDoC ECnt ESty SWCr
	'Prosperity' (HM) ♀H6	CSam CTri EPfP LRHS MCot MRav MWat NLar SLon SPer SWCr
	Pure Bliss = 'Dictator'[PBR] (HT)	ELon
	Pure Gold = 'Harhappen'[PBR] (F)	CSBt
	'Purezza' (Ra)	NLar
	'Purity' (ClHT)	EBee
	Purple Eden	see *R.* Ebb Tide
	Purple Moon = 'Dicmover' (F) **new**	IDic
	Purple Skyliner = 'Franwekpurp'[PBR] (ClS)	MCot SPer
	Purple Tiger = 'Jacpurr'[PBR] (F)	ESty SWCr
	quatre saisons	see *R.* × *damascena* var. *semperflorens*
	'Quatre Saisons Blanche Mousseuse' (DMo)	CPou NLar
	Queen Anne = 'Austruck'[PBR] (S)	CSBt EPfP ESty LBuc LRHS MAsh MBri SCoo
	Queen Elizabeth	see *R.* 'The Queen Elizabeth'
	Queen Mother = 'Korquemu'[PBR] (Patio) ♀H6	CSBt ELan EPfP MJak MRav SPer SPoG SWCr
	'Queen of Bourbons' (Bb)	LEdu NLar
	Queen of Denmark	see *R.* 'Königin von Dänemark'
	Queen of Sweden = 'Austiger'[PBR] (S)	CNec CRos ECnt EPfP LBuc LRHS MAsh MBri SCob SPer SWCr
	Rachel = 'Tangust'[PBR] (HT) ♀H6	CSBt ESty MRav SPoG SSea SWCr
	'Rachel' (HT)	CDoC COtt CPou LSRN
§	Rachel Louise Moran = 'Jacdrama'[PBR] (HT)	ESty
	Rainbow Magic = 'Dicxplosion'[PBR] (Patio)	MJak
	'Rambling Rector' (Ra) ♀H6	Widely available
	Rambling Rosie = 'Horjasper'[PBR] (Ra) ♀H6	CDoC CKel CRos CSBt EBee ECnt EPfP ESty EWTr LBuc LRHS LSRN MAsh MBri MSwo SSea SWCr
	'Raspberry Royale' (F/Patio) ♀H6	MAsh MBri SPoG
	'Raubritter' ('Macrantha' hybrid)	CPou EWTr SPer SWCr WBod
	Raymond Blanc = 'Delnado' (HT)	CDoC EBee EWTr LSRN MRav NLar SLon
	'Raymond Carver' (S)	LRHS NPri
	Rebecca (Patio)	ESty LSRN
	'Rebecca Claire' (HT)	LSRN
	Rebecca Mary = 'Dicjury'[PBR] (F)	IDic
	Reconciliation = 'Hartillery'[PBR] (HT)	SWCr
	Red Abundance	see *R.* Songs of Praise
	Red Blanket = 'Intercell' (S/GC)	LAst SPer
	Red Devil = 'Dicam' (HT)	IBoy MBri SCoo
	Red Drift = 'Meigalpio' (GC)	MAsh
	Red Eden Rose = 'Meidrason'[PBR] (Cl)	ESty SSea
	Red Finesse = 'Korvillade'[PBR] (F) ♀H6	EBee MBri SWCr
	'Red Grootendorst'	see *R.* 'F.J. Grootendorst'
	'Red Max Graf'	see *R.* Rote Max Graf
	Red Medley = 'Noapu'[PBR] (Min)	MAsh
	red moss	see *R.* 'Henri Martin'
	Red New Dawn	see *R.* 'Étendard'
	Red Parfum de Provence = 'Meiafone'[PBR] (HT)	ESty
§	'Red Patio' (F/Patio)	LSRN
	Red Perfumella = 'Meikeneza'[PBR] (HT)	ESty
	Red Rascal = 'Jacbed' (S/Patio)	CKel CSBt
	red rose of Lancaster	see *R. gallica* var. *officinalis*
	Redouté = 'Auspale'[PBR] (S)	LRHS
	Reflections = 'Simref' (F)	SWCr
	Regensberg = 'Macyoumis'[PBR] (F/Patio)	IBoy LEdu SPer
	'Reine des Violettes' (HP) ♀H7	CPou EAEE ELon EPfP IArd LAst LCro LRHS LSRN MBri MCot MRav NLar SPer SRGP SWCr
	'Reine Marie Henriette' (ClHT)	CPou
§	'Reine Victoria' (Bb)	CDoC EPfP LCro MBri MRav NLar SPer
§	Remember = 'Poulht001'[PBR] (HT) ♀H6	ECnt EPfP LBrs LRHS SPoG SWCr
	Remember Me = 'Cocdestin' (HT) ♀H6	CDoC COtt CSBt CWSG ECnt EPfP ESty IArd IBoy LCro LSRN MAsh MGos MRav NEgg NPri SCob SPer SPoG SWCr
	Remembrance = 'Harxampton'[PBR] (F)	CWSG ESty LBuc LRHS LSRN MAsh MBri MJak MRav MWat SCob SPer SPoG SSea SWCr
§	Renaissance = 'Harzart'[PBR] (HT)	CKel CSBt ELon MJak MRav SWCr
	'René André' (Ra)	CPou CRHN EBee NLar

	'Rescht'	see *R.* 'De Resht'
	'Rêve d'Or' (N)	MCot MMuc SLon SPer
	Rhapsody in Blue = 'Frantasia'PBR (S) ♀H6	Widely available
§	× ***richardii***	NLar
	Rick Stein = 'Tan96205'PBR (HT)	LSRN
	'River Gardens'	NPer
	Rob Roy = 'Cocrob' (F)	SPer
	'Robert le Diable' (Ce × G)	SPer
	Rock & Roll = 'Wekgobnez' (HT)	ESty
	'Roger Lambelin' (HP)	CPou
	Romance = 'Tanezamor'PBR (S)	IBoy LSRN MBri
	'Rosa Mundi'	see *R. gallica* 'Versicolor'
	'Rose à Parfum de l'Haÿ' (Ru)	CTri
	'Rose de Meaux'	see *R.* × *centifolia* 'De Meaux'
	'Rose de Meaux White'	see *R.* 'White de Meaux'
	'Rose de Rescht'	see *R.* 'De Resht'
	Rose des Cisterciens = 'Delarle' (HT)	ESty LRHS MRav
	'Rose du Maître d'Ecole'	see *R.* 'Du Maître d'Ecole'
	'Rose du Roi' (HP/DPo)	ELon LRHS
	Rose for Elaine = 'Rawdenqueen' (HT) **new**	LSRN
§	Rose Gaujard = 'Gaumo' (HT)	LRHS MAsh MBri
	Rose of Picardy = 'Ausfudge' (S)	LRHS MBri
	Rose In Memory of my Cat = 'Webyum' (HT) **new**	LSRN
	'Rose-Marie Viaud' (Ra)	CPou EBee MMuc
	Rosemary Harkness = 'Harrowbond' (HT)	ESty MJak MRav SPer SRGP
	'Rosemary Rose' (F)	SPer
	Rosemoor = 'Austough'PBR (S) ♀H6	CRos CSBt LBuc LRHS MBri
	'Roseraie de l'Haÿ' (Ru) ♀H7	Widely available
	Rosie = 'Benros' (Min)	LSRN
	Rosy Cushion = 'Interall' (S/GC)	LBuc LRHS MCot NLar SLon SPer WKif
	'Rosy Mantle' (ClHT)	CSBt SWCr
§	Rotary Sunrise = 'Fryglitzy' (HT)	CSBt
§	Rote Max Graf = 'Kormax' (GC/Ru)	CDul CKel
	Rouge Royale = 'Meikarouz' (HT)	ESty
	roxburghii	CBcs LEdu SKHP
	- PAB 7331 **new**	LEdu
	'Royal Air Force' (HT)	ELan
	Royal Bonica = 'Meimodac' (S)	COtt
§	Royal Brompton Rose = 'Meivildo' (HT)	ESty
	Royal Copenhagen	see *R.* Remember
	'Royal Gold' (ClHT)	SSea
	Royal Jubilee = 'Auspaddle' (S)	CSBt LCro LOPS MBri SCob SPer
	'Royal Occasion' (F)	SPer
	Royal William = 'Korzaun' (HT) ♀H6	CDoC CSBt ELan LRHS LSRN MAsh MBri MJak MRav MWat SCob SPer SWCr
§	***rubiginosa***	CArn CCVT CDul EPfP GPoy IFro LBuc MRav NWea SPer WMou
	rubrifolia	see *R. glauca* Pourr.
	Ruby Anniversary = 'Harbonny'PBR (Patio)	CDoC COtt CSBt ELon ESty LBuc LCro LRHS LSRN MAsh MBri MRav MWat NPri SCob SCoo SPoG SSea SVic SWCr
	'Ruby Baby' (Min)	MAsh
	Ruby Celebration = 'Peawinner'PBR (F) ♀H6	CKel COtt ESty MRav SWCr
	Ruby Ruby	see *R.* Ruby Slippers
§	Ruby Slippers = 'Weksactrumi' (Min)	LRHS SPoG
	'Ruby Wedding' (HT)	CBcs CKel CNec CSBt CTri ECnt ELan EPfP IArd IBoy LBrs LRHS LSRN MAsh MBri MGos MJak MRav SCob SPer SPoG SVic SWCr
	'Ruby Wedding Anniversary' (F)	LSRN
	rugosa (Ru)	CArg CDul CLnd CTri CTsd ECrN EPfP EPom LBuc LRHS MBri MHer MRav NWea SCob SGol SPlb SVic SWCr WHar WMat WMou
	- 'Alba' (Ru)	Widely available
	- 'Rubra' (Ru)	CBcs CCVT CDul CTri CWib ELan EPfP EPom LAst LBuc LCro LOPS NBes NWea SCob SEWo SPer SPoG SSea SVic WHar
	'Rugosa Atropurpurea' (Ru)	EPom
	'Rumba' (F)	ELan
	'Rural England' (Ra)	LRHS MBri NPri
	'Russelliana' (Ra)	EBee MMuc NLar
	Saint Boniface = 'Kormatt' (F/Patio)	CSBt
	Saint Edmunds Rose	see *R.* Bonita
	Saint Ethelburga = 'Beabimbo' (S)	LRHS MBri MCot NPri
	Saint John's rose	see *R.* × *richardii*
	Saint Swithun = 'Auswith'PBR (S)	EPfP ESty LRHS MBri MMuc SCob SSea SWCr
	'Salet' (DPMo)	CPou WHer
	'Sally Holmes' (S) ♀H7	CPou ECnt EPfP EWTr LRHS MRav MWat SEND SLon SMad SPer SWCr
	Sally Kane = 'Frygroovy'PBR (HT)	MRav
	Sally's Rose = 'Canrem' (HT)	ECnt LSRN
	Salsa	see *R.* Cheek to Cheek
	Salvation = 'Harlark'PBR (F)	ESty
§	Samaritan = 'Harverag'PBR (HT)	CSBt ESty MRav SWCr
	sambucina	WPGP
	sancta	see *R.* × *richardii*
	'Sander's White Rambler' (Ra) ♀H7	CRHN CSam CTri EPfP LRHS MBri MRav MSwo SPer SWCr WFar
	Sandra = 'Carsandra'	SLon
	Sandra = 'Koreinek' (HT)	LSRN
	Sandra = 'Poulen055'PBR (Renaissance Series) (S)	EBee LSRN
	'Sanguinea'	see *R.* × *odorata* Sanguinea Group
	Sarah (HT)	see *R.* Jardins de Bagatelle
	'Sarah van Fleet' (Ru)	CDoC CTri EBee EPfP IArd IBoy MBri MMuc MRav MSwo NEgg NLar SPer
	Sarah, Duchess of York	see *R.* Sunseeker
	Savoy Hotel = 'Harvintage' (HT)	EPfP MBri MRav SPer
	'Scabrosa' (Ru) ♀H7	ECnt EPfP LRHS NLar NWea SLon SPer SPoG
	Scarborough Fair = 'Ausoran' (S) ♀H6	LBuc LRHS MMuc
	Scarlet Fire	see *R.* 'Scharlachglut'

Scarlet Glow — see *R.* 'Scharlachglut'
Scarlet Hit = 'Poulmo'PBR (PatioHit Series) (Min/Patio) — ECnt IBoy LBMP LRHS LSRN SWCr
Scarlet Patio = 'Kortingle'PBR (Patio) — LBrs MAsh MBri MWat
Scarlet Queen Elizabeth = 'Dicel' (F) — CBcs
Scented Carpet = 'Chewground'PBR (GC) ♀H6 — ECnt ELan SWCr
Scented Garden = 'Chewscentity' (S) — ESty
Scented Memory = 'Poulht002'PBR (HT) — ECnt
Scentimental = 'Wekplapep'PBR (F) — CDoC EPfP ESty MAsh MBri MRav SCoo SSea SWCr
Scent-sation = 'Fryromeo'PBR (HT) — CKel MRav SCoo SPoG SWCr
Scepter'd Isle = 'Ausland'PBR (S) — CSBt EPfP LBuc LCro LOPS LRHS MAsh MBri SCob SCoo SPer SWCr
§ 'Scharlachglut' (ClS) — CPou EPfP GGal LRHS SPer WHer
Schloss Bad Homburg — see *R.* Alibaba
Schneewittchen — see *R.* Iceberg
§ 'Schneezwerg' (Ru) ♀H7 — EWTr NLar SPer
'Schoolgirl' (ClHT) — CBcs CDoC CTri CWSG EBee ELan EPfP IBoy LBuc LRHS MAsh MBri MRav MSwo NEgg SPer SSea SWCr
Scotch rose — see *R. spinosissima*
Scotch yellow (SpH) — see *R.* × *harisonii* 'Williams' Double Yellow'
'Sea Foam' (S) — WMoo
'Seagull' (Ra) ♀H6 — CTri EBee ECnt EPfP IBoy LAst LEdu LRHS LSRN MAsh MBri MRav NLar NWea SCob SLon SMad SPer SPoG SWCr WHer
'Seale Pink Diamond' (S) — SSea
'Sealing Wax' (*moyesii* hybrid) — CPou NLar
'Semiplena' — see *R.* × *alba* 'Alba Semiplena'
sempervirens (Ra) — SBrt
sericea var. ***morrisonensis*** B&SWJ 7139 — WCru
§ - subsp. ***omeiensis*** — LEdu WPGP
- - BWJ 7550 — WCru
- - PAB 2883 **new** — LEdu
- - f. ***pteracantha*** (S) — CBcs CDul CKel CSBt CTri ELan EPfP IDee LEdu LRHS MRav NLar NWea SCob SPer
seven sisters rose — see *R. multiflora* 'Grevillei'
Sexy Rexy = 'Macrexy' (F) — EPfP IBoy LSRN MAsh MBri MRav MWat SCob SPer SRGP SWCr
Sharifa Asma = 'Ausreef'PBR (S) — CSBt EBee ELan LSRN MBri MRav MSwo NEgg NLar SPer SWCr
Sheila's Perfume = 'Harsherry' (F) ♀H6 — CDoC EBee ECnt ESty IBoy LSRN MAsh MBri MRav SPer SPoG SWCr
Shine On = 'Dictalent'PBR (Patio) ♀H6 — CSBt ECnt IBoy MWat SWCr
Shining Light = 'Cocshimmer'PBR (Patio) — SCoo
'Shot Silk' (HT) — CKel
Show Star = 'Smi36-1-02' (HT) **new** — ESty
Showmee Sunshine = 'Kenveron' (GC) — ESty
Showtime = 'Baitime' (ClS) — LBuc MBri SWCr
§ Shrimp Hit = 'Poulshrimp'PBR (Patio) — ECnt SPoG
'Shropshire Lass' (S) — SPer
Silver Anniversary ambig. — LSRN
Silver Anniversary = 'Jaclav' (HT) — CKel MBri MJak
Silver Anniversary = 'Meiborfil' (HT) **new** — ELon
§ Silver Anniversary = 'Poulari'PBR (HT) ♀H6 — CDoC CSBt CWSG ECnt ELan LBrs LCro LRHS LSRN MGos MRav MWat NPri SCoo SPer SPoG SSea SVic SWCr
'Silver Jubilee' (HT) — CTri EPfP IArd IBoy LRHS MAsh MBri MRav SCob SPer SPoG SVic SWCr
'Silver Lining' (HT) — CKel
Silver Shadow = 'Frystereo' (HT) **new** — ESty
'Silver Wedding' (HT) — CBcs CNec COtt ELan IArd MJak MRav NEgg SCob SPer SVic SWCr
'Silver Wedding Celebration' (F) — ESty LSRN
Silver Wishes — see *R.* Pink Hit
Simba = 'Korbelma' (HT) — LSRN
'Simplex Multiflora' — CBot CWib
Simply Sally = 'Harpaint'PBR (Patio) — LSRN
§ Simply the Best = 'Macamster'PBR (HT) ♀H6 — CKel COtt CSBt CWSG ELan ESty LRHS LSRN MBri MGos MJak MRav SCob SCoo SPer SPoG SWCr
sinowilsonii — see *R. longicuspis* var. *sinowilsonii*
'Sir Cedric Morris' (Ra) — NLar SSea
I 'Sir Galahad' white-flowered (F) — CKel MRav
Sir John Betjeman = 'Ausvivid'PBR (S) — EPfP IBoy LBuc LRHS MBri
'Sir Joseph Paxton' (Bb) — CPou
Sir Paul Smith = 'Beapaul' (ClHT) — LRHS NPri
Sir Walter Raleigh = 'Ausspry' (S) — MRav
Sister Elizabeth = 'Auspalette'PBR (S) — LBuc LRHS LSRN MAsh MBri SCoo
Skylark = 'Ausimple'PBR (S) ♀H6 — LBuc LRHS MBri SCob
'Skyrocket' — see *R.* 'Wilhelm'
Smarty = 'Intersmart' (S/GC) — SPer
'Snow Dwarf' — see *R.* 'Schneezwerg'
Snow Goose = 'Auspom'PBR (ClS) — CSBt EPfP LRHS MBri NLar SSea
Snow Hit = 'Poulsnows'PBR (Min/Patio) — ECnt
Snow Sunblaze = 'Meigovin' (Min) — CSBt SPer
Snowball = 'Macangeli' (Min/GC) — LSRN
Snowcap = 'Harfleet'PBR (Patio) — ESty
'Snowdon' (Ru) — LRHS
Soeur Emmanuelle = 'Delamo'PBR (S) — CDoC ESty LSRN MRav
Soft Cover = 'Poultco10' (Min) ♀H7 — MAsh MBri
'Soldier Boy' (Cl) — CPou
§ Solo Mio = 'Poulen002'PBR (Renaissance Series) (S) — CTri EBee ECnt NLar
§ 'Sombreuil' (ClT) — EBee EPfP IArd LBuc LRHS MBri MRav NEgg NLar SPer SWCr
Something Special = 'Macwyo'PBR (HT) — ESty
Song and Dance = 'Frydishy'PBR (HT) — SWCr

Name	Suppliers
§ Songs of Praise = 'Harkimono'[PBR] (Abundance Series) (F)	ESty SWCr
'Sophia'	see *R.* Solo Mio = 'Poulen002'
'Sophie's Perpetual' (ClCh)	CPou CTri LRHS SLon SPer
Sophy's Rose = 'Auslot'[PBR] (S)	CRos LBuc LRHS LSRN MBNS MBri NEgg SPer SWCr
Sorbet Fruité = 'Meihestries'[PBR] (Cl)	SSea
'Soupert et Notting' (DPoMo)	CPou LRHS SPer
'Southampton' (F) ♀H6	LSRN SPer SSea SWCr
'Souvenir de Claudius Denoyel' (ClHT)	CPou SPer
'Souvenir de Jeanne Balandreau' (HP)	CPou
'Souvenir de la Malmaison' (Bb)	EPfP EWTr LRHS MRav MWat NLar SPer
'Souvenir de la Malmaison' (ClBb)	see *R.* 'Climbing Souvenir de la Malmaison'
'Souvenir de Madame Léonie Viennot' (ClT)	MRav
'Souvenir de Pierre Vibert' (DPMo)	CPou
'Souvenir de Saint Anne's' (Bb)	EWTr
'Souvenir du Docteur Jamain' (ClHP)	CPou CSBt ELan ELon EPfP ESty GGal LCro LRHS LSRN MCot MRav NLar SPer SPoG SSea SWCr WFar WKif
'Spanish Beauty'	see *R.* 'Madame Grégoire Staechelin'
Sparkle = 'Frymerlin'[PBR] (HT)	ECnt ESty LBrs SWCr
Sparkler	see *R.* Kent
Sparkling Scarlet = 'Meihati' (ClF)	MAsh
Special Anniversary = 'Whastiluc'[PBR] (HT) ♀H6	CDoC CKel COtt CSBt ECnt ELon EPfP ESty LBrs LCro LRHS LSRN LShp MBri MJak MRav MWat NPri SCoo SPoG SSea SWCr
Special Child = 'Taniripsa'[PBR] (F/Patio) ♀H6	CDoC MRav SSea SWCr
Special Event = 'Meibrelon' (HT)	ESty
Special Friend = 'Kirspec'[PBR] (Patio)	ESty LSRN SCob SWCr
Special Occasion = 'Fryyoung'[PBR] (HT)	CDoC MRav SWCr
Special Son (F)	ESty
'Spectabilis' (Ra)	CPou EBee SKHP
'Spencer' misapplied	see *R.* 'Enfant de France'
Spice of Life = 'Diccheeky'[PBR] (F/Patio)	IDic
§ ***spinosissima***	CArg CDul CSde LBuc LRHS MMuc NWea SCob SGol SPer
- 'Andrewsii' ♀H7	MRav
§ - double, pink-flowered	SKHP WBor
§ - double, white-flowered ♀H7	ECha EWTr LEdu
- 'Falkland'	ECha GCra
§ - 'Grandiflora'	LRHS
- 'Mary, Queen of Scots'	SRms
- 'Single Cherry'	SSea
- 'William III'	EWes GCra
Spirit of Freedom = 'Ausbite'[PBR] (S)	EPfP ESty LBuc LRHS MAsh MBri NEgg SSea
§ 'Splendens' (Ra)	GBin MMuc
St Helena = 'Canlish' (F)	ECnt
'Stanwell Perpetual'[7] (SpH) ♀H	CTri ELan EPfP EWTr IBoy MRav MWat NLar SEND SPer SSea
Star Dust = 'Morstar' (Min)	ELon
'Star Performer'[PBR] (ClPatio)	CSBt ECnt EPfP ESty LBMP MAsh MBri SPoG SSea SWCr
Stardust = 'Devstar' (HT)	WBor
Stardust = 'Peavandyke'[PBR] (Patio/F)	CPou ESty
Starlight Express = 'Trobstar'[PBR] (Cl)	IBoy LRHS MAsh NPri SCoo SPer
Stella (HT)	LSRN
Strawberries and Cream = 'Geestraw' (Min/Patio)	ELan ESty SWCr
Strawberry Fayre = 'Arowillip'[PBR] (Min/Patio)	CKel COtt ESty MRav SPoG
Strawberry Hill = 'Ausrimini'[PBR] (S) ♀H6	CSBt ESty LRHS MAsh MBri MMuc SCoo
Strike It Rich = 'Wekbepmey'[PBR] (HT) ♀H6	ECnt ESty MRav SWCr
§ Sue Hipkin = 'Harzazz'[PBR] (HT)	ESty MRav SWCr
'Suffolk' (HT)	SCob
Suffolk = 'Kormixal'[PBR] (S/GC) ♀H6	CSBt ELan LRHS MJak MRav SCob SEND SPer SSea
Sugar and Spice = 'Peaallure'[PBR] (Patio)	CDoC SPoG
Sugar Baby = 'Tanabagus'[PBR] (Patio)	ESty
Sugar 'n' Spice = 'Tinspice' (Min)	MRav
Suma = 'Harsuma' (GC)	ESty
Summer Beauty = 'Kororbe'[PBR] (F) ♀H6	EBee ESty SWCr
Summer Breeze = 'Korelasting'[PBR] (ClS)	MAsh
Summer Fragrance = 'Tanfudermos' (Castle Series) (HT)	ELon
§ Summer Gold = 'Poulreb'[PBR] (F)	MBri SWCr
'Summer Holiday' (HT)	SPer
Summer Love = 'Franluv' (F)	CBcs
Summer Memories = 'Koruteli'[PBR] (Palace Series) (F)	CKel
Summer Snow = 'Weopop' (Patio)	WBod
Summer Song = 'Austango'[PBR] (S)	CNec EPfP ESty IBoy LBuc LRHS LSRN MBri SCob SWCr
Summer Wine = 'Korizont'[PBR] (Cl) ♀H6	CSBt EBee ECnt EPfP LRHS MBri SCoo SPer SPoG SWCr
Summertime = 'Chewlarmoll'[PBR] (ClPatio) ♀H6	CDoC CSBt ECnt ELan EPfP IBoy LRHS MAsh MRav NPri SCoo SPer SPoG
Sun Hit = 'Poulsun'[PBR] (PatioHit Series) (Min/Patio)	CSBt ECnt MRav
'Sunblaze'	see *R.* Orange Sunblaze
Sunblest = 'Landora' (HT)	MAsh MRav SCob
Sunfire = 'Jacko' (F)	ECnt
Sunrise = 'Kormarter'[PBR] (S)	ESty MAsh SPoG SWCr
§ Sunseeker = 'Dicracer'[PBR] (F/Patio) ♀H6	COtt MAsh MRav SPoG
Sunset Boulevard = 'Harbabble'[PBR] (F)	COtt MRav SCoo SPer

	Name	Suppliers
	Sunset Celebration	see *R.* Warm Wishes
	Sunset Glow	see *R.* Alibaba
	Super Dorothy = 'Heldoro' (Ra) ♀H6	LSRN SSea SWCr
	Super Elfin = 'Helkleger'PBR (Ra)	CDoC COtt CRos LBuc LRHS MRav NLar SCob SPer SSea SWCr
	Super Excelsa = 'Helexa' (Ra) ♀H6	ESty IBoy LBuc SCob SSea SWCr
	Super Fairy = 'Helsufair'PBR (Ra) ♀H6	CDoC CKel COtt EBee ECnt MRav SMad SPer SSea SWCr
	Super Sparkle = 'Helfels'PBR (Ra)	EBee SCob SSea
§	Super Star = 'Tanorstar' (HT)	CKel MRav SWCr
	Super Trouper = 'Fryleyeca'PBR (F) ♀H6	CDoC COtt CSBt EBee ECnt ESty IBoy LBrs LRHS LSRN MBri MRav NPri SCoo SPer SWCr WCot
	Surrey = 'Korlanum' (GC) ♀H6	CKel CSBt CTri ELan ESty LCro LSRN MRav MSwo NLar SCob SPer SSea SWCr
	Susan = 'Poulsue' (S)	EBee ECnt LSRN NLar SLon SWCr
	Susan Williams-Ellis = 'Ausquirk'PBR (S)	CRos EPfP LBuc LRHS MBri SCob
	Sussex = 'Poulave'PBR (GC)	CDoC CSBt MRav MSwo SCob SPer SSea
	Swan Lake = 'Macmed' (Cl)	CPou EBee ECnt ELan EPfP EWTr IBoy MRav NLar SPer
	Swany = 'Meiburenac' (Min/GC)	ECrN ESty EWTr LSRN MJak MMuc MSwo SPer SWCr
	'Sweet Ballymaloe' (S)	IBoy
	Sweet Caroline = 'Micaroline' (Min)	LSRN
	Sweet Child of Mine (HT)	ESty
	Sweet Cover = 'Poulweeto'PBR (Towne & Country Series) (F)	MAsh
	Sweet Dream = 'Fryminicot' (Patio) ♀H6	COtt CSBt CTri ELan EPfP IBoy LAst LBrs LRHS LSRN MAsh MBri MJak MRav MWat SMad SPer SPoG SRGP SSea SWCr
	'Sweet Fairy' (Min)	CSBt
	Sweet Haze = 'Tan97274'PBR (F) ♀H6	CDoC CKel CSBt IBoy MBri MRav SCoo SPer SWCr
	Sweet Juliet = 'Ausleap'PBR (S)	CSBt ELan IBoy LRHS MSwo SPer SWCr
*	'Sweet Lemon Dream' (Patio)	CTri
	Sweet Magic = 'Dicmagic'PBR (Min/Patio) ♀H6	CTri EPfP IBoy MBri MRav SPoG
	Sweet Memories = 'Whamemo' (Patio)	CKel COtt CTri ECnt ELan EPfP ESty IBoy LBrs LRHS MAsh MBri MRav SCoo SPer SSea SWCr
	Sweet Parfum de Provence = 'Meiclusif'PBR (HT) ♀H6	ESty
	Sweet Pretty	see *R.* The Charlatan
	Sweet Remembrance = 'Kirr' (HT)	SCoo
	'Sweet Revelation'	see *R.* Sue Hipkin
	'Sweet Wonder' (Patio)	EPfP MAsh SPoG
	'Sweetie' (Patio)	ESty
	'Sydonie' (HP)	CPou
	'Sylvia Dot' (F)	LSRN
	'Sympathie' (ClHT)	SPer SSea
	Tall Story = 'Dickooky' (F) ♀H6	EBee MRav SWCr
	Tam O'Shanter = 'Auscerise'PBR (S)	EPfP LRHS
	Tangerine Tango = 'Cheworangemane' (Cl)	ECnt ESty
	Tango Showground = 'Chewpattens'PBR (GC)	ESty SSea
	Tatton = 'Fryentice'PBR (F)	COtt ESty MRav
	Tawny Tiger = 'Frygolly'PBR (F)	LBrs SWCr
	Tea Clipper = 'Ausrover'PBR (S)	CSBt LRHS MBri SCoo
	Tear Drop = 'Dicomo' (Min/Patio)	SCob SPer SSea SWCr
	Teasing Georgia = 'Ausbaker'PBR (S) ♀H6	CDoC CKel CRos ECnt EPfP ESty IBoy LBuc LRHS LSRN MBri MMuc NLar SCob SCoo SWCr
	Temptress = 'Korramal' (ClS) ♀H6	CPou EPfP EUJe MAsh
	Tenacious = 'Macblackpo'PBR (F)	ESty SWCr
	Tequila Sunrise = 'Dicobey' (HT) ♀H6	CKel CTri ELan EPfP ESty IBoy MBri MJak MRav MWat SPer SSea SWCr
	Terracotta = 'Meicobuis' (HT)	ESty
	Tess of the d'Urbervilles = 'Ausmove'PBR (S)	CRos EBee ELan EPfP EShb ESty IBoy LOPS LRHS LSRN MBri NEgg NLar SCob SCoo SPer SSea SWCr
	'Tessa' (F)	LSRN
	Thank You = 'Chesdeep'PBR (Patio)	CDoC ESty LBuc
§	That's Jazz = 'Poulnorm'PBR (Courtyard Series) (ClF)	ECnt LSRN
	The Albrighton Rambler = 'Ausmobile' (Ra) **new**	CRos LRHS
	The Alexandra Rose = 'Ausday'PBR (S)	EPfP GGal LBuc LRHS MAsh SEND SPer SSea
§	The Alnwick Rose = 'Ausgrab'PBR (S)	EPfP LBuc LRHS MBri NLar SCob SCoo SPer SSea
I	'The Anniversary Rose'	EPfP LBrs LBuc LRHS MBri SCoo
	The Birthday Rose (F)	LBuc
§	The Charlatan = 'Meiguimov'PBR (S)	CDoC
	The Compass Rose = 'Korwisco'PBR (S)	EPfP
	The Countryman = 'Ausman' (S)	CDoC IBoy LBuc LRHS SCob SSea
	The Coventry Cathedral Rose = 'Smi72-02' (F)	ESty
	The Dark Lady = 'Ausbloom'PBR (S)	MBri NEgg SPer
	The Diamond Wedding Rose (HT)	LBrs LSRN SWCr
§	'The Fairy' (Poly) ♀H7	CKel CSBt CTri EAEE ECnt ELan IBoy LAst LEdu LRHS MAsh MRav MWat NLar SCob SDix SEND SMad SPer SSea SWCr WBor WMoo
	'The Garland' (Ra) ♀H6	EPfP LBuc LRHS MBri MMuc NLar SPer SWCr
	The Generous Gardener = 'Ausdrawn'PBR (S) ♀H6	CKel COtt CRos ELan EPfP EShb ESty LBuc LRHS MBri MJak SCob SCoo SPer SSea SWCr
§	The Gold Award Rose = 'Poulac008' (Palace Series) (Patio)	ECnt
	The Herbalist = 'Aussemi' (S)	LRHS
	The Ingenious Mr Fairchild = 'Austijus'PBR (S)	EPfP LRHS MBri SCoo

	Name	Suppliers
	The Jubilee Rose = 'Poulbrido' PBR (F)	EBee ECnt SCoo
	The Lady Gardener = 'Ausbrass' **new**	CRos LRHS MAsh
	The Lady's Blush = 'Ausoscar' PBR (S)	EPfP LRHS MBri
	The Lakeland Rose = 'Harspiral' **new**	MAsh
	The Lark Ascending = 'Ausursula' (S)	LBuc LCro LOPS LRHS SCob SCoo
	The Maidstone Rose = 'Kordauerpa' (S)	SCoo
	'The Margaret Coppola Rose'	see *R.* White Gold
	The Mayflower = 'Austilly' PBR (S) ♀H6	CSBt ELon IBoy LBuc LRHS MBri MSwo SCob
§	The McCartney Rose = 'Meizeli' PBR (HT)	SPer
	'The New Dawn'	see *R.* 'New Dawn'
	The Nun = 'Ausnun' (S)	LRHS
	'The One and Only' (HT) **new**	LRHS
	The Painter = 'Mactemaik' PBR (F)	LSRN
§	The Pilgrim = 'Auswalker' PBR (S) ♀H6	CSBt EPfP LBuc LRHS MBri MJak NLar SCob SPer SSea SWCr
	The Prince = 'Ausvelvet' PBR (S)	LRHS NLar SPer
	The Prince's Trust = 'Harholding' PBR (Cl)	LBuc MAsh SPoG
§	'The Queen Elizabeth' (F)	CBcs CSBt CTri ELan IBoy LCro LSRN MAsh MBri MRav SCob SPer SPoG SRGP SSea SWCr WBor
	The Rotarian	see *R.* Rotary Sunrise
	'The Royal Brompton Rose'	see *R.* Royal Brompton Rose
I	'The Rugby Rose' (HT)	LSRN
	The Sheikh Khalifa Rose = 'Dickoolkid' (Patio)	IDic
	The Shepherdess = 'Austwist' PBR (S)	ELan IBoy LBuc LRHS MBri
	The Simple LIfe = 'Hartrifle' (Cl) **new**	LBuc
	The Times Rose = 'Korpeahn' (F) ♀H6	ECnt SCob SPer SWCr
	The Wedgwood Rose = 'Ausjosiah' PBR (ClS)	EPfP LBuc LRHS MBri SCob
	Thinking of You = 'Frydandy' PBR (HT) ♀H6	ESty IBoy LBrs MBri SRGP SSea SWCr
	'Thisbe' (HM)	CPou EBee SPer
	Thomas à Becket = 'Auswinston' **new**	CRos ESty LCro LOPS LRHS MAsh
	Thomas Barton = 'Meihirvin' (HT)	SSea
	'Threave' (Bb)	CPou
	threepenny bit rose	see *R. elegantula* 'Persetosa'
	Tickled Pink = 'Fryhunky' PBR (F) ♀H6	CDoC CKel COtt CSBt LRHS LSRN MBri MRav MWat SCoo SPer SPoG SSea
	Times Past = 'Harhilt' PBR (ClHT)	CKel EBee ELon ESty MRav SPoG SRGP SWCr
	'Tina Turner' (HT)	LSRN
	Tintinara = 'Dicuptight' PBR (HT) ♀H6	ECnt
	'Tipo Ideale'	see *R.* × *odorata* 'Mutabilis'
	Titanic = 'Macdako' PBR (F)	ESty
	Together Forever = 'Dicecho' PBR (F)	IDic SWCr
	'Tom Marshall'	EBee LSRN
	'Tony Jacklin' (F)	LSRN
	Top Marks = 'Fryministar' PBR (Min/Patio)	CSBt EPfP MJak MRav SCoo SWCr
	Topaz Jewel	see *R.* Yellow Dagmar Hastrup
	'Topsi' (F/Patio)	SPer
§	'Tour de Malakoff' (Ce)	CPou IBoy LRHS NLar SPer
	Tradescant = 'Ausdir' PBR (S)	SCob
	Tradition	see *R.* Tradition '95
§	Tradition '95 = 'Korkeltin' PBR (ClHT)	LBrs MAsh
	Tranquility = 'Barout' (HT)	EPfP LRHS SCob
	Tranquillity = 'Ausnoble' (S)	CRos CSBt ESty LBuc SCoo SPer
	'Treasure Trove' (Ra)	CRHN LRHS
	'Trier' (Ra)	CPou
	'Trigintipetala' misapplied	see *R.* × *damascena* 'Professeur Émile Perrot'
	'Triple Delight' (S) **new**	LSRN
I	'Trish's Rose'	LSRN
	Troika = 'Poumidor' (HT)	CSBt IBoy MAsh MBri MRav SPer SPoG SWCr
	'Tropicana'	see *R.* Super Star
	'Truly Loved' (F) **new**	LBrs
	Truly Scrumptious = 'Smi35-4-02' (HT)	ESty MRav
	Trumpeter = 'Mactru' (F) ♀H6	CTri EBee ECnt IArd IBoy MAsh MBri MRav MWat SPer SPoG SWCr
§	'Tuscany' (G)	SPer
	'Tuscany Superb' (G) ♀H7	CDoC CPou CSBt CTri EAEE ELan EPfP LCro LEdu LOPS LRHS MBri MRav MWat NChi NLar SKHP SPer SSea SWCr WBor WFar WHer WKif
	Twenty-one Again! = 'Meinimo' PBR (HT)	LSRN
	Twice in a Blue Moon = 'Tan96138' PBR (HT) ♀H6	CDoC CKel COtt CSBt ECnt ELon ESty IBoy LBrs MRav SCob SCoo SPoG SSea SWCr
	Twiggy's Rose = 'Harteam' PBR (F) **new**	LBrs
	Twist = 'Poulstri' PBR (Courtyard Series) (ClPatio)	ECnt ESty LBrs
	Tynwald = 'Mattwyt' (HT)	SPer
	'Unique Blanche'	see *R.* × *centifolia* 'Unique'
	Valencia = 'Koreklia' PBR (HT)	SPer
	Valentine Heart = 'Dicogle' PBR (F) ♀H6	CSBt CWSG ESty IArd LSRN MRav SWCr
	'Variegata di Bologna' (Bb)	EPfP LRHS MMuc MRav MWat SLon SWCr
	'Vatertag' (Min)	LSRN
	'Veilchenblau' (Ra) ♀H7	CDoC CKel CRHN CRos CSBt CTri EAEE EBee ECnt ELan EPfP ESty LCro LEdu LOPS LRHS MAsh MRav NEgg NLar SCob SEND SMad SPer SPoG SSea SWCr WBor WFar WKif
	Velvet Fragrance = 'Fryperdee' (HT)	CSBt ECnt ELon EPfP ESty MRav SPoG SSea SWCr
	'Verschuren' (HT/v)	ESty
	versicolor	see *R. gallica* 'Versicolor'
	'Vick's Caprice' (HP)	NLar
	Victoria Joy = 'Diciwill' (F)	IDic
	Viking Princess	see *R.* Imagination
	'Village Maid'	see *R.* × *centifolia* 'Unique Panachée'
	'Villia' **new**	GGal
	Violet Cloud = 'Harquick' PBR (Min) **new**	CKel ESty MRav

'Violette' (Ra) — CPou CRHN ESty LRHS SPer WFar WHer WKif
virginea — SPer
virginiana 🏆H7 — GCal NWea SDix
'Viridiflora' — see *R.* × *odorata* 'Viridiflora'
Waltz = 'Poulkrid'PBR (Courtyard Series) (ClPatio) — ECnt
Warm Welcome = 'Chewizz'PBR (ClMin) 🏆H6 — CDoC CKel CWSG ECnt ELan EPfP ESty IBoy LCro LRHS LSRN MAsh MRav MWat SMad SPer SPoG SSea SWCr
§ Warm Wishes = 'Fryxotic'PBR (HT) 🏆H6 — CDoC COtt CSBt ECnt IBoy LBuc LRHS LSRN MBri MJak MRav MWat NPri SCob SSea SWCr
'Warrior' (F) — SPer
webbiana — SKHP
Wedding Bells = 'Korsteflali'PBR (HT) **new** — LSRN
Wedding Celebration = 'Poulht006'PBR (HT) — ECnt LBrs LRHS
'Wedding Day' (Ra) — Widely available
Wee Jock = 'Cocabest' (F/Patio) — IBoy
'Weetwood' (Ra) — CRHN
Weisse Wolcke — see *R.* White Cloud
Well-Being = 'Harjangle'PBR (S) — CSBt ELon
'Wendy Cussons' (HT) — CTri MRav SCob SPer
Westerland = 'Korwest' (S) 🏆H6 — CDoC MRav NLar SWCr
Where the Heart Is = 'Cocoplan'PBR (HT) — ESty
Whisky Mac = 'Tanky' (HT) — CBcs CSBt CTri ELan LBuc LSRN MRav SCob SPer SRGP
'White Cécile Brünner' (Poly) — LAst
§ White Cloud = 'Korstacha'PBR (S/ClHT) — EPfP ESty SKHP SWCr
'White Cockade' (Cl) — CPou ESwi MSwo SPer SWCr
White Cover — see *R.* Kent
§ 'White de Meaux' (Ce) — LRHS
White Diamond = 'Interamon'PBR (S) — EBee ECnt
White Eden = 'Meiviowit'PBR (Cl) — ESty
§ White Gold = 'Cocquiriam'PBR (F) 🏆H6 — CSBt
'White Grootendorst' (Ru) — LRHS
White Max Graf — see *R.* × *jacksonii* White Max Graf
White Meidiland = 'Meicoublan' (S/GC) — LRHS
White Parfum de Provence = 'Meidiaphaz' (HT) — CSBt ESty
'White Patio' (Min/Patio) — MAsh MBri
White Perfumella = 'Meicalanq'PBR (HT) — ESty
§ 'White Pet' (Poly) 🏆H7 — CKel CSBt CTri EBee ECnt ELan EPfP EWTr LRHS MCot MRav NLar SEND SPer SSea SWCr WKif
white Provence — see *R.* × *centifolia* 'Unique'
'White Queen Elizabeth' (F) — SCob
white rose of York — see *R.* × *alba* 'Alba Semiplena'
White Star = 'Harquill' (ClHT) — ECnt MRav
White Wedding = 'Tan02360' **new** — LBuc
'White Wings' (HT) — IBoy WKif
wichurana (Ra) — CBcs EWTr GCal SDix SKHP
- 'Variegata' (Ra/v) — EPot
'Wickwar' (Ra) 🏆H6 — GCal GGal
Wild Edric = 'Aushedge'PBR (Ru) 🏆H6 — ECnt LBuc LRHS MMuc SCob SCoo
Wild Rover = 'Dichirap'PBR (F) 🏆H6 — ESty IDic LRHS
Wild Thing = 'Jactoose'PBR (S) 🏆H6 — IDic
Wild Thing = 'Ruiz510a'PBR — MBri
Wildeve = 'Ausbonny'PBR (S) 🏆H6 — LBuc LCro LOPS LRHS MBri
Wildfire = 'Fryessex' (Patio) — ECnt ESty IBoy LRHS MAsh MBri MRav SPoG SWCr
§ 'Wilhelm' (HM) — CPou SPer
William and Catherine = 'Ausrapper'PBR (S) — CRos CSBt ESty LBuc LCro LOPS LRHS MAsh SCob
'William Cobbett' (F) — SSea
§ 'William Lobb' (CeMo) 🏆H7 — CDoC CKel CPou EPfP IBoy LRHS MAsh MBri MNrw MRav MWat NEgg NLar SMad SPer WHer WKif
William Morris = 'Auswill'PBR (S) — CRos CSBt LBuc LRHS MBri NEgg SCob SPer
William Shakespeare = 'Ausroyal' (S) — CDoC IBoy LBrs MCot MJak SCob SPer
William Shakespeare 2000 = 'Ausromeo'PBR (S) — CKel CRos CSBt ECnt ELan EPfP EShb ESty IBoy LCro LOPS LRHS MAsh MBNS MBri MJak MSwo MWat NEgg NLar SCob SCoo SSea SWCr
'William Tyndale' (Ra) — CPou WBor
'Williams' Double Yellow' — see *R.* × *harisonii* 'Williams' Double Yellow'
Wiltshire = 'Kormuse'PBR (S/GC) 🏆H6 — CSBt CTri ECnt ELan ESty IBoy LRHS LSRN MRav NLar SCob SEND SLon SSea SWCr
Winchester Cathedral = 'Auscat'PBR (S) — CNec CRos CSBt CTri EBee ECnt ELan EPfP IBoy LCro LOPS LRHS LSRN MAsh MBri MJak MRav MSwo MWat NEgg NLar SCob SLon SPer SPoG SSea SWCr
Windflower = 'Auscross' (S) — LBuc
Windrush = 'Ausrush' (S) — SPer
Wisley = 'Ausintense'PBR (S) — SCoo
Wisley 2008 = 'Ausbreeze'PBR (S) — CSBt EPfP IBoy LBuc LRHS MBri SCob
With All My Love = 'Coczodiac'PBR (HT) — CSBt
With Thanks = 'Fransmoov'PBR (HT) — MJak
Wizard (HT) — ESty
Wollerton Old Hall = 'Ausblanket'PBR (S) — CSBt EPfP EShb ESty LBuc LRHS MBri SCob SCoo SPer
Wonderful = 'Poulpmt005'PBR (HT) — EBee ECnt
Wonderful News = 'Jonone'PBR (Patio) — ESty LBrs MWat
Worcestershire = 'Korlalon'PBR (GC) 🏆H6 — CDoC LRHS MRav SPer SWCr
Wymondham Abbey = 'Beadevil' (ClHT) — LRHS MBri NPri
§ ***xanthina*** 'Canary Bird' (S) 🏆H7 — CBcs CDoC CKel CSBt CTri EBee ECnt ELan EPfP ESty GKin IBoy LAst LRHS MBri MNrw MRav NEgg NLar SEND SKHP SMad SPer SPoG SSea SWCr SWvt
§ - f. ***hugonis*** — CTri ELan EWTr LRHS NLar SKHP SPer
'Yellow Cécile Brünner' — see *R.* 'Perle d'Or'

§ Yellow Dagmar Hastrup = 'Moryelrug'[PBR] (Ru)	CPou EBee EWTr NLar SCob SPer
Yellow Flower Carpet	see *R.* Flower Carpet Sunshine
'Yellow Patio' (Min/Patio)	LRHS MAsh MBri SPoG SWCr
yellow Scotch	see *R.* × *harisonii* 'Williams' Double Yellow'
Yellow Sunblaze = 'Meitrisical' (Min)	CSBt
'Yesterday' (Poly/F/S) ♀H6	CKel EWTr NLar
York and Lancaster	see *R.* × *damascena* 'Versicolor'
York Minster = 'Harquest' (F)	MRav
Yorkshire = 'Korbarkeit'[PBR] (GC)	CDoC ELan MRav
'Yorkshire Lady' (HT)	NEgg
Yorkshire Princess = 'Dicmouse' (Patio)	IDic
You Are My Sunshine = 'Frykwango'[PBR] (HT) ♀H6	SWCr
Young Lycidas = 'Ausvibrant'[PBR] (S)	CSBt EPfP IBoy LBuc LRHS LSRN MBri SCob
You're Beautiful = 'Fryracy' (F)	CBcs CDoC CKel COtt EBee ECnt EPfP ESty LBrs LBuc LCro LRHS LShp MBri MRav NPri SCoo SPer SPoG SWCr
Yves Piaget	see *R.* Royal Brompton Rose
'Yvonne Rabier' (Poly) ♀H7	EBee MRav NLar SLon SPer
'Zéphirine Drouhin' (Bb)	Widely available
§ 'Zigeunerknabe' (S)	NLar SKHP SPer WFar

Roscoea ✿ (*Zingiberaceae*)

sp.	CMac
alpina	CAby CBro CExl CLAP EBee ECho EPot GBuc GEdr GKev ILea WCru XLum
- CC 1820	IBlr
- 'Leaping Salmon'	CCon
- pink-flowered	IBlr
- purple-flowered	IBlr
- short	WCru
alpina* × *cautleyoides	IBlr
§ ***auriculata*** ♀H5	CAby CAvo CBct CBro CCon CEvo CLAP ECho EHrv EPfP EPot GBuc GCal GEdr GKev IBlr IFoB ILea LTro MPie NHar NWad SChF SDeJ SKHP SPer WCru WHar WSHC
- B&SWJ 2594	WCru
- B&SWJ 2687	WCru
- GWJ 9230	WCru
- 'Anorexia'	IBlr
- brown-stemmed × ***purpurea***	IBlr
- early-flowering	IBlr WCru
- 'Floriade'	CDes CLAP EBee GBuc GKev IBlr WSHC
- green-stemmed × ***purpurea***	IBlr
- late-flowering	WCru
- 'Special'	CLAP
- 'White Cap'	EBee ECho GKev
auriculata* × *australis	IBlr
auriculata* × *capitata	IBlr
auriculata* × *purpurea	WCru
australis	CSam CTal ELon GBuc GEdr LLHF MNrw WCru WThu
- pink-flowered KW 22124	IBlr
- purple-flowered KW 22124	IBlr
australis* × *humeana	IBlr
'Ballyrogan Lavender'	IBlr
'Ballyrogan White'	IBlr
× ***beesiana*** ♀H5	CAvo CBod ILea SHar
- 'Ballyrogan Purple'	IBlr
- Cream Group	CBct CDes CLAP CTal EBee EHrv EPfP EPot GBuc IBlr LEdu LTro MMHG NBir SKHP WCru WPGP
- Dark Group	IBlr
- Gestreept Group	CBro CCon CLAP CMea CTsd EPot EUJe GBuc GEdr GKev IBlr LAma LRHS MPie NHar SKHP SPer WCru WHar
- 'Lemon and Lavender'	IBlr
- 'Monique'	CDes EBee EPfP IBlr NHar WPGP
- 'Moonlight'	IBlr
- 'Petite Purple'	IBlr
bhutanica PAB 3826 **new**	LEdu
Blackthorn strain	IBlr WCru
brandisii misapplied	see *R. tumjensis*
cangshanensis BWJ 7848	WCru
capitata	CLAP IBlr
cautleyoides	CAby CAvo CBro CMea CWCL ECha ECho EHrv ELon ENun EPot GBuc GEdr GKev IBlr IFoB ILea LAma LHop LRHS MNrw NBid NGdn SPoG SRot WCru WHar XEll
- CLD 772	GEdr IBlr
I - 'Alba'	CTal
- var. ***cautleyoides*** f. ***atropurpurea***	IBlr
- - - 'Giraffe'	IBlr
- 'Crûg's Late Lemon'	WCru
- 'Doge Purple'	IBlr
- 'Early Purple'	CDes CLAP ECho GBuc WPGP
- 'Early Yellow'	CTal EBee
- 'Jeffrey Thomas' ♀H5	CBct CLAP CSam CTal EBee ECho ELan GBuc GCal GEdr GKev IBlr MLHP
- late, lavender-flowered	IBlr
- late, yellow-flowered	IBlr
- 'Lemon Giraffe'	IBlr
- 'Pennine Purple'	IBlr NHar
- plum-flowered	IBlr
- var. ***pubescens***	IBlr
- 'Purple Giant'	CLAP EBee SKHP
- 'Purple Queen'	EBee GKev
- purple-flowered	CAby IBlr NHar
- 'Reinier'	CLAP CTal ECho GCal IBlr SKHP
- f. ***sinopurpurea***	GKev IBlr
- 'Vanilla'	LEdu SKHP
- 'Washfield Purple'	IBlr
- 'Wine Red'	WHil
- 'Yeti'	CDes CTal ECho SKHP
aff. ***cautleyoides*** **new**	SPlb
cautleyoides* × *humeana	CLAP IBlr LRHS WHar
cautleyoides* × *praecox	IBlr
cautleyoides* × *scillifolia f. ***atropurpurea***	IBlr
debilis var. ***debilis***	IBlr
forrestii f. ***forrestii***	IBlr
- - pubescent	IBlr
- 'Ice Maiden'	IBlr
- f. ***purpurea***	IBlr
- f. ***purpurea* × *humeana***	IBlr
'Harvington Evening Star'	EBee ENun LLHF LRHS NHar
humeana	CAby CBro CLAP ECho EPot GBuc GEdr LAma LRHS WThu
- ACE 2539	IBlr
- from Cruickshank Botanic Garden	IBlr
- f. ***alba***	IBlr

- Forrest's form IBlr
- 'Guincho White Stripe' IBlr
- 'Harvington Raw Silk' 🏆H5 EBee ENun LLHF LRHS NHar
- 'Harvington Royale' EBee ENun LLHF LRHS NHar
- lavender-flowered IBlr
- 'Long Acre Sunrise' CDes CLAP WPGP
- f. ***lutea*** 🏆H5 CLAP IBlr
- pink-flowered IBlr
- 'Purple Streaker' CDes WPGP
- purple-flowered EBee ECho ENun
- 'Rosemoor Plum' CAby CDes CLAP WCot WPGP
- 'Snowy Owl' GEdr
- 'Two Tone' IBlr
- f. ***tyria*** 🏆H5 IBlr
- - 'Inkling' GBuc
'Ice Maiden' IBlr
'Kew Beauty' 🏆H5 CAby CBod CCon CDes CExl CLAP CMea CTal EPfP GBuc GCal LRHS NGdn SKHP SMHy WGwG WPGP
'Lavender Mist' IBlr
'McBeath's Pink' **new** ENun
'Pallid Sun' IBlr
'Pinky' CMea
praecox GEdr IBlr
procera misapplied see *R. auriculata*
procera Wall. see *R. purpurea*
§ ***purpurea*** CAvo CBod CBro CTal ECha ELan ELon EPfP EUJe GCal GKev IBal IBlr IFoB ILea LAma LRHS MAsh MMuc NBir NGdn SPer WCru WGwG WHer
- CC 1757 IBlr
- CC 3628 CExl IBlr
- HWJK 2020 WCru
- HWJK 2169 WCru
- HWJK 2175 WCru
- HWJK 2400 WCru
- HWJK 2407 WCru
- KW 13755 IBlr
- MECC 2 IBlr
- MECC 10 IBlr
- 'Ant Marian' **new** EBee
- 'Bronzed Albino' IBlr
- bronze-leaved CAby CLAP
- 'Brown Peacock' CAvo CDes CFil CLAP ECho GBuc GKev IBlr SKHP WCru WPGP
- 'Cinnamon Stick' CLAP CWGN ECtt GEdr MMHG NHar
- 'Dalai Lama' 🏆H4 EBee ECho GEdr GKev
- var. ***gigantea*** CC 1757 IBlr
- 'Himalayan Delight' IBlr
- 'Late Lavender' IBlr
- 'Nico' ECho ELan IBlr SKHP WCot
- 'Peacock' CLAP EBee ECho EPot GKev IBlr SKHP
- 'Peacock Eye' ECho GEdr GKev IBlr SKHP
- var. ***procera*** see *R. purpurea*
- 'Purple Dwarf' IBlr
- 'Purple Tower' IBlr
- 'Red Foot' EBee GKev
- 'Red Gurkha' see *R. purpurea* f. *rubra*
- Rosemoor form CLAP
- Royal Purple hybrids CLAP MAsh
§ - f. ***rubra*** 🏆H4 CAby CDes CLAP EBee ENun IBlr LLHF LRHS NHar
- - 'Gurkha Redstem' **new** WCru
- 'Salt 'n' Pepper' **new** EBee
- short CLAP IBlr
- 'Slender Wisp' IBlr
- 'Spice Island' CLAP CWGN ECtt
- tall CLAP WCru WPGP
- 'Twin Towers' EBee GKev
- 'Typico' IBlr
- 'Vannin' LEdu WCru
- 'Vincent' EBee EPot GKev
- 'Wisley Amethyst' CBro CLAP CTal EBee ENun IBlr LLHF LRHS SKHP SPoG
'Red Neck' 🏆H4 EBee IBlr SKHP
schneideriana IBlr WThu
- robust form IBlr
scillifolia CBro CCon ECho GBuc GEdr GKev LAma LHop LRHS NBir SDeJ WHar
- f. ***atropurpurea*** CAby CCon CDes EBee EHrv GBuc GCal IBal IBlr WCru WPGP WThu
- f. ***scillifolia*** EBee EHrv IBlr IFoB WCru WHar WHil WThu
aff. ***scillifolia*** purple-flowered GEdr IBlr
'Summer Deep Purple' 🏆H5 EBee ENun LRHS
tibetica CCon CEvo EBee GEdr GKev IBlr LEdu LLHF WCru WThu
- ACE 2538 IBlr WCru
- BWJ 7878 WCru
- f. ***atropurpurea*** BWJ 7640 WCru
- f. ***rosea*** **new** WCru
aff. ***tibetica*** IBlr
- f. ***albo-purpurea*** IBlr
§ ***tumjensis*** CTal IBlr WPGP
wardii 🏆H5 CExl IBlr

rosemary see *Rosmarinus officinalis*

Rosenia (*Asteraceae*)

humilis CPBP

Rosmarinus ✿ (*Lamiaceae*)

sp. LBMP LPar
corsicus 'Prostratus' see *R. officinalis* Prostratus Group
lavandulaceus misapplied see *R. officinalis* Prostratus Group
× ***noeanus*** XSen
officinalis Widely available
- f. ***albiflorus*** CArn ENfk EPfP GPoy LEdu LRHS MHer MNHC SDow SHDw SLim SPlb SRms WCFE WGwG WJek XSen
- - 'Lady in White' CSBt ELan EPfP LRHS MAsh SDow SLim SPer SRms WGwG WJek
- 'Alderney' MHer SDow WGwG
§ - var. ***angustissimus*** 'Benenden Blue' 🏆H4 CAbP CSBt CWib ELan GPoy LRHS SDix SDow SEND SPer SPlb SRms WGwG WJek
- - 'Corsican Blue' CArn CBod EBee ELan GPoy MHer MHol MNHC SGol SHDw SPer SRms
- 'Arp' CArn CBod ENfk EWes LHop
- 'Aureovariegatus' see *R. officinalis* 'Aureus'
§ - 'Aureus' (v) CBcs CPla SRms WJek
- 'Avicenna' **new** WGwG
- 'Baie d'Audierne' WGwG XSen
- 'Barbecue'PBR CLau ELan ENfk LEdu LRHS SRms
- 'Blue Lagoon' CBod CLau ENfk LRHS MHer MNHC SIde SPer SRms WGwG WHer WJek
- 'Blue Rain' CBod EPfP MHer MSwo WGwG WHfH
- 'Capercaillie' SDow WGwG XSen
- 'Collingwood Ingram' see *R. officinalis* var. *angustissimus* 'Benenden Blue'

- 'Cottage White' WGwG WHer
- dwarf, blue-flowered CLau
- 'Farinole' CArn CLau MNHC SRms WGwG
- 'Fota Blue' CArn CLau CWib IArd LRHS MHer MNHC SAko SDow SGol SHDw SIde SRms SVen SWvt WGwG WJek XSen
- 'Foxtail' CBod LRHS SRms WJek
- 'Frimley Blue' see *R. officinalis* 'Primley Blue'
- 'Genges Gold' (v) MHer WGwG
- 'Gold Dust' (v) CWGN EBee ENfk LAst
- 'Golden Rain' see *R. officinalis* 'Joyce DeBaggio'
- 'Gorizia' CArn CBcs CBod LRHS SDow SRms WPnn XSen
- 'Green Ginger' ♀H4 Widely available
- 'Guilded' see *R. officinalis* 'Aureus'
- 'Haifa' CBod CLau CSde EBtc ENfk NQui SRms WJek WPnn
- 'Henfield Blue' SHDw
- 'Huntington Carpet' ECtt
- 'Iden Blue Boy' EBee ELon
- 'Iden Pillar' WGwG
- 'Jekka Blue' **new** WJek

§ - 'Joyce DeBaggio' (v) MHer SDow WGwG WHer XSen
- 'Knightshayes Blue' LRHS
- 'Lady in Blue' WGwG
- × ***lavandulaceus*** see *R. officinalis* Prostratus Group
- 'Lilies Blue' GPoy WGwG
- 'Lockwood Variety' see *R. officinalis* (Prostratus Group) 'Lockwood de Forest'
- 'Logee Blue' CArn
- 'Madeline Hill' **new** LRHS
- 'Majorca Pink' CBcs CBod CLau COtt CSBt CSpe ENfk LRHS MHer MNHC MSCN NPri SDow SPer WGwG WJek XLum
- 'Marenca' CHll CLau MNHC SRms
- 'McConnell's Blue' ♀H4 CAbP CArn CDoC CLau CPrp ELan LHop LRHS MAsh MGos MNHC SCob SDow SHDw SHil SRms WGwG WHer WHoo WJek WPGP XSen
- 'Miss Jessopp's Upright' ♀H4 Widely available
- 'Pat Vlasto' WGwG
- 'Pointe du Raz' CAbP CArn CBod ELan EPfP LRHS MAsh SChF SLim SRms WGwG

§ - 'Primley Blue' CBcs CBod CLau COtt CSam ECtt MNHC MRav SGol SIde SRms WJek

§ - Prostratus Group Widely available
- - 'Capri' CAbP CBod CDul CLau EPfP LRHS MHer SCob SRms WFar WJek
- - 'Freda' **new** WGwG
- - 'Gethsemane' CArn WGwG
- - 'Jackman's Prostrate' SDix

§ - - 'Lockwood de Forest' WGwG WHer
- - 'Rampant Boule' CArn CBod CLau MHer SDow SRms WGwG WJek XLum XSen
- - 'Sea Level' CLau MHer WGwG
- - 'Sheila Dore' SPlb SVen
- - white-flowered GPoy
- - 'Whitewater Silver' **new** LRHS
- ***repens*** see *R. officinalis* Prostratus Group
- 'Rex' CLau WGwG
- 'Roman Beauty' PBR CAbP CBcs CSBt EHoe LAst LHop LRHS LSRN MBri MHol NPri SCob SLim SRms SWvt WHer
- 'Roseus' CArn CBot CHVG CLau CWib CWld ELan ENfk EPfP GPoy LHop LRHS MAsh MHer MNHC SDow SEND SLim SPoG SRms SVen WGwG WJek WPnn XSen
- 'Salem' CBod MHer
- 'Severn Sea' ♀H4 CArn CBod CLau COtt CSBt CSam CSde CTri ECtt ELan ENfk EPfP GPoy LRHS MAsh MGos MHer MNHC MRav MSwo SIde SLon SPer SRms SVen WCFE WGwG WHoo WJek
- 'Shimmering Stars' SDow WGwG XSen
- 'Silver Sparkler' WGwG WPat
- Silver Spires = 'Wolros' MNHC
- 'Sissinghurst Blue' ♀H4 CArn CBod CLau CSde CWCL EBee ECha ECrN ELan EPfP LRHS MAsh MHer MHtn MLHP MNHC MRav SDow SGol SLim SPer SPlb SPoG SRms SWvt WGwG WJek XSen
- 'Sissinghurst White' WGwG
- 'Sorcerer's Apprentice' SDow WGwG
- 'South Downs Blue' SHDw WGwG
- 'Spanish Snow' WGwG
- 'Spice Island' CBod LRHS SPad SPer
- 'Sudbury Blue' CBod CLau COtt ENfk MHer SDow SGol SHDw SRms WFar WJek XSen
- 'Sunkissed' CSBt LRHS SLim SRms
- 'Trusty' WGwG
- 'Tuscan Blue' CArn CBcs CBod CDoC CExl CLau COtt CPrp ECha ECrN ECtt ELan EPfP LRHS MHer MNHC MSwo NEgg NPri SDow SGol SPer SRms WGwG WHfH WJek WPGP WPnn XSen
- 'Variegatus' see *R. officinalis* 'Aureus'
- 'Vatican Blue' WJek
- 'Vicomte de Noailles' WGwG XSen
- 'Wisley Blue' **new** WGwG

repens see *R. officinalis* Prostratus Group
Salcombe form CHll
'Sappho' CHll

Rostrinucula (*Lamiaceae*)

dependens EBee ELon EPfP ESwi EWes MTPN NLar SBrt WCFE
sinensis CExl

Rosularia ✿ (*Crassulaceae*)

from Sandras Dağ, Turkey CWil

§ ***aizoon*** ECho EDAr LRHS
alba see *R. sedoides* var. *alba*

§ ***chrysantha*** ECho EDAr LRHS SFgr SPlb
crassipes see *Rhodiola wallichiana*
libanotica RCB RL 20 WCot

§ ***muratdaghensis*** SPlb
pallida A. Berger see *R. chrysantha*
pallida Stapf see *R. aizoon*
pallida ambig. EPot
platyphylla misapplied see *R. muratdaghensis*
sedoides CWil

§ - var. ***alba*** ECho EDAr EPot
sempervivum CWil ECho EWes

§ - subsp. ***glaucophylla*** CWil ECho LRHS MSCN WHal WThu
- subsp. ***pestalozzae*** **new** EPot
spatulata hort. see *R. sempervivum* subsp. *glaucophylla*

Rubia (*Rubiaceae*)

peregrina GPoy
tinctorum CArn CHab CHby GPoy MNHC SRms SWat WHfH WSFF

Rubus ✿ (Rosaceae)

RCB/Eq C-1	WCot
SDR 4635	GKev
acuminatus **new**	EBee ESwi LEdu SBrt
alceifolius Poir.	SDys
- B&SWJ 1833	WCru
arcticus	EBee ECtt EPPr LEdu NHar SHar SRot WThu XLum
- subsp. ***stellatus***	NHar
bambusarum	CBot EShb ESwi MRav WCru
'Benenden' ♀H5	Widely available
'Betty Ashburner'	CAgr CBcs CDoC CDul EBee EPPr EWTr GLog GQui MCoo MGos MRav MWhi SCob SPer WHar WMoo XLum
biflorus ♀H5	EWes LEdu MBlu MMuc SEND WPGP
'Boatsberry'	SDea
'Boysenberry' (F)	CArg ERea LEdu LRHS NPri
boysenberry, thornless (F)	CMac EMil GTwe LBuc LSRN NPri SDea SPer
buergeri B&SWJ 5555	WCru
caesius	WCot
calophyllus	WPGP
calycinoides Hayata ex Koidz.	see *R. rolfei*
calycinoides Kuntze	EBtc GKev SGol
chamaemorus	GPoy
'Clarke's Velvet Night' **new**	SBrt
cockburnianus (F)	CBcs CTri CWib EBee ELan EPfP EWTr GCra GKin IFoB LBuc MMuc MRav MSwo NSti NWea SCob SPer SPlb SRms WHar
- 'Goldenvale' ♀H5	CBcs CBot CDoC CDul EHoe ELon EPfP EWTr GQui IFro LHop LRHS MAsh MBlu MGos MMuc MRav MSwo MWhi NBir NEgg NLar NSti SCob SEND SLon SPer SPoG
crataegifolius	MRav
'Emerald Spreader'	WMoo
fockeanus misapplied	see *R. rolfei*
formosensis	SBrt
- B&SWJ 1798	ESwi WCru
fruticosus agg.	CArg NWea WSFF
- 'Adrienne' (F)	CAgr CHab CSBt LEdu MAsh MBri SBdl SRms WHar
- 'Apache' (F)	CHab LCro
- 'Ashton Cross' (F)	LBuc SBmr
- 'Bedford Giant' (F)	CHab CSBt LSRN MAsh MGos SBdl SBmr SEND SLim SPoG WHar
- 'Black Butte' (F)	CHab EPom SDea SLon SVic
- 'Black Satin' (F)	CAgr ECrN LRHS NLar SDea SVic
- 'Čačanska Bestrna' (F)	MCoo
- 'Chester' (F)	EPom ERea LEdu LRHS SFrt SKee SPer
- 'Godshill Goliath' (F)	SDea
- 'Helen' (F)	CAgr CSut MAsh MCoo SBmr SDea
- 'Himalayan Giant' (F)	CHab NEgg NLar SDea
- 'Karaka Black' (PBR) (F)	CHab ERea LBuc LRHS SBmr SPoG SVic
- 'Loch Maree'PBR (F/d)	CHab CMac EPom LEdu MCoo NPri SFrt SLon
- 'Loch Ness'PBR (F) ♀H6	CAgr CArg CHab CWib EPom GTwe IArd LBuc LCro LOPS LRHS LSRN NPri SBmr SCoo SDea SFrt SKee SPoG SVic WHar
- 'Loch Tay'PBR (F)	CArg CHab CMac EPom LRHS
- 'Merton Thornless' (F)	CSBt CWib ECrN LAst LEdu LSRN MAsh MBri MGos SBdl SPlb SRms WHar
- 'Natchez'PBR (F)	LBuc
- 'Navaho' (F)	CHab ERea LRHS
- 'No Thorn' (F)	SDea
- 'Oregon Thornless' (F)	CAgr CDoC CSBt CWib ECrN EPfP GTwe LCro LOPS LRHS LSRN MAsh MBri MJak MRav NLar NWea SBmr SCoo SDea SKee SLim SPoG SRms SVic WHar WMat
- 'Ouachita'PBR (F)	LCro LOPS LRHS SKee SPer SPoG
- 'Parsley Leaved' (F)	SDea
- 'Reuben' (F)	CHab EPom GQue LBuc LCro LOPS LRHS MCoo SBmr SKee SPer SPoG WMat
- 'Thornfree' (F)	CAgr CDoC CTri LRHS MBri NLar NPri SBmr SDea SKee SLim WMat
- 'Triple Crown' (F)	CHab CMac MCoo
- 'Variegatus' (v)	CMac MBlu WCot
- 'Waldo' (F)	CAgr CSBt CWib LBuc LSRN MAsh MBri MGos NPri SBdl SBmr SDea SRms WHar
'Glencoe' (F)	CSut MCoo
'Golden Showers'	CWib
henryi	CBcs ESwi LRHS WCot
ichangensis	CBot CFil ESwi
idaeus	GPoy
- 'All Gold' (F) ♀H6	EMil EPom ERea LBuc LRHS MAsh MCoo NLar NPri SBdl SCoo SFrt SPer SVic WHar WMat
- 'Aureus' (F)	ECha ELan LEdu MRav NBid WCot
- 'Autumn Bliss' (F) ♀H6	Widely available
- 'Autumn Treasure'PBR (F)	CSut EMil EPom ERea GTwe LRHS MCoo NPri SLon SVic
- 'Cascade Delight' (F)	EPom LBuc LCro LOPS LRHS MAsh SBdl
- 'Chemainus' (F) **new**	LCro LOPS
- 'Erika'PBR (F)	LCro LOPS LRHS MNHC SBmr SPer WMat
- 'Fallgold' (F)	CWib LSRN MMuc SBmr SKee SPoG
- 'Glen Ample'PBR (F) ♀H6	Widely available
- 'Glen Clova' (F)	CAgr CSBt CTri CWib ELan GTwe LRHS LSRN MAsh MGos NPri SBdl SBmr SKee SLim SPer SPoG WHar WMat
- 'Glen Doll'PBR (F)	CAgr GQue GTwe LRHS MAsh MCoo SBdl SCoo SPoG WMat
- 'Glen Fyne'PBR (F)	GTwe
- 'Glen Lyon'PBR (F)	CWib ECrN GKin LBuc MAsh MBri MJak NPri SBdl SCoo WHar
- 'Glen Magna'PBR (F) ♀H6	CAgr CArg CMac CSBt CWib ERea GKin MAsh MBri NPri SCoo SDea SKee SLim
- 'Glen Moy'PBR (F)	CAgr CArg CSBt CTri CWib ECrN EPfP GTwe LRHS LSRN MAsh MGos MJak NWea SCoo SDea SKee SLim SPer WHar
- 'Glen Prosen'PBR (F)	CAgr CSBt CWib EPfP ERea GKin GTwe LRHS LSRN MAsh MBri MGos NPri SBdl SBmr SCoo SDea SKee SLim SPer SPlb WHar WMat
- 'Glen Rosa' (F)	ERea MCoo SDea
- 'Heritage' (F)	CWib ELan MAsh SBdl SBmr SCoo
- Himbo Top = 'Rafzaqu'PBR (F)	CMac
- 'Joan J'PBR (F) ♀H6	CSut EPom ERea GTwe LSRN MCoo
- 'Leo'PBR (F) ♀H6	CSBt CTri CWib LSRN MAsh SBdl SBmr SCoo SKee SPer WHar

Plant	Suppliers
- 'Malling Admiral' (F) 🏆H6	CSBt CTri CWib EPom GTwe LAst LSRN MAsh NWea SBdl SCoo SKee WHar
- 'Malling Delight' (F)	CSBt CWib ELan SCoo SPlb
- 'Malling Jewel' (F) 🏆H6	CAgr CSBt CWib EPfP EPom GTwe LAst LBuc LSRN MAsh MJak SBdl SDea SKee
- 'Malling Promise' (F)	CWib MJak NLar
- 'Octavia'[PBR] (F)	CAgr CArg CSBt EMil EPom GQue GTwe LBuc LRHS MAsh MCoo NLar NWea SBdl SBmr SFrt SLim SPoG WHar WMat
- 'Polka'[PBR] (F) 🏆H6	CWSG EPfP EPom LBuc LCro LOPS LRHS LSRN MAsh MCoo MRav SBdl SBmr SCoo SKee SLim WHar WMat
- 'Sugana'[PBR] (F)	LRHS MAsh MCoo SBdl
- 'Summer Gold' (F)	GTwe
- 'Tadmor'[PBR] (F)	CArg ERea LCro LOPS LRHS SBmr SKee SPer WMat
- 'Tulameen' (F) 🏆H6	CAgr CSBt CWSG CWib ELan EMil EPom LBuc LCro LOPS LRHS LSRN MAsh MBri NLar SBdl SBmr SCoo SFrt SKee SLim SPer SPoG SVic WHar WMat
- 'Valentina' (F)	CSut SFrt
- 'Zeva Herbsternte' (F)	CWib MAsh SBdl
illecebrosus (F)	LEdu XLum
irenaeus	LEdu LRHS SEND
Japanese wineberry	see *R. phoenicolasius*
'Kenneth Ashburner'	CDoC NLar
lambertianus PAB 8931	LEdu
lineatus	CBot CDTJ CWib EPfP EWes GBin LHop LRHS MCot SBrt SKHP WCru WPGP WPat
- from Nepal	GCra
- B&SWJ 11261 from Sumatra	WCru
- HWJ 892 from Vietnam	ESwi WCru
- HWJK 2045 from Nepal	GQui WCru
× ***loganobaccus*** (F)	SBdl
- 'Brandywine' (F)	SDea
- 'Ly 59' (F) 🏆H5	ECrN EPfP MMuc SDea SKee SRms
- 'Ly 654' (F) 🏆H5	CSBt EPom ERea GTwe LBuc LRHS MBri NEgg NPri SBmr SDea SPer WHar
- thornless (F)	CAgr CTri CWib EPfP EPom GTwe LEdu MJak SDea SPoG SVic WMat
ludwigii	SBrt
'Malling Minerva' (F)	CAgr CSut EPom SFrt SVic
'Margaret Gordon'	MRav
microphyllus 'Variegatus' (v)	MRav
§ ***nepalensis***	CAgr GCra GKev LEdu WPGP
nutans	see *R. nepalensis*
'Obsidian' (F)	LEdu
odoratus	CBcs CExl EBee ELan EPPr EWTr IDee LEdu MBlu NBid SPer
'Ouachita'[PBR] (F) **new**	LOPS SPoG
palmatus var. ***coptophyllus***	MMuc
parkeri PAB 6891	LEdu
parviflorus	CArn IFro
- 'Bill Baker'	LEdu
- double-flowered (d)	EPPr
- 'Sunshine Spreader'	EHoe LEdu
parvus	LEdu WPGP
pectinellus var. ***trilobus***	SBrt
- - B&SWJ 1669B	WCru
peltatus	CFil NLar WPGP
pentalobus	see *R. rolfei*
§ ***phoenicolasius***	CAgr CBcs CDul CHGN ELan EPPr EPfP ERea EWTr GTwe LCro LEdu LHop LOPS LRHS MBlu MCoo MHer MRav SBmr SDea SPer SPoG SVic WBor WHea WPGP
§ ***rolfei***	CDul CTri GEdr IArd MCoo
- B&SWJ 3546 from Taiwan	WCru
- B&SWJ 3878 from the Philippines	WCru
- 'Emerald Carpet' 🏆H5	CAgr EAEE NLar
rosifolius NJM 10.142	WPGP
- 'Coronarius' (d)	ECrN LSou WCot
rubrisetulosus PAB 9532 **new**	LEdu
'Rushbrook Redleaf' **new**	SBrt
sanctus	CNat
saxatilis	LEdu
- PAB 3912	LEdu
setchuenensis	CMCN EPPr NLar
'Silvan' (F) 🏆H6	MCoo MMuc SEND
spectabilis	CBcs CWib ELan EPPr LEdu MMuc MRav WSHC
- 'Flore Pleno'	see *R. spectabilis* 'Olympic Double'
§ - 'Olympic Double' (d)	Widely available
- 'Olympic Gold' (d) **new**	CLet
splendidissimus B&SWJ 2361	ESwi WCru
squarrosus	ECou
'Sunberry' (F)	SBmr SDea
swinhoei B&SWJ 1735	WCru
taiwanicola	GEdr
- B&SWJ 317	ESwi WCru
- CWJ 12400	WCru
- 'Buckingham'	NPer
Tayberry Group (F) 🏆H5	CSBt CTri GTwe LRHS LSRN MGos NLar NPri SBdl SBmr SPer SRms SVic WHar
- 'Buckingham' (F)	CArg CSut EMil EPom ERea GTwe LBuc LCro LRHS NLar SBmr SVic WMat
- 'Medana Tayberry' (F)	CAgr ECrN EPfP GQue LEdu LRHS MBri NLar NWea SDea SKee WHar WMat
§ ***thibetanus*** 🏆H5	Widely available
- 'Silver Fern'	see *R. thibetanus*
treutleri B&SWJ 2139	WCru
tricolor	CAgr CBcs CDul CSBt CTri CWib ECrN GKev GKin MBlu MCoo MMuc MRav MSwo MWhi NLar SCob SDix SGol SPer WMoo
aff. ***tricolor***	WHar
trilobus B&SWJ 9096	WCru
'Tummelberry' (F)	EMil GQue LRHS MCoo SVic
ulmifolius 'Bellidiflorus' (d)	MRav
ursinus	SVic
xanthocarpus	LEdu NLar XLum
'Youngberry' (F)	SDea

Rudbeckia ✿ (*Asteraceae*)

Plant	Suppliers
alpicola **new**	EBee
Autumn Sun	see *R. laciniata* 'Herbstsonne'
'Berlin'	CWGN EBee ECtt GMaP IPot LHop LRHS LSou LSun MHol NLar SCob SPer SPoG WCot
californica	EBee LRHS
deamii	see *R. fulgida* var. *deamii*
'Denver Daisy'	LSun
'Dublin'	CWGN CWld ECtt IKil LRHS LSou MHol NLar SCob SPer SPoG WCot

	fulgida	SWvt WFar
	- 'City Garden'	CKno ECtt GBin LRHS MBri NLar SAko SRms
§	- var. ***deamii*** ♀H7	Widely available
	- 'Early Bird Gold'	CWGN EBee ECtt GBin LCro LOPS MHol NGBl NLar SAko SMad SPoG WCot
	- var. ***fulgida***	CMea EBee EPfP LEdu SPoG WTcb
	- 'Little Goldstar'[PBR]	CBod CKno CRos EBee ECtt ELan LBMP LCro LOPS LRHS MAsh MBri MPie NLar NPri SCob SHar SHil SLon SPoG WCot
§	- var. ***speciosa*** ♀H7	CPrp CWCL EBee ECha ECtt ELan EPfP GAbr MMuc SBch SDix SEND SHar SPlb SPtp SRms SWvt WFar WMoo WOld WOut WPtf WWEG WWtn XLum
I	- var. ***sullivantii*** 'Goldschirm'	EBee
	- - 'Goldsturm' ♀H7	Widely available
	- - 'Pot of Gold'	IKil MAsh NLar
	- Viette's Little Suzy = 'Blovi'	EBee SRms
	gloriosa	see *R. hirta*
	grandiflora new	CEvo LRHS
	- 'Sundance'	CHVG EBee LPla MMuc SAko SEND SPhx
§	***hirta***	ELan NBir SVic
	- 'Autumn Colours' (mixed)	CMea ELan SPhx
	- 'Cappuccino'	ELan EPfP
	- 'Cherokee Sunset' (d)	CSpe EPfP LRHS
	- 'Cherry Brandy'	LHop LRHS SGol SLon SPhx
	- 'Chim Chiminee'	IKil NGBl
	- 'Goldilocks'	CWCL SVic
	- 'Indian Summer' ♀H3	EPfP LRHS MHol MNHC SPav SPhx
	- 'Irish Eyes'	SPav SVic
	- 'Marmalade'	EPfP LRHS NGBl SVic
	- 'Prairie Sun'	CMea ELon EPfP LRHS NGBl SPhx
	- 'Sonora'	NGBl
	- 'Tiger Eye'	SPoG
	- 'Toto' ♀H3	SPav SWvt
	July Gold	see *R. laciniata* 'Juligold'
	laciniata	CElw CEvo CHVG CKno CMac CSpe EBee ELan GCal GQue LEdu MMuc MSpe NCGa NDov NGBl NLar SEND SMHy SPhx WCot WMoo WOld WPGP WTcb WWEG WWtn XLum
	- var. ***digitata***	IMou
	- 'Golden Glow'	see *R. laciniata* 'Hortensia'
	- 'Goldkugel' (d) ♀H7	MSpe
	- 'Goldquelle' (d)	CBod CLet CWCL EBee ECha ECtt ELan EPfP GMaP IVic LAst LHop LRHS MBri NGdn NPri SBea SCob SMad SPer SPoG SRms SRot SWvt WCAu WFar WMnd WWEG XLum
§	- 'Herbstsonne' ♀H7	Widely available
§	- 'Hortensia' (d)	EBee GQue MAvo MRav WBrk WCot WHoo WOld WWEG
§	- 'Juligold'	CPrp EBee ECtt LRHS MAvo MBNS MPie NEgg NGdn SPoG WWEG WWFP
	- 'Starcadia Razzle Dazzle'	EWld MAvo NGBl SAko WCot WWEG
	maxima	CAby CKno CSpe EBee ECha ELon EWoo GBin IFoB LEdu LHop LRHS LSun MBel MHol NCGa NGBl NLar NSti SBrt SKHP SMad SPhx SPlb WCot WTcb XLum
	missouriensis	EBee LRHS MMuc SEND
	mollis	EBee LRHS NBre
	newmannii	see *R. fulgida* var. *speciosa*
	nitida	IBoy
	occidentalis	LRHS NBre NChi WWEG
	- 'Black Beauty'[PBR]	ECtt EPfP
	- 'Green Wizard'	CBod CMac CWCL CWib EBee ECtt EHrv ELan EPfP EShb GBin IBoy LRHS MLHP NLar NSti SGSe SPav SPer SRms WHar WMnd WTcb WWEG
*	***paniculata***	EBee LLHF NBre WCot
	'Peking'[PBR]	CWGN ECtt IKil LRHS SCob SPoG WCot
	purpurea	see *Echinacea purpurea*
	speciosa	see *R. fulgida* var. *speciosa*
	subtomentosa	CEvo CSam EWes GCal LEdu LPla LRHS MSpe NDov NSti SCob SMHy WCot WOld XLum
	- 'Henry Eilers'	Widely available
	- 'Little Henry' new	EBee ECtt LRHS MAsh MHol SCob
	Summerina Series new	SCob
	- Summerina Brown = 'Et Rdb-o3' new	WCot WHil
	- Summerina Orange = 'ET Rdb-01' new	WCot WHil
	- Summerina Yellow = 'ET Rdb-02' new	WCot WHil
	triloba ♀H7	CDes CNec CSpe ECha ELon EPfP IBoy LCro LRHS MBel MMuc MNrw NCGa NGBl NGdn SDix SGSe SPhx WMoo WPGP
	- 'Prairie Glow'	CBod CBot CMea CNec EAJP IBoy IPot MSCN NCGa NDov SCob SGol SMad SPer SPhx

rue see *Ruta graveolens*

Ruellia (*Acanthaceae*)

	amoena	see *R. brevifolia*
§	***brevifolia***	ECre EShb
	caroliniensis subsp. ***ciliosa*** var. ***cinerascens*** new	SAko
	humilis	EBee EShb GEdr SBrt SPhx WHil
	macrantha	EShb
	makoyana ♀H1a	CTsd EShb WHil
	- white-flowered	EShb WHil
	strepens	EBee
	tweediana	EShb

Rulingia (*Sterculiaceae*)

	dasyphylla new	ECou
	hermanniifolia	MOWG

Rumex (*Polygonaceae*)

	acetosa	CAgr CArn CHab CHby CLau ENfk GPoy MCoo MHer MJak MMuc MNHC NBir SEND SIde SRms WHer WJek WSFF
	- 'Abundance'	CLau LEdu
	- subsp. ***acetosa*** 'Saucy' (v)	LEdu WCot
	- 'Profusion'	GPoy MHer
	acetosella	CAgr CHab NMir WSFF
	alpinus	EBee LEdu SDix SPhx WCot WPGP
	crispus	CLau
	flexuosus	CElw CSpe EPPr GCal LPot WJek
	hydrolapathum	CArn CBod CHab MMuc MSKA NLar SEND SPlb WCot WSFF
	patientia	CHab CLau
	sanguineus	CTri ENfk EShb LEdu MSKA NLar NQui SRms XLum

- var. ***sanguineus***	CElw CHby ELan GBin IFoB MHer MNHC NBro SGSe WHer WJek
scutatus	CArn CBod CHby CLau ENfk GPoy MNHC SIde SPlb SRms WHer WHfH WJek
- subsp. ***induratus***	SEND
- 'Silver Shield'	LEdu MHer SRms WJek

Rumohra (*Dryopteridaceae*)

adiantiformis ♀H1c	ISha LRHS NLos SEND WFib WPGP
- RCB/Arg D-2	WCot

Ruschia (*Aizoaceae*)

putterillii	SPlb
spinosa	SPlb
tumidula	SPlb

Ruscus ✿ (*Asparagaceae*)

aculeatus	CArn CBcs CDul CMac CTsd ELan EPfP GPoy LEdu LPal MGil MGos MRav NLar SDix SPlb SRms SWvt WRHF
- (f)	SCob
- hermaphrodite	EPfP GCal MMuc SEND SMad WPGP WThu
- var. ***aculeatus*** 'Lanceolatus' (f)	GCal
- var. ***angustifolius***	WPGP
- - PAB 254	LEdu
- 'Christmas Berry'	EPfP
- 'John Redmond'PBR ♀H5	CBcs ELan ELon EPfP EShb LHop LLHF LRHS MAsh NHol NLar NWad SCob SCoo SKHP SLon SPer SPoG SSpi SWvt WBor WFar WPGP
* - 'Wheeler's Variety' (f/m)	CJun MRav WPGP
hypoglossum	CMac MMuc SEND WCot WPGP
racemosus	see *Danae racemosa*

Russelia (*Plantaginaceae*)

§ ***equisetiformis*** ♀H1c	MOWG
- 'Lemon Falls' ♀H1c	MOWG
- 'Tangerine Falls'	MOWG
juncea	see *R. equisetiformis*

Ruta (*Rutaceae*)

chalepensis	CArn XLum
corsica	CArn XLum
graveolens	CBod CDul CHab ENfk GPoy LSun MJak MNHC SIde WJek XLum
- 'Jackman's Blue'	CBcs CTri EHoe EPfP GMaP GPoy MGos MHer MNHC MRav MSwo NLar SRms SWvt XLum
- 'Variegata' (v)	MNHC NPer SRms

Rytidosperma (*Poaceae*)

* ***arundinaceum***	EShb

S

Sabal (*Arecaceae*)

minor	CPHo LPal LTro NLos SBig SPlb
palmetto	LPal LTro
uresana	LPal LTro

Saccharum (*Poaceae*)

arundinaceum	CKno
brevibarbe var. ***contortum***	WCot
officinarum	SPlb
ravennae	SMad SPlb

sage see *Salvia officinalis*

sage, annual clary see *Salvia viridis*

sage, biennial clary see *Salvia sclarea*

sage, pineapple see *Salvia elegans*

Sageretia (*Rhamnaceae*)

§ ***thea***	CMen
theezans	see *S. thea*

Sagina (*Caryophyllaceae*)

subulata	ECho EHoe NPri SVic XLum
- var. ***glabrata***	MAsh
§ - - 'Aurea'	CMea CTri ECha ECho ECtt EDAr GMaP MHer SPoG

Sagittaria (*Alismataceae*)

australis	EWay
'Bloomin' Babe'	EWay
graminea	LLWG
- 'Crushed Ice' (v)	EWay
japonica	see *S. sagittifolia*
lancifolia	EWay LLWG
latifolia	MWts NPer
* ***leucopetala*** 'Flore Pleno' (d)	NPer
§ ***sagittifolia***	CWat EHon LLWG MSKA MWts WMAq WPnP XLum
- 'Flore Pleno' (d)	CWat EWay MWts WMAq XLum
- var. ***leucopetala***	WMAq

Saintpaulia ✿ (*Gesneriaceae*)

'Aca's Pink Delight'	WDib
'Aca's Red Ember' (v)	WDib
'Ajohn's Fruit Cocktail'	WDib
'Ajohn's Shimmering Star' **new**	WDib
'Allegro Appalachian Trail'	WDib
'Always Pink'	WDib
'Aly's Rosy Baby'	WDib
'Anouk'	WDib
'Anthoflores Edith'	WDib
'Arctic Frost' (d)	WDib
'Baby Brian'	WDib
'Baby's Breath'	WDib
'Baker's Pink Star'	WDib
'Ballet Snowcone' (d)	WDib
'Beacon Trail'	WDib
'Beatrice Trail'	WDib
'Betty Stoehr'	WDib
'Black Ace' (d)	WDib
'Blackie Bryant'	WDib
'Bliznecy' **new**	WDib
'Bloomlover's Cat' (d)	WDib
'Blue Dragon' (d)	WDib
'Blue Tail Fly'	WDib
'Blushing Ivory'	WDib
'Blushing Trail'	WDib
'Bob Serbin' (d)	WDib
'Bob's Omega'	WDib
'Bol's Evening Irja' **new**	WDib
brevipilosa	WDib
'Buckeye Carioca' **new**	WDib

'Buffalo Hunt' (d) WDib
'Calico Beauty' WDib
'Candy Fountain' **new** WDib
'Candy Swirls' WDib
'Cathedral' WDib
'Chantamara' WDib
'Chantaspring' WDib
'Cherries 'n' Cream' WDib
'Chiffon Fiesta' WDib
'Chiffon Moonmoth' WDib
'Chiffon Pageant' WDib
'Chiffon Vesper' WDib
'Colette' **new** WDib
'Coral Sparkle Trail' WDib
'Country Romance' (d) WDib
'Crimson Ice' WDib
'Cupid's Jewel' WDib
'Deep Sky' **new** WDib
'Deer Trail' WDib
'Delft' (d) WDib
'Desir' WDib
'Dibleys Kaarina' WDib
'Dibleys Mercedes' WDib
'Ek Lubasha' **new** WDib
'Electric Dreams' WDib
'Emerald Love' WDib
'Faded Denim' **new** WDib
'Falling Raindrops' WDib
'Favorite Child' WDib
'Festive Holiday' (d) WDib
'Fire Mountain' WDib
'Flashy Angel' (v) WDib
'Flower Drum' WDib
'Fun Trail' WDib
'Gecko's Vespa Vino' **new** WDib
'Genetic Blush' WDib
'Gillian' (d) WDib
'Golden Eye' WDib
'Golden Glow' (d) WDib
'Goluboi Tuman' **new** WDib
'Grandmother's Halo' WDib
'Green Dragon' **new** WDib
'Green Ice' WDib
'Green Lace' (d) WDib
'Halo's Aglitter' WDib
'Happy Cricket' WDib
'Hot Summer Day' WDib
'In The Pink' **new** WDib
'Indigo Ruffles' WDib
ionantha subsp. ***grotei*** WDib
- subsp. ***ionantha*** WDib
- subsp. ***rupicola*** WDib
- subsp. ***velutina*** WDib
'Irish Flirt' (d) WDib
'Joli Concerto' **new** WDib
'Jolly Cutie Pie' WDib
'Jolly Orchid' (d) WDib
'Jolly Texan' (d) WDib
'King's Trail' (d) WDib
'Kostina Fantaziia' WDib
'Lemon Drop' (d) WDib
'Lemon Whip' (d) WDib
'Little Axel' WDib
'Lollipop' WDib
'Looking Glass' WDib
'Louisiana Lagniappe' WDib
'Louisiana Lullaby' (d) WDib
'Love Spots' WDib
'Lubimaia Dochka' **new** WDib
'Lucky Lee Ann' (d) WDib
'Luminescence' WDib
'Lyon's Paprika' WDib
'Lyon's Plum Pudding' WDib
'Mac's Black Jack' WDib
'Mac's Blowing Bubbles' WDib
'Mac's Carnival Clown' WDib
'Mac's Cheery Cherry' WDib
'Mac's Circus Clown' WDib
'Mac's Coral Cutie' WDib
'Mac's Exquisite Extravaganza' WDib
'Mac's Just Jeff' (d/v) WDib
'Mac's Nocturne' (d) WDib
'Mac's Southern Springtime' (d) WDib
'Mac's Strawberry Sundae' WDib
'Mac's Will-o'-th'-Wisp' **new** WDib
'Mair' WDib
'Ma's Ching Dynasty' (d) WDib
'Ma's Corsage' WDib
'Ma's Easter Parade' WDib
'Ma's Lily Pad' WDib
'Masked Man' WDib
'Midget Lilian' (v) WDib
'Midnight Flame' (d) WDib
'Midnight Magic' WDib
'Midnight Rascal' (d) WDib
'Midnight Waltz' (d) WDib
'Milky Way Trail' WDib
'Mindi Brooke' **new** WDib
'Minnie Mine' WDib
'Minstrel's Mary Ruth' WDib
'Motley Crew' WDib
'Munchkin Kisses' (d) WDib
'Ness' Antique Red' WDib
'Ness' Bangle Blue' WDib
'Ness' Blueberry Puff' WDib
'Ness' Cherry Smoke' WDib
'Ness' Crinkle Blue' (d) WDib
'Ness' Dynomite' WDib
'Ness' Jesse' (d) WDib
'Ness' Midnight Fantasy' WDib
'Ness' Orange Pekoe' WDib
'Ness' Satin Rose' WDib
'Ness' Sheer Peach' WDib
'Ness' Viking Maiden' WDib
'Newtown Ohio' WDib
nitida WDib
'Nortex's Razzmatazz Haven' **new** WDib
'Ode to Beauty' WDib
'Okie Easter Bunny' WDib
'Oksana' WDib
'Optimara Chico' WDib
'Optimara Dali' WDib
'Optimara Hiroshige' **new** WDib
'Optimara Little Moonstone' WDib
'Optimara Little Ruby' **new** WDib
'Optimara Little Seneca' WDib
'Otoe' (d) WDib
'Parnikovyi Effekt' **new** WDib
'Pat Tracey' **new** WDib
'Peppermint Doll' WDib
'Petite Blarney' WDib
'Pink Wink' WDib
'Pirate's Treasure' WDib
'Pixie Blue' WDib
'Pixie Pink' WDib
'Pixie Show-off' WDib

'Podvenechnaia' (d)	WDib
'Powder Keg' (d)	WDib
'Powwow' (d/v)	WDib
'Prancing Pony' **new**	WDib
'Purple Passion'	WDib
'Rain Man'	WDib
'Rainbow's Limelight' (d)	WDib
'Rainbow's Quiet Riot'	WDib
'Ramblin' Amethyst'	WDib
'Ramblin' Angel' (d)	WDib
'Ramblin' Dots'	WDib
'Ramblin' Lassie'	WDib
'Ramblin' Magic' (d)	WDib
'Ramblin' Sunshine'	WDib
'Rare Tapestry'	WDib
'Raspberry Crisp'	WDib
'Red Lantern' (d)	WDib
'Red Summit'	WDib
'Reflections of Spring' (d)	WDib
'Rhapsodie Clementine'	WDib
'Rhapsodie Rosalie'	WDib
'Robert Mayer'	WDib
'Rob's Argyle Socks' (d)	WDib
'Rob's Bamboozle' (d)	WDib
'Rob's Blue Cat'	WDib
'Rob's Blue Socks'	WDib
'Rob's Boo Hoo'	WDib
'Rob's Boogie Woogie' **new**	WDib
'Rob's Chilly Willy' (d/v)	WDib
'Rob's Dandy Lion' (d/v)	WDib
'Rob's Dust Storm' (d)	WDib
'Rob's Fuzzy Navel'	WDib
'Rob's Hallucination'	WDib
'Rob's Heebie Jeebie'	WDib
'Rob's Hopscotch' (d)	WDib
'Rob's Hot Tamale'	WDib
'Rob's Ice Ripples' (d)	WDib
'Rob's Jitterbug'	WDib
'Rob's Love Bite' (d)	WDib
'Rob's Mad Cat' (d)	WDib
'Rob's Peedletuck'	WDib
'Rob's Pewter Bells' **new**	WDib
'Rob's Pink Buttercups' (v)	WDib
'Rob's Rinky Dink' (d)	WDib
'Rob's Ruff Stuff'	WDib
'Rob's Sarsparilla' (d)	WDib
'Rob's Scarecrow'	WDib
'Rob's Scrumptious'	WDib
'Rob's Seduction' (d/v)	WDib
'Rob's Shadow Magic' (d/v)	WDib
'Rob's Smarty Pants' (d)	WDib
'Rob's Sticky Wicket' (d)	WDib
'Rob's Toorooka' (d)	WDib
'Rob's Twinkle Blue' (d)	WDib
'Rob's Vanilla Trail' (d)	WDib
'Rob's Wooloomooloo' (d)	WDib
'Roll Along Blue' (d)	WDib
'RS-Strast'	WDib
'Ruffled Skies' **new**	WDib
'Ruffles 'n' Lace' **new**	WDib
'Saint Paul' **new**	WDib
'Santa Anita'	WDib
'Sapphire Halo' **new**	WDib
'Scarlet Ribbons'	WDib
'Senk's Beanstalk' **new**	WDib
shumensis	WDib
'Silly Girl'	WDib
'Silverglade Beads' **new**	WDib
'Silverglade Dolls' **new**	WDib
'Silverglade Dreams' **new**	WDib
'Silverglade Jingles' **new**	WDib
'Sky Bells' (v)	WDib
'Snow Leopard'	WDib
'Special Treat' **new**	WDib
'Sultan' (d)	WDib
'Sun Sizzle' **new**	WDib
'Sunkissed Rose' **new**	WDib
'Sweet Amy Sue' (d)	WDib
'Taffeta Blue' (d)	WDib
'Teen Thunder'	WDib
'The Madam'	WDib
'Tiger' (v) **new**	WDib
'Tina's April Fantasy'	WDib
'Toy Castle' **new**	WDib
'Tula'	WDib
'Twist 'n' Shout'	WDib
'Vampire's Kiss' (d)	WDib
'Warm Sunshine'	WDib
'Whirligig Star'	WDib
'Wild Irish Rose'	WDib
'Winnergreen' **new**	WDib
'Wisteria' (d)	WDib
'Witch Doctor' (d)	WDib
'Wrangler's Jealous Heart' **new**	WDib
'Yesterday's Child'	WDib

Salicornia (*Amaranthaceae*)

europaea	SVic

Salix ✿ (*Salicaceae*)

	acutifolia 'Blue Streak' (m) ♀H5	CWiW EPfP EWes MBlu NBir NLar SWat WMou
	- 'Pendulifolia' (m)	SGol
	'Aegma Brno' (f)	WMou
	aegyptiaca	CBot CLnd EBtc ECrN MBlu NWea WMou
	alba	CCVT CDul CHab CLnd CWiW ECrN LBuc NWea SEWo SGol WMou
	- f. ***argentea***	see *S. alba* var. *sericea*
	- 'Aurea'	CTho WMou
	- var. ***caerulea***	CDul NWea WMou
	- - 'Wantage Hall' (f)	CWiW
	- 'Cardinalis' (f)	CWiW SWat
	- 'Chermesina' hort.	see *S. alba* var. *vitellina* 'Britzensis'
	- 'Golden Ness' ♀H6	EBee MAsh MBlu WFar WMat
	- 'Hutchinson's Yellow'	CTho ECrN MBri NLar NWea
	- 'Liempde' (m)	NWea
	- 'Raesfeld' (m)	CWiW
§	- var. ***sericea*** ♀H6	CBcs CDul CLnd CTho EPfP MBlu MRav NLar NWea SPer WCot WMou
	- 'Splendens'	see *S. alba* var. *sericea*
	- 'Tristis' misapplied	see *S.* × *sepulcralis* var. *chrysocoma*
§	- 'Tristis' ambig.	CLnd CTri ELan IBoy LAst LRHS MBri MGos MRav MSwo NLar NWea SEWo SWat WHar
	- var. ***vitellina***	CDul CTri EPfP GQue LBuc MBNS MMuc NLar NWea SEND SGol SLon SWat
§	- - 'Britzensis' (m)	Widely available
	- - 'Nova'	SWat
§	- - 'Yelverton' ♀H6	EPfP GQue MAsh SPoG SWat WFar WMat
	- 'Vitellina Tristis'	see *S. alba* 'Tristis' ambig.
§	***alpina***	ECho GEdr NHar
	'Americana'	CWiW
	amplexicaulis 'Pescara' (m)	CWiW
	amygdaloides	CWiW

	'Aokautere'	see *S.* × *sepulcralis* 'Aokautere'
§	***arbuscula***	ECho XEll
	arenaria	see *S. repens* var. *argentea*
	aurita	NWea
	babylonica	CDul COtt LPal LPar WMou
	- 'Annularis'	see *S. babylonica* 'Crispa'
	- 'Bijdorp'	NLar
§	- 'Crispa'	ELan LHop LRHS MTPN NQui NSti SMad SPoG WFar
	- 'Pan Chih-kang'	CWiW NLar
	- var. ***pekinensis*** 'Pendula'	IArd
§	- - 'Tortuosa'	CBcs CDul CLnd CSBt CWib ECrN ELan EPfP IBoy IVic LRHS MGos MMuc MSCN NBir NOrn NPer NWea SCob SEND SGol SLon SPer SPlb SPoG SRms SWat WFar WHar WPos
*	- 'Tortuosa Aurea'	IBoy SGol SWvt
	× ***balfourii***	SDix
	'Blackskin' (f)	CWiW
	bockii	EBtc LLHF LRHS SDys SKHP
§	'Bowles's Hybrid'	WMou
	'Boydii' (f) ♀H7	CMea ECho EPot GAbr GBin GCrg ITim LEdu LRHS MGos NBir NHar NRya NSla SAko WAbe WFar WPat WThu
§	'Boyd's Pendulous' (m)	CWib
	caprea	CArg CBcs CCVT CDul CHab CLnd CTri EPfP LBuc MJak NBes NWea SCob SEWo SPer WMou WSFF
	- 'Black Stem'	CDul
§	- 'Kilmarnock' (m)	Widely available
	- 'Mas' (m)	CNWT
	- var. ***pendula*** (m)	see *S. caprea* 'Kilmarnock' (m)
	- - (f)	see *S. caprea* 'Weeping Sally'
§	- 'Weeping Sally' (f)	WMat
	capusii	WPGP
	cashmiriana	GEdr
*	***caspica rubra nana***	SWat
	'Chrysocoma'	see *S.* × *sepulcralis* var. *chrysocoma*
	cinerea	CBcs CTri MJak NWea SEWo WMou
	- 'Tricolor' (v)	NEoE
	daphnoides	CBcs CCVT CDul CLnd CMac EPfP MGos MMuc MSwo NWea SEND SGol SPer SRms SWat WMou WSFF
	- 'Aglaia' (m) ♀H6	CDul CTri GQue
	- 'Meikle' (f)	CWiW SWat
	- 'Netta Statham' (m)	CWiW
	- 'Ovaro Udine' (m)	CWiW
	- 'Oxford Violet' (m)	NWea
	- 'Stewartstown'	CWiW
	× ***dasyclados***	WPos
	- 'Grandis'	NWea
§	× ***doniana*** 'Kumeti'	CWiW
	'E.A. Bowles'	see *S.* 'Bowles's Hybrid'
	× ***ehrhartiana***	CNat
§	***elaeagnos***	CCVT CDul CTho CTri ECrN EPfP MBrN MMuc MSCN NWea SEND SLon SPer SWat WMou
§	- subsp. ***angustifolia*** ♀H5	CBcs CDul ELan EPfP MMuc MRav MSwo NLar NWea SCob SEND SRms
	'Elegantissima'	see *S.* × *pendulina* var. *elegantissima*
	eriocephala 'American Mackay' (m)	CWiW
	- 'Kerksii' (m)	CWiW
	- 'Mawdesley' (m)	CWiW
	- 'Russelliana' (f)	CWiW
	exigua ♀H5	CBcs CDul CLnd CTho ELan EPfP EWes IDee LAst LBuc LEdu LRHS MBlu MBrN MGos MSwo NBir NLar NWea SCob SCoo SMad SPer WMou WPGP
	fargesii ♀H6	Widely available
	fargesii × ***magnifica***	CFil
§	× ***finnmarchica***	WAbe
	formosa	see *S. arbuscula*
	fragilis	CCVT CDul CHab CLnd NWea WMou
§	- var. ***furcata***	CTri GCrg
	× ***fruticosa*** 'McElroy' (f)	CWiW
	fruticulosa	see *S. fragilis* var. *furcata*
	'Fuiri-koriyanagi'	see *S. integra* 'Hakuro-nishiki'
	furcata	see *S. fragilis* var. *furcata*
	glauca	CNat
	'Golden Curls'	see *S.* × *sepulcralis* 'Erythroflexuosa'
	gracilistyla	CTho NWea WMou
§	- 'Melanostachys' (m) ♀H5	CBcs CBot CDul CTho ECrN ELan EPfP EWTr GAbr LHop MAsh MBNS MBlu MBrN MGos MMuc MRav NBir NEgg NLar NWea SBrt SEND SGol SPer SRms SWat WBor WPtf
	× ***greyi***	NEoE
	hastata (f)	SWat
	- 'Wehrhahnii' (m) ♀H6	CBcs CDul CMea EBee ECho ELan EPfP GCra GKev IVic LEdu MBlu MJak MMuc MRav MSwo NBir NLar NWea SEND SPer SWat WKif
	helvetica ♀H7	CBcs CDul CLet CMac EBee ECho ELan EPfP GAbr IVic MBlu MRav NBir NEgg NLar NWea SAko SPer WAbe WFar
	herbacea	ECho GEdr WAbe
	herbacea × ***reticulata*** new	EPot
	hibernica	see *S. phylicifolia*
	hookeriana	CDul CExl CFil ELan MBlu MBrN NLar WCFE WMou
	incana	see *S. elaeagnos*
	integra 'Albomaculata'	see *S. integra* 'Hakuro-nishiki'
	- 'Flamingo' PBR	ELan SPoG
§	- 'Hakuro-nishiki' (v) ♀H5	Widely available
	- 'Pendula' (f)	MAsh MBri
	irrorata ♀H5	CDul CLnd EPfP MBlu MSwo NLar SCob SWat WMat
	'Jacquinii'	see *S. alpina*
	kinuyanagi (m)	LHop NSti
§	***koriyanagi***	CWiW
	'Kumeti'	see *S.* × *doniana* 'Kumeti'
	'Kuro-me'	see *S. gracilistyla* 'Melanostachys'
	lanata ♀H7	CBcs CBot CMac CMea ECho ELan ELon EPfP GAbr MAsh MGos MJak NBir NEgg NLar NWea SBrt SPer SWat WCFE
	lapponum	LEdu MMuc NLar NWea SRms
	- (m)	WAbe
	magnifica	CBot CDul CExl CFil EBee ELan EPfP EUJe IArd IDee LEdu LRHS MMuc MSnd NWea SKHP SWat WFar WHer WHor WMou WPGP
	'Mark Postill' (f)	CBot CDoC EBee ELon LRHS MBNS MMuc MNHC NLar SAko WWFP
	matsudana 'Tortuosa'	see *S. babylonica* var. *pekinensis* 'Tortuosa'
	- 'Tortuosa Aureopendula'	see *S.* × *sepulcralis* 'Erythroflexuosa'
	'Melanostachys'	see *S. gracilistyla* 'Melanostachys'

× ***meyeriana*** 'Lumley' (f) CWiW
× ***mollissima*** CWiW
var. ***hippophaifolia*** 'Jefferies' (m)
- - 'Notts Spaniard' (m) CWiW
- - 'Trustworthy' (m) CWiW
- 'Q83' WPos
- var. ***undulata*** 'Kottenheider Weide' (f) CWiW
aff. ***moupinensis*** from Vietnam CFil
§ ***myrsinifolia*** ELan LHop MBlu MMuc NLar SEND WGrn
- 'Black Knight' EPfP
myrsinites var. ***jacquiniana*** see *S. alpina*
myrtilloides 'Pink Tassels' (m) ECho GEdr SBrt
myrtilloides × ***repens*** see *S.* × *finnmarchica*
nakamurana var. ***yezoalpina*** CBot EBee ELan EPot EWes GKev GQui IVic LRHS MBlu MMuc MRav NHar NLar SBrt WFar WPat
nigricans see *S. myrsinifolia*
nivalis see *S. reticulata* subsp. *nivalis*
§ × ***pendulina*** var. ***elegantissima*** SWat
pentandra CBot CDul CLnd NWea WMou
- 'Patent Lumley' CWiW
§ ***phylicifolia*** NWea WMou
- 'Malham' (m) CWiW
§ ***purpurea*** CCVT CDul NWea SCob WMou
- 'Brittany Green' (f) CWiW
- 'Continental Reeks' CWiW
- 'Dark Dicks' (f) CWiW NLar WSFF
- 'Dicky Meadows' (m) CWiW
- 'Goldstones' CWiW NLar
- f. ***gracilis*** see *S. purpurea* 'Gracilis'
§ - 'Gracilis' MMuc NLar NWea SCob SEND SLon WCot
- 'Green Dicks' CWiW
- 'Helix' see *S. purpurea*
- 'Howki' (m) WMou
- 'Irette' (m) CWiW
- 'Jagiellonka' (f) CWiW
- var. ***japonica*** see *S. koriyanagi*
- subsp. ***lambertiana*** CWiW
- 'Lancashire Dicks' (m) CWiW
- 'Leicestershire Dicks' (m) CWiW
- 'Light Dicks' CWiW
- 'Lincolnshire Dutch' (f) CWiW
- 'Nancy Saunders' (f) ♀H6 CTho CWiW EHoe EWld GBin LEdu MBNS MBlu MBrN MRav NBir NLar NSti SDix SMHy WBod WCot
- 'Odeta' **new** LEdu
- 'Pendula' ♀H6 CCVT CMac ECrN LRHS MAsh MBri MSwo NOrn NWea
- 'Read' (f) CWiW
- 'Reeks' (f) CWiW
- 'Richartii' (f) CWiW
- 'Uralensis' (f) CWiW
pyrenaica EWes
pyrenaica × ***retusa*** ECho
repens NLar NWea SRms SWat WAbe
§ - var. ***argentea*** CDul ELan EPot EWes LRHS MMuc MRav NWea SPer
- ***pendula*** see *S.* 'Boyd's Pendulous' (m)
- 'Voorthuizen' (f) ECho
reticulata ♀H7 CMea ECho EPot GCrg NBir NHar NSla WAbe
§ - subsp. ***nivalis*** EPot
retusa CTri GEdr NBir NHar
rosmarinifolia misapplied see *S. elaeagnos* subsp. *angustifolia*
rosmarinifolia L. NLar WWtn
× ***rubens*** 'Basfordiana' (m) CDul CLnd CTho CWiW MBNS SWat WMou
- 'Bouton Aigu' CWiW
- 'Farndon' CWiW
- 'Flanders Red' (f) CWiW
- 'Fransgeel Rood' (m) CWiW
- 'Glaucescens' (m) CWiW
- 'Golden Willow' CWiW
- 'Jaune de Falaise' CWiW
- 'Jaune Hâtive' CWiW
- 'Laurina' CWiW
- 'Natural Red' (f) CWiW
- 'Parsons' CWiW
- 'Rouge Ardennais' CWiW
- 'Rouge Folle' CWiW
- 'Russet' (f) CWiW
× ***rubra*** CWiW
- 'Abbey's Harrison' (f) CWiW
- 'Continental Osier' (f) CWiW
- 'Eugenei' (m) CDul ECrN GQui MBlu SWat
- 'Fidkin' (f) CWiW
- 'Harrison's' (f) CWiW
- 'Harrison's Seedling A' (f) CWiW
- 'Mawdesley' CWiW
- 'Mawdesley Seedling A' (f) CWiW
- 'Pyramidalis' CWiW
I 'Salix Red' WJPR
Scarlet Curls = 'Scarcuzam' WPat
schraderiana NWea
× ***sepulcralis*** NWea
§ - 'Aokautere' CWiW
- 'Caradoc' CWiW
§ - var. ***chrysocoma*** ♀H5 Widely available
- 'Dart's Snake' ELan EPPr EShb MAsh MBrN MRav NLar WCot
§ - 'Erythroflexuosa' ♀H5 CBcs CDoC CDul EBee ELan EPPr EPfP LAst LBMP LHop MAsh MGos MMuc MRav NOrn NWea SCob SEND SGol SPer SPoG SWat WCFE WMat WPat
serpyllifolia CTri NHar WThu
- 'Chamonix' NSla WAbe
serpyllum see *S. fragilis* var. *furcata*
'Setsuka' see *S. udensis* 'Sekka'
sitchensis NWea
× ***smithiana*** NWea
× ***stipularis*** (f) NWea
subopposita EBtc ELan MMuc SBrt WAbe
triandra NWea WMou
- 'Black German' (m) CWiW
- 'Black Hollander' (m) CWiW NLar
- 'Black Maul' CWiW GQue WPos
- 'Grisette de Falaise' CWiW
- 'Grisette Droda' (f) CWiW
- 'Long Bud' CWiW
- 'Noir de Challans' CWiW
- 'Noir de Touraine' CWiW
- 'Noir de Villaines' (m) CWiW WJPR
- 'Rouge d'Orléans' EBtc
- 'Sarda d'Anjou' CWiW
- 'Whissander' CWiW
udensis NWea
- 'Golden Sunshine' **new** WCot
§ - 'Sekka' (m) CBcs ELan MBlu MMuc NBir NWea SWat WMou
uva-ursi WAbe

	Name	Suppliers
	viminalis	CCVT CLnd CMac EPfP LBuc MJak NWea SEWo SVic WJPR WMou WPos WSFF
	- 'Green Gotz'	CWiW
	vitellina 'Pendula'	see *S. alba* 'Tristis' ambig.
	'Yelverton'	see *S. alba* var. *vitellina* 'Yelverton'

Salvia ✿ (*Lamiaceae*)

	Name	Suppliers
	ACE 2172	SPin
	CD&R 1162	EPyc SPhx
	CD&R 1458	SPin
	CD&R 1495	SPin
	CD&R 3071	SPin
	PC&H 226	SPin
	from Catamarca, Argentina	SDys
	from Nur Daği, Saudi Arabia new	WCot
	absconditiflora	SPin
	acerifolia	SDys SPin
	acetabulosa	see *S. multicaulis*
	adenophora	SPin
	aethiopis	EWes SPav XSen
I	'African Sky'	LSou SDys SPin WHil
§	***africana***	EBee SPin
	africana-caerulea	see *S. africana*
	africana-lutea	see *S. aurea*
	agnes	SDys SPin
	'Alegría' new	SDys
	algeriensis	SPhx
	amarissima	SPin
	'Amber'	IMou LPla SBrt SPin
	ambigens	see *S. guaranitica* 'Blue Enigma'
	'Amistad'[PBR]	CAbb CBot CMos CPar CSpe CWGN EBee ECre ECtt EWld IFro IPot LBuc LHop LRHS MAsh MBri MCot MHer MRav NDov SCob SDys SPhx SPin WGrn WHil WNPC WOth
	ampelophylla	SDys
	- B&SWJ 10751	SPin
§	***amplexicaulis***	CBod MMuc NLar SEND SRms WHrl XSen
	amplifrons	SPin
	angustifolia Cav.	see *S. reptans*
	angustifolia Mich.	see *S. azurea*
	'Anna'	SDys
	'Anthony Parker'	WOut
	'Anthony Waterer'	EWld
	apiana	CArn EBee MHer SPin SPlb SRms SVen WHfH XSen
	arenaria	SPin
	argentea	CBcs CBod CSpe EAEE EAJP ECha ELan EPfP EWoo GMaP LHop LRHS MSpe SPer SPin SRkn SWat WJek WKif XLum XSen
	- 'Artemis'	EBee LSun
	arizonica	CSam EBee EWld GCal LHop LPla MAsh SDys SPin XSen
	aspera	SPin
	atrocyanea	CDoC CSam CSpe EBee ECre EWes EWld MAsh MAvo SDys SPin WHal WKif
	aucheri	SPin
§	***aurea***	CHll CSpe CTre ELan SPin SPlb SVen WBod XLum
	- 'Kirstenbosch'	CAby ECtt EPyc EWld NSti SDys SPin
	aurita	EBee SPin
	- var. ***galpinii***	SPin
	austriaca	SPin
§	***azurea***	SPhx SPin XSen
	- var. ***grandiflora***	SPin WCot
	bacheriana	see *S. buchananii*
§	***barrelieri***	EBee ESwi SPin XSen
	'Bee's Bliss'	XSen
	'Belhaven'	EBee GCal SPin WOut
	bertolonii	see *S. pratensis* Bertolonii Group
	bicolor	see *S. barrelieri*
	'Black Knight'	EPyc SDys SPin WOth WPGP
	blancoana	see *S. lavandulifolia* subsp. *blancoana*
	blepharophylla	CPrp ECtt EPyc EUJe LHop MCot MHer MSCN SPin WHea
	- 'Diablo'	ECtt
	- 'Painted Lady'	ECtt MAsh SDys SPin
	'Bleu Armor'[PBR]	MBri SPhx
	'Blue Chiquita'	SPin
	'Blue Ice' new	MHom
	'Blue Moon'	SDys
	'Blue Note'[PBR]	CMos CSpe CWGN CWld EBee MAvo MBel MHol NDov SCob SPoG SRkn WCot
	'Blue Sky'	EWld
§	'Blush Pink'	SDys
	bowleyana	SPin
	brandegeei	SPin
	brevilabra	SPin
	brevipes new	SPin
	'Bright Eyes'	CWGN SCob
	broussonetii	EBee SPin
§	***buchananii*** ♀H2	CBod CSam ECtt EPyc EWld LHop MAsh MCot MHer MRav SDys SPin SRkn XSen
	bulleyana misapplied	see *S. flava* var. *megalantha*
	bulleyana Diels	CExl EWes NQui WHea XSen
	- 'Blue Lips'	CBod EBee MBri SCob
	bullulata	SPin
	- pale-blue-flowered	SDys SPin
	cacaliifolia ♀H2	CExl CRHN CWCL ECtt EPyc EWld GCal MAsh MHer MSCN SDys SPin SRkn WOth
	cadmica	SPin
	caerulea misapplied	see *S. guaranitica*, *S. guaranitica* 'Black and Blue'
	caerulea L.	see *S. africana*
	caespitosa	XSen
	campanulata	SPin
	- B&SWJ 9232	WCru
	- DJHC C394	SPin
	- GWJ 9294	SPin WCru
	- aff. var. ***hirtella*** GWJ 9397	WCru
	canariensis	IDee SEND SPin WBod
	- f. ***albiflora***	EBee SVen
	- f. ***candidissima***	SPin
	candelabrum ♀H3	CAbP CSpe ECre EWes MHer SBch SPav SPhx SPin SVen WCot WKif WPnn XSen
	candidissima	XSen
	canescens	XSen
	cardinalis	see *S. fulgens*
	cardiophylla	SPin
	carnea	CSam SPin
	- from Valle de Bravo, Mexico	EPyc SDys
	castanea	EWld SPin
	caudata	SPin
	cedrosensis 'Baja Blanca' new	SPin
§	***chamaedryoides***	CFil EPyc MAsh SBrt SPhx SPin WHea XLum XSen
	- var. ***isochroma***	EPyc MAsh SDys SPin WPGP XSen
	- 'Marine Blue'	MAsh MCot

	Name	Suppliers
	- silver-leaved	CAby CSpe SPin XLum
	aff. ***chamaedryoides*** B&SWJ 9032 from Guatemala	SPin
	chamelaeagnea	EPyc GFai SBrt SDys SHar SPin
	'Cherry Queen'	CWGN EPyc MAsh
	chiapensis	EPyc MAsh SDys SPin
	chinensis	see *S. japonica*
	chionophylla	SPin
	'Christine Yeo'	CElw CNor EBee ECtt ELon EPri EPyc EWoo MAsh SAko SBch SDys SEND SPin WHil WHoo WMnd WPGP WSHC WTcb XSen
	cinnabarina	SPin
	cleistogama misapplied	see *S. glutinosa*
	clevelandii	MHer SPav SPin WJek
	- 'Winnifred Gilman'	SDys
	clinopodioides	CDes EBee SDys SPin
	'Clotted Cream'	SPoG
	coahuilensis misapplied	see *S. greggii* × *serpyllifolia*
	coahuilensis ambig.	EPyc LRHS LSou MAsh SKHP SLon SPin SRkn WSHC WTcb XLum
	coahuilensis Fernald	LHop
	coccinea	SPin
	- 'Brenthurst'	SPin
	- 'Coral Nymph' (Nymph Series)	SPav SPin
	- 'Lady in Red' (Nymph Series)	SPav
	concolor misapplied	see *S. guaranitica*
	concolor Lamb. ex Benth.	EPyc EWld GCal GGal MHom SDys SPin WSHC
	confertiflora	CAby CBot CDes CExl CSam CSpe CWCL EBee ECre ECtt ELan EPyc GCal MAsh MHer MHom MSCN SDix SDys SPin SPlb SRkn SVen WHea WKif WOth WPGP
	corrugata	CBcs CCon CDes CElw CPne EBee ECtt EPyc GBin GCal LRHS MAsh MHer SDys SPhx SPin WPGP
	'Crème Caramel'	EBee ECtt EPyc MAsh MHom SDys SPoG WHlf
	cruickshanksii	SPin
	cryptantha	XSen
	cuatrecasana **new**	SPin
	aff. ***curtiflora*** B&SWJ 10356	WCru
	curviflora	CSam CSpe EPyc MAsh SBch SDys SPin WOth
	- 'Tubular Bells'	CBot
	cyanescens	CFis CMea EPot EPyc LRHS SBrt SPin WPGP XSen
	cyanicalyx	EPyc SDys SPin
	cyclostegia	CExl
	daghestanica	GKev SPin XSen
	'Dancing Dolls'	CWGN EWTr LRHS SCob SHil
I	***dangitalis***	SPin
	- SDR 4332	CExl
	darcyi misapplied	see *S. roemeriana*
	darcyi J. Compton	CBot CExl CHll EPyc EWes MCot SDys SPin WOth WSHC XLum XSen
	davidsonii	SPin
	'Dayglo' **new**	ECtt
	deserta	WCot
	desoleana	EBee SPin XSen
	dichlamys	SPin
	'Didi'	NDov
	digitaloides	GBin XSen
	- BWJ 7777	SPin WCru
	discolor	CBot CHll CSpe ECtt ELan EPyc EWld GCal MAsh MCot MHer SCob SDys SPin WOth XSen
*	- ***nigra***	CCse
	disermas	SPin SPlb XSen
	- pink-flowered	SPin
	disjuncta	CElw SPin
	- 'Chimbango'	SPin
	divinorum	CArn GPoy LEdu
	dolichantha	CCon CTsd NBir NLar SPin WMoo XSen
	dolomitica	SPav SPin
	dombeyi	CAby CPne CSam SDys SPin
	dominica	SPin XSen
	dorisiana	MAsh SDys SPin SVen
	'Dorset Wonder'	NDov
	durifolia	SPin
	'Dyson's Crimson'	CAby CSde CSpe MCot SDys
	'Dyson's Gem'	SDys
	'Dyson's Joy'	LHop MCot SDys
	eigii	SPin XSen
	eizi-matudae	SDys SPin
§	***elegans***	CBot CLau EWes GCal GCra IDee WBod WOth XSen
	- 'Golden Delicious'	CAby CBod ECtt ENfk EWes MHer SPin SRms WOut
	- 'Honey Melon'	ENfk EPyc MAsh SDys
	- 'Scarlet Pineapple'	CArn CBod CExl CLau CPrp ECtt ELan ENfk GPoy MCot MHer MNHC SDys SPin SRms SVen WJek XSen
	- 'Sonoran Red'	SDys
	- 'Tangerine'	CArn CBod CLau CPrp ENfk EPyc MHer MNHC NQui SPin SRms WJek
	'Ember's Wish' **new**	CBot CMos SDys SPin
	'Endless Love'	EBee LSou MBri NDov SAko SPoG
	eremostachya	EBee
	euphratica	XSen
	evansiana	SPin XSen
	'Eveline'	CWGN EBee ECtt EPfP GBin LBMP LRHS MBri NLar SHar SPoG STPC WTor
	excelsa	SPin
	exserta **new**	EBee
	fallax	see *S. roscida*
	farinacea	SPin
§	***flava*** var. ***megalantha***	CAby CFis LRHS LSRN MSpe SPin WOut XSen
	forreri	EBee EPyc MAsh NDov SDys SPin WPGP
	- 'Karen Dyson'	SDys
§	***forsskaolii***	Widely available
	- white-flowered	EBee SPin XSen
§	***fruticosa***	CArn EPyc LRHS SLon SPin SRms XSen
§	***fulgens*** ♀H3	EPyc GCal MAsh SDys SPin SRkn WHea
	- from Mount Popocatépetl, Mexico	SPin
	'Germaine' **new**	SPin
	gesneriiflora	CCon ECtt EPyc SPin WOth WPGP
	- mountain form	SDys WPGP
	- 'Tequila'	SPin WOut
	gilliesii	SPin
	glabrescens	SPin
	- B&SWJ 11152	WCru
*	- var. ***robusta*** B&SWJ 11147	WCru
	glechomifolia	SPin

§	***glutinosa***	CArn CMac CSpe EBee EPyc EWld GCal IMou LRHS MMuc MNrw NBro NLar SEND SGSe SPav SPin SPtp WCAu WCot WHea XLum XSen
	graciliramulosa	SPin
	gracilis	SPin
	grahamii	see *S. microphylla* var. *microphylla* 'Newby Hall'
	'Great Comp'	NDov SDys
	greggii	ECtt EPfP EPyc EWes LRHS MHer SPlb SRms WHil WTcb XLum XSen
	- CD&R 1148	MCot SDys
	- 'Alba'	CSpe SPin XLum XSen
	- 'Blush Pink'	see *S.* 'Blush Pink'
	- 'Caramba' (v)	ESwi LRHS
	- 'Cream' **new**	EAJP
	- 'Devon Cream'	see *S. greggii* 'Sungold'
	- 'Diane'	MAsh
	- 'Emperor' **new**	LHop WTcb
	- 'Flame'	CWGN WHil
	- 'Icing Sugar'PBR	CNor CWGN CWld EAEE EBee ECtt ELan ENfk EPfP EWoo LBMP LHop LRHS MAsh MCot MSpe NDov NPri SAko SCob SDys SRkn WBor WSHC
	- 'Lipstick'	CExl ECtt LCro LOPS MAsh
	- 'Magenta'	SPin
	- (Navajo Series) 'Navajo Bright Red'	EPyc
*	- - 'Navajo Cream'	EPyc
*	- - 'Navajo Dark Purple'	EPyc
*	- - 'Navajo Purple'	EPyc
	- - Navajo Salmon Red = 'Rfds016'	EPyc
*	- - 'Navajo White'	EPyc
	- 'Peach' misapplied	see *S.* × *jamensis* 'Pat Vlasto'
	- 'Peach'	CLau CWGN EPfP EPyc MAsh SAko SDys WHea WPGP XLum XSen
	- 'Pink Preference'	MAsh SDys
	- 'Raspberry Red'	XLum
	- 'Sierra San Antonio'	see *S.* × *jamensis* 'Sierra San Antonio'
	- 'Sparkler' (v)	ELan EPfP LRHS MAsh SLon SPoG
	- 'Stormy Pink'	CAby CHll CPrp CSam CSpe CWld EPyc LRHS MCot NDov WOth WPGP WTcb XSen
§	- 'Sungold'	CWGN ECtt EPfP EPyc LRHS MAsh SAko SDys SPhx XSen
	- variegated (v)	XSen
	- yellow-flowered	CAby XLum
	greggii* × *lycioides	see *S. greggii* × *serpyllifolia*
§	***greggii* × *serpyllifolia***	CAbP CSpe EPyc MAsh SDys SPin SVen
	guadalujarensis	SPin
§	***guaranitica***	CBcs ECtt EShb MHer SPin WKif WPGP XLum XSen
	- 'Argentina Skies'	CAby CHGN ECtt EPPr EPyc SDys SPin XSen
§	- 'Black and Blue'	Widely available
§	- 'Blue Enigma' ♀H4	CAby CArn CBot CExl CWGN EBee ECha ECtt EHrv ELan EPfP EWoo GCal LHop LRHS MAsh MGos MRav SDix SDys SPin WHea WTcb XLum XSen
	- 'Costa Rica Blue'	EPyc SDys
	- 'Indigo Blue'	ECtt EPfP MAsh SPin
	- 'Midnight' **new**	CAby CSpe SAko
	- 'Omaha'	SPin
	- 'Omaha Gold' (v)	EPyc
	- 'Purple Emperor'	CBot CWld LHop
	- 'Purple Splendor'	MHer
	- purple-flowered	CSam SDys
	- 'Super Trouper' **new**	SPin
	haematodes	see *S. pratensis* Haematodes Group
	haenkei	CElw SPin
	- 'Prawn Chorus'	MAsh WOth
	hayatae	SPin
	heldreichiana	SMHy SPin XSen
	henryi	SPin
	hians	EWoo GCal GCra ILea SRms XLum
	- CC 1787	CExl
	hierosolymitana	CHid EBee XSen
	hirtella	SPin
	hispanica misapplied	see *S. lavandulifolia*
	hispanica L.	CSam SPin
	holwayi	SDys SPin
	horminum	see *S. viridis* var. *comata*
	huberi	XSen
	hypargeia	CPBP SIgm XSen
	inconspicua	SPin
	indica	EWTr XSen
	'Indigo Spires'	CBot CExl CHll CSam CSpe CWGN ECre ECtt EPfP EPyc EShb IMou MAsh MCot NDov SDix SDys SPhx SPin WBod WOth WSHC XLum XSen
	interrupta	EBee EWld MCot SPin WHea XSen
	involucrata ♀H3	CCon EPyc GCra MCot MHom NBro SDys SPin SVen WSHC
	- 'Bethellii' ♀H3	CArn CBod CBot CCon CDoC CMHG EBee ECtt ELan EPfP EPyc EWld EWoo LRHS MAsh MHer NSti SDix SDys SKHP SPin SRkn WGrn WKif WOth XLum
	- 'Boutin' ♀H3	CTsd EBee EPyc MAsh MHom SDys SPin
§	- 'Hadspen'	CBot CCon CDes CHll CRHN CSam CSpe EBee EPyc EWes GCal SBch SPin WOth WOut XLum
	- 'Mrs Pope'	see *S. involucrata* 'Hadspen'
	- 'Pink Icicles'	SDys
*	- var. ***puberula***	MHom
	involucrata* × *wagneriana	SDys
	iodantha	SPin
	- 'Louis Saso'	SPin
	iodochroa B&SWJ 10252	SPin WCru
	'Jackson's Cassis' **new**	WTcb
	'Jackson's Imperial' **new**	WTcb
	'Jackson's Kir Royale' **new**	WTcb
	'Jackson's Pink Gin' **new**	WTcb
	'Jackson's Purple' **new**	WTcb
	× ***jamensis***	CLau EWes MAsh SPin
	- 'Blue Amor'	MPkF
	- 'California Sunset'	MAsh SAko SDys
	- 'Dark Dancer'	MAsh SAko SDys SPhx WHil
	- 'Desert Blaze' (v)	CMos CWGN EAJP ECtt EPfP EPyc MRav SDys SPin WGrn WPGP WTcb XLum
	- 'Devantville'	NDov XLum
	- 'Dysons' Orangy Pink'	CSpe NDov SDys
	- 'El Durazno'	WTcb
	- 'Flammenn'PBR	LRHS MPkF SHil
	- 'Golden Girl' **new**	EBee
§	- 'Hot Lips'	Widely available
	- 'James Compton'	EPyc SIgm
	- 'Javier'	CSpe MAsh SDys SPin
	- 'Kentish Pink'	EPyc SDys WTcb
	- 'La Luna'	CDes CPrp CSam CSpe ECtt EPyc LHop MAsh MHer MRav NDov SPin

Plant	Suppliers
	WOth WPGP WSHC WTcb XLum XSen
- 'La Siesta'	EPyc MAsh WOth WTcb XSen
- 'La Tarde'	CTri EPyc MAsh MHom WTcb
- 'Los Lirios' 🏆H5	CTri EPyc GGal SPin WHil WOth WTcb
- 'Maraschino'	CDes EPfP EPyc LHop LRHS MAsh SDys SPin SRms WMnd WTcb XLum
- 'Melen' PBR	EBee SPin
- 'Moonlight Over Ashwood' (v)	EPyc MAsh SPin WSHC
- 'Moonlight Serenade'	EPyc MAsh SDys
- 'Nachtvlinder'	CAby CDes CPrp CSpe EAJP EPyc MAsh MCot NDov SAko SDys SPhx SPin WOth WSHC WTcb WTor
§ - 'Pat Vlasto'	EPyc SPin
- 'Peter Vidgeon'	CDes CWGN EPfP EPyc LCro LHop LRHS MAsh MCot SAko SDys SPhx SPin SPoG WSHC WTcb
- 'Pleasant Pink'	EPyc XSen
- 'Pluenn' PBR	LRHS MPkF SHil
- 'Raspberry Royale' 🏆H5	ECtt EPfP EPyc LHop LRHS MAsh MHer SAko SDys SPin WMnd WSHC XLum XSen
- 'Red Velvet'	EBee ECtt EPyc GGal MAsh MCot MHom SDys SPhx WHrl WSHC WTcb
- 'Señorita Leah'	CWGN EPyc MAsh MCot NDov SDys
§ - 'Sierra San Antonio'	CDes EPfP EPyc LRHS MAsh MHom NDov SAko SDys WHil WPGP XLum XSen
- 'Snow White' **new**	SPin
- 'Stormy Sunrise'	EPyc SDys
§ - 'Trebah'	CAby ECre EPyc EWoo LHop MAsh MCot MHom SAko SDys SPin SRot WHea WHil WKif WSHC
- 'Trenance'	ECre ELon EPyc LHop MHer MHom SPin SRot WHil
§ ***japonica***	SPin
- 'Alba'	SPin
'Jean's Purple Passion'	EPyc SDys SPin
'Jezebel'	SDys SPin
'Joan'	CWGN EPyc MAsh SDys SPin WHil WSHC
judaica	CMac SPin WGrn XSen
jurisicii	CWib EPfP LRHS SBrt SPav WHea WJek XLum XSen
- 'Alba'	XSen
- pink-flowered	XSen
karwinskyi	SDys SPin
karwinskyi* × *univerticillata	SDys
keerlii	SPin
koyamae	MBri SPin
- B&SWJ 10919	WCru
kronenburgii	XSen
'Lady Strybing'	SPin
'Lalarsha'	CElw EPyc MCot NDov SAko SDys
lanceolata	LHop SPin
lasiantha	SPin
§ ***lavandulifolia***	CArn EBee ECho ELan EPfP EWes GPoy LRHS MHer MLHP MNHC MRav SPin SRms WHoo WJek WKif WOut XLum XSen
§ - subsp. ***blancoana***	ECha EPyc MHer SPin WHea XSen
- subsp. ***gallica***	XSen
- subsp. ***pyrenaeorum***	SPin XSen
- 'Roquefure'	XSen

Plant	Suppliers
- subsp. ***vellerea***	XSen
lavanduloides	SPin
'Lavender Dilly Dilly' **new**	LRHS
lemmonii	see *S. microphylla* var. *wislizeni*
'Lemon Pie'	SDys SPin WHlf
leptophylla	see *S. reptans*
leucantha 🏆H2	CArn CBot CDoC CSpe ECre ELan EPyc EWld MAsh MCot MHer MOWG MRav MSCN SPin SPlb SRkn SVen WOth XSen
- Danielle's Dream = 'Ferpink'	SPin
- 'Eder' (v)	MAsh SDys
- 'Midnight'	CSam LHop
- 'Purple Velvet'	CAby CSpe CTsd EBee ECtt EPyc MAsh MHer MHom SDix SDys SPin WHea
- 'San Marcos Lavender'	EPyc SPin
- 'Santa Barbara'	CDes CHll LRHS MAsh SDys WPGP
- 'White Mischief'	SPin
leucocephala	CPne SDys SPin
leucophylla NNS 01-375	SPin
littae	SDys SPin
longispicata	SPin
longistyla	CFil SDys SPin SVen WPGP
lycioides misapplied	see *S. greggii* × *serpyllifolia*
lycioides A. Gray	CAbP CHll EPyc EWld LRHS SDys SPin
lyrata	CEvo
- 'Burgundy Bliss'	see *S. lyrata* 'Purple Knockout'
§ - 'Purple Knockout'	EPfP LRHS SPin XSen
- 'Purple Vulcano'	see *S. lyrata* 'Purple Knockout'
macellaria misapplied	see *S. microphylla*
macrophylla	GCal SDys SPin WPGP
- Cally selection	SPin
- purple-leaved	SDys
macrosiphon	SPin
'Madeline' PBR	CBod CMos CWGN EPfP EWTr GBin IBoy LBMP LCro LHop LOPS LRHS LSou MBri MNrw SPer SPin STPC
madrensis	SDys SPin
- 'Dunham'	EBee GCal
'Magenta Magic' **new**	SPin
'Magic Potion'	CWGN
mellifera	SPin XSen
mexicana	SPin
- B&SWJ 10288	WCru
- 'Limelight'	EPyc
- var. ***minor***	EPyc EWld SDys SPin
meyeri	EPyc GGal MHom SPin WHil
- CDPR 3071	WPGP
I ***miahuatlanensis***	SPin
§ ***microphylla***	CBod CLau CMHG CMac CPrp CTri EWes LAst MHer SVen WHea WOut WTcb XLum
- CD&R 1141	SPin
- 'Belize'	CPrp MAsh WHil WTcb
- 'Cerro Potosí'	CElw CPrp CSpe EBee EPyc LBMP MAsh MCot MHer SDix SDys SHar SIgm SPhx SPin WCFE WOth WTcb XLum
- 'Hot Lips'	see *S.* × *jamensis* 'Hot Lips'
- 'Huntington'	EPyc SPin
- 'Kew Red' 🏆H4	CBot CCon CHVG MNrw SPin WHil WHoo WPGP WTcb
I - 'Lutea'	MAsh SDys
- 'Maroon'	EPyc SDys WTcb
- 'Mauve'	EPyc NDov

§	- var. ***microphylla***	CRHN CTri CWib ECtt ELan ENfk EPyc EWoo LSRN MBri MCot MHer MNHC MRav SEND SPin SRkn WHfH WJek XLum XSen
	- - 'La Foux'	EPyc MCot SPhx XSen
§	- - 'Newby Hall' 🏆H4	CBot CDes ECtt EPyc EShb EWes EWoo SPhx WPGP WSHC
	- var. ***neurepia***	see *S. microphylla* var. *microphylla*
	- 'Norwell' **new**	MNrw
	- 'Orange Door'	EPyc SAko SDys
	- orange-red-flowered	MRav
	- 'Oregon Peach'	EPfP LRHS
	- 'Oxford'	SPin
	- 'Pink Blush' 🏆H4	CAby EABi EAJP ECtt ELan EPfP EPyc LRHS MAsh MCot MHer MHom MNHC MSpe SDix SEND SPin SRkn WHil WHoo WKif WPGP WSHC WTcb XSen
	- 'Pleasant View' 🏆H4	EPyc
	- 'Ribambelle'	EAJP MAsh XLum
	- 'Robin's Pride'	EPyc SDys WHil
	- 'Rodbaston Red'	WHil
	- 'Rosy Cheeks'	WOut
	- 'San Carlos Festival'	EPyc MAsh NCGa NDov SBch SDys SPhx SPin WPGP XSen
	- 'Trelawny Rose Pink'	see *S.* 'Trelawney'
	- 'Trelissick Creamy Yellow'	see *S.* 'Trelissick'
	- 'Trewithen Cerise'	see *S.* 'Trewithen'
	- 'Violette'	EPyc
	- 'Wendy's Surprise'	CBod CSpe SDys
	- 'Wild Watermelon'	CWGN EBee EPyc LHop MAsh MCot MHer NQui SDys WGrn WHil WWFP XSen
§	- var. ***wislizeni***	CElw EPyc SPhx
	- 'Wollerton White' **new**	MRav SDys
	- 'Zaragoza'	SPin
	microstegia	XSen
	miltiorhiza	CArn EBee MMuc SPin WOut XLum XSen
	miniata	SPin
	misella	SPin
	'Miss Elly'	MTis
	mocinoi	SPin
	mohavensis	XSen
	moorcroftiana	EPyc SPin WHea
	moschata	SPin
	'Mrs Beard'	XSen
	muelleri misapplied	see *S. greggii* × *serpyllifolia*
	muelleri ambig.	NDov
	muelleri Epling	EPyc
	muirii	SPin
	'Mulberry Jam'	CAby CDes CHGN CHll CSam EAJP ECtt EPfP EPyc EWes LHop MAsh MHom MSCN SDix SDys SPin SRkn WKif WOth WSHC WTcb
§	***multicaulis*** 🏆H3	MAsh SPin XSen
	munzii	SDys SPin
	Mystic Spires Blue = 'Balsalmisp'PBR	CSpe CWGN EPfP NDov SCob SPin SPoG
	namaensis	SPin
	nana	EBee
	- B&SWJ 10272	SPin
	- 'Curling Waves'PBR **new**	EBee LRHS
	napifolia	EBee LRHS MMuc NLar SPav SPin
	- 'Baby Blue'	EBee
	'Nazareth'	SPin XSen
	'Nel'	EWTr LHop
	nemorosa	SPin SRms XLum XSen
	- 'Amethyst' 🏆H7	EBee ELon EPfP GQue IKil LCro LOPS LPot LRHS MBel MHol MPie MRav MSpe MTis NDov SCob SMHy SPhx SPin SRms WCot WHoo WKif WWEG XSen
	- Blue Mound	see *S.* × *sylvestris* 'Blauhügel'
	- 'Bordeau Steel Blue'	EBee LRHS SRms
	- 'Caradonna' 🏆H7	Widely available
	- East Friesland	see *S. nemorosa* 'Ostfriesland'
	- 'Experimental Pink'	LRHS
	- 'Experimental Rose Compact'	LRHS
	- 'Experimental White'	LRHS
	- 'Grace' **new**	NDov
	- 'Lubecca' 🏆H7	ECtt EHrv EPfP LHop LRHS MAsh MCot MPie MSpe NDov NEgg NGdn NLar SPer WFar WMnd XSen
	- Lyrical Silvertone = 'Balyricsil'PBR	CBod
	- Marcus = 'Haeumanarc'PBR	EAEE EBee ECtt ELan EPfP EUJe LAst LBMP LRHS LSRN MBNS MBri MRav NDov NLar SAko SBod SDys SPoG WFar WHrl
	- 'New Dimension Blue'	EPfP
	- 'New Dimension Rose'	EBee
§	- 'Ostfriesland' 🏆H7	Widely available
	- 'Pink Friesland'PBR	CAby ECtt ELon EPfP GBin GMaP GQue LSou MGos NDov NSti SPoG WCAu
	- 'Plumosa'	see *S. nemorosa* 'Pusztaflamme'
	- 'Porzellan' 🏆H7	ECtt
§	- 'Pusztaflamme' 🏆H7	EBee ECha ECtt EPfP GQue MRav MTis SAko SMad WWEG XSen
	- 'Rose Queen'	CBod ELon GMaP MWat NBir NSti SCob SPhx SWat WCot WFar XLum XSen
	- 'Rosenwein'	LRHS NGdn SGbt SPhx XSen
	- 'Royal Distinction'	CBod ECtt
	- 'Schwellenburg'	ECGP ECtt GBin GBuc GQue LCro LHop LSou MHol NLar SCob WCot WMnd XSen
I	- (Sensation Series) 'Sensation Blue Improved'	LRHS
	- - 'Sensation Blue'	MBri
	- - 'Sensation Deep Blue'	EBee ELon LRHS SHil STPC
I	- - 'Sensation Deep Rose Improved'	IBoy LRHS MBel
	- - 'Sensation Rose'	CBod LAst LCro LLHF LRHS LSou MBri SHar SHil
	- - 'Sensation Sky Blue'	CBod
	- - 'Sensation White'	CWGN MHol
§	- subsp. ***tesquicola***	CBod LSRN MMuc MWhi NGdn SPhx WFar
	- 'Wesuwe'	ELon NDov XSen
	'Neon' **new**	SPin
	neurepia	see *S. microphylla* var. *microphylla*
*	***nevadensis***	SPin
	nilotica	SPin
	nipponica	GEdr SBrt
	- B&SWJ 5829	SPin WCru
	- 'Fuji Snow' (v)	EBee MBri
	- var. ***trisecta***	SPin
	nubicola	CExl GPoy SPin XSen
	- CC 4607	EBee
	- CC 4762	NLar
	'Nuchi'	SDys SPin
	nutans	CHVG SBrt SPin XSen
	officinalis	Widely available
	- 'Albiflora'	CArn CBod SPin WJek XSen
	- 'Aurea' ambig.	CWib ECho GPoy
	- 'Berggarten' 🏆H4	CArn CBod CBot CLau ECha GBin GCal LEdu LHop MHer MRav SCob

		SDix SPhx SPin WHer WJek XLum XSen
	- 'Bicolor'	SPin
§	- broad-leaved	CLau MHer SWat WJek
	- 'Crispa'	SPin XSen
	- 'Extrakta'	GCal
	- 'Grete Stolze'	LHop SEND XSen
	- 'Grower's Friend'	CTsd LAst
§	- 'Icterina' (v) ♀H4	Widely available
	- ***latifolia***	see *S. officinalis* broad-leaved
	- narrow-leaved	see *S. lavandulifolia*
	- 'Nazareth'	CLau WJek XSen
	- ***prostrata***	see *S. lavandulifolia*
	- 'Purpurascens' ♀H5	Widely available
	- 'Robin Hill'	EAEE LRHS
	- 'Rosea'	WJek XSen
	- 'Tricolor' (v)	CBcs CBod CTri CWld EBee ECho ELan ENfk EPfP GPoy LAst LBMP MAsh MBri MHer MNHC MRav SCob SGol SPer SPin SPoG SRms WHar WJek XSen
	- 'Variegata'	see *S. officinalis* 'Icterina'
	- variegated (v)	ECho MHer
	- 'Würzburg'	XSen
	ombrophila	SPin
	omeiana	SBrt
	- BWJ 8062	SPin WCru
	- 'Crûg Thundercloud'	EWld WCru
	oppositiflora misapplied	see *S. tubiflora*
	oppositiflora ambig.	EPyc SDys SPin
	oppositiflora Ruiz & Pav.	WPGP
	orbignaei	SPin
	'Out of the Mist'	WOut
	oxyphora	EPyc SDys SPin
	pachyphylla	LRHS SEND SPhx SPin XSen
	'Pakhuis Pass'	SPin
	palaestina	XSen
	pallida	SPin
	'Pam's Purple'	MAsh
§	***patens*** ♀H4	Widely available
	- 'Alba' misapplied	see *S. patens* 'White Trophy'
	- 'Blue Angel'	EPfP EWes SPad WCFE WGrn
	- 'Cambridge Blue' ♀H3	CAby CBod CExl CPrp CSpe CWGN EBee ECtt EHrv ELan EPfP EWoo LRHS MAsh MHer MRav MSpe NFav NLar NPer SDys SEND SIgm SPer SPhx SPin WOth WSHC
	- 'Chilcombe'	EPyc SDys SPin WOut
	- 'Dot's Delight'	CBod CExl CSpe ECtt EWes LHop LRHS MAsh NCGa SDys SHar SPer
	- 'Guanajuato'	CBcs CBot CExl CSam ECtt EPyc EWes EWoo MAsh MCot MHer NLar SDys SPad SPin SRot WOth WOut WSHC
	- 'Holbrook' **new**	CSam
	- large	CSpe EWld
	- 'Lavender Ice'	WOut
	- light blue-flowered	LRHS
	- Oceana Blue **new**	EBee
	- 'Oxford Blue'	see *S. patens*
	- (Patio Series) 'Patio Deep Blue'	CAby CWGN EPfP
	- - 'Patio Sky Blue'	NPri
	- 'Pink Ice'	EBee EPyc SDys WOut
	- pink-flowered	SPin
	- 'Royal Blue'	see *S. patens*
§	- 'White Trophy'	CExl ECtt ELan EPyc EWld LRHS SDys SPin
	pauciserrata	SPin

	'Peach Parfait' **new**	SDys
	pennellii	SPin
	'Penny's Smile'	CAby CBot ELon EPyc MAsh SAko SDys SPhx SPin SPoG WGrn WTcb
	'Peru Blue'	EBee SDys
	'Peter Vider'	EPfP
	'Phyllis' Fancy'	CAby CBot CDes CSam CSde CSpe EPyc MAsh MHer NDov NSti SAko SDys SPlb WOth
	pinguifolia	SPin
	'Pink Icing'	SPin
	pinnata	SPin
	pisidica	SPin XSen
	plectranthoides	SPin
	pogonochila	XSen
	polystachya	SPin
*	'Powis Castle'	MHom
	pratensis	CArn CWib CWld ELan EPfP GJos MHer MNHC MRav SPin WCot WOut XSen
	- W&B BGH-3 **new**	WCot
§	- Bertolonii Group	SPin XSen
	- 'Dear Anja'	see *S.* × *sylvestris* 'Dear Anja'
§	- Haematodes Group ♀H7	MNrw SPin SRms
	- 'Indigo' ♀H7	CAby CDes ECtt ELon GMaP LRHS LSou MPie MRav NEgg NLar SPhx SPin SPoG WCot WMnd WPGP
	- 'Lapis Lazuli'	EBee EWes LCro LRHS
	- 'Pink Delight' PBR	CMos EBee ECtt EPfP LRHS MPie NCGa NDov NLar SPoG
	- 'Rose Rhapsody' (Ballet Series)	EBee EPPr EPfP SPhx XSen
	- 'Rosea'	ECha SPin
	- 'Swan Lake' (Ballet Series)	CBod EBee EPPr NLar SPhx SPlb XSen
	- 'Sweet Esmeralda' (Ballet Series)	EAJP EBee NGdn NLar SPhx WOut XSen
	- 'Twilight Serenade' (Ballet Series)	CBod EBee ECtt EPfP IPot SPhx XSen
	pratensis* × *transylvanica	GJos
	procurrens	EBee EPyc SPin XSen
	przewalskii	CCon CExl EBee LRHS SPin WTcb XSen
	- ACE 1157	WCru
	- BWJ 7920	SPin WCru
	pulchella	SPin
	'Purple Majesty'	CBod CHll CSam ECtt EPyc EWTr LHop NSti SDys SPin SRkn WKif XLum
	'Purple Queen'	CAbP CAby CBod EBee EPyc LRHS LSou MCot SDys SPoG WTcb
	purpurea	LBMP LSRN
	quitensis	SPin
	radula	EBee SPin
	ranzaniana	SPin XSen
	recognita	LRHS WSHC XSen
	recurva	SPin
	'Red Swing'	SPoG
	reflexa	SPin
	regeliana misapplied	see *S. virgata* Jacq.
	regeliana Trautv.	NBir
	regla	EBee MAsh SDys SPin WPGP XSen
	- 'Jame'	SPin
	- 'Royal'	SPin
	repens	EPyc SPin XSen
§	***reptans***	EPyc SBrt SPin
	- from western Texas	CAby SDys WCot
	rhinosima	EBee
	ringens	SPin XSen

	Name	Suppliers
	riparia misapplied	see *S. rypara*
	roborowskii	SPin
§	***roemeriana***	CSpe IFoB SBrt WHea WPGP
	- 'Hot Trumpets'	LRHS
	'Rolando'	SDys SPin
§	***roscida***	SPin
	'Rose Queen' ambig.	SPer WMnd
	rosifolia	XSen
	'Royal Bumble'	Widely available
	'Royal Crimson Distinction'[PBR]	EBee ECtt EPPr LSou
	rubescens	SPin
	rubiflora new	SPin
	rubiginosa	SPin
	rufula new	SPin
	runcinata	SPin
	rutilans	see *S. elegans*
§	***rypara***	SPin
	sagittata	EBee GCal SPin WOut
	'Salmon Dance'	CWGN ECtt
	sanctae-luciae	SPin
	(Savannah Series) 'Savannah Purple'	SRot
	- 'Savannah Red'	EPfP
	- 'Savannah Salmon Rose'	SRot
	scabra	EBee SPin WOut
	schlechteri	EBee SPin
	sclarea	CBod CHby ECtt ENfk GPoy MHer MNHC SPin SRms WHfH WJek XLum XSen
	- var. ***turkestanica*** hort.	CBot CSpe EAJP ECha ECtt EHrv ELan EPfP EWoo LRHS LSRN LSun MCot MRav MSpe NEgg NGdn SEND SPav SPer SPhx SPtp SRkn SWat WBrk WKif WMnd XSen
	- var. ***turkestaniana*** Mottet	SPtp
§	- 'Vatican White'	CBot CNor CSpe EAJP EBee ELan LRHS LSun MNHC MSpe SAko SPhx SPtp WJek XSen
	- white-bracted	CWib SPin SWvt
	scutellarioides	SPin
	semiatrata misapplied	see *S. chamaedryoides*
	semiatrata Zucc.	CSpe SPin
	serboana	WPGP
	- B&SWJ 10236	WCru
	'Serenade'	MHol MTis NDov SPhx WCot
	serpyllifolia	SPin XSen
	- white-flowered	SPin
	sessei	SPin
	setulosa	SPin
	'Shame'	NCGa NDov
	'Shy Ruby' new	SPin
	'Silas Dyson'	CFil CSam ECre ECtt EPfP EPyc LRHS MAsh MHom NDov SAko SBch SDys SPhx SPin SPoG WPGP WTcb
	'Silke's Dream'	CDes CFil CSam ECtt EPfP EPyc LRHS MAsh SDys SPin SPoG WPGP WTcb XSen
	'Silke's Red' new	SDys
	sinaloensis	MAsh SPin
	smithii	SPin
	'Smoke'	SDys
	'Snow Cushion'	LRHS
	somalensis	CHVG EBee SPin SVen
	'Southern Belle'	SDys SPin
	spathacea ♀H4	SBrt SPin WOut
	- 'Avis Keedy'	SPin
	sphacelioides new	SPin
	splendens 'Dancing Flame' (v)	EPyc
	- 'Helen Dillon'	EPyc
	- 'Jimi's Good Red'	CSpe SDys WOth
	- 'Red Indian'	SDys
	- 'São Borja'	SDys
	- 'Vanguard'	LAst NPri
§	- 'Van-Houttei' ♀H3	EBee EPyc EWld SDys SVen
	- 'Vista Purple'	LAst
	sprucei	SPin
	squalens	SPin
	stachydifolia	SPin WHil WPGP
§	***staminea***	SPin
	stenophylla	SPin
	'Stephanie'	EPyc SDys SPin
	stepposa	SPin
	stolonifera	CAby CSam EPyc MAsh MHer SDys SPin WPGP
	striata	EPyc SDys SPin
	- red-flowered	SPin
	styphelus	SDys SPin
	subpalmatinervis	SPin
	subpatens new	SPin
	subrotunda	SDys SPin
	'Sunset Strip'	SDys WHlf
	× ***superba***	CSBt EBee ECha ECtt ELan EPfP EPyc LRHS LSRN NDov SDix SRms WCAu WGwG WHar WHoo
	- 'Adora Blue'	LRHS
	- 'Adrian'	EBee ECtt EPfP LRHS LSRN LSou MBel SPoG WCAu WCot
	- 'Merleau'	LRHS
	- 'Merleau Blue' new	SAko
	- 'Merleau Pink'	LRHS
	- 'Merleau Rose'	EBee LPot MRav SRms
*	- 'Rosea'	EBee
	- 'Rubin' ♀H7	ECtt NBre
I	- 'Superba'	ECtt MRav SPhx SRkn
	× ***sylvestris***	LSRN SPin
§	- 'Blauhügel' ♀H7	CSam EAJP ECha ECtt ELan EPfP LRHS MArl MRav MSpe NDov NLar NPri SHil SPhx WCAu WHoo WMnd WOth WPtf WWEG XSen
§	- 'Blaukönigin'	CNor EPfP GBin GMaP LAst LRHS NGBl NLar SCob SPer SPlb SPoG SRms SWvt WCot XSen
	- Blue Queen	see *S.* × *sylvestris* 'Blaukönigin'
§	- 'Dear Anja'	EBee IPot LCro LHop LPla LSou MAvo NDov NLar SPhx WCot
	- 'Lye End'	MRav MWat WCot
§	- 'Mainacht' ♀H7	Widely available
	- May Night	see *S.* × *sylvestris* 'Mainacht'
	- 'Negrito'	EBee ECtt GQue NGdn NLar XSen
	- 'Rhapsody in Blue'[PBR]	CAbP GBin LRHS MBNS MHol MTis NLar WCot
	- 'Rose Queen'	CBod ECha ECtt ELan ELon EPfP EShb LCro LHop LOPS LRHS MBel MHol MJak MRav NGBl SCob SCoo SPer SPhx SPoG SWvt WHar XSen
	- 'Rügen'	ELon GQue SAko XSen
	- 'Schneehügel'	CBod CMac CSBt EAJP EBee ECha ECtt EHoe ELan ELon EPPr EPfP GMaP LCro LRHS MBNS MRav MSpe MTis NLar NPri SHil SPer WCAu WHil WMnd WWEG XSen
	- 'Superba'	GBuc
	- 'Tänzerin' ♀H7	EBee ECtt ELon LPla LRHS MTis NDov NLar SAko XSen
	- 'Viola Klose'	EAEE EBee ECha ECtt ELan EPfP EShb GBuc LCro LOPS LRHS LSRN

	MBri MCot MSpe NCGa NDov NGdn NLar SPin SRms WAul XSen
tachiei hort.	see *S. forsskaolii*
taraxacifolia	LHop SPin XSen
tesquicola	see *S. nemorosa* subsp. *tesquicola*
texana new	EBee
'Theresia' new	SDys
thymoides	SPin WHil
tianschanica	SPin
tiliifolia	SPav SPin SRms WHea
tingitana	SPin XSen
tomentosa	EBee SPin XSen
tortuosa	COtt SPin
transcaucasica	see *S. staminea*
transsylvanica	GAbr IMou SPav SPhx SPin XSen
- 'Baumgartenii'	WHfH
- 'Blue Spire'	CMea MWhi SRkn
'Trebah Lilac White'	see *S.* × *jamensis* 'Trebah'
§ 'Trelawney'	EAEE ECtt EPPr EPyc EShb LHop LRHS MHom MPie SRot WBod WOth
§ 'Trelissick'	CBod CMea CWld EPPr EPyc LHop MAsh MCot MHom SDys SEND SPin SRkn SRot WHea WHil
§ 'Trewithen'	CBod CExl ECre EPyc EWoo MHom SPin SRot WHil WOut
trijuga	SPin WOut
triloba	see *S. fruticosa*
tubifera	SPin
§ ***tubiflora*** ♀H2	EPyc MAsh SPin
uliginosa ♀H4	Widely available
- 'African Skies'	CChe IPot LCro LRHS SMad SPin WTcb
- 'Ballon Azul'	CBot CSam CSpe MAsh SDys SPin WOth
'Ultra Violet'	WTcb
univerticillata	SPin
urica	EBee SPin
- short	SDys
'Valerie'	CAby EPyc SDys
'Van-Houttei'	see *S. splendens* 'Van-Houttei'
variana	SPin
'Vatican City'	see *S. sclarea* 'Vatican White'
vazquezii new	SPin
verbenaca	MHer SPin WOut XSen
verticillata	EPfP EPyc GAbr LEdu NLar SPin XSen
§ - 'Alba'	CAbP EBee ECtt EPfP GJos GQue LRHS MRav MTis NGdn NLar SPer SPin WAul XSen
- 'Hannay's Blue'	EPPr EPyc GMaP MAvo
- 'Hannay's Purple'	ECtt EPPr
- 'Purple Rain'	Widely available
- 'Smouldering Torches'	EBee LHop LPla NDov SMad SPhx
- 'White Rain'	see *S. verticillata* 'Alba'
villicaulis	see *S. amplexicaulis*
'Violin Music'[PBR]	CWGN ECtt
§ ***virgata*** Jacq.	EBee SPin XSen
viridis	CBod CHby MNHC SPin
- Claryssa Series new	SRms
§ - var. ***comata***	MCot WJek
- 'Marble Arch Blue' (Marble Arch Series)	CSpe
viscosa ambig.	EPyc
viscosa Jacq.	SPin WHil XSen
vitifolia	CSpe EPyc SDys
- B&SWJ 10236	SDix SPin
wagneriana	SPin
'Waverly'	CBot EBee EPyc EWld MAsh MCot MHer SDys
'Wendy's Wish'[PBR]	CAby CBot CHll CMos CSam EBee ECtt EPyc EWld LCro LHop LSou MAsh MCot MSCN NLar NPri SCob SDys SEND SPin SRkn WNPC WTcb
× ***westerae***	SPin
- 'Petra'	SDys
willeana	SPin
xalapensis	SPin
yunnanensis	SPin
- BWJ 7874	WCru
aff. ***yunnanensis***	SPin

Salvinia (*Salviniaceae*)

natans	LLWG MSKA

Sambucus ✿ (*Adoxaceae*)

adnata	SDix
caerulea	see *S. nigra* subsp. *caerulea*
coraensis	see *S. williamsii* subsp. *coreana*
ebulus	EPPr LEdu NSti SMad WCot WWtn
- 'Osmanli' new	SDix
formosana	WCot
* ***himalayensis***	WCot
mexicana B&SWJ 10349	WCot
miquelii	WCot
nigra	CArg CArn CBcs CCVT CDul ECrN EPom GPoy IBoy LBuc NBes NWea SEWo SPer WMat WMou WSFF
- 'Albomarginata'	see *S. nigra* 'Marginata'
- 'Ardwall'	CAgr GCal WCot
- 'Aurea'	CBcs CDul CMac CSBt ELan EPom MRav NWea SPer WCot WMoo
- 'Aureomarginata' (v)	ECrN ELan EPPr LPot MMuc MRav SEND WCot
- 'Bont Oosterwoldë' new	WCot
- 'Bradet'	CAgr NLar WCot
- 'Broadway' (v)	WCot
- 'Cae Rhos Lligwy'	CAgr WCot WHer
§ - subsp. ***caerulea***	WCot
- subsp. ***canadensis***	CDul SPhx
- - 'Adams' (F)	WCot
- - 'Aurea'	CWib NWea WCot WHar
- - 'Goldfinch'	MAsh
- - 'John's'	CAgr WCot
- - 'Maxima'	SDix SMad WCot
- - 'Rubra'	WCot
- - 'York' (F)	CAgr WCot
- 'Castledean'	WCot
- 'Dart's Greenlace'	WCot
- 'Dolomite' (v)	WCot
- 'Donau'	CAgr WCot
- 'Frances' (v)	EPPr WCot
- 'Franzi'	CAgr WCot
- 'Fructuluteo'	NLar WCot
- 'Godshill' (F)	CAgr SDea WCot
- 'Haschberg'	CAgr WCot
- 'Heterophylla'	see *S. nigra* 'Linearis'
- 'Hillier's Dwarf'	WCot
- 'Ina'	CAgr WCot
- 'Körsör' (F)	NLar WCot
- f. ***laciniata*** ♀H6	CBcs CDul EBee ELan EPPr EPfP GCal LPot LRHS MBlu MMuc MRav NWea SDix SLon SPer SPoG WCFE WCot WFar WPGP WPat
§ - 'Linearis'	ELan MRav NLar WCot
- 'Long Tooth'	CDul WCot
- 'Lutea Punctata'	WCot
- 'Madonna' (v)	CLet CMac LEdu MBlu MGos MRav NLar NPol NQui SMad SPer WCot

§ – 'Marginata' (v) CDul CMac CWib EHoe LBMP MHer MRav SDix WCot WFar WMoo
– 'Marion Bull' (v) CDul NLar WCot
I – 'Marmorata' NLar WCot
– 'Mint Julep' WCot
I – 'Monstrosa' WCot
– 'Nana' WCot
– 'Naomi' WCot
– 'Norfolk Speckled' (v) WCot
– 'Pingo Trail' WCot
– 'Plena' (d) WCot
– f. ***porphyrophylla*** see *S. nigra* f. *porphyrophylla*
'Black Beauty' 'Gerda'
– – 'Black Lace' see *S. nigra* f. *porphyrophylla* 'Eva'
– – Black Tower = 'Eiffel 1'[PBR] CHid CRos CSBt CWSG ELon EMil EPfP GBin LRHS MAsh MBri MMHG MMuc MPkF NLar NWea SCob SCoo SPer SPoG WCot WFar WGrn WMat WMoo
– – 'Blue Sheen' **new** CRos SCoo WCot
§ – – 'Eva'[PBR] 🏆[H6] Widely available
§ – – 'Gerda'[PBR] 🏆[H6] Widely available
§ – – 'Guincho Purple' CBcs CDul CMac CTri ELan EPPr EPfP EWTr LRHS MNHC MRav NLar NWea SPlb WCot WFar WMoo
– – 'Purple Pete' CDul WCot
– – 'Thundercloud' 🏆[H6] CDul CMHG ECrN ELon EPPr EWes GBin GCal MAsh MMHG MNrw NChi NEoE NLar SPhx WCot WFar WMoo
– 'Pulverulenta' (v) CWib EPPr GCal LHop MRav NLar NQui WCot
– 'Purpurea' see *S. nigra* f. *porphyrophylla* 'Guincho Purple'
– 'Pyramidalis' MRav SMad WCot
– 'Riese aus Vossloch' WCot
– 'Robert Piggin' (v) WCot
– var. ***rotundifolia*** WCot
– 'Sambu' (F) CAgr WCot
– 'Samdal' (F) CAgr WCot
– 'Samidan' (F) CAgr WCot
– 'Samnor' (F) CAgr WCot
– 'Sampo' (F) CAgr WCot
– 'Samyl' (F) CAgr WCot
– 'Urban Lace' CAgr WCot
– 'Variegata' see *S. nigra* 'Marginata'
– f. ***viridis*** CAgr WCot
– Welsh Gold = 'Walfinb'[PBR] LRHS SPoG
palmensis WCot
racemosa NWea WCot
– 'Altamont' **new** WCot
– 'Aurea' EHoe WFar
– var. ***callicarpa*** NLar WCot
– 'Goldenlocks' EWes
– subsp. ***kamtschatica*** WCot
– var. ***melanocarpa*** **new** WCot
– 'Plumosa Aurea' CBcs CDul CSBt CWib ELan EPfP GCra MGos MJak MRav MSwo NLar NWea SLim WCot
– var. ***pubens*** WCot
§ – var. ***sieboldiana*** WCot
– 'Sutherland Gold' 🏆[H7] Widely available
– 'Tenuifolia' WCot
– 'Welsh Gold' MAsh
sieboldiana see *S. racemosa* var. *sieboldiana*
tigranii WCot
§ ***williamsii*** subsp. ***coreana*** WCot

Samolus (*Primulaceae*)

repens ECou
valerandi LLWG

Sandersonia (*Colchicaceae*)

aurantiaca ECho EPot GKev LAma SDeJ

Sanguinaria (*Papaveraceae*)

canadensis CArn CBct CBro CCon CEvo EBee ECho EPfP EPot EWTr GBuc GEdr GKev GPoy LAma LEdu LRHS MMuc NHol NLar NRya SDeJ SEND SMHy SPer SWat WAbe WPnP
– f. ***multiplex*** (d) CEvo CLAP CTal EPot GEdr IFro LRHS NBir SPhx
– – 'Plena' (d) 🏆[H5] CBct CBro CWCL EBee ECha ECho ELon EPfP GAbr GBin GBuc GCra GKev GPoy LRHS MAvo MNrw NHar NHol NLar NRya NSla SDeJ SKHP SPer WAbe WCot WHil WKif WPnP

Sanguisorba ✿ (*Rosaceae*)

from Japan EBee MAvo
§ ***albiflora*** CKno EBee ELan EPfP EShb EWTr GBuc LBMP LEdu LPla LRHS MAvo MMuc MRav NEoE NGdn SEND SPhx SWat WCAu WMoo WOut
'All Time High' NDov
alpina GLog MMuc SEND
applanata WCot
armena CElw EBee EWes IMou MBel MNrw MPie WWtn XEll
'Autumn Bliss' EBee
'Blacksmith's Burgundy' MAvo
'Blackthorn' CKno EBee ECtt GMaP IKil MAvo MTis NDov NLar SMHy SPhx WCot WHoo
'Burr Blanc' CDes MAvo SMHy SPhx
canadensis Widely available
– hybrid MAvo
'Cangshan Cranberry' CDes CSpe EBee GBin MAvo MHol NDov SMHy WCot WWEG WWtn
* ***caucasica*** LEdu LPla SPhx
'Chocolate Tip' EBee ECtt EWTr IKil ILea IPot LHop MAvo NBro
'Coen's Cranberry' **new** NDov
dodecandra CDes EBee IMou MAvo MTis WPGP
'Figaro' WCot
hakusanensis CCon CKno EBee GBBs GCal IFro IPot LEdu LHop LRHS MAvo MMuc MNrw NBir NBro NChi NEoE NLar SMad WCot WFar WSHC WWEG
– B&SWJ 8709 WCru
– 'Lilac Squirrel' ECtt IPot LEdu MAvo MBel MTis NDov NLar
'Ivory Towers' MAvo
'John Coke' EBee NLar
magnifica EWes GCal LEdu MAvo
– ***alba*** see *S. albiflora*
menziesii Widely available
– 'Dali Marble' (v) EBee ECtt NLar SPoG WMoo WWEG
– 'Wake Up' MAvo
§ ***minor*** CAgr CArn CHby CLau EBee GPoy LEdu MHer MJak MNHC NBro NMir SIde SPhx SPlb SRms WHar WHer WHfH WJek WMoo WOut XLum

- subsp. ***minor***	CHab
'Misbourne Pink' new	LPla
'Nettlesworth Wand' new	SMHy
obtusa	Widely available
- 'Chatto'	MAvo NLar WPGP
- silver-leaved	MNrw
- white-flowered	EBee EWTr MAvo MBel MTis WPGP
officinalis	CArn CHab CKno EHoe GQue MHer MSCN NEoE NMir SPer SPhx SWat WHea WMoo WOut WWEG
- CDC 262	EPPr LEdu LPla SPhx
- CDC 282	CSpe SPhx
- CDC 292	GQue MAvo WCot
- DJHC 535	LEdu
- from Mongolia	CDes EBee
- 'Arnhem'	CCse CKno EBee ECtt EHrv EPPr ILea LEdu LPla LRHS MTis NDov SMHy SPhx WCot WWEG
- 'Crimson Queen'	EBee GQue MAvo MTis
- dark-flowered	MAvo
- early-flowering	CDes
- 'False Tanna'	CWib WFar
- 'Lemon Splash' (v)	EBee LEdu MAvo MMHG WCot WFar WWEG
- 'Martin's Mulberry'	CDes EBee EWes GCal LEdu MAvo NDov WPGP
- 'Morning Select'	EBee ECtt EPPr MAvo NLar STPC
- 'Red Buttons'	MAvo NDov
- 'Red Thunder'	CAby CDes CSpe CWld ECtt EPPr EWoo GBin ILea IPot LCro LEdu LOPS LPla LPot LRHS LSun MAvo MMHG MTis NDov NLar WCAu WCot WGwG WPGP WWEG
- 'Shiro-fukurin' (v)	CBot CHVG EBee ECtt EWes GKin GMaP IKil LEdu LSun MAvo MBel MCot MHol MSCN MTis NLar SBod SPer WCot WFar WHer WOut WSHC
- 'Tall Tanna' new	MAvo
- 'Tsetseguun'	LEdu MAvo WPGP
parviflora	see *S. tenuifolia* var. *parviflora*
pimpinella	see *S. minor*
'Pink Brushes'	ECtt GBin GQue IKil IMou IPot LPla MAvo MTis NLar
'Pink September'	MAvo
'Pink Tanna'	Widely available
'Raspberry Mivvi'	SPhx
'Rock and Roll'	ECtt EPPr GQue MTis NLar
sitchensis	see *S. stipulata*
§ ***stipulata***	CAby EBee GCal LEdu LPla LRHS MAvo MHer MNrw WWEG
- var. ***riishirensis***	EBee
'Tanna'	Widely available
'Tanna' seedling	EPPr EShb
tenuifolia	CCon EHrv GCal IFro LRHS MCot NChi NLar SDix SPhx
- var. ***alba***	Widely available
- - CDC	GCal MRav
- - 'Korean Snow'	CCse CMea GMaP LEdu LPla LRHS SMHy SMad SPhx WWEG
- 'Big Pink'	MAvo MNrw
- 'Bordeaux' new	EBee MTis
- 'Henk Gerritsen'	MAvo MTis NLar
§ - var. ***parviflora***	CDes EBee LEdu MAvo MNrw NLar WPGP
- 'Pink Elephant'	CKno EBee ECtt EPPr GBin GJos GQue ILea LEdu LHop LRHS MAvo MBel MTis NLar SMad WCAu WMoo
- var. ***purpurea***	CDes EBee
- 'Purpurea'	CKno EBee EPPr GQue ILea LEdu MAvo MTis SPhx WCot WPGP
- 'Stand Up Comedian'	GBin IMou LEdu MAvo NDov NLar WWEG
- 'Strawberry Frost' new	MAvo
- 'Sturdy Guard'	LEdu WWEG
- 'White Elephant'	ELan MAvo
- 'White Tanna'	EBee EPPr GQue LEdu MAvo MTis WWEG

Sanicula (*Apiaceae*)

europaea	GPoy IMou

Sansevieria (*Asparagaceae*)

cylindrica new	EShb
trifasciata	EShb
'Moonshine' ♀H1b	

Santolina (*Asteraceae*)

'Apple Court'	LRHS
benthamiana	XSen
§ ***chamaecyparissus***	Widely available
- var. ***corsica*** misapplied	see *S. chamaecyparissus* 'Nana'
- subsp. ***insularis***	XSen
- 'Lambrook Silver'	CDoC CFis EBee ECtt ENfk EPfP LRHS MAsh NLar SCoo SLim SPoG XSen
- 'Lemon Queen'	CDoC ENfk EPfP LRHS MAsh MGos MNHC MSwo NBir NLar SRms SWat XSen
- subsp. ***magonica***	XSen
§ - 'Nana' ♀H5	CBar CMHG ECho EPfP LRHS MAsh MHer MNHC MRav MSwo SCob SPoG SRms SWat XSen
- 'Pretty Carroll' ♀H5	CBod CBot EBee ECtt ELan EPfP LRHS LSRN MAsh MNHC NLar WFar
- 'Small-Ness'	CSma ECho ELan EPfP EWes LRHS MHer NLar SWvt WHer WTor XSen
- 'Weston'	ECho
impressa new	XSen
incana	see *S. chamaecyparissus*
* ***lindavica***	XSen
pectinata	see *S. rosmarinifolia* subsp. *canescens*
pinnata	CArn CTri MHer MLHP
§ - subsp. ***neapolitana*** ♀H5	CArn CSBt CWib EBee ECha ELan ENfk EPfP MMuc MRav SDix SEND WWEG
- - cream-flowered	see *S. pinnata* subsp. *neapolitana* 'Edward Bowles'
§ - - 'Edward Bowles'	Widely available
- - 'Sulphurea'	CArn CBot EPfP LRHS MAsh SPer SPhx WKif XSen
rosmarinifolia	CDoC CDul GPoy LRHS LSun MRav SBod SCob SEND SLon SPlb SPoG SRms
§ - subsp. ***canescens***	XSen
- 'Lemon Fizz' ♀H5	Widely available
§ - subsp. ***rosmarinifolia***	CLet ECha ECrN ELan ENfk EPfP MHer MRav SCob SDix SIgm SPer SRms SWvt WFar WHoo XLum XSen
- - 'Primrose Gem' ♀H5	CBcs CBod CDoC CSBt CTri EAJP ECha ELon EPfP LHop LRHS MAsh MMuc MNHC MSwo SCob SEND SGbt SPer SRms SWvt WHoo WWEG XSen
- - white-flowered	WHer XSen
Shades of Jade = 'Sant101'	ECrN
tomentosa misapplied	see *S. pinnata* subsp. *neapolitana*
villosa	XSen

virens	see *S. rosmarinifolia* subsp. *rosmarinifolia*
viridis	see *S. rosmarinifolia* subsp. *rosmarinifolia*

Sanvitalia (*Asteraceae*)

Aztekengold	see *S.* 'Starbini'
'Powerbini' **new**	NPri
procumbens 'Irish Eyes'	CSpe
§ 'Starbini'PBR	LAst
'Sunbini'PBR	CSpe LSou

Saponaria (*Caryophyllaceae*)

× ***boissieri***	ECho
'Bressingham' ♀H5	CPBP ECho ECtt EPot GCrg MHol NPri WAbe WIce
Bressingham hybrid	MAsh
caespitosa	ECho EDAr EWes
§ ***intermedia***	WCot
× ***lempergii*** 'Fritz Lemperg'	NDov WCot
- 'Max Frei'	CSam EBee ECtt ELon EPPr LCro LOPS LSou MCot MRav NDov SBch SDix SPhx WCot WOld WSHC XLum
ocymoides ♀H5	CMea EBee ECha ECho ECtt EDAr EHon EPfP GAbr LAst MAsh MMuc MNHC MSpe NFav NPri SEND SPer SPlb SPoG SRms SRot XLum
- 'Alba'	ECha
- 'Snow Tip'	ECho EDAr MSpe NGdn WAbe XLum
officinalis	CArn CBod CBre CPbn CWld ENfk GPoy MHer MLHP MNHC SIde SPlb SRms WHer WHfH WJek WMoo WPtf WSFF
- W&B BGB-7 **new**	WCot
- 'Alba Plena' (d)	CBre MMuc NLar SEND XLum
- 'Betty Arnold' (d)	CAby EBee ECtt EWes MHer WCot
§ - 'Dazzler' (v)	WWEG
- 'Flore Pleno' (d)	CBod GAbr
- 'Rosea Plena' (d)	CAby CBre CMac ECtt ELan EPfP GCra LEdu LLWP MHer MLHP MMuc NBid NBir NGdn SCob SEND SIde SPer WGwG WHlf WMoo WPtf
- 'Rubra Plena' (d)	CPrp ELan EWes MMuc MWhi SHar WHer
- 'Variegata'	see *S. officinalis* 'Dazzler'
× ***olivana*** ♀H5	CPBP ECho ECtt EPot GCrg GMaP MAsh NLar XLum
'Rosenteppich'	CPBP
sicula subsp. ***intermedia***	see *S. intermedia*
zawadskii	see *Silene zawadskii*

Sarcandra (*Chloranthaceae*)

§ ***glabra*** f. ***flava***	SRms

Sarcocapnos (*Papaveraceae*)

enneaphylla	LSRN

Sarcococca ✿ (*Buxaceae*)

sp.	LPar
confusa ♀H5	Widely available
hookeriana	ELon GKin IFoB LSRN MBlu MSwo NLar NWad SCob SGbt SWvt WFar WPGP
- B&SWJ 2585	WCru
- HWJK 2393	WCru
- HWJK 2428	WCru
- 'Daman'	CExl
- var. ***digyna***	Widely available
- - SDR 7816 **new**	GKev
- - 'Purple Stem' ♀H5	CExl CJun CLAP CNec CTri EPfP EUJe GKin LAst LCro LOPS LPfy LRHS MGos MNrw NLar SCob SCoo SPer SPoG SWvt WCru
- - 'Schillingii'	see *S. hookeriana* var. *digyna* 'Tony Schilling'
§ - - 'Tony Schilling'	CExl CJun WCru
- var. ***hookeriana***	CJun LSRN
- - GWJ 9222	WCru
- - GWJ 9344	WCru
- - GWJ 9369	WCru
- - HWJK 2102	WCru
- - HWJK 2366	WCru
- - HWJK 2393	WCru
- - 'Ghorepani' ♀H5 **new**	CRos LRHS
- var. ***humilis***	Widely available
- 'Winter Gem' ♀H5	CDoC EPfP LRHS LSRN MBri NHol SLon SPoG STPC
orientalis	CExl CJun CLAP CMCN CRos ELan ELon EPfP IMou LEdu LRHS MAsh MGos NLar NWad SPoG WPGP WPat
'Roy Lancaster'	see *S. ruscifolia* var. *chinensis* 'Dragon Gate'
'Rudolph'	EPfP LLHF LRHS
ruscifolia	Widely available
- var. ***chinensis***	CJun CSam SLon WCru WPGP WPat
§ - - 'Dragon Gate' ♀H5	CDoC CExl CJun CLAP CRos EBee ELan ELon EPfP LLHF LRHS LSRN MAsh SLim SLon SPoG SWvt WCru WPGP WPat
saligna	CBcs CJun EBtc ELan EPfP LRHS MRav SLon WCru WPat
- HWJK 2428 **new**	WCru
- MF P2056	WCru
trinervia B&SWJ 9500	WCru
vagans B&SWJ 7285	WCru
- B&SWJ 9766 from Vietnam	WCru
aff. ***vagans*** B&SWJ 7265 from north Thailand	WCru
wallichii	CDoC CExl ELon LEdu MBlu WPGP WPat
- B&SWJ 2291	CJun WCru WSHC
- GWJ 9427	WCru
zeylanica B&SWJ 10199	WCru
- var. ***brevifolia*** GWJ 9480	WCru

Sarmienta (*Gesneriaceae*)

repens ♀H2	CExl CFil WAbe WPGP

Sarothamnus see *Cytisus*

Sarracenia ✿ (*Sarraceniaceae*)

× ***ahlesii***	CHew NLos
alata	CHew EECP WSSs
- from Deer Park, Alabama, pubescent	NLos
- from Desoto National Forest, Mississippi	NLos
- from Robertson County, Texas	NLos
- from Stone County, Mississippi	NLos
- 'Black Tube' ♀H3	WSSs
- heavily veined	WSSs
- var. ***nigropurpurea***	WSSs
- var. ***ornata***	WSSs

- pubescent	EECP NLos WSSs
- 'Red Lid'	EECP NLos WSSs
- 'Red Lid' all red clone × ***flava*** var. ***rubricorpora***	NLos
- 'Red Lid' × ***flava*** red pitcher	EECP
- var. ***rubrioperculata***	WSSs
- wavy lid	WSSs
- white-flowered	WSSs
alata × ***flava***	NLos
alata × ***flava*** var. ***maxima***	NLos WSSs
alata × ***leucophylla***	NLos
(***alata*** red tube × ***flava*** 'Burgundy') × (***leucophylla*** × ***purpurea***)	NLos
× ***areolata***	CHew NLos WSSs
× ***catesbaei***	CHew NLos WSSs
× ***catesbaei*** × ***oreophila***	NLos
× ***catesbaei*** RV clone × ***oreophila***	NLos
× ***catesbaei*** × ***leucophylla***	NLos
× ***courtii*** × ***minor***	NLos
'Dixie Lace' ♀H3	NLos
'Eva'	WSSs
× ***excellens***	WSSs
- 'Judy'	NLos
× ***excellens*** × (***minor*** × ***rubra*** subsp. ***rubra***)	NLos
× ***excellens*** × (× ***rehdeii***)	NLos
× ***exornata***	SPlb
× ***farnhamii***	EECP NLos WSSs
flava	WSSs
- from Bay County, Florida	NLos
- from Carteret County, North Carolina	NLos
- from Dorchester County, South Carolina	NLos
- from Jedbury, Dorchester County, Florida	NLos
- from Marston Exotics	NLos
- from McClellanville, South Carolina	NLos
- from Santee Coastal Reserve, South Carolina	NLos
- from SB Creek Road	NLos
- from Shallotte, North Carolina	NLos
- all green giant	see *S. flava* var. *maxima*
- all red tube	NLos
- var. ***atropurpurea***	EECP WSSs
- - from Blackwater, Florida	NLos
- 'Claret'	WSSs
- var. ***cuprea***	WSSs
- var. ***flava***	CHew EECP WSSs
- - from Hurleyville, South Carolina	NLos
- - very tall, from Dahlia Bog, Virginia	NLos
- giant red tube	NLos
§ - var. ***maxima***	CHew EECP NLos WSSs
- - from North Carolina	NLos
- var. ***maxima*** × (× ***moorei*** Brook's hybrid)	NLos
- var. ***ornata***	CHew EECP NLos WSSs
- var. ***rubricorpora***	CHew EECP SPlb WSSs

- - from Apalachicola National Forest, Florida	NLos
- - 'Burgundy'	NLos WSSs
- var. ***rugelii***	CHew EECP NLos WSSs
- - from Homerville Airport, Ware County, Georgia	NLos
- stocky, from Appalachicola National Forest, Florida	NLos
((***flava*** × ***leucophylla***) × ***leucophylla***) × (***flava*** × ***rubra***)	NLos
(***flava*** × ***purpurea***) × (***purpurea*** subsp. ***purpurea***)	NLos
leucophylla	CHew NLos SPlb WSSs
- from Bens Bog, Baldwin County, Alabama	NLos
- from Citronelle, Alabama	NLos
- from Ctenium Fields, Perdido, Alabama	NLos
- from Gas Station Site, Perdido, Alabama	NLos
- from Hosford, Liberty County, Florida	NLos
- from Okaloosa Co., Florida	NLos
- from Southern Eglin Reserve, Oskaloosa County, Florida	NLos
- var. ***alba***	WSSs
- 'Deer Park Alabama'	NLos
- green	WSSs
- green and white	NLos WSSs
- pubescent	WSSs
- from Perdido, Alabama	NLos
- 'Schnell's Ghost' ♀H3	WSSs
- 'Tarnok'	WSSs
- f. ***viridescens***	WSSs
leucophylla × (***minor*** × ***rubra*** subsp. ***rubra***)	NLos
leucophylla × ***oreophila***	EECP
leucophylla × (× ***popei***)	EECP
leucophylla × ***rubra*** subsp. ***alabamensis***	NLos
'Lynda Butt' ♀H3	WSSs
× ***miniata***	EECP WSSs
minor	EECP WSSs
- from Berkeley County, South Carolina	NLos
- from Fitzgerald, Ben Hill County, Georgia	NLos
- var. ***minor***	CHew
§ - 'Okee Giant'	NLos WSSs
- 'Okefenokee Giant'	see *S. minor* 'Okee Giant'
- var. ***okefenokeensis***	CHew WSSs
(***minor*** × ***oreophila***) × (***leucophylla*** × ***purpurea***)	NLos
minor × ***rubra***	NLos
× ***mitchelliana***	NLos WSSs
- 'Juthatip Soper' ♀H3	NLos WSSs
× ***moorei***	CHew WSSs
I - 'Brook's Hybrid' ♀H4	CHew EECP NLos WSSs
- 'Marston Clone'	NLos
× ***moorei*** × ***purpurea*** subsp. ***venosa***	NLos
oreophila	CHew WSSs
- purple throat	NLos
oreophila × ***purpurea***	NLos

	oreophila* × *rubra subsp. ***wherryi*** 'Chatom Giant'	NLos
	× ***popei***	NLos WSSs
	'Pseudo-Judy'	NLos
	psittacina	CHew EECP WSSs
	purpurea	SPlb
	- subsp. ***purpurea***	CHew WSSs
	- - f. ***heterophylla*** 🏆H6	WSSs
	- subsp. ***venosa***	CHew WSSs
	- - var. ***burkii***	WSSs
	rubra	EECP WSSs
	- subsp. ***alabamensis*** 🏆H3	CHew WSSs
	- subsp. ***gulfensis***	CHew WSSs
*	- - f. ***heterophylla***	WSSs
*	- - - from Yellow River, North Florida	NLos
	- subsp. ***jonesii***	EECP NLos WSSs
*	- - f. ***heterophylla***	WSSs
	- subsp. ***rubra***	CHew WSSs
	- subsp. ***wherryi***	CHew EECP WSSs
	- - from near Perdido, Baldwin County, Alabama	NLos
	- - 'Chatom Giant'	NLos
	- - giant	WSSs
	- - yellow-flowered	WSSs
	'Vogel' 🏆H3	WSSs
	× ***wrigleyana***	NLos

Saruma (*Aristolochiaceae*)

	henryi	CAby CDes CLAP CTal ESwi EWld GEdr GKev GLog LEdu MAvo SBrt WCot WCru WPGP WSHC

Sasa (*Poaceae*)

	disticha 'Mirrezuzume'	see *Pleioblastus pygmaeus* 'Mirrezuzume'
	glabra f. ***albostriata***	see *Sasaella masamuneana* 'Albostriata'
	kurilensis	MWhi MWht WJun
§	- 'Shima-shimofuri' (v)	EPPr ERod EShb WJun
	- 'Shimofuri'	see *S. kurilensis* 'Shima-shimofuri'
	nana	see *S. veitchii* f. *minor*
§	***palmata***	CDul CWSG CWib EAla EHoe LCro LOPS MMuc MWhi SEND WHer
	- f. ***nebulosa***	CBcs ENBC LPal MBrN MWht WJun WMoo
	tessellata	see *Indocalamus tessellatus*
	tsuboiana	CBcs LPal LRHS MJak MWht NLar SBig SGol WMoo
§	***veitchii***	CBcs EHoe ENBC LPal MJak MMuc MRav MWht NLar SCob SEND SGol WFar WJun WMoo
§	- f. ***minor***	MMuc WMoo

Sasaella (*Poaceae*)

§	***masamuneana*** 'Albostriata' (v)	CDoC CEnt ENBC ERod LEdu LRHS MJak MMuc MWht SBig SEND WJun WMoo
§	***ramosa***	MWht

Sassafras (*Lauraceae*)

	albidum	CArn CBcs CMCN EBee ELan EPfP IDee LRHS MAsh NLar SChF SKHP SLon SPoG SSpi

satsuma see *Citrus reticulata*

Satureja ✿ (*Lamiaceae*)

	coerulea 🏆H5	EWes NBir XSen
	douglasii	CBod SHDw WJek
	- 'Indian Mint'PBR	ENfk MHer SRms
	hortensis	CBod CLau ENfk GPoy MHer MNHC SIde SRms WJek
	intricata	XSen
	montana	CHby CLau CSam EBee ENfk GKev GPoy LEdu LLWP MBri MHer MNHC SDix SEND SIde SRms SVic WHfH WJek XSen
*	- ***citriodora***	GPoy MHer MNHC XSen
§	- subsp. ***illyrica***	CPBP MMuc SPhx WJek XLum XSen
	- 'Purple Mountain'	GPoy MHer
	- ***subspicata***	see *S. montana* subsp. *illyrica*
	obovata	XSen
	repanda	see *S. spicigera*
§	***spicigera***	CArn CBod ENfk EPot LEdu MHer MMuc NBir SPhx SRms WJek WTor XLum
	spinosa	XSen
	thymbra	SHDw SRms XSen

Sauromatum (*Araceae*)

	gaoligongense	CDes
	guttatum	see *S. venosum*
§	***venosum***	CArn CCon CExl EBee ECho EShb LAma LEdu LRHS NLos SBig WCot WCru XLum

Saururus (*Saururaceae*)

	cernuus	CArn CBen CBod CWat EHon ELan LLWG MSKA SRms SWat WMAq WWtn XLum
	chinensis	LLWG

Saussurea (*Asteraceae*)

	costus	GPoy
	japonica B&SWJ 12672 **new**	WCru
	nepalensis	CArn
	pseudoalpina **new**	WCot

savory, summer see *Satureja hortensis*

savory, winter see *Satureja montana*

Saxegothaea (*Podocarpaceae*)

	conspicua	CBcs CDoC IArd IDee NLar SAko

Saxifraga ✿ (*Saxifragaceae*)

	JJH 9309174 **new**	NMen
	SEP 22 (7)	CPBP
	TJR 615/01 (7) **new**	EPot
	acerifolia (5)	GEdr
	aizoides (9)	ECho
	- var. ***atrorubens*** (9)	ECho
	aizoon	see *S. paniculata* subsp. *paniculata*
	× ***akinfievii*** (7) **new**	NMen
	'Alan Hayhurst' (8)	CPBP NSla WAbe
	'Alan Martin' (× *boydilacina*) (7)	ECho EPot EWes
	'Alba' ambig.	LRHS
	'Alba' (× *apiculata*) (7) 🏆H5	ECho NRya NSla SIgm SPlb
	'Alba' (*oppositifolia*) (7)	ECho ELan EWes GCrg ITim NWad WAbe
	'Albert Einstein' (× *apiculata*) (7) 🏆H5	CTal
	'Albertii' (*callosa*)	see *S.* 'Albida'
§	'Albida' (*callosa*) (8)	CTal ECho NWad WAbe
	'Albrecht Dürer' (Lasciva Group) (7)	NMen

'Alice' (Milford Group) (7)	NMen
'Alice Longbottom' (5) **new**	SAko
'Allendale Acclaim' (× *lismorensis*) (7)	NMen
'Allendale Accord' (7)	NMen
'Allendale Andante' (× *arco-valleyi*) (7)	NMen
'Allendale Angel' (× *kepleri*) (7)	NMen
'Allendale Argonaut' (7)	CPBP
'Allendale Ballet' (7)	NMen
'Allendale Bamby' (× *lismorensis*) (7)	NHar NMen
'Allendale Banshee' (7)	NMen
'Allendale Beau' (× *lismorensis*) (7)	CTal
'Allendale Beauty' (7)	NMen WAbe
'Allendale Billows' (7)	NHar
'Allendale Bonny' (7)	NHar NMen WAbe
'Allendale Bounty' (7)	NMen
'Allendale Bravo' (× *lismorensis*) (7)	NMen WAbe
'Allendale Cabal' (7)	CPBP NMen
'Allendale Carol' (7)	WAbe
'Allendale Cavalier' (7) **new**	NMen
'Allendale Charm' (7) (Swing Group)	ITim NMen WAbe WHoo
'Allendale Chick' (7)	NHar NMen
'Allendale Czech' (7)	NMen
'Allendale Delight' (7)	NMen
'Allendale Desire' (7)	NMen WAbe
'Allendale Dream' (7)	NMen
'Allendale Duo' (7)	NMen
'Allendale Elegance' (7)	CPBP WAbe
'Allendale Elf' (7)	WAbe
'Allendale Elite' (7)	WAbe
'Allendale Envoy' (7)	ITim NMen WAbe
'Allendale Epic' (7)	NHar
'Allendale Fairy' (7)	NHar NMen WAbe WHoo
'Allendale Frost' (7)	WAbe
'Allendale Ghost' (7)	WAbe
'Allendale Goblin' (7)	WAbe
'Allendale Grace' (7)	WAbe
'Allendale Gremlin' (7)	NMen
'Allendale Harvest' (7)	NMen WAbe
'Allendale Hobbit' (7)	NHar NMen
'Allendale Host' (7)	NMen WAbe
'Allendale Ice' (7)	NMen
'Allendale Icon' (× *polulacina*) (7)	WAbe
'Allendale Imp' (7)	WAbe
'Allendale Ina' (7)	NHar WAbe
'Allendale Jinn' (7)	WAbe
'Allendale Jo' (7)	WAbe
'Allendale Magic' (7)	NMen
'Allendale Nipper' (7) **new**	NMen
'Allendale Noon'	NMen
'Allendale Ruby' (7)	WAbe
'Allendale Snow' (× *rayei*) (7)	EPot NMen
'Alpenglow' (7)	NMen
alpigena (7)	EPot WAbe
'Amberine' (× *anglica*) (7)	NMen
'Amedeo Modigliani' (7) **new**	NMen
× ***andrewsii*** (8 × 11)	XLum
angustifolia Haw.	see *S. hypnoides*
'Anne Beddall' (× *goringiana*) (7)	NMen WAbe
'Antonio Vivaldi' (7)	WAbe
× ***apiculata*** (7)	ECho MAsh WGor
'Apple Blossom' (Mossy Group) (15)	ECtt EPfP NEoE NRya
'Apple Blossom' *sensu stricto* hort.	see *S.* 'Gregor Mendel'
'Arabella' (× *edithae*) (7)	ECho
§ 'Arco' (× *arco-valleyi*) (7)	ECho
× ***arco-valleyi*** *sensu stricto* hort.	see *S.* 'Arco'
× ***arendsii*** purple-flowered (15)	MMuc SEND SPlb
§ 'Aretiastrum' (× *boydii*) (7)	NMen
'Asahi' (*fortunei*) (5)	IVic SAko
aspera L. (10)	EDAr WAbe
'Atropurpurea' (*paniculata* subsp. *cartilaginea*) (8)	GMaP NHar NHol WHoo WIce XLum
'Aufheiter von Eri' (*fortunei*) (5)	IVic SAko
'Auguste Renoir' (Decora Group) (7)	WAbe
'Aurea Maculata' (*cuneifolia*)	see *S.* 'Aureopunctata'
'Aurea' (*umbrosa*)	see *S.* 'Aureopunctata'
§ 'Aureopunctata' (× *urbium*) (11/v)	CLet CMac CTri ECha ECho ELan EPfP GKev GMaP LEdu LPot LRHS MHer MLHP MRav SPer SPlb SPoG SRms WMoo XLum
'Autumn Tribute' (*fortunei*) (5)	GEdr WAbe
'Aya' (*fortunei*) (5) **new**	SAko
'Ayer's Rock' (7)	WAbe
'Balcana' (*paniculata*) (8)	NSla WAbe
'Baldensis'	see *S. paniculata* var. *minutifolia*
'Balkan' (*marginata* subsp. *marginata* var. *rocheliana*) (7) Υ^{H5}	ITim
'Beatles' (Beat Group) (7)	EPot
§ 'Beatrix Stanley' (× *angelica*) (7)	ECho LRHS MHer NWad
'Ben Loyal' (× *concinna*) (7) **new**	WAbe
'Benibana' (*fortunei*) (5) **new**	SAko
'Beni-komachi' (*fortunei*)	(5) SAko
'Bettina' (× *paulinae*) (7)	NMen
× ***biasolettoi*** *sensu stricto* hort.	see *S.* 'Phoenix'
× ***bilekii*** (7)	ECho
'Birch Yellow'	see *S.* 'Pseudoborisii'
'Black Beauty' (15)	ECtt GCrg LPot MHer
Black Ruby (*fortunei*) (5)	Widely available
'Blackberry and Apple Pie' (*fortunei*) (5)	CBct CElw CExl EBee ECho ECtt EPfP GEdr ITim LRHS MBrN MHol MLHP NHar NMyG SBch SWvt WCot WMoo
'Blush' (*fortunei*) (5)	LLHF
'Bob Hawkins' (Mossy Group) (15/v)	NHol NWad
'Bohemia' (7)	ECho NLar
× ***borisii*** *sensu stricto* hort.	see *S.* 'Sofia'
'Boston Spa' (× *elisabethae*) (7)	ECho ECtt GCrg LRHS MHer NLar SPlb WGor
'Brailes' (× *poluanglica*) (7)	NMen
'Brian Arundel' (Magnus Group) (7)	CPBP
'Bridget' (× *edithae*) (7)	CMea ECho LRHS NMen
'Brimstone' (7)	NMen WAbe
'Brno' (× *elisabethae*) (7)	EPot NMen
brunoniana	see *S. brunonis*
§ ***brunonis*** (1) CC 5315	GKev

	Name	Suppliers
	'Bryn Llwyd' (Vanessa Group) (7)	WAbe
	bryoides (10)	ECho
	'Buchholzii' (× *fleischeri*) (7)	NMen
*	'Buckland' (*fortunei*) (5)	WCot
	'Bürgel' (× *poluanglica*) (7)	GKev
	× ***burnatii*** (8)	ECho LRHS NSla WGor
	burseriana (7)	ECho NMen WAbe WGor
	× ***caesia*** misapplied (× *fritschiana*)	see *S.* 'Krain'
	caesia L. (8)	SRms WAbe
§	***callosa*** (8) ♀H5	ECho EDAr MHer MLHP MMuc SEND WAbe
	- subsp. ***callosa*** (8)	ECho
§	- - var. ***australis*** (8)	CTal GJos
§	- subsp. ***catalaunica*** (8)	WAbe
	- var. ***lantoscana***	see *S. callosa* subsp. *callosa* var. *australis*
	- *lingulata*	see *S. callosa*
	'Camyra' (7)	WAbe
	× ***canis-dalmatica***	see *S.* 'Canis-dalmatica'
§	'Canis-dalmatica' (× *gaudinii*) (8)	ECho ECtt GCrg GJos LRHS NHar NWad SIgm WGor
§	'Carmen' (× *elisabethae*) (7)	WAbe
§	'Carniolica' (*paniculata*) (8)	NBro NHol WOld
	'Carniolica' (× *engleri*) (8)	WAbe
	carolinica	see *S.* 'Carniolica' (*paniculata*)
	cartilaginea	see *S. paniculata* subsp. *cartilaginea*
	catalaunica	see *S. callosa* subsp. *catalaunica*
	'Caterhamensis' (*cotyledon*) (8)	NHar
	'Cathy Read' (× *polulacina*) (7)	NMen
	caucasica (7)	ECho WAbe
	cebennensis (15)	EPot NRya
	- dwarf (15)	WAbe
	'Celebration'	WAbe
	cespitosa (15)	WAbe
	'Chambers' Pink Pride'	see *S.* 'Miss Chambers'
	'Charles Chaplin' (7)	ECho NMen
	'Charles Darwin' (7)	NMen
	Cheap Confections (*fortunei*) (4)	CBct CCon ECtt GEdr IFoB LLHF NLar NMyG SBch SHar WBor WFar WMoo WOld WPGP
§	***cherlerioides*** (10)	NRya
	Cherry Pie (*fortunei*) (5)	CBct GEdr LLHF NBir NHar NMyG
	'Chodov' (Holenka's Miracle Group) (× *megaseiflora*) (7)	EPot NMen
	'Christine' (× *anglica*) (7)	ECho
	cinerea (7)	NMen WAbe
	- McB 1376	NWad
	'Cio-Cio-San' (Vanessa Group) (7)	NMen WAbe
	'Circe' (5) **new**	SAko
	'Citronella' (7)	ECho WAbe
	'Claire Felstead' (7)	WAbe
*	'Clare' (*paniculata*) (8)	NSla
	'Clare' (× *anglica*) (7)	ECtt NHol
§	'Clarence Elliott' (London Pride Group) (*umbrosa*) (11) ♀H5	CTri ECho EWTr EWes GAbr GBin GCal GJos GKev GMaP MHer NDov NLar NPri NRya WIce WThu WWEG
	'Claude Monet' (Impressio Group) (7)	NMen
	'Cloth of Gold' (*exarata* subsp. *moschata*) (15)	ECha ECho ECtt ELan GCrg GMaP LRHS MAsh MHer NHol NPri NRya NWad SBod SPlb SPoG SRms WAbe WIce
	cochlearis (8)	CTri LRHS MAsh NBro NMen NSla SBch SIgm WAbe WGor
	'Cockscomb' (*paniculata*) (8)	ECho NHar NLar NWad WAbe
	columnaris (7)	WAbe
	'Combrook' (× *poluanglica*) (7)	NMen
	'Conwy Snow' (*fortunei*) (5)	CDes CLAP WAbe WFar WMoo
	'Conwy Star' (*fortunei*) (5)	GEdr WAbe WFar
	'Coolock Gem' (7)	WAbe
	'Coolock Jean' (7)	WAbe
	'Coolock Kate' (7) ♀H5	WAbe
	'Corennie Claret'	see *S.* 'Glowing Ember'
	'Correvoniana' misapplied	see *S.* 'Lagraveana'
	'Correvoniana' Farrer (*paniculata*) (8)	EDAr MHer MMuc SEND WGor XLum
	cortusifolia (5)	CLAP EBee ECho
	- B&SWJ 5879	WCru
	- var. ***stolonifera*** (5)	CBct ECho GCal XLum
	Cotton Crochet (*fortunei*) (5/d)	CAbP CBct ECtt ESwi GEdr NHar NMyG SHeu WBor WCot WFar WMoo WOld
	cotyledon (8)	CTal ECho WAbe WCFE
	cotyledon* × *cuneifolia (8 × 11)	NSla
§	'Cranbourne' (× *anglica*) (7) ♀H5	CMea CPBP ECho EPot LRHS MAsh NMen
	'Cream' (*paniculata*) (8)	ECho
	'Cream Seedling' (× *elisabethae*) (7)	ECho
	'Crenata' (*burseriana*) (7) ♀H5	LRHS
	'Crimscote-love' (*poluanglica*) (7)	EPot
	'Crimson Rose' (*paniculata*)	see *S.* 'Rosea' (*paniculata*)
	'Crinoline' (7) **new**	WAbe
§	***crustata*** (8)	CPBP ECho NHar WAbe WThu XLum
	- var. ***vochinensis***	see *S. crustata*
	Crystal Pink (*fortunei*) (5/v)	CAbP CBct CBod CCon CExl EBee ECtt GEdr IFoB MNrw NHar NLar NMyG SGSe WCot WFar
	'Crystalie' (× *biasolettoi*) (7)	LRHS
	'Cultrata' (*paniculata*) (8)	NBro
	'Cumulus' (7) ♀H5	NMen WAbe
§	***cuneifolia*** (11)	ECho IMou MHer MLHP MWat NWad WMoo XLum
	- var. ***capillipes***	see *S. cuneifolia* subsp. *cuneifolia*
§	- subsp. ***cuneifolia*** (11)	ECtt GJos
*	- var. ***subintegra*** (11)	ECho
	'Cuscutiformis' (*stolonifera*) (5)	CAby CElw CExl CHid EWld GBuc GEdr MAvo MBel MSCN SBch SRms WBor WCru WPGP XLum
	cymbalaria (2)	WHil
	dahurica	see *S. cuneifolia*
	'Dainty Dame' (× *arco-valleyi*) (7)	LRHS NMen WAbe
	'Dana' (Prichard's Monument Group) (× *megaseiflora*) (7)	NMen
	'Dawn Frost' (7)	WIce
	'Dejvice' (7) **new**	NMen
	'Delia' (× *hornibrookii*) (7)	EPot
	densa	see *S. cherlerioides*
	'Dentata' (× *geum*)	see *S.* 'Dentata' (London Pride Group) (× *polita*)
§	'Dentata' (London Pride Group) (× *polita*) (11)	EAJP ECha ECho GCal WBor WMoo
	'Dentata' (× *urbium*)	see *S.* 'Dentata' (London Pride Group) (× *polita*)

I 'Diana' (× *lincolni-fosteri*) (7) WIce
diapensioides (7) WAbe
dinnikii (7) WAbe
× ***dinninaris*** (7) NSla
'Dobruška' (× *irvingii*) (7) NMen
'Doctor Clay' (*paniculata*) (8) CTal ECho EPot GCrg GKev LRHS NHar NHol NRya SPlb WAbe
'Doctor Ramsey' (8) ECho EWes LRHS NBro NWad WAbe WGor WPnn
'Dolores Umbridge' (5) **new** SAko
'Don Giovanni' (7) WAbe
'Donald Mann' (15) EWes
'Donnington Carpet' (7) **new** NMen
'Drakula' (*ferdinandi-coburgi*) (7) ECho EPot LRHS NMen
'Dwight Ripley' (7) NMen
'Edgar Irmscher' (7) NMen
'Edith' (× *edithae*) (7) CTal ECho LRHS
'Elegance' **new** SAko
'Elf' (7) see *S.* 'Beatrix Stanley'
'Elf' (*exarata* subsp. *moschata*) (15) ECtt MAsh SIgm SRms
'Elf Rose' (15) EPfP LRHS
'Eliot Hodgkin' (× *millstreamiana*) (7) NMen
× ***elisabethae*** *sensu stricto* hort. see *S.* 'Carmen'
'Ellie Brinckerhoff' (× *hornibrookii*) (7) NMen
'Elliott's Variety' see *S.* 'Clarence Elliott' (*umbrosa*)
'Emile Burnat' (× *burnatii*) (8) ♀H5 CTal
× ***engleri*** (8) CTal
epiphylla (5) BWJ 8177 WCru
§ 'Ernst Heinrich' (× *heinrichii*) (7) NMen
'Esther' (× *burnatii*) (8) CMea ECho LRHS NPri SRGP WAbe WHoo WPnn
§ 'Eulenspiegel' (× *geuderi*) (7) NWad
'Eva Hanzliková' (× *izari*) (7) WAbe
exarata (15) WAbe
'Excellent' (Exclusive Group) (7) CPBP EPot
'Exhibit' (Exclusive Group) (7) **new** NMen
fair maids of France see *S.* 'Flore Pleno'
'Fairy Dust' **new** SAko
'Fairy' (*exarata* subsp. *moschata*) (15) ECtt NBir
'Faldonside' (× *boydii*) (7) MAsh WAbe
'Falstaff' (*burseriana*) (7) WAbe
× ***farreri*** (15) WIce
'Favorit' (× *bilekii*) (7) EPot
§ ***federici-augusti*** ECho EPot GCrg LRHS NMen NSla
subsp. ***grisebachii*** (7) ♀H5 WAbe
ferdinandi-coburgi (7) ECtt WAbe
§ - subsp. ***chrysosplenifolia*** var. ***rhodopea*** (7) ECho EPot LRHS
- var. ***pravislavii*** see *S. ferdinandi-coburgi* subsp. *chrysosplenifolia* var. *rhodopea*
- var. ***radoslavoffii*** see *S. ferdinandi-coburgi* subsp. *chrysosplenifolia* var. *rhodopea*
'Findling' (Mossy Group) (15) EPfP GCrg NWad SPoG WAbe
'Firebrand' (× *kochii*) (7) WAbe
Five Color (*fortunei*) see *S.* 'Go-nishiki'
§ ***flagellaris*** (1) WAbe
'Flavescens' misapplied see *S.* 'Lutea' (*paniculata*)
§ 'Flore Pleno' (*granulata*) (15/d) CElw EWes NBir
'Flowers of Sulphur' see *S.* 'Schwefelblüte'
'Flush' (× *petraschii*) (7) NMen
fortunei (5) ♀H4 CLAP CMac ECho GMaP LEdu NBir SRms WAbe WFar
- B&SWJ 6346 WCru
- from John Fielding (5) WCot
- f. ***alpina*** from Hokkaido (5) WCru
- var. ***koraiensis*** (5) B&SWJ 8688 WCru
- var. ***obtusocuneata*** (5) CLAP ECho GEdr LLHF WAbe
- f. ***partita*** (5) CLAP WCot WCru
- var. ***pilosissima*** (5) B&SWJ 8557 WCru
- pink-flowered (5) WAbe
'Foster's Gold' (× *elisabethae*) (7) EPot NMen
'Four Winds' (Mossy Group) (15) EWes MBrN SPoG
'Francis Cade' (8) GAbr WAbe
'Franz Liszt' (7) NMen WAbe
'Freckles' GKev
'Frederik Chopin' (7) WAbe
'Friesei' (× *salmonica*) (7) CTal NMen
'Fumiko' (*fortunei*) (5) WAbe WCru
'G.W. Gould No. 1' NMen
'Gaiety' (15) ECho LRHS SPoG
× ***gaudinii*** (8) XLum
'Gelber Findling' (7) EPot NMen SIgm WAbe
'Gelbes Monster' (*fortunei*) (5) IVic
'Gem' (× *irvingii*) (7) WIce
'Gemma' (× *megaseiflora*) (7) LRHS
georgei (7) EPot WAbe
'Gerard Philipe' (7) NMen
× ***geuderi*** *sensu stricto* hort. see *S.* 'Eulenspiegel'
§ × ***geum*** (11) CHid ECho MRav WFar WMoo
- Dixter form (11) CElw ECha NDov SDix SMHy WWEG
'Gleborg' (Mossy Group) (15) SPoG
'Gloria' (*burseriana*) (7) ECho EPot LRHS MAsh NMen WIce
'Gloriana' see *S.* 'Godiva'
× ***gloriana*** *sensu stricto* hort. (7) see *S.* 'Godiva'
'Gloriosa' (× *gloriana*) (7) see *S.* 'Godiva'
§ 'Glowing Ember' (Mossy Group) (15) EWes
'Glückliches Mädchen' (*fortunei*) (5) IVic SAko
§ 'Godiva' (× *gloriana*) (7) WAbe
'Gold Dust' (× *eudoxiana*) (7) ECho GCrg NRya
'Golden Falls' (Mossy Group) (15/v) EWes SPlb SPoG
Golden Prague (× *pragensis*) see *S.* 'Zlatá Praha'
§ 'Go-nishiki' (*fortunei*) (5) GEdr LLHF NMyG
'Gorges du Verdon' (8) EWTr
'Goring White' (7) NMen
'Gothenburg' (7) EPot NMen WAbe
'Grace Farwell' (× *anglica*) (7) ECho NLar NMen

	Name	Suppliers
	granulata (15)	EChoEWes GJos NMir NSla WAbe
	'Grébovka' (× *megaseiflora*) (7) **new**	NMen
	'Greensleeves' (*fortunei*) (5)	LLHF
§	'Gregor Mendel' (× *apiculata*) (7) 🏆H5	CMea CTal ECho ECtt LRHS NLar NSla NWad SIgm SRms WAbe WHoo
	'Gregor' (× *poluanglica*) (7)	NMen WAbe
	grisebachii	see *S. federici-augusti* subsp. *grisebachii*
	'Haagii' (× *eudoxiana*) (7)	CTri ECho NPri WGor
	'Harbinger' (7)	NMen WAbe
	'Hare Knoll Beauty' (8)	CPBP ECho EPot LRHS NHar NHol NSla WAbe
	'Harlow Car' (× *anglica*) (7)	EPot NMen NSla
	'Harold Bevington' (*paniculata*) (8)	CTal
	'Harold Lloyd' (7)	NMen
	'Harry Marshall' (× *irvingii*) (7)	NWad
	'Harry Smith' (× *cimgani*) (7)	NMen
	'Harvest Moon' (*stolonifera*) (5)	WBor WHer
	'Hedwig' (× *malbyana*) (7)	WAbe
	× ***heinreichii*** *sensu stricto* hort.	see *S.* 'Ernst Heinrich'
	'Heisel Kurenai' (*fortunei*) (5)	IVic SAko
	'Henri Rousseau' (Conspecta Group) (7)	NMen
	'Hi-Ace' (Mossy Group) (15/v)	SPlb
	'Highlander Red Shades' (Mossy Group) (15)	WIce
	'Hime' (*stolonifera*) (5)	CDes WCru
	'Hindhead Seedling' (× *boydii*) (7)	ECho LRHS NMen WAbe
	hirsuta (11)	EHrv ESwi EWld GEdr LEdu MMuc SEND WCot WCru
	'Hirsuta' (× *geum*)	see *S.* × *geum*
	'Hirtella' Ingwersen (*paniculata*) (8)	EPot
	'Hirtifolia' (*paniculata*) (8)	CTal GJos
	'His Majesty' (× *irvingii*) (7)	NMen
	'Hiten' (*fortunei*) (5)	EBee
	'Hocker Edge' (× *arco-valleyi*) (7)	WAbe
	'Holden Seedling' (Mossy Group) (15)	ECtt
I	'Holden Variety' (*oppositifolia*) (7)	NRya NWad
	'Hradčany' (Holenka's Miracle Group) (× *megaseiflora*) (7)	NMen
	'Honington' (× *poluanglica*) (7)	NMen
	hostii (8)	ECho EDAr GKev NWad WGor XLum
	- subsp. ***hostii*** (8)	XLum
	- - var. ***altissima*** (8)	XLum
	- subsp. ***rhaetica*** (8)	NBro WThu XLum
	'Hsitou Silver' (*stolonifera*) (5)	EPPr WCot
§	***hypnoides*** (15)	NMir SPoG WAbe
	hypostoma (7)	WAbe
	'Iceland' (*oppositifolia*) (7)	EWes SIgm WAbe
	'Idlecote'	NMen
	'Ignaz Dörfler' (× *doerfleri*) (7)	WAbe
	imparilis (5)	EHrv GEdr WCru
	'Ingeborg' (Mossy Group) (15)	CElw ECha
	iranica (7)	EPot ITim NMen
	'Irena' (7)	NMen
	'Irene Bacci' (× *baccii*) (7)	NMen
	'Iris Prichard' (× *hardingii*) (7)	CTal NMen
	× ***irvingii*** (7)	ECho
	× ***irvingii*** *sensu stricto* hort.	see *S.* 'Walter Irving'
	'Ivan Urumonv' (× *urumoffii*) (7) **new**	NMen
	'James' (7)	NMen
	'Jan Amos Kómenský' (× *anglica*) (7)	NMen
	'Jan Neruda' (× *megaseiflora*) (7)	CPBP EPot
	'Jan Palach' (× *krausii*) (7)	WAbe
	'Jaromir' (8)	NHar NMen
	'Jaroslav Horný' (*maginata*) (7) **new**	NMen
	'Jason' (× *elisabethae*) (7)	NMen
	'Jenkinsiae' (× *irvingii*) (7)	CMea CTal ECho LRHS MAsh MMuc NLar NMen NRya NSla NWad SEND WAbe WGor WIce
	'Jocelynne Bacci' (7) **new**	NMen
§	'Johann Kellerer' (× *kellereri*) (7)	NMen
	'Johann Wolfgang Goethe' (7)	NMen WAbe
	'John Byam-Grounds' (Honor Group) (7)	NMen WAbe
	'John Tomlinson' (*burseriana*) (7)	NSla
	'Jorg' (× *biasolettoi*) (7)	NMen
	'Josef Mánes' (× *borisii*) (7)	NMen
	'Joy'	see *S.* 'Kaspar Maria Sternberg'
	'Judith Shackleton' (× *abingdonensis*) (7)	WAbe
	'Juliet'	see *S.* 'Riverslea'
§	***juniperifolia*** (7)	ECho SRms XLum
	'Jupiter' (Holenka's Miracle Group) (× *megaseiflora*) (7)	EPot SIgm
	'Kanna' (*fortunei*) (5)	IVic
	karadzicensis × ***scardica*** (7)	EPot
	'Karasin' (7)	NMen
	'Karel Čapek' (Prichard's Monument Group) (× *megaseiflora*) (7)	CPBP ECho EPot LRHS NMen WAbe
	'Karlštejn' (× *borisii*) (7)	EPot NMen
§	'Kaspar Maria Sternberg' (× *petraschii*) (7) 🏆H5	ECho LRHS
	'Kath Dryden' (7)	ECho ECtt ITim
	'Kathleen Pinsent' (8)	ECho WAbe
	'Kathleen' (× *polulacina*) (7)	NMen
	'Kath's Delight' (8)	GKev
	'Katie Bell' (5) **new**	SAko
	'Katrin' (× *borisii*) (7)	NMen
	'Kbley' **new**	NMen
	× ***kellereri*** *sensu stricto* hort.	see *S.* 'Johann Kellerer'
	'Kestoniensis' (× *salmonica*) (7)	NMen
	'Kew Gem' (× *petraschii*) (7)	ECho
	'King Lear' (× *bursiculata*) (7)	CTal ECho LRHS
	'Kinki Purple' (*stolonifera*) (5)	CBct EHrv EShb EWld WCru WPGP
	'Klondike' (× *boydii*) (7)	EPot

'Knapton Pink' (Mossy Group) (15)	ECtt EDAr EPfP NEoE NPri SPoG WAbe WIce
'Knebworth' (8)	ECho
'Kokaku' (*fortunei*) (5)	LLHF
§ 'Kolbiana' (× *paulinae*) (7)	NMen
kotschyi* × *wendelboi (7)	EPot
'Koukan' (*fortunei*) (5)	IVic
§ 'Krain' (× *fritschiana*) (8)	ECho WOld
'Labe' (× *arco-valleyi*) (7)	CPBP ECho LRHS
'Lady Beatrix Stanley'	see *S.* 'Beatrix Stanley'
§ 'Lagraveana' (*paniculata*) (8) 🏆H5	ECho EDAr GCrg LRHS
'Laka' (7)	WAbe
× ***landaueri*** *sensu stricto* hort.	see *S.* 'Leonore'
'Lantoscana' (*callosa* subsp. *callosa* var. *australis*) (8) **new**	GKev
'Lantoscana Superba' (*callosa* subsp. *callosa* var. *australis*) (8)	GKev WOld
'Lemon Puff'	CPBP WAbe WIce
'Lemon Spires' (7)	EPot
'Lenka' (× *byam-groundsii*) (7)	NMen WAbe
'Leo Gordon Godseff' (× *elisabethae*) (7)	ECho LRHS
'Leonardo da Vinci' (7)	NMen WAbe
§ 'Leonore' (× *landaueri*) (7)	ECho LRHS SIgm WAbe
'Letchworth Gem' (London Pride Group) (× *urbium*) (11)	ECho GAbr GCal
'Licht des Cerise' (*fortunei*) (5)	IVic
'Lidice' (7)	EPot WAbe WHoo
'Lilac Time' (× *youngiana*) (7)	NMen
lilacina (7)	WAbe WThu
'Lily Potter' (5) **new**	SAko
'Limelight' (*callosa* subsp. *callosa* var. *australis*) (8)	NWad
'Lincoln Foster' (8)	NHar
lingulata	see *S. callosa*
'Lismore Carmine' (× *lismorensis*) (7)	NMen
'Lismore Gem' (× *lismorensis*) (7)	ECho
'Lissadell' (*callosa*) (8)	GKev IFoB
* 'Little Piggy' (*epiphylla*) (5)	WCru
llonakhensis	WAbe
'Lohmuelleri' (× *biasolettoi*) (7)	GKev
lolaensis (7)	WAbe
London Pride Group (11) **new**	MHol
longifolia (8)	ECho EPot LRHS NSla
- var. ***aitanica*** (8)	WAbe
'Louis Armstrong' (Blues Group) (7)	WAbe
Love Me	see *S.* 'Miluj Mne'
lowndesii (7)	WAbe
'Lusanna' (× *irvingii*) (7)	NMen
'Luschtinetz' (Mossy Group) (15)	LRHS
'Lutea' ambig.	GJos NMen
'Lutea' (*aizoon*)	see *S.* 'Lutea' (*paniculata*)
§ 'Lutea' (*paniculata*) (8)	ECho EDAr EHoe EPot GMaP MMuc NBro NHol NPri NRya NSla NWad WGor
'Lužnice' (× *poluluteopurpurea*) (7)	CTal
macedonica	see *S. juniperifolia*
'Maigrün' (*fortunei*) (5)	EBee
'Marc Chagall' (Decora Group) (7)	WAbe
'Marcela' (× *megaseiflora*) (7) **new**	NMen
'Marco Polo' (7) **new**	NMen
marginata (7) 🏆H5	WAbe
- var. ***balcanica***	see *S. marginata* subsp. *marginata* var. *rocheliana*
- subsp. ***marginata*** var. ***boryi*** (7)	LRHS NMen WAbe
- - var. ***coriophylla*** (7)	EPot WAbe
§ - - var. ***rocheliana*** (7)	ECho LRHS
'Maria Callas' (× *poluanglica*) (7)	WAbe
'Maria Luisa' (× *salmonica*) (7)	NMen WAbe
'Marianna' (× *borisii*) (7)	CMea SIgm
'Maroon Beauty' (*stolonifera*) (5)	EBee ECtt EPPr LPot MCot NBid NBre WCot WWEG
'Mary Golds' (Swing Group) (7)	GKev ITim NLar NMen
'Masami' (5) **new**	SAko
'Medea' (5) **new**	SAko
× ***megaseiflora*** *sensu stricto* hort.	see *S.* 'Robin Hood'
'Merlin' (7) **new**	SAko
mertensiana (6)	EHrv GEdr NBir WCru WSHC
'Meteor' (7)	NHol NRya NSla
'Michle' (× *megaseiflora*) (7) **new**	NMen
micranthidifolia (4)	CLAP
'Mikuláš Koperník' (× *zenittensis*) (7)	WAbe
'Millstream Cream' (× *elisabethae*) (7)	ECho
§ 'Miluj Mne' (× *poluanglica*) (7)	CSma CTal ECho NMen WHoo
'Minnehaha' (× *elisabethae*) (7)	WAbe
'Minor' (*cochlearis*) (8) 🏆H5	CTal ECho EPot LRHS NHar NWad WGor
'Mirko Webr' (Harmonia Group) (7)	WAbe
§ 'Miss Chambers' (London Pride Group) (11)	EWes GCal WCot WMoo WSHC WWEG
'Moderne Zeit' (5) **new**	SAko
'Mollie Broom' (7)	WAbe
'Molly Weasley' (5) **new**	SAko
'Momo Sekisui' (*fortunei*) (5)	IVic SAko
'Momo Tarou' (*fortunei*) (5)	SAko
'Momobenkei' (*fortunei*) (5) **new**	SAko
'Mona Lisa' (× *borisii*) (7)	NWad SIgm
'Monarch' (8) 🏆H5	ECho GAbr GCrg GKev LRHS NWad WAbe WIce
§ 'Mondscheinsonate' (× *boydii*) (7)	WAbe
'Monika' (*webrii*) (7)	NMen
'Moon Beam' (× *boydilacina*) (7) **new**	NMen
'Moonlight Sonata' (× *boydii*)	see *S.* 'Mondscheinsonate'
'Moonlight' (× *boydii*)	see *S.* 'Sulphurea'
'Morava' (7)	EPot NMen

Mossy Group pink-flowered (15) MMuc SEND SPoG
- red-flowered (15) SPoG
- white-flowered (15) MMuc
'Mossy Triumph' see *S.* 'Triumph'
'Mother of Pearl' (× *irvingii*) (7) CMea ECho WIce
'Mount Nachi' (*fortunei*) (5) CBct CCon CDes ECho EPfP EWes GAbr GEdr GMaP LRHS MLHP NBro NMyG SPlb WAbe WCot WFar WMoo WPGP
'Mrs Helen Terry' (× *salmonica*) (7) ♀H5 LRHS NMen WIce
'Musgrove Pink' (*fortunei*) (5) CLAP
'Myra Cambria' (× *anglica*) (7) NWad
'Myra' (× *anglica*) (7) ECho WHoo
'Myriad' (7) WAbe
'Naarden' (7) NMen
'Nancye' (× *goringiana*) (7) EPot
'Neride' (7) **new** NMen
'Nicholas' (8) GKev
'Nisi' (*fortunei*) (5) IVic
'Norvegica' (*cotyledon*) (8) ITim
'Nottingham Gold' (× *boydii*) (7) ♀H5 EPot NMen NWad SIgm
§ ***obtusa*** (7) EPot MHer NMen
'Oh Yes' (*cochlearis*) (8) **new** WAbe
'Olsany' (× *megaseiflora*) (7) **new** NMen
'Olympus' (× *boydilacina*) (7) **new** NMen
'Omar Khayyám' (7) NMen WAbe
'Ontake-san' (5) **new** SAko
'Opalescent' (7) NMen
oppositifolia (7) GCrg MAsh MWat NHol NSla SPlb SRms WAbe WSHC
- subsp. ***oppositifolia*** var. ***latina*** (7) ECho GAbr
- subsp. ***paradoxa*** (7) EPot
'Pablo Picasso' (Conspecta Group) (7) EPot NMen WAbe
paniculata (8) ECho EDAr EHoe EPot GKev GMaP MHer MWat NSla SPlb SRms WAbe WHoo
§ - subsp. ***cartilaginea*** (8) GCrg
- subsp. ***kolenatiana*** see *S. paniculata* subsp. *cartilaginea*
§ - var. ***minutifolia*** (8) CPBP CTri ECho LRHS MSCN NBro NHar NRya NSla SIgm SPlb WAbe
§ - subsp. ***paniculata*** (8) MAsh
paradoxa (15) ECho EPot LRHS NHol NWad WGor
'Parcevalis' (× *finnisiae*) (7 × 9) NMen WAbe
'Paul Gaughin' (7) WAbe
'Paul Rubens' (7) NMen WAbe
'Peach Blossom' (7) NMen
'Peach Melba' (7) ♀H5 CSma CTal NLar NMen WAbe WHoo
'Peachy Head' (7) NMen WAbe
'Pearl Rose' (× *anglica*) (7) NMen
'Pearly Gates' (× *irvingii*) (7) CTal
'Pearly King' (Mossy Group) (15) ECtt GMaP WAbe
'Pearly King' variegated (15/v) CBod
× ***pectinata*** Schott, Nyman & Kotschy see *S.* 'Krain'
pedemontana from Mount Kazbek, Georgia (15) WAbe
'Penelope' (× *boydilacina*) (7) CTal ECho LRHS NLar WHoo
pensylvanica (4) CAby EBee GCal GCra IMou WCot
'Peter Burrow' (× *poluanglica*) (7) ECho WIce
'Peter Pan' (Mossy Group) (15) EDAr EPfP GCrg GMaP LRHS MAsh MHer NHol NLar NPri NWad SPoG WSHC
'Petra' (7) ECho
§ 'Phoenix' (× *biasolettoi*) (7) ECho LRHS NMen
'Pierantonio Micheli' (Renaissance Group) (7) NMen
'Pink Cloud' (*fortunei*) (5) GEdr NHar WAbe
'Pink Haze' (*fortunei*) (5) CLAP GEdr WAbe
'Pink Mist' (*fortunei*) (5) GEdr WAbe WFar WMoo
'Pink Pagoda' (*nipponica*) (5) CDes CLAP WCot WCru WPGP
'Pink Pearl' (7) SBch
'Pink Ray' (*fortunei*) (5) LLHF
'Pink Star' (× *boydilacina*) (7) NLar NMen
'Pixie' (15) CTal CTri ECtt GCrg MAsh NHol NRya NWad SPoG SRms
'Pixie Alba' see *S.* 'White Pixie'
'Plena' (*granulata*) see *S.* 'Flore Pleno'
'Polar Drift' NHar NSla WAbe
poluniniana (7) WAbe
poluniniana × 'Winifred' (× *poluanglica*) (7) ECho
'Pompadour' (15) NEoE
'Popelka' (*marginata* subsp. *marginata* var. *rocheliana*) (7) ECho LRHS
porophylla var. ***thessalica*** see *S. sempervivum* f. *stenophylla*
'Portae' (× *fritschiana*) (8) XLum
'Precious Piggy' (*epiphylla*) (5) WCru
'Primrose Bee' (× *apiculata*) (7) ITim
'Primrose Dame' (× *elisabethae*) (7) ECho WIce
'Primulaize' (9 × 11) GCrg
'Primulaize Salmon' (9 × 11) NHar WHoo
'Primuloides' (*umbrosa*) (11) ECho EDAr MMuc SEND SRms SWvt
'Prince Hal' (*burseriana*) (7) ECho LRHS
'Princess' (*burseriana*) (7) ECho LRHS
'Probynii' (*cochlearis*) (8) NMen NWad WAbe
'Prometheus' (× *prossenii*) (7) NMen
× ***prossenii*** *sensu stricto* hort. see *S.* 'Regina'
§ 'Pseudoborisii' (× *borisii*) (7) NMen
'Pseudo-paulinae' (× *paulinae*) (7) **new** NMen
'Pseudo-valdensis' (*cochlearis*) (8) WAbe
'Psycho' (7) WAbe
pubescens (15) WAbe
'Punctatissima' (*paniculata*) (8) NHar
* ***punctissima*** NWad
'Pungens' (× *apiculata*) (7) EPot
'Purple Piggy' (*epiphylla*) (5) CLAP WCru
'Purpurea' (*fortunei*) see *S.* 'Rubrifolia'
'Pygmalion' (× *webrii*) (7) NMen
'Pyramidalis' (*cotyledon*) (8) EPfP XLum

	Name	Suppliers
	'Pyrenaica' (*oppositifolia*) (7)	ECho
	quadrifaria (7)	WAbe
	'Radvan Horný' (× *cullinanii*) (7)	WAbe
	'Rainsley Seedling' (8)	GKev NBro
	'Ray Woodliffe' (× *dinninaris*) (7)	WAbe
	'Red Poll' (× *poluanglica*) (7)	GAbr ITim
*	'Regent'	WAbe
§	'Regina' (× *prossenii*) (7)	MHer NMen
	'Rembrandt van Rijn' (7)	NMen WAbe
	retusa (7)	WAbe
	'Rex' (*paniculata*) (8)	CMac ECho NWad
	rhodopetala (7)	ECho
	'Risa' (5) **new**	SAko
	'River Thame' (× *polulacina*) (7) **new**	NMen
§	'Riverslea' (× *bornibrookii*) (7)	NMen WAbe
§	'Robin Hood' (× *megaseiflora*) (7)	EPot WHoo
	'Rokujō' (*fortunei*) (5)	CLAP EBee IVic LHop NEoE NLar SHeu
	'Romulus' (7) **new**	NMen
	'Rosa Tubbs' (8)	EWTr GKev
	'Rosaleen' (× *salmonica*) (7) **new**	NMen
	'Rosalind' (7)	WHoo
	'Rosea' (*cortusifolia*) (5)	CLAP MHol NHar
§	'Rosea' (*paniculata*) (8) ♀H5	GMaP MMuc NBro NRya NSla SEND SRms WGor
	'Rosemarie' (7)	ECho NMen
	'Rosina Sündermann' (× *rosinae*) (7)	ECho LRHS
	'Rote Stadt' (*fortunei*) (5)	IVic
	rotundifolia (12)	CElw EBee ECha
	'Roy Clutterbuck' (7)	NMen
	'Roztyly' (× *megaseiflora*) (7) **new**	NMen
	'Rubella' (× *irvingii*) (7)	NMen
	'Rubra' (*aizoon*)	see *S.* 'Rosea' (*paniculata*)
§	'Rubrifolia' (*fortunei*) (5)	CAbP CBod CCon CLAP CMac CSpe ECha ECtt EHoe GAbr GEdr LSun NMyG SGSe SMad SWvt WBor WCot WCru WFar WMoo
*	'Ruby Red'	NEoE
	rufescens (5) BWJ 7510	EHrv WCru
	- BWJ 7684	GEdr WCru
	'Rusalka' (× *borisii*) (7)	NMen
	'Russell V. Prichard' (× *irvingii*) (7)	NWad
	'Ruth Draper' (*oppositifolia*) (7) ♀H5	GCrg WAbe
	'Ruth McConnell' (15)	CMea SBch
	'Ruznyě' (× *megaseiflora*) (7) **new**	NMen
	'Saint John's' (8)	ECho GKev
	'Saint Kilda' (*oppositifolia*) (7)	GCrg ITim NWad
	× ***salmonica*** *sensu stricto* hort.	see *S.* 'Salomonii'
§	'Salomonii' (× *salmonica*) (7)	SRms
	sancta (7)	ECho LRHS NMen SRms
	- subsp. ***pseudosancta***	see *S. juniperifolia*
	- - var. ***macedonica***	see *S. juniperifolia*
	'Sara Sinclair' (× *arco-valleyi*) (7)	CMea
	'Šárka' (7)	NMen
	sarmentosa	see *S. stolonifera*
	'Satchmo' (Blues Group) (7)	NMen
	'Saturn' (× *megaseiflora*) (7)	NMen
	'Sázava' (× *polulutcopurpurea*) (7)	CTal
§	***scardica*** (7)	EPot NBro WAbe WGor
	- var. ***dalmatica***	see *S. obtusa*
§	'Schelleri' (× *petraschii*) (7)	NMen
	'Schöne Mädchen' (*fortunei*) (5)	IVic
§	'Schwefelblüte' (15)	ECho GMaP LRHS
	sempervivum (7)	NGdn NSla WAbe
§	- f. ***stenophylla*** (7)	ECho MHer
	sendaica (5)	WCru
	'Seren y Gwanwyn' (*oppositifolia*) (7)	WAbe
	'Sergio Bacci' (7)	NMen
	'Setomidori' (5) **new**	SAko
	'Sherlock Holmes' (7)	CTal NMen WAbe
	'Shimmy'	WAbe
	'Shinkunomai' (*fortunei*) (5)	IVic
	'Shiragiku' (*fortunei*) (5)	WCot
§	'Silver Cushion' (15/v)	CMea CTri ECho ELan LRHS MAvo NPri SPlb SPoG WAbe
	'Silver Edge' (× *arco-valleyi*) (7)	EPot WAbe
	'Silver Hill' (*paniculata*) (8)	NSla SIgm
	'Silver Maid' (× *engleri*) (8)	GCrg NSla
	'Silver Mound'	see *S.* 'Silver Cushion'
	'Silver Velvet' (*fortunei*) (5)	CAbP CBct CLAP CSpe EBee ECtt ESwi GEdr IFoB MHol NMyG SGSe SHeu WBor WCot
	'Sissi' (7)	CPBP CTal EPot NMen WAbe
	'Slack's Ruby Southside' (Southside Seedling Group) (8) ♀H5	NSla NWad WIce
	'Slack's Sensation'	NSla
	'Slack's Supreme' (8)	NHar NSla WCot
	'Slzy Coventry' (× *proximae*) (7)	WAbe
	'Snowcap' (*pubescens*) (15)	WAbe
	'Snowflake' (Silver Farreri Group) (8) ♀H5	WAbe
§	'Sofia' (× *borisii*) (7)	EPot NMen
	Southside Seedling Group (8)	CMea CTal EAEE ECho EDAr EPfP EPot EWTr GAbr GJos GKev GMaP LHop LRHS MAsh MAvo MMuc NBro NHol NWad SAko SEND SPoG SRms WAbe WCFE WHoo WIce WOld XLum
	- red-flowered (8)	EPot
	'Southside Star' (Southside Seedling Group) (8) ♀H5	WAbe
	'Spartakus' (× *apiculata*) (7)	NMen
	spathularis (11)	WCot
	'Spinner's Snow-storm' (5) **new**	SAko
	'Splendens' (*oppositifolia*) (7) ♀H5	ECho EPfP GAbr MMuc NHar SIgm SRms WAbe WIce
	'Spotted Dog'	see *S.* 'Canis-dalmatica'
	'Sprite' (15)	SPoG
	spruneri (7)	ECho LRHS
	'Stansfieldii' (*rosacea*) (15)	GCrg SPlb SPoG
	'Star Dust' (7)	EPot
	startorii	see *S. scardica*
	'Štásek' (*dinnikii*) (7)	WAbe
	stellaris (4)	WAbe

	Name	Suppliers
	stenophylla subsp. ***stenophylla***	see *S. flagellaris*
	stolitzkae (7)	EPot
§	***stolonifera*** (5) 🏆H2	CSpe CTsd ECho EShb NBro SDix SWvt WCot WMoo WPnn WWtn
	- large-flowered (5)	WCot WGrn
	'Strawberry Melba' (7)	MHol NMen NPri
	'Sturmiana' (*paniculata*) (8)	SRms WOld
	'Sue Drew' (*fortunei*) (5)	LLHF
	'Sue Tubbs' (8)	GKev
	'Suendermannii Major' (× *kellereri*) (7)	ECho LRHS
	'Suendermannii' (× *kellereri*) (7)	ECho LRHS NMen
	'Sugar Plum Fairy' (*fortunei*) (5)	EBee ECtt EShb ESwi IVic
§	'Sulphurea' (× *boydii*) (7)	ECho EPot LRHS MAsh NSla NWad WHoo
	'Symons-Jeunei' (8)	NWad WAbe
	'Tamatsuzuri' (*fortunei*) (5)	SAko
	'Tankei' (5) **new**	SAko
	'Tenerife' (Swirly Group) (7)	EPot ITim NMen WAbe
	'Theoden' (*oppositifolia*) (7) 🏆H5	CMea ECho EWes NHar WAbe
	'Theresa Cooper' (7)	WAbe
	tolmiei (3)	WAbe
	tombeanensis (7)	NMen
	Touran Deep Red = 'Rockred' (Mossy Group) (15)	LBuc LRHS
	Touran Large White = 'Rocklarwhi'[PBR] (Mossy Group) (15)	EPfP LBuc LRHS
	'Teide' (Swirly Group) (7)	NMen
	'Tricolor' (*stolonifera*) (5) 🏆H2	EBak
§	'Triumph' (× *arendsii*) (15)	CBod ECtt EPfP GMaP MAsh MAvo NEgg SPoG
	'Tully' (× *elisabethae*) (7)	NMen WGor
	'Tumbling Waters' (8) 🏆H5	ECho EPot LHop LRHS MRav NHol NSla WAbe
§	'Tvoje Píseň' (× *poluanglica*) (7)	CTal GKev WHoo WThu
	'Tvůj Sen' (× *poluanglica*) (7)	NMen
§	'Tvůj Úsměv' (× *poluanglica*) (7) 🏆H5	NLar
§	'Tvůj Úspěch' (× *poluanglica*) (7)	WAbe
	'Tycho Brahe' (× *doerfleri*) (7)	WAbe
	umbrosa (11)	CMac CTri ECho EDAr LAst LEdu LRHS LSun MMuc MRav SBod SCob SEND SPlb SPoG SRms SWvt WMoo XLum
*	- ***subinteger***	MMuc SEND
	× ***urbium*** (11) 🏆H5	CBod CTri ECho ELan EPfP EWoo GMaP LEdu LPfy LPot MBel MCot NPri SPer SRms WBor WCAu WHoo WWEG
	'Vaccariana' (*oppositifolia*) (7)	ECho SHar
	'Valborg'	see *S.* 'Cranbourne'
	'Valentine'	see *S.* 'Cranbourne'
	'Valerie Finnis'	see *S.* 'Aretiastrum'
I	'Variegata' (*cuneifolia*) (11/v)	CBod ECho ECtt EPfP GCrg LRHS NHol NRya NWad SPlb SPoG WHoo WMoo
I	'Variegata' (*exarata* subsp. *moschata*) (15/v)	GMaP
	'Variegata' (*umbrosa*)	see *S.* 'Aureopunctata'
I	'Variegata' (× *urbium*) (11/v)	EBee ECho EPfP LRHS MBel MSpe NLar SBod SCob SMad SRms WWEG
	'Večerní Hvězda' (7)	WAbe
	veitchiana (5)	NBro XLum
	'Verona' (× *caroli-langii*) (7)	WAbe
	'Vinohrady' (7) **new**	NMen
	'Vítkov' (× *megaseiflora*) (7) **new**	NMen
	'Vladana' (× *megaseiflora*) (7)	ECho LRHS NMen WAbe
	'Vlasta' (7)	NMen
	'Vltava' (7)	NMen
	'Vreny' (8)	GKev
	'Vysoké Mýto' (7)	WAbe
	'Wada' (*fortunei*) (5)	CAbP CAby CBod CCon CDes CLAP CSpe EAEE ECtt ELon EPri GAbr GBuc GKev LAst MHol MNrw NBir NMyG SGSe WBor WCot WFar WOld WPGP WSHC WWtn
	'Walpole's Variety' (8)	NWad
	'Walter Ingwersen' (*umbrosa*) (11)	SRms
§	'Walter Irving' (× *irvingii*) (7) 🏆H5	WAbe
	'Warmes Herz' (*fortunei*) (5)	IVic
	'Welsh Dragon' (15)	WAbe
	'Welsh Red' (15)	WAbe
	'Welsh Rose' (15)	WAbe
	wendelboi (7)	CTal EPot WAbe
	'Wendrush' (× *wendelacina*) (7)	NMen
	'Wendy' (× *wendelacina*) (7)	WAbe
	'Wetterhorn' (*oppositifolia*) (7)	GCrg
	'Whatcote' (7) **new**	NMen
	'Wheatley Lion' (× *borisii*) (7)	NMen
	'Wheatley Rose' (7)	ECho LRHS
	'White Cap' (× *boydii*) (7)	NMen
§	'White Pixie' (15)	ECtt EDAr EPfP EWoo GCrg MAsh MHer NEoE NHol NPri NRya NWad SPlb SPoG SRms WIce
	'White Star' (*fortunei*) (5)	LLHF LRHS
	'White Star' (× *petraschii*)	see *S.* 'Schelleri'
	'Whitehill' (8) 🏆H5	CMea ECho ELan GEdr GJos GMaP LRHS NFav NRya NSla NWad SBch WHoo
	'William Boyd' (× *boydii*) (7)	WAbe
	'William Shakespeare' (Blues Group) (7)	NMen WAbe
	'Winifred Bevington' (8 × 11)	CPBP CSma CTal ECho EDAr GCrg LHop LRHS MHol MMuc NBro NLar NPri NRya NWad WAbe WHoo WOld WPnn
	'Winifred' (× *anglica*) (7)	CTal ECho WAbe
	'Winston Churchill' (15)	CTri ECho LRHS NHol NWad
I	'Winston Churchill Variegata' (15/v)	NHol NPri NWad
	'Wisley' (*federici-augusti* subsp. *grisebachii*) (7) 🏆H5	GKev
	'Wisley Primrose'	see *S.* 'Kolbiana'
	'Yellow Rock' (7)	NMen NRya
	'Youkuy' (*fortunei*) (5)	IVic
	Your Good Fortune	see *S.* 'Tvůj Úspěch'
	Your Smile	see *S.* 'Tvůj Úsměv'
	Your Song	see *S.* 'Tvoje Píseň'

Your Success	see *S.* 'Tvůj Úspěch'
'Yunagi' (*fortunei*) (5)	IVic SAko WOld
× ***zimmeteri*** (8 × 11)	ECho
§ 'Zlatá Praha' (× *pragensis*) (7)	NMen WAbe

Scabiosa (*Caprifoliaceae*)

africana	EWes SHar
- 'Jocelyn'	EWes SHar
alpina L.	see *Cephalaria alpina*
argentea	EWes WPGP
- PAB 1229 **new**	LEdu
atropurpurea	SPav
- 'Ace of Spades'	ELan EPfP MGos SCob SPav SPhx
- 'Beaujolais Bonnets'	CNor EAJP EPfP LBMP LRHS SHil SPer
- 'Black Knight'	CSpe SPav
- 'Blue Beau'	LRHS
§ - 'Chile Black'	CAby CBcs EAJP ECou EHoe EHrv ELan EPfP EUJe EWes IBoy LAst LRHS NPri SCob SPav SPer SRkn SWvt WBod WHar WMnd
§ - 'Chilli Pepper'	CWCL LRHS
§ - 'Chilli Sauce'	EBee
- 'Derry's Black'	CSpe SPtp
- 'Fata Morgana'	SPav
- 'Snowmaiden'	SPav
banatica	see *S. columbaria*
'Barocca'	CNor CSpe EBee EPfP LRHS WCot
'Black PomPom'	CBod CTsd CWld EBee GBin NLar
'Blackberry Fool' (Dessert Series)	WHlf
'Blue Diamonds'	EBee GJos IBoy LRHS MHol
'Blueberry Muffin' (Dessert Series)	WHlf
'Burgundy Blue'	MCot
Burgundy Bonnets = 'Scabon'[PBR]	CBod EPfP
§ 'Butterfly Blue'	Widely available
'Cambridge Blue'	EPfP
canescens	MSpe
caucasica	CMac EPfP GKev LAst LEdu LRHS WHoo XSen
- var. ***alba***	CBcs EPfP ILea NGBl WHoo
- 'Blausiegel'	CBod EHrv LRHS MRav MSpe NDov
- 'Clive Greaves' ♀H4	EBee ECha ECtt GBuc GMaP IBoy LRHS MBNS MSpe NDov SCob SGbt SPad SRms SWvt WCAu WCot WFar WHil
- 'Deep Waters'	CSpe EBee LRHS WPtf
- 'Fama'	COtt CSpe CWib NBir NGBl NLar SPlb SRms WFar
- 'Fama Deep Blue'	EWTr
- 'Goldingensis'	CWCL NGdn
- House's hybrids	CSBt MHol NGdn SRms
- 'Isaac House'	XLum
- 'Kompliment'	WFar
- 'Miss Willmott' ♀H4	CBod CMac CSam EBee ECha ECtt EHoe EHrv EPfP EWTr GBin IBoy LAst LHop LRHS MBri MLHP MRav MSpe NCGa NPri SGbt SPer SPoG SWvt WCAu WMnd
- Perfecta Series	CWib LRHS MMHG NGdn NLar SPoG SWat WHar
- - 'Perfecta Alba'	CBod CWib ELan ELon EPfP EWoo GMaP LAst LHop LRHS MBel MGos MHer MHol NLar SCob SPad SPer SPoG SWat WCAu WPtf XLum XSen
- - 'Perfecta Blue'	CBod CMac ELan ELon EPfP EWoo GMaP LSun MBel MGos MHer SBod WCot XLum
- - 'Perfecta Lilac Blue'	CWib EPfP SPer
- 'Stäfa'	EBee ECha GBee GBin LRHS NEgg NLar WMnd
- 'Thorp's Variegated' (v)	WCot
'Cherry Pie' (Dessert Series)	LBMP WHlf
'Chile Black'	see *S. atropurpurea* 'Chile Black'
'Chile Pepper'	see *S. atropurpurea* 'Chilli Pepper'
'Chile Sauce'	see *S. atropurpurea* 'Chilli Sauce'
cinerea	SPhx
§ ***columbaria***	CHab CWld EBee ECGP LRHS MLHP MMuc NEgg NMir SPhx WHer WJek WSFF
* - ***alpina***	GKev
- 'Blue Note'[PBR]	CBod EBee LRHS
- 'Mariposa Blue' **new**	MHol
- 'Misty Butterflies'	CAby ECtt EPfP GBin LBMP LHop MHol NEgg NGdn NLar WFar
- 'Nana'	CCse EBee GBin LRHS NBir NGdn NLar SBch SBea WCFE XLum
§ - subsp. ***ochroleuca***	CKno CSpe ECha EHrv LCro LRHS MCot MMuc MSpe NBir NLar SCob SEND SGSe SHar SPhx SPoG SRms WCAu WPGP
- - MESE 344	EBee
- - 'Moon Dance'	CCon CMea CSam EAJP GBin LBMP LLHF LRHS MSpe MTis NLar SAko SBea SGbt WHoo
- 'Pincushion Blue'	EDAr LRHS LSun
- 'Pincushion Pink'	EDAr LRHS NGdn SGSe
cretica	XLum XSen
drakensbergensis	CHid ELan EWes GKev IKil ILea LRHS MTPN SGSe SLon WCot WPtf
gigantea	see *Cephalaria gigantea*
graminifolia	ECho GKev LRHS NBir SBch SRms XLum
- ***rosea***	EWes
'Helen Dillon'	ECre EWes LSou
'Irish Perpetual Flowering'	see *S.* 'Butterfly Blue'
japonica var. ***acutiloba***	SPhx
- var. ***alpina***	CPrp EBee EPfP GKev MMuc MSpe NGdn SEND SPhx WHoo WWFP XLum
- - 'Blue Star'	EBee NBre NCGa SGbt
- 'Ritz Blue'	CMea EPfP MGos NCGa SPad
lachnophylla	GCal SPhx WCot
- 'Blue Horizon'	EBee
'Little Cracker'	CSpe GBin LRHS LSou SCob SLon
'Little Emily'	ELon LSou
lucida	CBod ECho ECtt EPfP LRHS MMuc MRav SEND WPGP XLum
Magic = 'Pmoore02'	EBee LCro LOPS LSou
'Midnight'	CMea
'Miss Havisham'	EWes
montana Mill.	see *Knautia arvensis*
ochroleuca	see *S. columbaria* subsp. *ochroleuca*
olgae	EBee
parnassi	see *Pterocephalus perennis*
'Perpetual Flowering'	see *S.* 'Butterfly Blue'
Pink Buttons = 'Walminipink'	CBod CCon EBee
'Pink Diamonds'	EBee ELan EPfP MHol
'Pink Mist'[PBR]	EBee ECtt ELan EPfP GBBs IBoy LCro LRHS MAsh MBri NBir NLar SCob SCoo SPer SPoG SRms

'Plum Pudding' (Dessert Series)	WHlf
pterocephala	see *Pterocephalus perennis*
rhodopensis	EBee
'Rhubarb Crumble' (Dessert Series)	WHlf
'Rosie's Pink'	ECtt
rumelica	see *Knautia macedonica*
'Satchmo'	see *S. atropurpurea* 'Chile Black'
'Strawberry Parfait' **new**	LBMP
succisa	see *Succisa pratensis*
tatarica	see *Cephalaria gigantea*
'Vivid Violet'	CAbb CSpe CWGN EBee ECtt LBuc LRHS LSRN LSou MBNS MHol MNrw NDov NLar SAko SHil WBor WBrk WCot

Scadoxus ✿ (*Amaryllidaceae*)

membranaceus	CLak GKev WCot
multiflorus	ECho GKev LAma SDeJ
§ - subsp. ***katherinae*** [H1b]	CLak CPne WCot
§ - subsp. ***multiflorus***	WCot
natalensis	see *S. puniceus*
§ ***puniceus***	CEvo CLak CPne GKev WCot

Scaevola (*Goodeniaceae*)

aemula 'Blue Fan'	see *S. aemula* 'Blue Wonder'
- Blue Print = 'Kingscablin'[PBR] **new**	NPri
§ - 'Blue Wonder'[PBR]	NPer SWvt
- 'Purple Fan'	LAst
- 'Sparkling Fan'	LAst
- 'Suntastic'	LAst
'Brillant'[PBR]	LAst LBMP LSou
crassifolia	SPlb
'Topaz Pink'	LAst LSou

Sceletium (*Aizoaceae*)

tortuosum	SPlb

Schefflera (*Araliaceae*)

alpina	CFil IVic
- B&SWJ 8247	WCru
- B&SWJ 11827	WCru
- HWJ 936	WCru
- large-leaved WWJ 11999	WCru
arboricola [H1c]	SEND XBlo
- 'Gold Capella' [H1c]	SEND XBlo
- 'Kalahari'	XBlo
brevipedicellata HWJ 870	WCru
- KWJ 12224	WCru
§ ***chapana*** B&SWJ 11848	WCru
- HWJ 983	WCru
delavayi	CFil CPne WCru WPGP
enneaphylla B&SWJ 11727	WCru
- HWJ 1018	WCru
fantsipanensis	CFil
- B&SWJ 11666	WCru
- B&SWJ 11671	WCru
- NJM 10.137	WPGP
gracilis HWJ 622	WCru
- HWJ 878	WCru
gracilis* × *taiwaniana	WCru
hoi B&SWJ 11747	WCru
kornasii B&SWJ 11830	WCru
- HWJ 918	WCru
macrophylla B&SWJ 8210	WCru
- B&SWJ 9788	WCru
- B&SWJ 11842	WCru
- PAB 2788	LEdu
microphylla B&SWJ 3872	WCru
multinervia B&SWJ 11727	WCru
aff. ***myriocarpa*** B&SWJ 11828	WCru
rhododendrifolia	CDoC CExl CFil CMHG EBee SMad WPGP
- GWJ 9375	WCru
taiwaniana [H4]	CFil CPne IVic
- B&SWJ 3575	WCru
- B&SWJ 7096	WCru
- RWJ 10000	WCru
- RWJ 10016	WCru
vietnamensis	see *S. chapana*

Schima (*Theaceae*)

argentea	CExl EBee EPfP
khasiana PAB 3447	LEdu
wallichii	CBcs CExl

Schinus (*Anacardiaceae*)

latifolius	CBcs
lentiscifolius	SPlb
molle	SPlb
polygamus	MGil SPlb

Schisandra (*Schisandraceae*)

sp.	LAst
arisanensis	MBlu NLar WPGP
- B&SWJ 3050	WCru
aff. ***bicolor***	WPGP
chinensis	CAgr CArn CBcs CRHN EShb GKev GPoy LEdu MSwo NLar
- B&SWJ 4204	WCru
- B&SWJ 4611A	WCru
- B&SWJ 4611B	WCru
- 'Bere'	LEdu WPGP
grandiflora [H5]	CBcs CBot CDoC CWCL EBee ELan EPfP ESwi IDee IMou LRHS MBlu SBrt SKHP SPer WBod
- B&SWJ 2245	WCru WSHC
- PAB 3673 **new**	LEdu
- var. ***cathayensis***	see *S. sphaerandra*
- 'Jamu' (m)	WCru
- 'Lahlu' (f/F)	WCru
grandiflora* × *rubriflora	WCru
henryi subsp. ***yunnanensis*** B&SWJ 6546	WCru
incarnata BWJ 7898	WCru
incarnata* × *rubriflora	WCru
lancifolia	MBlu WPGP
nigra	see *S. repanda*
perulata FMWJ 13100	WCru
aff. ***plena*** HWJ 664	WCru
propinqua	WSHC
- subsp. ***sinensis***	CBot CMac CRHN LEdu NLar WPGP
- - BWJ 8148	WCru
§ ***repanda***	EBee
- B&SWJ 5897	WCru
- B&SWJ 11455	WCru
rubriflora [H5]	CBcs CTri EBee EPfP IDee IMou LRHS MBlu MGos NLar SBrt SKHP SLon SMDP SPoG
- (f)	ESwi WSHC
- BWJ 7557	WCru
- 'Bodnant Redberry' (f)	WCru
§ ***sphaerandra*** BWJ 7739	WCru

- BWJ 8082	WCru
sphenanthera	EBee LRHS NLar WSHC
- BWJ 8151	WCru

Schizachyrium (*Poaceae*)

§ ***scoparium***	CKno EBee ECGP EHoe EPPr EPfP GQue SGSe XLum
- 'Blaze'	EPPr
- 'Blue Heaven'	ELon
- 'Prairie Blues'	ELon EPfP LRHS LSun SMea SPhx WCot

Schizocarphus (*Asparagaceae*)

nervosus	WCot

Schizocodon see *Shortia*

Schizophragma (*Hydrangeaceae*)

corylifolium	NLar
- BWJ 8150	WPGP
§ ***fauriei***	NLar WSHC
- B&SWJ 1701	WCru
- B&SWJ 6831	WCru
- B&SWJ 7052	WCru
- CWJ 12405	WCru
- CWJ 12433	WCru
hydrangeoides	CBcs CDoC CDul CRHN EBee ELan EPfP GKin LAst LCro LOPS LRHS MBlu MGos SGol SLim SLon SPer SWvt WCFE
- 'Brookside Littleleaf'	see *Hydrangea anomala* subsp. *petiolaris* var. *cordifolia* 'Brookside Littleleaf'
- var. ***concolor*** B&SWJ 5954	WCru
- - 'Moonlight' ♀H5	CBcs CDul CKel CMac CWGN ELan EPfP GKin LPal LRHS MBlu MGil MGos MMuc NLar SBrt SKHP SLon SPer SPoG SRkn SSpi SWvt WCot WCru WPGP WPat WSHC
- var. ***hydrangeoides*** B&SWJ 5489	WCru
- - B&SWJ 5732	WCru
- - 'Iwa Garami'	NLar
- - 'Roseum' ♀H5	CBcs CDoC CDul CMac ELan EPfP EWes GBin GKin IArd LRHS MBlu MGil MGos NLar SGol SKHP SLon SPer SSpi SWvt WCru WPGP
- 'Rose Sensation'	CBot EBee EPfP LRHS SLon SPoG
- var. ***taquetii*** B&SWJ 8771	WCru
- - 'Cheju's Early'	WCru
- var. ***ullungdoense*** B&SWJ 8505	WCru
- - B&SWJ 8522	WCru
- var. ***yakushimense*** B&SWJ 6119	WCru
integrifolium ♀H5	CBcs CBot CDul CRHN EBee ELan EPfP LRHS MBlu MMuc SKHP SPer WKif WPGP WSHC
- BWJ 8150	WCru
- var. ***fauriei***	see *S. fauriei*
molle HWJ 1011	WCru
- WWJ 11905	WCru

Schizostylis see *Hesperantha*

coccinea 'Gigantea'	see *Hesperantha coccinea* 'Major'
- 'Grandiflora'	see *Hesperantha coccinea* 'Major'
- 'Sunset'	see *Hesperantha coccinea* 'Sunrise'
'Pink Princess'	see *Hesperantha coccinea* 'Wilfred H. Bryant'

Schoenoplectus (*Cyperaceae*)

§ ***lacustris***	CWat MMuc MSKA MWLS MWts SEND
§ - subsp. ***tabernaemontani***	CSpe
- - 'Albescens' (v)	CBen CWat MMuc MNrw MSKA MWts SWat WHal XLum
- - 'Zebrinus' (v)	CBen CWat ELan MNrw MSKA MWts NPla SPlb SWat WMAq XLum

Schoenus (*Cyperaceae*)

pauciflorus	LLWG WMoo

Sciadopitys (*Sciadopityaceae*)

verticillata ♀H6	CBcs CDoC CDul CKen CMac CTho EFry EPfP GKin IDee MBlu MGos MMuc NHol NWad NWea SAko SCoo SEND SLim SPoG SSpi SWvt WHar
- 'Big Filip'	NLar
- 'Firework'	CKen NLar
- 'Globe'	CKen
- 'Gold Star'	CKen NLar
- 'Goldammer'	NLar
- 'Golden Rush'	CKen NLar
- 'Goldmahne'	CKen
- 'Grüne Kugel'	CKen NLar
- 'Jeddeloh Compact'	CKen
- 'Koja Maki'	NLar
- 'Kupferschirm'	CKen NLar
- 'Mecki'	CKen
- 'Megaschirm'	CKen
- 'Ossorio Gold'	CKen
- 'Perlenglanz'	CKen
- 'Picola'	CKen
- 'Pygmy'	CKen
- 'Richie's Cream'	CKen
- 'Richie's Cushion'	CKen
- 'Shorty'	CKen
- 'Speerspitze'	CKen
- 'Star Wars'	CKen
- 'Starburst'	CKen NLar
- 'Sternschnuppe'	CKen MAsh NLar
- 'Wintergreen'	CKen

Scilla (*Asparagaceae*)

adlamii	see *Ledebouria cooperi*
× ***allenii***	see × *Chionoscilla allenii*
amethystina	see *S. litardierei*
amoena	ECho WCot
autumnalis	CAvo CDes ECho EPot GKev LAma LLHF LRHS NRog WShi WThu
- white-flowered	NRog
bifolia ♀H5	CAvo CBro CTca ECho EPot GKev LAma LLWP SBch SDeJ SPhx WShi
- RS 156/83	ECho
- 'Alba'	ECho SPhx
- 'Rosea'	ECho GKev LAma LLWP MPie SDeJ
bithynica ♀H5	ECho EPot WCot WShi
campanulata	see *Hyacinthoides hispanica*
chinensis	see *S. scilloides*
cilicica	ECho
greilhuberi	CAvo ECho EPPr EPot LLHF WCot
hohenackeri	ECho LLHF SPhx WCot WThu
- BSBE 811	CDes WCot
§ ***hughii***	CDes EBee ECho
hyacinthoides	CDes ECho ERCP WCot
ingridiae	ECho
- var. ***taurica***	ECho
italica	see *Hyacinthoides italica*

japonica	see *S. scilloides*
kraussii	GKev
latifolia new	WCot
- from Morocco	ECho
liliohyacinthus	CBro ECho IBlr MMHG WShi
- 'Alba'	CAvo
lingulata	ECho LLHF WCot
- S&F 253	CDes
- var. ***lingulata***	ECho
§ ***litardierei*** ♀H5	CTca ECho EPPr EPfP EPot ERCP GKev LAma MMuc SBch SDeJ SEND SPhx WShi
lutea hort.	see *Ledebouria socialis*
madeirensis	CLak WCot
- from Madeira	CHll
melaina	ECho WCot
mesopotamica	ECho
messeniaca MS 38 from Greece	WCot
mischtschenkoana ♀H5	CAvo CBro CHid ECho EPot IFro LAma LCro LOPS LRHS MBri SBch SDeJ WShi
§ - 'Tubergeniana' ♀H5	CMea ECho GKev SPhx WCot
- 'Zwanenburg'	ECho
monophyllos	ECho WCot
morrisii	ECho
natalensis	see *Merwilla plumbea*
non-scripta	see *Hyacinthoides non-scripta*
nutans	see *Hyacinthoides non-scripta*
obtusifolia	ECho
persica ♀H4	CDes ECho WCot
peruviana	Widely available
- SB&L 20/1	WCot
- 'Alba'	CBro CTal CTca CWCL ECho GKev WCot WHil XLum
- var. ***elegans***	CDes
- 'Hughii'	see *S. hughii*
- var. ***venusta***	CDes EBee
- - S&L 311/2	WCot
pratensis	see *S. litardierei*
puschkinioides	ECho
rosenii	ECho
§ ***scilloides***	ECho NRog WCot
- B&SWJ 8812	WCru
* - 'Alba'	SDeJ
siberica ♀H5	CAby CAvo CBro CTca ECho ELan EPfP EShb GKev LAma LCro LOPS LPfy LRHS MMuc MWat SCob SPer SPhx WBor WHea WShi
- 'Alba'	CAvo CTca ECho EPfP EPot GKev LAma LRHS SDeJ WShi
- 'Spring Beauty'	CMea ECho EPot ERCP GKev LAma LRHS MBri SDeJ SPhx SRms WRHF
'Tubergeniana'	see *S. mischtschenkoana* 'Tubergeniana'
verna	ECho WShi WThu
vicentina	see *Hyacinthoides vincentina*
violacea	see *Ledebouria socialis*

Scirpoides (*Cyperaceae*)

§ ***holoschoenus***	EBee WDra

Scirpus (*Cyperaceae*)

cernuus	see *Isolepis cernua*
'Green Mist'	WCot
holoschoenus	see *Scirpoides holoschoenus*
lacustris	see *Schoenoplectus lacustris*
- 'Spiralis'	see *Juncus effusus* f. *spiralis*
maritimus	see *Bolboschoenus maritimus*
sylvaticus	WDra
tabernaemontani	see *Schoenoplectus lacustris* subsp. *tabernaemontani*

Scleranthus (*Caryophyllaceae*)

biflorus	ECho EDAr EPot EUJe EWes GBin LEdu MAsh SPlb XLum
uniflorus	ECho EPot LEdu SMad SPlb XLum

Sclerochiton (*Acanthaceae*)

harveyanus	EShb

Scoliopus (*Liliaceae*)

bigelowii	GEdr
hallii	CTal EBee LEdu MNrw WCru

Scolopendrium see *Asplenium*

Scopolia (*Solanaceae*)

anomala HWJK 2252 new	WCru
carniolica	CArn CAvo CCon EBee ELan EPPr EWld GPoy ILea LEdu MPhe NChi NLar NSti SPlb WCru WPGP WSHC XLum
- from Poland	LEdu
§ - var. ***brevifolia***	EBee EHrv EPPr EPfP EWld LEdu LRHS MNrw SPhx WCot WPGP
- - WM 9811	MPhe
- 'Zwanenburg'	ECho EHrv EPPr EWes LEdu NLar SPhx WPGP XLum
hladnikiana	see *S. carniolica* var. *brevifolia*
japonica	IMou
lurida	see *Anisodus luridus*
stramonifolia new	CArn

Scorzonera (*Asteraceae*)

hispanica	SVic

Scrophularia (*Scrophulariaceae*)

aquatica misapplied	see *S. auriculata*
§ ***auriculata***	CHab LLWG MHer NMir NPer WHer
§ - 'Variegata' (v)	CAby CBcs ECha EHoe ELan EPfP GCal GLog LLWG LRHS MHer NPri NSti SHar SPer SPoG
buergeriana 'Lemon and Lime' misapplied	see *Teucrium viscidum* 'Lemon and Lime'
- 'Lemon and Lime' (v)	EBee NEgg
macrantha	GEdr
nodosa	CArn GPoy NMir WHer WHfH
- ***variegata***	see *S. auriculata* 'Variegata'
umbrosa	MWLS
subsp. ***umbrosa*** new	
vernalis	CBgR

Scutellaria (*Lamiaceae*)

albida	EBee GJos
§ ***alpina***	ECho GJos SPlb SRms SRot
- 'Arcobaleno'	GJos LLHF
- 'Moonbeam'	GJos
altissima	CFis ECha ELan MMuc MSpe NBro SPlb WHea WOut WPtf WWtn XSen
'Amazing Grace'	EWes
baicalensis	CArn GJos GPoy IMou WPtf WTor
- 'Oriental Blue'	GJos
canescens	see *S. incana*
chungtiensis new	GEdr
diffusa	SBch
galericulata	CBod CHab ENfk GPoy MHer WHer
hastata	see *S. hastifolia*
§ ***hastifolia***	CTri ECtt

§	***incana***	ECGP ELan EWoo GMaP LCro LHop LOPS LPla LRHS MAvo MHol MPie SPhx WCot WMnd
	indica var. ***japonica***	see *S. indica* var. *parvifolia*
§	- var. ***parvifolia***	ECho EWes GJos ITim SRot WAbe
	- - 'Alba'	ECho LLHF
	lateriflora	CArn GJos GPoy SRms WJek
	- PAB 3921	LEdu
	maekawae	EBee WPGP
	- B&SWJ 557A	CDes WCru
	'Mood Indigo'	EPPr
	orientalis	ECtt WAbe
	- subsp. ***bicolor***	ECtt SIgm
	- subsp. ***pinnatifida***	XSen
	pontica	CPBP MMuc SPhx WIce
	scordiifolia	CFis CMea ECha ECho IMou LHop NRya NWad SRms
	- 'Seoul Sapphire'	CDes CSpe GBin LEdu LHop LRHS SPtp WPGP WPtf
	sevanensis	LHop WCot WIce
	'Sherbert Lemon'	CMea CPBP SRot WTor
	suffrutescens	GJos
	- 'Texas Rose'	CMea CSpe ECho GJos LHop LLHF LRHS MCot SBch SRot WAbe WHoo WIce
	supina	see *S. alpina*
	tournefortii	EBee ECtt LLWP LRHS WOut XSen
*	***zhongdianensis***	WPtf

seakale see *Crambe maritima*

Sebaea (*Gentianaceae*)

rehmanii	SPlb
thomasii	WAbe
- 'Bychan'	WAbe

Securigera (*Papilionaceae*)

§	***varia***	CArn EPPr LHop MMuc SEND SRms XLum

Sedastrum see *Sedum*

Sedella (*Crassulaceae*)

pumila new	GCal

× *Sedeveria* (*Crassulaceae*)

'Darley Dale'	CSuc
'Fanfare'	CSuc
'Harry Butterfield'	WCot
'Letizia'	CSuc EUJe

Sedum ✿ (*Crassulaceae*)

	sp.	SCob
	'Abbey Dore'	CKno CPrp ECtt ELan ELon EPfP GCal LPla LRHS LSou MSpe MTis NCGa SPhx WCAu WPGP
	acre	CTri ECho EPfP GPoy LEdu LRHS MAsh MNHC NMir SBod SCob SPlb XLum
	- 'Aureum'	ECho ECou EDAr EHoe ELan EPfP LAst MAsh NLar NPri NRya SCob SPoG XLum
	- 'Elegans'	ECtt GCrg
	- 'Golden Queen'	ECho EPot LRHS MSCN SPlb SPoG
	- 'Helvetica'	WCot
	- 'Minus'	ECho LRHS
§	- subsp. ***neglectum*** var. ***majus***	CChe EPfP NLar
	aizoon	ECho GCal LAst NBre SPlb WFar XLum
	- 'Aurantiacum'	see *S. aizoon* 'Euphorbioides'
§	- 'Euphorbioides'	ECha ECtt ELan LPot MHer MMuc MRav NLar SEND SHar SPer SPlb
§	- subsp. ***maximowiczii***	NWad
	alatum	WFar
	albescens	see *S. forsterianum* f. *purpureum*
	alboroseum	see *S. erythrostictum*
§	***album***	ECho GJos LRHS MMuc NBro NMir SEND XLum
	- 'Coral Carpet'	CTal ECho ECtt EDAr EPPr EPfP EPot GAbr GCrg GJos GKev MAsh MRav MWat NLar NPri NRya SFgr SPoG WCot XLum
	- subsp. ***teretifolium*** var. ***micranthum*** 'Chloroticum'	XLum
§	- - var. ***murale***	CTri LRHS XLum
	alpestre	XLum
	altissimum	see *S. sediforme*
*	***altum***	NBre
	Amber = 'Florseamb'	WCot
	anacampseros	MHer NWad SEND XLum
	'Aquarel'	GBin
	athoum	see *S. album*
	atlanticum	see *S. dasyphyllum* subsp. *dasyphyllum* var. *mesatlanticum*
	'Autumn Charm'	see *S.* (Herbstfreude Group) 'Lajos'
	Autumn Joy	see *S.* 'Herbstfreude'
	'Beach Party' (Party Hardy Series) new	LRHS
	beauverdii subsp. ***vietnamense*** HWJ 824	WCru
	'Bertram Anderson' 🏆H7	Widely available
	beyrichianum misapplied	see *S. glaucophyllum*
	'Birthday Party' (Party Hardy Series) new	EBee LRHS
	bithynicum 'Aureum'	see *S. hispanicum* var. *minus* 'Aureum'
	Black Beauty = 'Florseblab'	ECtt LRHS MBri MNrw NDov NLar SPoG
	'Blade Runner'	LRHS LSou
	brevifolium	EWes
§	- var. ***quinquefarium***	WIce
	'Carl' 🏆H7	Widely available
	cauticola 🏆H5	ECho EDAr EPot GBuc GCal MAsh MAvo MHer MRav SRms SRot WAbe WIce XLum
	- from Lida, Belarus	ECho
	- 'Coca-Cola'	CBod CMac CWGN EAEE ECtt EHoe GBin GJos GKev LAst LBMP LRHS MAsh MCot MRav NDov NPri SPhx SPoG SWvt WCAu WHoo
	- 'Lidakense' 🏆H5	CMea CSpe CTal CWCL ECha ECho ECtt EPot GBuc GCrg MAsh MLHP MSCN NHol NLar NSla SBch SPlb SRot XLum
	- 'Purpurine'	ECho
	- 'Robustum'	see *S.* 'Ruby Glow'
	'Cherry Tart' (SunSparkler Series) new	ECtt
	'Chocolate Drop' PBR	CMos CWGN EBee ECtt NLar SDys SPoG
	'Chocolate Sauce'	MAvo
	chrysicaulum	EPot
	'Class Act' PBR	ECtt LRHS MNrw NLar SPoG
	'Cloud Walker' PBR	ECtt LRHS MNrw NCGa SPoG
	confusum Hemsl.	SEND
	crassipes	see *Rhodiola wallichiana*

	crassularia	see *Crassula setulosa* 'Milfordiae'
	'Crazy Ruffles'	ECtt WCot
	cryptomerioides B&SWJ 054	WCru
	cyaneum 'Sakhalin'	WCot
	'Dark Jack'	CKno ECtt ELon EPfP MAvo MNrw MTis NGdn WCot
	dasyphyllum	ECho ECou NRya SPlb SRms
§	- subsp. ***dasyphyllum*** var. ***mesatlanticum***	NBir
	- ***mucronatis***	see *S. dasyphyllum* subsp. *dasyphyllum* var. *mesatlanticum*
	'Diamond Edge' (v)	EBee ECtt IKil
	divergens	XLum
	douglasii	see *S. stenopetalum* 'Douglasii'
	drymarioides	NBre
	'Dudley Field'	MHer
	'Eleanor Fisher'	see *S. telephium* subsp. *ruprechtii*
	ellacombeanum	see *S. kamtschaticum* var. *ellacombeanum*
	'Elworthy Rose'	CElw
§	***erythrostictum***	XLum
	- 'Frosty Morn' (v)	Widely available
§	- 'Mediovariegatum' (v)	CNec EAEE EBee ELan LRHS MHer MNrw NLar SWvt WFar WMnd WMoo XLum
	ewersii	ECho ECtt EDAr EPot EWTr GCrg MAsh MMuc NBro NLar SPhx SPlb WTor XLum
	- CC 5288	ITim
	- var. ***homophyllum*** 'Rosenteppich'	EPPr EPfP LBuc LRHS MAsh MBrN SWvt WMoo
	fabaria	see *S. telephium* subsp. *fabaria*
	fastigiatum	see *Rhodiola fastigiata*
	floriferum	see *S. kamtschaticum* var. *floriferum*
	forsterianum subsp. ***elegans***	NPri SEND SPlb XLum
	- - 'Silver Stone'	GJos MMuc
§	- f. ***purpureum***	NRya
	'Frosted Fire'	EBee LSou MAsh NSti
	furfuraceum	GEdr WAbe
	Garnet Brocade = 'Garbro'[PBR]	ECtt
§	***glaucophyllum***	EDAr XLum
	'Gold Mound'	EUJe LAst
	'Green Expectations'	ECtt GBin LRHS MRav NBre
	hakonense 'Chocolate Ball'	CPBP ECtt GBin LHop LSou LSun
	Herbstfreude Group	EHrv EWoo LRHS NWsh
	- 'Autumn Fire'	MAsh
	- 'Beka' (v)	LSou MAsh
	- 'Elsie's Gold' (v)	CBod EBee ECtt EPfP LRHS MAsh MNrw SPoG SRms WHil
§	- 'Herbstfreude' ♀H7	Widely available
	- 'Jaws'[PBR]	CAby CKno EBee ECtt IKil NLar WCot WFar XLum
§	- 'Lajos' (v)	LSou MAsh NEoE WCot
	- 'Mini Joy'	ELon LRHS MHol MNrw SHil
	heterodontum	see *Rhodiola heterodonta*
	hidakanum	ECtt EHoe EPot GMaP NBro NHol NWad SIgm WHoo
	himalense misapplied	see *Rhodiola* 'Keston'
	hispanicum	ECho SPlb
	- 'Blue Carpet'	EPPr EUJe MSCN NPri
	- ***glaucum***	see *S. hispanicum* var. *minus*
§	- var. ***minus***	ECho ECtt MMuc SEND SPlb WCot WMoo
§	- - 'Aureum'	ECho

§	***hybridum***	XLum
	- 'Czar's Gold'	NGdn
	'Ice Ruffles' (v)	MAvo SPoG
	'Indian Chief'	see *S.* (Herbstfreude Group) 'Herbstfreude'
	indicum var. ***yunnanense***	EShb
	ishidae	see *Rhodiola ishidae*
	'José Aubergine'[PBR]	CKno CMos EBee ECtt EWTr EWoo IPot LRHS MAvo MBri MRav MTis NCGa NDov NHol NLar NSti SCob SGol SPoG WPGP
	'Joyce Henderson'	EAEE ECtt ELan EPfP LHop LRHS MCot MRav MTis MWhi NChi NLar SPer SRGP WBrk WCot WMoo WOld
	kamtschaticum ♀H5	ECho EDAr GJos
	- B&SWJ 10870	WCru
§	- var. ***ellacombeanum*** ♀H5	MMuc SEND WCot XLum
	- - B&SWJ 8853	WCru
§	- var. ***floriferum***	XSen
§	- - 'Weihenstephaner Gold'	CTri ECho ECtt EDAr EPfP GMaP LPot MHer MMuc MRav MSCN NBir SPlb SPoG SRms XLum
	- var. ***kamtschaticum*** 'Variegatum' (v) ♀H5	CMea ECho EDAr EHoe EPfP GCrg LRHS MHer MJak MMuc NPri SPoG SRms SRot SWvt XLum
	kirilovii	see *Rhodiola kirilovii*
	'Knight Rider' **new**	EBee
	lanceolatum	NBre
	'Lime Zinger' (SunSparkler Series) **new**	ECtt
	lineare 'Variegatum' (v)	SBch WRHF XLum
	'Little Dove'	SBch
	'Little Missy' (v)	ECtt
§	***lydium***	CTri ECho MHer MSCN SFgr SPlb
	- 'Aureum'	see *S. hispanicum* var. *minus* 'Aureum'
	- 'Bronze Queen'	see *S. lydium*
I	'Marchants Best Red' ♀H7	ELon MRav SMHy SPhx WCot
	'Matrona' ♀H7	Widely available
	maweanum	see *S. acre* subsp. *neglectum* var. *majus*
	maximowiczii	see *S. aizoon* subsp. *maximowiczii*
	middendorffianum	ECho GCrg MBrN MHer SRms SRot XLum
§	***montanum*** **new**	MMuc
	moranense	XLum
	morganianum ♀H2	EBak EShb
	morrisonense B&SWJ 7078	WCru
	'Mr Goodbud'[PBR] ♀H7	CKno ECtt GBin LBMP LPla LRHS LSun MAvo MHol MNrw NDov NEgg NLar SAko SPoG WCot WTor
	'Munstead Red'	CBod CPrp CWCL EBee ECha ECtt EHrv ELon EPfP GBin LAst LRHS MNrw MRav MTis MWat NLar SBch SPer SPhx SPoG WCAu WKif WMnd WMoo
	murale	see *S. album* subsp. *teretifolium* var. *murale*
	nevii misapplied	see *S. glaucophyllum*
	nevii ambig.	SPlb
	nicaeense	see *S. sediforme*
	obtusatum misapplied	see *S. oreganum*
§	***obtusatum*** A. Gray	NBro NSla
	obtusifolium var. ***listoniae***	EDAr
	ochroleucum	NBre WCot
	- subsp. ***montanum***	see *S. montanum*
	oppositifolium	see *S. spurium* 'Album'

§	***oreganum***	ECha ECho EDAr GAbr GCrg GKev GMaP MHer MHtn NPri SMad SPlb SRms SRot XLum
	- 'Procumbens'	see *S. oreganum* subsp. *tenue*
§	- subsp. ***tenue***	NHol NRya NWad
§	***oregonense***	ECho LRHS MHer
	pachyclados	see *Rhodiola pachyclados*
	pachyphyllum	LAll
	palmeri	MRav NBir SChr XLum
	'Parish Plum'	SBch
	pilosum	EPot GKev WThu
	'Pink Dove'	SBch
§	***pluricaule***	ECho GCrg LRHS SPlb SRms
	'Pool Party'^{PBR} (Party Hardy Series) new	LRHS NLar
	populifolium	ECha GCal GEdr GJos IMou MHer MMuc NLar NPri SPhx XLum
	praealtum	SChr SEND
	pulchellum	ECtt
	'Purple Leaf'	LAst
	quinquefarium	see *S. brevifolium* var. *quinquefarium*
	'Red Cauli' 🏆^{H7}	Widely available
	'Red Rum'	GBin LPla SPhx
	'Red Setter'	WPGP
	reflexum L.	see *S. rupestre* L.
	rhodiola	see *Rhodiola rosea*
	rosea	see *Rhodiola rosea*
	rubroglaucum misapplied	see *S. oregonense*
	rubroglaucum Praeger	see *S. obtusatum* A. Gray
§	'Ruby Glow' 🏆^{H5}	Widely available
	'Ruby Port'	CSpe
§	***rupestre*** L.	ECho GJos LAst MMuc MNHC MWat SEND SPlb XLum
	- 'Angelina'	CKno CTal ECou ECtt EPPr EWes IMou MHer NBir NDov NEoE NHol NWad SPoG SRGP WCot WGrn XLum
	- 'Monstrosum Cristatum'	NBir SMad WCot XLum
	ruprechtii	see *S. telephium* subsp. *ruprechtii*
	sarcocaule hort.	see *Crassula sarcocaulis*
	sarmentosum	ECho XLum
§	***sediforme***	EDAr EPot GAbr MMuc SEND XSen
	- B&F MA 25	WCot
	- ***nicaeense***	see *S. sediforme*
	selskianum	GJos NBre NLar SBch XLum
	- 'Goldilocks'	GJos
	sempervivoides	ECho
	'September Ruby'	LRHS
	sexangulare	ECho EPot MHer MMuc NPri NRya SEND SFgr SPlb SRms XLum
	sibiricum	see *S. hybridum*
	sieboldii	ECho
	- 'Dragon'	LRHS MHCG
	- 'Mediovariegatum' (v) 🏆^{H3}	ECho EHoe LPot MHer MRav NWsh SPlb XLum
	'Silvermoon'	NWad
	spathulifolium	CTri ECha ECho
	- 'Aureum'	ECho ECtt MWat WAbe
	- 'Cape Blanco' 🏆^{H5}	Widely available
	- 'Purpureum' 🏆^{H5}	ECho ECtt EDAr EHoe EPfP EPot GAbr GKev GMaP LAst LBee LPot LRHS MBel MHer MHtn MWat NFav NHol NRya NWad SPer SPlb SPoG WAbe WMoo XLum
	- subsp. ***yosemitense*** new	WTor
	spectabile 🏆^{H7}	CArn CPrp CTri ELan EPfP GJos GMaP LRHS MCot MHer MRav NGdn SCob SPer SPlb SRms WBor WBrk WFar WSFF
	- Brilliant Group	CBar LAst LBMP MJak WCAu
	- - 'Brilliant' 🏆^{H7}	CBcs CBod COtt CSBt CTri EAEE ECha ECtt ELan EPfP LAst LCro LOPS LPal LRHS MBri MGos MRav NFav NGdn NLar SCob SPer SPoG SWvt WMoo
	- - 'Carmen'	XLum
	- - 'Hot Stuff'	CAby CNor EBee ECtt ELon EPfP LRHS LSRN MAvo MBri NPri SPoG SPtp SRot WCot
	- - 'Lisa'	GBin MTPN NLar
	- - 'Meteor'	CPrp LPla MRav MWat NLar SPhx
	- - 'Neon'	CKno EBee EPfP LRHS NDov
	- - 'Pink Fairy'	MNrw WHil
	- - 'Rosenteller'	CKno EBee GBin NBre
§	- - 'Septemberglut'	EAEE LRHS NBre XLum
	- - 'Steven Ward'	CKno EWes NLar SRGP
	- 'Crystal Pink'^{PBR}	LRHS MBri MNrw NLar
	- 'Humile'	XLum
	- 'Iceberg'	CBod EBee ECha ECtt EHrv EPfP EWTr LAst LPfy LRHS MAvo MCot MGos MRav MWat MWhi NGdn NLar SCob SPer SPhx SPtp SWvt WFar WHil WMnd WMoo WSFF XLum
	- 'Nordlicht'	GBin
	- 'Pink Chablis' (v)	NLar WCot
	- September Glow	see *S. spectabile* (Brilliant Group) 'Septemberglut'
	- 'Stardust'	CRos CTri EBee EPfP GBin GMaP LAst LCro LRHS LSou MBri MRav MTis NCGa SGol SPer WFar XLum
	- 'Variegatum'	see *S. erythrostictum* 'Mediovariegatum'
	- Walberton's Pizazz	EPfP LRHS
	spinosum	see *Orostachys spinosa*
	spurium	ECho GAbr GJos MMuc SEND SRms XSen
§	- 'Album'	NRya XLum
	- 'Atropurpureum'	ECha ECho WMoo XLum
	- 'Coccineum'	ECho GJos MMuc MNHC SEND
	- Dragon's Blood	see *S. spurium* 'Schorbuser Blut'
	- 'Fuldaglut'	CTri ECho ECtt EHoe GCrg GMaP GQue LRHS MNrw NRya WMoo WPnn
	- 'Green Mantle'	EBee ECha ECho EPfP LRHS
	- 'John Creech'	ECtt
	- Purple Carpet	see *S. spurium* 'Purpurteppich'
	- 'Purpureum'	SRms
§	- 'Purpurteppich'	ECho ECtt GJos MJak MRav NBro NLar NWad SRms SVen
	- 'Roseum'	SRms
	- 'Ruby Mantle'	GKev MSCN NBro NEoE SBch SPoG SRGP SWvt WMoo XLum
§	- 'Schorbuser Blut' 🏆^{H5}	EAEE ECho ECtt EPau EPfP GJos GKev LRHS MAsh MCot MLHP MWat NBir NDov NRya NSla SPlb SRGP SRms WHoo WIce XLum
I	- 'Splendens Roseum'	XLum
	- 'Summer Glory'	NLar
§	- 'Tricolor' (v)	CTri EBee ECha ECho EHoe EPfP GJos GKev MAsh MHer MHtn MLHP MRav NHol NRya NWad SPlb SPoG WMoo XLum
	- 'Variegatum'	see *S. spurium* 'Tricolor'
	- 'Voodoo'	ECou ECtt EPfP EWes LRHS MBel MHer NBro NDov NGdn XLum
	stefco	XLum
	stenopetalum	SPlb

§ - 'Douglasii'	MHer SRms
'Stewed Rhubarb Mountain'	CKno CPrp EAEE EBee ECha ECtt ELan EPfP LRHS MBNS MRav NLar SGbt WMoo
stoloniferum	ECho
stribrnyi	see *S. urvillei* Stribrnyi Group
'Sunset Cloud'	CMHG EBee ECtt EWes GCal LPot MRav
takesimense	XLum
- B&SWJ 8493	WCru
- B&SWJ 8518	WCru
tatarinowii	WCot
telephium	CArn IFro LPfy NBir SRms WSFF XLum
§ - Atropurpureum Group	MRav NLar SWvt
- - 'African Pearl'	GBin WCFE
- - 'Arthur Branch'	CPrp EBee ECtt GBin
- - 'Bon Bon'	LAst LRHS MAvo MBNS MTis NLar SPoG
- - 'Bressingham Purple'	EBee EPPr LRHS
- - 'Chocolate'	EAEE EBee ECtt EPPr NLar
- - 'Dark Knight'	LRHS
- - 'El Cid'	EWes
- - 'Karfunkelstein' ♀H7	CKno EBee ECha ECtt EPPr GBin GLog MAvo MHol MTis NDov SPhx WCot XLum
- - 'Leonore Zuuntz'	NBre
- - 'Lynda et Rodney'	EWes
- - 'Lynda Windsor'	ECtt EPfP MAvo NLar SWvt
- - 'Möhrchen'	EHrv EWTr GBin GMaP MHer MRav NGdn NLar NWsh SPhx WHil WMoo
- - 'Picolette'	EAEE ECtt EPfP LRHS LSou MNrw MSCN NCGa SPoG WCot WMoo
- - 'Postman's Pride'PBR	CKno CWGN ECtt EPfP GBin LPla LSou MNrw NGdn NQui
§ - - 'Purple Emperor' ♀H7	Widely available
- - 'Purple Moon'	SPhx
- - 'Ringmore Ruby'	MHer MNrw SPhx WCot WPGP
- - 'Xenox'PBR ♀H7	CWGN EAEE EBee ECtt EPfP GBin IPot LRHS MAvo MBNS MCot MNrw NLar SAko SCob SPoG WCAu WHil WPGP
- 'Coral Reef'PBR	EBee
- Emperor's Waves Group	NGdn NWad
§ - subsp. ***fabaria***	ECtt MRav NWsh WCot
- - var. ***borderei***	CElw LPla SBch SPhx
- 'Jennifer'	EBee ECtt LSun MBel MPie SBch WCot WHoo WRHF
- subsp. ***maximum*** 'Atropurpureum'	see *S. telephium* Atropurpureum Group
- - 'Gooseberry Fool'	CFis CMea CPrp EBee ECGP ECtt ELan EPfP GMaP SBch SPhx
- 'Moonlight Serenade'PBR	EBee ECtt LRHS
- 'Rainbow Xenox'PBR	LSou MBri
- 'Raspberry Truffle'	LBMP LRHS SDys
§ - subsp. ***ruprechtii***	CAby CPrp EAEE ECha ECtt EHoe EPPr EPfP GMaP LRHS LSou MCot MRav NLar NSti SPer SPhx WMoo WTor
- - 'Citrus Twist'	EBee ECtt LRHS MRav
- - 'Hab Gray'	CSpe EBee ECtt EWes EWld GBin GQue LRHS MAvo MTis NLar SAko SBch
- - 'Pink Dome'	ECha
- 'Strawberries and Cream'	Widely available
- 'Sunkissed'PBR	ECtt NCGa NLar
- subsp. ***telephium***	GCra
- 'Twinkling Star'PBR	ECtt MBri MNrw NLar
- 'Variegatum' (v)	MAvo
- 'Yellow Xenox'PBR	CBod EBee ECtt LRHS LSou MBri NLar WHil
ternatum	ECho MHer
tetractinum 'Coral Reef'	MHer MHtn XLum
'Thundercloud'PBR	LBuc LRHS MBri SHil
'Thunderhead'	LRHS WHlf
trollii	see *Rhodiola trollii*
'Twinkle Stars'	EBee
urvillei	CPBP
- Sartorianum Group	MHer XLum
§ - Stribrnyi Group	XLum
ussuriense	EPfP GCal NBir
- 'Chuwangsan'	EWld WCru
valens **new**	CPBP SPlb
'Veluwse Wakel'	ECtt GBin
'Vera Jameson' ♀H5	CMac CPrp CRos EAEE ECha ECtt EHoe ELan EPfP EShb GKev LAst LRHS LSRN MBel MBrN MCot MRav MWat NHol NSti NWsh SBch SPer SWvt WHoo WMoo
viviparum	NLar
- B&SWJ 8662	WCru
Walberton's Pink Whisper	EPfP LRHS
'Washfield Purple'	see *S. telephium* 'Purple Emperor'
'Weihenstephaner Gold'	see *S. kamtschaticum* var. *floriferum* 'Weihenstephaner Gold'
weinbergii	see *Graptopetalum paraguayense*
'Winky'	LSou
yezoense	see *S. pluricaule*
yunnanense	see *Rhodiola yunnanensis*

Seemannia see *Gloxinia*

Selaginella (*Selaginellaceae*)

apoda	CTsd LRHS
braunii	CLAP WCot
erythropus	LRHS
var. ***sanguinea***	
helvetica	EBee IMou XLum
kraussiana ♀H2	CKel CLAP CTsd EDAr NWad
- 'Aurea'	ISha LRHS
- 'Brownii' ♀H2	ISha LRHS
- 'Gold Tips'	CKel ISha LRHS
lepidophylla	GKev SVic
martensii ♀H1b	CKel
moellendorfii	ISha LPal LRHS
uncinata ♀H1b	CKel CLAP ISha LRHS

Selinum (*Apiaceae*)

CC 6869	EBee EWld MSpe
FMWJ 13465 **new**	CEvo
KWJ 12281 from northern Vietnam	WCru
carvifolium	CExl CMac CSpe ELan LEdu LHop LLWG SPhx SPtp WCAu
- PAB 2676	LEdu
cryptotaenium FMWJ 13250 **new**	WCru
- PAB 8948 **new**	LEdu
tenuifolium	see *S. wallichianum*
§ ***wallichianum***	Widely available
- CC 6869 **new**	GKev
- EMAK 886	EBee GPoy
- HWJK 2329 from Nepal **new**	WCru
- HWJK 2347	WCru
- PAB 3579	LEdu
- red-stemmed **new**	SBrt

Selliera (*Goodeniaceae*)

	radicans	GAbr GBin GEdr

Semele (*Asparagaceae*)

	androgyna	CRHN WCot

Semiaquilegia (*Ranunculaceae*)

	adoxoides double-flowered (d)	GKev
§	***ecalcarata*** 🏆H5	CWCL ECho EHrv EWld GCal GJos GKev MNrw NCGa NGdn SBea SRms WHal
	simulatrix	see *S. ecalcarata*
	'Sugar Plum Fairy'	CSma EPfP LBuc LRHS

Semiarundinaria (*Poaceae*)

§	***fastuosa*** 🏆H4	CBcs CBod CDoC CEnt CJun CTsd ENBC EPfP ERod EUJe IMou LPal MMuc MWht SEND SPlb WJun
	- var. ***viridis***	CEnt ERod MWht SBig WCru WJun
	kagamiana	CDoC ENBC EPfP IMou MMuc MWht SBig SEND WJun
§	***lubrica***	MWht
	makinoi	MWht WJun
I	***maruyamana***	MWht
	nitida	see *Fargesia nitida*
§	***okuboi***	CEnt ERod MWht
	villosa	see *S. okuboi*
	yamadorii	ERod MWht WJun
	yashadake	CEnt ERod MWht WJun
	- f. ***kimmei***	CBod CDoC CEnt ENBC ERod LCro LPal LRHS MMuc MWht NLar SBig SEND WJun WMoo WPGP
I	- - 'Inversa'	CEnt

Semnanthe see *Erepsia*

Sempervivella see *Rosularia*

Sempervivum ✿ (*Crassulaceae*)

	sp.	SCob SVic
	from Sierra Nova	ESem SFgr
	'Aalrika'	NMen
	'Aaroundina'	CWil NMen
	'Abba'	CMea EDAr ESem NMen WHal
	acuminatum	see *S. tectorum* var. *glaucum*
	'Adelaar'	CWil NMen
	'Adelmoed'	CWil NMen SFgr
	'Ageet'	CWil NMen
	'Aglow'	ESem MHom NMen
	'Aida' **new**	NMen
	'Aladdin'	CWil ESem GEdr MSCN NMen SRms
	'Alaric'	NMen
	'Alchimist'	ESem NMen XLum
	'Aldo Moro'	CTal CWil EDAr ESem LBee MHom NMen SFgr WIce XLum
	'Alenco' **new**	NMen
	'Alesia' **new**	NMen
	'Alfons-Roelands' **new**	NMen
	'Alice'	MSCN NMen
	'Alidae'	ESem
	allionii	see *Jovibarba allionii*
	'Allison'	CWil NMen SFgr
	'Alluring'	ESem GAbr NMen
	'Alpha'	CMea ESem LBee NMen SFgr SRms WHal XLum
	altum	CWil ECho ESem LRHS MHom NMen SPlb XLum
	'Amanda'	CWil EDAr ESem MBrN NMen SFgr SRms WHoo
	'Ambergreen'	NMen
	'Americanos' **new**	ESem
	andreanum	see *S. tectorum* var. *alpinum*
	'Andrenor'	ESem NMen
	'Andrenor' sport	NMen
	'Anna Marie'	ESem NMen
	'Apache' Haberer	ESem NMen
	'Apollo'	NMen SFgr XLum
	'Apple Blossom'	CMea ESem NMen
	'Apricot' **new**	NMen
	arachnoideum 🏆H5	Widely available
	- from the Abruzzi, Italy	NMen
	- 'Ararat'	SDys
	- 'Boria'	ESem
	- var. ***bryoides***	CWil ECho ESem LLHF LRHS SRms
	- 'Cebennense'	ESem
	- 'Clärchen'	ESem MSCN NSla WAbe
	- cristate	CWil
*	- ***densum***	EDAr EPPr WAbe
	- subsp. ***doellianum***	see *S. arachnoideum* subsp. *tomentosum* var. *glabrescens*
	- form No 1	ECho
	- 'Gusseri'	NMen
	- 'Laggeri'	see *S. arachnoideum* subsp. *tomentosum* (C.B. Lehm. & Schnittsp.) Schinz & Thell.
	- 'Red Papaver'	SFgr
	- 'Red Wings'	NMen XLum
	- 'Rubrum'	ECho ELon EUJe GMaP LRHS SPlb XLum
	- 'Sultan'	ESem
	- subsp. ***tomentosum*** misapplied	see *S.* × *barbulatum* 'Hookeri'
	- subsp. ***tomentosum*** ambig.	ECho EPot
§	- subsp. ***tomentosum*** (C.B. Lehm & Schnittsp.) Schinz & Thell. 🏆H5	ECho GCrg LRHS MSCN NPer NWad SFgr SPlb SRms WAbe
	- - GDJ 92.04	CWil
§	- - var. ***glabrescens***	SDys
	- - 'Minor' **new**	NPri
	- - 'Minus'	NPri
§	- - 'Stansfieldii'	ECho EPPr LRHS WHal
§	- 'White Christmas'	CWil MHer NMen
	arachnoideum × ***calcareum***	CWil
	arachnoideum × ***montanum***	see *S.* × *barbulatum*
	arachnoideum × ***nevadense***	SDys
	arachnoideum × ***pittonii***	NMen WAbe
	arenarium	see *Jovibarba arenaria*
	'Arlet'	EDAr
	armenum	ESem
	'Arondina'	CWil NMen
	'Aross'	CMea ESem NMen
	'Arrowheads Red'	NMen
	'Artist'	CWil ESem NMen SFgr
	'Ashes of Roses'	ESem MHom MSCN NHol NMen WAbe WGor XLum
	'Asteroid'	CWil ESem NMen
	'Astrid'	CWil NMen
	'Atlantic'	SRms
	atlanticum	CTal ESem MHom MMuc NMen NSla SFgr SRot
	- from Atlas Mountains, Morocco	ESem

	Name	Suppliers
	- from Oukaïmeden, Morocco	CWil ESem GAbr NMen SRms
	- 'Edward Balls'	ESem NMen SDys SFgr
	'Atlantis' Adams **new**	NWad
	'Atropurpureum' ambig.	CWil EDAr GEdr MBrN NMen SFgr WGor
	'Atropurpureum' Hemlich form	NMen
	'Attraction'	CWil NMen
	'Aureum'	see *Greenovia aurea*
	'Averil'	CWil NMen
	'Aymon Correvon'	ESem NMen
	'Baby Boo' **new**	ESem
	'Baby Skrocki'	CWil NMen
	balcanicum	CTal CWil EDAr NMen SRms XLum
	ballsii	ECho LLHF LRHS NMen SRms
	- from Kambeecho, Greece	MHom
	- from Smólikas, Greece	MHom NMen
	- from Tschumba Petzi, Greece	CWil MHom SDys XLum
	'Banderi'	NMen
	'Banjo'	NMen
	'Banyan'	CTal ECho LRHS NMen
§	× ***barbulatum***	ESem GAbr LBee NMen SDys WHoo
§	- 'Hookeri'	CTri CWil ESem WAbe WHoo XLum
	'Bascour Zilver'	CMea CWil LBee MSCN NMen SRms WHal
	'Be Mine'	MSCN
	'Beaute'	ESem NMen
	'Beautiful'	NMen
	'Bedazzled'	NMen
	'Bedivere'	LBee NMen SRms
	'Bedivere Crested'	NMen
*	'Bedley Hi'	MHom NMen
	'Bella Donna'	CWil ESem MHom NMen
	'Bella Meade'	EDAr ESem NMen SFgr SRms
	'Belle'	WGor
	'Bellotts Pourpre'	CWil ESem NMen
	'Benny Hill'	CWil
	'Bernstein'	CWil EDAr ESem MHer MSCN NMen NWad SFgr WHal XLum
	'Beta'	ESem MHom NMen WAbe XLum
	'Bethany'	CMea CWil NMen NWad SFgr WHal
	'Bicolor' ambig.	EPfP
	'Big Red'	NMen
	'Big Slipper'	ESem NMen
	'Bijou'	CWil NMen
	'Binstead'	ESem
	'Birchmaier'	NMen
	'Bitter Chocolate' **new**	SFgr
	'Black Beauty'	NMen
	'Black Cap'	ESem NMen
	'Black Claret'	NMen
	'Black Knight'	ECho LRHS MHer NMen SPlb SRms WHal
	'Black Mini'	CWil EPot GAbr GCrg GKev NBir NMen SRms
	'Black Mountain'	CWil ESem GKev LBee NMen
	'Black Prince'	ESem
	'Black Velvet'	NMen
	'Blood of Winter'	WGor
	'Blood Tip'	CMea CTal CWil ECho ELon EPfP ESem GAbr GCra GKev LAst LRHS LSun MHer MHtn MMuc MSCN NHol NMen NPri NRya NWad SEND SPlb SPoG SRms WHal WHoo
	'Bloodgood'	ECho
	'Bloody Goose'	ESem NMen
	'Blue Boy'	CTal CWil ECho ELon EPPr GAbr LBee LRHS MSCN NMen SFgr SRms WGor
	'Blue Moon'	ESem NMen
	'Blue Time'	GEdr LLHF SFgr WHoo XLum
	'Blush'	EDAr NMen
	'Boissieri'	see *S. tectorum* subsp. *tectorum* 'Boissieri'
	'Bold Chick'	NMen
	'Bombardier'	EDAr
	'Booth's Red'	NMen WGor
	'Boreale'	see *Jovibarba hirta* subsp. *borealis*
	borisii	see *S. ciliosum* var. *borisii*
	borissovae	EPot MHom NMen SDys
	'Boromir'	CWil EDAr NMen XLum
	'Boule de Neige'	GCrg GEdr NRya
	'Bowles's Variety'	NMen
	'Braune Maus'	ESem SFgr
I	'Braunella'	CWil NMen
	'Britta'	ESem SDys
	'Brock'	ECho LLHF LRHS MHom NMen SRms
	'Bronco' ♀H5	CTal CWil ECho ELon ESem GAbr GBin LBee LRHS MHom MMuc NHol NMen NRya NWad SEND SRms WCot WHfH WPGP WRHF XLum
	'Bronze Beauty'	EDAr NMen
	'Bronze Pastel'	CWil EDAr MHom MSCN NMen NSla SFgr SRms SRot WGor
	'Brown Owl'	CWil ECho ESem SRms
	'Brown Web' **new**	NMen
	'Brownii'	ESem NMen
	'Brunette'	ECho GAbr
	'Brunhilde' **new**	NMen
	bungeanum hort.	ESem NMen
	'Bunny Girl'	SFgr
	'Burgundy'	NMen
	'Burgundy Velvet'	NMen
	'Burnatii'	see *S. montanum* subsp. *burnatii*
	'Burning Desire'	ESem WGor
	'Burnished Bronze'	CWil NMen
	'Butterbur'	NMen
	'Butterfly'	ESem NMen
	'Café'	ELon MSCN NHol NMen SFgr SRms
*	***calabricum***	NHol
	calcareum	CBod CTal CWil ECho ECtt EUJe GKev LBMP LRHS MAsh NBro NHol NMen NPri SEND SPlb SPoG SRms SRot XLum
	- from the Alps, France	CWil ESem
	- from Calde la Vanoise, France	CWil
	- from Ceüze, France	CWil ESem
	- from Cleizé, France	see *S. calcareum* 'Limelight'
	- from Col Bayard, France	CWil GAbr NMen
	- from Colle St Michel, France	CWil ESem SRms
	- from Gorges supérieures du Cians, France	CWil ESem NMen
	- from Mont Ventoux, France	CWil ESem
	- from Petite Ceüse, France	ESem SRot
	- - GDJ 92.15	CWil
	- - GDJ 92.16	CWil SRms
	- from Queyras, France	CWil ESem NMen
	- from Route d'Annôt, France	CWil
	- from Triora, Italy	CWil NMen
	- 'Benz'	SDys
	- 'Extra' ♀H5	CDes CTal CWil ESem GAbr GEdr MSCN NMen SFgr SRms SRot

- 'Greenii'	CWil ECho ECtt ESem GKev LRHS MSCN NMen SPlb SRms
§ - 'Grigg's Surprise'	NMen SPlb
- 'Guillaumes' ♀H5	CTal CWil LBee LRHS NMen SFgr SRms SRot WHoo
§ - 'Limelight'	CMea CWil EDAr LBee LRHS NMen WHal WHoo
- 'Monstrosum'	see *S. calcareum* 'Grigg's Surprise'
- 'Mrs Giuseppi'	CTal CWil ECho ESem GAbr GCrg GEdr LBee LSun MHer NMen SBch SFgr SRms WAbe WIce XLum
- 'Nigricans'	NMen
- 'Pink Pearl'	CWil MSCN NMen SDys SFgr SPlb XLum
- 'Sir William Lawrence' ♀H5	CMea CWil ECho ECtt EDAr ESem LBee LRHS MMuc NMen SFgr SRms WAbe WHal WHoo WThu XLum
'Cameo'	see *Jovibarba heuffelii* var. *glabra* 'Cameo'
'Canada Kate'	NMen
'Cancer'	XLum
'Candy Floss'	ESem NMen
cantabricum	CWil ESem MMuc NMen WThu XLum
- from Navafria, Spain	CWil
- from Riaño, Spain	CWil
- from San Glorio, Spain	CWil
- from Ticeros	XLum
- from Valvanera, Spain	NMen
- subsp. ***cantabricum*** from Leitariegos, Spain	CWil GAbr MHom
- - GDJ 93.13 from Peña de Llesba, Spain	CWil
- - from Pico del Lobo, Spain	CWil NMen
I - subsp. ***gredense*** GDJ 95.04	CTal CWil
- subsp. ***guadarramense***	see *S. vicentei* subsp. *paui*
- - from Pico del Lobo, Spain, No 1	SRms SRot
- - from Valvanera, Spain, No 1	CWil
- subsp. ***urbionense***	CWil GEdr SRms
- - from El Gatón, Spain	CWil
- - from Picos de Urbión, Spain	CWil ESem
cantabricum × ***montanum*** subsp. ***stiriacum***	ESem
cantabricum × ***montanum*** subsp. ***stiriacum*** 'Lloyd Praeger'	CWil
'Caramel'	NMen
'Carluke'	NMen
'Carmen'	CWil GAbr NMen SFgr
'Carneum'	NMen
'Carnival'	CWil ESem NMen
caucasicum	CWil LRHS MHom NMen XLum
'Cavo Doro'	CWil NMen SFgr
'Celon'	CWil NMen
'Centennial'	NMen
charadzeae	CWil ESem LBee XLum
'Chartbury'	EDAr
'Cherry Frost'	ECho ESem NHol NMen XLum
'Cherry Glow'	see *Jovibarba heuffelii* 'Cherry Glow'
'Cherry Tart'	SPlb
'Chivalry'	ESem NMen
'Chocolate'	ESem NMen WAbe
§ × ***christii***	NMen
'Christmas Time'	NMen SFgr
chrysanthum	ESem

ciliosum ♀H4	CMea CWil ECho ESem NMen NRya SPlb
- from Alí Butús, Bulgaria	SDys
- from Ochrid, Macedonia	CWil
- from Pestani, Macedonia	ESem
§ - var. ***borisii***	CFis EPPr EPfP ESem GCal GKev MHtn NMen NRya WAbe WHal
- var. ***ciliosum*** × ***ciliosum*** var. ***borisii***	CTri
- var. ***galicicum***	CTal
- - 'Mali Hat'	ESem NMen
ciliosum × ***grandiflorum***	ESem NMen
'Cindy'	SRms
'Circlet'	NMen
'Clara Noyes'	NMen
'Clare'	MHer NMen SFgr
'Cleveland Morgan'	ESem MHom NMen XLum
'Climax' ambig.	ECho EPfP MHom
'Climax' Ford	NMen
'Cobweb Capers'	MHom NMen
'Cobweb Centres'	NMen
'Colchicum'	SRms
'Collage'	ESem
'Collecteur Anchisi'	CTal ESem SDys SFgr
'Commander Hay' ♀H5	CTal EDAr EPfP EWes GBin GCra GKev MHom MSCN NMen NPer NRya SRGP SRms WHal XLum
'Comte de Congae'	NMen
'Concorde'	LBee
'Congo'	NMen SFgr XLum
'Corio'	NMen
'Corona'	CWil ESem NMen
'Coronet'	NMen
'Corsair'	CTal CWil ELon EPPr ESem GEdr GKev MBrN MMuc NMen SFgr WGor WOld
'Cotopaxi'	CWil NMen
'Cranberry'	ESem NMen
'Crimson King'	SFgr
'Crimson Velvet'	CMea ESem LBee NMen XLum
§ 'Crispyn' ♀H5	CTal CWil ESem LBee LRHS MHer MHom MMuc MSCN NMen SEND SFgr
'Croton'	NMen
'Crucify'	ESem NMen
'Cupream'	CWil ESem NMen SRms
'Dakota'	CWil EDAr NMen SFgr
'Dallas'	CWil NMen SRms
'Damask'	CWil LBee NMen SFgr
'Dancer's Veil'	NMen
'Darjeeling'	CWil ESem NMen
'Dark Beauty'	ECho LRHS MSCN NHol NMen SFgr WAbe WCot WHal
'Dark Cloud'	CWil GAbr LBee NMen WGor WHoo XLum
'Dark Point'	CWil MHom MSCN NMen SFgr
'Dark Velvet'	CMea
'Darkie'	CWil SFgr
davisii	NMen
'De Kardijk'	NMen
'Deep Fire'	CWil NMen SRms
× ***degenianum***	SFgr XLum
'Delta' ♀H5	MHom NMen WHoo
densum	see *S. tectorum*
'Devil's Teeth' **new**	MSCN
'Devon Glow'	MSCN
'Devon Jewel'	WGor
'Diane'	ESem NMen SFgr
'Diavolo' **new**	NMen
'Director Jacobs'	CWil EDAr ESem NMen SFgr

'Dolle Dina's'	NMen
dolomiticum	NMen XLum
dolomiticum* × *montanum	NBro NMen SFgr
'Donarrose'	ESem SFgr
'Dornröschen' **new**	NMen
'Downland Queen'	CWil NMen
'Dr Fritz Köhlein' **new**	NMen
'Dragoness'	ESem NMen
'Dream Catcher'	CWil NMen
'Dusky'	NMen
'Dyke'	CTri CWil EDAr NMen SFgr WHal
dzhavachischvilii	CWil NMen XLum
'Edge of Night'	CWil NMen
'Eefje'	CWil ESem NMen
'El Greco'	ESem NMen
'El Toro'	MHom MSCN NMen
'Elgar'	NMen
'Else' **new**	NMen
'Elva' **new**	NMen
'Elvis'	CWil ESem MHom NMen SFgr
'Emerald Giant'	CWil ESem SFgr
'Emerson's Giant'	CWil NMen
'Eminent'	ESem
'Emmchen'	CWil NMen SFgr
'Engle's'	CMea CTri ECho LRHS MHer MMuc MSCN NMen SEND SFgr SPlb SRms WHal
'Engle's 13-2'	NMen
'Engle's Rubrum'	CTal EPot LBee NMen
'Erebus' **new**	ESem
erythraeum	ECho LLHF LRHS MHom NMen SPlb SRms WHal
- from Mesta Valley, Bulgaria **new**	NMen
- from Pirin, Bulgaria	NMen
- 'Red Velvet'	NMen
'Essence of Lime' **new**	SFgr
'Eugenia' **new**	ESem
'Eureka'	NMen
'Excalibur'	ESem NMen
'Exhibita'	CWil EPPr NMen SDys
'Exorna'	CWil EDAr ESem MHom NMen SFgr
'Fair Lady'	CWil MHom NMen
'Fairy'	NMen
'Fame'	CWil ESem NMen SPlb
'Faramir' **new**	NMen
'Fat Jack'	CWil NMen
× ***fauconnetii***	CTal CWil EDAr ESem
- 'Rubellum'	NMen
'Feldmaier'	GAbr NMen
'Fernwood'	CTal NMen
'Festival'	EDAr NMen
'Fiery Furness'	ESem NMen
'Fiesta' ambig.	NMen WHal
fimbriatum	see *S.* × *barbulatum*
'Finerpointe'	ESem NMen
'Fire Glint'	CWil GEdr NMen SRms
'Firgrove Big Bronze' **new**	SFgr
'Firgrove Silver'	SFgr
'First Try'	NMen
flagelliforme	XLum
'Flaming Heart'	CWil EDAr ESem MBrN NMen WGor
'Flamingo'	ESem NMen
'Flanders Passion'	EWes LBee NMen SRms
'Flasher'	NMen
'Fluweel'	MSCN NMen
'Forden'	MSCN NMen SFgr WGor
'Ford's Amiability'	SDys
'Ford's Giant'	XLum
'Ford's Shadows'	SDys
'Ford's Spring'	CWil ESem NMen
'Freckles'	NMen
'Freeland'	ESem
'Frolic'	ESem
'Fronika'	CWil NMen
'Frosty'	CWil NMen SFgr SRms
'Fuego' ♀H5	CWil LRHS MHom NMen SFgr
'Fuji'	NMen
× ***funckii***	EDAr ESem MBrN NMen NPri XLum
'Furryness'	ESem
'Fuzzy Wuzzy'	EDAr ESem NMen
'Galahad'	NMen
'Gallivarda' ♀H5	CWil LRHS MSCN NMen SFgr SRms
'Gambol'	NMen NWad
'Gamma'	CWil ESem LBee NMen
'Garnet'	ECho NMen WGor
'Gay Jester'	CTal CTri CWil NMen SFgr WHoo
'Gazelle'	NMen XLum
'Genevione'	CWil
'Georgette'	CWil ESem NMen XLum
'Georgia Rowan' **new**	CWil
'Gilosum'	EDAr
'Ginnie's Delight'	NMen
'Gipsy'	NMen
giuseppii ♀H5	ECho LBee LRHS MMuc NMen SRms
- from Coriscao, Spain	CTal LBee
- - GDJ 93.17	CWil
- from Peña Espigüete, Spain	CWil SDys SRms
- from Peña Prieta, Spain	CWil
'Gizmo'	NMen SFgr
'Glaucum'	see *S. tectorum* var. *glaucum*
globiferum subsp. ***globiferum*** 'Minor'	XLum
- subsp. ***hirtum***	SFgr
'Gloriosum' ambig.	EDAr ESem MSCN NMen SFgr
'Glowing Embers'	CWil ESem MHom NMen SFgr WHal XLum
'Godaert'	MMuc SEND XLum
'Goldie'	ESem
'Gollum'	NMen
'Granada'	EDAr NMen
'Granat'	ESem LBee MHer NMen SRms XLum
'Granby'	ECho ESem LBee SDys
grandiflorum	CTal CWil ESem NMen WThu XLum
- from Valpine	ESem
- 'Fasciatum'	ESem NMen
grandiflorum* × *montanum	see *S.* × *christii*
'Grannie's Favourite'	NMen
'Grapetone'	ESem MHom NMen SDys WHal
'Graupurpur'	CWil XLum
'Green Apple'	CWil GAbr MHom NMen SDys
'Green Disk'	SRms
'Green Dragon'	CTal ECho ESem LRHS MSCN NMen SRms WOut
'Green Gables'	EDAr ESem
'Green Ice'	CDes CWil ESem NMen SFgr
'Greenwich Time'	EDAr NMen
'Grey Dawn'	ECho ESem LRHS MHom NMen SRms XLum
'Grey Ghost'	ESem NMen
'Grey Green'	CWil
'Grey Lady'	CWil NMen

	'Grey Owl'	ECho LRHS MSCN NMen SFgr SRms
	'Grey Velvet'	CWil LBee NMen
	'Greyfriars'	CDes CMea CTal ECho EDAr LBee LRHS NMen SFgr WGor WOld
	'Greyolla'	CWil ESem NMen
	'Grünschnabel'	XLum
	'Gulle Dame'	CWil ESem MHom NMen SFgr
	'Halemaumau'	CWil ESem NMen
I	'Hall's Hybrid'	CWil GAbr MSCN NBro NMen
	'Happy'	CTal CWil ESem NMen SFgr SRms WGor
	'Hart'	CWil NMen
	'Havana'	CWil ESem NMen
	'Hayling'	ECho ESem LRHS NMen NWad SRms XLum
	'Heigham Red'	CWil ECho EPPr ESem GKev LBee LRHS NMen SRms WIce
	'Heike'	CWil NMen
	'Helen'	EDAr GEdr
	'Heliotroop'	NMen SDys SRot
	helveticum	see *S. montanum*
	'Hermann Näpfel' **new**	NMen
	'Hester'	CWil ECho ESem MBrN NBro NMen
	'Hey-hey'	CTal ECho ELon EPot GBin LBee LRHS MBrN NMen SPlb WCot XLum
	'Hidde'	CWil ESem SFgr SPlb
	'Hirsutum'	see *Jovibarba allionii*
	hirtum	see *Jovibarba hirta*
	'Hookeri'	see *S.* × *barbulatum* 'Hookeri'
	'Hopi'	CWil NMen
	'Hortulanus Smit'	XLum
	'Hot Boyz' **new**	NMen
	'Hot Peppermint'	ESem NMen
	'Hugo'	ESem
	'Hullabaloo'	EDAr NMen SFgr
	'Hurricane'	CWil ESem NMen
	'Ice Berry' **new**	SFgr
	'Icicle'	CMea ECho ELon LRHS MSCN NBro NHol NMen SRms WGor
	imbricatum	see *S.* × *barbulatum*
	'Imperial'	CWil MHom NMen SPlb
	'Infinity'	SFgr
	'Inge'	see *Jovibarba heuffelii* 'Inge'
	ingwersenii	CTal ESem MHom NMen XLum
	ingwersenii* × *pumilum	NMen SFgr SRms
	'Iophon'	LBee
	iranicum	NMen
	'Irazu'	CTal CWil ECho EPot ESem GAbr LRHS MSCN NMen SDys SFgr SRms
	'Irene'	ESem SFgr
	'Isaac Dyson'	SDys SRot
	'Isabelle'	CWil NMen
	italicum	MHom XLum
	'Itchen'	NMen
	'Ivonne'	NMen
	'Iwo'	NMen SFgr
	'Jack Frost'	NBro NMen SFgr XLum
	'Jacquette'	CWil ESem NMen
	'Jadestern'	CWil NMen
	'Jamie's Pride'	ESem WGor
	'Jelly Bean'	CWil MSCN NMen SFgr
	'Jet Stream' ♀H5	CWil ECho ELon ESem LRHS MHom MSCN NMen SDys SPlb SRms
	'Jetson'	WGor
	'Jewel Case'	CTal CWil ECho LRHS NMen
I	'John Hobbs seedling No. 2'	ESem NMen
	'John T.'	ESem NMen
	'John T.' × 'Saffron' **new**	NMen
	'Jolly Green Giant'	MHom NMen
	'Jo's Spark'	NMen
	'Jubilee'	CMea CWil ECho EDAr ELan ESem GEdr MAsh MHer NMen SFgr XLum
	'Jubilee Tricolor'	ESem GCrg GEdr NHol NMen SFgr WAbe
	'Jungle Fires'	CMea CWil ELon ESem NMen NPri SDys SRms WHoo
	'Jungle Shadows'	EDAr ESem NMen NWad XLum
	'Jupiter'	GKev NPri XLum
	'Jurrina'	NMen
	'Justine's Choice'	CWil ESem NMen SFgr SRms
	'Kalinda'	MHom
	'Kappa'	CTri CWil ESem NBro NMen SDys SRot
	'Katmai'	CWil ESem NMen SFgr
	'Kaya'	CWil
	'Keiko'	NMen
	'Kelly Jo'	CWil ECho ESem NBro NMen SFgr
	'Kelut'	ESem NMen
	'Kermit'	MHom NMen
	'Kia'	CWil NMen
	'Kiara'	CWil NMen
	'Kibo'	ESem NMen
	'Kim' **new**	NMen
	'Kimba'	CWil NMen
	'Kimble'	ESem NMen
	'Kimono'	NMen NWad
	kindingeri	CWil ESem MHom NMen XLum
	'King George'	CTal CTri CWil ESem LBee MMuc NMen SEND SFgr SRms WHal WHoo XLum
	'King Lear'	ESem GBin
	'Kip'	CMea NMen
	'Kismet'	NMen
	'Koko Flanel'	CTal CWil ESem NMen SFgr
	'Korspel Prince' **new**	NMen
	'Korspelsegietje'	CWil GAbr NMen SRms
	kosaninii	ESem NMen SFgr
	- from Koprivnik, Slovenia	MSCN NMen WAbe XLum
	- 'Hepworth'	SPlb
	'Krakeling'	NMen
	'Kramer's Purpur'	NMen
	'Kramer's Spinrad'	CMea CTal CWil EPPr ESem GAbr GEdr GKev LBee MBel NMen NPri SFgr SPlb SRms WGor WHoo
	'Krater'	CWil NMen
	'Kubi'	ESem
	'Larissa' **new**	SFgr
	'Laura Lee'	MMuc NMen SEND
	'Lavender and Old Lace'	CWil ECho EPot LBee LRHS MSCN NMen SPlb SRms WIce
	'Laysan'	CWil
	Le Clair's hybrid No 4	NMen
	'Le Congai' **new**	NMen
	'Legolas'	NMen
	'Lemon and Lime'	ESem
	'Lennik's Glory'	see *S.* 'Crispyn'
	'Lennik's Glory No.2'	NMen
	'Lentezon'	ESem SFgr
	'Leocadia's Nephew'	NMen
	'Les Yielding'	ESem
	leucanthum	XLum
	'Lilac Queen'	NMen
	'Lilac Time' ♀H5	CMea CTal CWil ECho ELon EPPr ESem GAbr LRHS MBrN MHer MSCN NMen SFgr SPlb SRms WHal XLum

	'Limbo'	NMen
	'Lion King'	CTal CWil ESem MSCN NMen SFgr
	'Lioness' **new**	CWil
	'Lipari'	NMen WCot XLum
	'Lipstick'	NMen
	'Little Coffee Cup'	SFgr
	'Little Flirt'	MSCN
	'Lively Bug'	CWil ECho EDAr EPPr ESem LBee LRHS MSCN NMen SDys SRms
	'Lloyd Praeger'	see *S. montanum* subsp. *stiriacum* 'Lloyd Praeger'
	'Long Shanks'	MSCN SFgr
	'Lonzo'	ESem NMen SRms
	'Lord Alan'	GKev NMen
	'Lord Morton' **new**	NMen
	'Louisse-Marie'	NMen
	'Lovely Roset' **new**	NMen
	'Lucy Liu' **new**	NMen
	'Lynn's Choice'	CWil GAbr NMen NWad SFgr WHal
	macedonicum	NMen SPlb SRms XLum
	- from Ljuboten, Macedonia/Kosovo	CWil
	'Madeleine'	ESem NMen
	'Magic Spell'	ESem NMen
	'Magical'	NMen
	'Magnificum'	CWil ESem NMen WGor
	'Mahogany'	CTal CTri CWil ECho EDAr ESem GKev LBee MHer MSCN NHol NMen NPri SFgr SRms WHal XLum
	'Maigret'	CWil NMen
	'Majestic'	ESem LBee NMen
	'Malby's Hybrid'	see *S.* 'Reginald Malby'
	'Maria Laach'	CWil ESem NMen
	'Marijntje'	CWil ESem NMen
	'Marjorie Newton'	CWil ESem NMen
	'Marland Ruby'	CWil NMen
	'Marmalade'	CMea NMen
§	***marmoreum***	ECho EPot LBee LRHS NMen SRms WHal
	- from Kanzan Gorge, Bulgaria	ESem XLum
	- from Okol, Albania	NMen
	- 'Brunneifolium'	CTal CWil GAbr LBee NMen NPri XLum
	- subsp. ***marmoreum*** var. ***dinaricum***	MHer NMen
§	- - 'Rubrifolium'	XLum
	'Marshall'	NMen
	'Mate'	ESem NMen
	'Matthew's Day Dream'	GKev
	'Mauna Kea'	ESem NMen
	'Mauvine'	NMen XLum
	'Mayfair'	EDAr
	'Mayfair Imp'	NMen
	'Medallion'	NMen
	'Meelah' **new**	NMen
	'Meisse'	ECho NMen
	'Melanie'	CWil ESem MBrN NMen
	'Memorial Merit'	ESem
	'Mercury'	CWil ECho GCrg LRHS NBro NMen SRms
	'Merlin'	ESem MSCN NMen
	mettenianum	NMen
	'Midas'	CTal CWil ECho ESem LRHS NMen SFgr
	'Mini Frost'	ESem NMen
	'Minuet'	NMen
	'Mira' **new**	MHol
	'Missouri Rose'	NMen
	'Mixed Spice'	NMen
	'Moerkerk's Merit'	CTal CWil LRHS NMen XLum
	'Mohair'	NMen
	'Mona Lisa'	NMen
	'Mondstein'	CWil ESem GKev MSCN
§	***montanum***	ESem MHtn
	- from Arbizion, France	CWil
	- from Monte Tirone, Italy	LBee
	- from Monte Tonale, Italy	CWil
	- from Windachtal, Germany	CWil
§	- subsp. ***burnatii***	CWil ESem MHom NMen
	- 'Caesar'	MSCN
	- subsp. ***carpaticum***	CWil XLum
	- - 'Cmiral's Yellow'	GKev MSCN WAbe
*	- Fragell form	SFgr
	- subsp. ***montanum***	CWil
	- 'Rubrum'	see *S.* 'Red Mountain'
	- subsp. ***stiriacum***	CWil ESem NMen SFgr SRms XLum
	- - from Mauterndorf, Austria	NMen
§	- - 'Lloyd Praeger'	CTal CWil ESem LBee NMen SDys SFgr
	montanum × ***tectorum*** var. ***boutignyanum***	NMen
	'More Honey'	CWil NMen
	'Morning Glow'	CMea ESem NMen WGor WHal
	'Mount Hood'	ECho ELon ESem LRHS NMen SRms WHal
	'Mount Usher'	NMen
	'Mulberry Wine'	CWil LBee NMen SFgr SRms WGor WHoo
	'Mystic'	CWil ESem MBrN NMen
	'Naemi' **new**	NMen
	'Neon'	CWil NMen
	'Neptune'	SFgr
	nevadense	CTal CWil EPot NMen SRms
	- from Puerto de San Francisco	CWil
	'Nico'	CWil NMen NWad SRms
	'Night Raven'	NMen
	'Nigrum'	see *S. tectorum* 'Nigrum'
	'Niobe'	CWil NMen SFgr WHal
	'Noellie'	CWil
	'Noir'	CWil EDAr ESem GKev MSCN NBro NMen WGor
	'Norbert'	CTal CWil EDAr NMen SRms XLum
	'Nörtofts Beauty'	NMen
	'Nouveau Pastel'	CFis CMea CWil ESem NMen WHal XLum
	'Octet'	NMen
	octopodes	NBir XLum
	- var. ***apetalum***	CTal CWil EPPr ESem GAbr MSCN NMen SRms WHoo
	'Oddity'	CWil GBin MBrN MHer MHtn NMen WHal
	'Ohio Burgundy'	ECho ESem LRHS MSCN NMen SRms WAbe
	'Old Copper'	ESem
	'Old Rose'	NMen SFgr
	'Olivette'	ESem NMen XLum
	'Olivine' **new**	SFgr
	'Omega'	ESem NMen
	'Ornatum'	ESem MHer MHom WHal
	ossetiense	CTal CWil EDAr GAbr NMen XLum
	'Othello' ♀H5	CDes CTri CWil EPfP GAbr GCra GKev NBir NMen WCot WPGP XLum
	'Ottelein'	NMen
	'Pacific Hep'	CWil NMen
	'Pacific Opal'	CWil
	'Pacific Purple Shadows'	CWil NMen
	'Pacific Spring Frost'	SFgr

	'Pacific Velveteen' new	SFgr
	'Packardian'	CWil ESem NMen NWad SFgr
	'Painted Lady'	ESem NMen
	'Palissander'	EDAr NMen XLum
	'Pam Wain'	MHom NMen
	'Passionata'	CWil NMen SFgr
	'Pastel'	CWil ESem MHer SFgr
	patens	see *Jovibarba heuffelii*
	'Patrician'	LBee SRms
	'Peggy'	CWil NMen WGor
	'Pekinese'	CTal ECho EDAr ESem GEdr LRHS MBrN NBro NMen SFgr SRms XLum
	'Peridot'	SFgr
	'Peterson's Ornatum'	SDys
	'Petsy'	ESem NMen SFgr SRms
	'Phoebe'	NMen
	'Pilatus'	MSCN SRms XLum
	'Pine Cone'	SFgr WGor
	'Pineapple Punch' new	SFgr
	'Pink Astrid'	CWil NMen
	'Pink Button'	CWil
	'Pink Cloud'	CWil NMen
	'Pink Dawn'	ESem
	'Pink Delight'	MSCN
	'Pink Flamingoes'	NMen
	'Pink Lemonade'	CWil MHom NMen
	'Pink Mist'	SRms
	'Pink Puff'	CWil MHom NMen SFgr
	'Pippin'	CMea CTal CWil ESem NMen SRms
	'Piran'	CWil
	pittonii ♀H5	CMea CWil ECho ESem NMen WHal XLum
	'Pixie'	CWil NMen SFgr
	'Plum Frosting'	ESem MSCN SFgr WGor
	'Plum Mist'	NWad
	'Plumb Rose'	CWil ESem NMen
	'Pluto'	CWil ESem LBee XLum
	'Poke Eat'	ESem
	'Polaris'	CWil MHom NMen
	'Poldark'	NMen
	'Ponderosa'	CWil NMen
	'Pottsii'	CWil ESem
I	'Powellii'	NMen
	'Prairie Sunset'	NMen
	'President Arsac'	XLum
	'Probus'	NMen
	'Procton'	ESem NMen
	'Proud Zelda'	CWil EDAr ESem GEdr MSCN NMen
	'Průhonice'	CWil NMen
	'Pseudo-ornatum'	LBee SRms
	'Pumaros'	SDys
	pumilum	CWil ECho GKev LRHS NMen SRms
	- from Adyl-Su, Chechnya, No 1	CWil
	- from El'brus, Russia, No 1	CWil
	- from Techensis, Caucasus Mountains	CWil SRms
	- 'Sopa'	CWil MSCN
	'Purdy'	MHom NMen WAbe
	'Purdy's 50-6'	CWil NMen
	'Purdy's 70-40'	NMen
	'Purdy's Big Red'	NMen
	'Purple Beauty'	GKev NMen
	'Purple Dazzler' new	CWil
	'Purple King'	CMea MHom NMen SDys
	'Purple Passion'	ESem NMen
	'Purple Queen'	CWil ECho EDAr ELon EPPr LRHS NMen SFgr SRms
	'Pygmalion'	ESem NMen
	'Queen Amalia'	see *S. reginae-amaliae*
	'Quintessence'	CWil MSCN NMen SRms
	'Racey'	ESem NMen SFgr
	'Ramses'	ESem SDys
	'Raspberry Ice'	CMea ESem GKev LBee MSCN NBro NMen
	'Rauer Kulm'	CWil NMen
	'Rauhreif'	ECtt XLum
	'Red Ace'	GEdr MBel NBro NMen NPri SFgr
	'Red Beam'	CWil LRHS MSCN NMen
	'Red Chief'	GKev
	'Red Chips'	EDAr MHom
	'Red Delta'	CDes NBir NMen SFgr WCot WPGP
	'Red Devil'	CMea CWil ECho ELon ESem LLHF LRHS NMen SFgr SPlb SRms WHoo
	'Red Giant'	NMen
	'Red King'	GBin NPri
	'Red Knight'	NMen
	'Red Lion'	NMen SFgr
	'Red Lynn'	CWil ESem
§	'Red Mountain'	CWil ESem LBee NMen SRms
	'Red Pink'	CWil NMen
	'Red Robin'	EDAr NMen
	'Red Shadows'	LBee
	'Red Spider'	EPPr EPot MHom NBro NMen
	'Red Summer'	ESem
	'Red West'	NMen
	'Regal'	ESem NMen
	reginae	see *S. reginae-amaliae*
§	***reginae-amaliae***	CWil GKev LRHS NMen SRms XLum
	- from Kambeecho, Greece, No 2	SDys
	- from Mavri Petri, Greece	CWil
	- from Sarpun, Turkey	CWil NMen SDys
	- from Vardusa, Serbia	CWil
§	'Reginald Malby'	CTri ECho ESem LRHS NMen SFgr SRms
	'Reinhard' ♀H5	CMea CTal CWil ECho EDAr ELon EPot ESem GCrg GEdr GKev LRHS MAsh MBrN MHer MSCN NMen NPri NRya SPlb SRms WHal WHoo
	'Remus'	ELan ESem NMen SFgr WGor
	'Rex'	NMen
	'Rhöne'	CWil LBee NMen
	'Rhubarb Crumble'	SFgr
	'Rich 'n' Fruity'	MSCN
	'Risque'	LBee
	'Rita Jane'	CWil ESem MHom NMen SFgr
	'Robin'	LBee NBro NHol NMen SFgr
	'Ronny'	CWil ESem NMen
	'Roosemaryn'	EDAr ESem
	'Rosa Mädchen' new	NMen
	× ***roseum***	ESem NMen
	'Rosie'	CMea CWil ECho ELon EPot ESem GAbr GEdr GMaP LBee LRHS MAsh MMuc MSCN NHol NMen NPri SRms WHal WHoo WIce
	'Rotkopf' ♀H5	CTal CWil LRHS MSCN NMen NPri NWad XLum
	'Rotmantel'	NMen
	'Rotund'	CWil GEdr MSCN
	'Rouge'	NMen
	'Royal Opera'	EDAr NMen NPri
	'Royal Ruby'	LBee NPri
	'Royale'	SFgr
	'Rubellum Mahogany'	SFgr

'Rubikon Improved' NMen
'Rubin' CBod CMea CTal CTri EPfP GBin GKev LBMP MAsh MMuc MSCN NBir NEgg NMen NPri SPoG SRms WAbe WIce XLum
I 'Rubra Ash' CWil ESem NMen WAbe
I 'Rubra Ray' CWil EDAr MMuc NMen SEND
'Rubrifolium' see *S. marmoreum* subsp. *marmoreum* 'Rubrifolium'
* 'Ruby Glow' EDAr
'Ruby Heart' EDAr
'Russian River' WHoo
'Rusty' CWil ESem NMen SFgr
ruthenicum CTal ECho EPPr LLHF LRHS MHom NMen NRya SRms XLum
- 'Regis-Fernandii' ECho XLum
'Safara' ESem
'Saga' MHom NMen
'Samwise' **new** NMen
'Sando' **new** NMen
'Sanford's Hybrid' NMen
'Santis' NMen
'Sarah' EDAr NMen
'Sarotte' CWil NMen
'Sassy Frass' NMen
'Saturn' ESem GEdr MSCN NMen SRms
schlehanii see *S. marmoreum*
schnittspahnii XLum
'Sea Breeze' SFgr
'Sea Urchin' SFgr
'Seminole' CWil ESem NMen
'Serendipity' EDAr
'Shannon Louise' **new** CWil
'Sharon's Pencil' CWil NMen
'Sheila' GAbr
'Shirley Moore' CWil EDAr NMen SFgr
'Shirley's Joy' NMen XLum
'Sideshow' NMen
'Sigma' NMen
'Silberkarneol' misapplied see *S.* 'Silver Jubilee'
'Silberkarneol' ambig. MMuc SEND
'Silberspitz' CTal CWil ECho ELon LRHS MHer MHom NBro NMen SPlb SRms
'Silken Threads' **new** SFgr
'Silver Crows' NMen
'Silver Cup' SFgr
§ 'Silver Jubilee' CMea CWil ECho EDAr ESem GBin LRHS MMuc NBro NMen NRya SPlb SRms XLum
'Silver Queen' CWil ESem
'Silver Shadow' MSCN
'Silver Sixpence' SFgr
'Silver Thaw' CWil EDAr GMaP LRHS NMen NPri
'Silverine' CWil EDAr NPri
'Silvertone' CWil ESem
'Simonkaianum' see *Jovibarba hirta*
'Sioux' CTal CWil ESem GAbr LBee MBrN NMen WHal
'Sirius' MHol NMen
'Skrocki's Beauty' **new** NMen
'Skrocki's Bronze' GAbr LRHS NMen SRms
'Slabber's Seedling' CWil NMen
'Smaragd' LBee NMen XLum
'Smit's Seedling' NMen
'Smokey Jet' ESem NMen SFgr
'Smokey Quartz' WGor
'Snowberger' CMea CTal CWil ESem MSCN NMen SFgr SRms WGor WHal
'Soarte' ESem
soboliferum see *Jovibarba sobolifera*
'Soothsayer' CWil NMen
sosnowskyi CWil NMen XLum
'Soul' NMen
'Soul Sister' ESem
'Spangle' NMen
'Spangle' sport NMen
'Spanish Dancer' NMen
'Sparkler' CTal
'Speciosum' ESem
'Spherette' CWil EDAr ESem MBrN MSCN NMen NPri WAbe
'Spice' NMen
'Spider's Lair' 🏆H5 EDAr MHom NMen
'Spinellii' NMen WThu
'Spiver's Velvet' ESem NMen
'Springmist' ECho ESem LRHS NMen NPri SFgr SRms WGor
'Sprite' CWil GEdr LRHS MBel NMen SDys SRms
'Squib' CDes CTal CWil ESem MSCN NMen
stansfieldii see *S. arachnoideum* subsp. *tomentosum* 'Stansfieldii'
'Starburst' CWil LRHS SFgr
'Starion' NMen
'Starshine' ESem SFgr
'State Fair' CWil EDAr NMen
'Steerosentern' **new** NMen
* ***stoloniferum*** GAbr
'Strawberry Fields' ESem
'Strawberry Sundae' ESem NMen
'Strider' CWil GAbr NMen
'Stuffed Olive' NMen SDys SRms SRot
'Sugary' NMen
'Sun Waves' CWil ESem NMen SDys
'Sunray Desire' CWil WGor
'Sunray Magic' WGor
'Super Dome' CWil NMen
'Superama' ESem NMen
'Supernova' ESem
'Syston Flame' NMen
'T'Pol' **new** NMen
'Tamberlane' EDAr
'Tambimuttu' NMen
'Tarita' CWil NMen
'Teck' NMen
§ ***tectorum*** 🏆H5 CArn CBod CHby CTal CTri ECho EDAr ELan EPfP GPoy LBee LPot MHer MNHC NMen SIde SPlb WJek XLum
§ - var. ***alpinum*** ECho LRHS MHom NBro NMen SRms
- var. ***andreanum*** CWil ESem XLum
- 'Atropurpureum' ECho ELan
- 'Atroviolaceum' EDAr NMen SPlb XLum
* - 'Aureum' NMen SFgr
- var. ***boutignyanum*** CWil
GDJ 94.02 from Sant Joan de Caselles, Andorra
- - GDJ 94.03 CWil
- - GDJ 94.04 from Route de Tuixén, Spain CWil SRms
- var. ***calcareum*** ECho ESem
§ - var. ***glaucum*** NMen
- 'Marin' NMen
- monstrose **new** SPlb
- 'Murale' **new** SFgr
§ - 'Nigrum' ESem LBee MHer NBro SDys WGor
- 'Red Flush' EDAr EPPr MBrN NMen SFgr
- 'Royanum' 🏆H5 ESem MSCN
* - subsp. ***sanguineum*** EDAr

	- 'Sunset'	CMea EDAr ESem GCrg SDys WHal
	- subsp. ***tectorum***	ESem GEdr NMen
§	- - 'Boissieri'	CWil NMen
	- - 'Triste'	CWil LBee NMen SFgr XLum
	- 'Tokajense'	ESem
	- 'Violaceum'	MHom NMen SPlb SRms WGor
	'Teddy Bear' **new**	MSCN
	'Tederheid'	NMen
	'Telfan'	NMen
	'Tenburg'	NMen
	'Terlamen'	CWil NMen
	'Terracotta Baby'	CTal CWil ELon ESem NMen SFgr
	'Thayne'	NMen
	'The Platters'	CWil NMen
	'The Rocket'	NMen
	× ***thompsonianum***	LBee SFgr
	'Thunder'	NMen
	'Tiger Bay'	NMen
	'Tintenblut' **new**	NMen
	'Tip Top'	CWil GEdr NMen SFgr
	'Titania'	CWil NBro NMen WHal
	'Topaz'	CWil LBee NMen NPri SRms XLum
	'Tordeur's Memory'	CWil ESem MMuc MSCN NMen SEND
I	'Tourmalyi'	NMen
	'Tracy Sue'	EDAr XLum
	'Traffic Lights' **new**	SFgr
	'Trail Walker'	CWil LBee NMen SRms
	transcaucasicum	XLum
	'Tree Beard'	CWil NMen
	'Trine'	CWil NMen
	'Tristesse' ♀H5	CWil ECtt EDAr GAbr LBee MBrN NMen NPri SFgr
	'Truva'	CWil ESem NMen SFgr
	'Tumpty'	SFgr
	'Twilight Blues'	CWil ECho ESem LRHS NMen SFgr SRms
	'Twizzler'	MSCN SFgr
	'Undine'	CWil ESem NMen SFgr
	'Unicorn'	ESem NMen
	'Uranus'	NMen
	'Urmina'	NMen
	× ***vaccarii***	XLum
	'Van der Steen'	GAbr NMen
	'Vanbaelen'	CWil GAbr NMen SDys
	'Vasi Petru' **new**	NMen
	'Vega' **new**	MHol
	'Veughelen'	NMen
	vicentei	ESem MHom NMen
	- from Gaton, Spain	ESem LBee NMen
§	- subsp. ***paui***	NSla
	'Video'	CWil ESem MHom NMen SFgr
	'Vignola'	CWil NMen
	'Viking'	NMen
	'Violet Queen'	ESem NMen
	'Virgil'	CWil EDAr ESem MBrN MSCN NMen NWad SDys SPlb WAbe WCot WIce
I	'Virginius'	CWil GAbr NMen
	'Vulcano'	NMen
	'Waldalina'	CWil NMen
	'Warrior'	EDAr
	'Wasti'	CWil NMen
	'Waterlily' **new**	NWad
	'Watermelon Rind'	ESem NMen
	webbianum	see *S. arachnoideum* L. subsp. *tomentosum* (C.B. Lehm. & Schnittsp.) Schinz & Thell.
	'Webby Flame'	CWil NMen
	'Webbyola'	ESem NMen
	'Weirdo'	CWil NMen
	'Wendy'	ESem SFgr
	'Westerlin'	CWil ESem NMen
	'White Bouquet'	NMen
	'White Christmas'	see *S. arachnoideum* 'White Christmas'
	'White Ladies'	NMen
	'Whitening'	EDAr EPot GEdr
	'Whitney'	ESem NMen
	× ***widderi***	NMen
	'Wilhelm Tell'	NMen
	'Winsome' **new**	NWad
	'Winter Beauty'	NMen
	'Wok' **new**	NMen
I	'Woolcott's Variety'	CWil ECho ESem MSCN NBir NMen SFgr
	wulfenii	CWil NMen
*	- ***roseum***	EDAr
	'Xaviera'	CWil NMen
	'Yanisha'	CWil NMen
	'Yarnton'	ESem NMen
	'Yolanda'	CWil NMen
	'Yvette'	CWil NMen
	'Zaccour' **new**	NMen
	'Zackenkrone'	NMen
	'Zaza'	CWil
	zeleborii	WHal
	'Zenith'	CWil EDAr ESem GAbr NMen SFgr SRms
	'Zenobia'	MHom
	'Zenocrate'	NHol WHal
	'Zepherin'	CWil MSCN NMen
	'Zilver Moon'	CWil ESem NMen
	'Zilver Snowflake'	NMen
	'Zilver Suzanna'	CWil ESem NMen
	'Zilverprinsesje'	NMen
	'Zircon'	EDAr NMen
	'Zone'	NMen
	'Zorba'	NMen
	'Zulu'	NMen

Senecio (Asteraceae)

	aquaticus	LLWG
§	***articulatus***	EShb
§	***barbertonicus***	EShb
	bidwillii	see *Brachyglottis bidwillii*
	candicans misapplied	see *S. cineraria*
	cannabifolius	CSpe
	christobalanensis	SDix
	chrysanthemoides	see *Euryops chrysanthemoides*
§	***cineraria***	LPot SEND
	- 'Silver Dust' ♀H4	EPfP MMuc
	cinerascens	SVen
*	***coccinilifera***	SBch
	compactus	see *Brachyglottis compacta*
	confusus	see *Pseudogynoxys chenopodioides*
	crassissimus	CDoC EShb
	cristobalensis	CSpe WCot
	doria	EBee EShb MMuc SAko WHrl
	elegans	SVen
	ficoides	EShb
	formosoides B&SWJ 10736	WCru
	formosus B&SWJ 10700	WCru
	gerberifolius B&SWJ 10357	WCru
	- B&SWJ 10361	WCru
	'Gregynog Gold'	see *Ligularia* 'Gregynog Gold'
	greyi misapplied	see *Brachyglottis* (Dunedin Group) 'Sunshine'

greyi Hook. f. — see *Brachyglottis greyi* (Hook. f.) B. Nord.
heritieri DC. — see *Pericallis lanata* (L'Hér.) B. Nord.
kleiniiformis — EShb
laxifolius hort. — see *Brachyglottis* (Dunedin Group) 'Sunshine'
leucostachys misapplied — see *S. viravira*
macroglossus — CHll EShb
- 'Variegatus' (v) ♀H1c — EShb
mandraliscae 'Blue Finger' **new** — WCot
maritimus — see *S. cineraria*
monroi — see *Brachyglottis monroi*
petasitis — CBcs CFil SDix WCot
polyodon **new** — GBuc LCro WHea
- var. **subglaber** — CMea CSpe EAJP EBee ECre EDAr EWes GBin GLog MHol MNrw MPie MSpe NDov NLar SPhx WCAu WCFE WMoo WPGP WSHC WWEG
- - S&SH 29 — NCGa
- - 'Harmony' — NDov
przewalskii — see *Ligularia przewalskii*
pulcher — CDTJ SBch SHar WPGP
rowleyanus — EBak
scandens — CExl EShb IMou WPGP
seminiveus — EBee
§ **serpens** — CDoC EShb EUJe MSCN SEND
§ **smithii** — ELan GBee NBid WWtn
subnivalis — XLum
subulatus var. **subulatus** CC 6516 — EBee
'Sunshine' — see *Brachyglottis* (Dunedin Group) 'Sunshine'
talinoides — see *S. barbertonicus*
subsp. **cylindricus** 'Himalaya'
tanguticus — see *Sinacalia tangutica*
§ **viravira** — EPri EUJe MCot WSHC

Senna (*Caesalpiniaceae*)

alexandrina — EShb LRHS WPGP
§ **corymbosa** — CBcs CRHN CTri ECre LTro
hebecarpa — SBrt
§ **marilandica** — CArn EBee ELan GBin MGil
multiglandulosa — WPGP
septemtrionalis — LRHS SEND

Sequoia (*Cupressaceae*)

sempervirens ♀H6 — CBcs CCVT CDoC CDul CLnd CMCN CMen CTho ECrN EFry EPfP EWTr LRHS MBlu MMuc NWea SEND SGol WMat WMou
- 'Adpressa' — CDoC CDul CTho EFry MAsh MGos NWea SCoo
- 'Cantab' — CDoC
- 'Glauca' — MAsh
- 'Henderson Blue' — SLim
- 'Prostrata' — CDoC SEND

Sequoiadendron (*Cupressaceae*)

giganteum ♀H6 — CBcs CCVT CDoC CDul CMCN CTho CTri EFry ELan EPfP EWTr LRHS MAsh MBlu MGos MMuc NEgg NOrn NWea SAko SEND SEWo SGol SPlb WMat WMou
- 'Barabits Requiem' — IArd MBlu SLim SMad
- 'Blauer Eichzwerg' — NLar
- 'Bultinck Yellow' — MBlu
- 'Curly Green' — NLar
- 'Glaucum' — CDoC CDul CTho MBlu SLim
* - 'Glaucum Compactum' — MBlu
- 'Greenpeace' — MBlu NLar
- 'Pendulum' — CCVT CDoC CDul CKen ERod ESwi LRHS MBlu SLim SMad
- 'Philip Curtis' — NLar
- 'Pirat' — NLar
- 'Powdered Blue' — NLar SLim WPGP

Serapias (*Orchidaceae*)

lingua — CDes SChF

Seriphidium see *Artemisia*

Serratula (*Asteraceae*)

bulgarica — NDov
coronata subsp. **insularis** B&SWJ 8698 — WCru
- - f. **alba** — GAbr
lycopifolia — WCot
§ **seoanei** — CKno CMea CPrp CSam EBee ELan LEdu LHop LPla MCot MHer MLHP MNrw MPie MRav NBid SHar SPhx SRms WCot WPGP
shawii — see *S. seoanei*
tinctoria — CArn NLar NMir SPhx WHer

Serruria (*Proteaceae*)

florida — SPlb
phylicoides — SPlb

Seseli (*Apiaceae*)

elatum — MAvo
gummiferum — CHid CSam CSpe EAJP MSpe SKHP SPhx WHil WPtf
hippomarathrum — LEdu MAvo SDix SPhx WCot WHal WHrl WPGP WWtn
lehmannii RCB UA 13 — WCot
§ **libanotis** — CArn CSam GBin LEdu LPla LRHS MAvo MBel NLar SDix SPhx WCot WPtf
montanum — CSam CSpe EBee IMou LHop LPla NDov SBrt WPGP
varium — CArn

Sesleria (*Poaceae*)

§ **albicans** — SCob
§ **argentea** — EHoe EPPr
autumnalis — CKno EBee ELon EShb IMou LCro LEdu LPla NDov SCob SPhx XLum
caerulea — CAby CBod CKno CSam CSde EHoe ELan ELon EPfP GQue IMou LEdu LPal MBrN MWhi SPhx SPoG WPtf XLum XSen
- subsp. **calcarea** — see *S. albicans*
- 'Malvern Mop' — EBee WHrl
* **candida** — EPPr
cylindrica — see *S. argentea*
glauca — EHoe NLar NOak
'Greenlee' — CKno NDov
heufleriana — CWCL EHoe EPPr GEdr IMou MBel NLar SMea SPhx SPlb WCot
insularis — EBee EPPr EShb
'Morning Dew' — EBee GCal
nitida — CKno EBee EHoe IMou LCro LEdu LRHS MBrN SDix SPhx WCot XLum XSen
rigida — EHoe
sadleriana — EBee EPPr EWes

Setaria (*Poaceae*)

macrostachya	LLWP SPhx
palmifolia ϒH2	EShb EUJe MMuc NLos SDix SGSe SPlb WCot
- BWJ 8132	WCru
viridis	CSpe WCot

Setcreasea see *Tradescantia*

shaddock see *Citrus maxima*

Sharon fruit see *Diospyros kaki*

Shepherdia (*Elaeagnaceae*)

argentea	CBcs NLar SAko

Shibataea (*Poaceae*)

kumasaca ϒH5	CAbb CBcs CDoC CEnt ENBC ERod GCal LEdu LRHS MBrN MWht SBig SGol WJun
lancifolia	WJun

Shortia (*Diapensiaceae*)

galacifolia	EPot
soldanelloides	EPot
var. ***magna***	
uniflora	GKev NHar WAbe

Sibbaldia (*Rosaceae*)

procumbens	GKev

Sibbaldiopsis (*Rosaceae*)

§ ***tridentata***	GJos GKev SBrt
- 'Lemon Mac'	NHar
- 'Nuuk'	CCon EPPr

Sibthorpia (*Plantaginaceae*)

europaea	CExl

Sida (*Malvaceae*)

hermaphrodita	EBee

Sidalcea (*Malvaceae*)

'Brilliant'	CBcs COtt EHrv GBin IBoy ILea LAst MJak MNrw MSCN NBir SPer WCAu WMoo WWEG
campestris from Oregon, USA	EPPr
candida	CBod CSam EBee ECtt ELan EPfP GCra GMaP ILea LAst LHop LRHS MAsh MBNS MMuc MRav MTis NChi NGdn NLar NSti SCob SPer WCAu WCot WPtf
- 'Bianca'	EBee EHrv EPfP NLar WFar WHal WMoo WOut WWEG
'Candy Girl'	CBod EBee NLar SCob WCot
'Crimson King'	WFar
'Croftway Red'	CBod CCon EBee ELan EWld GCra LRHS MBel NBro NGdn NHol NWad SPer SWvt WFar
'Elsie Heugh' ϒH7	Widely available
'Little Princess'PBR	COtt EBee EWes LRHS MHol MNrw NGdn NLar SCob SPoG WCot
'Loveliness'	CBod CPrp EBee ECtt ELan EShb LHop LRHS MRav NBro NCGa NGdn NWad WFar WGwG WMoo
malviflora	SRms
- 'Alba'	NChi
- 'Crimson Beauty'	EBee
- subsp. ***purpurea***	LRHS
'Moorland Rose Coronet'	WMoo
'Mr Lindbergh'	EBee MPie NLar
'Mrs Borrodaile'	CCon CMac MBel MRav NBro NEoE NGdn WMoo WWEG
'Mrs T. Alderson'	EBee
'My Love'	EBee NDov
'Oberon'	EBee LRHS MRav
oregana	NGdn
- subsp. ***spicata***	WMoo
'Party Girl'	CMac COtt CSBt CSam ELan EPfP GJos IBoy LRHS LSRN LSun MNHC MRav NBro NGdn NLar NPri SPlb SPoG WBor WFar WMnd WMoo XLum
'Purpetta'	CBod EBee ELan EPfP LSun NEoE NGBl NLar SPad
reptans	CDes EBee
'Reverend Page Roberts'	MRav WCot WWEG
'Rosaly'	CAby CSam EAJP IFoB LRHS MPie NLar
'Rosanna'	CBod CSam EAJP EPfP GMaP LRHS NLar WPtf
'Rose Bud'	EBee ELan
'Rose Queen'	CBod EBee ECha LHop LRHS MRav NBro NHol SHar SRms WFar
Stark's hybrids	LRHS SRms
'Sussex Beauty'	CMos CSam EBee LRHS MBel MLHP MRav NDov NEgg NGdn SBod WMoo
'Sweet Joy'	SPer
'Wensleydale'	CDes EBee LRHS
'William Smith' ϒH7	CBod CCon CSam EBee ECha ECtt EPfP EWes GBuc LRHS LSRN MBel MMuc MRav NBir NGdn NLar SEND SPer WFar WMnd WPtf WWEG
'Wine Red'	CBod CCon CMHG CMos EBee EShb LRHS NEgg NGdn SPoG SWvt WGwG WTor

Sideritis (*Lamiaceae*)

RCB UA 2	WCot
clandestina	XSen
cypria	EBee XSen
gomeraea new	WCot
hyssopifolia	SIgm
- subsp. ***guillonii***	XSen
phlomoides	SIgm XSen
romana	WAbe
scardica	CArn XSen
sericea new	SIgm
stachydioides	XSen
syriaca	MHer XSen

Sieversia (*Rosaceae*)

§ ***pentapetala***	GEdr WAbe
- 'Flore Pleno' (d)	WAbe
reptans	see *Geum reptans*

Silaum (*Apiaceae*)

silaus	NMir SBrt

Silene (*Caryophyllaceae*)

RBS	EPPr
from Uzbekistan	GCal
acaulis	ECho EDAr GCrg GJos SRms WAbe
§ - subsp. ***acaulis***	ECho SPlb SRms
- 'Alba'	ECho EWes SRms WAbe
- 'Blush'	ECho EDAr NSla WAbe WOld

§	- subsp. ***bryoides***	NLar
	- 'Correvoniana'	NLar
	- subsp. ***elongata***	see *S. acaulis* subsp. *acaulis*
	- subsp. ***exscapa***	see *S. acaulis* subsp. *bryoides*
	- 'Frances'	CPBP EDAr GCrg ITim NHar NLar NRya NSla WAbe
	- 'Francis Copeland'	ECho
	- 'Helen's Double' (d)	ECho GJos
	- 'Mount Snowdon'	ECho EWes MMuc NLar SPlb SPoG SRms SRot WHoo
	- 'Pedunculata'	see *S. acaulis* subsp. *acaulis*
	- 'Select'	EPot
	alba	see *S. latifolia* subsp. *alba*
§	***alpestris***	ECho SHar SRms SRot WMoo WThu
	- 'Flore Pleno' (d) ♀H5	CMea CPBP ECho EWes NSla SBch WIce
	araratica	ITim WAbe
	argaea	WAbe
	× ***arkwrightii***	see *Lychnis* × *arkwrightii*
	armeria	SDys
	- 'Aphrodite'	CSpe
	- 'Electra'	CSpe
	asterias	EBee GCal GCra MNrw SBrt WWFP
	- MESE 429	GBin
	atropurpurea	see *Lychnis viscaria* subsp. *atropurpurea*
	bolanthoides	WAbe
	catholica new	EBee
§	***compacta***	IMou WCot
	'Confetti'	CWld EAJP MMuc NSti SPhx
	'Country Comet'	NChi
§	***davidii***	EBee EPot GKev
	delavayi	GEdr
	dinarica	WAbe
§	***dioica***	CArn CHab CMac CWld GJos LEdu MHer MNHC NLar NMir SPhx SPoG SRms SWat WMoo WOut WSFF WShi
	- 'Clifford Moor' (v)	ECtt MHer MSCN NSti SCoo
	- 'Compacta'	see *S. dioica* 'Minikin'
	- 'Firefly'[PBR] (d)	CMac CWCL ECtt MBel NPri NSti SHar SRkn SWvt
§	- 'Flore Pleno' (d)	GCra MHer MRav NBid NBro NGdn WFar WHoo WTcb
	- golden-leaved	WFar
§	- 'Graham's Delight' (v)	NWad
	- 'Inane'	EBee ELon WBor WPGP WRHF WSHC
	- 'Innocence'	NChi
	- 'Kay's Winter Dream' new	MAvo
	- f. ***lactea***	MHer
§	- 'Minikin'	MAvo MSCN MTis NGdn NPri
	- 'Purple Prince'	MAvo MMuc SEND WFar WMoo WPtf
I	- 'Ray's Golden Campion'	GEdr NWad WOut WTou
	- 'Rollie's Favorite'[PBR]	EBee ECtt EPfP LBMP LRHS MBri MHol MNrw MSCN NDov NPri NSti SHar SPoG WBod WBor
	- 'Rubra Plena'	see *S. dioica* 'Flore Pleno'
	- 'Stella'	NChi
	- 'Thelma Kay' (d/v)	GBuc MAvo NGdn WMoo
	- 'Valley High' (v)	EBee ECtt EWes MHol MMuc WHil
	- 'Variegata'	see *S. dioica* 'Graham's Delight'
§	***fimbriata***	CCon CSpe EBee EHrv ELan EPPr EShb ILea LEdu LPla MCot MMHG MMuc MNrw MRav NChi NLar NSti SDix WBor WCot WKif WMoo WPGP WPtf WRHF
	hookeri Ingramii Group	WAbe
	kantzeensis	see *S. davidii*
	keiskei var. ***akaisialpina***	NSla
	- - f. ***leucantha*** new	NSla
	- var. ***minor***	ECho EWes LRHS NSla WAbe
	laciniata 'Jack Flash'	MSCN
	latifolia	CHab CWld MNHC NMir WOut
§	- subsp. ***alba***	SEND
	maritima	see *S. uniflora*
	multifida	see *S. fimbriata*
	noctiflora	CHab WSFF
	nutans	SRms WSFF
	orientalis	see *S. compacta*
	petersonii	LLHF
	plankii new	CPBP
	pusilla	ITim NLar
	quadridentata	see *S. alpestris*
	regia	EBee SBrt SPhx
	rubra	see *S. dioica*
	schafta ♀H5	CTri ECha ECho EPfP MAsh MMuc MRav NBid NFav NPri SEND SRms WHoo XLum
	- 'Abbotswood'	see *Lychnis* × *walkeri* 'Abbotswood Rose'
	- 'Persian Carpet'	SBch
	- 'Shell Pink'	CPBP CSam ECha ECtt EWes GJos LRHS MMuc NBid SBch SEND WHoo
	sieboldii	see *Lychnis coronata* var. *sieboldii*
	stellata new	SPhx
§	***uniflora***	CHab CWld ECho EPfP MMuc MSCN NBro NPri SPlb SRms SRot WHer WMoo WOut
	- 'Alba Plena'	see *S. uniflora* 'Robin Whitebreast'
I	- 'Compacta'	ECho NPri SHar WMoo
§	- 'Druett's Variegated' (v)	CTri ECho ECtt ELon EPot EWes GJos LHop LRHS MAsh MHer MHol NBid NPri SPlb SPoG SRms WIce XLum
	- 'Flore Pleno'	see *S. uniflora* 'Robin Whitebreast'
§	- 'Robin Whitebreast' (d)	ECha ECho ECtt EPfP NBid NBro SPhx SRms SRot WMoo WSHC XLum
	- 'Rosea'	ECho GCrg GJos MMuc SEND SPlb SRot
	- 'Swan Lake' (d)	SIgm
	- 'Variegata'	see *S. uniflora* 'Druett's Variegated'
	- Weisskehlchen	see *S. uniflora* 'Robin Whitebreast'
	- 'White Bells'	CTri WKif
	uralensis new	GEdr
	viridiflora	SPhx
§	***vulgaris***	CAgr CArn CHab CWld LEdu MHer MMuc MNHC NMir SEND SRms WHer WOut
	- subsp. ***maritima***	see *S. uniflora*
	wallichiana	see *S. vulgaris*
	'Wisley Pink'	ECtt
	yunnanensis	SPhx WSHC
§	***zawadskii***	GKev MMuc NWad SBrt SEND

Siler (*Umbelliferae*)

	montanum	see *Laserpitium siler*

Silphium (*Asteraceae*)

	integrifolium	NBre SMad SPhx WCot WOld XLum
	laciniatum	CMac LEdu NBre SMad SPhx WHal XLum
	perfoliatum ♀H7	CArn CFis EBee GPoy IMou LCro MMuc NBre NDov NLar SDix SEND SPhx WCot WWEG XLum
	- from Great Dixter	IMou
	- var. ***connatum***	SPhx

	simpsonii new	CEvo
	terebinthinaceum	SBrt SPhx WCot XLum
	trifoliatum	EPPr SPhx WCot

Silybum (*Asteraceae*)

	marianum	ELan GAbr GPoy LRHS MNHC SIde SPav SRms WHfH WOut WTou

Simmondsia (*Simmondsiaceae*)

	chinensis	EOHP

Sinacalia (*Asteraceae*)

§	***tangutica***	CBod CSam EPPr GQue ILea LHop MBel MSCN NBid NLar SDix WCot WOld WWtn

Sinapis (*Brassicaceae*)

	alba	SVic

Sinarundinaria (*Poaceae*)

	anceps	see *Yushania anceps*
	jaunsarensis	see *Yushania anceps*
	maling	see *Yushania maling*
	murielae	see *Fargesia murielae*
	nitida	see *Fargesia nitida*

Sinningia (*Gesneriaceae*)

	sp.	EABi
*	***caerulea***	WDib
	calcaria	WDib
	canescens ♀H1c	LToo WDib
§	***cardinalis***	EBak WDib
	- 'Innocent'	WDib
	conspicua	WDib
	nivalis	WDib
	speciosa 'Blanche de Méru'	SDeJ
	- 'Hollywood'	SDeJ
	- 'Kaiser Friedrich'	SDeJ
	- 'Kaiser Wilhelm'	SDeJ
	- 'Mont Blanc'	SDeJ
	tubiflora	CSpe WCot WKif XLum

Sinobambusa (*Poaceae*)

	tootsik	WJun

× *Sinocalycalycanthus* see *Calycanthus*

Sinocalycanthus see *Calycanthus*

Sinocrassula (*Crassulaceae*)

	yunnanensis new	SPlb

Sinofranchetia (*Lardizabalaceae*)

	chinensis	CFil CRHN IArd LEdu WPGP WSHC
	- DJHS 4117	WCru

Sinojackia (*Styracaceae*)

	xylocarpa	CBcs CMCN NLar

Sinopanax (*Araliaceae*)

	formosanus new	CFil

Sinopodophyllum (*Berberidaceae*)

§	***hexandrum***	CArn CBct CBro CWCL EBee ECho ELan EPot GBuc GCra GKev GMaP GPoy MNrw MRav NBid NBir NChi NHar NLar SKHP SPlb WPnP WSHC
	- CC 7324 new	GKev
§	- var. ***chinense***	CLAP ECho EWld GCal LEdu WCru
	- - BWJ 7908	WCru
	- - SDR 4409	CExl
	- 'Chinese White'	CExl
§	- var. ***emodi***	CArn EPfP GBuc ITim
	- - 'Majus'	CCon CLAP EWTr GBin WHal

Sinowilsonia (*Hamamelidaceae*)

	henryi	CBcs IArd NLar SAko

Siphocranion (*Lamiaceae*)

§	***macranthum***	CDes EBee EWes WPGP

Sison (*Apiaceae*)

	amomum	CBre

Sisymbrium (*Brassicaceae*)

§	***luteum***	EBee

Sisyrinchium ✿ (*Iridaceae*)

	× ***anceps***	see *S. angustifolium*
§	***angustifolium***	CMHG ECha EDAr MCot NBir NChi SChF SPlb SRms WBrk
	- f. ***album***	MCot NChi NLar
§	***arenarium***	CWCL GAbr GEdr
	atlanticum	NBro
	bellum hort.	see *S. idahoense* var. *bellum*
	bermudiana	see *S. angustifolium*
	- 'Album'	see *S. graminoides* 'Album'
	'Biscutella'	CBod CKno CPrp CTri ECho EPfP EWoo GMaP ITim LEdu LHop MCot NFav SPlb SRot WHal WHoo WKif
	'Blue Ice'	ITim LRHS NLar WAbe WMoo
	'Blue Skies'	ITim
	boreale	see *S. californicum*
	brachypus	see *S. californicum* Brachypus Group
	'Californian Skies'	CAby CBro CElw CExl CKno CTri EAJP ECha ECho ECtt EWoo GMaP LHop LRHS MNrw NBir NDov NSla SWvt WKif WMoo
§	***californicum***	CBen ECho EDAr EHon IMou LLWG LRHS NBro WMAq XLum
§	- Brachypus Group	ECho EPfP LPot MAsh NBir NLar SPlb SWvt WMoo
	- 'Yellowstone'	EPfP MHtn NPri
*	***capsicum***	CExl
	convolutum	NDov
	- B&SWJ 9117	WCru
	cuspidatum	see *S. arenarium*
	depauperatum	MNrw
	'Devon Skies'	CElw CPBP CWCL ECho ECtt EWoo GCrg LRHS MNrw NLar SBch SWvt WAbe WIce
	'Doctor Bailey'	EBee
	douglasii	see *Olsynium douglasii*
	'Dragon's Eye'	CElw CKno CMea CPBP EAJP ECtt EDAr EWes EWoo MBrN MHer NPri SCob WIce
	'E.K. Balls'	Widely available
	'Emmeline'	EWoo
	graminoides	IFoB NBro
§	- 'Album'	NBro
	grandiflorum	see *Olsynium douglasii*
	'Hemswell Sky'	ECtt EHoe EWoo GAbr NLar NRya
	'Iceberg'	CElw CKno EAJP ECha EWes LSun
	idahoense	ECha ECtt GAbr MHer NDov NRya SPlb SRms
§	- var. ***bellum***	CKno ECho EPfP NFav SRms WMoo XLum
	- - pale-flowered	CKno
	- - 'Rocky Point'	CKno EBee EPfP EWes LRHS SPoG

Plant	Suppliers
- var. ***macounii***	GEdr SPlb
§ - - 'Album' ♀H5	CAby CElw CMea ECho ECtt EWes GAbr GCrg GEdr GKev LPot NFav WAbe WIce
iridifolium	see *S. micranthum*
'Janet Denman' (v)	ECho EWes MAvo
junceum	see *Olsynium junceum*
littorale	CExl
macrocarpon misapplied	see *S. macrocarpum*
macrocarpon E.P. Bicknell ♀H4	CPBP MNrw
§ ***macrocarpum***	ECho
'Marion'	CMea CPBP ECtt MBrN WHoo
'May Snow'	see *S. idahoense* var. *macounii* 'Album'
'Miami'	EWoo
§ ***micranthum***	ECho
montanum* × *nudicaule	ECho GAbr SRot
'Mrs Spivey'	CSpe MHer NBir
'North Star'	see *S.* 'Pole Star'
palmifolium	CAby CBod CSpe EBee LEdu MHer MNrw SBch SMad SPad WSHC XLum
patagonicum	CExl CTal ECho
§ 'Pole Star'	EWoo NLar
'Quaint and Queer'	CExl EAJP ECha EHoe EWoo MBrN MCot MLHP MNrw NBir WMnd WSHC
'Raspberry'	CKno CMea EDAr EWoo
'Sapphire'	CAby CKno CWCL ECha ECtt EDAr EHoe GCrg LPot LRHS MHol NLar NPri SCob SPoG WBor WGrn WMoo
§ ***striatum***	Widely available
§ - 'Aunt May' (v)	CBcs CBod CMac CSBt ECha ECho EHoe EPfP EWoo GMaP LAst LRHS LSRN MBel MGos MRav MSpe NLar NPri NSti SCob SGSe SPer SPoG SRms SWat SWvt WCot WPGP WWEG
- 'Variegatum'	see *S. striatum* 'Aunt May'
aff. ***unispathaceum*** B&SWJ 10683	WCru

Sium (*Apiaceae*)

Plant	Suppliers
sisarum	CAgr CArn CLau GPoy LEdu MAvo MHer

Skimmia ✿ (*Rutaceae*)

Plant	Suppliers
sp.	LPar
anquetilia	CMac
- (f)	IVic WCru
- (m)	WCru
arborescens B&SWJ 11799	WCru
- subsp. ***nitida*** B&SWJ 8239	WCru
- - FMWJ 13377 **new**	CEvo
arisanensis B&SWJ 7114	WCru
- CWJ 12417	WCru
black-fruited B&SWJ 8259 from northern Vietnam (f/m)	WCru
× ***confusa*** 'Kew Green' (m) ♀H5	Widely available
japonica	CDul CMHG CMac CWib LPar MGos NPla NWea SCob SSta WBod WFar
- (f)	CMac CTri ELan EPfP GGal LPar SRms
- - B&SWJ 5053	WCru
- (m)	GGal
- - B&SWJ 5053	WCru
- 'Alba'	see *S. japonica* 'Wakehurst White'
- 'Bowles's Dwarf Female' (f)	CDoC CMHG ELan MGos MRav MWht SLim SLon
- 'Bowles's Dwarf Male' (m)	CMHG ELan LRHS SLim
- 'Bronze Knight' (m)	CMac EBee IVic MRav NLar NWad
- 'Carberry' (f)	CMac IVic
- 'Chameleon' (f)	NLar
- compact (f)	GGal
- 'Dad's Red Dragon' (f)	CMac MAsh
- 'Emerald King' (m)	MAsh WFar
- 'Finchy'PBR (m)	MBri
- 'Foremanii'	see *S. japonica* 'Veitchii'
§ - 'Fragrans' (m) ♀H5	CDoC CMac CRos CSBt CTri CWSG CWib EBee EPfP LPal LRHS LSRN MAsh MGos MJak MRav NLar NPri NWea SCob SHil SLim SPer SPoG SWvt WFar WGwG
- 'Fragrant Cloud'	see *S. japonica* 'Fragrans'
- 'Fructu Albo'	see *S. japonica* 'Wakehurst White'
- 'Godrie's Dwarf' (m)	CRos EBee EPfP LRHS NLar SHil WFar
- 'Humpty Dumpty' (f)	WFar
- var. ***intermedia*** f. ***repens*** B&SWJ 5560	WCru
- - B&SWJ 11165	WCru
- 'Kew White' (f)	CAbP CDoC CWib ELan EPfP IArd LPar LRHS MAsh MGos MRav NHol NWad SAko SLon SPer SSta SWvt WCFE
- Luwian = 'Wanto' (m)	LRHS SHil
- 'Macpenny Dwarf' (m)	CMac
- 'Magic Marlot'PBR (m/v) ♀H5	EBee EMil EPfP LRHS LSRN MAsh MGos MRav NLar SCob SPoG
- 'Marlot' (m)	LRHS NLar NWad SPoG
- 'Nymans' (f) ♀H5	CDoC CRos EBee ELan EPfP LCro LRHS MAsh MGos MRav SCob SHil SLim SPer SPoG SRms SSpi SWvt
- Obsession = 'Obsbolwi'PBR (m/f)	CRos LPar LRHS MAsh MGos NPri SCob SHil
- 'Olympic Flame' (f)	CDoC CRos EPfP IArd LRHS MBlu MJak SHil SPoG
- 'Pabella'PBR (f)	LRHS MAsh
- 'Pigmy' (f)	CExl
- 'Red Diamonds' **new**	LRHS
- 'Red Princess' (f)	MAsh
- 'Red Riding Hood' (f)	CRos ELan ELon LRHS MAsh NLar SHil SLon SPer
- 'Redruth' (f)	CBcs CDoC CMac CSBt CTsd ELon MAsh MGos NLar SEND
§ - subsp. ***reevesiana***	CBcs CDoC CDul CMHG CMac CSBt CTri CWSG CWib ELan EPfP IVic LCro LHop LOPS LRHS MBri MGos MRav MSwo NLar SCob SPoG SSpi SWvt
- - B&SWJ 3763	MAsh WCru
- - 'Chilan Choice' (f/m)	LRHS WPGP
- - var. ***reevesiana***	MJak
- - B&SWJ 3544	WCru
§ - Rogersii Group	CMac CTri
- - 'George Gardner' (m)	EPfP LRHS
- - 'Nana Mascula' (m)	CTri
- - 'Rogersii' (f)	CMac
- 'Rubella' (m) ♀H5	Widely available
- 'Rubinetta' (m)	EPfP IArd MAsh SCob
- 'Ruby Dome' (m)	MAsh NWad
- 'Ruby King' (m)	CDoC CSBt IArd LSRN NLar SAko
- 'Scarlet Dwarf' (f)	MAsh NHol WHar
- Sensation = 'Whitebolwi'PBR **new**	EBee

	- 'Smits Shandy'[PBR] new	MGos
	- 'Snow White'[PBR] (m)	MAsh
	- 'Tansley Gem' (f)	LRHS MAsh MWht SPoG
	- 'Temptation'[PBR] (f)	CDoC ELan EPfP LRHS SCob SHil
	- 'Thereza'[PBR] (m)	EPfP
§	- 'Veitchii' (f)	CBar CBcs CDoC CDul CMac CRos CSBt CTri ELan EPfP IArd LRHS LSRN MAsh MGos MMuc MRav NLar SCob SEND SLim SPer SPoG SWvt
§	- 'Wakehurst White' (f)	CMHG CMac CSBt CTri EPfP IVic LRHS MAsh MRav SLim SLon SPoG WFar
	- 'White Bella' (m)	LRHS SHil
	- 'Winifred Crook' (f)	LRHS
	- 'Wisley Female' (f)	CTri
	laureola	CExl MRav SRms WSHC
	- GWJ 9364	WCru
	- 'Kew Green'	NWad
	- subsp. ***laureola*** HWJK 2095	WCru
	- subsp. ***multinervia*** GWJ 9374	WCru
	'Red Diamonds'	LRHS SHil
	reevesiana	see *S. japonica* subsp. *reevesiana*
	rogersii	see *S. japonica* Rogersii Group

Smallanthus (*Asteraceae*)

	sonchifolius	CAgr LEdu
	- 'Morado'	LEdu WPGP
§	***uvedalius***	CArn

Smelowskia (*Brassicaceae*)

calycina	GKev

Smilacina see *Maianthemum*

Smilax (*Smilacaceae*)

sp.	WBor
B&SWJ 6628 from Thailand	WCru
aspera	CArn CMac EShb LEdu WCru WPGP
china B&SWJ 4427	WCru
discotis	CBcs SEND
glaucophylla B&SWJ 2971	WCru
nipponica B&SWJ 4331	WCru
rotundifolia	LEdu
sieboldii	LEdu MRav
- B&SWJ 744	WCru

Smithiantha (*Gesneriaceae*)

	'Anni'	EABi
	'Extra Sassy'	EABi
	'Heartland's Charm'	EABi
	'Little One'	WDib
	'Moana'	EABi
	'Santa Clara'	EABi
I	'Temple Bells'	EABi

× *Smithicodonia* (*Gesneriaceae*)

'Heartland's Joy'	EABi

Smyrnium (*Apiaceae*)

olusatrum	CArn CHab CSpe MHer MNHC SRms SWat WHer WSFF
perfoliatum	CHid CSpe EHrv ELan ELon EWes LEdu NBir SDix WCot WHal WSHC
rotundifolium	LEdu WCot

Solandra (*Solanaceae*)

	grandiflora misapplied	see *S. maxima*
	hartwegii	see *S. maxima*
§	***maxima***	WCot

Solanum (*Solanaceae*)

	atropurpureum	CDTJ CSpe SPlb WCot
	betaceum (F)	SVic
	- yellow-fruited (F) new	SPlb
	burchellii new	SPlb
	capsicastrum	SPlb
	conchifolium hort.	see *S. linearifolium*
	crispum	CBot
	- 'Autumnale'	see *S. crispum* 'Glasnevin'
§	- 'Glasnevin' ♀[H4]	Widely available
	dulcamara	CArn GPoy WHfH
	- var. ***album***	LSRN
	- 'Lucia' (v)	CNat
	- 'Variegatum' (v)	CMac EHoe MAsh
	incanum	LEdu
	jasminoides	see *S. laxum*
	- 'Blue Ice'	LSou
	laciniatum	CDTJ CExl IDee MPie SBig SEND SPav SPlb WOut
§	***laxum***	EBee GGal LRHS SPer SRms SWvt WSHC
	- 'Album' ♀[H4]	Widely available
	- 'Album Variegatum' (v)	CWib SCob WSHC
*	- 'Aureovariegatum' (v)	CMac EShb LBMP NEgg SLim SPlb
	- 'Coldham'	EShb SDix SMad
	- 'Creche ar Pape'	ECha LRHS
§	***linearifolium***	CSpe LBMP SKHP WHer WPGP WSHC
	muricatum (F)	CHII EShb SPlb
	pinnatum	SPlb
	pseudocapsicum variegated (v)	WCot
	pyracanthum	CDTJ SPlb WCot
	quitoense (F)	CDTJ SBig SPlb
	- 'Cannington Purple' new	SPlb
	rantonnetii	see *Lycianthes rantonnetii*
	rigescentoides	SPlb
	sisymbriifolium	SPlb
	aff. ***stenophyllum*** B&SWJ 10744	WCru
	wendlandii	CHII

Solaria (*Alliaceae*)

sp.	GCal

Soldanella (*Primulaceae*)

	alpicola	GJos GKev
	alpina	CCon CTal EBee ECho GBin GCra GKev LLHF SRms WAbe
	- SDR 3504	GKev
	- SDR 6332	GKev LEdu
	- SDR 6915	LEdu
I	- 'Alba'	ECho WAbe
	carpatica	CTal ECho GKev LEdu LLHF WAbe
	- 'Alba'	ECho GEdr LEdu NHar WAbe
	carpatica* × *pusilla	CPBP ECho ITim MNrw NHar NRya NWad WAbe WSHC
	carpatica* × *villosa	ECho LEdu
	cyanaster	EBee ECho GBin GBuc GEdr GJos GKev LEdu LLHF NQui NRya WAbe
	dimoniei	CTal EBee ECho GKev ITim LEdu WAbe
	hungarica	ECho GEdr WAbe

minima	ECho GEdr GJos GKev LEdu NHar NSla WAbe
montana	CFis ECho GBin GJos LEdu LLHF NLar SBch
pindicola	CTal ECho GEdr LEdu WAbe
pusilla	NWad
'Spring Symphony'	CTal ECho GEdr GMaP ITim LEdu LLHF NHar SAko WTcb
'Sudden Spring'	CTal ECho GEdr LEdu NWad WAbe
villosa ♀H5	CCon CTal EBee ECho EPot GAbr GBin GEdr GKev LEdu NRya NWad SBch WAbe WMoo WSHC

Soleirolia (*Urticaceae*)

soleirolii	CTri EUJe LLWG LPfy MMuc MSCN MWhi SCob SEND SMad SPer SVic SWvt WHer XLum
- 'Argentea'	see *S. soleirolii* 'Variegata'
§ - 'Aurea'	CTri SVic SWvt
- 'Golden Queen'	see *S. soleirolii* 'Aurea'
- 'Silver Queen'	see *S. soleirolii* 'Variegata'
§ - 'Variegata' (v)	LLWG SCob SVic WHer

Solenopsis (*Campanulaceae*)

axillaris	see *Isotoma axillaris*

Solenostemon ✿ (*Lamiaceae*)

'Autumn Rainbow'	WDib
'Beauty' (v)	WDib
'Beauty of Lyons'	EShb WDib
'Black Heart'	WDib
'Black Prince' ♀H1c	WDib
'Brilliant' (v)	WDib
'Bronze Pagoda'	WDib
'Buttercup'	WDib
'Chamaeleon' (v)	WDib
'City of Sunderland'	WDib
'Combat' (v) ♀H1c	WDib
'Crimson Ruffles' (v) ♀H1c	WDib
'Dazzler' (v)	WDib
'Display' (v)	WDib
'Durham Gala' ♀H1c	WDib
'Firelight' (v)	WDib
'Flamingo'	WDib
'Freckles' (v)	WDib
'Gingernut'	EUJe
'Illumination'	WDib
'Inky Fingers' (v)	WDib
'Juliet Quartermain' ♀H1c	EUJe WDib
'Jupiter'	WDib
'Kentish Fire' (v)	WDib
'Kiwi Fern' (Stained Glassworks Series) (v)	WDib
'Lemon Chiffon'	WDib
'Lord Falmouth' (v) ♀H1c	WDib
'Midnight'	EUJe
'Mrs Pilkington' (v)	WDib
'Muriel Pedley' (v)	WDib
'Paisley Shawl' (v)	WDib
'Palisandra'	CSpe
'Peter Wonder' (v)	WDib
'Picturatus' (v) ♀H1c	WDib
'Pineapple Beauty' (v) ♀H1c	NPri WDib
'Pineapplette' (v) ♀H1c	WDib
'Pink Chaos' (v) ♀H1c	WDib
'Red Angel'	WDib
'Red Velvet' (v)	WDib
Redhead = 'Ufo646'PBR ♀H1c	NPri
'Rose Blush' (v)	WDib
'Roy Pedley' ♀H1c	WDib
'Royal Scot' (v) ♀H1c	WDib
'Salmon Plumes' (v)	WDib
'Saturn' (v)	WDib
scutellarioides Henna = 'Balcenna'PBR ♀H1c	ECtt NPri
'The Flume'	WDib
thyrsoideus	see *Plectranthus thyrsoideus*
'Timotei'	WDib
Trusty Rusty = 'Uf06419'PBR ♀H1c	NPri
'Walter Turner' (v) ♀H1c	ECtt NPri WDib
'Watermelon' (v) new	LAst
'Winsome' (v) ♀H1c	WDib
'Winter Sun' (v)	WDib
'Wisley Flame'	WDib
'Wisley Tapestry' (v) ♀H1c	WDib

Solidago (*Asteraceae*)

Babygold	see *S.* 'Goldkind'
brachystachys	see *S. cutleri*
caesia	CMea EBee EWes LRHS NBir SMHy
canadensis	CTri ELan SPlb WBrk WHer WOld WWtn XLum
- var. ***salebrosa***	EBee LRHS
'Citronella'	ECtt GQue
'Cloth of Gold'	CMac COtt ECtt EPfP NEoE NHol SPoG SWvt WGwG WMnd
§ 'Crown of Rays'	ECtt ELon EPfP MRav SCob WFar WWEG
§ ***cutleri***	ECho NLar SBch SIgm SPlb SRms WFar WThu
I - ***nana***	ECho
'Ducky'	SCob
'Early Bird'	NLar WFar
faucibus new	CEvo
'Featherbush'	EBee WWEG
flabelliformis	WCot
§ ***flexicaulis***	GMaP WCot XLum
- 'Variegata' (v)	EBee ECtt ELan EShb GMaP LRHS NLar WMoo WWEG XLum
'Foxbrook Gold' new	MAvo
'Gardone' ♀H7	WFar
gigantea	WFar
glomerata	MMuc NLar SEND
Golden Baby	see *S.* 'Goldkind'
§ 'Golden Dwarf'	CWCL WBod WPtf WWEG XLum
'Golden Fleece'	see *S. sphacelata* 'Golden Fleece'
'Golden Thumb'	see *S.* 'Queenie'
'Golden Wings'	CBre MWat
'Goldenmosa' ♀H7	CSBt EWes GKev GMaP SPer WFar
'Goldilocks'	SRms
§ 'Goldkind'	CAgr CBod CBre CNec CSBt CTri EBee ECtt ELan EPfP IBoy LPot LRHS MBri MMuc MWhi NEgg NPri SEND SWvt WBrk WHar WWEG WWtn XLum
Goldzwerg	see *S.* 'Golden Dwarf'
'Harvest Gold'	CBre CElw
'Hiddigeigei' (v)	WCot
hybrida	see *S.* × *luteus*
latifolia	see *S. flexicaulis*
'Laurin'	NLar XLum
'Ledsham'	ECtt LEdu LRHS NBre SPoG
'Lena'	SRms
'Linner Gold'	NBre
'Little Lemon'PBR	EBee ELan LRHS LSou MBri SCob
§ × ***luteus***	EBee EWTr SRms WHil WOut XLum
- 'Lemore' ♀H7	CBod CMea EAJP EBee ECha ELan EPfP GBuc GMaP GQue LAst LHop

	LSou MSpe NCGa NSti SPer SPhx SPoG SRms WFar WWEG WWtn XLum
* ***minutissima***	MHol
subsp. ***minuta*** new	
ohioensis	XLum
§ ***ptarmicoides***	EBee XEll XLum
§ 'Queenie'	ECha MHer MLHP WWEG
rugosa	ECha MBNS MMuc SEND SPhx WCot WWtn
- 'Fireworks' ♀H7	CAby CBre CHVG CMHG CMac CMea CSam EBee ECtt ELon GQue IBoy ILea LHop LRHS MAvo MSpe NLar SDys SPhx WBrk WCot WFar WHoo WOld WWEG XLum
- 'Loydser Crown'	NDov
sempervirens	EBee IMou LRHS WOld WWEG
'Septembergold'	CSam
shortii 'Solar Cascade' new	EBee
'Sonnenschein'	NBre
speciosa	SPhx
spectabilis var. ***confinis***	EBee
- - KM 27-01	EBee
§ ***sphacelata*** 'Golden Fleece'	CBcs ELan EPfP IMou NBre SRms WMnd WWEG
spiraeifolia	EBee
Strahlenkrone	see *S.* 'Crown of Rays'
'Summer Sunshine'	WWEG
Sweety = 'Barseven'PBR	LRHS MBri
'Tom Thumb'	MRav NBir SRms
uliginosa	EShb XLum
ulmifolia	EBee
virgaurea	CArn GPoy MHer MNHC NLar SRms WHer
- subsp. ***alpestris*** var. ***minutissima***	GEdr
- var. ***cambrica***	see *S. virgaurea* subsp. *minuta*
§ - subsp. ***minuta***	GBin GCrg
§ - 'Variegata' (v)	CBre EHoe NEoE
vulgaris 'Variegata'	see *S. virgaurea* 'Variegata'
'Yellow Stone'	EBee

× *Solidaster* see *Solidago*

hybridus	see *Solidago* × *luteus*

Sollya (*Pittosporaceae*)

sp.	WBod
fusiformis	see *S. heterophylla*
§ ***heterophylla*** ♀H3	Widely available
- 'Alba'	CBcs CFlo CKel EBee ELan EPfP LRHS SEle SLim SLon SWvt WSHC
- mauve-flowered	ECou
- 'Pink Charmer'	CBcs ELan LRHS SLon SPoG
- pink-flowered	LBMP LRHS SWvt

Solms-laubachia (*Brassicaceae*)

pulcherrima new	GKev

Sonchus (*Asteraceae*)

arboreus	WCot
pinnatus	SPlb

Sophora (*Papilionaceae*)

arizonica	SIgm
cassioides NJM 08.008	WPGP
- 'Goldilocks'	WPGP
- 'Goughensis'	WPGP
§ ***davidii***	CBcs CExl CWGN CWib EBee EPfP LRHS MBlu MGos MMuc MOWG SBrt SEND SSpi WGrn WPGP WSHC
- dark blue-flowered	WPGP
flavescens	SBrt
fulvida	EBee ECou EPfP WPGP
howinsula	ECou
japonica	see *Styphnolobium japonicum*
§ 'Little Baby'	CAbP CWib EBee ELan EPfP EUJe LBrs LRHS LSRN MGos SEle SPoG SWvt WGrn
longicarinata	ECou
macrocarpa	SWvt
microphylla	CTri ECou LEdu LHop MGil WPGP
molloyi	ECou
- 'Dragon's Gold'	CBcs ECou ELan EPfP LRHS MAsh SCob SCoo SEND SEle SPoG SSta SWvt WPGP
- 'Early Gold'	WPGP
prostrata misapplied	see *S.* 'Little Baby'
prostrata ambig.	CBcs
prostrata Buchanan	CMac
stenophylla new	SIgm
Sun King = 'Hilsop'PBR ♀H4	CBcs CBot CDul CWGN ELan EPfP EWes LRHS LSRN MBri MGos NLar SCob SCoo SHil SLim SLon SPoG SWvt WCot
tetraptera	CAbP CBcs CDul CTsd ECou EPfP LRHS MMuc SEND SWvt WCFE WPGP
viciifolia	see *S. davidii*

Sorbaria (*Rosaceae*)

aitchisonii	see *S. tomentosa* var. *angustifolia*
arborea	see *S. kirilowii*
aff. ***assurgens*** BWJ 8185	WCru
§ ***kirilowii***	CExl CMac MRav NLar SMad WOut
- AC 3433	MSnd
sorbifolia	CAbP CBcs CMCN ELan MGil MLHP MMuc SCob SEND SPer SPlb WFar WWtn
- 'Sem'PBR ♀H5	Widely available
- var. ***stellipila*** B&SWJ 776	WCru
§ ***tomentosa*** var. ***angustifolia*** ♀H5	CBcs CDul CTri ELan EPfP IDee LRHS MMuc MRav NBid SCob SEND SLon SPer WHer

× *Sorbaronia* (*Rosaceae*)

fallax	EPfP NLar
- 'Ivan's Beauty'	ECrN

× *Sorbopyrus* (*Rosaceae*)

auricularis	MCoo
- 'Shipova' (F)	CAgr

Sorbus ✿ (*Rosaceae*)

sp.	CMen
NJM 09.203	WPGP
adamii	CMCN
alnifolia	CJun CLnd CMCN EPfP LRHS MBlu WHer
- B&SWJ 8461	WCru
- B&SWJ 10948	WCru
- 'Red Bird' ♀H5	EPfP MBlu WPat
'Amber Light' new	LRHS WMat
americana	CLnd NWea WHer
anglica	CDul CTho
'Apricot Queen'	CDul CLnd EBee ECrN LAst MJak SGol WFar
aria	CCVT CDul CHab CLnd CSBt CTri ECrN IBoy LBuc MGos MMuc NWea SCob SEND SEWo SGol WHar WMou

	- 'Aurea'	CLnd SPer
	- 'Chrysophylla'	CDul CSBt ECrN NWea
	- 'Decaisneana'	see *S. aria* 'Majestica'
	- 'Gigantea'	EWTr
	- 'Lutescens' ♀H6	Widely available
	- 'Magnifica'	ECrN ELan ESwi NEgg NLar SEWo WJas
§	- 'Majestica' ♀H6	CCVT CDoC CDul CLnd CMac EBee ECrN LHop MRav NWea SCob SPer WFar WHar WJas
	- 'Mitchellii'	see *S. thibetica* 'John Mitchell'
	aria* × *pseudovilmorinii	WPGP
	arnoldiana 'Golden Wonder'	see *S.* 'Lombarts Golden Wonder'
	aronioides misapplied	see *S. caloneura*
	aronioides Rehder	GKev
	arranensis	CDul CLnd WPat
§	***aucuparia***	Widely available
	- 'Aspleniifolia'	CBcs CCVT CDul CLnd CMCN CMac CSBt ECrN ERea EUJe GBin IBoy LRHS MGos MJak MRav NLar NOrn NWea SCob SLim SPer WFar WJas WMat WMou
§	- 'Beissneri'	CAgr CDul MRav NWea SLon
	- Cardinal Royal = 'Michred'	CCVT CDoC CDul CLnd ECrN EWTr MMuc NEgg SCoo SEND SEWo SLon
	- 'Dirkenii'	SGol WJas WMat
§	- var. ***edulis*** (F)	CArg CBcs CDul CLnd CTho ECrN LBuc MGos SCob SPer
	- - 'Rossica' misapplied	see *S. aucuparia* var. *edulis* 'Rossica Major'
§	- - 'Rossica Major'	CDul ECrN GQui SEWo
§	- 'Fastigiata'	CTri ELan EPfP GKin MGos SCob
	- 'Hilling's Spire'	CBcs CTho
	- subsp. ***maderensis***	WPat
	- 'Pendula'	ELan
	- ***pluripinnata***	see *S. scalaris* Koehne
	- var. ***rossica*** Koehne	see *S. aucuparia* var. *edulis*
	- 'Sheerwater Seedling' ♀H6	CBcs CCVT CDoC CDul CMCN COtt CSBt EBee ECrN ELan EPfP GKin IBoy LAst LHop MGos MMuc MRav MSwo NOrn NWea SCob SEND SEWo SGol SPer WFar
	- var. ***xanthocarpa***	ECrN ELan EWTr
	aucuparia* × *scalaris new	NOrn
	Autumn Spire = 'Flanrock' ♀H6	CDoC CDul CLnd CTsd EBee ELan ERea ESwi IBoy LRHS LSRN MAsh MBri MGos NLar NWea SCoo SEWo SLim SLon SPoG SWvt WHar WMat
	bissetii	WPat
	- Yu 14299	WCru
	brevipetiolata B&SWJ 11771	WCru
§	***caloneura***	EBee EPfP LEdu MBlu WPGP
	- Guiz 80	WCru
	- NJM 11.004	WPGP
	carmesina B&L 12545	EBee EPfP GKev WCru
	- 'Emberglow'	WMat
	cashmiriana Hedl. ♀H6	Widely available
	aff. ***cashmiriana***	GKev LCro LOPS MAsh MJak NHol NOrn WFar
	- B 751	WCru
	'Chinese Lace'	Widely available
§	***commixta***	CBcs CDul CLnd CMCN CTho EBee ECrN IBoy LAst LCro MBlu MGos MJak MMuc MSwo NLar SCob SEND SGol SLim SPer WHer WJas
	- B&SWJ 10839	WCru
	- B&SWJ 11043	WCru
	- B&SWJ 12640 from Ulleungdo, South Korea new	WCru
	- 'Embley' ♀H6	CBcs CCVT CDul CMCN CSBt CTho CTri EBee ECrN ELan EPfP LCro LHop LOPS MBlu MGos MMuc MRav NEgg NOrn NWea SCob SEND SGol SPer
	- Olympic Flame = 'Dodong' ♀H6	CDul COtt EBee EMil EPfP ERea IArd LBuc LRHS LSRN MBlu MBri NLar NWea SCoo SEWo SLim SPer SPoG WHar WMat WMou
	- 'Ravensbill'	EBee EPfP NLar NWea SCoo WHar WMat
	- var. ***rufoferruginea***	GQui
	- - B&SWJ 11486	WCru
	- var. ***sachalinensis*** B&SWJ 8515	WCru
	aff. ***commixta***	MSnd
	conradinae misapplied	see *S. pohuashanensis* (Hance) Hedl.
	conradinae Koehne	see *S. esserteauana*
	'Copper Kettle' ♀H6	EBee EPfP MAsh MBri NLar SCoo WHar WMat
	'Coral Beauty'	CLnd
	corymbifera WWJ 11860	WCru
	croceocarpa	CDul
	'Croft Coral'	MAsh WHar
	cuspidata	see *S. vestita*
*	***decora*** 'Grootendorst'	CDul
	- var. ***nana***	see *S. aucuparia* 'Fastigiata'
	devoniensis	CDoC CDul CTho
	- 'Devon Beauty'	CAgr
	discolor misapplied	see *S. commixta*
§	***discolor*** (Maxim.) Maxim.	EBee LAst MBlu MJak NWea WJas
	- MF 96172	MAsh
	- MF 97103	WCru
	domestica	CDul EPfP MMuc SEND WCot
	- 'Maliformis'	see *S. domestica* f. *pomifera*
§	- f. ***pomifera***	LEdu WThu
§	- f. ***pyrifera***	LEdu
	- 'Pyriformis'	see *S. domestica* f. *pyrifera*
	- 'Rosie'	CAgr
	dunnii	EBee WPGP
	'Eastern Promise' ♀H6	CDul COtt EBee EPfP GBin LCro MAsh MBri MSwo NLar NOrn NWea SCob SCoo SLim WHCr WHar WMat WMou
§	***eburnea*** Harry Smith 12799	GKev GQui WPGP
	eminens	CDul CNat WPat
	epidendron WWJ 11930	WCru
§	***esserteauana***	CLnd CTho WPGP WPat
	fansipanensis NJM 09.176	WPGP
	'Fastigiata'	see *S. aucuparia* 'Fastigiata', *S.* × *thuringiaca* 'Fastigiata'
	aff. ***filipes*** KR 5095 new	GKev
	- KR 6844 new	GKev
	folgneri	CJun MBri
	- 'Emiel' ♀H6	EPfP MBlu MBri WMat
	- 'Lemon Drop'	CDul CJun CLnd EPfP MAsh MBri SCoo WHar WMat
	foliolosa	CLnd
	forrestii ♀H6	CBcs CMCN EBee EPfP GKev MBri NLar
*	***fosteri***	EBee
§	***frutescens*** ♀H6	NWea WMou WPGP
	- Rock 14987 new	GKev
	fruticosa Crantz	GKev NSla
	- 'Koehneana'	see *S. koehneana* C.K. Schneid.
	'Ghose'	EBee MBri WMat

	Name	Suppliers
	glabriuscula	EBee GKev
	'Glendoick Gleam'	GGGa
	'Glendoick Glory'	GGGa
	'Glendoick Ivory'	GGGa
	'Glendoick Pearl'	GGGa
	'Glendoick Ruby'	GGGa
	'Glendoick Spire'	GGGa LRHS MBri WMat
	'Glendoick White Baby'	GGGa LRHS MBri WMat
	glomerulata	LLHF
	'Golden Wonder'	see *S.* 'Lombarts Golden Wonder'
	gonggashanica	EBee EPfP GKev NLar WPGP WPat
*	***gorrodini***	CLnd
§	***graeca***	WPat
	granulosa HWJ 1041	WCru
	harrowiana	GCal LLHF WMat WPGP WPat
	- KR 21009	CDul LRHS WPGP
	hedlundii	CDul CExl EBee EBtc EPfP LRHS NLar NWea SKHP WMat WPGP
	- GWJ 9363 new	WCru
	- KR 1687	WPGP
	- KR 1810	WPGP
	helenae	WPGP
	- EN 3088 new	GKev
	hemsleyi	CBcs CDul CExl EPfP WPGP WPat
	- 'John Bond' ♀H6	CDoC EBee NLar SPoG WMat
	× ***hostii***	CLnd
	hugh-mcallisteri CLD 310	EBee GKev
	hupehensis misapplied	see *S. pseudohupehensis*
	hupehensis C.K.Schneid.	see *S. discolor* (Maxim.) Maxim.
	- 'November Pink'	see *S. pseudohupehensis* 'Pink Pagoda'
	- var. ***obtusa*** misapplied	see *S. pseudohupehensis* 'Pink Pagoda'
	- 'Rosea'	see *S. pseudohupehensis* 'Pink Pagoda'
	aff. ***hupehensis*** ambig.	ECrN NOrn WFar
	hybrida L.	ECrN
	- 'Gibbsii' ♀H6	CDoC EBee ELan EPfP EWTr MAsh NOrn WHar WMat
	insignis	LLHF WPGP WPat
	intermedia	CBcs CCVT CDul CLnd CSBt CTho CTri CWib ECrN ELan MGos MMuc NWea SEND SGol WHar WMou
	- 'Brouwers'	CDoC CLnd ELan
	japonica	CDul EBee WMat
	- B&SWJ 10813	WCru
	- B&SWJ 11048	WCru
	'Joseph Rock'	Widely available
I	***keenanii*** KR 7746	WPGP
§	× ***kewensis***	CDul CLnd NWea SPlb
	khumbuensis new	GKev
	'Kirsten Pink'	CWib EBee
	koehneana misapplied	see *S. frutescens*
	koehneana ambig.	GEdr
§	***koehneana*** C.K.Schneid.	CLnd ELan GKev GQui MMHG NWea WMou
	aff. ***koehneana*** C.K.Schneid.	see *S. eburnea*
	lanata misapplied	see *S. vestita*
	lancastriensis	CNat
	latifolia	CLnd NWea
	- 'Henk Vink'	CCVT
	'Leonard Messel' ♀H6	CDoC EPfP LRHS MAsh MBri NLar WHCr WMat
	'Leonard Springer'	ECrN
	'Likjornaja'	EPfP MBri
§	'Lombarts Golden Wonder'	CBcs CDul MMuc NWea SEND
*	***maculata*** KR 5334 new	GKev
	matsumurana misapplied	see *S. commixta*
	matsumurana (Makino) Koehne	WPGP
	megalocarpa	CBcs CDoC CJun SKHP WPGP
	meliosmifolia B&SWJ 11709	WCru
	microphylla agg.	CMCN GKev
	- GWJ 9252	WCru
	- SICH 1009 new	EBee
	minima	WPat
	monbeigii (Cardot.) N.P.Balakr.	CLnd
	moravica 'Laciniata'	see *S. aucuparia* 'Beissneri'
	muliensis F 22177 new	GKev
§	***munda***	CTho EBee GKev MBri
	needhamii NJM 11.005	WPGP
	- PAB 9853 new	LEdu
	olivacea new	EPfP
	aff. ***ovalis*** H 1948	EBee
	parvifructa new	GKev WPGP
	'Peaches and Cream' new	LCro LOPS
	'Pearly King'	CTho MAsh WJas
§	'Pink Pearl'	CDul EPfP
	'Pink-Ness'	EPfP MBlu SCoo WMat
	pohuashanensis misapplied	see *S.* × *kewensis*
§	***pohuashanensis*** (Hance) Hedl.	WPat
	porrigentiformis	CDul
	poteriifolia ♀H5	GEdr GKev NHar WPat
	prattii misapplied	see *S. munda*
	pseudobakyonensis	CBcs
§	***pseudohupehensis*** ♀H6	CBcs CDul CLnd CMCN CMac CTho CTri EBee EPfP EWTr GKev MMuc MRav MSnd NWea SEND SGol SPer WHar WJas
	- MF 96170	GKev
§	- 'Pink Pagoda' ♀H6	Widely available
	pseudovilmorinii	CDul GKev LRHS MBri NLar WCru WMat
	- CLD 1437	GKev
	randaiensis	EBee GKev GQui MBri NLar SPlb WPGP
	- B&SWJ 3202	EPfP WCru
	'Red Robin'	IBoy
	'Red Tip'	CDul
	reducta ♀H5	CBcs GAbr GBin GCal GKev GQui MMuc NHar NHol NLar NSla SBrt SPer WPat
	aff. ***reducta***	MSnd
	reflexipetala misapplied	see *S. commixta*
	rehderiana misapplied	see *S. aucuparia*
	rehderiana Koehne	CLnd GKev
	- AC 3459	MSnd
	rosea	GEdr GKev
	- SEP 492	WCru WPGP
	- 'Rosiness' ♀H6	CLnd EBee EPfP LRHS MBri WHar WMat
	'Rowancroft Coral Pink'	EBee
	rubescens new	GKev
	- Yu 1381 new	EBee
	rupicola	NWea
	rushforthii KR 5789 new	GKev
	rutilans new	GKev
	'Salmon Queen'	CLnd
	sambucifolia	EBee SKHP
	sargentiana ♀H6	CCVT CDul CLnd CMCN CTho CTri EBee ECrN ELan EPfP GQui LCro MBlu MBri MGos MRav MSwo NLar NOrn NWea SLim SPer SPoG WMat WMou WPat

- EGM 291 WCru
'Savill Orange' MMuc
scalaris ambig. CBcs CMCN CNWT ELan LRHS MAsh MSwo NWea WHar WMou
§ ***scalaris*** Koehne CCVT CDul CLnd CTho CTri EBee EPfP LHop MBlu MGos SPer WJas WMat
'Schouten' ECrN
scopulina misapplied see *S. aucuparia* 'Fastigiata'
(sect. Discolores) KR 5585 WCru WPGP
- KR 6308 **new** WCru
setschwanensis BWJ 8053 WCru
subulata HWJ 925 WCru
- KWJ 12272 WCru
'Sunshine' CCVT CDoC CDul CLnd EWTr MAsh MBri MGos MMuc SEND WJas
thibetica AGS/ES 347 WPGP
§ - 'John Mitchell' ♀H6 CAgr CDul CMCN CWib EBee ECrN EPfP MBlu MBri MGos NOrn NWea SLim WMat
aff. ***thibetica*** BWJ 7757a WCru
thomsonii GWJ 9363 WCru
- HWJ 984 WCru
- WWJ 12004 WCru
§ × ***thuringiaca*** 'Fastigiata' CBcs CCVT CDul CLnd CSBt EBee EPfP NEgg SCoo WJas WMat
'Titan' **new** EPfP
× ***tomentella*** CLnd
torminalis CBcs CCVT CDul CHab CLnd CMCN CMac CTho CTri ELan EPfP LEdu MBri MGos MMuc MRav MSnd NLar NWea SCoo SEND SEWo SPer SPoG WHar WMou
umbellata var. ***cretica*** see *S. graeca*
§ ***vestita*** CDoC CLnd CMCN CTho EPfP WCru
vexans CDul GBin WPat
vilmorinii ♀H6 Widely available
- 'Pink Charm' **new** EBee EPfP LRHS WMat
- 'Robusta' see *S.* 'Pink Pearl'
aff. ***vilmorinii*** GKin IBoy LOPS MJak
- KR 6453 GKev WCru WPGP
wardii CDul CLnd CTho EPfP MBlu WPat
'White Wax' CDul LAst MGos NWea SPer SPoG
wilmottiana CDul WPat
wilsoniana CLnd GGGa GQui
- NN 0929 MSnd
'Wisley Gold' ♀H6 EBee GBin LRHS MAsh SCoo SLim WMat
yuana WPGP

Sorghastrum (*Poaceae*)

avenaceum see *S. nutans*
§ ***nutans*** CBod SMad
- 'Indian Steel' CBod EBee GQue LSun SGSe XLum

sorrel, common see *Rumex acetosa*

sorrel, French see *Rumex scutatus*

Souliea see *Actaea*

soursop see *Annona muricata*

Sparaxis (*Iridaceae*)

bulbifera ECho
elegans SPlb
'Fire King' GKev NRog
grandiflora subsp. ***acutiloba*** ECho NRog
- subsp. ***grandiflora*** CGrW CTre ECho
mixed NRog SDeJ
'Moonlight' LAma NRog
parviflora ECho
'Red Reflex' ECho GKev NRog
'Sunshine' LAma NRog
tricolor CGrW CTre ECho NRog SDeJ
variegata ECho
villosa ECho NRog

Sparganium (*Sparganiaceae*)

RCB RA G-1 WCot
§ ***erectum*** CWat EHon NMir NPer SWat WMAq WSFF XLum
ramosum see *S. erectum*

Sparrmannia (*Malvaceae*)

africana ♀H1c CHII ELan EShb SEND SVen
- 'Flore Pleno' (d) CBcs

Spartina (*Poaceae*)

pectinata SGol XLum
- 'Aureomarginata' (v) CBod CWCL EBee EHoe ELan EPPr EPfP GMaP LRHS MLHP MMuc MWhi NLar NOak NWsh SEND SPer WMoo WWEG WWtn

Spartium (*Papilionaceae*)

junceum ♀H5 CArn CBcs CDoC CDul COtt CSde CWld EBee ECrN ELan EPfP EWTr LAst LRHS MGos MMuc SCob SDix SEND SPer SPoG SRms XSen
- 'Brockhill Compact' CDoC ELan EPfP LRHS

Spartocytisus see *Cytisus*

Spathantheum (*Araceae*)

orbignyanum WCot

Spathipappus see *Tanacetum*

Spathiphyllum (*Araceae*)

wallisii NGBl SPre

Spathodea (*Bignoniaceae*)

campanulata SPlb

spearmint see *Mentha spicata*

Speirantha (*Asparagaceae*)

§ ***convallarioides*** CCon CDoC CLAP CTal EBee ECho EHrv ELon EPPr EPfP LEdu MNrw SGSe WCru WHil WPGP
gardenii see *S. convallarioides*

Sphacele see *Lepechinia*

Sphaeralcea (*Malvaceae*)

ambigua EBee SPlb XSen
'Childerley' CSpe CWGN ECtt LHop SPad WCot
coccinea EBee SPlb
fendleri CHII CSam CSde
- subsp. ***venusta*** LHop
gierischii **new** EBee
grandiflora **new** EBee
'Hopleys Lavender' EWoo LAst LHop LSou SWvt
'Hyde Hall' MHom

incana	CSpe LHop LSou
- 'Sourup'	CBod CSpe EBee ECtt ELan WCot
laxa	EBee
malviflora	CDTJ
miniata	CHII
munroana	CDTJ ECtt ELan SRkn
- pale pink-flowered	CSam ECtt
'Newleaze Coral'	CBod CWGN ECtt ELan EWoo LAst LBMP LHop MAsh MHom MNrw SPad SRkn SWvt WBor WCot WWFP
'Newleaze Pink'	SRkn
parvifolia	EBee
remota	CExl CMea SPlb
umbellata	see *Phymosia umbellata*

Sphenomeris (*Dennstaedtiaceae*)

chinensis B&SWJ 6108	WCru

Spigelia (*Loganiaceae*)

marilandica	EBee GKev SKHP SMad WHil WSHC
- 'Red Feather'	NLar
- 'Wisley Jester'	SKHP

Spiloxene (*Hypoxidaceae*)

capensis	NRog

Spiraea (*Rosaceae*)

	alba var. ***latifolia***	MMuc SEND
	albiflora	see *S. japonica* 'Albiflora'
	arborea	see *Sorbaria kirilowii*
	× ***arguta*** 'Bridal Wreath'	see *S.* 'Arguta'
§	'Arguta' ♀H6	Widely available
	aff. 'Arguta'	SHil
	betulifolia aff.	GKin MRav SCob WFar
	- var. ***aemiliana*** aff.	CAbP ECtt MAsh MMuc SCob
	- 'Tor'	CLet EPPr
	- 'Tor Gold'PBR	CBcs EBee EPPr LRHS
	× ***billardii*** misapplied	see *S.* × *pseudosalicifolia*
	blumei CWJ 12829	WCru
	× ***bumalda*** 'Wulfenii'	see *S. japonica* 'Walluf'
	callosa 'Alba'	see *S. japonica* 'Albiflora'
	canescens	CExl GKin
	- AC 1354	MSnd
	- CC 7281 **new**	CEvo EWld
	- var. ***glaucophylla***	MMuc SEND
	chamaedryfolia	GKev
	× ***cinerea*** 'Grefsheim' ♀H6	CBcs CDoC COtt CSBt ELan LBuc MBri MGos MMuc NLar SCob SEND SGol SLim SPer SPlb
	crispifolia misapplied	see *S. japonica* 'Bullata'
	densiflora	GKev
	douglasii	CMac GKev SCob
	formosana B&SWJ 1597	CExl WCru
	fritschiana	CMac
	hayatana	GKev
	- RWJ 10014	WCru
	hendersonii	see *Petrophytum hendersonii*
	henryi	GKev
§	***japonica*** 'Albiflora'	CDoC CDul CLet CMac CSBt CTri CWib ELan ELon LBMP LRHS MAsh MGos MRav MSwo NEgg NWad SCob SGbt SGol SLim SPad SPer SRms SWvt WMoo
	- 'Alpina'	see *S. japonica* 'Nana'
	- 'Alpine Gold'	NEoE
	- 'Anthony Waterer' (v)	Widely available
	- 'Barkby Gold'	MGos
	- 'Blenheim'	SRms
§	- 'Bullata'	CMac GCrg NLar SRms WAbe WPat
	- 'Candlelight' ♀H6	CDoC CSBt ELan EPfP GKin LAst LRHS LSou MAsh MGos NEgg NLar SCob SCoo SGol SLim SPer SPoG SWvt WMoo
	- 'Crispa'	EPfP NEoE NWad WFar WGrn WMoo
	- 'Dart's Red' ♀H6	CDul ELan GKin IVic LRHS WMoo
	- 'Firelight'	Widely available
§	- var. ***fortunei*** 'Macrophylla'	WPat
§	- 'Genpei'	CMac MJak MMuc SEND SGol SPer SPoG
	- 'Gold Mound'	CBar CExl CMac COtt CWib EHoe ELan EPfP LAst LRHS MAsh MGos MJak MMuc MRav MSwo NLar SCoo SEND SLim SPlb SRms WFar WHar
	- Golden Princess = 'Lisp' ♀H6	CDoC CMac COtt CTri ELan EPfP IBoy LAst LBuc LRHS MAsh MGos NEgg NLar NPri SCoo SGol SHil SPer SRms SSta WFar WMoo
	- 'Goldflame'	Widely available
	- 'Little Princess'	CBar CBcs CDoC CDul CLet CMac COtt CWib EBee ELan EShb LBMP LRHS MAsh MRav MSwo NLar NWea SCob SCoo SGol SHil SLim SPer SRGP SRms SWvt WFar WHar WMoo
	- Magic Carpet = 'Walbuma'PBR (v) ♀H6	CDoC COtt EPfP GBin LBuc LRHS MAsh MBri MMuc NLar SCob SCoo SEND SPoG
	- 'Magnifica'	see *S. japonica* var. *fortunei* 'Macrophylla'
§	- 'Nana' ♀H6	CMac CSBt ECho GCrg MAsh MRav SRms
	- 'Nyewoods'	see *S. japonica* 'Nana'
	- 'Shiburi'	see *S. japonica* 'Albiflora'
	- 'Shirobana' misapplied	see *S. japonica* 'Genpei'
	- 'Shirobana'	see *S. japonica* 'Albiflora'
	- 'Snow Cap'	CWib
§	- 'Walluf'	CMac CTri CWib
	- 'White Cloud'	CTsd
	- 'White Gold'PBR	CBod CDoC CMac COtt CSBt ELan EPfP LAst LRHS MAsh NEoE NHol NWad SCoo SLim SPer SPoG SWvt WHar WMoo
	× ***margaritae***	SPer SWvt
	micrantha	CExl
	nipponica	CBcs
	- 'Halward's Silver'	MRav NEoE
§	- 'Snowmound' ♀H6	Widely available
	- var. ***tosaensis*** misapplied	see *S. nipponica* 'Snowmound'
	- var. ***tosaensis*** (Yatabe) Makino	LHop
	palmata 'Elegans'	see *Filipendula purpurea* 'Elegans'
	prunifolia (d)	CMac ELan EPfP LRHS MRav SPer WCFE WFar WGrn WPat
	× ***pseudosalicifolia*** 'Triumphans'	MMuc SEND SPer
	rosthornii **new**	GKev
	salicifolia	GKev
	sargentiana **new**	GKev
	'Sparkling Champagne'	CSBt LBuc LRHS NWad SLim SLon
	Sundrop = 'Bailcarol'	LBuc
	thunbergii ♀H6	CBcs CDul CMac CTri CWib EPfP MMuc MRav NWea SBrt SCob SEND SGol SLim SRms
	- 'Golden Times'	LRHS SPoG

	- 'Mount Fuji'	CMac CWib MRav NEoE WFar
	ulmaria	see *Filipendula ulmaria*
	× ***vanhouttei***	CBcs CBod CDul CTri ELan EPfP MMuc MRav MSwo SEND SLim SPer SRms WFar WMoo
	- 'Gold Fountain'	CMac ELan EMil EPfP EShb GBin LSRN MMuc NHol NLar SCoo SEND SPer SPoG WFar WMoo
	- 'Pink Ice' (v)	CDoC COtt CWib EHoe EPfP LAst LHop LRHS MAsh MGos MMuc MRav NLar SEND SPer SPlb SPoG SWvt
	veitchii	MRav
	venusta 'Magnifica'	see *Filipendula rubra* 'Venusta'

Spiranthes (*Orchidaceae*)

	aestivalis	NLAp
	cernua	NGdn
	odorata	LSou
	- 'Chadd's Ford' ϒH4	CBcs CBro CDes CExl EBee ECho ECtt EHrv IKil LAma LEdu LHop LRHS MBel MNrw NBir WCot WPtf WSHC
	spiralis	NLAp WHer

Spirodela (*Araceae*)

§	***polyrrhiza***	EWay

Spodiopogon (*Poaceae*)

	sibiricus	CKno EBee EHoe EPPr NDov NLos SGSe SMHy SMad WPtf XLum
	- 'West Lake'	IMou

Sporobolus (*Poaceae*)

	airoides	CBod CKno EBee EHoe EPPr EShb LPla SGSe SMHy SMad WHrl
	heterolepis	CKno CSpe EBee EHoe GQue LRHS NDov SGSe SMHy SMea SPhx WCot
	- 'Cloud'	GBin
I	- 'Wisconsin Strain'	EBee EPPr IMou LPla SPhx
	heterolepsis 'Blue Dust'	NDov
	wrightii	EPPr SMad SPhx

Sprekelia (*Amaryllidaceae*)

	formosissima	CCon CGrW ECho LAma LEdu SDeJ SPav

Stachys (*Lamiaceae*)

	aethiopica 'Danielle'	see *S. thunbergii* 'Danielle'
§	***affinis***	CArn GPoy LEdu SPlb SVic XLum
	albens	XSen
	alpina	EBee
	balcanica	GKev
	- MESE	EBee WPGP
	betonica	see *S. officinalis*
§	***byzantina***	Widely available
§	- 'Big Ears'	Widely available
§	- 'Cotton Boll'	ECha GCal LCro LRHS SPer WFar WWEG
	- 'Countess Helen von Stein'	see *S. byzantina* 'Big Ears'
	- 'Fuzzy Wuzzy'	CBod
	- gold-leaved	see *S. byzantina* 'Primrose Heron'
	- large-leaved	see *S. byzantina* 'Big Ears'
	- 'Limelight'	ECtt WCot WSHC XLum
§	- 'Primrose Heron'	EBee ECha GKev MRav NLar SPer SPoG SWvt WCAu XLum
	- 'Sheila McQueen'	see *S. byzantina* 'Cotton Boll'
	- 'Silky Fleece'	CBod ECha ELan EPfP GKev LRHS MMuc NBre SEND SRms WWEG XSen
	- 'Silver Carpet'	Widely available
	chamissonis var. ***cooleyae***	EBee
	citrina	CMea GCal XSen
	coccinea	CPla ECtt GEdr WMoo
	densiflora	see *S. monieri* (Gouan) P.W. Ball
§	***discolor***	CFis CMea EWes GEdr IKil LRHS NLar WCAu WCot
	germanica	NBre WHfH
	grandidentata	WPGP
	grandiflora	see *S. macrantha*
	'Hidalgo'	CSpe
	lanata Jacq.	see *S. byzantina*
	lavandulifolia	WAbe XSen
§	***macrantha***	CBod CKno CMac CTri ECha EWTr GKev GLog LEdu LRHS LSRN MCot MLHP NBir NChi NSti SPhx SRms SWat WCFE WCot WWEG
*	- 'Alba'	ECha
	- 'Ben' (v)	LEdu MAvo
	- 'Hummelo'	see *S. officinalis* 'Hummelo'
	- 'Morning Blush'	CAby GEdr SPhx WFar
*	- 'Nivea'	CSam ELan NBir
	- 'Robusta' ϒH7	ELan ELon GCal LEdu MAvo MMuc NBro NGdn WCot WWEG
	- 'Rosea'	CElw CMHG ELan GBee GMaP LLWP LRHS MArl MAvo MLHP SCob SPlb SWat
	- 'Superba' ϒH7	CPrp CSpe ECtt EPfP GCra GMaP IBoy LEdu MAvo MRav NEgg NLar SCob SPer SWvt WBor WCAu WCot WFar WMnd WMoo XLum
	- 'Violacea' ϒH7	CDes EBee GKev MBrN NChi WCot WOut
	mexicana misapplied	see *S. thunbergii*
	monieri misapplied	see *S. officinalis*
	monieri ambig.	CPrp EShb GKev NLar NSti WOut
§	***monieri*** (Gouan) P.W. Ball	LEdu MSpe
*	- 'Rosea'	EBee LEdu NBre NLar SRms
	nivea	see *S. discolor*
	obliqua	NBre WOut
§	***officinalis***	CArn CHab CPrp CWld EBee GPoy ILea LEdu MHer MMuc MNHC MWhi NMir SEND SRms WCot WHer WHfH WJek WOut
	- 'Alba'	CArn EBee LEdu MMuc NBro SCob SEND
	- 'Cally Bicolor' **new**	GCal
	- 'Cally Pink' **new**	GCal
	- dwarf, white-flowered	GCal
§	- 'Hummelo'	Widely available
	- 'Marchant's Pink'	SMHy
	- 'Pink Cotton Candy'	STPC WNPC
	- 'Powder Puff'	EBee
	- 'Rosea'	EAJP GCal GQue NBro SCob WFar WWEG
	- 'Rosea Superba'	ECha NBre SDix WCot
	- 'Saharan Pink'	CMHG EPfP LSRN NLar WOut WWEG
	- 'Wisley White'	CAby ECtt GKev GQue LPot LRHS MHol NPri SRms WCot WFar WHfH WOut WTor
	olympica	see *S. byzantina*
	ossetica	CDes CFis EBee GEdr
	palustris	CArn CBod CHab EBee EWay LLWG MMuc MWLS NLar NMir SEND
	- from Islay, Hebrides	MMuc SEND

- pale-flowered	WOut
recta	EBee MMuc
setifera	NBre XLum
spicata	see *S. macrantha*
sylvatica	CHab NMir WHer WOut WSFF
thirkei	WCot XSen
§ ***thunbergii***	LEdu MBrN SBch WHrl WPGP
§ - 'Danielle'	CElw ECtt GJos LAst LRHS NLar SDys SPhx SRkn SRms WOut
tuberifera	see *S. affinis*
tymphaea	XSen

Stachyurus (*Stachyuraceae*)

chinensis	CBcs CJun CMCN CTri CWib MGos NLar
- 'Celina' ♀H4	CJun EPfP GKin LRHS MGos NLar SHil SPoG
- 'Goldbeater'	NLar
- 'Joy Forever' (v) ♀H4	CBcs CBot CDoC CMac EBee EMil EPfP IArd IVic LLHF LRHS LSRN MGos NLar SHil SKHP SLim SPer SSpi SSta SWvt
- 'Senna'	NLar
- 'Wonderful Image'	NLar
himalaicus	CBcs NLar
- HWJCM 009	WCru
- HWJK 2035	WCru
- 'Dolly'	NLar
aff. ***himalaicus*** HWJK 2052	WCru
'Magpie' (v)	CJun EPfP NLar WFar
praecox ♀H5	Widely available
- B&SWJ 8898	WCru
- B&SWJ 10899	IDee LCro LHop WCru
- var. ***leucotrichus***	CJun NLar
- var. ***matsuzakii***	CJun NLar
- - B&SWJ 2817	WCru
- - B&SWJ 11229	WCru
- - 'Issai'	LRHS SHil
- 'Petra'	CJun
retusus	CExl
'Rubriflorus'	CJun EPfP LRHS MAsh NLar WPGP
salicifolius	CBcs CBot CExl CFil CJun CTho EBee EPfP IDee SChF SKHP WPGP WPat
sigeyosii	CBcs CExl CFil
- B&SWJ 6915	WCru
- CWJ 12420	WCru
- RWJ 10094	WCru
aff. ***szechuanensis***	CExl
- BWJ 8153	WCru
yunnanensis	CBcs CFil CJun IArd IDee NLar WPGP WPat WSHC

Staehelina (*Asteraceae*)

dubia	SBrt

Stangeria (*Stangeriaceae*)

eriopus	LPal

Staphylea ✿ (*Staphyleaceae*)

bolanderi	CBcs NLar
bumalda	CJun LEdu NLar
- B&SWJ 11053	WCru
- B&SWJ 12744 from Korea	WCru
colchica	CBcs CDul CHll CJun CMCN EBee ELan EPfP ESwi EWTr EWes LEdu LRHS MGos MMHG MRav NLar SPer WKif WSHC
holocarpa	CJun EPfP
- 'Innocence'	CBcs NLar SAko
- var. ***rosea***	CBcs CJun EPfP MBlu NLar SAko SMad SSpi SWvt WPGP
pinnata	CAgr CBcs CJun EBtc EPfP IVic MMuc NLar SEND
- PAB 8427 **new**	LEdu
trifolia	CBcs CJun EBee ESwi

Statice see *Limonium*

Stauntonia (*Lardizabalaceae*)

sp.	CKel
FMWJ 13177 from northern Vietnam	WCru
aff. ***chinensis*** DJHV 06175	WCru
hexaphylla	CBcs CHll CTri CWGN EBee EPfP ESwi EUJe LEdu LPal LRHS MAsh NLar SAdn SKHP SPer SPoG SSpi SSta WSHC
- B&SWJ 4858	WCru
aff. ***libera*** KWJ 12218	WCru
aff. ***maculata*** FMWJ 13055 **new**	CEvo WCru
aff. ***nova*** FMWJ 13177 **new**	CEvo
obovata CWJ 12353	WCru
obovatifoliola B&SWJ 3685	WCru
purpurea B&SWJ 3690	WCru
yaoshanensis B&SWJ 8223	WCru
- HWJ 1024	WCru WPGP

Stegnogramma (*Thelypteridaceae*)

pozoi	EFer

Stellaria (*Caryophyllaceae*)

graminea	CHab
holostea	CHab CWld MMuc NBir NMir WHer WPtf WShi

Stemmacantha (*Asteraceae*)

carthamoides	CArn
§ ***centaureoides***	CAby CBot CDes EBee ECGP ECha EWTr GCal GQue IBoy IPot LPla MAvo MHol MSpe MTis NBid NSti WCot
§ ***rhapontica***	MMuc

Stenanthium (*Melanthiaceae*)

gramineum	CFil EWes WPGP

Stenomesson (*Amaryllidaceae*)

coccineum	NRog
incarnatum apricot-flowered	NRog
§ ***miniatum***	WCot
pearcei	ECho NRog WCot
variegatum	WCot
- orange-flowered	NRog
- red-flowered	NRog
- yellow-flowered	NRog WCot

Stenotaphrum (*Poaceae*)

secundatum 'Variegatum' (v) ♀H1c	EShb LSou XLum

Stephanandra (*Rosaceae*)

chinensis	SLon
incisa	CBcs CExl SCob

§ - 'Crispa' CDoC CDul CMac CTri EBee ELan EPfP EWTr GKin IDee LAst LHop MBlu MJak MRav NEgg NHol SCob SPer WHar WMoo
- 'Prostrata' see *S. incisa* 'Crispa'
tanakae CBcs CDul CExl CTri EBee ELan EPfP EWTr LAst MBlu MGil MRav NEgg SLon SPer

Stephania (*Menispermaceae*)

japonica CWJ 12823 WCru
longa KWJ 12163 WCru
sinica BWJ 8094 WCru
aff. **tetrandra** WWJ 11896 WCru

Stephanotis (*Asclepiadaceae*)

floribunda ♀H1b CBcs MBri

Sterculia (*Malvaceae*)

rupestris see *Brachychiton rupestris*

Sternbergia (*Amaryllidaceae*)

'Autumn Gold' ECho
candida CBro NRog
§ **clusiana** NRog
colchiciflora GKev NRog
fischeriana CBro NRog
greuteriana ECho NRog
lutea ♀H4 CAvo CBro CTri ECha ECho EPfP EPot ERCP EWes LAma LCro LHop LOPS LRHS NRog SBch SCob SDeJ SDix WHoo XLum
- Angustifolia Group CAvo CBro CMea ECho
macrantha see *S. clusiana*
sicula CBro EBee ECho EPot GKev NRog
- 'Arcadian Sun' ECho GKev NRog
- var. **graeca** ECho NRog
- - from Crete ECho
- 'John Marr' CDes WThu

Stevia (*Asteraceae*)

rebaudiana CArn CBod ENfk EOHP GPoy SHDw SRms WCot WJek

Stewartia ✿ (*Theaceae*)

sp. LPar
gemmata see *S. sinensis*
'Korean Splendor' see *S. pseudocamellia* Koreana Group
koreana see *S. pseudocamellia* Koreana Group
malacodendron ♀H5 LRHS
monadelpha CBcs CJun CMen IDee MBlu MPkF NLar
ovata LRHS
pseudocamellia ♀H5 Widely available
- B&SWJ 11044 from North Japan WCru
§ - Koreana Group ♀H5 CDul CJun CMCN EBee EPfP GKin LRHS MBri NLar SLim SSpi WPGP
pteropetiolata CMHG IVic
- B&SWJ 11726 WCru
- NJM 10.107 WPGP
- WWJ 11939 WCru
rostrata CBcs CJun ELan GBin LRHS MBlu MBri MPkF NLar SSpi WCru
- 'Hulsdonk Pink' **new** CJun
serrata CJun CMen GBin MPkF WPGP
§ **sinensis** ♀H5 CBcs CJun EPfP IArd IDee IMou MBlu MPkF NLar SAko SSpi WBod WPGP

Stipa (*Poaceae*)

sp. ETod
F&M 248 EBee
arundinacea see *Anemanthele lessoniana*
- 'Sunrise' EAEE
barbata CKno CSpe EAJP ECha ELon EPPr ETod EWes NCGa SCob WKif XSen
- 'Silver Feather' CBot ETod WPtf
brachytricha see *Calamagrostis brachytricha*
§ **calamagrostis** Widely available
- 'Allgäu' WCot
- 'Lemperg' IMou LRHS NDov
capillata EBee EPPr GCal LRHS MBel MMuc MNrw NDov SDix XSen
- 'Brautschleier' CBod CWib
comata SPhx
elegantissima CKno EHoe NLos SHDw
extremiorientalis EPPr EWoo MMuc SEND SMad
gigantea ♀H7 Widely available
- 'Gold Fontaene' CDes CKno EBee EPPr EWes LRHS MAvo MNrw NDov SMHy SMad WCot WMoo WPGP WWEG
- 'Pixie' GCal LRHS SGSe WWEG
grandis EPPr WMoo
ichu CKno CRos LRHS MAvo NLos SDix SHDw SMad SPoG
- F&M 32 CFil WPGP
joannis EBee GCal
lasiagrostis see *S. calamagrostis*
leptostachya WCot
lessingiana CExl EBee EHoe EPPr ETod LRHS NLos SEND SPhx WMoo
offneri EPPr
papposa SPhx
pennata CBod EPPr ETod NDov XSen
§ **poeppigiana** EBee
pseudoichu CAbP CBod CFil CSpe EPPr ESwi ETod MAvo MBel SMad WCot
- RCB/Arg Y-1 EBee ELon NCGa
pulcherrima EBee EPPr GCal
- 'Windfeder' CCon
ramosissima CKno
robusta SPhx
splendens misapplied see *S. calamagrostis*
splendens Trin. ECha MMuc SAko
tenacissima CDul IBoy MAsh
tenuifolia misapplied see *S. tenuissima*
tenuifolia Steud. CMea EBee EPfP LRHS MBri MRav NBir NBro NOak NSti WHal WMoo XLum XSen
§ **tenuissima** Widely available
- 'Wind Whispers' CBod CExl CSpe EUJe GBin LEdu LRHS MBel
turkestanica NDov SWat
ucrainica NDov

Stoebe (*Asteraceae*)

alopecuroides SPlb

Stokesia ✿ (*Asteraceae*)

cyanea see *S. laevis*
§ **laevis** ECGP ECha EPfP LRHS MMuc NLar SCob SEND SPlb WCAu WMoo WPGP WWEG XLum
- 'Alba' ECha EHrv ELan EPfP EPri LEdu LRHS MRav NLar WCAu
- 'Blue Star' CAby CBcs CBod CSam CWGN ELan ELon EPfP EWoo LAst LEdu LRHS MBel MHer MRav SGbt SPad

	SPer SPhx SPoG SRkn SWvt WHoo WHrl WMnd WMoo
- 'Color Wheel'	CMos ECtt LRHS SCob
- 'Honeysong Purple' new	NLar
- 'Klaus Jelitto'	IPot LEdu LRHS MBri SPoG WHrl
- 'Mary Gregory'	CBod CCon CMac CMos CSam EBee ECtt EHrv ELan EPfP IKil LEdu LRHS LSou MBel MNrw MRav NCGa NLar SPer SPhx SRGP SWvt WGwG WHrl WPGP WWEG
- 'Mel's Blue'	EBee ECtt
- mixed	CPou
- 'Omega Skyrocket'	CPou SBea
- 'Peach Melba'	ECtt NCGa WMoo
- 'Peachie's Pick'	ECtt
- 'Purple Parasols'	CBod CMac CWGN ECtt EPfP GBin IKil LRHS LSou MBel NCGa SCob SPoG STPC SWvt WHrl WMoo WWEG
- 'Purple Pixie'PBR	ECtt LRHS
- 'Silver Moon'	CMos ECtt EPfP GBin LRHS MBel MTPN NBir SPer STPC WHrl WMoo WWEG
§ - 'Träumerei'	CWGN EAEE EBee ECtt EPfP LRHS MMuc NLar SEND SPoG WHrl WMnd WMoo WWEG XLum
- 'White Star'	see *S. laevis* 'Träumerei'

Stranvaesia see *Photinia*

× *Stranvinia* see *Photinia*

Stratiotes (*Hydrocharitaceae*)

aloides	CBen CWat EHon EWay MWts NPer SVic SWat WMAq WPnP

strawberry see *Fragaria*

Strelitzia (*Strelitziaceae*)

juncea	LPal XBlo
nicolai	LPal NPer SPlb XBlo
reginae ♀H1c	CAbb CBcs CTsd ELan EShb ETod EUJe LPal NPer NPla SBig SChr SEND SPlb XBlo
- 'Kirstenbosch Gold'	LPal XBlo

Streptocarpella see *Streptocarpus*

Streptocarpus ✿ (*Gesneriaceae*)

'Adele'	WDib
'Albatross'	CSpe CTsd WDib
'Alissa'	WDib
'Amanda' Dibley	WDib
'Ambiente' ♀H1c new	WDib
'Anne' (d)	CTsd WDib
'Awena'	WDib
baudertii	WDib
'Bella' new	WDib
'Bethan' ♀H1c	CTsd WDib
'Bianca'	WDib
'Black Gardenia'	CTsd WDib
'Black Panther'	CTsd WDib
'Blue Bird'	SBrm
'Blue Frills' ♀H1c	WDib
'Blue Gem'	WDib
'Blue Leyla'	see *S.* 'Leyla'
'Blue Moon'	WDib
'Blue Nymph'	WDib
'Blushing Bride' (d)	WDib
'Boysenberry Delight'	WDib
'Branwen'	CTsd WDib
'Brimstone'	SBrm
'Bristol's Black Bird'	WDib
'Bristol's Very Best'	WDib
'Burgundy Ice' ♀H1c	SBrm
'Buttons'	SBrm
caeruleus	WDib
'Caitlin'	CTsd WDib
candidus	WDib
'Cappuccino'	WDib
'Carol'	WDib
'Carolyn Ann'	SBrm
'Carys' ♀H1c	CTsd WDib
caulescens	WDib
- var. ***pallescens***	WDib
'Celebration' new	WDib
'Charlotte' ♀H1c	SBrm WDib
'Chloe'	WDib
'Chorus Line'	CTsd WDib
'Christine'	SBrm
'Concord Blue'	WDib
'Constant Nymph'	WDib
'Copper Knob'	SBrm
'Crystal Beauty'	WDib
'Crystal Blush'	WDib
'Crystal Charm'	WDib
'Crystal Dawn'	WDib
'Crystal Ice'PBR ♀H1c	LCro LOPS WDib
'Crystal Snow'	WDib
'Crystal Wonder'	WDib
cyaneus	WDib
- subsp. ***polackii***	WDib
'Cynthia'	WDib
'Dainty Lady'	SBrm
'Daphne'	WDib
'Dark Eyes Mary'	SBrm
'Dee' new	WDib
'Delia' new	WDib
'Denim'	WDib
denticulatus	WDib
'Diana'	WDib
'Dinas'	WDib
'Double Delight' (d)	SBrm
'Dreamtime'	SBrm
dunnii	WDib
'Elegance'	SBrm
'Elizabeth'	SBrm
'Ella'	SBrm
'Ella Mae'	SBrm
'Ellie'	WDib
'Elsi'	CTsd WDib
'Emily'	WDib
'Eve'	WDib
'Falling Stars' ♀H1c	CTsd WDib
'Festival Wales'	WDib
'Fiona'	WDib
floribundus	WDib
'Frances'	SBrm
'Frances Elizabeth'	SBrm
'Franken Alison'	SBrm
'Franken Jenny'	SBrm
'Franken Kelly' ♀H1c	SBrm
'Franken Misty Blue'	SBrm
'Franken Texas Sunset'	SBrm
'Frosty Diamond' ♀H1c	CTsd WDib
'Full Moon' new	WDib
gardenii	WDib
'Gillian'	SBrm
glandulosissimus ♀H1c	WDib
'Gloria' ♀H1c	CTsd WDib

Name	Suppliers
'Gwen'	WDib
'Hannah' 🏆[H1c]	WDib
'Hannah Ellis'	SBrm
'Harlequin Blue'[PBR] 🏆[H1c]	WDib
'Harlequin Damsel'	WDib
'Harlequin Dawn'	WDib
'Harlequin Delft'	WDib
'Harlequin Lace' 🏆[H1c]	WDib
'Harlequin Purple'	WDib
'Harriet'	WDib
'Hayley'	WDib
'Heather Ice'	SBrm
'Heidi'	CTsd WDib
'Helen'	CTsd WDib
'Hope'	WDib
'Ida'	SBrm
'Inky Fingers'	SBrm
'Iona'	WDib
'Isabella'	WDib
'Izzy'	SBrm
'Jacquie'	WDib
'Jane Elizabeth'	SBrm
'Jennifer' 🏆[H1c]	WDib
'Jessica' 🏆[H1c]	WDib
'Joanna'	CTsd WDib
johannis	WDib
'Josie'	SBrm
'Joy'	WDib
'Judith'	SBrm
'Karen'	WDib
'Katie'[PBR] 🏆[H1c]	WDib
kentaniensis	WDib
'Kerry's Gold'	SBrm
'Kim' 🏆[H1c]	WDib
kirkii	WDib
'Kisie'	SBrm
'Lady Lavender'	SBrm
'Largesse'	SBrm
'Laura' 🏆[H1c]	WDib
§ 'Leyla'[PBR]	WDib
'Louise'	WDib
'Lucy'	WDib
'Lyndee'	WDib
'Lynne'	WDib
'Maassen's White'	WDib
'Magpie'	SBrm
'Margaret' Gavin Brown	WDib
'Marie'	WDib
'Mary'	SBrm
'Megan'	WDib
'Melanie' Dibley	WDib
meyeri	WDib
'Midnight Flame'	CTsd WDib
'Mini Nymph'	WDib
'Misty Pink'	SBrm
'Modbury Lady'	SBrm
modestus	WDib
'Molly'	SBrm
'Monica's Magic'	SBrm
'Myfanwy'	WDib
'Natalie'	WDib
'Nerys'	CTsd WDib
'Nia'	CTsd WDib
'Nicola'	CTsd WDib
'Olga'	WDib
'Olivia'	WDib
'Padarn'	WDib
'Pale Rider'	SBrm
'Patricia'	SBrm
'Paula'	WDib
'Pearl'	WDib
'Penelope'	SBrm
pentherianus	WDib
'Pink Leyla'[PBR] 🏆[H1c]	WDib
'Pink Souffle'	WDib
polyanthus subsp. ***dracomontanus***	WDib
primulifolius	WDib
- subsp. ***formosus***	WDib
'Princesse' (Marleen Series)	WDib
prolixus	WDib
'Purple Pride'	SBrm
'Raspberry Dream'	SBrm
rexii	WDib
'Rhiannon'	CTsd WDib
'Rose Halo'	WDib
'Rosebud'	WDib
(Roulette Series) 'Roulette Azur'[PBR]	WDib
- 'Roulette Cherry'	WDib
'Rubina'[PBR]	WDib
'Rubina Pink' 🏆[H1c] **new**	WDib
'Ruby'	CTsd WDib
'Ruby Anniversary'	SBrm
'Ruffles'	SBrm
'Ruth'	WDib
'Sally'	WDib
'Sandra'	WDib
'Sarah'	WDib
saxorum	CDoC CTsd WDib
- compact 🏆[H1c]	WDib
- 'Concord Blue' **new**	EBee
'Scarlett'	WDib
'Seren'[PBR]	WDib
'Shannon'	SBrm
'Sian'	WDib
silvaticus	WDib
'Sioned' 🏆[H1c]	WDib
'Snow White' 🏆[H1c]	CSpe WDib
'Spirit'[PBR] 🏆[H1c]	WDib
'Stacey'	SBrm
'Stella'[PBR] 🏆[H1c]	WDib
'Stephanie'	WDib
stomandrus	WDib
'Strawberry Fondant'	SBrm
'Summer Skies'	SBrm
'Susan' 🏆[H1c]	CTsd WDib
'Swaybelle'	SBrm
'Sweet Melys'	WDib
'Targa' (Marleen Series)	WDib
'Tatan Blue'	SBrm
'Teleri'	WDib
'Terracotta'	SBrm
'Texas Hot Chili'	CTsd WDib
'Texas Sunrise'	SBrm
thompsonii	WDib
'Tina' 🏆[H1c]	WDib
'Tracey'	WDib
'Twice as Nice'	SBrm
vandeleurii	WDib
'Vanessa'	SBrm
variabilis	WDib
'Velvet Underground'	SBrm
'Vera'	SBrm
'Watermelon Wine'	WDib
wendlandii	WDib
'Wendy'	WDib
'White Butterfly' 🏆[H1c]	WDib
'White Wings'	SBrm
'Wiesmoor Red'	WDib

'Winifred'	WDib

Streptopus (*Liliaceae*)

amplexifolius	EBee ECho EHrv GAbr MNrw NMyG WCru
roseus	ECho
streptopoides	EBee EPPr EPfP LEdu LRHS MMHG

Streptosolen (*Solanaceae*)

jamesonii ♀H1c	CHll EBak EShb MOWG SWvt

Strobilanthes (*Acanthaceae*)

sp.	WBor
CC 4071	CExl
CC 4573	CExl
anisophylla	EShb SDys
atropurpurea misapplied	see *S. attenuata*
atropurpurea Nees	see *S. wallichii*
§ ***attenuata***	CCon EBee ECGP ECtt EPfP GCal GCra ILea ITim IVic LEdu LHop LRHS MBel MRav NChi NDov NSti SDix SGSe WCru WMoo
- 'Blue Carpet'	EBee NDov
- 'Cally Bicolor' **new**	GCal
- subsp. ***nepalensis***	CHll XLum
dyeriana ♀H1b	EBak MPie WCot
flexicaulis	WPGP
- B&SWJ 354	WCru
aff. ***inflata*** B&SWJ 7754	WCru
* ***lactea***	EShb
nutans	CCon CPou EBee EWld NSti SBrt XLum
pentstemonoides	WCot
aff. ***pentstemonoides*** HWJK 2019	WCru
rankanensis	CCon EBee EPPr SDys SMHy XLum
- B&SWJ 1771	WCru
violacea	CHVG CPrp EShb IArd LHop
§ ***wallichii***	CMac CSam EBee EWes EWld LLWP MMuc NSti SEND WCAu WCru WMoo WWEG
- PAB 8440 **new**	LEdu

Stromanthe (*Marantaceae*)

sanguinea 'Triostar'PBR (v)	XBlo

Strongylodon (*Papilionaceae*)

macrobotrys	MOWG

Strophanthus (*Apocynaceae*)

speciosus	CHll EShb

Strumaria (*Amaryllidaceae*)

chaplinii	NRog
discifera subsp. ***bulbifera***	NRog WCot
gemmata	NRog
karooica	NRog
salteri	NRog
tenella subsp. ***orientalis***	NRog
truncata	NRog WCot
watermeyeri subsp. ***watermeyeri***	NRog

Stuartia see *Stewartia*

Stylidium (*Stylidiaceae*)

adnatum	ECou
graminifolium	CTsd SPlb
- Little Saphire = 'St116'	SRot

Stylophorum (*Papaveraceae*)

diphyllum	CPou EWld GCal IMou LEdu MAvo WCru WPGP WPnP WWtn
lasiocarpum	CExl CSpe EBee EWes EWld GEdr MMHG NBid WCot WCru WHil

Stypandra (*Phormiaceae*)

glauca	CLak

Styphelia (*Epacridaceae*)

colensoi	see *Leucopogon colensoi*

Styphnolobium (*Papilionaceae*)

§ ***japonicum***	CAbP CBcs CDul CHab CLet CLnd CTho CWib EPfP MGos SCob SPlb
- 'Flavirameum' **new**	LRHS
- 'Pendulum'	CDul

Styrax (*Styracaceae*)

americanus	NLar
confusus	CBcs CExl
dasyanthus	CBcs CExl
faberi	CBcs CExl
formosanus	CBcs CExl CFil CJun EPfP MBlu
var. ***formosanus***	WPGP
- - B&SWJ 3803	WCru
- - B&SWJ 6786	WCru
- var. ***hayatiana*** B&SWJ 6823	WCru
grandiflorus	CExl
hemsleyanus ♀H5	CBcs CExl CTho EPfP GBin MBlu MMuc NLar SPer
hookeri	CExl
japonicus	CBcs CDoC CDul CExl CLnd CMCN CTho CTri CWib ELan EPfP GGal GKin LRHS MAsh MBlu MGos MMuc MRav NLar SPer SPoG SReu SSpi WPGP WPat
- B&SWJ 4405	WCru
- B&SWJ 8770	WCru
- B&SWJ 11078	WCru
- Guiz 216	CExl WPGP
- PAB 8366 **new**	LEdu
§ - Benibana Group	WPGP
- - 'Pink Chimes' ♀H5	CBcs CExl CJun CMCN CMac EBee ELan EPfP ESwi GBin GKin IDee MBlu MPkF NLar WMat
- 'Carillon'	CJun
- 'Fargesii' ♀H5	CBcs CDoC CDul CExl CJun CTho EPfP GBin IVic LRHS SKHP
- 'Fragrant Fountain'	MBlu NLar
- 'Herkenrode'	MBri
- 'Hyme'	NLar
- 'Issai'	NLar
- 'Pendulus'	EBee EPfP WPGP
- 'Purple Dress' ♀H5	CJun MBlu MBri NLar
- 'Roseus'	see *S. japonicus* Benibana Group
- 'Snowfall'	CJun NLar
- 'Sohuksan' ♀H5	CExl CFil CJun MBlu NLar WPGP
limprichtii	CExl CFil
obassia	CBcs CDul CLnd CMCN CTho EBee EPfP GBin IVic LRHS MBlu MBri NLar WPGP
- B&SWJ 6023	WCru
- B&SWJ 10890	WCru
odoratissimus	CExl
officinalis	CBcs
platanifolius var. ***mollis***	CFil

serrulatus	CExl
shiraianus	CExl CFil NLar WPGP
suberifolius WWJ 11868	WCru
* ***taiwanensis***	SKHP
tonkinensis FMWJ 13134 new	WCru
'Wespelaar' new	SAko
wilsonii	CExl
wuyuanensis	CBcs NLar WPGP

Succisa (*Caprifoliaceae*)

§ ***pratensis***	CAby CArn CHab CMac CWld EPri LEdu LHop LLWG MHer MPie NLar SBch SGSe SMHy SPhx WCAu WHer WHoo WPGP WPtf WSFF WWFP XLum
- 'Alba'	EWes
- 'Cassop'	NRya
- 'Derby Purple'	CSpe WPtf
- 'Peddar's Pink'	EWes LEdu LLWG SPhx

Succisella (*Caprifoliaceae*)

inflexa	EBee LEdu MSpe SPhx WCot
- 'Frosted Pearls'	CFis CMHG LEdu LLWP MAvo MMuc WWFP

Sullivantia (*Saxifragaceae*)

sullivantii dwarf	WThu

sunberry see *Rubus* 'Sunberry'

Sutera (*Scrophulariaceae*)

(Abunda Series) Abunda Blue Improved = 'Balabimblu'	LAst
- Abunda Colossal Blue = 'Balabolue' new	LAst
- Abunda Colossal Pink new	LAst LBMP
- Abunda Colossal Sky Blue = 'Balabolav'	LBMP NPri
- Abunda Colossal White = 'Balabowite'PBR	LBMP NPri
(Copia Series) Copia Dark Pink = 'Dancop19'PBR	LAst
- Copia Double White (d)	LAst
- Copia Gulliver White = 'Dangul14'PBR	LAst
cordata 'Blizzard'	LSou
- 'Olympic Gold' (v)	SCoo
- (Scopia Series) Scopia Double Pink Pearl	LAst
- - Scopia Golden Leaves White = 'Dancop15' new	LAst NPri
- - Scopia Great Classic Pink = 'Dancop46' new	NPri
§ - 'Snowflake'	LAst NPer SCoo SPoG SWvt
Great Purple = 'Dancop21'PBR (Scopia Series)	LSou
microphylla	see *Jamesbrittenia microphylla*
neglecta	WPGP
(Scopia Series) Scopia Double Ballerina Pink (d) new	LAst
- Scopia Double White (d) new	LAst
(Secrets Series) 'Secrets Blue Delight'	LSou
- 'Secrets Central Pink'	LSou
- 'Secrets Silver Sky'	LSou

Sutherlandia ✿ (*Papilionaceae*)

frutescens	CBod CSpe CTre GDun SPlb WJek
- fine-leaved	GDun
- 'Prostrata'	SIgm
montana	CSpe CTre SBrt

Swainsona (*Papilionaceae*)

galegifolia	CHll
- 'Albiflora'	MOWG

sweet cicely see *Myrrhis odorata*

Swertia (*Gentianaceae*)

bimaculata PAB 8845 new	LEdu
perennis	GEdr
petiolata CC 7335 new	GKev

Swietenia (*Meliaceae*)

mahogani	SPlb

Syagrus (*Arecaceae*)

botryophora	XBlo
§ ***romanzoffiana***	XBlo
weddelliana	see *Lytocaryum weddellianum*

× *Sycoparrotia* (*Hamamelidaceae*)

semidecidua	CBcs CJun MBlu NLar
- 'Purple Haze'	CJun NLar WPGP

Sycopsis (*Hamamelidaceae*)

sinensis	CAbP CBcs CExl CWib EBee EPfP GCal LRHS MMuc NLar SKHP SPoG SSpi SWvt WPGP WSHC

Symphoricarpos (*Caprifoliaceae*)

albus	CDul CMac MSwo NWea SCob
- 'Constance Spry'	SRms
§ - var. ***laevigatus***	EPfP LBuc
× ***chenaultii*** 'Brain de Soleil'PBR	EBee
- 'Hancock'	CBar CDul CMac ECrN ELan EPfP IDee MBri MGos MMuc MRav MSwo SCob SEND SGol SLim SPer WCFE
× ***doorenbosii*** 'Magic Berry'	MHtn MRav NWea SGol
- 'Mother of Pearl'	ELan EPfP MMuc MRav NWea SCob SEND SPer
- 'White Hedge'	ELan LBuc MMuc NWea SEND SPer SPlb
guatemalensis B&SWJ 1016	WCru
Magical Candy = 'Kolmcan'PBR	ELan EPfP SPoG
Magical Galaxy = 'Kolmgala'PBR	ELan EPfP SPoG
Magical Sweet = 'Kolmaswet'PBR	SPoG
orbiculatus	SLon
- 'Albovariegatus'	see *S. orbiculatus* 'Taff's Silver Edge'
- 'Argenteovariegatus'	see *S. orbiculatus* 'Taff's Silver Edge'
- 'Bowles's Golden Variegated'	see *S. orbiculatus* 'Foliis Variegatis'
§ - 'Foliis Variegatis' (v)	CMac CTri EHoe ELan MGos MRav SGol SPer
- 'George Gardiner'	CMac
§ - 'Taff's Silver Edge' (v)	SGol

- 'Variegatus' see *S. orbiculatus* 'Foliis Variegatis'
rivularis see *S. albus* var. *laevigatus*

Symphyandra see *Campanula*

asiatica see *Hanabusaya asiatica*

Symphyotrichum see *Aster*

Symphytum (*Boraginaceae*)

'Angela Whinfield' CDes CMea EBee
asperum ECha MRav NLar WMoo
* ***azureum*** NChi WCAu WMnd
'Belsay' GBuc
'Belsay Gold' NBid NBir SDix WBor
bulbosum Schimp. PAB 4886 LEdu
caucasicum CElw CMHG CSde EBee ECha GPoy GQue IFro LEdu NLar NSti SEND SIde WHer WHil WMoo WOut WWtn XLum
- 'Eminence' WWEG
- 'Norwich Sky' CExl
cordatum EPPr LEdu MNrw SKHP
'Denford Variegated' (v) NBid
§ 'Goldsmith' (v) CBod CMea CSam EBee ECha EHrv ELan EPfP EWoo LAst MBri MCot MHol MPie NBid NBir NEgg NLar NPer SPer WJek WMnd WWEG
grandiflorum CMac CTri GKev GPoy LEdu SPer
- 'Sky-blue-pink' IFro
'Hidcote Blue' CBod CBre CLet CNec CTri ECha ECtt EPPr EPfP LRHS MMuc NBro NEgg SCob SEND SPer SPoG WGwG WHea WMoo WOut WPnP WWEG WWtn
§ 'Hidcote Pink' CBod CNec ECha ECtt EPPr LBMP LPot LRHS MMuc MNrw NBir SEND SPer SPoG WFar WGwG WMoo WPnP WWEG WWtn XLum
'Hidcote Variegated' (v) CMac WOut
ibericum CSam ECha EHrv GKev GMaP GPoy LHop LRHS MLHP MMuc NSti SEND SRms WGwG WJek WMoo WOut WWtn
- 'All Gold' ECha LRHS MHer MNrw WMoo
- 'Blaueglocken' ECha LPla WMoo
- dwarf IFro WMoo
- 'Gold in Spring' NLar WFar
- 'Jubilee' see *S.* 'Goldsmith'
- 'Lilacinum' CFis WHer
- 'Variegatum' see *S.* 'Goldsmith'
- 'Wisley Blue' CBcs CBod ILea SCob WFar WMoo WWEG
'Lambrook Gold' LHop
'Lambrook Sunrise' CMac LEdu NBro WCot WMoo WWEG
'Langthorns Pink' ELan GCal
'Mereworth' see *S.* × *uplandicum* 'Mereworth'
officinale CAgr CArn CHab ENfk GJos GPoy MHer MNHC MNrw NPer NPri SIde SPoG SRms WHea WHer WHfH WJek XLum
- blue-flowered SEND
- var. ***ochroleucum*** WHer
orientale EBee EPPr GCal MBel
peregrinum see *S.* × *uplandicum*
'Romanian Red' **new** SDix
'Roseum' see *S.* 'Hidcote Pink'
'Rubrum' CBod CLet EHrv ELan EPfP EWes GBin GCra LEdu LRHS MMuc NBro NLar SPer WCAu WGwG WPGP XLum
'Sera Howys' WOut
tuberosum CBre CElw CFis CSam EPPr GPoy LEdu MHer MMuc SEND WBor WCot WHer WOut
§ × ***uplandicum*** CTri ELan GCra GPoy MMuc SEND SVic WJek
- 'Axminster Gold' (v) CMea EWes NChi WCot
- 'Bocking 14' CAgr CBod CHby CPbn EOHP EShb GAbr LEdu MHer MNHC SIde WSFF XLum
- 'Droitwich' (v) WCot
§ - 'Mereworth' (v) CBct SEND
- 'Moorland Heather' CDes MHer MMHG MNrw WMoo WWEG
- 'Variegatum' (v) CBot ECha ECtt ELan EPfP EWes GBuc GCal LAst LRHS NBir NGdn NSti SPoG WMoo WWtn

Symplocarpus (*Araceae*)

foetidus CDes

Symplocos (*Symplocaceae*)

sawafutagi CBcs NLar WPGP

Synadenium (*Euphorbiaceae*)

grantii 'Rubrum' **new** EShb

Syncarpha (*Asteraceae*)

vestita SPlb

Syncolostemon (*Lamiaceae*)

'Candy Kisses' WCot

Syneilesis (*Asteraceae*)

aconitifolia GEdr WCot WHal
- B&SWJ 879 EHrv LEdu WCru
palmata GEdr WCot
- B&SWJ 1003 WCru
- B&SWJ 11226 WCru
- 'Kiko' GEdr
subglabrata B&SWJ 298 WCru
aff. ***tagawae*** B&SWJ 11191 WCru

Syngonium (*Araceae*)

podophyllum ♀H1b XBlo

Synnotia see *Sparaxis*

Synsepalum (*Sapotaceae*)

dulcificum SCit

Synthyris (*Plantaginaceae*)

laciniata EBee LLHF
missurica EWld
- subsp. ***missurica*** EBee GBuc
- subsp. ***stellata*** CAby CBod CLAP EAEE EBee ECre EPfP EPri EWes GBin GBuc GCal LEdu LRHS MMHG NCGa SPoG WCot WGwG WHal WMoo WPGP WPtf WSHC WWEG
reniformis CLAP GBuc WPGP WWEG

Synurus (*Asteraceae*)

pungens SBrt

Syringa ✿ (*Oleaceae*)

afghanica misapplied see *S. protolaciniata*
afghanica C.K. Schneid. IVic WSHC

× ***chinensis*** 'Alba' — see *S.* 'Correlata'
- 'Saugeana' — MMuc SPer

§ 'Correlata' (graft-chimaera) — EBee EPfP IDee
× ***diversifolia*** new — NLar
emodi 'Aurea' — NLar
- 'Aureovariegata' — see *S. emodi* 'Variegata'
- 'Elegantissima' (v) — CBcs CDoC CMac EBtc ELan EPfP GQui LRHS MAsh NEgg NLar SKHP SPoG SSpi
§ - 'Variegata' (v) — CBot EMil LRHS NLar
× ***hyacinthiflora*** 'Anabel' (d) — NLar
- 'Clarke's Giant' — NLar
- 'Esther Staley' 🏆H6 — EPfP MRav SKHP
- 'Lavender Lady' — NLar
- 'Pocahontas' 🏆H6 — GBin LRHS
- 'Sweetheart' (d) — WMat
Josée = 'Morjos 060f' — CDoC ELan ELon EPfP LBrs LSou MAsh SCob SMDP SWvt WFar WPat
× ***josiflexa*** — CExl
- 'Agnes Smith' — EBee LRHS MMuc NLar
- 'Bellicent' 🏆H6 — CBot CMac ELan EPfP IDee IFro LRHS MAsh MMuc MRav NLar SAko SEND SKHP SPer SPoG SRms SWvt WCFE WFar WPat
- 'Lynette' — NEoE
- 'Redwine' — SKHP
§ - 'Royalty' — NLar SKHP
josikaea — CMCN CSBt NLar SPer
'Kim' — MRav
komarowii — GGGa IDee WPat
§ - subsp. ***reflexa*** — CDul EPfP EWTr IDee NLar SLon
§ × ***laciniata*** Mill. — CJun CWld EBee ELan EPfP IDee LRHS MGos MRav NLar SPer SPoG SSpi WCFE WHar WPGP
'Lark Song' — NLar
meyeri — SVen
- 'Inge' — NLar
§ - 'Palibin' 🏆H5 — Widely available
'Minuet' — CBcs LBuc SKHP
Miss Japan new — EBee
oblata — CMCN
palibiniana misapplied — see *S. meyeri* 'Palibin'
patula misapplied — see *S. meyeri* 'Palibin'
patula (Palib.) Nakai — see *S. pubescens* subsp. *patula*
pekinensis — see *S. reticulata* subsp. *pekinensis*
- Beijing Gold — see *S. reticulata* subsp. *pekinensis* 'Zhang Zhiiming'
× ***persica*** 🏆H6 — CExl CJun CTri EPfP MGos MRav NLar SLon SPer WFar
- 'Alba' 🏆H6 — CJun MRav WFar WSHC
- var. ***laciniata*** — see *S.* × *laciniata* Mill.
'Pink Perfume'PBR — LRHS
pinnatifolia — CBcs CBot GBin LRHS NLar SAko
× ***prestoniae*** 'Desdemona' — EBtc LRHS MMuc SEND SKHP
- 'Elinor' 🏆H6 — CBot CMHG ELan EMil EPfP MRav SKHP
- 'Nocturne' — WFar
- 'Royalty' — see *S.* × *josiflexa* 'Royalty'
§ ***protolaciniata*** — NLar SKHP SLim
pubescens subsp. ***julianae*** 'George Eastman' — MRav
- subsp. ***microphylla*** 'Superba' 🏆H6 — Widely available
§ - subsp. ***patula*** — CMac EPfP LRHS MMuc MRav NWea SEND SLim SVen
- - 'Miss Kim' 🏆H6 — Widely available
'Red Pixie' — CMac ELon EPfP LCro LRHS MBri MGos MMHG SCoo SHil SKHP
reflexa — see *S. komarowii* subsp. *reflexa*
reticulata — MBlu
- 'Ivory Silk' — EPfP LRHS NLar SKHP WMat
§ - subsp. ***pekinensis*** — CMCN GBin GKev
- - China Snow = 'Morton' 🏆H6 — SKHP
- - 'Yellow Fragrance' — NLar
§ - - 'Zhang Zhiiming' — EBee
× ***swegiflexa*** — CDul CExl
tomentella — EBee NWea SRms WPGP
- subsp. ***sweginzowii*** — GKin MMuc NLar SPer
- subsp. ***yunnanensis*** — CExl GGGa
velutina Kom. — see *S. pubescens* subsp. *patula*
villosa — SPlb
vulgaris — CDul EPfP NWea
§ - 'Andenken an Ludwig Späth' 🏆H6 — Widely available
- 'Aurea' — MRav NEoE
- Beauty of Moscow — see *S. vulgaris* 'Krasavitsa Moskvy'
- 'Belle de Nancy' (d) — CDul CLnd CMac CWib EBee ECrN ELan ELon LAst MAsh MMuc MRav NLar SCob SEND SGol SPoG SWvt
- Carpe Diem — see *S. vulgaris* 'Evert de Gier'
- 'Charles Joly' (d) 🏆H6 — Widely available
- 'Comtesse d'Harcourt' — EPfP SEND
- 'Congo' — LSRN
- 'Edward J. Gardner' (d) 🏆H6 — ELon SEND
§ - 'Evert de Gier' new — CBcs
- 'Firmament' 🏆H6 — ELan MRav SEND SPer
- 'G. J. Baardse' — EWTr
- 'Katherine Havemeyer' (d) 🏆H6 — Widely available
§ - 'Krasavitsa Moskvy' (d) 🏆H6 — CDoC ECrN EPfP EWes GBin LRHS MAsh MBri NLar SEND WMat
- 'Lee Jewett Walker' — SSta
- 'Lila Wonder'PBR — EBee EPfP
- 'Madame Florent Stepman' — CMac
- 'Madame Lemoine' (d) 🏆H6 — Widely available
- 'Masséna' — SPer
- 'Michel Buchner' (d) — CBcs CDul CWib EBee ECrN ELan MBlu MGos NLar SCob SCoo SLim SPer WMat
- 'Miss Ellen Willmott' (d) — IArd NLar
- 'Mrs Edward Harding' (d) 🏆H6 — EBee ECrN EPfP MRav NLar NWea SPer
- 'Pavlinka' (d) — IArd
- 'Président Grévy' (d) — CBar CDoC CMac EPfP MAsh SLim SPer
- 'Primrose' 🏆H6 — CBcs CMac CWib EBee ELan ELon EPfP GBin LRHS MAsh MGos MJak MSnd NLar NOrn SCoo SEND SHil SKHP SPer WMat
- 'Prince Wolkonsky' (d) — EBee EPfP LSRN MAsh SEND SPer WFar
- Rose de Moscou = 'Minkarl'PBR — EPfP SHil
- 'Sensation' 🏆H6 — Widely available
- 'Souvenir d'Alice Harding' (d) 🏆H6 — MBri
- 'Souvenir de Louis Spaeth' — see *S. vulgaris* 'Andenken an Ludwig Späth'
- variegated (v) — EWes
- variegated double (d/v) — WCot
- 'Vesper' — IArd
- 'Viviand-Morel' (d) — CMac LLHF SKHP
wolfii — CArn EBtc NLar

Syzygium (*Myrtaceae*)

luehmannii new	EShb
paniculatum	CExl

T

Tacca (*Taccaceae*)

chantrieri	GKev
- 'Green Isle'	GKev
integrifolia	GKev LPal

Taccarum (*Araceae*)

weddellianum	WCot

Tacitus see *Graptopetalum*

Tagetes (*Asteraceae*)

'Cinnabar'	CSpe SDix
lemmonii	SDix SHDw WJek
- 'Martin's Mutant'	WCot
'Lemon Gem'	WJek
lucida	CArn ENfk LEdu MHer SRms WJek
patula Durango Series	NPri
- - 'Durango Bee'	NPri
- - 'Durango Flame'	NPri
- - 'Durango Orange'	NPri
- - 'Durango Yellow'	NPri
- 'Harlequin'	see *T. patula* 'Old Scotch Pride'
§ - 'Old Scotch Pride'	SPav

Taiwania (*Cupressaceae*)

cryptomerioides	IArd IDee SAko

Talinum (*Portulacaceae*)

'Zoe'	CPBP

tamarillo see *Solanum betaceum*

tamarind see *Tamarindus indica*

Tamarindus (*Caesalpiniaceae*)

indica (F)	SPlb

Tamarix (*Tamaricaceae*)

gallica	NWea SEND WSHC
hampeana	SEND
§ ***parviflora*** ♀H5	CDul CMac EPfP IVic LRHS NLar SCob SPoG
pentandra	see *T. ramosissima* 'Rosea'
ramosissima	CLet CTri ECrN ELan EPfP MAsh NLar SCob SEWo SLim SLon SRms WHar
- 'Hulsdonk White'	CBcs SPer
- 'Pink Cascade' ♀H5	CBcs CDul CMac EBee ELon EPfP LCro LRHS MBlu MGos MMuc MRav NEgg SBod SCob SEND SGbt SGol SPer SPoG SWvt WBor
§ - 'Rosea'	CBcs
§ - 'Rubra'	CDoC EPfP IVic MBri SEND SLon SPer
- 'Summer Glow'	see *T. ramosissima* 'Rubra'
tetrandra ♀H5	CBcs CCVT CChe CDul CLet CSde CTsd CWSG CWib ELan EPfP LBMP LRHS MBlu MBri MGil MGos MMuc MRav MSwo NPer SEND SGol SHil SPer SPlb SRms SWvt WHar
- var. ***purpurea***	see *T. parviflora*

Tamus (*Dioscoreaceae*)

communis	CArn

Tanacetum ✿ (*Asteraceae*)

sp.	CHab
§ ***argenteum***	ECho MRav SIde
- subsp. ***canum***	ECho LRHS SLon
§ ***balsamita***	CArn CBod CHby CLau CPrp EBee ELan ENfk GPoy LEdu MHer MMuc MNHC SEND SRms WHer WHfH WJek WSFF XLum XSen
§ - subsp. ***balsamita***	GPoy SIde
§ - subsp. ***balsamitoides***	CBod CPrp MHer SRms WJek
- var. ***tanacetoides***	see *T. balsamita* subsp. *balsamita*
- ***tomentosum***	see *T. balsamita* subsp. *balsamitoides*
§ ***cinerariifolium***	CArn CBod CPrp GPoy MNHC WJek
§ ***coccineum***	SVic WFar
- 'Bees' Pink Delight'	CBod ECtt NEgg
- 'Duro'	LRHS
- 'Eileen May Robinson'	CBod EPfP LSRN NGdn
- 'Garden Treasure'	EBee ECtt SPoG
- 'H.M. Pike'	EBee
- 'James Kelway'	EPfP NBir
- 'Laurin'	EBee LRHS
- Robinson's crimson-flowered	LRHS MNHC
- Robinson's giant-flowered	CTsd LRHS SRms
- Robinson's pink-flowered	EBee EPfP GMaP MHol SCob SGSe XLum
- Robinson's red-flowered	CBod CSBt EAJP EPfP GMaP LRHS MHol SGSe SPlb SWvt WTcb XLum
- Robinson's rose-flowered	EAJP LPal
- 'Snow Cloud'	CBod ECtt EPfP LRHS WWEG
- 'Vanessa'	MNrw
§ ***corymbosum***	GCal LRHS NLar WCot
- 'Bukke' new	LEdu
- 'Festtafel'	LEdu LPla
densum	ECho WCFE
- subsp. ***amani***	ECha ECho GMaP LRHS SEND XSen
- - 'Beth Chatto'	XSen
§ ***haradjanii***	ECho MCot SBch WKif
huronense	EBee
kittaryanum subsp. ***uralense*** new	EBee
macrophyllum misapplied	see *Achillea grandifolia* Friv.
§ ***macrophyllum*** (Waldst. & Kit.) Sch.Bip.	CPrp EBee ECtt EPPr LPla SPhx
- 'Cream Klenza'	WCot
niveum	ECha SDix WCot
- 'Jackpot'	CBot CFis CWib EPfP EWes SWvt
§ ***parthenium***	CArn CBod CHab CHby CLau CPbn ENfk GPoy MHer MNHC NPer SIde SRms SVic WHer WJek XLum
- 'Aureum'	CBod CHid CPbn ECha ELan ENfk EWes GPoy LEdu LPot MBri MHer MLHP MNHC NPri SPer SPlb SRms SWvt WCot WHer WJek WMoo XLum
- double white-flowered (d)	NPer SRms
- 'Golden Ball'	EPfP
- 'Golden Moss'	XLum
- 'Plenum' (d)	MNrw
§ - 'Rowallane' (d)	MMuc SEND WCot
- 'Sissinghurst White'	see *T. parthenium* 'Rowallane'

	- 'Snowball' (d)	EPfP
	poteriifolium	EBee LRHS MAvo
	ptarmiciflorum 'Silver Feather'	SRms SVen
*	***tommansii***	EBee LRHS
	vulgare	CArn CHab CHby CLau CMac ECha ECtt ENfk GPoy LCro MHer MNHC SIde SRms SVic WJek WMoo WSFF XSen
	- 'All Gold'	SMad SRms
	- var. ***crispum***	CLau CPrp EBee ENfk MHer MNHC MRav SIde SMad SRms WJek
	- 'Gold Sticks'	CBod
	- 'Golden Fleece'	EBee ECtt EWes LEdu LRHS LSou NSti SPer WCot WGrn
	- 'Isla Gold' (v)	ECtt EWes LEdu LHop LPla MHer MMuc MRav SEND WCot WHil WMoo
	- 'Silver Lace' (v)	CBre EBee EWes NBid WHer WJek WMoo

Tanakaea (*Saxifragaceae*)

	radicans	GEdr WCru
	- B&SWJ 11407	WCru

tangelo see *Citrus* × *aurantium* Tangelo Group

tangerine see *Citrus reticulata* Tangerine Group

tangor see *Citrus* × *aurantium* Tangor Group

Taraxacum (*Asteraceae*)

	faeroense	NWad WCot
	officinale agg.	CHab
	- 'Nettleton'	CNat
	rubrifolium	CBre EPPr

tarragon see *Artemisia dracunculus*

Tasmannia (*Winteraceae*)

§	***lanceolata***	Widely available
	- (f)	EUJe SPer WPat
	- (m)	CDoC SPer WPat
	- 'Mount Wellington'	GCal
	- 'Red Spice'	EPfP ESwi LSRN
	- 'Suzette' (v)	LRHS MBlu SRms

Taxodium ✿ (*Cupressaceae*)

	ascendens 'Nutans'	see *T. distichum* var. *imbricarium* 'Nutans'
	distichum ♀H5	Widely available
	- 'Cascade Falls'	CDul LRHS MBlu MGos NLar SAko SLim
	- 'Falling Waters'	CBcs SGol SKHP
	- 'Gee Wiz'	SLim
	- var. ***imbricarium***	CMCN EPfP
§	- - 'Nutans'	CBcs EPfP IArd LRHS MBlu SGol SLim WMat
	- 'Little Leaf'	SMad
	- 'Minaret'	MBlu
*	- 'Pendulum'	IDee
	- 'Peve Minaret'	CMen LRHS MGos NLar SAko SCob SGol SKHP SLim SPoG
	- 'Peve Yellow'	MBlu SLim
	- 'Schloss Herten'	SLim
	- 'Secrest'	MBlu
	- Shawnee Brave = 'Mickelson'	MBlu
	mucronatum	CDoC CExl CFil
	- NJM 09.037	WPGP

Taxus ✿ (*Taxaceae*)

	sp.	ETod LPar
	baccata ♀H6	Widely available
	- 'Adpressa Variegata' (m/v)	CDoC
	- 'Aldenham Gold'	CKen
	- 'Amersfoort'	CDoC NLar
	- 'Argentea Minor'	see *T. baccata* 'Dwarf White'
	- Aurea Group	CDul ELan LPar SRms
I	- 'Aureomarginata' (v)	CBcs MAsh NEgg SWvt
	- 'Autumn Shades'	CBcs NLar
	- 'Bridget's Gold'	CKen
	- 'Corleys Coppertip'	CKen EBtc MBri MRav NLar SEND SLim
	- 'Cristata'	CKen MBlu NLar
	- 'David'	IArd LRHS MGos NLar SPoG SWvt
	- 'Dovastoniana' (f)	CMac NLar NWea
	- 'Dovastonii Aurea' (m/v)	CBcs GKin MBlu MBri NLar NWea SGol SLim
	- 'Drinkstone Gold' (v)	SLim
§	- 'Dwarf White' (v)	NLar
	- 'Elegantissima' (f/v)	CTho EFry EPfP NEgg NWea SCoo SLim
§	- 'Fastigiata' (f) ♀H6	CBcs CDul CLet CMac CNWT CSBt CTho CTri CWib EFry ELan EPfP EUJe LAst LPar MGos MRav MSwo NEgg NOrn NWea SCob SEWo SGol SPer SPoG SRms SWvt WHar WMat
	- Fastigiata Aurea Group	CLnd CMac CWib EPfP IArd LPar LRHS MAsh MGos MJak NLar NOrn SCob SGol SRms WHar
	- 'Fastigiata Aureomarginata' (m/v) ♀H6	CDoC CDul CMac CSBt CTri EPfP LBee LRHS MBri MGos NWea SCoo SLim SLon SPer SPoG SWvt
	- 'Fastigiata Robusta' (f)	CDoC CSBt EBtc ELan EPfP LRHS MAsh MBri MGos MJak NLar SCoo SLim SPoG WGor WMat
	- 'Goldener Zwerg' **new**	MBlu
	- 'Great Column' **new**	MBlu
	- 'Green Column'	CKen MMuc
	- 'Green Diamond'	CKen MBlu
	- 'Green Rocket'	CDul
	- 'Hibernica'	see *T. baccata* 'Fastigiata'
	- 'Icicle' ♀H6	CBcs MAsh NHol NLar NWad
	- 'Itsy Bitsy'	CKen
	- 'Ivory Tower'	CBcs CDoC CKen ELan LRHS NHol NLar NWad SLim
	- 'Jack's Gold' **new**	NLar
	- 'Klitzeklein'	CKen
	- 'Micro'	CKen MAsh
	- 'Nutans'	CDoC CKen
	- 'Prostrata'	CMac
	- 'Pygmaea'	CKen
	- 'Repandens' (f) ♀H6	CDul IArd NWea
I	- 'Repens Aurea' (v) ♀H6	CDoC CDul CKen CMac EFry LAst MBri NLar SCoo SLim
	- 'Rushmore'	NLar
	- 'Semperaurea' (m) ♀H6	CBcs CDoC CMac EFry LBuc MAsh MBri NLar NWea SCoo SGol SLim SPoG
	- 'Standishii' (f) ♀H6	Widely available
	- 'Stove Pipe'	CKen
	- 'Summergold' (v)	EFry ELan LRHS MGos MRav NBir NLar SCoo SLim
	brevifolia	NLar
	cuspidata	CMen LPar
	- 'Aurescens' (v)	CKen NLar
	- 'Minuet'	CKen
	- 'Straight Hedge'	SLim

× ***media*** new LPar
- 'Hicksii' (f) CDul LBuc NWea SGol
- 'Hillii' LBuc
- 'Lodi' LBee
- 'Nixe' SLim

tayberry see *Rubus* Tayberry Group

Tecoma (*Bignoniaceae*)

capensis ♀H1c CHll CRHN EBee SVen
- 'Lutea' EPfP
ricasoliana see *Podranea ricasoliana*

Tecomanthe (*Bignoniaceae*)

speciosa CRHN ECou

Tecomaria see *Tecoma*

Tecophilaea (*Tecophilaeaceae*)

cyanocrocus ♀H3 ECho EPot GKev LAma LLHF LRHS
- 'Leichtlinii' ♀H3 CAvo ECho EPot GKev LAma LLHF LRHS SDeJ
- 'Purpurea' see *T. cyanocrocus* 'Violacea'
- Storm Cloud Group ECho EPot GKev LLHF
§ - 'Violacea' CAvo ECho EPot GKev LLHF LRHS
violiflora ECho

Telekia (*Asteraceae*)

§ ***speciosa*** CCon CMac CSam CSpe ELan EPPr EPfP GAbr GLog MBel MMuc NBro NChi NLar NSti SDix SPlb WBrk WHer WHoo WMoo WWEG

Telephium (*Molluginaceae*)

imperati SBrt

Telesonix see *Boykinia*

Teline see *Genista*

Tellima (*Saxifragaceae*)

grandiflora Widely available
- 'Bob's Choice' WCot
- 'Delphine' (v) EPPr EWld WCot XLum
- 'Forest Frost' CBod CFis CMac EHoe ELan EPPr EShb LAst LRHS MBNS MPnt NLar SCob SWvt WCAu WCot WGwG WHoo WMoo WOut
- Odorata Group CBre ECha EHrv WCot WMoo
- 'Purpurea' see *T. grandiflora* Rubra Group
- 'Purpurteppich' CBod ECha EHrv EPPr LHop LRHS MPnt MRav SWvt WCot WMnd WMoo WPnP
§ - Rubra Group Widely available
- 'Silver Select' EPPr

Telopea (*Proteaceae*)

'Emperor's Torch' LRHS MPkF
oreades GGal SPlb
speciosissima CTre SPlb
truncata SPlb WCru

Templetonia (*Papilionaceae*)

retusa ECou

Temu see *Blepharocalyx*

Tephroseris (*Asteraceae*)

integrifolia subsp. ***capitata*** SPlb

Tephrosia (*Papilionaceae*)

virginiana EBee

Ternstroemia (*Pentaphylacaceae*)

chapaensis WWJ 11918 WCru
gymnanthera WCru
luteoflora WCru
FMWJ 13360 new

Tetracentron (*Trochodendraceae*)

sinense CBcs CMCN EPfP IArd NLar

Tetradenia (*Lamiaceae*)

riparia EOHP

Tetradium (*Rutaceae*)

austrosinense NJM 09.215 EBee WPGP
§ ***daniellii*** CBcs CDul CMCN CTho EPfP ESwi IArd LEdu LRHS SAko WHar WMat WPGP
§ - Hupehense Group CMCN CTho GBin MSnd NLar WPGP
fraxinifolium PAB 9101 LEdu
aff. ***fraxinifolium*** WWJ 11615 WCru
glabrifolium SAko
- B&SWJ 6882 WCru
- CWJ 12364 WCru
ruticarpum LEdu WPGP
- B&SWJ 3541 WCru

Tetragonolobus see *Lotus*

Tetraneuris (*Asteraceae*)

§ ***grandiflora*** SPlb WIce
scaposa EPot
torreyana CPBP

Tetrapanax (*Araliaceae*)

sp. ETod
§ ***papyrifer*** ♀H4 CBrP CDTJ CHGN ELan ESwi LPal NLos SBig SDix SEND SVen XBlo
- B&SWJ 7135 WCru
- 'Di-Sue-Shan' WCru
- 'Empress' WCru
- 'Rex' Widely available
- 'Steroidal Giant' CDTJ SBig SKHP

Tetrapathaea see *Passiflora*

Tetrastigma (*Vitaceae*)

obtectum EBee ECre ESwi EWes SEND WCFE
voinierianum ♀H1b WCot

Tetratheca (*Elaeocarpaceae*)

ciliata var. ***alba*** MOWG
thymifolia pink-flowered MOWG

Teucridium (*Lamiaceae*)

parvifolium ECou MPie

Teucrium (*Lamiaceae*)

* ***ackermannii*** ♀H5 CMea ECho MHer SBch SIgm WAbe WHoo XSen
arduinoi XSen
aroanium CTal ECho EPot SIgm XSen
asiaticum XSen
aureum XSen
botrys MHer

chamaedrys misapplied	see *T.* × *lucidrys*
chamaedrys L.	CBar CWib ELon ENfk GMaP GPoy LAst LRHS LSRN MCot MNHC MRav MSwo NWad SBod SCob SEND SIgm SLim SPer SPlb SRms SVen SWvt WBrk WHar WHfH WJek WWEG XSen
- 'Nanum'	ECho
- 'Rose'	SRms
- 'Summer Sunshine'	LRHS
dunense	XSen
flavum	CArn EBee EDAr EPPr GCal SBrt XSen
fruticans	Widely available
- 'Azureum' ♀H3	CBcs CBod CSde CTsd EBee ELan EPfP LAst LHop LRHS LSRN MRav SBrt SEND SMad SPer SPoG SWvt WCFE WHil WKif XSen
I - 'Azureum Compactum' **new**	CLet
- 'Compactum'	CDoC ELan EWTr LAst LSRN SLim SLon SPer SPoG SWvt WCFE WPGP WPnn
- 'Drysdale'	CDoC CSBt ELan LRHS SWvt
hircanicum	CAby CArn CSam ECha ECtt ELan GAbr IFro LLWP LRHS LSRN MMuc MNrw NBir SEND SPhx SRkn WCFE WMoo XSen
- 'Paradise Delight'	ECtt IKil NLar
- 'Purple Tails'	CBod CSpe CTsd CWib CWld EPfP GQue LSou MCot MHol MNHC MRav NBir WGwG
lamiifolium W&B BGB-7	WCot
§ × ***lucidrys***	CArn CChe CMea ECha ECrN ELan ENfk EPfP EWoo LPla LRHS MHer MNHC MPie SPer SPoG SRms SWvt WCFE WHar WHoo WJek WPnn XSen
- 'Lucky Gold' PBR	EBee LRHS SPoG
lucidum	GCal SLon
marum	CArn CTri LEdu SBrt SIgm SRms WJek XSen
massiliense misapplied	see *T.* × *lucidrys*
montanum	WJek XSen
musimonum	EPot SIgm
orientale	XSen
polium	ECho SPhx WThu XSen
pseudochamaepitys	XSen
pyrenaicum ♀H5	CMea CPBP ECho EPot EWes GEdr ITim SBch SIgm XSen
- subsp. ***guarense***	XSen
scorodonia	CArn CHab GPoy MCot MHer MNHC NLar NMir SRms WHer WJek XSen
- 'Binsted Gold'	EBee NSti
- 'Crispum'	CWld LEdu LRHS MHer MMuc NBro NLar SPer SRms WGrn WJek WKif WMnd WMoo WOut
- 'Crispum Marginatum' (v)	CFis EBee ECGP ECha EHoe EPPr EPfP EWld IKil LEdu LSou MNrw MRav WWEG
- 'Winterdown' (v)	EBee LRHS SBch
subspinosum	ECho LLHF SIgm WHoo WThu
§ ***viscidum*** 'Lemon and Lime' (v)	EBee
webbianum	ECho

Thalia (*Marantaceae*)

dealbata	CBen EUJe EWay LLWG MSKA MWts NLar SBig SLon WMAq XLum

Thalictrum (*Ranunculaceae*)

CC 4576	CExl
Cox 6118	ITim
from Afghanistan	see *T. isopyroides*
actaeifolium	CLAP CWib
- B&SWJ 4664	WCru
- B&SWJ 6310	WCru
- var. ***brevistylum*** B&SWJ 8819	CDes WCru
- compact B&SWJ 4946	WCru
- 'Perfume Star'	CMos CPar ECtt GBin IPot MMHG NDov NLar SCob WCot
adiantifolium	see *T. minus* 'Adiantifolium'
alpinum	CTal EDAr EPPr GJos
angustifolium	see *T. lucidum*
'Anne' PBR	EBee ECtt EWTr IKil ILea IPot LRHS MNrw NLar WCot
aquilegiifolium	Widely available
- SDR 5463	GKev
- 'Album'	EBee ECha ELan EPfP GBin GCra GKin LAst LBMP LHop LRHS MBel MCot MMuc NBid SEND SKHP SPer SPhx SWvt WBor WCAu WFar WMnd WSHC
- 'Constable's Clouds'	EPPr
* - 'Hybridum'	SGSe WMoo
- var. ***intermedium*** B&SWJ 10965	WCru
- 'Purpureum'	NLar NQui WWtn
- var. ***sibiricum***	IMou
- - B&SWJ 11007	WCru
- 'Small Thundercloud'	GCal
- 'Thundercloud' ♀H5	Widely available
baicalense	EPPr
'Black Stockings'	CExl CKno CMac EBee ECtt ELan EPPr EPfP EShb EWoo GBin ILea IPot LRHS LSou MBel MCot MHol NDov NLar NPri SCob SKHP SMad SPad SPoG WCAu WHil
calabricum	NLar
chelidonii	EPPr NLar
- HWJK 2216	WCru
clavatum	CAby CLAP WPGP
coreanum	see *T. ichangense*
coriaceum	CEvo
cultratum	CDes EBee LRHS WPGP
dasycarpum	CEvo EPPr GJos WCot WPnP
§ ***delavayi*** ♀H7	Widely available
- BWJ 7800	WCru
- BWJ 7903	WCru
- var. ***acuminatum***	MBel
- - BWJ 7535	WCru
- - BWJ 7971	WCru
- 'Album'	Widely available
- 'Ankum'	CKno EBee MNrw NLar
- var. ***decorum***	CElw CLAP CWCL ECtt ELon EPPr MBel SHar SPad WCot WCru WPGP WSHC
- - BWJ 7770	WCru
- aff. var. ***decorum***	CExl
- 'Gold Laced'	NLar
- 'Hewitt's Double' (d) ♀H7	Widely available
- 'Hinkley'	NLar
- var. ***mucronatum***	WCru
- - DJHC 473	WCru
- purple-stemmed BWJ 7748	WCru
- 'White Cloud'	GBin

	Name	Suppliers
	aff. ***delavayi***	GKin IBoy MGos NDov
	diffusiflorum	IMou WAbe WCru WSHC
	dipterocarpum misapplied	see *T. delavayi*
	dipterocarpum Franch.	CMac EBee LRHS XLum
	'Elin'	Widely available
	fendleri	GBin
	- var. ***polycarpum***	EBee IMou WOut
	filamentosum	EPPr IMou
	- B&SWJ 777	WCru
	- B&SWJ 4145	WCru
	- var. ***yakusimense*** B&SWJ 6094	WCru
	aff. ***finetii*** DJHC 473	CLAP
	flavum	CHab CMac EHon ELan EWld GKin LLWG MSCN NBro NMir SPhx SWat WFar WShi
	- 'Chollerton'	see *T. isopyroides*
§	- subsp. ***glaucum*** ♀H7	Widely available
	- - dwarf	WPGP
	- - 'True Blue'	SGbt
	- 'Illuminator'	CElw CTri EPfP IBoy LRHS MArl MRav NLar WCot WFar
	flexuosum	see *T. minus* subsp. *minus*
	honanense	SKHP
	- BWJ 7962	WCru
	- 'Marble Leaf'	SKHP
§	***ichangense***	CBot CHid CSpe EPot EPri GEdr IPot LRHS MAvo MBel MHol MPie MTis NMyG NWad SDix SPad SPer WCot WRHF
	- B&SWJ 8203	WCru
	- Evening Star strain (v)	CAby CSpe ECtt GBin MHol SCob SPad SPoG
	- var. ***minus*** 'Chinese Chintz'	WCru
	- 'Purple Marble'	CWGN GEdr LEdu MSCN WCot
§	***isopyroides***	CCon CEvo EAEE EBee GCal GKev GKin LAst LRHS MHol MMuc MRav NLar NWad SEND SHar WCot
	javanicum	LEdu WPGP
	- B&SWJ 9506	WCru
	- PAB 9431 new	LEdu
	- var. ***puberulum*** B&SWJ 6770	WCru
	johnstonii B&SWJ 9127	WCru
	kiusianum	CAby CTal EBee ECha ECho EHoe ELan EWes GCra ITim LRHS LSun MBel MHer MHol MPie NBir NLar NSla SKHP SRot SWvt WAbe WCot WFar XEll
	- Kew form	WSHC
	koreanum	see *T. ichangense*
§	***lucidum***	CDoC CElw CExl EBee ECtt EHoe ELan EShb GBin GCal GKin IMou LEdu LPla LRHS MHol MMuc MPie MTis NGBl NLar NSti SDix SEND SKHP SPhx WCot
	minus	CArn GBin LEdu LRHS MMuc SEND
§	- 'Adiantifolium'	GBin GJos IPot MBel MRav NGdn NLar SHar SRms XLum
	- var. ***hypoleucum*** B&SWJ 8634	WCru
	- subsp. ***kemense***	EBee
§	- subsp. ***minus***	GJos NBre
	- var. ***sipellatum*** B&SWJ 5051	WCru
	morisonii	EBee LRHS NBid
	omeiense BWJ 8049	WCru
	- DJHC 762	CDes
	orientale	EBee LRHS
	osmundifolium	WCru
	petaloideum	EPPr
	platycarpum B&SWJ 2261	WCru
	polygamum	see *T. pubescens* Pursh
	przewalskii	WCru
§	***pubescens*** Pursh	EBee ECha ECtt GBin GJos GMaP LRHS NDov NLar SHar SPhx
	punctatum B&SWJ 1272	WCru
	ramosum BWJ 8126	CEvo WCru
	reniforme	EBee WCot
	- B&SWJ 2610	WCru
	- GWJ 9311	WCru
	- HWJK 2403	WCru
	rochebrunianum	Widely available
	rubescens B&SWJ 10006	WCru
	rugosum	EBee LRHS
	sachalinense	CCon WOut WPGP
	- RBS 0279	EBee EPPr NLar
	shensiense	CExl
	simplex var. ***brevipes*** B&SWJ 4794	WCru
	speciosissimum	see *T. flavum* subsp. *glaucum*
*	***sphaerostachyum***	CElw EBee ECtt EPPr LRHS MBel MNrw MPie MWhi WHal
	'Splendide'	CAby CDoC CExl CSpe EBee ECtt ELan ELon EPfP EWTr GBin IMou IPot LPla LRHS MAvo MBel MHol MNrw MSCN MTis NDov NEgg NLar SMad STPC WCot WHil
	'Splendide White'	CMos CSpe ECtt IPot LRHS MCot NDov NLar SHar STPC
	squarrosum	CDes EBee WPGP
	tenuisubulatum BWJ 7929	WCru
	tuberosum	CElw CSpe LLHF WCot
	- 'Rosy Hardy'	SHar
	tubiferum B&SWJ 10999	WCru
	'Tukker Princess'	EBee ECtt GBin IKil ILea LHop MBel MHol NLar WCot
	uchiyamae	CDes EBee GBin GJos WCot WPGP
	urbainii B&SWJ 7085	WCru
	- 'Taiwan Baika' new	CEvo
	'Yubari Mountains'	GEdr
	yunnanense	WCru

Thamnocalamus (*Poaceae*)

	Name	Suppliers
	crassinodus	SBig
	- 'Gosainkund'	CEnt ERod MWht
	- 'Kew Beauty' ♀H3	CAbb CDTJ CDoC CEnt EPfP ERod MBrN MWht SBig WCot WJun WPGP
	- 'Langtang'	CEnt ERod MWht WJun WPGP
	- 'Merlyn'	CDoC CEnt EPfP ERod MWht WJun WPGP
	falconeri	see *Himalayacalamus falconeri*
	khasianus	see *Drepanostachyum khasianum*
	maling	see *Yushania maling*
	spathaceus misapplied	see *Fargesia murielae*
§	***spathiflorus***	CEnt WJun
	- subsp. ***nepalensis***	ERod MWht SBig
	tessellatus	see *Bergbambos tessellata*

Thamnochortus (*Restionaceae*)

	Name	Suppliers
	cinereus	CTre LRHS
	insignis ♀H2	CSpe CTre MPkF SPlb
	lucens	SPlb

Thapsia (*Apiaceae*)

decipiens — see *Melanoselinum decipiens*
villosa — CArn

Thea see *Camellia*

Thelypteris (*Thelypteridaceae*)

dentata — SGSe
kunthii — EBee ISha
limbosperma — see *Oreopteris limbosperma*
noveboracensis — see *Parathelypteris novae-boracensis*
ovata var. **lindheimeri** — ISha
palustris — CKel EBee EShb NLar SRms WFib WPnP XLum
phegopteris — see *Phegopteris connectilis*

Themeda (*Poaceae*)

japonica — SGSe
triandra — SMad

Thermopsis (*Papilionaceae*)

caroliniana — see *T. villosa*
chinensis — CLet EAJP EBee ELon LRHS MHer MMuc SBea SEND WBor WTcb
fabacea — see *T. lupinoides*
lanceolata — CMea CTri EBee ELon EPfP LRHS MMuc NQui NSti SEND SHar SPad WCot WFar WKif
§ **lupinoides** — ECha EHrv
macrophylla — EBee
mollis — CExl NBid WTcb
montana — see *T. rhombifolia* var. *montana*
§ **rhombifolia** var. **montana** — CBod CWCL EAEE EBee EHrv ELan EPfP GAbr GCra GMaP LHop LRHS MMuc NBir NCGa NPol NSti NWad SEND SGSe SPer SPoG WBor WTcb WWEG
§ **villosa** — CAbP CWCL ELon LRHS MRav NGdn NLar SMHy WCot WFar WHoo WWEG

Therorhodion see *Rhododendron*

Thladiantha (*Cucurbitaceae*)

dubia — EBee SDix WCot

Thlaspi (*Brassicaceae*)

sp. — NGdn
biebersteinii — see *Pachyphragma macrophyllum*
§ **cepaeifolium** subsp. **rotundifolium** — GEdr GKev WAbe
densiflorum — GEdr
rotundifolium — see *T. cepaeifolium* subsp. *rotundifolium*
zaffrani — GEdr WAbe

Thryptomene (*Myrtaceae*)

saxicola — ECou

Thuja ✿ (*Cupressaceae*)

sp. — LPar
'Extra Gold' — see *T. plicata* 'Irish Gold'
§ **koraiensis** — NLar SLim
occidentalis — NWea SEND
- 'Amber Glow' — CDoC CKen CSBt MAsh NHol NLar NWad SCoo SLim SPoG WGor
- 'Anniek'[PBR] — CKen SPoG
- 'Aureospicata' — EFry
- 'Bateman Broom' — CKen
- 'Beaufort' (v) — CKen
- 'Brabant' 🏆H6 — CDul LPar MGos MJak NLar NPri NWea SCob SCoo SLim
- 'Brobeck's Tower' 🏆H6 — CDoC CKen NLar SLim
- 'Caespitosa' — CKen
- 'Danica' 🏆H6 — CMac EFry GKin IBoy LCro MAsh MBri MGos MJak NOrn NWea SCob SCoo SLim SPoG SRms WCFE
- 'Danica Gold' **new** — SLim
- 'Degroot's Spire' — CKen NLar SLim
- 'Douglasii Aurea' (v) — CKen
- Emerald — see *T. occidentalis* 'Smaragd'
- 'Ericoides' — CDoC EFry SRms
- 'Europa Gold' 🏆H6 — NLar SGol
- 'Fastigiata' — WMou
- 'Filiformis' — CKen
- 'Filips Magic Moment'[PBR] **new** — SPoG
- 'Globosa' — ELan
I - 'Globosa Variegata' (v) — CKen
- 'Gold Drop' — CKen
- 'Golden Anne' — WGor
- 'Golden Globe' — CDoC EFry IBoy MGos MJak SCoo SLim
- 'Golden Minaret' — EFry
- Golden Smaragd = 'Janed Gold'[PBR] — CCVT SLim SPoG
- 'Golden Tuffet' 🏆H6 — CDoC CKen EFry ELan GKin LBee MBri MPkF NLar NWad SCob SCoo SLim SPer SPoG WGor
- 'Hetz Midget' 🏆H6 — CKen EFry GKin IBoy LAst MBri NLar NWad SCob SCoo SLim SPlb WGor
- 'Holmstrup' 🏆H6 — CDoC CDul CMac CWib EFry MAsh MBri MGos NOrn SGol SLim SRms
- 'Hoveyi' — CTri EFry
- 'Jantar'[PBR] — NLar
- 'Linesville' — CKen
- 'Little Champion' — EFry IBoy
- 'Little Gem' — EFry SRms
- 'Lutea Nana' — EFry
- 'Malonyana Holub' — SLim
- 'Marrisen's Sulphur' — CDoC EFry
- 'Meineke's Zwerg' (v) — CKen
- 'Mirjam'[PBR] (v) — CKen SPoG WGor
- 'Mr Bowling Ball' — CDoC NLar
- 'Ohlendorffii' — CKen
- 'Perk Vlaanderen' (v) — LRHS
I - 'Pygmaea' — CKen
- 'Pyramidalis Aurea' — ECrN
- 'Pyramidalis Compacta' — EFry
- 'Recurva Nana' — NWad
- 'Rheingold' 🏆H6 — Widely available
§ - 'Smaragd' 🏆H6 — CCVT CDoC CDul CSBt CWib EFry ELan EPfP IBoy LAst LBuc LCro LRHS MAsh MBri MGos MJak NLar NOrn NWea SCob SCoo SGol SLim SPoG SWvt WCFE WMou
* - 'Smaragd Variegated' (v) — CKen
- 'Smokey' — CKen
- 'Spiralis' — EFry NLar WCFE
- 'Starstruck' **new** — SPoG
§ - 'Stolwijk' (v) — EFry
- 'Sunkist' 🏆H6 — CKen CMac COtt CWib EFry LAst MAsh MBri MGos MJak NEgg SCoo SGol WGor
- 'Teddy' — EFry EPfP LBee MAsh MBri MGos NHol SCoo SPoG

- 'Tiny Tim'	CDoC CMac CWib EFry IBoy MBri MGos SGol
- 'Trompenburg'	CDoC EFry NLar
- 'Wansdyke Silver' (v)	CMac EFry
- 'Wareana'	CMac
- 'Wareana Aurea'	see *T. occidentalis* 'Wareana Lutescens'
§ - 'Wareana Lutescens'	CWib
- 'Waterfield'	NLar NWad
- 'Yellow Ribbon'	CDul CKen CSBt EFry MJak SCob SGol
orientalis	see *Platycladus orientalis*
- 'Miller's Gold'	see *Platycladus orientalis* 'Aurea Nana'
plicata	CBcs CCVT CDul CMac CTho EFry ELan EPfP LPar NBes NWea SCob SPer WHar WMou
- 'Atrovirens' ♀H6	CDul CLet CTri ECrN LBee LBuc LCro LRHS MAsh MBri MGos MMuc SCob SCoo SEND SEWo SGol SRms SWvt WHar WMat WMou
- 'Aurea' ♀H6	EFry MAsh SRms
- 'Can-can' (v)	ELan MAsh
I - 'Cole's Variety'	CWib MMuc
- 'Collyer's Gold'	CDul EFry SRms
- 'Copper Kettle'	CKen EFry GKin LRHS SLim
- 'Cuprea'	CKen EFry
- 'Doone Valley'	CKen EFry NWad
- 'Emerald'PBR	EUJe
- 'Excelsa'	CDul
- 'Fastigiata'	CDul
- 'Gelderland' ♀H6	EFry ELan EPfP NEgg SCoo SLim
- Goldy = '4ever'PBR	CDoC MBri SLim SPoG
- 'Hillieri'	CDoC CDul
- 'Holly Turner'	SLim
§ - 'Irish Gold' (v)	CDul CMac SLim SMad
- 'Martin'	CJun SWvt
- 'Rogersii' ♀H6	CDoC CKen CMac EFry MAsh NHol SCoo SRms WThu
- 'Semperaurescens' (v)	CMac
- 'Stolwijk's Gold'	see *T. occidentalis* 'Stolwijk'
- 'Stoneham Gold' ♀H6	CDoC CMac EFry GKin MAsh MGos MMuc SEND SRms WCFE
- Verigold = 'Courtapli'	CCVT MMuc SEND
- 'Whipcord' ♀H6	CBcs CKen EFry ELan EPfP EUJe LRHS MPkF NHol NLar SCoo SLim SPoG WBor
* - 'Windsor Gold'	EFry
- 'Winter Pink' (v)	CKen
- 'Zebrina' (v) ♀H6	CBcs CDoC CDul CMac CTri CWib EFry ELan EPfP LRHS MAsh MGos MMuc NLar NPri NWea SCob SCoo SEND SLim SPoG SWvt WHar
standishii	WThu

Thujopsis (*Cupressaceae*)

dolabrata ♀H6	CBcs CDul EFry GKin MMuc NEgg NWea SEND SWvt
- 'Aurea' (v)	CDoC CKen EFry LRHS NLar SLim
- var. ***hondae***	IArd SLim
- 'Laetevirens'	see *T. dolabrata* 'Nana'
§ - 'Nana'	CDoC CKen CMac EFry LRHS MGos NLar SLim SRms
- 'Variegata' (v)	CMac EFry GKin NLar SLim
koraiensis (Nakai) hort.	see *Thuja koraiensis*

Thunbergia (*Acanthaceae*)

alata	EPfP SPoG
- 'African Sunset'	CSpe EShb
- 'Lemon Queen'	CHll SWvt
- 'Orange Beauty'	LBuc LSou SWvt
battiscombeii	EShb MOWG
erecta	MOWG
fragrans GWJ 9441	WCru
grandiflora ♀H1a	CBcs CHll MOWG WSFF
- 'Alba'	CHll
gregorii ♀H1c	CHll EShb MOWG
laurifolia B&SWJ 7166	WCru
'Lemon Star'	LBuc
natalensis	EShb

thyme, caraway see *Thymus herba-barona*

thyme, garden see *Thymus vulgaris*

thyme, lemon see *Thymus citriodorus*

thyme, wild see *Thymus serpyllum*

Thymus ✿ (*Lamiaceae*)

from Albania	CArn
from Turkey	EWes LEdu SHDw
'A Touch of Frost'	SHDw
§ 'Alan Bloom'	LRHS
'Albus'	CBod ENfk
'Anderson's Gold'	see *T. pulegioides* 'Bertram Anderson'
'Aureus' ambig.	MJak
azoricus	see *T. caespititius*
'Bressingham'	CArn CBod CMea CTri ECtt EDAr GCrg GMaP LEdu LLWP LRHS MHer MMuc MNHC NDov NYoL SEND SPlb SRms WIce WJek
'Caborn Fragrant Cloud'	LLWP
'Caborn Grey Lady'	LLWP
'Caborn Lilac Gem'	LLWP SHDw
'Caborn Pink Carpet'	LLWP
'Caborn Royale'	LLWP
'Caborn Wine and Roses'	ENfk LLWP SRms WJek
§ ***caespititius***	CArn GCrg GPoy MHer NRya NYoL SPlb SRms SRot WJek
caespitosus	CTri LEdu
camphoratus	ENfk ESwi EWes GCrg MHer SPhx WJek
capitatus	CArn
§ ***carnosus*** Boiss.	MHer NYoL WJek XSen
'Carol Ann' (v)	ENfk EWes MNHC NYoL SRms
cephalotos	WAbe
ciliatus	CBod XSen
cilicicus misapplied	see *T. caespititius*
cilicicus ambig.	MNHC SRms
cilicicus Boiss. & Bail.	WAbe
citriodorus misapplied	see *T.* 'Culinary Lemon'
citriodorus ambig.	CTal CTsd MMuc NDov SBod SRms XLum
citriodorus (Pers.) Schreb.	LEdu NYoL
- 'Archer's Gold'	see *T. pulegioides* 'Archer's Gold'
- 'Aureus'	see *T. pulegioides* 'Aureus'
- 'Bertram Anderson'	see *T. pulegioides* 'Bertram Anderson'
- 'Silver Posie'	see *T.* 'Silver Posie'
'Coccineus'	see *T.* Coccineus Group
'Coccineus Major'	CMea EDAr LRHS MHer MNHC SCob SRms WJek
§ Coccineus Group ♀H5	Widely available
- 'Atropurpureus' Schleipfer	see *T.* 'Purple Beauty'
§ - 'Purple Beauty'	EPot GCrg LRHS MHer SHDw SRms

§ - 'Red Elf'	CBod GAbr GCrg MHer NYoL
comosus misapplied	CBod NYoL SHDw
'Creeping Lemon' misapplied	see *T. pulegioides* 'Kurt'
§ 'Culinary Lemon'	CArn CHby CLau EDAr ENfk GPoy MBrN MHer MNHC NPri NYoL WJek XLum XSen
'Dark Eyes'	SHDw
'Dartmoor'	CBod SHDw WJek
'Desboro'	see *T. serpyllum* 'Desborough'
'Dillington'	ENfk
doerfleri	NYoL XSen
'Doone Valley' (v)	Widely available
drucei	see *T. polytrichus* subsp. *britannicus*
'E.B.Anderson'	see *T. pulegioides* 'Bertram Anderson'
'Eastgrove Pink'	SHDw
'Elfin Pink Carpet' **new**	MHol
erectus	see *T. carnosus*
'Fragrantissimus'	CArn CLau ENfk GPoy LLWP MHer MNHC NPri SIde SPlb WJek WOut XSen
'Golden King' (v)	ECha EDAr ELan ENfk LHop LSRN MAsh MBri MHer MMuc SRms
'Golden Lemon' misapplied	see *T. pulegioides* 'Aureus'
'Golden Lemon' (v)	WJek
'Golden Queen' (v)	CBod EDAr MHol NPri NYoL SRms
'Gratian'	SHDw
§ 'Hartington Silver' (v)	CBod ECha ECho ECtt ENfk EPot EWes GCrg GKev LAst LBMP LEdu LHop LRHS MAsh MHer MMuc NPri NRya NYoL SBod SPlb SPoG SRms WHoo WJek
herba-barona	CArn CBod CLau CMea CTri EDAr ENfk GPoy LEdu LLWP MHer MNHC NYoL SIde SRms WJek
- ***citrata***	see *T. herba-barona* 'Lemon-scented'
§ - 'Lemon-scented'	CBod ECha GPoy LEdu LLWP MHer NYoL SHDw SRms WJek
'Highdown'	ECtt SHDw
'Highdown Adur'	SHDw
'Highdown Lemon'	SHDw
'Highdown Red'	SHDw
'Highdown Stretham'	SHDw
'Highland Cream'	see *T.* 'Hartington Silver'
hirsutus	XSen
hyemalis	GPoy
§ 'Iden'	CBod WJek
'Jekka'	CBod SRms WJek
'Kurt'	see *T. pulegioides* 'Kurt'
'Lavender Sea'	EWes
'Lemon Caraway'	see *T. herba-barona* 'Lemon-scented'
'Lemon Curd'	CLau ENfk LLWP MNHC NHol NYoL SHDw SPlb SPoG SRms WJek
'Lemon Sorbet'	SHDw
* 'Lemon Variegated' (v)	CLau EDAr ENfk EPfP MNHC NYoL SPer SPoG
leucotrichus	XSen
'Lilac Time'	ECtt ENfk EWes LEdu LLWP MHer SHDw SPlb SRms WJek
'Lime'	LEdu
linearis	XSen
longicaulis	CBod CLau ECha LLWP MHer SRms
'Magic Carpet'	MAvo SPhx
marschallianus	see *T. pannonicus*
§ 'Massa'	SHDw
mastichina	SPhx XSen
- 'Didi'	MHer
membranaceus	WAbe
micans	see *T. caespititius*
minus	see *Calamintha nepeta*
'Mountain Select'	SHDw
neiceffii	CMea ECha SBch XSen
'Orange'	CBod LEdu SRms
§ Orange Spice = 'Tm95'	SHDw XSen
pallasianus	CLau SHDw
§ ***pannonicus***	MHer NYoL
'Peter Davis'	CBod ENfk LHop LRHS LSRN MHer NBir NYoL SIde SPoG SRms WAbe WIce WTor XSen
§ 'Pinewood'	CTal LEdu MHer WJek XSen
'Pink Ripple'	CBod CLau CMea CTal ECtt ENfk EWes LEdu LLWP MHer MNHC NPri SHDw SIgm SRms WHal WHoo WJek
polytrichus misapplied	see *T. praecox*
§ ***polytrichus*** A. Kern ex Borbás subsp. ***britannicus***	CArn CBod CTri ECha GEdr GJos GMaP GPoy LEdu MBNS MBri MHer MLHP MMuc MNHC NBir NPri NYoL SEND SHDw SPlb SRms WHoo WJek XLum
§ - - 'Thomas's White' 🏆H5	CTri NYoL
'Porlock'	CBod CLau CMea CSam CTri EPfP GPoy MHer NPri NYoL SRms WHoo WJek
§ ***praecox***	CBod CWld EWoo GJos MHer NMir
- 'Albiflorus'	EWoo MRav NPri
- subsp. ***arcticus***	see *T. polytrichus* subsp. *britannicus*
- - 'Albus'	see *T. polytrichus* subsp. *britannicus* 'Thomas's White'
prostrate	CBod
pulegioides	CArn CBod CHby CLau CPrp ENfk GPoy LLWP MBri MHer MNHC MSCN NYoL SHDw SIde SRms WJek
§ - 'Archer's Gold'	CBar CLau CTri ECtt EDAr EHoe ENfk EPfP EPot GJos GKev LEdu LHop LLWP LPot LRHS LSRN MAsh MBri MHer MHol MNHC MRav NBir NHol NWad NYoL SCob SRms WJek
§ - 'Aureus' 🏆H5	CBod ENfk GMaP LCro LLWP MAsh MBri MMuc SPer SPlb SRms WHoo WJek
§ - 'Bertram Anderson' 🏆H5	CBod CMea CTal ECha ECtt ENfk EPfP GCrg GMaP LAst LLWP MAsh MCot MHer MMuc NBir NRya NYoL SCob SEND SPer SPoG SRms WAbe WHoo WJek
- 'Elliott's Gold' **new**	LBMP
- 'Foxley' (v)	CBod CLau EHoe ENfk EPfP GAbr LLWP MHer MMuc MNHC NPri NYoL SEND SHDw SIde SPlb SPoG SRms WJek
§ - 'Kurt'	CBod ENfk LEdu LLWP MHer SHDw SRms WJek
- 'Sir John Lawes'	MHer
- 'Tabor'	CBod ENfk MNHC NYoL SHDw SRms

'Rainbow Falls' (v)	EPfP MNHC NYoL SHDw SRms
'Rasta' (v)	MHer
'Redstart'	CBod ECha ECtt ENfk LEdu LLWP MHer NYoL SHDw SRms WJek
richardii subsp. ***nitidus*** 'Compactus Albus'	see *T. vulgaris* 'Snow White'
'Rosa Ceeping'	SHDw
'Rosalicht'	see *T.* 'Rosedrift'
§ 'Rosedrift'	SHDw
rotundifolius misapplied	see *T. vulgaris* 'Elsbeth'
'Ruby Glow'	ECtt EWes GCrg MHer SHDw
serpyllum ambig.	EWoo NPri SCob SVic XLum
serpyllum L.	CArn GJos LBuc MBri MMuc SPlb SRms WJek
- var. ***albus***	CTal ECha GMaP GPoy LAst LLWP LRHS MNHC SPer SRms WHoo WJek
- 'Albus Variegatus'	see *T.* 'Hartington Silver'
- 'Annie Hall'	CBod CTal EDAr EPfP EPot LHop LLWP LRHS MAsh MNHC SRms WJek
- 'Atropurpureus'	see *T.* (Coccineus Group) 'Purple Beauty'
- ***coccineus*** 'Minor' misapplied	see *T.* Coccineus Group
- - 'Minor' Bloom	see *T.* 'Alan Bloom'
- 'Conwy Rose'	CPBP WAbe
§ - 'Desborough'	MHer
- 'East Lodge'	LLWP MNHC SRms
- 'Elfin'	ECho EWes EWoo GCrg MBri MRav SPlb WAbe
- 'Goldstream' (v)	CBod CMea ENfk LEdu LHop LRHS MBri MHer NYoL SPlb SRms WJek
- 'Iden'	see *T.* 'Iden'
- 'Minimalist'	see *T. serpyllum* 'Minor'
- 'Minimus'	see *T. serpyllum* 'Minor'
§ - 'Minor'	CArn CMea CTal CTri ECha ECtt ENfk GCrg LLWP LRHS MBri MHer MLHP MMuc MNHC NRya NSla NYoL SEND SPlb SRms SRot WAbe WHoo WJek
- 'Minus'	see *T. serpyllum* 'Minor'
- 'Pink Chintz' ♀H5	CArn CBod ECha ECtt EDAr ENfk EPfP EPot GEdr GMaP GPoy LCro LEdu LLWP LOPS LRHS MBri MHer MNHC NYoL SPer SPlb SPoG SRms WIce WJek
- 'Posh Pinky'	CPBP
- 'Purple Beauty'	see *T.* (Coccineus Group) 'Purple Beauty'
- 'Red Carpet'	ECtt GCrg NPri NWad NYoL
- 'Red Elf'	see *T.* (Coccineus Group) 'Red Elf'
- 'Russetings'	CBod CTsd CWld ECtt ENfk EPfP EWoo LEdu MHer MNHC NYoL SCob SIde SPoG SRms WJek
- 'September'	MHer
- 'Snowdrift'	CArn CMea ECtt EPfP LEdu LLWP MHer MNHC NWad SIde SPlb SRms WCFE WJek
- 'Variegatus'	see *T.* 'Hartington Silver'
- 'Vey'	CBod CTal EWes LHop LRHS MHer SHDw SRms WJek
'Silver King' (v)	ENfk
§ 'Silver Posie'	Widely available
'Silver Queen' (v) ♀H5	CBcs CSam ECha EDAr ELan ENfk EPfP GCrg GKev GMaP LAst MCot MHer MNHC NHol NPri NYoL SCob SPer SPlb SRms WJek
'Spicy Orange'	see *T.* Orange Spice
striatus	LEdu
valesiacus	see *T.* 'Massa'
§ ***vulgaris***	Widely available
* - 'Compactus'	ENfk GPoy LEdu LLWP MHer MNHC MRav SPhx SRms WCAu WJek
- 'Deutsche Auslese'	see *T. vulgaris*
- 'Dorcas White'	MHer
§ - 'Elsbeth'	CLau LLWP MHer
- English, winter **new**	SRms
- French	see *T. vulgaris*
- 'Golden Pins'	MHer
- 'Lemon Queen'	CLau
- 'Lucy'	LLWP MHer
- 'Pinewood'	see *T.* 'Pinewood'
§ - 'Snow White'	CLau EWes WJek
'Widecombe' (v)	SHDw
zygioides	SIgm

Tiarella ✿ (*Saxifragaceae*)

'Appalachian Trail'	CBcs CBod EBee ECtt GBin LBMP LCro LSou MAvo MHol MPnt NWad SHeu SPoG WCot WNPC
'Black Snowflake'	MPnt SHeu
'Black Velvet'	MBel MPnt SHeu
'Braveheart'	EPfP LHop MPnt SHeu SPoG WNPC
'Butter and Sugar'	MPnt
'Butterfly Wings'	MPnt
'Candy Striper'	ECtt MPnt NCGa SHeu
'Cascade Creeper'PBR	ECtt LAst LRHS LSou MPnt NWad SHeu WNPC
collina	see *T. wherryi*
cordifolia ♀H5	Widely available
- 'Glossy'	CCon MPnt
- 'Milk Chocolate'	MPnt
- 'Oakleaf'	CCon MPnt NBro SHeu
- 'Rosalie'	see × *Heucherella alba* 'Rosalie'
- 'Running Tapestry'	MPnt SHeu
- 'Slick Rock'	EPPr
'Crow Feather'PBR	CNec MPnt NWad SHeu SPoG WNPC
'Cygnet'	CLAP ECtt MPnt SHeu SRot
'Dunvegan'	MPnt
'Elizabeth Oliver'	MPnt
'Freckles'	MRav
'Happy Trails'PBR	EBee MPnt NWad SHeu WCot WNPC
'Hidden Carpet'	CHid
'Inkblot'	ELan LRHS MPnt NBro SHeu WMoo
'Iron Butterfly'PBR (v)	CAby CLAP CMac CWCL EBee ECha ECtt EHoe EPfP EWoo GBin GMaP LAst LCro LRHS LSRN MBel MPnt MRav SCob SGbt SPer SPoG SRot
'Iron Cross'	SPlb
'Jeepers Creepers'PBR	CHid EBee ECha ECtt LBMP LRHS MJak MPnt NWad SHeu WNPC
'Martha Oliver'	CCon CLAP EBee MPnt
'Mint Chocolate'	CLAP EAEE ECtt EHoe EHrv ELan GMaP LPot LRHS MNrw MPnt MRav NBir NGdn NLar SHeu SWvt
'Moorgrün'	EPPr GCal SHeu
Morning Star = 'Tntia042'PBR	CBod CHid ECtt MPnt SHeu SRkn SRot WHoo
'Mystic Mist'PBR (v)	CHid CWGN EAEE ECtt LAst LBMP LRHS LSou MPnt MWhi NDov NWad SHeu SPoG WNPC

'Neon Lights'PBR	CHid ECtt ELan MPnt NBir NWad SCob SHeu SWvt WNPC
§ 'Ninja'	CHid ECtt EHrv ELan EUJe GMaP LRHS MPnt NBir NLar SPer SWvt
'Oregon Trail'	ECtt GBin MBel MNrw MPnt NWad SHeu WCot WNPC
'Pacific Crest'	EBee ECtt MPnt NWad SHeu WNPC
'Pink Bouquet'	CBct CLAP CMac CSpe EAEE ECtt EHrv ELan GJos IKil LSun MBel MBri MHol MPie MPnt NBro NDov NLar SBch SBod SHeu WCot WGwG WMoo WPnP
'Pink Brushes'PBR	CLAP MPnt SHeu WPnP
'Pink Skyrocket'PBR	CLAP ECtt ELan LBMP LHop LLHF LRHS LSRN MBel MHol MPnt NBir NGdn NHol NWad SHeu SPad SPer SPoG SWvt WCot
'Pinwheel'	MPnt
'Pirate's Patch'PBR	LLHF MPnt SHeu WNPC
polyphylla	MPnt SHeu WCru
- 'Baoxing Pink'	CFis CLAP MPnt WCru
- 'Filigran'	EPfP IBoy MPnt NHol NLar NWad SHar SHeu
- pink-flowered	EHrv
'Running Tiger'	MPnt
'Sea Foam'	MPnt SHeu
'Simsalabim'	MPnt
'Skeleton Key'	MPnt
'Skid's Variegated' (v)	CCon ECtt LLWG LRHS MHol MNrw MPnt NSti SHeu SPoG SWvt WCot
'Skyrocket'	ECtt MCot NLar
'Spanish Cross'	EBee MPnt SHeu
'Spring Symphony'PBR	CBod CCon CLAP CNec ECtt EShb GBin GBuc GKev LRHS MBel MBri MPnt NCGa NPer NWad SHar SHil WSHC
Starburst = 'Tntia041'PBR	ECtt MPnt NWad SHeu
'Sugar and Spice'PBR	CNec CWGN EAEE EPfP LRHS MBrN MPnt MWhi NDov NWad SHeu WNPC
'Sunset Ridge'	EBee ECtt MPnt NWad SHeu WNPC
'Tiger Stripe'	EPfP LRHS MPnt NBro SHeu
'Timbuktu'	EBee ECtt MAsh MPnt SHeu WNPC
trifoliata	MPnt MRav
- var. ***unifoliata***	MHer MPnt
'Viking Ship'	see × *Heucherella* 'Viking Ship'
§ ***wherryi*** 🏆H5	CAby CBar CBcs EBee ELan ELon EPfP GAbr IBoy LAst LPot LRHS LSun MPnt NBir NBro NPri NRya SCob SPer SPlb SWvt WHar WPnP XLum
- 'Bronze Beauty'	CLAP GBuc MPnt SBch SHeu
- bronze-leaved	SCob
- 'Green Velvet'	ECha MPnt SHeu
- 'Heronswood Mist' (v)	CAbP CBct ECtt ELan MHol MNrw MPnt SHeu SWvt

Tibouchina (*Melastomataceae*)

granulosa	MOWG
'Jules'	MOWG WCot
organensis	CBcs CDoC CHll EUJe MMuc SEle SHeu SWvt
paratropica	CRHN GCal
- RCB/Arg X-4	WCot
semidecandra misapplied	see *T. urvilleana*
§ ***urvilleana*** 🏆H1c	CBcs CBod CDoC CMan CRHN CSBt CTri CTsd EAla EBak EUJe MOWG NLos SDix SPer SRkn SWvt
- 'Edwardsii' 🏆H1c	SAdn WCot
- 'Nana'	CDoC
- 'Rich Blue Sun'	CDoC
- variegated (v)	CMan SPer SWvt WCot

Tigridia (*Iridaceae*)

catarinensis	SDeJ
immaculata B&SWJ 10393	WCru
lutea	ECho
orthantha 'Red-Hot Tiger'	WCru
pavonia	CAby CBro CExl ECho SDeJ WSHC
- 'Alba'	ECho
- 'Alba Grandiflora'	GKev WHil
- 'Aurea'	ECho GKev
- 'Canariensis'	CTca ECho GKev WHil
- 'Lilacea'	ECho GKev SDeJ WHil
- red-flowered	ECho
- 'Speciosa'	CTca GKev SDeJ WHil
- yellow-flowered	ECho

Tilia ✿ (*Malvaceae*)

HRS 2808	WPGP
americana	CLnd CMCN
- 'Dentata'	CDul
argentea	see *T. tomentosa*
begoniifolia	see *T. dasystyla* subsp. *caucasica*
§ ***caroliniana***	CDul CMCN EBee ELan EPfP MBlu
subsp. ***heterophylla***	WPGP
chinensis	CMCN WPGP
- F 30558	WPGP
chingiana	CDul CMCN EBee SLon WPGP
cordata	Widely available
§ - 'Böhlje'	CDul ECrN
- 'Dainty Leaf'	CDul
- 'Erecta'	see *T. cordata* 'Böhlje'
- 'Greenspire' 🏆H6	CArg CCVT CDul CLnd CWib ECrN EPfP IBoy MRav SCob SEWo WMat WMou
- 'Len Parvin'	EBee WPGP
- 'Roelvo'	CDul
- 'Swedish Upright'	CDul
- 'Winter Orange' 🏆H6	CBod CDul EBee EPfP GQue LAst MBlu MBri SBir SCoo SEWo WMat WPat
dasystyla	CMCN
§ - subsp. ***caucasica***	CMCN WPGP
- - A&L 16	WPGP
endochrysea	WPGP
× ***euchlora***	CArg CCVT CDul CLnd CMCN EBee ECrN EPfP NWea SCob SEWo SPer WMat
§ × ***europaea***	CBcs CDul CLnd ELan EWTr MMuc NWea SCob SEND
- 'Koningslinde'	CDul
- 'Pallida'	CDul CLnd MBlu NLar NWea
- 'Wratislaviensis' 🏆H6	CDul EBee MBlu NLar NWea
§ 'Harold Hillier'	CMCN MBlu
henryana	CBcs CDoC CDul CLnd CMCN CTho CWib EBee ELan EMil EPfP ERod IArd IDee LRHS MBlu MMuc SBir SCoo SEND WMat WMou WPGP WPat
- 'Arnold Select' 🏆H5	WCot
- large	WPGP

'Hillieri'	see *T.* 'Harold Hillier'
insularis misapplied	see *T. japonica*
intonsa	CMCN
§ ***japonica***	CDul CMCN EBee EPfP WPGP
- 'Ernest Wilson' 🏆H6	CMCN MBlu
kiusiana	CDul CMCN EBee MBlu WMou WPGP WPat
mandshurica	CDul CMCN EBee WPGP
maximowicziana	WPGP
mexicana	WPGP
- CD&R 1318	EBee WPGP
miqueliana	CMCN IDee
× ***moltkei***	CDul CMCN EBee IArd IDee WPGP
mongolica	CBcs CDul CMCN EPfP MBlu SCoo WMou WPGP
- 'Harvest Gold' **new**	MBlu
monticola	see *T. caroliniana* subsp. *heterophylla*
nobilis KR 226	WPGP
oliveri	CDul CMCN EBee MBlu NWea WMou WPGP
paucicostata	WPGP
platyphyllos	CAgr CCVT CDul CHab CLnd CMCN CSBt CTho CTri ECrN EPfP LAst LBuc MMuc NWea SCob SCoo SEND SPer WMat WMou
- 'Aurea'	CDul CTho ECrN MBlu WMat
- 'Corallina'	see *T. platyphyllos* 'Rubra'
- 'Erecta'	see *T. platyphyllos* 'Fastigiata'
§ - 'Fastigiata'	CDul
- 'Laciniata'	CDul CMCN CTho MBlu
§ - 'Rubra' 🏆H6	CCVT CDul CLnd CTho IBoy MGos NWea SEWo
- 'Tortuosa'	MBlu
§ ***tomentosa***	CDul CLnd CMCN MMuc NWea SCob SCoo WMou
- 'Brabant' 🏆H6	CDul ELan EPfP
- 'Petiolaris' 🏆H6	CArg CBcs CCVT CDul CLnd CMCN ECrN ELan EPfP MBlu MSwo NWea SCob SEND SPer WMou
tuan	WPGP
- var. ***chenmoui***	CMCN EPfP MBlu WPGP
× ***vulgaris***	see *T.* × *europaea*

Tilingia (*Apiaceae*)

ajanensis B&SWJ 11202	IMou WCru

Tillaea see *Crassula*

Tillandsia (*Bromeliaceae*)

sp.	XBlo
abdita	LAir
aeranthos	LAir SChr
- 'Major'	LAir
albertiana	LAir
albida	LAir SPlb
araujei	LAir
- 'Bronze'	LAir
baileyi	LAir NEve
balbisiana	LAir
bandensis	LAir
bartramii	LAir
bergeri	LAir NEve SPlb
brachycaulos	LAir
bulbosa	LAir NEve SPlb
butzii	LAir NEve
cacticola	SPlb
caliginosa	LAir
capillaris	LAir
capitata red-leaved	LAir
caput-medusae	LAir NEve
'Chantilly'	LAir
chiapensis	LAir
concolor	LAir
- 'Cicatlan'	LAir
'Cotton Candy' **new**	NEve
cyanea 🏆H1a	LAir NEve
diaguitensis large	LAir
- small	LAir
duratii	LAir NEve
dyeriana	LAir NEve
edithae	LAir
ehlersiana	LAir
exserta	LAir
fasciculata	LAir
- from Central America	LAir
- var. ***fasciculata***	LAir
- 'Tropiflora'	LAir
'Feather Duster'	LAir
festucoides	LAir
flabellata	LAir NEve SPlb
× ***floridana***	LAir
fuchsii	SPlb
- f. ***gracilis***	LAir NEve
funckiana	LAir NEve
gardneri	LAir
glabrior	LAir
harrisii	NEve
'Heather's Blush'	LAir
heteromorpha	LAir
hondurensis	LAir
'Houston'	LAir
'Humbug'	LAir
intermedia	LAir
ionantha	LAir NEve
- from Honduras	LAir
- from Mexico	LAir
* - 'Fuego'	LAir
- var. ***ionantha*** 'Druid'	LAir
- var. ***maxima*** 'Huamelula'	see *T. ionantha* var. *stricta*
- 'Rubra'	LAir
§ - var. ***stricta***	LAir
- var. ***vanhyningii***	LAir
ixioides	LAir
'Jackie Loinaz'	LAir
juncea	LAir NEve
'Kashkin'	LAir
kirchhoffiana	LAir
latifolia var. ***divaricata***	LAir
- var. ***divaricata*** soft-leaved	LAir
leiboldiana 'Mora'[PBR]	LAir NEve
leonamiana	LAir
loliacea	LAir
lorentziana	LAir
magnusiana	LAir
mallemontii	LAir
melanocrater tricolor	LAir
mooreana **new**	SPlb
myosura	LAir
'Mystic Albert'	LAir
neglecta	LAir
oaxacana	LAir
oerstediana	LAir
'Oeseriana'	LAir
paleacea	LAir NEve
- 'Canta'	LAir
'Perfectly Peachy'	LAir

plagiotropica	LAir
polystachia	LAir
pruinosa	LAir SPlb
pseudobaileyi	LAir
punctulata	LAir
recurvata	LAir
reichenbachii	LAir
'Samantha'	LAir NEve
schiedeana	LAir
- 'Major'	LAir
seleriana	NEve SPlb
'Sparkler'	LAir
streptocarpa	LAir
streptophylla	LAir
stricta	LAir
- var. ***albifolia***	LAir
- green-leaved	LAir
- 'Hard Leaf'	LAir
sucrei	LAir
'Sweet Isabel'	LAir
tectorum	LAir
tenuifolia 'Amethyst'	LAir
- 'Blue Flower'	LAir
- 'Rubra'	LAir
- var. ***saxicola***	LAir
tricholepis	LAir
tricolor	LAir NEve
- var. ***melanocrater***	LAir
usneoides	LAir NEve SPlb
utriculata	LAir NEve
- subsp. ***pringlei***	LAir
variabilis	LAir
velutina	LAir
vernicosa	LAir
'Veronica's Mariposa'	LAir
'Victoria'	LAir
'White Star'	LAir
xerographica	LAir NEve SPlb

Tinantia (*Commelinaceae*)

pringlei	EWld GEdr LEdu MNrw MPie SBrt SDys WPGP
- AIM 77	EBee MAvo MNrw WCot
- variegated (v)	WCot

Tinnea (*Lamiaceae*)

barbata	GFai

Titanotrichum (*Gesneriaceae*)

oldhamii	GEdr

Tithonia (*Asteraceae*)

rotundifolia 'Torch'	CSpe

Tofieldia (*Tofieldiaceae*)

coccinea	CTal GCal GEdr WCru
japonica new	GEdr
- 'Rosea' new	GEdr

Tolmiea (*Saxifragaceae*)

menziesii	CBod CMac EWld MCot WTou XLum
- 'Goldsplash'	see *T. menziesii* 'Taff's Gold'
- 'Maculata'	see *T. menziesii* 'Taff's Gold'
§ - 'Taff's Gold' (v)	EHoe EHrv GMaP LRHS NBid SHil SPlb WPtf XLum
- 'Variegata'	see *T. menziesii* 'Taff's Gold'

Tolpis (*Asteraceae*)

barbata	IMou

Toona (*Meliaceae*)

§ ***sinensis***	CArn CBcs CDul CTho CWib EBee ELan EPfP LEdu SEND WPGP
- 'Flamingo' (v)	CBcs CTho EBee EPfP ESwi EUJe GKin IVic LCro LEdu LOPS LRHS MAsh MGos NLar SHil SPoG SWvt WCot WMat

Torenia (*Linderniaceae*)

'Lovely White'	LAst
(Moon Series) Blue Moon = 'Dantmoon'	LAst
- Purple Moon = 'Dantopur'PBR	LAst LSou
- Rose Moon = 'Dantoromoon'	LAst
- White Moon = 'Dantorwhite'PBR	LAst
- Yellow Moon = 'Danmoon20'PBR	LAst
Summer Wave Series	SCoo

Torilis (*Apiaceae*)

japonica	CBre

Townsendia (*Asteraceae*)

§ ***alpigena*** var. ***alpigena***	CPBP
formosa	CPBP ECho
hookeri	CPBP
incana	WAbe
leptotes	CPBP
mensana	GKev
montana	see *T. alpigena* var. *alpigena*
parryi	GKev
spathulata	CPBP

Toxicodendron see *Rhus*

verniciflum	see *Rhus verniciflua*

Trachelium (*Campanulaceae*)

§ ***asperuloides***	WAbe
caeruleum 'Black Knight'	CSpe
lanceolatum	WCot

Trachelospermum ✿ (*Apocynaceae*)

sp.	EAla ETod LPar
from Nanjing, China	EShb
§ ***asiaticum*** ♀H4	Widely available
- B&SWJ 4814	WCru
- 'Golden Memories'	CBcs CExl CKel CWGN EBee ELan ELon EPfP LRHS LSRN NLar SKHP SLon SPoG SSpi SSta SWvt WPat
- 'Goshiki' (v)	EShb WPat
- var. ***intermedium***	WPGP
* - 'Kiejiu Chirimen'	SKHP
- 'Kulu Chirimen'	WCot
- 'Nagaba' (v)	SKHP
- 'Ōgon-nishiki' (v)	LRHS MPkF SKHP SPoG
- 'Pink Showers'	SKHP
- 'Shirofu Chirimen' (v)	SKHP
- 'Summer Sunset'	CWCL EPfP LRHS MPkF WCot
- 'Theta'	SKHP WCot WPGP WPat
'Chameleon'	SKHP
jasminoides ♀H4	Widely available
- B&SWJ 5117	LPar WCru
- 'Major'	CMac EBee ELan MAsh

§ - var. ***pubescens*** 'Japonicum'	CRHN LRHS NPri SLon SPer SPoG WBor WSHC
- 'Star of Toscana'	IArd IDee LCro LRHS NLar SAko SCob
- 'Tricolor' (v)	LRHS SCob SEle SGol SWvt
- 'Variegatum' (v) ♀H4	Widely available
- 'Waterwheel'	CKel CMac EBee ELan ELon GCal LRHS NLar SCob SKHP SPoG SWvt WPGP WSHC
- 'White Wings' **new**	EBee
- 'Wilsonii'	CExl CHll CMac ELan ELon EPfP EUJe LRHS LSRN MRav NLar SAdn SEND SKHP SLim SPer SPoG SWvt WCot WCru WHar WPGP WPat
majus misapplied	see *T. jasminoides* var. *pubescens* 'Japonicum'
majus Nakai	see *T. asiaticum*

Trachycarpus ✿ (*Arecaceae*)

sp.	ETod
from Manipur	CPHo
§ ***fortunei*** ♀H5	Widely available
fortunei × ***wagnerianus***	LPal LPar
geminisectus	LPal NLos
latisectus	CBlu LTro NLos SBig
martianus	LPal SBig
- from Nepal	LTro
'Naggy'	LPal
oreophilus	NLos
princeps	CBlu CBrP LPal
takil ambig.	LPal
takil Becc.	LPal
wagnerianus	CBlu CBrP CDTJ CExl CPHo EPfP ETod EUJe LPal LRHS LTro NLos NPla SBig SChr WPGP

Trachymene (*Apiaceae*)

coerulea	CSpe CWld

Trachystemon (*Boraginaceae*)

orientalis	Widely available

Tradescantia (*Commelinaceae*)

albiflora	see *T. fluminensis*
× ***andersoniana*** W. Ludwig & Rohw. nom. inval.	see *T.* Andersoniana Group
§ Andersoniana Group	CWib WWtn
- 'Angelic Charm' (Charm Series)	CWGN ECtt SHeu
- 'Baby Doll'	XLum
- 'Bilberry Ice'	CBod CMac CPrp CWCL ECtt EPfP GMaP IKil LBMP LRHS MBel MWat MWhi NBir NBro NGBl NGdn NLar SBod SCob SGSe SGbt SPad SWvt WMnd WWEG WWtn XLum
- 'Blanca'	WWEG
- 'Blue and Gold'	CBcs EBee ECtt ELon EPfP LAst LHop MHol MRav NSti SGSe WCot WFar WHil WWEG
- 'Blue Stone'	CCse CMea CSBt ECha ECtt IKil MAvo MRav SRkn SRms WHoo WWEG XLum
- 'Bridal Veil'	CHll SChr WDib
- 'Caerulea Plena'	see *T. virginiana* 'Caerulea Plena'
- Carmine Glow	see *T.* (Andersoniana Group) 'Karminglut'
- 'Charlotte'	ECha ECtt ELan LRHS LSRN NBro NGdn NLar WMnd WWEG WWtn XLum
- 'Chedglow'	WWEG
- 'Concord Grape'	Widely available
- 'Danielle'	EPfP
- 'Domaine de Courson'	ECtt IKil XLum
- 'Good Luck'PBR	MHol
- 'In the Navy'	NLar
- 'Innocence'	CAby CMHG CSBt CTri ECha ECtt ELan EPfP GCra GMaP IBoy LHop LRHS MBel MMuc NBir NCGa NGdn NSti SCob SEND SPer SWvt XLum
- 'Iris Prichard'	EBee ELan GCra GLog GMaP NLar
- 'Isis'	CPrp CTri EBee ECtt ELan EPfP GCra LBMP LRHS MMuc MRav NBir NCGa NGdn SBod SEND SPer SWvt WKif WMnd WWtn
- 'J.C. Weguelin'	EPfP LPot NBir SRms WCAu WMnd WWEG XLum
§ - 'Karminglut'	EBee ECtt ELan EPfP GLog GMaP IBoy NBir NGdn SGSe WHoo WWEG XLum
- 'Leonora'	MMuc NLar SCob SEND XLum
- 'Little Doll'	CWCL ECtt EPfP GLog LAst LRHS MPie NBro NLar WWEG XLum
- 'Little White Doll'	CPrp ECtt EPfP LAst NLar WWEG
- 'Mac's Double' (d)	CMos EBee IKil
- 'Mariella'	EBee
- 'Melissa'	XLum
- 'Merlot Clusters'	SCob
- 'Mrs Loewer'	MAvo
- 'Osprey'	CBcs CTri ECha ECtt ELan EPfP EWoo GCal LRHS LSun MLHP MRav MWhi NCGa NGdn NSti SGSe SPer SPoG SRms WCAu WGwG WHoo WKif WWEG WWtn XLum
- 'Pauline'	ECtt ELon LSun MRav NBir NLar WWEG XLum
- 'Perinne's Pink'	CWCL ECtt EPfP LRHS NSti
- 'Pink Chablis'	CMos CWCL ECtt EPfP IKil MHol NBro NLar
- 'Purewell Giant'	CMac CTri GLog LHop LRHS NBro NLar SPer SWvt WKif WMnd
- 'Purple Dome'	CAby CMos ECtt EPfP GMaP LAst LRHS MAvo MMuc MRav NBir NBro NGdn SEND SPoG WMnd
- 'Red Grape'	LBMP LPot LRHS MWhi NSti SCob WWEG
- 'Regal Charm' (Charm Series)	EBee SHeu
- 'Rosi'	EBee
- 'Rubra'	CPrp SCob SRms XLum
- 'Satin Doll'PBR	CBcs ECtt EPfP
- 'Snowbank'	EBee
- 'Sunshine Charm'PBR (Charm Series)	CWCL EBee LRHS NLar SHeu WHil
- 'Sweet Kate'	CMac CWCL ECtt LBMP LRHS LSRN MBNS NBro NLar SGbt SHil SPoG XLum
- 'Sylvana'	EBee
- 'Valour'	CSBt EBee EPfP LRHS
- 'Zwanenburg Blue'	ECha ECtt EHrv ELan GLog LAst LPal LRHS MLHP NLar SGSe SPlb SPoG WMnd WWEG XLum
'Angel Eyes'	ECtt
crassifolia	CFil
- F&M 258	WPGP
§ ***fluminensis***	SChr WDib
§ - 'Aurea' ♀H1c	SChr
- 'Maiden's Blush' (v)	CSpe EShb SChr SPlb SRms SVen

	- 'Quicksilver' (v) ♀H1c	EShb NGBl
	- 'Variegata'	see *T. fluminensis* 'Aurea'
	'Lucky Charm'	EBee NLar SHeu
§	'Magic Birdtail' **new**	EBee
	pallida 'Kartuz Giant'	EShb WCot
	- 'Pale Puma'	EShb
§	- 'Purpurea' ♀H1c	EOHP EShb NGBl
	pendula	see *T. zebrina*
	'Purple Sabre'	CBcs EUJe LAst SPlb
	purpurea	see *T. pallida* 'Purpurea'
	sillamontana ♀H1c	EShb MPie SChr
	spathacea	EShb
	- 'Versicolor'	EShb
	'Swallowtail'	see *T.* 'Magic Birdtail'
	tricolor	see *T. zebrina*
	virginiana	LPot MWhi
	- 'Alba'	CMac GCal
*	- 'Brevicaulis'	EBee ECha NBro WWEG
§	- 'Caerulea Plena' (d)	ELan EPfP MRav SPer SRms WWEG
	- 'Rubra'	SPlb
§	***zebrina*** ♀H1c	EShb NGBl
	- ***pendula***	see *T. zebrina*
	- 'Purpusii' ♀H1c	SRms WDib

Tragopogon (*Asteraceae*)

	crocifolius	CSpe SPhx
	porrifolius	CFis GCal MCot NGBl SDix SVic WCot
	pratensis	CArn CWld NMir

Trautvetteria (*Ranunculaceae*)

	sp.	CEvo
	carolinensis	IMou WSHC
	- var. ***japonica***	CLAP GEdr WCru
	- - B&SWJ 10861	WCru
	- var. ***occidentalis***	EBee EPPr LEdu WCru

Triadica (*Euphorbiaceae*)

	sebifera	LEdu WCru
	- CWJ 12819	WCru

Trichodiadema (*Aizoaceae*)

	intonsum	SPlb

Trichopetalum (*Asparagaceae*)

§	***plumosum***	CBro

Trichostema (*Lamiaceae*)

	'Blue Bonnets'	SEND

Tricuspidaria see *Crinodendron*

Tricyrtis (*Liliaceae*)

	B&SWJ 3229 from Taiwan	WCru
	'Abdane'	SGSe
	'Adbane'	CChe CLAP ELan EWes GBuc WGwG
	affinis B&SWJ 2804	CLAP WCru
	- B&SWJ 5645	WCru
	- B&SWJ 6182	WCru
	- B&SWJ 11169	WCru
	- B&SWJ 11442	WCru
	- 'Early Bird'	WCru
	'Amanagowa'	GEdr
	bakeri	see *T. latifolia*
	'Blue Wonder'	CBod EBee ELon IBal LRHS SPer
	dilatata	see *T. macropoda*
	'Empress'	CBct CExl ECha ELon EPfP EThi EWes GBuc IBal LEdu LRHS LSou NEgg NWad SBea SGSe SRkn SRot WWEG
	flava	EBee LRHS WCru
	formosana	CAby CAvo CTri ECha ECho EHrv ELan EPfP EWoo GKev GLog GMaP IBoy LEdu LPal LPot LRHS MCot MMuc MNrw SBea SDys SEND SRms SRot WKif
	- B&SWJ 3073	WCru
	- B&SWJ 355	WCru
	- B&SWJ 3616	CExl WCru
	- B&SWJ 3635	CLAP
	- B&SWJ 3712	WCru
	- B&SWJ 6741	WCru
	- B&SWJ 6970	WCru
	- RWJ 10109	WCru
	- 'Autumn Glow' (v)	GEdr
	- 'Dark Beauty'	CBot CDes CExl CLAP CWCL ECtt EHrv ELan GBuc LCro MNrw MWat SBea SCob WCAu WPGP
	- 'Daruma'	GEdr
I	- 'Donkere Selectie' **new**	EBee
	- 'Emperor' (v)	EBee ESwi
	- 'Gilt Edge' (v)	CBct CBod CExl CWCL ECtt ELan EPfP EThi GBuc IBal LSou MBNS NBro NEgg NLar NSti NWad SGSe SWvt WHil WWEG
	- f. ***glandosa*** B&SWJ 7084	WCru
	- aff. f. ***glandosa*** 'Blu-Shing Toad'	MAvo WCru
	- var. ***grandiflora*** 'W-Ho-ping Toad'	WCru
	- 'Kestrel' (v)	WCot
	- pale-flowered	EThi
	- 'Purple Beauty'	MNrw MPie MPkF
	- 'Samurai' (v)	CWCL EWes
	- 'Seiryu'	EBee
	- 'Shelley's'	CLAP NBro
	- 'Small Wonder'	WCru
	- 'Spotted Toad'	LEdu MAvo WCru
§	- Stolonifera Group	CAvo CBcs CLAP CMac EHrv ELan EPfP LEdu LRHS MCot MWat NWad SHar
	- - B&SWJ 7046	WCru
	- 'Taiwan Toad'	CExl
	- 'Taroko Toad'	WCru
	- 'Tiny Toad'	WCru
	- 'Variegata' (v)	LEdu NBir WCru
	- 'Velvet Toad'	WCru
	'Golden Leopard'	EBee LSou
	'Harlequin'	LEdu WWEG
§	***hirta***	CBcs CHid CMac CTri CTsd ECho IBoy ILea LOPS LRHS LTro MCot MJak NBro NHol SEND SGSe SGbt SPlb SWvt WWEG
	- B&SWJ 5971	WCru
	- B&SWJ 11182	WCru
	- B&SWJ 11227	WCru
	- 'Alba'	CMac SGSe
	- 'Albomarginata' (v)	CMac EAEE GCra LRHS NEgg NLar NSti SGSe SWvt
	- 'Golden Gleam'	WCot
	- var. ***masamunei***	WCru
	- 'Matsukaze'	CExl CLAP EWes
	- 'Miyazaki'	CCon CLAP CMac ECha ECtt EPfP GBuc IFoB LRHS MHer MNrw MPkF WCAu WRHF XLum
	- 'Taiwan Atrianne'	CLAP CMos ECtt ELan LRHS MNrw NEgg NWad SGbt WCAu

- 'Variegata' (v) CTri EBee EWes GCra GKev LRHS WCot WWEG
Hototogisu CExl CLAP CMos EAEE ECha ECtt ELan LHop LRHS MWat NBir NHol NLar WWEG
ishiiana CLAP CTal EBee EHrv WCru WSHC
- var. ***surugensis*** LEdu WCru
japonica see *T. hirta*
'Kohaku' CLAP EBee WHil WWEG
lasiocarpa EHrv LEdu MAvo XLum
- B&SWJ 3635 CAby CExl WCru
- B&SWJ 6861 WCru
- B&SWJ 7013 WCru
- B&SWJ 7103 WCru
- 'Royal Toad' WCru
§ ***latifolia*** ELan GLog GMaP LEdu SGSe WCru
- 'Saffron' WCru
- 'Yellow Sunrise' EBee NCGa NSti
'Lemon Lime' (v) SGSe
'Lightning Strike' (v) EBee ECha ECtt LEdu WCot
'Lilac Towers' WCru
macrantha GAbr GLog WCru WSHC
§ - subsp. ***macranthopsis*** CAby CBct CExl CLAP GBuc LHop WCot WCru
- - 'Juro' (d) WCru
macranthopsis see *T. macrantha* subsp. *macranthopsis*
* ***macrocarpa*** XLum
macropoda ELan GLog ILea LEdu LHop LRHS MAvo SGSe WCAu
- B&SWJ 1271 from Korea WCru
- B&SWJ 5013 WCru
- B&SWJ 5556 WCru
- B&SWJ 5847 from Japan WCru
- B&SWJ 6209 WCru
- B&SWJ 8700 WCru
- B&SWJ 8829 from Korea WCru
- from Yungi Temple, China CLAP NCGa
maculata HWJCM 470 WCru
- HWJK 2010 WCru
- HWJK 2411 WCru
- PAB 3188 LEdu
'Mine-no-yuki' GEdr
'Momoyama' GEdr
'Moonlight Treasure'[PBR] CExl CLAP EBee IBoy NHol WCot
nana WCru
- B&SWJ 11399 WCru
ohsumiensis CAby CLAP ECha EHrv GBuc WCru
perfoliata CLAP LEdu WCru
- 'Spring Shine' (v) WCru
pilosa EBee LEdu
Pink Freckles = 'Innotripf'[PBR] CBct CLAP CMos EBee ELon ESwi EThi LAst LSou MPnt SRot SWvt WHil
'Raspberry Mousse' CLAP CWCL EPfP IFoB LHop MBNS NSti
ravenii B&SWJ 3229 WCru
- RWJ 10012 WCru
setouchiensis WCru
'Shimone' CExl CHid CLAP EBee ECha SGSe
'Sinonome' EBee IPot MAvo MNrw MPkF
stolonifera see *T. formosana* Stolonifera Group
suzukii RWJ 10111 WCru
'Taipei Silk'[PBR] ESwi IFoB LSun NCGa
'Tojen' EAEE ECha ECtt ELon EPfP EWes GKev IBal LAst LEdu LHop LRHS MNrw NBid NBir SPer WCAu
'Variegata' (*affinis* hybrid) (v) CLAP WWEG
'Washfields' EBee
'White Towers' CBro CCon CExl CHid CLAP CWCL ECha EHrv EWoo GBuc IFoB LRHS MRav NEgg NLar NSti SRms XLum

Trifolium (*Papilionaceae*)

angustifolium CArn
arvense PAB 7952 new LEdu
brandegeei SPhx
dubium SPre
incarnatum CSpe MHer
macrocephalum EBee SPhx
nanum LLHF
ochroleucon CAby EAJP ECha EHrv EPPr GMaP ILea LEdu MAvo MCot MPie NSti SBch SGSe SHar SMHy SMad SPhx WAul WMoo WPGP
pannonicum CMea GCal MNrw WOut WWFP
- 'White Tiara' MMHG
pratense CHab MHer NMir WSFF
- 'Dolly North' see *T. pratense* 'Susan Smith'
- 'Ice Cool' see *T. repens* 'Green Ice'
§ - 'Susan Smith' (v) LEdu
repens SVic WSFF
- 'Debbie' LEdu
- 'Dragon's Blood' CBod CMea EPPr LBMP LEdu LLWG MMuc MPie SEND SPer WPGP WTor
- 'Gold Net' see *T. pratense* 'Susan Smith'
§ - 'Green Ice' EBee LLWG NSti WHal
- 'Harlequin' (v) MHer WCot WMoo WOut
- 'Hullavington' CNat
- 'Isabella' LEdu WPGP
- 'Josephine' LEdu
- 'Purpurascens' CArn CBre LLWG LRHS MBNS MHer MPie NSti SPoG
§ - 'Purpurascens Quadrifolium' CAby CBod CMea ECha EHoe EPau EWes GAbr LBMP MCot NMir NPer SPer SPlb WRHF WTor
- 'Tetraphyllum Purpureum' see *T. repens* 'Purpurascens Quadrifolium'
- 'Wheatfen' CNat NDov NPer
- 'William' CBre ECGP LEdu MMuc NDov SEND WCot WOut
rubens CAby CArn CBod CMea CWCL EAJP ELan EPPr EShb GCal LEdu LRHS MAvo MBel MHer MMHG MMuc MNHC MNrw MSCN NChi SPer SPhx SPlb WAul WCAu WMoo WSHC WTcb
- 'Drama' ELon MNrw
- 'Peach Pink' ELon EPPr LHop MAvo MMHG SPhx WCot
- 'Red Feathers' CWCL CWld ELon EPPr EWes LBMP LSun MHol SGSe SHar SMad
'Spring' LEdu
trichocephalum EPPr

Trigonella (*Papilionaceae*)

foenum-graecum WSFF

Trillidium see *Trillium*

Trillium ✿ (*Melanthiaceae*)

albidum ♀H5 EBee ECho ENun GBin GBuc GEdr LAma LLHF LRHS NHar SKHP SSpi WBor

	angustipetalum	EPot GEdr GKev
	apetalon	GEdr LAma
	camschatcense	CExl GEdr GKev LAma
§	***catesbyi***	CCon CExl CWCL EBee ECho EPot EWTr GEdr GKev LAma LLHF MNrw NWad
	cernuum	CWCL ECho GCra GKev LAma
	chloropetalum	CBro CEvo ENun GBin GBuc GEdr LRHS NWad SSpi
	- var. ***chloropetalum***	GBuc
	- var. ***chloropetalum*** × ***parviflorum***	SKHP
§	- var. ***giganteum*** 🏆H5	CExl GBuc SPhx WCru
	- pink-flowered	GEdr
	- var. ***rubrum***	see *T. chloropetalum* var. *giganteum*
	cuneatum	CArn CBcs CBct CBro CExl CWCL ECho EHrv EPot GAbr GBuc GEdr GKev GMaP LAma LEdu LRHS MNrw NBir NHol NWad SDeJ SKHP SSpi WPnP
	- 'Ghost'	SKHP
	- 'Moonshine'	SKHP
	decipiens	CEvo GEdr
	decumbens	CEvo GEdr SKHP
	discolor	CEvo GEdr
	erectum 🏆H5	Widely available
	- f. ***albiflorum***	CCon ECha ECho GBuc MNrw NWad SKHP SSpi WPnP
	- - Harvington clone **new**	ENun
	- 'Beige'	GKev
	- Harvington dark form **new**	ENun
	- f. ***luteum***	GEdr SKHP
	- red-flowered	CEvo ECho GKev
	erectum × ***flexipes***	EBee ECho EHrv GBuc MNrw NBir SKHP SSpi
	flexipes	CBct CEvo CWCL ECho EHrv EPot GEdr GKev LAma LRHS MNrw NHar NHol NWad SKHP SSpi
	- 'Harvington Dusky Pink' **new**	ENun
I	- 'Harvington Selection'	EBee ENun LRHS SKHP
	flexipes × ***simile*** Harvington hybrids **new**	ENun
	foetidissimum	GEdr SKHP
	govanianum	GEdr GKev LAma LRHS
	gracile	GEdr
	grandiflorum 🏆H5	Widely available
	- 'Beige'	CBct
	- Gothenburg pink	GEdr
	- f. ***polymerum*** 'Flore Pleno' (d)	EBee ENun GEdr LLHF LRHS SKHP
	- - 'Snowbunting' (d)	EWes GKev LAma LRHS MMHG NHar WThu
	- 'Quicksilver'	SKHP
	- f. ***roseum***	EBee ENun GEdr LRHS
	- white-flowered	MAvo
	kurabayashii	CExl CPne CTal EBee ECho EHrv ENun EPot EWld GBin GBuc GEdr LRHS MNrw SKHP SSpi WBor WCru WPGP
	lancifolium	GEdr
	ludovicianum	GEdr
	luteum 🏆H5	Widely available
	maculatum	GEdr
	nivale	CBct GEdr NHar
	ovatum	SSpi
	- f. ***hibbersonii***	GBuc NHar
	- 'Roy Elliott'	CExl
	parviflorum	GEdr MNrw SKHP
	pusillum	CEvo CExl CWCL EBee ECho EPot GEdr GKev LAma LLHF MNrw NHol
*	- var. ***alabamicum***	SKHP
I	- var. ***georgianum***	SKHP
	recurvatum	CBcs CCon CEvo CWCL EBee ECho EHrv EPot GEdr GKev LAma LEdu NHol NWad SKHP WPnP
	reliquum	CEvo GEdr
	rivale 🏆H4	CExl ECho GBuc GEdr GKev SCob
	- Purple Heart Group	GEdr
	rugelii	EBee ECho EHrv EWes GEdr GKev LAma MNrw SKHP SSpi WSHC
	- Askival hybrids	ECho GAbr GBuc MNrw SKHP SSpi
	rugelii × ***vaseyi***	EBee EHrv EWes MNrw SKHP SSpi
	sessile	CEvo CExl CWCL ECho EWTr GBuc GEdr GKev LAma MAvo MNrw NBir NWad SDeJ SKHP WCot WKif WSHC WShi
	- 'Rubrum'	see *T. chloropetalum* var. *giganteum*
	simile	EBee ECho ENun GAbr GEdr LLHF LRHS MNrw NHar SKHP SSpi
	smallii	GEdr
	stamineum	CWCL GEdr LAma
	stylosum	see *T. catesbyi*
	sulcatum	CExl CWCL EBee ECho EHrv ENun GBuc GEdr GKev GMaP LAma LRHS MNrw NHar SKHP SSpi WCot WSHC
	- cream-flowered	GBBs
	taiwanense B&SWJ 3411	WCru
	texanum	SKHP
	tschonoskii	GEdr GKev LAma
	underwoodii	CEvo GEdr
	undulatum	GEdr MNrw
	vaseyi	CEvo CWCL EBee ECho EHrv ENun EWes GEdr GKev LAma LRHS MNrw NHar SKHP SSpi
	- large-flowered	SKHP
	viride	GBBs
	viridescens	GEdr LAma

Triosteum (*Caprifoliaceae*)

	angustifolium **new**	CEvo
	erythrocarpum	EBee EWTr SMad
	himalayanum	GCal GKev WSHC
	- BWJ 7907	CLAP WCru
	pinnatifidum	CLAP EBee EWTr EWld GCal IMou WCru

Tripleurospermum (*Asteraceae*)

§	***maritimum***	WHer

Tripsacum (*Poaceae*)

	dactyloides	EPPr

Tripterospermum (*Gentianaceae*)

	fasciculatum B&SWJ 11297	WCru
	japonicum	GEdr LLHF
	- B&SWJ 10876	WCru
	lanceolatum RWJ 9918	WCru

Tripterygium (*Celastraceae*)

	doianum B&SWJ 11467	WCru
	aff. ***doianum*** CWJ 12852	WCru
	regelii B&SWJ 5453	WCru

- B&SWJ 8666 from Korea WCru
- B&SWJ 10921 WCru
wilfordii GCal LEdu
- BWJ 7852 from China WCru
- NJM 11.029 from China WPGP
- WWJ 12009 WCru

Tristagma (*Alliaceae*)

nivale EBee

Triteleia (*Asparagaceae*)

'4U' CAvo EBee ECho EPfP GKev
bridgesii ECho
californica see *Brodiaea californica*
§ 'Corrina' CAvo CBro EBee ECho EPot GKev
'Crystal Pink' SDeJ
'Double Touch' (d) new ERCP
'Foxy' new EBee EPot
grandiflora ECho WCot
hyacinthina EBee ECho GKev WCot
ixioides ECho
- 'Splendens' ECho
- 'Starlight' CAvo CBro CTri ECho EPfP EPot ERCP GKev SDeJ
§ ***laxa*** ECha ECho
- 'Allure' EBee ECho
- 'Dexter' CAbP
§ - 'Koningin Fabiola' CBro CSpe CTri EBee ECho GKev LAma MLHP MNrw NBir SCob SDeJ SEND SPer WCot WRHF
- Queen Fabiola see *T. laxa* 'Koningin Fabiola'
lilacina ECho
'Ocean Queen' CMea EBee ERCP
§ ***peduncularis*** ECho WCot
'Rudy' CAvo CBro CHid CMea CWCL EBee ECho ERCP GKev SCob SDeJ WCot WRHF
'Silver Queen' CBro CMea EBee ECho EPot ERCP
× ***tubergenii*** ECho
uniflora see *Ipheion uniflorum*
'White Sweep' EBee ECho
'www'PBR ECho

Trithrinax (*Arecaceae*)

brasiliensis LPal SBig
campestris CBrP LPal SBig

Tritoma see *Kniphofia*

Tritonia (*Iridaceae*)

crocata ♀H2 ECho
- 'Baby Doll' EBee LEdu
- 'Pink Sensation' CDes EBee ECho
- 'Plymouth Pastel' CDes
- 'Prince of Orange' CDes EBee
- 'Princess Beatrix' CDes
- 'Serendipity' CDes EBee EPri
- 'Tangerine' CDes EBee
deusta CDes EPri
disticha new SMad
§ - subsp. ***rubrolucens*** Widely available
- - short, red-pink-flowered CDes
- - tall, clear pink-flowered CDes CTca WPGP
flabellifolia ECho
laxifolia CDes CTca ECho EPot GKev NRog
lineata CDes CTca EBee ECho EPri LEdu WPGP
- 'Parvifolia' GKev
pallida ECho SPlb
rosea see *T. disticha* subsp. *rubrolucens*
securigera CDes ECho LEdu
squalida ECho EPri

Trochocarpa (*Ericaceae*)

clarkei WThu
gunnii WThu
thymifolia WThu
- white-flowered WThu

Trochodendron (*Trochodendraceae*)

aralioides Widely available
- B&SWJ 6080 from Japan WCru
- from Taiwan CFil
- - B&SWJ 1651 WCru
- - CWJ 12357 WCru
- - RWJ 9845 WCru

Trollius (*Ranunculaceae*)

ACE 1187 CExl
acaulis ECho ELon EWes GAbr
altaicus LRHS
buddae CDes CWCL EWes MRav
§ ***chinensis*** ECha GCal GKev NChi SWat
- 'Golden Queen' ♀H7 Widely available
- 'Imperial Orange' GBin
× ***cultorum*** CAby
- 'Alabaster' Widely available
- 'Baudirektor Linne' MRav NGdn
- 'Byrne's Giant' ECtt IKil
- 'Canary Bird' ELan GCal MJak NGdn SRms
- 'Cheddar' CMos CWCL ECtt ELon EPfP GBin GCal GEdr GMaP ILea LRHS LSou MBNS MBel MCot MRav MSCN MWts NBro NEoE NLar SKHP SPoG SWvt WBor WFar
- 'Earliest of All' CSam CWCL NGdn NLar SPer WWEG
- 'Etna' GBin WWEG
§ - 'Feuertroll' ECha ECtt MRav NEoE NGdn
- Fireglobe see *T.* × *cultorum* 'Feuertroll'
- 'Golden Cup' NBir NGdn
- 'Goldquelle' ♀H7 EBee GBuc
- 'Goliath' NLar
- 'Helios' CSam GBin GBuc LLHF
- 'Lemon Queen' CBod CMac COtt CWCL CWat ECtt EHrv EPfP GBin GKev GMaP LRHS MRav NLar NQui SCob SGol SPer SWat
- 'New Moon' CAby CLet CWCL EBee EShb GAbr GBin GBuc IKil LRHS NChi NQui SPad WSHC
- 'Orange Crest' EBee ECtt GCal
- 'Orange Globe' GMaP
- 'Orange Princess' ♀H7 COtt CWCL CWat LRHS NBro NLar SPer SRms
- 'Orange Queen' SWvt
- 'Prichard's Giant' CDes CMHG ECtt ELan ELon NBro NGdn WCFE
§ - 'Superbus' ♀H7 CCon CWCL ELan ELon EPfP GMaP LRHS MSCN NGdn SPer WFar
- 'T. Smith' ECtt NBro
- 'Taleggio' LEdu
'Dancing Flame' new SHar
europaeus CAby CBod CWCL ECha ELan EWoo GCal LAst LEdu LHop LRHS LSun MLHP MRav MWat NGdn SRot SWat WCFE WHoo WWEG

	- SDR 6306	GKev
	- subsp. ***europaeus***	WFar
	- 'Lemon Supreme'	GBuc GKev LRHS
	- 'Superbus'	see *T.* × *cultorum* 'Superbus'
	hondoensis	LLHF NEoE
	ircuticus	GKev WCot
	laxus 'Albiflorus'	CExl EWTr
	ledebourii misapplied	see *T. chinensis*
	pumilus	ECha ECho ELan EPfP GKev LLHF LRHS NLar NSla SGSe SPer WAbe
	- ACE 1818	CExl MHer
	- 'Wargrave'	ECho
	vaginatus	EBee
	yunnanensis ♀H6	EBee GBin GKev LRHS
	- orange-flowered	CExl GKev

Tropaeolum ✿ (*Tropaeolaceae*)

	azureum	CExl CFil CPla
	brachyceras	CPne EBee ECho GKev
	ciliatum	CFil CPla ECho EWld GKev NBid WCot WCru WPGP
	Gleam Series	NPri
	hookerianum	CExl
	- subsp. ***austropurpureum***	CExl CFil
	- subsp. ***hookerianum***	CFil
	incisum	CWCL EBee ECho WCot
	lepidum	CPla
	majus	ENfk GPoy SVic
	- Alaska Series (v) ♀H3	CWCL ENfk LCro MNHC SIde WJek
	- 'Apricot Twist'	GBee
	- 'Black Velvet' (Tom Thumb Series) **new**	LCro
	- 'Crimson Beauty'	CSpe
§	- 'Darjeeling Double' (d) ♀H3	WCot
	- 'Darjeeling Gold'	see *T. majus* 'Darjeeling Double'
	- 'Empress of India'	MNHC WJek
	- 'Hermine Grashoff' (d)	CSpe GBee GCal
	- Jewel of Africa Group (v)	CWCL
	- Jewel Series	ENfk
	- 'Margaret Long' (d)	CSpe GCal WCot
	- 'Peaches and Cream'	WJek
	- 'Red Wonder'	CSpe EPfP WCot
	- Tom Thumb Series	MNHC WJek
	nubigenum* × *polyphyllum	CFil
	pentaphyllum	CExl CFil CPne CSpe EBee ECho GCal
	peregrinum	ECho
	polyphyllum ♀H3	CWCL EBee ECho EPot GBuc LHop NBir SMHy WCot WPGP
	sessilifolium	CFil EBee ECho
	smithii	GCal WCot
	speciosum ♀H5	Widely available
	sylvestre	EWld
	tricolor ♀H2	CAvo CFil ECho GKev WBor XEll
	tuberosum	CAgr GKev GPoy SDeJ
	- var. ***lineamaculatum*** 'Ken Aslet' ♀H3	CBcs CBro CKel CWCL EBee ECha ELan EPfP EPot GCra GKev LAma LEdu LRHS NLar SPer SPoG WCot

Tsuga ✿ (*Pinaceae*)

	canadensis	CDul CMac EPfP NWea
	- 'Abbott's Dwarf'	CKen MGos NHol
§	- 'Abbott's Pygmy'	CKen
	- 'Bacon Cristate'	CKen
	- 'Beehive'	NLar
	- 'Bennett'	NLar
	- 'Betty Rose' (v)	CKen
	- 'Birkett's White'	CKen
	- 'Brandley'	CKen
§	- 'Branklyn'	CKen WCFE
	- 'Cappy's Choice'	CKen
	- 'Cinnamonea'	CKen
	- 'Coffin'	CKen
	- 'Cole's Prostrate' ♀H7	CKen MAsh SLim
	- 'Creamey' (v)	CKen
	- 'Curley'	CKen
	- 'Curtis Ideal'	CKen
	- 'Dr Hornbeck'	see *T. canadensis* 'Hornbeck'
	- 'Eisburg'	SLim
	- 'Essex'	CKen NWad
*	- 'Everitt's Dense Leaf'	CKen
	- 'Everitt's Golden'	CKen SLim
	- 'Fantana'	MAsh NHol
	- 'Gracilis'	WThu
	- 'Greenwood Lake'	WThu
	- 'Hedgehog'	NLar
§	- 'Hornbeck'	CKen
	- 'Horsford'	CKen NWad
	- 'Horstmann' No 1	CKen
	- 'Hussii'	CKen NHol
	- 'Jacqueline Verkade'	CKen MAsh NLar
	- 'Jeddeloh' ♀H7	CDoC MAsh MGos NEgg NHol NLar SCob SGol SLim
	- 'Jervis'	CKen NHol NWad
	- 'Julianne'	CKen
	- 'Kingsville Spreader'	CKen
	- 'Little Joe'	CKen
	- 'Livingston'	SLim
I	- 'Lutea'	CKen
	- 'Many Cones'	CKen
	- 'Minima'	CKen
	- 'Minuta' ♀H7	CKen MGos NHol NWad
	- 'Palomino'	CKen
	- 'Pendula' ♀H7	CKen MAsh MBri
	- 'Pincushion'	CKen
	- 'Prostrata'	see *T. canadensis* 'Branklyn'
	- 'Pygmaea'	see *T. canadensis* 'Abbott's Pygmy'
	- 'Rugg's Washington Dwarf'	CKen
	- 'Snowflake'	CKen
	- 'Stewart's Gem'	CKen
	- 'Verkade Petite'	CKen
	- 'Verkade Recurved'	CKen
	- 'Von Helms' Dwarf'	CKen
	- 'Warnham'	CKen MAsh
	caroliniana 'La Bar Weeping'	CKen NLar
	- 'Planting Fields Broom'	CKen
	chinensis	CKen
	diversifolia 'Gotelli'	CKen
	dumosa	CKen
	heterophylla ♀H6	CBcs CCVT CDul EPfP MMuc NWea SCob SEWo SGol
	- 'Iron Springs'	CKen
	- 'Laursen's Column'	CKen
	- 'Ray Godfrey'	NLar
	- 'Thorsens Weeping'	CKen
	menziesii	see *Pseudotsuga menziesii*
	mertensiana 'Blue Star'	CKen MAsh NLar
	- 'Elizabeth'	CKen
	- 'Glauca'	CKen
I	- 'Glauca Nana'	CKen
I	- 'Horstmann'	CKen
	- 'Quartz Mountain'	CKen
	sieboldii 'Baldwin'	CKen

	- 'Green Ball'	CKen NLar
	- 'Honeywell Estate'	CKen
	- 'Nana'	CKen

Tuberaria (*Cistaceae*)

	lignosa	WAbe

Tulbaghia ✿ (*Alliaceae*)

	acutiloba	CTca EBee GKev LEdu MHom NHoy
	'African Moon'	NHoy
	alliacea	ECho EPri LEdu NHoy WCot
	alliacea* × *violacea	CAvo ECho
*	***allioides***	CBro
	'Bob Brown'	CDes LEdu WPGP
	'Bright Eyes'	NHoy
	capensis	CPou LEdu NBir NHoy
	'Cariad'	LEdu
	cernua CD&R 199	CDes EBee LEdu
	- hybrid	EPri NHoy
§	***coddii***	CPne GKev LEdu MHom NHoy
	coddii* × *violacea	NHoy
	cominsii	CExl ECho EPri LEdu SBch
	- 'Harry Hay's Pink'	NHoy
	cominsii* × *violacea	CAvo CExl CTca MHom NHoy
	'Cosmic'	CDes CPou EBee EPPr EPri LEdu NHoy WPGP
	'Crystal'	NHoy
	'Dreaming Spires'	NHoy
	dregeana	NHoy
	'Elaine Ann'	NHoy
	'Enigma'	NHoy
	'Fairy Snow'	CDes LEdu
	'Fairy Star'	CDes CTca EBee EPri EShb LEdu LSou NHoy SMHy WCot
	fragrans	see *T. simmleri*
	- 'Alba'	ECho ELan EPot SDeJ
	galpinii	GKev NHoy
	'Grey Dawn'	NHoy
	'Hazel'	CDes CPou EBee LEdu MHer NHoy WPGP
	'Janet'	NHoy
	'John May's Special'	CDes CKno EShb LEdu MHom NHoy WCot WHoo WPGP
	leucantha ♀H2	CDes CTca ECho EPri GKev LEdu MHom NHoy NWad
	- H&B 11996	CDes LEdu
	ludwigiana	CPne MHer
	maritima	see *T. violacea* var. *maritima*
	Marwood seedling	ECho LEdu MHer MHom MTPN NHoy
	montana	EBee LEdu MHer MPie NHoy
	'Moshoeshoe'	LEdu
	'Moya' **new**	CDes
	natalensis ♀H2	CBro CPou CPrp ECho GKev NHoy
	- B&V 421	EPri
	- Burtt 6949	CPne
	- CD&R 84	NHoy
	- clone 1 white B&V 421	CDes NHoy
	- clone 2 pink B&V 421	LEdu NHoy
	- pink-flowered	CTca ECho MHom NHoy
	- white-flowered	CTca
	natalensis* × *violacea	NHoy
	poetica	see *T. coddii*
	'Premier'	NHoy
	'Purple Eye' ♀H2	CBro CDes CKno CPne CSpe EBee EWoo GBin LEdu NHoy NSti SPoG WCot
	'Rainbow'	NHoy
§	***simmleri*** ♀H2	CMos CPou EBee ECho EHrv EPri EWes GKev LAma LEdu NHoy NLar SDeJ
	- 'Cheryl Renshaw'	WCot
	- pink-flowered	CTca
	- 'Snow Queen'	CPrp
	- white-flowered	CPou CPrp CTca ECho GKev NHoy
	'Snow White'	WCot
	'Snowball'	NHoy
	'Suzanne'	NHoy
	verdoorniae	LEdu NHoy
	violacea ♀H2	Widely available
	- from RBGE	MHom NHoy
*	- 'Alba'	CKno EBee ECho EPri EWoo GKev MHer NHoy SChF SWat WKif
	- 'Dissect White'	NHoy
I	- 'Fine Form'	CKno NHoy WKif
	- 'John Rider'	EPri NHoy
*	- var. ***maritima***	CPne EShb LEdu MHer MHom NHoy WCot
	- var. ***obtusa***	NHoy
	- 'Pallida'	CAvo CBro CCse CDes CPou CTca ECho LEdu NHoy WPGP
	- 'Pearl'	CPou NHoy
	- 'Peppermint Garlic'	CDes CTca LEdu WPGP
	- var. ***robustior***	CAby CPou CTca ECha EWes NHoy
	- 'Seren'	LEdu
§	- 'Silver Lace' (v) ♀H2	Widely available
	- 'Variegata'	see *T. violacea* 'Silver Lace'
	- var. ***violacea***	NHoy
	- 'White Goddess'	CPou

Tulipa ✿ (*Liliaceae*)

	sp.	LRHS
	'Abba' (2)	LAma SCob SDeJ
	'Absalon' (9)	GKev LAma
	'Abu Hassan' (3)	CAvo ERCP LAma LCro MBri SDeJ
	acuminata (15)	CAvo CBro CTca ECho ERCP GKev LAma MGib SCob SDeJ SPhx
	'Ad Rem' (4)	MBri SDeJ
	'Addis' (14)	LAma
	'Agrass White' (3)	NBri
	'Air' (10)	ERCP
	aitchisonii	see *T. clusiana*
	'Akebono' (11)	LAma
	'Akela' (5)	LAma
	'Alabaster' (5)	LAma
	'Aladdin' (6)	LAma LCro LOPS NBri SDeJ
	'Aladdin's Record' (6)	CBro LAma SDeJ
	'Alba Regalis' (1)	LAma
	'Albert Heijn' (13)	SDeJ
	albertii (15)	ECho LAma
	Albion Star = 'Mieke Telkamp' (13)	EPfP SDeJ
	'Aleppo' (7)	SDeJ
	'Alexander Pushkin'PBR (3)	LAma
	'Alfred Cortot' (12) ♀H6	LAma SDeJ
	'Ali Baba' (14) ♀H6	LAma NBri
	'Alice Leclercq' (2)	LAma
	'Allegretto' (11)	LAma MBri
	'Alliance' (2)	LAma
	altaica (15) ♀H6	ECho LAma
	amabilis	see *T. hoogiana*
	'Talisman' ambig.	LAma
	'American Dream' (4)	LAma

'American Eagle' (7)	LAma SDeJ
'Analita' (13)	LAma
'Ancilla' (12) ♀H6	CBro LAma NBri
'André Rieu' (5) **new**	LCro
'Angélique' (11) ♀H6	CAvo CBro CTca EPfP ERCP GKev LAma LCro LOPS LPfy MBri NBir NBri SCob SDeJ SPer
'Angels Wish' (5) ♀H6	CAvo LAma MGib SDeJ
'Annie Schilder' (3)	ERCP LAma
'Antarctica'[PBR] (3)	LAma
'Anthony Eden' (2)	LAma
'Antoinette'[PBR] (5)	CAby EPfP LAma LCro LOPS
'Antraciet' (11)	ERCP LAma LCro LOPS
'Apeldoorn' (4)	EPfP GKev LAma LCro LOPS MBri NBri SCob SDeJ
'Apeldoorn's Elite' (4) ♀H6	LAma MBri NBri SDeJ
'Apricot Beauty' (1) ♀H6	CTca ERCP LAma LCro MBri NBir NBri SDeJ
'Apricot Emperor' (13)	MCot SDeJ
'Apricot Foxx' (3) **new**	EPfP LAma
'Apricot Impression'[PBR] (4)	LAma LPfy
'Apricot Jewel'	see *T. linifolia* (Batalinii Group) 'Apricot Jewel'
'Apricot Magic' (1)	LAma
'Apricot Parrot' (10) ♀H6	LAma MBri MCot NBri SDeJ
'Aquilla' (11)	LAma SDeJ
'Arabian Mystery' (3)	ERCP LAma NHol SDeJ
'Aria Card' (7)	LAma SDeJ
'Artist' (8) ♀H6	ERCP LAma SDeJ
'Atlantis' (5)	LAma MBri NBri
'Attila' (3)	CAvo LAma
'Attila Graffiti' (3)	LAma
'Attila's Elite' (3)	LAma
aucheriana (15) ♀H5	CBro ECho EPot LAma LLHF
australis (15)	ECho
'Avignon' (5)	SDeJ
aximensis (15)	ECho EPot LAma
'Bacchus' (7)	LAma
'Backpacker' (11) **new**	MGib
bakeri	see *T. saxatilis* Bakeri Group
'Ballade' (6) ♀H6	CAvo ERCP LAma LCro MCot SDeJ
Ballade Dream = 'Sonnet' (6)	LAma SDeJ
'Ballade Gold' (6)	LAma
'Ballerina' (6) ♀H6	CAby CAvo CBro CTca ECho EPfP ERCP LAma LCro LOPS MBri MCot NBri SCob SDeJ SPer
'Banja Luka' (4)	LAma NBri SDeJ
'Barbados' (7)	LAma SCob SDeJ
'Barcelona' (3) ♀H6	ERCP LAma LCro LOPS
'Baronesse' (5)	SDeJ
'Bastogne' (3)	LAma SCob
'Bastogne Parrot' (10)	LAma
batalinii	see *T. linifolia* Batalinii Group
'Beau Monde' (3) ♀H6	SDeJ
'Beauty of Apeldoorn' (4)	LAma MBri
'Beauty of Bath' (9)	LAma
'Beauty of Spring' (4) **new**	LAma
'Beauty Queen' (1)	LAma SDeJ
'Bel Air'[PBR] (2)	LAma
'Belcanto' (3)	LAma
'Belicia' (2)	LAma
'Bellflower' (7)	LAma
'Bellona' (3)	LAma SDeJ
'Berlioz' (12)	LAma SDeJ
'Bessie' (5)	LAma
'Bestseller' (1)	SDeJ
biebersteiniana (15)	ECho

§	***biflora*** (15)	ECho EPot GKev LAma MGib SDeJ
	bifloriformis (15)	ECho LAma LLHF
I	- 'Maxima' (15)	SPhx
	'Big Chief' (4) ♀H6	LAma
	'Black and White' (9)	LAma
	'Black Charm' (3)	CAby
	'Black Hero' (11)	CAby CAvo EPfP ERCP LAma LCro MCot SDeJ
	'Black Horse' (5)	LAma
	'Black Jewel' (7)	ERCP LAma SDeJ
	'Black Parrot' (10) ♀H6	CAvo CBro EPfP ERCP LAma LCro LOPS MBri NBri SCob SDeJ SPer
	'Black Stallion' (11)	LAma
	'Black Swan' (5)	SDeJ
	'Blackjack' (3)	LAma
	'Bleu Aimable' (5)	CAvo ERCP LAma MCot SDeJ
	'Blue Diamond' (11)	CAvo ERCP LAma NBri SDeJ
	'Blue Heron' (7) ♀H6	ERCP LAma LCro SDeJ
	'Blue Parrot' (10)	EPfP ERCP LAma LCro NBri SCob SDeJ SPer
	'Blue Ribbon' (3)	CAvo LCro LOPS
	Blueberry Ripple	see *T.* 'Zurel'
	'Blumex Favourite'[PBR] (10)	SCob
	'Blushing Apeldoorn' (4)	LAma
	'Blushing Beauty' (5)	LAma SDeJ
	'Blushing Bride' (5)	SDeJ
	'Blushing Girl' (5)	LAma MGib SDeJ
	'Blushing Lady' (5)	LAma MCot
	'Border Legend' (13)	LAma
	'Boston' (3)	LAma
	'Boutade' (14)	NPer
	'Bridesmaid' (5)	LAma
	'Bright Parrot' (10)	LAma MGib
	'Brilliant Star' (1)	LAma
	'Brown Sugar' (3)	EPfP ERCP
	'Bruine Wimpel' (5)	LAma
	'Buddy' (14) **new**	SCob
	'Bulldog' (7)	CAvo SDeJ
	'Burgundy' (6)	CTca ERCP LAma LCro LOPS SDeJ SPer
	'Burgundy Lace' (7)	LAma LCro LOPS SDeJ
	'Burning Heart' (4) ♀H6	LAma SDeJ
	'Burning Love' (1)	LAma
	butkovii (15)	EPot
	'Buttercup' (14)	SDeJ
	'Café Noir' (5)	ERCP LAma NHol
	'Cairo' (3)	LCro LOPS
	'Calgary' (3) ♀H6	CAvo LAma SCob SDeJ
	'Calibra' (7)	LAma
	'Californian Sun' (14)	LAma
	'Calypso' (14) ♀H6	LAma LRHS NBri
	'Canasta' (7)	LAma SDeJ
	'Candela' (13) ♀H6	LAma NBri SDeJ
	'Candy Club' (5)	LAma
	'Candy Prince'[PBR] (1)	LAma NBri SDeJ
	'Canova' (7)	SDeJ
	'Cantata' (13)	LAma
	'Cape Cod' (14)	LAma NBri SDeJ
	'Cardinal Mindszenty' (2)	ERCP LAma LRHS SDeJ
	carinata (15)	ECho
	'Carlton' (2)	LAma NBri
	'Carnaval de Nice' (11/v) ♀H6	CAby CBro CTca ERCP LAma LCro LOPS MBri SDeJ SPer
	'Carola' (3)	LAma
	'Carrousel' (7)	SDeJ
	'Cartouche' (11)	LAma SDeJ
	'Cassini' (3)	LAma SDeJ
§	***celsiana*** (15)	ECho LAma

'Chanson d'Amour' (14)	LAma
'Charmeur'[PBR] (3)	SDeJ
'Cheers' (3)	LAma
'China Lady' (14)	SDeJ
'China Pink' (6) ♀[H6]	CAvo CBro CTca ERCP LAma LCro LOPS MBri SDeJ
'China Town' (8) ♀[H6]	ERCP LAma LCro MBri MGib SDeJ
'Chopin' (12)	LAma NHol
'Christmas Dream' (1)	GKev LAma SDeJ
'Christmas Marvel' (1)	LAma NBri SDeJ
'Christmas Sweet' (1)	LAma
chrysantha Boiss. ex Baker	see *T. montana*
'Cilesta' (2)	LAma
'Cistula' (6)	SDeJ
'City Flower' (14)	LAma
'City of Vancouver' (5)	LAma
'Claudia' (6)	LAma NBri SDeJ
'Clearwater'[PBR] (5)	CAby LAma SDeJ
§ ***clusiana*** (15)	CBro ECho ERCP LAma MBri WHer
- var. ***chrysantha*** (15) ♀[H5]	CExl ECho LAma WShi
- - 'Tubergen's Gem' (15)	ECho EPot GKev LAma MBri
- 'Cynthia' (15) ♀[H6]	CAby CTca ECGP ECho EPot ERCP GKev LAma MBri SBod SDeJ
- 'Sheila' (15)	CBro ECho LAma SPhx
§ - var. ***stellata*** (15)	CBro ECho LAma MGib
'Colour Spectacle'[PBR] (5)	CAby LAma
'Columbine' (5)	ECho LAma
'Come-Back' (4)	LAma
'Comedian' (14)	LAma
'Concerto' (13)	CBro LAma LPfy MBri NPer SDeJ
'Continental' (3)	LAma
'Cool Crystal' (7)	LAma
'Coquette' (1)	LAma SDeJ
'Coquette Yellow' (1)	LAma
'Cordell Hull' (5)	LAma
'Corona' (12)	LAma NBri SDeJ
'Corsage' (14) ♀[H6]	LAma SDeJ
'Cortina' (9)	SDeJ
'Cottage Boy' (1)	LAma
'Cotton Candy Clouds' **new**	LAma
'Couleur Cardinal' (3)	CBro ERCP LAma LCro LOPS LRHS NBri SDeJ
'Cracker'[PBR] (3)	LAma
'Cream Perfection' (3)	LAma
'Creme Upstar' (11)	ERCP LAma LCro LOPS MBri SDeJ
cretica (15)	ECho LAma LLHF
'Crispion Dark' (7)	ERCP
'Crystal Beauty' (7) ♀[H6]	LAma
'Cuban Night' (7)	LAma
'Cum Laude' (5)	LAma SDeJ
'Cummins' (7)	CAvo ERCP LAma
'Curly Sue' (7)	ERCP LAma LCro LOPS MCot SPer
'Czaar Peter' (14) ♀[H6]	CAvo EPfP MBri NBri NPer SDeJ
'Daladier' (11)	LAma
'Dallas' (7)	LAma
'Dance' (13)	LAma SDeJ
'Dancing Queen' (2)	MBri
'Dancing Show' (8)	LAma
dasystemon (15)	ECho LAma LLHF
'Davenport' (7)	ERCP
'David Teniers' (2)	ERCP LAma SDeJ
'Daydream' (4) ♀[H6]	LAma NBri SCob SDeJ SPer
'Daylight' (12)	LAma
'Daytona' (7)	CAvo LAma
'Deep River' (5)	LAma
'Deirdre' (8)	LAma
'Deshima' (3)	LAma
'Design Impression' (4)	LAma
'Destiny' (10)	LAma
'Diana' (1)	LAma
'Dior' (2) **new**	LCro LOPS
'Doll's Minuet' (8)	EPfP ERCP LAma LCro LOPS NBri
'Dom Pedro' (5)	LAma
'Dominiek' (3)	LAma LRHS
'Don Quichotte' (3) ♀[H6]	LAma LCro LOPS MBri SDeJ
'Donald Duck' (14) ♀[H6]	MBri
'Donauperle' (14)	SDeJ
'Donna Bella' (14)	SDeJ
'Dordogne' (5) ♀[H6]	LAma SDeJ
'Double Dazzle' (2)	LAma
'Double Flaming Parrot'[PBR] (10) **new**	LAma
'Double Price' (2)	ERCP
'Double Princess'[PBR] (2)	LAma
'Double Red Riding Hood' (14v)	LAma SCob SDeJ
'Double Sugar' (11)	LAma
'Douglas Bader' (5)	LAma
'Dragon King' (3)	SDeJ
'Dream Touch' (11)	LAma LCro LOPS
'Dreamboat' (14)	LAma MBri
'Dreaming Maid' (3)	LAma MBri
'Dreamland' (5) ♀[H6]	LAma MBri SDeJ
'Duc van Tol Aurora'	LAma
'Duc van Tol Max Cramoisie' (1)	LAma
'Duc van Tol Primrose' (1)	LAma
'Duc van Tol Red and Yellow' (1)	GKev LAma WHer
'Duc van Tol Rose' (1)	LAma
'Duc van Tol Salmon' (1)	LAma
'Duc van Tol Scarlet' (1)	LAma
'Duc van Tol Violet' (1)	LAma
'Duc van Tol White' (1)	LAma
'Dutch Gold' (3)	MBri
'Dyanito' (6)	LAma
'Early Glory' (3)	LAma LCro
'Early Harvest' (12) ♀[H6]	CAvo LAma SDeJ
'Early Star' (14)	LAma
'Easter Parade' (13)	LAma
'Easter Surprise' (14) ♀[H6]	LAma MBri SDeJ
'Ego Parrot' (10) **new**	LCro
'Electra' (5)	LAma MBri NHol
'Elegans Alba' (6)	LAma
'Elegant Lady' (6)	CAvo LAma NBri SDeJ
'Erna Lindgreen' (10)	LAma
'Escape'[PBR] (3)	LAma
'Esperanto' (8/v) ♀[H6]	LAma SDeJ
'Esprit' (7) **new**	LAma
'Estella Rijnveld' (10)	ERCP LAma LCro LOPS SDeJ
'Esther' (5)	LAma
'Eternal Flame' (2)	LAma LCro
'Evita'[PBR]	LAma
'Exotic Emperor' (13)	CAvo LAma LCro SDeJ
'Eye Catcher' (8)	LAma
'Fabio' (7)	LAma LRHS
'Fairy Nymph' (5)	LAma
'Fancy Frills' (7) ♀[H6]	ERCP LAma SDeJ
'Fantasy' (10) ♀[H6]	LAma NBri
'Fashion' (12)	LAma SDeJ
ferganica (15)	ECho LAma
'Fidelio' (3) ♀[H6]	SDeJ
'Fire of Love' (14)	LAma
'Fire Queen' (3) ♀[H6]	LAma
'First Impression' (14)	LAma
'Flair' (1)	LAma LRHS NBri SDeJ

	'Flamenco' (7)	SDeJ
	'Flaming Club' (5)	LAma
	'Flaming Coquette'PBR (1)	LAma
	'Flaming Evita'PBR (2)	SDeJ
	'Flaming Jewel' (4)	LAma
	'Flaming Parrot' (10)	CAby CAvo ERCP GKev LAma LCro LOPS MBri
I	'Flaming Purissima' (13)	CAvo LAma MBri SDeJ
	'Flaming Springgreen' (8)	CAvo ERCP LAma LCro SDeJ
	'Flashback' (10)	ERCP LAma
	'Flig Flag' (3)	ERCP
	'Florette'PBR (5)	LAma
	'Florijn Chic' (6)	LAma
	'Florosa' (8)	ERCP LCro LOPS SDeJ
	'Fontainebleau' (3)	LAma SDeJ
	'Formosa' (8)	EPfP LAma
	'Foxtrot'PBR (2)	EPfP ERCP LAma
	'Françoise' (3)	LAma SDeJ
	'Franz Léhar' (12)	SDeJ
	'Freeman' (11)	LAma
	'Fringed Elegance' (7) ♀H6	LAma LCro LOPS
	'Fringed Family' (7)	SDeJ
	'Fringed Golden Apeldoorn' (7)	LAma
	'Fringed Red Riding Hood' (7) **new**	CAby
	'Fritz Kreisler' (12)	LAma SDeJ
	'Fulgens' (6)	LAma
	'Fulton' (5)	LAma
	'Für Elise' (14)	LRHS NBri SDeJ
	'Gabriella' (3)	LAma
	'Gaiety' (12)	SDeJ
	'Gander's Rhapsody' (3)	LAma
	'Garanza' (2)	LAma
	'Garden Party' (3)	LAma SDeJ
	'Garden Show' (14)	LAma
	'Gavota' (3) ♀H6	CAvo CBro LAma NBri NHol SCob SDeJ
	'Generaal de Wet' (1)	LAma SDeJ
	'Georges Grappe' (5)	LAma
	'Georgette' (5)	LAma MBri
	'Gerbrand Kieft' (11) ♀H6	ERCP
	'Gipsy Love' (7)	SDeJ
	'Giuseppe Verdi' (12)	LAma LRHS MBri
	'Glück' (12) ♀H6	ECho EPfP LAma LRHS
	'Golden Apeldoorn' (4)	LAma LCro LOPS MBri NBri SCob SDeJ
	'Golden Artist' (8)	LAma MBri SDeJ
	'Golden Dynasty' (3) **new**	MGib
	'Golden Emperor' (13)	LAma SDeJ
	'Golden Melody' (3)	LAma SDeJ
	'Golden Nizza' (11)	LAma
	'Golden Oxford' (4)	LAma
	'Golden Parade' (4)	LAma
	'Goldwest' (14)	SDeJ
	'Gordon Cooper' (4)	LAma SDeJ
	'Gorilla' (7) **new**	LAma
	'Goudstuk' (12)	LAma
	'Goya' (2)	LAma
	'Grand Perfection'PBR (3) ♀H6	LCro LOPS
	'Grand Prestige' (14)	LAma
	'Grand Style' (5) ♀H6	LAma
	'Granny Award' (11)	LAma
	'Green Eyes' (8)	SDeJ
	'Green River' (8)	LAma SDeJ
	'Green Unique'	LAma
	'Green Village' (8)	LAma
	'Green Wave' (10)	ERCP LAma LCro LOPS SDeJ
	'Greenstar' (6)	LAma
	greigii (14)	LAma
	grengiolensis (15)	LAma
	'Greuze' (5)	LOPS
	'Groenland' (8)	CAvo CBro LAma LCro MBri MCot NBri SDeJ
	'Gudoshnik' (4)	LAma
	hageri (15)	ECho LAma LLHF MBri
	- 'Splendens' (15)	LAma SBod SDeJ SPhx
	'Hakuun' (4)	LAma
	'Halcro' (5) ♀H6	LAma
	'Hamilton' (7)	LAma SDeJ
	'Happy Family' (3)	LAma
	'Happy Generation' (3)	LAma LCro LOPS MBri
	'Happy Hour' (7)	ERCP
	'Havran' (3)	CAvo CBro ERCP LAma LCro LOPS
	'Heart's Delight' (12)	CBro ECho LAma MBri NBri SDeJ
	'Helmar' (3)	LAma SDeJ
	'Hemisphere' (3)	EPfP ERCP LAma SDeJ
	'Hermitage' (3)	ERCP LAma
	heweri (15)	EPot LAma
	'Hocus Pocus' (5)	LAma SDeJ
	'Holland Baby' (2)	LAma SDeJ
	'Holland Bouquet' (3)	LAma
	'Holland Chic' (6)	LAma MCot SDeJ
	'Holland Emotions' (4)	LAma
	'Holland Happening' (10)	LAma
	'Holland Queen'PBR (3)	LAma
	'Holland Ruby' (11)	LAma
	'Holland Sun' (3)	LAma
	'Hollandia' (3)	LAma MBri
	'Hollands Glorie' (4)	LAma SDeJ
	'Hollywood' (8)	LAma
	'Hollywood Star' (8)	LAma
	'Honeymoon' (7)	LAma
	'Honky Tonk' (15) ♀H6	CAvo ECho GKev LAma MBri
§	***hoogiana*** (15)	ECho
	'Hot Chocolate' (3)	LAma
	'Hotpants' (3)	LAma SCob
	'Huis Ten Bosch' (7)	LAma
§	***humilis*** (15)	CBro ECho EWTr GKev LAma LRHS MBri SDeJ WShi
	- 'China Carol' (15)	ECGP ECho LAma LLHF SDeJ
	- 'Eastern Spice' (15)	ECho LAma
	- 'Eastern Star' (15)	ECho GKev LAma MBri
§	- 'Lilliput' (15)	CBro ECho EPot GKev LAma LRHS MGib NBri
	- 'Magenta Queen' (15)	LAma
	- 'Odalisque' (15)	ECho EPot ERCP GKev LAma LRHS SBod
	- 'Persian Pearl' (15)	CAvo ECho EPfP EPot ERCP GKev LAma LCro LOPS MBri SCob SDeJ
	- var. ***pulchella*** Albocaerulea Oculata Group (15)	CTca ECho EPot ERCP GKev LLHF MCot
	- 'Tête-à-tête' (15)	LAma
§	- Violacea Group (15)	ECho LRHS MBri
	- - black base (15)	CMea ECho EPot ERCP GKev LAma MBri
	- - yellow base (15)	ECho EPot GKev LAma
	'Humming Bird' (8)	LAma
	'Ice Cream' (11)	LAma SDeJ
	'Ice Stick' (12)	CBro SDeJ
	'Ile de France' (5)	ERCP LAma LCro LOPS SDeJ
	iliensis (15)	CMea EPot LAma LLHF
	'India' (3)	LAma
	'Indian Velvet' (5) **new**	LCro LOPS
	ingens (15)	ECho LAma
	'Innuendo' **new**	SPer

Name	Suppliers
'Insulinde' (9)	LAma
'Inzell' (3)	EPfP LAma
'Ivory Floradale' (4) ♀H6	LAma SDeJ
'Jaap Groot' (4)	LAma
'Jackpot' (3)	EPfP LAma SCob
'Jacqueline' (6)	LAma LOPS
'Jan Reus' (3)	CAvo CBro ERCP LAma LCro LOPS
'Jazz' (6)	ERCP
'Jewel of Spring' (4)	LAma
'Jimmy' (3)	LAma
'Jochem' (3)	LAma
'Joffre' (1)	LAma MBri
'Johann Strauss' (12)	LAma MBri NBri
'Juan' (13) ♀H6	LAma MBri
'Judith Leyster' (3)	LAma
'Juliette' (4)	LAma
'Karel Doorman' (10)	LAma
'Kathleen Truxton' (5)	LAma
kaufmanniana (12)	ECho EPot
§ 'Kees Nelis' (3)	MBri NBri
'Keizerskroon' (1)	LAma SDeJ
'Kikomachi' (3) **new**	LRHS
'Kingsblood' (5) ♀H6	LAma SDeJ
'Kleurenpracht'	see *T.* 'Princess Margaret Rose'
kolpakowskiana (15) ♀H6	EPot ERCP LAma LLHF MBri WShi
kurdica (15)	ECho LAma SPhx
- purple-flowered (15)	ECho
'La Belle Époque' (2)	CAvo ERCP LCro LOPS SCob SDeJ
'La Courtine' (5)	LAma
'La Douceur' (5)	LAma
'Lac van Rijn' (1)	GKev LAma
* 'Lady Diana' (14)	MBri
'Lady Jane' (15) ♀H6	CAvo CMea ECho LAma MBri SPhx WShi
'Large Copper' (14)	LAma
'Lasting Love' (3)	LAma
'Latvian Gold' (15)	ECho
'Le Mogol' (5)	LAma
'Leen van der Mark' (3)	LAma MBri NBri
'Leo Visser' (3)	LAma
'Libretto Parrot' (10)	LAma SDeJ
'Light and Dreamy' (4) **new**	LCro LOPS
'Lighting Sun' (4)	LAma
'Lila Star'	LAma
'Lilac Perfection' (11)	CTca ERCP LAma MBri SDeJ
'Lilac Time' (6)	LAma
'Lilac Wonder'	see *T. saxatilis* (Bakeri Group) 'Lilac Wonder'
'Lilliput'	see *T. humilis* 'Lilliput'
'Lilybeauty' (6)	LAma
'Lilyfire' (6)	LAma SDeJ
'Limelight' **new**	LAma
'Lingerie' (7)	LAma
linifolia (15) ♀H5	CAvo ECho EPot ERCP GKev LAma MBri MGib SDeJ WShi
§ - Batalinii Group (15) ♀H5	ECho MBri
§ - - 'Apricot Jewel' (15)	CBro ECho EPot ERCP GKev LAma
- - 'Bright Gem' (15) ♀H5	CBro ECho EPot GKev LAma MBri NPer SPhx WHoo
- - 'Bronze Charm' (15)	CAvo CMea ECGP ECho EPot LAma MBri SDeJ SPhx
- - 'Red Gem' (15)	ECho GKev SPhx
- - 'Red Hunter' (15) ♀H6	CAby CBro CMea ERCP GKev LAma MBri
- - 'Red Jewel' (15)	ECho LAma
- - 'Salmon Gem' (15)	ECho
- - 'Yellow Jewel' (15)	ECho GKev LAma WShi
§ - Maximowiczii Group (15)	ECho LAma
'Lipgloss' (3)	LAma NHol
'Little Beauty' (15) ♀H6	CAby CAvo CBro CMea ECho EPfP EPot GKev LAma LCro LOPS LRHS MBri NBri SBod SDeJ SPhx WHoo
'Little Diamond' (12)	LRHS
'Little Girl' (14) **new**	LCro
'Little Princess' (15) ♀H6	CAvo CBro CTca ECho EPfP EPot ERCP GKev LAma NBri SDeJ SPhx
'Little Star' (15) ♀H6	GKev LAma
'London' (4)	LAma
'Long Lady' (5)	LAma
'Louvre' (7) ♀H6	LAma
'Love Song' (12)	LAma
'Lovely Surprise' (14)	SDeJ
'Lucky Strike' (3)	MBri
§ 'Lustige Witwe' (3)	LAma SDeJ
'Lydia' (3)	LAma
'Mabel' (9)	LAma
§ 'Madame Lefeber' (13)	LAma LOPS MBri NBri SDeJ
'Madonna' (10)	EPfP LAma
'Magier' (5)	MBri
'Maja' (7)	LAma MBri
'Makassar' (3)	LAma
'Mango Charm' (3) **new**	LAma
'March of Time' (14)	LAma MBri
'Margaret Herbst' (14)	LAma
'Margarita' (2)	LAma LCro SPer
'Marie José' (14)	SDeJ
'Marie Louise' (5)	LAma
'Mariette' (6)	CBro LAma MBri SDeJ
'Marilyn' (6)	ERCP LAma SDeJ
'Marit' (4) ♀H6	LAma
'Marjolein' (6)	LAma
marjolletii (15)	LAma
'Maroon' (7)	ERCP
'Mary Ann' (14)	LAma
'Mata Hari' (3)	LAma
'Matchpoint' (7/d)	ERCP LAma SDeJ
'Maureen' (5) ♀H6	ERCP LAma LCro LOPS SDeJ
'Maureen Double' (11) **new**	LCro
mauritiana 'Cindy' (15)	LAma
maximowiczii	see *T. linifolia* Maximowiczii Group
'Maytime' (6)	LAma LCro LOPS MBri MCot SDeJ
'Maywonder' (11)	MBri
'Melody d'Amour' (5)	LAma
'Melrose' (2)	LAma
'Menton' (5) ♀H6	ERCP LAma LCro LOPS SDeJ
'Menton Exotic' (11)	ERCP SPer
'Merlot' (6)	LAma LOPS
'Merry Christmas' (1)	LAma
'Merry Christmas Design' (1)	LAma
Merry Widow	see *T.* 'Lustige Witwe'
'Mickey Mouse' (1)	LAma LCro MBri
'Miranda' (11)	LAma
'Miskodeed' (14)	SDeJ
'Miss Elegance' (3)	LAma
'Miss Holland' (3)	MBri
'Mistress' (3)	LAma LCro
'Modern Style' (5)	LAma
'Mona Lisa' (6)	LAma SDeJ
'Mondial' PBR (2)	LAma
'Moneymaker' (6)	ERCP
'Monsella' (2)	LAma NBri
§ ***montana*** (15)	CTca ECho EPot LAma
- yellow-flowered	ECho GKev LAma
'Monte Carlo' (2) ♀H6	CBro LAma LCro MBri NBri SDeJ
'Montreux' (2)	LAma
'Moonshine' (6)	LAma
'Moonwalker' (4)	LAma

'Mount Tacoma' (11)	CAvo CBro ERCP LAma LCro LOPS MBri SDeJ SPer
'Mr Van der Hoef' (2)	LAma MBri SDeJ
'Mrs John T. Scheepers' (5)	LAma SDeJ
'Muriel' (10)	ERCP
'National Velvet' (3) **new**	LCro
'Negrita' (3)	ERCP LAma LCro LOPS MBri NBri SCob SDeJ
neustruevae (15)	ECho LAma
'New Design' (3/v)	LAma MBri
'Nicholas Heyek' (3) **new**	LCro
'Nightrider' (8)	CAvo ERCP LAma LCro MCot SDeJ
'Noranda' (7)	LAma
'Ollioules' (4) ♀H6	LAma SDeJ
'Olympic Flame' (4) ♀H6	LAma LCro LOPS SDeJ
'Orange Angelique' (11)	GKev XEll
'Orange Bouquet' (3) ♀H6	LAma MBri SDeJ
'Orange Brilliant' (13)	LAma
'Orange Cassini' (3)	LAma NBri
'Orange Elite' (14)	MBri
'Orange Emperor' (13) ♀H6	CAvo ERCP LAma LPfy MBri SDeJ
'Orange Favourite' (10)	ERCP LAma
'Orange Lion' (4)	LAma
'Orange Monarch' (3)	LAma
'Orange Princess' (11) ♀H6	CBro CTca ERCP LAma LCro LOPS SCob SDeJ
'Orange Queen' (4)	LAma
'Orange Sun'	see *T.* 'Oranjezon'
'Orange Toronto' (14)	LAma
'Orange Triumph' (11)	MBri
'Oranje Nassau' (2) ♀H6	MBri
§ 'Oranjezon' (4) ♀H6	ERCP LAma
'Oratorio' (14) ♀H6	LAma MBri SDeJ
'Oriental Beauty' (14) ♀H6	LAma
orphanidea (15)	ECho LAma
- 'Flava' (15)	ECho LAma
§ - Whittallii Group (15) ♀H6	EPot ERCP GKev LCro LOPS SDeJ SPhx WShi
'Oscar' (3)	LAma NHol
ostrowskiana (15)	ECho LAma
'Oxford' (4) ♀H6	LAma
'Oxford's Elite' (4)	LAma
'Page Polka' (3)	LAma MBri SDeJ
'Palestrina' (3)	LAma SPer
'Pandour' (14)	LAma MBri
'Panorama' (5)	LAma
'Papillon' (9)	LAma
'Parade' (4) ♀H6	LAma MBri
'Parrot King' (10)	SDeJ
'Passionale' (3) ♀H6	EPfP LAma LCro LOPS NBri SDeJ SPer
'Paul Scherer' (3) ♀H6	CAvo ERCP LAma LCro LOPS SDeJ
'Pax' (3)	LAma
'Peach Blossom' (2)	ERCP LAma LCro LRHS MBri NBri SCob SDeJ SPer
Peacock Group	SDeJ
'Peppermintstick' (15) ♀H6	CAvo CBro CTca ECho EPfP LAma MPie SCob SDeJ SPer
'Perestroyka' (5)	LAma MBri SDeJ
persica	see *T. celsiana*
'Philippe de Comines' (5)	LAma
'Piccolo' (15)	LAma
'Picture' (5)	ERCP LAma SDeJ
'Pieter de Leur' (6)	LAma MBri
'Pimpernel' (8/v)	LAma SDeJ
'Pink Diamond' (5)	CAvo ERCP NHol SDeJ
'Pink Dwarf' (12)	SDeJ
'Pink Impression' (4) ♀H6	LAma LCro MBri SDeJ
'Pink Lady' (3)	LAma
'Pink Sensation' (14)	SDeJ
'Pinkeen' (13)	LAma
'Pinocchio' (14)	LAma LRHS MBri NBri SDeJ
'Pirand' (13) ♀H6	SDeJ
'Pittsburg' (3) **new**	LCro LOPS
'Plaisir' (14) ♀H6	LAma MBri
platystigma (15)	ECho LAma
'Poco Loco' (13)	SDeJ
polychroma	see *T. biflora*
praestans (15)	ECho SPer WShi
- 'Bloemenlust' (15)	GKev
- 'Fusilier' (15) ♀H6	CBro CExl EPot LAma MBri NBir NBri SDeJ
- 'Shogun' (15)	ERCP NBri SDeJ
- 'Unicum' (15/v)	EPot ERCP LAma MBri MGib NBri SBod SDeJ
- 'Van Tubergen's Variety' (15)	ECho LAma NPer
- 'Zwanenburg Variety' (15)	ECho
'Pretty Woman' (6)	LAma SPer
'Princeps' (13)	LAma MBri SDeJ
§ 'Princess Margaret Rose' (5)	LAma
'Princess Unique'[PBR] (11)	LAma
'Princess Victoria' (3) **new**	GKev
'Princesse Charmante' (14) ♀H6	LAma LCro LOPS MBri
'Prins Carnaval' (1) ♀H6	LAma
'Prinses Irene' (3) ♀H6	CAvo CBro CMea CTca EPfP ERCP LAma LCro LOPS LRHS MBri MCot NBir NBri NHol SDeJ
'Prinses Margriet' (3)	ERCP LAma
'Professor Einstein' (3)	LAma
'Professor Röntgen' (10)	ERCP LAma LCro LOPS SDeJ
'Professor Schotel' (15)	LAma
pulchella humilis	see *T. humilis*
§ 'Purissima' (13) ♀H6	CAvo CBro LAma LCro LOPS MBri NBri SCob SDeJ SPer
'Purple Bouquet' (3)	LAma SDeJ
'Purple Dream' (6)	CBro LAma SDeJ
'Purple Flag' (3)	LAma LCro LOPS
'Purple Jacket' (11) **new**	LCro LOPS
'Purple Prince' (5)	LAma LCro LOPS LPfy LRHS SDeJ
'Purple Rain' (3)	LAma
'Purple Tower' **new**	ERCP
'Purple Voice'	LAma
'Quebec' (14)	LAma LPfy SDeJ
'Queen of Marvel' (2)	LAma SDeJ
'Queen of Night' (5)	CAvo CBro CMea CTca EPfP ERCP GKev LAma LCro LPfy MBri NBri SCob SPer SPhx
'Queensday' (11)	LAma
'Queensland' (7)	CAvo ERCP LAma
'Quest' (3)	LAma
'Rai' (10)	ERCP LAma LCro
'Rainbow'	LAma
'Real Time' (7)	LAma
'Recreado' (5)	CAvo ERCP LAma SDeJ
'Red Baby Doll' (2)	LAma
'Red Emperor'	see *T.* 'Madame Lefeber'
'Red Georgette' (5) ♀H6	CAby LAma MBri NBir
'Red Hat' (7) **new**	LCro LOPS MGib
'Red Impression'[PBR] (4) ♀H6	LAma LCro LOPS
'Red Mark'[PBR] (3)	LAma
'Red Present' (3)	LAma
'Red Princess' (11) ♀H6	ERCP LAma
'Red Revival' (1)	LAma
'Red Riding Hood' (14) ♀H6	CAvo CBro EPfP GKev LAma LRHS MBri NBir NBri SCob SDeJ SPer

Name	Suppliers
'Red Rover' (3) **new**	LCro
'Red Shine' (6) ♀^{H6}	CAvo CBro LAma LCro MBri SDeJ
'Red Springgreen' (8)	ERCP LAma LCro LOPS SDeJ
'Red Wing' (7) ♀^{H6}	LAma SDeJ
'Redwood' (14)	SDeJ
Rembrandt mix (9)	MBri
(Rembrandt Group) 'Saskia' (15)	LAma
'Rems Favourite' (3)	CAvo LCro LOPS
'Renown' (5)	LAma SDeJ
'Renown Unique' (11)	LAma
'Request' **new**	LAma
'Rex Rubrorum' (2)	LAma
rhodopea	see *T. urumoffii*
'Ringo'	see *T.* 'Kees Nelis'
'Robert Schuller' (14)	LAma
'Rockery Master' (14)	LAma
'Rococo' (10)	CBro ERCP LAma LCro LOPS MBri NBri SDeJ
'Roi du Midi' (5)	LAma SDeJ
'Ronaldo' (3)	ERCP LAma LCro LOPS
'Rosalie' (3)	LAma
'Rose des Dames' (5)	LAma
* 'Rose Emperor' (13)	MBri
'Rosy Dream' (13)	LAma SDeJ
'Roulette' (3)	LAma
'Royal Acres' (2)	LAma
'Royal Elegance' (7)	LAma
'Ruud Lubbers' (14)	LAma
'Sahara Rally' (4)	LAma
'Salmon Impression'^{PBR} (4)	LAma MBri NBri
'Salmon Jewel' (3)	EPot
'Salmon Parrot' (10)	LAma
'Salut' (13)	LAma
'Sanne' (3)	LAma
'Sapporro' (6)	CMea ERCP LAma LCro LOPS NBri
saxatilis (15)	CBro ECho EPfP GKev LAma LCro LOPS MBri SDeJ WShi
§ - Bakeri Group (15)	SCob SEND
§ - - 'Lilac Wonder' (15) ♀^{H6}	CAby CAvo CBro CExl ECho EPot ERCP GKev LAma LCro LOPS MBri NPer SCob SPhx
'Scarlet Baby' (12)	EPfP LAma MBri NBri
'Schoonoord' (2)	LAma MBri
schrenkii (15)	EPot ERCP LAma
'Scotland' (2)	LAma
'Seadov' (3)	LAma LCro
'Sensual Touch' (7) ♀^{H6}	LAma SDeJ
'Sevilla' (3) ♀^{H6} **new**	LPfy
'Sexy Lady' (10)	LAma
'Shakespeare' (12)	CBro LAma SDeJ
'Shirley' (3)	CAvo ERCP LAma LCro LOPS LPfy MBri NBri NChi SCob SDeJ SPer
'Shirley Dream' (3)	LAma SDeJ
'Shirley Flame' (3)	LAma
'Showtime' (14)	SDeJ
'Showwinner' (12) ♀^{H6}	CAvo CBro LAma MBri NBri NHol SDeJ
'Sihouette Bouquet' (3)	LAma
'Silver Dollar' (3)	LAma
'Silver Parrot' (10)	LAma LCro LOPS
'Silverado' (5)	LAma
'Silverstream' (4)	LAma
'Sinopel' (8)	LAma
'Snow Parrot' (10)	ERCP
'Snow Valley' (7) **new**	LCro
'Snowboard' (3)	LAma
'Snowpeak' (5)	LAma
sogdiana (15)	ECho LAma LLHF
'Sorbet' (5) ♀^{H6}	LAma SDeJ
sprengeri (15) ♀^{H6}	CAvo CBro CDes CExl CLAP CSpe CTca ECha ECho ERCP LAma LLHF WHal WShi
- Trotter's form (15)	WCot
'Spring Green' (8) ♀^{H6}	CAvo CBro EPfP ERCP GKev LAma LCro LOPS MBri NBri SCob SDeJ SPer SPhx
'Spryng' (3) ♀^{H6}	SDeJ
'Starfighter' (7)	SDeJ
stellata	see *T. clusiana* var. *stellata*
'Stockholm' (2) ♀^{H6}	LAma
'Stresa' (12) ♀^{H6}	CBro LAma LRHS NBri SDeJ
'Striped Sail' (3)	LAma
'Strong Gold' (3) ♀^{H6}	LAma MGib SDeJ
'Stunning Apricot' (5)	LAma LCro LOPS
subpraestans (15)	LAma
'Sun Dance' (14)	LAma
'Sun Lover' (11)	LAma
'Sunny Prince'^{PBR} (1)	CBro
'Super Parrot' (10)	LAma
'Supertwins' (3)	LAma
'Survivor' (5)	SDeJ
'Swan Wings' (7)	ERCP LAma LCro LOPS SDeJ
'Sweet Harmony' (5)	LAma MBri
'Sweet Lady' (14)	LAma SDeJ
'Sweetheart' (13)	LAma LCro LOPS MBri NBri SDeJ
'Sweety' (3)	LAma
sylvestris (15)	CAby CAvo CBro CSpe CTca ECho EPfP EPot ERCP LAma LCro MBri MGib NBir SDeJ SPhx WCot WHer WOut WShi
'Sylvia Warder' (14)	LAma
'Synaeda King' (6) ♀^{H6}	LAma
'Synaeda Orange' (6)	LAma
systola (15)	LAma
'Taco' (15)	LAma MBri
'Talisman' (5) **new**	GKev
'Tarafa' (14)	LAma
tarda (15) ♀^{H5}	CAvo CBro CExl ECho EPfP ERCP GKev LAma LCro LOPS LPot LRHS MBri NBri SBod SDeJ SPhx WShi
'Temple of Beauty' (5) ♀^{H6}	LAma SDeJ
'Temple's Favourite' (5)	MBri
'Tennessee' (3)	LAma
'Tequila Sun' (3)	LAma
tetraphylla (15)	ECho LAma
'Texas Flame' (10)	LAma MBri NBri SDeJ
'Texas Gold' (10)	LAma SDeJ
'The First' (12)	LAma NBri
'The Lizard' (9)	LAma
'Theeroos' (2)	LAma
'Tinka' (15) ♀^{H6}	CMea ECho LAma SCob
'Tiny Timo' (15)	LLHF
'Tom Pouce' (3) **new**	LCro LOPS
'Ton Angustinus' (4)	LAma
'Toplips' (11)	LAma SDeJ
'Topparrot' (10)	LAma SDeJ
'Toronto' (14) ♀^{H6}	CTca LAma MBri NBri SCob SDeJ
'Toronto Double' (2)	LAma SDeJ
'Totum' (11)	LAma
'Toucan' (3)	LAma
'Toulon' (13)	MBri
'Toyota' (5)	SDeJ
'Très Chic' (6)	CAvo CTca EPfP LAma LCro LOPS MBri
'Tricolored Beauty' (8)	ERCP

	'Trinket' (14) 🏆H6	LAma
	'Tropical Dream' (3) **new**	LAma
	'Tropical Lady' (3)	LAma
	tschimganica (15)	LAma
	tubergeniana (15)	LAma
	turkestanica (15) 🏆H5	CAby CBro CExl CHid CTca ECho EPfP EPot ERCP GKev LAma LPot MBri NBri NPer SDeJ WHoo WShi
	'Turkish Delight' (14)	NPer
	'Twilight Princess' (8)	LAma
	'Typhoon' (3)	LAma
	'Uncle Tom' (11)	CAvo ERCP LAma MBri NBri SDeJ
	'United States' (14)	LAma NPer
	'Upstar' (11)	LAma
	urumiensis (15) 🏆H5	CHid ECho EPot GKev LAma LPot MBri SDeJ SPhx
	- 'Tity's Star' (15) **new**	SBod
§	***urumoffii*** (15)	ECho LAma
	'Valentine' (3)	LAma SDeJ
	'Valery Gergiev' (7)	ERCP LAma
	'Van der Neer' (1)	SDeJ
	'Van Eijk'PBR (4)	LAma NBri SCob
	'Verona' (2)	LAma SDeJ
	'Véronique Sanson' (3)	ERCP LCro LOPS SDeJ
	'Victoria's Secret' (3) **new**	EPfP LCro LOPS
	'Viking'	LAma
	'Vincent van Gogh' (7)	LAma
	violacea	see *T. humilis* Violacea Group
	'Violet Beauty' (5)	LAma LCro SDeJ
	'Violet Bird' (8)	LAma LCro LOPS SDeJ
	'Virichic' (8)	ERCP LAma LCro LOPS MCot
	'Vivex' (4)	LAma
	'Vivienne Westwood' (10) **new**	LCro LOPS
	vvedenskyi (15)	ECho EPot GKev
	- 'Bernadette'	LAma
	- 'Tangerine Beauty' (15) 🏆H6	ECho GKev LAma MBri
	'Wallflower' (5)	ERCP LAma
	'Wapen van Leiden' (1)	LAma
	'Warbler' (7)	LAma SDeJ
	'Washington' (3)	LCro
	'Weber's Parrot' (10)	ERCP LAma LCro LOPS MBri MCot
	'Weisse Berliner' (3)	CBro LAma
	'West Point' (6)	CAvo CBro CTca LAma LCro LOPS MBri SDeJ
*	'White Bouquet' (5)	LAma
	'White Dream' (3)	LAma LCro LOPS MBri NBri SDeJ
	'White Elegance' (6)	LAma
	'White Emperor'	see *T.* 'Purissima'
	'White Lieberstar' **new**	ERCP
	'White Marvel' (3)	LAma LRHS
	'White Parrot' (10)	CAvo ERCP LAma LCro LOPS SDeJ
	'White Sea' (13)	LAma
	'White Triumphator' (6) 🏆H6	CAvo CBro CMea ERCP GKev LAma LCro LOPS MBri NBir SDeJ SPhx
	whittallii	see *T. orphanidea* Whittallii Group
	'Wildhof' (3) 🏆H6	ERCP
§	'Willem van Oranje' (2)	LAma LRHS SDeJ
	'Willemsoord' (2)	LAma LRHS MBri SDeJ
	William of Orange	see *T.* 'Willem van Oranje'
	wilsoniana	see *T. montana*
	'Winterberg' (3)	LAma
	'Wirosa' (11) 🏆H6	NBri
	'Wisley' (5)	LCro MBri SCob
	'World Expression' (5) 🏆H6	LAma SDeJ
	'Yellow Apeldoorn' **new**	SPer
	'Yellow Crown' (3)	LAma
	'Yellow Emperor' (5)	MBri
	'Yellow Flight' (3)	LAma SDeJ
	'Yellow Pompenette'PBR (11) 🏆H6	SDeJ
	'Yellow Present' (3)	LAma
I	'Yellow Purissima' (13) 🏆H6	LAma
	'Yellow Springgreen' (8)	CBro ERCP LAma LCro LOPS SDeJ
	'Yellow Wave' (4)	LAma
	'Yoko Parrot' (10)	SDeJ
	'Yokohama' (3)	LAma NBri SCob SDeJ SPer
	'Yonina' (6)	LAma LCro LOPS NBri
	'Zampa' (14) 🏆H6	LAma MBri
	'Zombie' (13)	LAma
	'Zomerschoon' (5)	LAma
§	'Zurel' (3)	ERCP LAma MCot SCob

tummelberry see *Rubus* 'Tummelberry'

Tunica see *Petrorhagia*

Tupistra (*Asparagaceae*)

aurantiaca	LEdu
- B&SWJ 2267	WCot WCru
- B&SWJ 2401	WCru
chinensis 'Eco China Ruffles'	WCot
grandistigma	WCot
- B&SWJ 11773	WCru
jinshanensis	WCot
urotepala HWJ 562	WCru
wattii B&SWJ 8297	WCru

Tussilago (*Asteraceae*)

farfara	GPoy MHer NMir WHer WHfH WSFF

Tweedia (*Asclepiadaceae*)

§	***coerulea*** 🏆H1c	CBcs CDTJ CFlo CKel CSpe SWvt

Typha (*Typhaceae*)

	angustifolia	CBen CKno CWat LLWG MMuc MSKA NPer SEND SPlb SWat WMAq WPnP
	latifolia	CBen CWat EHon MSKA NBir NPer SVic SWat WMAq WPnP XLum
	- 'Variegata' (v)	CWat LLWG MSKA MWts NPla WMAq
§	***laxmannii***	CBen EHon LLWG MSKA WMAq WPnP XLum
	lugdunensis	MWts
	minima	CBen CWat EHoe EHon MSKA MWts NPer SWat WMAq WPnP XLum
	shuttleworthii	CBen LLWG
	stenophylla	see *T. laxmannii*

Typhonium (*Araceae*)

giganteum	CAby SKHP WCot
horsfieldii	LEdu WCot
roxburghii	LTro
trilobatum	WCot
venosum	EUJe LTro

Typhonodorum (*Araceae*)

lindleyanum	XBlo

U

Uapaca (*Euphorbiaceae*)

kirkiana (F)	XBlo

ugli see *Citrus* × *aurantium* Tangelo Group 'Ugli'

Ugni ✿ (*Myrtaceae*)

candollei	SVen
§ ***molinae***	CBcs CBod CCon CDul CExl CHll CTsd EBee ELan ELon EPfP EShb GGal IDee IVic LEdu LPal LRHS MGil MGos MHer SAdn SBrt SChF SEle SWvt WGwG WHar WJek
- PAB 1347	LEdu
- 'Butterball'	CBcs EBee EPfP LRHS LSou SPoG SWvt WBor
- 'Flambeau' (v)	CBcs CBod CDul CExl CMac CSde ELan EPfP EShb IVic LEdu LRHS MAsh MGil NLar SEle SHil SLon SPoG SRkn SWvt
- orange-leaved	SRms WJek
- 'Variegata' (v)	LEdu LRHS WJek

Ulex (*Papilionaceae*)

europaeus	CArn CBcs CCVT CDoC CDul CHab CMac CTri ECrN ELan EPfP MCoo MGil MGos MMuc NBes NWea SCob SEWo SPer WHar
§ - 'Flore Pleno' (d) 🏆H4	CBcs CBod CDoC CDul CLet CMac CSBt CSde CTri ELan EPfP GCal IArd LAst MBlu MGos MMuc NWea SCob SEND SPer WFar WHer
- 'Plenus'	see *U. europaeus* 'Flore Pleno'
gallii	NLar
- 'Mizen Head'	GCal NLar

Ullucus (*Basellaceae*)

tuberosus	LEdu

Ulmus ✿ (*Ulmaceae*)

americana 'Princeton'	SEWo
carpinifolia var. ***suberosa***	CDul
chenmoui new	IArd
'Columella' new	SAko
'Dodoens'	IArd MBlu SCoo
'Frontier'	SGol
§ ***glabra***	CDul EPfP MJak NWea SCob SCoo
- 'Camperdownii'	CMac ECrN ELan LAst WMou
- 'Exoniensis'	CTho IVic
- 'Gittisham'	CTho
- 'Horizontalis'	see *U. glabra* 'Pendula'
- 'Lutescens'	CTho CTri NLar NWea SCoo SEWo WMat
§ - 'Pendula'	CMac
§ × ***hollandica*** 'Dampieri Aurea' 🏆H6	CDul CTho EBee ELan EPfP LBuc MAsh MBlu MGos MRav NLar NWea SCob SPer SPoG WMat WPat
- 'Jacqueline Hillier'	CDul CMac CSpe ECho ELan LAst LRHS MMuc NLar SEND SGol WCFE WFar WPat
- 'Wredei'	see *U.* × *hollandica* 'Dampieri Aurea'
laevis	CDul EGFP
'Lobel'	CCVT
Lutèce = 'Nanguen'	CDoC CDul SGol
minor	CDul
- 'Dampieri Aurea'	see *U.* × *hollandica* 'Dampieri Aurea'
montana	see *U. glabra*
'Morfeo' new	CArg WMat
parvifolia	CMen WPGP
- 'Frosty' (v)	ECho
- 'Geisha' (v)	ECho ELan MAsh WPat
§ - 'Hokkaido'	CMen ECho EWes LLHF SIgm WAbe WFar WPat WThu
- 'Pygmaea'	see *U. parvifolia* 'Hokkaido'
- 'Yatsubusa'	ECho MRav
procera	CDul MCoo MGos SLon WSFF
- 'Argenteovariegata' (v)	NLar
pumila 'Beijing Gold'	ELan NLar
rubra	CArn
'Sapporo Autumn Gold'	CCVT EBee LBuc MRav SGol WCFE
uyematsui	WPGP
Vada = 'Wanoux'[PBR]	SGol

Umbellularia (*Lauraceae*)

californica	CArn IDee SAko SSpi WPGP

Umbilicus (*Crassulaceae*)

rupestris	CArn SChr WHer WShi

Uncinia (*Cyperaceae*)

* ***cyparissias*** from Chile	NBir
egmontiana	CBar EBee EPfP LRHS NWad SHil WGrn WMoo
erinacea new	GCal
rubra	Widely available
§ - 'Belinda's Find'[PBR]	CHid CKno EBee ELan ESwi IBoy LRHS MAsh MHol NLar SPoG WCot
- Everflame	see *U. rubra* 'Belinda's Find'
uncinata	CBcs ECha SDix
* - ***rubra***	CBod CKno CTri ELon IFro MAsh SCob SLim SRms SWvt

Uniola (*Poaceae*)

latifolia	see *Chasmanthium latifolium*

Urceolina (*Amaryllidaceae*)

miniata	see *Stenomesson miniatum*
peruviana	see *Stenomesson miniatum*

Urginea (*Asparagaceae*)

macrocentra	ECho
maritima	EBee ECho LAma WCot
ollivieri	CTal ECho
undulata	ECho

Urospermum (*Asteraceae*)

dalechampii	CSam

Ursinia (*Asteraceae*)

alpina	CPBP WHil

Urtica (*Urticaceae*)

from Casa Meca, Spain	CNat
dioica 'Chedglow 2' (v)	CNat
- 'Curly-Wurly'	CNat
- OGG mutant	CNat
- 'Winter Yellow'	CNat

Utricularia (*Lentibulariaceae*)

sp.	EECP
australis	EFEx

biloba	CHew
bisquamata 'Betty's Bay' ♀H2	CHew
dichotoma	CHew EFEx
exoleta R. Brown	see *U. gibba*
§ ***gibba***	EFEx
heterosepala	CHew
intermedia	EFEx
lateriflora	CHew EFEx
livida ♀H2	CHew EFEx
menziesii	EFEx
microcalyx	CHew
monanthos	CHew EFEx
nephrophylla	CHew
novae-zelandiae	CHew
ochroleuca	EFEx
paulineae	CHew
praelonga	CHew
prehensilis	CHew
reniformis	EFEx
I - ***nana***	EFEx
sandersonii ♀H2	CHew
simplex	CHew
subulata	EFEx
tricolor	CHew
uniflora	CHew
vulgaris	EFEx
warburgii	CHew
welwitschii	CHew

Uvularia (*Colchicaceae*)

§ ***caroliniana***	ECho
disporum	ECho
grandiflora ♀H5	Widely available
- dwarf	ECho
- gold-leaved	CAby CBct
- 'Lynda Windsor'	CDes CTal LEdu SKHP
- orange-flowered	SKHP
- var. ***pallida***	CAby CAvo CBct CDes CLAP CTal EBee ECho EHrv EPPr EPfP EPot GBin GCal GEdr IBlr ILea LEdu LRHS MRav NCGa NHar SMHy WCru WPnP
- 'Susie Lewis'	WCru
grandiflora* × *perfoliata	ECho NBir WWEG
perfoliata	CBct CEvo CExl CLAP CTal EBee ECha ECho EPPr EPfP EPot GBuc GKev IBlr IMou LEdu MRav NBir WCru
- tall	EPPr
pudica	see *U. caroliniana*
sessilifolia	CBct CEvo CExl ECho EPfP GEdr GKev IMou LEdu LRHS MMHG WCru
- 'Cobblewood Gold' (v)	EPPr WCru

V

Vaccinium ✿ (*Ericaceae*)

arctostaphylos	SWvt
'Berkeley' (F)	CAgr CWib GKin LBuc LSRN MAsh MBlu NPla SDea SPre WHar
'Bluejay' (F)	CWib ELan LAst LRHS MAsh MBri SCoo SLon WHar
'Blueray' (F)	CWib GKin
'Brigitta' (F)	CTrh EMil GTwe LRHS NPla SPoG SPre
chaetothrix	WAbe WThu
'Chandler' (F)	CAgr CArg CMac CTrh EMil EPom GKin LCro LOPS LRHS LSRN NPla SKee
consanguineum B&SWJ 10486	WCru
corymbosum (F)	CBcs MNHC SCoo SSta
- 'Aurora'PBR (F)	LCro LOPS SPer
- 'Blauweiss-Goldtraube' (F)	CAgr CSBt CWib EPfP ESwi GKin LSRN MAsh NLar NPri SDea SPoG SVic WHar
- 'Blue Duke' (F)	LSRN SFrt
- 'Blue Pearl' (F)	LBuc SFrt
- 'Bluecrop' (F)	Widely available
- 'Bluegold' (F)	CTrh LRHS MAsh SFrt
- 'Bluetta' (F)	CAgr CTri CWib ELan GTwe SCoo SPoG
- 'Coville' (F)	CWib NLar
- 'Darrow' (F)	CAgr GTwe MBri NPla SBdl WMat
- 'Dixie' (F)	CSBt LEdu NPla
- 'Duke' (F) ♀H6	CArg CMac CTrh CWib ELan EPfP EPom LCro LOPS LRHS MGos NPla NWea SBmr SDea SPre WHar
- 'Elliott' (F)	LSRN SPer
- 'Hardyblue' (F)	CAgr
- 'Heerma' (F)	NLar
- 'Ivanhoe' (F)	GKin
- 'Jersey' (F)	CAgr CWib EPfP LAst LRHS MAsh MGos MMuc NPla SCoo SDea SPer SVic WHar
- 'Nelson' (F)	LRHS NPla SCoo
- 'Nui' (F)	EPom LSRN MRav
- 'Patriot' (F)	CAgr CSBt CTrh CWib GKin GQue GTwe LBuc LRHS MBri MGos MPkF MRav NPla NPri SBdl SBmr SCoo SDea SHil SPer SPoG SPre WMat
- 'Polaris' (F)	CTrh
- 'Reka' (F)	CAgr NPer
- 'Spartan' (F) ♀H6	CTrh CWib EPom GTwe LCro LEdu LOPS LRHS LSRN MGos NPla SKee SPer
- 'Stanley' (F)	ELan EPfP LRHS
- 'Toro' (F)	GTwe LRHS NPla SFrt SPre
- 'Weymouth' (F)	SDea
crassifolium	LRHS SPoG
subsp. ***sempervirens*** 'Well's Delight' (F)	
cylindraceum ♀H5	CBcs EBee NLar WPat
- 'Tinkerbell'	ITim
delavayi	LRHS MAsh NHar NLar WAbe WThu
donianum	see *V. sprengelii*
dunalianum	CBcs
- var. ***caudatifolium*** B&SWJ 1716	WCru
- var. ***megaphyllum*** HWJ 515	WCru
'Earliblue' (F)	CAgr CMac CSBt GKin MBri NPla SBdl SDea SFrt SPoG WMat
floribundum	CBcs CDoC CMHG LRHS MAsh SSpi WPat
glaucoalbum ♀H5	CAbP CDoC CMac EBee EPfP LRHS MAsh MBlu MRav WBod WPGP WPat
'Goldtraube 71'	MAsh NPla
* ***grandiflorum***	ECho
griffithianum	SSta
'Herbert' (F)	CAgr CMac EPom LBuc
macrocarpon (F)	CArn ECho ELan GTwe LRHS MAsh MMuc NHar SDea SPre SRms

- 'Centennial' (F)	NHar
- 'CN' (F)	CAgr NLar
- 'Early Black' (F)	ELan EPom GKin NLar SVic
- 'Franklin' (F)	CAgr
- 'Hamilton'	LLHF WThu
- 'Howes' (F)	NHar
- 'Langlois' (F)	NLar
- 'Olson's Honkers' (F)	CAgr NLar
- 'Pilgrim' (F)	CAgr CMac GEdr GKin LCro LEdu LOPS LRHS MAsh MCoo NHar SBmr WHar WMat
- 'Red Star' (F)	CTrh
- 'Stevens' (F)	CAgr
moupinense	GEdr LRHS MAsh WThu
- 'Variegatum' (v)	LLHF
myrtillus	CAgr EPom GPoy NLar SVic
'Northland' (F)	CSBt CWib EPfP GQue GTwe MBri NLar NPla NPri SBdl SCoo SDea SPoG WMat
nummularia	ECho GEdr LRHS NHar NLar SSpi WAbe WThu
ovatum	CBcs CMHG CMac CTsd GKin WPat WThu
- 'Thundercloud'	CAbP LRHS MAsh
§ ***oxycoccos*** (F)	CAgr GPoy MCoo NHar WThu
'Ozarkblue' (F)	EPom GTwe LCro LOPS LSRN
pallidum	IBlr
palustre	see *V. oxycoccos*
'Pink Lemonade'	EPom LCro LOPS LRHS SBmr SPer
retusum	WThu
§ ***sprengelii***	CFil
'Spring Surprise'	WAbe
'Sunrise' (F)	GTwe
'Sunshine Blue' (F)	CAgr CTrh EPom LBuc LRHS SBmr SDea SPoG
'Tophat' (F)	LEdu MPkF
vitis-idaea	CArn EPfP EWes GPoy NWea SVic
- 'Aalshorst'	NLar
- 'Autumn Beauty'	NLar
- 'Compactum'	EWes LLHF
- 'Erntetraum'	NLar
- 'Ida'	LBuc
- Koralle Group ♀H5	CAgr GKin MBri NLar NWad
- 'Leucocarpa'	NLar
- subsp. ***minus***	GEdr NLar WAbe WThu
- 'Red Candy'	ELan EPfP LCro LOPS LRHS MSCN NLar SCob
- 'Red Pearl'	CSBt EPom LRHS MAsh NLar SBmr
- 'Red Shank' **new**	ITim

Valeriana (*Caprifoliaceae*)

'Alba'	see *Centranthus ruber* 'Albus'
alliariifolia	CSam EBee GCal MSpe NBro
- PAB 3001	LEdu WPGP
'Coccinea'	see *Centranthus ruber*
dioica	LLWG
fauriei **new**	WHil
hardwickii PAB 8999 **new**	LEdu
jatamansi	CArn GPoy SRms WJek
- PAB 6846	LEdu WPGP
montana	MMuc NBro NRya SEND SRms SWat
officinalis	Widely available
- subsp. ***sambucifolia***	EPPr GCal MNrw MSpe SHar
phu 'Aurea'	CArn CBod CHby CMac EBee ECha EHoe EHrv ELan EPfP GKin LHop LRHS MCot MLHP MRav NBid NBir NBro NEgg NLar NSti NWad SPer SRms WCAu WMoo
pyrenaica	EBee ECha EHrv EPPr GCal LPla LRHS MMHG MMuc MNrw SDix SEND SHar SPhx WCot WMoo
saxatilis	NRya
supina	CPBP
wallrothii	WCot

Valerianella (*Caprifoliaceae*)

§ ***locusta***	CBod GPoy SVic
olitoria	see *V. locusta*

Vallea (*Elaeocarpaceae*)

stipularis	CTsd

Vallisneria (*Hydrocharitaceae*)

asiatica var. ***biwaensis*** **new**	XBlo
gigantea **new**	XBlo
spiralis **new**	XBlo
- 'Tortifolia' **new**	XBlo

Vallota see *Cyrtanthus*

Vancouveria (*Berberidaceae*)

chrysantha	CCon CExl CFil CTal EBee EPPr EPfP GBuc GEdr GLog MRav NRya SKHP SMad WMoo WPGP
hexandra	CExl CFil CMac CTal ECha EHrv EPPr EPfP EWld GBuc GEdr GKev GLog ILea LEdu NSti SKHP SPhx WCru WMoo WPGP WWEG
planipetala	CTal IMou WCru

Vania see *Thlaspi*

veitchberry see *Rubus* 'Veitchberry'

Veltheimia ✿ (*Asparagaceae*)

§ ***bracteata*** ♀H2	CCse CLak ECho EPri LToo NRog WCot
- 'Lemon Flame'	ECho NRog
- yellow-flowered	NRog
§ ***capensis*** ♀H2	NRog
viridifolia misapplied	see *V. capensis*
viridifolia Jacq.	see *V. bracteata*

× *Venidioarctotis* see *Arctotis*

Venidium see *Arctotis*

Veratrum ✿ (*Melanthiaceae*)

album ♀H7	CBct CCon CEvo CPne EBee ECha GKev GPoy ILea MAvo MNrw MRav NBid WCru
- PAB 537	LEdu
- var. ***flavum***	LPla MNrw SPhx WCot WCru
- subsp. ***lobelianum***	GCal
- 'Lorna's Green'	EBee GCal MNrw WCot
- var. ***oxysepalum***	WCru
californicum	EBee ECha GCal MNrw NBid SMad WCot
dolichopetalum B&SWJ 4195	WCru
formosanum	CDes EBee MNrw WSHC
- B&SWJ 1575	WCru
- RWJ 9806	WCru
grandiflorum B&SWJ 4416	WCru
longebracteatum	WCru
maackii	CEvo EBee GCal MNrw
- B&SWJ 5875	WCru

	- green-flowered **new**	GCal
	- var. ***japonicum***	MNrw WCru
	- var. ***maackii***	MNrw
	- - B&SWJ 5831	WCru
	nigrum ♀^{H7}	CBct CCon EBee ECha GCal GEdr GMaP IKil ILea LEdu LPla LRHS MAvo MLHP MNrw MRav NBid NBir NLar SMad SPhx SPlb WCot WCru WPnP
	- B&SWJ 4450 from South Korea	WCru
	schindleri	GEdr MNrw
	- B&SWJ 4068	WCru
	stamineum	WCru
	viride	CBct EBee EWes GCal MNrw NBid WCot WCru

Verbascum (*Scrophulariaceae*)

	'Annie May'	LSRN
	'Arctic Summer'	see *V. bombyciferum* 'Polarsommer'
	'Bill Bishop'	ECho
	blattaria	NBir SPav SWat WHer
	- f. ***albiflorum***	CSpe EWTr GBBs IFro LLWP NDov SPlb WHer WMoo
	- yellow-flowered	SPav SWat
	'Blue Lagoon'	CBcs CMos CSpe CWGN EPfP GBin MNrw SCob SHil STPC
	'Blushing Bride'^{PBR}	LLHF
§	***bombyciferum***	CBre ECha ELan GMaP LRHS MMuc MSpe NGBl SCob SEND
*	- 'Arctic Snow'	SPav SPoG
§	- 'Polarsommer'	CSpe EPfP GJos LCro LRHS NBir SPer SWat
	- 'Silver Lining'	NPer
	'Broussa'	see *V. bombyciferum*
	'Buttercup'	ECtt LRHS NPri SHil
	'Camelot'	LRHS
	'Caribbean Crush'	CBcs ECtt ELan ELon GBin IBoy LRHS MHol SPer SPoG
	chaixii	CSam ECha MMHG NBir SDix WFar WMoo
	- 'Album'	Widely available
	- 'Sixteen Candles'	GJos LSun MBNS MHol NLar WFar
	- 'Wedding Candles'	CBod CWld ELan NGdn NLar SBea SPtp WFar
	'Cherry Helen'^{PBR}	LCro LOPS LRHS LSRN MBri NLar SCob
	'Christo's Yellow Lightning' ♀^{H7}	CSpe ECtt MHol SDix WCot WRHF
	'Clementine'	CBcs CMos CRos EBee ECtt ELan EPfP LCro LRHS MBri MHol SCob SHil SPhx
	'Coneyhill Yellow'	EPPr
	(Cotswold Group) 'Cotswold Beauty'	CSam CSpe ECtt EPfP EWoo LRHS MMuc MRav MWat NDov NGdn SBea SHar SPer WHoo WMnd
	- 'Cotswold Gem'	ECtt
	- 'Cotswold Queen'	CSam ECtt ELan EPPr EPfP LRHS MMuc MRav MWat NDov SBea SGol SHar SPer SWvt
	- 'Gainsborough' ♀^{H6}	Widely available
	- 'Mont Blanc'	ECtt LRHS SWat
	- 'Pink Domino' ♀^{H6}	CBod COtt CSam ECtt ELan EPPr EPfP GMaP LOPS LRHS LSun MJak MLHP MRav NSti SBea SPer SWvt WMnd WWFP
	- 'Royal Highland'	CSam ECtt ELan EPfP LRHS NGdn SPoG SWvt
	- 'White Domino'	ECtt
	'Cotswold King'	see *V. creticum*
§	***creticum***	CSpe IKil WCot
	'Dark Eyes'^{PBR}	CWGN ECtt LRHS SCob
§	***densiflorum***	CArn EAJP
	epixanthinum ♀^{H5}	CPla EBee
	'Flower of Scotland'	MBNS MHol
	'Golden Wings' ♀^{H4}	CPla WAbe
	'Guinevere'	LRHS
	'Helen Johnson'	CBod CWCL EAEE ECtt ELan EPfP LOPS LRHS LSRN MGos MRav NLar NPri SCob SCoo SHil SPer SRkn SWvt WMnd
	× ***hybridum*** 'Banana Custard'	NGBl
	- 'Copper Rose'	EBee LRHS MHer
	- 'Snow Maiden'	CTri EPfP
	'Jackie'	CBod ECtt ELan GBBs LBMP LRHS LSRN MBri SCob SCoo SPad
	'Jackie in Pink'	LRHS MBri SHil
	'Jackie in Yellow'^{PBR}	LLHF MBri
	'Jester'	CBcs CBod CTsd CWld LRHS MBNS MHol SCob
	'June Johnson'	EAEE ECtt LRHS
	'Kynaston'	IPot LRHS MBNS
	'Lavender Lass'	MHol SPer
	'Letitia' ♀^{H4}	CPla ECho ECtt ELan EPot EWes GCal ITim LRHS SWvt WAbe WCot
	'Linda'	ECtt
	longifolium var. ***pannosum***	see *V. olympicum*
	lychnitis	SPhx
	lydium **new**	EBee
	'Megan's Mauve'	EAEE
	'Merlin'^{PBR}	EAEE ECtt LRHS LSRN MBNS WMnd
	nigrum	CArn CDes CHab EBee NGdn NLar WHer WMoo
	- var. ***album***	NChi NGdn NLar WMoo WOut
§	***olympicum***	ELan EPfP GJos LPot LRHS MBNS MLHP MMuc NGBl NSti SCob SDix SEND SVen WCot WWEG
	'Petra'	LRHS SPhx
	phlomoides	SPhx
	phoeniceum	CBod EBee ELan EPfP GJos NBid NBro SPlb SPoG WFar WMoo
*	- 'Album'	CSpe
	- 'Flush of White'	CBod CBot EAJP ECtt EPfP GBin GQue NGBl NGdn NLar SCob WCAu WHar WMoo WWFP
	- hybrids	CTri GMaP NEgg NGdn SRms SWat WFar
	- 'Rosetta'	CBod EAJP EPfP MCot NGBl NGdn SPad
	- 'Violetta'	CBod CBot CSpe EAJP ECtt EPPr EPfP EShb LCro LRHS MCot MHol MLHP MSpe MWat NChi NDov NEgg NGBl NGdn SGbt SPav SPer SPhx WCFE WHrl WMoo
	'Pink Kisses'	LLHF LRHS LSRN MBNS
	'Pink Petticoats'	COtt EBee LBuc LRHS SPoG
	(Pixie Series) 'Pixie Apricot'	ECtt MBri
	- 'Pixie Blue'	EBee ECtt LRHS MBri
	- 'Pixie Pink'	MBri
	- 'Pixie White'	ECtt MBri
	'Plum Smokey'^{PBR}	ECtt IBoy LLHF
	'Primrose Path'	ECtt EPfP LRHS NLar
	pulverulentum	EBee
	pyramidatum	EBee SPhx
	'Queen of Hearts'	LRHS
	'Raspberry Ripple'	LLHF MHer MRav SPer
	'Rosie'	SCob
	'Sierra Sunset'	LRHS NLar
	'Southern Charm'	COtt EPfP GJos GMaP NQui WPtf

'Spica'	CBot LRHS
'Sugar Plum'[PBR]	ECtt ELon LBuc LLHF MBri MHol SPoG WCAu
'Summer Sorbet'	CBcs ECtt MNrw SPoG
Sunset shades	GJos WOut
'Temptress Purple' **new**	CBot
thapsiforme	see *V. densiflorum*
thapsus	CHab ENfk GJos GPoy MHer MNHC NBir NMir SEND SRms WOut
'Tropic Sun' ♀H5	WHoo
'Wessex'	LRHS
xanthophoeniceum	WCot

Verbena (Verbenaceae)

(Aztec Series) Aztec Cherry Red = 'Balazcherd'[PBR] (G)	NPri
- Aztec Pearl = 'Balazpearl'[PBR] (G)	SCoo
- Aztec Plum Magic = 'Balazplum'[PBR] (G)	NPri
- Aztec Red = 'Balazred' (G)	SCoo
- Aztec Silver Magic = 'Balazsilma'[PBR] (G)	NPri SCoo
'Blue Prince' (G)	CSpe
§ ***bonariensis*** ♀H4	Widely available
- 'Little One'	SPad
- 'Lollipop'[PBR]	Widely available
brasiliensis misapplied	see *V. bonariensis*
canadensis 'Perfecta' (G)	CSpe
chamaedrifolia	see *V. peruviana*
§ 'Claret' (G)	CMac CSpe EAJP EBee ECtt EHrv ELan EPfP LRHS LSRN LSou MCot MNrw SCoo SPhx SPoG WWEG
'Corsage Peach' (Corsage Series) (G/d)	LRHS
corymbosa	CHid CHll CWld EBee ECha EWoo LRHS SPer SPhx WMoo
- 'Gravetye'	LPot
'Diamond Merci' (G)	WHoo
'Edith Eddleman' (G)	CMac CWGN EPfP LRHS SPoG
elegans	NDov
(Empress Series) Empress Flair Burgundy = 'Duefarburg'[PBR] (G) **new**	LBMP
- Empress Flair Red = 'Duempflare'[PBR] (G) **new**	LBMP
- Empress Flair Royal Blue = 'Duempflarobu'[PBR] (G) **new**	LBMP
- Empress Flair Violet Blue = 'Duempflavibu'[PBR] (G) **new**	LBMP
- Empress Flair White = 'Duempflawi'[PBR] (G) **new**	LBMP
- Empress Hot Pink Charme = 'Duemphopich'[PBR] (G) **new**	LBMP
- Empress Lavender Blue = 'Duemplavbu'[PBR] (G) **new**	LBMP
- Empress Peach Flair (G)	LAst LBMP
- Empress Soft Pink Charme (G) **new**	LBMP
Estrella Voodoo Pink Star = 'Wesverepista' **new**	LBMP
Estrella Voodoo Red Star = 'Wesverevoo'[PBR] **new**	LBMP
(Fuego Series) Fuego Blues Dark Purple (G) **new**	LBMP
- Fuego Pink = 'Kleve04334'[PBR] (G) **new**	LBMP
- Fuego Red with Eye = 'Klevp10409'[PBR] (G) **new**	LBMP
- Fuego Violet with Eye = 'Klevp07355'[PBR] (G) **new**	LBMP
goddingii (G)	EBee
'Hammerstein Pink'	EBee EPfP
hastata	CSpe EBee ECtt EPfP LAst LEdu LRHS MNrw NSti SCob SPhx SPlb SRms SWat SWvt WCAu WFar WMnd WMoo WOld WOut WTcb XLum
* - 'Alba'	CTsd EBee ELan EPfP GBin NLar SCob SDix WCAu WMoo
- 'Blue Spires'	EPfP IPot SCob
- f. ***rosea***	CBre CElw CMea CSpe EHoe ELan EPfP GKev IPot LRHS MCot MLHP MNrw MRav NDov SDix SPer SPhx SWat WCAu WHea WMoo WSHC
- - 'Pink Spires'	EBee ECtt ELan EPfP LHop LRHS SCob
- 'White Spires'	CMea EPfP
'Homestead Purple' (G)	CBod CMac CRos EAJP EBee ECtt ELan EPfP LOPS LRHS LSRN MCot MNrw SCob SDix SRkn SWvt WHoo WWEG
'Jenny's Wine'	see *V.* 'Claret'
'La France' (G)	CHGN ECha EPfP LRHS SDix SMHy SPhx SPoG
(Lanai Series) Lanai Blue Denim = 'Bludena'[PBR] (G)	MCot
- Lanai Candy Cane Red = 'Veaz0011' (G)	LAst
- Lanai Lime Green = 'Veaz0013'[PBR] (G)	LAst
- Lanai Pink Twister = 'Flagdena'[PBR] (G) **new**	LAst
- Lanai Red 07 = 'Lan Reda07'[PBR] (G) **new**	LAst
- Lanai Royal Purple with Eye = 'Lan Roypureye'[PBR] (G)	MCot
- Lanai White (G) **new**	LAst
Lascar White = 'Kleve04340'[PBR] (Lascar Series) (G) **new**	LBMP
lasiostachys	EBee
'Lois' Ruby'	see *V.* 'Claret'
macdougalii	WMoo
- 'Lavender Spires'	LPla NDov SDix SPhx
officinalis	CArn ENfk GPoy MHer MNHC SIde SRms WHer WJek WSFF
- var. ***grandiflora*** 'Bampton'	CAby CElw CSpe ECtt LEdu LHop MNrw WCot WHoo WPGP
patagonica	see *V. bonariensis*
§ ***peruviana*** (G)	EBee ECho LRHS SRms XLum
'Pink Bouquet'	see *V.* 'Silver Anne'
'Pink Parfait' (G)	EPfP
Quartz Series	LAst NPri
- 'Quartz Red Polka Dot'	ELan EPfP
- 'Quartz Waterfall' (mixed)	LAst
§ ***rigida*** ♀H3	Widely available
- f. ***lilacina***	LSRN

- - 'Lilac Haze'	CMac EPfP LBMP LRHS NSti SPoG SRkn
- - 'Polaris'	CBod CMea CMos CSam EAJP EBee ELan ELon EPfP EShb GCal LHop LRHS MNrw MRav SCob SDix SHar SMHy SPer SPoG
'Rococo Peach'	LRHS
'Rococo Pink'	LRHS
'Samira Scarlet'	LRHS
scabridoglandulosa	see *Junellia succulentifolia*
Seabrook's Lavender = 'Sealav'[PBR]	CBod EBee EPfP ESwi LOPS LRHS LSRN SCoo SHar SPer SRkn SWvt
serpyllifolia	see *Junellia micrantha*
§ 'Silver Anne' (G) 🏆H3	MCot SDix
§ 'Sissinghurst' (G) 🏆H2	CAby CSam ECtt SRms
'Strawberry Kiss'	EPfP SPoG
stricta	EBee EWes NDov NLar SPhx
(Superbena Series) Superbena Burgundy = 'Usbenal5'[PBR] (G)	CAby
- Superbena Coral Star (G) **new**	NPri
- Superbena Scarlet Lace = 'Akiv341'[PBR] (G) **new**	NPri
§ - Superbena Violet Blue = 'Usbenas10'[PBR] (G)	NPri
- Superbena Violet Lace	see *V.* Superbena Violet Blue
(Tapien Series) Tapien Compact Red = 'Suntapicore'[PBR] (G)	LAst
- Tapien Pink = 'Sunver'[PBR] (G)	LAst MCot
- Tapien Salmon = 'Suntapiro'[PBR] (G)	LAst LSou
- Tapien Sky Blue = 'Suntapilabu'[PBR] (G)	LAst
- Tapien Violet = 'Sunvop'[PBR] (G)	LAst LSou
- Tapien White = 'Suntapipurew'[PBR] (G)	LAst
(Temari Series) Temari Blue = 'Sunmariribu'[PBR] (G)	LAst MCot
- Temari Coral Pink = 'Sunmariripi'[PBR] (G)	LAst LSou
- Temari Neon Red = 'Sunmarineopi'[PBR] (G)	LAst
- Temari Vanilla = 'Sunmarivani'[PBR] (G)	LSou
'Tenerife'	see *V.* 'Sissinghurst'
venosa	see *V. rigida*
'Venturi Rose'	LRHS
Vepita Hot Pink (Vepita Series) **new**	NPri

Verbesina (*Asteraceae*)

alternifolia	CArn SDix
- 'Goldstrahl'	EPPr

Vernicia (*Euphorbiaceae*)

fordii	SPlb

Vernonia (*Asteraceae*)

angustifolia* × *missurica	WCot
§ ***arkansana***	CHGN CSam EBee ECha ECtt EPPr EWTr EWes IPot LEdu MAvo NLar SDix SEND SPhx WWEG
- 'Alba'	EBee ECtt MAvo
- 'Betty Blindeman'	EBee LEdu
- 'Mammuth'	CDes EBee ECtt EWes EWoo GQue ILea IPot LCro LEdu LHop LPla LRHS MAvo MNrw MTis SMad SPhx WCot
baldwinii	EBee MAvo SPhx
crinita	see *V. arkansana*
fasciculata	EShb EWes LEdu LPla LRHS MAvo MMuc MRav NLar SEND SPhx WCot
gigantea	ELon EWes MAvo MMuc MNrw NLar SEND SMad SPhx
glauca	SPhx WCot
lettermannii 'Iron Butterfly'	EBee
missurica	SPhx
noveboracensis	EBee LEdu MAvo MTis NLar SGSe SMad XLum
- 'Albiflora'	EPPr EWes

Veronica (*Plantaginaceae*)

'Amethyst Plume' **new**	EBee MHol
amethystina	see *V. spuria* L.
anagallis-aquatica	LLWG
'Anna'[PBR]	MTis NDov
armena	ECho EDAr EWes MHer MMuc SBch SEND SRot WIce XSen
'Atomic Hot Pink' **new**	EBee
'Atomic Lilac'	LSou
'Atomic Pink'	LSou
'Atomic Pink-White Ray' **new**	LBMP
'Atomic Silvery Pink Ray'	LCro
'Atomic Sky Ray'[PBR]	LSou
'Atomic Violet Ray'[PBR]	LSou
'Atomic White Ray' **new**	LCro
§ ***austriaca***	EWoo NBre NChi WMoo
- dark blue-flowered	NChi
- var. ***dubia***	see *V. prostrata*
- 'Ionian Skies'	CTri ECha ECho ECtt EPPr MMuc NWad SEND SHar SIgm SPer WIce WKif WSHC WWEG
§ - subsp. ***teucrium***	CArn CSam CTri EBee ECho SRms WKif
- - 'Blue Fountain'	LRHS
- - 'Crater Lake Blue' 🏆H6	EBee ECtt ELan EPfP EWld EWoo LEdu LHop LRHS MAvo MBel MHol MRav SPhx SPlb SRms WCot WFar WMnd WSHC
- - 'Kapitän'	ECha ECho GBuc LHop LRHS NGdn WFar
- - 'Knallblau'	EAJP
- subsp. ***teucrium*** 'Lapis Lazuli' **new**	EBee
- - 'Mammuth' **new**	IKil
- - 'Royal Blue' 🏆H6	CPrp EAJP EBee ECGP EPfP EShb GMaP LRHS MBri MHol MWhi NSti SPer SRms WFar WKif WMnd WMoo XLum XSen
- subsp. ***vahlii***	LLHF
'Baby Blue'[PBR]	CBod
'Baby Doll'[PBR]	LRHS MBNS MBri
'Baby Pink' **new**	CBod
beccabunga	CBen CBod CHab CWat EHon EWay GPoy MMuc MSKA MWLS MWts NMir NPer SEND SWat WHer WMAq WSFF
'Bergen's Blue'	NLar SHar WSHC
Blue Bouquet	see *V. longifolia* 'Blaubündel'
'Blue Indigo'	MNrw NBre NGdn
'Blue Spire'	SWat
bombycina	ITim WAbe
- subsp. ***bolkardaghensis***	WAbe
bonarota	see *Paederota bonarota*
caespitosa	CPBP

- subsp. ***caespitosa***	EPot WAbe
candida	see *V. spicata* subsp. *incana*
× ***cantiana*** 'Kentish Pink'	WAul WCFE WMoo WWEG XLum
caucasica	MSCN XSen
chamaedrys	NMir XLum
- 'Pam' (v)	ECtt
'Christa Bubblegum'	EPfP
Christy = 'Henslerone'[PBR]	CBod EPfP LBuc LRHS MBri NPri
cinerea ♀H5	MLHP SBch SBrt WHoo WSHC WTor XSen
dabneyi	EBee WPGP
'Dark Martje'	EBee IPot
'Darwin's Blue'	NLar WHrl
'Ellen Mae'	CElw ECtt EWes LPla MNrw WCot WMnd
'Eveline'[PBR]	ECtt EPfP LRHS MHol NDov NLar
exaltata (d)	NChi
'Fairytale'[PBR]	EWTr LRHS MBNS MBri NGdn WHil
'Fantasy'	NDov
filiformis	XLum
'First Love'	ECtt EPfP LRHS LSou MAsh MBri MNrw NGdn
formosa	see *Parahebe formosa*
§ ***fruticans***	ECho GJos
fruticulosa	LLHF
gentianoides	Widely available
- 'Alba'	CMea GCal LEdu NBre NChi
- 'Barbara Sherwood' ♀H7	EBee EWTr LRHS NGdn WWEG
- 'Blue Streak'	EPfP SGSe XLum
- 'Nana'	EBee
- 'Pallida'	EWoo GAbr GKev MBrN MMuc MRav SCob SEND SPlb WBor WWEG XLum
- 'Robusta'	CAby CBod ECtt GMaP LRHS NGdn WFar WHoo WMnd
- 'Tissington White'	Widely available
- 'Variegata' (v)	EBee ECha ECtt ELan GCra GMaP LAst LRHS MHer MRav MSCN NBir NEgg NWad SBea SPer SWat WFar WRHF WWEG
'Giles van Hees'	ECtt
grandis	EBee EWTr IFro LEdu MMuc MWhi NChi NLar SEND WHrl WMoo WPtf XLum
× ***guthrieana***	SRms
incana	see *V. spicata* subsp. *incana*
* - 'Candidissima'	GCal
'Ink'	MAvo SPhx
'Inspiration'	CCse NBre NDov
'Inspire Blue'	LPot LRHS LSou MMuc MPnt SEND SHil
'Inspire Pink'	LRHS LSou MPnt SHil
kellereri	see *V. spicata*
kiusiana	CMHG EBee IFro LEdu LPla NLar NWad SPhx WHrl
* - var. ***maxima***	CAby WPtf
kotschyana	XSen
'Lavender Plume'	CWGN EBee EPfP WHil
liwanensis Mac&W 5936	EPot
longifolia	CMac CSBt ECha ELan GCra MBel MSpe NSti WMoo XLum
- 'Alba'	ELan MMuc SEND WMoo
- 'Antarctica'	EBee
- 'Blaubart'	XLum
§ - 'Blaubündel'	CCse LRHS NGdn
- 'Blauer Sommer'	EBee EPfP LRHS NDov NEgg NGdn
§ - 'Blauriesin'	CTri ECtt ELan EPfP GMaP MBri NLar NSti SAko SPer
- Blue Giantess	see *V. longifolia* 'Blauriesin'
- 'Blue Gown' **new**	CAbP
- 'Blue John'	CAbP ECGP ECtt EPfP GBin LSou MPie MTis NBre NDov NSti WCot WHoo
- blue-flowered	CBod SGSe WHar
- 'Charlotte'[PBR] (v)	CBod CSpe EBee ECtt EHoe GBin LCro LHop LRHS MBel MHol MTis NDov SCob SHar WCot WHil WRHF
- 'Charming Pink'	LRHS MSCN SAko
- 'Christa'[PBR]	EPfP MBri
- 'Fascination'	ECtt EHoe LAst NEoE NGdn
- 'Foerster's Blue'	see *V. longifolia* 'Blauriesin'
- 'Incarnata'	EBee LRHS
- 'Joseph's Coat' (v)	NBre
- 'Lilac Fantasy'	LHop MBri MRav MSCN
- 'Marietta' **new**	WCot
- 'Oxford Blue'	CBar CBod WBor WHoo
- 'Pacific Ocean'[PBR]	ECtt
- 'Pink Eveline'[PBR]	ECtt LRHS MBel MSpe NDov NLar SPad STPC
- pink-flowered	CBod EShb
- 'Rose Tone'	GJos WMoo
- 'Schneeriesin'	EBee ECha ECtt EPfP GMaP LEdu LRHS MAvo MRav MTis NBir NLar SAko SPer
lyallii	see *Parahebe lyallii*
macrostachya	SKHP
'Martje'	XLum
'Mini Spires Blue'	MBri
'Mini Spires Pink'	MBri
montana 'Corinne Tremaine' (v)	NBir SRms
officinalis	GJos XLum XSen
oltensis	CPBP ECho EPot EWld GCrg ITim LLHF MHer SIgm
orchidea	SRms
ornata	WOld
'Pacific Ocean'	ECtt NLar
pectinata	ECtt
- 'Rosea'	ECho ECtt EWes XSen
peduncularis 'Oxford Blue'	see *V. umbrosa* 'Georgia Blue'
perfoliata	see *Parahebe perfoliata*
petraea 'Madame Mercier'	XLum
'Pink Damask'	ECtt ELan ELon EPfP GMaP MAvo MCot MLHP MRav MSpe MTis NDov NGdn NLar SDys SPhx WHoo WMnd WWEG
'Pink Harmony'	CBod MAsh MHol NGBl NSti
pinnata	SBrt
- 'Blue Feathers'	EDAr
piroliformis	WAbe
porphyriana	CBod CMea EBee EDAr MMuc NLar WTor
prenja	see *V. austriaca*
§ ***prostrata*** ♀H5	CBod CMea CSpe CTri ECho ECtt EDAr EPfP GCrg GJos LAst LRHS MAsh MHol MLHP NEgg NHar NHol NPri SEND SRms WHoo WIce WMoo XLum
- 'Alba'	MLHP
- 'Aztec Gold'[PBR]	CMac
§ - 'Blauspiegel'	CPBP SIgm
- Blue Mirror	see *V. prostrata* 'Blauspiegel'
- 'Blue Sheen'	ECho ECtt EPfP LRHS NBir NPri
- 'Goldwell'	EBee ECtt EPPr LAst NPri SRot
- 'Lavender Mist'	LRHS
- 'Lilac Time'	CBod ECho ECtt EPot LHop LRHS NBir NHol SBch SRms WHil WIce WTor

	- 'Little Nell' **new**	ECtt
	- 'Loddon Blue'	NPri SRms WCot
	- 'Mrs Holt'	ECho ECtt GCrg LHop LRHS MHer NBir NLar NPri NWad SRms WHoo XLum
	- 'Nana'	CPBP ECho ECtt EPot EWes GCrg MWat WAbe
	- 'Nestor'	CTri EAJP ECtt NPri WPtf XLum
	- 'Rosea'	ECho
	- 'Spode Blue' ♀[H5]	CBod CMac CMea EBee ECho ECtt GCrg GMaP LBMP LHop LRHS MHer MMuc SEND SPoG SRms WWEG
	- 'Trehane'	ECho ECtt EDAr EPfP GCrg LEdu LHop LRHS MAsh MHer MHol NEgg NRya NWad SPlb SPoG SRms WIce
	'Purpleicious Harmony'[PBR]	EBee EPfP GBin MCot WHil
	repens	ECho EPfP GJos NEoE SPlb
	- 'Sunshine'	WRHF
	'Rosalinde'	NGdn
	'Royal Pink'	CPrp LAst LHop MRav NLar
	rupestris	see *V. prostrata*
	saturejoides	GCrg SRms
	saxatilis	see *V. fruticans*
	schmidtiana 'Nana'	ITim
	selleri	see *V. wormskjoldii*
	'Shirley Blue' ♀[H6]	CPrp CWib ELan EPfP ILea LCro LOPS LPot LSRN MHer MJak MMuc MWat SEND SPer SPhx SRms WCAu WCFE WWEG
§	***spicata***	CSam ELan EPfP GJos LRHS MLHP MRav NBid SCob SRms WBrk WMoo WShi XLum
	- 'Alba'	EBee EPfP GJos LPot LRHS MRav NLar XLum
§	- 'Blaufuchs'	CSam
	- 'Blue Candles'	GQue MTis
	- Blue Fox	see *V. spicata* 'Blaufuchs'
§	- 'Erika'	CSam ECtt EPfP GBin IBoy MAsh MNrw NBid NBir NGdn NLar WHil
§	- 'Glory'[PBR]	CBod CWGN ECtt ELan ELon LOPS LRHS MBri MMuc MPie SCob SEND SPad SPoG WCot WHoo WMnd
	- 'Heidekind'	CBod EBee ECha ECho ECtt EDAr ELan EPot GCrg LAst LHop LPot MWat NBir NGdn SRms SRot SWat WHil WHoo WIce XLum
	- 'High Five'[PBR]	EBee
	- subsp. ***hybrida***	WHer
	- - 'Elaine's Form'	WCot
§	- 'Icicle'	EBee SCob WCAu
§	- subsp. ***incana*** ♀[H4]	ECho EHoe ELan EPfP GJos MMuc SEND SPlb SRms SWat WCFE WMoo XSen
	- - 'Nana'	MLHP NBir SRms
	- - 'Silbersee'	MLHP
	- - 'Silver Carpet'	ECtt LAst LHop LRHS MRav SPer WMnd
	- - 'Wendy'	GCal LPla SPhx
	- 'Nana Blauteppich'	EDAr NLar
	- 'Pink Goblin'	EDAr ELan EPfP
	- 'Pink Panther'[PBR]	LSou WCot
	- Red Fox	see *V. spicata* 'Rotfuchs'
	- 'Romiley Purple'	EBee SPer
	- 'Rosalind'	NLar
	- ***rosea***	see *V. spicata* 'Erika'
§	- 'Rotfuchs'	CBod ECtt EHoe ELan ELon EPfP LAst LCro LPot LRHS LSou MHer MMuc MRav NBid NBir NGdn NLar SCob SPad SPer SPoG SRms WCAu WCFE WWEG
	- 'Royal Candles'	see *V. spicata* 'Glory'
	- 'Sightseeing'	CWib GJos NBir SRms
	- subsp. ***spicata*** 'Nana'	XSen
	- 'Twilight'[PBR]	ECtt EPfP LRHS NLar
	- 'Ulster Blue Dwarf'	EBee EPfP EWTr GMaP IBoy IMou LHop LRHS LSou MAsh MAvo MBri NBid NGdn SHil WCAu
	- Younique Baby Blue **new**	WCot
	- Younique Baby Red = 'Versbabyred' **new**	WCot
§	***spuria*** L.	SEND
	stelleri	see *V. wormskjoldii*
	subsessilis 'Blaue Pyramide'	WPtf
	'Sunny Border Blue'	CBod EPfP IKil MHol NLar WCot
	tauricola	XSen
	teucrium	see *V. austriaca* subsp. *teucrium*
	thessalica	EPot WAbe
	thymoides subsp. ***pseudocinerea***	SIgm
§	***umbrosa*** 'Georgia Blue' ♀[H5]	Widely available
	urticifolia	SBrt
	virginica	see *Veronicastrum virginicum*
	'Waterperry Blue'	ECtt NPri
	'White Icicle'	see *V. spicata* 'Icicle'
	'White Jolanda'	NSti
	whitleyi	MMuc
§	***wormskjoldii***	ECho GBin GCrg MBrN MMuc SEND SRms
	- 'Alba'	MLHP

Veronicastrum ✿ (*Plantaginaceae*)

	'Adoration'	CSpe EBee ECtt LPla MAvo MTis NDov SMHy SPhx STPC WCAu
	axillare	IMou
	brunonianum	GCal WSHC
	japonicum var. ***australe*** B&SWJ 11009	WCru
	latifolium	CDes EBee WCot
	- BWJ 8158	WCru WSHC
	'Red Arrows'	Widely available
	sibiricum	CKno CSpe EBee ECha EShb GCal GQue ILea LRHS MLHP MMuc SEND SHar WMoo WWtn XLum
	- BWJ 6352	WCru WFar
	- 'Kobaltkaars'	SMHy
	- var. ***yezoense***	IMou WHoo
	- - RBS 0290	NEoE
	villosulum	EBee EWes IMou NBid NBro WSHC
§	***virginicum***	CArn CKno EBee ECtt GCra GPoy MAvo MWhi NBir NLar SRms WFar WMoo WWEG WWtn XLum
	- 'Album'	Widely available
	- 'Apollo'	CBct CBod CBre CSpe ECtt EHrv ELon EPPr EPfP EWTr GBin GMaP IBoy ILea LEdu LPla LRHS MAvo NBro NLar NSti SMHy SPhx SWvt WAul WBor WCAu WHrl WPGP WWEG
	- 'Cupid'	CMos EBee ECtt GBin MNrw NDov STPC
	- 'Diane'	EBee EPPr GMaP ILea IPot LPla LRHS MAvo MTis NDov NLar SPhx SWvt WCAu
	- 'Erica'	Widely available
	- 'Fascination'	Widely available
	- var. ***incarnatum***	see *V. virginicum* f. *roseum*

	- 'Lavendelturm'	Widely available
	- light blue-flowered	SGSe
	- 'Pointed Finger'	CMea GCal GMaP LEdu MAvo NLar SMHy SPhx WCot
§	- f. ***roseum***	CAby CPrp ECha ELan GMaP LBMP LPla LRHS MAvo MHol MJak MRav NBro NDov SGbt SPad SPer SPhx SWvt WBor WHrl WKif WMoo XLum
	- - 'Pink Glow'	Widely available
	- 'Spring Dew'	CBod CBre EPPr LEdu LPla LRHS MNrw NBid NBro NEoE NLar SPhx WCAu WFar
	- 'Temptation'	EBee GMaP IPot LEdu LPla MRav NBro NEoE NLar SPhx

Verschaffeltia (*Arecaceae*)

	splendida	XBlo

Vestia (*Solanaceae*)

§	***foetida***	CBcs CExl CTsd CWib EBee ELan EPfP LRHS MGil MNrw MPie SBig SBrt SEND WSHC
	lycioides	see *V. foetida*

Viburnum ✿ (*Adoxaceae*)

	acerifolium	LLHF NWad WPat
	alnifolium	see *V. lantanoides*
	atrocyaneum	CExl CJun NWad SBrt SKHP WPat
	- B&SWJ 7272	EPfP WCru
	- HIRD 113	WPGP
	odoratissimum var. ***awabuki*** B&SWJ 11374 from Wabuka, Japan	WCru
	betulifolium	CAbP CBcs CExl CJun CMCN EBee ELan EPfP EWes GKin IDee NLar SAko WPGP
	- f. ***aurantiacum***	CJun
	- 'Hohuanshan'	SSta WCru
	bitchiuense	CJun NLar
	× ***bodnantense***	CMac CTri EBee EWTr WFar WHar
	- 'Charles Lamont' 🏆H6	Widely available
	- 'Dawn' 🏆H6	Widely available
	- 'Deben' 🏆H6	EBee EPfP NLar SPer WPat
	brachyandrum B&SWJ 5784	WCru
	bracteatum	NLar
	buddlejifolium	CMac EBee EBtc EPfP EWes LRHS MMuc SKHP WCru WPat
	× ***burkwoodii***	Widely available
	- 'Anika'	NLar
	- 'Anne Russell'	Widely available
	- 'Chenaultii'	MRav
	- 'Compact Beauty'	CJun WPat
	- 'Conoy'	CJun EBee ELon LEdu NLar WPat
	- 'Fulbrook'	CAbP CRos EPfP LEdu LRHS MAsh NLar WHar WPat
	- 'Mohawk' 🏆H6	CAbP CDoC CJun CRos ELan ELon EPfP LCro LEdu LRHS MAsh MGos NLar SCob SCoo SHil SKHP SWvt WPat
	- 'Park Farm Hybrid' 🏆H6	CAbP CDoC CExl CJun CMac CRos CSam CTri CWib EBee ECrN ELan ELon EPfP EWoo LAst LEdu LRHS MAsh MGos MRav NHol NLar SAko SPer SPoG SRms SWvt WKif WPat
	calvum	CExl
	aff. ***calvum*** WWJ 12012	WCru
	× ***carlcephalum*** 🏆H6	Widely available
	- 'Cayuga' 🏆H5	ELon LPar MAsh NLar WPat
	- 'Van der Maat'	NLar
*	- 'Variegatum' (v)	CJun
	carlesii	CBcs CCVT CDul CMac CTri CWib EPfP GKin LPar LSRN MBlu MGos MRav MSwo SCob SEWo SGol SLim SPer WFar
	- B&SWJ 8838	WCru
	- 'Aurora' 🏆H6	Widely available
	- 'Charis'	CJun CSBt LRHS NLar WKif
	- 'Compactum'	CJun NLar WPat
	- 'Diana' 🏆H6	CDoC CJun CMHG CMac CRos EPfP LRHS LSRN MAsh MBlu NLar SCob SPer SSta WCFE WPat
	- 'Marlou'	CJun NLar WPat
	cassinoides	CJun WPGP
	- 'Nanum'	EPfP
	- 'Sear Charm'	WPGP
	'Chesapeake'	CDul CJun EWes MMuc NLar SEND
	chingii	CJun WCru WPGP WPat
	'Chippewa'	CJun
	cinnamomifolium 🏆H5	CAbP CBcs CBot CExl CSde ELan EPfP EWTr GBin LRHS MAsh NLar SBrt SCob SEND SLon SPer SPoG SSpi WSHC
	cotinifolium	CExl
	- CC 4541	CExl NLar
	cylindricum	CBot CEvo EPfP LRHS NLar SBrt SKHP WCru WPGP WPat
	- B&SWJ 6479 from Thailand	WCru
	- B&SWJ 7239	WCru
	- B&SWJ 9719 from Vietnam	WCru
	- HWJCM 434 from Nepal	WCru
	- 'Chino-Crûg'	WCru
	dasyanthum	NLar
	davidii 🏆H5	Widely available
	- (f)	CBcs CDoC CMac CRos CSBt ELan EPfP EWTr LAst MAsh SPer SPoG SRms WCFE WHar WPat
	- (m)	CBcs CDoC CMac CRos CSBt ELan EPfP SGbt SPer SPoG SRms WHar WPat
	- 'Angustifolium'	CJun WPGP
	dentatum	EBtc MAsh
	- Autumn Jazz	see *V. dentatum* 'Ralph Senior'
	- Blue Muffin = 'Christom'	LRHS WPat
	- Chicago Lustre	see *V. dentatum* 'Synnestvedt'
§	- 'Ralph Senior'	NLar
§	- 'Synnestvedt'	NLar
	- 'White and Blue'	CJun NLar
	dilatatum	LEdu
	- B&SWJ 5844	WCru
	- B&SWJ 8734	WCru
	- B&SWJ 10830	WCru
	- PAB 6831	LEdu
	- 'Erie'	EPfP NLar
	- 'Inneke'	NLar
	- 'Sealing Wax'	NLar
	'Emerald Triumph'	CJun
	erosum B&SWJ 8735	WCru
	- B&SWJ 8893	WCru
	- B&SWJ 11083	WCru
	erubescens	CAbP CJun EPfP NLar SBrt
	- HWJK 2163	WCru
	- var. ***gracilipes***	CJun LLHF
	- 'Ward van Teylingen'	NLar
	'Eskimo' 🏆H5	CAbP CBcs CCVT CJun CMac CRos CSBt EBee ELan EPfP GBin LRHS MAsh MBNS MBlu MGos SCob SCoo SKHP SLim SPoG SSta SWvt

	Name	Suppliers
	fansipanense B&SWJ 8302	WCru
	- KWJ 12239	WCru
§	***farreri*** ℽH6	Widely available
	- 'Album'	see *V. farreri* 'Candidissimum'
§	- 'Candidissimum'	CBot CDul CExl CMac EBee ELan EPfP IArd LHop LRHS MAsh MRav NLar SGol SPer SWvt
	- 'December Dwarf'	CJun NLar
	- 'Farrer's Pink'	CAbP CExl CJun
	- 'Joni'	NLar
	- 'Nanum'	CJun CMac EBtc ELan ELon EPfP LRHS MAsh MBrN MRav SKHP WPat
	foetens	see *V. grandiflorum* f. *foetens*
	foetidum	IArd
	- var. ***ceanothoides***	NLar
	- var. ***rectangulatum*** B&SWJ 1888	WCru
	- - B&SWJ 3451	WCru
	formosanum CWJ 12460	WCru
	fragrans Bunge	see *V. farreri*
	'Fragrant Cloud'	ECrN SWvt
	furcatum ℽH6	CBot EPfP GKin IArd MBri NLar SAko SKHP WPat
	- B&SWJ 5939	WCru
	× ***globosum*** 'Jermyns Globe'	CAbP CDoC CJun CMHG CMac EPfP LHop MRav NLar SCob SEND SLon SPoG WFar
	grandiflorum	CJun NLar
	- 'De Oirsprong'	NLar
§	- f. ***foetens***	CJun LRHS
	- - GWJ 9227	WCru
	- 'Snow White'	CJun
	aff. ***griffithianum*** GWJ 9388	WCru
	harryanum	CAbP EBtc EWTr IArd MBNS NLar WCru WPat WRHF WSHC
	henryi	CAbP CJun EPfP IArd NLar WPat
	× ***hillieri***	CHGN
	- 'Winton' ℽH5	CAbP CDoC CJun CMac CWib EBee EPfP GBin IArd IDee LCro LHop LRHS LSRN MBri MGos MMuc NLar SHil SKHP SLon SPoG SVen WFar WPGP
	hoanglienense B&SWJ 8281	WCru
	- KWJ 12283 new	WCru
	'Huron'	EPfP NLar
	ichangense	CJun NLar
	japonicum	CExl EPfP NLar SLon
	- B&SWJ 5968	WCru
	× ***juddii***	Widely available
	kansuense	CExl
	- BWJ 7737	WCru
	koreanum	WBod
	- B&SWJ 4231	WCru
	lantana	CCVT CDul CHab CLnd CNWT CTri CWib EAEE ECrN ELan EShb EWTr LAst LBuc NWea SCob SEND SEWo SPer SVic WMat WMou
	- 'Aureum'	CBot CMHG EHoe EPfP MAsh MBlu NLar
	- var. ***discolor***	NLar
	- 'Mohican'	NLar
	- 'Variefolium' (v)	CJun
	- 'Xanthocarpum'	SWvt WFar
§	***lantanoides***	SSpi
	aff. ***lautum*** B&SWJ 10290	WCru
	'Le Bois Marquis'PBR	CDoC CRos EBee EMil EPfP EShb EUJe LCro LRHS MGos SHil SPoG
	lentago	CAbP CMac EPfP
	lobophyllum	NLar
	luzonicum	CJun
	- B&SWJ 3637	WCru
	- var. ***formosanum*** B&SWJ 3585	WCru
	- var. ***oblongum*** B&SWJ 3549	WCru
	- var. ***sinuatum*** B&SWJ 4009	WCru
	macrocephalum	CJun NLar SLon
	mariesii	see *V. plicatum* f. *tomentosum* 'Mariesii'
	mullaha B&SWJ 2251A	WCru
	- GWJ 9227	WCru
	nervosum	EBee
	- HWJK 2241	WCru
	- HWJK 2373 new	WCru
	nudum	ECrN IDee
	- Brandywine = 'Bulk'	LRHS WPGP
	- 'Pink Beauty'	CJun CRos EPfP LCro LOPS LRHS LSRN MBri MMHG NLar SHil SWvt WFar WPGP WPat
	- 'Winterthur'	CJun NLar
	odoratissimum misapplied	see *V. odoratissimum* var. *awabuki*
	odoratissimum Ker Gawl.	EBee LEdu
	- RWJ 10046	WCru
	- aff. 'Arboricolum'	WCru
§	- var. ***awabuki***	CExl ELon EPfP EUJe LEdu LRHS MAsh MBlu MGos NLar SEND SLim WCot WPat
	- - B&SWJ 8404	EBee WCru
	- - 'Emerald Lustre'	CBcs EBee LRHS
	aff. ***odoratissimum*** B&SWJ 3913 from the Philippines	WCru
	oliganthum 'Kyo Kanzashi'	WPGP
	'Oneida'	CJun
	opulus	Widely available
	- var. ***americanum*** 'Hans'	NLar
	- - 'Phillips'	CAgr
	- - 'Spring Red'	NLar
	- - 'Wentworth'	CAgr
	- 'Amy's Magic Gold'	NLar
	- 'Apricot'	NLar
	- 'Aureum'	CLet CMac CWib EHoe ELan EPfP EWTr LBMP LRHS MAsh MGos MMuc MRav NEgg NLar SCob SEND SPer WCFE WMoo
	- var. ***calvescens*** B&SWJ 10544	WCru
	- 'Compactum' ℽH6	Widely available
	- 'Fructuluteo'	SCob SGol
*	- 'Harvest Gold'	SCoo SLim SPoG
	- 'Lady Marmalade'	NLar
	- 'Nanum'	CAbP CBcs ELan EPfP EShb MRav NLar
	- 'Notcutt's Variety' ℽH6	MAsh WPat
	- 'Park Harvest'	CDul EBee EBtc EPfP LRHS NLar SKHP SMad SWvt
§	- 'Roseum' ℽH6	Widely available
	- 'Sterile'	see *V. opulus* 'Roseum'
*	- 'Sterile Compactum'	LAst SWvt
	- 'Sylvie'	NLar
	- 'Xanthocarpum' ℽH6	CBcs CDoC CDul CExl CMac EBee ELan EPfP GBin GKin LRHS MAsh MBlu MGos MMuc MRav MSwo NLar SCob SEND SKHP SLon SPer SRms SWvt WBod WFar WPat WWtn

parvifolium	EPfP NLar WPat
- B&SWJ 3375	WCru
- B&SWJ 6768	WCru
phlebotrichum B&SWJ 11058	WCru
pichinchense B&SWJ 10660	WCru
plicatum	CTri CWib
- 'Janny'	IArd
- 'Nanum'	see *V. plicatum* f. *tomentosum* 'Nanum Semperflorens'
§ - f. ***plicatum***	EPfP SChF
- - 'Grandiflorum'	CAbP CDoC CMac CNec EPfP LRHS NLar SCob SPer SPoG WFar WMoo
- - 'Mary Milton'	CJun EBee ELan GBin NLar
- - Newport = 'Newzam'	EBee NLar
- - 'Pink Sensation'	CJun GBin
- - 'Popcorn' ♀H5	CAbP CDoC CExl CJun CMac CRos EBee ELan ELon EPfP EShb LEdu LRHS LSRN MAsh MBri NHol NLar SKHP SLim SPoG SSta WPat
- - 'Rosace'	EBee EPfP LRHS MBlu NLar SAko SSpi
- - 'Rotundifolium'	CRos IArd LRHS MAsh MBri MGos MRav NLar SHil WPat
- - Triumph = 'Trizam'	NLar
- 'Sterile'	see *V. plicatum* f. *plicatum*
- f. ***tomentosum***	CJun EWTr LRHS NLar SAko SKHP
'Cascade' ♀H5	SSpi
- - 'Dart's Red Robin'	ECtt LLHF MAsh SAko WPat
- - 'Elizabeth Bullivant'	EPfP LLHF LRHS MAsh
- - 'Igloo'	WPat
- - Kilimanjaro = 'Jww1'PBR	EBee EPfP GBin IDee LCro LOPS LPfy LRHS LSou MBlu NLar WMoo
- - 'Lanarth'	Widely available
§ - - 'Mariesii' ♀H5	Widely available
- - 'Mariesii Great Star'	LRHS
- - 'Molly Schroeder'	CJun EBee MMHG NLar
§ - - 'Nanum Semperflorens'	CBcs CDoC CMac ECtt EShb LRHS MGos NLar SPoG WFar WPat WSHC
- - 'Pink Beauty' ♀H5	Widely available
- - 'Rowallane'	NLar WPat
- - 'Saint Keverne'	ELan GKin
- - 'Shasta'	CDoC CDul CJun CMCN EPfP EWTr LEdu LRHS NLar SKHP WFar
- - 'Shoshoni'	GBin NLar
- - 'Summer Snowflake' ♀H5	CDoC COtt CRos CWGN ECrN EPfP EShb LBMP LRHS MAsh MSwo NLar SKHP SLim SPer SPoG WFar
- 'Watanabe'	see *V. plicatum* f. *tomentosum* 'Nanum Semperflorens'
'Pragense' ♀H6	CAbP CBcs CBot CDul CJun CMCN EBee EPfP GBin LRHS MGos NHol NLar SEND SLon SPer
propinquum	CAbP NLar WPat
- CWJ 12426	WCru
prunifolium	EBtc SGol WCru
- 'Mrs Henry's Large'	CJun EPfP NLar
* 'Regenteum'	CWib
× ***rhytidophylloides***	IBoy
- 'Alleghany'	NLar
- Dart's Duke = 'Interduke'	WPat
- 'Willowwood'	ELan LRHS MAsh NLar SPer WPat
rhytidophyllum	CBcs CDoC CDul CMac CNWT EAEE ECrN EPfP LAst LCro LHop LRHS MGos MJak MMuc MSwo NEgg NWea SCob SEND SGol SPer SRms SWvt WCFE WHar WMoo WSFF
- 'Aldenham'	LSRN
- 'Roseum'	CBot CExl SWvt
- 'Variegatum' (v)	CJun WPat
- 'Wisley Pink'	LRHS SSpi
'Royal Guard'	CJun LLHF
sambucinum HWJ 838	WCru
- var. ***tomentosum*** HWJ 733	WCru
sargentii B&SWJ 8695	WCru
- f. ***flavum***	NLar
- 'Onondaga' ♀H6	Widely available
- 'Susquehanna'	EPfP
semperflorens	see *V. plicatum* f. *tomentosum* 'Nanum Semperflorens'
§ ***setigerum***	EPfP NLar WPat
- BWJ 8409 **new**	WCru
- 'Aurantiacum'	NLar
sieboldii B&SWJ 2837	WCru
- CWJ 12808	WCru
- 'Seneca'	CJun
sphaerocarpum B&SWJ 3052	WCru
subalpinum	NLar
sympodiale	CFil
taitoense CWJ 12406 **new**	WCru
taiwanianum B&SWJ 3009	WCru
theiferum	see *V. setigerum*
tinoides B&SWJ 10612	WCru
tinus	Widely available
- 'Bewley's Variegated' (v)	EBee SCob SPer
I - 'Compactum'	SWvt
- 'Eve Price' ♀H4	Widely available
- 'French White' ♀H4	CDoC CDul CMac EBee ELan EPfP EWTr LCro LRHS MGos MRav NLar SAko SCob SCoo SLim SPoG SWvt WFar WHar
- 'Gwenllian' ♀H4	Widely available
- 'Israel'	MBNS
- 'Ladybird' **new**	CWSG
- 'Lisarose'PBR	EPfP MBri NLar SPoG SWvt
- 'Little Bognor'	NLar
- 'Lucidum'	CBcs CJun CSde ECrN EPfP LPar NLar SGol
- 'Lucidum Variegatum' (v)	CJun CMac SLim WFar
* - 'Macrophyllum'	EPfP LRHS NLar SPoG SWvt
- 'Pink Prelude'	SCob
- 'Purpureum'	CBcs CJun CNec CSBt ECrN EHoe ELon EPfP LRHS MAsh MGos MSwo NEgg NLar SCob SCoo SGol SLim SPer SPoG WMoo WPat
- Spirit = 'Anvi'PBR	CAbP COtt CSBt EBee ELan LRHS LSou MAsh MBri NLar NWad SCob SCoo SPoG SWvt
- 'Spring Bouquet'	CJun MAsh
- subsp. ***subcordatum*** B&SWJ 12544	WCru
- 'Variegatum' (v)	CBot CLet CMac CTri CWib EBee EHoe ELan ELon EPfP LAst LPar LPfy LRHS MAsh MGos NEgg NLar NPol SCob SEND SGol SLim SRms SWvt WPat
triphyllum B&SWJ 5784	WCru
urceolatum B&SWJ 6988	WCru
utile	WThu

aff. ***venustum*** B&SWJ 10477	WCru
wrightii	EPfP IArd IDee MRav NLar
- B&SWJ 5871	WCru
- 'Hessei'	WPat
- var. ***stipellatum*** B&SWJ 5856	WCru
- - B&SWJ 8780A	WCru

Vicia (*Papilionaceae*)

americana	EBee
cracca	CHab CWld NMir WSFF
oroboides	EBee
sativa	CHab CWld
sepium	CWld

Villaresia see *Citronella*

Vinca (*Apocynaceae*)

sp.	SCob
difformis	CNec CSam CTri ECha EWoo LCro LLWP MGos SDix WBod WHer XLum
- 'Alba'	CBot CSam
- Greystone form	CExl EPPr MMuc SEND
- 'Jenny Pym'	CBod CChe CExl CMac CSam EBee EPPr EPfP EWes EWld LHop LRHS MBNS MBri MMuc NLar SBch SEND SPoG WBor WRHF
- 'Ruby Baker'	EPPr EWes LRHS NChi
- subsp. ***sardoa***	CBot EPPr EWes LRHS
- 'Snowmound'	CSBt LRHS MRav NLar SPoG SWvt
herbacea RCB UA 21	WCot
'Hidcote Purple'	see *V. major* var. *oxyloba*
major	CBcs CDul CMac CSBt CWib ELan EShb GPoy LBuc LCro LPal LRHS MGos MJak MSwo NPol NPri NWea SCob SGbt SGol SHil SLim SPer SRms WHar WMoo XLum XSen
- 'Alba'	CMac CWib
- subsp. ***balcanica***	IMou XLum
- 'Elegantissima'	see *V. major* 'Variegata'
- 'Expoflora' (v)	NLar
- var. ***hirsuta*** misapplied	see *V. major* var. *oxyloba*
§ - subsp. ***hirsuta*** (Boiss.) Stearn	CMac LPla WCot XLum
§ - 'Maculata' (v)	CBcs CDoC CSBt ECrN EHoe EShb LRHS MMuc MRav MSwo NPri SCob SEND SGol SLim SPer SPoG SWvt WMoo WOut
§ - var. ***oxyloba***	CExl CFis CTri ECha ELan EPfP EPri EWld LHop LPot LRHS MRav NLar SRms WBor WHer XSen
- var. ***pubescens***	see *V. major* subsp. *hirsuta* (Boiss.) Stearn
- 'Surrey Marble'	see *V. major* 'Maculata'
§ - 'Variegata' (v) ♀H6	Widely available
- 'Wojo's Jem' (v)	CDoC CMac ELan EPfP EWes LRHS MBri MGos NLar NPri SCob SHil SLim SPoG SWvt WCot WMoo
minor	CBar CBcs CBod CDoC CDul CMac CSBt ELan EWoo GAbr GKin GPoy LAst LCro LOPS LRHS MAsh MGos MJak NPri NWea SCob SLim SVic WHar XLum
- f. ***alba***	CBcs CBod CDoC CDul CMac ECha EPPr EPfP EWTr LAst LOPS LPfy LRHS LSRN MAsh NLar NPri SCob SGol SPer WCot WHar XLum
§ - - 'Alba Variegata' (v)	CBar CExl EHoe IFro LBMP LSRN NEoE SPer SRms WCot WHoo WOut
- 'Alba Aureovariegata'	see *V. minor* f. *alba* 'Alba Variegata'
- f. ***alba*** 'Gertrude Jekyll'	Widely available
§ - 'Argenteovariegata' (v) ♀H6	CBcs CDoC CDul CMac CSBt CSam CTri ECha ELan ELon EPfP LAst LBuc LRHS MBri MGos MJak MMuc MSwo NLar NPri NWea SCob SEND SGol SLim SPer SRms
§ - 'Atropurpurea' ♀H6	Widely available
I - 'Aureomarginata'	WMoo
§ - 'Aureovariegata' (v)	CBcs CMac EBee ELan EPPr EPfP GAbr LRHS MGos MRav NPri SGol SHil SLim SPer SPlb WRHF
- 'Azurea'	CHid
§ - 'Azurea Flore Pleno' (d) ♀H6	CArn CBot CMac CWib ECha EPPr EPfP GAbr GCra IFro LHop LLWP LRHS MAsh MRav NLar NPri SHil SLim SPer SPoG SRms SWvt WHoo WKif WMoo XLum
* - 'Blue and Gold'	EAEE ELon SCob
- 'Blue Drift'	EWes MSwo
- 'Bowles's Blue'	see *V. minor* 'La Grave'
- 'Bowles's Cunningham'	LAst
- 'Bowles's Purple'	CBod CTsd GMaP LBMP WBor
- 'Bowles's Variety'	see *V. minor* 'La Grave'
- 'Burgundy'	SRms
- 'Caerulea Plena'	see *V. minor* 'Azurea Flore Pleno'
- 'Dartington Star'	see *V. major* var. *oxyloba*
- 'Double Burgundy'	see *V. minor* 'Multiplex'
- 'Flower Power'	EPPr
- Green Carpet	see *V. minor* 'Grüner Teppich'
§ - 'Grüner Teppich'	SGol
- 'Halstenbek'	XLum
- 'Illumination' (v)	Widely available
- 'Josephine'	MHol
§ - 'La Grave' ♀H6	Widely available
- 'Marie'	EPPr
- 'Mrs Betty James' (d)	WCot
§ - 'Multiplex' (d)	EPPr MSwo SGol SLim SRms WOut
- 'Purpurea'	see *V. minor* 'Atropurpurea'
- 'Ralph Shugert' ♀H6	CBod CBot CExl CMac CNec ELon EPPr EPfP EWTr EWes EWoo LAst LCro LHop LRHS MBri MGos NLar NPri SCob SCoo SEle SGol SHil SPoG WMoo
- 'Rubra'	see *V. minor* 'Atropurpurea'
- 'Sabinka'	CHid EPPr
- 'Silver Service' (d/v)	CHid MRav
- 'Snowdrift'	EPPr
- 'Variegata'	see *V. minor* 'Argenteovariegata'
- 'Variegata Aurea'	see *V. minor* 'Aureovariegata'
- 'White Gold'	NEoE
- 'White Power'	EPPr

Vincetoxicum (*Apocynaceae*)

cretaceum PAB 3432	LEdu
forrestii	CExl
fuscatum	IMou
hirundinaria	EBee EPPr GEdr GPoy LEdu
nigrum	CArn EBee GCal LEdu NChi NMyG WCot WTou

Viola ✿ (*Violaceae*)

'Admiration' (Va)	WGoo
adunca var. ***minor***	see *V. labradorica* ambig.
§ ***alba***	EWes
'Alethia' (Va)	SDys WGoo

	'Alice' (Vt)	CLAP
	'Alice Kate'	WGoo
	'Alice Witter' (Vt)	LLHF WPtf
*	'Alison' (Va)	WGoo
	alpina	WAbe
	'Amelia' (Va)	WGoo
	'Annette Ross' (Va)	NDov WGoo
I	'Annie' (Vt)	CLAP LLHF
	arborescens	SBrt
	'Ardross Gem' (Va)	ECho ECtt WGoo WKif
	arenaria	see *V. rupestris*
	'Arkwright's Ruby' (Va)	MAsh
	arvensis	CHab
	'Aspasia' (Va) ♀H5	EWoo MAsh WGoo
	'Avril Lawson' (Va)	SHar WGoo
	'Barbara' (Va)	WGoo
	'Baroness de Rothschild' misapplied	see *V.* 'Baronne Alice de Rothschild'
	'Baroness de Rothschild' ambig. (Vt)	CLAP
§	'Baronne Alice de Rothschild' (Vt)	NLar WCot
	'Beatrice' (Vtta)	WGoo
	'Becky Groves' (Vt)	CLAP
§	'Belmont Blue' (C)	CSam CSpe CTri EBee ECho ELon EWes EWoo GAbr GCal GMaP IFro LCro LRHS MAsh MCot MHer MRav MSCN NBir NCGa NDov SCob SHar SPer SPhx WGoo
§	***bertolonii***	WGoo
	'Beshlie' (Va) ♀H5	WGoo
	biflora	CMHG CPla EWld MNrw
	'Blackout'	MHol
	'Blue Butterfly' (C)	EWoo SPhx
	'Blue Horns' (C)	ELon
	'Blue Moon' (C)	MAsh WGoo
	'Blue Moonlight' (C)	CElw MPie
	'Boughton Blue'	see *V.* 'Belmont Blue'
§	'Bowles's Black' (T)	CSpe EPfP EShb LEdu NBro NChi SRms WJek
	brevistipulata var. ***hidakana***	GEdr
	'Bruneau' (dVt)	CBre EBee ECtt LEdu WCot
*	'Bryony' (Vtta)	WGoo
	'Bullion' (Va)	WGoo
	'Burncoose Yellow'	WGoo
	'Buttercup' (Vtta)	ECtt LSRN SDys SPhx SPoG WGoo
	'Butterpat' (C)	MAsh NDov SHar SPhx WGoo
	'Buxton Blue' (Va)	WGoo
	Can Can Series	CWCL
	'Candy' (Vt)	EBee
	canina	NBro NMir
	'Carol Loxton' (Vt)	EBee
	'Catalina'	CLAP
	chaerophylloides 'Beni-zuru'	GEdr
§	- var. ***sieboldiana***	SBrt
	- - pink-flowered	SBrt
	'Chantreyland' (Va)	EShb
	'Charles William Groves' (Vt)	CLAP ELon
	'Charlotte'	WGoo
	'Clementina' (Va) ♀H5	MRav WGoo
	'Cleo' (Va)	WGoo
	'Clive Groves' (Vt)	CLAP ELon
	'Coeur d'Alsace' (Vt)	CLAP EBee ECtt GMaP NCGa NLar SHar WHal XLum
	'Colette' (Va)	WGoo
	'Colombine' (Vt)	CAby MAsh
	'Columbine' (Va)	ECtt EPfP GMaP LRHS MHer NBir NDov NPri SPer SPoG WBrk WCot WGoo
§	'Conte di Brazza' (dPVt)	EHrv SHar
	'Cordelia' (Vt)	CLAP
	cornuta ♀H5	CElw CMea CPla ECho GKev LRHS MLHP MMuc MNrw NBir NBro SCob SEND SRms WGoo WHoo WTou
	- Alba Group ♀H5	Widely available
	- 'Alba Minor'	ECho EPfP EWes EWoo NBro NChi NSla SPhx
	- 'Blaue Schönheit'	EShb
	- blue-flowered	ECho MHer MLHP WMoo
	- 'Brimstone'	SPhx
	- 'Cleopatra' (C)	MNrw MPie SPhx
	- 'Clouded Yellow'	EWoo MNrw
	- 'Gypsy Moth' (C)	EWoo SPhx
	- 'Icy But Spicy'	MAsh MCot MRav NDov WGoo
	- Lilacina Group (C)	ECha MRav SWat WMnd WPtf
	- 'Maiden's Blush'	SPhx
	- 'Mark's Dainty'	MPie
	- 'Minor'	CPla CSam EWoo LSun MAsh NBro NDov NSla WGoo WTor
	- 'Netta Statham'	EWoo MPie WGoo
	- 'Pale Apollo' (C)	SPhx
	- Purpurea Group	CMea ECha WMnd WSHC
	- 'Rosea'	ECha
	- 'Spider'	MAsh MPie SDys WGoo WTor
	- 'Victoria's Blush' (C)	CElw CSpe ELon GMaP LCro MAsh MCot MPie NBir NDov SHar SPhx WGoo
	- 'Violacea'	EWoo MAsh
	corsica	CMea CSpe EPPr NChi SBch SEND SPhx WHea
§	***cucullata*** ♀H5	ECho SRms
§	- 'Alba' (Vt)	CBro ECho LLWP NBir SRms
*	- 'Striata Alba'	NBro
	'Czar'	see *V.* 'The Czar'
	'Daisy Smith' (Va)	WGoo
	'Danielle Molly'	WGoo
	'Dawn' (Vtta)	CAby CBod CMea ECtt EPfP GMaP NLar SPoG WGoo
	'Delicia' (Vtta)	NDov SPhx WGoo
	'Desdemona' (Va)	EWoo NDov SPhx WGoo
	'Devon Cream' (Va)	WGoo
	dissecta var. ***sieboldiana***	see *V. chaerophylloides* var. *sieboldiana*
	'Donau' (Vt)	WCot
	'Duchesse de Parme' (dPVt)	IFro SRms
	'D'Udine' (dPVt)	ECtt SRms WCot WHil
	'Dusk'	WGoo
	'E.A. Bowles'	see *V.* 'Bowles's Black'
	'Eastgrove Blue Scented' (C)	EWoo SDys WGoo WOut
	'Eastgrove Ice Blue' (C)	MCot WGoo WOut
	'Elaine Quin'	ECtt MCot NDov NEgg NLar NPri SPoG WGoo WKif
§	***elatior***	CPla EPPr MNrw SBrt SMHy WHil WPtf
	'Elizabeth' (Va)	WGoo
	'Elizabeth Lee'	WCot
	'Elliot Adam' (Va)	WGoo
	'Emma' (Va)	CElw
	'Emperor Blue Vein'	EBee EPfP
	erecta	see *V. elatior*
	'Eris' (Va)	WGoo
	'Etain' (Va)	CAby ECho ECtt ELan EPfP EWoo GBuc GMaP LBMP LRHS MAsh NDov NEgg NLar NPri SCob SPoG WBrk WGoo WIce

	Name	Suppliers
	'Fabiola' (Vtta)	EWoo
*	'Fantasy'	WGoo
	'Fiona' (Va)	EWoo MCot SPhx WGoo
	'Fiona Lawrenson' (Va)	WGoo
	'Florence' (Va)	WGoo
	'Foxbrook Cream' (C)	MAsh WGoo
	'Francesca' (Va)	WGoo
	'Freckles'	see *V. sororia* 'Freckles'
	Friolina Creamy Pink (Friolina Series)	LAst
	glabella	SBrt
	'Gladys Findlay' (Va)	WGoo
	'Glanmore'	WCot
*	'Glenda'	WGoo
	'Glenholme'	EWoo MAsh
	'Governor Herrick' (Vt)	CLAP EBee ECtt EHrv LLHF NLar WCot
§	***gracilis***	NBir
	- 'Lutea'	CSam
	- 'Major'	WGoo
	'Green Goddess' PBR	EPfP
	'Green Jade' (v)	CPla
	'Grey Owl' (Va)	SPhx WGoo
	'Grovemount Blue' (C)	CMea EPfP WTor
	grypoceras new	CEvo
	- var. ***exilis*** 'Sylettas'	LEdu
	'Gustav Wermig' (C)	MAsh WGoo
	'Haslemere'	see *V.* 'Nellie Britton'
	'Heartthrob' (v)	EBee ECtt LSou WHil WNPC
*	'Heaselands'	SMHy
§	***hederacea***	CExl CTsd ECho GQui IFoB MBNS SCob SRms
	- 'Putty Road' (Vt)	ECho
§	'Helen Mount' (T)	ECho
	'Helena' (Va)	WGoo
	'Hespera' (Va)	WGoo
	heterophylla subsp. ***epirota***	see *V. bertolonii*
*	'Hetty Gatenby'	WGoo
	'Holdgate'	WGoo
	'Hudsons Blue'	CElw MNrw
	'Huntercombe Purple' (Va) ♀H5	ECho LHop LRHS MAsh NBir SCob WGoo WHal WKif
	'Iden Gem' (Va)	WGoo
	'Inverurie Beauty' (Va) ♀H5	EWoo GBin GMaP SDys WGoo WKif WTor
	'Irish Elegance'	see *V.* 'Sulfurea'
	'Irish Molly' (Va)	CSpe ECho ECtt ELan EPfP EWTr GBuc MAsh NEgg SPer SPoG SRms WGoo WIce
	'Isabel'	NDov SRms WGoo
	'Isabella' (Vt)	CLAP EBee
	'Isobel'	MAsh
	'Ivory Queen' (Va)	EWoo MRav SPhx WGoo
	'Jack Sampson' (Vt)	EBee
	'Jackanapes' (Va) ♀H5	EBee ECho ECtt ELan EPfP LRHS MAsh SPer SPoG SRms WGoo WIce
	'Jane Mott' (Va)	EWoo
	'Janet' (Va)	EBee ECtt LSRN SDys SPoG
	'Janette'	WGoo
	japonica	SBrt
	'Jean Arnot' (Vt)	EBee
	'Jean Jeanie'	WGoo
	'Jeannie Bellew' (Va)	SPhx WGoo
	'Jennifer Andrews' (Va)	WGoo
	'Joanna' (Va)	WGoo
	'Johnny Jump Up'	see *V.* 'Helen Mount'
	'Joker Violet Gold' (Joker Series)	CWCL
	jooi	ECho EPfP GKev NBir SIgm SPhx WAbe WPtf
	'Josie' (Va)	WGoo
	'Joyce Gray' (Va)	WGoo
	'Judy Goring' (Va)	EWTr EWoo SPhx
	'Julian' (Va)	EWoo WGoo
	'Juno' (Va)	EWoo
	'Jupiter' (Va)	WCot
	'Katerina' (Va)	SPhx WGoo
	'Kim'	CLAP
	'Kimberley's Alice' (Vt) new	EBee
	'Kitten'	EWoo MAsh SDys SPhx WGoo
	'Kitty White' (Va)	EWoo SDys SPhx
§	'Königin Charlotte' (Vt)	GBBs GBin GMaP LRHS MHer WCot WMoo
	'Kurenai'	SBrt
	labradorica misapplied	see *V. riviniana* Purpurea Group
	- ***purpurea***	see *V. riviniana* Purpurea Group
§	***labradorica*** ambig.	EHrv GJos GQui NPri SCob WCAu
	'Lady Saville'	see *V.* 'Sissinghurst'
	'Lees Peachy Pink' (Vt)	CLAP
	'Letitia' (Va)	ECho MAsh MCot MNrw MRav SDys WGoo
	'Lianne' (Vt)	CLAP LLHF WCot
	'Lindsay'	WGoo
	'Lisa Tanner' (Va)	WGoo
	'Little Angel'	ECtt
	'Little David' (Vtta) ♀H5	CSam CTri ECtt MCot NDov SPhx WGoo
	'Lizzy Wootten' (Va)	EWoo
	'Lord Plunket' (Va)	WGoo
§	'Lord Primrose'	ECtt MHol
	'Lorna Cawthorne' (C)	MAsh SDys WGoo
	'Louisa' (Va)	EWoo WGoo
	'Lucy' (Va)	MAsh
§	***lutea***	WGoo
	- subsp. ***elegans***	see *V. lutea*
	'Lydia Groves' (Vt)	CLAP ECtt ELon LLHF LSou SRms WCot
	'Maggie Mott' (Va) ♀H5	ECha ECho ECtt EWTr EWoo LHop MAsh MCot MRav WGoo
	'Magic'	NDov WGoo
	mandshurica f. ***albiflora***	EPPr SBrt
	- 'Fuji Dawn' (v)	CPla SGSe
	- f. ***hasegawae***	EPPr
	- f. ***plena*** (d) new	GEdr
	- - white-flowered new	GEdr
	mandshurica × ***patrinii***	SBrt
	'Margaret' (Va)	WGoo
	'Marie-Louise' (dPVt)	SHar
	'Mars' (Va)	LEdu
I	'Mars'	CAbP LSRN
	'Martin' (Va) ♀H5	CAby CBod CMea ECha EPfP EWoo GMaP LHop LSRN MAsh MAvo MHer MPie NDov SPer SPoG WGoo
	'Mary Mouse'	WGoo
	'Mauve Haze' (Va)	WGoo
	'Mauve Radiance' (Va)	EWoo WGoo
	'May Mott' (Va)	SPhx WGoo
	'Melinda' (Vtta)	WGoo
	'Mercury' (Va)	MCot NDov WGoo
	'Midnight' (Va)	EWoo
	'Milkmaid' (Va)	ELon EWoo GBin NBir
	(Miracle Series) 'Miracle Bride White' (Vt)	SHar
	- 'Miracle Classy Pink' (Vt)	SHar
	- 'Miracle Ice White' (Vt)	NLar SHar
	- 'Miracle Intense Blue' (Vt)	NCGa NLar

	Name	Suppliers
	- 'Miracle Vanilla White' (Vt)	SHar
	'Miss Brookes' (Va)	WGoo
	'Misty Guy' (Vtta)	MAsh WGoo
	'Molly Sanderson' (Va) ♀H5	CAby EAJP ECha ECho ECtt ELan EPfP EWoo GMaP LAst LHop LRHS MAsh MHer NEgg SCob SPer SPlb SPoG WBrk WGoo WIce
	'Moonlight' (Va) ♀H5	ECho ELan LHop LRHS WGoo
	'Morwenna' (Va)	ECtt MAsh MCot NDov WGoo WKif
	'Mrs Lancaster' (Va)	EBee ECtt ELan EWoo GMaP LHop LSRN MCot NBir NLar SDys SPoG WGoo
	'Mrs Pinehurst' (Vt)	EBee GMaP
	'Mrs R. Barton' (Vt)	CLAP ELon SHar
	'Myfawnny' (Va)	ECho LRHS MCot SDys SRms WGoo
§	'Nellie Britton' (Va) ♀H5	ECho SRms
	'Netta Statham'	see *V.* 'Belmont Blue'
	'Nora'	NDov WGoo
	'Norah Church' (Vt)	CLAP
	'Norah Leigh' (Va)	WGoo
	obliqua	see *V. cucullata*
	odorata (Vt)	CArn CBcs CBod CHab EPfP GPoy LCro MRav NMir NPri SEND SIde SRms SVic WJek WOut
	- 'Alba' (Vt)	EBee ECho ELan EPfP GBin LEdu MHer MMuc SEND SRms WMoo
	- 'Alba Plena' (dVt)	EHrv
	- 'Albiflora' (Vt)	CLAP EPfP
	- apricot-flowered	see *V.* 'Sulfurea'
	- 'Bethan Davies' (d/Vt)	WCot
	- 'Dawnie' (Vt)	EBee
	- 'Double Rose' (d) **new**	WCot
	- var. ***dumetorum***	see *V. alba*
	- 'Elsmeer' (Vt)	ECtt LSou WCot
	- 'Hungarian Beauty' (Vt)	EBee LCro
	- 'Katy' (Vt)	CLAP ELon
	- 'King of Violets' (dVt)	ECtt LSou SHar SPer
	- 'Melanie' (Vt)	CLAP WCot
	- 'Mrs R.O. Barlow' (Vt)	CLAP WCot WSHC
	- pink-flowered	see *V. odorata* Rosea Group
	- 'Princeana'	CBod
	- ***rosea***	see *V. odorata* Rosea Group
§	- Rosea Group (Vt)	GBin IFoB LSou MMuc MPie MRav SEND SIde SPer SRms WCot WSHC
*	- subsp. ***subcarnea*** (Vt)	MMuc SEND
	- 'Sulphurea'	see *V.* 'Sulfurea'
	- 'Vin d'André Thorp' (Vt)	ECtt LEdu WCot WWEG
I	- 'Violett Charm' (Vt)	WCot
	- 'Weimar' (Vt)	GBin
	- 'Wismar' (Vt)	WCot
	'Olive Edwards'	WGoo
	'Opéra' (Vt)	CLAP LLHF
	'Orchid Pink' (Vt)	CLAP GMaP
	orientalis **new**	GEdr
	palustris	EWay LLWG WHer WSFF WShi
	'Pamela Zambra' (Vt)	CLAP WSHC
	papilionacea	see *V. sororia*
	papuanum **new**	MHer
	'Parchment' (Vt)	EBee
	'Parme de Toulouse' (dPVt)	NLar XLum
	'Pasha' (Va)	EWoo SDys SPhx
	'Pat Creasy' (Va)	NDov WGoo
	'Pat Kavanagh' (C)	MAsh WGoo
	'Patience'	NDov WGoo
	'Pearl Rose'	ELon
	pedata	CBro ECho WAbe
	- f. ***alba***	GEdr MHer
	- 'Bicolor'	ECho WAbe
	pedatifida	IFoB
	pensylvanica	see *V. pubescens* var. *eriocarpa*
	'Peppered-palms'	EHrv SGSe
	'Perle Rose' (Vt)	CLAP EHrv
	'Petra' (Vtta)	EWoo SPhx WGoo
	phalacrocarpa	SBrt
	'Phyl Dove' (Vt)	CLAP EBee WCot
	'Pickering Blue' (Va)	WGoo
	pinnata	SBrt
	'Primrose Dame' (Va)	WGoo
	'Primrose Pixie' (Va)	WGoo
	'Prince Henry' (T)	MNHC
	'Prince John' (T)	MNHC
	'Princess Diana' (Vt)	EBee
	'Princess Mab' (Vtta)	WGoo
	'Princess of Prussia' (Vt)	WCot
	'Princess of Wales'	see *V.* 'Princesse de Galles'
§	'Princesse de Galles' (Vt)	CTri
	prionantha **new**	GEdr
§	***pubescens*** var. ***eriocarpa***	SRms
	'Purple Wings' (Va)	WGoo
	Queen Charlotte	see *V.* 'Königin Charlotte'
	'Raven'	SPhx WGoo
	'Rebecca' (Vtta)	CAby CBod CPla CSam ECho ECtt ELan EPfP GBuc GMaP LAst LRHS LSRN MAsh MCot MHer NBir NDov NEgg NLar SDys SPer SPoG SRms WBrk WGoo WIce
	'Red Giant' (Vt)	EHrv LEdu MBNS
	'Red Queen' (Vt)	CLAP
	reichenbachiana	GJos
	'Reine des Blanches' (dVt)	EBee ECtt GBin LEdu LLWP NGdn SPer SRms WCot
	'Reine des Neiges' (Vt)	EBee
	reniforme	see *V. hederacea*
	riviniana	CWld GJos MHer MMuc SEND WHer WOut WSFF WShi
	- dark pink-flowered	MMuc
	- 'Ed's Variegated' (v)	EPPr
§	- Purpurea Group	Widely available
	- 'Rosea'	SEND
	- white-flowered	CWld EWes MMuc SEND
	'Roscastle Black'	CMea EPfP EWoo MAsh NDov SBch WGoo
	rotundifolia	LEdu
	'Rubin' (C)	EShb
	'Rubra' (Vt)	EPfP XLum
§	***rupestris***	CTri MHer
*	- ***rosea***	CPla IFro LLWP SGSe WHer WPtf
	sagittata	LPot
	'Saint Helena' (Vt)	WCot
	selkirkii Pursh ex Goldie	CPla WThu
	- 'Variegata' (v)	XEll
	sempervirens	SBrt
	seoulensis	LLHF
	septentrionalis	see *V. sororia*
	'Serena' (Va)	WGoo
	'Sherbet Dip'	WGoo
	'Sidborough Poppet'	EWes
	'Silver Samurai'	WCot
§	'Sissinghurst' (Va)	NBir
	'Smugglers' Moon'	WGoo
	somchetica	WCot
	'Sophie' (Vtta)	WGoo
	'Sorbet Series'	NPri
§	***sororia***	ECha ECho EPPr EWoo MLHP MNrw NBir NBro SCob SPhx
*	- 'Albiflora' ♀H6	CHid EAJP ECho EPPr EPfP EWTr EWoo LEdu LLWG LSun MRav SCob SPhx WCFE WJek XLum

- 'Dark Freckles' EBee ECho EWTr LHop NLar NRya SPhx XLum
§ - 'Freckles' Widely available
- 'Priceana' ECGP EPri EWTr LEdu LPla MRav NBir SPlb WCot
- 'Sorority Sisters' NChi
- 'Speckles' (v) WCot
- 'Sweet Emma' SPhx
* 'Spencer's Cottage' WGoo
Starry Night see V. 'Lord Primrose'
'Steyning' (Va) WGoo
stojanowii CSpe ECho GCrg LLHF
§ 'Sulfurea' (Vt) CLAP CPBP EHrv LLWP MMHG MRav NRya WCot
'Susie' (Va) MHol WGoo
'Swanley White' see V. 'Conte di Brazza'
'Sybil' (SP) NDov WGoo
§ 'The Czar' (Vt) CBre CLAP ELon SHar WCot
'Tiger Eyes' (Va) CBod SPoG
'Titania' (Va) EBee
'Tom Tit' (Va) ECtt WGoo
'Tony Venison' (C/v) ELon EPfP NEgg NLar WGoo WHer
tricolor CHab CWld ECho ENfk EPfP GPoy LCro MHer MNHC NDov SIde SRms WBod WJek
- 'Sawyer's Black' ENfk
velutina see *V. gracilis*
verecunda WSHC
- B&SWJ 604a WCru
§ - var. ***yakusimana*** WThu
'Victoria Cawthorne' (C) ECho EWoo GBuc MAsh MHer WBod WGoo
'Violacea' (C) EWoo
'Virginia' (Va) WGoo
'Vita' (Va) EWoo SRms WGoo
'White Ladies' see *V. cucullata* 'Alba'
'White Pearl' (Va) SPhx WGoo
'White Perfection' (C) EShb
'White Swan' (Va) MAsh
'White Witch' (Vt) new EBee
'Winifred Jones' (Va) WGoo
'Winona Cawthorne' (C) EWoo NDov
'Wisley White' LHop LPla LRHS
× ***wittrockiana*** Matrix Series NPri
'Woodlands Cream' (Va) MHer WGoo
'Woodlands Lilac' (Va) WGoo
yakusimana see *V. verecunda* var. *yakusimana*
yezoensis SBrt
'Zara' (Va) NDov WGoo
'Zoe' (Vtta) CBod ECtt EPfP MAsh NEgg SPoG WGoo

Viscaria (*Caryophyllaceae*)

vulgaris see *Lychnis viscaria*

Vitaliana (*Primulaceae*)

§ ***primuliflora*** ECho EDAr GKev NRya NSla
- subsp. ***chionantha*** WAbe
- subsp. ***cinerea*** GKev
- subsp. ***praetutiana*** CPBP GCrg NHar NWad WAbe WThu

Vitex (*Lamiaceae*)

agnus-castus CArn CBcs CMCN COtt CSde EPri EShb GPoy IDee LCro LEdu LRHS MRav NLar SEND SLon SPer SPoG WSHC XSen
- f. ***alba*** CDul CWib MBlu NLar
- f. ***latifolia*** ♀H5 CBot CWib EBee ECre ELan EPfP LRHS LSRN MGos MHer NLar SDix SPoG WPGP XSen
- 'Silver Spire' CBot EBee ECre ELan EMil EPfP LRHS NLar SPoG SSpi WPGP
chinensis see *V. negundo* var. *heterophylla*
incisa see *V. negundo* var. *heterophylla*
negundo CArn LEdu
§ - var. ***heterophylla*** EWes XSen

Vitis ✿ (*Vitaceae*)

sp. ETod
'Abundante' (F) WSuV
'Alden' (O/B) WSuV
'Amandin' (G/W) WSuV
amurensis EPfP EWoo
- B&SWJ 4138 WCru
- B&SWJ 4299 WCru
- B&SWJ 12568 WCru
'Atlantis' (O/W) WSuV
§ 'Aurore' (W) CAgr WSuV
'Baco Noir' (O/B) CAgr CLet SDea WSuV
'Beauty Seedless' (B/S) SDea
betulifolia EPfP
'Bianca' (O/W) SBmr WSuV
'Birstaller Muscat' (W) WSuV
Black Hamburgh see *V. vinifera* 'Schiava Grossa'
* 'Black Strawberry' (B) CAgr SDea WSuV
'Blanc Seedless' (W/S) SDea
§ 'Boskoop Glory' (O/B) ♀H5 CMac ERea ETod LBuc MCoo NLar SCob SCoo SDea WHar WSuV
'Brant' (O/B) ♀H5 Widely available
'Brilliant' (B) WSuV
'Buffalo' (B) WSuV
californica (F) NLar
'Canadice' (O/R/S) SDea WSuV
'Cascade' see V. Seibel 13053
Castel 19637 (B) WSuV
'Chambourcin' (B) WSuV
Claret Cloak = 'Frovit'PBR ♀H5 CBot CLet ELan EPfP EUJe LRHS LSRN MAsh MBlu NLar SCoo SPer SPtp WPGP
coignetiae ♀H5 Widely available
- B&SWJ 4550 from Korea WCru
- B&SWJ 4744 WCru
- B&SWJ 8553 from Korea WCru
- B&SWJ 10882 from Japan WCru
- B&SWJ 10908 from Japan WCru
- var. ***glabrescens*** B&SWJ 8537 WCru
- 'Purple Cloak' SCob
- Sunningdale form NLar WGrn
'Dalkauer' (W) WSuV
I 'Diamond' (B) WSuV
'Dutch Black' (O/B) WSuV
'Edwards No 1' (O/W) WSuV
'Eger Csillaga' (O/W) WSuV
'Einset' (B/S) WSuV
ficifolia see *V. thunbergii*
flexuosa B&SWJ 5568 WCru
- var. ***choii*** B&SWJ 4101 WCru
- var. ***parvifolia*** NLar
- - B&SWJ 1946 WCru
'Fragola' (O/R) CAgr CDul CMac CTri ECha EPom ERea GTwe MCoo MRav NLar SBdl SDea SLim SPer SPoG SRms WMat WSuV
'Gagarin Blue' (O/B) CAgr EPom GTwe SDea SVen WSuV
'Glenora' (F/B/S) CAgr WSuV
'Hecker' (O/W) WSuV

	henryana	see *Parthenocissus henryana*
	'Himrod' (O/W/S)	ELan ERea GTwe SDea WSuV
	'Horizon' (O/W)	WSuV
	inconstans	see *Parthenocissus tricuspidata*
	'Interlaken' (O/W/S)	CAgr ERea SDea WSuV
	'Johanniter' (W)	SPre WSuV
	'Kempsey Black' (O/B)	CAgr WSuV
	'Kozmapalme Muscatoly' (O/W)	WSuV
	'Kuibishevski' (O/R)	WSuV
	Landot 244 (O/B)	WSuV
	Landot 3217 (O/B)	WSuV
	'L'Arcadie Blanche' (W)	WSuV
	'Léon Millot' (O/G/B)	CAgr CSBt LSRN SDea WSuV
	'Lucy Kuhlman' (B)	WSuV
	'Maréchal Foch' (O/B)	WSuV
	'Maréchal Joffre' (O/R)	CAgr GTwe WSuV
	'Mars' (O/B/S)	WSuV
	'Merzling' (O/W)	WSuV
	'Munson R.W.' (O/R)	WSuV
	'Muscat Bleu' (O/B)	EPom LRHS NLar SBmr SKee SLim SPoG WMat WSuV
	'Nero'PBR	CAgr
	'New York Muscat' (O/B) ♀H5	WSuV
	'New York Seedless' (O/W/S)	WSuV
	'Niagara' (O/W)	WSuV
	'Niederother Monschrebe' (O/R)	WSuV
	Oberlin 595 (O/B)	WSuV
	'Orion' (O/W)	LRHS MAsh WSuV
	'Paletina' (O/W)	WSuV
	'Perdin' (O/W)	WSuV
	'Phönix' (O/W)	CAgr EPom GTwe LCro LOPS LRHS LSRN MAsh MBri MGos NLar NPla SBmr SKee SLim SPoG SPre SVic WMat WSuV
	piasezkii	WCru
	- var. ***pagnuccii***	WCru
*	'Pink Strawberry' (O)	WSuV
	'Pirovano 14' (O/B)	GTwe SDea WSuV
§	'Plantet' (O/B)	WSuV
	'Poloske Muscat' (W)	EPom ERea WMat WSuV
	purpurea 'Spetchley Park' (O/B)	CAgr WSuV
	quinquefolia	see *Parthenocissus quinquefolia*
	'Ramdas' (O/W)	WSuV
	Ravat 51 (O/W)	WSuV
	'Rayon d'Or' (O/W)	WSuV
	'Regent'PBR (O/B)	CAgr EPom ERea GTwe LCro LOPS LRHS MBri MCoo MGos NLar SKee SLim SPoG SPre SVic WMat WSuV
	'Reliance' (O/R/S)	CAgr ERea WSuV
	'Rembrant' (R)	CAgr WSuV
	riparia	CArn NLar
	'Romulus' (O/G/W/S)	WSuV
	'Rondo' (O/B)	CAgr NPla SPre SVic WMat WSuV
	'Saturn' (O/R/S)	CAgr WSuV
	'Schuyler' (O/B)	CAgr WSuV
	Seibel (F)	GTwe SDea
	Seibel 5279	see *V.* 'Aurore'
	Seibel 5409 (W)	WSuV
	Seibel 5455	see *V.* 'Plantet'
	Seibel 7053	WSuV
	Seibel 9549	WSuV
§	Seibel 13053 (O/B)	CMac LRHS MAsh SDea SEND WSuV
	Seibel 138315 (R)	WSuV
	'Seneca' (W)	WSuV
	'Serena' (O/W)	WSuV
§	'Seyval Blanc' (O/W)	CAgr GTwe MAsh SDea SEND SVic WSuV
	Seyve Villard 12.375	see *V.* 'Villard Blanc'
	Seyve Villard 20.473 (F)	NPer
	Seyve Villard 5276	see *V.* 'Seyval Blanc'
	Seyve Villard ambig.	LRHS NPer
	'Sirius' (B)	WSuV
	'Solaris' (O/W)	LRHS MGos SFrt WMat WSuV
	'Stauffer' (O/W)	WSuV
	'Suffolk Seedless' (B/S)	ERea GTwe WSuV
	'Tereshkova' (O/B)	CAgr SDea WSuV
	'Thornton' (O/S)	WSuV
§	***thunbergii*** B&SWJ 4702	WCru
	'Triomphe d'Alsace' (O/B)	CAgr CSBt LRHS MCoo NPer SDea WSuV
	'Trollinger'	see *V. vinifera* 'Schiava Grossa'
	'Vanessa' (O/R/S)	SDea WSuV
§	'Villard Blanc' (O/W)	WSuV
	vinifera	EUJe LPal MGos
	- EM 323158B	WSuV
	- 'Abouriou' (O/B)	WSuV
	- 'Acolon' (O/B)	WSuV
	- 'Adelheidtraube' (O/W)	WSuV
	- 'Albalonga' (W)	WSuV
§	- 'Alicante' (G/B)	CBcs CMac GTwe SDea WSuV
	- 'Augusta Louise' (O/W)	WSuV
	- 'Auxerrois' (O/W)	WSuV
	- 'Bacchus' (O/W)	CAgr ERea LRHS MBri NLar SDea SFrt SLim SVic WMat WSuV
	- 'Baresana' (G/W)	NPla WSuV
	- 'Beauty'	CAgr
	- 'Black Alicante'	see *V. vinifera* 'Alicante'
	- 'Black Corinth' (G/B/S)	ERea
	- 'Black Frontignan' (G/O/B)	WSuV
	- Black Hamburgh	see *V. vinifera* 'Schiava Grossa'
	- 'Black Monukka' (G/B/S)	WSuV
	- 'Black Prince' (G/B)	CAgr WSuV
	- 'Blue Portuguese'	see *V. vinifera* 'Portugieser'
§	- 'Bouvier' (W)	WSuV
	- 'Bouviertraube'	see *V. vinifera* 'Bouvier'
	- 'Buckland Sweetwater' (G/W)	CLet GTwe SDea SLim WSuV
	- 'Cabernet Sauvignon' (O/B)	EPfP EUJe LRHS MAsh MGos NPer NPri SDea SVic WSuV
	- 'Cardinal' (O/R)	WSuV
	- 'Carla' (O/R)	WSuV
	- 'Centennial' (O/N/S)	WSuV
	- 'Chardonnay' (O/W)	CAgr LRHS LSRN MAsh NPer NPri SDea SPer SPre SVic WSuV
§	- 'Chasselas' (G/O/W)	LRHS SDea WSuV
	- 'Chasselas de Fontainebleau' (F)	SVic
	- 'Chasselas d'Or'	see *V. vinifera* 'Chasselas'
	- 'Chasselas Rosé' (G/R)	CAgr WSuV
	- 'Chasselas Rosé Royal' (O/R)	SVic
	- 'Chasselas Vibert' (G/W)	WSuV
	- 'Chenin Blanc' (O/W)	SVic WSuV
	- 'Ciotat' (F)	ERea EShb MRav SDea WSuV
	- 'Cot Précoce de Tours' (O/B)	WSuV
	- 'Crimson Seedless' (R/S)	ERea WSuV
	- 'Csabyongye' (O/W)	WSuV
	- 'Dattier de Beyrouth' (G/W)	WSuV
	- 'Dattier Saint Vallier' (O/W)	SVic WSuV
	- 'Dolcetto' (O/B)	WSuV

	- 'Dornfelder' (O/R)	ERea SLim SPoG SVic WMat WSuV
	- 'Dunkelfelder' (O/R)	WSuV
	- 'Early Van der Laan' (F)	CMac
	- 'Ehrenfelser' (O/W)	WSuV
	- 'Elbling' (O/W)	WSuV
	- 'Exalta' (G/W/S)	WSuV
	- 'Excelsior' (W)	WSuV
	- 'Faber' (O/W)	WSuV
	- 'Fiesta' (W/S)	WSuV
	- 'Findling' (W)	WSuV
	- 'Flame'	CAgr NPla SBdl SVic WHar WMat
	- 'Flame Red' (O/D)	EPom
	- 'Flame Seedless' (G/O/R/S)	CMac EPom GTwe LRHS SFrt SPoG WSuV
	- 'Forta' (O/W)	WSuV
	- 'Foster's Seedling' (G/W)	MJak SDea SVic WSuV
	- 'Freisamer' (O/W)	WSuV
	- 'Frühburgunder' (O/B)	WSuV
	- 'Gamay Hâtif des Vosges'	WSuV
	- 'Gamay Noir' (O/B)	SVic WSuV
	- Gamay Teinturier Group (O/B)	WSuV
	- 'Gewürztraminer' (O/R)	LRHS MAsh SDea SVic WSuV
	- 'Glory of Boskoop'	see *V.* 'Boskoop Glory'
	- 'Golden Chasselas'	see *V. vinifera* 'Chasselas'
	- 'Goldriesling' (O/W)	WSuV
	- 'Gros Colmar' (G/B)	WSuV
	- 'Grüner Veltliner' (O/W)	WSuV
	- 'Gutenborner' (O/W)	WSuV
	- 'Helfensteiner' (O/R)	WSuV
	- 'Huxelrebe' (O/W)	SVic WSuV
	- 'Incana' (O/B)	ELon LRHS MRav SVen WCFE WCot WPGP WSHC
	- 'Italia' (O/W)	NPla
	- 'Juliaumsrebe' (O/W)	WSuV
	- 'Kanzler' (O/W)	WSuV
	- 'Kerner' (O/W)	WSuV
	- 'Kernling' (F)	WSuV
	- 'King's Ruby' (F/S)	ERea WSuV
	- 'Lady Hastings' (G/B)	ERea
	- 'Lakemont' (O/W/S)	CAgr CMac ELan EPfP EPom ERea GTwe MBri MGos NLar NPla NPri SBmr SDea SEWo SFrt SKee SLim SPoG SPre SVic WHar WMat WSuV
	- 'Lival' (O/B)	WSuV
	- 'Madeira Frontignan' (G/R)	ERea
	- 'Madeleine Angevine' (O/W)	CAgr GTwe LRHS LSRN MAsh NPer NPri SDea SPoG SVen SVic WSuV
	- 'Madeleine Celine' (B)	WSuV
	- 'Madeleine Royale' (G/W)	WSuV
	- 'Madeleine Silvaner' (O/W)	CSBt GTwe LRHS MAsh NPer SDea SPoG WSuV
	- 'Madresfield Court' (G/B)	GTwe WSuV
	- 'Merlot' (G/B)	EUJe LRHS SDea SVic WSuV
§	- 'Meunier' (B)	SVic WSuV
	- 'Mireille' (F)	SDea WSuV
	- 'Morio Muscat' (O/W)	WSuV
	- 'Mrs Pearson' (G/W)	ERea
§	- 'Müller-Thurgau' (O/W)	LRHS LSRN MAsh MGos SDea SVic WSuV
	- 'Muscat Blanc à Petits Grains' (O/W)	SWvt WSuV
	- 'Muscat Cannon Hall' (G/W)	CHll
	- 'Muscat de Lierval' (O/B)	WSuV
	- 'Muscat de Saumur' (O/W)	WSuV
	- 'Muscat Hamburg' (G/B)	COtt LRHS LSRN MAsh MGos SDea SWvt WSuV
	- 'Muscat of Alexandria' (G/W)	CBcs CMac CRHN ERea LRHS MRav SDea SFrt SLim SPer SVic WHar WMat
	- 'Muscat Ottonel' (O/W)	WSuV
	- 'Muscat Saint Laurent' (W)	WSuV
	- 'Nebbiolo' (O/B)	WSuV
	- 'No 69' (W)	WSuV
	- 'Noblessa' (W)	WSuV
	- 'Noir Hâtif de Marseille' (O/B)	WSuV
	- 'Olive Blanche' (O/W)	WSuV
	- 'Oliver Irsay' (O/W)	WSuV
	- 'Optima' (O/W)	WSuV
	- 'Ora' (O/W/S)	WSuV
	- 'Ortega' (O/W)	WSuV
	- 'Palatina' (O/W)	SFrt
	- 'Perle' (O/W)	WSuV
	- 'Perle de Czaba' (G/O/W)	WSuV
	- 'Perlette' (O/W/S)	EPom ERea GTwe LRHS WSuV
	- 'Petit Rouge' (R)	WSuV
	- 'Pinot Blanc' (O/W)	LCro LOPS LRHS MAsh SVic WSuV
	- 'Pinot Gris' (O/B)	SDea SVic WSuV
	- 'Pinot Noir' (O/B)	SVic WSuV
§	- 'Portugieser' (O/B)	WSuV
	- 'Précoce de Bousquet' (O/W)	WSuV
	- 'Précoce de Malingre' (O/W)	CAgr SDea
	- 'Prima' (O/B)	WSuV
	- 'Primavis Frontignan' (G/W)	WSuV
	- 'Purpurea' (O/B) ♀H5	Widely available
	- 'Queen of Esther' (B)	MBri SKee SLim WSuV
	- 'Regner' (O/W)	WSuV
	- 'Reichensteiner' (O/G/W)	CAgr SDea SVic WSuV
	- 'Riesling' (O/W)	LRHS MAsh SVic WSuV
	- Riesling-Silvaner	see *V. vinifera* 'Müller-Thurgau'
	- 'Rotberger' (O/G/B)	WSuV
	- 'Royal Muscadine' (G/O/W)	GQue SBdl WMat WSuV
	- 'Saint Laurent' (G/O/W)	SVic WSuV
	- 'Sauvignon Blanc' (O/W)	LRHS SVic WSuV
	- 'Scheurebe' (O/W)	WSuV
§	- 'Schiava Grossa' (G/B/D)	Widely available
	- 'Schönburger' (O/W)	SDea SVic WSuV
	- 'Schwarzriesling'	see *V. vinifera* 'Meunier'
	- 'Sémillon'	LRHS LSRN MAsh SVic
	- 'Senator' (O/W)	WSuV
	- 'Septimer' (O/W)	WSuV
	- 'Shiraz' (B)	WSuV
	- 'Siegerrebe' (O/W/D)	CAgr GTwe LBuc LRHS MAsh NPer SDea SPoG SVic WSuV
	- 'Silvaner' (O/W)	WSuV
	- 'Spetchley Red' (O/B) ♀H5	CKel CRHN NLar WAvo WCot WCru WPGP WPat
	- strawberry grape	see *V.* 'Fragola'
	- 'Suffolk Red' (G/R/S)	ERea
§	- 'Sultana' (W/S)	CAgr GTwe NPla SDea WSuV
	- 'Theresa' (O/W)	LRHS MBri SLim WSuV
	- 'Thompson Seedless'	see *V. vinifera* 'Sultana'
*	- 'Triomphe' (O/B)	SVic
	- 'Triomphrebe' (W)	WSuV
	- 'Vroege van der Laan' (O/W)	ETod MJak NLar

	- 'Wrotham Pinot' (O/B)	SDea WSuV
	- 'Würzer' (O/W)	WSuV
	- 'Zweigeltrebe' (O/B)	WSuV
*	'White Strawberry' (O/W)	WSuV
	'Zalagyöngye' (W)	CAgr WSuV

Vriesea (*Bromeliaceae*)

'Astrid'	LAir NEve
carinata	NEve
corcovadensis	LAir
espinosae	LAir
gigantea	LAir NEve
- 'Nova'	LAir NLos
hieroglyphica	LAir NEve
imperialis	NEve
'Kallisto'	LAir NEve
'Lacy' **new**	LAir
saundersii ♀H1a	NEve
splendens ♀H1a	LAir NEve SPlb XBlo

W

Wachendorfia (*Haemodoraceae*)

multiflora	CLak SVen
paniculata	CLak CTal
thyrsiflora	CCon CDes CExl CPne EAla EBee GGal LEdu NLos SVen WPGP WSHC

Wahlenbergia (*Campanulaceae*)

albomarginata	ECho GBin
- 'Blue Mist'	ECho
congesta	ECho NPri
gloriosa	MOWG
pumilio	see *Edraianthus pumilio*

Waldsteinia (*Rosaceae*)

	fragarioides	EBee IMou
	geoides	EBee EPPr EWTr LAst MGil MMuc NEoE SPer WMoo XLum
	- 'Goldkäfer'	IMou
	ternata	Widely available
§	- 'Mozaick' (v)	EBee EShb EWes NBir NEoE
	- 'Variegata'	see *W. ternata* 'Mozaick'

walnut, black see *Juglans nigra*

walnut, common see *Juglans regia*

Wasabia (*Brassicaceae*)

wasabi	CArn CExl GPoy LEdu

Washingtonia (*Arecaceae*)

filifera ♀H1c	CPHo LTro SBig SEND SPlb
robusta	EAla LPal LTro MHin SHil SPlb

Watsonia (*Iridaceae*)

	aletroides	CDes CTre EBee ECho GCal GKev SDeJ SVen
	amatolae	IBlr
	angusta	CDes CExl CPne CPrp EBee IBlr SGSe SPlb WPGP
	'Apricot Queen'	IDee
	ardernei	see *W. borbonica* subsp. *ardernei* (Sander) Goldblatt 'Arderne's White'
	beatricis	see *W. pillansii*
§	***borbonica***	CDes CPrp EBee
	- subsp. ***ardernei*** misapplied	see *W. borbonica* subsp. *ardernei* (Sander) Goldblatt 'Arderne's White'
§	- subsp. ***ardernei*** (Sander) Goldblatt 'Arderne's White'	CBre CDes CExl CPrp GCal IBlr
	- subsp. ***borbonica***	IBlr WPGP
	- 'Peach Glow'	ERCP GKev
	brevifolia	see *W. laccata*
	brick red-flowered	CDes EBee WPGP
	coccinea Herb. ex Baker	CBlu CTre
	'Dart Sea Trout'	CDes EBee
	densiflora	IBlr
	early pink-flowered **new**	CPne
	fourcadei	GCal
	fulgens	LEdu
	galpinii	CCon
	- lavender-flowered	IBlr
	- pink-flowered	IBlr
	galpinii × ***knysnana***	IBlr
§	***humilis***	EBee GCal SKHP
	knysnana	CDes EBee IBlr
§	***laccata***	CPne CTre
	- orange-flowered	CDes
	- pink-flowered	CDes EBee
	latifolia	IBlr
	lepida	CTre ECho SPlb
	× ***longifolia*** dark red-flowered **new**	GCal
	marginata	CPrp CTre EBee ECho
	- ***alba***	SKHP
	marlothii	CDes
	meriania	EBee ERCP GBin GKev IBlr MHer
	- var. ***bulbillifera***	CCon CPne CPrp EBee ECho GAbr GCal GCra GGal IBlr LTro WSHC
	'Peachy Pink Orphan'	CDes EBee WPGP
§	***pillansii***	CAbb CCon CExl CPne CPrp EBee EPri EWld IBlr ILea LEdu LRHS NCGa SVen
	- peach-flowered	CExl
	- pink-flowered	CExl CPrp IVic
	- red-flowered	CExl IVic
	- soft pink-flowered	EPri
	pink-flowered	CDes
	pyramidata	see *W. borbonica*
	roseoalba	see *W. humilis*
	'Stanford Scarlet'	CAby CCon CDes CExl CPrp EBee ELon IBlr WPGP
	stenosiphon	IBlr
	strubeniae	IBlr
	tabularis	CPrp IMou
	transvaalensis	EBee
	'Tresco Dwarf Pink'	CCon CDes CExl EBee IBlr LEdu WPGP
	Tresco hybrids	CAbb CExl CTre EPri GGal SRkn
	'Tresco Mauve' **new**	CCon
	vanderspuyae	CExl CPne CPrp EPri IBlr
	wilmaniae	CExl CPrp EBee IBlr WPGP
	- JCA 3.955200	SKHP
	- 'Ice Angel'	SKHP
	wordsworthiana	GCal
	zeyheri	EBee

Wattakaka see *Dregea*

Wedelia (*Asteraceae*)

trilobata	LLWG

Weigela ✿ (*Caprifoliaceae*)

CC 1231	CExl

'Abel Carrière' CMac CTri ECtt GKin MGos NWea WCFE
§ 'Avalanche' EPfP
'Avalanche' misapplied see *W.* 'Candida'
'Avalanche' Lemoine see *W.* 'Avalanche'
'Avant Garde' MAsh WPat
Black and White = 'Courtacad1'PBR CBot CWGN EBee EPfP LRHS LSRN NLar SCob SGol SPoG
'Boskoop Glory' GQui SPer
'Bouquet Rose' LPot
§ Briant Rubidor = 'Olympiade' (v) CBcs CBot CDoC CMac COtt EBee ECrN EHoe LRHS MAsh MBri MGos MMuc MRav NEgg NLar SCob SEND SGol SHil SLim SPer SPlb SPoG WHar
'Bristol Ruby' Widely available
'Bristol Snowflake' CDul CMac EPfP MBlu MHer MSwo NBir NLar SLon
§ 'Candida' CTri ELan MRav NLar SGol SPer WOut
Cappuccino = 'Verweig 2'PBR MBlu MGos MJak NBro NLar SGol
Carnaval = 'Courtalor'PBR ♀H6 CBcs COtt CWib LAst LSou MRav NLar SCob
'Chameleon' MPkF
coraeensis ♀H6 CHll EPfP IArd MBlu MMHG MNrw SBrt SPer WPat
- 'Alba' CHll
decora GQui
- B&SWJ 10834 WCru
'Eva Rathke' NBir NLar NWea
'Evita' IBoy MBlu
floribunda B&SWJ 10831 WCru
florida CDul CMac NBes
- B&SWJ 8439 WCru
- f. ***alba*** CBcs
* - 'Albovariegata' (v) CExl
- 'Bicolor' CMac ELan
- 'Foliis Purpureis' Widely available
- 'Gustave Malet' CMCN GQui
- Magical Fantasy see *W. florida* Sunny Fantasy
- Magical Rainbow = 'Kolmagira'PBR LBuc LRHS MPkF SGol SPoG
- 'Milk and Honey' LRHS
- Minor Black = 'Verweig 3'PBR COtt EPfP GBin LRHS MGos MPkF NBro NHol NLar SPoG WMoo
- Monet = 'Verweig'PBR (v) Widely available
- Moulin Rouge = 'Brigela'PBR CBcs CDoC ELan EPfP LRHS MAsh MBri MGos NQui SLim WCot
- 'Pink Princess' EMil LRHS MSwo WHar
- Rubigold see *W.* Briant Rubidor
§ - Sunny Fantasy = 'Kolsunn' MPkF
- 'Tango' LRHS MAsh NEoE
- 'Versicolor' CExl CMHG CMac CWib GQui SLon
- Wine and Roses = 'Alexandra'PBR ♀H6 Widely available
- 'Wings of Fire' **new** LBuc LRHS SCob
'Florida Variegata' (v) ♀H6 Widely available
'Gold Rush' NLar
'Golden Candy' NEoE SCob
hortensis CExl
'Hulsdonk' NLar
japonica 'Dart's Colourdream' EHoe EWes LAst MMuc SCob SEND SGol WGrn
- 'Variegated Dart's Colourdream' (v) ELon
'Jean's Gold' ELan MBlu MRav
'Kosteriana Variegata' (v) CSBt EBee EPfP LRHS MAsh MMuc NEgg SEND SHil
'Little Red Robin' ELon MPkF SCob
'Looymansii Aurea' CBot CExl CMHG CTri ELan EPfP NLar SGol SPer WBod WHar
Lucifer = 'Courtared'PBR CDoC
maximowiczii CBod CExl EBee GQui LLHF
§ ***middendorffiana*** Widely available
'Minuet' LRHS MRav MSwo NEoE
'Mont-Blanc' MAsh MMHG
Nain Rouge = 'Courtanin'PBR CTri NLar
'Nana Variegata' (v) CExl ECrN ELon EPfP LCro LRHS MJak NLar SCob
Naomi Campbell = 'Bokrashine'PBR EShb GBin GKin MMHG NEgg NLar SEND SGol WHar WMoo
'Newport Red' see *W.* 'Vanicek'
Pink Poppet = 'Plangen'PBR CAbP CBot CLet COtt CSBt CWSG EPfP GKin LBMP LRHS LSRN LSou MAsh MBri MGos MPkF NLar SCob SCoo SHil SLim SPoG SRkn SWvt
praecox ECrN
- B&SWJ 8705 WCru
'Praecox Variegata' (v) ♀H6 CMac CTri EPfP LAst LRHS MAsh MRav NBir SDix SPer SPoG SRms WCFE WPat
'Red Prince' ♀H6 ELan EPfP LRHS MGos MSwo NLar SCob SGol SHil SPoG WBod
Rubidor see *W.* Briant Rubidor
Rubigold see *W.* Briant Rubidor
'Ruby Anniversary' CBcs LBuc LRHS SLon
'Ruby Queen'PBR CMac EPfP
Ruby Wedding LSRN
'Rumba' CMac CWSG MRav
sessilifolia see *Diervilla sessilifolia*
'Snowflake' ECrN LPot SRms
'Stelzneri' MMuc
subsessilis B&SWJ 1056 WCru
- B&SWJ 4206 WCru
'Suzanne' (v) EPPr
§ 'Vanicek' MBNS NWea WHar
'Victoria' CDul CMac CWib ECrN EHoe ELan EPPr EPfP LRHS MGos MSwo NBir NWad SCob SGol SPer WHar WMoo

Weinmannia (*Cunoniaceae*)

racemosa CDul IVic

Weldenia (*Commelinaceae*)

candida ECho GEdr IBlr LLHF NHar SChF

Westringia (*Lamiaceae*)

angustifolia MOWG
brevifolia ECou SVen
- 'Grace' **new** LRHS
§ ***fruticosa*** ♀H1c CBcs CHll CSde CTsd SRms SVen WJek
- 'Smokie' (v) CTsd MOWG
- 'Variegata' (v) CTre SRms SVen WJek
rosmariniformis see *W. fruticosa*
'Wynyabbie Gem' CAbb LRHS SEND SVen

whitecurrant see *Ribes rubrum* (W)

Wigandia (*Boraginaceae*)

caracasana CHll

Wikstroemia (*Thymelaeaceae*)

gemmata LRHS

Wilkesia (*Asteraceae*)

	gymnoxiphium	CBrP

wineberry see *Rubus phoenicolasius*

Wisteria ✿ (*Papilionaceae*)

	sp.	LPar
	'Betty's Dwarf Blue'	NLar
§	***brachybotrys***	SCob
§	- Murasaki-kapitan	CTri CWGN EBtc EMil EPfP LRHS MMuc SEND SKHP
	- 'Okayama' ♀H5	EPfP SKHP SLau WMat
	- 'Pink Chiffon'	CWGN EMil EPfP LRHS SKHP SPoG
§	- 'Shiro-kapitan' ♀H5	CBcs CFlo CTri CWGN EPfP IArd LRHS LSRN MAsh MBri MGos MMuc MRav NHol NLar SEND SHil SKHP SLau SLim SPer WPGP WPat
	- 'Showa-beni' ♀H5	CDoC CFlo CKel CRHN CTri CWGN EPfP MGos MMuc NLar SCoo SEND SKHP SLau SLim WPGP
*	- 'White Silk'	CBcs CKel COtt EPfP LRHS LSRN MGos NPla SLon SPoG
§	'Burford' ♀H5	CFlo CKel CWGN EBee EPfP LRHS LSRN MAsh MBri SCob SCoo SKHP SLau SLim WHar WMat WPGP
	'Caroline'	CBcs CDoC CFlo CWGN EBee EBtc EPfP LRHS LSRN MAsh MGos MJak MRav NLar SCob SHil SLau SPer SPoG SRms SSpi WMat WPGP WSHC
	floribunda	CBcs CRHN CWib ELan EPfP IBoy SCob SEWo SGol
	- B&SWJ 12748 from South Korea	WCru
§	- 'Alba' ♀H5	Widely available
	- 'Black Dragon'	see *W. floribunda* 'Yae-kokuryū' (d)
	- 'Burford'	see *W.* 'Burford'
	- 'Cascade'	CBcs COtt LPfy MBri SHil
§	- 'Domino' ♀H5	CBcs CKel CMac CWGN ELon EPfP IArd LBMP LPar LRHS LSRN MAsh MGos MMuc MRav MSwo NLar NOrn NPla SCoo SEND SGol SKHP SLau SLim SPer SPoG SSta
	- 'Ed's Blue Dragon' (d)	NPla SHil
	- 'Fragrantissima'	see *W. sinensis* 'Jako'
	- 'Geisha'	CBcs CFlo CKel EBee EMil EWTr LRHS SEND SKHP
	- 'Golden Dragon'	EPfP
	- 'Harlequin'	CBcs CFlo COtt ELon LRHS MMuc NPla SEND SKHP
	- 'Hocker Edge'	SLau
	- 'Hon-beni'	see *W. floribunda* 'Rosea'
	- 'Honey Bee Pink'	see *W. floribunda* 'Rosea'
	- 'Honko'	see *W. floribunda* 'Rosea'
	- 'Issai Perfect'	LRHS LSRN NLar SCoo SLon
	- 'Issai-naga'	NLar
	- 'Jakohn-fuji'	see *W. sinensis* 'Jako'
	- 'Kimono' **new**	SKHP SLau
§	- 'Kuchi-beni'	CBcs CKel ELan EWTr GBin IBoy LCro LRHS LSRN MBri MGos MMuc MRav NHol NLar SEND SHil SKHP SLau SPer SPoG SRms
	- 'Lawrence' ♀H5	CBcs CDoC CFlo CKel CWGN EBtc LRHS NLar SKHP SLau
	- 'Lipstick'	see *W. floribunda* 'Kuchi-beni'
	- 'Longissima'	see *W. floribunda* 'Multijuga'
	- 'Longissima Alba'	see *W. floribunda* 'Alba'
	- 'Macrobotrys'	see *W. floribunda* 'Multijuga'
	- 'Magenta'	LRHS NPla
§	- 'Multijuga' ♀H5	Widely available
	- 'Nana Richin's Purple'	LRHS SLau
	- 'New Pink'	LRHS
	- 'Peaches and Cream'	see *W. floribunda* 'Kuchi-beni'
	- 'Pink Ice'	see *W. floribunda* 'Rosea'
	- Reindeer	see *W. sinensis* 'Jako'
§	- 'Rosea' ♀H5	Widely available
	- 'Royal Purple' ♀H5	EPfP IArd MBri NLar SGol SKHP SLau SPoG
	- 'Russelliana'	CBcs CFlo CKel GBin
	- 'Shiro-naga'	see *W. floribunda* 'Alba'
	- 'Shiro-nagi'	see *W. floribunda* 'Alba'
	- 'Shiro-noda'	see *W. floribunda* 'Alba'
	- 'Snow Showers'	see *W. floribunda* 'Alba'
	- 'Variegata' (v)	CWGN
	- 'Violacea Plena' (d) ♀H5	CBcs CDoC CMac SKHP SWvt
	- 'Yae-kokuryū' (d)	Widely available
	× ***formosa***	LCro LOPS SLau SLim
	- 'Black Dragon'	see *W. floribunda* 'Yae-kokuryū'
	- 'Domino'	see *W. floribunda* 'Domino'
	- 'Issai' Wada pro parte	see *W. floribunda* 'Domino'
	- 'Kokuryū'	see *W. floribunda* 'Yae-kokuryū'
	- 'Yae-kokuryū'	see *W. floribunda* 'Yae-kokuryū'
	frutescens	EBee EPfP
	- 'Alba'	see *W. frutescens* 'Nivea'
	- 'Amethyst Falls' PBR	CBcs CWGN EBee EShb IArd LCro LRHS LSRN MGos SCoo SKHP SLon SPoG WMoo
	- 'Longwood Purple'	LRHS
§	- 'Nivea'	LRHS
	Kapitan-fuji	see *W. brachybotrys*
	'Lavender Lace'	CBcs CKel COtt EPfP LRHS LSRN MAsh MJak NLar SLau
	macrostachya 'Aunt Dee'	CWGN NLar
	- 'Blue Moon'	WHar
	- 'Clara Mack'	CWGN IArd
	multijuga 'Alba'	see *W. floribunda* 'Alba'
	sinensis	Widely available
	- 'Alba'	CBcs CDoC CMen CWib ELan EPfP EWTr IBoy LAst LCro LPar LRHS LSRN MAsh MGos MSwo NPla SCob SLau SPer SPoG
	- 'Amethyst' ♀H5	CBcs CKel COtt EPfP LCro LOPS LRHS LSRN MAsh MBri MGos MJak MRav NPla SHil SKHP SLau SLim SPer SPoG WPat
	- 'Consequa'	see *W. sinensis* 'Prolific'
	- 'Cooke's Special'	CWGN
§	- 'Jako' ♀H5	NHol
	- 'Oosthoek's Variety'	see *W. sinensis* 'Prolific'
	- 'Prematura'	see *W. floribunda* 'Domino'
	- 'Prematura Alba'	see *W. brachybotrys* 'Shiro-kapitan'
§	- 'Prolific' ♀H5	Widely available
	- 'Rosea'	LSRN SCob SWvt
	- 'Shiro-capital'	see *W. brachybotrys* 'Shiro-kapitan'
	'Tiverton'	CBcs EUJe MJak NPla
	venusta	see *W. brachybotrys* 'Shiro-kapitan'
	- 'Alba'	see *W. brachybotrys* 'Shiro-kapitan'
	- var. ***violacea*** misapplied	see *W. brachybotrys* Murasaki-kapitan

Withania (*Solanaceae*)

	somnifera	CArn GPoy

Wittsteinia (*Alseuosmiaceae*)

	vacciniacea	SBrt WCru

Wodyetia (*Arecaceae*)

bifurcata XBlo

Wollemia (*Araucariaceae*)

nobilis CDTJ CDoC CDul CTho EPfP ESwi EUJe GBin LPar LRHS MGos MHtn

Woodsia (*Woodsiaceae*)

ilvensis NLos
obtusa CDTJ CKel CLAP CWCL EBee EFer EPfP ISha LPal LRHS MBri NBro NLar SGol SPoG SRot XLum
polystichoides SRms
pseudopolystichoides new NLos

Woodwardia (*Blechnaceae*)

areolata SKHP
fimbriata ♀H3 CBod CCon CDoC CLAP CTal CWCL EFer ELon EPfP ERod EWTr GCal GEdr LEdu LRHS NBro NHol NLar SBig SBod SEND SGSe SPer WFib WMoo WPGP XLum
orientalis CCon ESwi ISha LEdu LPal LRHS NLos SGSe WFib WPGP
- var. ***formosana*** B&SWJ 6865 ESwi WCru
radicans ♀H3 CHid CKel CLAP EWes WCot WFib
unigemmata ♀H4 CLAP EFer EShb EWes ISha LRHS NLos SGSe SKHP WAbe WFib WHal
virginica CLAP ISha LRHS

Worcesterberry see *Ribes* 'Worcesterberry'

Wulfenia (*Plantaginaceae*)

amherstiana GEdr LEdu
baldaccii GKev
carinthiaca CTal EBee ECho GAbr GEdr GKev LEdu NBir NLar XLum
orientalis CTal
× ***schwarzii*** CDes EBee IMou LEdu WPGP WSHC

Wurmbea (*Colchicaceae*)

dioica CLak
stricta WCot

Wyethia (*Asteraceae*)

angustifolia SBrt

X

Xanthoceras (*Sapindaceae*)

sorbifolium ♀H5 CAgr CBcs CDul CMCN CWib EBee ELan EPfP IArd IDee IMou MBlu NLar SSpi

Xanthocyparis (*Cupressaceae*)

nootkatensis 'Glauca' MGos NWea
- 'Green Arrow' ♀H6 CKen EBee MBri SCoo SLim WHar WMat
- 'Jubilee' SCoo SLim WCFE WHar WMat
- 'Lutea' MGos NWea
- 'Pendula' ♀H6 CCVT CDoC CDul CKen CLet ELan EPfP GKin IDee LRHS MBlu MBri NEgg NWea WCFE
- 'Strict Weeper' CKen SLim

Xanthorhiza (*Ranunculaceae*)

simplicissima CArn CBcs CDoC CDul EPfP IVic LEdu MGil NLar SDys SSpi WCot WPGP

Xanthorrhoea (*Xanthorrhoeaceae*)

australis SPlb
fulva SPlb
johnsonii SPlb
preisii GBin SPlb

Xerochrysum (*Asteraceae*)

§ ***bracteatum*** SVen
§ - 'Coco' CMHG CSpe
§ - 'Dargan Hill Monarch' CHll CSpe SRms

Xeronema (*Xeronemataceae*)

callistemon CBcs

Xylotheca (*Flacourtiaceae*)

kraussiana SPlb

Y

Youngberry see *Rubus* 'Youngberry'

Ypsilandra (*Melanthiaceae*)

cavaleriei CExl EBee GEdr WCot
thibetica CBct CCon CDes CExl CHid CLAP CPrp EBee ELon EPfP GCal GKev LEdu LLHF LRHS NLar SChF SMad WCru WPGP WSHC
- narrow-leaved WCru

Yucca ✿ (*Asparagaceae*)

sp. ETod LPar
SDR 3701 GKev
aloifolia CDoC EAla ETod LPal SBig SCob SPlb
§ - f. ***marginata*** (v) EAla SBig
- 'Purpurea' EBee
- 'Tricolor' (v) EAla
- 'Variegata' see *Y. aloifolia* f. *marginata*
angustifolia see *Y. glauca*
angustissima SIgm
baccata EAla ETod NLos SIgm SPlb XSen
brevifolia EAla
campestris EAla
carnerosana EAla WCot
cernua new WCot
constricta EAla
decipiens EAla
§ ***elata*** EAla WPGP XSen
§ ***elephantipes*** ♀H2 CDTJ ETod SEND
- 'Jewel' (v) SEND
- 'Puck' (v) SEND
- variegated (v) SEND
faxoniana EAla SPlb
filamentosa Widely available
- 'Antwerp' GCal
- 'Bright Edge' (v) ♀H3 CBcs CDoC CDul CMHG CMac CTri ELan ELon EPfP LAst LEdu

	LPal LRHS LSRN MBri MJak MRav MSwo SChr SCob SLim SPer SWvt
- 'Color Guard' (v) 🏆^{H5}	EPfP EUJe LAst LRHS MBri NLar SChr
- 'Garland's Gold' (v)	CBcs CDoC MAsh MJak SBig
- 'Gold Heart' (v)	MBri
- 'Variegata' (v)	CBcs SCob SRms
filifera	EAla EUJe LPal SPlb
flaccida	SCob
- 'Golden Sword' (v) 🏆^{H3}	CBcs CDoC CLet CMac CTsd EBee ELan EPfP GMaP LAst LRHS LSRN MAsh MGos MSwo NLar SCob SGol SLim SPer SWvt WHar
- 'Ivory' 🏆^{H5}	CDoC CTsd ELan ELon GCal GMaP LRHS LSRN MBri MRav NLar SPer SRms
§ ***glauca***	EAla EPfP LRHS MBri SPlb WCot XSen
gloriosa 🏆^{H5}	CBcs CDoC CMac CTri ETod EUJe GKev LPal LPar MMuc NPla SCob SEND SPer SPlb SPoG SWvt
- 'Aureovariegata'	see *Y. gloriosa* 'Variegata'
- Bright Star = 'Walbristar'^{PBR}	LBuc LHop LRHS SCob SPer SPoG WCot
§ - 'Variegata' (v) 🏆^{H5}	CBcs CChe CDoC CDul CMHG CMac CSBt ECrN ELan ELon EPfP EUJe GMaP LAst LEdu LRHS MMuc MRav NLos SCob SEND SLim SPer SPlb SPoG SRms SWvt WCFE
guatemalensis	see *Y. elephantipes*
harrimaniae	SIgm
- var. ***neomexicana***	CEvo
jaliscensis	EAla
linearifolia	WCot
linearis	see *Y. thompsoniana*
madrensis	EAla
pallida	EAla WPGP
radiosa	see *Y. elata*
recurvifolia 🏆^{H5}	EBee EPfP ETod
- Banana Split = 'Monvil' (v)	EBee EPfP LBuc LRHS MAsh MBri SPoG
- 'Gold Stream' (v)	WCot
reverchonii	EAla
rigida	CDTJ WCot WPGP XSen
rostrata	CDTJ EAla ETod EUJe LPal LPar SPlb WCot XSen
- 'Sapphire Skies'	EUJe MAvo NLos WCot
rupicola	EAla WCot
schidigera	EAla
schottii	EShb WCot
§ ***thompsoniana***	CDTJ EAla LPal WCot XSen
torreyi	SIgm
treculeana	EAla
'Vittorio Emanuele II'	SMad
whipplei	CBcs CDoC EAla EBee ELan EPfP LRHS LTro SBig WPGP XSen
- subsp. ***caespitosa*** NNS 01-412	WCot
- subsp. ***intermedia*** NNS 01-413	WCot
- subsp. ***parishii***	CEvo
- subsp. ***whipplei***	CEvo
- - NJM 11.001	WPGP

Yushania (*Poaceae*)

KR 7698	ERod MWht
§ ***anceps***	CBcs CDoC CDul CEnt CExl ENBC MMuc MWht SBig SEND WMoo
- 'Pitt White'	CEnt CExl MWht WJun
- 'Pitt White Rejuvenated'	ERod
brevipaniculata	ERod WJun
chungii	CDul CEnt CExl ERod MWht WJun
* ***equatus***	WJun
maculata	CDul CEnt CExl ERod MWht SBig WJun
§ ***maling***	CExl ERod WJun
Yunnan 5	CExl MWht

Z

Zabelia (*Caprifoliaceae*)

§ ***biflora***	LRHS
§ ***triflora***	CAbP CExl CWib LHop MMuc NLar SBrt SEND SKHP WFar WSHC

Zaluzianskya (*Scrophulariaceae*)

JCA 15665	WAbe
elongata	SPlb
microsiphon	SPlb
'Orange Eye'	CPBP CTal CWCL EBee EPot GKev NSla WAbe WIce WTor
ovata	CElw CPBP CSpe CTal CTre CWCL EPfP EWld GKev LCro LOPS MHer MSCN NSla SIgm SPad SPlb SPoG SPtp WAbe WIce
- orange-eyed **new**	SBrt
pulvinata	SPlb
'Semonkong'	GCal SWvt

Zamia (*Zamiaceae*)

furfuracea	LPal
pumila	SPlb

Zantedeschia (*Araceae*)

§ ***aethiopica***	Widely available
- 'Apple Court Babe'	ELon
- 'Crowborough' 🏆^{H4}	Widely available
- 'Glencoe' **new**	GCal
- 'Glow'	CExl CMac ECtt EWoo WAvo WGwG
- 'Green Goddess' 🏆^{H2}	Widely available
- 'Little Gem'	SMad
- 'Luzon Lovely'	WCru
- 'Marshmallow'	CAby ECtt ELan EPfP LRHS
- 'Mr Martin'	ECtt ELon SBig SMad SWvt WCot
- 'Pershore Fantasia' (v)	CExl WAvo WCot WWEG
- 'Snow White'^{PBR}	LRHS
- 'White Gnome'	WCot
- 'White Sail'	ECtt ELan LRHS MRav NGdn SWat WGwG
albomaculata	CTca GKev LAma SPlb WWEG
'Anneke'	GKev
'Apricot Glow'	CHll ECho GKev
'Auckland'^{PBR}	GKev SDeJ
'Barcelona' **new**	NBri
'Best Gold'	see *Z.* 'Florex Gold'
'Black Eyed Beauty'	GKev LAma
'Black Magic'	CMac GKev
'Black Pearl'	LAma
'Black Star'	see *Z.* 'Edge of Night'
'Cameo'	GKev LAma SDeJ
'Cantor'^{PBR}	NBri
(Captain Series) 'Captain Marrero'^{PBR} **new**	NBri

– 'Captain Murano'PBR	SPoG
– 'Captain Prado'PBR	EPfP LRHS NBri
– 'Captain Reno'PBR	EPfP SPoG
– 'Captain Romance'PBR	LCro LOPS
– 'Captain Tendens'PBR	GKev SDeJ
'Chianti'	GKev SDeJ
'Crystal Blush'	GKev LAma SDeJ
§ 'Edge of Night'	CBcs GKev NBri SDeJ
'Elegant Swan'PBR	NBri SCob
elliottiana ♀H1c	CBcs CCon CTri LAma
'Esm Puc'PBR	ECho
'Flame'	CBcs GKev SPad
'Flamingo'PBR	WCot
'Flavo Gold'	ECho
§ 'Florex Gold'	GKev
'Galaxy'	GKev
'Helen O'Connor'	CExl
'Hercules'	ESwi
'Hot Shot'	GKev
'Kiwi Blush'	CAby CBro CExl CLet CSpe ELan ELon EPfP LLWG LRHS SEND SKHP SPer SRkn SWat
'Lemon Drop'PBR **new**	GKev
'Lime Lady'	ECha EWay
'Majestic Red'	GKev
'Mango'	EPri GKev LAma MPie WCot
'Medusa'PBR **new**	GKev
'Mozart'	GKev
'Odessa'PBR	LCro LOPS SPoG
odorata **new**	CDes
'Orange Tycoon'PBR **new**	NBri
'Philomena'	LRHS
'Picasso'PBR	CBcs EPfP GKev NBri SDeJ SPad SPoG WCot
'Pink Mist'	LAma LLWG NBri SMad
'Pink Persuasion'	GKev LAma
'Pot of Gold'	GKev
'Purple Sensation'	MPie
'Red Alert'PBR	GKev NBri
'Red Sox'PBR	GKev SDeJ
'Red Star'PBR **new**	GKev
rehmannii ♀H1c	ECho GKev LAma SDeJ SRms
'Samur'PBR	NBri
'Sapporo'PBR **new**	GKev
'Schwarzwalder'PBR	GKev
'Siberia'PBR	NBri
'Solfatare'	GKev
'Sunshine'	WCot
'Treasure'	GKev
'White Giant'	EWay WPGP
'White Pixie'	EPfP

Zanthorhiza see *Xanthorhiza*

Zanthoxylum (*Rutaceae*)

acanthopodium GWJ 9287	WCru
– PAB 8760 **new**	LEdu
ailanthoides B&SWJ 11115 from Japan	WCru
– B&SWJ 11394 from Japan	WCru
– f. ***inermis*** RWJ 10048	WCru
americanum	ELan LEdu
armatum	CAgr SBrt
– HWJK 2178	WCru
bungeanum BWJ 8040	WCru
clava-herculis **new**	CFil
fauriei B&SWJ 11080	WCru
aff. ***fauriei*** B&SWJ 11371	WCru
– B&SWJ 11523	WCru
laetum	CFil
– FMWJ 13175 **new**	CEvo
– WWJ 11678	WCru
– WWJ 11914	WCru
myriacanthum B&SWJ 11844	WCru
oxyphyllum	LEdu
– GWJ 9428	WCru
– HWJK 2131	WCru
piperitum	CAgr GPoy SBrt
– B&SWJ 8543	WCru
– B&SWJ 11377	WCru
– B&SWJ 11433	WCru
– purple-leaved	CExl CFil WPGP WPat
schinifolium	CAgr LEdu
– B&SWJ 8593	WCru
– B&SWJ 11080	WCru
– B&SWJ 11391	WCru
simulans	CAgr CArn CBcs CDul CExl GBin IVic LEdu
stenophyllum	CMCN

Zauschneria (*Onagraceae*)

arizonica	see *Z. californica* subsp. *latifolia*
§ ***californica***	CFis CHll CTri ECho MBrN SLon SWat SWvt WBod WPnn XLum
§ – 'Dublin' ♀H4	Widely available
– 'Ed Carman'	ECha ECtt MMuc SEle XLum
* – subsp. ***garrettii***	ECho SDys SWat
– 'Glasnevin'	see *Z. californica* 'Dublin'
§ – subsp. ***latifolia***	XLum
§ – subsp. ***mexicana***	SRms
– 'Olbrich Silver'	EBee ECha ECho ECtt EWes LRHS SBrt SIgm WHoo WKif XLum
– 'Western Hills' ♀H5	CCon CSpe CTri ECha ECho EPfP EWld LHop LRHS LSou MMuc MRav SEND SPhx SWvt WHoo XLum
§ ***cana***	ECha SWat
– 'Sir Cedric Morris'	EPfP LRHS
– ***villosa***	see *Z. californica* subsp. *mexicana*
I 'Pumilio'	EPot MHer
§ ***septentrionalis***	WAbe

Zebrina see *Tradescantia*

Zehneria (*Cucurbitaceae*)

scabra	SVic

Zelkova ✿ (*Ulmaceae*)

carpinifolia	CDul CMCN SPlb WPGP
'Kiwi Sunset'	EPfP NWea WMat
serrata ♀H6	CBcs CCVT CDul CLnd CMCN CMen CTho EBee ECrN ELan EPfP EShb IDee MBri MGos MMuc NWea SEND SGol WMou
– B&SWJ 8491 from Korea	WCru
– 'Goblin'	CJun MBlu NLar WPat
– 'Green Vase'	MBlu SCob
– 'Green Veil' **new**	IArd
– 'Kiwi Sunset'PBR	CDul MGos
– 'Musashino'	SGol
– 'Ogon'	EPfP SGol
– 'Variegata' (v)	CJun CMac MBlu NLar SGol SMad
sinica	CMen
× ***verschaffeltii***	CMCN EPfP IArd IDee MBlu

Zenobia (*Ericaceae*)

pulverulenta	CAbP CBcs CDoC CDul CMac ELan EPfP IVic LRHS MAsh MBlu MGil

	MGos SCob SLon SSta WAbe WPat WSHC
- 'Blue Sky'	CAbP CBcs CBct CDoC CMCN EBee EPfP GBin GKin IDee LRHS MAsh MBlu MBri MGos MPkF NLar SCob SPer SPoG SSpi WPGP
- f. ***nitida***	CMac NLar
- 'Raspberry Ripple'	CBcs LRHS MAsh MBri NLar SSta
- 'Viridis'	NLar

Zephyranthes (*Amaryllidaceae*)

atamasca	SKHP WHil
'Big Dude'	SKHP
candida	CAby CBro CTal EBee ECho EPot EShb EWld GKev LAma LPot LRHS NRog SChF SDeJ WHil
- 'Lemon Drops'	NRog
citrina	CExl ECho GKev LAma SDeJ
drummondii	ECho GKev NRog
flavissima	ECho GKev
'Ivory Crocus'	NRog
katherinae	NRog
'Krakatau'	WCot
La Bufa Rosa Group	CEvo CExl GKev WCot
lindleyana	NRog
mexicana	ECho
minima ♀H2	ECho NRog
minuta	ECho GKev NRog
'Pink Beauty'	ECho
primulina	ECho NRog
robusta	see *Habranthus robustus*
rosea	ECho GKev SDeJ
'Snow White'	ECho
traubii from San Carlos	NRog
versicolor	NRog

Zigadenus (*Melanthiaceae*)

elegans	EBee ECha EPri GAbr LEdu LRHS MAvo MHer SMad WCot WSHC
nuttallii	CTal ECho GKev

Zingiber ✿ (*Zingiberaceae*)

mioga	CAgr CCon CFil EBee GPoy ILea IMou LEdu SChr SPlb WPGP
- 'Crûg's Zing'	LEdu WCru WPGP
- 'Dancing Crane' (v)	CFil CMac EUJe LEdu
- 'White Feather'	LEdu
officinale	SPre SRms

Zinnia (*Asteraceae*)

elegans	SVic
'Envy' (d)	CSpe
'Profusion Cherry'	CWCL
'Red Spider'	CSpe
'Swizzle Scarlet and Yellow'	CWCL
Zahara Series **new**	LAst

Zizia (*Apiaceae*)

aptera	SPhx
aurea	SDix SPhx WSHC XLum

Ziziphus (*Rhamnaceae*)

§ ***jujuba*** (F)	CAgr CBcs CDul SAko
- 'Lang' (F)	CAgr
- 'Li' (F)	CAgr
- var. ***spinosa***	CArn
sativa	see *Z. jujuba*

Bibliography

This is by no means exhaustive but lists some of the more useful works used in the preparation of the *RHS Plant Finder*. The websites of raisers of new plants (not listed here) are also an invaluable source of information.

General

Allan, H.H., et al. 2000. *Flora of New Zealand.* Wellington. http://floraseries.landcareresearch.co.nz

Bean, W.J. 1988. *Trees and Shrubs Hardy in the British Isles.* (8th ed.) Sir George Taylor, D.L. Clarke (eds). Supp. D.L. Clarke (ed.). London: John Murray.

Beckett, K. (ed.). 1994. *Alpine Garden Society Encyclopaedia of Alpines.* Pershore, Worcs.: Alpine Garden Society.

Boufford, D.E., et al. (eds). 2003. *Flora of Taiwan Checklist.* A checklist of the vascular plants of Taiwan. Taipei, Taiwan: NTU. http://tai2.ntu.edu.tw

Bramwell, D. & Bramwell, Z.I. 2001. *Wild Flowers of the Canary Islands.* (2nd ed.). Madrid: Editorial Rueda, S.L.

Brickell, C. (ed.). 2008. *The Royal Horticultural Society A-Z Encyclopedia of Garden Plants.* (3rd ed.) London: Dorling Kindersley.

Brickell, C.D. et al (eds.). 2009. *International Code of Nomenclature for Cultivated Plants* (8th ed.). ISHS.

Brummitt, R.K. (comp.). 1992. *Vascular Plant Families and Genera.* Kew: Royal Botanic Gardens. http://data.kew.org

Castroviejo, S. et al. (eds). *Flora Iberica.* 1987-2007. (Vols 1-8, 10, 14, 15, 21). Madrid: Real Jardín Botánico, C.S.I.C.

Cave, Y. & Paddison, V. 1999. *The Gardener's Encyclopaedia of New Zealand Native Plants.* Auckland: Godwit.

Cooke, I. 1998. *The Plantfinder's Guide to Tender Perennials.* Newton Abbot, Devon: David & Charles.

Cullen, J. et al. (eds). 2011. *The European Garden Flora* (2nd ed.). Cambridge: Cambridge University Press. (5 vols).

Davis, P.H., Mill, R.R. & Tan, K. (eds). 1965-88. *Flora of Turkey and the East Aegean Island.* (Vols 1-10). Edinburgh University Press.

Dirr, M.A. 1997. *Dirr's Hardy Trees & Shrubs: An Illustrated Encyclopedia.* Portland, Oregon: Timber Press.

Gardiner, J. 2012. *The Timber Press Encyclopedia of Flowering Shrubs.* Portland, Oregon: Timber Press.

Goldblatt, P. & Manning, J. 2000. *Cape Plants. A Conspectus of the Cape Flora of South Africa.* South Africa/USA: National Botanical Institute of South Africa/Missouri Botanical Garden.

Greuter, W., Brummitt, R.K., Farr, E., Kilian, N., Kirk, P.M. & Silva, P.C. (comps). 1993. *NCU-3.*

Grierson, A.J.C., Long, D.G. & Noltie, H.J. et al. (eds). 2001. *Flora of Bhutan.* Edinburgh: Royal Botanic Garden.

Grimshaw, J. & Bayton, R. 2009. *New Trees. Recent Introductions to Cultivation.* Kew: Royal Botanic Gardens.

Güner, A., Özhatay, N., Ekîm, T., Baser, K.H.C. & Hedge, I.C. 2000. *Flora of Turkey and the East Aegean Islands.* Supp. 2. Vol. 11. Edinburgh: Edinburgh University Press.

Hinkley, D.J. 2009. *The Explorer's Garden: Shrubs and Vines from the Four Corners of the World.* Portland, Oregon: Timber Press.

Hoffman, M. (ed.). 2005. *List of Woody Plants. International Standard ENA 2005-2010.* Netherlands: Applied Plant Research.

Huxley, A., Griffiths, M. & Levy, M. (eds). 1992. *The New RHS Dictionary of Gardening.* London: Macmillan.

Iwatsuki, K., et al. 1995. *Flora of Japan.* Vols I-IIIb. Tokyo, Japan: Kodansha Ltd.

Jelitto, L. & Schacht, W.R., Simon, H. 2002. *Die Freiland-Schmuchstauden.* Germany: Verlag Eugen Ulmer.

Krüssmann, G. (trans.). 1984-86. *Manual of Cultivated Broad-leaved Trees & Shrubs.* London: Batsford (3 vols).

Leslie, A.C. (trans.). *New Cultivars of Herbaceous Perennial Plants 1985-1990.* Hardy Plant Society.

Mabberley, D.J. 2008. *Mabberley's Plant Book. A Portable Dictionary of Plants, their Classification and Uses.* (3rd ed.). Cambridge: Cambridge University Press.

McNeill, J. et al. 2012. *International Code of Nomenclature for Algae, Fungi, & Plants* (Melbourne Code). Regnum Vegetabile 154. Königstein, Germany: Koeltz Scientific Books.

Metcalf, L.J. 1987. *The Cultivation of New Zealand Trees and Shrubs.* Auckland: Reed Methuen.

Nelson, E.C. 2000. *A Heritage of Beauty: The Garden Plants of Ireland: An Illustrated Encyclopaedia.* Dublin: Irish Garden Plant Society.

Ohwi, J. 1965. *Flora of Japan.* Washington DC: Smithsonian Institution.

Phillips, R. & Rix, M. 1997. *Conservatory and Indoor Plants.* London: Macmillan. (2 vols).

Press, J.R. & Short, M.J. (eds). 1994. *Flora of Madeira.* London: Natural History Museum/HMSO.

Rehder, A. 1940. *Manual of Cultivated Trees and Shrubs Hardy in North America.* (2nd ed.). New York: Macmillan.

Rice, G. (ed.), 2006. *Encyclopedia of Perennials.* London: Dorling Kindersley.

Stace, C. 2010. *New Flora of the British Isles.* (3rd ed.). Cambridge: Cambridge University Press.

Thomas, G.S. 1990. *Perennial Garden Plants. A Modern Florilegium.* (3rd ed.). London: Dent.

Trehane, P. (comp.). 1989. *Index Hortensis. Vol. 1: Perennials.* Wimborne: Quarterjack

Tutin, T.G., et al. 1964. *Flora Europaea.* Cambridge University Press. Vols 1-5.

General Websites

Annotated Checklist of the Flowering Plants of Nepal. Jan 2010 www.efloras.org/flora_page-aspx?_id=110

Australian Cultivar Registration Authority. Jan 2010. www.anbg.gov.au/acra

Australian Plant Breeders Rights: Database Search. Jan 2010. http://pbr.ipaustralia.optus.com.au

Australian Plant Names Index. Australian National Botanic Gardens (comp.). Jan 2010. www.anbg.gov.au/apni/index.html

Bolivia Checklist. Jan 2010. www.efloras.org/flora_page.aspx?flora_id=40

Botanical Expedition in Myanmar Checklist. Jan 2010. http://botany.si-edu/myanmar/checklistNames.cfm

Canadian Ornamental Plant Foundation. Jan 2010. www.copf.org

Canadian Plant Breeders Rights Office: Canadian Food Inspection Agency. Jan 2010. www.inspection.gc.ca

Catalogue of the Vascular Plants of Madagascar: www.efforas.org/flora_page.aspx?flora_id+12

Darwin Checklist of Moroccan Vascular Plants www.herbarium.rdg.ac.uk/

DEFRA Plant Varieties and Seeds Gazette. Jan 2010. www.defra.gov.uk

Flora Himalaya Database. Jan 2010. www.leca.univ-savoie.fr

Flora Mesoamericana Internet Version (W3FM). Jan 2013. Missouri Botanical Garden. www.tropicos.org/Project/FM

Flora of Australia Online. Jan 2010. Australian Biological Resources Study. www.environment.gov.au/biodiversity/abrs/online-resources/flora/index.html

Flora of Chile. Jan 2010. www.efloras.org/flora_page.aspx?flora_id=60

Flora of China Checklist. Jan 2010. http://flora.huh.harvard.edu/china

Flora of Pakistan. Jan 2010. www.efloras.org/flora_page.aspd?flora_id=5

Flora of North America Website. Jan 2010. Morin, N.R., et al. www.efloras.org-page.aspx/flora_id=1

GRIN (Germplasm Resources Information Network) Taxonomy. Jan 2010. www.ars-grin.gov

Hatch, D. Jan 2010. New Ornamentals Society Database. http://members.tripod.com/~Hatch_L/nos.html

International Plant Names Index. Jan 2010. www.ipni.org

International Plant Names Index: Author Query. Jan 2010. www.ipni.org/ipni

Manaaki Whenua: Landcare Research in New Zealand Plants Database Jan 2010. http://nzflora.landcareresearch.co.nz

Manual de plantas de Costa Rica. Jan 2010. www.mobot.org/manual.plantas

Plant List, The. A working list of all plant species www.theplantlist.org.

Plants Database. USDA, NRCS. Jan 2010. http://plants.usda.gov

Plants of Southern Africa: an Online Checklist. Jan 2010. http://posa.sanbi.org

PLUTO: Plant Variety Database www.upov.int/pluto/en

New Zealand Plant Variety Rights Office www.iponz.govt.nz/cms/pvr

Royal Horticultural Society. www.rhs.org.uk/plants/RHS-Publications/Plant-registers

Tropicos. Jan 2010. www.tropicos.org

US Patent Full-Text Database. US Patent and Trademark Office, (comp.). Jan 2010. www.uspto.gov/patft

World Checklist of Selected Families. 2010. apps.kew.org/wcsp

Genera And Other Plant Groupings

Acer

Gregory, P. & Angus, H. 2008. *World Checklist of Maple Cultivar Names.* Forestry Commission National Arboreta.

Harris, J.G.S. 2000. *The Gardener's Guide to Growing Maples.* Newton Abbot, Devon: David & Charles.

Van Gelderen, C.J. & Van Gelderen, D.M. 1999. *Maples for Gardens.* A Color Encyclopedia. Portland, Oregon: Timber Press.

van Gelderen, D.M., de Jong, P.C., Oterdoom, H.J. 1994. *Maples of the World.* Portland, Oregon: Timber Press.

Yano, M. 2003. *Book for Maples. Wild Maples of Japan and Maple Cultivars.* Japan: Japan Maple Publishing Group.

Vertrees, J.D. 2001. *Japanese Maples.* Momiji and Kaede. (3rd ed.). Portland, Oregon: Timber Press.

Actaea

Compton, J.A., Culham, A. & Jury, S.L. 1998. Reclassification of *Actaea* to Include *Cimicifuga* and *Souliea* (*Ranunculaceae*). *Taxon* 47:593-634.

Adiantum
Goudey, C.J. 1985. *Maidenhair Ferns in Cultivation.* Melbourne: Lothian.
Agapanthus
Snoeijer, W. 2004. *Agapanthus. A Revision of the Genus.* Portland, Oregon: Timber Press.
Agavaceae
Irish, M. & Irish, G. 2000. *Agaves, Yuccas and Related Plants.* A Gardener's Guide. Portland, Oregon: Timber Press.
Aizoaceae
Burgoyne, P. et al. 1998. *Mesembs of the World. Illustrated Guide to a Remarkable Succulent Group.* South Africa: Briza Publications.
Allium
Davies, D. 1992. *Alliums. The Ornamental Onions.* London: Batsford
Gregory, M., et al. 1998. *Nomenclator Alliorum.* Kew: Royal Botanic Gardens.
Mathew, B. 1996. *A Review of Allium Section Allium.* Kew: Royal Botanic Gardens.
Androsace
Smith, G. & Lowe, D. 1997. *The Genus Androsace.* Pershore, Worcs.: Alpine Garden Society.
Anemone, Japanese
McKendrick, M. 1990. Autumn Flowering Anemones. *The Plantsman* 12(3):140-151.
McKendrick, M. 1998. Japanese Anemones. *The Garden* (RHS) 123(9):628-633.
Anthemis
Leslie, A. 1997. Focus on Plants: *Anthemis tinctoria. The Garden* (RHS) 122(8):552-555.
Apiaceae
Pimenov, M.G. & Leonov, M.V. 1993. *The Genera of the Umbelliferae.* Kew: Royal Botanic Gardens.
Aquilegia
Munz, P.A. 1946. *Aquilegia:* the Cultivated and Wild Columbines. *Gentes Herb.* 7(1):1-150.
Araceae
Govaerts, R. & Frodin, D.G. 2002. *World Checklist and Bibliography of Araceae (and Acoraceae).* Kew:Royal Botanic Gardens
Araliaceae
Govaerts, R. & Frodin, D.G. 2002. *World Checklist and Bibliography of Araliaceae.* Kew:Royal Botanic Gardens
Arecaceae (palms)
Craft, P. & Riffle, R.L. 2003. *Encyclopedia of Cultivated Palms.* Portland, Oregon: Timber Press.
Uhl, N.W. & Dransfield, J. 1987. *Genera Palmarum.* A Classification of Palms Based on the Work of Harold E. Moore Jr. Lawrence, Kansas: Allen Press.
Argyranthemum
Humphries, C.J. 1976. A Revision of the Macaronesian Genus *Argyranthemum. Bull. Brit. Mus. (Nat. Hist.) Bot.* 5(4):145-240.
Arisaema
Gusman, G. & Gusman, L. 2002. *The Genus Arisaema: A Monograph for Botanists and Nature Lovers.* Ruggell, Leichtenstein: A.R. Gantner Verlag Kommanditgesellschaft.
Pradhan, U.C. 1997. *Himalayan Cobra Lilies* (Arisaema). Their Botany and Culture. (2nd ed.). Kalimpong, West Bengal, India: Primulaceae Books.
Arum
Bown, D. 2000. *Plants of the Arum Family.* (2nd ed.). Portland, Oregon: Timber Press.
Boyce, P. 1993. *The Genus Arum.* London: HMSO.
Asclepiadaceae
Eggli, U. (ed.). 2002. *Illustrated Handbook of Succulent Plants: Asclepiadaceae.* Heidelberg, Germany: Springer-Verlag.
Aster
Picton, P. 1999. *The Gardener's Guide to Growing Asters.* Newton Abbot: David & Charles.
Asteraceae
Bremer, K. et al. 1994. *Asteraceae: Cladistics and Classification.* Portland, Oregon: Timber Press.
Cubey, J. & Grant, M. 2004. *Perennial Yellow Daisies: RHS Bulletin No 6.* Wisley, Surrey: RHS.
Astilbe
Noblett, H. 2001. *Astilbe.* A Guide to the Identification of Cultivars and Common Species. Cumbria: Henry Noblett.
Aubrieta
1975. *International Registration Authority Checklist.* Weihenstephan, Germany: (Unpublished).
Bamboos
Ohrnberger, D. 1999. *The Bamboos of the World.* Amsterdam: Elsevier.
Whittaker, P. 2005. *Hardy Bamboos – Taming the Dragon.* Portland, Oregon: Timber Press.
Begonia
American Begonia Society Astro Branch Begonia Data Base. Jan 2010. http://absastro.tripod.com
American Begonia Society Registered Begonias. Jan 2010. http://www.begonias.org
Ingles, J. 1990. *American Begonia Society Listing of Begonia Cultivars.* Revised Edition Buxton Checklist. American Begonia Society.
Tebbitt, M.C. 2005. *Begonias: Cultivation, Identification and Natural History.* Portland, Oregon: Timber Press.
Berberidaceae
Ahrendt, L.W.A. 1961. *Berberis and Mahonia. A Taxonomic Revision.* Cambridge: Cambridge University Press.
Stearn, W.T. & Shaw, J.M.H. 2002. *The Genus Epimedium and Other Herbaceous Berberidaceae including the Genus Podophyllum.* Kew: Royal Botanic Gardens.

Betula
Ashburner, K.B. & McAllister, H. 2013. *The Genua Betula: Taxonomic Revision of Birches*. Kew: Royal Botanic Gardens.
Hunt, D. (ed.). 1993. *Betula: Proceedings of the IDS Betula Symposium 1992*. Richmond, Surrey: International Dendrology Society.
Boraginaceae
Bennett, M. 2003. *Pulmonarias and the Borage Family*. London: Batsford.
Bougainvillea
Gillis, W.T. 1976. Bougainvilleas of Cultivation (*Nyctaginaceae). Baileya* 20(1):34-41.
Iredell, J. 1994. *Growing Bougainvilleas*. London: Cassell.
MacDaniels, L.H. 1981. A Study of Cultivars in *Bougainvillea (Nyctaginaceae). Baileya* 21(2):77-100.
Singh, B., Panwar, R.S., Voleti, S.R., Sharma, V.K. & Thakur, S. 1999. *The New International Bougainvillea Check List*. (2nd ed.). New Delhi: Indian Agricultural Research Institute.
Bromeliaceae
Bromeliad Cultivar Registry Online Databases. Bromeliad Society International. Jan 2010. www.bsi.org
Brugmansia
Wreggitt, L. et al. (comp.). Jan 2010. *Register of Brugmansia Cultivars and Checklist of Names in Use*. American Brugmansia and Datura Society. www.abads.org
Buddleja
Stuart, D.D. 2006. *Buddlejas: Royal Horticultural Society Collector Guide*. Portland, Oregon: Timber Press.
Bulbs
Leeds, R. 2000. *The Plantfinder's Guide to Early Bulbs*. Newton Abbot, Devon: David & Charles.
KAVB Online registration pages. Jan 2010. http://kavb.back2p.soft-orange.com
Buxus
Batdorf, L.R. 1995. *Boxwood Handbook. A Practical Guide to Knowing and Growing Boxwood*. Boyce, VA, USA: The American Boxwood Society. Jan 2010. www.boxwoodsociety.org
Cactaceae
Hunt, D. et al. 2006. *New Cactus Lexicon*. (2 vols.) Sherborne, Dorset: DH Books.
Camellia
Ferrari, D. & Sfondrini, N. Web *Camellia* Register. Camellia-unipv.it/camelliadb2
Savige, T.J. (comp.). 1993. *The International Camellia Register*. (Vol 1-2). Supps. 1-2. 1997-2011. The International Camellia Society.
Trehane, J. 2007. *Camellias: The Gardener's Encyclopedia*. Portland, Oregon: Timber Press. The International Camellia Society.
Trujillo, D. J. (ed.). 2002. *Camellia Nomenclature*. (24th revd ed.). Southern California Camellia Society.
Campanula
Lewis, P. & Lynch, M. 1998. *Campanulas*. A Gardeners Guide. (2nd ed.). London: Batsford.
Lewis, P 2002. *Campanulas in the Garden*. Pershore, Worcs.: Hardy Plant Society.
Campanulaceae
Lammers, T.G. 2007. *World Checklist and Bibliography of Campanulaceae*. Kew Publishing.
Canna
Cooke, I. 2001. *The Gardener's Guide to Growing Cannas*. Newton Abbot, Devon: David & Charles.
Gray, J. & Grant, M. 2003. Canna: RHS Bulletin No 3. Wisley, Surrey: RHS.
Hayward, K. Jan 2010. www.hartcanna.com
Carnivorous Plants
Schlauer, J. (comp.). Jan 2010. Carnivorous Plant Database. www.omnisterra.com
Ceanothus
Fross, D. & D. Wilken. 2006. *Ceanothus*. Portland, Oregon: Timber Press.
Cercidiphyllum
Dosmann, M.S. 1999. Katsura: a Review of *Cercidiphyllum* in Cultivation and in the Wild. *The New Plantsman* 6(1):52-62.
Dosmann, M., Andrews, S., Del Tredici, P. & Li, J. 2003. Classification and Nomenclature of Weeping Katsuras. *The Plantsman* 2(1):21-27.
Chaenomeles
Weber, C. 1963. Cultivars in the Genus *Chaenomeles. Arnoldia (Jamaica Plain)* 23(3):17-75.
Chrysanthemum
Brummitt, D. 1997. *Chrysanthemum* Once Again. *The Garden* (RHS) 122(9):662-663.
Chrysanthemums in Aberdeen. Directory of popular cultivars. www.chrysanthemums.info
Gosling, S.G. (ed.). 1964. *British National Register of Chrysanthemums*. Whetstone, London: National Chrysanthemum Society.
National Chrysanthemum Society. 2000. *British National Register of Names of Chrysanthemums Amalgamated Edition 1964-1999*. Tamworth, Staffordshire: National Chrysanthemum Society. Cultivar database. Jan 2010. www.nationalchrysanthemumsociety.org.uk
Cistus
Bygrave, P. & Page, R.G. (ed.). 2001. *Cistus – A Guide to the Collection at the Chelsea Physic Garden*. London: Chelsea Physic Garden Company.
Citrus
Davies, F.S. & Albrigo, L.G. 1994. *Citrus*. Wallingford, Oxon: Cab International.
Page, M. 2008. *Growing Citrus*. London: Timber Press
Saunt, J. 1990. *Citrus Varieties of the World*. An Illustrated Guide. Norwich: Sinclair

Clematis

Donald, D., *The International Clematis Register and Checklist*, Supp. 4. 2012

Evison, R.J. 1998. *The Gardener's Guide to Growing Clematis*. Newton Abbot, Devon: David & Charles.

Grey-Wilson, C. 2000. *Clematis: the Genus*. London: Batsford

HelpMeFind Clematis. Nov 2006. www.helpmefind.com/clematis

Johnson, M. 2001. *The Genus Clematis*. Södertälje, Sweden: Magnus Johnsons Plantskola AB & Bengt Sundström.

Matthews, V. (comp.). 2002. *The International Clematis Register and Checklist 2002* & Supps 1-3. 2004-2009. London: RHS.

Toomey, M. & Leeds, E. 2001. *An Illustrated Encyclopedia of Clematis*. Portland, Oregon: Timber Press.

Conifers

Anders, A.G. & Spicer, D.P. 2012 *RHS Encyclopedia of Conifers*. (2 vols). London:RHS & Kingsblue Publishing.

Bitner, R.L. 2007. *Conifers for Gardens. An Illustrated Encyclopedia*. Portland, Oregon: Timber Press.

Bloom, A. 2001. *Gardening with Conifers*. London: Frances Lincoln.

den Ouden, P. & Boom, B.K. 1965. *Manual of Cultivated Conifers*. The Hague: Martinus Nijhof.

Eckenwalder, J.E. 2009. *Conifers of the World*. China:Timber Press

Farjon, A. 1998. *World Checklist and Bibliography of Conifers*. Kew: Royal Botanic Gardens.

Farjon, A. 2008. *A Natural History of Conifers*. Portland, Oregon: Timber Press.

Farjon, A. 2010. *A Handbook of the World's Conifers*. (2 vols). Leiden-Boston: Brill.

Knees, S.G. & Springate, L.S. 2009. *The International Conifer Register, Pt 5*. London: RHS.

Krüssmann, G. & Epp, M.E. (trans.). 1985. *Manual of Cultivated Conifers*. London: Batsford.

Lewis, J. & Leslie, A.C. 1987-1998. *The International Conifer Register. Pts 1-4*. London: RHS.

Welch, H.J. 1979. *Manual of Dwarf Conifers*. New York: Theophrastus.

Welch, H.J. 1993. *The World Checklist of Conifers*. Bromyard, Herefordshire: Landsman's Bookshops.

Cornus

Cappiello, P. & Shadow, D. 2005. *Dogwoods*. Portland, Oregon: Timber Press.

Corydalis

Lidén, M. & Zetterlund, H. 1997. *Corydalis. A Gardener's Guide and a Monograph of the Tuberous Species*. Pershore, Worcs.: Alpine Garden Society Publications Ltd.

Corylus

Crawford, M. 1995. *Hazelnuts: Production and Culture*. Dartington, Devon: Agroforestry Research Trust.

Cotoneaster

Fryer, J. & Hylmö, B. 2009. *Cotoneasters. A Comprehensive Guide to Shrubs for Flowers, Fruit and Foliage*. Portland, Oregon: Timber Press.

Crassulaceae

Rowley, G. 2003. *Crassula: A Grower's Guide*. Venegono superiore, Italy: Cactus & Co.

Eggli, U. (ed.) 2003. *Illustrated Handbook of Succulent Plants*. Springer.

Crataegus

Phipps, J.B. 2003. *Hawthorns and Medlars. RHS Plant Collector Guide*. Portland, Oregon: Timber Press.

Crocosmia

Goldblatt, P., Manning, J.C. & Dunlop, G. 2004. *Crocosmia and Chasmanthe*. Portland, Oregon: Timber Press.

Crocus

Jacobsen, N., van Scheepen, J. & Ørgaard, M. 1997. The *Crocus chrysanthus – biflorus* Cultivars. *The New Plantsman* 4(1):6-38.

Mathew, B. 1982. *The Crocus. A Review of the Genus Crocus (Iridaceae)*. London: Batsford.

Mathew, B. 2002. *Crocus* Up-date. *The Plantsman* 1(1):44-56.

Cyclamen

Clennett, C. Jan. 2003. Register of Cultivar Names. www.cyclamen.org

Grey-Wilson, C. 2003. *Cyclamen. A Guide for Gardeners, Horticulturists & Botanists*. London: Batsford.

Cypripedium

Cribb, P. 1997. *The Genus Cypripedium*. Portland, Oregon: Timber Press.

Dahlia

American Dahlia Society website. Jan 2010. www.dahlia.org

Bates, D. Dahlia Plant Finder 2007. Jan 2010. www.dahliaworld.co.uk

McDonald, S., & Hedge, R. (comps). 1969. *Tentative Classified List and International Register of Dahlia Names 1969* & Supps 1-23. 1986-2013. London: RHS.

National Dahlia Society. 2005. *Classified Directory and Judging Rules*. (28th ed.) Aldershot, Hants: National Dahlia Society.

Winchester Growers Ltd English National Dahlia Collection website. Jan 2010. www.national-dahlia-collection.co.uk

Daphne

Brickell, C.D. & Mathew, B. 1976. *Daphne. The Genus in the Wild and in Cultivation*. Woking, Surrey: Alpine Garden Society.

Grey-Wilson, C. (ed.). 2001. *The Smaller Daphnes. The Proceedings of 'Daphne 2000', a Conference held at the Royal Horticultural Society*. Pershore, Worcs.: Alpine Garden Society.
White, R. 2006. *Daphnes: A Practical Guide for Gardeners*. Portland, Oregon: Timber Press.
Delphinium
1949. *A Tentative Check-list of Delphinium Names*. London: RHS.
1970. *A Tentative Check-list of Delphinium Names*. Addendum. London: RHS.
Bassett, D. & Wesley, W. 2004. *Delphinium: RHS Bulletin No 5*. Wisley, Surrey: RHS.
Leslie, A.C. 1996. *The International Delphinium Register Cumulative Supp. 1970-1995*. London: RHS.
Leslie, A.C. 1996-2005. The International Delphinium Register Supp. 1994-99. *The Delphinium Society Year Book 1996-2005*. London: RHS.
Dianthus
Galbally, J. & Galbally, E. 1997. *Carnations and Pinks for Garden and Greenhouse*. Portland, Oregon: Timber Press.
Leslie, A.C. *The International Dianthus Register*. 1983-2002. (2nd ed. & Supps 1-19). Supps 19-29, 2002-12. London: RHS.
Dierama
Hilliard, O.M. & Burtt, B.L. 1991. *Dierama. The Harebells of Africa*. Johannesburg; London: Acorn Books.
Dionysia
Grey-Wilson, C. 1989. *The Genus Dionysia*. Woking, Surrey: Alpine Garden Society.
Douglasia
Mitchell, B. 1999. Celebrating the Bicentenary of David Douglas: a Review of *Douglasia* in Cultivation. *The New Plantsman* 6(2):101-108.
Dracaena
Bos, J.J., Graven, P., Hetterscheid, W.L.A. & van de Wege, J.J. 1992. Wild and cultivated *Dracaena fragrans*. *Edinburgh J. Bot.* 49(3):311-331.
Echeveria
Schulz, L. & Kapitany, A. *Echeveria Cultivars*. Teesdale, Australia: Schulz Publishing.
Episcia
Dates, J.D. 1993. *The Gesneriad Register 1993*. Check List of Names with Descriptions of Cultivated Plants in the Genera *Episcia* & *Alsobia*. Galesburg, Illinois: American Gloxinia & Gesneriad Society, Inc.
Erodium
Clifton, R. 1994. *Geranium Family Species Checklist. Pt 1 Erodium*. (4th ed.). The Geraniaceae Group.
Toomey, N., Cubey, J. & Culham, A. 2002. *Erodium × variabile*. *The Plantsman* 1(3): 166-172
Victor, D.X. (comp.). 2000. *Erodium: Register of Cultivar Names*. The Geraniaceae Group.
Erythronium
Mathew, B. 1992. A Taxonomic and Horticultural Review of *Erythronium* L. (*Liliaceae*). *J. Linn. Soc., Bot.* 109:453-471.
Mathew, B. 1998. The Genus *Erythronium*. *Bull. Alpine Gard. Soc. Gr. Brit.* 66(3):308-321.
Eupatorium sensu lato
Hind, D.J.N. 2006. Splitting *Eupatorium*. *The Plantsman* (n.s.) 5(2):185-189.
Euonymus
Brown, N. 1996. Notes on Cultivated Species of *Euonymus*. *The New Plantsman* 3(4):238-243.
de Jong, P. & Kolster, H. 2013. *Euonymus: Een kleurrijk geslacht*. Zeist, Netherlands: KNNV Uitgeverij.
Lancaster, C.R. 1981. An Account of *Euonymus* in Cultivation and its Availability in Commerce. *The Plantsman* 3(3):133-166.
Lancaster, C.R. 1982. *Euonymus* in Cultivation – Addendum. *The Plantsman* 4:61-64, 253-254.
Euphorbia
Govaerts, R., Frodin, D.G. & Radcliffe-Smith, A. 2000. *World Checklist and Bibliography of Euphorbiaceae*. Kew: Royal Botanic Gardens.
Turner, R. 1995. *Euphorbias. A Gardeners Guide*. London: Batsford.
Witton, D. 2000. *Euphorbias*. Pershore, Worcs.: Hardy Plant Society.
Fagales
Gocaerts, R. & Frodin, D.G. 1998. *World Checklist and Bibliography of Fagales*. RBG Kew.
Fagus
Dönig, G. 1994. *Die Park-und Gartenformen der Rotbuche Fagus sylvatica L.* Erlangen, Germany: Verlag Gartenbild Heinz Hansmann.
Fascicularia
Nelson, E.C., Zizka, G., Horres, R. & Weising, K. 1999. Revision of the Genus *Fascicularia* Mez (*Bromeliaceae*). *Botanical Journal of the Linnean Society* 129(4):315-332.
Ferns
Checklist of World Ferns. Jan 2010. http://homepages.caverock.net.nz/nbj/fern
Johns, R.J. 1996. *Index Filicum*. Supplementum Sextum pro annis 1976-1990. Kew:Royal Botanic Gardens.
Jones, D.L. 1987. *Encyclopaedia of Ferns*. Melbourne, Australia: Lothian.
Kaye, R. 1968. *Hardy Ferns*. London: Faber & Faber
Rickard, M.H. 2000. *The Plantfinder's Guide to Garden Ferns*. Newton Abbot, Devon: David & Charles.
Rush, R. 1984. *A Guide to Hardy Ferns*. London: British Pteridological Society.
Forsythia
INRA Forsythia website. Jan 2010. www.angers.inra.fr/forsy

Fritillaria

Clark, T. & Grey-Wilson, C. 2003. Crown Imperials. *The Plantsman* 2(1):33-47.

Mathew, B., et al. 2000. *Fritillaria* Issue. *Bot. Mag.* 17(3):145-185.

Pratt, K. & Jefferson-Brown, M. 1997. *The Gardener's Guide to Growing Fritillaries.* Newton Abbot: David & Charles.

Turrill, W.B. & Sealy, J.R. 1980. *Studies in the Genus Fritillaria (Liliaceae).* Hooker's Icones Plantarum Vol. 39 (1 & 2). Kew: Royal Botanic Gardens.

Fruit

Brogdale Horticultural Trust National Fruit Collection. Jan 2010. www.nationalfruitcollection.org.uk

Bowling, B.L. 2000. *The Berry Grower's Companion.* Portland, Oregon: Timber Press.

Hogg, R. 1884. *The Fruit Manual.* (5th ed.). London: Journal of Horticulture Office.

Fuchsia

American Fuchsia Society Registration Database. Jan 2010. www.americanfuchsiasociety.org

Bartlett, G. 1996. *Fuchsias – A Colour Guide.* Marlborough, Wilts: Crowood Press.

Boullemier, Leo.B. (comp.). 1991. *The Checklist of Species, Hybrids and Cultivars of the Genus Fuchsia.* London, New York, Sydney: Blandford Press.

Boullemier, Leo.B. (comp.). 1995. *Addendum No 1 to the 1991 Checklist of Species, Hybrids and Cultivars of the Genus Fuchsia.* Dyfed, Wales: The British Fuchsia Society.

Goulding, E. 1995. *Fuchsias: The Complete Guide.* London: Batsford.

Johns, E.A. 1997. *Fuchsias of the 19th and Early 20th Century.* An Historical Checklist of Fuchsia Species & Cultivars, pre-1939. Kidderminster, Worcs.: British Fuchsia Society

Stevens, R. Jan 2010. Find That Fuchsia. www.findthatfuchsia.info

Galanthus

Bishop, M., Davis, A. & Grimshaw, J. 2001. *Snowdrops. A monograph of cultivated Galanthus.* Maidenhead: Griffin Press.

Davis, A.P., Mathew, B. (ed.) & King, C. (ill.). 1999. *The Genus Galanthus. A Botanical Magazine Monograph.* Oregon: Timber Press.

Gentiana

Bartlett, M. 1975. *Gentians.* Dorset: Blandford Press.

Halda, J.J. 1996. *The Genus Gentiana.* Dobré, Czech Republic: Sen.

Ho T.N. & Liu S. 2001. *Worldwide Monograph of Gentiana.* Beijing: Science Press.

Geranium

Armitage, J. 2005-2007. *Hardy Geraniums – Stages 1-3: RHS Bulletin Nos 10 , 14* & *18.* Wisley, Surrey: RHS.

Bath, T. & Jones, J. 1994. *The Gardener's Guide to Growing Hardy Geraniums.* Newton Abbot, Devon: David & Charles.

Bendtsen, B.H. 2005. *Gardening with Hardy Geraniums.* Portland, Oregon: Timber Press.

Clifton, R.T.F. 1995. *Geranium Family Species Check List Pt 2.* Geranium. (4th ed. issue 2). Dover: The Geraniaceae Group.

Jones, J., et al. 2001. *Hardy Geraniums for the Garden.* (3rd ed.). Pershore, Worcs.: Hardy Plant Society.

Victor, D.X. 2004. *Register of Geranium Cultivar Names.* (2nd ed.). The Geraniaceae Group.

Yeo, P.F. 2002. *Hardy Geraniums.* (3rd ed.). Kent: Croom Helm.

Gesneriaceae

The Gesneriad Society. Listing of registered gesneriads. Jan 2010. www.aggs.gesneriadsociety.org

Dates, J.D. 1986-1990. *The Gesneriad Register 1986-1987 & 1990.* Galesburg, Illinois: American Gloxinia & Gesneriad Society, Inc.

Gladiolus

British Gladiolus Society List of Cultivars Classified for Show Purposes 1994. Mayfield, Derbyshire: British Gladiolus Society.

1997-1998. British Gladiolus Society List of European, New Zealand & North American Cultivars Classified for Exhibition Purposes 1997 & 1998. Mayfield, Derbyshire: British Gladiolus Society.

Goldblatt, P. & Manning, J. 1998. *Gladiolus in Southern Africa.* Vlaeberg, South Africa: Fernwood Press.

Goldblatt, P. 1996. *Gladiolus in Tropical Africa.* Systematics Biology and Evolution. Oregon: Timber Press.

Gleditsia

Santamour, F.S. & McArdle, A.J. 1983. Checklist of Cultivars of Honeylocust (*Gleditsia triacanthos* L.). *J. Arboric.* 9:271-276.

Grevillea

Olde, P. & Marriott, N. 1995. *The Grevillea Book.* (3). Kenthurst, NSW: Kangaroo Press.

Haemanthus

Snijman, D. 1984. A Revision of the Genus *Haemanthus. J. S. African Bot.* (Supp. Vol. 12).

Hamamelis

Lane, C. 2005. *Witch Hazels.* Portland, Oregon: Timber Press.

Heathers

Baker, H.A. & Oliver, E.G.H. 1967. *Heathers in Southern Africa.* Cape Town: Purnell.

Nelson, E.C. 2011. *Hardy Heathers from the Northern Hemisphere.* London: Kew Publishing

Nelson, E.C. & Small, D.J. (eds). 2000. *International Register of Heather Names.* (Pts 1-4). The Heather Society.

Schumann, D., Kirsten, G. & Oliver, E.G.H. 1992. *Ericas of South Africa.* Vlaeberg, South Africa: Fernwood Press.

Small, D. & Wulff, E.M.T. 2008. *Gardening with Hardy Heathers.* Portland, Oregon: Timber Press.

Hebe

Hutchins, G. 1997. *Hebes: Here and There.* A Monograph on the Genus *Hebe.* Caversham, Berks: Hutchins & Davies.

Metcalf, L.J. 2001. *International Register of Hebe Cultivars.* Canterbury, New Zealand: Royal New Zealand Institute of Horticulture (Inc.).

Metcalf, L.J. 2006. *Hebes: A Guide to Species, Hybrids and Allied Genera.* Portland, Oregon: Timber Press.

Hedera

Jury, S. et al. 2006. *Hedera algeriensis,* a Fine Species of Ivy. *Sibbaldia* 4: 93-108.

McAllister, H. 1988. Canary and Algerian Ivies. *The Plantsman* 10(1):27-29.

Rose, P.Q. 1996. *The Gardener's Guide to Growing Ivies.* Newton Abbot, Devon: David & Charles.

Rutherford, A., McAllister, H. & Mill, R.R. 1993. New Ivies from the Mediterranean Area and Macaronesia. *The Plantsman* 15(2):115-128.

Heliconia

Berry, F. & Kress, W.J. 1991. *Heliconia.* An Identification Guide. Washington: Smithsonian Institution Press.

Helleborus

Burrell, C.C. & Tyler, J.K. 2006. *Hellebores: A Comprehensive Guide.* Portland, Oregon: Timber Press.

Mathew, B. 1989. *Hellebores.* Woking: Alpine Garden Society.

Rice, G. & Strangman, E. 1993. *The Gardener's Guide to Growing Hellebores.* Newton Abbot, Devon: David & Charles.

Hemerocallis

Baxter, G.J. (comp.). American Daylily Society Registry of Daylily Cultivars. Jan 2010. www.daylilies.org

Herbs

Phillips, R. & Foy, N. 1990. *Herbs.* London: Pan Books Ltd.

Heuchera and × ***Heucherella***

Heims, D. & Ware, G. 2005. *Heucheras and Heucherellas: Coral Bells and Foamy Bells.* Portland, Oregon: Timber Press.

Hibiscus

Noble, C. Apr 2007. Australian Hibiscus Society Database Register. www.australianhibiscus.com/

Hosta

Hosta Library. Aug 2006. www.hostalibrary.org

Grenfell, D. & Shadrack, M. 2004. *The Color Encyclopedia of Hostas.* Portland, Oregon: Timber Press.

Schmid, W.G. 1991. *The Genus Hosta.* London: Batsford.

Zilis, M.R. 2009. *The Hostapedia. An Encyclopedia of Hostas.* Q.22 Nursery Inc.

Hyacinthaceae (***Asparagaceae*** pro parte)

Dashwood, M. & Mathew, B. 2006. *Hyacinthaceae – little blue bulbs: RHS Bulletin No 11.* Wisley, Surrey: RHS.

Mathew, B. 2005. *Hardy Hyacinthaceae* Pt 1: *Muscari. The Plantsman* 4(1):40-53.

Mathew, B. 2005. *Hardy Hyacinthaceae* Pt 2: *Scilla, Chionodoxa* and × *Chinoscilla. The Plantsman* 4(2):110-121.

Hydrangea

Dirr, M.A. 2004. *Hydrangeas for American Gardens.* Portland, Oregon: Timber Press.

Haworth-Booth, M. 1975. *The Hydrangeas.* London: Garden Book Club.

Van Gelderen, C.J. & Van Gelderen, D.M. 2004. *Encyclopedia of Hydrangeas.* Portland, Oregon: Timber Press.

Hypericum

Lancaster, R. & Robson, N. 1997. Focus on Plants: Bowls of Beauty. *The Garden* (RHS) 122(8):566-571.

Ilex

Bailes, C. 2006. *Hollies for Gardeners.* Portland, Oregon: Timber Press.

Dudley, T.R. & Eisenbeiss, G.K. 1973 & 1992. *International Checklist of Cultivated Ilex, Pts 1 & 2.*. Washington DC: United States Dept of Agriculture.

Galle, F.C. 1997. *Hollies: the Genus Ilex.* Portland, Oregon: Timber Press.

Impatiens

Morgan, R.J. 2007. *Impatiens: The Vibrant World of Busy Lizzies, Balsams and Touch-me-nots.* Portland, Oregon: Timber Press.

Iris

Austin, C. 2005. *Irises: A Gardener's Encyclopedia.* Oregon:Timber Press.

Hoog, M.H. 1980. Bulbous Irises . *The Plantsman* 2(3):141-64.

Lowe, A. & Lowe, M. *Iris Check List of Registered Cultivar Names 2000-2009.* Hannibal, New York.

Mathew, B. 1981. *The Iris.* London: Batsford.

Mathew, B. 1993. The Spuria Irises. *The Plantsman* 15(1):14-25.

Stebbings, G. 1997. *The Gardener's Guide to Growing Iris.* Newton Abbot: David & Charles.

The Species Group of the British Iris Society, (ed.). 1997. *A Guide to Species Irises.* Their Identification and Cultivation. Cambridge: Cambridge University Press.

Jasminum

Green, P. & Miller, D. 2009. *The Genus Jasminum in Cultivation.* Kew: Royal Botanic Gardens.

Jovibarba **see under** Sempervivum

Kalmia

Jaynes, R.A. 2009. *Kalmia. Mountain Laurel and Related Species.* (3rd ed.). Portland, Oregon: Timber Press.

Kniphofia
Taylor, J. 1985. *Kniphofia* – a Survey. *The Plantsman* 7(3):129-160.
Whitehouse, C.M. 2012. Preliminary checklist of *Kniphofia* epithets. *Hanburyana* 6: 9-82.
Kohleria
Dates, J.D. (ed.) & Batcheller, F.N. (comp.). 1985. *The Gesneriad Register 1985. Check List of Names with Descriptions of Cultivated Plants in the Genus Kohleria.* Lincoln Acres, California: American Gloxinia and Gesneriad Society, Inc.
Lachenalia
Duncan, G.D. 1988. *The Lachenalia Hand Book.* Kirstenbosch, South Africa: National Botanic Gardens.
Duncan, G.D. 2012. *The Genus Lachenalia.* London: Kew Publishing.
Lantana
Howard, R.A. 1969. A Check List of Names Used in the Genus *Lantana. Arnoldia.* 29(11):73-109.
Lathyrus
Norton, S. 1996. *Lathyrus. Cousins of Sweet Pea.* Surrey: NCCPG.
Lavandula
Upson, T. & Andrews, S. 2004. *The Genus Lavandula.* Kew: Royal Botanic Garden.
Leptospermum
Check List of *Leptospermum* Cultivars. 1963. *J. Roy. New Zealand Inst. Hort.* 5(5):224-30.
Dawson, M. 1997. A History of *Leptospermum scoparium* in Cultivation – Discoveries from the Wild. *The New Plantsman* 4(1):51-59.
Dawson, M. 1997. A History of *Leptospermum scoparium* in Cultivation – Garden Selections. *The New Plantsman* 4(2):67-78.
Lewisia
Davidson, B.L.R. 2000. *Lewisias.* Portland, Oregon: Timber Press.
Elliott, R. 1978. *Lewisias.* Woking: Alpine Garden Society.
Mathew, B. 1989. *The Genus Lewisia.* Bromley, Kent: Christopher Helm.
Lilium
Donald, D. *The International Lily Register 1982-2002.* (4th ed.). Supp. 3, 2012. London: RHS.
Leslie, A.C. *The International Lily Register 1982-2002.* (4th ed.). Supps 1-2, 2008-2010. London: RHS.
Lonicera
Blahník, Z. 2006. *Lonicera* Cultivar Names: The First World List. *Acta Pruhoniciana* 81:59-64.
Bradshaw, D. 1996. *Lonicera. Climbing Honeysuckles.* Surrey: NCCPG.
Magnolia
Callaway, D.J. Sep 2001. Magnolia Cultivar Checklist. www.magnoliasociety.org
Frodin, D.G. & Govaerts, R. 1996. *World Checklist and Bibliography of Magnoliaceae.* Kew: Royal Botanic Garden.
Gardiner, J. 2000. *Magnolias: A Gardener's Guide.* Portland, Oregon: Timber Press.
Hunt, D. (ed.). 1998. *Magnolias and their Allies.* London: International Dendrology Society & The Magnolia Society.
Liu, Y. 2004. *Magnolias of China.* Beijing: Beijing Science and Technology Press.
Maianthemum
Cubey, J.J. 2005 *The Incorporation of Smilacina within Maianthemum. The Plantsman* N.S.4(4).
Malus
Crawford, M. 1994. *Directory of Apple Cultivars.* Devon: Agroforestry Research Trust.
Fiala, J.L. 1994. *Flowering Crabapples.* The genus *Malus.* Portland, Oregon: Timber Press.
Rouèche, A. Oct 2007. Les Crets Fruits et Pomologie. www.pomologie.com
Spiers, V. 1996. *Burcombes, Queenies and Colloggetts.* St Dominic, Cornwall: West Brendon.
Meconopsis
Grey-Wilson, C. 1992. A Survey of the Genus *Meconopsis* in Cultivation. *The Plantsman* 14(1): 1-33.
Grey-Wilson, C. 2002. The True Identity of *Meconopsis napaulensis. Bot. Mag.* 23(2):176-209.
Meconopsis Group website. Jan 2010. www.meconopsis.org
Stevens, E. & Brickell, C. 2001. Problems with the Big Perennial Poppies. *The New Plantsman* 8(1):48-61.
Stevens, E. 2001. Further Observations on the Big Perennial Blue Poppies. *The New Plantsman* 8(2):105-111.
Miscanthus
Jones, L. 2004. Miscanthus: RHS Bulletin No 7. Wisley, Surrey: RHS.
Moraea
Goldblatt, P. 1986. *The Moraeas of Southern Africa.* Kirstenbosch, South Africa: National Botanic Gardens.
Musa
Banana and Plantain Section of Biodiversity International 2001. http://bananas.bioversityinternational.org
INIBAP *Musa* Germplasm Information System. Jan 2010. www.crop-diversity.org/banana
Narcissus
Blanchard, J.W. 1990. *Narcissus – A Guide to Wild Daffodils.* Woking, Surrey: Alpine Garden Society.
Kington, S. (comp.). 2008. *The International Daffodil Register and Classified List 2008* (4th ed.)
McDonald, S. (comp.) *The International Daffodil Register and Classified List 2008,* Supps 1-5. 2008-2012. London: RHS.
Nematanthus
Arnold, P. 1978. *The Gesneriad Register 1978.* Check List of *Nematanthus.* American Gloxinia and Gesneriad Society, Inc.

Nerium

Pagen, F.J.J. 1987. *Oleanders. Nerium L. and the Oleander Cultivars*. Wageningen, The Netherlands: Agricultural University Wageningen.

Nymphaea

Knotts, K. & Knotts, B. Victoria Adventure Website. Checklist of Waterlily Cultivars. Jan 2010. www.victoria-adventure.org

Orchidaceae

Shaw, J.M.H. Jan 2010. The International Orchid Register. http://apps.rhs.org.uk/horticultural database/orchidregister/orchidregister.asp

Origanum

White, S. 1998. *Origanum. The Herb Marjoram and its Relatives*. Surrey: NCCPG.

Paeonia

HelpMeFind Peonies. Jan 2010. www.helpmefind.com/peony/index.php

Jakubowski, R. American Peony Society Peony Checklist. www.americanpeonysociety.org

Jakubowski, R. 2008. *Peonies 1997-2007. Registered Peony Cultivars, with a Checklist of Peony Names, References and Originators*. Missouri: American Peony Society.

McLewin, W & Dezhong, C. 2008. *Peony rockii and the Gansu Mudan*. Massachusetts: Wellesley-Cambridge Press.

Osti, G.L. 1999. *The Book of Tree Peonies*. Turin: Umberto Allemandi.

Wang, L., et al. 1998. *Chinese Tree Peony*. Beijing: China Forestry Publishing House.

Papaver

Grey-Wilson, C. 1998. Oriental Glories. *The Garden* (RHS) 123(5):320-325.

Papaveraceae

Grey-Wilson, C. 2000. *Poppies. The Poppy Family in the Wild and in Cultivation*. London: Batsford.

Tebbitt, M. Liden, M. Zetterlund, H. 2008. *Bleeding Hearts, Corydalis and their Relatives*. Portland, Oregon: Timber Press

Passiflora

King, L.A. Jan 2008. Passiflora online passion flower cultivar register. www.passionflow.co.uk

Ulmer, T. & MacDougal, J.M. 2004. *Passiflora – Passion Flowers of the World*. Portland, Oregon: Timber Press.

Pelargonium

Anon. 1978 & 1985. *A Checklist and Register of Pelargonium Cultivar Names*. Pts 1 & 2. Australian Pelargonium Society.

Clifton, R. 1999. *Geranium Family Species Checklist, Pt 4: Pelargonium*. The Geraniaceae Group.

Key, H. 2000. *1001 Pelargoniums*. London: Batsford.

Miller, D. 1996. *Pelargonium*. A Gardener's Guide to the Species and Cultivars and Hybrids. London: Batsford.

Pelargonium Palette: The Geranium and Pelargonium Society of Sydney Incorporated. Varieties – Alphabetical List. July 2010. www.elj.com/geranium

Van der Walt, J.J.A., et al. 1977. *Pelargoniums of South Africa*. (1-3). Kirstenbosch, South Africa: National Botanic Gardens.

Penstemon

Lindgren, D.T. & Davenport, B. 1992. List and description of named cultivars in the genus *Penstemon*. University of Nebraska.

Nold, R. 1999. *Penstemons*. Portland, Oregon: Timber Press.

Way, D. & James, P. 1998. *The Gardener's Guide to Growing Penstemons*. Newton Abbott, Devon: David & Charles.

Way, D. 2006. *Penstemons*. Pershore, Worcs.: Hardy Plant Society.

Phlomis

Mann Taylor, J. 1998. *Phlomis: The Neglected Genus*. Wisley: NCCPG.

Phlox

Harmer, J. & Elliott, J. 2001. *Phlox*. Pershore, Worcs.: Hardy Plant Society.

Stebbings, G. 1999. Simply Charming. *The Garden* (RHS) 124(7):518-521.

Wherry, E.T. 1955. *The Genus Phlox*. Philadelphia, Pennsylvania: Morris Arboretum.

Phormium

Heenan, P.B. 1991. *Checklist of Phormium Cultivars*. Royal New Zealand Institute of Horticulture.

McBride-Whitehead, V. 1998. Phormiums of the Future. *The Garden* (RHS) 123(1):42-45.

Pieris

Bond, J. 1982. *Pieris* – a Survey. *The Plantsman* 4(2):65-75.

Wagenknecht, B.L. 1961. Registration Lists of Cultivar Names in the Genus *Pieris* D. Don. *Arnoldia (Jamaica Plain)* 21(8):47-50.

Pittosporum

Miller, D.M. 2006. RHS Plant Assessments: *Pittosporum tenuifolium* hybrids & cultivars.

Plectranthus

Miller, D. & Morgan, N. 2000. Focus on Plants: A New Leaf. *The Garden* (RHS) 125(11):842-845.

Shaw, J.M.H. 1999. Notes on the Identity of Swedish Ivy and Other Cultivated *Plectranthus*. *The New Plantsman* 6(2):71-74.

Van Jaarsveld, E.J. 2006. *South African Plectranthus*. Vlaeberg, South Africa: Fernwood Press.

Pleione

Cribb, P. & Butterfield, I. 1999. *The Genus Pleione*. (2nd ed.). Kew: Royal Botanic Gardens.

Shaw, J.M.H. (comp.). Oct 2002. Provisional List of *Pleione* Cultivars. RHS.

Poaceae

Clayton, W.D., Harman, K.T. & Williamson, H. Jan 2010. GrassBase : The Online World Grass Flora. www.kew.org/data/grasses-syn

Darke, R. 2007. *Encyclopedia of Grasses for Livable Landscapes*. Portland, Oregon: Timber Press.
Grounds, R. 1998. *The Plantfinder's Guide to Ornamental Grasses.* Newton Abott, Devon: David & Charles.
Wood, T. 2002. *Garden Grasses, Rushes and Sedges.* (3rd ed.). Abingdon, Oxon: John Wood.
Polemonium
Nichol-Brown, D. 2000. *Polemonium.* Wisley: NCCPG.
Potentilla
Davidson, C.G., Enns, R.J. & Gobin, S. 1994. *A Checklist of Potentilla fruticosa: the Shrubby Potentillas.* Morden, Manitoba: Agriculture & Agri-Food Canada Research Centre.
Miller, D.M. 2002. *Shrubby Potentilla: RHS Bulletin No 1*. Wisley, Surrey: RHS.
Primula
Richards, J. 2002 (2nd ed.). *Primula.* London: Batsford.
Primula allionii
Archdale, B. & Richards, D. 1997. *Primula allionii Forms and Hybrids.* National Auricula & Primula Society, Midland & West Section.
Primula auricula
Baker, G. *Double Auriculas.* National Auricula & Primula Society, Midland & West Section.
Baker, G. & Ward, P. 1995. *Auriculas*. London: Batsford.
Guest, A. 2009. *The Auricula History, Cultivation and Varieties*. Woodbridge, Suffolk: Garden Art Press
Hawkes, A. 1995. Striped Auriculas. National Auricula & Primula Society, Midland & West Section.
Nicholle, G. 1996. *Border Auriculas.* National Auricula & Primula Society, Midland & West Section.
Robinson, M.A. 2000. *Auriculas for Everyone.* How to Grow and Show Perfect Plants. Lewes, Sussex: Guild of Master Craftsmen Publications.
Telford, D. 1993. *Alpine Auriculas.* National Auricula & Primula Society, Midland & West Section.
Ward, P. 1991. *Show Auriculas.* National Auricula & Primula Society, Midland & West Section.
Proteaceae
International *Proteaceae* Register. July 2002. (7th ed.).
Rebelo, T. 1995. *Proteas.* A Field Guide to the Proteas of Southern Africa. Vlaeberg: Fernwood Press/National Botanical Institute.
Prunus
Crawford, M. 1996. *Plums.* Dartington, Devon: Agroforestry Research Trust.
Jacobsen, A.L. 1992. *Purpleleaf Plums.* Portland, Oregon: Timber Press.
Jefferson, R.M. & Wain, K.K. 1984. *The Nomenclature of Cultivated Flowering Cherries (Prunus).* The Sato-Zakura Group. Washington DC: USDA.
Kuitert, W. 1999. *Japanese Flowering Cherries.* Portland, Oregon: Timber Press.
Pulmonaria
Bennett, M. 2003. *Pulmonarias and the borage family*. London: B.T. Batsford.
Hewitt, J. 1994. *Pulmonarias.* Pershore, Worcs.: Hardy Plant Society.
Hewitt, J. 1999. Well Spotted. *The Garden* (RHS) 124(2):98-103.
Pyracantha
Egolf, D.R. & Andrick, A.O. 1995. *A Checklist of Pyracantha Cultivars.* Washington DC: Agricultural Research Service.
Pyrus
Crawford, M. 1996. *Directory of Pear Cultivars.* Totnes, Devon: Agroforestry Research Institute.
Smith, M.W.G. 1976. *Catalogue of the British Pear.* Faversham, Kent: MAFF.
Quercus
International Oak Society. Oak Name Checklist. www.oaknames.org.
Miller, H.A. & Lamb, S.H. 1985. *Oaks of North America.* Happy Camp, California: Naturegraph Publishers.
Mitchell, A. 1994. The Lucombe Oaks. *The Plantsman* 15(4):216-224.
Rhododendron
Argent, G., Fairweather, C. & Walter, K. 1996. *Accepted Names in* Rhododendron *section Vireya.* Edinburgh: Royal Botanic Garden.
Argent, G., Bond, J., Chamberlain, D., Cox, P. & Hardy, A. 1997. *The Rhododendron Handbook 1998.* Rhododendron Species in Cultivation. London: RHS.
Chamberlain, D.F. & Rae, S.J. 1990. A Revision of *Rhododendron* IV. Subgenus *Tsutsusi. Edinburgh J. Bot.* 47(2).
Chamberlain, D.F. 1982. A Revision of *Rhododendron* II. Subgenus *Hymenanthes. Notes Roy. Bot. Gard. Edinburgh* 39(2).
Chamberlain, D., Hyam, R., Argent, G., Fairweather, G. & Walter, K.S. 1996. *The Genus Rhododendron.* Edinburgh:Royal Botanic Garden.
Cox, K.N.E. 2005. *Rhododendrons and Azaleas. A Colour Guide.* Wiltshire: The Crowood Press.
Cox, P.A. & Cox, K.N.E. 1988. *Rhododendron Hybrids*. London: Batsford.
Cox, P.A. & Cox, K.N.E. 1997. *The Encyclopedia of Rhododendron Species*. Perth: Glendoick Publishing.
Cullen, J. 2005. *Hardy Rhododendron Species. A Guide to Identification.* Portland, Oregon: Timber Press.
Davidian, H.H. 1982-1992 *The Rhododendron Species* (Vols 1-4). London: Batsford.

Galle, F.C. 1985. *Azaleas.* Portland, Oregon: Timber Press.
Leslie, A.C. (comp.) 2004. *The International Rhododendron Register and Checklist* (2nd ed.) & Supps 1-6, 2004-2012. London: RHS.
McQuire, J.F.J. & Robinson, M.L.A. 2009. *Pocket Guide to Rhododendron Species.* Kew: Royal Botanic Gardens.
Tamura, T. (ed.). 1989. *Azaleas in Kurume.* Kurume, Japan: International Azalea Festival '89.
van Gelderen, D.M. & van Hoey-Smith, J.R.P. 1992. *Rhododendrons.* London: Batsford.

Ribes

Crawford, M. 1997. *Currants and Gooseberries: Production and Culture.* Dartington, Devon: Agroforestry Research Trust.

Rosa

Beales, P., Cairns, T. 1998. *Botanica's Rose: The Encyclopedia of Roses.* Hoo, Kent: Grange Books.
Cairns, T. (ed.). 2000. *Modern Roses XI. The World Encyclopedia of Roses.* London: Academic Press.
Dickerson, B.C. 1999. *The Old Rose Advisor.* Portland, Oregon: Timber Press.
Haw, S.G. 1996. Notes on Some Chinese and Himalayan Rose Species of Section *Pimpinellifoliae. The New Plantsman* 3(3):143-146.
HelpMeFind Roses. Jan 2010. www.helpmefind.com
McCann, S. 1985. *Miniature Roses.* Newton Abbot, Devon: David & Charles.
Pawsey, Angela (ed.) 2013. *Find That Rose! 2013-2014.* (31st ed.) Colchester, Essex.
Phillips, R. & Rix, M. 1993. *The Quest for the Rose.* London: BBC Books.
Phillips, R. & Rix, M. 2004. *The Ultimate Guide to Roses.* Lonon: Macmillan.
Quest-Ritson, C. 2003. *Climbing Roses of the World.* Portland, Oregon: Timber Press.
Quest-Ritson, C. & B. 2003. *The Royal Horticultural Society Encyclopedia of Roses: The Definitive A-Z Guide.* London: Dorling Kindersley.
Thomas, G.S. 1995. *The Graham Stuart Thomas Rose Book.* London: John Murray.
Verrier, S. 1996. *Rosa Gallica.* Balmain, Australia: Florilegium.

Roscoea

Cowley, J. 2007. *The Genus Roscoea.* Kew Publishing.

Rosularia

Eggli, U. 1988. A Monographic Study of the Genus *Rosularia. Bradleya* (Supp.) 6:1-118.

Saintpaulia

Goodship, G. 1987. *Saintpaulia Variety List* (Supp.). Slough, Bucks: Saintpaulia & Houseplant Society.
Moore, H.E. 1957. *African Violets, Gloxinias and Their Relatives.* A Guide to the Cultivated Gesneriads. New York: Macmillan.

Salix

Newsholme, C. 1992. *Willows.* The Genus *Salix.* London: Batsford.

Salvia

Clebsch, B. 2003. *A Book of Salvias.* (2nd ed.). Portland, Oregon: Timber Press.
Compton, J. 1994. Mexican Salvias in Cultivation. *The Plantsman* 15(4):193-215.
Middleton, R. *Robin's Salvias.* www.robinssalvias.com

Saxifraga

Bland, B. 2000. *Silver Saxifrages.* Pershore, Worcs.: Alpine Garden Society.
Dashwood, M. & Bland, B. 2005. Silver Saxifrages: RHS Bulletin No 9. Wisley, Surrey: RHS.
McGregor, M. Jan 2010. Saxbase. Saxifrage Society. www.saxifraga.org
McGregor, M. 1995. *Saxifrages: The Complete Cultivars & Hybrids: International Register of Saxifrages.* (2nd ed.). Driffield, E. Yorks: Saxifrage Society.
Webb, D.A. & Gornall, R.J. 1989. *Saxifrages of Europe.* Bromley, Kent: Christopher Helm.

Sedges

Govaerts, R. & Simpson, D.A. 2007 *World Checklist of Cyperaceae: Sedges.* Richmond, Surrey: RBG Kew

Sedum

Evans, R.L. 1983. *Handbook of Cultivated Sedums.* Motcombe, Dorset: Ivory Head Press.
Lord, T. 2006. *Sedum* up for assessment. *The Plantsman* 5(4):244-252.
Stephenson, R. 1994. *Sedum.* The Cultivated Stonecrops. Portland, Oregon: Timber Press.

Sempervivum

Diehm, H. Jan 2010. www.semperhorst.de
Miklánek, M. 2000. *List of Cultivars: Sempervivum and Jovibarba* v. 15.1. http://miklanek.tripod.com

Sinningia

Dates, J.D. 1988. *The Gesneriad Register 1988. Check List of Names with Descriptions of Cultivated Plants in the Genus Sinningia.* Galesburg, Illinois: American Gloxinia and Gesneriad Society, Inc.

Solenostemon

Addink, Wouter. Jan 2010. Coleus Finder. http://coleusfinder.org
Pedley, W.K. & Pedley, R. 1974. *Coleus – A Guide to Cultivation and Identification.* Edinburgh: Bartholemew.

Sorbus

McAllister, H. 2005. *The Genus Sorbus: Mountain Ash and Other Rowans.* Kew: Royal Botanical Gardens.
Snyers d'Attenhoven, C. 1999. *Sorbus* Lombarts hybrids *Belgische Dendrologie*: 76-81. Belgium.

Spiraea

Miller, D.M. 2003. *Spiraea japonica with coloured leaves: RHS Bulletin No 4.* Wisley, Surrey: RHS

Streptocarpus
Arnold, P. 1979. *The Gesneriad Register 1979: Check List of Streptocarpus.* Binghamton, New York: American Gloxinia & Gesneriad.
Succulents
Eggli, U. (ed.) 2002. *Illustrated Handbook of Succulent Plants.* Heidelberg, Germany: Springer-Verlag.
Eggli, U. & Taylor, N. 1994. *List of Names of Succulent Plants other than Cacti Published 1950-92.* Kew: Royal Botanic Gardens.
Grantham, K. & Klaassen, P. 1999. *The Plantfinder's Guide to Cacti and Other Succulents.* Newton Abbot, Devon: David & Charles.
Jacobsen, H. 1973. *Lexicon of Succulent Plants.* London: Blandford.
Syringa
Fiala, J.L. & Vrugtman, F. 2008. *A Gardener's Encyclopedia of Lilacs.* Portland, Oregon: Timber Press.
Vrugtman, F. 2000. *International Register of Cultivar Names in the Genus Syringa L. (Oleaceae).* (Contribution No 91). Hamilton, Canada: Royal Botanic Gardens.
Thymus
Easter, M. 2009. *International* Thymus *Register and Checklist.* UK: Owl Prints.
Tilia
Piggott, D. 2012. *Lime-trees and Basswoods. A Biological Monograph of the Genus Tilia.* Cambridge: Cambridge University Press.
Tiliaceae (_Malvaceae_ pro parte)
Wild, H. 1984. *Flora of Southern Africa 21 (1: Tiliaceae).* Pretoria: Botanical Research Institute, Dept of Agriculture.
Tillandsia
Kiff, L.F. 1991. *A Distributional Checklist of the Genus Tillandsia.* Encino, California: Botanical Diversions.
Trillium
Case, F.W.J. & Case, R.B. 1997. *Trilliums.* Portland, Oregon: Timber Press.
Jacobs, D.L. & Jacobs, R.L. 1997. *American Treasures.* Trilliums in Woodland Garden. Decatur, Georgia: Eco-Gardens.
Tulipa
KAVB Online registration pages. http://kavb.back2p.soft-orange.com
Ulmus
Green, P.S. 1964. Registratration of Cultivar Names in *Ulmus. Arnoldia (Jamaica Plain)* 24:41-80.
Vaccinium
Trehane, J. 2004. *Blueberries, Cranberries and Other Vacciniums.* Portland, Oregon: Timber Press.
Vegetables
Official Journal of the European Communities. Oct 2007. Common catalogue of varieties of agricultural plant species: consolidated version. http://ec.europa.eu/food
Viburnum
Dirr, M.A. 2007. *Viburnums: Flowering Shrubs for Every Season.* Portland, Oregon: Timber Press.
Kenyon, L. 2001. *Viburnum.* Surrey: NCCPG.
Viola
Coombes, R.E. 2003. *Violets.* (2nd ed.). London: Batsford.
Fuller, R. 1990. *Pansies, Violas & Violettas.* The Complete Guide. Marlborough: The Crowood Press.
Perfect, E.J. 1996. *Armand Millet and his Violets.* High Wycombe: Park Farm Press.
Robinson, P.M. & Snocken, J. 2003. Checklist of the Cultivated Forms of the Genus *Viola* including the Register of Cultivars. American Violet Society. http://americanvioletsociety.org
Vitis
Robinson, J. 1989. *Vines, Grapes and Wines.* London: Mitchell Beazley.
Watsonia
Goldblatt, P. 1989. *The Genus Watsonia.* A Systematic Monograph. South Africa: National Botanic Gardens.
Weigela
Howard, R.A. 1965. A Checklist of Cultivar Names in *Weigela. Arnoldia (Jamaica Plain)* 25:49-69.
Wisteria
Valder, P. 1995. *Wisterias.* A Comprehensive Guide. Balmain, Australia: Florilegium.
Yucca
Smith, C. 2004. *Yuccas: Giants among the Lilies.* NCCPG.
Zauschneria
Robinson, A. 2000. Focus on Plants: Piping Hot (*Zauschneria* Cultivars). *The Garden* (RHS) 125(9):698-699.
Zingiberaceae
Branney, T.M.E. 2005. *Hardy Gingers. Including Hedychium, Roscoea and Zingiber.* Cambridge: Timber Press.

Nurseries

The following nurseries between them stock an unrivalled choice of plants. Before making a visit, please remember to check with the nursery that the plant you seek is currently available.

Nursery Codes and Symbols

The first letter of each nursery code represents the area of the country in which the nursery is situated.

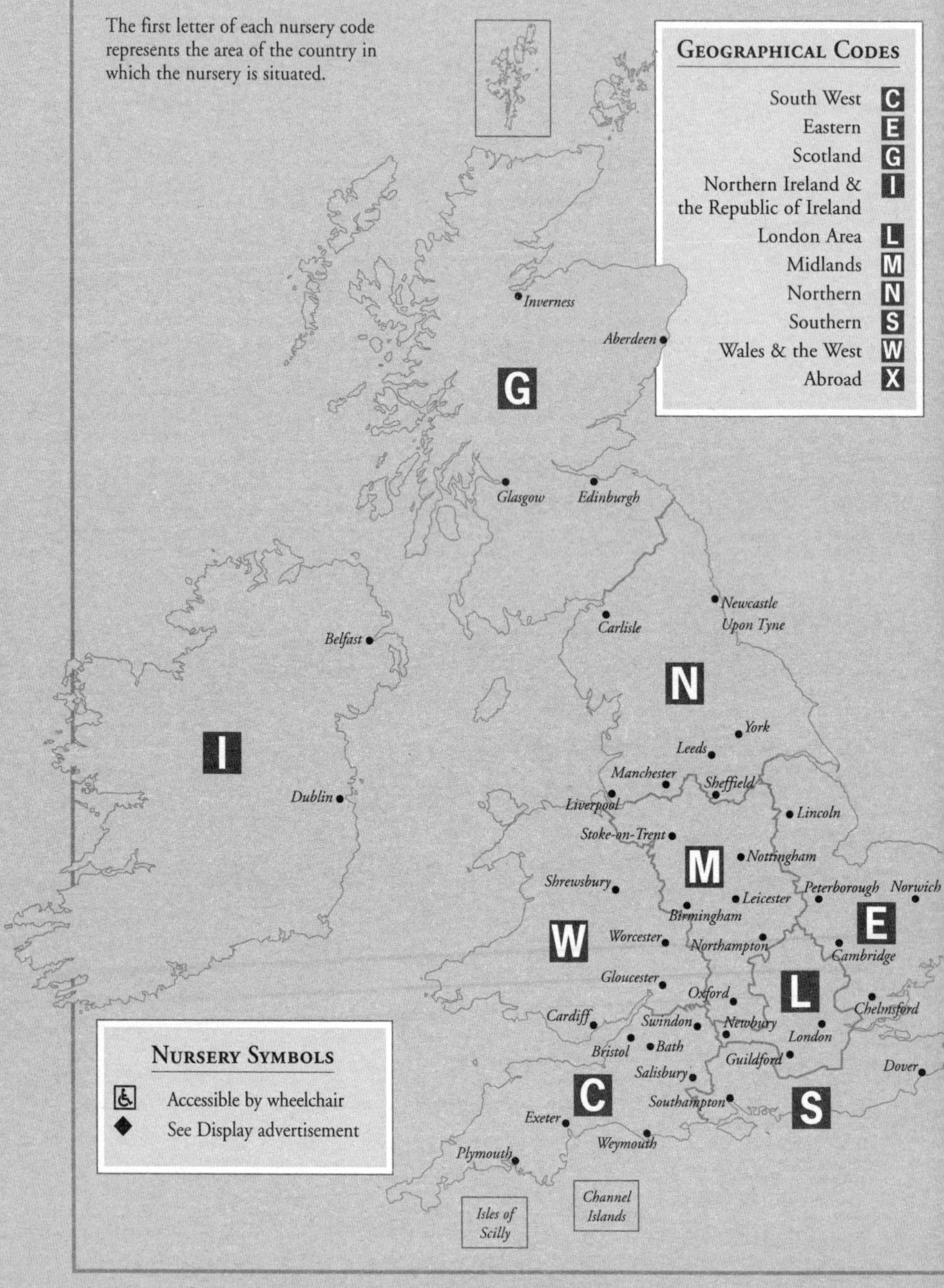

USING THE NURSERY LISTINGS

Your main reference from the Plant Directory is the Nursery Details by Code listing, which includes all relevant information for each nursery in order of nursery code. The Nursery Index by Name is an alphabetical list for those who know a nursery's name but not its code and wish to check its details in the main list.

1 NURSERY DETAILS BY CODE

Once you have found your plant in the Plant Directory, turn to this list to find out the name, address, opening times and other details of the nurseries whose codes accompany the plant.

KEY

♿ Accessible by wheelchair ◆ See Display advertisement

A geographical code is followed by three letters reflecting the nursery's name

SFrt **FRUIT GARDEN PLANTS** ♿ ◆
Woolton Farm, Bekesbourne, Canterbury, Kent CT4 5EA
Ⓣ (01227) 830525
Ⓜ 07710 253690
Ⓕ (01227) 831969
Ⓔ sales@fruitgardenplants.co.uk
Ⓦ www.fruitgardenplants.co.uk
Contact: Mark Mount
Opening Times: 1000-1600 Thu-Sat, 1st Nov-31st Mar. 1000-1700 Thu-Sun, 1st Apr-31st Oct.
Min Mail Order UK: £10.00
Min Mail Order EU: £35.00
Credit Cards: MasterCard, Visa
Specialities: Tree fruits & soft fruits.
Notes: Fruit display garden where visitors can see particular varieties & the methods used for growing them. Small café. Medieval tythe barn. Also sells wholesale. Delivers to shows. Wheelchair accessible.
Map Ref: S, C5 **OS Grid Ref:** TR191568

Other information about the nursery

A brief summary of the plants available

The map letter is followed by the map square in which the nursery is located

The Ordnance Survey national grid reference for use with OS maps

2 NURSERY INDEX BY NAME

If you are looking for a particular nursery, use this alphabetical index to find it, note its code and then turn to the Nursery Details by Code listing for full information.

Forest Edge Nurseries	CFst
Frogswell Nursery	IFro
Frosch Exclusive Perennials	XFro
Fruit Garden Plants	SFrt
Fuchsia Michiels	**XMic**
Galloway Plants	GGal
Garden Blooms	NGBl
Garden House Nursery	NGdn

How to Use the Nursery Listings

The details given for each nursery have been compiled from information supplied to us in answer to a questionnaire. In some cases, because of constraints of space, the entries have been slightly abbreviated.

This year we have removed several of the symbols from the nursery details. We found that more and more nurseries wanted to expand on what they offered and a simple "yes/no" answer was no longer appropriate. Information on mail order, exporting beyond the EU, whether payment in euros is accepted and whether nurseries will deliver to shows is now all given in **Notes**. We hope that this will clarify what services nurseries offer.

We have retained the wheelchair symbol for those nurseries that tell us their site is fully accessible. Please note that this does not necessarily relate to any gardens to which the nursery may be attached. It is important, however, to read the **Notes** section of each nursery's details, as many will offer restricted wheelchair access.

Nurseries are not charged for their entries and inclusion in no way implies a value judgement.

Nursery Details by Code (*page 832*)

Each nursery is allocated a code, for example GPoy. The first letter of each code indicates the main area of the country in which the nursery is situated. In this example, G=Scotland. The remaining three letters reflect the nursery's name, in this case Poyntzfield Herb Nursery.

In this main listing the nurseries are given in alphabetical order of codes for quick reference from the Plant Directory. All of the nurseries' details, such as address, opening times, mail order service etc., will be found here.

Opening Times

Although opening times have been published as submitted and where applicable, **it is always advisable, especially if travelling a long distance, to check with the nursery first.** The initials NGS indicate that the nursery is open under the National Gardens Scheme.

Mail Order

Many nurseries provide a mail order service. **This is, however, often restricted to certain times of the year or to particular genera.** Please check the **Notes** section of each nursery's entry for any restrictions or special conditions.

In some cases, the mail order service extends to all members of the European Union. Where this is offered, the minimum charge to the EU will be noted in the Nursery entry.

Where **'No minimum charge'** (Nmc) is shown, please note that to send even one plant may involve the nursery in substantial postage and packing costs. Some nurseries may not be prepared to send tender or bulky plants.

Where a nursery offers a **mail order only** service, this will be noted under **Opening Times** in the nursery entry. Many nurseries also offer an online mail order facility.

Export

Export refers to mail order beyond the European Union. Nurseries that are prepared to consider exporting are indicated. There is usually a substantial minimum charge and, in addition, all the costs of phytosanitary certificates and Customs have to be met by the purchaser.

Catalogue Cost

Some nurseries may not charge for their printed catalogues or may ask for a few stamps to bear the cost of postage, although a large (at least A5) stamped address envelope is always appreciated. Overseas customers should use an equivalent number of International Reply Coupons (IRC) in place of stamps.

If catalogues (or plant lists) are available in an electronic format, some nurseries have indicated that they will email them to enquirers.

An increasing number of nurseries now publish their catalogues only on the internet as this is more cost-effective for them than producing a printed copy and enables them to reflect stock changes throughout the year.

Wheelchair Access ♿

Nurseries are asked to indicate if their premises are suitable for wheelchair users. Where only partial access is indicated, this is noted in the **Notes** field and the nursery is not marked with the symbol.

The assessment of ease-of-access is entirely the responsibility of the individual nursery.

Specialities

Nurseries list here the plants or genera that they supply and any National Collections of plants they may hold. Please note that some nurseries may charge an entry fee to visit a National Collection. Always enquire before visiting. Charges may also be levied to visit a garden attached to the nursery.

Nurseries will also note here if they only have small quantities of individual plants available for sale or if they will propagate to order.

Notes

In this section, you will find notes on any restrictions to mail order or export; on limited wheelchair access; or the nursery site address, if this differs from the office address; together with any other non-horticultural information.

Delivery to Shows

Many nurseries will deliver pre-ordered plants to flower shows for collection by customers. Contact the nursery for details of shows they will be attending.

Payment in Euros

A number of UK nurseries have indicated that they will accept payment in Euros. You should, however, check with the nursery concerned before making such a payment, as some will only accept cash and some only cheques, whilst others will expect the purchaser to pay bank charges.

Maps

If you wish to visit a nursery you can find its approximate location on the relevant map (following p.933), unless the nursery has requested this is not shown. Nurseries are also encouraged to provide their Ordnance Survey national grid reference for use with OS publications such as the Land Ranger series.

Nursery Index by Name

For convenience, an alphabetical index of nurseries is included (*page 927*). This gives the names of all nurseries listed in the book in alphabetical order of nursery name together with their code.

Deleted Nurseries

Every year some nurseries ask to be removed from the book. This may be a temporary measure because, for example, they are relocating or because their plant stocks are low due to adverse growing conditions, or it may be permanent following closure, sale, retirement or a change in the way they trade.

Occasionally, nurseries are unable to meet the closing date and may ask to re-enter the book in the following edition.

Some nurseries simply do not respond at all and, as we have no current information on them, they are not included in the book.

Please, never use an out of date edition

Nursery Details by Code

Please note that all these nurseries are listed in alphabetical order by their code. All nurseries are listed in alphabetical order by their name in the **Nursery Index by Name** on page 927.

South West

CAbb **Abbotsbury Sub-Tropical Gardens** ♿
Abbotsbury, Nr Weymouth, Dorset DT3 4LA
Ⓣ (01305) 871344
Ⓕ (01305) 871344
Ⓔ info@abbotsburygardens.co.uk
Ⓦ www.abbotsburyplantsales.co.uk
Contact: David Sutton
Opening Times: 1000-1800 daily, mid Mar-1st Nov. 1000-1500, Nov-mid Mar.
Min Mail Order UK: Nmc
Credit Cards: Access, Visa, MasterCard, Switch
Specialities: Less common & tender shrubs incl. palms, tree ferns, bamboos & plants from Australia, New Zealand & S. Africa.
Notes: Wheelchair accessible.

CAbP **Abbey Plants** ♿
Chaffeymoor, Bourton, Gillingham, Dorset SP8 5BY
Ⓣ (01747) 840841
Contact: K Potts
Opening Times: 1000-1300 & 1400-1700 Wed-Sat, Mar-Nov. Dec-Feb by appt.
Min Mail Order UK: Nmc
Cat. Cost: 2 × 2nd class.
Credit Cards: None
Specialities: Flowering trees & shrubs.
Notes: Wheelchair accessible.
Map Ref: C, B4 **OS Grid Ref:** ST762304

CAby **The Abbey Nursery** ♿
Forde Abbey, Chard, Somerset TA20 4LU
Ⓣ (01460) 220088
Ⓔ theabbeynursery@hotmail.com
Contact: Paul Bygrave
Opening Times: 1000-1700 7 days, 1st Mar-31st Oct.
Cat. Cost: None issued.
Credit Cards: All major credit/debit cards
Specialities: Hardy herbaceous perennials.
Notes: Wheelchair accessible.
Map Ref: C, C4 **OS Grid Ref:** ST359052

CAgr **Agroforestry Research Trust**
46 Hunters Moon, Dartington, Totnes, Devon TQ9 6JT
Ⓕ (01803) 840776
Ⓔ mail@agroforestry.co.uk
Ⓦ www.agroforestry.co.uk
Contact: Martin Crawford
Opening Times: Not open. Mail order only.
Min Mail Order UK: Nmc
Min Mail Order EU: Nmc
Cat. Cost: 4 × 1st class.
Credit Cards: All major credit/debit cards
Specialities: Top & soft fruit, nut trees incl. *Castanea, Corylus, Juglans, Pinus*. Also seeds. Some plants in small quantities only.
Notes: Euro accepted.

CAni **Anita Allen**
Shapcott Barton Estate, East Knowstone, South Molton, Devon EX36 4EE
Ⓣ (01398) 341664
Contact: Anita Allen
Opening Times: By appt. only. Garden open under NGS & Plant Heritage.
Min Mail Order UK: Nmc
Cat. Cost: 5 × 1st class & state which catalogue: Shasta daisies or *Buddleja*.
Credit Cards: None
Specialities: National Collections of *Leucanthemum* × *superbum* & *Buddleja davidii* & hybrids, 70+ cvs. 80+ accurately named Shasta daisies, a few in very short supply. Also many hardy perennials. Some *Buddleja* propagated to order.
Map Ref: C, B3 **OS Grid Ref:** SS846235

CArg **Ashridge Trees Ltd** ◆
Grove Cross Barn, Castle Cary, Somerset BA7 7NJ
Ⓣ (01963) 359444
Ⓕ (01963) 359445
Ⓔ support@ashridgetrees.co.uk
Ⓦ www.ashridgetrees.co.uk

Contact: Catherine Young
Opening Times: 0900-1730, Mon-Fri.
Min Mail Order UK: £20.00
Credit Cards: MasterCard, Visa
Specialities: Trees, hedging & fruit.

CArn **Arne Herbs** ♿
Limeburn Nurseries, Limeburn Hill,
Chew Magna, Bristol
BS40 8QW
Ⓣ (01275) 333399
Ⓔ arneherbs@aol.com
Ⓦ www.arneherbs.co.uk
Contact: A Lyman-Dixon & Jenny Thomas
Opening Times: By appt. only.
Min Mail Order UK: Nmc
Min Mail Order EU: Nmc
Cat. Cost: Online only.
Specialities: Herbs, some very rare. North American, Mediterranean & UK wild flowers. Also plants for research, conservation projects & historical recreations.
Notes: Euro accepted. Wheelchair accessible.
Map Ref: C, A5 **OS Grid Ref:** ST563638

CAvo **Avon Bulbs**
Burnt House Farm, Mid-Lambrook,
South Petherton, Somerset
TA13 5HE
Ⓣ (01460) 242177 or 249060
Ⓕ (01460) 249025
Ⓔ info@avonbulbs.co.uk
Ⓦ www.avonbulbs.co.uk
Contact: C Ireland-Jones
Opening Times: Mail order only. Collection of pre-booked orders by arrangement.
Min Mail Order UK: Nmc
Min Mail Order EU: Nmc
Cat. Cost: 4 × 2nd class.
Credit Cards: All major credit/debit cards
Specialities: Some special snowdrops are only available in small quantities.
Notes: Delivers to some shows.
Map Ref: C, B5 **OS Grid Ref:** ST422187

CBar **Barters Plant Centre & Nursery** ♿
Chapmanslade, Westbury, Wiltshire
BA13 4AL
Ⓣ (01373) 832694
Ⓕ (01373) 832677
Ⓔ plantcentre@barters.co.uk
Ⓦ www.barters.co.uk
Contact: Andrew Stone
Opening Times: 0900-1700 Mon-Thu, 0900-1730 Fri & Sat, summer. 0900-1630 Mon-Thu, 0900-1700 Fri & Sat, winter. 1030-1630 Sun.
Cat. Cost: None issued.
Credit Cards: All, except American Express
Specialities: Wide range of shrubs. Ground cover, container trees, ferns, half-hardy perennials, grasses, herbaceous & climbers. Hedging, fruit trees, old fashioned roses & bare-root stock.
Notes: Also sells wholesale. Wheelchair accessible.
Map Ref: C, B5 **OS Grid Ref:** ST830480

CBcs **Burncoose Nurseries** ♿
Gwennap, Redruth, Cornwall TR16 6BJ
Ⓣ (01209) 860316
Ⓕ (01209) 860011
Ⓔ info@burncoose.co.uk
Ⓦ www.burncoose.co.uk
Contact: C H Williams
Opening Times: 0830-1700 Mon-Sat & 1100-1700 Sun.
Min Mail Order UK: Nmc
Min Mail Order EU: Individual quotations for EU sales.
Cat. Cost: Free
Credit Cards: Visa, MasterCard, Maestro
Specialities: Extensive range of over 3500 ornamental trees & shrubs and herbaceous. Rare & unusual *Magnolia*, *Rhododendron*. Conservatory plants. 30 acre garden.
Notes: Also sells wholesale. Delivers to shows. Wheelchair accessible.

CBct **Barracott Plants** ♿
Old Orchard, Calstock Road, Gunnislake,
Cornwall PL18 9AA
Ⓣ (01822) 832234
Ⓜ 07811 207186
Ⓔ geoffandthelma@barracott.eclipse.co.uk
Ⓦ www.barracottplants.co.uk
Contact: Geoff & Thelma Turner
Opening Times: 0900-1700 Thu & Fri, Mar-end Sep. Other times by appt.
Min Mail Order UK: Nmc
Cat. Cost: 1st class stamp.
Credit Cards: None
Specialities: Herbaceous plants: shade-loving, foliage & form. *Acanthus*, *Aspidistra*, *Astrantia*, *Bergenia*, *Convallaria*, *Disporum*, *Liriope*, *Maianthemum*, *Polygonatum*, *Roscoea*, *Trillium* & *Uvularia*.
Notes: Also sells wholesale. Delivers to shows. Euro accepted. Wheelchair accessible.
Map Ref: C, C3 **OS Grid Ref:** SX436702

CBen **Bennetts Water Gardens**
Putton Lane, Chickerell, Weymouth, Dorset
DT3 4AF
Ⓣ (01305) 785150
Ⓔ info@waterlily.co.uk
Ⓦ www.waterlily.co.uk
Contact: James Bennett
Opening Times: 1000-1700 Apr-Sep, Sun-Fri.
Min Mail Order UK: Nmc
Min Mail Order EU: Nmc

C

Credit Cards: Visa, MasterCard, JCB, Maestro
Specialities: National Collection of *Nymphaea* (hardy water lilies).
Notes: Loose plants available by mail order. Potted plants available in store. Partially wheelchair accessible.
Map Ref: C, C5 **OS Grid Ref:** SY650797

CBgR **Beggar's Roost Plants**
Lilstock, Bridgwater, Somerset TA5 1SU
Ⓣ (01278) 741519
Ⓔ ro@lilstock.eclipse.co.uk
Ⓦ www.ladyrosemaryfitzgerald.co.uk
Contact: Lady Rosemary FitzGerald
Opening Times: Not open. Mail order only.
Min Mail Order UK: £10.00
Min Mail Order EU: £15.00
Cat. Cost: 3 × large 2nd class.
Credit Cards: None
Specialities: *Hemerocallis* (incl. heritage) grown in British conditions.
Notes: Mail order for specialities *Hemerocallis*. Ask for list. Euro accepted.
Map Ref: C, B4 **OS Grid Ref:** ST168450

CBlu **Blue Nurseries Ltd**
(Office) Brook Cottage, 2 Bleet, Steeple Ashton, Wiltshire BA14 6EA
Ⓜ 07745 067119 or 07813 894026
Ⓔ office@bluenurseries.com
Ⓦ www.bluenurseries.com
Contact: Richard Hill
Opening Times: Not open. Mail order only.
Min Mail Order UK: £4.95
Min Mail Order EU: £6.95
Cat. Cost: Online only.
Credit Cards: Paypal
Specialities: South African plants & hardy palms with slowly expanding range of plants but focussed on the architectural & rare.
Notes: Online-based but displays at plant and horticultural shows. Euros accepted via Paypal only. Also sells wholesale.

CBod **Bodmin Nursery** ♿
Laveddon Mill, Laninval Hill, Bodmin, Cornwall PL30 5JU
Ⓣ (01208) 72837
Ⓕ (01208) 76491
Ⓔ bodminnursery@aol.com
Ⓦ www.bodminnursery.co.uk
Contact: Mark Lawlor
Opening Times: 0900-1700 Mon-Sat. 1000-1600 Sun.
Credit Cards: All major credit/debit cards
Specialities: Herbs, herbaceous & grasses, hardy geraniums & coastal plants. Interesting shrubs, fruit & ornamental trees.
Notes: Wheelchair accessible.
Map Ref: C, C2 **OS Grid Ref:** SX053659

CBot **The Botanic Nursery**
Coombe Lane, Atworth, Nr Melksham, Wiltshire SN12 8NU
Ⓜ 07850 328756
Ⓔ office@botanicnursery.co.uk
Ⓦ www.botanicnursery.co.uk
Contact: Terence Baker
Opening Times: 1000-1700 Tue-Sat, Mar-Oct.
Min Mail Order UK: 5 plugs or 3 plants.
Min Mail Order EU: Nmc
Cat. Cost: Online only.
Credit Cards: MasterCard, Visa
Specialities: Specialists in propagation of rare shrubs. All plants are lime-tolerant. National Collection of *Digitalis*.
Notes: Mail order Oct-Mar. Plugs also available, see website or contact nursery. Delivers to shows. Only partially accessible for wheelchairs.
Map Ref: C, A5 **OS Grid Ref:** ST852655

CBre **Bregover Plants**
Middlewood, North Hill, Nr Launceston, Cornwall PL15 7NN
Ⓣ (01566) 782661
Ⓔ jenbousfield@gmail.com
Contact: Jennifer Bousfield
Opening Times: 1100-1700 Wed, Mar-mid Oct and by appt.
Min Mail Order UK: Nmc
Min Mail Order EU: Nmc
Cat. Cost: 3 × 1st class. Plant list available as PDF download.
Credit Cards: None
Specialities: Unusual hardy perennials grown in small garden nursery. Available in small quantities only.
Notes: Mail order Oct-Mar only. Delivers to shows.
Map Ref: C, C2 **OS Grid Ref:** SX273752

CBro **Broadleigh Gardens** ♿
Bishops Hull, Taunton, Somerset TA4 1AE
Ⓣ (01823) 286231
Ⓕ (01823) 323646
Ⓔ info@broadleighbulbs.co.uk
Ⓦ www.broadleighbulbs.co.uk
Contact: Lady Skelmersdale
Opening Times: 0900-1600 Mon-Fri for viewing only (charity donation). Orders may be collected if notice given.
Min Mail Order UK: Nmc
Min Mail Order EU: Nmc
Cat. Cost: 2 × 1st class.
Credit Cards: All major credit/debit cards
Specialities: January catalogue: bulbs in growth (*Galanthus*, *Cyclamen* etc.) & herbaceous woodland plants (trilliums, hellebores etc). Extensive list of *Agapanthus*.

June catalogue: dwarf & unusual bulbs, *Iris* (DB & PC). National Collection of Alec Grey hybrid daffodils.
Notes: Delivers to shows. Euro accepted as cash payment only. Wheelchair accessible.
Map Ref: C, B4 **OS Grid Ref:** ST195251

CBrP **Brooklands Plants**
25 Treves Road, Dorchester,
Dorset DT1 2HE
Ⓣ (01305) 265846
Ⓔ cycads@btinternet.com
Ⓦ botanicalgardenphotography.com
Contact: Ian Watt
Opening Times: By appt. only for collection of plants.
Min Mail Order UK: £25.00 + p&p
Cat. Cost: 2 × 2nd class or by email.
Credit Cards: None
Specialities: Cycad nursery specialising in the more cold-tolerant species of *Encephalartos*, *Dioon*, *Macrozamia* & *Cycas*. Also specialist in cold-tolerant palms as well as plants from New Zealand. Some species available in small quantities only.
Notes: Euro accepted.
Map Ref: C, C5 **OS Grid Ref:** SY682897

CBur **Burnham Nurseries**
Forches Cross, Newton Abbot, Devon
TQ12 6PZ
Ⓣ (01626) 352233
Ⓔ mail@orchids.uk.com
Ⓦ www.orchids.uk.com
Contact: Any member of staff
Opening Times: 1000-1600 Mon-Sun.
Min Mail Order UK: Nmc
Min Mail Order EU: £100.00 + p&p
Cat. Cost: 1 × 2nd class or online.
Credit Cards: Visa, MasterCard, Maestro
Specialities: Many types of tropical orchid species and hybrids.
Notes: Exports beyond EU, please ask for details. Delivers to shows. Euro accepted. Partial wheelchair accessiblity.
Map Ref: C, C4 **OS Grid Ref:** SX841732

CCac **Cactus Shop** ♿
Caldicott, Winkleigh, Devon
EX19 8DW
Ⓣ (01837) 83610
Ⓜ 07586 880472
Ⓕ (01837) 83610
Ⓔ ralph@cactusshop.co.uk
Ⓦ www.cactusshop.co.uk
Contact: Ralph Northcott
Opening Times: 1000-1600 daily.
Min Mail Order UK: Nmc
Min Mail Order EU: Nmc
Cat. Cost: Online only.
Credit Cards: All major credit/debit cards
Specialities: Epiphytes. Cacti hardy in the UK.
Notes: Also sells wholesale. Exports beyond EU. Euro accepted. Delivers to shows. Wheelchair accessible.
Map Ref: C, C3 **OS Grid Ref:** SS 61815 09718

CChe **Cherry Tree Nursery** ♿
(Sheltered Work Opportunities Project)
off New Road Roundabout, Northbourne,
Bournemouth, Dorset BH10 7DA
Ⓣ (01202) 593537
Ⓕ (01202) 590626
Ⓔ contactus@cherrytreenursery.org.uk
Ⓦ www.cherrytreenursery.org.uk
Contact: Stephen Jailler
Opening Times: 0830-1530 Mon-Fri, 0900-1500 Sat, Apr-Sep & 0900-1300 Sat, Oct-Mar. 1000-1500 Sun, Apr to Jul.
Cat. Cost: A4 sae + £2.20 stamps.
Credit Cards: All, except American Express
Specialities: Hardy shrubs, perennials, climbers, grasses & bamboos.
Notes: A registered charity providing work for adults with severe and enduring mental illness. Also sells wholesale. Debit cards accepted. Wheelchair accessible.
Map Ref: C, C6 **OS Grid Ref:** SZ 08335 96581

CCht **Chestnut Nursery** ♿
(Sheltered Work Opportunities Project)
75 Kingland Road, Poole, Dorset
BH15 1TN
Ⓣ (01202) 685999
Ⓔ info@chestnutnursery.org.uk
Ⓦ www.chestnutnursery.org.uk
Contact: Angela Mansbridge
Opening Times: 0830-1530 Mon-Fri, 1000-1530 Sat.
Specialities: Wide variety of perennials, shrubs, ornamental grasses and seasonal crops.
Notes: A registered charity providing work for adults with severe and enduring mental illness. Wheelchair accessible.
Map Ref: C, C6 **OS Grid Ref:** SZ018909

CCon **Constantine Garden Nursery** ♿
Tresahor, Constantine, Falmouth, Cornwall
TR11 5PL
Ⓣ (01326) 340593
Ⓔ plants@cornwallgardens.com
Ⓦ www.cornwallgardens.com
Contact: Sorcha Hitchcox
Opening Times: 1000-1700 Wed-Sat, 1100-1600 Sun, Feb-Sep. By appt. Oct-Jan.
Min Mail Order UK: £15.00 + p&p
Min Mail Order EU: £40.00 + p&p
Cat. Cost: 6 × 1st class.
Credit Cards: Access, Delta, Switch, Visa

C

Specialities: Over 4000 varieties of cottage garden & rare perennials with many specialities. Also 80 varieties of *Clematis*. Some rare varieties available in small quantities only.
Notes: Display gardens. Dogs welcome. Free planting plans. Expert advice. Garden design. Horticultural courses. Plenty of car parking. Tea, coffee & cake. Delivers to shows. Euro accepted. Wheelchair accessible.
Map Ref: C, D1

CCse **CHASE PLANTS**
Hookswood Cottage, Farnham, Blandford Forum, Dorset DT11 8DQ
Ⓣ (01725) 516394
Ⓔ sales@chaseplants.co.uk
Contact: Sue Lees & Eddie Wheatley
Opening Times: By appt. only.
Min Mail Order UK: £10.00
Cat. Cost: Large 1st class.
Credit Cards: None
Specialities: Hardy perennials, shrubs & some conservatory plants.
Notes: Delivers to shows.

CCVN **CULM VIEW NURSERY**
Waterloo Farm, Clayhidon, Devon EX15 3TN
Ⓣ (01823) 680698
Ⓔ plants@culmviewnursery.co.uk
Ⓦ www.culmviewnursery.co.uk
Contact: Brian & Alison Jacobs
Opening Times: By appt. only for collection.
Min Mail Order UK: Nmc
Min Mail Order EU: Nmc
Credit Cards: Paypal
Specialities: Hebaceous perennials grown in peat-free compost.
Notes: Mail order seed & some plants. Exports beyond EU. Delivers to shows.

CCVT **CHEW VALLEY TREES** ♿
Winford Road, Chew Magna, Bristol BS40 8HJ
Ⓣ (01275) 333752
Ⓔ info@chewvalleytrees.co.uk
Ⓦ www.chewvalleytrees.co.uk
Contact: S Scarth
Opening Times: 0800-1700 Mon-Fri all year. 0900-1600 Sat. Closed Sun. Closed B/hols & Sats Jul & Aug.
Min Mail Order UK: Nmc
Cat. Cost: Free.
Credit Cards: All major credit/debit cards
Specialities: Native British & ornamental trees, shrubs, fruit trees & hedging.
Notes: Also sells wholesale. Wheelchair accessible.
Map Ref: C, A5 **OS Grid Ref:** ST558635

CDes **DESIRABLE PLANTS**
(Office) Pentamar, Crosspark, Totnes, Devon TQ9 5BQ
Ⓣ (01803) 864489 evenings
Ⓔ desirableplants@gmail.com
Ⓦ www.desirableplants.com
Contact: Sarah & Julian Sutton
Opening Times: Not open. Mail order only.
Min Mail Order UK: £15.00
Cat. Cost: 4 × 2nd class. During 2014 changing to twice-yearly, short-lived availability lists by email (print-outs available for those without internet access).
Credit Cards: None
Specialities: Choice & interesting bulbs & perennials by mail order. Emphasis moving towards dormant bulbs, many uncommon, & in small numbers.
Notes: Nursery not at this address.

CDob **DOBIES OF DEVON**
Long Road, Paignton, Devon TQ4 7SX
Ⓣ 0844 701 7623
Ⓕ 0844 701 7624
Ⓦ www.dobies.co.uk
Contact: Customer Services
Opening Times: Not open. Mail order only. Phone line open 0830-1700 Mon-Fri (office). Also answerphone.
Min Mail Order UK: Nmc
Min Mail Order EU: £5.00
Cat. Cost: Free.
Credit Cards: Delta, MasterCard, Switch, Visa
Specialities: Wide selection of popular flower & vegetable seeds. Also includes young plants, summer-flowering bulbs & garden sundries.
Notes: Mail order to UK & Rep. of Ireland only.

CDoC **DUCHY OF CORNWALL** ◆
Cott Road, Lostwithiel, Cornwall PL22 0HW
Ⓣ (01208) 872668
Ⓕ 01208 871809
Ⓔ sales@duchyofcornwallnursery.co.uk
Ⓦ www.duchyofcornwallnursery.co.uk
Contact: Jim Stephens
Opening Times: 0900-1700 Mon-Sat, 1000-1700 Sun & B/hols.
Min Mail Order UK: £10.00
Cat. Cost: None issued.
Credit Cards: All major credit/debit cards
Specialities: *Camellia*, *Fuchsia*, conifers & *Magnolia*. Also a huge range of garden plants incl. trees, shrubs, roses, perennials, fruit & conservatory plants.
Notes: Nursery partially accessible to wheelchair users.
Map Ref: C, C2 **OS Grid Ref:** SX112614

CDoy **Caradoc Doy**
PO Box 28, Exeter, Devon EX3 0WY
Ⓣ (01392) 877225
Ⓕ (01392) 877225
Ⓔ info@caradocdoy.co.uk
Ⓦ www.caradocdoy.co.uk
Contact: Caradoc Doy
Opening Times: Open by appt. only.
Min Mail Order UK: Nmc
Cat. Cost: Online.
Credit Cards: All major credit/debit cards
Specialities: Olive trees.
Notes: Euro accepted.

CDTJ **Desert to Jungle** ♿
Henlade Garden Nursery, Lower Henlade, Taunton, Somerset TA3 5NB
Ⓣ (01823) 443701
Ⓕ (01458) 250521
Ⓔ plants@deserttojungle.com
Ⓦ www.deserttojungle.com
Contact: Rob Gudge
Opening Times: 1000-1700 Mon, Tues & Thu-Sun (closed Wed), 1st Mar-31st Oct. Thu, Fri & Sat only Nov-Feb. Opening times may vary during RHS shows, so please phone to check.
Min Mail Order UK: Nmc
Credit Cards: All major credit/debit cards
Specialities: Exotic-looking plants giving a desert or jungle effect in the garden. Incl. *Agave*, *Canna*, aroids, succulents, ferns, tree ferns & bamboos.
Notes: Nursery shares drive with Mount Somerset Hotel. Also sells wholesale. Delivers to shows. Wheelchair accessible.
Map Ref: C, B4 **OS Grid Ref:** ST273232

CDul **Dulford Nurseries** ♿
Cullompton, Devon EX15 2BY
Ⓣ (01884) 266361
Ⓔ dulford.nurseries@virgin.net
Ⓦ www.dulford-nurseries.co.uk
Contact: Paul Rawlings
Opening Times: 0730-1630 Mon-Fri.
Min Mail Order UK: Nmc
Min Mail Order EU: Nmc
Cat. Cost: Free.
Credit Cards: All major credit/debit cards
Specialities: Native, ornamental & unusual trees, hedging & shrubs incl. oaks, maples, beech, birch, chestnut, lime, *Malus*, *Sorbus* & pines.
Notes: Wheelchair accessible.
Map Ref: C, C4 **OS Grid Ref:** SY062062

CEls **Elsworth Herbs**
Farthingwood, Broadway, Sidmouth, Devon EX10 8HS
Ⓣ (01395) 578689
Ⓔ john.twibell@btinternet.com
Contact: Drs J D & J M Twibell
Opening Times: By appt. only.
Min Mail Order UK: £10.00
Cat. Cost: By email only.
Credit Cards: None
Specialities: National Collection of *Artemisia*. Wide range of *Artemisia*. Stock available in small quantities only. Orders may require propagation from Collection material, for which we are the primary reference source.
Notes: Mail order only on small scale in exceptional situations. Partially accessible for wheelchairs.
Map Ref: C, C4 **OS Grid Ref:** SY119881

CElw **Elworthy Cottage Plants** ♿
Elworthy Cottage, Elworthy, Nr Lydeard St Lawrence, Taunton, Somerset TA4 3PX
Ⓣ (01984) 656427
Ⓔ mike@elworthy-cottage.co.uk
Ⓦ www.elworthy-cottage.co.uk
Contact: Mrs J M Spiller
Opening Times: 1000-1700 Thu, late Mar-end Aug. Also by appt. Feb-Oct.
Cat. Cost: 3 × 2nd class.
Credit Cards: None
Specialities: Unusual herbaceous plants esp. hardy *Geranium*, *Geum*, *Crocosmia*, *Monarda*, *Phlox*, *Pulmonaria* & *Epimedium*. Some varieties only available in small quantities. *Galanthus* available by mail order in Feb.
Notes: Nursery on B3188, 5 miles north of Wiveliscombe, in centre of Elworthy village. Delivers to shows. Wheelchair accessible.
Map Ref: C, B4 **OS Grid Ref:** ST084349

CEnt **Entwood Farm Plants**
Harcombe, Lyme Regis, Dorset DT7 3RN
Ⓣ (01297) 444034
Ⓔ jennyhlyme@hotmail.co.uk
Contact: Jenny & Ivan Harding
Opening Times: By prior arrangement only.
Credit Cards: None
Specialities: Bamboo specialist. Plus selection of shrubs & perennials. Some stock in small quantities.
Notes: Delivers to shows.
Map Ref: C, C4 **OS Grid Ref:** SY335953

CEvo **Evolution Plants**
19a Lower South Wraxall, Bradford on Avon, Wiltshire BA15 2RU
Ⓣ (01225) 867761
Ⓜ 07788 747869
Ⓔ info@evolution-plants.com
Ⓦ www.evolution-plants.com
Contact: Helen Bailey
Opening Times: Mail order only. Not open except by prior appt.
Min Mail Order UK: Nmc

Min Mail Order EU: Nmc
Credit Cards: All, except American Express
Specialities: Specialist nursery with a broad list with emphasis on plants grown from wild-collected seed. *Acer, Agapanthus, Crocosmia, Epimedium, Galanthus, Helleborus* (species), *Iris, Paeonia, Trillium* & *Veratrum.*
Notes: Exports beyond EU. Euro accepted.

CExl **EXCLUSIVE PLANTS NURSERY**
Tretawn, High Cross, Constantine, Falmouth, Cornwall TR11 5RE
Ⓣ (01326) 341496
Ⓜ 07775 811385
Ⓕ (01326) 341496
Ⓔ info@exclusiveplants.com
Ⓦ www.exclusiveplants.com
Contact: Paul Bonavia
Opening Times: Weekends or by appt. only.
Min Mail Order UK: Nmc
Min Mail Order EU: £25.00
Cat. Cost: 2 × 1st class.
Credit Cards: All major credit/debit cards
Specialities: A plantsperson's nursery, offering rare & unusual plants from around the world. Also new introductions & the best form of our better known plants.
Notes: Euro accepted.

CFen **FENTONGOLLAN FARM** ♿
Merther Lane, St Michael Penkivel, Tresillian, Truro, Cornwall TR2 4AQ
Ⓣ (01872) 520209
Ⓕ (01872) 520606
Ⓔ admin@flowerfarm.co.uk
Ⓦ www.flowerfarm.co.uk
Contact: James Hosking
Opening Times: 0900-1700 7 days, Aug-end Nov.
Min Mail Order UK: Nmc
Min Mail Order EU: Nmc
Cat. Cost: Free.
Credit Cards: All major credit/debit cards
Specialities: *Narcissus.*
Notes: Also sells wholesale. Delivers to shows. Euro accepted. Wheelchair accessible.
Map Ref: C, D2

CFil **FILLAN'S PLANTS**
Tuckermarsh Gardens, Yelverton, Devon PL20 7HN
Ⓣ (01822) 841551
Ⓜ 07813 161276
Ⓕ (01822) 841551
Ⓔ fillansplants@yahoo.co.uk
Ⓦ www.tuckermarshplants.co.uk
Contact: Mark Fillan
Opening Times: By appt. only. Please phone or email.
Min Mail Order UK: Nmc

Min Mail Order EU: £50.00
Cat. Cost: 4 × 1st class
Credit Cards: None
Specialities: *Hydrangea* & unusual woody plants. Some plants available in small quanitities only.
Notes: Also sells wholesale.

CFis **MARGERY FISH PLANT NURSERY** ♿
East Lambrook Manor Gardens, East Lambrook, South Petherton, Somerset TA13 5HH
Ⓣ (01460) 240328
Ⓜ 07710 484745
Ⓔ enquiries@eastlambrook.com
Ⓦ www.eastlambrook.com
Contact: Tom Wild
Opening Times: 1000-1700 Tue-Sat, Feb-Oct, plus B/hol Mons & Suns Feb, May-Jul. Nov-Jan by appt.
Cat. Cost: None issued.
Credit Cards: All major credit/debit cards
Specialities: Hardy geraniums & cottage garden herbaceous plants. Stock available in small quantities only. Major collection of hardy geraniums on site.
Notes: Wheelchair accessible.
Map Ref: C, B5 **OS Grid Ref:** ST431188

CFlo **FLOYDS CLIMBERS AND CLEMATIS**
36 Dowding Drive, Lower Compton, Calne, Wiltshire SN11 8QL
Ⓣ (01249) 823200
Ⓜ 07762 499416
Ⓔ sales@floydsclimbers.co.uk
Ⓦ www.floydsclimbers.co.uk
Contact: Marcel Floyd
Opening Times: Open w/ends twice a year. See website or phone for dates.
Min Mail Order UK: Nmc
Credit Cards: Paypal
Specialities: *Clematis* and climbers.
Notes: Also sells wholesale. Euro accepted. Delivers to shows.
Map Ref: C, A6

CFst **FOREST EDGE NURSERIES**
Verwood Road, Woodlands, Wimborne, Dorset, BH21 8LJ
Ⓣ (01202) 829564
Ⓕ (01202) 829564
Ⓔ heathers@forestedgenurseries.co.uk
Ⓦ www.forestedgenurseries.co.uk
Contact: David Edge
Opening Times: 0900-1630 Mon. Collection available by arrangement on other days.
Cat. Cost: £2.00
Credit Cards: Paypal
Specialities: Heathers: *Calluna, Erica, Daboecia.*

Notes: Also sells wholesale. Euro accepted.
Map Ref: C, B6

CFwr **The Flower Bower**
Woodlands, Shurton, Stogursey,
Nr Bridgwater, Somerset
TA5 1QE
Ⓣ (01278) 732134
Ⓔ theflowerbower@yahoo.co.uk
Ⓦ www.theflowerbower.co.uk
Contact: Sheila Tucker
Opening Times: By appt. only. Visitors welcome during bloom times: May-Jul for *Epiphyllum* & May-Sep for daylilies.
Min Mail Order UK: Nmc
Min Mail Order EU: Nmc
Cat. Cost: Online only.
Credit Cards: None
Specialities: *Hemerocallis*, esp. newer varieties & spiders. Over 700 varieties of *Epiphyllum*. National Collection of *Epiphyllum*.
Notes: Daylilies: newer & rarer varieties mostly available in small quantities. *Epiphyllum*: please send email address to obtain a link to the list.
Map Ref: C, B4 **OS Grid Ref:** ST203442

CGrW **The Great Western Gladiolus Nursery**
17 Valley View, Clutton, Bristol
BS39 5SN
Ⓣ (01761) 452036
Ⓔ clutton.glads@btinternet.com
Ⓦ www.greatwesterngladiolus.co.uk
Contact: G F Hazell
Opening Times: Mail order only. Open by appt. only.
Min Mail Order UK: Nmc
Min Mail Order EU: Nmc
Cat. Cost: 4 × 1st class (2 catalogues).
Credit Cards: None
Specialities: *Gladiolus* species & hybrids, corms & seeds. Other South African bulbous plants. Only available in small quantities.
Notes: Also sells wholesale. Euro accepted.

CHab **Habitat Aid Ltd.**
Hookgate Cottage, South Brewham,
Somerset BA10 0LQ
Ⓣ (01749) 812355
Ⓔ info@habitataid.co.uk
Ⓦ www.habitataid.co.uk
Contact: Nick Mann
Opening Times: Not open. Mail order only.
Min Mail Order UK: £50.00, incl. p&p.
Cat. Cost: None issued.
Credit Cards: All major credit/debit cards
Specialities: British trees, wildflowers and seeds. Local provenance seed mixes. Native aquatic plants. Cottage garden perennials. Heritage fruit trees.
Notes: Also sells wholesale. Delivers to shows.

CHby **The Herbary**
161 Chapel Street, Horningsham,
Warminster, Wiltshire
BA12 7LU
Ⓣ (01985) 844442
Ⓔ info@beansandherbs.co.uk
Ⓦ www.beansandherbs.co.uk
Contact: Pippa Rosen
Opening Times: May-Sep strictly by appt. only.
Min Mail Order UK: Nmc
Min Mail Order EU: Nmc
Cat. Cost: Online only.
Credit Cards: None
Specialities: Culinary, medicinal & aromatic herbs organically grown in small quantities.
Notes: Mail order for seed only and all year for organic vegetable seed & large variety of organic bean & herb seed. Also sells wholesale. Euro accepted.

CHew **Hewitt-Cooper Carnivorous Plants**
The Homestead, Glastonbury Road,
West Pennard, Somerset BA6 8NN
Ⓣ (01458) 832844
Ⓕ (01458) 832712
Ⓔ sales@hccarnivorousplants.co.uk
Ⓦ www.hccarnivorousplants.co.uk
Contact: Nigel Hewitt-Cooper
Opening Times: By appt.
Min Mail Order UK: £10.00 + p&p
Min Mail Order EU: £30.00
Cat. Cost: 1 × 1st class/1 × IRC.
Credit Cards: All major credit/debit cards
Specialities: Carnivorous plants.
Notes: Mail order May-Nov. Euro accepted. Delivers to shows.

CHGN **High Garden Nurseries** ♿
Chiverstone Lane, Kenton, Exeter, Devon
EX6 8NJ
Ⓣ (01626) 899106
Ⓔ highgarden@highgarden.co.uk
Ⓦ highgardenkenton.wordpress.com
Contact: Chris Britton
Opening Times: 0900-1700 Tue-Fri
Cat. Cost: None issued.
Credit Cards: All major credit/debit cards
Specialities: Quality shrubs, trees & perennials, some unusual & different.
Notes: Wheelchair accessible.
Map Ref: C, C4 **OS Grid Ref:** SX957836

CHid **Hidden Valley Nursery**
Umberleigh, Devon EX37 9BU
Ⓣ (01769) 560567

Ⓜ 07899 788789
Ⓔ plalindley@itsosbroadband.co.uk
Contact: Linda & Peter Lindley
Opening Times: Daylight hours, but please phone first.
Cat. Cost: None issued.
Credit Cards: None
Specialities: Hardy perennials esp. shade lovers & Chatham Islands forget-me-nots (*Myosotidium hortensia*).
Notes: Nursery not easy to find using Sat Nav or Google Street Map. Delivers to shows. Euro accepted.
Map Ref: C, B3 **OS Grid Ref:** SS567205

CHII **HILL HOUSE NURSERY LTD**
Landscove, Nr Ashburton, Devon TQ13 7LY
Ⓣ (01803) 762273
Ⓔ bluebird@hillhousenursery.com
Ⓦ www.hillhousenursery.com
Contact: Raymond, Sacha & Matthew Hubbard
Opening Times: 1100-1700 7 days, all year. Open all B/hols incl. Easter Sun. Closed Friday before Xmas Eve for two weeks only. Tearoom open 1st Mar-30th Sep.
Min Mail Order UK: Nmc
Cat. Cost: None issued.
Credit Cards: Delta, MasterCard, Switch, Visa, Paypal
Specialities: 3000+ varieties of plants, most propagated on premises, many rare or unusual. The garden, open to the public, was laid out by Edward Hyams. Pioneers of glasshouse pest control by beneficial insects.
Notes: Groups welcome with prior notice. Also sells wholesale. Euro accepted. Tea room & garden wheelchair accessible, access limited in nursery.
Map Ref: C, C3 **OS Grid Ref:** SX774664

CHVG **HIDDEN VALLEY GARDENS** ♿
Treesmill, Nr Par, Cornwall PL24 2TU
Ⓣ (01208) 873225
Ⓔ hiddenvalleygardens@yahoo.co.uk
Ⓦ www.hiddenvalleygardens.co.uk
Contact: Mrs P Howard
Opening Times: 1000-1800 Thu-Mon (closed Tue & Wed), 20th Mar-15th Oct. Please phone for directions. Garden open as nursery.
Cat. Cost: None issued.
Credit Cards: All major credit/debit cards
Specialities: Cottage garden plants, *Dahlia* & many perennials which can be seen growing in the garden. Some stock available in small quantities. Display garden.
Notes: Award-winning Garden In Cornwall, 2010 & 2011. Euro accepted. Wheelchair accessible.
Map Ref: C, D2 **OS Grid Ref:** SX094567

CIri **THE IRIS GARDEN**
Yard House, Pilsdon, Bridport, Dorset, DT6 5PA
Ⓣ (01308) 868797
Ⓔ info@theirisgarden.co.uk
Ⓦ www.theirisgarden.co.uk
Contact: Clive Russell
Opening Times: Show garden open by appt. only. Please email or phone for details.
Cat. Cost: None issued.
Specialities: Modern bearded & beardless *Iris* from breeders in UK, USA, France, Italy & Australia. National Collection of Space Age *Iris*. Collection of 6-Fall & Novelty Bearded *Iris* in preparation for ratification.
Notes: No mail order or sales from website. Ordering in garden only. Plants can be ordered on site with a 25% deposit but customers must be prepared to return & collect at a later date. Euro accepted.
Map Ref: C, C5 **OS Grid Ref:** SY421988

CJun **JUNKER'S NURSERY LTD.**
Higher Cobhay, Milverton, Somerset TA4 1NJ
Ⓣ (01823) 400075
Ⓔ karan@junker.co.uk
Ⓦ www.junker.co.uk
Contact: Karan Junker
Opening Times: Strictly by appt. only.
Min Mail Order UK: Nmc
Min Mail Order EU: Nmc
Cat. Cost: 6 × 1st class.
Credit Cards: None
Specialities: Choice & unusual shrubs & trees incl. grafted *Acer palmatum*, *Cornus*, *Daphne*, *Magnolia*. Many available in larger, more mature sizes. Small quantities only of some hard to propagate plants, esp. daphnes.
Notes: Extensive planted areas showing how the plants look growing in "real world" conditions. We propagate & grow all our own plants with an increasing number grown naturally in open ground as well as in pots, incl. larger sizes. Limited wheelchair access.
Map Ref: C, B4

CKel **KELWAYS** ♿
Picts Hill, Langport, Somerset TA10 9EZ
Ⓣ (01458) 250521
Ⓕ (01458) 253351
Ⓔ sales@kelways.co.uk
Ⓦ www.kelways.co.uk
Contact: Dave Root, Andy Martin
Opening Times: 0900-1700 Mon-Fri, 0900-1700 Sat, 1000-1600 Sun.
Min Mail Order UK: £4.00 + p&p
Min Mail Order EU: £8.00 + p&p
Cat. Cost: Online only.
Credit Cards: All major credit/debit cards

Specialities: *Paeonia, Iris, Hemerocallis* & herbaceous perennials. Wide range of trees, shrubs & herbaceous. Hardy ferns & tree ferns.
Notes: Also sells wholesale. Exports beyond EU. Delivers to shows. Euro accepted. Wheelchair accessible.
Map Ref: C, B5 **OS Grid Ref:** ST434273

CKen **Kenwith Conifer Nursery (Gordon Haddow)** ♿
Blinsham, Nr Torrington, Beaford, Winkleigh, Devon EX19 8NT
Ⓣ (01805) 603274
Ⓕ (01805) 603663
Ⓔ info@kenwithconifernursery.co.uk
Ⓦ www.kenwithconifernursery.co.uk
Contact: Gordon Haddow
Opening Times: 1000-1630 Tue-Sat all year. Closed all B/hols. If travelling a long distance, please phone previous day to ensure nursery will be open.
Min Mail Order UK: £20 + p&p
Min Mail Order EU: £50 + p&p
Cat. Cost: Online only.
Credit Cards: MasterCard, Visa
Specialities: All conifer genera. Grafting a speciality.
Notes: Wheelchair accessible.
Map Ref: C, B3 **OS Grid Ref:** SS518160

CKno **Knoll Gardens**
Hampreston, Wimborne, Dorset BH21 7ND
Ⓣ (01202) 873931
Ⓕ (01202) 870842
Ⓔ enquiries@knollgardens.co.uk
Ⓦ www.knollgardens.co.uk
Contact: N R Lucas
Opening Times: 1000-1700 Tue-Sat, Feb-Dec. Open B/hol Mons. See website for further details.
Min Mail Order UK: Nmc
Min Mail Order EU: Nmc
Cat. Cost: £2.00 + 50p postage.
Credit Cards: MasterCard, Visa,
Specialities: Grasses (main specialism). Flowering perennials. National Collection of *Pennisetum*.
Notes: Also sells wholesale.
Map Ref: C, C6

CLak **Lakka Bulbs**
(Office) 127 Mill Street, Torrington, North Devon EX38 8AW
Ⓣ (01805) 625071
Ⓔ jonathan.hutchinson@talktalk.net
Contact: Jonathan Hutchinson
Opening Times: Not open. Mail order only.
Min Mail Order UK: Nmc
Min Mail Order EU: Nmc
Cat. Cost: None issued.
Credit Cards: None
Specialities: National Collections of *Veltheimia bracteata* & cvs and *Scadoxus*. All available in small quantities only.

CLAP **Long Acre Plants** ♿
South Marsh, Charlton Musgrove, Nr Wincanton, Somerset BA9 8EX
Ⓣ (01963) 32802
Ⓕ (01963) 32802
Ⓔ info@plantsforshade.co.uk
Ⓦ www.plantsforshade.co.uk
Contact: Nigel & Michelle Rowland
Opening Times: 0900-1300 & 1330-1630 Thu & Fri only, Mar-Jun, Sep & Oct.
Min Mail Order UK: £20.00 + p&p
Min Mail Order EU: Nmc
Cat. Cost: 3 × 1st class.
Credit Cards: MasterCard, Maestro, Visa,
Specialities: Ferns, woodland bulbs & perennials. Marginal/bog plants.
Notes: Some plants available in small numbers only and only seasonally available. Ship to EU in autumn and winter only. Delivers to shows. Wheelchair accessible.
Map Ref: C, B5

CLau **Laurel Farm Herbs**
Moorland Barn, Whiddon Down, Okehampton, Devon EX20 2QL
Ⓣ Not available at time of going to print. Check website.
Ⓜ 07905 518666
Ⓔ laurelfarmherbs@aol.com
Ⓦ www.laurelfarmherbs.co.uk
Contact: Chris & Jenny Seagon
Opening Times: Please phone or check website for opening hours as times can vary.
Min Mail Order UK: 3 plants + p&p
Min Mail Order EU: 3 plants + p&p
Cat. Cost: Online only.
Credit Cards: MasterCard, Switch, Visa,
Specialities: Herbs, especially rosemary, thyme, mint & sage.
Notes: Nursery has relocated from Suffolk to Devon. Also sells wholesale. Delivers to shows (payment in advance).
Map Ref: C, C3

CLet **Letsgoplanting** ♿
Otters Reach, West Buckland, Wellington, Somerset, TA21 9LD
Ⓣ (01823) 660175
Ⓕ (01823) 661107
Ⓔ mail@letsgoplanting.co.uk
Ⓦ www.letsgoplanting.co.uk
Contact: Ian Phillips
Opening Times: 0900-1700, Mon-Fri.
Min Mail Order UK: Nmc

Min Mail Order EU: Nmc
Cat. Cost: Online only.
Credit Cards: All major credit/debit cards
Specialities: Shrubs, herbaceous perennials, grasses, climbers, ferns and bamboos. Most plants propagated and grown on the nursery. All hardy stock comes with a one-year guarantee.
Notes: Payment can be taken over the phone. Euro accepted. Wheelchair accessible.
Map Ref: C, B4

CLnd LANDFORD TREES
Landford Lodge, Landford, Salisbury, Wiltshire SP5 2EH
Ⓣ (01794) 390808
Ⓕ (01794) 390037
Ⓔ trees@landfordtrees.co.uk
Ⓦ www.landfordtrees.co.uk
Contact: C D Pilkington
Opening Times: 0800-1700 Mon-Fri.
Cat. Cost: Free.
Credit Cards: All, except American Express
Specialities: Deciduous ornamental trees.
Notes: Also sells wholesale.
Map Ref: C, B6 **OS Grid Ref:** SU247201

CLng LONGCOMBE NURSERY AND GARDEN CENTRE ♿
Longcombe, Totnes, Devon TQ9 6PL
Ⓣ (01803) 863098
Ⓔ info@simplyclematis.co.uk
Ⓦ www.simplyclematis.co.uk
Contact: Linda Clarke
Opening Times: 0900-1700 Mon-Sat, 1000-1600 Sun.
Min Mail Order UK: Nmc
Min Mail Order EU: Nmc
Cat. Cost: Online only.
Credit Cards: All major credit/debit cards
Specialities: *Clematis.*
Notes: Also sells wholesale. Delivers to shows. Wheelchair accessible.
Map Ref: C, C3 **OS Grid Ref:** SX834601

CLoc C S LOCKYER (FUCHSIAS) ◆
Lansbury, 70 Henfield Road, Coalpit Heath, Bristol BS36 2UZ
Ⓣ (01454) 772219
Ⓕ (01454) 772219
Ⓔ Stuart@lockyerfuchsias.co.uk
Ⓦ lockyerfuchsias.co.uk
Contact: C S Lockyer
Opening Times: 1000-1300, 1430-1700 most days, please ring.
Min Mail Order UK: 6 plants + p&p
Min Mail Order EU: £12.00 + p&p
Cat. Cost: 4 × 1st class or online
Credit Cards: All major credit/debit cards
Specialities: *Fuchsia.*
Notes: Many open days & coach parties. Also sells wholesale. Exports beyond EU. Delivers to shows. Euro accepted. Partial wheelchair access.
Map Ref: C, A5

CMac MAC PENNYS NURSERIES
154 Burley Road, Bransgore, Christchurch, Dorset BH23 8DB
Ⓣ (01425) 672348
Ⓕ (01425) 673917
Ⓔ office@macpennys.co.uk
Ⓦ www.macpennys.co.uk
Contact: T & V Lowndes & S Lowndes
Opening Times: 0900-1700 Mon-Sat, 1000-1700 Sun & B/hols, except closed Xmas-New Year.
Min Mail Order UK: Nmc
Cat. Cost: A4 sae with 4 × 1st class.
Credit Cards: All major credit/debit cards
Specialities: General. Plants available in small quantities only.
Notes: Mail order available Sep-Mar, UK only. Also sells wholesale. Nursery partially accessible for wheelchairs.
Map Ref: C, C6

CMan MANDY PLANTS ♿
(Office) 4 St Mary's Place, Ipplepen, Devon TQ12 5FF
Ⓣ (01803) 813647
Ⓜ 07432 112245
Ⓔ enquiries@mandyplants.com
Contact: Liz Spanton
Opening Times: By appt. only.
Min Mail Order UK: Nmc
Min Mail Order EU: £25.00
Cat. Cost: 2 × 1st class
Credit Cards: Paypal
Specialities: *Mandevilla* & *Dipladenia.*
Notes: Nursery is at Bishopsteignton, Devon. Also sells wholesale. Delivers to shows. Wheelchair accessible.
Map Ref: C, C3 **OS Grid Ref:** SX836667

CMCN MALLET COURT NURSERY ♿
Marshway, Curry Mallet, Taunton, Somerset TA3 6SZ
Ⓣ (01823) 481493
Ⓜ 07713 091521
Ⓕ (01823) 481493
Ⓔ malletcourtnursery@btinternet.com
Ⓦ www.malletcourt.co.uk
Contact: J G S & P M E Harris F.L.S.
Opening Times: 0930-1700 Mon-Fri summer, 0930-1600 winter. Sat & Sun by appt.
Min Mail Order UK: Nmc
Min Mail Order EU: Nmc

Cat. Cost: £1.50
Credit Cards: All major credit/debit cards
Specialities: Maples, oaks, *Magnolia*, hollies & other rare and unusual plants incl. those from China & South Korea.
Notes: Mail order Oct-Mar only. Also sells wholesale. Exports beyond EU. Euro accepted. Wheelchair accessible.
Map Ref: C, B4

CMea **The Mead Nursery** ♿
Brokerswood, Nr Westbury, Wiltshire
BA13 4EG
Ⓣ (01373) 859990
Ⓔ info@themeadnursery.co.uk
Ⓦ www.themeadnursery.co.uk
Contact: Steve & Emma Lewis-Dale
Opening Times: 0900-1700 Wed-Sat & B/hol Mons, 1200-1700 Sun, 1st Feb-10th Oct. Closed Easter Sun.
Cat. Cost: 5 × 1st class.
Credit Cards: All major credit/debit cards
Specialities: Perennials, alpines, pot-grown bulbs and grasses.
Notes: Wheelchair accessible.
Map Ref: C, B5 **OS Grid Ref:** ST833517

CMen **Mendip Bonsai Studio**
Byways, Back Lane, Downside, Shepton Mallet, Somerset BA4 4JR
Ⓣ (01749) 344274
Ⓜ 07711 205806
Ⓔ john@mendipbonsai.co.uk
Ⓦ www.mendipbonsai.co.uk
Contact: John Trott
Opening Times: Private nursery. Visits by appt. only.
Min Mail Order UK: £15.00
Cat. Cost: Large sae for plant & workshop lists
Credit Cards: All major credit/debit cards
Specialities: Bonsai, Potensai, accent plants & garden stock. Acers, conifers, incl. many *Pinus thunbergii* species, *Aciphylla*, *Davallia* & *Pyrrosia*. Many plants available in small numbers only. Young trees for garden or bonsai culture.
Notes: Education classes, lectures, demonstrations & club talks on bonsai. Stockist of most bonsai, pots, related bonsai sundries & a large range of bronze figures. Mail orders will normally be despatched late Mar-early Apr, late Sep-Oct. Delivers to shows by arrangement.
Map Ref: C, B5

CMHG **Marwood Hill Gardens** ♿
Marwood, Barnstaple, Devon EX31 4EB
Ⓣ (01271) 342528
Ⓕ (01271) 342528
Ⓔ info@marwoodhillgarden.co.uk
Ⓦ www.marwoodhillgarden.co.uk
Contact: Malcolm Pharoah
Opening Times: 1100-1630, 7 days. Closed Nov-Feb.
Cat. Cost: 3 × 1st class.
Credit Cards: Delta, MasterCard, Solo, Switch, Visa
Specialities: Large range of unusual trees & shrubs. *Eucalyptus*, alpines, *Camellia*, *Astilbe*, bog plants & perennials. National Collections of *Astilbe*, *Tulbaghia* & *Iris ensata*.
Notes: Wheelchair accessible.
Map Ref: C, B3 **OS Grid Ref:** SS545375

CMil **Mill Cottage Plants** ♿
Henley Mill, Henley Lane,
Wookey, Somerset
BA5 1AW
Ⓣ (01749) 676966
Ⓜ 07851 698759
Ⓔ millcottageplants@gmail.com
Ⓦ www.millcottageplants.co.uk
Contact: Sally Gregson
Opening Times: By appt. only. Phone for directions.
Min Mail Order UK: Nmc
Min Mail Order EU: £25.00 + p&p
Cat. Cost: Online only.
Credit Cards: All major credit/debit cards
Specialities: Rare *Hydrangea serrata* cvs, *H. aspera* cvs, *Epimedium*, shade & damp-loving plants.
Notes: Euro accepted. Wheelchair accessible.
Map Ref: C, B5

CMos **Ian & Teresa Moss** ♿
(Office) 'Iona', Woolmersdon,
Bridgwater, Somerset
TA5 2BP
Ⓣ (01278) 661352
Ⓜ 07903 268718
Ⓔ teresa@hardyandunusualplants.co.uk
Ⓦ www.hardyandunusualplants.co.uk
Contact: Teresa Moss
Opening Times: 1000-1630, daily, 30th Mar-31st Oct 2014.
Cat. Cost: £1.50
Credit Cards: All, except American Express
Specialities: Hardy & unusual plants. Range of perennials incl. the best of recent introductions as well as more unusual varieties & reliable old favourites. Wide range of hardy geraniums.
Notes: Plant sales through Kilver Court Gardens, Kilver Street, Shepton Mallet, Somerset, BA4 5NF. Delivers to shows (see website for details of which shows attended). Wheelchair accessible.
Map Ref: C, B4

C

CMus **MUSGROVE WILLOWS** ♿
Willowfields, Lakewall,
Westonzoyland, Bridgwater,
Somerset TA7 0LP
Ⓣ (01278) 691105
Ⓕ (01278) 699107
Ⓔ info@musgrovewillows.co.uk
Ⓦ www.musgrovewillows.co.uk
Contact: Ellen Musgrove
Opening Times: 0900-1700 Mon-Fri.
Min Mail Order UK: £12.50
Min Mail Order EU: Nmc
Credit Cards: All major credit/debit cards
Specialities: *Salix* (willow). A family nursery since 1928.
Notes: Exports beyond EU. Wheelchair accessible.
Map Ref: C, B4

CNat **NATURAL SELECTION**
1 Station Cottages, Hullavington,
Chippenham, Wiltshire
SN14 6ET
Ⓣ (01666) 837369
Ⓜ 07800 583999
Ⓔ martin@worldmutation.demon.co.uk
Ⓦ www.worldmutation.demon.co.uk
Contact: Martin Barber
Opening Times: Please phone first.
Min Mail Order UK: £9.00 + p&p
Min Mail Order EU: Nmc
Cat. Cost: 2 × 2nd class.
Credit Cards: None
Specialities: Unusual British natives & others. Also seed. Only available in small quantities.
Notes: Euro accepted.

CNec **NECTAR PLANTS GARDEN NURSERY**
646 Dorchester Road, Upwey, Weymouth,
Dorset DT3 5LG
Ⓣ (01305) 855988 or 814473
Ⓔ martinyoung100@btinternet.com
Ⓦ www.nectarplants.co.uk
Contact: Martin Young
Opening Times: 1000-1700 Fri, Sat, Sun only, mid-March to mid-Oct.
Cat. Cost: A5 sae for availability list.
Credit Cards: All major credit/debit cards
Specialities: Small scale nursery specialising in plants for bees & butterflies, cottage garden favourites & coastal plants. Wide selection of *Buddleja davidii*, *B. weyeriana* & hardy geraniums. Good selection of David Austin roses & many flowering shrubs. Some own-propagated plants in small quantities only.
Notes: Nursery is on old Dorchester-Weymouth road. Follow signs to Upwey. Large copper beech tree next to green gate. Delivers to shows.
Map Ref: C, C5 **OS Grid Ref:** SY674838

CNMi **NEWPORT MILLS NURSERY**
Wrantage, Taunton, Somerset, TA3 6DJ
Ⓣ (01823) 490231
Ⓔ john@newportmillsnursery.net
Ⓦ www.newportmillsnursery.net
Contact: John Barrington
Opening Times: Not open. Mail order only.
Min Mail Order UK: Nmc free p&p
Min Mail Order EU: Nmc. EU postal rate per order.
Cat. Cost: Free.
Credit Cards: All major credit/debit cards
Specialities: *Delphinium elatum* hybrids. English scented perpetual flowering carnations. *Dianthus*. Pinks, Exhibition, Modern & Old World.
Notes: Mail order Apr-Sep for young delphiniums in 7cm pots. Dormant plants can be sent out in autumn/winter if requested. Euro accepted.
Map Ref: C, B4 **OS Grid Ref:** ST318234

CNor **NORTHBROOK NURSERY** ♿
47 Northbrook Road, Broadstone, Dorset,
BH18 8HD
Ⓣ (01202) 695256
Ⓔ marg@northbrooknursery.co.uk
Ⓦ www.northbrooknursery.co.uk
Contact: Margaret Bailey
Opening Times: 1000-1600, Tue-Fri, Apr-Oct.
Min Mail Order UK: Nmc
Cat. Cost: None issued.
Credit Cards: Paypal
Specialities: Perennials. Plants available in small quantities only.
Notes: Delivers to shows. Wheelchair accessible.
Map Ref: C, C6 **OS Grid Ref:** SZ 001947

CNWT **NEW WOOD TREES**
Oldwood House, Aish Road, Stoke Gabriel,
Totnes, Devon TQ9 6PX
Ⓣ (01803) 782666
Ⓔ info@newwoodtrees.co.uk
Ⓦ www.newwoodtrees.co.uk
Contact: Philip Nieuwoudt
Opening Times: 0900-1700 Mon-Fri.
Credit Cards: None
Specialities: Trees. Multi-stem ornamentals; small to medium sized trees and large shrubs.
Notes: Specialises in specimen trees so when a species is sold out it takes a while to replenish stocks. Also sells wholesale. Delivers to shows.
Map Ref: C, C3 **OS Grid Ref:** SX847580

COtt **OTTER NURSERIES LTD** ♿
Gosford Road, Ottery St. Mary, Devon
EX11 1LZ
Ⓣ (01404) 815815
Ⓜ 07875 268429

Ⓕ (01404) 815816
Ⓔ otter@otternurseries.co.uk
Ⓦ www.otternurseries.co.uk
Contact: Garden centre plant information desk
Opening Times: 0800-1730 Mon-Sat, 1030-1630 Sun. Closed Xmas, Boxing Day & Easter Sun.
Cat. Cost: None issued
Credit Cards: All, except American Express
Specialities: Large garden centre & nursery with extensive range of trees, shrubs, conifers, climbers, roses, fruit & hardy perennials.
Notes: Wheelchair accessible.

CPar **Parks Perennials**
242 Wallisdown Road, Wallisdown, Bournemouth, Dorset BH10 4HZ
Ⓣ (01202) 524464
Ⓜ 07977 878546
Ⓔ parks.perennials@ntlworld.com
Contact: S. Parks
Opening Times: Apr-Oct most days, please phone first.
Cat. Cost: None issued.
Credit Cards: None
Specialities: Hardy herbaceous perennials.
Notes: Delivers to shows.
Map Ref: C, C6

CPbn **Penborn Goat Farm** ♿
Penborn, Bounds Cross, Holsworthy, Devon EX22 6LH
Ⓣ (01288) 381569
Ⓔ penborngoats@btinternet.com
Ⓦ www.penborngoats.com
Contact: P R Oldfield
Opening Times: By appt. only.
Min Mail Order UK: £20.00
Min Mail Order EU: £24.00
Cat. Cost: Online.
Credit Cards: None
Specialities: *Mentha*, *Melissa*. Available in small quantities only.
Notes: Wheelchair accessible.
Map Ref: C, C2 **OS Grid Ref:** SS290021

CPBP **Parham Bungalow Plants**
Parham Lane, Market Lavington, Devizes, Wiltshire, SN10 4QA
Ⓣ (01380) 812605
Ⓔ jjs@pbplants.freeserve.co.uk
Contact: Mrs D E Sample
Opening Times: Please ring first.
Min Mail Order UK: Nmc
Min Mail Order EU: Nmc
Cat. Cost: Sae.
Credit Cards: None
Specialities: Alpines.
Notes: Delivers to shows. Euro accepted.
Map Ref: C, B6

CPen **Pennard Plants**
3 The Gardens, East Pennard, Shepton Mallet, Somerset, BA4 6TU
Ⓣ (01749) 860039
Ⓔ sales@pennardplants.com
Ⓦ www.pennardplants.com
Contact: Chris Smith
Opening Times: By appt. only.
Min Mail Order UK: Nmc
Min Mail Order EU: Nmc
Cat. Cost: 3 × 1st class.
Credit Cards: All major credit/debit cards
Specialities: *Agapanthus*.
Notes: Nursery at The Walled Garden at East Pennard. Exports beyond EU. Delivers to shows. Euro accepted.
Map Ref: C, B5

CPhi **Alan Phipps Cacti**
62 Samuel White Road, Hanham, Bristol BS15 3LX
Ⓣ (0117) 9607591
Ⓦ www.cactus-mall.com/alan-phipps/index.html
Contact: A Phipps
Opening Times: 1000-1700 but prior phone call essential to ensure a greeting.
Min Mail Order UK: £5.00 + p&p
Min Mail Order EU: £20.00 + p&p
Cat. Cost: Sae or 2 × IRC (EC only).
Credit Cards: None
Specialities: *Mammillaria*, *Astrophytum* & *Ariocarpus*. Species & varieties will change with times. Ample quantities exist in spring. Limited range of *Agave*.
Notes: Specimen-size plants not available by mail order. Euro accepted as cash only.
Map Ref: C, A5 **OS Grid Ref:** ST644717

CPHo **The Palm House**
8 North Street, Ottery St Mary, Devon EX11 1DR
Ⓣ (01404) 815450
Ⓜ 07815 673397
Ⓔ george@thepalmhouse.co.uk
Ⓦ www.thepalmhouse.co.uk
Contact: George Gregory
Opening Times: Mail order only. Open by appt. only.
Min Mail Order UK: £15.00
Min Mail Order EU: £10.00
Cat. Cost: 2 × 1st class.
Credit Cards: All major credit/debit cards
Specialities: Palms.
Notes: Also sells wholesale.

CPla **Plant World Botanic Gardens** ♿
St Marychurch Road, Newton Abbot, Devon TQ12 4SE
Ⓣ (01803) 872939
Ⓕ (01803) 875018

C

Ⓔ raybrown@plant-world-seeds.com
Ⓦ www.plant-world-seeds.com
Contact: Ray Brown
Opening Times: 0930-1700 7 days a week, Apr (Easter if earlier)-Oct.
Min Mail Order UK: Nmc
Min Mail Order EU: Nmc
Cat. Cost: 3 ×1st class or 2 × IRC.
Credit Cards: Access, EuroCard, MasterCard, Visa
Specialities: Alpines & unusual herbaceous plants.
Notes: 4 acre garden planted as map of the world (entry charge). Mail order seed only. Also sells wholesale. Exports beyond EU. Euro accepted. Wheelchair access to nursery & café only.

CPne **Pine Cottage Plants** ♿
Pine Cottage, Fourways, Eggesford, Chulmleigh, Devon EX18 7QZ
Ⓣ (01769) 580076
Ⓜ 07718 505053
Ⓔ sales@pcplants.co.uk
Ⓦ www.pcplants.co.uk
Contact: Dick Fulcher
Opening Times: By appt. only. Please phone first.
Min Mail Order UK: £20.00
Min Mail Order EU: £20.00
Cat. Cost: 3 × 1st class.
Credit Cards: Maestro, MasterCard, Visa
Specialities: *Agapanthus*, South African bulbous plants, species *Rhododendron* & other unusual plants.
Notes: Mail order *Agapanthus* from Sep-Jun. Exports beyond EU. Wheelchair accessible.
Map Ref: C, B3 **OS Grid Ref:** SS683099

CPou **Pounsley Plants** ♿
Pounsley Combe, Spriddlestone, Brixton, Plymouth, Devon PL9 0DW
Ⓣ (01752) 402873
Ⓜ 07770 758501
Ⓕ (01752) 406682
Ⓔ pou599@aol.com
Ⓦ www.pounsleyplants.com
Contact: Mrs Jane Hollow
Opening Times: Normally 1000-1600 Mon-Sat but please phone first.
Min Mail Order UK: £10.00 + p&p
Min Mail Order EU: €20.00 + p&p
Cat. Cost: 2 × 1st class.
Credit Cards: None
Specialities: Unusual herbaceous perennials & *Clematis*. Comprehensive range of Old Roses & large selection of modern roses.
Notes: Mail order solely bare root roses, Nov-Mar. Also sells wholesale. Delivers to shows. Euro accepted. Wheelchair accessible.
Map Ref: C, D3 **OS Grid Ref:** SX521538

CPrp **ProperPlants.com**
Penknight, Edgcumbe Road, Lostwithiel, Cornwall PL22 0JD
Ⓣ (01208) 872291
Ⓔ info@ProperPlants.com
Ⓦ www.ProperPlants.com
Contact: Sarah Wilks
Opening Times: 1000-1800 or dusk if earlier, Tue & B/hols mid-Mar to end-Sep & by appt.
Min Mail Order UK: Nmc
Min Mail Order EU: Nmc
Cat. Cost: 2 × 1st class.
Credit Cards: All major credit/debit cards
Specialities: *Agapanthus*, *Crocosmia* & *Hesperantha*.
Notes: Exports beyond EU. Delivers to shows.
Map Ref: C, C2 **OS Grid Ref:** SX093596

CQua **Quality Daffodils**
14 Roscarrack Close, Falmouth, Cornwall TR11 4PJ
Ⓣ (01326) 317959
Ⓜ 07989 243450
Ⓕ (01326) 317959
Ⓔ rascamp@daffodils.uk.com
Ⓦ www.qualitydaffodils.com
Contact: R A Scamp
Opening Times: Not open. Mail order only. Viewing by appt. only.
Min Mail Order UK: Nmc
Min Mail Order EU: Nmc
Cat. Cost: 4 × 1st class.
Credit Cards: All major credit/debit cards
Specialities: *Narcissus* hybrids & species. Some stocks are less than 100 bulbs.
Notes: Also sells wholesale. Exports beyond EU. Euro accepted.
Map Ref: C, D1

CRHN **Roseland House Nursery**
Chacewater, Truro, Cornwall TR4 8QB
Ⓣ (01872) 560451
Ⓔ clematis@roselandhouse.co.uk
Ⓦ www.roselandhouse.co.uk
Contact: C R Pridham
Opening Times: 1300-1700 Tue & Wed, Apr-Sep. Other times by appt.
Min Mail Order UK: Nmc
Min Mail Order EU: Nmc
Cat. Cost: Online only.
Credit Cards: All major credit/debit cards
Specialities: Climbing & conservatory plants. National Collections of *Clematis viticella* & *Lapageria rosea*. Named *Lapageria* in short supply but occasionally available.
Notes: Garden open to the public. Credit cards accepted from mail order customers only. Delivers to shows.
Map Ref: C, D1 **OS Grid Ref:** SW752445

CRos **RHS Garden Rosemoor Plant Centre** ♿ ◆
RHS Garden Rosemoor, Torrington, Devon EX38 8PH
Ⓣ (01805) 626842
Ⓕ (01805) 622422
Ⓔ rosemooradmin@rhs.org.uk
Ⓦ www.rhs.org.uk/rosemoor
Contact: Emma Van-Huysse or Sam Smith
Opening Times: 1000-1800 Mon-Sat, 11.30-1730 Sun, Apr-Sep (summer). 1000-1700 Mon-Sat, 1030-1630 Sun, Oct-Mar (winter). Closed Easter Sun & Xmas Day.
Cat. Cost: None issued
Credit Cards: All major credit/debit cards
Specialities: Wide range of shrubs, herbaceous plants, roses, climbers, alpines & seasonal lines, reflecting where possible the diversity of planting in the garden. Display highlighting a selection of plants for sale that are looking good in the garden. Also displays of AGM plants & Plants for Pollinators.
Notes: Plant Centre attached to RHS Garden. Free entry to Plant Centre & Gift Shop & Kitchen Garden Restaurant. Plants subject to seasonal availability but will source plants whenever possible. Wheelchair accessible.
Map Ref: C, B3 **OS Grid Ref:** SS500176

CSam **Sampford Shrubs**
Sampford Peverell, Tiverton, Devon EX16 7EN
Ⓣ (01884) 821164
Ⓔ via website
Ⓦ www.samshrub.co.uk
Contact: M Hughes-Jones & S Proud
Opening Times: 1000-1700 Wed-Fri, 2nd Apr-12th Sep incl.
Min Mail Order UK: Nmc
Cat. Cost: Online only.
Credit Cards: All major credit/debit cards
Specialities: Plants particularly suitable for naturalistic gardening.
Notes: Mail order only via dedicated ecommerce website. Despatched Oct-Mar. Euro accepted.
Map Ref: C, B4 **OS Grid Ref:** ST043153

CSBt **St Bridget Nurseries Ltd** ♿
Old Rydon Lane, Exeter, Devon EX2 7JY
Ⓣ (01392) 873672
Ⓕ (01392) 876710
Ⓔ sales@stbridgetnurseries.co.uk
Ⓦ www.stbridgetnurseries.co.uk
Contact: Sales Dept
Opening Times: 0900-1700 Mon-Sat, 1030-1630 Sun. Closed Xmas Day, Boxing Day, New Year's Day & Easter Sunday.
Min Mail Order UK: Nmc
Cat. Cost: Free.
Credit Cards: All major credit/debit cards
Specialities: Large general nursery, with two garden centres.
Notes: Mail order available, please contact for prices & carriage charges. Also sells wholesale. Wheelchair accessible.
Map Ref: C, C4 **OS Grid Ref:** SX955905

CSde **Seaside Plants**
Marsh Lane Nursery, West Charleton, Kingsbridge, Devon TQ7 2AQ
Ⓜ 07747 661272
Ⓔ info@seasideplants.co.uk
Ⓦ www.seasideplants.co.uk
Contact: Michael Hornby
Opening Times: Not open. View by appt. only.
Min Mail Order UK: Nmc
Min Mail Order EU: Nmc
Cat. Cost: Online only.
Credit Cards: All major credit/debit cards
Specialities: Wide range, esp. coastal plants, *Elaeagnus*, *Euonymus*, *Fuchsia*, grasses, *Griselinia*, *Hydrangea*, *Olearia* & *Pittosporum*.
Notes: Euro accepted.

CSma **Plants for Small Gardens**
Goosegate, Bridford, Exeter, Devon EX6 7LW
Ⓜ 07845 793582
Ⓔ sales@plantsforsmallgardens.co.uk
Ⓦ www.plantsforsmallgardens.co.uk
Contact: Sue Hearnden
Opening Times: Not open. Mail order online only.
Min Mail Order UK: £12.50
Cat. Cost: Online only.
Credit Cards: Paypal
Specialities: Dwarf hardy, rockery and alpine plants, all grown on our nursery in Devon. Range to suit all types of gardeners from *Aubrieta* & *Helianthemum* to more specialist plants such as kabschia saxifrages & *Meconopsis*.

CSna **Snape Cottage**
Chaffeymoor, Bourton, Dorset SP8 5BZ
Ⓣ (01747) 840330 (evenings only).
Ⓔ ianandangela@snapecottagegarden.co.uk
Ⓦ www.snapestakes.com
Contact: Mrs Angela Whinfield
Opening Times: 1400-1700 last Sat in months Feb-Jun incl.
Min Mail Order UK: Nmc
Cat. Cost: Sae.
Credit Cards: None
Specialities: 'Old' forms of many popular garden plants. Plantsman's garden open same time as nursery. Stock available in small quantities. Snape Stakes plant supports.

C

Notes: Mail order *Galanthus* only. List issued in Feb. Group visits welcome all year.
Map Ref: C, B5 **OS Grid Ref:** ST762303

CSpe **SPECIAL PLANTS**
Hill Farm Barn, Greenways Lane,
Cold Ashton, Chippenham, Wiltshire
SN14 8LA
Ⓣ (01225) 891686
Ⓔ derry@specialplants.net
Ⓦ www.specialplants.net
Contact: Derry Watkins
Opening Times: 1000-1700 7 days Mar-Oct. Other times please ring first to check.
Min Mail Order UK: £10.00 + p&p
Cat. Cost: 2 × 1st class for seed list.
Credit Cards: All major credit/debit cards
Specialities: Tender perennials, *Pelargonium*, *Salvia*, *Streptocarpus*, hardy geraniums, *Anemone*, *Erysimum*, *Papaver*, *Viola* & grasses. Many varieties propagated in small numbers only.
Notes: Mail order Sep-Mar only. Delivers to shows. Euro accepted.
Map Ref: C, A5 **OS Grid Ref:** ST749726

CSta **STADDON FARM NURSERIES** ♿
Staddon Road, Holsworthy, Devon
EX22 6NH
Ⓜ 07547 711189
Ⓔ penny.staddonfarm@yahoo.co.uk
Ⓦ www.pennysprimulas.co.uk
Contact: Penny Jones
Opening Times: By appt. only.
Min Mail Order UK: Nmc
Cat. Cost: Online only.
Credit Cards: All major credit/debit cards
Specialities: *Primula*. National Collection of *Primula sieboldii* Japanese cvs.
Notes: Wheelchair accessible.

CSto **STONE LANE GARDENS**
Stone Farm, Chagford, Devon TQ13 8JU
Ⓣ (01647) 231311
Ⓔ paul.bartlett@stonelanegardens.com
Ⓦ www.stonelanegardens.com
Contact: Paul Bartlett
Opening Times: Open by appt. only. Not open to casual visitors. Website ordering available.
Min Mail Order UK: Nmc
Min Mail Order EU: Nmc
Cat. Cost: 6 × 1st class for colour catalogue with photos or online.
Credit Cards: All major credit/debit cards
Specialities: Comprehensive selection of wild origin *Betula* & *Alnus*, both bare-root & in pots. Choice selection of specially grafted cvs. National Collection of Birch & Alder.
Notes: Arboretum open all year with summer sculpture exhibition (charges apply). Planting service available in West Country, details on request. Also sells wholesale. Credit cards accepted online only.
Map Ref: C, C3 **OS Grid Ref:** SX708908

CSuc **SURREAL SUCCULENTS**
Clowance Wood Nursery, Praze-an-Beeble,
Cornwall TR14 0NW
Ⓜ 07707 314823
Ⓔ info@surrealsucculents.co.uk
Ⓦ www.surrealsucculents.co.uk
Contact: Colin Skelly
Opening Times: Mail order only. Open by appt.
Min Mail Order UK: Nmc
Min Mail Order EU: Nmc
Cat. Cost: Online only.
Credit Cards: Paypal
Specialities: Hardy & half-hardy succulents. *Aeonium*, *Echeveria*. Some in small quantities only. National Collection of *Aeonium* applied for.
Notes: Euro accepted.

CSut **SUTTONS SEEDS**
Woodview Road, Paignton, Devon TQ4 7NG
Ⓣ 0844 922 2899
Ⓕ 0844 922 2265
Ⓦ www.suttons.co.uk
Contact: Customer Services
Opening Times: Office: 0830-1700 Mon-Fri. Also answerphone.
Min Mail Order UK: Nmc
Min Mail Order EU: £5.00
Cat. Cost: Free.
Credit Cards: Delta, MasterCard, Switch, Visa
Specialities: Over 1,000 varieties of flower & vegetable seed, bulbs, plants & sundries.

CTal **TALE VALLEY NURSERY**
Barratt's Cottage, Cullompton, Devon
EX15 2NQ
Ⓣ (01884) 277614
Ⓜ 07791 676162
Ⓔ contactus@talevalleynursery.co.uk
Ⓦ www.talevalleynursery.co.uk
Contact: Lorraine & Chris Birchall
Opening Times: Not open.
Min Mail Order UK: £10.00 + p&p
Min Mail Order EU: £25.00 + p&p
Cat. Cost: 4 × 1st class or PDF download from website.
Credit Cards: None
Specialities: Alpines, shade/woodland herbaceous plants & bulbs. National Collections of *Rhodohypoxis* & × *Rhodoxis*. Some specialist plants available in small numbers only.

Notes: Mail order for selection of National Collections, other bulbs & a few select plants. Delivers to shows.

CTca **Trecanna Nursery**
The Old Barn, Chilsworthy, Cornwall PL18 9PB
Ⓣ (01822) 834680
Ⓜ 07785 242148
Ⓔ mark@trecanna.com
Ⓦ www.trecanna.com
Contact: Mark Wash
Opening Times: Not currently open to the public.
Min Mail Order UK: £22.00
Min Mail Order EU: £45.00
Cat. Cost: £2.00
Credit Cards: All major credit/debit cards
Specialities: Hardy South African plants. Good collections of *Crocosmia*, *Eucomis*, *Kniphofia*, *Watsonia*, *Crinum*, *Albuca*, nerines, *Zantedeschia*, *Lachenalia* & *Moraea*. Wide range of dry bulbs from around the globe.
Notes: Talks to garden societies. Exports beyond EU. Delivers to shows.
Map Ref: C, B5 **OS Grid Ref:** SX247733

CTho **Thornhayes Nursery**
St Andrews Wood, Dulford, Cullompton, Devon EX15 2DF
Ⓣ (01884) 266746
Ⓕ (01884) 266739
Ⓔ trees@thornhayes-nursery.co.uk
Ⓦ www.thornhayes-nursery.co.uk
Contact: K D Croucher
Opening Times: 0800-1600 Mon-Fri. 0930-1400 Sat.
Min Mail Order UK: £30
Min Mail Order EU: £30
Credit Cards: All major credit/debit cards
Specialities: A broad range of forms of ornamental, amenity & fruit trees incl. West Country apple varieties.
Notes: Also sells wholesale. Euro accepted. Limited wheelchair accessible.
Map Ref: C, C4

CTre **Trewidden Nursery**
Buryas Bridge, Penzance, Cornwall TR20 8TT
Ⓣ (01736) 362087
Ⓕ (01736) 331470
Ⓔ info@trewidden-nursery.com
Ⓦ www.trewidden-online.co.uk
Contact: Jeff Rowe
Opening Times: Not open. Mail order & RHS shows. Open w/ends, one in spring & one in autumn, contact nursery for details.
Min Mail Order UK: Nmc
Min Mail Order EU: Nmc
Cat. Cost: Online only.
Credit Cards: None
Specialities: *Protea*, *Restio*, succulents and other unusual plants.
Notes: Sells at shows around the country and online. Card payments accepted at shows. Mail order through website only.

CTrh **Trehane Nursery** ♿
Stapehill Road, Hampreston, Wimborne, Dorset BH21 7ND
Ⓣ (01202) 873490
Ⓔ nursery@trehane.co.uk
Ⓦ www.trehane.co.uk
Contact: Lorraine Keets
Opening Times: 0830-1630 Mon-Fri all year (excl. Xmas & New Year). 1000-1600 Sat-Sun in spring & by special appt.
Min Mail Order UK: Nmc
Min Mail Order EU: Nmc
Cat. Cost: £1.50 cat./book.
Credit Cards: All major credit/debit cards
Specialities: Extensive range of *Camellia* species, cultivars & hybrids. Many new introductions. Evergreen azaleas & blueberries.
Notes: Also sells wholesale. Wheelchair accessible.
Map Ref: C, C6 **OS Grid Ref:** SU059000

CTri **Triscombe Nurseries** ♿ ◆
West Bagborough, Nr Taunton, Somerset TA4 3HG
Ⓣ (01984) 618267
Ⓔ info@triscombenurseries.co.uk
Ⓦ www.triscombenurseries.co.uk
Contact: S Parkman
Opening Times: 0900-1730 Mon-Sat. 1400-1730 Sun & B/hols.
Min Mail Order UK: Nmc
Cat. Cost: 1 × 1st class.
Credit Cards: None
Specialities: Trees, shrubs, roses, fruit, *Clematis*, herbaceous & rock plants.
Notes: Wheelchair accessible.
Map Ref: C, B4

CTsd **Treseders** ♿
Wallcottage Nursery, Lockengate, St. Austell, Cornwall PL26 8RU
Ⓣ (01208) 832234
Ⓔ Treseders@btconnect.com
Ⓦ www.treseders.co.uk
Contact: James Treseder
Opening Times: 0900-1700 Mon-Sat, 1000-1600 Sun. Closed Wed.
Min Mail Order UK: Nmc
Min Mail Order EU: Nmc
Cat. Cost: Plant list available on request.
Credit Cards: All major credit/debit cards
Specialities: A wide range of choice & unusual plants grown in peat-free compost.

C

Establishing collection of *Prostanthera*.
Notes: Plants sometimes only available in small quantities. Enquiries welcome. Delivers to shows. Wheelchair accessible.
Map Ref: C, C2 **OS Grid Ref:** SX034620

CWat **THE WATER GARDEN** ♿
Hinton Parva, Swindon, Wiltshire
SN4 0DH
Ⓣ (01793) 790558
Ⓕ (01793) 791298
Ⓔ mike@thewatergarden.co.uk
Ⓦ www.thewatergarden.co.uk
Contact: Mike & Anne Newman
Opening Times: 1000-1700 Wed-Sun.
Min Mail Order UK: £10.00 + p&p
Cat. Cost: 4 × 1st class.
Credit Cards: Access, Switch, Visa
Specialities: Water lilies, marginal & moisture plants, oxygenators & alpines.
Notes: Also sells wholesale. Wheelchair accessible.
Map Ref: C, A6

CWCL **WESTCOUNTRY NURSERIES**
Donkey Meadow, Woolsery, Devon
EX39 5QH
Ⓣ (01237) 431111
Ⓔ info@westcountry-nurseries.co.uk
Ⓦ www.westcountry-nurseries.co.uk
Contact: Sarah Conibear
Opening Times: 1000-1600 Mar-mid Jul. Closed for lunch 1300-1330. Before travelling at a w/end, please check with nursery.
Min Mail Order UK: Nmc
Cat. Cost: 2 × 1st class + A5 sae for full colour cat.
Credit Cards: All major credit/debit cards
Specialities: *Lupinus*, *Lewisia*, *Helleborus*, *Clematis*, cyclamen, lavender, select perennials, grasses, ferns & climbers. National Collection of Lupins.
Notes: Delivers to shows.
Map Ref: C, B2 **OS Grid Ref:** SS351219

CWGN **WALLED GARDEN NURSERY** ♿
Brinkworth House, Brinkworth,
Nr Malmesbury, Wiltshire
SN15 5DF
Ⓣ (01666) 826637
Ⓜ 07921 436863
Ⓔ f.wescott@btinternet.com
Ⓦ www.clematis-nursery.co.uk
Contact: Fraser Wescott
Opening Times: 1000-1700, 7 days Mar-Oct. 1000-dusk, Mon-Fri Nov & Feb. Closed Dec & Jan.
Min Mail Order UK: £15.00
Credit Cards: All major credit/debit cards
Specialities: *Clematis* & climbers, with a selection of unusual perennials & shrubs.
Notes: Wheelchair accessible.
Map Ref: C, A6 **OS Grid Ref:** SU002849

CWhe **WHETMAN PINKS LTD**
Houndspool, Dawlish, Devon EX7 0QP
Ⓣ (01626) 863328
Ⓜ 07860 198238
Ⓕ (01626) 888911
Ⓔ orders@whetmanpinks.com
Ⓦ www.whetmanpinks.com
Contact: Mrs Carolyn Bourne
Opening Times: Not open. Mail order only.
Min Mail Order UK: £10.00
Min Mail Order EU: £10.00
Cat. Cost: Free.
Credit Cards: All, except American Express
Specialities: Garden pinks & hybrid *Dianthus*.
Notes: Nursery tours for clubs & societies can be arranged by appt. Also sells wholesale. Euro accepted.

CWhl **WHITEHALL GARDEN CENTRE** ♿
Corsham Road, Lacock, Chippenham, Wiltshire SN15 2LZ
Ⓣ (01249) 730204
Ⓕ (01249) 730755
Ⓔ info@whitehallgardencentre.co.uk
Ⓦ www.whitehallgardencentre.co.uk
Contact: Peter Self
Opening Times: 0830-1800 Mon-Wed & Sat, 0830-2000 Thu & Fri, 1030-1630 Sun.
Min Mail Order UK: Nmc
Cat. Cost: Online only.
Credit Cards: All major credit/debit cards
Specialities: Large selection incl. shrubs, roses, *Clematis*, conifers, herbs, herbaceous, ornamental trees and alpines. Also bedding plants.
Notes: Farm shop. Restaurant. Wheelchair accessible.
Map Ref: C, A5

CWib **WIBBLE FARM NURSERIES** ♿
Wibble Farm, West Quantoxhead,
Nr Taunton, Somerset TA4 4DD
Ⓣ (01984) 632303
Ⓕ (01984) 633168
Ⓔ sales@wibblefarmnurseries.co.uk
Ⓦ www.wibblefarmnurseries.co.uk
Contact: Mrs M L Francis
Opening Times: 0800-1700 Mon-Fri, 1000-1600 Sat. 1400-1600 Sun (open Sun Mar-Sep only). All year incl. some B/hols.
Min Mail Order UK: Nmc
Min Mail Order EU: Nmc
Cat. Cost: 3 × 1st class.
Credit Cards: All major credit/debit cards
Specialities: Growers of a wide range of hardy

plants, many rare & unusual. Display gardens.
Notes: Also sells wholesale. Wheelchair accessible.
Map Ref: C, B4

CWil **Fernwood Nursery**
Peters Marland, Torrington, Devon EX38 8QG
Ⓣ (01805) 601446
Ⓜ 07794 133116
Ⓔ hw@fernwood-nursery.co.uk
Ⓦ www.fernwood-nursery.co.uk
Contact: Howard Wills
Opening Times: Any time by appt. Please phone or email first.
Min Mail Order UK: Nmc
Min Mail Order EU: Nmc
Cat. Cost: Sae for list.
Credit Cards: Paypal
Specialities: National Collection of *Sempervivum, Jovibarba* & *Rosularia.*
Notes: Mail order for *Sempervivum, Jovibarba* & *Rosularia* only. 5 miles from RHS Rosemoor.
Exports beyond EU. Euro accepted.
Map Ref: C, C3 **OS Grid Ref:** SS479133

CWiW **Windrush Willow**
Higher Barn, Sidmouth Road, Aylesbeare, Exeter, Devon EX5 2JJ
Ⓣ (01395) 233669
Ⓕ (01395) 233669
Ⓔ windrushw@aol.com
Ⓦ www.windrushwillow.com
Contact: Richard Kerwood
Opening Times: Mail order only. Open by appt.
Min Mail Order UK: Nmc
Min Mail Order EU: Nmc
Cat. Cost: 2 × 1st class.
Credit Cards: All major credit/debit cards
Specialities: *Salix*. Unrooted cuttings available Dec-Mar.
Notes: Also sells wholesale. Euro accepted.

CWld **Wild Thyme**
(Office) The Old Orchard, Friggle Street, Frome, Somerset BA11 5LH
Ⓣ (01373) 464417
Ⓜ 07956 888477
Ⓔ jess@wildthymeplants.co.uk
Ⓦ www.wildthymeplants.co.uk
Contact: Monica Ashman
Opening Times: Not open. Mail order only via online shop.
Min Mail Order UK: £15.00
Credit Cards: MasterCard, Maestro, Visa
Specialities: Wildflowers & fragrant plants.
Notes: Delivers to shows.

CWri **Nigel Wright Rhododendrons** ♿
The Old Glebe, Eggesford, Chulmleigh, Devon EX18 7QU
Ⓣ (01769) 580632
Ⓔ wrightrhodos@aol.com
Ⓦ www.wrightrhodos.com
Contact: Nigel Wright
Opening Times: 7 days, by appt. only.
Cat. Cost: 2 × 1st class.
Credit Cards: None
Specialities: *Rhododendron* & deciduous azaleas. 200 varieties field grown, root-balled, some potted. For collection only. Specialist grower. Free advice & planting plans.
Notes: Also sells wholesale. Wheelchair accessible.
Map Ref: C, B3 **OS Grid Ref:** SS684106

CWSG **West Somerset Garden Centre** ♿
Mart Road, Minehead, Somerset TA24 5BJ
Ⓣ (01643) 703812
Ⓕ (01643) 706476
Ⓔ wsgc@btconnect.com
Ⓦ www.westsomersetgardencentre.co.uk
Contact: Ms J K Webber
Opening Times: 0800-1700 Mon-Sat, 1000-1600 Sun.
Min Mail Order UK: Nmc
Cat. Cost: None issued.
Credit Cards: American Express, Maestro, MasterCard, Solo, Visa
Specialities: Wide general range. *Clematis* & rose varieties change throughout the season.
Notes: Wheelchair accessible.
Map Ref: C, B4

CWVF **White Veil Fuchsias** ♿
Verwood Road, Three Legged Cross, Wimborne, Dorset BH21 6RP
Ⓣ (01202) 813998
Contact: A. C. Holloway
Opening Times: 0900-1300 & 1400-1700 Mon-Sat, 1000-1300 & 1400-1600 Sun, Jan-Aug. The nursery will be closed from 31st Aug to Jan 2015.
Cat. Cost: 4 × 1st class.
Credit Cards: None
Specialities: Fuchsias. Small plants grown from Jan-Apr. Available in small quantities only.
Notes: Wheelchair accessible.

CYeo **South Yeo Nursery**
Poughill, Crediton, Devon EX17 4LF
Ⓣ (01363) 866401
Ⓜ 07971 412132
Ⓕ (01363) 866740
Ⓔ davidross350@btinternet.com
Ⓦ hesperantha.co.uk
Contact: David Ross

Opening Times: By appt. only.
Min Mail Order UK: £10
Min Mail Order EU: £30
Cat. Cost: 6 × 1st class
Credit Cards: Paypal
Specialities: All plants grown are from micro-propagated plugs, virus-checked by FERA, and have been through an extensive verification programme. More cvs will become available during the year. National Collection of *Hesperantha coccinea* cvs.
Notes: Also sells wholesale. Exports beyond EU. Delivers to shows. Euro accepted.
Map Ref: C, C3 **OS Grid Ref:** SS865085

E

Eastern

EABi **Alison Bilverstone**
22 Kings Street, Swaffham, Norfolk PE37 7BU
Ⓣ (01760) 725026
Ⓔ a.bilverstone@tiscali.co.uk
Contact: Alison Bilverstone
Opening Times: Not open. Mail order only.
Min Mail Order UK: Nmc
Min Mail Order EU: Nmc
Cat. Cost: A5 sae 2nd class (large letter rate postage).
Credit Cards: None
Specialities: *Achemene*, *Kohleria* & *Smithiantha* rhizomes, available Dec to mid-Apr. Stocked in small quantities.
Notes: Euro accepted.

EACa **Alpine Campanulas (Bellflower Nursery)**
Langham Hall Walled Garden, Langham, Nr Bury St Edmunds, Suffolk IP31 3EE
Ⓜ 07879 644958
Ⓔ campanulas@btinternet.com
Ⓦ www.bellflowernursery.co.uk
Contact: Sue Wooster
Opening Times: 1000-1630 Thu & Fri, mid-Mar to end Oct. Other times by appt.
Min Mail Order UK: £10.00
Cat. Cost: A5 sae 1 × 1st class (large letter rate postage).
Credit Cards: None
Specialities: *Campanula*. National Collection of Alpine Campanulas. Most stock in small numbers only.
Notes: Hardy plant nursery within the Walled Garden, Langham Hall. Groups welcome by appt.
Map Ref: E, C3 **OS Grid Ref:** TL978691

EAEE **AEE – A Lover of Plants** ♿
Snetterton Park, Harling Road (off A11), Snetterton, Norfolk NR16 2JU
Ⓣ (01379) 651230
Ⓜ 07874 214182
Ⓔ aeesales@fsmail.net
Ⓦ www.aeesupplyingplantlovers.com
Contact: Anne Etheridge
Opening Times: 0900-1700 7 days, Mar-Sep. 1000-1600 Tue, Thu, Fri, Sun, Oct-Feb.
Min Mail Order UK: Nmc
Min Mail Order EU: Nmc
Credit Cards: All major credit/debit cards
Specialities: Perennials & grasses plus a few enticing alpines & shrubs. Alpines available in small quantities only.
Notes: Talks available Mar-Oct. For information on group & trade discounts please contact nursery. Plants delivered free within 10 miles of Roydon, Diss or Snetterton Park. Coffee shop on site. Wheelchair accessible.

EAJP **A & J Plants**
Scenterfields, Chapel Road, Great Tey, Colchester, Essex CO6 1JR
Ⓣ (01206) 212124
Ⓕ (01206) 212124
Ⓔ mail@aandjplants.com
Ⓦ www.aandjplants.com
Contact: Jackie Rhodes
Opening Times: Not open. Mail order only. Orders can be collected from nursery by prior arrangement.
Min Mail Order UK: Nmc
Credit Cards: MasterCard, Visa
Specialities: Wide variety of choice perennials and ornamental grasses propagated on the nursery, some in small quantities.
Notes: Plant Centre at Marks Hall Garden (CO6 1TG) stocked with seasonal selection of perennials & grasses. Also sells wholesale. Delivers to shows.

EAla **Alafin Arids & Exotics**
Alafin, Langford Road, Maldon, Essex CM9 4SU
Ⓣ (01621) 858384
Ⓜ 07725 876187
Contact: David Griffin
Opening Times: Open by appt. only (not Wed.). Please phone mobile number for appt.
Credit Cards: None
Specialities: *Yucca*, *Agave*. All plants available in small numbers.

EBak **B & H M Baker** ♿
Bourne Brook Nurseries, Greenstead Green, Halstead, Essex CO9 1RB
Ⓣ (01787) 476369
Contact: Clive Baker
Opening Times: 0800-1600 Mon-Fri, 0900-1200 & 1400-1600 Sat & Sun, Mar-30th Jun.
Cat. Cost: 2 × 1st class + 33p.
Credit Cards: All major credit/debit cards

Specialities: *Fuchsia* & conservatory plants.
Notes: Also sells wholesale. Wheelchair accessible.
Map Ref: E, C2

EBar **Barcham Trees PLC**
Eye Hill Drove, Ely, Cambridgeshire CB7 5XF
Ⓣ (01353) 720748
Ⓜ 07801 917566
Ⓕ (01353) 723060
Ⓔ mike@barchamtrees.co.uk
Ⓦ www.barcham.co.uk
Contact: Mike Glover
Opening Times: 0900-1700 Mon-Fri. Visits to the nursery by appt. only.
Cat. Cost: £10.00
Credit Cards: All major credit/debit cards
Specialities: Large grower of containerised trees. 478 varieties available, from 10-12cm to 40cm girth.
Notes: As trees range from 3-8 metres all are despatched on lorries rather than through the mailing service. Also sells wholesale. Exports beyond EU. Euro accepted. E-commerce site: www.buythetreeyousee.com.

EBee **Beeches Nursery** ♿
Village Centre, Ashdon, Saffron Walden, Essex CB10 2HB
Ⓣ (01799) 584362
Ⓕ (01799) 584421
Ⓔ sales@beechesnursery.co.uk
Ⓦ www.beechesnursery.co.uk
Contact: Alan Bidwell/Kevin Marsh
Opening Times: 0830-1700 Mon-Sat, 1000-1700 Sun & B/hols.
Min Mail Order UK: £15.00
Min Mail Order EU: £20.00
Cat. Cost: Online.
Credit Cards: All major credit/debit cards
Specialities: Herbaceous specialists & extensive range of other garden plants. Rarieties available in limited numbers only.
Notes: Plants dispatched Oct-Feb only. Orders accepted throughout the year. No trees by mail order. Wheelchair accessible.
Map Ref: E, C2 **OS Grid Ref:** TL586420

EBen **Bennison Peonies**
The Grange, East Firsby, Market Rasen, Lincolnshire LN8 2DB
Ⓣ (01673) 878289
Ⓔ info@BennisonPeonies.co.uk
Ⓦ www.BennisonPeonies.co.uk
Contact: Jo Bennison
Opening Times: W/ends 7th/8th & 14th/15th June 2014.
Min Mail Order UK: £10 + p&p
Min Mail Order EU: £10 + p&p
Cat. Cost: Online only.
Credit Cards: None
Specialities: *Paeonia.*
Map Ref: E, A1 **OS Grid Ref:** TF022857

EBtc **Botanica**
Chantry Farm, Campsea Ashe, Wickham Market, Suffolk IP13 0PZ
Ⓣ (01728) 747113
Ⓜ 07887 423964
Ⓕ (01728) 747725
Ⓔ sales@botanica.org.uk
Ⓦ www.botanicaplantnursery.co.uk
Contact: Daniel Everett
Opening Times: 1000-1700 6 days summer, 1000-1700 5 days August, 1000-1600 7 days winter.
Min Mail Order UK: £15 + p&p
Cat. Cost: Online only.
Credit Cards: All, except American Express
Specialities: Range of rare & unusual hardy plants. All stock is English-grown on our nursery and in non-peat based compost.
Notes: Also sells wholesale.
Map Ref: E, C3 **OS Grid Ref:** TM328550

ECGP **Cambridge Garden Plants** ♿
The Lodge, Clayhithe Road, Horningsea, Cambridgeshire CB25 9JD
Ⓣ (01223) 861370
Ⓔ kit@cambridgegardenplants.co.uk
Contact: Kit Buchdahl
Opening Times: 1100-1730 Thu-Sun mid Mar-31st Oct. Other times by appt.
Cat. Cost: 4 × 1st class.
Credit Cards: None
Specialities: Hardy perennials incl. wide range of *Geranium, Allium, Euphorbia, Cyclamen, Digitalis.*
Notes: Euro accepted. Wheelchair accessible.
Map Ref: E, C2 **OS Grid Ref:** TL497637

ECha **The Beth Chatto Gardens Ltd** ♿
Clacton Road, Elmstead Market, Colchester, Essex CO7 7DB
Ⓣ (01206) 822007
Ⓕ (01206) 825933
Ⓔ info@bethchatto.co.uk
Ⓦ www.bethchatto.co.uk
Contact: Beth Chatto
Opening Times: 0900-1700 Mon-Sat, 1000-1700 Sun, 1st Mar-31st Oct. 0900-1600 Mon-Sat, 1000-1600 Sun, Nov-end Feb.
Min Mail Order UK: Nmc
Min Mail Order EU: Ask for details
Cat. Cost: Free.
Credit Cards: All, except American Express
Specialities: Predominantly herbaceous. Many unusual for special situations.
Notes: Wheelchair accessible.
Map Ref: E, D3 **OS Grid Ref:** TM069238

E

ECho **Choice Landscapes** ♿
Priory Farm, 101 Salts Road,
West Walton, Wisbech,
Cambridgeshire
PE14 7EF
Ⓣ (01945) 585051
Ⓔ info@choicelandscapes.org
Ⓦ www.choicelandscapes.org
Contact: Jillian Agg
Opening Times: By appt.
Min Mail Order UK: £15.00
Min Mail Order EU: £15.00 + p&p
Cat. Cost: 4 × 1st class.
Specialities: Alpines, bulbs, lilies & South African bulbs.
Notes: Delivers to shows. Wheelchair accessible.
Map Ref: E, B1

ECnt **Cants of Colchester Ltd**
Nayland Road, Mile End,
Colchester, Essex
CO4 5HA
Ⓣ (01206) 844008
Ⓕ (01206) 855371
Ⓔ enquiries@cantsroses.co.uk
Ⓦ www.cantsroses.co.uk
Contact: Angela Pawsey
Opening Times: 0900-1300, 1400-1630 Mon-Fri. Sat varied, please phone first. Sun closed.
Min Mail Order UK: Nmc
Min Mail Order EU: Nmc
Cat. Cost: Free
Credit Cards: Delta, MasterCard, Maestro, Visa
Specialities: Roses. Unstaffed rose field can be viewed dawn-dusk every day from end Jun to end Sep.
Notes: Bare-root mail order end Oct to end Mar, containers Apr-Aug. Exports beyond EU. Partial wheelchair access.
Map Ref: E, C3

ECou **County Park Nursery**
Essex Gardens,
Hornchurch, Essex
RM11 3BU
Ⓜ 07935 906866
Ⓔ info@countyparknursery.co.uk
Ⓦ www.countyparknursery.co.uk
Contact: Paul Boosey
Opening Times: By appt. only.
Cat. Cost: Online only.
Credit Cards: None
Specialities: Alpines & rare and unusual plants from New Zealand, Tasmania & the Falklands. Many plants available in small quantities only.
Notes: Euro accepted.

ECrc **The Crocosmia Gardens**
9 North Street, Caistor, Lincolnshire
LN7 6QU
Ⓣ (01472) 859269
Ⓜ 07747 304620
Ⓔ mark@thecrocosmiagardens.net
Ⓦ www.thecrocosmiagardens.net
Contact: Mark Fox
Opening Times: 1000-1700 Mon-Sun.
Min Mail Order UK: £5.00
Min Mail Order EU: £5.00
Credit Cards: None
Specialities: *Crocosmia*. National Collection of *Crocosmia*.
Notes: Exports beyond EU. Euro accepted.
Map Ref: E, A1

ECre **Creake Plant Centre** ♿
Leicester Road, South Creake, Fakenham,
Norfolk NR21 9PW
Ⓣ (01328) 823018
Ⓜ 07760 762499
Ⓕ (01328) 823018
Ⓔ trevor-harrison@btconnect.com
Ⓦ www.creakeplantcentre.co.uk
Contact: Mr T Harrison
Opening Times: 1000-1300 & 1400-1730 7 days excl. Xmas.
Cat. Cost: None issued
Credit Cards: All major credit/debit cards
Specialities: Unusual shrubs, herbaceous, conservatory plants, old roses. Hellebores. Some plants only available in small quantities.
Notes: Wheelchair accessible.
Map Ref: E, B1 **OS Grid Ref:** TF864353

ECrN **Crown Nursery** ♿
High Street, Ufford, Suffolk IP13 6EL
Ⓣ (01394) 460755
Ⓕ (01394) 460142
Ⓔ enquiries@crown-nursery.co.uk
Ⓦ www.crown-nursery.co.uk
Contact: Jill Proctor
Opening Times: 0900-1700 (1600 in winter) Mon-Sat.
Min Mail Order UK: Nmc
Credit Cards: All major credit/debit cards
Specialities: Mature & semi-mature native, ornamental & fruit trees. Heritage fruit varieties.
Notes: Mail order for small/young stock only. Also sells wholesale. Wheelchair accessible.
Map Ref: E, C3 **OS Grid Ref:** TM292528

ECtt **Cottage Nurseries** ♿
Thoresthorpe, Alford, Lincolnshire
LN13 0HX
Ⓣ (01507) 466968
Ⓕ (01507) 463409
Ⓔ bill@cottagenurseries.net

Ⓦ www.cottagenurseries.net
Contact: W H Denbigh
Opening Times: 0900-1700, 7 days 1st Mar-31st Oct. 1000-1500, Nov-Feb. Closed 15th Dec-6th Jan.
Min Mail Order UK: £15.00
Cat. Cost: 4 × 1st class.
Credit Cards: MasterCard, Maestro, Visa
Specialities: Hardy perennials. Wide general range.
Notes: Wheelchair accessible.
Map Ref: E, A2 **OS Grid Ref:** TF461776

EDAr **D'Arcy & Everest**
(Office) PO Box 78, St Ives, Huntingdon, Cambridgeshire PE27 6ZA
Ⓣ (01480) 497672 answerphone
Ⓜ 07715 374440
Ⓕ (01480) 466042
Ⓔ angela@darcyeverest.co.uk
Ⓦ www.darcyeverest.co.uk
Contact: Angela Whiting, Richard Oliver
Opening Times: 1000-1500 Wed-Sat, Mar-end Sep. Nursery gardens open Sat only, but close at 1400 if an event on. Winter by appt. Coach parties welcome by appt.
Min Mail Order UK: £15.00 + p&p
Min Mail Order EU: £50.00 + p&p
Cat. Cost: 6 × 1st class.
Credit Cards: All major credit/debit cards
Specialities: Alpines & sempervivums.
Notes: Nursery is at Pidley Sheep Lane (B1040), Pidley, Huntingdon, Cambs PE28 3FL. Delivers to shows. Euro accepted. Partial wheelchair access.
Map Ref: E, C2 **OS Grid Ref:** TL338762

EDel **Delfland Nurseries Ltd** ♿
Benwick Road, Doddington, March, Cambridgeshire PE15 0TU
Ⓣ (01354) 740553
Ⓕ (01354) 741200
Ⓔ info@delfland.co.uk
Ⓦ www.organicplants.co.uk
Contact: Jill Vaughan
Opening Times: 0900-1600 Mon-Fri, 0900-1300 Sat, all year. Additionally, at peak season, 0900-1600 Sat & 1000-1600 Sun.
Min Mail Order UK: £1.95 + p&p
Cat. Cost: Free or online.
Credit Cards: All major credit/debit cards
Specialities: Vegetable, bedding & container plants.
Notes: Mail order and retail organic & peat-free from stock (mainly veg. plants) or to order (for large orders). Retail bedding & container plants not organic or peat-free. Also sells wholesale. Wheelchair accessible.
Map Ref: E, C2 **OS Grid Ref:** TL386908

EECP **Essex Carnivorous Plants**
12 Strangman Avenue, Thundersley, Essex SS7 1RB
Ⓣ (01702) 551467
Ⓜ 07957 196391
Ⓔ Mark@essexcarnivorousplants.com
Ⓦ www.essexcarnivorousplants.com
Contact: Mark Haslett
Opening Times: By appt. only.
Min Mail Order UK: Nmc
Min Mail Order EU: Nmc
Cat. Cost: 2 × 1st class or online.
Credit Cards: None
Specialities: Good range of carnivorous plants. *Sarracenia*, *Dionaea*. Some stock available in small quantities only.
Notes: Also sells wholesale. Delivers to shows.
Map Ref: E, D2 **OS Grid Ref:** TQ797875

EFer **The Fern Nursery** ♿
Grimsby Road, Binbrook, Lincolnshire LN8 6DH
Ⓣ (01472) 398092
Ⓔ rtimm@fernnursery.co.uk
Ⓦ www.fernnursery.co.uk
Contact: R N Timm
Opening Times: 0900-1700 Fri, Sat & Sun Apr-Oct or by appt.
Min Mail Order UK: Nmc
Min Mail Order EU: Nmc
Cat. Cost: 2 × 1st class.
Credit Cards: None
Specialities: Ferns. Display garden.
Notes: Only plants in the mail order part of the catalogue can be sent mail order. Also sells wholesale. Euro accepted. Wheelchair accessible.
Map Ref: E, A1 **OS Grid Ref:** TF212942

EFEx **Flora Exotica**
Pasadena, South-Green, Fingringhoe, Colchester, Essex CO5 7DR
Ⓜ 07989 456094
Contact: J Beddoes
Opening Times: Not open. Mail order only.
Min Mail Order UK: Nmc
Min Mail Order EU: Nmc
Cat. Cost: 4 × 1st class.
Credit Cards: None
Specialities: Exotica flora incl. orchids.
Notes: Exports beyond EU. Euro accepted.

EFly **The Fly Trap Plants** ♿
Cookes Road, Thurton, Norwich, Norfolk NR14 6AE
Ⓣ (01508) 480348
Ⓜ 07769 256556
Ⓔ sales@tftplants.co.uk
Ⓦ www.tftplants.co.uk
Contact: Pauline Steward

Opening Times: By appt. only.
Min Mail Order UK: Nmc
Cat. Cost: 1 × 1st class sae
Credit Cards: None
Specialities: All kinds of carnivorous plants, from *Sarracenia*, *Drosera*, *Pinguicula*, to *Utricularia* aquatic plants.
Notes: Delivers to shows. Euro accepted. Wheelchair accessible.

EFry **Jack Fryer Conifer Specialist (formerly Hull Farm)**
Sunnyside, Spring Valley Lane, Ardleigh, Colchester, Essex CO7 7SB
Ⓜ 07587 777085 or 07900 298366
Ⓔ jack.wendyfryer@mail.com
Contact: Jack Fryer
Opening Times: By appt. only. Please phone for appt.
Min Mail Order UK: £50.00 + p&p
Cat. Cost: 5 × 2nd class.
Credit Cards: None
Specialities: Conifers.
Notes: Also sells wholesale.
Map Ref: E, C3 **OS Grid Ref:** GR043274

EGFP **Grange Farm Plants** ♿
Grange Farm, 38 Fishergate Road, Sutton St James, Spalding, Lincolnshire PE12 0EZ
Ⓣ (01945) 440240
Ⓜ 07742 138760
Ⓕ (01945) 440355
Ⓔ ellis.family@tinyonline.co.uk
Contact: M C Ellis
Opening Times: Mail order only. Open by appt. only.
Min Mail Order UK: Nmc
Min Mail Order EU: Nmc
Cat. Cost: 1 × 1st class.
Credit Cards: None
Specialities: Rare trees & shrubs, esp. *Juglans*, *Fraxinus*. Some species available in small quantities only.
Notes: Euro accepted. Wheelchair accessible.

EHoe **Hoecroft Plants** ♿
Severals Grange, Holt Road, Wood Norton, Norfolk NR20 5BL
Ⓣ (01362) 684206
Ⓔ hoecroft@hotmail.co.uk
Ⓦ www.hoecroft.co.uk
Contact: Jane Lister
Opening Times: 1000-1600 Thu-Sun, 1st Apr-31st Oct or by appt.
Min Mail Order UK: Nmc
Min Mail Order EU: Nmc
Cat. Cost: 5 × 2nd class.
Credit Cards: None
Specialities: An extensive range of coloured & variegated-leaved shrubs & herbaceous perennials. 260 ornamental grasses. Free entry to display gardens.
Notes: Nursery 2 miles north of Guist on B1110. Euro accepted. Wheelchair accessible.
Map Ref: E, B3 **OS Grid Ref:** TG008289

EHon **Honeysome Aquatic Nursery**
The Row, Sutton, Nr Ely, Cambridgeshire CB6 2PB
Ⓣ (01353) 778889
Ⓕ (01353) 777291
Ⓔ info@honeysomeaquaticnursery.co.uk
Ⓦ www.honeysomeaquaticnursery.co.uk
Contact: Mrs L S Bond
Opening Times: At all times by appt. only.
Min Mail Order UK: Nmc
Cat. Cost: 2 × 2nd class.
Credit Cards: Paypal
Specialities: Hardy aquatic, bog & marginal.
Notes: Also sells wholesale.
Map Ref: E, C2

EHrv **Harveys Garden Plants** ♿
Great Green, Thurston, Bury St Edmunds, Suffolk IP31 3SJ
Ⓣ (01359) 233363
Ⓕ (01359) 233363 & answerphone
Ⓔ admin@harveysgardenplants.co.uk
Ⓦ www.harveysgardenplants.co.uk
Contact: Roger Harvey
Opening Times: 0930-1630 Mon-Sun, excl. Xmas & New Year's Day.
Min Mail Order UK: £20.00
Min Mail Order EU: £20.00
Cat. Cost: £3.00
Credit Cards: All major credit/debit cards
Specialities: *Helleborus*, *Anemone*, *Epimedium*, *Galanthus*, *Astrantia*, *Pulmonaria* & other herbaceous perennials, plus shade & woodland plants.
Notes: Full garden design & maintenance service. Delivers to shows. Euro accepted. Wheelchair accessible.
Map Ref: E, C2 **OS Grid Ref:** TL94127

EIri **Irisesonline**
Slade Cottage, Petts Lane, Little Walden, Essex CB10 1XH
Ⓣ (01799) 526294
Ⓔ sales@irisesonline.co.uk
Ⓦ www.irisesonline.co.uk
Contact: Clare Kneen
Opening Times: By appt. only.
Min Mail Order UK: Nmc
Cat. Cost: 3 × 1st class or online.
Credit Cards: None
Specialities: *Iris*. Small family-run nursery. Some varieties available in small quantities only.
Notes: Delivers to shows.
Map Ref: E, C2 **OS Grid Ref:** TL546416

ELad **LADYBIRD NURSERIES** ♿
Gromford Lane, Snape, Saxmundham, Suffolk IP17 1RD
Ⓣ (01728) 688289
Ⓔ ladybirdnurseriessnape@gmail.com
Ⓦ www.ladybirdnurseries.co.uk
Contact: Mrs M Booker
Opening Times: 0900-1700, Mon-Sat, 1000-1600 Sun.
Credit Cards: All major credit/debit cards
Notes: Wheelchair accessible.

ELan **LANGTHORNS PLANTERY** ♿
High Cross Lane West, Little Canfield, Dunmow, Essex CM6 1TD
Ⓣ (01371) 872611
Ⓕ 0871 661 4093
Ⓔ info@langthorns.com
Ⓦ www.langthorns.com
Contact: E Cannon
Opening Times: 1000-1700 or dusk (if earlier) 7 days excl. Xmas fortnight.
Min Mail Order UK: £15.00
Cat. Cost: Online only.
Credit Cards: Access, Delta, MasterCard, Switch, Visa
Specialities: Wide general range with many unusual plants.
Notes: Mail order anything under 4ft tall. Mail order not available during spring & summer months. Wheelchair accessible.
Map Ref: E, D2 **OS Grid Ref:** TL592204

ELon **LONG HOUSE PLANTS** ♿
The Long House, Church Road, Noak Hill, Romford, Essex RM4 1LD
Ⓣ (01708) 371719
Ⓔ tim@longhouse-plants.co.uk
Ⓦ www.longhouse-plants.co.uk
Contact: Tim Carter
Opening Times: 1000-1700 Fri, Sat & B/hols, 1000-1600 Sun, Mar to end Sep, or by appt.
Cat. Cost: None issued.
Credit Cards: All major credit/debit cards
Specialities: Interesting range of choice trees, shrubs, climbers, roses, grasses, herbaceous perennials & ferns. Many unusual varieties. Specialities incl. *Agapanthus*, asters, *Camellia*, *Hemerocallis*, *Iris sibirica*, *Kniphofia*, *Papaver orientale* & *Phlox*. Some plants available in small quantities.
Notes: Wheelchair accessible.
Map Ref: E, D2 **OS Grid Ref:** TQ554194

EMac **FIRECREST TREES & SHRUBS NURSERY** ♿
Hall Road, Little Bealings, Woodbridge, Suffolk IP13 6LG
Ⓣ (01473) 625937
Ⓕ (01473) 625937
Ⓔ mac@firecrest.org.uk
Ⓦ www.firecrest.org.uk
Contact: Mac McGregor
Opening Times: 0900-1600 Mon-Fri, 1230 Sat.
Min Mail Order UK: Nmc
Cat. Cost: 2 × 1st class (bare root only).
Credit Cards: None
Specialities: Trees & shrubs. Japanese maples. Bare-root hedging.
Notes: Also sells wholesale. Euro accepted. Wheelchair accessible.

EMal **MARSHALL'S MALMAISONS** ♿
Hullwood Barn, Shelley, Ipswich, Suffolk IP7 5RE
Ⓣ (01473) 822400
Ⓜ 07768 454875
Ⓔ jim@malmaisons.plus.com
Ⓦ www.malmaisonsandiris.co.uk
Contact: J M Marshall/Sarah Cook
Opening Times: By appt. only.
Min Mail Order UK: £33.00 incl. p&p
Min Mail Order EU: £36.00 incl. p&p
Cat. Cost: 1st class sae.
Credit Cards: None
Specialities: National Collections of Malmaison Carnations & Cedric Morris Irises. *Iris* stock only available in small quantities.
Notes: Also sells wholesale. Wheelchair accessible.
Map Ref: E, C3 **OS Grid Ref:** TM006394

EMic **MICKFIELD HOSTAS** ♿
The Poplars, Mickfield, Stowmarket, Suffolk IP14 5LH
Ⓣ (01449) 711576
Ⓕ (01449) 711576
Ⓔ mickfieldhostas@btconnect.com
Ⓦ www.mickfieldhostas.co.uk
Contact: Mr & Mrs R L C Milton
Opening Times: Nursery open every day, all season.
Min Mail Order UK: Nmc
Min Mail Order EU: Nmc
Cat. Cost: 1st class.
Credit Cards: All, except American Express
Specialities: National Collection of *Hosta* containing over 2000 varieties. See website for details of cvs held & latest availability. Operates waiting list for rarities & some limited quantity plants only available at nursery. Will divide parent plants for collectors if feasible. Expect to pay more for root divisions of mature plants.
Notes: Delivers to shows. Euro accepted. Wheelchair accessible.
Map Ref: E, C3 **OS Grid Ref:** TM136619

E

EMil **Mill Race Garden Centre** ♿
New Road, Aldham, Colchester, Essex
CO6 3QT
Ⓣ (01206) 242521
Ⓔ plantdesk@millracegardencentre.co.uk
Ⓦ www.millracegardencentre.co.uk
Contact: Annette Bayliss
Opening Times: 0900-1730 Mon-Sat, 1000-1630 Sun.
Min Mail Order UK: £9.00
Credit Cards: All major credit/debit cards
Specialities: Stock available in small quantities only.
Notes: Trees & large shrubs not sent by mail order. Wheelchair accessible.
Map Ref: E, C2 **OS Grid Ref:** TL918268

ENBC **Norfolk Bamboo Company**
Vine Cottage, The Drift, Ingoldisthorpe, King's Lynn, Norfolk
PE31 6NW
Ⓣ (01485) 543935
Ⓜ 07970 310880
Ⓔ Lewdyer@hotmail.com
Ⓦ www.norfolkbamboo.co.uk
Contact: Lewis Dyer
Opening Times: 1000-1600 Fri & 1000-1400 Sat, Apr-Sep, or by appt.
Min Mail Order UK: £10.00 + p&p
Cat. Cost: 1 × 1st class sae for price list.
Credit Cards: None
Specialities: Bamboos.
Map Ref: E, B2

ENfk **Norfolk Herbs** ♿
Blackberry Farm, Dillington, Dereham, Norfolk NR19 2QD
Ⓣ (01362) 860812
Ⓕ (01362) 860812
Ⓔ info@norfolkherbs.co.uk
Ⓦ www.norfolkherbs.co.uk
Contact: Rosemary or Oliver Clifton-Sprigg
Opening Times: 0900-1700 Mon-Sat, 1000-1600 Sun, Apr-Aug. 1000-1600 Fri & Sat, Feb, Oct & Nov. 1000-1600 Wed-Sat, Mar, Sept & Dec. Closed from Xmas to end Jan. To visit at other times, please contact nursery.
Min Mail Order UK: £6.90
Cat. Cost: 2 × 2nd class.
Credit Cards: All major credit/debit cards
Specialities: Growers & suppliers of naturally raised culinary, medicinal & aromatic herb plants. Bay trees & scented pelagoniums.
Notes: Established 1986. Sells from nursery, online & at local shows. A founding member of Norfolk Nursery Network. Also sells wholesale. Delivers to shows. Wheelchair accessible.
Map Ref: E, B2 **OS Grid Ref:** TF967150

ENun **Twelve Nunns** ◆
16 Carisbrook Grove, Stamford, Lincolnshire
PE9 2GF
Ⓣ (01778) 590455
Ⓔ penny@twelvenunns.co.uk
Ⓦ www.twelvenunns.co.uk
Contact: Penny Dawson
Opening Times: Not open. Mail order only.
Min Mail Order UK: Nmc
Min Mail Order EU: Nmc
Cat. Cost: Free.
Credit Cards: All major credit/debit cards
Specialities: *Helleborus*, incl. plants with "Harvington" prefix, *Roscoea*, *Erythronium* & *Trillium*. Plants bred, propagated & grown on nursery.
Notes: Also sells wholesale.

EOHP **Old Hall Plants**
1 The Old Hall, Barsham, Beccles, Suffolk
NR34 8HB
Ⓣ (01502) 717475
Ⓔ info@oldhallplants.co.uk
Ⓦ www.oldhallplants.co.uk
Contact: Janet Elliott
Opening Times: By appt. only. Please phone first.
Min Mail Order UK: Nmc
Min Mail Order EU: Nmc
Cat. Cost: 4 × 1st class.
Credit Cards: Paypal
Specialities: A variety of rare herbs, house plants, *Plectranthus*. Some plants available in small quantities.
Notes: Partial wheelchair access. Paypal accepted for overseas orders only.
Map Ref: E, C3 **OS Grid Ref:** TM396904

EPau **Paugers Plants Ltd**
Bury Road, Depden, Bury St Edmunds, Suffolk IP29 4BU
Ⓣ (01284) 850527
Ⓜ 07906 618603
Ⓔ enquiries@paugers-plants.co.uk
Ⓦ www.paugers-plants.co.uk
Contact: Geraldine Arnold
Opening Times: 0900-1730 Wed-Sat, 1000-1700 Sun & B/hols, 1st Mar-30th Nov.
Min Mail Order UK: Nmc
Cat. Cost: None issued.
Credit Cards: All major credit/debit cards
Specialities: Hardy shrubs & perennials in large or small quantities.
Notes: Also sells wholesale.
Map Ref: E, C2 **OS Grid Ref:** TL783568

EPfP **The Place for Plants**
East Bergholt Place, East Bergholt, Suffolk
CO7 6UP
Ⓣ (01206) 299224

Ⓕ (01206) 299229
Ⓔ sales@placeforplants.co.uk
Ⓦ www.placeforplants.co.uk
Contact: Marie Pertwee
Opening Times: 1000-1700 (or dusk if earlier) 7 days. Closed Easter Sun. Garden open Mar-Oct.
Min Mail Order UK: Nmc
Cat. Cost: Online only.
Credit Cards: All major credit/debit cards
Specialities: Wide range of specialist & popular plants. National Collection of Deciduous *Euonymus*. 20 acre mature garden with free access to RHS members during season (excl. Sun).
Notes: Mail order from Sep-Feb. Delivers to shows. Euro accepted.
Map Ref: E, C3

EPom **Pomona Fruits Ltd**
Pomona House, 12 Third Avenue, Walton-on-the-Naze, Essex CO14 8JU
Ⓣ 0845 676 0607
Ⓕ 0845 676 0608
Ⓔ Info@PomonaFruits.co.uk
Ⓦ www.PomonaFruits.co.uk
Contact: Ming Yang/Claire Higgins
Opening Times: Not open. Mail order only.
Min Mail Order UK: Nmc
Cat. Cost: Free.
Credit Cards: All major credit/debit cards
Specialities: Fruit stock.
Map Ref: E, D3

EPot **Pottertons Nursery** ♿
Moortown Road, Nettleton, Caistor, Lincolnshire LN7 6HX
Ⓣ (01472) 851714
Ⓕ (01472) 852580
Ⓔ sales@pottertons.co.uk
Ⓦ www.pottertons.co.uk
Contact: Robert Potterton
Opening Times: 1000-1600 Tue-Sat, Mar-Oct. 1000-1530 Tue-Fri, Nov-Feb.
Min Mail Order UK: Nmc
Min Mail Order EU: Nmc
Cat. Cost: £2.00 in stamps
Credit Cards: MasterCard, Visa
Specialities: Alpines, dwarf bulbs & woodland plants. Hardy orchids & *Pleione*.
Notes: External talks nationally & internationally to garden clubs & societies. Group nursery tours by arrangement. Delivers to shows. Euro accepted. Wheelchair accessible.
Map Ref: E, A1 **OS Grid Ref:** TA091001

EPPr **The Plantsman's Preference** ♿
Church Road, South Lopham, Diss, Norfolk IP22 2LW
Ⓣ Office (evenings): (01953) 681439
Ⓜ Nursery (day): 07799 855559
Ⓔ tim@plantpref.co.uk
Ⓦ www.plantpref.co.uk
Contact: Tim Fuller
Opening Times: 0930-1700 Fri, Sat & Sun Mar-Oct. Other times by appt.
Min Mail Order UK: Nmc
Min Mail Order EU: Nmc
Cat. Cost: Online only.
Credit Cards: All major credit/debit cards
Specialities: Hardy geraniums & ornamental grasses. Unusual & interesting perennials incl. shade/woodland. Some choice shrubs esp. *Caprifoliaceae*. National Collection of *Molinia*.
Notes: Delivers to shows. Wheelchair accessible.
Map Ref: E, C3 **OS Grid Ref:** TM041819

EPri **Priory Plants** ♿
1 Covey Cottages, Hintlesham, Nr Ipswich, Suffolk IP8 3NY
Ⓣ (01473) 652656
Ⓜ 07798 627618
Ⓕ (01473) 652656
Ⓔ sue.mann3@btinternet.com
Ⓦ www.prioryplants.co.uk
Contact: Sue Mann
Opening Times: By appt. only. Please ring first to avoid disappointment.
Min Mail Order UK: £15.00 + p&p
Min Mail Order EU: £25.00
Cat. Cost: Online only.
Credit Cards: None
Specialities: Cottage garden perennials, as well as increasing range of South African plants. *Agapanthus, Astrantia, Dierama, Dietes, Geum*, Siberian *Iris, Kniphofia, Nerine, Papaver, Tritonia, Tulbaghia* & *Watsonia*.
Notes: Sells at plant fairs & agricultural shows. Also sells wholesale. Delivers to shows. Wheelchair accessible.
Map Ref: E, C3 **OS Grid Ref:** TM070448

EPts **Potash Nursery** ♿
Cow Green, Bacton, Stowmarket, Suffolk IP14 4HJ
Ⓣ (01449) 781671
Ⓔ enquiries@potashnursery.co.uk
Ⓦ www.potashnursery.co.uk
Contact: M W Clare
Opening Times: Pre-ordered plants can be collected by appt. only.
Min Mail Order UK: £21.00
Cat. Cost: 1 × 1st class.
Credit Cards: Delta, MasterCard, Visa
Specialities: *Fuchsia*.
Notes: Peat free. Delivers to shows. Wheelchair accessible.
Map Ref: E, C3 **OS Grid Ref:** TM0565NE

E

EPyc **Pennycross Plants**
Earith Road, Colne, Huntingdon, Cambridgeshire PE28 3NL
Ⓣ (01487) 841520
Ⓔ salvias@pennycrossplants.co.uk
Contact: Janet M Buist
Opening Times: 1000-1600 Mon-Fri, 1st Apr-31st Jul. Sep by appt.
Cat. Cost: 1 × 2nd class for *Salvia* list only.
Credit Cards: None
Specialities: Hardy perennials. Salvias. Some plants available in limited quantities only. Will propagate salvias to order.
Notes: Delivers to shows.
Map Ref: E, C2 **OS Grid Ref:** TL378759

ERCP **Rose Cottage Plants**
Bay Tree Farm, Epping Green, Essex CM16 6PU
Ⓣ (01992) 573775
Ⓔ anne@rosecottageplants.co.uk
Ⓦ www.rosecottageplants.co.uk
Contact: Anne & Jack Barnard
Opening Times: By appt. & for special events (see website for details).
Min Mail Order UK: Nmc
Min Mail Order EU: £20.00
Cat. Cost: Online only.
Credit Cards: All major credit/debit cards
Specialities: Bulbs.
Notes: Mail order, bulbs only. Delivers to shows.
Map Ref: E, B1 **OS Grid Ref:** TL435053

ERea **Reads Nursery**
Douglas Farm, Bungay, Suffolk NR35 2JG
Ⓣ (01986) 895555
Ⓔ plants@readsnursery.co.uk
Ⓦ www.readsnursery.co.uk
Contact: Stephen Read
Opening Times: Not open. Mail order only.
Min Mail Order UK: Nmc
Min Mail Order EU: Nmc
Cat. Cost: Free.
Credit Cards: All major credit/debit cards
Specialities: Ornamental & unusual fruit trees. Soft fruit. *Magnolia*.

ERod **The Rodings Plantery** ♿
Anchor Lane, Abbess Roding, Essex CM5 0JW
Ⓣ (01279) 876421
Ⓜ 07790 020940
Ⓔ janeandandy@therodingsplantery.co.uk
Ⓦ www.therodingsplantery.co.uk
Contact: Jane & Andy Mogridge
Opening Times: 1000-1600 Wed & Sat. By appt. only. Occasional open days, please phone for details.
Min Mail Order UK: Nmc
Min Mail Order EU: £500.00 + p&p
Cat. Cost: 3 × 1st class.
Credit Cards: None
Specialities: Bamboos. Rare & unusual trees.
Notes: Delivers to shows. Euro accepted. Wheelchair accessible.
Map Ref: E, D2

ESem **Semps by Post**
28 Mill Road, Newbourne, Woodbridge, Suffolk IP12 4NP
Ⓣ (01473) 736440
Ⓔ Tricia@sempsbypost.co.uk
Ⓦ www.sempsbypost.co.uk
Contact: Tricia Newell
Opening Times: Not open.
Min Mail Order UK: Nmc
Min Mail Order EU: Nmc
Cat. Cost: Online only.
Credit Cards: Paypal
Specialities: *Sempervivum*. Some stock available in small quantities.

ESgI **Seagate Irises** ♿
A17 Long Sutton By-Pass, Long Sutton, Lincolnshire PE12 9RX
Ⓣ (01406) 365138
Ⓜ 07887 856389
Ⓔ sales@irises.co.uk
Ⓦ www.irises.co.uk
Contact: Julian Browse or Wendy Browse
Opening Times: 1000-1700 daily Apr-mid Jul. Please phone for appt. mid-Jul to Mar.
Cat. Cost: £3.50 or €8.00.
Credit Cards: Maestro, MasterCard, Visa
Specialities: Different types of *Iris*, bearded, beardless & species hybrids with about 1000 varieties in all, both historic & modern. Some only available in small quantities. Many container-grown available to callers.
Notes: Wheelchair accessible.
Map Ref: E, B1 **OS Grid Ref:** TF437218

EShb **Shrubland Park Nurseries**
Maltings Farm, Whatfield Road, Elmsett, Ipswich, Suffolk IP7 6LZ
Ⓣ (01473) 657012
Ⓜ 07890 527744
Ⓔ gill@shrublandparknurseries.co.uk
Ⓦ www.shrublandparknurseries.co.uk
Contact: Gill & Catherine Stitt
Opening Times: 1000-1600 daily, 1st Mar-30th Oct. 1000-1500 Fri, Sat & Sun, 1st Nov-1st Mar. Please ring or check website for any changes if travelling a long distance.
Min Mail Order UK: Nmc
Min Mail Order EU: Nmc
Cat. Cost: 6 × 2nd class or free by email.
Credit Cards: All major credit/debit cards, Paypal

Specialities: Conservatory plants, succulents, hardy perennials, climbers, shrubs, ferns & grasses.
Notes: Delivers to shows.
Map Ref: E, C3 **OS Grid Ref:** TM052466

ESMi **Straight Mile Nursery Gardens** ♿
Ongar Road, Pilgrims Hatch, Brentwood, Essex CM15 9SA
Ⓣ (01277) 374439
Ⓔ gdlsisley@aol.com
Ⓦ www.gardendesignsandlandscapes.co.uk
Contact: David Sisley
Opening Times: 1000-1700, 7 days (but closed some Weds, phone first.)
Min Mail Order UK: Nmc
Min Mail Order EU: Nmc
Cat. Cost: Online only.
Credit Cards: All, except American Express
Specialities: General nursery stock. Japanese maples, *Epimedium*. Some in small quantities only.
Notes: Delivers to shows. Wheelchair accessible.
Map Ref: E, D2 **OS Grid Ref:** TQ571964

EStr **Strictly Daylilies**
2 Primes Corner, Histon, Cambridgeshire CB24 9AG
Ⓣ (01223) 236239
Ⓜ 07765 236880
Ⓔ info@strictlydaylilies.com
Ⓦ www.strictlydaylilies.com
Contact: Paula & Chris Dyason
Opening Times: Mail order only. Open by appt.
Min Mail Order UK: Nmc
Min Mail Order EU: Nmc
Cat. Cost: No charge.
Credit Cards: All major credit/debit cards
Specialities: *Hemerocallis*. Some stock available in small quantities only.
Notes: Also sells wholesale. Delivers to shows.

ESty **Style Roses** ♿
10 Meridian Walk, Holbeach, Spalding, Lincolnshire PE12 7Nr
Ⓣ (01406) 424089
Ⓜ 07760 626750 or 07780 860415
Ⓕ (01406) 490006
Ⓔ mail@styleroses.co.uk
Ⓦ www.styleroses.co.uk
Contact: Margaret Styles
Opening Times: Vary. Nursery address is different from office, so please make an appt. before visiting.
Min Mail Order UK: Nmc
Min Mail Order EU: Nmc
Cat. Cost: Free in UK.
Credit Cards: MasterCard, Maestro, Visa
Specialities: Standard & bush roses.
Notes: Export to EU during bare-root season Nov-Mar. Also sells wholesale. Exports beyond EU. Delivers to shows. Wheelchair accessible.
Map Ref: E, B1

ESwi **Swines Meadow Farm Nursery** ♿ ◆
47 Towngate East, Market Deeping, Peterborough PE6 8LQ
Ⓣ 01778 343340
Ⓜ 07432 627766
Ⓔ ceveandsons@btconnect.com
Ⓦ www.swinesmeadowfarmnursery.co.uk
Contact: Colin Ward
Opening Times: 0900-1600 Mon-Sat, 1000-1600 Sun. Closed Jan. Open by appt. only in Jan.
Min Mail Order UK: £10.00
Min Mail Order EU: £10.00
Credit Cards: All, except American Express
Specialities: Hardy exotics, tree ferns, bamboos & phormiums. Wollemi pine stockist. Many specialities available in small quantities only.
Notes: Delivers to shows. Euro accepted. Wheelchair accessible.
Map Ref: E, B1 **OS Grid Ref:** TF150113

EThi **Thistlefield Plants and Design**
65 Westgate Street, Shouldham, Kings Lynn, Norfolk PE33 0BL
Ⓣ (01366) 347365
Ⓜ 07899 994071
Ⓕ (01366) 347365
Ⓔ paul@thistlefieldplants.co.uk
Ⓦ www.thistlefieldplants.co.uk
Contact: Paul Welford
Opening Times: Not open. Sells at plant fairs & shows only.
Min Mail Order UK: Nmc
Cat. Cost: Online only.
Credit Cards: None
Specialities: Perennials. *Tricyrtis* available in small quantities only.
Notes: Delivers to shows.

ETho **Thorncroft Clematis Ltd** ♿
The Lings, Reymerston, Norwich, Norfolk NR9 4QG
Ⓣ (01953) 850407
Ⓔ sales@thorncroftclematis.co.uk
Ⓦ www.thorncroftclematis.co.uk
Contact: Peter Skeggs-Gooch
Opening Times: Not open. Mail order only. Telephones manned 0900-1600 Mon-Sat. Orders can be collected from the nursery by prior arrangement.
Min Mail Order UK: Nmc
Min Mail Order EU: Nmc
Cat. Cost: 6 × 2nd class.

Credit Cards: All major credit/debit cards
Specialities: *Clematis*.
Notes: Exports beyond EU but does not export to USA, Canada or Australia. Delivers to shows. Wheelchair accessible.
Map Ref: E, B3 **OS Grid Ref:** TG039062

E

ETod **TODD'S BOTANICS**
West Street, Coggeshall,
Colchester, Essex
CO6 1NT
Ⓣ (01376) 561212
Ⓔ info@toddsbotanics.co.uk
Ⓦ www.toddsbotanics.co.uk
Contact: Mark Macdonald
Opening Times: Not open, except by appt. Mail order only.
Min Mail Order UK: Nmc
Cat. Cost: Online only.
Credit Cards: All major credit/debit cards
Specialities: Hardy exotics, herbaceous. Bamboos, palms, ferns, grasses, *Canna* & *Hedychium*. Olives, incl. named varieties. *Citrus*. Drought-resistant plants.
Notes: Not all plants available mail order, contact nursery for details. Also sells wholesale. Delivers to shows. Euro accepted. Nursery partially accessible for wheelchairs.

EUJe **URBAN JUNGLE**
Ringland Lane, Old Costessey, Norwich, Norfolk NR8 5BG
Ⓣ (01603) 744997
Ⓕ (0709) 2366869
Ⓔ lizzy@urbanjungle.uk.com
Ⓦ www.urbanjungle.uk.com
Contact: Elizabeth Browne
Opening Times: 1000-1700 1st Feb-31st Oct 7 days incl B/hols. 1000-1600 Nov-Dec Thu, Fri, Sat, Sun. Closed Jan.
Min Mail Order UK: Nmc
Min Mail Order EU: Nmc
Credit Cards: All major credit/debit cards
Specialities: Wide range of choice plants from exotic bedding to hardy evergreens.
Notes: Display gardens & living walls. Delivers to shows. Limited wheelchair access.
Map Ref: E, B3 **OS Grid Ref:** TG153127

EVic **VICTORIAN VIOLAS**
85 Fulmar Road, Lincoln, Lincolnshire
LN6 0RX
Ⓣ (01522) 686343
Ⓔ victorianviolasinfo@fsmail.net
Ⓦ www.victorianviolas.co.uk
Contact: Robert Chapman
Opening Times: Not open.
Min Mail Order UK: Nmc
Cat. Cost: 2 × 1st class
Credit Cards: None
Specialities: Hardy perennial violas (summer flowering).
Notes: Delivers to shows.

EWay **WAYSIDE AQUATICS**
Blackmore Road, Doddinghurst, Brentwood, Essex CM15 0HU
Ⓜ 07709 791317
Ⓔ sales@watergardenplants.co.uk
Ⓦ www.watergardenplants.co.uk
Contact: Anna Robinson
Opening Times: Mail order only. With prior notice, plants may be collected between 1000-1700, Wed-Sun.
Min Mail Order UK: Nmc
Cat. Cost: Online.
Credit Cards: All major credit/debit cards
Specialities: Range of water garden plants: waterlilies; floating plants; oxygenating plants; marginals; marsh plants. Some stock in small quantities.
Map Ref: E, D2 **OS Grid Ref:** TQ585995

EWes **WEST ACRE GARDENS** ♿
Tumbleyhill Road, West Acre,
King's Lynn, Norfolk
PE32 1UJ
Ⓣ (01760) 755562
Ⓔ info@westacregardens.co.uk
Ⓦ www.westacregardens.co.uk
Contact: J J Tuite
Opening Times: 1000-1700 7 days 1st Feb-30th Nov. Other times by appt.
Cat. Cost: None issued.
Credit Cards: Delta, MasterCard, Switch, Visa
Specialities: Very wide selection of herbaceous & other garden plants incl. *Rhodohypoxis*, *Primula auricula* & *Galanthus*.
Notes: Delivers to shows. Wheelchair accessible.
Map Ref: E, B1 **OS Grid Ref:** TF792182

EWld **WOODLANDS**
Peppin Lane, Fotherby, Louth, Lincolnshire
LN11 0UW
Ⓣ (01507) 603586
Ⓔ annbobarmstrong@btinternet.com
Ⓦ www.woodlandsplants.co.uk
Contact: Ann Armstrong
Opening Times: Flexible, but please phone or email to avoid disappointment.
Min Mail Order UK: Nmc
Min Mail Order EU: Nmc
Cat. Cost: None issued.
Credit Cards: None
Specialities: Small but interesting range of unusual plants, esp. woodland, *Codonopsis* and *Salvia*, all grown on the nursery in limited quantity.

Notes: Mature garden, art gallery & refreshments. Euro accepted.
Map Ref: E, A2 **OS Grid Ref:** TF322918

EWoo **Woottens Plants** ♿
Wenhaston, Blackheath,
Halesworth, Suffolk
IP19 9HD
Ⓣ (01502) 478258
Ⓕ (01502) 478888
Ⓔ info@woottensplants.co.uk
Ⓦ www.woottensplants.co.uk
Contact: Elizabeth Loftus
Opening Times: 0930-1700 7 days.
Min Mail Order UK: Nmc
Min Mail Order EU: Nmc
Cat. Cost: Online only.
Credit Cards: All, except American Express
Specialities: *Pelargonium*, *Hemerocallis*, *Primula auricula*, *Iris*, *Chrysanthemum* & *Clivia*.
Notes: Also sells wholesale. Wheelchair accessible.
Map Ref: E, C3 **OS Grid Ref:** TM426749

EWTr **Walnut Tree Garden Nursery**
Flymoor Lane, Rocklands,
Attleborough, Norfolk
NR17 1BP
Ⓣ (01953) 488163
Ⓔ info@wtgn.co.uk
Ⓦ www.wtgn.co.uk
Contact: Jim Paine & Clare Billington
Opening Times: 0900-1800 Tue-Sun Feb-Nov & B/hols.
Min Mail Order UK: Nmc
Cat. Cost: Online.
Credit Cards: All major credit/debit cards
Map Ref: E, B1 **OS Grid Ref:** TL978973

Scotland

GAbr **Abriachan Nurseries** ♿
Loch Ness Side, Inverness, Inverness-shire
IV3 8LA
Ⓣ (01463) 861232
Ⓔ info@lochnessgarden.com
Ⓦ www.lochnessgarden.com
Contact: Mr & Mrs D Davidson
Opening Times: 0900-1900 daily (dusk if earlier) Feb-Nov.
Min Mail Order UK: Nmc
Cat. Cost: 4 × 1st class.
Credit Cards: All major credit/debit cards
Specialities: Herbaceous perennials, old-fashioned *Primula*, *Helianthemum*, hardy geraniums, *Sempervivum* & *Primula auricula*.
Notes: Delivers to shows. Wheelchair access to nursery only.
Map Ref: G, B2 **OS Grid Ref:** NH571347

GAgs **Angusplants**
3 Balfour Cottages,
Menmuir, by Brechin,
Angus DD9 7RN
Ⓣ (01356) 660280
Ⓜ 07972 026109
Ⓔ alison@angusplants.co.uk
Ⓦ www.angusplants.co.uk
Contact: Dr Alison S. Goldie & Mark A. Hutson
Opening Times: By appt. only. Please phone first.
Min Mail Order UK: Nmc
Min Mail Order EU: Nmc
Cat. Cost: 2 × 2nd large letter stamps.
Credit Cards: None
Specialities: Predominantly *Primula auricula*, although other *Primula* species are offered. A few available in small quantities only. National Collection of Alpine Auriculas.
Notes: Mail order available all year.
Map Ref: G, B3 **OS Grid Ref:** NO528643

GBBs **Border Belles**
Old Branxton Cottages,
Innerwick, Nr Dunbar, East Lothian
EH42 1QT
Ⓣ (01368) 840325
Ⓔ mail@borderbelles.com
Ⓦ www.borderbelles.com
Contact: Gillian Moynihan
Opening Times: Open by appt. only.
Min Mail Order UK: Nmc
Cat. Cost: Online only.
Credit Cards: All major credit/debit cards
Specialities: Hardy perennials & woodland plants.
Notes: Also sells wholesale.

GBee **Beeches Cottage Nursery** ♿
High Boreland, Lesmahagow, South
Lanarkshire ML11 9PY
Ⓣ (01555) 893369
Ⓜ 07930 343131
Ⓔ thebeeches.nursery@talktalk.net
Ⓦ www.beechescottage.co.uk
Contact: Margaret Harrison, Steven Harrison
Opening Times: 1000-1630 7 days incl. Apr-end Jun. 1000-1630 Wed-Sat, Jul-end Sep.
Cat. Cost: None issued.
Credit Cards: None
Specialities: Traditional & unusual hardy cottage garden perennials which can be seen growing in display gardens at 850ft. Some plants available in small quantities only. Hanging basket specialists. Cottage gardens designed and planted.
Notes: Also sells wholesale. Wheelchair access to nursery only.
Map Ref: G, C2 **OS Grid Ref:** NS837403

GBin **Binny Plants** ♿
West Lodge, Binny Estate, Ecclesmachan Road, Nr Broxbourn,
West Lothian EH52 6NL
Ⓣ (01506) 858931
Ⓜ 07753 626117
Ⓔ contact@binnyplants.com
Ⓦ www.binnyplants.com
Contact: Billy Carruthers
Opening Times: 1000-1700 7 days. Closed mid-Dec to mid-Jan.
Min Mail Order UK: £25.00
Min Mail Order EU: £25.00
Cat. Cost: £2.50 refundable on ordering.
Credit Cards: MasterCard, EuroCard, Maestro, Visa
Specialities: Perennials incl. *Astilbe*, *Geranium*, *Hosta*, *Paeonia* & *Iris*. Plus large selection of grasses & ferns.
Notes: Mail order Sep-Apr only. Also sells wholesale. Euro accepted. Wheelchair accessible.
Map Ref: G, C3 **OS Grid Ref:** NT050732

GBuc **Buckland Plants** ♿
Whinnieliggate, Kirkcudbright,
Kirkcudbrightshire DG6 4XP
Ⓣ (01557) 331323
Ⓕ (01557) 331323
Ⓔ via website
Ⓦ www.bucklandplants.co.uk
Contact: Rob Asbridge
Opening Times: 1000-1700 Thu-Sun 1st Mar-1st Nov & B/hols.
Min Mail Order UK: £20.00 + p&p
Min Mail Order EU: Nmc
Cat. Cost: 3 × 1st class.
Credit Cards: All major credit/debit cards
Specialities: A very wide range of scarce herbaceous, woodland plants & larger alpines incl. *Anemone*, *Cardamine*, *Erythronium*, *Helleborus*, *Lilium*, *Meconopsis*, *Nomocharis*, *Primula*, *Tricyrtis* & *Trillium*.
Notes: Euro accepted. Assisted wheelchair access.
Map Ref: G, D2 **OS Grid Ref:** NX719524

GCal **Cally Gardens** ♿
Gatehouse of Fleet, Castle Douglas,
Kirkcudbrightshire DG7 2DJ
Ⓣ (01557) 815029 recorded information only.
Ⓔ info@callygardens.co.uk
Ⓦ www.callygardens.co.uk
Contact: Michael Wickenden
Opening Times: 1000-1730 Sat-Sun, 1400-1730 Tue-Fri. Easter Sat-last Sun in Sept.
Min Mail Order UK: £15.00 + p&p
Cat. Cost: 3 × 1st class.
Credit Cards: None
Specialities: Unusual perennials & grasses. Some rare shrubs, climbers & conservatory plants. 3500 varieties growing in an 2.7 acre walled garden built in the 1760s.
Notes: Also sells wholesale. Wheelchair accessible.
Map Ref: G, D2 **OS Grid Ref:** NX604549

GCra **Craigieburn Garden** ♿
Craigieburn House, by Moffat, Dumfriesshire DG10 9LF
Ⓣ (01683) 221250
Ⓜ 07824 390519
Ⓔ ajmw1@aol.com
Ⓦ www.craigieburngarden.com
Contact: Janet & Andrew Wheatcroft
Opening Times: 1030-1800 daily, Easter-31st Oct. Other times by appt.
Specialities: *Meconopsis* plants for damp gardens, herbaceous perennials.
Notes: Wheelchair accessible.
Map Ref: G, D3

GCrg **Craigiehall Nursery**
Carnwath, Lanark, Lanarkshire ML11 8LH
Ⓣ 01555 840027 (answering machine)
Ⓕ 01555 840027
Ⓔ sales@craigiehallnursery.co.uk
Ⓦ www.craigiehallnursery.co.uk
Contact: Innes Hogg
Opening Times: Not open. Mail order only.
Min Mail Order UK: Nmc
Cat. Cost: Online only.
Credit Cards: All major credit/debit cards
Specialities: A very wide range of alpine and rock garden plants; over 500 different varieties on the nursery. Some are quite common, others much less so.
Notes: Online sales only, no telephone ordering.

GCro **Croft 16 Daffodils**
16 Midtown of Inverasdale, Poolewe,
Achnasheen, Ross-shire IV22 2LW
Ⓣ (01445) 781717
Ⓔ sales@croft16daffodils.co.uk
Ⓦ www.croft16daffodils.co.uk
Contact: Duncan & Kate Donald
Opening Times: Not open. Mail order only.
Min Mail Order UK: Nmc
Min Mail Order EU: Nmc
Cat. Cost: Online. Customers without internet access send 4 × 1st for sales list without pictures.
Credit Cards: Paypal
Specialities: National Collection of Daffodils bred pre-1930. Some stocks only available in small quantities. A waiting list for *desiderata* is in operation.
Notes: Limited availability, so please order by late Jun if possible. Orders unfulfilled in one

season will take priority the following year. Customers outside the EU should contact nursery.
Map Ref: G, A1 **OS Grid Ref:** NG822851

GDun **Dunskey Gardens & Maze** ♿
Portpatrick, Stranraer, Wigtownshire DG9 8TJ
Ⓣ (01776) 810905
Ⓜ 07899 092070
Ⓕ (01776) 810581
Ⓔ gabygardeners@btinternet.com
Ⓦ www.dunskey.com
Contact: Gabrielle Reynolds
Opening Times: 1000-1600 w/ends only Feb, 1000-1700 daily Easter-Oct. See website for details.
Credit Cards: All major credit/debit cards
Specialities: Broad range, propagated from the gardens, incl. bulbs, tender perennials, herbaceous, trees and shrubs. Available in small quantities only. National Collections of *Clianthus* & *Sutherlandia*.
Notes: Dunskey Estate Walled Garden & Maze open to the public. Sells at local plant shows. Wheelchair accessible.
Map Ref: G, D2 **OS Grid Ref:** NX004560

GEdr **Edrom Nurseries**
Coldingham, Eyemouth, Berwickshire TD14 5TZ
Ⓣ (01890) 771386
Ⓕ (01890) 771387
Ⓔ info@edrom-nurseries.co.uk
Ⓦ www.edrom-nurseries.co.uk
Contact: Mr Terry Hunt
Opening Times: 0900-1700 Thu, Fri, Sat & Mon (closed Tue & Wed), 1000-1600 Sun.
Min Mail Order UK: Nmc
Min Mail Order EU: Nmc
Cat. Cost: Free.
Credit Cards: All major credit/debit cards
Specialities: *Cypripedium*, *Epimedium*, *Gentiana*, *Primula*, *Meconopsis*, *Rhodohypoxis*, *Trillium* & Japanese *Hepatica*.
Notes: Delivers to shows.
Map Ref: G, C3 **OS Grid Ref:** NT873663

GFai **Fairholm Plants**
Fairholm, Larkhall, Lanarkshire ML9 2UQ
Ⓣ (01698) 881671
Ⓕ (01698) 888135
Ⓔ fairholm.plants@stevenson-hamilton.co.uk
Contact: Mrs J M Hamilton
Opening Times: Apr-Oct by appt.
Min Mail Order UK: Nmc
Cat. Cost: 1 × 2nd class for descriptive list.
Credit Cards: None
Specialities: *Abutilon* & unusual half-hardy perennials esp. South African. National Collection of *Abutilon* cvs. Plants & rooted cuttings available in small quantities only.
Notes: Mail order for young/small plants. Euro accepted.
Map Ref: G, C2 **OS Grid Ref:** NS754515

GGal **Galloway Plants** ♿
Claymoddie, Whithorn, Newton Stewart, Dumfries & Galloway DG8 8LX
Ⓣ (01988) 500422
Ⓔ gallowayplants@aol.com
Ⓦ www.gallowayplants.co.uk
Contact: Robin & Mary Nicholson
Opening Times: 1400-1700 Fri, Sat & Sun, Apr-Sep, other times by prior appt.
Min Mail Order UK: £50.00 + p&p
Cat. Cost: 2 × 1st class.
Credit Cards: None
Specialities: Southern hemisphere plants. *Hydrangea*. Available in small quantities only.
Notes: Also sells wholesale. Delivers to shows. Wheelchair accessible.
Map Ref: G, D2 **OS Grid Ref:** NX450377

GGGa **Glendoick Gardens Ltd** ♿
Glendoick, Perth, Perthshire PH2 7NS
Ⓣ (01738) 860205
Ⓕ (01738) 860630
Ⓔ orders@glendoick.com
Ⓦ www.glendoick.com
Contact: Kenneth Cox
Opening Times: Nursery not open to the public. Garden centre open 0900-1730 (summer), 0900-1700 (winter) 7 days. Gardens open Apr & May, details on website.
Min Mail Order UK: £40.00
Min Mail Order EU: £100.00
Cat. Cost: £1.00.
Credit Cards: All, except American Express
Specialities: Rhododendrons, azaleas and ericaceous, *Primula* & *Meconopsis*. Plants from wild seed. Many catalogue plants available at garden centre. 3 National Collections.
Notes: Exports beyond EU. Wheelchair access to Garden Centre.
Map Ref: G, C3

GJos **Jo's Garden Enterprise** ♿
Easter Balmungle Farm, Eathie Road, by Rosemarkie, Ross-shire IV10 8SL
Ⓣ (01381) 621006
Ⓔ josgardenenterprise@hotmail.co.uk
Contact: Joanna Chance
Opening Times: 1000 to dusk, 7 days.
Cat. Cost: None.
Credit Cards: None
Specialities: Alpines & herbaceous perennials. Selection of native wild flowers.
Notes: Wheelchair accessible.
Map Ref: G, B2 **OS Grid Ref:** NH600742

G

GKev **Kevock Garden Plants**
Kevock Road, Lasswade, Midlothian
EH18 1HT
Ⓣ 0131 454 0660
Ⓜ 07811 321585
Ⓕ 0131 454 0660
Ⓔ info@kevockgarden.co.uk
Ⓦ www.kevockgarden.co.uk
Contact: Stella Rankin
Opening Times: Not open. Mail order & plant stalls only.
Min Mail Order UK: £25.00
Min Mail Order EU: £25.00
Cat. Cost: 3 × 1st class.
Credit Cards: MasterCard, Switch, Visa
Specialities: Chinese & Himalayan plants. *Androsace*, *Daphne*, *Paeonia*, *Primula*, *Meconopsis*, *Iris*, woodland plants, alpines, rock plants, marginal & bog plants, bulbs.
Notes: Also sells wholesale. Delivers to shows. Euro accepted.

GKin **Kinlochlaich Garden Plant Centre**
Appin, Argyll
PA38 4BB
Ⓣ (01631) 730342
Ⓜ 07881 525754
Ⓔ fiona@kinlochlaich.plus.com
Ⓦ www.kinlochlaichgardencentre.co.uk
Contact: Fiona Hutchison
Opening Times: 0900-1730, 7 days.
Cat. Cost: None issued
Credit Cards: All major credit/debit cards
Specialities: Hardy shrubs, trees, azaleas, perennials. Also Gulf Stream plants such as *Tropaeolum*, *Embothrium*, *Eucryphia*, *Drymis* & more. Good selection of hardy seaside plants.
Notes: Do not offer mail order but will post where possible.
Map Ref: G, C2

GLet **Letham Plants**
11a Letham Mains Holdings,
Haddington, East Lothian
EH41 4NW
Ⓣ (01620) 822350
Ⓜ 07842 211712
Ⓔ lethamplants@hotmail.co.uk
Ⓦ www.letham-plants.co.uk
Contact: Caroline Samuel
Opening Times: By appt. only.
Min Mail Order UK: Nmc
Min Mail Order EU: Nmc
Credit Cards: All major credit/debit cards
Specialities: *Astrantia*, *Dicentra*.
Notes: Also sells wholesale. Delivers to shows. Euro accepted.
Map Ref: G, C3 **OS Grid Ref:** NT487730

GLog **Logie Steading Plants** ♿
Forres, Moray IV36 2QN
Ⓣ (01309) 611222 or 611278
Ⓕ (01309) 611300
Ⓔ panny@logie.co.uk
Ⓦ www.logie.co.uk
Contact: Mrs Panny Laing
Opening Times: 1030-1700 hours, 7 days, April-Christmas.
Credit Cards: All major credit/debit cards
Specialities: Unusual hardy plants, grown in Scotland for Scottish gardens. Large range of hardy geraniums, bold herbaceous plants, grasses & marginal plants.
Notes: Logie House Garden open every day. Café, farm shop, river walk, heritage centre. Wheelchair accessible.
Map Ref: G, B2 **OS Grid Ref:** NJ006504

GMaP **Macplants** ♿
Berrybank Nursery, 5 Boggs Holdings,
Pencaitland, East Lothian
EH34 5BA
Ⓣ (01875) 341179
Ⓕ (01875) 340842
Ⓔ sales@macplants.co.uk
Ⓦ www.macplants.co.uk
Contact: Gavin McNaughton
Opening Times: 1030-1700, 7 days, Mar-end Sep.
Min Mail Order UK: Nmc
Cat. Cost: 4 × 2nd class.
Credit Cards: MasterCard, Switch, Visa
Specialities: Herbaceous perennials, alpines, hardy ferns, violas & grasses. *Meconopsis*. National Collection of *Sanguisorba*.
Notes: Also sells wholesale. Delivers to shows. Wheelchair accessible.
Map Ref: G, C3 **OS Grid Ref:** NT447703

GPoy **Poyntzfield Herb Nursery** ♿
Nr Balblair, Black Isle, Dingwall, Ross-shire
IV7 8LX
Ⓣ (01381) 610352 (phone between 1200-1300 & 1800-1900 Mon-Sat only.)
Ⓕ (01381) 610352
Ⓔ info@poyntzfieldherbs.co.uk
Ⓦ www.poyntzfieldherbs.co.uk
Contact: Duncan Ross
Opening Times: 1300-1700 Mon-Sat 1st Mar-30th Sep, 1300-1700 Sun May-Aug.
Min Mail Order UK: £10.00 + p&p
Min Mail Order EU: £20.00 + p&p
Cat. Cost: 4 × 1st class.
Credit Cards: All major credit/debit cards
Specialities: Over 400 popular, unusual & rare herbs esp. medicinal. Also seeds.
Notes: Mail order operates in the spring & autumn. Wheelchair accessible.
Map Ref: G, B2 **OS Grid Ref:** NH711642

GPPs **POGS Penstemons**
The Gatehouse, Moniaive, Dumfries & Galloway DG3 4HZ
Ⓣ (01848) 200472
Ⓜ 07905 825818
Ⓔ info@pogspenstemons.co.uk
Ⓦ www.pogspenstemons.co.uk
Contact: Allison Fitz-Earle
Opening Times: Not open. Mail order only.
Min Mail Order UK: Nmc
Cat. Cost: Free.
Credit Cards: All major credit/debit cards, Paypal
Specialities: Penstemons.
Notes: Mail order plants available all year. Also sells wholesale.

GQue **Quercus Garden Plants Ltd** ♿
Whitmuir Farm, Lamancha, West Linton, Scottish Borders EH46 7BB
Ⓣ (01968) 661908
Ⓔ colin@quercus.uk.net
Ⓦ www.quercuslandart.com
Contact: Colin McBeath or Jennie Sinclair
Opening Times: Contact nursery for details.
Cat. Cost: Online, or £2.00 for a paper copy.
Credit Cards: All major credit/debit cards
Specialities: Easy & unusual plants for contemporary Scottish gardens.
Notes: Nursery has moved to a new site from Rankeilour Gardens, Fife. Delivery service available on large orders at nursery's discretion. Wheelchair accessible.
Map Ref: G, C3

GQui **Quinish Garden Nursery**
Dervaig, Isle of Mull, Argyll PA75 6QL
Ⓣ (01688) 400344
Ⓕ (01688) 400344
Ⓔ quinishplants@aol.com
Ⓦ www.Q-gardens.org
Contact: Nicholas Reed
Opening Times: By appt. only.
Min Mail Order UK: Nmc
Min Mail Order EU: Nmc
Cat. Cost: 2 × 1st class.
Credit Cards: None
Specialities: Choice garden shrubs & conservatory plants.
Map Ref: G, C1

GSPN **Spring Park Nursery**
The Gatehouse, Moniaive, Dumfries & Galloway DG3 4HZ
Ⓣ (01848) 200472
Ⓜ 07905 825818
Ⓔ info@springparknursery.co.uk
Ⓦ www.springparknursery.co.uk
Contact: Julian Fitz-Earle
Opening Times: Not open. Mail order only.
Min Mail Order UK: Nmc
Credit Cards: All major credit/debit cards, Paypal
Specialities: Heathers.
Notes: Mail order plants available all year. Also sells wholesale.

GTwd **Tweed Valley Fruit Trees Ltd**
Tighnuilt House, Innerleithen, Peeblesshire EH44 6RD
Ⓣ (01896) 831147
Ⓜ 07885 105813
Ⓔ info@tweedvalleyfruittrees.co.uk
Ⓦ www.tweedvalleyfruittrees.co.uk
Contact: Nick Edwardson
Opening Times: Not open. Visits may be possible by prior arrangement only.
Min Mail Order UK: Nmc
Cat. Cost: Online or phone for information.
Specialities: Wide selection of apple, pear and plum trees on a range of different rootstocks, focussing on varieties considered especially suitable for the whole UK and the heritage Scottish varieties in particular.
Notes: Also sells wholesale.

GTwe **J Tweedie Fruit Trees**
Maryfield Road Nursery, Nr Terregles, Dumfriesshire DG2 9TH
Ⓣ (01387) 720880
Contact: John Tweedie
Opening Times: Please ring for times. Collections by appt.
Cat. Cost: Sae
Credit Cards: None
Specialities: Fruit trees & bushes. A wide range of old & new varieties.
Map Ref: G, D2

N. Ireland & Republic

IArd **Ardcarne Garden Centre** ♿
Ardcarne, Boyle, Co. Roscommon, Republic of Ireland
Ⓣ +353 7196 67091
Ⓕ +353 7196 67341
Ⓔ ardcarne@indigo.ie
Ⓦ www.ardcarneplantsplus.ie
Contact: James Wickham, Mary Frances Dwyer, Kirsty Ainge
Opening Times: 0900-1800 Mon-Sat, 1300-1800 Sun & B/hols.
Credit Cards: Access, American Express, Visa
Specialities: Native & unusual trees, choice perennials, roses, plants for coastal areas, fruit trees, incl. heritage Irish apple trees, vegetable plants, specimen plants & semi-mature trees. Wide general range.
Notes: Euro accepted. Wheelchair accessible.
Map Ref: I, B1

IBal **Bali-Hai Mail Order Nursery**
42 Largy Road, Carnlough, Ballymena, Co. Antrim, N. Ireland BT44 0EZ
Ⓣ 028 2888 5289
Ⓜ 07708 257164
Ⓕ 028 2888 5289
Ⓔ balihainursery@btinternet.com
Ⓦ www.mailorderplants4me.com
Contact: Mrs M E Scroggy
Opening Times: Mon-Sat by appt. only.
Min Mail Order UK: Nmc
Min Mail Order EU: Nmc
Cat. Cost: Online only.
Credit Cards: All major credit/debit cards
Specialities: National Collection of *Hosta*, part planted in 1.5 acres, open to the public by appt. *Agapanthus*, *Crocosmia*, *Rhodohypoxis*, tree ferns & other perennials. Hostas grown to order.
Notes: Also sells wholesale. Export beyond EU restricted to bare root perennials, no grasses. Euro accepted.
Map Ref: I, A3 **OS Grid Ref:** D287184

IBlr **Ballyrogan Nurseries** ♿
The Grange, Ballyrogan, Newtownards, Co. Down, N. Ireland BT23 4SD
Ⓣ 028 9181 0451 (evenings)
Ⓔ gary.dunlop@btinternet.com
Contact: Gary Dunlop
Opening Times: Only open by appt.
Min Mail Order UK: £10.00 + p&p
Min Mail Order EU: £20.00 + p&p
Cat. Cost: 2 × 2nd class.
Credit Cards: None
Specialities: Choice herbaceous. *Agapanthus*, *Crocosmia*, *Rodgersia*, *Dierama*, *Erythronium*, *Roscoea* & *Watsonia*.
Notes: Also sells wholesale. Euro accepted. Wheelchair accessible.
Map Ref: I, B3

IBoy **Boyne Garden Centre**
Ardcalf, Slane, Co. Meath, Republic of Ireland
Ⓣ +353 419 824350
Ⓕ +353 419 824350
Ⓔ boynegardencentre@eircom.net
Ⓦ www.boynegardencentre.com
Contact: Aileen Muldoon Byrne
Opening Times: 0930-1800 Mon-Sat, 1400-1800 Sun, Mar-Sep. 0930-1800 B/hols. W/ends only Oct-Feb.
Credit Cards: All major credit/debit cards
Specialities: Hardy herbaceous perennials. David Austin roses. Trees, shrubs, climbers, grasses, bamboos & ferns.
Notes: Pre-ordered plants delivered to shows. Euro accepted.
Map Ref: I, B3

IDee **Deelish Garden Centre**
Skibbereen, Co. Cork, Republic of Ireland
Ⓣ +353 28 21374
Ⓕ +353 28 21374
Ⓔ deel@eircom.net
Ⓦ www.deelish.ie
Contact: Bill & Rain Chase
Opening Times: 1000-1800 Mon-Sat, 1400-1800 Sun.
Cat. Cost: Sae
Credit Cards: Access, Visa
Specialities: Unusual plants for the mild coastal climate of Ireland. Conservatory plants. Sole Irish agents for Chase Organic Seeds.
Notes: No mail order outside Ireland & UK. Euro accepted.
Map Ref: I, D1

IDic **Dickson Nurseries Ltd**
Milecross Road, Newtownards, Co. Down, N. Ireland BT23 4SS
Ⓣ 028 9181 2206
Ⓜ 07522 222161
Ⓕ 028 9181 3366
Ⓔ mail@dickson-roses.co.uk
Ⓦ www.dickson-roses.co.uk
Contact: Colin Dickson
Opening Times: 0800-1230 & 1300-1515 Mon-Thu. 0800-1230 Fri.
Min Mail Order UK: Nmc
Min Mail Order EU: £25.00 + p&p
Cat. Cost: Free
Credit Cards: None
Specialities: Roses esp. modern Dickson varieties. Limited selection, check website. Most varieties available in small quantities only.
Notes: Also sells wholesale. Only glasshouses accessible for wheelchairs.
Map Ref: I, B3

IFoB **Field of Blooms** ♿
Ballymackey, Lisnamoe, Nenagh, Co. Tipperary, Republic of Ireland
Ⓣ +353 67 29974
Ⓜ +353 8764 06044
Ⓔ guy2002@eircom.net
Ⓦ www.fieldofblooms.com
Contact: Guy de Schrijver
Opening Times: Strictly by appt.
Min Mail Order UK: Nmc
Min Mail Order EU: Nmc
Cat. Cost: Online only.
Credit Cards: None
Specialities: Hellebores, herbaceous, hardy perennials, ornamental grasses, woodland plants & some alpines.
Notes: Euro accepted. Wheelchair accessible.
Map Ref: I, C2

IFro **Frogswell Nursery**
Clooncolan, Straide, Foxford, Co. Mayo, Republic of Ireland
Ⓣ +353 94 903 1420
Ⓜ +353 8621 06166
Ⓔ frogswell@gmail.com
Ⓦ www.frogswellhardyplants.com
Contact: Celia Graebner
Opening Times: Feb-Oct by appt. Please phone first. Also Garden Open Days & occasional workshops; see website for details.
Credit Cards: None
Specialities: A small garden-based nursery specialising in shade & woodland plants incl. hybrid hellebores & hardy geraniums, plus unusual flowering perennials, bee & wild pollinator plants for the Irish climate, all raised on site & without chemical inputs. Some in very limited quantities.
Notes: Group visits & talks by arrangement. See website for location map. Euro accepted.
Map Ref: I, B1 **OS Grid Ref:** M2497

IKil **Kilmurry Nursery** ♿
Gorey, Co. Wexford, Republic of Ireland
Ⓣ +353 53 948 0223
Ⓜ +353 8681 80623
Ⓕ +353 53 948 0223
Ⓔ kilmurrynursery@eircom.net
Ⓦ www.kilmurrynursery.com
Contact: Paul & Orla Woods
Opening Times: 0900-1700 Mon-Fri, Mar-Sep. Wintertime by appt.
Min Mail Order UK: Nmc
Min Mail Order EU: Nmc
Cat. Cost: Online only.
Credit Cards: None
Specialities: Herbaceous perennials and grasses.
Notes: Tea rooms open during summer. Also sells wholesale. Delivers to shows. Euro accepted. Wheelchair accessible.
Map Ref: I, C3 **OS Grid Ref:** 3C

ILea **Leamore Nursery**
Cronroe, Ashford, Co. Wicklow, Republic of Ireland
Ⓣ +353 87 227 8850
Ⓕ +353 404 70126
Ⓔ info@leamorenursery.com
Ⓦ www.leamorenursery.com
Contact: Phil Havercroft
Opening Times: Not open to the public.
Min Mail Order UK: Nmc
Min Mail Order EU: Nmc
Cat. Cost: Online only.
Credit Cards: All major credit/debit cards
Specialities: *Paeonia* & other perennials. Most items in large quantities. Itoh peonies & some more unusual items only available in small quantities.
Notes: Bare root peonies supplied in autumn, available to order from July (on website). Founding members of the Irish Specialist Nursery Association (ISNA). Also sells wholesale. Delivers to shows. Euro accepted.

IMou **Mount Venus Nursery** ♿
The Walled Garden, Mutton Lane, Dublin 16, Republic of Ireland
Ⓣ +353 1493 3813
Ⓜ +353 8632 18789
Ⓔ mountvenusnursery@gmail.com
Ⓦ www.mountvenusnursery.com
Contact: Oliver & Liat Schurmann
Opening Times: 1000-1800 Mon-Sat, Feb-Nov.
Min Mail Order UK: €20
Min Mail Order EU: €35
Credit Cards: All major credit/debit cards
Specialities: Specialist perennials. Grasses & bamboos. Unusual woodland plants.
Notes: Also sells wholesale. Delivers to shows. Euro accepted. Wheelchair accessible.
Map Ref: I, C3

IPen **Peninsula Primulas**
72 Ballyeasborough Road, Kircubbin, Co. Down, N. Ireland BT22 1AD
Ⓣ 028 4277 2193
Ⓜ 07714 465834
Ⓔ peninsula.primulas@btinternet.com
Ⓦ www.penprimulas.com
Contact: Philip Bankhead
Opening Times: Mail order only. Not open.
Min Mail Order UK: Nmc
Min Mail Order EU: Nmc
Cat. Cost: Free
Credit Cards: Paypal
Specialities: Extensive selection of *Primula* species, plus auriculas. Also *P. allionii* cvs and European hybrid alpines.
Notes: Also sells wholesale. Delivers to shows. Euro accepted.

IPot **The Potting Shed** ♿
Bolinaspick, Camolin, Enniscorthy, Co. Wexford, Republic of Ireland
Ⓣ +353 5393 83629
Ⓔ susan@camolinpottingshed.com
Ⓦ www.camolinpottingshed.com
Contact: Susan Carrick
Opening Times: 1100-1700, Wed-Sat (incl.), Mar-Sep 2014. Other times by appt.
Min Mail Order UK: Nmc
Min Mail Order EU: Nmc
Cat. Cost: 3 × 1st class.
Credit Cards: MasterCard, Visa
Specialities: We grow a wide range of unusual, hard to find and new introductions of herbaceous perennials, ornamental grasses and

Clematis, many of which can be seen growing to their full potential in our many display beds.
Notes: Member of the Irish Specialist Nursery Assoc. (ISNA). Orders outside Ireland can only be delivered by courier, charges at cost. Delivers to shows. Euro accepted. Wheelchair accessible.
Map Ref: I, C3

IPPN **Perennial Plants Nursery**
Nr Ballymaloe, Barnabrow, Midleton, Co. Cork, Republic of Ireland
Ⓣ +353 21 465 2122
Ⓔ perennialplants@eircom.net
Ⓦ www.sandysgarden.ie
Contact: Sandy McCarthy
Opening Times: Please ring for times.
Min Mail Order UK: Nmc
Min Mail Order EU: Nmc
Cat. Cost: None issued.
Credit Cards: None
Specialities: Many unusual herbaceous, ornamental grasses, tender perennials. Some available in small quantities only.
Notes: Delivers to shows. Euro accepted. Sterling accepted.
Map Ref: I, D2 **OS Grid Ref:** W9568

IRhd **Ringhaddy Daffodils**
Ringhaddy Road, Killinchy, Co. Down, N. Ireland BT23 6TU
Ⓣ 028 9754 1007
Ⓜ 07762 337534
Ⓔ info@ringhaddy-daffodils.com
Ⓦ www.ringhaddy-daffodils.com
Contact: Nial Watson
Opening Times: Mail order only. Not open.
Min Mail Order UK: £20.00 + p&p
Min Mail Order EU: £50.00 + p&p
Cat. Cost: £3.00
Credit Cards: Paypal
Specialities: Daffodil bulbs, some varieties only available in small numbers.
Notes: Exports beyond EU. Euro accepted.

IRos **Ros Ban Wildlife Garden** ♿
Common, Raphoe, Co. Donegal, Republic of Ireland
Ⓣ +353 74 91 45336
Ⓜ +353 8608 05214
Ⓔ Rosbangarden@gmail.com
Contact: Ann Kavanagh
Opening Times: Garden open all year, morning to evening.
Credit Cards: None
Notes: Plants available in season from the garden. Please check plant availability with nursery before travelling. Euro accepted. Wheelchair accessible.
Map Ref: I, A2 **OS Grid Ref:** C254037

ISha **Shady Plants** ♿
Coolbooa, Clashmore, Youghal, Co. Cork, Republic of Ireland
Ⓣ +353 24 86998
Ⓜ +353 8605 42171
Ⓔ mike@shadyplants.ie
Ⓦ www.shadyplants.net
Contact: Mike Keep
Opening Times: 1300-1700, Tue-Sat, by appt. only.
Min Mail Order UK: Nmc
Min Mail Order EU: Nmc
Cat. Cost: £1.00
Credit Cards: Paypal
Specialities: Specialist fern nursery based near the south coast of Ireland.
Notes: Delivers to shows. Euro accepted. Wheelchair accessible.
Map Ref: I, D2 **OS Grid Ref:** 613,585

ISsi **Seaside Nursery** ♿
Claddaghduff, Co. Galway, Republic of Ireland
Ⓣ +353 95 44687
Ⓜ +353 8633 91555
Ⓔ Tom@seasidenursery.biz
Ⓦ www.seasidenursery.biz
Contact: Tom Dyck
Opening Times: 1000-1700 Mon-Sat. Closed Sun.
Min Mail Order UK: Nmc
Min Mail Order EU: Nmc
Cat. Cost: €3.50
Credit Cards: MasterCard, Visa
Specialities: Plants & hedging suitable for seaside locations. Rare plants originating from Australia & New Zealand esp. *Phormium*, *Astelia*.
Notes: Also sells wholesale. Euro accepted. Wheelchair accessible.

ITim **Timpany Nurseries & Gardens** ♿
77 Magheratimpany Road, Ballynahinch, Co. Down, N. Ireland BT24 8PA
Ⓣ 028 9756 2812
Ⓕ 028 9756 2812
Ⓔ s.tindall@btconnect.com
Ⓦ www.timpanynurseries.com
Contact: Susan Tindall
Opening Times: 1000-1730 Tue-Sat, Sun by appt.
Min Mail Order UK: £40.00 + p&p
Min Mail Order EU: £40.00 + p&p
Cat. Cost: £2.00
Credit Cards: All, except American Express
Specialities: *Androsace*, *Campanula*, *Cassiope*, *Celmisia*, *Cyclamen*, *Dianthus*, *Galanthus*, *Meconopsis*, *Primula*, *Primula auricula*, *Rhodohypoxis* & *Saxifraga*.
Notes: Delivers to shows. Wheelchair accessible.
Map Ref: I, B3

IVic **VICTORIA'S NURSERY & GARDEN**
Upper Kells, Kells, Cahirceveen, Co Kerry, Republic of Ireland
Ⓣ +353 66 947 7605
Ⓜ +353 8791 11465
Ⓔ kellshouse@eircom.net
Contact: Victoria Vogel
Opening Times: 1000-1700 Wed-Sun all year except Xmas. Closed Mon & Tue, except B/hols & by arrangement.
Cat. Cost: None issued.
Credit Cards: None
Specialities: *Rhododendron*, azaleas, *Acer*, tree ferns, seaside & woodland plants, *Saxifraga fortunei* forms.
Notes: Drive along Ring of Kerry, at Kells follow signs to Kells Bay Garden towards Kells Beach, nursery to left after little bridge. Euro accepted.
Map Ref: I, D1

LONDON AREA

LAir **JUST AIRPLANTS**
272a Herndean Road, Caversham, Reading, Berkshire RG4 7QT
Ⓣ 0118 324 3949
Ⓕ 0118 324 3955
Ⓔ info@justairplants.com
Ⓦ www.justairplants.com
Contact: Gill Passman
Opening Times: Not open. Mail order only.
Specialities: Bromeliads. *Neoregelia*, *Tillandsia*, *Aechmea*, *Billbergia*, *Cryptanthus*.
Notes: Mail order only by phone or online shop. Plants can be ordered for collection at events across UK. Also sells wholesale. Delivers to shows.

LAll **ALLWOODS** ♿
Cuddington Way, Cheam, Surrey SM2 7JB
Ⓣ 020 8393 7616
Ⓔ info@allwoods.net
Ⓦ www.allwoods.net
Contact: David & Emma James
Opening Times: Office 0900-1630 Mon-Fri. Answer machine all other times. Nursery open to visitors Mar-Jun, check website for detailed opening times.
Min Mail Order UK: Nmc
Min Mail Order EU: Nmc
Cat. Cost: 2 × 1st class.
Credit Cards: Access, MasterCard, Maestro, Switch, Visa
Specialities: *Dianthus* incl. hardy border carnations, pinks, perpetual flowering & spray carnations, Malmaisons & *D. allwoodii*. Unusual & collectors' geraniums & *Pelargoniums*. *Fuchsia*, Penstemons & other garden plants. Succulents.
Notes: All listed varieties available as plugs but choice varies depending on time of year. Please phone before travelling to avoid disappointment and/or to ensure order is ready for collection. Also sells wholesale. Wheelchair accessible.

LAma **JACQUES AMAND INTERNATIONAL LTD** ♿
The Nurseries, 145 Clamp Hill, Stanmore, Middlesex HA7 3JS
Ⓣ 020 8420 7110
Ⓕ 020 8954 6784
Ⓔ www.jacquesamandintl.com
Ⓦ www.jacquesamand.com
Contact: Louise Houghton
Opening Times: 0900-1700 Mon-Fri, 1000-1600 Sat.
Min Mail Order UK: Nmc
Min Mail Order EU: Nmc
Cat. Cost: 1 × 1st class.
Credit Cards: All major credit/debit cards
Specialities: Rare and unusual species bulbs esp. *Arisaema*, *Trillium*, *Fritillaria*, tulips.
Notes: Also sells wholesale. Exports beyond EU. Delivers to shows. Euro accepted. Wheelchair accessible.
Map Ref: L, B3

LAst **ASTERBY & CHALKCROFT NURSERY** ♿
The Ridgeway, Blunham, Bedfordshire MK44 3PH
Ⓣ (01767) 640148
Ⓔ sales@asterbyplants.co.uk
Ⓦ www.asterbyplants.co.uk
Contact: Simon & Eva Aldridge
Opening Times: 1000-1700 7 days. Closed Xmas & Jan.
Min Mail Order UK: Nmc
Credit Cards: All major credit/debit cards
Specialities: Hardy shrubs, herbaceous & trees.
Notes: Please ring for mail order information. Exports beyond EU. Wheelchair accessible.
Map Ref: L, A3 **OS Grid Ref:** TL151497

LAyl **AYLETT NURSERIES LTD** ♿ ◆
North Orbital Road, St Albans, Hertfordshire, AL2 1DH
Ⓣ (01727) 822255
Ⓕ (01727) 823024
Ⓔ info@aylettnurseries.co.uk
Ⓦ www.aylettnurseries.co.uk
Contact: Julie Aylett
Opening Times: 0830-1730 Mon-Fri, 0830-1700 Sat, 1030-1630 Sun.
Cat. Cost: Free.
Credit Cards: All major credit/debit cards
Specialities: *Dahlia*. 2-acre trial ground adjacent to garden centre.

Notes: Wheelchair accessible.
Map Ref: L, B3 **OS Grid Ref:** TL169049

LBee **Beechcroft Nursery** ♿
127 Reigate Road, Ewell, Surrey
KT17 3DE
Ⓣ 020 8393 4265
Ⓕ 020 8393 4265
Ⓔ enquiries@beechcroft-nursery.co.uk
Ⓦ www.beechcroft-nursery.co.uk
Contact: C Kimber
Opening Times: 1000-1600 Mon-Sat, 1000-1400 Sun and B/hols. Closed Xmas-New Year week.
Cat. Cost: None issued.
Credit Cards: All major credit/debit cards
Specialities: Conifers.
Notes: Wheelchair accessible.
Map Ref: L, C3

LBMP **Blooming Marvellous Plants**
Korketts Farm, Aylesbury Road, Winslow, Buckinghamshire MK18 3JL
Ⓣ (01296) 714714
Ⓜ 07963 747305
Ⓔ alex@bmplants.co.uk
Ⓦ www.bmplants.co.uk
Contact: Alexia Ballance
Opening Times: 0900-1700 Tue-Sat & 1000-1600 Sun, 1st Mar-26th Oct 2014. Closed Mon (except B/hols). Nov-Feb by appt. only.
Min Mail Order UK: Nmc
Credit Cards: All major credit/debit cards
Specialities: A wide range of unusual and familiar perennials, shrubs, grasses, ferns & bedding plants, most in more generous sizes than usually found in nurseries. *Heuchera*, *Heucherella*, *Tiarella* & other shade-loving plants. Some more unusual plants available in small quantities only.
Notes: Located on the A413 just outside Winslow (heading in the Aylesbury direction). Cannot send large shrubs by mail order. Delivers to shows. Partial wheelchair access.
Map Ref: L, A2 **OS Grid Ref:** SP777271

LBrs **Burstow Nurseries & Garden Centre** ♿
Antlands Lane, Horley, Surrey RH6 9SR
Ⓣ (01293) 771942
Ⓕ (01293) 771942
Ⓔ enquiries@burstownurseries.co.uk
Ⓦ www.burstownurseries.co.uk
Contact: Chris Corke
Opening Times: 0900-1700 Mon-Sat, 0930-1600 Sun.
Credit Cards: All major credit/debit cards
Specialities: Roses & shrubs as well as a good range of herbaceous perennials & seasonal bedding plants.
Notes: Please note no mail order. Wheelchair accessible.

LBuc **Buckingham Nurseries** ♿ ◆
14 Tingewick Road, Buckingham
MK18 4AE
Ⓣ (01280) 822133
Ⓕ (01280) 815491
Ⓔ enquiries@buckingham-nurseries.co.uk
Ⓦ www.buckingham-nurseries.co.uk
Contact: R J & P L Brown
Opening Times: 0830-1730 (1800 in summer) Mon-Sat, 1030-1630 Sun.
Min Mail Order UK: Nmc
Min Mail Order EU: Nmc
Cat. Cost: Free.
Credit Cards: MasterCard, Maestro, Visa
Specialities: Bare rooted and container grown hedging. Fruit trees, soft fruit, trees, shrubs, herbaceous perennials, alpines, grasses & ferns.
Notes: Garden centre with restaurant. Euro accepted. Wheelchair accessible.
Map Ref: L, A2 **OS Grid Ref:** SP675333

LCla **Clay Lane Nursery**
3 Clay Lane, South Nutfield, Nr Redhill, Surrey RH1 4EG
Ⓣ (01737) 823307
Ⓔ claylane.nursery@btinternet.com
Ⓦ www.claylane-fuchsias.co.uk
Contact: K W Belton
Opening Times: Variable opening times. Please phone before travelling.
Min Mail Order UK: £10.00
Cat. Cost: 3 × 2nd class.
Credit Cards: None
Specialities: *Fuchsia*. Many varieties in small quantities only.
Notes: Mail order by telephone pre-arangement only. Delivers to shows.
Map Ref: L, C4

LCro **Crocus.co.uk**
Nursery Court, London Road, Windlesham, Surrey GU20 6LQ
Ⓣ 0844 557 2233
Ⓕ (01344) 629600
Ⓔ customerservices@crocus.co.uk
Ⓦ www.crocus.co.uk
Contact: Customer Care Team
Opening Times: Mail order only. Order lines open 24hrs, 7 days. Nursery has four Open Days a year; see website or phone for details.
Min Mail Order UK: Nmc + delivery charges (see website or phone for details).
Cat. Cost: Free.
Credit Cards: All, except American Express
Specialities: Large general nursery.
Notes: Also sells wholesale.
Map Ref: L, C3

LEdu **Edulis** ♿
(Office) 1 Flowers Piece, Ashampstead, Reading, Berkshire RG8 8SG
Ⓣ (01635) 578113
Ⓜ 07802 812781
Ⓔ edulisnursery@gmail.com
Ⓦ www.edulis.co.uk
Contact: Paul Barney
Opening Times: By appt. only.
Min Mail Order UK: £20.00 + p&p
Min Mail Order EU: £50.00 + p&p
Cat. Cost: 5 × 1st class.
Credit Cards: All, except American Express
Specialities: Unusual edibles, architectural plants, permaculture plants & many of our own collections.
Notes: Nursery is at The Walled Garden, Tidmarsh Lane, Pangbourne, RG8 8HT. Also sells wholesale. Euro accepted. Delivers to shows. Wheelchair accessible.
Map Ref: L, B2 **OS Grid Ref:** SU615747

LHel **Herts Hellebores** ♿
Green Lane Farm, Levens Green, Nr Ware, Hertfordshire
SG11 1HD
Ⓣ (01920) 438458
Ⓔ lorna@herts-hellebore.co.uk
Ⓦ www.herts-hellebore.co.uk
Contact: Lorna Jones
Opening Times: 1000-1600 Wed & Sat only, 1st Feb-29th Mar 2014. Other times Jan-Apr by appt. only. Check with nursery for 2015 opening times.
Min Mail Order UK: £18
Min Mail Order EU: £18
Cat. Cost: Free.
Credit Cards: All major credit/debit cards
Specialities: Hellebore hybrids. Specialising in developments of double & anemone centred hybrids. Seed-raised plants offered by colour. Some available in small quantities only.
Notes: Euro accepted. Wheelchair accessible.
Map Ref: L, A4 **OS Grid Ref:** TL357224

LHop **Hopleys Plants Ltd** ♿
High Street, Much Hadham, Hertfordshire
SG10 6BU
Ⓣ (01279) 842509
Ⓕ (01279) 843784
Ⓔ plants@hopleys.co.uk
Ⓦ www.hopleys.co.uk
Contact: Mr Aubrey Barker
Opening Times: 0900-1700 Mon & Wed-Sat, 1230-1700 Sun. Closed Jan, Feb except by appt.
Min Mail Order UK: Nmc
Credit Cards: Access, Switch, Visa
Specialities: Wide range of hardy & half-hardy shrubs & perennials.
Notes: Also sells wholesale. Delivers to shows. Wheelchair accessible.
Map Ref: L, A4 **OS Grid Ref:** TL428196

LLHF **Little Heath Farm (UK)** ♿
Little Heath Lane, Potten End, Berkhamsted, Hertfordshire HP4 2RY
Ⓣ (01442) 864951
Ⓔ lhfnursery@gmail.com
Ⓦ www.littleheathfarmnursery.co.uk
Contact: John Spokes
Opening Times: 1000-1700 or dusk if earlier, 7 days.
Cat. Cost: Online only.
Credit Cards: MasterCard, Visa
Specialities: Large range of alpines, herbaceous, shrubs, many available in small quantities only.
Notes: Wheelchair accessible. Delivers to shows.
Map Ref: L, B3

LLoc **W & S Lockyer**
39 Mitchley Avenue, Riddlesdown, Purley, Surrey CR8 1BZ
Ⓣ 020 8660 1336
Ⓕ 020 8660 1336
Ⓔ williamlockyer@btinternet.com
Contact: William Lockyer
Opening Times: Not open.
Min Mail Order UK: Nmc
Cat. Cost: £2.00: no stamps.
Credit Cards: None
Specialities: Auriculas. Nerines. National Collection of Double Auriculas.
Notes: Also sells wholesale. Delivers to Shows.

LLWG **Lilies Water Gardens** ♿
Broad Lane, Newdigate, Surrey
RH5 5AT
Ⓣ (01306) 631064
Ⓜ 07801 166244
Ⓔ mail@lilieswatergardens.co.uk
Ⓦ www.lilieswatergardens.co.uk
Contact: Simon Harman
Opening Times: 0900-1700 Wed-Sat, Mar-Aug. By appt. only Sep-Feb.
Min Mail Order UK: Nmc but flat rate £6.50 delivery charge.
Min Mail Order EU: Nmc
Cat. Cost: Online only.
Credit Cards: All major credit/debit cards
Specialities: Waterlilies, moist perennials, bog-garden plants, primulas, marginal plants, ferns, oxygenating plants. Pond, incl. submerged & free-floating, aquatic, water iris, water-garden, floating, stream & deep-water plants. Alpine, rock & creeping plants. Rushes & grasses.
Notes: Wheelchair accessible.

L

LLWP **LW Plants**
23 Wroxham Way, Harpenden, Hertfordshire AL5 4PP
Ⓣ (01582) 768467
Ⓔ mail@thymus co.uk
Ⓦ www.thymus.co.uk
Contact: Mrs Margaret Easter
Opening Times: 1100-1630 most days, but please phone first.
Cat. Cost: Online only.
Credit Cards: None
Specialities: Plants from a plantsman's garden, esp. *Geranium*, grasses & *Thymus*. Some available in small quantities only. National Collections of *Thymus* (Scientific), *Hyssopus* & *Satureja*. Brickell award 2011. *Thymus* ICRA.
Map Ref: L, B3 **OS Grid Ref:** TL141153

LMil **Millais Nurseries** ♿
Crosswater Farm, Crosswater Lane, Churt, Farnham, Surrey GU10 2JN
Ⓣ (01252) 792698
Ⓔ sales@rhododendrons.co.uk
Ⓦ www.rhododendrons.co.uk
Contact: David Millais
Opening Times: 1000-1700 Mon-Fri all year. Daily in spring. Please phone or see website for w/end opening in spring.
Min Mail Order UK: Nmc
Min Mail Order EU: Nmc
Cat. Cost: Free list on request. Full catalogue Online.
Credit Cards: All major credit/debit cards
Specialities: Rhododendrons, azaleas, magnolias, camellias & acers. Garden open in spring.
Notes: Mail order all year. Also sells wholesale. Wheelchair accessible.
Map Ref: L, C3 **OS Grid Ref:** SU856397

LOPS **RHS Online Plant Shop** ◆
Nursery Court, London Road, Windlesham, Surrey GU20 6LQ
Ⓣ 0844 557 2623
Ⓕ 0844 557 2234
Ⓔ customerservices@rhsplants.co.uk
Ⓦ www.rhsplants.co.uk
Contact: Customer Care Team
Opening Times: Not open. Online mail order only.
Min Mail Order UK: Nmc
Credit Cards: All, except American Express

LPal **The Palm Centre**
Ham Central Nursery, Ham, Richmond, Surrey TW10 7HA
Ⓣ 020 8255 6191
Ⓕ 020 8255 6192
Ⓔ info@palmcentre.co.uk
Ⓦ www.palmcentre.co.uk
Contact: Toby Shobbrook
Opening Times: 0900-1700, 7 days.
Min Mail Order UK: £10.00 + p&p
Min Mail Order EU: £10.00 + p&p
Cat. Cost: Free.
Credit Cards: All, except American Express
Specialities: Palms, ferns, bamboos. National Collection of *Trachycarpus*.
Notes: Also sells wholesale. Delivers to shows. Euro accepted.
Map Ref: L, B3

LPar **Paramount Plants & Gardens Ltd** ♿
131 Theobalds Park Road, Crews Hill, Enfield, Middlesex EN2 9BH
Ⓣ 020 8367 8809
Ⓜ 07802 952517
Ⓔ info@paramountplants.co.uk
Ⓦ www.paramountplants.co.uk
Contact: Lucas & Karen Mariconda
Opening Times: 0900-1600 7 days.
Min Mail Order UK: Nmc
Credit Cards: All major credit/debit cards
Specialities: Fully mature hardy plants incl. trees, large shrubs, bamboos, topiary, acers, tree ferns, palms, climbers and evergreen screening trees.
Notes: Also sells wholesale. Delivers to shows. Wheelchair accessible.
Map Ref: L, B4

LPfy **Plantify**
Unit 6, Windsor Business Centre, Windsor, Berkshire SL41 1SP
Ⓣ (01753) 257452
Ⓔ info@plantify.co.uk
Ⓦ www.plantify.co.uk
Contact: Peter Laughton
Opening Times: Not open. Mail order only.
Min Mail Order UK: Nmc
Cat. Cost: Online only.

LPla **The Plant Specialist**
7 Whitefield Lane, Great Missenden, Buckinghamshire HP16 0BH
Ⓣ (01494) 866650
Ⓕ (01494) 866650
Ⓔ enquire@theplantspecialist.co.uk
Ⓦ www.theplantspecialist.co.uk
Contact: Sean Walter
Opening Times: 1000-1700 Wed-Sat, 1000-1600 Sun, Apr-Oct.
Cat. Cost: None issued.
Credit Cards: All major credit/debit cards
Specialities: Herbaceous perennials, grasses, half-hardy perennials, bulbs.
Notes: Limited wheelchair access.

LPmr **Primrose Hall Nursery**
Dingley Dell Nursery, Toddington Road, Westoning, Bedfordshire MK45 5AH
Ⓣ (01525) 874989
Ⓔ alec.white@dingleydellnursery.co.uk
Ⓦ www.dingleydellnursery.co.uk
Contact: Alec White
Min Mail Order UK: Nmc
Min Mail Order EU: Nmc
Credit Cards: All, except American Express
Specialities: Small, independent nursery specialising in alpines, perennials, hardy shrubs, climbers, vegetables, herbs & bedding plants.
Notes: Also sells wholesale. Delivers to shows.

LPot **Potash Plants** ♿
Potash Nursery, Drayton Parslow, Buckinghamshire MK17 0JE
Ⓣ (01296) 720578
Ⓔ info@potashplants.co.uk
Ⓦ www.potashplants.co.uk
Contact: Gill Gallon
Opening Times: 0900-1730 Mon-Sat. 1030-1630 Sun.
Cat. Cost: Online.
Credit Cards: All, except American Express
Specialities: Wide range of traditional and unusual hardy perennials, grasses, trees & shrubs. Some available in small quantities only.
Notes: Nursery on B4032 mid-way between Aylesbury and Milton Keynes. Also sells wholesale. Delivers to shows. Wheelchair accessible.
Map Ref: L, A3 **OS Grid Ref:** SP834279

LRHS **Wisley Plant Centre (RHS)** ♿ ◆
RHS Garden, Wisley, Woking, Surrey GU23 6QB
Ⓣ (01483) 211113
Ⓕ (01483) 212372
Ⓔ wisleyplantcentre@rhs.org.uk
Ⓦ www.rhs.org.uk/wisleyplantcentre
Opening Times: 0900-1700 Mon-Sat, Oct-Feb. 0900-1800 Mon-Sat, Mar-Sep. 1100-1700 Sun all year, browsing from 1030. Closed Xmas Day.
Cat. Cost: Online only.
Credit Cards: All major credit/debit cards
Specialities: Over 10,000 plants, many rare or unusual, reflecting the range of the RHS flagship garden at Wisley. Plants subject to seasonal availability. For plants not in stock, we operate a reservation service by phone & in person.
Notes: Programme of free plant events throughout the year. Please ring or check website for details. Wheelchair accessible.
Map Ref: L, C3

LShp **Squire's Garden Centre, Shepperton** ♿
Halliford Road, Upper Halliford, Shepperton, Middlesex TW17 8SG
Ⓣ (01932) 784121
Ⓕ (01932) 785386
Ⓔ shepp.plants@squiresgardencentres.co.uk
Ⓦ www.squiresgardencentres.co.uk
Contact: Plant Area Manager
Opening Times: 0900-1800 Mon-Sat, 1030-1630 Sun.
Cat. Cost: None issued.
Credit Cards: All major credit/debit cards
Specialities: Roses.
Notes: Other garden centres in Middlesex, Surrey, Berkshire and West Sussex. Wheelchair accessible.

LSou **Southon Plants** ♿
Mutton Hill, Dormansland, Lingfield, Surrey RH7 6NP
Ⓣ (01342) 870150
Ⓔ lyn@southon-plants.co.uk
Ⓦ www.southonplants.com
Contact: Mr Southon
Opening Times: 0900-1730 Mar-Oct. Closed Mon from Jul-Dec. For Nov, Dec, Jan & Feb times, please phone first. See website for up-to-date opening hours.
Cat. Cost: Online only.
Credit Cards: All major credit/debit cards
Specialities: New & unusual hardy & tender perennials, specialising in *Agapanthus* (over 30 varieties), & *Heuchera* (over 40 varieties). Many new varieties for tender perennials/patio plants.
Notes: Wheelchair accessible.
Map Ref: L, C4

LSqH **Squire's Garden Centre, West Horsley** ♿
Epsom Road, West Horsley, Leatherhead, Surrey KT24 6AR
Ⓣ (01483) 282911
Ⓕ (01483) 281380
Ⓔ hors.plants@squiresgardencentres.co.uk
Ⓦ www.squiresgardencentres.co.uk
Contact: Plant Area Manager
Opening Times: 0900-1800 Mon-Sat, 1030-1630 Sun.
Cat. Cost: None issued.
Credit Cards: All major credit/debit cards
Specialities: Herbaceous.
Notes: Other garden centres in Middlesex, Surrey, Berkshire and West Sussex. Wheelchair accessible.

LSRN **Spring Reach Nursery** ♿
Long Reach, Ockham, Guildford, Surrey GU23 6PG
Ⓣ (01483) 284769

Ⓜ 07884 432666
Ⓕ (01483) 284769
Ⓔ info@springreachnursery.co.uk
Ⓦ www.springreachnursery.co.uk
Contact: Nick & Lissa Hourhan
Opening Times: 7 days. 1000-1700 Mon-Sat, 1030-1630 Sun. Open B/hols. Closed 23rd Dec-2nd Jan.
Min Mail Order UK: Nmc
Min Mail Order EU: Nmc
Credit Cards: All major credit/debit cards
Specialities: Shrubs, evergreen climbers, *Clematis*, perennials, roses, grasses, ferns, bamboos, trees, hedging, soft fruit & top fruit. Plants for chalk & clay. Deer & rabbit proof plants. Specimen & acid-loving plants.
Notes: Please ring for mail order details. Also sells wholesale. Delivers to shows. Wheelchair accessible.
Map Ref: L, C3

M

LSun **Sunnyside Nursery**
Upper Allotments, New Road, Northchurch, Hertfordshire HP4 1NJ
Ⓜ 07743 552154
Ⓔ philsmith2004@yahoo.co.uk
Ⓦ www.thesunnysidenursery.co.uk
Contact: Philip Smith
Opening Times: 0900-1700 Tue-Fri. Closed Mon. Sat, Sun & B/hols Mar-Sep at the Bridgewater Monument, National Trust Ashridge Estate.
Cat. Cost: Availability list on request.
Credit Cards: All major credit/debit cards
Specialities: Hardy perennials, alpines & ornamental grasses.
Notes: Please phone for stock availability & updates. Trade discounts available with orders of £100+.

LToo **Toobees Exotics**
20 Inglewood, St Johns, Woking, Surrey GU21 3HX
Ⓣ (01483) 722600
Ⓜ 07836 334011
Ⓕ (01483) 751995
Ⓔ bbpotter@woking.plus.com
Ⓦ www.toobees-exotics.com
Contact: Bob Potter
Opening Times: Not open. Mail order & online shop only. Visits by appt. only.
Min Mail Order UK: Nmc
Min Mail Order EU: Nmc
Cat. Cost: Sae
Specialities: South African & Madagascan succulents, many rare & unusual species, *Euphorbia* & *Pachypodium*. Stock varies constantly.
Notes: Credit cards accepted online only. Exports beyond EU. Euro accepted.

LTop **Topiary Arts**
(Office) 224 Hospital Bridge Road, Whitton, Twickenham, Middlesex TW2 6LF
Ⓣ 020 8894 2816
Ⓜ 07775 602704
Ⓔ jcb@topiaryarts.com
Ⓦ www.topiaryarts.com
Contact: James Crebbin-Bailey
Opening Times: By appt. only.
Min Mail Order UK: £30
Cat. Cost: Online only.
Credit Cards: None
Specialities: Topiary. Small quantities of *Buxus*, *Philyrea*, *Taxus* & *Ligustrum*.
Notes: Nursery is at Copped Hall Walled Garden, Upshire, Epping, Essex CM16 5HS. Also sells wholesale. Delivers to shows.

LTro **Tropical Britain Ltd** ◆
Hagthorn Farm, Pennypot Lane, Chobham, Woking, Surrey GU24 8DG
Ⓔ info@tropicalbritain.co.uk
Ⓦ www.tropicalbritain.co.uk
Contact: John Edmiston
Opening Times: Not open. Mail order only.
Min Mail Order UK: Nmc
Min Mail Order EU: Nmc
Cat. Cost: Online only.
Credit Cards: All major credit/debit cards
Specialities: Hardy exotics, rare plants & perennials, incl. palms, *Agave*, *Yucca*, bananas, hardy gingers, ferns & grasses.
Notes: Mail order online only. Euro accepted.

LYaf **Yaffles** ♿
Harvest Hill, Bourne End, Buckinghamshire SL8 5JJ
Ⓣ (01628) 525455
Contact: I Butterfield
Opening Times: 0900-1300 & 1400-1700. Please phone beforehand in case we are attending shows.
Min Mail Order UK: Nmc
Min Mail Order EU: £30.00 + p&p
Cat. Cost: 2 × 2nd class.
Credit Cards: None
Specialities: *Pleione*.
Notes: Only *Pleione* by mail order. Delivers to shows. Wheelchair accessible.

Midlands

MArl **Arley Hall Nursery** ♿
Northwich, Cheshire CW9 6NA
Ⓣ (01565) 777479 or 777231
Ⓕ (01565) 777465
Ⓦ www.arleyhallandgardens.com
Contact: Jane Foster, Rosie Jackson
Opening Times: 0930-1730 Mon-Fri, 1100-

1730 Sat & Sun, 29th Mar-29th Sep.
Cat. Cost: 4 × 1st class.
Credit Cards: All major credit/debit cards
Specialities: Wide range of herbaceous incl. many unusual varieties, some in small quantities. Wide range of unusual pelargoniums.
Notes: Nursery is beside car park at Arley Hall Gardens. Wheelchair accessible.
Map Ref: M, A1 **OS Grid Ref:** SJ673808

MAsh **Ashwood Nurseries Ltd** ♿
Ashwood Lower Lane, Ashwood, Kingswinford, West Midlands DY6 0AE
Ⓣ (01384) 401996
Ⓕ (01384) 401108
Ⓔ mailorder@ashwoodnurseries.com
Ⓦ www.ashwoodnurseries.com
Contact: Karrina Gilbert & Steve Lampitt
Opening Times: 0900-1700 Mon-Sat & 0930-1700 Sun, excl. Xmas & Boxing Day.
Min Mail Order UK: Nmc
Min Mail Order EU: Nmc
Cat. Cost: 4 × 1st class.
Credit Cards: All major credit/debit cards
Specialities: Large range of hardy plants, shrubs & dwarf conifers. Roses, alpines & herbaceous plants. Also specialises in *Auricula*, *Cyclamen*, *Galanthus*, hellebores, *Hepatica*, *Hydrangea* & *Salvia*. National Collection of *Lewisia*.
Notes: Tea room overlooking display garden. Ample parking. Regular events. Groups by appt. to visit private garden. Wheelchair accessible.
Map Ref: M, C2 **OS Grid Ref:** SO865879

MAvo **Avondale Nursery** ♿
(Office) 3 Avondale Road, Earlsdon, Coventry, Warwickshire CV5 6DZ
Ⓣ (024) 766 73662
Ⓜ 07979 093096
Ⓔ enquiries@avondalenursery.co.uk
Ⓦ www.avondalenursery.co.uk
Contact: Brian Ellis
Opening Times: 1000-1230, 1400-1700 Mon-Sat, 1030-1630 Sun, Mar-Sep. Other times by appt.
Cat. Cost: 4 × 1st class.
Credit Cards: All major credit/debit cards
Specialities: Rare & unusual perennials esp. *Aster*, *Eryngium*, *Leucanthemum*, *Geum*, *Crocosmia*, *Sanguisorba* & grasses. National Collections of *Aster novae-angliae*, *Anemone nemorosa* & *Sanguisorba*. Display garden open. Groups welcome.
Notes: Nursery is at Russell's Nursery, Mill Hill, Baginton, Nr Coventry, CV8 3AG. Delivers to shows. Wheelchair accessible.
Map Ref: M, C2 **OS Grid Ref:** SP339751

MBel **Bluebell Cottage Nursery** ♿
Lodge Lane, Dutton, Cheshire WA4 4HP
Ⓣ (01928) 713718
Ⓔ info@bluebellcottage.co.uk
Ⓦ www.bluebellcottage.co.uk
Contact: Sue Beesley
Opening Times: 1000-1700 Wed-Sun & B/hols, 1st Apr-end Sep. By appt. only outside these dates.
Min Mail Order UK: £5.95
Cat. Cost: Online only.
Credit Cards: All major credit/debit cards
Specialities: *Achillea*, *Anthemis*, *Brunnera*, *Centaurea*, *Echinacea*, *Geranium*, *Geum*, *Lychnis*, *Persicaria*, *Potentilla*, *Sanguisorba*, *Thalictrum* & ornamental grasses. Some items stocked in small quantities. Mail order plants are fully established, ready to plant out.
Notes: Mail order available all year round. Refreshments available. Delivers to shows. Wheelchair accessible.
Map Ref: M, A1 **OS Grid Ref:** SJ586779

MBlu **Bluebell Arboretum & Nursery** ♿
Annwell Lane, Smisby, Nr Ashby de la Zouch, Derbyshire LE65 2TA
Ⓣ (01530) 413700
Ⓕ (01530) 417600
Ⓔ sales@bluebellnursery.com
Ⓦ www.bluebellnursery.com
Contact: Robert & Suzette Vernon
Opening Times: 0900-1700 Mon-Sat & 1030-1630 Sun Mar-Oct, 0900-1600 Mon-Sat (not Sun) Nov-Feb. Closed 24th Dec-1st Jan incl. & Easter Sun.
Min Mail Order UK: £7.95
Min Mail Order EU: Nmc
Cat. Cost: £1.50 + 3 × 1st class.
Credit Cards: Access, MasterCard, Switch, Visa
Specialities: Uncommon trees & shrubs. Rare *Acer*, *Betula*, *Cornus*, *Fagus*, *Magnolia*, *Liquidambar*, *Quercus* & *Tilia*. Woody climbers.
Notes: Display garden & arboretum. 9-acre woodland garden with unusual trees. Guide dogs only. Working nursery, so wear appropriate clothing & sturdy footwear when visiting. Delivers to shows. Wheelchair accessible.
Map Ref: M, B1 **OS Grid Ref:** SK344187

MBNS **Barnsdale Gardens** ♿
Exton Avenue, Exton, Oakham, Rutland LE15 8AH
Ⓣ (01572) 813200
Ⓔ info@barnsdalegardens.co.uk
Ⓦ www.barnsdalegardens.co.uk
Contact: Nick Hamilton
Opening Times: 0900-1700 Mar-May & Sep-

Oct, 0900-1900 Jun-Aug, 1000-1600 Nov-Feb, 7 days. Closed 24th & 25th Dec.
Min Mail Order UK: Nmc
Min Mail Order EU: Nmc
Cat. Cost: Online only.
Credit Cards: All major credit/debit cards
Specialities: Wide range of choice & unusual garden plants. *Penstemon*, *Hemerocallis*.
Notes: Mail order from website or by telephone ordering only. Delivers to shows. Wheelchair accessible.
Map Ref: M, B3 **OS Grid Ref:** SK912108

M

MBri **Bridgemere Nursery & Garden World** ♿
Bridgemere, Nr Nantwich, Cheshire CW5 7QB
Ⓣ (01270) 521100
Ⓕ (01270) 520215
Ⓔ bridgemere.plantinfo@thegardencentregroup.co.uk
Ⓦ www.bridgemere.co.uk
Contact: Ann Foster, Roger Pierce
Opening Times: 0900-1800 7 days. Closed 25th & 26th Dec.
Min Mail Order UK: Nmc
Cat. Cost: None issued.
Credit Cards: Access, MasterCard, Switch, Visa
Notes: Mail order restricted to "click & collect" & home delivery service available on www.thegardencentregroup.co.uk. Euro accepted. Wheelchair accessible.
Map Ref: M, B1 **OS Grid Ref:** SJ727435

MBrN **Bridge Nursery** ♿
Tomlow Road, Napton-on-the-Hill, Nr Rugby, Warwickshire CV47 8HX
Ⓣ (01926) 812737
Ⓔ pemartino@tiscali.co.uk
Ⓦ www.Bridge-Nursery.co.uk
Contact: Christine Dakin & Philip Martino
Opening Times: 1000-1600 Mon-Sun mid Feb-mid Nov. Other times by appt.
Cat. Cost: Online only.
Credit Cards: All major credit/debit cards
Specialities: Ornamental grasses, sedges & bamboos. Also range of shrubs & perennials. Display garden.
Notes: Also sells wholesale. Euro accepted. Wheelchair accessible.
Map Ref: M, C2 **OS Grid Ref:** SP463625

MCms **Chrysanthemums Direct**
Holmes Chapel Road, Over Peover, Knutsford, Cheshire WA16 9RA
Ⓣ 0800 046 7443
Ⓜ 07977 312593
Ⓔ sales@chrysanthemumsdirect.co.uk
Ⓦ www.chrysanthemumsdirect.co.uk
Contact: Martyn Flint
Opening Times: Not open. Mail order only.
Min Mail Order UK: Nmc
Min Mail Order EU: Nmc
Cat. Cost: 4 × 1st class.
Credit Cards: All major credit/debit cards
Specialities: Chrysanthemums. Young plants grown to order. Delivery within 14 days.
Notes: Delivers to shows.

MCoo **Cool Temperate**
(Office) 45 Stamford Street, Awsworth, Nottinghamshire NG16 2QL
Ⓣ (0115) 916 2673
Ⓕ (0115) 916 2673
Ⓔ phil.corbett@cooltemperate.co.uk
Ⓦ www.cooltemperate.co.uk
Contact: Phil Corbett
Opening Times: 0900-1700, 7 days. Please ring/write first.
Min Mail Order UK: £30.00
Min Mail Order EU: £50.00
Cat. Cost: 3 × 1st class.
Credit Cards: None
Specialities: Tree fruit, soft fruit, nitrogen-fixers, hedging, own-root fruit trees. Many species available in small quantities only.
Notes: Nursery at Newton's Lane, Cossall, Notts. Also sells wholesale. Exports beyond EU.
Map Ref: M, B2 **OS Grid Ref:** SK474434

MCot **Coton Manor Garden**
Guilsborough, Northampton, Northamptonshire NN6 8RQ
Ⓣ (01604) 740219
Ⓔ nursery@cotonmanor.co.uk
Ⓦ www.cotonmanor.co.uk
Contact: Caroline Tait
Opening Times: 1200-1730 Tue-Sat, 1st Apr-27th Sep. Also Sun Apr, May & B/hol w/ends. Other times in working hours by appt.
Cat. Cost: Online only.
Credit Cards: All major credit/debit cards
Specialities: Wide-range of herbaceous perennials (1200+ varieties), some available in small quantities only. Also many tender perennials & selected shrubs.
Notes: Garden open. Tea rooms. Garden school. Partial wheelchair access.
Map Ref: M, C3 **OS Grid Ref:** SP675715

MCri **Crin Gardens**
79 Partons Road, Kings Heath, Birmingham B14 6TD
Ⓜ 07805 591475
Ⓔ cringardens@tiscali.co.uk
Ⓦ www.cringardens.co.uk
Contact: M Milinkovic
Opening Times: Not open. Mail order only.

Min Mail Order UK: Nmc
Min Mail Order EU: Nmc
Cat. Cost: 2 × 1st class + 1 × 2nd.
Credit Cards: None
Specialities: Lilies. Limited stock available on first come, first served basis.
Notes: Euro accepted.

MDon **DONINGTON NURSERIES LTD** ♿
Kings Mills, Park Lane, Castle Donington, Derbyshire DE74 2RS
Ⓣ (01332) 853004
Ⓕ (01332) 853793
Ⓔ sales@doningtonnurseries.co.uk
Ⓦ www.doningtonnurseries.co.uk
Contact: Rebecca Faulkner
Opening Times: Open daily (hours vary depending on season).
Cat. Cost: None.
Credit Cards: All major credit/debit cards
Specialities: Family-owned nursery stocking wide range of trees, shrubs, perennials & alpines. 50% of stock grown on nursery set within 4-acre former walled garden of Donington Hall. Home grown laurel & *Thuja* hedging available in large quantities.
Notes: Wheelchair accessible.
Map Ref: M, B2 **OS Grid Ref:** SK421273

MFie **FIELD HOUSE NURSERY** ♿
Leake Road, Gotham, Nottinghamshire NG11 0JN
Ⓣ (01159) 830278
Ⓜ 07504 125209
Ⓔ val.woolley@btinternet.com
Contact: Valerie A Woolley & Bob Taylor
Opening Times: By appt. only.
Cat. Cost: 4 × 1st class (auriculas/primulas). 2 × 1st class (astrantias).
Credit Cards: MasterCard, Electron, Maestro, Solo, Visa
Specialities: *Primula auricula* & seed, *Astrantia*. National Collections of *Primula auricula* (show & alpine) & *Astrantia*.
Notes: Mail order for *Astrantia*, *Primula* & auricula seeds. Euro accepted. Delivers to shows. Wheelchair accessible.

MGib **JOHN GIBSON DAFFODILS**
14 Waverley Road, Kettering, Northamptonshire NN15 6NT
Ⓣ (01536) 523350
Ⓔ gibbo.john@ntlworld.com
Ⓦ johngibson-daffodils.co.uk
Contact: John Gibson
Opening Times: Not open. Mail order only.
Min Mail Order UK: Nmc
Min Mail Order EU: Nmc
Cat. Cost: Free.
Credit Cards: None
Specialities: Small mail order business selling specialist exhibition *Narcissus* bulbs, many of own breeding, miniatures and species, plus hyacinths, tulips and other spring bulbs. Stocked in small quantities.
Notes: Exports beyond EU. Euro accepted.

MGil **JOHN GILLIES** ♿
(Office) 15 Newey Road, Coventry, Warwickshire CV2 5GZ
Ⓜ 07546 064961
Ⓔ enquiries@gilliesrareplants.com
Ⓦ www.gilliesrareplants.com
Contact: John Gillies
Opening Times: 1000-1700 Mon-Sat, 1030-1630 Sun, Mar-Sep. Oct-Feb by appt.
Cat. Cost: 4 × 1st class or online.
Specialities: A range of choice & rare trees, shrubs & climbers, incl., but not limited to, *Azara*, *Clethra*, *Colquhounia*, *Diostea*, *Embothrium*, *Ercilla*, *Fabiana*, *Mutisia* & *Rhapiolepis*. Most available in small quantities only. Contact nursery if plant not on plant list.
Notes: Nursery at Russell's Nursery, Mill Hill, Baginton, CV8 3AG, situated beside Avondale Nursery. Can deliver pre-purchased plants to attended plant fairs (see website for details or contact nursery). Wheelchair accessible.
Map Ref: M, C2 **OS Grid Ref:** SP337750

MGos **GOSCOTE NURSERIES LTD** ♿
Syston Road, Cossington, Leicestershire LE7 4UZ
Ⓣ (01509) 812121
Ⓔ enquiries@goscote.co.uk
Ⓦ www.goscote.co.uk
Contact: James Toone
Opening Times: 7 days, year round, apart from between Xmas & New Year.
Cat. Cost: Online only.
Credit Cards: Access, Delta, MasterCard, Switch, Visa
Specialities: Japanese maples, rhododendrons & azaleas, *Magnolia*, *Camellia*, *Pieris* & other *Ericaceae*. Ornamental trees & shrubs, conifers, fruit, heathers, alpines, roses, *Clematis* & unusual climbers.
Notes: Design & landscaping service available. Café & show garden. Also sells wholesale. Wheelchair accessible.
Map Ref: M, B3 **OS Grid Ref:** SK602130

MHCG **HILL CLOSE GARDENS** ♿
Bread and Meat Close, Warwick, Warwickshire CV34 6HF
Ⓣ (01926) 493339
Ⓜ 07533 401934
Ⓔ gardenssupervisor@hcgt.org.uk
Ⓦ www.hillclosegardens.com

Contact: Gary Leaver
Opening Times: 1100-1700, Mon-Fri, all year. 1100-1700 Sat & Sun, Apr-Oct.
Cat. Cost: Online only.
Credit Cards: All major credit/debit cards
Specialities: Small retail nursery attached to heritage garden which is open to the public. *Chrysanthemum* & *Aster*. Many other rare plants offered under the Plant Heritage plant exchange
Notes: Wheelchair accessible.
Map Ref: M, C2 **OS Grid Ref:** SP277647

M

MHed **Hedgexpress**
Buckland Road, Bampton,
Oxfordshire
OX18 2AA
Ⓣ (01993) 850979
Ⓕ (01993) 850100
Ⓔ info@hedgexpress.co.uk
Ⓦ www.hedgexpress.co.uk
Contact: Gavin Stevens
Opening Times: 0900-1600, Mon-Fri.
Min Mail Order UK: Nmc
Cat. Cost: Online only.
Credit Cards: Paypal
Specialities: Hedging & lavenders.
Notes: Also sells wholesale.
Map Ref: M, D2 **OS Grid Ref:** SP322024

MHer **The Herb Nursery** ♿
Thistleton, Oakham, Rutland
LE15 7RE
Ⓣ (01572) 767658
Ⓔ herbnursery@southwitham.net
Ⓦ www.herbnursery.co.uk
Contact: Peter Bench
Opening Times: 0900-1800 (or dusk) 7 days excl. Xmas-New Year.
Cat. Cost: Free with A5 sae.
Credit Cards: All major credit/debit cards
Specialities: Herbs, wild flowers, cottage garden plants, scented-leaf pelargoniums. *Thymus*, *Mentha*, *Lavandula*.
Notes: Wheelchair accessible.
Map Ref: M, B3

MHin **Hinwick Hall Plant Centre** ♿
Hinwick Hall College, Hinwick,
Wellingborough, Northamptonshire
NN29 7JD
Ⓣ (01933) 350543
Ⓕ (01933) 412470
Ⓔ RHockney@hinwick.livability.org.uk
Contact: Richard Hockney
Opening Times: 0900-1700 Mon-Sat, 1000-1600 Sun, Mar-Nov.
Credit Cards: All major credit/debit cards
Specialities: Range of unusual and common plants, grasses & a selection of sub-tropical.
Notes: Small retail nursery attached to a specialist college working with young adults with learning difficulties and disabilities. Wheelchair accessible.

MHol **Hollies Farm Plant Centre**
Uppertown, Bonsall, Nr Matlock,
Derbyshire, DE4 2AW
Ⓣ (01629) 822734
Ⓔ rbrt.wells@gmail.com
Ⓦ www.holliesfarmplantcentre.co.uk
Contact: Robert or Linda Wells
Opening Times: 0900-1700 every day except Wed.
Credit Cards: None
Specialities: Range of rare & unusual herbaceous perennials.
Notes: Also sells wholesale.

MHom **Homestead Plants**
The Homestead, Normanton,
Bottesford, Nottingham
NG13 0EP
Ⓣ (01949) 842745
Ⓦ www.homesteadplants.com
Contact: Mrs S Palmer
Opening Times: By appt.
Min Mail Order UK: Nmc
Cat. Cost: 2 × 2nd class.
Credit Cards: None
Specialities: Unusual hardy & half-hardy perennials, esp. *Argyranthemum*, *Galanthus*, *Hosta*, *Jovibarba*, *Salvia*, *Sempervivum* & heliotrope. Drought-tolerant asters. Most available only in small quantities. National Collection of *Heliotropium* cultivars.
Notes: Mail order not offered year round. Please check with nursery for details.
Map Ref: M, B3 **OS Grid Ref:** SK812407

MHtn **Hintons Nursery** ♿
Coventry Road, Guy's Cliffe, Warwick,
Warwickshire CV34 5FJ
Ⓣ (01926) 492273
Ⓔ info@hintonsnursery.co.uk
Ⓦ www.hintonsnursery.co.uk
Contact: S. Ridgeway
Opening Times: 0900-1700 Mon-Sat, 1000-1600 Sun. Closed Xmas Day-New Year's Day (incl.)
Min Mail Order UK: Nmc
Credit Cards: All, except American Express
Specialities: Wide selection of shrubs, herbaceous perennials, trees, alpines, herbs, acquatics, seasonal bedding, fruit and vegetables. Most grown on site.
Notes: Larger plants only available for collection. Groups welcome by prior arrangement. Wheelchair accessible.
Map Ref: M, C2 **OS Grid Ref:** SP289667

MJac **JACKSON'S NURSERIES**
Clifton Campville, Nr Tamworth,
Staffordshire B79 0AP
Ⓣ (01827) 373307
Contact: N Jackson
Opening Times: 0900-1800 Mon & Wed-Sat, 1000-1700 Sun.
Cat. Cost: 2 × 1st class.
Credit Cards: None
Specialities: *Fuchsia.*
Notes: Also sells wholesale.
Map Ref: M, B2

MJak **JACKSON'S NURSERIES** ♿
Thorney Edge Road, Bagnall, Stoke-on-Trent,
Staffordshire ST9 9LE
Ⓣ (01782) 502741
Ⓕ (01782) 504932
Ⓔ sales@jacksonsnurseries.co.uk
Ⓦ www.jacksonsnurseries.co.uk
Contact: Sherrie Davison
Opening Times: 0800-1700 7 days, Mar-Oct. 0800-1630, Nov-Feb.
Credit Cards: MasterCard, Visa
Specialities: Good general range.
Notes: Family-run nursery, established for over 50 years, a short distance from the Peak District. Tea room. Also sells wholesale. Wheelchair accessible.

MLea **LEA RHODODENDRON GARDENS LTD** ♿
Lea, Matlock, Derbyshire DE4 5GH
Ⓣ (01629) 534380/534260
Ⓕ (01629) 534260
Ⓔ lea.gardens@hotmail.co.uk
Ⓦ www.leagarden.co.uk
Contact: Peter Tye
Opening Times: 1000-1730 7 days 20 Mar-30 Jun. Out of season by appt.
Min Mail Order UK: £15.00 + p&p
Min Mail Order EU: £15.00 + p&p
Cat. Cost: 30p + sae.
Credit Cards: All major credit/debit cards
Specialities: Rhododendrons & azaleas.
Notes: Exports beyond EU. Wheelchair accessible.
Map Ref: M, B1 **OS Grid Ref:** SK324571

MLHP **LONGSTONE HARDY PLANT NURSERY** ♿
Station Road, Great Longstone,
Nr Bakewell, Derbyshire
DE45 1TS
Ⓣ (01629) 640136
Ⓜ 07762 083674
Ⓔ lucyinlongstone@hotmail.com
Ⓦ www.longstonehardyplants.co.uk
Contact: Lucy Wright
Opening Times: 1000-1700 Wed-Mon (closed Tue), 1st Mar-31st Oct.
Credit Cards: All major credit/debit cards
Specialities: Peat-free nursery displaying all our own hardy perennials, ornamental grasses, herbs & shrubs, incl. many unusual varieties. Some stock available in small quantities only. Can propagate to order.
Notes: Turn across village green between the White Lion Pub & the Cripin Inn. Nursery 100 yds on right. Wheelchair accessible.
Map Ref: M, A2 **OS Grid Ref:** SK198717

MLod **LODGE FARM PLANTS & WILDFLOWERS** ♿
Case Lane, Fiveways, Hatton, Warwickshire
CV35 7JD
Ⓣ (01926) 484649
Ⓜ 07977 631368
Ⓔ lodgefarmplants@btinternet.com
Ⓦ www.lodgefarm-plants.com
Contact: Janet Cook & Nick Cook
Opening Times: Open 7 days all year, except Xmas Day & Boxing Day.
Min Mail Order UK: Nmc
Cat. Cost: Availability list online.
Credit Cards: All major credit/debit cards
Specialities: All forms of fruit trees: bush; espalier; fan; stepovers; cordons. Soft fruit. Wildflower plants. Native trees & hedging.
Notes: Courier service to all UK. Also sells wholesale. Delivers to shows. Euro accepted. Wheelchair accessible.
Map Ref: M, C2 **OS Grid Ref:** SP223700

MMHG **MORTON NURSERIES LTD** ♿
Morton, Retford, Nottinghamshire
DN22 8HE
Ⓣ (01777) 702530
Ⓜ 07940 434398
Ⓔ enquiries@morton-nurseries.com
Ⓦ www.morton-nurseries.co.uk
Contact: Gill McMaster
Opening Times: By appt.only
Min Mail Order UK: £5.00 + p&p
Cat. Cost: 3 × 1st class.
Credit Cards: All major credit/debit cards
Specialities: Shrubs & perennials.
Notes: Delivers to shows. Wheelchair accessible.
Map Ref: M, A3

MMuc **MUCKLESTONE NURSERIES**
Rock Lane, Mucklestone, Nr Market Drayton,
Shropshire TF9 4DN
Ⓣ (01630) 674284
Ⓜ 07714 241668
Ⓔ info@botanyplants.co.uk
Ⓦ www.botanyplants.co.uk
Contact: William & Louise Friend
Opening Times: 0900-1700 (or dusk) 7 days, winter times may vary, please phone first.
Min Mail Order UK: Nmc

Cat. Cost: Online.
Credit Cards: All major credit/debit cards
Specialities: Trees, shrubs, grasses, bamboos, rhododendrons, ferns & perennials for acid & damp soils of the north & west UK. Our nursery in Kent grows complementary range for dry, chalk & coast. See entry under code SEND. Extensive grounds where plants can be seen growing.
Notes: Any plants on website or listed under nursery code SEND can be collected to order or sent.
Map Ref: M, B2 **OS Grid Ref:** SJ728373

MNai **Naieus Exotics**
432 Burton Road, Midway, Swadlingcote, Derbyshire DE11 0DW
Ⓜ 07871 315312
Ⓔ naieus@live.co.uk
Ⓦ www.naieusexotics.co.uk
Contact: Ian
Opening Times: 0900-1800, Mon-Sat. 1000-1630 Sun.
Min Mail Order UK: £15.00
Min Mail Order EU: € 15.00
Cat. Cost: £1.00 + 1 × 1st class.
Credit Cards: All major credit/debit cards
Specialities: *Brugmansia*. Available in small quantities only.
Notes: Exports beyond EU. Delivers to shows. Euro accepted.

MNew **Newington Nurseries** ♿
Newington, Nr Stadhampton, Wallingford, Oxfordshire OX10 7AW
Ⓣ (01865) 400533
Ⓔ plants@newington-nurseries.co.uk
Ⓦ www.newington-nurseries.co.uk
Contact: Mrs A T Hendry
Opening Times: 0830-1700 Wed-Sun Jan-Dec.
Min Mail Order UK: Nmc
Credit Cards: Access, MasterCard, Switch, Visa
Specialities: Unusual cottage garden plants, hardy exotics, herbs, orchids, grasses, topiary & specimen plants. National Collection of *Alocasia* (*Araceae*).
Notes: Also sells wholesale. Euro accepted. Wheelchair accessible.
Map Ref: M, D3

MNHC **The National Herb Centre** ♿
Banbury Road, Warmington, Nr Banbury, Oxfordshire OX17 1DF
Ⓣ (01295) 690999
Ⓕ (01295) 690034
Ⓔ info@herbcentre.co.uk
Ⓦ www.herbcentre.co.uk
Contact: Plant Centre Staff
Opening Times: 0900-1730 Mon-Sat, 1030-1700 Sun.
Min Mail Order UK: Nmc but carriage charge of £10.00 for orders valued up to £50, more for larger orders.
Credit Cards: All major credit/debit cards
Specialities: Herbs, culinary & medicinal. Extensive selection of rosemary, thyme & lavender, in particular.
Notes: Next day delivery UK mainland only, signature required. Wheelchair accessible.
Map Ref: M, C2 **OS Grid Ref:** SP413471

MNrw **Norwell Nurseries** ♿
Woodhouse Road, Norwell, Newark, Nottinghamshire NG23 6JX
Ⓣ (01636) 636337
Ⓔ wardha@aol.com
Ⓦ www.norwellnurseries.co.uk
Contact: Dr Andrew Ward
Opening Times: 1000-1700 Mon, Wed-Fri & Sun (Wed-Mon May & Jun). By appt. Aug & 20th Oct-1st Mar.
Min Mail Order UK: £15.00 + p&p
Min Mail Order EU: £40.00
Cat. Cost: 3 × 1st class or online.
Credit Cards: None
Specialities: A large collection of unusual & choice herbaceous perennials esp., hardy geraniums, *Geum*, pond & bog plants, cottage garden plants, *Hemerocallis*, grasses, *Trillium*, hardy chrysanthemums & woodland plants. Over 2500 different species & cvs grown. One acre garden open.
Notes: Talks given. Also sells wholesale. Delivers to shows. Wheelchair accessible.
Map Ref: M, B3 **OS Grid Ref:** SK767616

MOld **Old Hall Nursery** ♿
Winkhill, Leek, Staffordshire ST13 7PN
Ⓣ (01538) 308257
Ⓜ 07866 175881
Ⓔ oldhallnursery@hotmail.co.uk
Ⓦ www.oldhallnursery.com
Contact: Sandra Henshall
Opening Times: 1000-1600, 7 days.
Cat. Cost: Not available.
Credit Cards: None
Specialities: Large selection of herbaceous, herbs & alpines. Also shrubs, climbers & fruit trees. All hardy.
Notes: Wheelchair accessible.
Map Ref: M, B2 **OS Grid Ref:** SK051521

MOWG **The Old Walled Garden** ♿
Honeybourne Road, Pebworth, Stratford-upon-Avon, Warwickshire CV37 8XP
Ⓣ (01789) 720788
Ⓕ (01789) 721162
Ⓔ Heather@oldwalledgarden.com

Ⓦ www.oldwalledgarden.com
Contact: Heather Godard-Key
Opening Times: 0900-1700 Mon-Sat, 3rd Mar-29th Aug. 0900-1600 Mon-Fri, 1st Sep-27th Feb. 1030-1600 Sat & Sun, 5th Apr-27th Jul. Closed last 2 weeks of Dec-1st week Jan, Easter Sun & Aug B/hol Mon.
Min Mail Order UK: Nmc
Min Mail Order EU: £30
Cat. Cost: 3 × 1st class
Credit Cards: MasterCard, Maestro, Visa
Specialities: Many rare & unusual shrubs. Wide range of conservatory plants esp. Australian. *Callistemon* & *Hibiscus*.
Notes: Delivers to shows. Wheelchair accessible.
Map Ref: M, C2 **OS Grid Ref:** SP133458

MPhe **Phedar Nursery**
42 Bunkers Hill, Romiley, Stockport, Cheshire SK6 3DS
Ⓣ (0161) 430 3772
Ⓔ mclewin@phedar.com
Ⓦ www.phedar.com
Contact: Will McLewin
Opening Times: Frequent but irregular. Please phone to arrange appt.
Min Mail Order UK: Nmc
Min Mail Order EU: Nmc
Cat. Cost: Online or write for printed version.
Credit Cards: None
Specialities: *Helleborus*, *Paeonia*. Limited stock of some rare items.
Notes: Exports beyond EU subject to destination & on an ad hoc basis only. Please contact nursery for details. Also sells wholesale. Euro accepted.
Map Ref: M, A2 **OS Grid Ref:** SJ936897

MPie **Piecemeal Plants** ♿
Whatton House Gardens, Nr Kegworth, Loughborough, Leicestershire LE12 5BG
Ⓣ (01509) 672056
Ⓜ 07950 757444
Ⓔ nursery@piecemealplants.co.uk
Ⓦ www.piecemealplants.co.uk
Contact: Mary Thomas
Opening Times: 1300-1600 (normally 1700 in summer) early Apr-mid Sep, Thu, Fri & some Sun. For up to date details, please ring or see website. Also by arrangement throughout the year.
Cat. Cost: Online only.
Credit Cards: None
Specialities: Interesting range of herbaceous perennials & bulbs, many unusual. Some half-hardy or tender. Majority in small quantities.
Notes: Nursery located at entrance to Whatton Gardens, off A6 between Kegworth & Hathern. Car parking in front of Whatton House at top of drive. Wheelchair accessible.
Map Ref: M, B3 **OS Grid Ref:** SK494242

MPkF **Packhorse Farm Nursery** ♿
Sandyford House, Lant Lane, Tansley, Matlock, Derbyshire DE4 5FW
Ⓣ (01629) 57206
Ⓜ 07974 095752
Ⓕ (01629) 57206
Contact: Hilton W Haynes
Opening Times: 1000-1700 Tues & Wed, 1st Mar-31st Oct. Any other time by appt. only.
Cat. Cost: 2 × 1st class for plant list.
Credit Cards: None
Specialities: *Acer*, rare stock is limited in supply. Other more unusual hardy shrubs, trees & conifers.
Notes: Delivers to shows. Wheelchair accessible.
Map Ref: M, B2 **OS Grid Ref:** SK322617

MPnt **Plantagogo.com**
Jubilee Cottage Nursery, Snape Lane, Englesea Brook, Crewe, Cheshire CW2 5QN
Ⓣ (01270) 820335
Ⓜ 07713 518271
Ⓔ info@plantagogo.com
Ⓦ www.plantagogo.com
Contact: Vicky & Richard Fox
Opening Times: By appt. only. Also Open Days: 4th, 5th, 6th Apr; 10th, 11th, 12th Oct 2014, 1000-1600.
Min Mail Order UK: £9.95 single payment.
Min Mail Order EU: Price on application or see website.
Cat. Cost: 4 × 1st class.
Credit Cards: All major credit/debit cards
Specialities: *Heuchera*, *Heucherella*, *Tiarella*, also large selection of perennials. National Collections of *Heuchera*, *Heucherella* & *Tiarella*. Plants listed in the *RHS Plant Finder* are available in good quantities. Others, not listed here, are available from our collections on request.
Notes: Also sells wholesale. Delivers to shows. Limited wheelchair access.
Map Ref: M, B1 **OS Grid Ref:** SJ750516

MRav **Ravensthorpe Nursery** ♿
6 East Haddon Road, Ravensthorpe, Northamptonshire NN6 8ES
Ⓣ (01604) 770548
Ⓕ (01604) 770548
Ⓔ ravensthorpenursery@hotmail.com
Contact: Jean & Richard Wiseman
Opening Times: 1000-1800 (or dusk if earlier) Tue-Sat. B/hol w/ends in May. Easter Mon.
Min Mail Order UK: Nmc

Min Mail Order EU: Nmc
Cat. Cost: None issued.
Credit Cards: Delta, MasterCard, Visa
Specialities: Huge range of perennials, shrubs & trees with numerous unusual varieties, many of which can be seen growing in the display garden.
Notes: Search & delivery service for large orders, winter months only. Wheelchair accessible.
Map Ref: M, C3 **OS Grid Ref:** SP665699

MSCN **Stonyford Cottage Nursery** ♿
Stonyford Lane, Cuddington, Northwich, Cheshire CW8 2TF
Ⓣ (01606) 888970/888128 (answerphone)
Ⓜ 07714 205177
Ⓔ stonyfordcottage@yahoo.co.uk
Ⓦ www.stonyfordcottagenursery.co.uk
Contact: Andrew Overland
Opening Times: 1000-1700 Tue-Sun & B/hol Mons 1st Feb-31st Oct.
Min Mail Order UK: Nmc
Min Mail Order EU: Nmc
Cat. Cost: None.
Credit Cards: All major credit/debit cards
Specialities: Wide range of herbaceous perennials, *Iris*, hardy *Geranium*, moisture-loving & bog plants. *Sempervivum*, *Paeonia*, candelabra *Primula*.
Notes: Also sells wholesale. Wheelchair accessible.
Map Ref: M, A1 **OS Grid Ref:** SJ580710

MSKA **Sweet Knowle Aquatics** ♿
Wimpstone-Ilmington Road, Stratford-upon-Avon, Warwickshire CV37 8Nr
Ⓣ (01789) 450036
Ⓕ (01789) 450036
Ⓔ sweetknowleaquatics@hotmail.com
Ⓦ www.sweetknowleaquatics.co.uk
Contact: Zoe Harding
Opening Times: 0930-1700 Sun-Fri, closed Sat. Open B/hols.
Min Mail Order UK: Nmc
Min Mail Order EU: Nmc
Cat. Cost: By email only.
Credit Cards: All major credit/debit cards
Specialities: Aquatics. Hardy & tropical water lilies, marginals & oxygenators. 2-acre display garden open to the public (no charge).
Notes: Wheelchair accessible.
Map Ref: M, C2 **OS Grid Ref:** SP207480

MSmi **John Smith & Son** ♿
Fuchsia Centre, Thornton Nurseries, Thornton, Leicestershire LE67 1AN
Ⓣ (01530) 230331
Ⓕ (01530) 230331
Ⓔ sales@fuchsiaplants.co.uk
Ⓦ www.fuchsiaplants.co.uk
Contact: David Smith
Opening Times: 0800-1730 Mon-Fri, 1000-1600 Sat & Sun all year round.
Min Mail Order UK: Nmc
Cat. Cost: Online only.
Credit Cards: None
Specialities: Hardy, Half-hardy & large American fuchsias.
Notes: Also sells wholesale. Wheelchair accessible.
Map Ref: M, B3

MSnd **Sound Garden Rhododendrons**
7 Lumber Lane, Burtonwood, Warrington, Cheshire WA5 4AS
Ⓣ (01925) 229100
Ⓜ 07931 340836
Ⓔ timothyatkinson@msn.com
Ⓦ www.sound-garden-designs.co.uk
Contact: Tim Atkinson
Opening Times: By appt. only.
Cat. Cost: 2 × 1st class
Credit Cards: None
Specialities: Species *Rhododendron*. Species *Sorbus*.
Notes: Nursery formerly at Middledale Farm, Dale Road, Marple, Cheshire SK6 6NL. Delivers to shows.
Map Ref: N, B1 **OS Grid Ref:** SJ948901

MSpe **SpecialPerennials.com**
Yew Tree House, Hall Lane, Hankelow, Crewe, Cheshire CW3 0JB
Ⓣ (01270) 811443
Ⓜ 07980 910000
Ⓔ plants@specialperennials.com
Ⓦ www.specialperennials.com
Contact: Janet & Martin Blow
Opening Times: Nursery only open when garden open for NGS & National Collection of *Helenium* & *Centaurea* Open Days. See website or phone for details.
Min Mail Order UK: Nmc
Cat. Cost: Online or A5 sae (large letter rate postage) for descriptive catalogue.
Credit Cards: Paypal
Specialities: Herbaceous perennials. *Geum*, border *Phlox*, *Hemerocallis*, *Monada* & *Persciaria*. National Collections of *Helenium* cvs & *Centaurea*. All plants available in small quantities only.
Notes: All plants grown in garden nursery, most in small quantities & some sell out quickly. Garden open for NGS. Talks given. Group visits to garden & nursery welcomed. See website or send sae for details. Orders can be delivered to Plant Hunters' Fairs.
Map Ref: M, B1 **OS Grid Ref:** SJ699452

MSwo **SWALLOWS NURSERY** ♿
Mixbury, Brackley,
Northamptonshire
NN13 5RR
Ⓣ (01280) 847721
Ⓔ enq@swallowsnursery.co.uk
Ⓦ www.swallowsnursery.co.uk
Contact: Chris Swallow
Opening Times: 0900-1300 & 1400-1700 (earlier in winter) Mon-Fri, 0900-1300 Sat.
Min Mail Order UK: £15.00
Cat. Cost: 3 × 1st class (plus phone number).
Credit Cards: All major credit/debit cards
Specialities: Growing a wide range, particularly shrubs, climbers, trees & roses.
Notes: Trees not for mail order unless part of larger order. Nursery transport used where possible, esp. for trees. Also sells wholesale. Wheelchair accessible.
Map Ref: M, C3 **OS Grid Ref:** SP607336

MTis **TISSINGTON NURSERY** ♿
The Old Kitchen Gardens,
Tissington, Ashbourne, Derbyshire
DE6 1RA
Ⓣ (01335) 390650
Ⓜ 07929 720284
Ⓔ info@tissington-nursery.co.uk
Ⓦ www.tissington-nursery.co.uk
Contact: Mairi Longdon
Opening Times: 1030-1700 daily, end Mar-end Sep.
Min Mail Order UK: Nmc
Cat. Cost: 4 × 1st class or online.
Credit Cards: All major credit/debit cards
Specialities: Choice & unusual perennials esp. *Achillea*, *Aster*, *Geranium*, *Geum*, *Helenium*, *Helianthus*, *Nepeta*, *Phlox*, *Salvia*, *Sanguisorba* & *Sedum*.
Notes: Delivers to shows. Wheelchair accessible.
Map Ref: M, B1 **OS Grid Ref:** SK176521

MTPN **SMART PLANTS**
Sandy Hill Lane, off Overstone Road,
Moulton, Northampton NN3 7JB
Ⓣ (01604) 454106
Ⓜ 07519 339508
Ⓔ smartplants@hotmail.co.uk
Contact: Stuart Smart
Opening Times: 1000-1500 Thu & Fri, 1000-1700 Sat. Other times by appt.
Min Mail Order UK: Nmc
Cat. Cost: 3 × 1st class
Credit Cards: None
Specialities: Wide range of herbaceous, alpines, shrubs, grasses, hardy *Geranium*. Some plants available in small quantities only.
Notes: Delivers to shows. Limited wheelchair access.

MWat **WATERPERRY GARDENS LTD** ♿
Waterperry, Nr Wheatley, Oxfordshire
OX33 1JZ
Ⓣ (01844) 339226/254
Ⓕ (01844) 339883
Ⓔ pmaxwell@waterperrygardens.co.uk
Ⓦ www.waterperrygardens.co.uk
Contact: Mr R Jacobs
Opening Times: 1000-1730 summer. 1000-1700 winter.
Min Mail Order UK: £30.00
Cat. Cost: Online only.
Credit Cards: All major credit/debit cards
Specialities: General, large range of herbaceous esp. *Aster*, also National Collection of *Saxifraga* (subsect. *Kabschia* & *Engleria*).
Notes: Wheelchair accessible.
Map Ref: M, D3 **OS Grid Ref:** SP630064

MWhi **WHITEHILL FARM NURSERY** ♿
Whitehill Farm, Burford, Oxfordshire
OX18 4DT
Ⓣ (01993) 823218
Ⓕ (01993) 822894
Ⓔ a.youngson@virgin.net
Ⓦ www.whitehillfarmnursery.co.uk
Contact: P J M Youngson
Opening Times: 0900-1800 (or dusk if earlier) daily, except Mon, Mar-Oct. Nov-Feb & Mons by appt.
Min Mail Order UK: £15 + p&p
Min Mail Order EU: £25 + p&p
Credit Cards: All major credit/debit cards
Specialities: Grasses & bamboos, less common shrubs & perennials. Some available in small quantities only.
Notes: Euro accepted. Wheelchair accessible.
Map Ref: M, D2 **OS Grid Ref:** SP268113

MWht **WHITELEA NURSERY** ♿
Whitelea Lane, Tansley, Matlock, Derbyshire
DE4 5FL
Ⓣ (01629) 55010
Ⓔ sales@uk-bamboos.co.uk
Ⓦ www.uk-bamboos.co.uk
Contact: David Wilson
Opening Times: By appt.
Min Mail Order UK: Nmc
Cat. Cost: Online only. Price list available 2 × 1st class.
Credit Cards: None
Specialities: Bamboos. Substantial quantities of 45 cvs & species of bamboo, remainder stocked in small numbers only. Limited stocks of grasses, trees & shrubs.
Notes: Mail order limited by carrier restrictions, please contact nursery or see website for details. Also sells wholesale. Wheelchair accessible.
Map Ref: M, B1 **OS Grid Ref:** SK325603

MWLS **Water Line Solutions** ◆
Lilford Lodge Farm, Barnwell, Nr Oundle, Northamptonshire PE8 5SA
Ⓣ (01832) 272725
Ⓔ alex@water-lines.co.uk
Ⓦ www.water.lines.co.uk
Contact: Alexandra Budaiova
Opening Times: 0830-1700, Mon-Thu, 0830-1630, Fri.
Min Mail Order UK: Nmc
Min Mail Order EU: £50.00
Cat. Cost: Online only.
Credit Cards: All major credit/debit cards
Specialities: Wetlands nursery supplying acquatic plants.
Notes: Delivers to shows. Also sells wholesale.
Map Ref: M, C3

N

MWts **Waterside Nursery**
Sharnford, Leicestershire
Ⓣ (01455) 273730
Ⓜ 07931 557082
Ⓔ watersidenursery@yahoo.co.uk
Ⓦ www.watersidenursery.co.uk
Contact: Linda Smith
Opening Times: By appt. only.
Min Mail Order UK: Nmc
Cat. Cost: Online only.
Credit Cards: All major credit/debit cards
Specialities: Aquatics, marginal pond plants, miniature waterlilies, waterlilies, bog garden plants & moisture-loving plants.
Notes: Delivers to shows.

Northern

NAbi **Abi and Tom's Garden Plants** ♿
Halecat Nurseries, Witherslack, Grange Over Sands, Cumbria LA11 6RT
Ⓣ (01539) 552946
Ⓔ info@halecatplants.co.uk
Ⓦ www.halecatplants.co.uk
Contact: Tom & Abi Attwood
Opening Times: 0900-1700 Mon-Sat, 1000-1600 Sun, Mar-Oct incl. Check online or phone for winter opening times.
Cat. Cost: Online.
Credit Cards: All major credit/debit cards
Specialities: Hardy herbaceous perennials.
Notes: Wheelchair accessible.
Map Ref: N, C1 **OS Grid Ref:** SD433838

NBes **Best4Hedging**
Five Acres Nursery, Dawbers Lane, Euxton, Lancashire PR7 6EE
Ⓣ (01257) 261243
Ⓔ enquiries@best4hedging.co.uk
Ⓦ www.best4hedging.co.uk
Contact: Kate James
Opening Times: 0800-1800 Mon-Fri, 0800-1600 Sat, 1000-1600 Sun.
Min Mail Order UK: Nmc
Cat. Cost: Online.
Specialities: Hedging.
Notes: Delivers to shows.
Map Ref: N, D1

NBFr **Bee Friendly Garden Plants**
Five Acres Nursery, Dawbers Lane, Euxton, Lancashire PR7 6EE
Ⓣ (01257) 263876
Ⓔ buzz@beefriendlygardenplants.co.uk
Ⓦ www.beefriendlygardenplants.co.uk
Contact: Any member of staff
Opening Times: 0800-1800, Mon-Fri, 0800-1600, Sat & 1000-1600 Sun.
Cat. Cost: Online.
Specialities: Plants for attracting wildlife.
Notes: Delivers to shows.
Map Ref: N, D1

NBid **Bide-A-Wee Cottage Gardens** ♿
Stanton, Netherwitton, Morpeth, Northumberland NE65 8PR
Ⓣ (01670) 772238
Ⓜ 07976 559416
Ⓕ (01670) 772238
Ⓔ info@bideawee.co.uk
Ⓦ www.bideawee.co.uk
Contact: Mark Robson
Opening Times: 1330-1700 Sat & Wed, 19th Apr-30th Aug 2014. Group visits at other times, except Sun.
Min Mail Order UK: £20.00
Cat. Cost: Online only.
Credit Cards: All major credit/debit cards
Specialities: Unusual herbaceous perennials, *Agapanthus*, *Primula*, ferns, grasses. National Collection of *Centaurea*.
Notes: Wheelchair accessible.
Map Ref: N, B2 **OS Grid Ref:** NZ132900

NBir **Birkheads Secret Gardens & Nursery** ♿
Birkheads Lane, Sunniside, Gateshead, Tyne & Wear NE16 5EL
Ⓣ (01207) 232262
Ⓜ 07778 447920
Ⓕ (01207) 232262
Ⓔ birkheadsnursery@gmail.com
Ⓦ www.birkheadssecretgardens.co.uk
Contact: Mrs Christine Liddle
Opening Times: 1000-1700 Wed-Sun (closed Mon & Tues), early Mar to late Sep. Open B/hol Mons. Coach groups by appt. See website or phone for details.
Cat. Cost: None issued.
Credit Cards: All major credit/debit cards
Specialities: Hardy herbaceous perennials, grasses, bulbs & herbs. *Allium*, *Digitalis*,

Euphorbia, *Galanthus* & *Geranium*.
Notes: Nursery & coffee chop wheelchair accessible, please ring for special access directions.
Map Ref: N, B2 **OS Grid Ref:** NZ220569

NBre **Breezy Knees Nurseries** ♿
Common Lane, Warthill, York YO19 5XS
Ⓣ (01904) 488800
Ⓦ www.breezyknees.co.uk
Contact: Any member of staff
Opening Times: 1000-1700 7 days (open 1100 Sun), 1st Apr-30th Sep.
Credit Cards: All major credit/debit cards
Specialities: Very wide range of perennials. All can be viewed in 15-acre gardens (open 24th May-30th Sep).
Notes: Wheelchair accessible.
Map Ref: N, C3 **OS Grid Ref:** SE675565

NBri **Brighter Blooms**
Walton Flats Nursery, Gillibrand Street, Walton-le-Dale, Preston, Lancashire PR5 4AX
Ⓜ 07884 430732
Ⓔ matthew@brighterblooms.co.uk
Ⓦ www.brighterblooms.co.uk
Contact: Matthew Smith
Opening Times: By appt. only.
Credit Cards: All major credit/debit cards
Specialities: *Zantedeschia*, potted & bulbs. Spring & summer bulbs (dry format). Potted bulbs available in small quantities only.
Notes: Also sells wholesale. Delivers to shows.

NBro **Brownthwaite Hardy Plants** ♿
Fell Yeat, Casterton, Kirkby Lonsdale, Lancashire LA6 2JW
Ⓣ (01524) 271340 (after 1800 hours).
Ⓦ www.hardyplantsofcumbria.co.uk
Contact: Chris Benson
Opening Times: 1000-1700, 1st Apr-20th Sep.
Min Mail Order UK: Nmc
Cat. Cost: 4 × 1st class for *Hydrangea* catalogue.
Credit Cards: None
Specialities: Herbaceous perennials incl. *Geranium*, *Hosta*, *Primula*, hardy ferns, *Hydrangea paniculata* & *H. serrata* varieties.
Notes: Follow brown signs from A65 between Kirkby Lonsdale & Cowan Bridge. Mail order for *Hydrangea* & *P. auricula*. Delivers to shows. Wheelchair accessible.
Map Ref: N, C1 **OS Grid Ref:** SD632794

NCGa **Caths Garden Plants** ♿
The Walled Garden, Heaves Hotel, Heaves, Levens, Cumbria LA8 8EF
Ⓣ (01539) 561126
Ⓔ cath@cathsgardenplants.co.uk
Ⓦ www.cathsgardenplants.co.uk
Contact: Bob Sanderson
Opening Times: 1030-1700 most days, Mar-Oct. Please ring to check to be certain. 1030-1600 Tue-Sat, Nov, Dec & Feb. Closed Xmas & New Year weeks & all Jan.
Min Mail Order UK: £15.00 + p&p
Min Mail Order EU: £25.00
Cat. Cost: Online only.
Credit Cards: All major credit/debit cards
Specialities: Wide variety of perennials, incl. uncommon varieties & selections of grasses, ferns, shrubs & climbing plants.
Notes: On A590 follow signs for Heaves (not in Levens village). Delivers to shows. Wheelchair accessible.
Map Ref: N, C1 **OS Grid Ref:** SD497867

NChi **Chipchase Castle Nursery** ♿
Chipchase Castle, Wark, Hexham, Northumberland NE48 3NT
Ⓣ (01434) 230083
Ⓜ 07881 630398
Ⓔ info@chipchaseplants.co.uk
Ⓦ www.chipchaseplants.co.uk
Contact: Joyce Hunt & Alison Jones
Opening Times: 1000-1700 Thu-Sun & B/hol Mons Easter (or 1st Apr)-end Aug.
Min Mail Order UK: Nmc
Min Mail Order EU: Nmc
Cat. Cost: A5 sae for list
Credit Cards: All major credit/debit cards
Specialities: Unusual herbaceous esp. *Eryngium*, *Geum* & *Geranium*. Some plants only available in small quantities.
Notes: Delivers to shows. Suitable for accompanied wheelchair users.
Map Ref: N, B2 **OS Grid Ref:** NY880758

NCot **Cottage Garden Plants**
1 Kelton Croft, Kirkland, Cumbria CA26 3YE
Ⓣ (01946) 862664
Ⓔ expressplants@aol.com
Ⓦ simplesite.com/hardy_geraniums
Contact: Mrs J Purkiss
Opening Times: Open by appt. only for collecting orders & viewing garden. Consult local press & radio for charity openings.
Min Mail Order UK: £10.00
Min Mail Order EU: £15.00
Cat. Cost: 4 × 1st class sae.
Credit Cards: Paypal
Specialities: Small quantities only of all plants. New & exclusive introductions of *Geranium* cvs occasionally available. National Collection of *Geranium phaeum* Group. Other hardy geraniums plus hardy perennials sometimes available during the season.
Map Ref: N, C1

NCro **CROSTON CACTUS** ♿
43 Southport Road, Eccleston, Chorley, Lancashire PR7 6ET
Ⓣ (01257) 452555
Ⓕ (01257) 452555
Ⓔ sales@croston-cactus.co.uk
Ⓦ www.croston-cactus.co.uk
Contact: John Henshaw
Opening Times: 0930-1700 by appt. only.
Min Mail Order UK: £5.00 + p&p
Min Mail Order EU: £10.00 + p&p
Cat. Cost: Online only.
Credit Cards: All major credit/debit cards
Specialities: Mexican cacti, *Echeveria* hybrids & some bromeliads & *Tillandsia*. Some items held in small quantities only. See catalogue.
Notes: Credit card payment accepted for online orders only. Euro accepted. Wheelchair accessible.
Map Ref: N, D1 **OS Grid Ref:** SD522186

NCum **CUMBRIA WILDFLOWERS** ♿
Unit 8, Westwood, Orton Grange, Carlisle, Cumbria CA5 6LB
Ⓣ (01228) 711282
Ⓕ (01228) 711282
Ⓔ cdunt@cumbriawildflowers.co.uk
Ⓦ www.cumbriawildflowers.co.uk
Contact: Chris Dunt
Min Mail Order UK: Nmc
Min Mail Order EU: Nmc
Cat. Cost: Free.
Credit Cards: Paypal
Specialities: Native British wildflowers.
Notes: Also sells wholesale. Exports beyond EU. Wheelchair accessible.

NDav **DAVE PARKINSON PLANTS**
4 West Bank, Carlton, Goole, East Yorkshire DN14 9PZ
Ⓣ (01405) 860693
Ⓜ 07773 564945
Ⓦ www.daveparkinsonplants.co.uk
Contact: Mary Parkinson
Opening Times: Not open. Mail order only. Sells at RHS & Orchid Shows.
Min Mail Order UK: £12 + p&p
Min Mail Order EU: Nmc
Cat. Cost: 1st class stamp.
Credit Cards: None
Specialities: Hardy orchids. Terrestrial South African *Disa* orchids, species & hybrids.
Notes: Delivers to shows.

NDov **DOVE COTTAGE NURSERY & GARDEN** ♿
Shibden Hall Road, Halifax, West Yorkshire HX3 9XA
Ⓣ (01422) 203553
Ⓔ info@dovecottagenursery.co.uk
Ⓦ www.dovecottagenursery.co.uk
Contact: Stephen & Kim Rogers
Opening Times: 1000-1700 Wed-Sat, Mar-Sep. 1000-1700 Sun & B/hols Mar-Jun.
Cat. Cost: Free.
Credit Cards: All major credit/debit cards
Specialities: Herbaceous perennials & selected grasses, many displayed in adjoining naturalistic garden.
Notes: Wheelchair accessible.
Map Ref: N, D2 **OS Grid Ref:** SE115256

NDro **DROINTON NURSERIES** ♿
Plaster Pitts, Norton Conyers, Ripon, North Yorkshire HG4 5EF
Ⓣ (01765) 641849
Ⓜ 07909 971529
Ⓔ info@auricula-plants.co.uk
Ⓦ www.auricula-plants.co.uk
Contact: Robin & Annabel Graham
Opening Times: Open days in spring, otherwise by appt. only.
Min Mail Order UK: Nmc
Min Mail Order EU: Nmc
Cat. Cost: 4 × 1st class.
Credit Cards: All major credit/debit cards
Specialities: *Primula auricula*. More than 900 cvs of show, alpine, double & border auriculas. Limited stock of any one cultivar. National Collection of *Primula auricula* (Borders).
Notes: Also sells wholesale. Exports beyond EU. Delivers to shows. Wheelchair accessible.
Map Ref: N, C2 **OS Grid Ref:** SE315753

NEgg **EGGLESTON HALL GARDENS** ♿
Eggleston, Barnard Castle, Co. Durham DL12 0AG
Ⓣ (01833) 650230
Ⓔ mbhock@btinternet.com
Ⓦ www.egglestonhallgardens.co.uk.
Contact: Malcolm Hockham
Opening Times: 1000-1700 7 days. Closed 24th Dec to 6th Jan each year.
Cat. Cost: Online only.
Credit Cards: All major credit/debit cards
Notes: Collection from nursery only. Euro accepted. Wheelchair accessible.

NEoE **EAST OF EDEN NURSERY** ♿
Ainstable, Carlisle, Cumbria CA4 9QN
Ⓣ (01768) 896604
Ⓜ 07788 142969
Ⓔ roger@east-of-eden-nursery.co.uk
Ⓦ www.east-of-eden-nursery.co.uk
Contact: Roger Proud
Opening Times: By appt. only, Mar-Oct.
Min Mail Order UK: £10.00

Cat. Cost: None issued
Credit Cards: All major credit/debit cards
Specialities: Interesting & unusual shrubs, perennials & alpines, esp. astilbes and geums with over 60 new *Geum* cvs, bred & raised on nursery.
Notes: Mail order available for geums & astilbes only. Delivers to shows. Wheelchair accessible.
Map Ref: N, B1 **OS Grid Ref:** NY467504

NEqu EQUATORIAL PLANT CO.
The Dovecote, Newgate, Barnard Castle, Co. Durham DL12 8NW
Ⓣ (01833) 908127
Ⓕ (01833) 908127
Ⓔ Equatorial99@talktalk.net
Ⓦ www.equatorialplants.com
Contact: Dr Richard Warren
Opening Times: Mail order only. Open by appt. only.
Min Mail Order UK: Nmc
Min Mail Order EU: Nmc
Cat. Cost: Free.
Credit Cards: Access, Visa, Paypal
Specialities: Laboratory-raised orchids only.
Notes: Also sells wholesale. Exports beyond EU. Delivers to shows. Euro accepted.

NEve EVERY PICTURE TELLS A STORY ♿
Lydiate Barn Nursery & Garden Centre, Southport Road, Lydiate, Merseyside L31 4EE
Ⓣ 0151 286 2033
Ⓜ 07847 939867
Ⓔ don@every-picture.com
Ⓦ www.every-picture.com
Contact: Don Billington
Opening Times: 1000-1700.
Min Mail Order UK: Nmc
Credit Cards: All major credit/debit cards
Specialities: *Aechmea*, *Guzmania* & *Tillandsia*. Other plants available in small quantities. National Collections of *Neoregelia*, *Billbergia* & *Aechmea*.
Notes: Wheelchair accessible. Delivers to shows.
Map Ref: N, D1

NFav PERENNIAL FAVOURITES LTD ♿
East Park View, Blyth, Northumberland NE24 3AY
Ⓣ (01670) 540653
Ⓔ adam.greenwold@googlemail.com
Contact: Adam Greenwold
Opening Times: 0730-1700, 7 days, Apr-Oct. 0900-1600, Mon-Sat, (closed Sun) Nov-Mar.
Credit Cards: All major credit/debit cards
Specialities: Specialising in hardy herbaceous perennials, but also supplying alpines and shrubs with a bent for surviving on the north sea coast.
Notes: Also sells wholesale. Wheelchair accessible.
Map Ref: N, B2 **OS Grid Ref:** NZ320812

NFir FIR TREES PELARGONIUM NURSERY ♿
Stokesley, Middlesbrough, Cleveland TS9 5LD
Ⓣ (01642) 713066
Ⓕ (01642) 713066
Ⓔ mark@firtreespelargoniums.co.uk
Ⓦ www.firtreespelargoniums.co.uk
Contact: Helen Bainbridge
Opening Times: 1000-1600 7 days, 1st Apr-31st Aug, 1000-1530 Mon-Fri, 1st Sep-31st Mar.
Min Mail Order UK: £4.00 + p&p
Cat. Cost: 4 × 1st class or £1.00 coin.
Credit Cards: All major credit/debit cards
Specialities: All types of *Pelargonium*, fancy leaf, regal, decorative regal, oriental regal, angel, miniature, zonal, ivy leaf, stellar, scented, dwarf, unique, golden stellar & species.
Notes: Delivers to shows. Wheelchair accessible.
Map Ref: N, C2

NGBl GARDEN BLOOMS
Fieldgate, Mill Field Road, Fishlake, Doncaster, Yorkshire DN7 5GH
Ⓣ 0845 5440964
Ⓔ info@gardenblooms.co.uk
Ⓦ www.gardenblooms.co.uk
Contact: Liz Webster
Opening Times: Open by appt. only.
Min Mail Order UK: Nmc
Cat. Cost: Online only.
Credit Cards: None
Specialities: Hardy & tender perennials & small range of conservatory/house plants. Some plants available in small quantities only.
Notes: Credit cards accepted online only. Delivers to shows.
Map Ref: N, D2 **OS Grid Ref:** SE659148

NGdn GARDEN HOUSE NURSERY ♿
The Square, Dalston, Carlisle, Cumbria CA5 7LL
Ⓣ (01228) 710297
Ⓜ 07595 219082
Ⓔ stephickso@hotmail.co.uk
Ⓦ www.gardenhousenursery.co.uk
Contact: Stephen Hickson
Opening Times: 0900-1700 7 days Mar-Oct.
Cat. Cost: Plant list online only.
Credit Cards: None
Specialities: *Geranium*, *Hosta*, *Hemerocallis*, *Iris*, grasses, *Brunnera*, *Pulmonaria* & *Aconitum*.

Notes: Also sells wholesale. Wheelchair accessible.
Map Ref: N, B1 **OS Grid Ref:** NY369503

NHal **HALLS OF HEDDON**
West Heddon Nurseries, Heddon-on-the-Wall, Northumberland NE15 0JS
Ⓣ (01661) 852445
Ⓕ (01661) 852398
Ⓔ enquiry@hallsofheddon.co.uk
Ⓦ www.hallsofheddon.co.uk
Contact: David Hall
Opening Times: 0900-1700 Mon-Sat 1000-1700 Sun.
Min Mail Order UK: £10.00
Min Mail Order EU: £35.00
Cat. Cost: 3 × 2nd class
Credit Cards: Delta, MasterCard, Switch, Visa
Specialities: *Chrysanthemum* & *Dahlia.*
Notes: Also sells wholesale.
Map Ref: N, B2 **OS Grid Ref:** NZ122679

NHar **HARTSIDE NURSERY GARDEN**
Nr Alston, Cumbria CA9 3BL
Ⓣ (01434) 381372
Ⓕ (01434) 381372
Ⓔ enquiries@plantswithaltitude.co.uk
Ⓦ www.plantswithaltitude.co.uk
Contact: S L & N Huntley
Opening Times: 1130-1630 Mon-Fri, 1230-1600 w/ends & B/hols, Mar-Jun (incl.). 1130-1630 Tue-Fri, 1230-1600 B/hols, w/ends by appt., Jul-Oct (incl.). Winter months by appt. Times may vary during show season, so please phone before travelling.
Min Mail Order UK: Nmc
Min Mail Order EU: £50.00 + p&p
Cat. Cost: 4 × 1st class or 3 × IRC
Credit Cards: All major credit/debit cards
Specialities: Alpines grown at altitude of 1100 feet in Pennines. *Primula*, ferns, *Gentian* & *Meconopsis.*
Notes: Delivers to shows.
Map Ref: N, B1 **OS Grid Ref:** NY708447

NHaw **THE HAWTHORNES NURSERY** ♿
Marsh Road, Hesketh Bank, Nr Preston, Lancashire PR4 6XT
Ⓣ (01772) 812379
Ⓔ richardhaw@talktalk.net
Ⓦ www.hawthornes-nursery.co.uk
Contact: Irene & Richard Hodson
Opening Times: 0900-1800 7 days 1st Mar-30th Jun, Thu-Sun July-Oct. Gardens open for NGS. Check with nursery for National Collection Open Day 2014.
Min Mail Order UK: £10.00
Min Mail Order EU: Nmc
Cat. Cost: None issued.
Credit Cards: None
Specialities: *Clematis.* National Collection of *Clematis viticella.*
Notes: Euro accepted. Wheelchair accessible.

NHer **HERTERTON HOUSE GARDEN NURSERY**
Hartington, Cambo, Morpeth, Northumberland NE61 4BN
Ⓣ (01670) 774278
Contact: Mrs M Lawley & Mr Frank Lawley
Opening Times: 1330-1730 Mon, Wed, Fri-Sun 1st Apr-end Sep. (Earlier or later in the year weather permitting.)
Cat. Cost: None issued.
Credit Cards: None
Specialities: Country garden flowers.
Map Ref: N, B2 **OS Grid Ref:** NZ022880

NHip **HIPPOPOTTERING NURSERY**
Orchard House, East Lound, Nr Doncaster, South Yorkshire DN9 2LR
Ⓜ 07979 764677
Ⓔ hippomaples@hotmail.co.uk
Ⓦ www.hippopottering.com
Contact: Pat Gibbons
Opening Times: By appt. only & Open Days.
Min Mail Order UK: £15.00 + p&p
Min Mail Order EU: £15.00 + p&p
Cat. Cost: Online only.
Credit Cards: MasterCard, Visa
Specialities: Japanese maples. Many available only from us.
Notes: Mail order to UK throughout year; to EU during winter. Delivers to shows. Wheelchair accessible in dry weather only.

NHol **HOLDEN CLOUGH NURSERY LTD.** ♿
Holden, Bolton-by-Bowland, Clitheroe, Lancashire BB7 4PF
Ⓣ (01200) 447615
Ⓔ info@holdencloughnursery.co.uk
Ⓦ www.holdencloughnursery.co.uk
Contact: John Foley
Opening Times: 0900-1700 Mon-Sat, 1030-1630 Sun, incl. B/hols. Closed Xmas Day & Boxing Day.
Min Mail Order UK: Nmc
Min Mail Order EU: Nmc
Cat. Cost: 2 × 1st class.
Credit Cards: All major credit/debit cards
Specialities: Large general list incl. perennials, esp. *Crocosmia*, shrubs, dwarf conifers, alpines, heathers, grasses & ferns.
Notes: Seasonal mail order on some items. Also sells wholesale on some items. Exports beyond EU. Delivers to shows. Wheelchair accessible.
Map Ref: N, C2 **OS Grid Ref:** SD773496

NHoy **HOYLAND PLANT CENTRE** ♿
54 Greenside Lane, Hoyland,
Barnsley, Yorkshire
S74 9PZ
Ⓣ (01226) 744466
Ⓜ 07717 182169
Ⓕ (01226) 744466
Ⓔ stevenhickman@btconnect.com
Ⓦ www.somethingforthegarden.co.uk
Contact: Steven Hickman
Opening Times: All year round by appt. only.
Min Mail Order UK: Nmc
Min Mail Order EU: Nmc
Cat. Cost: 4 × 1st class.
Credit Cards: All major credit/debit cards
Specialities: *Agapanthus* (400+ cvs) & *Tulbaghia* (80+ cvs). Some available in small quantities only. National Collections of *Agapanthus* & *Tulbaghia*.
Notes: Daily practical workshops available, ring for details. Also sells wholesale. Exports beyond EU. Delivers to shows. Euro accepted. Wheelchair accessible.

NJRG **JRG DAHLIAS**
22 Summerville Road, Milnthorpe, Cumbria
LA7 7DF
Ⓣ (01539) 562691
Ⓔ jack@jrg-dahlias.co.uk
Ⓦ www.jrg-dahlias.co.uk
Contact: Jack Gott
Opening Times: By appt. only.
Min Mail Order UK: £10.00 + p&p
Min Mail Order EU: Price with order.
Cat. Cost: Sae: 110mm × 220mm, 2nd class.
Credit Cards: None
Specialities: *Dahlia*.
Notes: Delivers to Shows.
Map Ref: N, C1

NLAp **LANESIDE HARDY ORCHID NURSERY** ♿
74 Croston Road, Garstang, Preston,
Lancashire PR3 1HR
Ⓣ (01995) 605537
Ⓜ 07946 659661
Ⓔ jcrhutch@aol.com
Ⓦ www.lanesidehardyorchids.com
Contact: Jeff Hutchings
Opening Times: By telephone appt. only. Details of Open Days on website.
Min Mail Order UK: £35.00
Min Mail Order EU: £35.00
Cat. Cost: Sae or lists updated every month online.
Credit Cards: All major credit/debit cards
Specialities: 150+ species of hardy terrestrial orchids plus composts & cultivation notes. Species suitable for garden, cold or frost-free greenhouse or meadow plantings.
Notes: Mail order for orchids during appropriate dormancy period as plants only sent bare-rooted. Also hardy orchid composts & pumice from the nursery or from shows if ordered. See website for shows & talks. Also sells wholesale. Delivers to shows. Wheelchair accessible.
Map Ref: N, D1

NLar **LARCH COTTAGE NURSERIES** ♿ ◆
Melkinthorpe, Penrith, Cumbria CA10 2DR
Ⓣ (01931) 712404
Ⓕ (01931) 712727
Ⓔ plants@larchcottage.co.uk
Ⓦ www.larchcottage.co.uk
Contact: Peter Stott & Joanne McCullock
Opening Times: Daily from 1000-1730 (or dusk in winter), all year round.
Min Mail Order UK: Nmc
Min Mail Order EU: Nmc
Cat. Cost: £7.00
Credit Cards: All major credit/debit cards
Specialities: Comprehensive plant collection in unique garden setting. Rare & unusual plants; particularly shrubs, trees, perennials, dwarf conifers & Japanese maples. *Acer*, *Hamamelis*, *Magnolia* & *Cornus kousa* cvs. Old-fashioned roses, bamboo & alpines.
Notes: Terraced restaurant & art gallery. Wheelchair accessible.
Map Ref: N, C1 **OS Grid Ref:** NY315602

NLos **THE LOST WORLD NURSERY** ♿
The Hawthorns, Hesketh Bank, Nr Preston,
Lancashire PR4 6XT
Ⓜ 07810 547629
Ⓔ plants@thelostworldnursery.com
Ⓦ www.thelostworldnursery.com
Contact: Phil Ball
Opening Times: By prior appt. only. Please phone in advance when planning a visit.
Min Mail Order UK: Nmc
Min Mail Order EU: Nmc
Cat. Cost: Online.
Credit Cards: Paypal
Specialities: Carnivorous plants: *Sarracenia*, *Nepenthes*. Ferns, bromeliads, bananas, palms, grasses, gingers, bamboo. Plants for exotic effect.
Notes: Plants may be pre-ordered for collection either at the nursery or at shows or plant fairs. Delivers to shows. Euro accepted. Wheelchair access in dry weather.
Map Ref: N, D1 **OS Grid Ref:** SD447239

NMat **MATTHEWMAN SWEET PEAS**
14 Chariot Way, Thorpe Audlin, Pontefract,
West Yorkshire WF8 3EZ
Ⓣ (01977) 621381
Ⓕ (01977) 621381

Ⓔ sales@sweetpeasonline.co.uk
Ⓦ www.sweetpeasonline.co.uk
Contact: Pauline Matthewman
Min Mail Order UK: £1.25
Min Mail Order EU: £3.00
Cat. Cost: Free.
Credit Cards: All major credit/debit cards
Specialities: Sweet peas.
Notes: Exports beyond EU. Delivers to shows.

NMen **MENDLE NURSERY** ♿
Holme, Scunthorpe, North Lincolnshire DN16 3RF
Ⓣ (01724) 850864
Ⓔ annearnshaw@lineone.net
Ⓦ www.mendlenursery.com
Contact: Mrs A Earnshaw
Opening Times: 1000-1600 Tue-Sun.
Min Mail Order UK: Nmc
Min Mail Order EU: Nmc
Cat. Cost: 3 × 1st class.
Credit Cards: Paypal
Specialities: *Jovibarba*, *Saxifraga* & *Sempervivum*.
Notes: Wheelchair accessible.
Map Ref: N, D3 **OS Grid Ref:** SE925070

NMir **MIRES BECK NURSERY** ♿
Low Mill Lane, North Cave, Brough, East Riding, Yorkshire
HU15 2Nr
Ⓣ (01430) 421543
Ⓕ (01430) 421543
Ⓔ admin@miresbeck.co.uk
Ⓦ www.miresbeck.co.uk
Contact: Judy Burrow & Martin Rowland
Opening Times: 1000-1600 Mon-Sat 1st Mar-30th Sep. 1000-1500 Mon-Fri 1st Oct-30th Nov & by appt.
Min Mail Order UK: Nmc
Cat. Cost: 3 × 1st class.
Credit Cards: None
Specialities: Wildflower plants of Yorkshire provenance.
Notes: Mail order for wildflower plants & plugs only. Also sells wholesale. Wheelchair accessible.

NMyG **MARY GREEN** ♿
The Walled Garden, Hornby, Lancaster, Lancashire LA2 8LD
Ⓣ (01524) 221989
Ⓜ 07778 910348
Ⓔ Marygreenplants@btinternet.com
Contact: Mary Green
Opening Times: By appt. only.
Cat. Cost: None issued.
Credit Cards: None
Specialities: Hostas, ferns & other shade-loving perennials.
Notes: Delivers to shows. Wheelchair accessible.
Map Ref: N, C1 **OS Grid Ref:** SD588688

NNor **NORCROFT NURSERIES** ♿
Roadends, Intack, Southwaite, Carlisle, Cumbria CA4 0LH
Ⓣ (01697) 473933
Ⓔ info@norcroftnurseries.co.uk
Ⓦ www.norcroftnurseries.co.uk
Contact: Keith Bell
Opening Times: Every afternoon excl. Mon (open B/hol), Apr-Jul, or ring for appt.
Min Mail Order UK: Nmc
Cat. Cost: 2 × 2nd class
Credit Cards: None
Specialities: Hardy herbaceous, *Dianthus*, *Aquilegia*, hostas, *Lilium*, *Papaver*.
Notes: Wheelchair accessible.
Map Ref: N, B1 **OS Grid Ref:** NY474433

NOak **OAK TREE NURSERY** ♿
Mill Lane, Barlow, Selby, North Yorkshire YO8 8EY
Ⓣ (01757) 618409
Ⓜ 07706 505688
Ⓔ gill@oaktreenursery.plus.com
Ⓦ www.oaktreenursery.com
Contact: Gill Plowes
Opening Times: By appt. only.
Min Mail Order UK: £10.00 + p&p
Min Mail Order EU: Nmc
Cat. Cost: 4 × 1st class.
Credit Cards: All major credit/debit cards
Specialities: Ornamental grasses & grass-like plants.
Notes: Will export seeds only beyond the EU. Also sells wholesale. Delivers to shows. Wheelchair accessible.

NOra **ORANGE PIPPIN LTD**
(Office) 33 Algarth Rise, Pocklington, York, Yorkshire YO42 2HX
Ⓣ (01759) 392007
Ⓔ trees@orangepippin.com
Ⓦ www.orangepippintrees.co.uk
Contact: Maureen Borrie
Opening Times: Not open. Mail order online only.
Min Mail Order UK: Nmc
Min Mail Order EU: Nmc
Cat. Cost: Online only.
Credit Cards: MasterCard, Visa
Specialities: Wide range of many types of fruit tree, incl. traditional & modern varieties. Wide choice of rootstocks. Fruit tree expert available most days & at w/ends. Website incl. extensive tasting notes & variety comparisons.
Notes: Order online all year round, deliveries from end Aug-end Mar. Exports beyond EU.

NOrn **Ornamental Trees Ltd**
Five Acres Nursery, Dawbers Lane, Euxton, Lancashire PR7 6EE
Ⓣ (01257) 365232
Ⓔ sales@ornamental-trees.co.uk
Ⓦ www.ornamental-trees.co.uk
Contact: Any member of staff
Opening Times: Mail order only. 0800-1800, Mon-Fri, 0800-1600, Sat & 1000-1600 Sun.
Specialities: Trees & hedging.
Notes: Delivers to shows.
Map Ref: N, D1

NPer **Perry's Plants** ♿
The River Garden, Sleights, Whitby, North Yorkshire YO21 1RR
Ⓜ 07879 498623
Ⓔ sharon.perry@virgin.net
Ⓦ www.perrysplants.co.uk
Contact: Sharon & Richard Perry
Opening Times: 1000-1700 mid-March to Oct.
Cat. Cost: None published.
Credit Cards: None
Specialities: *Lavatera, Malva, Erysimum, Euphorbia, Anthemis, Osteospermum* & *Hebe.* Uncommon hardy & container plants & aquatic plants.
Notes: Euro accepted. Wheelchair accessible.
Map Ref: N, C3 **OS Grid Ref:** NZ869082

NPla **The Plant Directory**
Scawsby Hall Nurseries, Barnsley Road, Scawsby, Doncaster, South Yorkshire DN5 7UB
Ⓣ (01302) 783434
Ⓔ mail@the-plant-directory.co.uk
Ⓦ www.the-plant-directory.co.uk
Contact: David Lawson
Opening Times: Not open. Mail order only.
Min Mail Order UK: Nmc
Cat. Cost: None issued
Credit Cards: American Express, MasterCard, Visa, Paypal
Specialities: A wide range of herbaceous perennials, hardy trees, shrubs & indoor plants. Some indoor & aquatic plants in small quantities only.

NPol **Polemonium Plantery**
28 Sunnyside, Trimdon Grange, Co. Durham TS29 6HF
Ⓣ (01429) 881529
Ⓔ dandd@polemonium.co.uk
Ⓦ www.polemonium.co.uk
Contact: David or Dianne Nichol-Brown
Opening Times: By appt. only.
Min Mail Order UK: £10.00
Cat. Cost: 3 × 1st class
Credit Cards: None
Specialities: National Collections of *Polemonium, Collomia, Gilia, Leptodactylon* (*Polemoniaceae*) & *Hakonechloa.*
Notes: Also sells wholesale. Delivers to shows.
Map Ref: N, B2 **OS Grid Ref:** NZ369353

NPri **Primrose Cottage Nursery** ♿
Ringway Road, Moss Nook, Wythenshawe, Manchester M22 5WF
Ⓣ (0161) 437 1557
Ⓜ 07798 754457
Ⓔ info@primrosecottagenursery.co.uk
Ⓦ www.primrosecottagenursery.co.uk
Contact: Caroline Dumville
Opening Times: 0830-1730 Mon-Sat, 0930-1730 Sun (summer). 0830-1700 Mon-Sat, 0930-1700 Sun (winter).
Cat. Cost: Plant lists can be sent by email.
Credit Cards: All major credit/debit cards
Specialities: Perennials, herbs, roses, patio & hanging basket plants. Shrubs, houseplants, ornamental trees, fruit trees, soft fruit bushes & vegetable plants.
Notes: Coffee shop open daily. Wheelchair accessible.
Map Ref: N, D2

NQui **Quiet Corner Plants** ♿
(Office) 20 Grove Road, Brandon, Co. Durham DH7 8AW
Ⓜ 07932 159204
Ⓔ hal@uwclub.net
Ⓦ www.quietcornerplants.co.uk
Contact: Howard Leslie
Opening Times: 1000-1700 (or sunset in winter), 7 days.
Min Mail Order UK: Nmc
Cat. Cost: Online only.
Credit Cards: All major credit/debit cards
Specialities: Hardy herbaceous & shrubby perennials, incl. small quantities of lesser known and harder to find plants.
Notes: Also sells wholesale. Delivers to shows. Wheelchair accessible.
Map Ref: N, B2

NRib **Ribblesdale Nurseries** ♿
Newsham Hall Lane, Woodplumpton, Preston, Lancashire PR4 0AS
Ⓣ (01772) 863081
Ⓕ (01772) 861884
Ⓔ philsd@btinternet.com
Ⓦ www.ribblesdalenurseries.co.uk
Contact: Mr & Mrs Dunnett
Opening Times: 0900-1800 Mon-Sat Apr-Sep, 0900-1700 Mon-Sat Oct-Mar. 1030-1630 Sun.
Credit Cards: Delta, MasterCard, Switch, Visa
Specialities: Trees, shrubs & perennials.

Conifers, hedging, alpines, fruit, climbers, herbs, aquatics, ferns & wildflowers. Own grown plants in peat-free compost.
Notes: Wheelchair accessible.

NRob **W Robinson & Son (Seeds & Plants) Ltd** ♿
Sunny Bank, Forton, Nr Preston, Lancashire PR3 0BN
Ⓣ (01524) 791210
Ⓕ (01524) 791933
Ⓔ info@mammothonion.co.uk
Ⓦ www.mammothonion.co.uk
Contact: Miss Robinson
Opening Times: 1000-1600 7 days Mar-Jun, 0800-1700 Mon-Fri Jul-Feb.
Min Mail Order UK: Nmc
Min Mail Order EU: Nmc
Cat. Cost: Free.
Credit Cards: All major credit/debit cards
Specialities: Mammoth vegetable seed. Onions, leeks, tomatoes & beans. Range of vegetable plants in the spring.
Notes: Also sells wholesale. Exports beyond EU. Delivers to shows. Wheelchair accessible.

NRog **R V Roger Ltd** ♿
The Nurseries, Pickering, North Yorkshire YO18 7JW
Ⓣ (01751) 472226
Ⓕ (01751) 476749
Ⓔ sales@rvroger.co.uk
Ⓦ www.rvroger.co.uk
Contact: Ian Roger
Opening Times: 0900-1700 Mon-Sat, 1000-1600 Sun.
Min Mail Order UK: Nmc
Min Mail Order EU: Nmc
Cat. Cost: £1.00
Credit Cards: All major credit/debit cards
Specialities: Holders of National Collection of *Erythronium*.
Notes: Also sells wholesale. Wheelchair accessible.
Map Ref: N, C3 **OS Grid Ref:** SE801827

NRya **Ryal Nursery** ♿
East Farm Cottage, Ryal, Northumberland NE20 0SA
Ⓣ (01661) 886562
Ⓔ alpines@ryal.freeserve.co.uk
Contact: R F Hadden
Opening Times: Mar-Jul by appt., please phone.
Cat. Cost: Sae.
Credit Cards: None
Specialities: Alpine & woodland plants, mainly available in small quantities only. National Collection of *Primula marginata*.
Notes: Also sells wholesale. Delivers to shows. Wheelchair accessible.
Map Ref: N, B2 **OS Grid Ref:** NZ015744

NSla **Slack Top Nurseries**
Alpine House, 22A Slack Top, Hebden Bridge, West Yorkshire HX7 7HA
Ⓣ (01422) 845348
Ⓜ 07508 953804
Ⓔ enquiries@slacktopnurseries.co.uk
Ⓦ www.slacktopnurseries.co.uk
Contact: Michael & Allison Mitchell
Opening Times: 1000-1700 Fri-Sun 1st Mar-31st Aug & B/hols. Other times by appt.
Min Mail Order UK: £20.00
Min Mail Order EU: £50.00
Cat. Cost: 2 × 1st class A5 sae or online.
Credit Cards: None
Specialities: Alpine, rockery & woodland plants.
Notes: Talks given to gardening clubs & other groups by appt. Delivers to shows. Euro accepted. Some areas of garden inaccessible for wheelchairs.
Map Ref: N, D2 **OS Grid Ref:** SD977286

NSti **Stillingfleet Lodge Nurseries** ♿
Stewart Lane, Stillingfleet, North Yorkshire YO19 6HP
Ⓣ (01904) 728506
Ⓔ info@stillingfleetlodgenurseries.co.uk
Ⓦ www.stillingfleetlodgenurseries.co.uk
Contact: Vanessa Cook
Opening Times: 1300-1700 Wed & Fri, 1st Apr-30th Sep. 1300-1700, 1st & 3rd Sat & Sun in each month.
Cat. Cost: Online only.
Credit Cards: None
Specialities: Foliage & unusual perennials. Hardy geraniums, *Pulmonaria*, variegated plants & grasses, interesting climbers.
Notes: Wheelchair accessible.
Map Ref: N, D2

NSue **Sue Proctor Plants**
69 Ings Mill Avenue, Clayton West, Huddersfield, West Yorkshire HD8 9QG
Ⓣ (01484) 866189
Ⓜ 07917 006636
Ⓔ sueproctor@talktalk.net
Ⓦ www.sueproctorplants.co.uk
Contact: Richard Proctor
Opening Times: By appt. only. Please phone first.
Min Mail Order UK: £3.50
Cat. Cost: Large 1st sae.
Credit Cards: All major credit/debit cards
Specialities: *Hosta*, especially miniature hostas.
Notes: Delivers to shows.

N

NSum **Summerdale Garden Nursery**
Summerdale House, Cow Brow,
Lupton, Carnforth, Lancashire
LA6 1PE
Ⓣ (01539) 567210
Ⓔ sheals@btinternet.com
Ⓦ www.summerdalegardenplants.co.uk
Contact: Gail Sheals
Opening Times: 0930-1630 Thu, Fri & Sat, 1st Apr-31st Aug. Other times by appt. only.
Min Mail Order UK: £25.00
Cat. Cost: Online only.
Credit Cards: None
Specialities: Wide variety of perennials, large collection of *Primula*. Many moist and shade-loving plants incl. *Meconopsis* & hellebores.
Notes: Mail order for primulas only.
Map Ref: N, C1 **OS Grid Ref:** SD545819

NTay **Taylors Clematis Nursery** ♿
Sutton Road, Sutton, Nr Askern, Doncaster, South Yorkshire DN6 9JZ
Ⓣ (01302) 700716
Ⓔ info@taylorsclematis.co.uk
Ⓦ www.taylorsclematis.co.uk
Contact: Chris & Suzy Cocks
Opening Times: Open by appt. only. Please ring for details Mon-Fri, before 0900 or after 1500 hours. Ticket only Open Days 2014: 10th May, 7th,14th, 21st & 28th Jun. For tickets see website or contact nursery by post/phone.
Min Mail Order UK: Nmc
Min Mail Order EU: Nmc
Cat. Cost: 4 × 2nd class.
Credit Cards: All major credit/debit cards
Specialities: *Clematis* (over 350+ varieties). 2-year old mature specimens, all grown on nursery.
Notes: Talks/presentations to clubs & societies in Feb, Mar & and Oct. Also offers next day delivery courier service. Delivers to shows. Wheelchair accessible.
Map Ref: N, D2 **OS Grid Ref:** SE552121

NTPC **Tree Peony Company**
Willow Cottage, Rillington, Malton, North Yorkshire YO17 8JU
Ⓣ (01944) 758280
Ⓔ info@treepeony.co.uk
Ⓦ www.treepeony.co.uk
Contact: Thelma Scruton, Roger Scruton
Min Mail Order UK: Nmc
Min Mail Order EU: Nmc
Cat. Cost: None.
Credit Cards: None
Specialities: Tree peonies. *Paeonia suffruticosa*. *P.* Gansu Group. *P. rockii*.
Notes: Also sells wholesale. Euro accepted. Delivers to shows.

NTre **Treetyme**
Prospect Hill House, Kirkoswald,
Penrith, Cumbria
CA10 1ER
Ⓣ (01768) 800238
Ⓕ (01768) 897138
Ⓔ sales@treetyme.co.uk
Ⓦ www.treetyme.co.uk
Contact: Hugh Povey
Opening Times: Not open. Mail order via website only. Visits by appt. only.
Min Mail Order UK: Nmc
Min Mail Order EU: Nmc
Cat. Cost: Online only.
Credit Cards: All major credit/debit cards
Specialities: *Cercis*. Stock available in small quantities only. National Collection of *Cercis*.
Notes: Also sells wholesale.

NWad **Waddow Lodge Garden** ♿
Clitheroe Road, Waddington,
Clitheroe, Lancashire
BB7 3HQ
Ⓣ (01200) 429145
Ⓔ peterfoleyhcn@hotmail.co.uk
Ⓦ www.gardentalks.co.uk
Contact: Peter Foley
Opening Times: By appt. only all year.
Min Mail Order UK: Nmc
Min Mail Order EU: Nmc
Cat. Cost: Online only.
Credit Cards: None
Specialities: A developing plantsman's garden with a wide-ranging & interesting plant collection.
Notes: Open for group visits by appt., incl. evenings. Also open under NGS again in 2015. Wheelchair accessible.
Map Ref: N, C1 **OS Grid Ref:** SD732434

NWea **Weasdale Nurseries Ltd.**
Newbiggin-on-Lune,
Kirkby Stephen, Cumbria
CA17 4LX
Ⓣ (01539) 623246
Ⓕ (01539) 623277
Ⓔ sales@weasdale.com
Ⓦ www.weasdale.com
Contact: Andrew Forsyth
Opening Times: 0830-1300 & 1400-1730 Mon-Fri. Closed w/ends, B/hols, Xmas through to the New Year.
Min Mail Order UK: Nmc
Min Mail Order EU: Nmc
Cat. Cost: Free of charge in UK or £2.00 to EU.
Credit Cards: All major credit/debit cards
Specialities: Hardy forest trees, hedging, broadleaved & conifers. Specimen trees & shrubs grown at 850 feet (260 metres)

elevation. Some rarer plants are grown in small batches, so availability can't be guaranteed.
Notes: Mail order a speciality. Mail order Nov-Apr only. Also sells wholesale to VAT registered customers.
Map Ref: N, C1 **OS Grid Ref:** NY690039

NWit **D S Witton** ♿
26 Casson Drive, Harthill,
Sheffield, Yorkshire
S26 7WA
Ⓣ (01909) 771366
Ⓔ donshardyeuphorbias@btopenworld.com
Ⓦ www.euphorbias.co.uk
Contact: Don Witton
Opening Times: By appt. only. Open Day, 1300-1600, Sun 4th May 2014.
Min Mail Order UK: Nmc
Cat. Cost: 1 × 1st class sae.
Credit Cards: None
Specialities: National Collection of Hardy *Euphorbia*. Over 130 varieties.
Notes: Mail order seed only, Oct-June. Wheelchair accessible.
Map Ref: N, D2 **OS Grid Ref:** SK494812

NWsh **Westshores Nurseries**
82 West Street, Winterton, Lincolnshire
DN15 9QF
Ⓣ (01724) 733940
Ⓜ 07875 732535
Ⓔ westshnur@aol.com
Ⓦ www.westshores.co.uk
Contact: Gail & John Summerfield
Opening Times: 1st Mar-31st Oct. Please check before visiting.
Min Mail Order UK: £15.00
Cat. Cost: Online only.
Credit Cards: All major credit/debit cards
Specialities: Ornamental grasses.
Notes: Wide selection of talks for gardening clubs and HPS groups.
Map Ref: N, D3 **OS Grid Ref:** SE927187

NYoL **Yorkshire Lavender** ♿
Terrington, York, North Yorkshire
YO60 6PB
Ⓣ (01653) 648008
Ⓔ lavenderworld@btconnect.com
Ⓦ www.yorkshirelavender.com
Contact: Julia Snowball
Opening Times: 1000-1700 7 days, 5th Apr to 25th Oct 2014.
Min Mail Order UK: £10.00
Cat. Cost: None issued
Credit Cards: All major credit/debit cards
Specialities: *Lavandula, Mentha, Thymus.* Herbs.
Notes: Wheelchair accessible.
Map Ref: N, C3 **OS Grid Ref:** SE655710

S

Southern

SAdn **Ashdown Forest Garden Centre & Nursery** ♿
Duddleswell, Ashdown Forest, East Sussex
TN22 3JP
Ⓣ (01825) 712300
Ⓔ victoria@ashdownforestgardencentre.co.uk
Ⓦ www.ashdownforestgardencentre.co.uk
Contact: Victoria Falletti
Opening Times: 0900-1700 winter, 0900-1800 summer.
Min Mail Order UK: Nmc
Cat. Cost: Online only.
Credit Cards: All major credit/debit cards
Specialities: Ornamental grasses, *Lapageria, Fuchsia*, conservatory climbers, unusual shrubs.
Notes: Wheelchair accessible.
Map Ref: S, C4 **OS Grid Ref:** TQ468283

SAdu **Adur Valley Growers**
(Office) 4 Newland Road, Upper Beeding, Steyning, West Sussex BN44 3JJ
Ⓣ (01903) 813780
Ⓔ clivethecannaman@gmail.com
Ⓦ www.adurvalleygrowers.co.uk
Contact: Clive Parker
Opening Times: Not open. Mail order only.
Min Mail Order UK: Nmc
Min Mail Order EU: Nmc
Cat. Cost: Online only.
Credit Cards: Paypal
Specialities: A wide range of disease-free *Canna*, many only available in very small numbers. All plants grown in own peat-free compost without the use of chemical pesticides. Will propagate to order.
Notes: Plants only available from May-Oct. Euro accepted.

SAko **Akorn and Oake**
18 Twyford Avenue, Southampton, Hampshire
SO15 5NP
Ⓣ (02380) 344040
Ⓜ 07973 149404
Ⓔ stefan.rau@hotmail.co.uk
Contact: Stefan Rau
Opening Times: Mail order only. Open by appt. only.
Min Mail Order UK: £15.00
Specialities: *Saxifraga.*
Notes: Plants only sent out in dormant state. Delivers to shows.

SBch **Birchwood Plants**
(Office) 10 Westering, Romsey, Hampshire
SO51 7LY
Ⓣ (01794) 502192
Ⓔ info@birchwoodplants.co.uk

Ⓦ www.birchwoodplants.co.uk
Contact: Lesley Baker
Opening Times: Not open to the public. Plants can be collected by arrangement from nursery or from sales & shows as posted on website or phone for details.
Min Mail Order UK: £15 + p&p
Min Mail Order EU: £15+ p&p
Cat. Cost: Online only.
Credit Cards: Paypal
Specialities: Plants to attract bees & butterflies. Alpines & drought-tolerant plants. Predominantly growing peat-free. National Collection of *Geranium nodosum*. Most stock only available in very small quantities unless ordered in advance.
Notes: Nursery at Silverwood House, Gardener's Lane, Nr Romsey, SO51 6AD. Mail order mostly for small plants. No mail order sent Dec-Jan. Delivers to shows.
Map Ref: S, D2 **OS Grid Ref:** SU333190

SBdl **Grow at Brogdale**
Brogdale Farm, Brogdale Road, Faversham, Kent ME13 8XZ
Ⓣ (01795) 531888
Ⓕ (01795) 531710
Ⓔ fruit@brogdaleonline.co.uk
Ⓦ www.brogdaleonline.co.uk
Contact: Donna Cooper
Min Mail Order UK: Nmc
Min Mail Order EU: Nmc
Cat. Cost: £4.95
Credit Cards: MasterCard, Switch, Visa
Specialities: Over 5000 fruit varieties, most of which can be propagated to order. Holders of several National Collections of Fruit.
Notes: Also sells wholesale. Exports beyond EU. Euro accepted.

SBea **Bean Place Nursery**
Watersfield, Bletchenden Road, Headcorn, Kent TN27 9JB
Ⓜ 07841 484822
Ⓔ info@beanplace.co.uk
Ⓦ www.beanplace.co.uk
Contact: Anita or Tim Waters
Opening Times: By appt. only.
Cat. Cost: Online.
Credit Cards: None
Specialities: Ornamental grasses, herbaceous perennials & cottage garden plants.
Notes: Also sells wholesale. Only sells at shows. Contact nursery for details of shows attended.

SBig **Big Plant Nursery** ♿ ◆
Hole Street, Ashington, West Sussex RH20 3DE
Ⓣ (01903) 891466
Ⓜ 07957 262845
Ⓕ (01903) 892829
Ⓔ info@bigplantnursery.co.uk
Ⓦ www.bigplantnursery.co.uk
Contact: Bruce Jordan
Opening Times: 0900-1700 Mon-Sat, 1000-1600 Sun & B/hols.
Min Mail Order UK: Please phone for further info.
Cat. Cost: A5 sae with 2 × 1st class.
Credit Cards: All major credit/debit cards
Specialities: Bamboos, hardy exotics & palms, *Ginkgo, Betula.*
Notes: Programme of events & propagation tuition, see nursery website for details. Also sells wholesale. Delivers to shows. Wheelchair accessible.
Map Ref: S, D3 **OS Grid Ref:** TQ132153

SBir **Birchfleet Nurseries** ♿ ◆
Greenfields Close, Nyewood, Petersfield, Hampshire GU31 5JQ
Ⓣ (01730) 821636
Ⓕ (01730) 821636
Ⓔ gammoak@aol.com
Ⓦ www.birchfleetnurseries.co.uk
Contact: John & Daphne Gammon
Opening Times: By appt. only. Please phone.
Cat. Cost: 2 × 1st class.
Credit Cards: None
Specialities: Oaks. Beech. *Nyssa*. National Collection of *Liquidambar*.
Notes: Also sells wholesale. Nursery accessible for wheelchairs in dry weather.
Map Ref: S, C3

SBmr **Blackmoor Nurseries**
Blackmoor Estate, Blackmoor, Liss, Hampshire GU33 6BS
Ⓣ (01420) 477978
Ⓕ (01420) 487813
Ⓔ sales@blackmoor.co.uk
Ⓦ www.blackmoor.co.uk
Contact: Jon Munday
Opening Times: 0730-1600.
Min Mail Order UK: Nmc
Min Mail Order EU: Nmc
Cat. Cost: None issued.
Credit Cards: All major credit/debit cards
Specialities: Fruit trees, soft fruit & ornamental trees.
Notes: Also sells wholesale.

SBod **Bodiam Nursery**
Bodiam, Robertsbridge, East Sussex TN32 5RA
Ⓣ (01580) 830811
Ⓜ 07971 419302
Ⓔ enquiries@bodiamnursery.co.uk
Ⓦ www.bodiamnursery.co.uk

Contact: Jill Kaye
Opening Times: 1000-1700, 7 days, 1st Mar-31st Oct. Closed Nov-Feb.
Cat. Cost: None issued.
Credit Cards: All major credit/debit cards
Specialities: Wide range of *Acer palmatum*, available in small numbers of each variety. Coastal & Mediterranean plants. Many other compact or slow-growing shrubs & perennials suitable for small gardens & containers.
Notes: Between Great Dixter & Merriments Gardens, situated opposite Bodiam Castle, next to the level crossing for the steam railway.

SBri **Brickwall Cottage Nursery** ♿
1 Brickwall Cottages, Frittenden, Cranbrook, Kent TN17 2DH
Ⓣ (01580) 852425
Ⓜ 07714 529946
Ⓔ sue.martin@talktalk.net
Ⓦ www.geumcollection.co.uk
Contact: Sue Martin
Opening Times: By appt. only.
Min Mail Order UK: Nmc
Min Mail Order EU: Nmc
Credit Cards: None
Specialities: Hardy perennials. Stock available in small quantities only. National Collection of *Geum*.
Notes: Wheelchair accessible.
Map Ref: S, C5 **OS Grid Ref:** TQ815410

SBrm **Brambly Hedge**
Mill Lane, Sway, Hampshire SO41 8LN
Ⓣ (01590) 683570
Contact: Kim Williams
Opening Times: By appt. only in Jul & Aug.
Min Mail Order UK: Nmc
Cat. Cost: Sae for descriptive list.
Credit Cards: None
Specialities: National Collections of *Streptocarpus* & *Begonia rex* cvs. Plants available in small quantities only.
Notes: Mail order Mar-Aug, small quantities only.

SBrt **Brighton Plants** ♿
New Hall Lane, Small Dole, Sussex BN5 9YJ
Ⓜ 07955 744802
Ⓔ brighton.plants@gmail.com
Ⓦ www.brightonplants.blogspot.com/
Contact: Steve Law
Opening Times: 1000-1700 w/ends, May-Oct & B/hols. Please email/phone first.
Min Mail Order UK: Nmc
Min Mail Order EU: Nmc
Cat. Cost: 3 × 1st class.
Credit Cards: None
Specialities: Hardy herbaceous and woody plants. Drought-tolerant plants.
Notes: Exports beyond EU. Delivers to shows. Wheelchair accessible.
Map Ref: S, D3 **OS Grid Ref:** TQ208132

SCac **Cacti & Succulents**
Hammerfield, Crockham Hill, Edenbridge, Kent TN8 6RR
Ⓣ (01732) 866295
Contact: Geoff Southon
Opening Times: Flexible. Please phone first.
Min Mail Order UK: Nmc
Cat. Cost: None issued.
Credit Cards: None
Specialities: *Echeveria* & related genera & hybrids. Haworthias & gasterias. A large range of aeoniums, both species & hybrids. Many available in small quantities only.

SCam **Camellia Grove Nursery** ♿
Market Garden, Lower Beeding, West Sussex RH13 6PP
Ⓣ (01403) 891412
Ⓔ lp@hortic.com
Ⓦ www.camellia-grove.com
Contact: Chris Loder
Opening Times: 1000-1600 Mon-Sat, please phone first so we can give you our undivided attention.
Min Mail Order UK: Nmc
Min Mail Order EU: Nmc
Cat. Cost: 2 × 1st class.
Credit Cards: All, except American Express
Specialities: *Camellia japonica*, *C. williamsii*, *C. sasanqua* & *C. reticulata*, from the purest white to richest red flowers.
Notes: Also sells wholesale. Exports beyond EU. Delivers to shows. Euro accepted. Wheelchair accessible.
Map Ref: S, C3 **OS Grid Ref:** TQ221255

SChF **Charleshurst Farm Nursery**
Loxwood Road, Plaistow, Billingshurst, West Sussex RH14 0NY
Ⓣ (01403) 752273
Ⓜ 07736 522788
Ⓔ Charleshurstfarm@aol.com
Ⓦ www.charleshurstplants.co.uk
Contact: Clive Mellor
Opening Times: Normally 0900-1730 Fri, Sat, Sun, Feb-Oct, but please ring first before travelling.
Min Mail Order UK: Nmc
Min Mail Order EU: Nmc
Cat. Cost: 2 × 1st class.
Credit Cards: All major credit/debit cards
Specialities: Shrubs incl. some more unusual species. Good range of daphnes & Japanese maples.
Notes: Delivers to shows. Euro accepted.
Map Ref: S, C3 **OS Grid Ref:** TQ015308

SChr **John Churcher**
47 Grove Avenue, Portchester, Fareham, Hampshire PO16 9EZ
Ⓣ (023) 9232 6740
Ⓜ 07717 495861
Ⓔ johnchurcher47@btinternet.com
Contact: John Churcher
Opening Times: By appt. only. Please phone or email.
Min Mail Order UK: Nmc
Min Mail Order EU: Nmc
Cat. Cost: None issued.
Credit Cards: None
Specialities: Hardy exotics for the Mediterranean-style garden, incl. palms, tree ferns, *Musa*, hedychiums, cycads, *Agave*, *Aloe*, *Opuntia* & echiums. Stock available in small quantities only.
Map Ref: S, D2 **OS Grid Ref:** SU614047

SCit **The Citrus Centre** ♿
West Mare Lane, Marehill, Pulborough, West Sussex RH20 2EA
Ⓣ (01798) 872786
Ⓔ enquiries@citruscentre.co.uk
Ⓦ www.citruscentre.co.uk
Contact: Amanda & Chris Dennis
Opening Times: 0930-1600 Tue-Sat. Phone for Xmas & B/hol opening times.
Min Mail Order UK: Nmc
Min Mail Order EU: Nmc
Cat. Cost: Online.
Credit Cards: MasterCard, Visa
Specialities: *Citrus* & *Citrus* relatives.
Notes: Wheelchair accessible.
Map Ref: S, D3

SCmr **Cromar Nursery** ♿
39 Livesey Street, North Pole, Wateringbury, Maidstone, Kent ME18 5BQ
Ⓣ (01622) 812380
Ⓔ CromarNursery@aol.com
Ⓦ www.cromarnursery.co.uk
Contact: Debra & Martin Cronk
Opening Times: 0930-1700 daily except Wed. Winter opening 0930-1630 Thu, Fri, Sat, Sun. Please check website or phone if travelling far.
Min Mail Order UK: Nmc
Min Mail Order EU: Nmc
Cat. Cost: 2 × 1st class.
Credit Cards: All major credit/debit cards
Specialities: Ornamental & fruit trees.
Notes: Wheelchair accessible.
Map Ref: S, C4 **OS Grid Ref:** TQ697547

SCob **Coblands Nurseries** ♿
Trench Road, Tonbridge, Kent TN11 9NG
Ⓣ (01732) 770999
Ⓔ info@coblands.co.uk
Ⓦ www.coblands.co.uk
Contact: Lewis Normand
Opening Times: 0900-1630 Mon-Sat, all year. Closed for Xmas/New Year.
Min Mail Order UK: Nmc
Min Mail Order EU: Nmc
Cat. Cost: Online & seasonal postings to existing customers.
Credit Cards: All major credit/debit cards
Specialities: Wide range of plants esp. herbaceous perennials of garden-worthiness incl. *Hebe*, *Hydrangea*, *Phormium*, *Brunnera*, *Echinacea*, *Epimedium*, *Heuchera*, *Hosta*, *Rudbeckia* & ferns. Wide range of established specimen plants. New introductions may be in limited supply.
Notes: Direct online ordering service. Bare-rooted fruit trees, ornamental trees & hedging available seasonally. Also sells wholesale. Wheelchair accessible.
Map Ref: S, C4 **OS Grid Ref:** TQ586487

SCog **Coghurst Camellias** ♿
Ivy House Lane, Near Three Oaks, Hastings, East Sussex TN35 4NP
Ⓣ (01424) 756228
Ⓔ rotherview@btinternet.com
Ⓦ www.rotherview.com
Contact: R Bates & W Bates
Opening Times: 1000-1530 7 days, all year.
Min Mail Order UK: Nmc
Min Mail Order EU: Nmc
Cat. Cost: 6 × 1st class.
Credit Cards: All major credit/debit cards
Specialities: *Camellia*.
Notes: Nursery is on the same site as Rotherview Nursery. Also sells wholesale. Delivers to shows. Euro accepted. Wheelchair accessible.
Map Ref: S, D5

SCoo **Cooling's Nurseries Ltd** ♿
Rushmore Hill, Knockholt, Sevenoaks, Kent TN14 7NN
Ⓣ (01959) 532269
Ⓕ (01959) 534092
Ⓔ Plantfinder@coolings.co.uk
Ⓦ www.coolings.co.uk
Contact: Mark Reeve or Toby Davies
Opening Times: 0900-1700 Mon-Sat & 1000-1630 Sun.
Cat. Cost: None issued
Credit Cards: All, except American Express
Specialities: Large range of perennials, conifers & bedding plants. Many unusual shrubs & trees. Third generation family business.
Notes: Display garden. Coffee shop. Wheelchair accessible.
Map Ref: S, C4 **OS Grid Ref:** TK477610

SDay **A LA CARTE DAYLILIES**
Little Hermitage, St Catherine's Down, Nr Ventnor, Isle of Wight
PO38 2PD
Ⓣ (01983) 730512
Ⓔ andy@alacartedaylilies.co.uk
Ⓦ www.alacartedaylilies.co.uk
Contact: Jan & Andy Wyers
Opening Times: Mail order only. Open by appt. only. Difficult to find on an unmade private road, phone/email for directions.
Min Mail Order UK: Nmc
Min Mail Order EU: Nmc
Cat. Cost: 3 × 1st class.
Credit Cards: None
Specialities: *Hemerocallis*. National Collections of Miniature & Small Flowered *Hemerocallis* & Large Flowered *Hemerocallis* (post-1960 award-winning cultivars).
Notes: Euro accepted.
Map Ref: S, D2 **OS Grid Ref:** SZ499787

S

SDea **DEACON'S NURSERY** ◆
Moor View, Godshill, Isle of Wight
PO38 3HW
Ⓣ (01983) 840750 (24 hrs) or (01983) 522243
Ⓕ (01983) 523575
Ⓔ info@deaconsnurseryfruits.co.uk
Ⓦ www.deaconsnurseryfruits.co.uk
Contact: G D & B H W Deacon
Opening Times: 0800-1600 Mon-Fri May-Sep, 0800-1700 Mon-Fri 0800-1200 Sat Oct-Apr.
Min Mail Order UK: Nmc
Min Mail Order EU: Nmc
Cat. Cost: Free.
Credit Cards: All major credit/debit cards
Specialities: Over 300 varieties of apple, old & new, apricots, cherries, damsons, gages, nectarines, peaches, pears, plums. Modern soft fruit, grapes, hops, nuts & family trees.
Notes: Also sells wholesale. Exports beyond EU. Euro accepted.
Map Ref: S, D2

SDeJ **P. DE JAGER & SONS LTD** ♿ ◆
Church Farm, Ulcombe, Maidstone, Kent
ME17 1DN
Ⓣ (01622) 840229
Ⓕ (01622) 844073
Ⓔ flowerbulbs@dejager.co.uk
Ⓦ www.dejager.co.uk
Contact: George Clowes
Opening Times: Mail order only. Orders taken from 0900-1700 Mon-Fri
Min Mail Order UK: Nmc
Min Mail Order EU: Nmc
Cat. Cost: Free
Credit Cards: All major credit/debit cards
Specialities: Wide range of all flower bulbs.
Notes: Also sells wholesale. Exports beyond EU. Euro accepted. Wheelchair accessible.

SDix **GREAT DIXTER NURSERIES**
Northiam, Rye, East Sussex TN31 6PH
Ⓣ (01797) 254044
Ⓕ (01797) 252879
Ⓔ nursery@greatdixter.co.uk
Ⓦ www.greatdixter.co.uk
Contact: Michael Morphy
Opening Times: 0900-1700 7 days, Apr-Oct. 0900-1630 Mon-Fri, 0900-1230 Sat, closed Sun, Nov-Mar.
Min Mail Order UK: Nmc
Min Mail Order EU: Nmc
Cat. Cost: 5 × 1st class.
Credit Cards: All major credit/debit cards
Specialities: *Clematis*, shrubs and plants. Gardens open.
Notes: Plants dispatched Sep-Mar only. Partially accessible for wheelchairs.
Map Ref: S, C5 **OS Grid Ref:** TQ821251

SDow **DOWNDERRY NURSERY** ♿
Pillar Box Lane, Hadlow, Nr Tonbridge, Kent
TN11 9SW
Ⓣ (01732) 810081
Ⓕ (01732) 811398
Ⓔ info@downderry-nursery.co.uk
Ⓦ www.downderry-nursery.co.uk
Contact: Dr Simon Charlesworth
Opening Times: 1000-1700 Wed-Sun 1st May-30th Sep & B/hols. Other times by appt.
Min Mail Order UK: Nmc
Min Mail Order EU: Nmc
Cat. Cost: Free.
Credit Cards: Delta, MasterCard, Maestro, Visa
Specialities: National Collections of *Lavandula* and *Rosmarinus*.
Notes: Exports beyond EU. Euro accepted. Wheelchair accessible.
Map Ref: S, C4 **OS Grid Ref:** TQ625521

SDys **DYSONS NURSERIES** ♿
Great Comp Garden, Platt, Sevenoaks, Kent
TN15 8QS
Ⓣ (01732) 885094
Ⓜ 07887 997663
Ⓔ dysonsorders@greatcompgarden.co.uk
Ⓦ www.greatcompgarden.co.uk
Contact: William T Dyson
Opening Times: 1100-1700 7 days 1st Apr-31st Oct. Other times by appt.
Cat. Cost: Online only.
Credit Cards: All major credit/debit cards
Specialities: Salvias & an eclectic range of choice and uncommon plants.

Notes: Delivers to shows. Wheelchair accessible.
Map Ref: S, C4

SEle **Eleplants Nursery**
32 Framfield Road, Uckfield, East Sussex TN22 5AH
Ⓣ (01825) 760356
Ⓔ eleplantsnursery@talk21.com
Ⓦ www.eleplantsnursery.co.uk
Contact: Martin Batchelor
Opening Times: Not open but can be visited by prior appt. only.
Credit Cards: All major credit/debit cards, Paypal
Specialities: Shrubs.
Notes: Exports beyond EU. Delivers to shows.

SEND **East Northdown Farm & Gardens** ♿
George Hill Road (B2052), Margate, Kent CT9 3TS
Ⓣ (01843) 862060
Ⓜ 07714 241668 or 7
Ⓔ info@botanyplants.co.uk
Ⓦ www.botanyplants.co.uk
Contact: Louise & William Friend
Opening Times: 0900-1700 7 days, all year except Sun in Nov & Jan. Closed Xmas week.
Min Mail Order UK: Nmc
Cat. Cost: Online only.
Credit Cards: All major credit/debit cards
Specialities: Chalk & coast-loving plants. Specimen shrubs & bamboos available.
Notes: Plants from our other nursery MMuc available to order. Tearoom & gardens. Wheelchair accessible.
Map Ref: S, B6 **OS Grid Ref:** TR383702

SEWo **English Woodlands** ♿
Burrow Nursery, Herrings Lane, Cross-in-Hand, Heathfield, East Sussex TN21 0UG
Ⓣ (01435) 862992
Ⓕ (01435) 867742
Ⓔ sales@englishwoodlands.com
Ⓦ www.englishwoodlands.com
Contact: Joanne Carter
Opening Times: 0800-1700 Mon-Fri. 0800-1630 Sat. Closed Sun & B/hols.
Min Mail Order UK: £25.00
Cat. Cost: Free.
Credit Cards: All, except American Express
Specialities: Trees, shrubs, hedging.
Notes: Also sells wholesale. Wheelchair accessible.
Map Ref: S, C4 **OS Grid Ref:** TQ567222

SFai **Fairweather's Garden Centre** ♿
High Street, Beaulieu, Hampshire SO42 7YB
Ⓣ (01590) 612307
Ⓕ (01590) 612519
Ⓔ info@fairweathers.co.uk
Ⓦ www.fairweathers.co.uk
Contact: Sue Greaves
Opening Times: 0900-1700 7 days.
Min Mail Order UK: Nmc
Cat. Cost: None issued.
Credit Cards: MasterCard, Visa
Specialities: *Agapanthus* & *Lavandula*.
Notes: Wheelchair accessible.
Map Ref: S, D2

SFgr **Firgrove Plants**
24 Wykeham Field, Wickham, Fareham, Hampshire PO17 5AB
Ⓣ (01329) 835206 after 1900 hours.
Ⓔ jenny@firgroveplants.demon.co.uk
Ⓦ www.firgroveplants.demon.co.uk
Contact: Jenny MacKinnon
Opening Times: Not open. Mail order only.
Min Mail Order UK: £10.50
Cat. Cost: Sae.
Credit Cards: None
Specialities: Wide range of houseleeks in small quantities.
Notes: Houseleeks by mail order Apr-mid Oct.

SFrt **Fruit Garden Plants** ♿ ◆
Woolton Farm, Bekesbourne, Canterbury, Kent CT4 5EA
Ⓣ (01227) 830525
Ⓜ 07710 253690
Ⓕ (01227) 831969
Ⓔ sales@fruitgardenplants.co.uk
Ⓦ www.fruitgardenplants.co.uk
Contact: Mark Mount
Opening Times: 1000-1600 Thu-Sat, 1st Nov-31st Mar. 1000-1700 Thu-Sun, 1st Apr-31st Oct.
Min Mail Order UK: £10.00
Min Mail Order EU: £35.00
Credit Cards: MasterCard, Visa
Specialities: Tree fruits & soft fruits.
Notes: Fruit display garden where visitors can see particular varieties & the methods used for growing them. Small café. Medieval tythe barn. Also sells wholesale. Delivers to shows. Wheelchair accessible.
Map Ref: S, C5 **OS Grid Ref:** TR191568

SGbt **Gilbert's Nursery** ♿
Dandy's Ford Lane, Sherfield English, Romsey, Hampshire SO51 6DT
Ⓣ (01794) 322566
Ⓔ gilbertsnursery@aol.com
Ⓦ www.gilbertsnursery.co.uk
Contact: Nick Gilbert
Opening Times: 0900-1700 Tue-Sat, 10.00-16.30 Sun, all year round. *Dahlia* field open from 2nd week Aug to 2nd week Oct.

Min Mail Order UK: Nmc
Min Mail Order EU: Nmc
Cat. Cost: 2 × 1st class
Credit Cards: All, except American Express
Specialities: *Dahlia*. Proper plant nursery with many unusual plants & staff happy to share their knowledge & help with plant selection.
Notes: *Dahlia* field with over 400 cvs on view (grass pathways). See above for opening times or go to www.gilbertsdahlias.co.uk. Tea room. Delivers to shows. Wheelchair accessible.
Map Ref: S, C2

SGol **Golden Hill Nurseries** ♿
Lordsfield, Goudhurst Road, Marden, Kent TN12 9LT
Ⓣ (01622) 833218
Ⓜ 07826 523655
Ⓕ (01622) 832528
Ⓔ enquiries@goldenhillplants.com
Ⓦ www.goldenhillplants.com
Contact: Roger Butler
Opening Times: 0900-1700 Mon-Sat, 1st Mar-31st Oct. 0900-1600 Mon-Sat, 1st Nov-28th Feb. 1100-1600 Sun from 3rd Sun in Feb until Xmas.
Min Mail Order UK: Nmc
Cat. Cost: Online only.
Credit Cards: All major credit/debit cards
Specialities: Specimen plants, shrubs, grasses, bamboos, Japanese maples, conifers & trees.
Notes: Also sells wholesale. Euro accepted. Wheelchair accessible.

SGSe **Garden Secrets Nursery**
Boldre Nurseries, Southampton Road, Sway, Lymington, Hampshire SO41 8ND
Ⓜ 07779 084245
Ⓔ hazelwoodpreschool@hotmail.co.uk
Ⓦ www.gardensecretsnursery.co.uk
Contact: Tim Woodford
Opening Times: 0900-1700 w/ends or by appt. only.
Credit Cards: None
Specialities: Perennials, grasses and ferns.

SHaC **Hart Canna** ♿
25-27 Guildford Road West, Farnborough, Hampshire GU14 6PS
Ⓣ (01252) 514421
Ⓜ 07762 950000
Ⓔ sales@hartcanna.com
Ⓦ www.hartcanna.co.uk
Contact: Keith Hayward
Opening Times: By arrangement.
Min Mail Order UK: Nmc
Min Mail Order EU: Nmc
Cat. Cost: Sae.
Credit Cards: All major credit/debit cards
Specialities: *Canna*. National Collection of *Canna*.
Notes: Also sells wholesale. Euro accepted. Delivers to shows. Wheelchair accessible.
Map Ref: S, C3

SHal **Hall's Court Nursery** ♿
Pluckley Road, Bethersden, Ashford, Kent TN26 3ET
Ⓣ (01233) 820828
Ⓜ 07729 418275
Ⓔ info@hallscourt.co.uk
Ⓦ www.hallscourt.co.uk
Contact: Jeanette Jahnz
Opening Times: 0900-1700 every w/end, end Mar-beginning Oct. Weekdays by appt.
Cat. Cost: Online only.
Credit Cards: None
Specialities: Around 90 varieties of hardy geraniums & around 50 varieties of pelargoniums, incl. some species. Also alpines, herbs, some succulents, perennials & hardy fuchsias. Some plants available in small quantities only.
Notes: Small nursery, situated midway between Ashford and Tenterden in rural Kent. Wheelchair accessible.
Map Ref: S, C5 **OS Grid Ref:** TQ919414

SHar **Hardy's Cottage Garden Plants** ♿
Priory Lane Nursery, Freefolk Priors, Whitchurch, Hampshire RG28 7NJ
Ⓣ (01256) 896533
Ⓔ info@hardys-plants.co.uk
Ⓦ www.hardys-plants.co.uk
Contact: Rosemary Hardy
Opening Times: 1000-1700 7 days, 1st Mar-30th Sep. 1000-1600 Mon-Fri, Oct, 1000-1500 Mon-Fri, 1st Nov-28th Feb. Closed 23rd Dec-4th Jan.
Min Mail Order UK: Nmc
Cat. Cost: Online only.
Credit Cards: Access, Electron, Switch, Solo, Visa
Specialities: Wide range of herbaceous perennials incl. *Achillea*, *Gaura*, *Geum*, *Geranium*, *Hemerocallis*, *Heuchera*, *Lathryus vernus*, *Paeonia*, *Penstemon* & *Salvia*.
Notes: Accepts HTA Gift Tokens. Offers trade discount. Also sells wholesale. Delivers to shows. Wheelchair accessible.
Map Ref: S, C2

SHDw **Highdown Nursery**
New Hall Lane, Small Dole, Nr Henfield, West Sussex BN5 9YH
Ⓣ (01273) 492976
Ⓜ 07900 956456
Ⓕ (01273) 492976

Ⓔ highdown.herbs@btinternet.com
Ⓦ www.highdownnursery.com
Contact: A G & J H Shearing
Opening Times: 0900-1700 7 days.
Min Mail Order UK: £10.00 + p&p
Cat. Cost: 3 × 1st class.
Credit Cards: None
Specialities: Herbs. Grasses.
Notes: Also sells wholesale. Delivers to shows. Euro accepted. Partial wheelchair access.
Map Ref: S, D3 **OS Grid Ref:** TV214134

SHeu **HEUCHERAHOLICS** ♿
(Office) The Paddock, Pilley Street, Pilley, Lymington, Hampshire SO41 5QP
Ⓣ (01590) 670581
Ⓜ 07973 291062
Ⓔ jooles.heucheraholics@gmail.com
Ⓦ www.heucheraholics.co.uk
Contact: Julie Burton/Sean Atkinson
Opening Times: Visits to nursery by appt. only. Please phone first. No need to make an appt. for Open Days.
Min Mail Order UK: Nmc
Cat. Cost: No charge.
Credit Cards: All major credit/debit cards
Specialities: *Heuchera*, *Heucherella*, *Pulmonaria* & *Tiarella*. Other foliage plants. *Helleborus*.
Notes: Nursery is located at Boldre Nurseries, Southampton Road, Boldre, Lymington, Hants. Toilet facilities. Well-behaved dogs welcome. Also sells wholesale. Delivers to shows. Wheelchair accessible.
Map Ref: S, D2 **OS Grid Ref:** SZ310934

SHil **HILLIER GARDEN CENTRES**
Ampfield House, Ampfield, Romsey, Hampshire SO51 9PA
Ⓣ (01794) 368944
Ⓕ (01794) 367830
Ⓔ info@hillier.co.uk
Ⓦ www.hillieronline.co.uk
Opening Times: Office 0830-1700 Mon-Fri. Garden Centres: 0900-1730 Mon-Sat, 1000-1630 Sun.
Min Mail Order UK: Nmc
Min Mail Order EU: £250
Cat. Cost: None issued.
Notes: Other nursery branches in the south of England.

SHyH **HYDRANGEA HAVEN** ♿
Market Garden, Lower Beeding, West Sussex RH13 6PP
Ⓣ (01403) 891412
Ⓔ lp@hortic.com
Ⓦ www.hydrangea-haven.com
Contact: Chris Loder
Opening Times: 1000-1600 Mon-Sat, please phone first, so we can give you our undivided attention.
Min Mail Order UK: Nmc
Min Mail Order EU: Nmc
Cat. Cost: 2 × 1st class.
Credit Cards: All, except American Express
Specialities: *Hydrangea*: mophead, lacecap & panicle. *Agapanthus*.
Notes: Also sells wholesale. Exports beyond EU. Delivers to shows. Euro accepted. Wheelchair accessible.
Map Ref: S, C3 **OS Grid Ref:** TQ221255

SIde **IDEN CROFT HERBS** ♿
Frittenden Road, Staplehurst, Kent TN12 0DH
Ⓣ (01580) 891432
Ⓔ idencroftherbs@yahoo.co.uk
Ⓦ www.uk-herbs.com
Contact: Tracey Connors-Parry
Opening Times: 0900-1700 Mon-Sat & 1100-1700 Sun & B/hols, Mar-Sep. Closed Oct-Feb.
Min Mail Order UK: £10.00
Min Mail Order EU: £25.00
Cat. Cost: Online only.
Credit Cards: All major credit/debit cards
Specialities: Herbs, aromatic & wildflower plants & plants for bees & butterflies. National Collections of *Mentha* & *Origanum*.
Notes: Wheelchairs available at nursery.
Map Ref: S, C5

SIgm **TIM INGRAM** ♿
Copton Ash, 105 Ashford Road, Faversham, Kent ME13 8XW
Ⓣ (01795) 535919
Ⓔ coptonash@yahoo.co.uk
Ⓦ coptonash.plus.com
Contact: Dr T J Ingram
Opening Times: 1400-1800 Fri & Sat, Mar-Oct. Other times by appt.
Credit Cards: None
Specialities: Small, specialised nursery, offering mainly alpines and spring plants. Many unusual plants available in small quantities.
Notes: Delivers to shows. Wheelchair accessible.
Map Ref: S, C5 **OS Grid Ref:** TR015598

SIri **IRIS OF SISSINGHURST**
Roughlands Farm, Goudhurst Road, Marden, Kent TN12 9NH
Ⓣ (01622) 831511
Ⓔ orders@irisofsissinghurst.com
Ⓦ www.irisofsissinghurst.com
Contact: Sue Marshall
Opening Times: Contact nursery or see website for opening times.
Min Mail Order UK: Nmc

Min Mail Order EU: Nmc
Cat. Cost: 2 × 1st class.
Credit Cards: None
Specialities: *Iris*, short, intermediate & tall bearded, *ensata*, *sibirica* & many species.
Notes: Euro accepted.
Map Ref: S, C4 **OS Grid Ref:** TQ735437

SKee **KEEPERS NURSERY**
Gallants Court, Gallants Lane, East Farleigh, Maidstone, Kent ME15 0LE
Ⓣ (01622) 726465
Ⓕ 0870 705 2145
Ⓔ info@keepers-nursery.co.uk
Ⓦ www.keepers-nursery.co.uk
Contact: Hamid Habibi
Opening Times: Only on a limited number of Open Days & for collection of trees & plants by arrangement.
Min Mail Order UK: Nmc
Cat. Cost: Online only.
Credit Cards: MasterCard, Switch, Maestro, Visa
Specialities: A very large range of fruit trees incl. old & rare as well as modern varieties. Soft fruit plants & nut trees.

S

SKHP **KEVIN HUGHES PLANTS** ♿
(Office) Heale House, Middle Woodford, Salisbury, Wiltshire SP4 6NT
Ⓣ (01722) 782504
Ⓜ 07720 718671
Ⓔ info@kevinsplants.co.uk
Ⓦ www.kevinsplants.co.uk
Contact: Kevin Hughes
Opening Times: 1100-1700 Wed-Sat, 1st Feb-31st Oct. Other times by appt. only.
Min Mail Order UK: £10.00
Min Mail Order EU: £20.00
Cat. Cost: 3 × 1st class
Credit Cards: All, except American Express
Specialities: Less common & new hardy garden plants with a particular emphasis on *Magnolia*, *Trillium*, climbers, *Philadelphus*, *Viburnum* & *Syringa*. We try to select plants that are garden-worthy & attract wildlife. Many plants are slow to propagate & will always be in short supply. None are from wild-dug sources.
Notes: Nursery at Heale Garden, Middle Woodford, Salisbury, SP4 5NT. Exports beyond EU. Euro accepted. Wheelchair accessible.
Map Ref: S, C1 **OS Grid Ref:** SU125363

SKin **KINGS BARN TREES**
Kings Barn Farm, Kent Street, Cowfold, West Sussex RH13 8BB
Ⓣ (01403) 865405
Ⓔ sales@kingsbarntrees.co.uk
Ⓦ www.kingsbarntrees.co.uk
Contact: Adrian Rumble
Opening Times: Not open. Mail order via website only.
Min Mail Order UK: £9.95
Min Mail Order EU: £9.95
Cat. Cost: Not available.
Credit Cards: All major credit/debit cards
Specialities: Mainly grow containerised trees, specialising in *Eucalyptus*. Also grow willow for sale as whips & setts during the winter/early spring. *Eucalyptus* available in small quantities only.

SLau **THE LAURELS NURSERY** ♿
Benenden, Cranbrook, Kent TN17 4JU
Ⓣ (01580) 240463
Ⓦ www.thelaurelsnursery.co.uk
Contact: Peter or Sylvia Kellett
Opening Times: 0800-1600 Wed-Fri, 0900-1200 Sat, Sun by appt. only.
Min Mail Order UK: £30
Cat. Cost: Free.
Credit Cards: All major credit/debit cards
Specialities: Open ground & container ornamental trees, shrubs & climbers especially birch, beech & *Wisteria*.
Notes: Mail order of small *Wisteria* only. Also sells wholesale. Euro accepted. Wheelchair accessible.
Map Ref: S, C5 **OS Grid Ref:** TQ815313

SLay **LAYHAM GARDEN CENTRE & NURSERY** ♿
Lower Road, Staple, Nr Canterbury, Kent CT3 1LH
Ⓣ (01304) 813267
Ⓕ (01304) 814007
Ⓔ info@layhamgardencentre.co.uk
Ⓦ www.layhamgardencentre.co.uk
Contact: Ellen Wessel
Opening Times: 0900-1700 7 days.
Min Mail Order UK: Nmc
Min Mail Order EU: £25.00 + p&p
Cat. Cost: Free.
Credit Cards: MasterCard, Visa
Specialities: Roses, herbaceous, shrubs, trees & hedging plants.
Notes: Mail order roses only. Also sells wholesale. Euro accepted. Wheelchair accessible.
Map Ref: S, C6 **OS Grid Ref:** TR276567

SLBF **LITTLE BROOK FUCHSIAS** ♿
Ash Green Lane West, Ash Green, Nr Aldershot, Hampshire GU12 6HL
Ⓣ (01252) 329731
Ⓔ carol.gubler@ntlbusiness.com
Ⓦ www.littlebrookfuchsias.co.uk
Contact: Carol Gubler

Opening Times: 1000-1700 Wed-Sun 1st Jan-29th Jun.
Cat. Cost: 50p + sae.
Credit Cards: All major credit/debit cards
Specialities: Fuchsias, old & new.
Notes: Nursery located off White Lane in Ash Green. Wheelchair accessible.
Map Ref: S, C3 **OS Grid Ref:** SU901496

SLdr **Loder Plants** ♿
Market Garden, Lower Beeding, West Sussex RH13 6PP
Ⓣ (01403) 891412
Ⓔ sales@rhododendrons.com
Ⓦ www.rhododendrons.com
Contact: Chris Loder
Opening Times: 1000-1600 Mon-Sat, please ring first so we can give you our undivided attention.
Min Mail Order UK: Nmc
Min Mail Order EU: Nmc
Cat. Cost: 2 × 1st class.
Credit Cards: All, except American Express
Specialities: Rhododendrons & azaleas in all sizes. Some in very limited quantities only. *Agapanthus.*
Notes: Also sells wholesale. Exports beyond EU. Delivers to shows. Euro accepted. Wheelchair accessible.
Map Ref: S, C3 **OS Grid Ref:** TQ221255

SLim **Lime Cross Nursery** ♿
Herstmonceux, Hailsham, East Sussex BN27 4RS
Ⓣ (01323) 833229
Ⓕ (01323) 833944
Ⓔ info@limecross.co.uk
Ⓦ www.limecross.co.uk
Contact: Jonathan Tate, Anita Green
Opening Times: 0830-1700 Mon-Sat & 1000-1600 Sun.
Min Mail Order UK: Nmc
Min Mail Order EU: £50.00
Cat. Cost: Online only.
Credit Cards: All major credit/debit cards
Specialities: Conifers, trees & shrubs, climbers.
Notes: Wheelchair accessible.
Map Ref: S, D4 **OS Grid Ref:** TQ642125

SLon **Longstock Park Nursery** ♿
Longstock, Stockbridge, Hampshire SO20 6EH
Ⓣ (01264) 810894
Ⓕ (01264) 810924
Ⓔ longstocknursery@leckfordestate.co.uk
Ⓦ www.longstocknursery.co.uk
Contact: Mark Pitman
Opening Times: 0830-1730 Mon-Sat, 1000-1700 Sun. Closed 25th-27th Dec & 1st Jan.
Min Mail Order UK: £15.00
Cat. Cost: Lists of *Buddleja*, *Penstemon*, roses, fruit trees & bushes.
Credit Cards: All major credit/debit cards
Specialities: A wide range, over 2000 varieties, of trees, shrubs, perennials, climbers, aquatics & ferns. Extensive collection of *Penstemon*. National Collections of *Buddleja* & *Clematis viticella*.
Notes: Mail order for *Buddleja* only. Wheelchair accessible.
Map Ref: S, C2 **OS Grid Ref:** SO365389

SMad **Madrona Nursery** ♿
Pluckley Road, Bethersden, Kent TN26 3DD
Ⓣ (01233) 820100
Ⓕ (01233) 820091
Ⓔ madrona@hotmail.co.uk
Ⓦ www.madrona.co.uk
Contact: Liam MacKenzie
Opening Times: 1000-1700 Sat-Tue 15th Mar-28th Oct. Other times by appt.
Cat. Cost: Free
Credit Cards: All major credit/debit cards
Specialities: Unusual shrubs, conifers & perennials. *Eryngium*, *Colletia*.
Notes: Delivers to shows. Euro accepted. Wheelchair accessible.
Map Ref: S, C5 **OS Grid Ref:** TQ918419

SMDP **Marcus Dancer Plants**
Kilcreggan, Alderholt Road, Sandleheath, Fordingbridge, Hampshire SP6 1PT
Ⓣ (01425) 652747
Ⓜ 07709 922730
Ⓔ marcus.dancer@btopenworld.com
Ⓦ www.clematisplants.co.uk
Contact: Marcus Dancer
Opening Times: By appointment only.
Min Mail Order UK: Nmc
Cat. Cost: 4 × 1st class.
Credit Cards: None
Specialities: Wide range of *Clematis*, smaller range of *Daphne*. Some varieties available in small quantities only.
Notes: Mail order available for all plants. Delivers to shows.
Map Ref: S, D1

SMea **Meadowgate Nursery**
Street End Lane, Sidlesham, Chichester, West Sussex PO20 7RG
Ⓣ (01243) 641997
Ⓜ 07736 523262
Ⓔ meadowgatenursery@tiscali.co.uk
Ⓦ www.meadowgatenursery.co.uk
Contact: David Allen
Opening Times: 1000-1700 Sat-Wed.
Min Mail Order UK: Nmc
Credit Cards: All major credit/debit cards

Specialities: Ornamental grasses and complimentary perennials.
Notes: Also sells wholesale. Delivers to shows.

SMHy **Marchants Hardy Plants** ♿
2 Marchants Cottages, Mill Lane,
Laughton, East Sussex
BN8 6AJ
Ⓣ (01323) 811737
Ⓕ (01323) 811737
Ⓔ graham@marchantsplants.plus.com
Ⓦ www.marchantshardyplants.co.uk
Contact: Graham Gough
Opening Times: 0930-1730 Wed-Sat, 12th Mar-18th Oct 2014.
Cat. Cost: 3 × 2nd class
Credit Cards: MasterCard, Visa
Specialities: Uncommon herbaceous perennials. *Agapanthus*, *Erodium*, choice grasses, *Galanthus*, *Miscanthus*, *Molinia*.
Notes: Euro accepted. Wheelchair accessible.
Map Ref: S, D4 **OS Grid Ref:** TQ506119

SMor **Morehavens** ♿
Stocks Lane, Meonstoke, Hampshire
SO32 3NQ
Ⓣ (01489) 878501
Ⓔ morehavens@camomilelawns.co.uk
Ⓦ www.camomilelawns.co.uk
Contact: E. Clements
Opening Times: Mail order only. Open for collection only.
Min Mail Order UK: £18.00
Min Mail Order EU: £18.00 + p&p
Cat. Cost: Free.
Credit Cards: Paypal
Specialities: *Camomile nobile* 'Treneague' and *C. nobile* dwarf.
Notes: Also sells wholesale. Wheelchair accessible.

SPad **Paddock Plants**
The Paddock, Upper Toothill Road,
Rownhams, Southampton, Hampshire
SO16 8AL
Ⓣ (023) 8073 9912
Ⓜ 07763 386717
Ⓔ rob@paddockplants.co.uk
Ⓦ www.paddockplants.co.uk
Contact: Rob & Joanna Courtney
Opening Times: By appt. only. Please telephone in advance.
Min Mail Order UK: £10.00
Cat. Cost: Online only.
Credit Cards: All major credit/debit cards
Specialities: Family-run nursery offering interesting range of perennials, grasses, ferns & shrubs, incl. some unusual varieties, using peat-free growing medium. Some varieties grown in small quantities.
Notes: Local delivery by our own transport. Courier delivery throughout UK. Delivers to shows.
Map Ref: S, D2 **OS Grid Ref:** SU383177

SPav **Pavilion Plants**
18 Pavilion Road, Worthing,
West Sussex
BN14 7EF
Ⓣ (01903) 821338
Contact: Andrew Muggeridge
Opening Times: Mail order only. Please phone for details.
Min Mail Order UK: Nmc
Cat. Cost: 4 × 1st class.
Credit Cards: None
Specialities: Perennials and bulbs. *Digitalis*.
Notes: Also sells wholesale.
Map Ref: S, D3

SPer **Perryhill Nurseries Ltd** ♿
Edenbridge Road, Hartfield, East Sussex
TN7 4JP
Ⓣ (01892) 770377
Ⓕ (01892) 770929
Ⓔ sales@perryhillnurseries.co.uk
Ⓦ www.perryhillnurseries.co.uk
Contact: P J Chapman
Opening Times: 0900-1700 7 days 1st Mar-31st Oct. 0900-1630 1st Nov-28th Feb.
Min Mail Order UK: Nmc
Cat. Cost: Online only.
Credit Cards: Access, Maestro, MasterCard, Visa
Specialities: Wide range of trees, shrubs, perennials, roses, fruit trees, soft fruit. Unusual & rare plants may be available in small quantities.
Notes: Mail order despatch depends on size & weight of plants. Wheelchair accessible.
Map Ref: S, C4 **OS Grid Ref:** TQ480375

SPhx **Phoenix Perennial Plants** ♿
Paice Lane, Medstead,
Alton, Hampshire
GU34 5PR
Ⓣ (01420) 560695
Ⓜ 07909 528191
Ⓕ (01420) 563640
Ⓔ marina@phoenixperennialplants.co.uk
Ⓦ www.phoenixperennialplants.co.uk
Contact: Marina Christopher
Opening Times: Open by appt. only.
Cat. Cost: 4 × 1st class.
Credit Cards: All major credit/debit cards
Specialities: Perennials, many uncommon & hardy, selected for beneficial insects particularly pollinators. *Agastache*, *Centaurea*, *Monarda*, *Sanguisorba*, *Sedum*, *Thalictrum*, *Verbascum*, bulbs, prairie plants, grasses,

S

especially *Molinia* & late-flowering perennials.
Notes: Co-located with Select Seeds SSss. Also sells wholesale. Delivers to shows. Wheelchair accessible.
Map Ref: S, C2 **OS Grid Ref:** SU657362

SPin **John and Lynsey's Plants** ♿
2 Hillside Cottages, Trampers Lane, North Boarhunt, Fareham, Hampshire PO17 6DA
Ⓣ (01329) 832786
Ⓔ landjpink@tiscali.co.uk
Contact: Mrs Lynsey Pink
Opening Times: By appt. only. Open under NGS.
Cat. Cost: None issued.
Credit Cards: None
Specialities: Mainly *Salvia* with a wide range of other unusual perennials. Stock is only available in small quantities but we are happy to try & propagate anything that we have. National Collection of species *Salvia*.
Notes: Wheelchair accessible.
Map Ref: S, D2 **OS Grid Ref:** SU603109

SPlb **Plantbase** ♿
Sleepers Stile Road, Cousley Wood, Wadhurst, East Sussex TN5 6QX
Ⓣ (01892) 785599
Ⓜ 07967 601064
Ⓔ graham@plantbase.freeserve.co.uk
Ⓦ www.plantbase.co.uk
Contact: Graham Blunt
Opening Times: 1000-1700, 7 days all year (appt. advisable).
Min Mail Order UK: Nmc
Min Mail Order EU: Nmc
Cat. Cost: Online only.
Credit Cards: All major credit/debit cards
Specialities: Wide range of alpines, perennials, shrubs, climbers, waterside plants, herbs, Australasian, South African & South American plants in particular. Some available in small quantities only.
Notes: Delivers to shows. Euro accepted. Wheelchair accessible.
Map Ref: S, C5

SPoG **The Potted Garden Nursery** ♿
Ashford Road, Bearsted, Maidstone, Kent ME14 4NH
Ⓣ (01622) 737801
Ⓦ www.thepottedgarden.co.uk
Contact: Any staff member
Opening Times: 0900-1730 (dusk in winter), 7 days. Xmas/New Year period opening times on website or answerphone.
Credit Cards: All major credit/debit cards
Notes: Mail order not available. Wheelchair accessible.
Map Ref: S, C5 **OS Grid Ref:** TQ810550

SPol **Pollie's Perennials and Daylily Nursery** ♿
Lodore, Mount Pleasant Lane, Sway, Lymington, Hampshire SO41 8LS
Ⓣ (01590) 682577
Ⓜ 07712 713765
Ⓕ (01590) 682577
Ⓔ terry.maasz@btinternet.com
Ⓦ www.polliesdaylilies.co.uk
Contact: Pollie Maasz
Opening Times: 1000-1730 w/ends & 1400-1730 Mon-Fri during the daylily season, late-May to mid-Aug. Other times by appt. only.
Min Mail Order UK: Nmc
Min Mail Order EU: £20.00
Cat. Cost: 2 × 1st class.
Credit Cards: Paypal
Specialities: *Hemerocallis*, also less commonly available hardy perennials. Stock available in small quantities only. National Collection of Spider & Unusual Form *Hemerocallis*. 1700+ different cvs can be viewed, mid Jun-mid Sep.
Notes: Mail order, daylilies only. Euro accepted. Wheelchair accessible.
Map Ref: S, D2

SPop **Pops Plants**
Pops Cottage, Barford Lane, Downton, Salisbury, Wiltshire SP5 3PZ
Ⓣ (01725) 511421
Ⓔ mail@popsplants.com
Ⓦ www.popsplants.com
Contact: Lesley Roberts
Opening Times: By appt. only, please.
Min Mail Order UK: 5 plants.
Min Mail Order EU: 5 plants.
Cat. Cost: £2.50
Credit Cards: Paypal
Specialities: *Primula auricula*. Some varieties in limited numbers. National Collection of Show, Alpine, Double & Striped Auriculas.
Notes: Credit cards accepted online only. Exports beyond EU (min. mail order outside EU 10 plants). Delivers to shows. Euro accepted.

SPpl **Popular Plants**
(Office) 13 River Gardens, Milford-on-Sea, Lymington, Hampshire SO41 0QA
Ⓣ (01590) 641218
Ⓜ 07563 603075
Ⓔ popularplants@gmail.com
Ⓦ www.popular-plants.co.uk
Contact: Chris Hammond
Opening Times: Not open. Mail order online only. For Open Days see website or phone nursery.
Min Mail Order UK: Nmc
Credit Cards: All major credit/debit cards

Specialities: *Lavandula* & herbs.
Notes: Nursery at Rodlease Rough Nursery, Rodlease Lane, Boldre, SO41 5PG. Also sells wholesale. Delivers to shows.

SPre **Plants4Presents ◆**
The Glasshouses, Fletching Common, Newick, Lewes, East Sussex
BN8 4JJ
Ⓣ (01825) 721162
Ⓔ plants@4presents.co.uk
Ⓦ www.plants4presents.co.uk
Contact: Emily Rae
Opening Times: Not open. Mail order only.
Min Mail Order UK: Nmc
Min Mail Order EU: Nmc
Cat. Cost: Online only.
Credit Cards: All major credit/debit cards
Specialities: Well-established nursery offering a range of unusual flowering and fruiting plants, incl. citrus trees.
Notes: Delivers to shows.

S

SPtp **Plantstoplant**
Fromefield Nurseries Ltd, Church Lane, Awbridge, Romsey, Hampshire
SO51 0HN
Ⓣ (01794) 341123
Ⓕ (01794) 341351
Ⓔ info@plantstoplant.com
Ⓦ www.plantstoplant.com
Contact: David West
Opening Times: Not open. Mail order only.
Min Mail Order UK: £12.00
Cat. Cost: Online only.
Credit Cards: All major credit/debit cards, Paypal
Specialities: Unusual plants.
Notes: Also sells wholesale.

SRea **Really Wild Flowers**
H V Horticulture Ltd, Glenwood, 55 Balcombe Road, Haywards Heath, West Sussex RH16 1PE
Ⓣ (01444) 413376
Ⓕ 0844 443 2503
Ⓔ info@reallywildflowers.co.uk
Ⓦ www.reallywildflowers.co.uk
Contact: Grahame Dixie
Opening Times: Not open. Mail order only.
Min Mail Order UK: £10 + p&p
Cat. Cost: 3 × 1st class.
Credit Cards: All major credit/debit cards
Specialities: Native wild flowers for grasslands, woodlands & wetlands. Seeds & bulbs. Hedge plants & trees. Advisory & soil analysis services.
Notes: Credit card payment accepted for online orders only. Also sells wholesale. Delivers to shows.

SReu **G Reuthe Ltd**
Crown Point Nursery, Sevenoaks Road, Ightham, Nr Sevenoaks, Kent TN15 0HB
Ⓣ (01732) 865614
Ⓔ reuthe@hotmail.co.uk
Contact: C & P Tomlin
Opening Times: 0900-1600 Thu-Sat. Closed Jan, Feb, Jul & Aug. Please phone before visiting as we are sometimes closed due to circumstances beyond our control. Please ask for details of special spring openings.
Min Mail Order UK: £30.00 + p&p
Credit Cards: Access, Visa
Specialities: Rhododendrons & azaleas, trees, shrubs & climbers. Some plants only available in larger sizes. Large specimen plants available in pots & open ground.
Notes: Landscaping & planting service.
Map Ref: S, C4

SRGP **Rosie's Garden Plants**
Fieldview Cottage, Pratling Street, Aylesford, Kent
ME20 7DG
Ⓣ (01622) 715777
Ⓜ 07740 696277
Ⓕ (01622) 715777
Ⓔ jcaviolet@aol.com
Ⓦ www.rosiesgardenplants.biz
Contact: J C Aviolet
Opening Times: Not open. Mail order only.
Min Mail Order UK: Nmc
Min Mail Order EU: Nmc
Cat. Cost: Online only.
Specialities: Hardy *Geranium*, *Buddleja* & *Aster*. Herbaceous & shrubs. Roses. Grows & sells asters, hardy geraniums, roses, plants & shrubs with people's names.
Notes: Exports beyond EU. Delivers to shows. Check web for dates of shows, talks & farmers' markets.

SRiv **River Garden Nurseries**
Troutbeck, Otford, Sevenoaks, Kent
TN14 5PH
Ⓣ (01959) 525588
Ⓕ (01959) 525810
Ⓔ box@river-garden.co.uk
Ⓦ www.river-garden.co.uk
Contact: Jenny Alban Davies
Opening Times: By appt. only.
Min Mail Order UK: £10.00 + p&p
Min Mail Order EU: £50.00 + p&p
Cat. Cost: 2 × 1st class.
Credit Cards: None
Specialities: *Buxus* species, cultivars & *Buxus* hedging. *Buxus* topiary.
Notes: Also sells wholesale. Euro accepted.
Map Ref: S, C4 **OS Grid Ref:** TQ523593

SRkn **RAPKYNS NURSERY** ♿
Street End Lane, Broad Oak, Heathfield, East Sussex TN21 8UB
Ⓣ (01825) 830065
Ⓜ 07771 916933
Ⓕ (01825) 830065
Ⓔ rapkyns@homecall.co.uk
Ⓦ www.rapkynsnursery.co.uk
Contact: Steven Moore
Opening Times: 1000-1700 Tue, Thu & Fri, Mar-Oct incl.
Min Mail Order UK: Nmc
Min Mail Order EU: Nmc
Cat. Cost: 2 × 1st class or online.
Credit Cards: None
Specialities: Unusual shrubs, perennials & climbers. Asters, campanulas, *Ceanothus*, geraniums, lavenders, *Clematis*, penstemons & grasses. New collections of *Crocosmia*, *Anemone*, *Heuchera*, *Heucherella*, *Phlox*, *Coreopsis* & *Helleborus*. Extensive range of salvias.
Notes: Nursery next door to Scotsford Farm, TN21 8UB. Mail order Sep-Apr incl. Also sells wholesale. Delivers to shows. Wheelchair accessible.
Map Ref: S, C4 **OS Grid Ref:** TQ604248

SRms **RUMSEY GARDENS** ♿
117 Drift Road, Clanfield, Waterlooville, Hampshire PO8 0PD
Ⓣ (023) 9259 3367
Ⓔ info@rumsey-gardens.co.uk
Ⓦ www.rumsey-gardens.co.uk
Contact: Mrs M A Giles
Opening Times: 0900-1700 Mon-Sat & 1000-1600 Sun & B/hols. Closed Sun Nov-Feb.
Min Mail Order UK: £15.00
Cat. Cost: Online only.
Credit Cards: American Express, MasterCard, Visa
Specialities: Wide general range. Herbaceous, alpines, heathers & ferns. National & International Collection of *Cotoneaster*.
Notes: Wheelchair accessible.
Map Ref: S, D2

SRot **ROTHERVIEW NURSERY** ♿
Ivy House Lane, Three Oaks, Hastings, East Sussex TN35 4NP
Ⓣ (01424) 756228
Ⓔ rotherview@btinternet.com
Ⓦ www.rotherview.com
Contact: Ray & Wendy Bates
Opening Times: 1000-1700 Mar-Oct, 1000-1530 Nov-Feb, 7 days.
Min Mail Order UK: Nmc
Min Mail Order EU: Nmc
Cat. Cost: 6 × 1st class.
Credit Cards: All major credit/debit cards
Specialities: Alpines. Ferns. *Camellia*.
Notes: Nursery is on same site as Coghurst Camellias. Also sells wholesale. Delivers to shows. Euro accepted. Wheelchair accessible.
Map Ref: S, D5

SSea **SEALE NURSERIES** ♿
Seale Lane, Seale, Farnham, Surrey GU10 1LD
Ⓣ (01252) 782410
Ⓔ catherine@sealenurseries.demon.co.uk
Ⓦ www.sealenurseries.co.uk
Contact: David & Catherine May
Opening Times: 1000-1600 Tue-Sat incl. Other times by appt. Closed 25th Dec-mid Jan.
Cat. Cost: None issued.
Credit Cards: Access, Delta, MasterCard, Visa
Specialities: Roses & *Pelargonium*. Some varieties in short supply, please phone first.
Notes: Wheelchair accessible.
Map Ref: S, C3 **OS Grid Ref:** SU887477

SSpi **SPINNERS GARDEN** ♿
School Lane, Boldre, Lymington, Hampshire SO41 5QE
Ⓣ (01590) 612196 (admin)
Ⓜ 07545 432090
Ⓔ info@spinnersgarden.co.uk
Ⓦ www.spinnersgarden.co.uk
Contact: Andrew Roberts
Opening Times: 1000-1700 Wed-Sat, Apr-Sep. Other times by appt. only.
Min Mail Order UK: £50.00
Cat. Cost: Online only.
Credit Cards: All major credit/debit cards
Specialities: Less common trees & shrubs esp. *Acer*, *Magnolia*, species & lacecap *Hydrangea*. Bog & woodland plants.
Notes: Limited mail order. Wheelchair accessible.

SSss **SELECT SEEDS** ♿
Paice Lane, Medstead, Nr Alton, Hampshire GU34 5PR
Ⓣ (01420) 560695
Ⓜ 07909 528191
Ⓕ (01420) 563640
Ⓔ marina@phoenixperennialplants.co.uk
Contact: Marina Christopher
Opening Times: Not open. Mail order only.
Min Mail Order UK: £10.00
Cat. Cost: 3 × 1st class.
Credit Cards: All major credit/debit cards
Specialities: Seeds. Unusual hardy perennial seed selection incl. many prairie plants & ornamental umbellifers. Genera incl. *Agastache*, *Angelica*, *Centaurea*, *Seseli*, *Sanguisorba* & *Silphium*.

Notes: Only sells seed by mail order. Credit cards not accepted by phone. Co-located with Phoenix Perennial Plants SPhx. Delivers to shows. Wheelchair accessible.
Map Ref: S, C2 **OS Grid Ref:** SU657362

SSta **Starborough Nursery** ♿
Starborough Road, Marsh Green, Edenbridge, Kent
TN8 5RB
Ⓣ (01732) 865614
Ⓔ starborough@hotmail.co.uk
Contact: C & P Tomlin
Opening Times: 0900-1600 Thu, Fri & Sat. Closed Jan, Jul & Aug.
Min Mail Order UK: £30.00 + p&p
Min Mail Order EU: Certain plants only to EU.
Credit Cards: Access, Visa
Specialities: Rare & unusual shrubs esp. *Daphne*, *Acer*, *Cercis*, rhododendrons & azaleas, *Magnolia* & *Nyssa*. Some plants only available in larger sizes.
Notes: Mail order only between Oct & Apr. Planting & landscaping services available. Wheelchair accessible.
Map Ref: S, C4

S

STPC **The Plant Company** ♿
Coolham Road, West Chiltington, Pulborough, West Sussex
RH20 2LH
Ⓣ (01403) 740100
Ⓔ sales@theplantco.co.uk
Ⓦ www.theplantco.co.uk
Contact: Tim Ricketts
Opening Times: 0900-1730 Mon-Sat.
Min Mail Order UK: £8.95
Min Mail Order EU: Nmc
Cat. Cost: Online only.
Credit Cards: MasterCard, Visa
Specialities: A range of herbaceous, shrubs and grasses.
Notes: Also sells wholesale. Delivers to shows. Wheelchair accessible.
Map Ref: S, C3 **OS Grid Ref:** TQ111196

STrG **Terrace Gardener**
8 Foxbush, Hildenborough, Kent
TN11 9HT
Ⓣ (01732) 832762
Ⓔ johan@terracegardener.com
Ⓦ www.terracegardener.co.uk
Contact: Mr J Hall
Opening Times: Not open. Mail order only, incl. online & by phone. Telephone orders 0930-1500 Mon-Fri.
Min Mail Order UK: Nmc
Cat. Cost: Online only
Credit Cards: All major credit/debit cards
Specialities: Patio plants & topiary trees. Container gardening. Architectural & hardy exotics.
Notes: Euro accepted.

SVen **Ventnor Botanic Garden** ♿
Undercliff Drive, Ventnor, Isle of Wight
PO38 1UL
Ⓣ (01983) 855397
Ⓔ sales@botanic.co.uk
Ⓦ www.botanic.co.uk
Contact: Jason Melia
Opening Times: 1000-1700 7 days, all year.
Min Mail Order UK: Nmc
Min Mail Order EU: Nmc
Cat. Cost: None issued
Credit Cards: All, except American Express
Specialities: Coastal, drought-tolerant, Mediterranean & southern hemisphere plants. Rare & esoteric half-hardy trees, shrubs & perennials.
Notes: Wheelchair accessible.
Map Ref: S, D2 **OS Grid Ref:** SZ548768

SVic **Victoriana Nursery Gardens** ♿
Challock, Ashford, Kent, TN25 4DG
Ⓣ (01233) 740529
Ⓕ 0203 292 1529
Ⓔ info@victoriananursery.co.uk
Ⓦ www.victoriananursery.co.uk
Contact: Serena Shirley
Opening Times: 0930-1630 (or dusk if sooner) Mon-Fri, 1030-1500 (or dusk if sooner) Sat.
Min Mail Order UK: Nmc
Cat. Cost: Free by post or online.
Credit Cards: All major credit/debit cards
Specialities: Heritage & unusual vegetable plants, seeds, fruit trees & bushes. Also 600+ varieties of *Fuchsia*.
Notes: Also sells wholesale. Wheelchair accessible.
Map Ref: S, C5 **OS Grid Ref:** TR018501

SWat **Water Meadow Nursery** ♿
Cheriton, Nr Alresford, Hampshire
SO24 0QB
Ⓣ (01962) 771895
Ⓔ plantaholic101@btinternet.com
Ⓦ www.plantaholic.co.uk
Contact: Mrs Sandy Worth
Opening Times: 1000-1700 Fri & Sat, 23rd Mar-28th Jul. Other times by prior telephone appt. only.
Min Mail Order UK: £10.00 + p&p
Min Mail Order EU: £50.00 + p&p
Cat. Cost: Full catalogue online only. 2 × 1st class for individual plant lists, please indicate with application.
Credit Cards: All major credit/debit cards

Specialities: Waterlilies, extensive water garden plants, unusual herbaceous perennials, aromatic herbs & wildflowers. National Collection of *Papaver orientale* Group. Re-blooming *Papaver* Super Poppy Series.
Notes: Mail order by 24 or 48 hour courier service only. Also sells wholesale. Exports beyond EU. Delivers to shows. Wheelchair accessible.
Map Ref: S, C2

SWCr **Wych Cross Nurseries** ♿
Wych Cross, Forest Row, East Sussex
RH18 5JW
Ⓣ (01342) 822705
Ⓕ (01342) 828246
Ⓔ jp@wychcross.co.uk
Ⓦ www.wychcross.co.uk
Contact: John Paisley
Opening Times: 0900-1730 Mon-Sat.
Min Mail Order UK: Nmc
Cat. Cost: Free
Credit Cards: All major credit/debit cards
Specialities: Roses.
Notes: Wheelchair accessible.
Map Ref: S, C4 **OS Grid Ref:** TQ420320

SWhi **John Hall Plants Ltd** ♿
Whitehall Nursery, Red Lane (Off Churt Road), Headley Down, Hampshire
GU35 8SR
Ⓣ (01428) 715505
Ⓜ 07714 344327
Ⓔ info@johnhallplants.com
Ⓦ www.johnhallplants.com
Contact: John Hall
Opening Times: 0900-1630 Mon-Fri, 0900-1300 Sat, by appt. only.
Min Mail Order UK: Nmc
Min Mail Order EU: Nmc
Cat. Cost: By email only.
Credit Cards: None
Specialities: *Erica*, *Calluna* & *Daboecia*.
Notes: Planting plans supplied. Also sells wholesale. Exports beyond EU. Euro accepted. Wheelchair accessible.
Map Ref: S, C3 **OS Grid Ref:** SU837371

SWvt **Wolverton Plants Ltd** ♿ ◆
Wolverton Common, Tadley, Hampshire
RG26 5RU
Ⓣ (01635) 298453
Ⓕ (01635) 299075
Ⓔ Julian@wolvertonplants.co.uk
Ⓦ www.wolvertonplants.co.uk
Contact: Julian Jones
Opening Times: 0900-1800 (or dusk Nov-Feb), 7 days. Closed Xmas/New Year.
Cat. Cost: Online only.
Credit Cards: All major credit/debit cards
Specialities: Wide range of herbaceous perennials & shrubs grown on a commercial scale for the public.
Notes: Horticultural club visits welcome by prior arrangement. Also sells wholesale. Euro accepted. Wheelchair accessible.
Map Ref: S, C2 **OS Grid Ref:** SU555589

Wales and the West

WAbe **Aberconwy Nursery**
Graig, Glan Conwy, Colwyn Bay, Conwy
LL28 5TL
Ⓣ (01492) 580875
Contact: Keith & Tim Lever
Opening Times: 1000-1600 Tue-Sun Mar-Sep incl.
Cat. Cost: 2 × 2nd class.
Credit Cards: MasterCard, Visa
Specialities: Alpines, incl. specialist varieties, esp. gentians, dionysias, dwarf *Dianthus*, *Primula*, *Saxifraga* & dwarf ericaceous plants. Some choice shrubs & woodland plants incl. smaller ferns.
Notes: Delivers to shows.
Map Ref: W, A3 **OS Grid Ref:** SH799744

WAln **L. A. Allen**
Windy Ridge, Llandrindod Wells, Powys
LD1 5NY
Ⓔ leslie.allen@mypostoffice.co.uk
Contact: Les Allen
Opening Times: Mail order only. Open by prior appt.
Min Mail Order UK: Nmc
Min Mail Order EU: Nmc
Cat. Cost: 6 × 1st class.
Credit Cards: None
Specialities: All sections of *Primula auricula*: alpine auricula, show-edged, show-self, doubles, show-stripe. Surplus plants from private collection so available in small quantities. Occasionally only 1 or 2 available of some cvs.
Notes: Also sells wholesale.

WAul **Aulden Farm**
Aulden, Leominster, Herefordshire
HR6 0JT
Ⓣ (01568) 720129
Ⓔ pf@auldenfarm.co.uk
Ⓦ www.auldenfarm.co.uk
Contact: Alun Whitehead
Opening Times: 1000-1700 Thu & Fri, Apr-Jul. Thu only in Aug-Sep.
Min Mail Order UK: £25.00
Cat. Cost: Online only.
Credit Cards: Paypal
Specialities: National Collection of Siberian *Iris*.

Notes: Three acre garden, also open to groups by arrangement. Talks given. If travelling some distance please email to check availability of plants.

WAvo **Pershore College of Horticulture**
Avonbank, Pershore, Worcestershire
WR10 3JP
Ⓣ (01386) 551149
Ⓔ plantcentre@warkscol.ac.uk
Ⓦ www.warwickshire.ac.uk/plantcentre
Contact: Jo Gildea
Opening Times: 0900-1700 Mon-Sat, 1000-1630 Sun (1600 in winter).
Cat. Cost: £1.00
Credit Cards: All major credit/debit cards
Specialities: National Collections of *Penstemon* & *Philadelphus*.
Notes: Also sells wholesale.
Map Ref: W, C5

W

WBla **Black Mountain Auriculas**
Whitegrove Nurseries, Fferm Gelliwen, Llanedi, Pontardulais, Swansea, West Glamorgan SA4 0FR
Ⓣ (01269) 832509
Ⓜ 07967 488782
Ⓕ (01269) 832509
Ⓔ whitegrovenurseries@tiscali.co.uk
Contact: Richard Williams
Opening Times: Mail order only. Open by prior appt. only.
Min Mail Order UK: Nmc
Min Mail Order EU: £50
Cat. Cost: Email for list.
Credit Cards: None
Specialities: *Primula auricula*. Many cultivars available in very small quantities only. Other species of *Primula* available, esp. *P. sieboldii*. *Hosta*, *Rhodohypoxis* & *Pleione* in small quantities.
Notes: Also sells wholesale. Delivers to shows. Euro accepted.
Map Ref: W, D3 **OS Grid Ref:** SN573083

WBod **Bodnant Garden Nursery** ♿
Tal-y-Cafn, Conwy, Gwynedd LL28 5RE
Ⓣ (01492) 650501
Ⓜ 07971 389771
Ⓕ (01492) 650863
Ⓔ sales@bodnant-plants.co.uk
Ⓦ www.bodnant-plants.co.uk
Contact: Graham Marsh
Opening Times: 0900-1730, 7 days. Closed Xmas Day, Boxing Day & New Year's Day.
Min Mail Order UK: £12.99
Cat. Cost: None issued.
Credit Cards: Connect, MasterCard, Switch, Visa
Specialities: *Rhododendron*, *Camellia*. Wide range of unusual trees and shrubs.
Notes: Wheelchair accessible. Also sells wholesale.

WBor **Bordervale Plants** ♿
Nantyderi, Sandy Lane, Ystradowen, Cowbridge, Vale of Glamorgan
CF71 7SX
Ⓣ (01446) 774036
Ⓔ lonytwod@gmail.com
Ⓦ www.bordervale.co.uk
Contact: Claire E Jenkins
Opening Times: 1000-1700 Fri-Sun & B/hols Mar-early Oct. Very often open Mon-Thu but please make an appt. on these days if travelling some distance.
Min Mail Order UK: £20.00 + p&p
Cat. Cost: 3 × 1st class.
Credit Cards: None
Specialities: Unusual herbaceous perennials, trees, shrubs & roses, as well as cottage garden plants, many displayed in the 2-acre garden.
Notes: Mail order available for smaller items, subject to season. Garden open May-Sep when nursery open. Also open for NGS. See website for details. Delivers to shows. Nursery wheelchair accessible.
Map Ref: W, D3 **OS Grid Ref:** ST022776

WBrk **Brockamin Plants** ♿
Brockamin, Old Hills, Callow End, Worcestershire WR2 4TQ
Ⓣ (01905) 830370
Ⓔ stone.brockamin@btinternet.com
Contact: Margaret Stone
Opening Times: By appt. only.
Cat. Cost: Free.
Credit Cards: None
Specialities: National Collections of *Aster novae-angliae*, *Erigeron* cvs, *Geranium sanguineum*, *G. macrorrhizum* & *G.* × *cantabrigiense*. Plants available in small quantities only.
Notes: Wheelchair accessible.
Map Ref: W, C5 **OS Grid Ref:** SO830488

WBuc **Bucknell Nurseries** ♿
Bucknell, Shropshire SY7 0EL
Ⓣ (01547) 530606
Ⓕ (01547) 530699
Ⓔ nickcoull@yahoo.co.uk
Contact: A N Coull
Opening Times: 0800-1700 Mon-Fri & 1000-1300 Sat.
Min Mail Order UK: Nmc
Cat. Cost: Free
Credit Cards: All major credit/debit cards
Specialities: Bare-rooted hedging conifers & forest trees.

Notes: Also sells wholesale. Wheelchair accessible.
Map Ref: W, C4 **OS Grid Ref:** SO356736

WCas **Castree's Garden Plants**
Bromsash (B4224), Ross-on-Wye, Herefordshire HR9 7PL
Ⓣ (01989) 750315
Ⓔ castrees@btconnect.com
Contact: Susan and Richard Edwards
Opening Times: 0900-1700 7 days, 1st Mar-1st Dec.
Credit Cards: All major credit/debit cards
Specialities: Good general range. Perennials, seasonal bedding plants & hanging baskets.

WCAu **Claire Austin Hardy Plants**
White Hopton Farm, Wern Lane, Sarn, Newtown, Powys SY16 4EN
Ⓣ (01686) 670342
Ⓔ enquiries@claireaustin-hardyplants.co.uk
Ⓦ www.claireaustin-hardyplants.co.uk
Contact: Claire Austin
Opening Times: Mail order only. Open during Jun when *Iris* field is in flower. See website for details.
Min Mail Order UK: Nmc
Min Mail Order EU: Nmc
Cat. Cost: UK free; Europe 5.00
Credit Cards: MasterCard, Switch, Visa
Specialities: *Paeonia*, *Iris*, *Hemerocallis* & hardy plants. National Collections of Bearded *Iris* & Hybrid Herbaceous *Paeonia*.
Notes: Euro accepted.

WCFE **Charles F Ellis**
Oak Piece Nurseries, Stanton, Nr Broadway, Worcestershire WR12 7NQ
Ⓣ (01386) 584077
Ⓕ (01386) 584491
Ⓔ ellisplants@cooptel.net
Ⓦ www.ellisplants.co.uk
Contact: Charles Ellis
Opening Times: 1000-1600 7 days, 1st Apr-30th Sep. Closed all of July
Min Mail Order UK: Nmc
Cat. Cost: None issued.
Credit Cards: All, except American Express
Specialities: Wide range of shrubs, conifers & climbers, some of them unusual. Some available in small quantities only.
Notes: Euro accepted.
Map Ref: W, C5

WChG **Chennels Gate Gardens & Nursery** ♿
Eardisley, Herefordshire HR3 6LT
Ⓣ (01544) 327288
Ⓔ mark.richard.dawson60@gmail.com
Contact: Mark Dawson
Opening Times: 1000-1700 7 days Mar-Oct.
Cat. Cost: None issued.
Credit Cards: None
Specialities: Interesting & unusual cottage garden plants, grasses & shrubs.
Notes: Wheelchair accessible.
Map Ref: W, C4

WCJW **CJ WildBird Foods Ltd** ♿
The Rea, Upton Magna, Shrewbury, Shropshire SY4 4UR
Ⓣ 0800 731 2820
Ⓕ (01743) 709505
Ⓔ sales@birdfood.co.uk
Ⓦ www.birdfood.co.uk
Contact: Martin George
Opening Times: 0900-1700, Mon-Fri, 0900-1200 Sat, closed Sun.
Min Mail Order UK: Nmc
Min Mail Order EU: Nmc
Cat. Cost: Free.
Credit Cards: All major credit/debit cards
Specialities: Perennials, bulbs, fruit bushes, climbers and roses. Also garden wildlife specialists.
Notes: For EU information see www.vivara.com. Euro accepted. Wheelchair accessible.
Map Ref: W, B4 **OS Grid Ref:** SJ568121

WCot **Cotswold Garden Flowers**
Sands Lane, Badsey, Evesham, Worcestershire WR11 7EZ
Ⓣ nursery: (01386) 833849 or mail order: (01386) 422829
Ⓜ 07812 833849
Ⓕ nursery: (01386) 49844
Ⓔ info@cgf.net
Ⓦ www.cgf.net
Contact: Mandie Potter, Bob Brown
Opening Times: 0900-1730 Mon-Fri, 1000-1730 Sat & Sun, 8th Mar-30th Sep. 0900-1630 Mon-Fri only, 1st Oct-7th Mar. Closed winter B/hols.
Min Mail Order UK: Nmc
Min Mail Order EU: Nmc
Cat. Cost: £1.50 or 6 × 1st class.
Credit Cards: All, except American Express
Specialities: A very wide range of easy & unusual perennials.
Notes: Also sells wholesale. Delivers to shows. Euro accepted. Limited wheelchair access.
Map Ref: W, C5 **OS Grid Ref:** SP077426

WCra **Cranesbill Nursery** ◆
Greenhayes, Upper Westmancote, Tewkesbury, Gloucestershire GL20 7ES
Ⓣ (01684) 773770
Ⓜ 07970 103168
Ⓔ john@cranesbillnursery.com

Ⓦ www.cranesbillnursery.com
Contact: John Dilks
Opening Times: Mail order only. Visitors by appt. only.
Min Mail Order UK: Nmc
Min Mail Order EU: Nmc
Cat. Cost: 4 × 1st class. Current availability list on request.
Credit Cards: Delta, MasterCard, Maestro, Visa, Paypal
Specialities: Specialist nursery offering a wide range of hardy geraniums. Some of the more unusual cvs available in small quantities.
Map Ref: W, C5 **OS Grid Ref:** SO940378

WCre **Crescent Plants** ♿
Stoney Cross, Marden,
Hereford, Herefordshire
HR1 3EW
Ⓣ (01432) 880262
Ⓜ 07990 970539
Ⓔ crescent@btinternet.com
Ⓦ www.auriculas.co.uk
Contact: June Poole
Opening Times: Open Days in Apr & May (contact nursery for details). Other times by appt. only. Essential to phone first.
Min Mail Order UK: Nmc
Min Mail Order EU: Nmc
Cat. Cost: Free
Credit Cards: Paypal
Specialities: Named varieties of *Primula auricula* incl. selfs, alpines, double, striped, edges, fancies & border types. Help & advice freely given. Own special recipe auricula compost available for collection only.
Notes: Payment by Paypal via website or send cheque with order. Wheelchair accessible.
Map Ref: W, C4 **OS Grid Ref:** SO525477

WCru **Crûg Farm Plants** ♿
Caernarfon, Gwynedd
LL55 1TU
Ⓣ (01248) 670232
Ⓜ 07774 980842
Ⓔ mailorder@crug-farm.co.uk
Ⓦ www.mailorder.crug-farm.co.uk
Contact: B. & S. Wynn-Jones
Opening Times: 0900-1630 Thu-Sat, last Thu in Mar to 3rd Sat in Sep, incl. Fri B/hol. Or all year Mon-Fri by appt.
Min Mail Order UK: Nmc
Min Mail Order EU: Nmc
Cat. Cost: Online only.
Credit Cards: All major credit/debit cards
Specialities: Unusual & rare incl. trees, shrubs, herbaceous & bulbous, mostly self-collected new introductions from the Far East & the Americas. Rare woody & climbers esp. *Acer, Araliaceae, Carpinus, Hydrangeaceae* & *Magnolia* with many other extraordinary introductions. Shade plants esp. *Asparagaceae, Convallariaceae, Liliaceae, Ranunculaceae* & *Saxifragaceae*. Many supplied bare-rooted. National Collections of *Coriaria, Paris* & *Polygonatum.*
Notes: Delivery by overnight carrier for UK & Ireland. Courier for rest of EU. Delivers to shows. Wheelchair accessible.
Map Ref: W, A2 **OS Grid Ref:** SH509652

WDib **Dibleys Nurseries** ♿ ◆
Llanelidan, Ruthin, Denbighshire LL15 2LG
Ⓣ (01978) 790677
Ⓕ (01978) 790668
Ⓔ sales@dibleys.com
Ⓦ www.dibleys.com
Contact: R Dibley
Opening Times: 1000-1700 7 days, Apr-Aug. 1000-1700 Mon-Fri, Mar, Sep & Oct.
Min Mail Order UK: Nmc
Min Mail Order EU: Nmc
Cat. Cost: Free
Credit Cards: Access, Electron, Solo, Switch, Visa
Specialities: *Streptocarpus, Columnea, Solenostemon, Saintpaulia* & other gesneriads & *Begonia.* National Collections of *Streptocarpus* & *Saintpaulia.*
Notes: Also sells wholesale. Euro accepted. Delivers to shows. Wheelchair accessible.
Map Ref: W, A3

WDra **Dragonfly Flora**
(Office) 7 Delfryn, Bryn, Llanelli,
Carmarthenshire SA14 9AF
Ⓜ 07885 643513
Ⓔ lewises@talktalk.net
Contact: Lew Lewis
Opening Times: By appt. only.
Min Mail Order UK: Nmc
Min Mail Order EU: Nmc
Specialities: Grasses, sedges and all UK native wetland & aquatic species..
Notes: Also sells wholesale. Delivers to shows.

WEuc **Hardy-Eucalyptus**
Grafton Nursery, Worcester Road, Grafton
Flyford, Worcester, Worcestershire
WR7 4PW
Ⓣ (01905) 888098
Ⓜ 07515 261511
Ⓔ office@hardy-eucalyptus.com
Ⓦ www.hardy-eucalyptus.com
Contact: Hilary Collins
Opening Times: Mail order only. Not open to the public but plants may be collected by appt. Phone or email to arrange a time.
Specialities: Garden-hardy *Eucalyptus.*
Notes: Also sells wholesale. Delivers to shows.

WFar **FARMYARD NURSERIES** ♿
Dol Llan Road, Llandysul, Carmarthenshire SA44 4RL
Ⓣ (01559) 363389
Ⓜ 01267 220259
Ⓕ (01559) 362200
Ⓔ sales@farmyardnurseries.co.uk
Ⓦ www.farmyardnurseries.co.uk
Contact: Richard Bramley
Opening Times: 0900-1700 7 days, excl. Xmas Day, Boxing Day & New Year's Day.
Min Mail Order UK: Nmc
Min Mail Order EU: Nmc
Cat. Cost: 4 × 1st class.
Credit Cards: MasterCard, Switch, Visa
Specialities: Large range of home grown shrubs & herbaceous perennials, incl. *Geranium*, *Helleborus* & *Primula*. Trees, shrubs, climbers, alpines, conifers & bedding plants.
Notes: Additionally sells from shop/yard in Carmarthen. Also sells wholesale. Euro accepted. Wheelchair accessible.
Map Ref: W, C2 **OS Grid Ref:** SN421406

WFib **FIBREX NURSERIES LTD** ♿
Honeybourne Road, Pebworth, Stratford-on-Avon, Warwickshire CV37 8XP
Ⓣ (01789) 720788
Ⓕ (01789) 721162
Ⓔ sales@fibrex.co.uk
Ⓦ www.fibrex.co.uk
Contact: U Key-Davis & R L Godard-Key
Opening Times: 0900-1700 Mon-Fri, 3rd Mar-29th Aug. 0900-1600 Mon-Fri, 1st Sep-27th Feb. 1030-1600 Sat & Sun,5th Apr-27th Jul. Closed last 2 weeks Dec & 1st week Jan. Closed Easter Sun & Aug B/hol Mon.
Min Mail Order UK: £10.00 + p&p
Min Mail Order EU: £20.00 + p&p
Cat. Cost: 3 × 1st class.
Credit Cards: MasterCard, Maestro, Visa
Specialities: *Hedera*, ferns, *Pelargonium*, named tuberous begonias. National Collections of *Pelargonium* & *Hedera*. Plant collections subject to time of year, please check by phone.
Notes: Also sells wholesale. Delivers to shows. Wheelchair accessible.
Map Ref: W, C5 **OS Grid Ref:** SP133458

WGoo **WILDEGOOSE NURSERY HOME OF BOUTS VIOLAS**
12 Beambridge Cottage, Millichope, Munslow, Craven Arms, Shropshire SY7 9HD
Ⓣ (01584) 841890
Ⓜ 07717 265212
Ⓔ flowers@boutsviolas.co.uk
Ⓦ www.boutsviolas.co.uk
Contact: Laura Crowe
Opening Times: Mail order only. Open strictly by appt. only.
Min Mail Order UK: Nmc
Min Mail Order EU: Nmc
Cat. Cost: 1st class sae.
Credit Cards: All major credit/debit cards
Specialities: *Viola*.
Notes: Taken over *Viola* stock from Bouts Cottage Nursery. Delivers to shows. Euro accepted.

WGor **GORDON'S NURSERY** ♿
1 Cefnpennar Cottages, Cefnpennar, Mountain Ash, Mid-Glamorgan CF45 4EE
Ⓣ (01443) 474593
Ⓕ (01443) 475835
Ⓔ sales@gordonsnursery.co.uk
Ⓦ www.gordonsnursery.co.uk
Contact: D A Gordon
Opening Times: 1000-1800 7 days Mar-Jun. 1000-1700 7 days Jul-Oct. 1100-1600 weekends only Nov & Feb. Closed Dec-Jan.
Min Mail Order UK: Nmc
Cat. Cost: 3 × 1st class.
Credit Cards: All major credit/debit cards
Specialities: Shrubs, perennials, alpines & dwarf conifers. Some plants available in small quantities only.
Notes: Mail order only available in some cases, please check for conditions in catalogue. Delivers to shows. Wheelchair accessible.
Map Ref: W, D3 **OS Grid Ref:** SO037012

WGrn **GREEN'S LEAVES** ♿
36 Ford House Road, Newent, Gloucestershire GL18 1LQ
Ⓣ (01531) 820154
Ⓜ 07890 413036
Ⓔ r.paul.green@hotmail.co.uk
Ⓦ www.greensleavesnursery.co.uk
Contact: Paul Green
Opening Times: By appt. only. Please phone to arrange.
Min Mail Order UK: £10.00 + p&p
Cat. Cost: 4 × 2nd class.
Credit Cards: None
Specialities: Range of rare & choice shrubs, also some perennials. Ornamental grasses, sedges & phormiums.
Notes: Also sells wholesale. Delivers to shows. Wheelchair accessible.
Map Ref: W, C4 **OS Grid Ref:** SO732273

WGwG **GWYNFOR GROWERS**
Gwynfor, Pontgarreg, Llangrannog, Llandysul, Ceredigion SA44 6AU
Ⓣ (01239) 654151
Ⓔ info@gwynfor.co.uk
Ⓦ www.gwynfor.co.uk
Contact: Steve & Angie Hipkin

Opening Times: Usually 1000-1800 or sunset if earlier, Wed, Thu & Sun, all year round.
Min Mail Order UK: Nmc
Cat. Cost: PDF list available by email.
Credit Cards: Paypal
Specialities: National Collection of *Rosmarinus* cvs. Specialist supplier of Welsh fruit trees. Classic & contemporary plants grown organically & peat-free. Some plants available in small quantities only. Rarities propagated to order.
Notes: Plants also available at local farmers' markets, plant fairs & some NGS Open Gardens. Delivers to shows.
Map Ref: W, C2 **OS Grid Ref:** SN331536

WHal **Hall Farm Nursery**
Vicarage Lane, Kinnerley, Nr Oswestry, Shropshire SY10 8DH
Ⓣ (01691) 682135
Ⓔ info@hallfarmnursery.co.uk
Ⓦ www.hallfarmnursery.co.uk
Contact: Christine & Nick Ffoulkes-Jones
Opening Times: 1000-1700, Tues-Sat, 1st Mar-4th Oct 2014.
Min Mail Order UK: £20.00 +p&p
Cat. Cost: Online only.
Credit Cards: Electron, MasterCard, Maestro, Visa
Specialities: Wide range of herbaceous perennials, woodland plants, alpine & scree plants.
Notes: Partially accessible for wheelchairs.
Map Ref: W, B4 **OS Grid Ref:** SJ333209

WHar **Harley Nursery** ♿
Harley, Shrewsbury, Shropshire SY5 6LN
Ⓣ (01952) 510241
Ⓔ plants@harleynursery.co.uk
Ⓦ www.harleynursery.co.uk
Contact: Nick Murphy & Debbie Plant
Opening Times: 0900-1730 Mon-Sat, 1000-1600 Sun & B/hols. Winter hours 0830-1630 Mon-Sat, 1000-1600 Sun & B/hols.
Min Mail Order UK: £50.00
Cat. Cost: Online only.
Credit Cards: All major credit/debit cards
Specialities: Wide range of trees & shrubs. Large selection of fruit trees & bushes, many old & unusual varieties. Seasonal selection of conifers, climbing & herbaceous plants. Wide range of hedging & forestry plants, many available bare-root.
Notes: Wheelchair accessible.
Map Ref: W, B4 **OS Grid Ref:** SJ598020

WHCr **Hergest Croft Gardens**
Kington, Herefordshire HR5 3EG
Ⓣ (01544) 230160
Ⓜ 07968 435627
Ⓕ (01544) 232031
Ⓔ gardens@hergest.co.uk
Ⓦ www.hergest.co.uk
Contact: Stephen Lloyd
Opening Times: 1200-1730, 7 days, Apr-Oct.
Cat. Cost: None issued
Credit Cards: All major credit/debit cards
Specialities: *Acer*, *Betula* & unusual woody plants.
Notes: Limited wheelchair access.

WHea **Heath Garden** ♿
Heath Hill, Sheriffhales, Shifnal, Shropshire TF11 8RR
Ⓣ (01952) 691341
Ⓔ 1malt@supanet.com
Contact: Gordon Malt
Opening Times: 1000-1800 Tues, Apr-Sep. Other times by appt.
Cat. Cost: None issued.
Credit Cards: None
Specialities: Interesting range of hardy & tender perennials. *Geranium*, *Salvia*, ornamental grasses & silver foliage plants. Bulbous plants.
Notes: Plants available in small quantities only. Talks & demonstrations to horticultural clubs. Garden open for groups by appt. Wheelchair accessible.
Map Ref: W, B5 **OS Grid Ref:** SJ376313

WHer **The Herb Garden & Historical Plant Nursery**
Frondeg, Gilfachreda, New Quay, Ceredigion SA45 9SP
Ⓣ (01545) 580893
Ⓔ corinnetremaine@gmail.com
Ⓦ www.HistoricalPlants.co.uk
Contact: Corinne Tremaine
Opening Times: By appt. only.
Min Mail Order UK: £15.00 + p&p
Min Mail Order EU: £50.00 + p&p sterling only.
Cat. Cost: Online only.
Credit Cards: None
Specialities: Rarer herbs, rare natives & wild flowers; rare & unusual & historical perennials & old roses.

WHfH **Herbs for Healing** ♿
Barnsley Herb Garden, Barnsley, Nr Cirencester, Gloucestershire GL7 5EE
Ⓣ (01285) 740638
Ⓜ 07773 687493
Ⓔ herbs@herbsforhealing.net
Ⓦ www.herbsforhealing.net
Contact: Davina Wynne-Jones
Opening Times: 1000-1700 Wed, mid Apr-Sep, or by appt.

Min Mail Order UK: Nmc
Credit Cards: Paypal
Specialities: Medicinal & some culinary herbs. Display garden.
Notes: Nursery in Clapton's Lane, Barnsley, behind Barnsley House Hotel. See web for directions. Courses and workshops on use of herbs. Sells at local farmers markets. Euro accepted. Wheelchair accessible.
Map Ref: W, D5 **OS Grid Ref:** SP048177

WHil **Hillview Hardy Plants** ♿
(off B4176) Worfield, Nr Bridgnorth, Shropshire WV15 5NT
Ⓣ (01746) 716454
Ⓜ 07974 391608
Ⓕ (01746) 716454
Ⓔ hillview@onetel.net
Ⓦ www.hillviewhardyplants.com
Contact: Ingrid, John & Sarah Millington
Opening Times: 0900-1700 Mon-Sat Mar-mid Oct. At other times, please phone first.
Min Mail Order UK: £10.00 + p&p
Min Mail Order EU: £10.00 + p&p
Cat. Cost: Online only.
Credit Cards: All major credit/debit cards
Specialities: Choice herbaceous perennials incl. *Acanthus* & *Acanthaceae*, *Albuca*, *Aquilegia*, auricula, *Primula*, *Canna*, *Crocosmia*, *Eucomis*, *Ixia*, South African bulbs. National Collections of *Acanthus* & *Albuca*.
Notes: Also sells wholesale. Exports beyond EU. Delivers to shows. Euro accepted. Wheelchair accessible.
Map Ref: W, B4 **OS Grid Ref:** SO772969

WHlf **Hayloft Plants**
Manor Farm, Pensham, Pershore, Worcestershire WR10 3HB
Ⓣ (01386) 554440 or (01386) 562999
Ⓕ (01386) 553833
Ⓔ info@hayloftplants.co.uk
Ⓦ www.hayloftplants.co.uk
Contact: Yvonne Walker
Opening Times: Not open. Mail order only.
Min Mail Order UK: Nmc
Min Mail Order EU: Nmc
Cat. Cost: Free.
Credit Cards: All major credit/debit cards

WHod **Hodgehill Nursery** ♿
Birmingham Road, Kidderminster, Worcestershire DY10 3Nr
Ⓣ (01562) 822058
Ⓔ hodgehill-ltd@btconnect.com
Ⓦ www.hodgehill-ltd.co.uk
Contact: Bev Gerrard
Opening Times: 0830-1730 Mon-Sat, 1030-1630 Sun.
Credit Cards: All major credit/debit cards
Notes: Also sells wholesale. Wheelchair accessible.
Map Ref: W, C5 **OS Grid Ref:** SO857773

WHoo **Hoo House Nursery** ◆
Hoo House, Gloucester Road, Tewkesbury, Gloucestershire GL20 7DA
Ⓣ (01684) 293389
Ⓕ (01684) 293389
Ⓔ nursery@hoohouse.co.uk
Ⓦ www.hoohouse.co.uk
Contact: Robin & Julie Ritchie
Opening Times: 1000-1700 Mon-Sat, 1100-1700 Sun.
Cat. Cost: 3 × 1st class.
Credit Cards: All major credit/debit cards
Specialities: Wide range of herbaceous & alpines grown peat-free. *Aster*, *Cyclamen*, *Geranium*, *Penstemon* & many later-flowering varieties. National Collections of *Platycodon* & *Gentiana asclepiadea* cvs.
Notes: Also sells wholesale. Euro accepted. Partially wheelchair accessible.
Map Ref: W, C5 **OS Grid Ref:** SO893293

WHor **Horticultural Sales**
Upper Brockington, Berrington Street, Bodenham, Herefordshire HR1 3HT
Ⓣ (01568) 797747
Ⓜ 07966 635005
Ⓕ (01568) 600484
Ⓔ pdavies@hortsales.fsnet.co.uk
Ⓦ www.hortplants.co.uk
Contact: Peter Davies
Opening Times: By appt. only.
Min Mail Order UK: Nmc
Min Mail Order EU: Nmc
Cat. Cost: Free but available by email only.
Credit Cards: Paypal
Specialities: Wide selection of less commonly grown shrubs, available in small quantities only.
Notes: Plant finding service. 38 years experience in trade. Also sells wholesale. Euro accepted.

WHrl **Harrells Hardy Plants**
(Office) 15 Coxlea Close, Evesham, Worcestershire WR11 4JS
Ⓣ (01386) 443077
Ⓜ 07799 577120 or 07733 446606
Ⓔ mail@harrellshardyplants.co.uk
Ⓦ www.harrellshardyplants.co.uk
Contact: Liz Nicklin & Kate Phillips
Opening Times: By appt. only. Please telephone.
Min Mail Order UK: Nmc

Cat. Cost: Online plant list.
Credit Cards: None
Specialities: Display gardens showcase wide range of hardy perennials, esp. *Hemerocallis* & grasses.
Notes: Nursery located off Rudge Rd, Evesham. Please phone for directions or see website. Mail order Nov-Mar only. Partial wheelchair access.
Map Ref: W, C5 **OS Grid Ref:** SP033443

WIce **Ice Alpines** ♿
Lyehead, Bewdley, Worcestershire DY12 2UW
Ⓣ (01299) 269219
Ⓕ (01562) 510003
Ⓔ icealpines@gmail.com
Ⓦ www.Icealpines.co.uk
Contact: Mark Lagomarsino
Opening Times: Mail order. Open by appt. only.
Min Mail Order UK: Nmc
Min Mail Order EU: £18
Credit Cards: Paypal
Specialities: British grown alpine & rockery plants.
Notes: Delivers to shows. Wheelchair accessible.

WJas **Paul Jasper Trees**
(Office) The Lighthouse, Bridge Street, Leominster, Herefordshire HR6 8DX
Ⓕ (01568) 616499 for orders.
Ⓔ jaspertreescouk@aol.com
Ⓦ www.jaspertrees.co.uk
Contact: Paul Jasper
Opening Times: Not open. Mail order only.
Min Mail Order UK: £20.00 + p&p
Cat. Cost: Online only.
Credit Cards: All major credit/debit cards
Specialities: Full range of fruit & ornamental trees. Over 100 modern and traditional fruit tree varieties plus 100 ornamental tree varieties, all direct from the grower. Many unusual varieties of *Malus domestica* & *Prunus*.
Notes: Regular updates & notes on website. Also sells wholesale. Delivers to shows.
Map Ref: W, C4 **OS Grid Ref:** SO495595

WJek **Jekka's Herb Farm** ♿
Rose Cottage, Shellards Lane, Alveston, Bristol, South Gloucestershire BS35 3SY
Ⓣ (01454) 418878
Ⓕ (01454) 424907
Ⓔ sales@jekkasherbfarm.com
Ⓦ www.jekkasherbfarm.com
Contact: Jekka McVicar
Opening Times: Please check website or phone nursery for dates.
Min Mail Order UK: £10.00
Min Mail Order EU: Charges per order on application.
Cat. Cost: Online only.
Credit Cards: Delta, MasterCard, Maestro, Visa
Specialities: Culinary, medicinal, aromatic, decorative herbs.
Notes: Only sell seeds via mail order. Plants can be ordered for collection from the farm with 24 hours notice. Wheelchair accessible.
Map Ref: W, D4

WJPR **JPR Environmental**
The Malt House, Standish, Stonehouse, Gloucestershire GL10 3DL
Ⓣ (01453) 811537
Ⓔ enquiries@jprenvironmental.co.uk
Ⓦ www.jprwillow.co.uk
Contact: John Robinthwaite
Opening Times: Mail order only. 0900-1700.
Min Mail Order UK: £6.00
Credit Cards: All, except American Express
Specialities: *Salix*.
Notes: Also sells wholesale.

WJun **Jungle Giants** ♿
Ferney, Onibury, Craven Arms, Shropshire SY7 9BJ
Ⓣ (01584) 856200
Ⓕ (01584) 856663
Ⓔ bamboo@junglegiants.co.uk
Ⓦ www.junglegiants.co.uk
Contact: Michael Brisbane
Opening Times: 7 days. By appt. only please.
Min Mail Order UK: £25.00 + p&p
Min Mail Order EU: £100.00 + p&p
Cat. Cost: Online only.
Credit Cards: Access, MasterCard, Visa
Specialities: Bamboos.
Notes: Also sells wholesale. Exports beyond EU. Euro accepted. Wheelchair accessible.
Map Ref: W, C4 **OS Grid Ref:** SO430779

WKif **Kiftsgate Court Gardens** ♿
Kiftsgate Court, Chipping Camden, Gloucestershire GL55 6LN
Ⓣ (01386) 438777
Ⓕ (01386) 438777
Ⓔ anne@kiftsgate.co.uk
Ⓦ www.kiftsgate.co.uk
Contact: Mrs J Chambers
Opening Times: 1200-1800 Sat-Wed, May, Jun & Jul. 1400-1800 Sat-Wed, Aug. 1400-1800 Sun, Mon & Wed, Apr & Sep.
Cat. Cost: None issued
Credit Cards: All, except American Express
Specialities: Small range of unusual plants.
Notes: Wheelchair accessible.
Map Ref: W, C5 **OS Grid Ref:** SP170430

WLav **The Lavender Garden**
Ashcroft Nurseries, Nr Ozleworth, Kingscote, Tetbury, Gloucestershire GL8 8YF
Ⓣ (01453) 860356 or 549286
Ⓜ 07837 582943
Ⓔ Andrew007Bullock@aol.com
Ⓦ www.TheLavenderG.co.uk
Contact: Andrew Bullock
Opening Times: 1100-1700 Sat & Sun. Weekdays variable, please phone. 1st Nov-1st Mar by appt. only.
Min Mail Order UK: £10.00 + p&p
Min Mail Order EU: £20.00 + p&p
Cat. Cost: 2 × 1st class.
Credit Cards: All major credit/debit cards
Specialities: *Lavandula*, *Buddleja*, plants to attract butterflies. Herbs, wildflowers. National Collection of *Buddleja*.
Notes: Also sells wholesale. Delivers to shows.
Map Ref: W, D5 **OS Grid Ref:** ST798948

WMAq **Merebrook Water Plants**
Kingfisher Barn, Merebrook Farm, Hanley Swan, Worcestershire WR8 0DX
Ⓣ (01684) 310950
Ⓜ 07876 777066
Ⓔ enquiries@pondplants.co.uk
Ⓦ www.pondplants.co.uk
Contact: Roger Kings & Biddi Kings
Opening Times: Not open. Mail order only.
Min Mail Order UK: Nmc
Min Mail Order EU: £25.00
Cat. Cost: Online only.
Credit Cards: All major credit/debit cards
Specialities: *Nymphaea*, Louisiana irises & other aquatic plants. International Waterlily & Water Gardening Soc. accredited collection.

WMat **The Tree Shop** ♿
Frank P Matthews Ltd, Berrington Court, Tenbury Wells, Worcestershire WR15 8TH
Ⓣ (01584) 812800
Ⓕ (01584) 811830
Ⓔ treeshop@fpmatthews.co.uk
Ⓦ www.frankpmatthews.com
Contact: Steve Grosvenor
Opening Times: 0730-1700 Mon-Fri
Cat. Cost: 4 × 1st class.
Credit Cards: All major credit/debit cards
Specialities: Fruit & deciduous ornamental Trees.
Notes: Also sells wholesale. Wheelchair accessible.
Map Ref: W, C4 **OS Grid Ref:** SO571676

WMil **Anne Milner**
Meadow House, Baunton, Cirencester, Gloucestershire GL7 7BB
Ⓣ (01285) 643731
Ⓔ anne.milner@btinternet.com
Ⓦ www.blissiris.co.uk
Contact: Anne Milner
Opening Times: By appt. only.
Min Mail Order UK: Nmc
Min Mail Order EU: Nmc
Cat. Cost: 50p (UK) £1.00 (EU) to cover postage.
Credit Cards: None
Specialities: National Collection of *Iris* (A.J. Bliss introductions). Available in small quantities only.
Notes: Euro accepted. Delivers to some shows, check with nursery.

WMnd **Mynd Hardy Plants Ltd** ♿
Delbury Hall Estate, Diddlebury, Craven Arms, Shropshire SY7 9DH
Ⓣ (01584) 841222
Ⓔ myndhardyplants@aol.com
Ⓦ www.myndplants.co.uk
Contact: Richard & Jill Rallings
Opening Times: 1300-1700 Wed-Fri, 1000-1700 Sat, 16th Mar-14th Sep. 1300-1700 B/Hol Mons. 1300-1700 Sun May-Jul. Other times, phone for appt.
Cat. Cost: 4 × 2nd class.
Credit Cards: All major credit/debit cards
Specialities: Herbaceous plants, specialising in American bred, British grown, *Hemerocallis*. Home to New Hope Garden's *Hemerocallis* plants.
Notes: Also sells wholesale. Wheelchair accessible.
Map Ref: W, B4 **OS Grid Ref:** SO510852

WMoo **Moorland Cottage Plants**
Rhyd-y-Groes, Brynberian, Crymych, Pembrokeshire SA41 3TT
Ⓣ (01239) 891363
Ⓦ www.moorlandcottageplants.co.uk
Contact: Jennifer Matthews
Opening Times: 1030-1730 daily excl. Wed 1st Mar-30th Sep.
Min Mail Order UK: £35.00
Cat. Cost: 4 × 1st class.
Credit Cards: All major credit/debit cards
Specialities: Traditional & unusual hardy perennials. Many garden-worthy rarities. Cottage garden plants, ferns & many shade plants, moisture lovers, ornamental grasses, colourful ground cover.
Notes: Display garden open for NGS from mid-May to end Sep. Partial wheelchair access.
Map Ref: W, C2 **OS Grid Ref:** SN091343

WMou **Mount Pleasant Trees** ♿
Rockhampton, Berkeley, Gloucestershire GL13 9DU
Ⓣ (01454) 260348
Ⓔ info@mountpleasanttrees.com

Ⓦ www.mountpleasanttrees.com
Contact: Tom Locke & Elizabeth Murphy
Opening Times: 0830-1630 Mon-Fri, 0830-1230 Sat, Oct-Apr.
Min Mail Order UK: Nmc but p&p quoted on individual basis.
Cat. Cost: Free.
Credit Cards: All major credit/debit cards
Specialities: Wide range of trees for forestry, hedging, woodlands & gardens esp. *Populus, Salix, Tilia* & *Quercus*.
Notes: Mail order available for plants under 1m in height, quotes on request. Also sells wholesale. Wheelchair accessible.
Map Ref: W, D4 **OS Grid Ref:** ST654929

WNHG **NEW HOPE GARDENS** ♿
(Office) The Old Chapel, Cefn Einion, Nr Bishops Castle, Shropshire SY9 5LF
Ⓣ Office: (01588) 630750 or Nursery: (01584) 841222
Ⓔ Newhopegardensmz@aol.com
Ⓦ www.newhopegardens.com
Contact: Mark Zenick
Opening Times: 1300-1700 Wed-Fri, 1000-1700 Sat, 22nd Mar-28th Sep. 1300-1700 B/hol Mons during season. 1300-1700 Sun, May-Sep. Other times phone nursery for appt. Daylily Open W/ends: 28th/29th Jun, 5th/6th Jul, 12th/13th Jul, 19th/20th Jul. (NGS Open Days: 1300-1700, 8th & 20th Jul.)
Min Mail Order UK: Nmc
Min Mail Order EU: Nmc
Cat. Cost: Online only. Plant list on request.
Credit Cards: All major credit/debit cards
Specialities: American bred, British grown, *Hemerocallis*. Ships bare-rooted plants. Daylily plants are growing and for sale at Mynd Hardy Plants.
Notes: Nursery co-located with Mynd Hardy Plants (code WMnd). Wheelchair accessible.
Map Ref: W, B4 **OS Grid Ref:** SO510852

WNPC **NEWENT PLANT CENTRE** ♿
Ledbury Road, Newent, Gloucestershire GL18 1DL
Ⓣ (01531) 828488
Ⓕ (01531) 828488
Ⓔ markmoir999@btinternet.com
Ⓦ www.newentplantcentre.co.uk
Contact: Mark Moir
Opening Times: 0900-1700 Mon-Sat, 1000-1600 Sun. Closed Jan.
Credit Cards: All major credit/debit cards
Specialities: Extensive range of *Heuchera* & *Euphorbia*. Herbaceous perennials, climbers, shrubs, trees, alpines, herbs, roses & fruit.
Notes: Delivers to shows. Wheelchair accessible.
Map Ref: W, C4 **OS Grid Ref:** SO716282

WOld **OLD COURT NURSERIES**
Colwall, Nr Malvern, Worcestershire WR13 6QE
Ⓣ (01684) 540416
Ⓜ 07971 522891
Ⓔ oldcourtnurseries@btinternet.com
Ⓦ www.autumnasters.co.uk
Contact: Paul, Meriel or Helen Picton
Opening Times: 1400-1700 Wed-Sat, May-Aug. 1100-1700 Wed-Sun, Aug. 1100-1700 7 days, 1st week Sep-2nd week Oct. Also by appt. May to Oct.
Min Mail Order UK: Nmc
Min Mail Order EU: Nmc
Credit Cards: None
Specialities: National Collection of Michaelmas Daisies. Herbaceous perennials.
Notes: Mail order sent in spring only. Display garden open Aug-Oct.
Map Ref: W, C4 **OS Grid Ref:** SO759430

WOth **OTHER FELLOW FUCHSIAS**
25 Spring Meadow Road, Lydney, Gloucestershire GL15 5LF
Ⓣ (01594) 844452
Ⓜ 07564 357637
Ⓔ info@otherfellow.co.uk
Ⓦ otherfellow.co.uk
Contact: Nick Egginton
Opening Times: Not open. Mail order only.
Min Mail Order UK: Nmc
Min Mail Order EU: £10.50 + p&p
Cat. Cost: Free.
Credit Cards: All major credit/debit cards
Specialities: Expanding collection of *Fuchsia*, esp. unusual, single & exhibition varieties. Small selection of *Salvia* & other tender perennials. Some stock available in small quantities only. Can propagate to order.
Notes: Exports beyond EU. Euro accepted.

WOut **OUT OF THE COMMON WAY**
(Office) Penhyddgan, Boduan, Pwllheli, Gwynedd LL53 8YH
Ⓣ office: (01758) 721577 or nursery: (01407) 720431
Ⓔ ziggymen22@hotmail.co.uk
Contact: Joanna Davidson (nursery) Margaret Mason (office & mail order)
Opening Times: By arrangement.
Min Mail Order UK: Nmc
Min Mail Order EU: Nmc
Cat. Cost: A5 sae (large letter rate postage).
Credit Cards: None
Specialities: *Labiates*, esp. *Nepeta* & *Salvia*. *Aster, Geranium* & *Crocosmia*. Native plants. Some plants propagated in small quantities only. Will propagate salvias to order.
Notes: Nursery is at Pandy Treban, Bryngwran, Anglesey. Delivers to shows.

W

Euro accepted. Partially accessible for wheelchairs.
Map Ref: W, A2 **OS Grid Ref:** SH370778

WPat **Chris Pattison** ♿
Brookend, Pendock, Gloucestershire
GL19 3PL
Ⓣ (01531) 650480
Ⓕ (01531) 650480
Ⓔ cp@chris-pattison.co.uk
Ⓦ www.chris-pattison.co.uk
Contact: Chris Pattison
Opening Times: 0900-1700 Mon-Fri. W/ends by appt. only.
Min Mail Order UK: £10.00 +p&p
Cat. Cost: 3 × 1st class.
Credit Cards: None
Specialities: Choice rare shrubs & trees. Grafted stock esp. Japanese maples & *Liquidambar*. Wide range of *Viburnum* & dwarf/miniature trees & shrubs suitable for bonsai or rockery.
Notes: Mail order Nov-Feb only. Also sells wholesale. Euro accepted. Wheelchair accessible.
Map Ref: W, C5 **OS Grid Ref:** SO781327

WPGP **Pan-Global Plants** ♿
The Walled Garden, Frampton Court, Frampton-on-Severn, Gloucestershire
GL2 7EX
Ⓣ (01452) 741641
Ⓜ 07801 275138
Ⓔ info@panglobalplants.com
Ⓦ www.panglobalplants.com
Contact: Nick Macer
Opening Times: 1100-1700 Wed-Sun 1st Feb-31st Oct. Also B/hols. Closed 2nd Sun in Sep. Winter months by appt., please phone first.
Min Mail Order UK: £15.00
Min Mail Order EU: £15.00
Cat. Cost: 6 × 1st class.
Credit Cards: Delta, Maestro, MasterCard, Solo, Visa
Specialities: A plantsman's nursery offering a very wide selection of correctly named rare & desirable trees, shrubs, herbaceous, bamboos, exotics, climbers, ferns etc. Specialities incl. *Magnolia*, *Hydrangea*, *Tilia*, *Betula*, *Sorbus*, *Bamboo* & *Agavaceae*.
Notes: Wheelchair accessible.
Map Ref: W, D5 **OS Grid Ref:** SO750080

WPhe **Pheasant Acre Plants**
3 Pheasant Walk, Pen-y-Fai, Bridgend, Mid Glamorgan CF31 4DU
Ⓣ (01656) 664086
Ⓜ 07816 236462
Ⓔ sales@pheasantacreplants.co.uk
Ⓦ www.pheasantacreplants.co.uk
Contact: Rob Evans
Opening Times: Nursery visits by appt. only and on Open Days.
Min Mail Order UK: Nmc
Min Mail Order EU: Nmc
Cat. Cost: £1.00
Credit Cards: All major credit/debit cards
Specialities: Bulbous. Ornamental. *Gladiolus*.
Notes: Delivers to shows. Euro accepted.

WPnn **The Perennial Nursery**
Rhosygilwen, St Davids, Haverfordwest, Pembrokeshire SA62 6DB
Ⓣ (01437) 721954
Ⓜ 07717 783492
Ⓔ theperennialnursery@tesco.net
Ⓦ www.droughttolerantplants.co.uk
Contact: Mrs Philipa Symons
Opening Times: 1030-1700 Mar-Oct. Closed Tue.
Min Mail Order UK: Nmc
Min Mail Order EU: Nmc
Cat. Cost: Online only.
Credit Cards: MasterCard, Visa
Specialities: *Lampranthus*, wind & drought-tolerant plants.
Notes: Tea room.
Map Ref: W, C1 **OS Grid Ref:** SM775292

WPnP **Penlan Perennials** ♿
Wern Rhos, Newchapel, Boncath, Pembrokeshire SA37 0EN
Ⓣ (01239) 842260
Ⓜ 07857 675312
Ⓔ info@penlanperennials.co.uk
Ⓦ www.penlanperennials.co.uk
Contact: Richard Cain
Opening Times: Open for collection of orders & by appt..
Min Mail Order UK: Nmc
Min Mail Order EU: Nmc
Cat. Cost: Online PDF, or sae for CD-ROM.
Credit Cards: All major credit/debit cards
Specialities: Aquatic, marginal & bog plants. Shade-loving & woodland perennials, ferns & hardy geraniums, all grown organically in peat-free compost.
Notes: Mail order all year, next day delivery. Secure online web ordering. Also sells wholesale. Euro accepted. Wheelchair accessible. Delivers to shows.
Map Ref: W, C2 **OS Grid Ref:** SN217392

WPos **Poshplants**
Glanaber, Waunfawr, Caernarfon, Gwynedd
LL55 4EZ
Ⓔ na.horticulture@btinternet.com
Ⓦ www.poshplants.biz
Contact: Neil Alcock

Opening Times: Not open. Mail order online only.
Min Mail Order UK: Nmc
Min Mail Order EU: £6.00
Cat. Cost: Online only.
Credit Cards: Paypal
Specialities: Unusual perennials. Range of *Salix*.

WPtf **Pantyfod Garden Nursery**
Llandewi Brefi, Tregaron, Ceredigion SY25 6PE
Ⓣ (01570) 400564 (answering service)
Ⓔ sales@pantyfodgarden.co.uk
Ⓦ www.pantyfodgarden.co.uk
Contact: Susan Rowe
Opening Times: Nursery & garden open1100-1700, Fri & Sat, 11th Apr-5th Oct 2014. Garden open for 3 days under the National Gardens Scheme when plants are offered for sale. Please check with NGS for Open Days.
Min Mail Order UK: Nmc
Min Mail Order EU: Nmc
Cat. Cost: Online only.
Credit Cards: Paypal
Specialities: Hardy geraniums, unusual hardy perennials, grasses, plants for moist soil, black plants, woodland plants. All plants grown largely peat-free. Many plants available in small quantities.
Notes: Stock changes throughout the year. Some plants ready later in the year. Not all plants available for mail order. See website for regular updates or phone/email. Emails welcome to enquire about plants not listed on website.
Map Ref: W, C3 **OS Grid Ref:** SN654540

WRHF **Red House Farm** ♿
Flying Horse Lane, Bradley Green, Nr Redditch, Worcestershire B96 6QT
Ⓣ (01527) 821269
Ⓔ redhousenursery@googlemail.com
Ⓦ www.redhousefarmgardenandnursery.co.uk
Contact: Mrs Maureen Weaver
Opening Times: 0900-1700 Mon-Sat all year. 1000-1700 Sun & B/hols.
Cat. Cost: 2 × 1st class.
Credit Cards: None
Specialities: Cottage garden perennials.
Notes: Wheelchair accessible.
Map Ref: W, C5 **OS Grid Ref:** SO986623

WSFF **Saith Ffynnon Wildlife Plants** ♿
Whitford, Holywell, Flintshire CH8 9EQ
Ⓣ (01352) 711198
Ⓕ (01352) 716777
Ⓔ jan@7wells.org
Ⓦ www.7wells.co.uk
Contact: Jan Miller
Opening Times: By appt. only.
Min Mail Order UK: Nmc
Min Mail Order EU: Nmc
Cat. Cost: 2 × 1st class (list only) or full catalogue online.
Credit Cards: All major credit/debit cards
Specialities: Plants and seeds to attract bees, butterflies and moths. Natural dye plants. National Collection of *Eupatorium*. Stock available in small quantities unless ordered well in advance.
Notes: Percentage of profits go to conservation. Credit cards accepted via website only. Also sells wholesale. Euro accepted. Wheelchair accessible.

WSHC **Stone House Cottage Nurseries** ♿
Stone, Nr Kidderminster, Worcestershire DY10 4BG
Ⓣ (01562) 69902
Ⓔ louisa@shcn.co.uk
Ⓦ www.shcn.co.uk
Contact: L N Arbuthnott
Opening Times: 1000-1700 Wed-Sat, late Mar-early Sep only.
Cat. Cost: Sae
Credit Cards: None
Specialities: Small general range esp. wall shrubs, climbers & unusual plants.
Notes: Wheelchair accessible.
Map Ref: W, C5 **OS Grid Ref:** SO863750

WShi **Shipton Bulbs**
Y Felin, Henllan Amgoed, Whitland, Carmarthenshire SA34 0SL
Ⓣ (01994) 240125
Ⓕ (01994) 241180
Ⓔ admin@shiptonbulbs.co.uk
Ⓦ www.shiptonbulbs.co.uk
Contact: John Shipton & Astra Shipton
Opening Times: By appt. only.
Min Mail Order UK: Nmc
Min Mail Order EU: Nmc
Cat. Cost: Sae.
Credit Cards: All major credit/debit cards
Specialities: Native British bulbs. Bulbs & plants for naturalising.
Notes: Delivers to shows. Euro accepted.
Map Ref: W, D2 **OS Grid Ref:** SN188207

WSSs **Shropshire Sarracenias** ♿
5 Field Close, Malinslee, Telford, Shropshire TF4 2EH
Ⓣ (01952) 501598
Ⓔ mike@carnivorousplants.uk.com
Ⓦ www.carnivorousplants.uk.com
Contact: Mike King
Opening Times: By appt. only.
Min Mail Order UK: Nmc

Min Mail Order EU: Nmc
Cat. Cost: 2 × 1st class.
Credit Cards: Paypal
Specialities: *Sarracenia. Dionaea muscipula* & forms. Some stock available in small quantities only. National Collections of *Sarracenia* & *Dionaea.*
Notes: Exports beyond EU. Delivers to shows. Euro accepted. Wheelchair accessible.
Map Ref: W, B4 **OS Grid Ref:** SJ689085

WSuV **SUNNYBANK VINE NURSERY (NATIONAL VINE COLLECTION)**
Cwm Barn, King Street, Ewyas Harold, Rowlestone, Herefordshire HR2 OEE
Ⓣ (01981) 240256
Ⓔ Sarah@sunnybankvines.co.uk
Ⓦ www.sunnybankvines.co.uk
Contact: Sarah Bell
Opening Times: Not open. Mail order only. Open day once a year advertised on both nursery & Plant Heritage websites.
Min Mail Order UK: £12.00 incl. p&p
Min Mail Order EU: £15.00 incl. p&p
Cat. Cost: Online only.
Credit Cards: None
Specialities: Vines. National Collection of *Vitis vinifera* (hardy, incl. dessert & wine). Small quantities of 60-70 varieties available as rooted plants, the entire Collection usually available as bare wood cuttings for own propagation depending upon wood ripening this season.
Notes: EU sales by arrangement. Exports beyond EU.

WTan **TAN-Y-LLYN NURSERIES**
Meifod, Powys SY22 6YB
Ⓣ (01938) 500370
Ⓔ info@tanyllyn-nursery.co.uk
Ⓦ www.tanyllyn-nursery.co.uk
Contact: Callum Johnston
Opening Times: By appt. only. Please phone.
Min Mail Order UK: Nmc
Cat. Cost: 2 × 1st class or online.
Credit Cards: Paypal
Specialities: Herbs, alpines, perennials.
Map Ref: W, B3 **OS Grid Ref:** SJ167125

WTcb **T3 PLANTS** ♿
Wall End Nursery, Wall End Barn, Stoke Prior, Leominster, Herefordshire HR6 0ND
Ⓣ (01568) 760152
Ⓜ 07775 001287
Ⓔ t3plants@aol.com
Ⓦ www.t3plants.co.uk
Contact: Leila Jackson
Opening Times: 1000-1500 Mon-Wed, Apr-Sep.
Min Mail Order UK: 10 plants.
Cat. Cost: 3 × 1st class.
Specialities: Family nursery specialising in *Abutilon* & *Salvia. Campanula, Persicaria, Sanguisorba* & autumn-flowering plants. Some stock propagated to order. Large collection of sub-shrub *Salvia.* National Collection of *Abutilon.*
Notes: Wheelchair accessible. Delivers to shows. Also sells wholesale.

WThu **THUYA ALPINE NURSERY**
Glebelands, Hartpury, Gloucestershire GL19 3BW
Ⓣ (01452) 700548 (after dark)
Contact: S W Bond
Opening Times: 1000-dusk Sat & B/hols. 1100-dusk Sun, Weekdays appt. advised.
Min Mail Order UK: £6.00 + p&p
Min Mail Order EU: £12.00 + p&p
Cat. Cost: 4 × 2nd class.
Credit Cards: None
Specialities: Wide and changing range incl. rarities, available in smallish numbers.
Notes: Will deliver plants to AGS shows only. Partially accessible for wheelchair users.
Map Ref: W, C5

WTor **TORTWORTH PLANTS LTD**
Old Lodge Farm, Tortworth, Wotton-under-Edge, Gloucestershire GL12 8HF
Ⓣ (01454) 260020
Ⓕ (01454) 260020
Ⓔ info@tortworthplants.co.uk
Ⓦ www.tortworthplants.co.uk
Contact: Rebecca Flint or Tim Hancock
Opening Times: By appt. only.
Min Mail Order UK: Nmc
Cat. Cost: Online or 2 × 1st for plant list.
Specialities: Herbaceous perennials & alpines, incl. rare & unusual.
Notes: Also sells wholesale. Delivers to shows.

WTou **TOUCHWOOD PLANTS**
4 Clyne Valley Cottages, Killay, Swansea, West Glamorgan SA2 7DU
Ⓣ (01792) 522443
Ⓔ Carrie.Thomas@ntlworld.com
Ⓦ www.touchwoodplants.co.uk
Contact: Carrie Thomas
Opening Times: Most reasonable days/times. Please phone first.
Min Mail Order UK: Nmc
Min Mail Order EU: Nmc
Cat. Cost: Online only.
Credit Cards: All major credit/debit cards, Paypal
Specialities: Seeds & plants. National Collections of *Aquilegia vulgaris* cvs & *Aquilegia* hybrids. Plant stocks held in small

quantities. Main stock is seed. Garden & *Aquilegia* Collection open.
Notes: Plants sent bare-rooted at relevant times of the year. Only seeds (not plants) exported outside UK. Credit cards accepted online only. Exports beyond EU.
Map Ref: W, D3 **OS Grid Ref:** SS600924

WTre **Walled Garden Treberfydd**
Llangasty, Brecon, Powys LD3 7PX
Ⓣ (01874) 730169
Ⓜ 07711 222700
Ⓔ alison@walledgardentreberfydd.com
Ⓦ www.walledgardentreberfydd.com
Contact: Alison Sparshatt
Opening Times: 1000-1600 7 days.
Credit Cards: All, except American Express
Specialities: Beautiful plant nursery set in the walled garden of a Victorian Gothic house. Hardy plants grown in Wales which are structural, unusual, herbal or fragrant.
Notes: Also sells wholesale.
Map Ref: W, C4 **OS Grid Ref:** SO128255

W

WViv **Viv Marsh Postal Plants** ♿
Walford Heath, Shrewsbury, Shropshire SY4 2HT
Ⓣ (01939) 291475
Ⓔ mail@postalplants.co.uk
Ⓦ www.postalplants.co.uk
Contact: Mr Viv Marsh
Opening Times: Open 2 w/ends a year. Please phone or see website for details.
Min Mail Order UK: £33.00
Min Mail Order EU: £33.00
Cat. Cost: Free.
Credit Cards: All major credit/debit cards
Specialities: Specialists in *Alstroemeria* & *Lathyrus*. National Collection of *Alstroemeria*, viewing by appt.
Notes: Wheelchair access to tunnels. No disabled toilet.
Map Ref: W, B4 **OS Grid Ref:** SJ445197

WWct **Walcot Organic Nursery**
Lower Walcot Farm, Walcot Lane, Drakes Broughton, Pershore, Worcestershire WR10 2AL
Ⓣ (01905) 841587
Ⓜ 07780 547983
Ⓕ (01905) 841587
Ⓔ enquiries@walcotnursery.co.uk
Ⓦ www.walcotnursery.co.uk
Contact: Kevin O'Neill
Opening Times: 0800-1700 Mon-Fri. 1000-1300 Sat. Nov-Mar only.
Min Mail Order UK: £12.00
Cat. Cost: 1 × 2nd class.
Credit Cards: All major credit/debit cards
Specialities: Organic fruit trees. Apples, plums, pears, cherries, quinces etc on different rootstocks.
Notes: Also sells wholesale.

WWEG **World's End Garden Nursery** ♿
Moseley Road, Hallow, Worcester, Worcestershire WR2 6NJ
Ⓣ (01905) 640977
Ⓕ (01905) 641373
Ⓔ info@worldsendgarden.co.uk
Ⓦ www.worldsendgarden.co.uk
Contact: Kristina & Robin Pearce
Opening Times: 1000-1700, Mon-Fri, Mar-Oct. Other times by appt. only.
Min Mail Order UK: £20.00
Min Mail Order EU: £20.00
Cat. Cost: Online only.
Credit Cards: All major credit/debit cards
Specialities: Extensive range of herbaceous perennials & ornamental grasses. Especially *Geum*, *Hosta*, *Leucantheum*, *Miscanthus* & *Panicum*.
Notes: Delivers to shows. Wheelchair accessible.
Map Ref: W, C5 **OS Grid Ref:** SO815597

WWFP **Whitehall Farmhouse Plants**
Sevenhampton, Cheltenham, Gloucestershire GL54 5TL
Ⓣ (01242) 820772
Ⓜ 07711 021034
Ⓕ (01242) 821226
Ⓔ info@wfplants.co.uk
Ⓦ www.wfplants.co.uk
Contact: Victoria Logue
Opening Times: By appt. only.
Min Mail Order UK: Nmc
Credit Cards: None
Specialities: A small nursery producing a range of interesting & easy hardy perennials for the garden. Some plants held in small quantities only.
Notes: Delivers to shows.
Map Ref: W, C5 **OS Grid Ref:** SP018229

WWtn **Westonbury Mill Water Garden** ♿
Pembridge, Herefordshire HR6 9HZ
Ⓣ (01544) 388650
Ⓕ (01544) 388650
Ⓔ richardpim@btinternet.com
Ⓦ www.westonburymillwatergardens.com
Contact: Richard Pim
Opening Times: 1100-1700 daily, 1st Apr-30th Sep. By appt. only at other times & to arrange collection.
Specialities: Range of plants, mostly herbaceous, with special emphasis on plants for the water garden. Some plants available in small quantities. Contact nursery to confirm

availability as stock sells out quickly when in flower.
Notes: Café. Wheelchair accessible.

Abroad

XBar **Barnhaven Primroses ◆**
11 rue du Pont Blanc, Plestin-les-grèves, 22310, France
Ⓣ +33 2 9635 6841
Ⓜ +33 6 6124 7739
Ⓕ +33 2 9635 6841
Ⓔ info@barnhaven.com
Ⓦ www.barnhaven.com
Contact: Lynne & David Lawson
Opening Times: 1400-1700 Feb-Apr. For visits outside this period, please phone first.
Min Mail Order UK: Nmc
Min Mail Order EU: Nmc
Credit Cards: MasterCard, Visa
Specialities: Barnhaven strains of polyanthus, incl. gold-laced & anomalous. Also auriculas & alpines. Seeds & plants available worldwide.
Notes: Exports beyond EU. Euro accepted. Delivers to shows.

XBlo **Table Bay View Nursery**
PO Box 12123, Mill Street, Cape Town, 8010, South Africa
Ⓣ +27 21 683 5108
Ⓕ +27 21 683 5108
Ⓔ info@tablebayviewnursery.co.za
Contact: Terence Bloch
Opening Times: Mail order only. No personal callers.
Min Mail Order UK: £15.00 + p&p
Min Mail Order EU: £15.00
Cat. Cost: £3.40 (postal order)
Credit Cards: None
Specialities: Tropical & sub-tropical ornamental & fruiting plants. Self-harvested seed, predominently from our own inventory of mother stock plants.
Notes: Due to high local bank charges, can no longer accept foreign bank cheques, only undated postal orders. To comply with UK import regulations, prospective buyers must register with DEFRA before placing an order. Exports beyond EU. Euro accepted.

XEll **Ellebore**
La Chamotière, 61360 Saint-Jouin-de-Blavou, France
Ⓣ +33 2 3383 3772
Ⓜ +33 6802 28674
Ⓕ +33 2 3383 3773
Ⓔ pepiniere.ellebore@orange.fr
Ⓦ www.pepiniere-ellebore.fr
Contact: Nadine Albouy & Christian Geoffroy
Opening Times: 1000-1800 Wed-Sat, mid-Feb to late Jun & Sep-Dec. 1500-1800 Thu, Fri & Sat, Jul, Aug & Jan to mid-Feb.
Min Mail Order UK: Nmc
Min Mail Order EU: Nmc
Cat. Cost: Free.
Credit Cards: All major credit/debit cards
Specialities: *Helleborus*. Bulbs. *Clematis*.
Notes: Also sells wholesale. Euro accepted. Delivers to shows.

XFro **Frosch Exclusive Perennials**
Ziegelstadelweg 5, D-83623 Dietramszell-Lochen, Germany
Ⓣ +49 172 842 2050
Ⓕ +49 8027 904 9975
Ⓔ info@cypripedium.de
Ⓦ www.cypripedium.de
Contact: Michael Weinert
Opening Times: Not open. Mail order only. Orders taken between 0700-2200 hours.
Min Mail Order UK: £350.00 + p&p
Min Mail Order EU: £350.00 + p&p
Cat. Cost: Online only.
Credit Cards: None
Specialities: *Cypripedium* hybrids. Hardy orchids.
Notes: Also sells wholesale. Exports beyond EU. Euro accepted.

XGra **Graefswinning**
Diestersteenweg 222, 3850, Nieuwerkerken, Belgium
Ⓣ +32 1188 3611
Ⓔ info@graefswinning.be
Ⓦ www.graefswinning.be
Contact: Jeaninne Lemmens
Opening Times: Open Apr-Jun to view flower fields. Check website for further information.
Min Mail Order UK: Nmc
Min Mail Order EU: Nmc
Cat. Cost: Online only.
Credit Cards: MasterCard, Visa, Paypal
Specialities: Herbaceous, tree & Itoh peonies. Several acres of peonies in the field. Sell containerised peonies in sturdy 7L pots as well as bare root plants. Landscape & cut-flower varieties.
Notes: Bare root peonies are shipped in autumn to countries within the EU. Container plants available at nursery & garden shows. Exports beyond EU. Euro accepted.

XLum **Lumen Plantes Vivaces**
Les Coutets, 24100 Creysse-Bergerac, Occitania, France
Ⓣ +33 5 5357 6215
Ⓕ +33 5 5358 5488
Ⓔ lumenviva@aol.com
Ⓦ www.lumen.fr

Contact: Michel Lumen
Opening Times: 0900-1200 & 1300-1630 Mon-Thu, 0900-1200 & 1300-1530 Fri. Closed Sat, Sun & B/hols. 0900-1200 & 1300-1830 Mon-Sat, Mar-Jun.
Min Mail Order UK: Nmc
Min Mail Order EU: Nmc
Cat. Cost: Online only.
Credit Cards: MasterCard, Visa
Specialities: Hardy perennials. French National Collection of *Miscanthus*.
Notes: Also sells wholesale. Exports beyond EU. Delivers to shows. Euro accepted.
Grid Ref: N44 51.789 E0 32.0518

XMic **Fuchsia Michiels**
Kruisstraat 51, 2500 Lier–Koningshooikt, Belgium
Ⓣ +32 474 440706
Ⓔ fuchsia.michiels@skynet.be
Ⓦ www.fuchsia.be
Contact: Katrien Michiels
Opening Times: 0900-1200 & 1300-1700, Thu-Sat.
Min Mail Order UK: € 25
Min Mail Order EU: € 25
Credit Cards: MasterCard, Visa
Specialities: Large range of *Fuchsia*, *Pelargonium*, *Streptocarpus*.
Notes: Family nursery established over 30 years ago. Euro accepted.

XPou **Koen Van Poucke** ♿
Heistraat 106, Sint-Niklaas, Oost-Vlaanderen, 9100 Belgium
Ⓣ +32 377 77642
Ⓕ +32 376 61698
Ⓔ kvanpoucke@skynet.be
Ⓦ www.koenvanpoucke.be
Contact: Koen Van Poucke
Opening Times: 0900-1230 & 1300-1800, Tue-Sat. Closed Sun & Mon. Closed Jul. Check website before travelling a long distance.
Min Mail Order UK: € 100
Min Mail Order EU: € 100
Credit Cards: None
Specialities: *Epimedium*. Also rare Asian shade plants. *Dahlias*.
Notes: Mail order Sep-Apr. Collector's garden open to the public. Delivers to shows. Euro accepted. Wheelchair accessible.

XSen **Les Senteurs Du Quercy** ♿
Mas de Fraysse, Escamps, Lot, 46230, France
Ⓣ +33 5 652 10167
Ⓔ melie.fred@aliceadsl.fr
Ⓦ www.senteursduquercy.com
Contact: Frédéric Prévot
Opening Times: 1400-1800 spring & summer (excl. Aug). Other times, incl. Aug, by appt.
Min Mail Order UK: Nmc
Min Mail Order EU: Nmc
Cat. Cost: €5.00
Specialities: *Salvia*, *Iris*, *Phlomis*, *Teucrium*, *Lavandula* and drought tolerant plants. French National Coll. of *Salvia* species.
Notes: Euro accepted. Wheelchair accessible.

XTur **Etablissements Pierre Turc** ♿ ◆
63 Route de Seiches, 49630 Mazé, France
Ⓣ +33 2 4180 6408
Ⓜ +33 6 4756 3327
Ⓕ +33 2 4180 2696
Ⓔ export@turcieflor.com
Ⓦ www.turcieflor.com
Contact: Mark Hodson
Opening Times: 0800-1215 & 1400-1700 Mon-Fri.
Min Mail Order UK: Nmc + p&p
Min Mail Order EU: Nmc + p&p
Credit Cards: None
Specialities: *Alstroemeria*, *Agapanthus* & *Canna*. Also *Arum*, *Begonia*, *Dahlia*, *Fuchsia* & *Hippeastrum*.
Notes: Also sells wholesale. Exports beyond EU. Delivers to shows. Euro accepted. Wheelchair accessible.

Nursery Index by Name

Nurseries that are included in the *RHS Plant Finder* for the first time this year (or have been reintroduced after a significant absence) are marked in **bold type**.

Full details of the nurseries will be found in **Nursery Details by Code** on page 832. For a key to the geographical codes, see the start of **Nurseries**.

A & J Plants	EAJP
A La Carte Daylilies	SDay
Abbey Nursery, The	CAby
Abbey Plants	CAbP
Abbotsbury Sub-Tropical Gardens	CAbb
Aberconwy Nursery	WAbe
Abi and Tom's Garden Plants	NAbi
Abriachan Nurseries	GAbr
Adur Valley Growers	SAdu
AEE - a lover of plants	EAEE
Agroforestry Research Trust	CAgr
Akorn and Oake	**SAko**
Alafin Arids & Exotics	EAla
Alan Phipps Cacti	CPhi
Allen, Anita	CAni
Allen, L.A.	WAln
Allwoods	LAll
Alpine Campanulas (Bellflower Nursery)	EACa
Angusplants	GAgs
Ardcarne Garden Centre	IArd
Arley Hall Nursery	MArl
Arne Herbs	CArn
Ashdown Forest Garden Centre & Nursery	SAdn
Ashridge Trees Ltd	**CArg**
Ashwood Nurseries Ltd	MAsh
Asterby & Chalkcroft Nursery	LAst
Aulden Farm	WAul
Avon Bulbs	CAvo
Avondale Nursery	MAvo
Aylett Nurseries Ltd	LAyl
B & H M Baker	EBak
Bali-Hai Mail Order Nursery	IBal
Ballyrogan Nurseries	IBlr
Barcham Trees PLC	EBar
Barnhaven Primroses	XBar
Barnsdale Gardens	MBNS
Barracott Plants	CBct
Barters Plant Centre & Nursery	CBar
Bean Place Nursery	SBea
Bee Friendly Garden Plants	**NBFr**
Beechcroft Nursery	LBee
Beeches Cottage Nursery	GBee
Beeches Nursery	EBee
Beggar's Roost Plants	CBgR
Bennetts Water Gardens	CBen
Bennison Peonies	**EBen**
Best4Hedging	**NBes**
Beth Chatto Gardens Ltd., The	ECha
Bide-A-Wee Cottage Gardens	NBid
Big Plant Nursery	SBig
Bilverstone, Alison	EABi
Binny Plants	GBin
Birchfleet Nurseries	SBir
Birchwood Plants	SBch
Birkheads Secret Gardens & Nursery	NBir
Black Mountain Auriculas	WBla
Blackmoor Nurseries	SBmr
Blooming Marvellous Plants	LBMP
Blue Nurseries Ltd	**CBlu**
Bluebell Arboretum & Nursery	MBlu
Bluebell Cottage Nursery	MBel
Bodiam Nursery	SBod
Bodmin Nursery	CBod
Bodnant Garden Nursery	**WBod**
Border Belles	GBBs
Bordervale Plants	WBor
Botanic Nursery, The	CBot
Botanica	EBtc
Boyne Garden Centre	IBoy
Brambly Hedge	SBrm
Breezy Knees Nurseries	NBre
Bregover Plants	CBre
Brickwall Cottage Nursery	SBri
Bridge Nursery	MBrN
Bridgemere Nursery & Garden World	MBri
Brighter Blooms	NBri
Brighton Plants	SBrt
Broadleigh Gardens	CBro
Brockamin Plants	WBrk
Brooklands Plants	CBrP

Fruit Garden Plants	SFrt
Fuchsia Michiels	**XMic**
Galloway Plants	GGal
Garden Blooms	NGBl
Garden House Nursery	NGdn
Garden Secrets Nursery	SGSe
Gilbert's Nursery	SGbt
Gillies, John	MGil
Glendoick Gardens Ltd	GGGa
Golden Hill Nurseries	SGol
Gordon's Nursery	WGor
Goscote Nurseries Ltd	MGos
Graefswinning	XGra
Grange Farm Plants	EGFP
Great Dixter Nurseries	SDix
Great Western Gladiolus Nursery, The	CGrW
Green, Mary	NMyG
Green's Leaves	WGrn
Grow at Brogdale	**SBdl**
Gwynfor Growers	WGwG
Habitat Aid Ltd.	CHab
Hall Farm Nursery	WHal
Halls of Heddon	NHal
Hall's Court Nursery	SHal
Hardy-Eucalyptus	WEuc
Hardy's Cottage Garden Plants	SHar
Harley Nursery	WHar
Harrells Hardy Plants	WHrl
Hart Canna	SHaC
Hartside Nursery Garden	NHar
Harveys Garden Plants	EHrv
Hawthornes Nursery, The	NHaw
Hayloft Plants	WHlf
Heath Garden	WHea
Hedgexpress	**MHed**
Herb Garden & Historical Plant Nursery, The	WHer
Herb Nursery, The	MHer
Herbary, The	CHby
Herbs for Healing	WHfH
Hergest Croft Gardens	WHCr
Herterton House Garden Nursery	NHer
Herts Hellebores	LHel
Heucheraholics	SHeu
Hewitt-Cooper Carnivorous Plants	CHew
Hidden Valley Gardens	CHVG
Hidden Valley Nursery	CHid
High Garden Nurseries	CHGN
Highdown Nursery	SHDw
Hill Close Gardens	**MHCG**
Hill House Nursery Ltd	CHll
Hillier Garden Centres	SHil
Hillview Hardy Plants	WHil
Hintons Nursery	**MHtn**
Hinwick Hall Plant Centre	MHin
Hippopottering Nursery	NHip
Hodgehill Nursery	**WHod**
Hoecroft Plants	EHoe
Holden Clough Nursery Ltd.	NHol
Hollies Farm Plant Centre	MHol
Homestead Plants	MHom
Honeysome Aquatic Nursery	EHon
Hoo House Nursery	WHoo
Hopleys Plants Ltd	LHop
Horticultural Sales	WHor
Hoyland Plant Centre	NHoy
Hydrangea Haven	SHyH
Ice Alpines	WIce
Iden Croft Herbs	SIde
Ingram, Tim	SIgm
Iris Garden, The	CIri
Iris of Sissinghurst	SIri
Irisesonline	EIri
JPR Environmental	WJPR
Jack Fryer Conifer Specialist (formerly Hull Farm)	EFry
Jackson's Nurseries	MJak
Jackson's Nurseries	MJac
Jacques Amand International Ltd	LAma
Jekka's Herb Farm	WJek
Jo's Garden Enterprise	GJos
John and Lynsey's Plants	SPin
John Gibson Daffodils	**MGib**
John Hall Plants Ltd	SWhi
JRG Dahlias	NJRG
Jungle Giants	WJun
Junker's Nursery Ltd.	CJun
Just Airplants	LAir
Keepers Nursery	SKee
Kelways	CKel
Kenwith Conifer Nursery (Gordon Haddow)	CKen
Kevin Hughes Plants	SKHP
Kevock Garden Plants	GKev
Kiftsgate Court Gardens	WKif
Kilmurry Nursery	IKil
Kings Barn Trees	SKin
Kinlochlaich Garden Plant Centre	GKin
Knoll Gardens	CKno
Ladybird Nurseries	ELad
Lakka Bulbs	CLak
Landford Trees	CLnd
Laneside Hardy Orchid Nursery	NLAp
Langthorns Plantery	ELan
Larch Cottage Nurseries	NLar
Laurel Farm Herbs	CLau
Laurels Nursery, The	SLau
Lavender Garden, The	WLav
Layham Garden Centre & Nursery	SLay
Lea Rhododendron Gardens Ltd	MLea
Leamore Nursery	**ILea**
Letham Plants	**GLet**
Letsgoplanting	**CLet**
Lilies Water Gardens	LLWG
Lime Cross Nursery	SLim

INDEX MAP

The maps on the following pages show the approximate location of the nurseries whose details are listed in this directory.

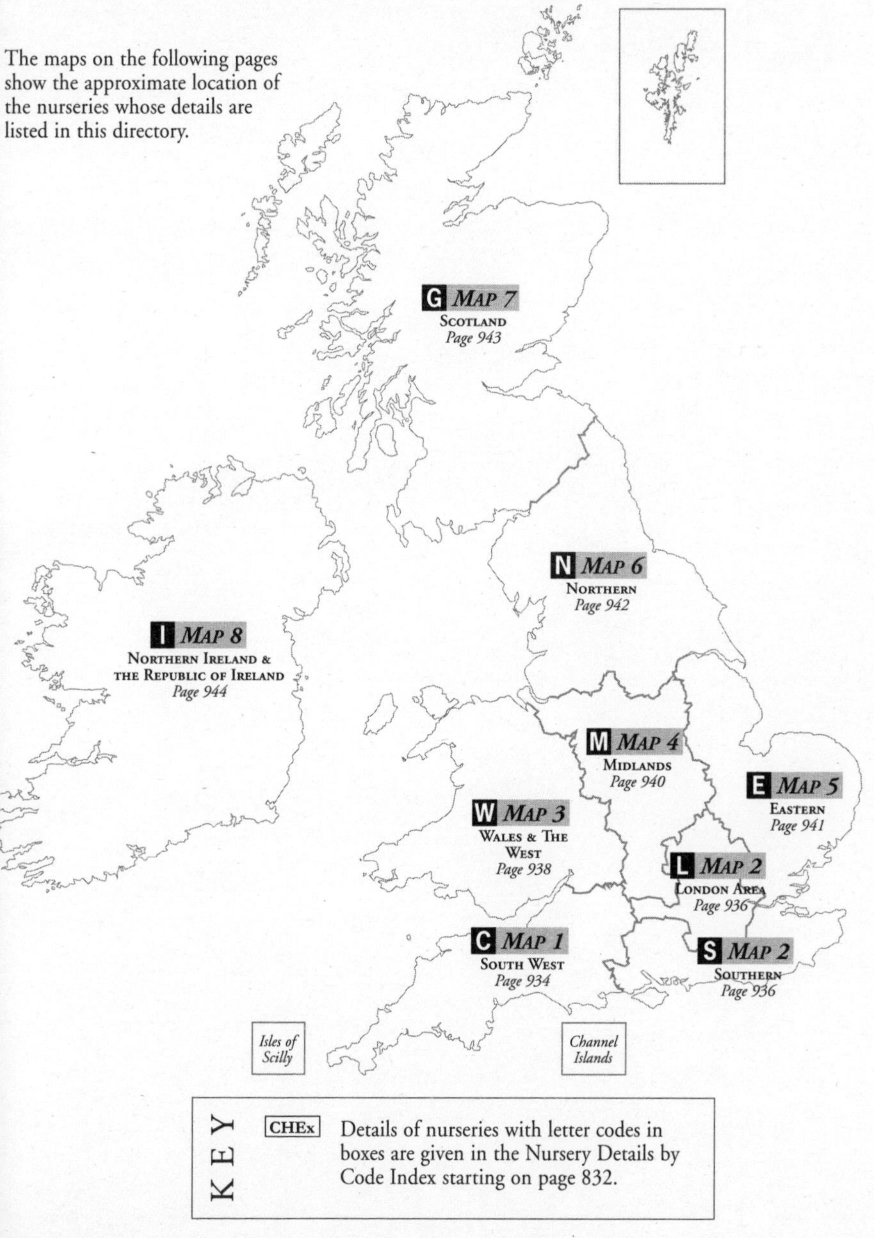

KEY

CHEx — Details of nurseries with letter codes in boxes are given in the Nursery Details by Code Index starting on page 832.

1
2
3
A
B
C
D
C
MAP ONE
South West
Llanelli
M4
Swansea
Neath
Port
Ilfracombe
Combe Martin
CMHG
Barnstaple
Bideford
CHid
CWCL
CRos
CKen
CWri
CPne
Bude
CWil
CCac
A39
CPbn
Okehampton
CSto
Launceston
CBre
Tavistock
Wadebridge
CBod
CBct
Newton
CTca
CHll
Bodmin
Liskeard
A38
CTsd
CDoC
Newquay
CPrp
Plymouth
CNW
A30
CHVG
CPou
CRHN
St Austell
Truro
St Ives
Redruth
CFen
Camborne
CBcS
Penzance
Helston
Falmouth
CCon
CQua

4
5
6
A
B
C
D
Stroud
Cirencester
Tydfil
Pontypool
Cwmbran
Newport
CARDIFF
Bristol
Clevedon
Weston Super Mare
Swindon
Chippenham
Calne
Marlborough
Newbury
Melksham
Devizes
Bath
Trowbridge
Burnham on Sea
Minehead
Williton
Bridgwater
Wells
Frome
Warminster
Glastonbury
Andover
Salisbury
Wincanton
Taunton
Shaftesbury
Wellington
Yeovil
Southampton
Chard
Ringwood
Blandford Forum
Honiton
Lymington
Wimborne Minster
Bridport
Lyme Regis
Dorchester
Bournemouth
Poole
Exmouth
Weymouth
Torquay
M4
M5
M3
A36
A303
A354
A35
CLoc
CWGN
CWat
CPhi
CSpe
CWhi
CFlo
CBot
CArn
CCVT
CPBP
CMea
CMil
CMen
CFwr
CBgR
CMus
CTri
CSna
CElw
CPen
CAbP
CBro
CMos
CKel
CLAP
CJun
CDTJ
CNMi
CFis
CLet
CMCN
CAvo
CLnd
CFst
CKno
CDul
CNor
CTrh
CMac
CAby
CIri
CEnt
CPar
CChe
CSBt
CBrP
CCht
CNec
CEls
CBen

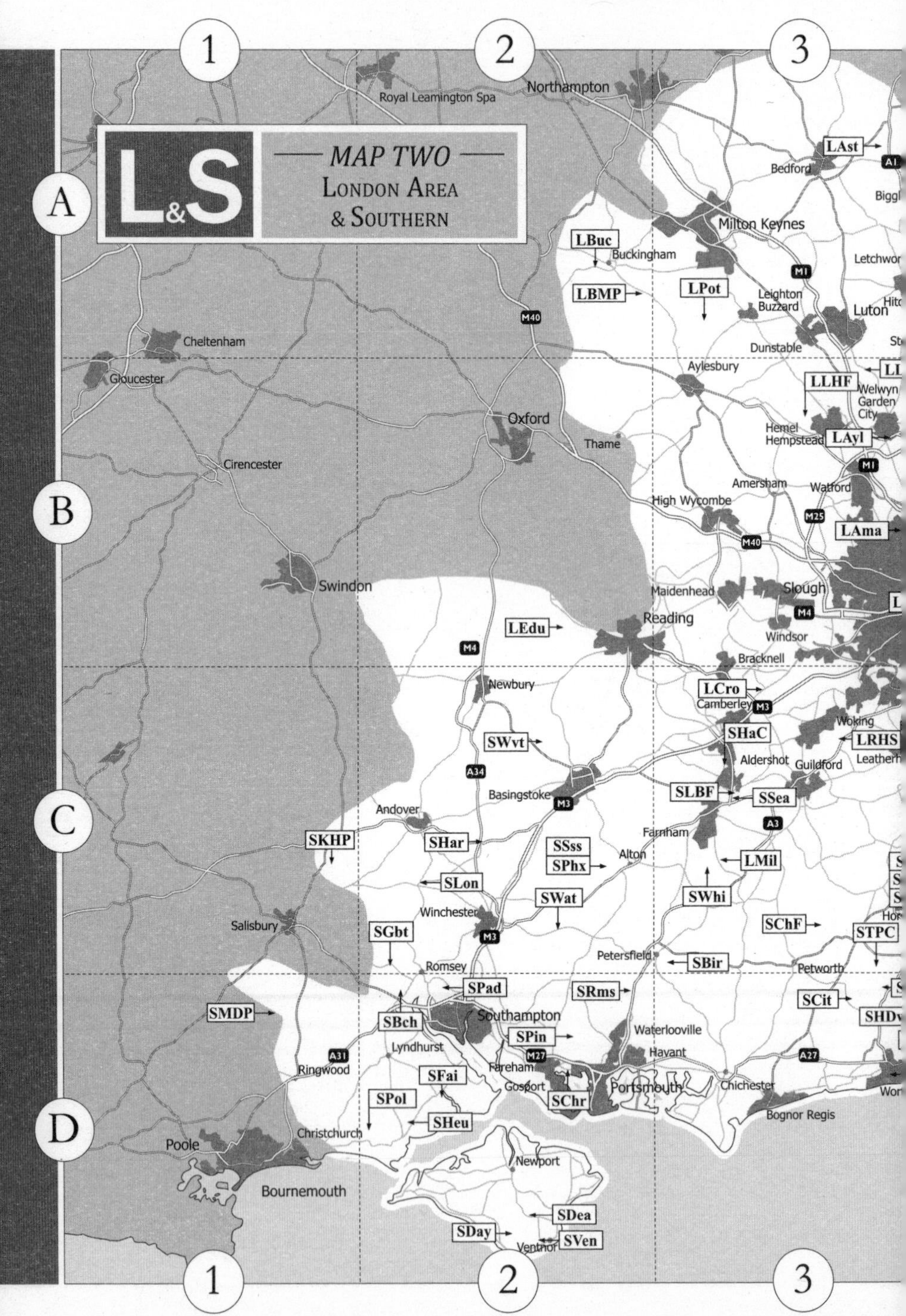
L&S
MAP TWO
London Area
& Southern
1
2
3
A
B
C
D
Royal Leamington Spa
Northampton
Bedford
LAst
Milton Keynes
LBuc
Buckingham
LBMP
LPot
Leighton Buzzard
Luton
Letchwor
Dunstable
Cheltenham
Gloucester
Oxford
Thame
Aylesbury
LLHF
Welwyn Garden City
Hemel Hempstead
LAyl
Cirencester
Amersham
Watford
High Wycombe
LAma
Swindon
Maidenhead
Slough
Reading
Windsor
LEdu
Bracknell
Newbury
LCro
Camberley
SHaC
Woking
LRHS
SWvt
Aldershot
Guildford
Basingstoke
SLBF
SSea
Andover
Farnham
SKHP
SHar
SSss
SPhx
Alton
LMil
SLon
SWat
SWhi
Winchester
Salisbury
SGbt
SChF
STPC
Petersfield
SBir
Petworth
Romsey
SPad
SRms
SCit
SMDP
SBch
Southampton
SPin
Waterlooville
Havant
Lyndhurst
Ringwood
Fareham
SFai
Gosport
Portsmouth
Chichester
SChr
SPol
SHeu
Bognor Regis
Christchurch
Poole
Newport
Bournemouth
SDea
SDay
SVen
Ventnor
M1
M4
M3
M25
M40
M27
A1
A3
A27
A31
A34

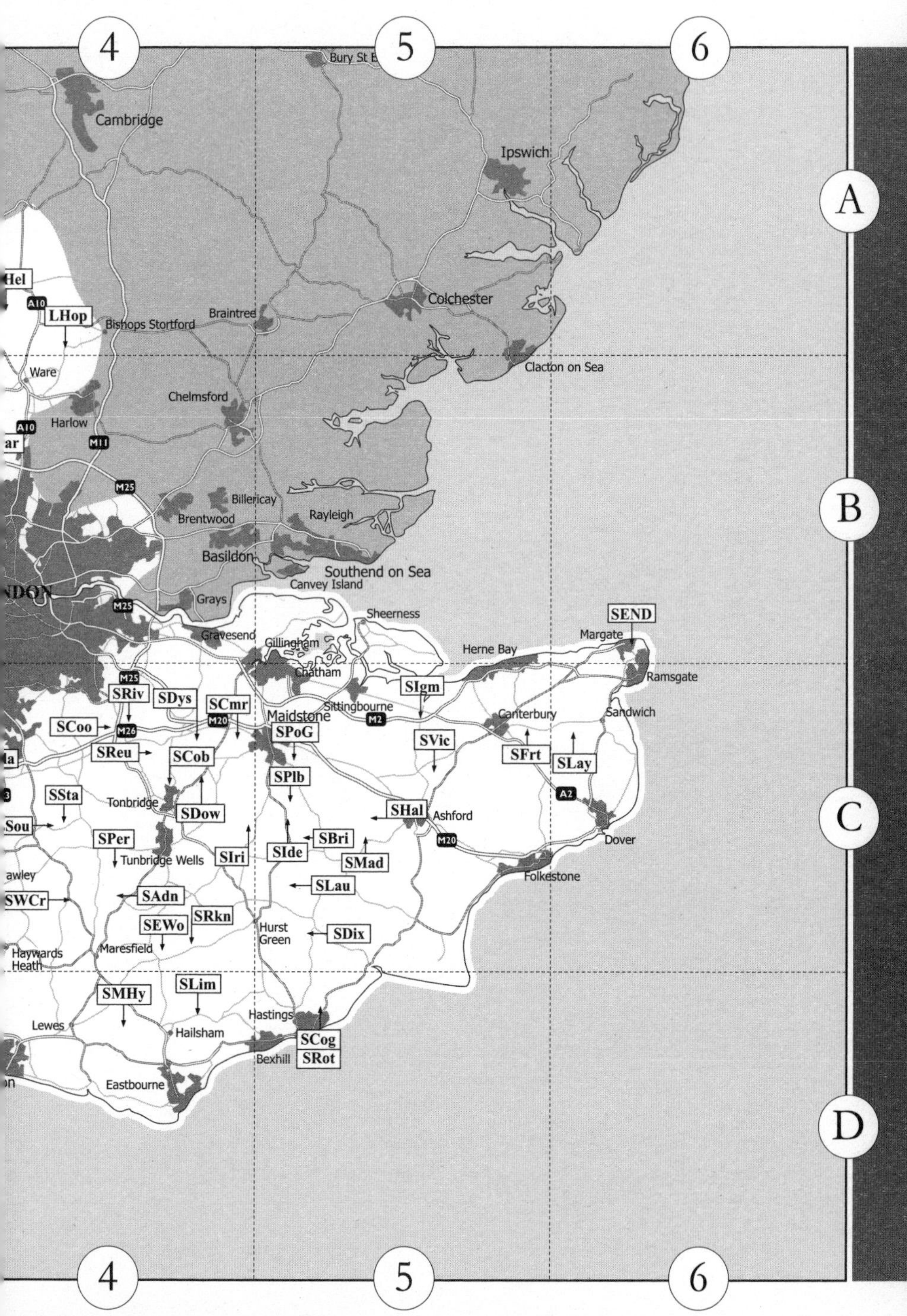
4
5
6
A
B
C
D
Bury St E
Cambridge
Ipswich
Hel
A10
LHop
Bishops Stortford
Braintree
Colchester
Ware
Clacton on Sea
Chelmsford
Harlow
A10
ar
M11
M25
Billericay
Brentwood
Rayleigh
Basildon
Southend on Sea
Canvey Island
NDON
M25
Grays
Sheerness
SEND
Margate
Gravesend
Gillingham
Herne Bay
Chatham
Ramsgate
M25
SRiv
SDys
SCmr
SIgm
Sittingbourne
Sandwich
SCoo
M20
Maidstone
M2
Canterbury
M26
SPoG
SVic
SReu
SCob
SFrt
SLay
la
SPlb
A2
SSta
Tonbridge
SDow
SHal
Ashford
Sou
SBri
M20
Dover
SPer
SIri
SIde
SMad
Tunbridge Wells
Folkestone
awley
SLau
SWCr
SAdn
SRkn
SEWo
Hurst Green
SDix
Maresfield
Haywards Heath
SMHy
SLim
Hastings
Lewes
Hailsham
SCog
Bexhill
SRot
Eastbourne
on
4
5
6

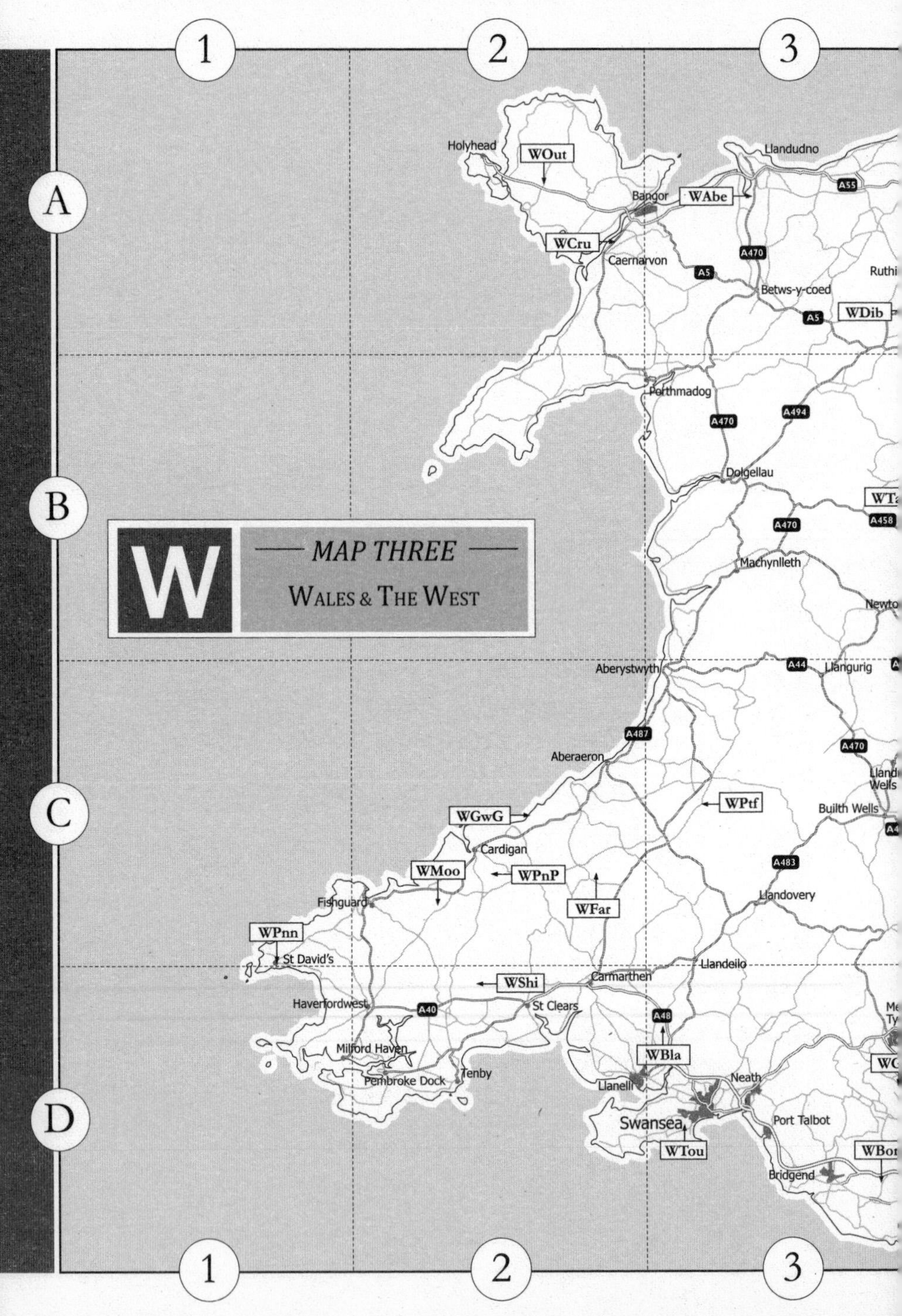
1
2
3
A
B
C
D
MAP THREE
WALES & THE WEST
Holyhead
WOut
Llandudno
Bangor
WAbe
A55
WCru
Caernarvon
A470
A5
Betws-y-coed
WDib
Porthmadog
A494
Dolgellau
A458
Machynlleth
Aberystwyth
A44
Llangurig
A487
Aberaeron
A470
Builth Wells
WGwG
WPtf
Cardigan
WMoo
WPnP
A483
Fishguard
WFar
Llandovery
WPnn
St David's
Llandeilo
WShi
Carmarthen
Haverfordwest
A40
St Clears
A48
Milford Haven
WBla
Pembroke Dock
Tenby
Llanelli
Neath
Swansea
Port Talbot
WTou
Bridgend

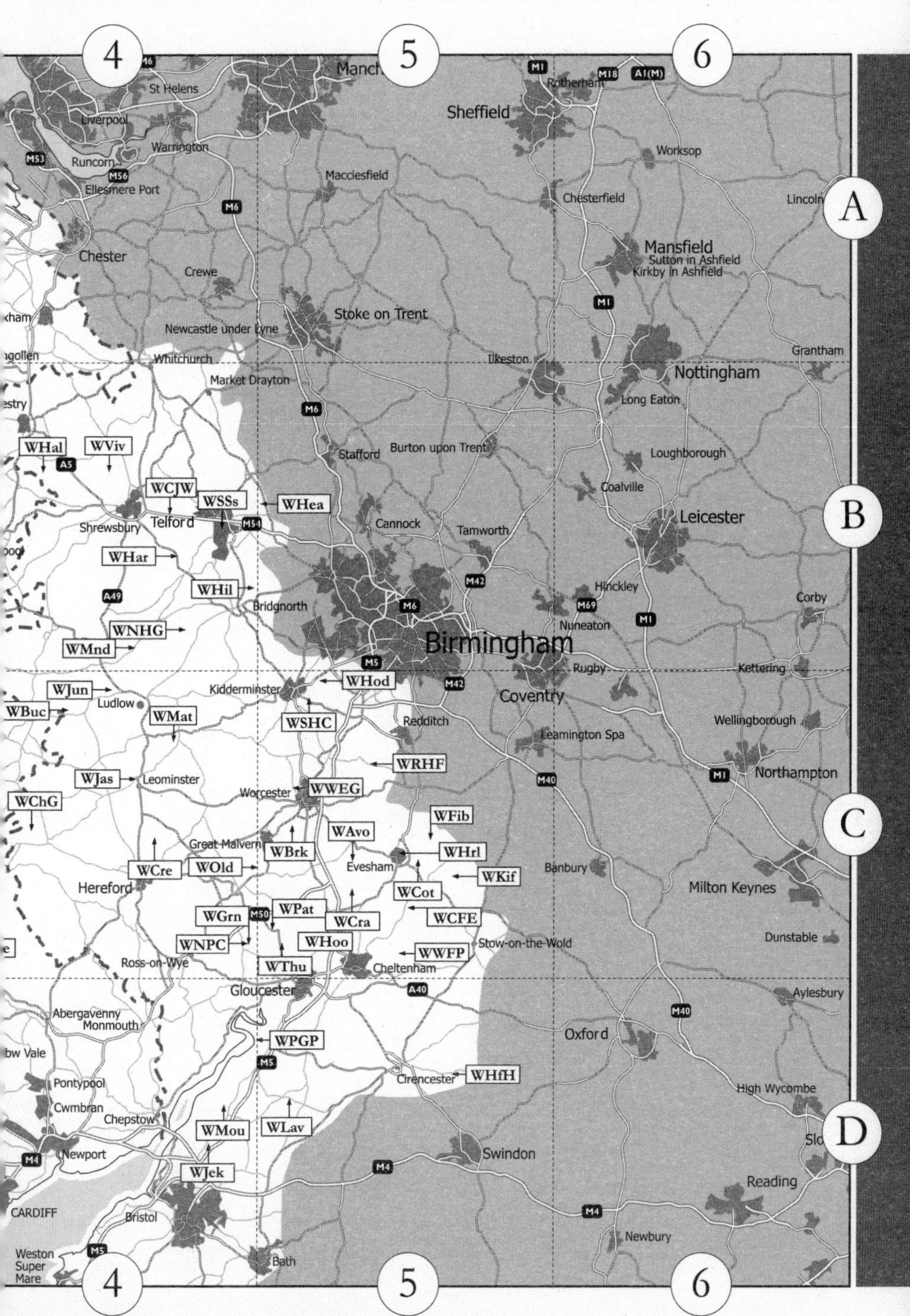
4
5
6
A
B
C
D
Manchester
St Helens
Liverpool
Warrington
Runcorn
Ellesmere Port
Macclesfield
Sheffield
Rotherham
Worksop
Chesterfield
Lincoln
Chester
Crewe
Mansfield
Sutton in Ashfield
Kirkby in Ashfield
Stoke on Trent
Newcastle under Lyne
Whitchurch
Market Drayton
Ilkeston
Nottingham
Grantham
Long Eaton
Stafford
Burton upon Trent
Loughborough
Coalville
Leicester
Shrewsbury
Telford
Cannock
Tamworth
Hinckley
Corby
Bridgnorth
Nuneaton
Birmingham
Rugby
Kettering
Kidderminster
Ludlow
Coventry
Redditch
Wellingborough
Leamington Spa
Leominster
Worcester
Northampton
Great Malvern
Evesham
Banbury
Hereford
Milton Keynes
Stow-on-the-Wold
Dunstable
Ross-on-Wye
Cheltenham
Gloucester
Aylesbury
Abergavenny
Monmouth
Oxford
Pontypool
Cwmbran
Chepstow
Cirencester
High Wycombe
Newport
Swindon
Reading
CARDIFF
Bristol
Newbury
Weston Super Mare
Bath
M1
M18
A1(M)
M53
M56
M6
M54
A5
A49
M42
M69
M5
M40
M50
A40
M4
WHal
WViv
WCJW
WSSs
WHea
WHar
WHil
WNHG
WMnd
WJun
WBuc
WMat
WHod
WSHC
WRHF
WJas
WWEG
WChG
WFib
WAvo
WBrk
WHrl
WCre
WOld
WKif
WCot
WGrn
WPat
WCra
WCFE
WNPC
WHoo
WWFP
WThu
WPGP
WHfH
WMou
WLav
WJek

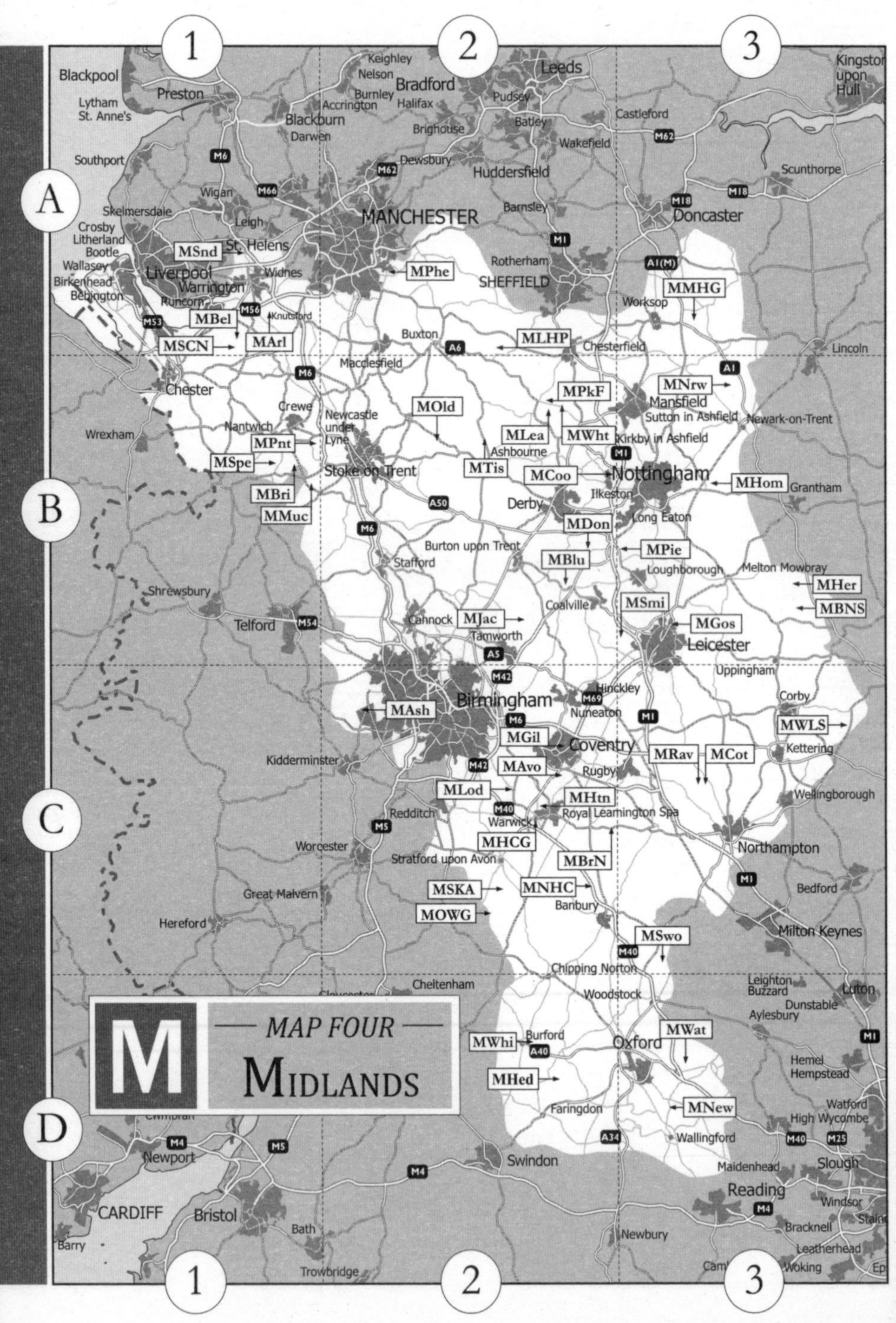
MAP FOUR
MIDLANDS

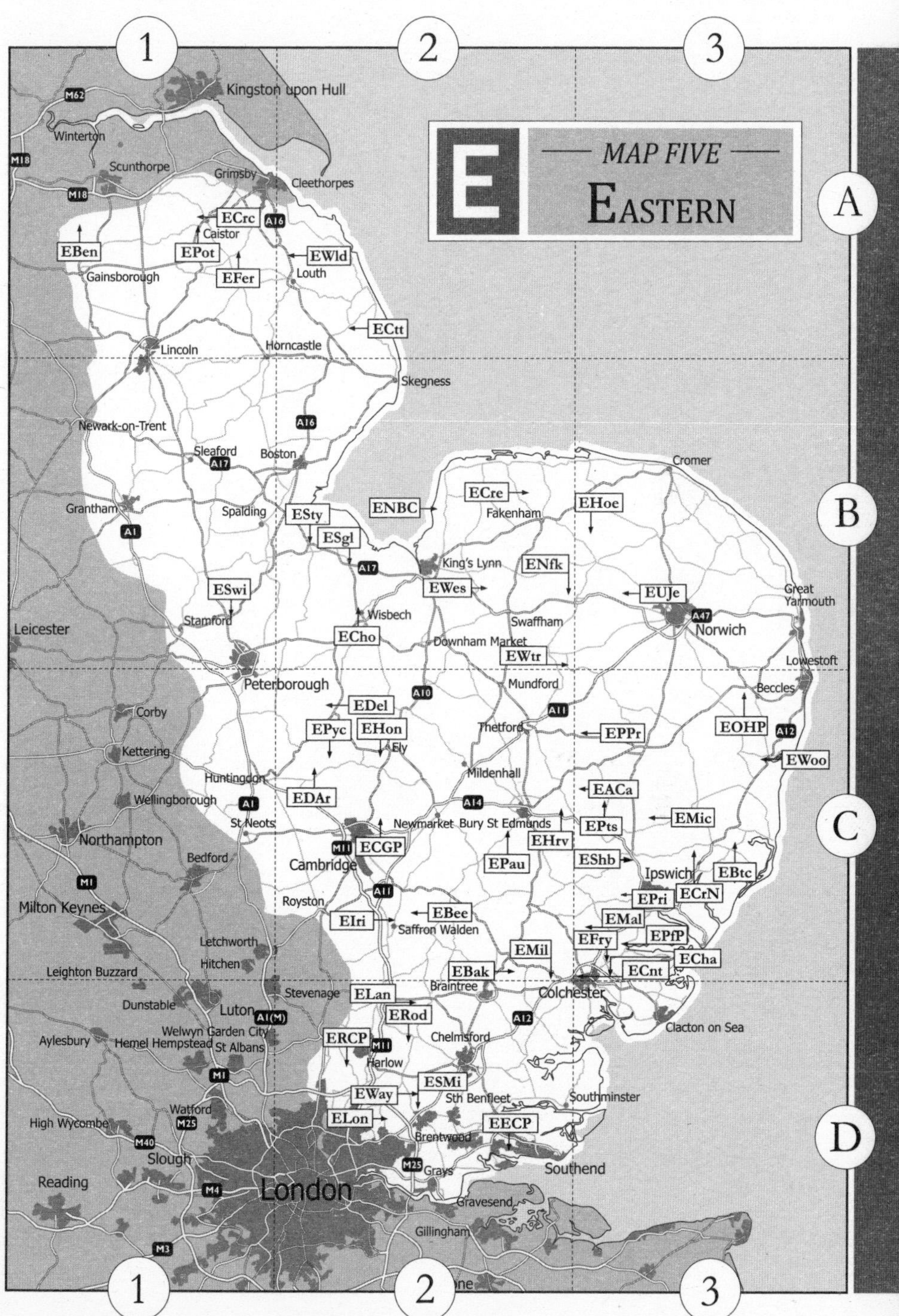

E
MAP FIVE
EASTERN
1
2
3
A
B
C
D
Kingston upon Hull
Winterton
Scunthorpe
Grimsby
Cleethorpes
ECrc
Caistor
EBen
EPot
EWld
Gainsborough
EFer
Louth
ECtt
Lincoln
Horncastle
Skegness
Newark-on-Trent
Sleaford
Boston
Cromer
ECre
ENBC
Fakenham
EHoe
Grantham
Spalding
ESty
ESgl
King's Lynn
ENfk
ESwi
EWes
EUJe
Great Yarmouth
Wisbech
Swaffham
Norwich
Leicester
Stamford
ECho
Downham Market
EWtr
Lowestoft
Peterborough
Mundford
Beccles
EDel
Corby
EPyc
EHon
Thetford
EPPr
EOHP
Ely
Kettering
EWoo
Mildenhall
Huntingdon
EACa
Wellingborough
EDAr
EMic
St Neots
Newmarket
Bury St Edmunds
EPts
Northampton
ECGP
EHrv
EPau
EShb
Bedford
Cambridge
Ipswich
EBtc
ECrN
EPri
Milton Keynes
Royston
EBee
EIri
Saffron Walden
EMal
Letchworth
EFry
EPfP
EMil
Hitchen
ECha
Leighton Buzzard
EBak
ECnt
Braintree
Colchester
Stevenage
ELan
Dunstable
Luton
ERod
Clacton on Sea
Welwyn Garden City
Aylesbury
Hemel Hempstead
St Albans
ERCP
Chelmsford
Harlow
ESMi
EWay
Sth Benfleet
Southminster
Watford
High Wycombe
ELon
EECP
Brentwood
Slough
Southend
Reading
Grays
London
Gravesend
Gillingham

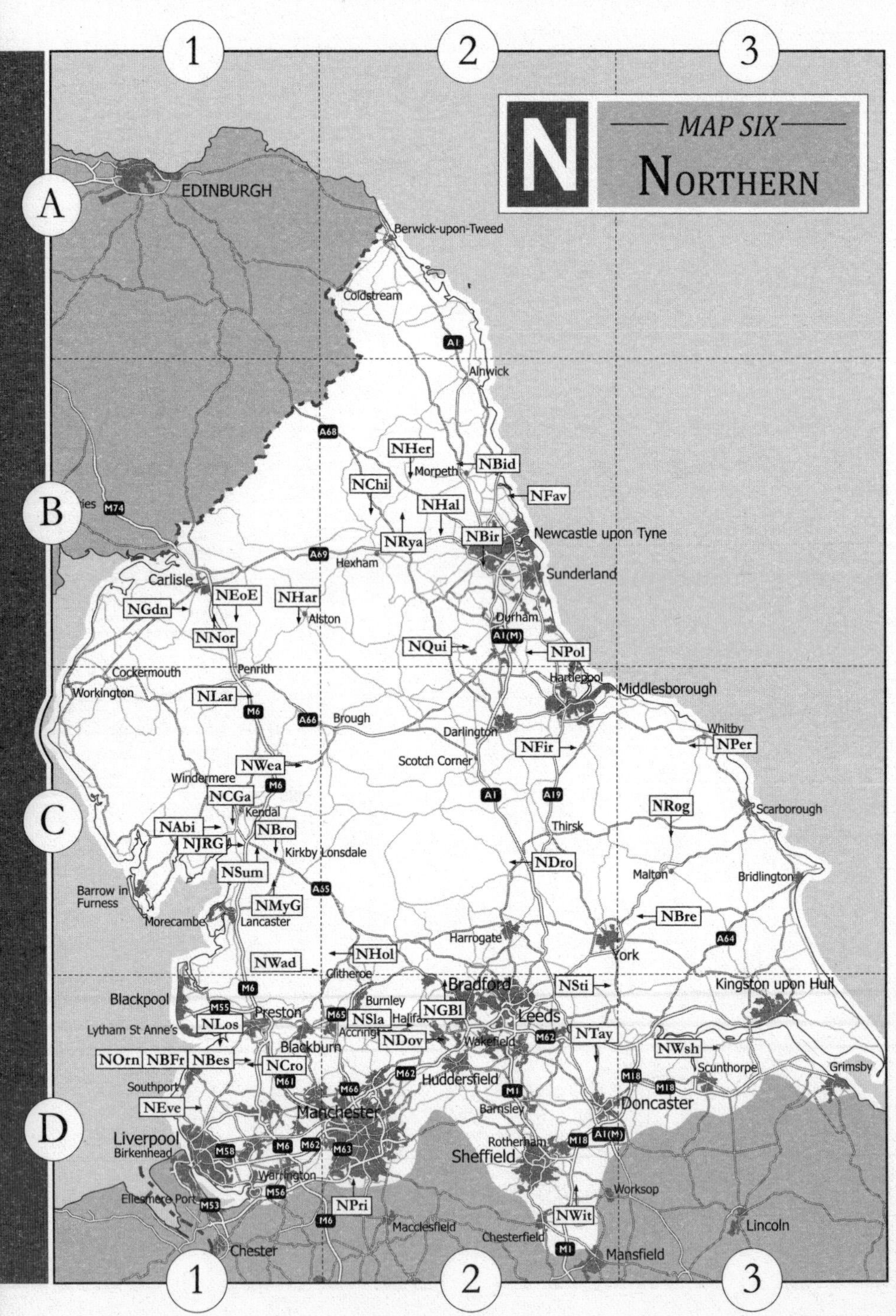

N
MAP SIX
Northern
1
2
3
A
B
C
D
EDINBURGH
Berwick-upon-Tweed
Coldstream
A1
Alnwick
A68
NHer
Morpeth
NBid
NChi
NFav
NHal
M74
NRya
NBir
Newcastle upon Tyne
A69
Hexham
Sunderland
Carlisle
NEoE
NHar
NGdn
Alston
Durham
NNor
NQui
A1(M)
NPol
Penrith
Cockermouth
Hartlepool
Middlesborough
Workington
NLar
M6
A66
Brough
Darlington
Whitby
NFir
NPer
NWea
Scotch Corner
Windermere
M6
NCGa
A1
A19
NRog
Scarborough
Kendal
NAbi
Thirsk
NBro
NJRG
Kirkby Lonsdale
NDro
NSum
Malton
Bridlington
Barrow in Furness
A65
NMyG
NBre
Morecambe
Lancaster
Harrogate
A64
York
NHol
NWad
Clitheroe
M6
Bradford
NSti
Kingston upon Hull
Blackpool
Burnley
M55
NGBl
Preston
M65
NSla
Halifax
Leeds
NLos
Accrington
Lytham St Anne's
NDov
M62
NTay
Blackburn
Wakefield
NWsh
NOrn
NBFr
NBes
NCro
M62
M18
Scunthorpe
Grimsby
M61
Huddersfield
Southport
M66
M1
M18
NEve
Manchester
Barnsley
Doncaster
Liverpool
Birkenhead
M58
M6
M62
M63
Rotherham
M18
A1(M)
Sheffield
Warrington
M56
Worksop
Ellesmere Port
M53
NPri
M6
NWit
Macclesfield
Chesterfield
Lincoln
M1
Mansfield
Chester
1
2
3

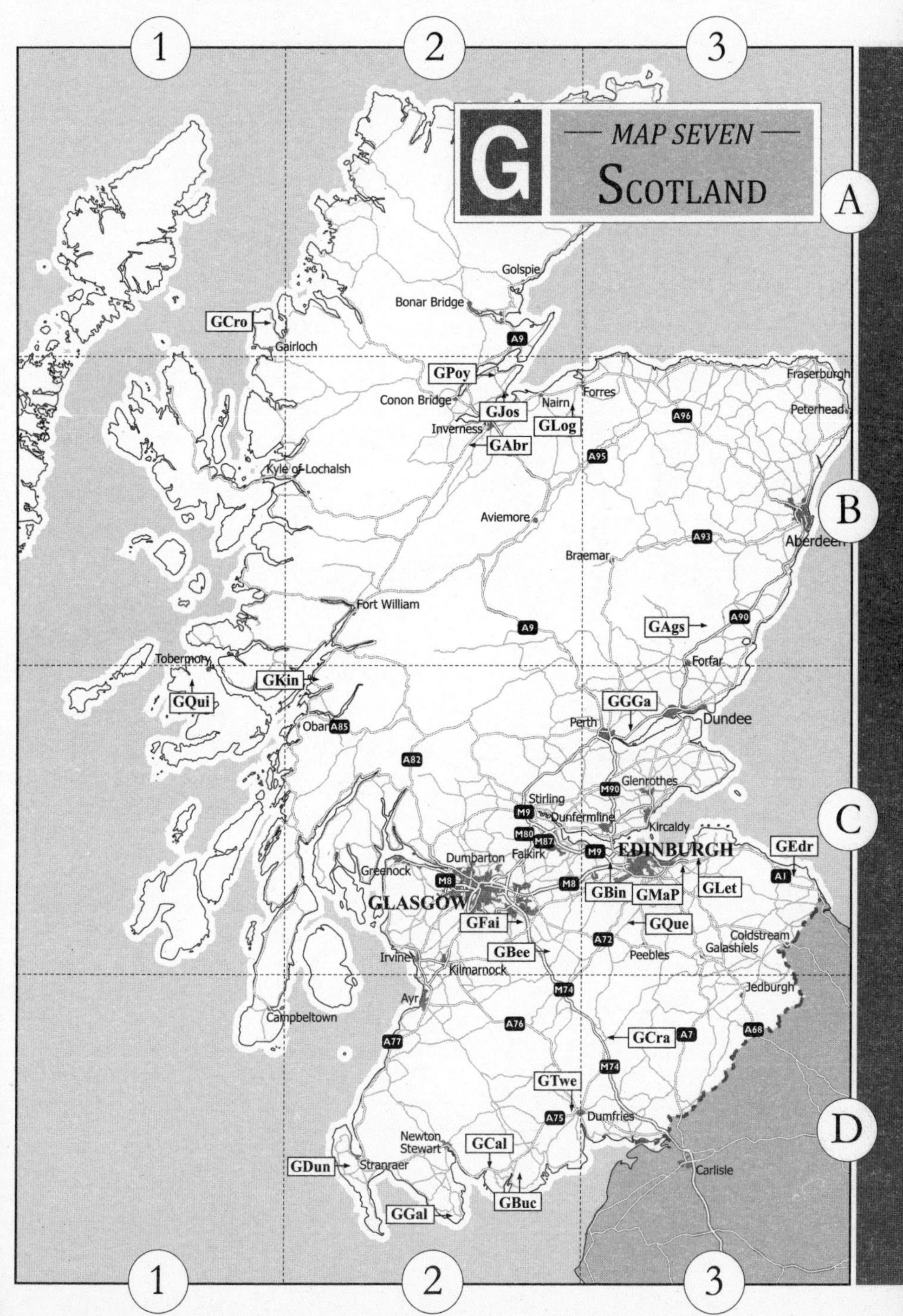
1
2
3
G
— MAP SEVEN —
SCOTLAND
A
B
C
D
Golspie
Bonar Bridge
GCro
Gairloch
A9
GPoy
Conon Bridge
GJos
Nairn
Forres
GLog
Inverness
GAbr
Fraserburgh
Peterhead
A96
A95
Kyle of Lochalsh
Aviemore
Aberdeen
A93
Braemar
Fort William
A9
GAgs
A90
Forfar
Tobermory
GKin
GQui
GGGa
Perth
Dundee
Oban
A85
A82
Glenrothes
M90
Stirling
M9
Dunfermline
M80
M87
Kircaldy
Dumbarton
Falkirk
M9
EDINBURGH
GEdr
Greenock
M8
M8
A1
GLASGOW
GBin
GMaP
GLet
GFai
GQue
A72
Coldstream
Galashiels
GBee
Peebles
Irvine
Kilmarnock
M74
Jedburgh
Ayr
Campbeltown
A76
A77
GCra
A7
A68
M74
GTwe
A75
Dumfries
Newton Stewart
GCal
GDun
Stranraer
Carlisle
GBuc
GGal

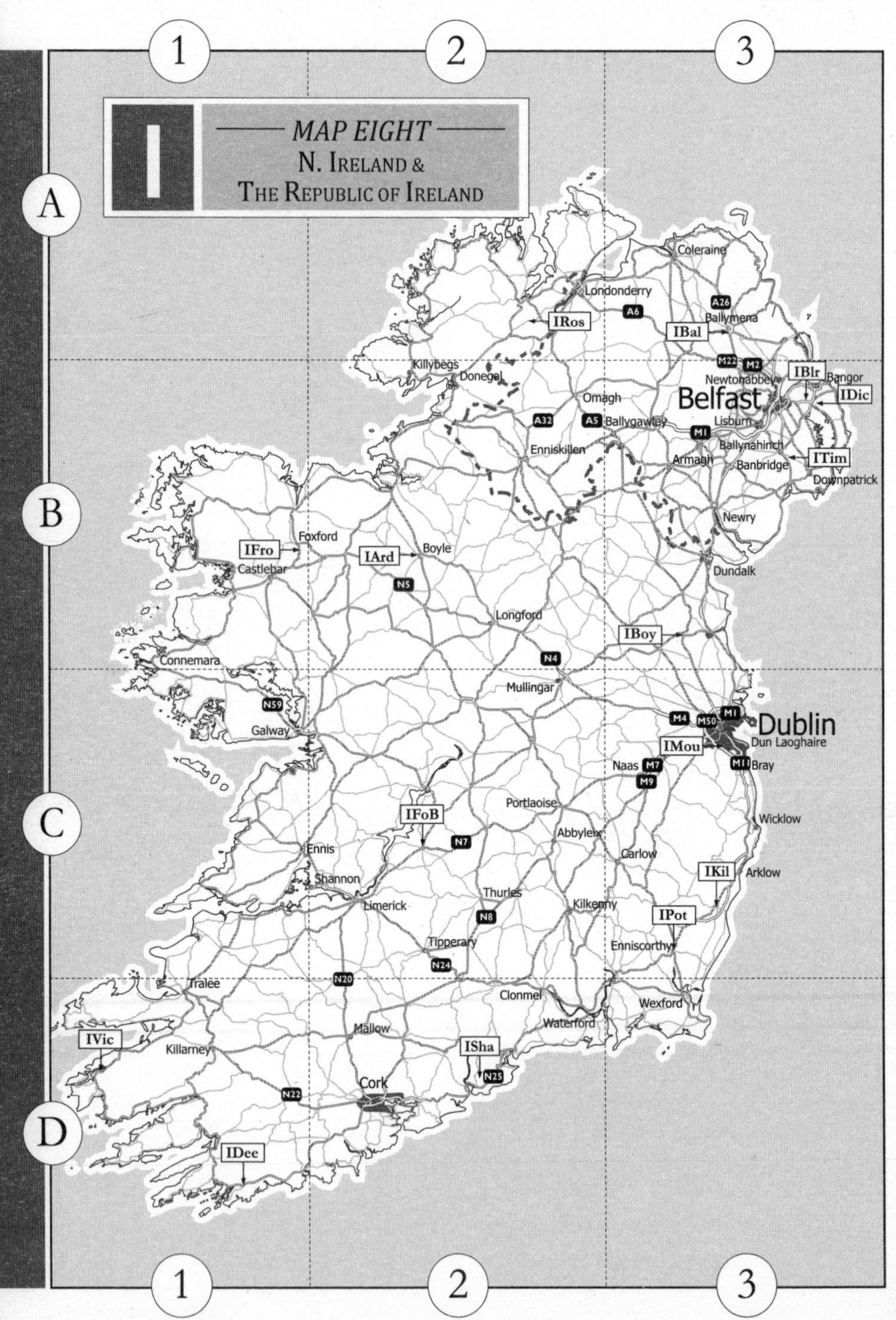

1
2
3
A
B
C
D
I
MAP EIGHT
N. IRELAND &
THE REPUBLIC OF IRELAND
Coleraine
Londonderry
A6
A26
Ballymena
IRos
IBal
M22
M2
Newtonabbey
IBlr
Bangor
IDic
Killybegs
Donegal
Omagh
Belfast
A32
A5
Ballygawley
Lisburn
M1
Ballynahinch
Enniskillen
Armagh
Banbridge
ITim
Downpatrick
Newry
Foxford
IFro
Castlebar
IArd
Boyle
N5
Dundalk
Longford
IBoy
N4
Connemara
Mullingar
N59
M4
M50
M1
Dublin
Galway
IMou
Dun Laoghaire
Naas
M7
M11
Bray
M9
Portlaoise
IFoB
Wicklow
N7
Abbyleix
Ennis
Carlow
IKil
Arklow
Shannon
Thurles
Kilkenny
Limerick
IPot
N8
Tipperary
Enniscorthy
N24
N20
Tralee
Clonmel
Wexford
Mallow
Waterford
IVic
Killarney
ISha
N25
Cork
N22
IDee

big plant
nursery

Aylett Nurseries
The Complete Garden Centre
"The home of the Gold Medal Dahlias"
Trees, shrubs and seasonal plants.
Garden sundries & landscape materials.
Garden furniture, BBQ's, gifts & clothing.
Coffee House serving home-cooked food.
Easy parking and delivery service.
Opening Hours
Mon - Fri 8.30am - 5.30pm,
Sat 8.30am - 5pm,
Sun 10.30am - 4.30pm
North Orbital Road, St. Albans, Herts. AL2 1DH
Tel: 01727 822255 Email: info@aylettnurseries.co.uk
www.aylettnurseries.co.uk

Barnhaven
Primroses

INDEX OF ADVERTISERS